WHEN THEY READ

MANUSCRIPTS

How the manuscript's form and contents depict the idea

A writing style that informs, entertains, and touches the reader

Verifiable research facts (in nonfiction)

Anecdotes and quotes from your interviews with people

How the manuscript will serve their readers and the market

Perfect copy; SASE enclosed

1987 Writer's Market

Acknowledgement
*The editor wishes to thank Paula Deimling
(*Writer's Market *editor, 1984-86) for her
efforts in planning and preparing much of
this edition.*

*Distributed in Canada by Prentice-Hall of
Canada Ltd., 1870 Birchmount Road,
Scarborough, Ontario M1P 2J7.*

*Managing Editor, Market Books Department:
Constance J. Achabal*

*Library of Congress Catalog Number
31-20772
International Standard Serial Number
0084-2729
International Standard Book Number
0-89879-243-6*

1987

Writer's Market

Where to Sell What You Write

Editor: *Becky Hall Williams*

Assistant Editors: *Sheila Freeman*
Glenda Tennant
Editorial Assistant: *Kathleen Vonderhaar*

Writer's Digest Books

Cincinnati, Ohio

The Writing Profession

From the Editors
Using *Writer's Market*

The Markets

Contents

The Writing Profession

From the Editors

Welcome to our book. We think of it as a partnership—a joint effort of the *Writer's Market* staff and you, our readers. We want the information in this book to fit your needs—needs of beginning writers as well as those of fulltime freelancers.

Our efforts

Our work on the 58th edition of *Writer's Market* began with the questions and suggestions we received from you. Then we asked writers, editors and publishers for answers. Another of our roles in this partnership is to tell you what we've learned about market opportunities and how you can use this information most effectively. To meet these goals, we've made many changes and additions in *Writers Market '87:*

• More than 900 new market opportunities, plus thousands of changes in titles; addresses; editors and editorial requirements.

• Articles on magazine agreements and book contracts, with general information for new writers and specific details for all writers who wonder whether or not to sign on the dotted line . . . and why.

• Close-up interviews with 13 writers and editors who share their insight, experience and advice about the writing life.

• Section introductions with greater emphasis on how trends and transitions of the publishing industry affect every writer.

• An Author's Agents section—new from beginning to end—that includes both commission-only and commission- and fee-charging agents, plus numerous questions and answers to help you get ready, find, and then evaluate an agent.

• Revised and expanded information in the Appendix including Developing a Strategy, Equipment and Supplies, Approaching Your Markets, Manuscript Mechanics, Mailing Your Submissions, Financial Records, Tax Information, Rights and the Writer, and How Much Should I Charge?

• A reorganized version of Using Writer's Market featuring a step-by-step approach to reading a market listing and getting the most out of this book.

Your efforts

The effectiveness of our partnership depends on the information in *Writer's Market '87*, but it also depends on you. We had the same question as previous editors of this book: Who is our "average" reader? Is this your first copy of *Writer's Market*—or your twenty-first?

You may be a "recreational writer," enjoying your private hobby but wondering if you, too, could be published. Perhaps you're a student who's curious about writing as a career. Or you may be a fulltime or part-time freelancer, relying on your writing skills for all or part of your income.

We know that experienced freelancers use *Writer's Market* because it has the most complete information on current freelance opportunities. These writers have already learned how to use the market listings; they know all the writer's jargon included in the Glossary; they know most of the information in the Appendix.

Beginning freelancers use *Writer's Market* because it opens up a whole world of possibilities. It includes specific information on how to approach editors and all the details of how to get started—and keep on going—with a writing career.

We've given you information that will help you become a successful writer—by whatever definition of success you choose. It's up to *you* to use this information well.

You and *Writer's Market*

One reader wrote to tell us that she wouldn't buy another copy of *Writer's Market* until we made editors respond more promptly and publishers pay higher rates. Well, we wish we could do that, too. Unfortunately, we can only report what editors and publishers tell us.

We hope you understand that—between the time our book goes to press and the time you read it—some of the details in the market listings may change. Publishers go out of business, editors find other jobs, and publications change their focuses or their payment policies.

We appreciate the help we receive from readers who send us information about new market opportunities. And we want to know when you have complaints about nonpayment from any market listed here. Always enclose a stamped, self-addressed envelope (SASE) if you expect a reply.

Our partnership with you continues to be important to us. Thank you for giving us the opportunity to be a part of your writing life.

Becky Hall Williams, Sheila Freeman, Glenda Tennant, Kathleen Vonderhaar

Read this

● Listings are based on editorial questionnaires and interviews. They are *not* advertisements; publishers do not pay for their listings. Markets are *not* endorsed by *WM* editors.

● All listings have been verified prior to the publication of this book. If a listing has not changed from last year, then the editor has told us that his needs have not changed—and that the previous listing still accurately reflects what he buys. We require documentation in our files for each listing and *never* run a listing without its editorial office's approval.

● Listings for new markets and changes in others can be found throughout the year in *Writer's Digest*, the monthly magazine for freelancers.

● When looking for a specific market, check the index. A market might not be listed for one of these reasons: 1) It doesn't solicit freelance material. 2) It has gone out of business. 3) It doesn't pay for material; we have, however, included nonpaying listings in the Journalism and Lifestyles categories because publication in these magazines could be valuable to a writer. *Some* magazines in the In-Flight section compensate writers with coupons for air travel. 4) It has failed to verify or update its listing for the 1987 edition. 5) It hasn't answered *Writer's Market* inquiries satisfactorily. (To the best of our ability—and with our readers' help—we try to screen out dishonest listings.) 7) It buys few manuscripts, thereby constituting a very small market for freelancers. 8) It was in the midst of being sold at press time, and rather than disclose premature details, we chose not to list it.

● *Writer's Market* reserves the right to exclude any listing.

Using Writer's Market

Think of this section as an informal guided tour through *Writer's Market*—an introduction to the information you'll find in most individual market listings. The Table of Contents is a good place to start. That way you'll know where to find all the sections mentioned here.

Be sure to read the introductions to each market category. You'll find helpful information on trends, industry practices, and special methods for submitting your material.

Review the symbols and abbreviations used throughout *Writer's Market '87*. They're explained in the box on the following page. The most important abbreviation is SASE—self-addressed, stamped envelope. Always enclose one whenever you write to an editor or publisher. This rule is not included in the individual market listings because it's a "given" *you must follow if you expect to receive a reply*.

Reading a listing

Now let's get acquainted with what you can find in a typical market listing.

● One or more symbols (*, ‡, □) may precede the name and address of the publication or other market. Check the key on the following page for their meanings.

● A phone number in a listing does *not* mean that the market accepts phone queries. Make a phone query only when your story's timeliness would be lost by following the usual procedures. As a rule, don't call unless you've been invited to do so.

● In most listings, names of contact persons are given in the first paragraph or under the bold subheadings. Address a query or submission to a specific name whenever possible. If the name is not easily recognizable by gender, use the full name (e.g., Dear Dale Smith:). If no contact name is given, consult a sample copy. As a last resort, you could address your query to "Articles Editor" or whatever seems appropriate. Read Approaching Your Markets in the Appendix.

● A market's general openness to writers is indicated by the percentage of freelance material used or by the percentage of published manuscripts from new and unagented writers.

● A general description of the market gives you an indication of its focus and audience. Use this information to decide if you'd like to see a sample copy and/or guidelines.

● The date a market was established can help you evaluate its stability. Newer markets may be more open to freelancers, but they can also be riskier.

● Circulation figures are the total of subscriptions (individual and library) plus off-the-shelf sales.

● General payment policies and other practices are usually described in the first paragraph of each listing. Look for markets that pay on acceptance—not on publication. Look for markets that do not buy all rights or make "work for hire" agreements. Retain rights you might be able to resell. Look for markets that publish accepted material promptly and give writers a byline.

● General submission requirements include how far in advance you should submit seasonal material and whether or not previously published material will be considered.

● Send manuscripts or queries to one market at a time unless it is indicated that simultaneous submissions are OK. If you send a manuscript to two or more markets at one time, always mention in your cover letter that it is a simultaneous submission.

● Computer printouts and electronic submissions (by computer disk or modem) are mentioned only when the market accepts them. See Equipment and Supplies in the Appendix for additional information.

● Reporting times indicate how soon a market will respond to your query or manuscript, but times listed are approximate. Quarterly publications, book publishers, literary magazines, and all new listings may be especially slow to respond. Wait six weeks beyond the stated reporting time before you send a polite inquiry.

• If you're interested in writing for a particular market, you should request writer's guidelines. "Writer's guidelines for SASE" means that a business-size envelope with one First Class stamp will be adequate. You should request a sample copy if you are unable to find the publication at your local library. A sample copy (or book catalog) is often available for a 9x12 SAE with a specified number of stamps or IRCs. Most publishers will send writer's guidelines with sample copies at no extra charge if you request them.

• Subheads in bold (Nonfiction, Photos, Columns/Departments, Fiction, Poetry, Fillers, etc.) guide you to the types of material used in a publication. Sometimes the name of an editor appears here. If so, send your submission to that person.

• Contact people often describe the specific kinds of material they want—or do *not* want to see. Follow their requests! For example, do not send fiction or poetry to a publication that uses only nonfiction; do not send a children's book manuscript to a publisher of men's adventure novels.

• The number of each type of manuscript purchased per issue or per year gives you an idea of how easy (or difficult) it may be to sell your work to a particular market. With new listings, these figures may change dramatically, depending on the submissions they receive or sudden changes in policy.

• If the market wants to see queries, that's what you should send. The same goes for outlines and sample chapters, etc. Don't send a complete manuscript unless the listing indicates that it's OK.

• Editors know the length of most material they buy; follow their stated range of words or pages. Of course a story should be as long—or as short—as it needs to be. If your manuscript doesn't fit the requirements of the magazine you wrote it for, find another market.

• Payment ranges tell you what the market *usually* paid at the time *Writer's Market* was published.

• Helpful suggestions are listed under the bold subhead Tips in many listings. They describe the best way to 'break in' at that market; suggest a particular slant; or give you some special insight into special needs and preferences.

Other information

Listings for other types of markets (Scriptwriting, Gags, Greeting Cards, etc.) sometimes contain additional information, which is explained in the introductions to each section. The Appendix at the back of *Writer's Market* should answer most of your questions about the business of writing. In the Glossary, you'll find definitions of many words and phrases that pertain to writing. Remember to use a standard dictionary if you come across other words you don't understand. Turn to the Index when you want to locate a specific market.

Take just enough time away from your writing to get well-acquainted with *Writer's Market* '87. Then settle down at that typewriter or personal computer and write, write, write.

Key to Symbols and Abbreviations

‡ New listing in all sections
* Subsidy publisher in Book Publishers section
□ Cable TV market in Scriptwriting section
ms Manuscript; mss Manuscripts
b&w Black and white (photo)
SASE Self-addressed, stamped envelope
SAE Self-addressed envelope
IRC International Reply Coupon for replies from foreign markets

Your First Book Contract

by Linda Hayes

Finally! Your ultimate dream has been realized. After you've suffered seemingly endless research, revisions and rejections, a discerning publisher has just offered you a contract. At last, you're only a signature away from literary stardom, not to mention unthinkable wealth. Right? Not really. There's at least one more major hurdle to overcome—negotiating a good contract. While the outcome may have little effect on your literary star's rising or falling, it does determine whether you will reap dividends, disappointment or perhaps even disaster.

Note to writers still waiting for that first offer: Read on. You're in an even stronger position if you plan ahead.

There are several ways to tackle a contract: 1) get a lawyer (not your uncle, the patent attorney); 2) find an experienced literary agent; or 3) do it yourself.

If you choose the third option, you'll need to know almost as much about book contracts as you know about the topic or characters in your book. Even if you work with an agent or attorney, it's wise to be as informed as possible. Remember, that's *your* name at the bottom of the contract. To give you an idea of what to expect, some basic elements of the offer/contract process are outlined here.

The offer

Let's assume at this point that the discerning editor has phoned or written to say that XYZ Publishing loves your book and wants to publish it. Such news is often enough to render first-time authors totally incoherent. When you're once again of sound mind, double check the offer's details. Typically, the initial offer spells out the advance and basic royalty rates, the rights the publisher is buying, and perhaps the way subsidiary rights income will be split.

If you did your homework before submitting your manuscript to XYZ Publishing, you're already familiar with their books and reputation. Now—before you finally agree on any of these points—you need to know more about the publishing house, its policies and plans for your book.

Questions to ask

You may think that asking a lot of questions will demonstrate your ignorance or antagonize XYZ Publishing. Relax. Asking questions is the best way to learn—and you certainly want to learn as much as you can about your book's future. It's best to ask your questions as soon after receiving the offer as possible.

Because publishers don't make an offer unless they have a good idea of how to market a book, you can bet that XYZ has developed a tentative plan for yours. Call or write the editor who made the initial offer. If you phone, be sure that the editor will confirm the conversation in writing.

Remember that the answers to the following questions will help you understand what the terms of the offer—and the subsequent contract—really mean.

Linda Hayes is a founder and marketing director of Columbia Literary Associates in the Washington/Baltimore area. As a literary agent, she has placed a variety of fiction and nonfiction titles with major publishers. Her own articles and short fiction have appeared in magazines such as Writer's Digest, Lady's Circle and Weight Watcher's Magazine.

- Are royalties based on list price? Or on net price (after discounts/shipping are deducted)? If net, what's the average discount and cost deduction?
- What are XYZ's main sales outlets (bookstores, direct mail, schools, libraries, bookclub, etc.)? What's the typical ratio of these sales? What's the typical ratio of regular vs. special discount sales? Should this hold true for my book?
- What are the short-and long-term sales projections for my book? What's XYZ's sales experience with similar books?
- Is any promotion planned (budgeted) for my book? What specifically? Were the similar books mentioned above handled the same way?
- What are the plans for my book's formatting? Hardcover/cloth, tradepaper/quality paperback, mass market paperback, library edition, etc.? Is more than one format planned? Will they be released together or in sequence? If in sequence, what's the planned schedule?
- What are the projected prices and initial print run, i.e. number to be printed? (This often changes.)
- How will my book be distributed? By XYZ's sales force, independent reps, via another publisher, etc.?
- How aggressively does XYZ exploit subsidiary rights? What kinds of success has it had with similar books?
- What's XYZ's policy on keeping books in print?

The contract

Armed with the answers to all (or most) of these questions, you can decide whether or not to accept the initial offer. If you do, your contract should arrive a few weeks later. Don't let its formality intimidate you. Although it is a legally binding document, a contract is simply a written agreement between two parties to meet the needs of both. If you don't agree on all points, you can negotiate to have them modified. It's not only acceptable, it's expected. (Unless, of course, you're thrilled with every clause.)

Although there are countless varieties of publishing contracts and different ways to word even the simplest clause, the basic elements of a trade book contract are fairly standard. The clauses may appear in almost any order or combination. Each project requires its own contract adjustments, of course, but the following issues are common to most books.

Grant of rights

The first clause usually states that you're granting the publisher specific rights to your book for distribution or sublicensing. These rights may be limited to certain territories, ranging from the United States, Canada and the Philippines alone, up to world rights. It's rumored that at least one foresighted publisher includes lunar distribution in his contract!

Besides book rights, there are several subsidiary rights you either grant your publisher to sublicense, reserve to sell yourself, or divide between you. These rights include: periodical or newspaper publication before or after publication (first or second serial rights), bookclub, dramatic and nondramatic performance, British Commonwealth, foreign language, reprint, merchandising, abridgements, audiovisual, etc.

The decision on which rights to grant or hold depends on how they'll best be sold—through the publisher, you or your agent. If the publisher handles them, you split the fee and your share will be held until the advance is earned back—unless you can negotiate a "pass-through" clause to get it sooner. If you or your agent hold and sell the rights, the money is yours right away. Some authors insert contract clauses to revert certain rights back to them, if the publisher has not exploited the rights after a reasonable time. Be sure to look for a clause that specifies separate royalty percentages for each subsidiary right.

Manuscript preparation and delivery

This section (or these clauses) of the contract describe what XYZ Publishing expects to receive from you and when it should be received.

- *What you're providing*—You agree to produce a manuscript of an approximate length, on a certain topic, with a tentative title. Be specific to avoid misunderstandings. You may also be required (or allowed) to read the copyedited manuscript and/or correct the proofs in a timely manner.
- *Additional materials*—You may be asked to provide supplementary materials such as illustrations, index or bibliography. If you plan to use a quotation or excerpt from someone else's work in your book, you must provide XYZ with written permission from the original publisher. You are usually responsible for the cost of these additional materials. Sometimes you can negotiate a split of the cost and put a limit on your portion of the expense.
- *The due date*—If the manuscript is due by May 15, but supplemental materials aren't due 'til June 1, make sure the contract says so. Late manuscripts jeopardize the book's acceptance and marketability, as well as your professional reputation.
- *Any extensions allowed*—Although editors are human and will—if they can—allow extra time when you break your arm, make sure there's wording to cover uncontrollable emergencies. (Such protection for the publisher is labeled Force Majeure, or Acts of God). Sometimes extensions are allowed for less serious reasons, but if the contract doesn't say so, don't count on it.
- *Nondelivery*—If you don't deliver the finished manuscript when due or after extensions, you can expect a penalty. Normally, the contract terminates and the previously paid advance must be returned.

Manuscript acceptance

Some of the most vital parts of the contract, these clauses describe XYZ's right to accept, reject, or request revisions in your manuscript.

- *Acceptance*—This highly controversial clause was traditionally based on the publisher's interpretation of the phrase "satisfactory in form and content." XYZ may be more—or less—specific in its acceptance policies. Some experienced nonfiction writers have been able to delete this restrictive wording and substitute "will deliver a manuscript in accordance with the attached proposal." If this works, keep a copy of your book proposal and if alterations must be made, verify them in a letter to your editor.
- *Chance to revise unsatisfactory manuscript*—The contract should guarantee you the opportunity to make any necessary revisions, based on a letter from XYZ specifically detailing what's needed.
- *Rejected manuscript*—Suppose that you've delivered the manuscript and made all requested revisions, but it's still not satisfactory. Normally, the contract terminates and the publisher requires the return of the first part of the advance. Authors and agents vehemently (and reasonably) argue that repayment shouldn't be necessary, since that money was meant to cover expenses while writing. If that argument fails, you can promise repayment when you resell the manuscript. Or, if the publisher absolutely refuses to strike the repayment clause, you can haggle wording to keep part of the advance (like a magazine article kill fee) or at least that portion you have valid expense receipts for.

Royalties and advances

Here's what you've been looking for. How much will you be paid and when?

- *Royalties*—You'll want to maximize your royalty percentages for various editions or uses of your book. These might include hardcover, mass market paperback, trade paperback, export, discount sales, bookclub, remainders and overstock. If XYZ is buying subsidiary rights, the royalty percentage for each one should be listed separately. Remember, the most important detail is whether royalties are based on net receipts (after discounts and shipping costs are deducted) or on list price (either the jacket price or the slightly lower bookseller's catalog price.)

• *Advances*—The publisher's initial payment to you, this is an advance against your expected royalties. Your book must earn this amount for XYZ before you get any more money. Unless your project is complete, the advance will be spread over two or more payments: part on signing the contract and the rest as the manuscript is completed. Some contracts delay final payment until publication, but you should get paid when *your* work is done. How much should the advance be? In his Writer's Digest book on contracts, Richard Balkin says that "roughly 75% of advances in trade publishing are below $10,000, 20% in the $10,000 to $30,000 range, and no more than 5% upward of $30,000."

• *Payments/accounting*—Payments are usually made three to four months after each six-month royalty period. Be sure that statements will be sent even when no royalty's due. You'll want complete income information on these regular statements or at your request. Statements should specify number of copies printed, shipped, sold and returned; royalty type and rate; reserve against returns; and details of subsidiary rights sales.

• *Reserve against returns*—Publishers' sales to booksellers are returnable, so the reserve policy will allow XYZ to reserve a percentage of your royalties to cover these returns. A few publishers don't hold reserves, but most do—from 20-60% of your earnings. What's left after returns is gradually paid out over several royalty periods. Ask about typical returns for your kind of book and negotiate a reasonable limitation on what percentage can be held and when it will be released.

• *Author's copies*—Contrary to your friends' belief that authors have an unlimited supply of free copies, you're usually offered only ten or so. You can often nudge that number higher. You're also normally granted a 40-50% discount on additional copies, as long as you're not reselling them. Some authors have had that limitation lifted when they can tap special markets unavailable to the publisher. You might consider this if your book's ideal for lecture tour promotion.

Option/right of first refusal

Since XYZ Publishing is planning a costly promotional campaign to make your name a household word and your book the new national bestseller, it certainly doesn't want you to sell your next book to someone else. Realistically, the majority of books get little promotional support, but most publishers want you "under option" in case your book should take off on its own.

Of course, if XYZ sells millions of copies of your book, you'll be delighted to have XYZ handle your next one. But if the company did a lousy job; or you disagree on everything; or your next book is a blockbuster novel definitely not designed for XYZ's typical distribution, then you'll understand why you should have reworded your option clause.

A few publishers will delete option clauses, but when the clause must stay, try to define or make it less limiting.

• Watch out for clauses that option more than one book or claim *any* book you write next. Limit the clause to what's right for the publisher or situation; say your "next cookbook" or "young adult novel" rather than "book."

• Don't let XYZ delay reviewing your next book until long after the first book's out. If you earn your living writing, you may starve by then. Specify how soon they must consider your second manuscript and put a time limit on how long they may hold it for review.

• Avoid freezing the same terms for the purchase of your second book. Usually you'll want, need, and deserve better terms by then.

• Don't let XYZ require too much material for your next submission, e.g., a complete man-

uscript when an outline and sample material would be more reasonable.
● Avoid "matching clauses." Suppose that you've negotiated with XYZ on your next book, turned down its offer, and gotten a better one from another publisher. A matching clause would allow XYZ to match the other offer and obligate you to accept XYZ's contract.

Other important details

You'll want to look at several more clauses that need your careful attention. Whether they're located at the beginning of the contract or buried at the end, these clauses can be critical to your future.

● *Copyright*—Normally, this says the publisher will apply for copyright in your name and will abide by copyright regulations. It also authorizes XYZ to represent you in this. As a rule, the copyright should not be registered in the publisher's name. Even if XYZ supplied much of the book's material, a joint registration would be possible.

● *Publication date*—This clause specifies a time frame within which the book must be published. You'll want to allow enough time for subsidiary sales, but if publication is delayed, so are your royalties. Also, enthusiasm for your book can evaporate due to changes in the market, editor, or publishing house policies.

● *Warranties/indemnities*—XYZ will surely include warranties and indemnities, as they are the most sensitive and least changeable clauses in a contract. In effect, you swear that in preparing the manuscript you've done nothing to invite lawsuits. This section also describes your responsibilities if suits do arise. Whole chapters are written on these clauses alone; study them carefully. The good news is that more publishers are now including authors in their liability insurance coverage.

● *Publisher's determinations*—Hoping to avoid later conflicts, XYZ declares it has the final word on the book's design, title, price, distribution, promotion, etc. Conflicts arise anyway, but remember, if you've chosen a good publisher, its staff has a lot more professional book experience than you do. Some publishers include or will add the opportunity for author's approval on some elements, "...such approval not to be unreasonably withheld." If any of these points are critically important to you, make sure you have that approval in the contract.

● *Revision for later editions*—XYZ may expect you to revise your nonfiction book if it sells well but some of the information is outdated. You don't want to do unnecessary, unpaid revisions, yet some books suffer if revisions aren't allowed. Work for wording that balances both concerns.

● *Out of print/termination*—Make sure your contract specifies when the book is considered out of print; how to request reprinting; and procedures for termination (notification, purchase of copies, rights reversion).

● *Competing works/next work*—This clause keeps you from selling to another publisher a second book that would compete with and potentially hurt the sale of the current work. With fiction, this clause sometimes keeps you from using the same characters. Nonfiction's another matter, particularly if you're a specialist actively writing in your field. Define exactly what kinds of books you can't do.

XYZ Publishing doesn't want the final manuscript of your book to be late because you're working on another book for a competitor. That's understandable; but if you're already under contract, make sure your editor knows and that it's reflected here. The limitation most often applies to accepting new contracts while working on this book, so if you're an active writer, be sure to reword or delete unreasonable language. This clause can sometimes prohibit another publisher from releasing one of your books close to XYZ's publication date for this book.

● *Bankruptcy*—The contract will terminate and rights revert to you if XYZ goes into bankruptcy. It's safer to include wording that termination/reversion will occur if the firm defaults in its payments to you or if it becomes involved in any insolvency, bankruptcy, or reassignment action.

What's not there

Not every contract addresses each of these points. Beware. Sometimes what's *not* in a contract can hurt. Important points too often omitted are: arbitration of disputes, termination/reversion of rights procedures, specific income information the publisher must provide, and the author's right to inspect the publisher's records (audit clause).

Of course, if certain clauses detrimental to you are missing—like the option clause—you'd certainly not want to argue them into the contract!

The fine print

You'll learn through more extensive research that there are dozens of innocent-looking little "gotchas" hiding between the lines of your contract. "Time is of the essence" sounds like a pleasant reminder to get the manuscript in on time. It actually means that if the manuscript doesn't arrive precisely on the dot, terrible things will happen (e.g., abrupt termination—of the contract, not you.) Agents' least favorite three little words—"Or any other,"— often create unfair drains of your money. This phrase allows charges from an unprofitable book to be assessed against the account of your bestseller. Learn the language.

Get it in writing

Book contract negotiations are like marriage proposals. They come at a time when you're feeling sought after, optimistic and trusting. But all honeymoons end. Realistically, the editor who loved your book will move on to something else. Or XYZ Publishing may be bought by a larger company with different policies. Short of that, misunderstandings occur and memories of what was said during contract negotiations fade rapidly. The message here? If it's important, get it in writing.

If a contract phrase seems to mean one thing, but the negotiator says it means something else, have the language clarified in writing. The same is true when you're told that "the Legal Department won't let us change the contract, but we'll give you 100 free copies of your book anyway;" or "we can't make promotional commitments in the contract, but we definitely plan to take ads in major magazines." For any detail or promise that can't go into the contract, be sure to verify it in a letter (called a sideletter) and get it countersigned.

Other resources

We've tried to introduce some of the countless details to be negotiated in every book contract. Don't be daunted. Of course you'll need to do further research. It takes more than a brief article to define the language of the industry and to explore the hundreds of possible variations in contract clauses. Remember that contracts also vary according to the type of book (trade, textbook, scholarly, technical) and the type of publisher (general, professional, or university press).

As you continue your study, you may want to consult the following books: *How to Understand & Negotiate a Book Contract or Magazine Agreement*, by Richard Balkin (a Writer's Basic Bookshelf Book from Writer's Digest Books); *How to Be Your Own Literary Agent*, by Richard Curtis (Houghton Mifflin Company); and *Author Law & Strategies—A Legal Guide for the Working Writer*, by Brad Bunnin and Peter Beren (Nolo Press).

Research thoroughly, choose what's best for you, and negotiate creatively. Despite all the work and worry, remember that you've just entered one of the most exciting professions in the world. You're an author!

Negotiating Magazine Agreements

by Dean R. Lambe

By some accounts, there are over 75,000 consumer, trade, and small press magazines in North America. Over half—certainly most of those that the beginning freelancer encounters—don't have formal agreements for the work they publish. Legal contracts, like those offered by book publishers, are rare with magazines. Typically, prior verbal agreements are made or "boilerplate" form-letter contracts are sent *after* the work has been accepted. Sometimes, the only agreement a writer sees is on the back of the payment check, whereupon the writer's endorsement may constitute acceptance of the printed terms. Attorneys disagree whether such a legal ploy is enforceable. You can avoid it by depositing the check in your account with "For Deposit Only" and no signature.

Prior agreements are rare for fiction and poetry. The best arrangements are reserved for nonfiction sales. While a Stephen King or a James Michener (or their agents) might negotiate for everything they write, most of us have less flexibility. All writers should be aware of the issues involved in magazine agreements, however. The freelancer who is professionally knowledgable will be treated professionally by editors.

Submission specifics

Let's consider the best agreement terms, then, mindful of the differences between fiction and nonfiction, as well as the differences among the three submission categories: over-the-transom, on speculation, and by assignment.

Through the window. Before air conditioning, most publishers had little windows—transoms—above their doors. Neophyte writers would toss their manuscripts through this open ventilation space, often after hours. To this day, a work from a writer with no prior editorial contact is called "over-the-transom," and it remains in the weakest bargaining position. Most fiction and poetry fall into this submission category, although prior sales do make a difference with any editor.

On spec is out on a limb. The negotiation position isn't much improved for the second category, on speculation. When a writer submits "on spec," it means the editor has been queried by mail or phone, and has shown tentative interest. The initial contact often establishes some of the terms—article length, slant, and rights offered—but a formal agreement depends on final acceptance.

Many working professionals—those who support themselves by writing—refuse to work on spec, for there is no guarantee that their efforts will ever be rewarded, or the the work will appear as they would wish. Those most successful with on spec sales restrict the works to short humor, mood pieces, interview/profiles or editorial essays. Such articles have the best chance of finding a home elsewhere if rejected by the first editor. In my experience, articles in

Dean R. Lambe *has written fiction and nonfiction for many magazines including* OMNI, Analog Science Fiction, The Magazine of Fantasy & Science Fiction, Advanced Computing, *and* Writer's Digest. *His novel,* The Odysseus Solution *(Baen Books) was co-written with Michael A. Banks. He handles grievances with magazine publishers for his colleagues in the Science Fiction Writers of America, Inc. and the Computer Writers' Association.*

newspaper Sunday supplements and in airline in-flight magazines often represent on spec sales.

Could you give us 3,000 words. The best opportunity for agreement negotiation comes with assignment or commission. Either through a query initiated by the writer, or by a phone call from an editor, a writer receives an assignment to do a particular piece. Assignments are offered to well-established professionals who have a demonstrated track record of prior sales to the magazine or to similar publications. (Exceptions include prominent politicians, Hollywood celebrities, and ball players.) While new freelancers rarely get an assignment, when special qualifications are presented well in a query, even *National Geographic* may offer a $3,000 commission.

Upon assignment, the terms should be finalized by both parties, on paper, before writing begins. It's up to the writer to raise the issues, for editors won't offer all relevant items. Sometimes, editors aren't even allowed to negotiate, but it never hurts to ask. When an assignment is initiated by telephone, the better publications will follow up with a formal agreement. You *always* should make sure such a letter is forthcoming; if it isn't, submit it yourself (in two signed copies, one for the editor to keep, one to sign and return).

Know your markets

Whatever your submission category, from first over-the-transom short story to commissioned *Playboy* interview, you must study the market listings. Your chances are much improved for negotiation either before or after acceptance if you know something about the magazine's policies and its people. There's no point in asking a dollar a word from *Isaac Asimov's Science Fiction Magazine*; even *Omni* doesn't pay that much.

Fortunately, you're now reading an excellent source of annual market information. If your library doesn't maintain the most recent editions of *Writer's Market* and the companion *Fiction Writer's Market* (Writer's Digest Books), seek them out. Other useful annual listings include the *International Directory of Little Magazines and Small Presses* (Dustbooks), and *The Writer's Guide to Magazine Markets* (both Fiction and Nonfiction volumes; New American Library). Helpful periodicals include *Writer's Digest, The Writer*, and *Publisher's Weekly*. Before you stamp that query letter, check the magazine's masthead to make sure that your targeted *Family Circle* editor isn't now working for *Redbook.*

These sources provide information about payment rates, indications of rights purchased, article needs, payment timeliness, and openness to beginners. The highest paying markets, however, often don't publish their top rates, and magazine circulation or even number of major advertisers isn't always a reliable measure of payment rates.

Once qualified for membership, the writer should join an appropriate writers' organization. Groups like the Mystery Writers of America, the American Society of Journalists and Authors, and the Science Fiction Writers of America provide regular news of markets and editorial changes. Writers' groups also provide "insider" tips on newly-opened markets.

Terms of importance

Now, let's consider specific magazine agreement terms in descending order of importance. Few issues are "deal-breakers," terms so important that you will risk losing the sale for them.

Payment rate. Paying markets usually deal on an *x* cents per word schedule. Often, a lower rate will be offered newcomers, so a range of word rates is listed. For those that pay a flat page rate, or a flat rate for the typical 3,000 word article, experienced pros often get more, as do longer articles. Over-the-transom work can count on the lowest rates, especially if it's fiction or poetry.

Richard Balkin, a New York agent and author of *How to Understand and Negotiate a Book Contract or Magazine Agreement* (Writer's Digest Books) says: "I recommend *always* asking for 50 percent more than was offered. . . ." As a horse-trader, I suspect Mr. Balkin's 50 percent does a lot of walking. Push for more only if you have a track record of published work, or have factors the editor may have failed to consider (hardship of a short deadline, extra research, difficulty in locating interviewee, etc.).

High rates are most often requested for assigned work, and then only with polite discretion. Editors have publishers to whom they must answer, and more than one editor has gone job hunting after being generous. Hard-luck stories will work—sometimes—but don't try an editor's patience or credulity.

Do try for higher rates for sales after your first to a particular magazine. You probably won't get it for fiction or poetry, but the nonfiction gravy often thickens the second time it's passed.

The right rights. After money, the rights to the work have highest priority. Always put a copyright notice on your first manuscript page, e.g., "Copyright (or ©) 1987 by I.M. Writer." Under the 1978 U.S. Copyright Law, you own all rights to a work from the moment of its creation. You must agree to assign (sell) those rights; such assignments should be in writing. Ideally, a one-time right to publication is all a magazine needs, but "first North American serial rights" (where *serial* means magazine) are usually required. If internationally distributed, then "first English serial rights" to the work are necessary and acceptable. If the publisher wants second serial rights for no extra money, then you lose reprint income. Ditto for British and other foreign rights; negotiate more money or ask to keep secondary rights. Try to keep all other rights, especially performing rights (stage, TV, film), even with nonfiction. The Broadway musical and movie *The Best Little Whorehouse in Texas* began as nonfiction in *Playboy.* Video games and computers have added a new category of electronic rights that you should try to retain as well.

If a magazine requests "all rights," you should run the other way. "All rights" is a deal breaker for most writers; no matter how good the original money, you'll never see another penny. A number of publishers have "standard, all rights" agreements that the editor will change readily. Those who don't ask are not writers; they're amateurs. The same deal-breaker advice holds on "work for hire" clauses. Here, "work for hire" is a form of slavery. Since freelancers lack the benefits of magazine staff, we shouldn't ever "work for hire."

Consumer and trade magazines, and some other publications, file a collective copyright that registers your work. Writers may register on their own, and definitely should, if the magazine doesn't carry a collective copyright notice. See this book's Appendix for more specific copyright information.

Worries about piracy and plagiarism are greatly exaggerated; it rarely happens. Copyright is formal notice of ownership, however, so make sure that it's filed. While most of the West has joined the International Copyright Union, many nations have not. So, don't lose sleep over unlikely rip-offs.

Payment schedule and publication date. Better publications pay "on acceptance" within 30 days of the date the editor buys the material. (With most fiction sales, this is also the time when the agreement is sent). Too many magazines pay well after publication—euphemistically called "payment *on* publication." Many writers simply won't work for on-publication money. For those who must, try to negotiate at least partial payment on acceptance. The writer loses control of other terms when a work languishes unpaid "in inventory."

There are times when a writer may wish to schedule delayed payment. Toward the end of one income tax year, freelancers may wish to have large advances or magazine fees extended into the following year. A fellow novelist ran afoul of the IRS when our mutual publisher dated her check December 31st, rather than January 1st. With a little foresight, you may get a better tax break.

Just as writers need their money as soon as possible, their reputations require early publication. Prominent writers can specify which issue will contain their work. Try to include "publication within 12 months of acceptance, or all rights revert to the writer" into your agreements, although many magazines will insist on 24 months.

Deadline and length. Both the length of the work, and the date that it's due, are crucial numbers. While not relevant to over-the-transom work, make "how long" and "when" a part of your on spec and assignment agreements. Delivery date is not the calendar day you slip the manila envelope into *your* mailbox, but the day it reaches the editor. If you require changes in either number, call for an extension. Sometimes, when a writer finds the article running longer than previously expected, payment is renegotiated. Failure to give advance notice of changes in length or delivery date will earn large demerits in the editor's memory book.

Editing and galleys. In a perfect world, editors would lose a toe for every cut. Editors are still walking; obviously we settle for less than perfection. Try for an agreement that requires your approval of cuts or other editorial changes, but don't be surprised if an editor says no. Often, there isn't time during the final paste-up to clear changes with the writer. With on spec and assigned work, it's not unusual for editors to request two rewrites without additional payment. Raise the matter at the outset, by all means—and hope for the best.

Some control of editorial changes comes with the right to receive galleys or "final edit." Galleys are copies of the typeset format as the work will actually appear, while final edit manuscript represents the stage just prior to typesetting. In both cases, editors are usually finished doing their worst. Legitimate errors of fact, mistakes in spelling or grammar, and sometimes lost text may be repaired at this time. Galleys must be returned promptly—in one week—so the busy freelancer often takes on quite a burden, but most writers want the opportunity. Many publications argue that they can do the job faster and more accurately inhouse.

Editing and galley approval are issues at the very core of our artistic integrity. If you choose to go to the wall over these terms, you must decide how badly you want to sell the work, or the next piece, to that editor.

Expenses and kill fees. New freelancers, fiction writers, and over-the-transom contributors rarely hear about these issues. For on spec and commissioned nonfiction, some of the costs of creation are paid by the publisher. Discuss these details before you begin work. Expense reimbursement is offered at three levels: limited, reasonable, and all incidentals. In the first case a limited amount is paid for phone calls, travel mileage, and photocopying. "Reasonable expenses" will cover a little more—dinner and drinks with your interview subject, for example.

"All incidentals" covers everything from a temporary secretary to plane tickets to St. Bart's. That Caribbean travel expense will be among your receipts only when a major magazine wants to hear about the funny way airplanes land near the Eden Rock Hotel. At all levels, prior approval and complete records are mandatory.

Kill fees are paid for acceptable, completed work that is finally rejected. The policy is most commonly followed for the better assigned nonfiction articles. Usually the kill fee is 20 to 25 percent of the original offer, although it may be more or less. The writer is free to sell a killed work elsewhere, but some magazines then require a return of the kill fee.

But is it art? Even the lowest-paying markets will sometimes accept artwork—photographs or illustrations—with over-the-transom and on spec nonfiction, but they rarely pay much additional for it. In most cases, artwork is chosen by the magazine's art director, not your editor. If you have special experience of a travel-related, architectural, or scientific nature, and are very good with 35 mm camera or paint brush, then offer artwork. Negotiation for photos or original drawings should be conducted separately from the writing agreement.

Other boilerplate issues. Although, as with formal book contracts, all parts of a magazine agreement ought to be open to negotiation, some are not. Principal among the "stand or fall" clauses are the writer's warranty and indemnification for libel.

With the warranty clause, few object to agreement that the work is original, wholly their own creation, and not an infringement on anybody else's copyright. With indemnification, on the other hand, many writers would prefer to cross it out. Most magazines won't agree. Technically, the indemnification clause requires the writer to guarantee that he has libeled no one, and has not through action or inaction placed the magazine open to a lawsuit. In practice, the freelancer must be accurate with descriptions and quotations, and must be willing to make any changes required by the magazine's attorney. In our increasingly litigious society, even writers of fiction have been sued successfully. "Malpractice" insurance has become available to writers. When warranty and indemnification clauses are included in magazine agreements, sources like *Law and the Writer* (Writer's Digest Books) will help clarify this quagmire.

Few of the above issues will, *or should*, be raised with every magazine sale. Payment rates and schedule, length and delivery date, and rights sold will be standard items of any agreement, but even those may not be open to negotiation. The wise writer, whether faced with an after-sale agreement or an editor's assignment, will keep a list of all possible issues handy. Be polite, but don't be afraid to ask.

What Editors Say...

The most over-rated selling tool for a new writer is the telephone. We are writers and readers in this business. If you can't write a thoughtful query and give me time to give it a thoughtful reading, then you probably don't have an idea for us.

—William B. McMorris, *Boy's Life*

We're a quarterly, so we work in three month increments. If an article isn't seasonal, we might let it sit around a while before we decide to use it. Give us time to respond.

—Ann Cuniff, *Openers*

The use of new developments in technology and science—even world events—is critical to science fiction. Our authors are our visionaries of tomorrow; their works are appropriate for us if they are focusing on new developments, new scientific discoveries, or extrapolations thereof. If dealing with older topics, ie., time travel, authors must present a new "twist" so that the tale doesn't appear trite or timeworn.

—Patrick Lucien Price, *Amazing Stories*

Editorial staffs are overworked; as a result time is in short supply. Writers must be thoroughly professional—from query to manuscript. Correspondence must be to the point and brief.

—Bruce Nygren, Thomas Nelson Publishers

We seem to have a lot of writers who keep submitting even though we have rejected them consistently for years. I'm not one for giving up, but what does it take to get through to some writers that perhaps they would be better suited to another publication?

—Pamela Yearsley, *UNITY Magazine*

One writer had scheduled a trip to Ireland. He called to ask if we would be interested in having him interview executives of Irish subsidiaries of Ohio firms. We were.

—R.W. Gardner, *Ohio Business*

One writing team landed an assignment by submitting a clear, short, to-the-point query accompanied by a one-page outline and SASE. They told us who'd be interested in the article and why—and they were right. They have since received a half-dozen assignments—*always* on time and *always* professional.

Another writer lost an assignment by submitting a six-page query insisting we were wrong in our assessment of our audience's interests. He suggested a series of 12 articles, sketchily described, and virtually demanded about 30% more than we usually pay.

—Diane Ingalls, *PROFILES Magazine*

In selecting writers for possible assignments, we look for people who are qualified in their particular subjects, who are dedicated enough to research their articles thoroughly, and who can write good, snappy, interesting copy.

—Laura L. Vitale, *Better Health & Living*

Try to use the word that conveys your *exact* meaning—not one that almost does the job. Pay careful attention to syntax; correct syntax is a great aid to *clarity* in writing.

—Clarissa Silitch, Yankee Books

A writer who "cleans up" his own writing is valuable to us. We want manuscripts that have been labored over—tight writing, good, direct sentence structure, as well as lively, descriptive style that will really involve the reader.

—Marjorie H. Rice, *Bridal Fair*

One of our writers double-submitted material to us and to a competitor. We found out when reviewing contracts that in addition to signing the copyright release he had added a note saying, "I'm not sure whether you ought to use this, since so-and-so has also bought it." The other magazine and ours were already in production so the article will appear in both, the same month. This person will not write for us again soon.

—Mary Lou Redding, *The Upper Room*

We look for writers who can tell a story that is both entertaining and *clear* to the 8-through-12-year-old reader. We want writers who talk *with* children, not *at* or *down* to them. Simplicity and good explanations are vital; however, children today are quite sophisticated. They are also easily bored. So we look for writers who can capture young imaginations with a lively style, original touches and humor. We always advise new writers to read the piece they have just written to a child in our age range. Most children will give you a frank—and sometimes surprising—critique.

—Pat Robbins, *National Geographic WORLD*

A Washington D.C. freelancer dropped me a query letter for a feature story, which didn't really appeal to our market. I responded negatively, but I was, at the time, looking for a Washington writer for a profile on an alumnus-senator. She sent samples of her writing and was given the assignment, which she did so well that we've been associated for three years.

—Gay L. Totten, *Purdue Alumnus*

We receive between 1,500 and 2,000 freelance/over-the-transom articles a year. Any article that gets published will have been reviewed by up to eight editors before acceptance. That takes time!

—Norman Perry, *St. Anthony Messenger*

It's hard for me not to consider it a waste of time when I receive communications—letters or phone calls—from writers who have no knowledge of our publication. Read before you write.

—Frank Bentayou, *Cleveland Magazine*

Getting the assignment for a book is only half the job. We have had writers sign a contract and then proceed to write the book that *they* always wanted, not necessarily what *we* wanted or what was agreed to in the contract.

—Rick Wolff, Alexander Hamilton Institute

Teenagers are growing more interested in topical issues and political activity, and we are trying to keep them informed on the issues that directly affect them. Many writers think that writing for a teenage audience means writing down to them, and that's demeaning to both reader and writer. At the same time, if a writer doesn't have a feel for teenagers, he or she won't grasp their frames of reference, and therefore, won't be able to connect with them. Some of the best writers can't write for *Seventeen*. Then again, some of the very best can—and do.

—Sarah Crichton, *Seventeen*

There is very little room in an editor's schedule for special treatment of writers; deadlines are not flexible; no material is "a must" for any publication.

—T.L. Solomon, *IBM PC UPDATE*

I prefer query letters WITH outlines. Query letters need to contain a lot of information on the subject. Anything that simply teases is rejected. A writer can land an assignment by presenting a well-focused query with plenty of 35mm slides of the artist's work. Articles with a step-by-step structure often have the best chances of acceptance for first-time writers. Slide sheets clearly labeled with an artwork's medium and size and title help.

—Mike Ward, *The Artist's Magazine*

The biggest trend seems to be every other publisher now wants to publish in Trade paperback. It just makes us more selective about everything we do. We are not particularly affected by fads or trends in publishing.

—George Young, Ten Speed Press

One writer sent a query letter misspelling both the company name and my name. Another way to lose an assignment is by not catching my attention in the first two lines of the query.

—Ed Rabinowitz, *Volkswagen's World*

The Romance Writers of America (R.W.A.) holds an annual contest for unpublished romance writers, the Golden Heart awards. Last year Harlequin bought two manuscripts that were read for this contest.

Our editors often give writing workshops or seminars associated with R.W.A. or local writer's groups. Attending these can be a valuable way of meeting an editor or getting up-to-date information.

—Laurie Bauman, Harlequin Books

What Writers Say...

Choose writing as a profession only if your drive is very strong and your talent becomes clear in your early attempts. Convinced of your ability, you have to be willing to work hard, make sacrifices of time and economic security. For most writers, a second career is essential.

—Flora Rheta Schreiber

The "secret" of writing is that there's no secret. Just sit down and do it, instead of blathering about it. Attach the seat of the pants to the seat of the chair. If you write two pages a day (about 20 minutes work) at the end of a year you'll have a book.

—Marion Zimmer Bradley

Too many beginning writers are in love with words and have not learned the fine art of using one simple word instead of a dozen fancy ones. In *Up the Down Staircase*, I had a whole chapter on racial prejudice. In my subsequent drafts, I condensed that chapter into a paragraph, and that paragraph into one sentence—a youngster writes, "Can you tell by my handwriting if I'm white or not?"

—Bel Kaufman

One thing I have stopped attempting is to judge whether what I write is any good. That is someone else's job. What I ask myself is—"Do I love this story, these people enough to stay with the book through thick and thin to The End?"

—Dorothy Cannell

After *Berlin Wild*, a big book, I was loathe to begin again. I found myself adding chapters to my just completed novel. John Hersey suggested I try a "little" book—and so I am.

—Elly Welt

Anyone involved in a long project is going to have seductive little ideas flitting by. Lately I try to retain some of these in fragmentary form. That way something is always more or less ongoing, and the crushing feeling of completion does not occur at the end of a project, so the theory goes.

—Madison Smartt Bell

My first "novel"—it was probably about ten pages—was completed when I was eight. I gathered my family together to hear it and found I could not read my own handwriting. It was the first great tragedy of my life.

—John Guinther

When I was having difficulty translating technical-speak into English, I was approached by my mentor, Irving Stone (not *the* Irving Stone; better). He knew instantly what the problem was. We looked down 28 floors to 42nd Street, and could see a guy standing on the corner, opening a copy of a tabloid newspaper. Irv pointed down, and said four words that constituted the best writing advice I ever received—"Write it for him."

—David A. Anderton

For rewriting, of which I do a great deal, I reread, looking for words that can be deleted without loss of sense—tautologies, unneeded adverbs. Then I reread it aloud, for rhythm and euphony. I try to make sure that every page has at least something colorful, amusing, or otherwise interesting.

—L. Sprague de Camp

Too many times I have been asked, "What do you do?" and when I respond, "I'm a writer," I immediately get the follow-up question, "Oh, and do you work?"

—Cork Millner

You can't live on what you make from a syndicated column—at least it takes lots of time to build up subscribers. Be sure to *not* put all your eggs in one basket. Have other, *paying*, ongoing writing work.

—Peter Weaver

I think if there is one area where there's a bit of prejudice against writers, it's in terms of finances. It takes an incredible amount of work to reach the same level as a well-paid secretary, and many people tend to look down on writers when they learn how low their incomes are. But, how many people are likely to be able to incorporate new interests—from Victorian history to birdwatching—into their work lives and earn money from it?

—Cheryl MacDonald

If I encounter an editor who is unfair and refuses to pay for work done, I complain, but if they are still unfair, I don't submit to them anymore. It's not their fault, usually. It's an unethical publisher who takes a writer's work without paying for it.

—Walter Olesky

I'm always entertained at writers' meetings here in Maine when I hear people who have never published anything worrying about copyright. For seven years I've been trying to write something good enough for someone to steal, but it has never happened.

—Robert Skoglund

Develop a good track record first, then look for an agent when you've got a book-length work in mind. It's a trial and error proposition. I've been with my current agent for more than ten years, but had an unsatisfactory relationship with another agent before that.

—John H. Lavin

I don't know of many people who earn an adequate income via self-syndication. If I were beginning today, and didn't have any subcribers, I would not try to syndicate myself.

—Robert Yoakum

Be successful in your primary endeavor before trying to attain syndication. Your reputation will sell your work.

—Murray Olderman

The arts are very much like athletics in that your body takes a real beating. The romanticization of alcohol, especially by male writers, deeply disturbs me. It's the road to self-defeat as a writer and self-hate as a person.

—Rita Mae Brown

The Markets

Book Publishers

Why do we begin this market section with a rather discouraging quote? Because it's good advice—a realistic statement on a common theme.

Book publishers receive far too many manuscripts that are clones of current bestsellers, manuscripts that have no audience or are not (yet) publishable. It's easy for beginning writers to blame "blind editors" or "dollar-hungry publishers" instead of recognizing that they, themselves, have failed to produce professional, timely and compelling manuscripts.

Of course many fine books do remain unpublished. Some of them have resided in desk drawers for years because the writer has no idea how to find a publisher. While there's no guarantee that *your* well-written manuscript will find a home in 1987, you'll increase your chances of success if you read—and re-read—this entire section.

The business of book publishing

If you want to satisfy a publisher's needs, you must understand a few facts about the industry as a whole. Book publishing is a blend of business and intuition that varies from one publishing house to the next. In deciding which books to publish, some rely on an editor's enthusiasm for a manuscript; others listen more carefully to the people who analyze each book's sales potential. Some publishers consider books that look like bestsellers—and nothing else. Others are proud to produce a few "literary" novels that will have only moderate sales compared to the other books on their list.

Like most businesses, publishing companies have been at the mercy of economic changes in the last few years. You may think that you, as a writer, are not affected when two publishers merge or when a conglomerate buys a publishing firm. Think again. Such changes are made for economic reasons, and the usual effect is "belt tightening."

As a result, many publishers now have smaller editorial staffs that are unable to review every query, proposal and manuscript. Yes, they still want to publish books of the highest quality, but it's no longer possible for them to consider hundreds—or thousands—of manuscripts each year. That's why more and more editors must rely on agents to "sift through the chaff."

All publishers must be profitable if they want to survive. When they look at their own financial performance, they recognize the importance of "big" books. Publishers want hot topics that are easily promotable through author tours and interviews. It's no wonder that "celebrity" books are as popular with editors as they are with readers.

As you continue writing and trying to sell your book(s), take some time to learn more about the publishing industry. Once you understand the role of editors and the complexities of the business, you'll see how you can improve your queries and manuscripts. Your study of specific publishers will also be a good investment in your future.

Trends and transitions

Predicting topics and types of books that will be popular in the next year is always risky. Tastes change as rapidly in books as in fashion, and there's always the chance that a "can't fail" book will be published six months too late. On the other hand, some books can be popular across the generations. An unusual number of reprints of children's books and romances is scheduled for 1987.

Do trends make books, or do books make trends? The answer, of course, is "yes." During one week in 1986, we read about the success of a number of publishers who have specialized in books about China or by Chinese writers; then we saw a brief news item reporting that "traveling to China" is the most common "fantasy" shared by men and women in the U.S.

Current events and population trends will certainly influence the types of books to be published in 1987 and 1988. You'll have to be one step ahead of the most recent information and events. Remember that publishers may be swamped with books on aerospace and nuclear safety, AIDS, and the upswing in conservative religion and politics—just as they were inundated with computer books a few years ago. Books that reflect general population trends such as the increasing affluence of "baby boomers" and "senior citizens" are probably on safer ground.

With those disclaimers in mind, here are some trends that may affect what editors buy this year:

• Self-help and how-to books continue to be popular. Topics range from home-remodeling to health and fitness—anything that affects readers' lives. Many people are too busy to read for entertainment alone; they want to *learn* as they read. If you know your subject well and can express yourself clearly, editors will be interested.

• Books for and about children should find a ready market. First-time parents want to know more about child care and parenting. They also want to provide good books for their children.

• Books for young people are on the increase. Juvenile series books are popular, and at least one publisher has announced plans for "prequels" of teen books that are geared toward pre-teen readers.

• Technical books are expected to remain steady as electronic and print data bases increase. These specialized books help professionals supplement their educations and keep up with advances in their fields.

• Headline-inspired books, like those about (and by) celebrities and experts, help readers satisfy their curiosity. Almost everyone wants to know more about people and events in the news. Books in this category must be especially timely or capable of sustaining interest beyond 1987.

• Books with film and video potential will continue to be sought by publishers. Writers, agents and publishers all want to increase the possibility of sales through these subsidiary rights.

• Mainstream fiction is always a good bet—if the publisher is convinced that it will have a large enough audience. The recent trend toward short story collections may have peaked out, but don't give up yet.

• Romance, science fiction and mysteries continue to be popular. Is this an escapist trend? Hybrid books, like romantic/suspense and science fiction/mystery novels, seek to attract larger audiences.

Remember that trends are constantly changing—that's what makes them *trends*, rather than absolutes. The publishing industry is in a state of transition, too, with changes in policies and personnel. Serious writers work to keep up-to-date.

Finding the right publisher

Don't spend years writing a book and only a few days looking for a publisher. Give your book the best publisher possible. For some writers, the best is a publisher whose books regularly appear on the bestseller lists. For others, the best is a small press where each author gets personal attention from the editor.

No matter what type of book you've written, this Book Publisher section can help you. You'll find more than 800 publishers listed. Not all of them buy the kind of work you write, but the Subject Indexes for nonfiction and fiction at the end of the section will tell you which ones do. You might want to review the appropriate index before you turn to the individual listings.

When you read the detailed listings of publishers, choose two or three that buy what you're writing. Send for their catalogs and writer's guidelines. You'll learn the most current information about the books they've published, as well as their preferences for receiving manuscripts. Try to read a couple of the publishers' books; a visit to the library is all that's necessary.

You may be frustrated by the manuscript preparation or writer's guidelines you receive. It seems that each publisher prefers a different type of submission. Some will read only a query letter; some want a letter with an outline/synopsis; others want a one-page proposal; few will read a completed manuscript. More and more editors accept submissions only through agents; don't waste their time (and yours) by submitting material directly. To see if you and your manuscript are ready for an agent, read the Author's Agents section.

Most editors like specific information in query letters. Show that you understand their concerns by mentioning the audience for your book, the competition, and why your book is different. The editor will also want to know if you have previous publishing experience or special training relevant to your book. Do *not* claim to have written "the next blockbuster bestseller"—even if you're certain that you have.

You may notice that more publishers are accepting electronic submissions—manuscripts prepared on a computer and sent on a disk or over phone lines. This isn't just a fad; publishers save typesetting costs when manuscripts are submitted electronically. At least one book publisher shares this savings by paying writers an extra 50¢/page for electronic submissions.

Remember that only a fraction of today's writers sell a book to the first place it's submitted. Prepare a list of at least a dozen publishers that might be interested in your book. Learn more about them; send for catalogs and guidelines a few at a time. If your submission comes back with a polite rejection, send it to the next publisher on your list.

You may be able to speed up this process with simultaneous submissions of your query letter or manuscript. It's usually OK to send queries to several editors at the same time—as long as each letter is individually addressed. Never send a "form letter" as a query. If more than one editor responds favorably, you may be able to submit your manuscript simultaneously. Some publishers, however, refuse to consider simultaneous submissions; their *Writer's Market* listings (and their guidelines) should tell you so. Otherwise, you can send your manuscript to two or more publishers at the same time—but you *must* notify the editors that it's a simultaneous submission.

Publishing alternatives

At the *Writer's Market* office, we receive many calls and letters asking about subsidy publishing and self-publishing. As you read more about the publishing industry, you'll undoubtedly find advertisements and articles describing the benefits of these alternatives. Be cautious. Know what *you* want from your writing.

Of course most writers want to make money from the books they write; not many succeed at first. Those who aspire to be professional writers know that it may take years to perfect a book, find the right publisher, and receive royalty payments. They are willing to invest their time and effort to meet that goal.

Some writers are more impatient. They've tried to sell a book and have met only rejection—*encouraging* rejection, perhaps, but still rejection. They know they haven't written bestsellers, but they don't believe their books can be improved by further revision. They're convinced that a specific market exists, and they want their books published *now*.

Other writers simply write for their own satisfaction, or for the pleasure of family and friends. Their writing may be "just a hobby," but with some encouragement they begin to wonder if they, too, could "be published." They haven't tried to market a manuscript before and are confused about the differences between "regular" publishers, subsidy publishers and self-publishing.

As a rule, we suggest you work with publishers that *pay writers*. Most publishers do this through a royalty arrangement, paying the author 3 to 25 percent of the wholesale or retail price. These "regular" publishers actively market their books; you'll find them in bookstores and libraries, read about them in the newspaper and sometimes see the author on TV. Whenever a copy of one of these books is sold, both the writer and the publisher make money.

Subsidy publishers, on the other hand, expect writers to *pay them* to cover all or part of the cost of producing a book. They may ask for $1,000 or sometimes as much as $8,000, explaining that "with the current economic conditions in book publishing, we would like you to share some of the risks involved. . . ." Subsidy publishers rarely market books as effectively as major publishing companies. They make money by selling their services to writers, not by selling their products to bookstores and libraries. Some subsidy publishers offer royalties but expect the writer to pay for promotion expenses.

Problems can arise when writers don't understand the policies and terms in a subsidy publisher's "proposal" or contract. Don't sign anything unless you understand and are comfortable with all the terms. If you are willing to pay to have your book published, you should be willing to hire an attorney to advise you on a contract.

A subsidy publisher is sometimes called a "vanity press" because the company appeals to the writer's ego with compliments and offers to "publish" the writer's book. Most subsidy publishers are offended when they are called vanity presses, but at *Writer's Market*, we don't distinguish between the two. Any publishing effort that asks the writer to pay all or part of the cost is identified as a subsidy publisher. Companies that subsidy publish more than 50% of their books each year are listed in *Writer's Market after* the "royalty" publishers.

This doesn't mean that subsidy publishing is always a bad choice. In Canada, for example, books are often subsidized by government grants. In the U.S. a special-interest book might be subsidized by the writer's friends, a foundation or church. Sometimes a "royalty" publisher will offer a subsidy arrangement to a writer whose talent outweighs the marketing potential of the book. Companies that occasionally do this (50% of the time or less) are identified with an asterisk in the listings.

Do it yourself

Self-publishing is another option for some writers. Are you willing to pay for a few hundred to several thousand copies of your book? Can you supervise all stages of its production? Do you have the time and energy to promote and distribute the book yourself?

"Self-publishing is probably preferable to subsidized publishing," said Sanford G. Thatcher, editor-in-chief of Princeton University Press. "Self-publishing doesn't seem to carry the same 'taint' as subsidized publishing, and I know of more successes among self-published books than subsidized ones."

Writers interested in self-publishing can approach a small press publisher and agree to split the cost of a press run. Some companies also call themselves self-publishers. More often, writers contract with a local printer to produce a specific number of books for a specific price.

As with subsidy publishing, be sure you know what's involved. "Done properly, self-publishing is an exciting and viable way to get your book into print," say Marilyn and Tom Ross, authors of *The Complete Guide to Self-Publishing* (Writer's Digest Books).

Your book

If you receive a number of rejections, don't give up. Many successful writers submit a manuscript to dozens of publishers before finding a "home" for their book.

Make sure that you've done everything in your power to improve your book's chances. Study writing and revision techniques; take a writing class; join a writer's group; continue to study the markets.

No matter which publishing route you choose for your book—royalty, subsidy, or self-publishing—remember that the writing of a good book comes first. Think of your book as a manuscript in transition; help it evolve into the best book it can be . . . while you continue your search for the best possible publisher.

‡**AASLH PRESS**, American Association for State and Local History, 172 2nd Ave. N., Nashville TN 37201. (615)255-2971. Director: Gerald George. Publishes hardcover originals and reprints. Averages 2-6 titles/year; receives 20-30 submissions annually. 50% of books from first-time authors; 100% of books from unagented writers. Pays 5-10% royalty on retail price. Publishes book an average of 1 year after acceptance. Photocopied submissions OK. Computer printout submissions acceptable; prefers letter-quality to dot-matrix. Reports in 3 months on submissions. Free book catalog.
Nonfiction: How-to, reference, self-help and textbook. "We publish books, mostly technical, that help people do effective work in historical societies, sites and museums, or do research in, or teach, history. No manuscripts on history itself—that is, on the history of specific places, events, people." Submit outline/synopsis and sample chapters. Reviews artwork/photos.
Recent Nonfiction Title: *Interpretation of Historic Sites*, by W.T. Alderson and Shirley Low (how-to paperback).
Tips: "Explain why our market will buy your book, use it, need it."

‡**ABBOTT, LANGER & ASSOCIATES**, 548 1st St., Crete IL 60417. (312)672-4200. President: Dr. Steven Langer. Publishes trade paperback originals and loose-leaf books. Averages 12 titles/year; receives 25 submissions annually. 75% of books from first-time authors; 100% of books from unagented writers. Pays 10-15% royalty; no advance. Publishes book an average of 1 year after acceptance. Photocopied submissions OK. Electronic submissions OK via disk, but requires hard copy also. Computer printout submissions acceptable. Reports in 2 weeks on queries; 1 month on mss.
Nonfiction: How-to, reference, technical on some phase of personnel administration, industrial relations, sales management, etc. Especially needs "a very limited number (3-5) of books dealing with very specialized topics in the field of personnel management, wage and salary administration, sales compensation, training, recruitment, selection, labor relations, etc." Publishes for personnel directors, wage and salary administrators, training directors, sales/marketing managers, security directors, etc. Query. Reviews artwork/photos.
Recent Nonfiction Title: *How to Develop, Conduct, and Use a Pay/Fringe Benefit Survey*, by Carl F. Lutz.
Tips: "A how-to book in personnel management, sales/marketing management or security management has the best chance of selling to our firm."

ABINGDON PRESS, 201 8th Ave. S., Box 801, Nashville TN 37202. (615)749-6403. Director of Publishing: Ronald P. Patterson. Executive Editor Trade Books: Michael E. Lawrence. Executive Editor Reference/Academic books; Carey J. Gifford. Executive Editor Church Resources; Leslie Pomeroy. Publishes paperback originals and reprints; church supplies. Averages 100 titles/year; receives approximately 2,500 submissions annually. 10% of books from first-time authors; 90-95% of books from unagented writers. Average print order for a writer's first book is 4,000-5,000. Pays royalty. Publishes book an average of 18 months after acceptance. Electronic submissions OK—"we have a Shaffstall converter." Requests advance consultation and sample disk. Computer printout submissions acceptable; prefers letter-quality to dot-matrix. Query with outline and samples only. Ms guidelines for SASE. Reports in 6 weeks.
Nonfiction: Religious-lay and professional, children's religious books and academic texts. Length: 32-300 pages. Reviews artwork/photos.
Recent Nonfiction Title: *Winning Through Integrity*, by Cliff C. Jones.
Fiction: Juveniles only. Reviews artwork/photos.

‡ *The double dagger before a listing indicates that the listing is new in this edition. New markets are often the most receptive to freelance contributions.*

Recent Fiction Title: *Wolfhunter*, by Joel Kaufmann.

Tips: "A short, pithy book is ahead of the game. Long, rambling books are a luxury few can afford. Religious nonfiction work geared to church professionals is the area in which we see our best sales."

HARRY N. ABRAMS, INC., Subsidiary of Times Mirror Co. 100 5th Ave., New York NY 10011. (212)206-7715. President, Publisher and Editor-in-Chief: Paul Gottlieb. Publishes hardcover and "a few" paperback originals. Averages 65 titles/year; receives "thousands" of submissions annually. 5% of books from first-time authors; 25% of books from unagented writers. "We are one of the few publishers who publish almost exclusively illustrated books. We consider ourselves the leading publishers of art books and high-quality artwork in the U.S." Offers variable advance. Publishes book an average of 1-2 years after acceptance. Photocopied submissions OK. Computer printout submissions acceptable; no dot-matrix. Reports in 3 months. Free book catalog.

Nonfiction: Art, nature and science, and outdoor recreation. Needs illustrated books for art and art history, museums. Submit outline/synopsis and sample chapters and illustrations. Reviews artwork/photos as part of ms package.

Recent Nonfiction Title: *Renoir, His Life, Art, and Letters*, by Barbara Ehrlich White.

Tips: "We publish *only* high-quality illustrated art books, i.e., art, art history, museum exhibition catalog, written by specialists and scholars in the field. Once the author has signed a contract to write a book for our firm the author must finish the manuscript to agreed-upon high standards within the schedule agreed upon in the contract."

ACADEMY CHICAGO, 425 N. Michigan Ave., Chicago IL 60611. (312)644-1723. Editorial Director/Senior Editor: Anita Miller. Publishes hardcover and paperback originals and reprints. Averages 60 titles/year; receives approximately 2000 submissions annually. 10% of books from first-time authors; 25% of books from unagented writers. Average print order for a writer's first book 1,500-3,500. Pays 7-10% royalty; no advance. Publishes book an average of 18 months after acceptance. Photocopied submissions OK. No computer printout submissions. Reports in 2 months.

Nonfiction: Adult, travel, and historical. No how-to, cookbooks, self-help, etc. Query and submit first four consecutive chapters. Reviews artwork/photos.

Recent Nonfiction Title: *Age of Agony*, by Guy Williams.

Fiction: "Mysteries, mainstream novels." No "romantic" fiction, or religious or sexist material; nothing avant-garde. "We can no longer do children's books or young adults."

Recent Fiction Title: *Carlyle Simpson*, by Karen Lee Osborne.

Tips: "The writer has the best chance of selling our firm a good mystery, because the response to these is predictable, relatively."

‡ACCELERATED DEVELOPMENT INC., 3400 Kilgore Ave., Muncie IN 47304. (317)284-7511. President: Dr. Joseph W. Hollis. Executive Vice President: Mrs. Marcella Hollis. Publishes textbooks/paperback originals and software. Averages 10-12 titles/year; receives 120 submissions annually. 50% of books from first-time authors; 100% of books from unagented writers. Electronic submissions OK if compatible with CPT equipment (schedule needs to be arranged), but requires hard copy also. Computer printout submissions acceptable; prefers letter-quality to dot-matrix. Pays 6-15% royalty on net price. Publishes book an average of 1 year after acceptance. Reports in 3 months. Free book catalog.

Nonfiction: Reference books and textbooks on psychology, counseling, guidance and counseling, teacher education and death education. Especially needs "psychologically-based textbook or reference materials, death education material, theories of counseling psychology, techniques of counseling, and gerontological counseling." Publishes for professors, counselors, teachers, college and secondary students, psychologists, death educators, psychological therapists, and other health-service providers. "Write for the graduate level student." Submit outline/synopsis, 2 sample chapters, prospectus, and author's resume. Reviews artwork/photos.

Recent Nonfiction Title: *Bulimia: Book for Therapist and Client*, by B. Bauer, Ph.D., W.Anderson, Ph.D., and R. Hyatt, M.D.

Tips: "Freelance writers should be aware of American Psychological Association style of preparing manuscripts."

ALWAYS submit mss or queries with a stamped, self-addressed envelope (SASE) within your country or International Reply Coupons (IRCs) purchased from the post office for other countries.

ACCENT BOOKS, A division of Accent Publications, 12100 W. 6th Ave., Box 15337, Denver CO 80215. (303)988-5300. Managing Editor: Mary B. Nelson. Publishes evangelical Christian paperbacks, the majority of which are nonfiction, though fiction books are considered if they contain underlying Christian message and are either contemporary mystery/romance or frontier romance. Averages 18-24 titles/year. 30% of books from first-time authors; 100% of books from unagented writers. Pays royalty on cover price. Publishes book an average of 9 months after acceptance. Computer printout submissions acceptable; no dot-matrix. Query or submit 2 sample chapters with a brief synopsis and chapter outline. Do not submit full ms unless requested. Reports in 2-3 months. Ms guidelines for SASE.
Recent Nonfiction Title: *The Woman God Can Use.*
Recent Fiction Title: *Moonshell.*
Tips: "How-to books and 'helping' books for the Christian emphasizing the importance of God's Word in the lives of individuals, books that address issues today's Christians need information on, and books for the professional and the volunteer in church ministry have the best chance of selling to our firm."

ACE SCIENCE FICTION, The Berkley Publishing Group, 200 Madison Ave., New York NY 10016. (212)686-9820. Publishes paperback originals and reprints. Publishes 120 titles/year.
Fiction: Science fiction and fantasy. Query with outline and 3 sample chapters. Reports in 3 months.

ACROPOLIS BOOKS, LTD., Subsidiary of Colortone Press, 2400 17th St. NW, Washington DC 20009. (202)387-6805. Publisher: Alphons J. Hackl. Publishes hardcover and trade paperback originals. Averages 25 titles/year. Pays individually negotiated royalty. Publishes book an average of 7 months after acceptance. Electronic submissions OK, but requires hard copy also. Computer printout submissions acceptable; prefers letter-quality to dot-matrix. Reports in 2 months. Free book catalog.
Nonfiction: How-to, reference and self-help. Subjects include health, beauty/fashion and money management. "We will be looking for manuscripts dealing with fashion and beauty, and self development. We also will be continuing our teacher books for early childhood education. Our audience includes general adult consumers, professional elementary school teachers and children." Submit outline/synopsis and sample chapters. Reviews artwork/photos as part of ms package.
Recent Nonfiction Title: *Earn College Credit for What you Know,* by Susan Simosko.

ACS PUBLICATIONS, INC., Box 16430, San Diego CA 92116-0430. (619)297-9203. Editorial Director: Maritha Pottenger. Publishes trade paperback originals and reprints. Averages 10 titles/year; receives 400 submissions annually. 50% of books from first-time authors; 95% of books from unagented writers. Average print order for a writer's first book is 3,000. Pays 15% royalty "on monies received through wholesale and retail sales." No advance. Publishes book an average of 2 years after acceptance. Photocopied submissions OK "if neat." Electronic submissions OK if CP/M compatible with Cromemco, DEC VT180, IBM CPM-86, Osborne, and Xerox (5¼" diskettes; 9 track, 800 bpi, ½ inch magnetic tape; ASCII also acceptable). Prefers hard copy first to evaluate. Computer printout submissions acceptable; prefers letter-quality to dot-matrix. Reports in 1 month on queries; 2 months on mss. Free book catalog. Manuscript guidelines for 9x12 SAE and 4 first class stamps.
Nonfiction: Self-help, astrology and New Age. Subjects include holistic health alternatives, psychology, numerology, and psychic understanding. "Our most important market is astrology. We are seeking pragmatic, useful, immediately applicable contributions to field; prefer psychological approach. Specific ideas and topics should enhance people's lives. Research also valued. No determinism ('Saturn made me do it.') No autobiographies. No airy-fairy 'space cadet' philosophizing. Keep it grounded, useful, opening options (not closing doors) for readers." Query or submit outline/synopsis and 3 sample chapters.
Recent Nonfiction Title: *Seven Paths to Understanding,* by Zipporah Dobyns and William Wrobel.
Tips: "Our readers are astrology students and professionals plus the general public interested in increased fulfillment through nontraditional paths. The writer has the best chance of selling us a book that is inspiring and immediately useful, one emphasizing personal responsibility. Our publishing philosophy is opposed to fatalism."

‡ADDISON-WESLEY PUBLISHING CO., INC., General Books Division, Jacob Way, Reading MA 01867. Publisher: Ann Dilworth. Publishes hardcover and paperback originals. Publishes 50 titles/year. Pays royalty. Simultaneous and photocopied submissions OK. Reports in 1 month. Free book catalog.
Nonfiction: Biography, business/economics, health, how-to, photography, politics, psychology and science. "Also needs books on 'tools for living' related to finance, health, education, and parenting by people well-known and respected in their field." Query, then submit outline/synopsis and 1 sample chapter.
Recent Nonfiction Title: *The New Joy of Photography,* by Eastman Kodak.
Tips: Queries/mss may be routed to other editors in the publishing group.

‡ADLER & ADLER, PUBLISHERS, INC., Suite 705, 4550 Montgomery Ave., Bethesda MD 20814. (301)654-4271. Editor-in-Chief: George Walsh. Publishes hardcover and trade paperback originals, and hardcover reprints. Averages 20-25 titles/year. 25% of books from first-time authors; 15% of books from unagented writers. Pays 7½-15% royalty on wholesale price. Offers variable advance. Simultaneous and photocopied submissions OK. Electronic submissions OK via IBM-PC Wordperfect, but requires hard copy also. Computer printout submissions OK; prefers letter-quality to dot-matrix. Reports in 2 weeks on queries; 6 weeks on mss. Book catalog free on request.

Nonfiction: Biography, reference, and general trade nonfiction. Subjects include business and economics, health, history, politics, psychology, sociology, travel, science, education, and current events. Submit outline/synopsis and sample chapters or complete ms.

Recent Nonfiction Title: *The Price of a Life: One Woman's Death from Toxic Shock*, by Tom Riley (current affairs).

Fiction: Submit outline/synopsis and sample chapters or complete ms.

Recent Fiction Title: *Daughters of Jerusalem*, by Roger Cleeve.

Tips: Writer has the best chance of selling nonfiction to this press.

AFFIRMATION BOOKS, 22 The Fenway, Boston MA 02215. (617)266-8792. Executive Editor: Marie Kraus. Publishes trade paperback originals. Publishes 4 titles/year; receives 75 submissions annually. 50% of books from first-time authors; 100% of books from unagented writers. Pays 5-10% royalty on retail or wholesale price. Publishes book an average of 1 year after acceptance. Simultaneous and photocopied submissions OK. Computer printout submissions acceptable; no dot-matrix. Reports in 1 month on queries; 3 months on mss. Book catalog for #10 SAE and 1 first class stamp.

Nonfiction: Self-help. Subjects include psychology (combined with religion) and religion (combined with psychology; Christian, no dogma). "Affirmation Books is part of the ministry of the House of Affirmation, international therapeutic residential centers for clergy and religious suffering from emotional unrest (not alcohol or drug problems). We need books for an audience that is primarily clergy and religious or lay people working in or for the Catholic Church. Topics on healthy emotional living that will help people improve the quality of their lives. Not pop psychology; some research or mention of previous literature in the field." No personal journeys, alcohol or drug problems, or books aimed at parents only. Query or submit outline/synopsis and sample chapters. Reviews artwork/photos.

Recent Nonfiction Title: *Midlife Wanderer: The Woman Religious in Midlife Transition*, by Sheila Murphy.

Tips: "We are primarily a mail-order business although we are looking to expand our bookstore outlets. Because we have a specific audience, clergy, men and women religious, lay people, none of our backlist has gone out of print. We are interested in expanding our audience. The writer has the best chance of selling our firm a book that combines psychology and Christianity in a way that helps our audience improve the quality of their lives. No autobiographical material or personal journeys."

AGLOW PUBLICATIONS, A ministry of Women's Aglow Fellowship International, Box I, Lynnwood WA 98046-1557. (206)775-7282. Editor: Gwen Weising. Publishes mass market paperback originals. Averages 10 titles/year; receives 1,000 submissions annually. 50% of books from first-time authors; 95% of books from unagented writers. Average print order of a writer's first book is 10,000. Pays up to 7½% maximum royalty on retail price "depending on amount of editorial work needed"; buys some mss outright. No advance. Publishes book 1 year after acceptance. Photocopied submissions OK. Computer printout submissions acceptable; prefers letter-quality to dot-matrix. Reports in 1 month on queries; 2 months on mss. Free book catalog. Ms guidelines for SASE.

Nonfiction: Bible studies, self-help, inspirational and cookbooks. Subjects include religion (Christian only). "Familiarize yourself with our materials before submitting. Our needs and formats are very specific." Query or submit outline/synopsis and first 3 sample chapters.

Recent Nonfiction Title: *Living Fully*, by George O. Wood.

Fiction: "We are a Christian women's publishing house and are looking for manuscripts for both teenage girls and women. No secular material or material directed toward a men's audience." Query or submit outline/synopsis and sample chapters.

Tips: "The writer has the best chance of selling our firm a book that shows some aspect of the Christian life."

AHSAHTA PRESS, Boise State University, Dept. of English, 1910 University Dr., Boise ID 83725. (208)385-1246. Co-Editor: Tom Trusky. Publishes trade paperback originals. Averages 3 titles/year; receives 500 submissions annually. 75% of books from first-time authors; 75% of books from unagented writers. Pays 25% royalty on retail price. "Royalty commences with third printing." Publishes books an average of 8 months after acceptance. Simultaneous and photocopied submissions OK. Computer printout submissions acceptable; prefers letter-quality to dot-matrix. Reports in 2 weeks on queries; 3 months on mss. Ms guidelines for SASE.

Poetry: Contemporary Western American (cultural ecological or historical) poetry collections only. No "rhymed verse, songs of the sage, buckaroo ballads, purple mountain's majesty, coyote wisdom; Jesus-in-the-prairie, or 'nice' verse." Accepts poetry translations from native American languages, Spanish and Basque. Submit 15 samples between February and April. "Write incredible, original poetry."

Recent Poetry Title: *Flights of the Harvest-Mare*, by Linda Bierds (two-time Writer's Choice award-winner).

‡***ALASKA NATURE PRESS**, Box 632, Eagle River AK 99577. Editor/Publisher: Ben Guild. Publishes hardcover and paperback originals. Plans to offer subsidy publishing "as needed—estimated 10%." Averages 2 titles/year. 75-80% of books from first-time authors; 100% of books from unagented writers. Pays 10% royalty on retail price; no advance. Publishes book 24-30 months after acceptance. Simultaneous and photocopied submissions OK. Computer printout submissions acceptable; prefers letter-quality to dot-matrix. Reports in 4 months.
Nonfiction: Alaska material only: animals, biography, history, how-to, juveniles, nature, photography, poetry, recreation, wildlife, nature and self-help. No hunting or fishing tales. Query or submit outline/synopsis and 2-3 sample chapters or complete ms. Reviews artwork/photos as part of ms package. "As a specialty publishing house (we take *only* Alaskans' material) the work *must* have an impact on Alaska or people interested in Alaska—for Alaska."
Fiction: Alaska material only—*adventure, historical,* romance and suspense. Query editor/publisher. Reports in 4 months.

ALASKA NORTHWEST PUBLISHING CO., 130 Second Ave., Edmonds WA 98020. Editor and Publisher: Robert A. Henning. Publishes primarily paperback originals. Averages 12 titles/year; receives 250 submissions annually. 80% of books from first-time authors; 95% of books from unagented writers. Most contracts call for 10% royalty. "Rejections are made promptly, unless we have three or four possibilities in the same general field, and it's a matter of which one gets the decision. That could take three months." Publishes book an average of 2 years after acceptance. Computer printout submissions acceptable; prefers letter-quality to dot-matrix. Free book catalog.
Nonfiction: "Alaska, northern British Columbia, Yukon, Northwest Territories and northwest U.S. are subject areas. Emphasis on life in the last frontier, history, biography, cookbooks, travel, field guides and outdoor subjects. Writer must be familiar with area first-hand. We listen to any ideas." Query with outline, sample chapters, and any relevant photographs preferred. Reviews artwork/photos as part of ms package.
Tips: "First-person nonfiction, preferably resource- but not development-oriented, and informal prose (well organized, syntax reasonably good) have the best chance of selling to our firm."

ALBA HOUSE, 2187 Victory Blvd., Staten Island, New York NY 10314. (212)761-0047. Editor-in-Chief: Anthony L. Chenevey. Publishes hardcover and paperback originals and reprints. Specializes in religious books. "We publish shorter editions than many publishers in our field." Averages 15 titles/year; receives 1,000 submissions annually. 50% of books from first-time authors; 80% of books from unagented writers. Pays 10% royalty on retail price. Publishes book an average of 9 months after acceptance. Computer printout submissions acceptable; prefers letter-quality to dot-matrix. Query. State availability of photos/illustrations. Simultaneous and photocopied submissions OK. Reports in 1 month. Book catalog and ms guidelines for SASE. Reviews artwork/photos.
Nonfiction: Publishes philosophy, psychology, religion, sociology, textbooks and Biblical books. Accepts nonfiction translations from French, German or Spanish. Submit outline/synopsis and 1-2 sample chapters.
Recent Nonfiction Title: *The Making of a Pastoral Person*, by Gerald Niklas.
Tips: "We look to new authors." Queries/mss may be routed to other editors in the publishing group.

THE ALBAN INSTITUTE, INC., 4125 Nebraska Ave. NW, Washington DC 20016. (202)244-7320. Director of Publications: Celia A. Hahn. Publishes trade paperback originals. Averages 6 to 8 titles/year; receives 100 submissions annually. 100% of books from unagented writers. Pays 7% royalty; $50 on publication for 2- to 8-page articles relevant to congregational life—practical—ecumenical. Publishes book an average of 1 year after acceptance. Computer printout submissions acceptable; prefers letter-quality to dot-matrix. Reports in 2 months. Prefers queries. Book catalog and ms guidelines for SASE.
Nonfiction: Religious—focus on local congregation—ecumenical. Must be accessible to general reader. Research preferred. Needs mss on the task of the ordained leader in, the congregation, the career path of the ordained leader in the congregation, problems and opportunities in congregational life, and ministry of the laity in the world and in the church. No sermons, devotional, anecdotal, inspirational type or prayers. Query or submit outline/synopsis and sample chapters.
Recent Nonfiction Title: *So You're on the Search Committee*, by Bunty Ketcham.
Tips: "Our audience is intelligent, probably liberal mainline Protestant and Catholic clergy and lay leaders, executives and seminary administration/faculty—people who are concerned with the local church at a practical level and new approaches to its ministry."

*Asterisk preceding a listing indicates that individual subsidy publishing or co-publishing (where author pays part or all of publishing costs) is also available. Firms whose subsidy programs comprise more than 50% of their total publishing activities are listed at the end of the Book Publishers section.

ALBATROSS PUBLISHING HOUSE, 500 Fifth Ave., New York NY 10110. Editor: Candace Maté. Publishes hardcover originals. Averages 4 titles/year. Pays 5-15% royalty on retail price; offers "open" advance. Simultaneous submissions OK. SAE and IRCs. Reports in 2 weeks on queries; 1 month on mss.
Nonfiction: How-to and reference (nautical). "We're looking for practical books on any aspect of sailing, boat building, seamanship, navigation, and the related fields." No cruising stories. Query or submit outline/synopsis and sample chapters.
Recent Nonfiction Title: *The World's Best Sailboats*, by Ferenc Maté.

ALLEN & UNWIN, INC., 8 Winchester Place, Winchester MA 01890. (617)729-0830. Publisher: John Michel. Publishes hardcover and paperback originals. Averages 150 titles/year. Publishes book an average of 1 year after acceptance. Simultaneous and photocopied submissions OK. Computer printout submissions acceptable. Reports in 3 weeks. Book catalog for SASE.
Nonfiction: Business/economics, history, literature, literary criticism, philosophy, politics, reference, science, sociology, technical and textbooks. Especially needs advanced university material; must be of international interest. Submit outline/synopsis and sample chapters.

ALLEN PUBLISHING CO., 7324 Reseda Blvd., Reseda CA 91335. Publisher: Michael Wiener. Publishes paperback originals. Averages 3 titles/year; receives 50 submissions annually. 50% of books from first-time authors; 100% of books from unagented writers. Pays 10% royalty on net price; no advance. Publishes book an average of 6 months after acceptance. Simultaneous and photocopied submissions OK. Computer printout submissions acceptable; prefers letter-quality to dot-matrix. "Author queries welcome from new or established writers. Do not send manuscript or sample chapter." Reports in 2 weeks. SASE "essential." One-page author guidelines available for SASE.
Nonfiction: Self-help material, 20,000-30,000 words, aimed at wealth-builders. "We want to reach the vast audience of opportunity seekers who, for instance, purchased *Lazy Man's Way to Riches*, by Joe Karbo. Material must be original and authoritative, not rehashed from other sources. Most of what we market is sold via mail order in softcover book form. No home fix-it, hobby hints, health or 'cure' books, or 'faith' stories, poetry or fiction. We are a specialty publisher and will not consider any book not fitting the above description." Reviews artwork/photos as part of ms package.
Recent Nonfiction Title: *How To Start Your First Business*.
Tips: "We are looking for books that appeal to down-and-out people who want to start a business of their own or otherwise turn around their financial status. We do not aim at the sophisticated, highly-educated person looking for such things as tax shelters and complicated investments. Our audience is looking for uncomplicated answers to their financial problems. Any manuscript we consider must meet that criterion while, at the same time, avoiding the trap of claiming to offer a get-rich-quick approach."

ALMAR PRESS, 4105 Marietta Dr., Binghamton NY 13903. (607)722-0265. Editor-in-Chief: A.N. Weiner. Managing Editor: M.F. Weiner. Publishes hardcover and paperback originals and reprints. Averages 6 titles/year; receives 100 submissions annually. 75% of books from first-time authors; 100% of books from unagented writers. Average print order for a writer's first book is 2,000. Pays 10% royalty; no advance. Publishes book an average of 3 months after acceptance. Prefers exclusive submissions; however, simultaneous (if so indicated) and photocopied submissions OK. Electronic submissions OK if compatible with IBM-PC. Computer printout submissions acceptable; prefers letter-quality to dot-matrix. Reports in 1 month. Book catalog for SASE.
Nonfiction: Publishes business, technical, and consumer books and reports. "These main subjects include general business, financial, travel, career, technology, personal help, hobbies, general medical, general legal, and how-to. *Almar Reports* are business and technology subjects published for management use and prepared in 8½x11 and book format. Publications are printed and bound in soft covers as required. Reprint publications represent a new aspect of our business." Submit outline/synopsis and sample chapters. Reviews artwork/photos as part of ms package. Looks for information in the proposed book that makes it different or unusual enough to attract book buyers. Reviews artwork/photos.
Recent Nonfiction Title: *How to Buy, Install and Maintain Your Own Telephone Equipment*, by La Carrubba and Zimmer.
Tips: "We look for timely subjects. The type of book the writer has the best chance of selling to our firm is something different or unusual—*no* poetry or fiction, also *no* first-person travel or family history. The book must be complete and of good quality."

*ALYSON PUBLICATIONS, INC., 40 Plympton St., Boston MA 02118. (617)542-5679. Publisher: Sasha Alyson. Publishes trade paperback originals and reprints. Averages 20 titles/year; receives 500 submissions annually. 50% of books from first-time authors; 80% of books from unagented writers. Average print order for a writer's first book is 6,000. Subsidy publishes 5% of books. Pays 8-15% royalty on net price; buys some mss outright for $200-1,000; offers average $600 advance. Publishes book an average of 15 months after acceptance. Computer printout submissions acceptable; no dot-matrix. Reports in 2 weeks on queries; 5 weeks on mss. Looks for "writing ability and content suitable for our house." Book catalog and ms guidelines for business-size SAE and 3 first class stamps.

Nonfiction: Subjects include gay/lesbian. "We are especially interested in nonfiction providing a positive approach to gay/lesbian issues." Accepts nonfiction translations. Submit one-page synopsis. Reviews artwork/photos as part of ms package.

Recent Nonfiction Title: *The Men With the Pink Triangle,* by Heinz Heger (history).

Fiction: Gay novels. Accepts fiction translations. Submit one-page synopsis.

Recent Fiction Title: *Between Friends,* by Gillian E. Hanscombe (lesbian fiction).

Tips: "We publish many books by new authors. The writer has the best chance of selling to our firm well-researched, popularly-written nonfiction on a subject (e.g., some aspect of gay history) that has not yet been written about much. With fiction, create a strong storyline that makes the reader want to find out what happens. With nonfiction, write in a popular style for a non-academic audience."

*AMEREON LTD., Box 1200, Mattituck NY 11952. (516)298-5100. Subsidiaries include J.M. Carroll & Co., Box 44, Bryan TX 77806, and Amereon House. Editor: Kay B. Russell. Will not consider unsolicited manuscripts in 1987.

AMERICAN ASTRONAUTICAL SOCIETY, (Univelt, Inc., Publisher), Box 28130, San Diego CA 92128. (619)746-4005. Editorial Director: H. Jacobs. Publishes hardcover originals. Averages 8-10 titles/year; receives 12-15 submissions annually. 5% of books from first-time authors; 5% of books from unagented writers. Average print order for a writer's first book is 600-2,000. Pays 10% royalty on actual sales; no advance. Publishes book an average of 4 months after acceptance. Simultaneous and photocopied submissions OK. Computer printout submissions acceptable; prefers letter-quality to dot-matrix. Reports in 1 month. Free book catalog; ms guidelines for SAE and 39¢ postage.

Nonfiction: Proceedings or monographs in the field of astronautics, including applications of aerospace technology to Earth's problems. "Our books must be space-oriented or space-related. They are meant for technical libraries, research establishments and the aerospace industry worldwide." Submit outline/synopsis and 1-2 sample chapters. Reviews artwork/photos as part of ms package.

Recent Nonfiction Title: *Soviet Lunar and Planetary Exploration,* by N.L. Johnson.

‡*AMERICAN ATHEIST PRESS, American Atheists, Box 2117, Austin TX 78768-2117. (512)458-1244. Editor: R. Murray-O'Hair. Publishes trade paperback originals and trade paperback reprints. Averages 12 titles/year; receives 200 submissions annually. 40-50% of books from first-time authors; 100% of books from unagented writers. Subsidy publishes 0-5% of books. "If a work does not meet the overall standards or goals of our press, we will consider publishing it under subsidy arrangements, providing that it is of an adequate quality." Pays 5-10% royalty on retail price. Publishes book an average of 8 months after acceptance. Simultaneous and photocopied submissions OK. Computer printout submissions acceptable; prefers letter-quality to dot-matrix. Reports in 3 weeks on queries; 6 weeks on submissions. Free book catalog.

Imprints: Gusttav Broukal Press, R. Murray-O'Hair, editor.

Nonfiction: Biography, humor, reference and general. Subjects include history (of religion and Atheism, of the effects of religion historically); philosophy and religion (from an Atheist perspective, particularly criticism of religion); politics (separation of state and church, religion and politics); Atheism (particularly the lifestyle of Atheism; the history of Atheism; applications of Atheism). "We are interested in hard-hitting and original books expounding the lifestyle of Atheism and criticizing religion. We would like to see more submissions dealing with the histories of specific religious sects, such as the L.D.S., the Worldwide Church of God, etc. We are generally not interested in biblical criticism." Submit outline/synopsis and sample chapters or complete ms. Reviews artwork/photos.

Recent Nonfiction Title: *The Trial of C.B. Reynolds,* by Madalyn O'Hair.

Fiction: Humor (satire of religion or of current religious leaders); anything of particular interest to Atheists. "We rarely publish any fiction. But we have occasionally released a humorous book." No mainstream. "For our press to consider fiction, it would have to tie in with the general focus of our press, which is the promotion of Atheism and free thought." Submit outline/synopsis and sample chapters.

Tips: "Our press will look at a good variety of perspectives (though not religious ones)—authors would be surprised at what we might be interested in. A manuscript of 200-500 pages of scholarly quality and popular approach has the best chance of selling to us."

AMERICAN CATHOLIC PRESS, 1223 Rossell Ave., Oak Park IL 60302. (312)386-1366. Editorial Director: Father Michael Gilligan. Publishes hardcover originals and hardcover and paperback reprints. "Most of our sales are by direct mail, although we do work through retail outlets." Pays by outright purchase of $25-100; no advance. Publishes book an average of 8 months after acceptance. Simultaneous and photocopied submissions OK. Computer printout submissions acceptable. Reports in 2 months. Free book catalog.

Nonfiction: "We publish books on the Roman Catholic liturgy—for the most part, books on religious music and educational books and pamphlets. We also publish religious songs for church use, including Psalms, as

well as choral and instrumental arrangements. We are very interested in new music, meant for use in church services. Books, or even pamphlets, on the Roman Catholic Mass are especially welcome. We have no interest in secular topics and are not interested in religious poetry of any kind." Query.
Recent Nonfiction Title: *The Role of Music in the New Roman Liturgy*, by W. Herring (educational).

AMERICAN COUNCIL FOR THE ARTS, 570 7th Ave., New York NY 10018. (212)354-6655. Editor-in-Chief: Robert Porter. Publishes hardcover and trade paperback originals. Averages 5-8 titles/year; 50-100 submissions annually. 75% of books from first-time authors; 100% of books from unagented writers. Average print order of a writer's first book is 3,000. Pays 10-15% royalty on wholesale or retail price. Publishes book an average of 1 year after acceptance. Simultaneous and photocopied submissions OK. Electronic submissions OK if compatible with DECmate II, but requires hard copy also. Computer printout submissions acceptable. Reports in 1 month on queries; 2 months on mss. Free book catalog.
Nonfiction: How-to, reference, technical, textbook and professional books on business and economics—nonprofit management, recreation, sociology, and travel—all as they pertain to the arts. Books on the arts in areas of management, reference, public policy, and role in society (i.e., city life, travel, recreation, education, etc.). Especially needs books on nonprofit management skills, especially the arts (i.e., marketing, planning); public policy in the arts; resource directories for the arts; and practical discussions of ways the arts can be integrated into specific aspects of everyday life. Publishes for artists, professionals, and trustees of arts organizations and agencies; university faculty and students; professionals and trustees of nonprofit institutions. No mss on the aesthetics of specific arts disciplines or biographies. Query or submit outline/synopsis and 3-4 sample chapters. Reviews artwork/photos as part of ms package.
Recent Nonfiction Title: *The Road Show: A Handbook for Successful Booking and Touring in the Performing Arts*, by Rena Shagan.

‡AMERICAN FEDERATION OF INFORMATION PROCESSING SOCIETIES, INC. (AFIPS), 1899 Preston White Dr., Reston VA 22091. (703)620-8918. Director: Chris Hoelzel. Publishes hardcover and trade paperback originals. Averages 6 titles/year; receives 15 submissions annually. Simultaneous and photocopied submissions OK. Electronic submissions OK via IBM system 38, PC, XT, but requires hard copy also. Computer printout submissions acceptable; prefers letter-quality to dot-matrix. Book catalog free on request.
Nonfiction: Reference, technical and textbook on computing. Query. Reviews artwork/photos.
Recent Nonfiction Title: *Information Processing in the U.S.* (reference).
Tips: "The writer has the best chance of selling to our firm books on current computer technology (cutting edge), computing history and computing security."

THE AMERICAN PSYCHIATRIC PRESS, INC., (associated with the American Psychiatric Association), 1400 K St. NW, Washington DC 20005. (202)682-6268. Managing Editor: Tim Clancy. Publishes hardcover and trade paperback originals and software. Averages 40 titles/year, 2-4 trade books/year; receives about 150 submissions annually. About 10% of books from first-time authors; 95% of books from unagented writers. Pays 10% minimum royalty based on all money actually received, maximum varies; offers average $3,000-7,500 advance. Publishes book an average of 9 months after acceptance. Simultaneous and photocopied submissions OK (if made clear in cover letter). Electronic submissions OK on IBM PC, but requires hard copy also. Computer printout submissions acceptable; no dot-matrix. Reports in 6 weeks "in regard to an *initial* decision regarding our interest. A *final* decision requires more time (8-12 weeks)." Ms guidelines for SASE.
Nonfiction: Reference, self-help, technical, textbook and general nonfiction. Subjects include psychology/psychiatry and sociology (as it relates to psychiatry). Authors must be well qualified in their subject area. Especially looking for books that discuss major psychiatric topics for the general public. Also interested in books for children. No first-person accounts of mental illness or anything not clearly related to psychiatry. Query with outline/synopsis and sample chapters.
Recent Nonfiction Title: *Anxiety and Its Treatment: Help Is Available*, by John H. Greist, M.D., James W. Jefferson, M.D., and Isaac M. Marks, M.D.
Tips: "Because we are a specialty publishing company, books written by or in collaboration with a psychiatrist have the best chance of acceptance. Make it authoritative and professional."

AMPHOTO, 1515 Broadway, New York NY 10036. (212)764-7300. Senior Editor: Marisa Bulzone. Publishes hardcover and paperback originals. Averages 20 titles/year. Pays royalty, or makes outright purchase; offers variable advance. Publishes book an average of 9 months after acceptance. Simultaneous and photocopied submissions OK. Electronic submissions OK, but requires hard copy also. Computer printout submissions acceptable; prefers letter-quality to dot-matrix. Reports in 1 month. Free book catalog.
Nonfiction: "Photography instruction only. We cover all technical and how-to aspects. Few portfolios or picture books." Submit outline/synopsis, sample chapters and sample photos. Reviews artwork/photos as part of ms package. Looks for "practical value to the readers, marketing information."
Recent Nonfiction Title: *Secrets of Studio Still Life Photography*, by Gary Perweiler.
Tips: "Consult the photo magazines for book ideas."

‡ANCESTRY INCORPORATED, Box 476, Salt Lake City UT 84110. (801)531-1790. Managing Editor: Robert J. Welsh. Publishes hardcover and mass market paperback originals. Averages 4-6 titles/year; receives 10-20 submissions annually. 80% of books from first-time authors; 100% of books from unagented writers. Pays 8-12% royalty; purchases mss outright for varying amount or pays royalty on gross sales. Offers variable advance. Publishes book an average of 8 months after acceptance. Simultaneous and photocopied submissions OK. Electronic submissions OK via IBM PC, Wordstar, but requires hard copy also. Computer printout submissions acceptable. Reports in 1 month on queries; 2 months on mss. Free book catalog and ms guidelines.
Nonfiction: Biography, how-to, reference, and genealogy. Subjects include Americana; history (family and local); and hobbies (genealogy). "Our publications are almost exclusively genealogical in nature. We consider everything from short monographs to book length works on immigration, migration, record collections, etc. Good local histories and heraldic topics are considered." No mss that are not genealogical or historical. Query, or submit outline/synopsis and sample chapters, or complete ms. Reviews artwork/photos.
Recent Nonfiction Title: *The Source: A Guidebook of American Genealogy*, by Eakle & Cerny (reference).
Tips: "Genealogical reference, how-to, and descriptions of source collections have the best chance of selling to our firm. Be precise in your description."

*AND/OR PRESS, Box 522, Berkeley CA 94701. Contact: Ronin Publishing, Box 1035, Berkeley CA 94201. (415)540-6278. Publisher: Sebastian Orfali. Publishes paperback originals, and hardcover and paperback reprints. Averages 8 titles/year; receives 500 submissions annually. 100% of books from unagented writers. Specializes in "nonfiction works with young urban professional interest. We function as an alternative information resource. 75% are funded by investors and author receives small advance. 25% are funded by author; Ronin works with author to produce, promote and distribute. Also obtains foreign and domestic subsidiary rights." Pays 5-10% royalty; offers average advance of 10% of first print run. Publishes ms an average of 1 year after acceptance. Electronic submissions OK via IBM PC, 300 Baud, but requires hard copy also. Computer printout submissions acceptable. Reports in 3 months. Submit outline with 1-3 sample chapters; "we do guarantee return of manuscript."
Nonfiction: Publishes appropriate technology, human potential, the future, health and nutrition, travel and psycho-pharmacology books. Also alternative lifestyle books. Reviews artwork/photos as part of ms package.
Recent Nonfiction Title: *Beating Job Burnout*, by Dr. Beverly Potter.
Tips: "Ronin recognizes that the author is not merely an outside vendor but is an integral part of all phases of the publishing process. Ronin uses a decentralized form—relying on freelance professionals: artists, editors, etc., and a novel distribution approach in addition to the traditional. A successful book, previously published by a major house, now out of print has the best chance of selling to our firm."

ANDREWS, McMEEL & PARKER, 4900 Main St., Kansas City MO 64112. Editorial Director: Donna Martin. Publishes hardcover and paperback originals. Averages 30 titles/year. Pays royalty on retail price. "Query only. No unsolicited manuscripts. Areas of specialization include humor, how-to, and consumer reference books, such as *The Writer's Art* by James J. Kilpatrick, and *Roger Ebert's Movie Home Companion*."

ANGEL PRESS/PUBLISHERS, 561 Tyler, Monterey CA 93940. (408)372-1658. Contact: Editor. Publishes hardcover originals and reprints and mass market softcover originals. Averages 2-4 titles/year; receives 600-700 submissions annually. 10% of books from first-time authors; 80% of books from unagented writers. Average print order from a writer's first book is 2,000. Pays negotiable royalty; cash return (actual). No advance. Publishes book an average of 1 year after acceptance. Simultaneous and photocopied submissions OK. Computer printout submissions acceptable; prefers letter-quality to dot-matrix. Reports in 3 weeks on queries; "several" months on mss.
Nonfiction: Biography, how-to, humor, self-help and spiritual/metaphysical. Subjects include Americana, health, history, hobbies, nature, philosophy, photography, psychology, recreation, religion and sociology. Especially needs "well-written, well-conceived books in the areas of controversy, feminist, humor, satire; plus any book that is unusually well-written and is potentially a good seller in its field." Query before submitting ms. Reviews artwork/photos as part of ms package.
Recent Nonfiction Title: *Living with Angels*, by Dorie D'Angelo (spiritual/inspirational).
Fiction: Adventure, fantasy, humor, mainstream, metaphysical, and human potential. "Fiction is not our main thrust." Query before submitting ms.
Recent Fiction Title: *Re'lize Whut Ahm Talkin' 'Bout?*, by Steve Chennault (black English).
Tips: Spiritual/metaphysical or holistic health books have the best chance of selling to this firm.

APPALACHIAN MOUNTAIN CLUB, 5 Joy St., Boston MA 02108. (617)523-0636. Editorial Director: Mr. Aubrey Botsford. Imprint: AMC Books. Publishes hardcover and trade paperback originals. Averages 3-6 titles/year; receives 30 submissions annually. 80% of books from first-time authors; 99% of books from unagented writers. Pays 10% royalty on retail price; offers $500-1,000 advance. Publishes book 1 year after acceptance. Simultaneous and photocopied submissions OK. Electronic submissions OK via ASCII file, composed on IBM-compatible machine or Microsoft Word, but requires hard copy also. Computer printout submissions acceptable; prefers letter-quality to dot-matrix. Reports in 6 weeks on queries; 3 months on mss. Book catalog for 9x12 SASE.

Nonfiction: How-to, illustrated book, reference and guidebook. Subjects include history (Northeast, mountains), nature, photography, recreation, "self-propelled" outdoors activities, and travel. "We want manuscripts about the outdoors, ecology, the environment, mountains and their history and culture, non-motorized recreation, and guidebooks and field guides. We would also like to see semi-philosophical works on the outdoors. Relevant fiction will be considered, too." No physical fitness manuals. Query or submit outline/synopsis and sample chapters only. Reviews artwork/photos.

Recent Nonfiction Title: *River Rescue* , by Les Bechdel and Slim Ray.

Tips: "We are expanding into the Southeast (North Carolina, South Carolina, Washington DC, Maryland, Virginia, West Virginia), with basically the same interests as here in New England. Be patient. The AMC makes decisions slowly, mainly because it cannot afford to take financial risks."

APPLEZABA PRESS, Box 4134, Long Beach CA 90804. (213)591-0015. Publisher: D.H. Lloyd. Publishes trade paperback originals. Averages 3-4 titles/year; receives 800-1,000 submissions annually. 10% of books from first-time authors; 100% of books from unagented writers. Pays 8-12% royalty on retail price plus several author copies. Seldom offers advance. Publishes book an average of 3 years after acceptance. Simultaneous and photocopied submissions OK. Computer printout submissions acceptable; prefers letter-quality to dot-matrix. Reports in 1 month on queries; 2 months on mss. Free book catalog (when available)..

Nonfiction: Cookbook and humor. Subjects include cooking and foods. "Our needs are not great here. However, we are working on a 'poets' cookbook at present and are soliciting contributions. We need individual recipes from poets as well as a few short, upbeat poems relating to food, recipes, restaurants, etc." No how-to, reference, sports or self-help books. Query. Reviews artwork/photos.

Fiction: Experimental, humor, mainstream, novella and short story collections. "We prefer to see short, novella length, or short story collections. No confession, gothic, horror or western manuscripts. Submit outline/synopsis and sample chapters.

Recent Fiction Title: *Case of the Missing Blue Volkswagen*, by Gerald Locklin.

Poetry: "The poetry that attracts us is *usually* short, conversational prose poems. We don't let this limit us, however." No traditional forms. Submit complete ms.

Recent Poetry Title: *Madonna Who Shifts For Herself*, by Lyn Lifshin (conversational/feminist).

Tips: The freelancer has the best chance of publishing collections of poetry or short fiction. "They are economical enough for us to produce, and we have developed a market for them."

ARBOR HOUSE, A member of the Hearst Trade Book group, 235 E. 45th St., New York NY 10017. President and Publisher: Eden Collinsworth. Editor-in-Chief: Ann Harris. Publishes hardcover and trade paperback originals and selected reprints. Pays standard royalty; offers negotiable advance. Publishes book an average of 9 months after acceptance. Computer printout submissions acceptable; prefers letter-quality to dot-matrix. Free book catalog.

Nonfiction: Autobiography, cookbook, how-to and self-help. Subjects include Americana (possibly), art (possibly), business and economics, cooking and foods, health, history, politics, psychology, recreation, inspiration and sports. Query first to "The Editors." Reviews artwork/photos as part of ms package.

Recent Nonfiction Title: *Takecover: The New Wall Street Warriors*, by Moira Johnston.

Fiction: "Quality fiction—everything from romance to science fiction, fantasy, adventure and suspense." Query or submit outline/synopsis and sample chapters to "The Editors."

Recent Fiction Title: *Sweetie Baby Cookie Honey*, by Fredric Gershon.

Tips: "Freelance writers should be aware of a greater emphasis on agented properties and market resistance to untried fiction."

ARCsoft PUBLISHERS, Box 132, Woodsboro MD 21798. (301)845-8856. Publisher: Anthony R. Curtis. Publishes trade paperback originals. Averages 20 titles/year. "We now offer only 'buyout' contracts in which all rights are purchased. Typically, an advance of 20 percent is paid at contract signing and 80 percent at acceptable completion of work. Royalties are no longer offered since writers suffer under royalty contracts for small-volume technical books." Offers variable advance. Publishes book an average of 6 months after acceptance. Computer printout submissions acceptable; no dot-matrix. Reports in 1 month on queries; 10 weeks on mss. Free book catalog.

Nonfiction: Technical. "We publish technical books including space science, personal computers and hobby electronics, especially for beginners." Accepts nonfiction translations. Query or submit outline/synopsis and 1 sample chapter. Reviews artwork/photos as part of ms package.

Recent Nonfiction Title: *IBM PCjr Games Programs*, by Howard Bridges.

Tips: "We look for the writer's ability to cover our desired subject thoroughly, writing quality and interest."

*M. ARMAN PUBLISHING, INC., 28 N. Ridgewood Ave., Rio Vista, Ormond Beach FL 32074. (904)673-5576. Mailing address: Box 785, Ormond Beach FL 32074. Contact: Mike Arman. Publishes trade paperback originals, reprints and software. Averages 6-8 titles/year; receives 20 submissions annually. 20% of books from first-time authors; 100% of books from unagented writers. Average print order for a writer's first book is 1,500. Subsidy publishes 20% of books. Pays 10% royalty on wholesale price. No advance. Publishes book (on royalty basis) an average of 8 months after acceptance; 6 weeks on subsidy basis. Photocopied submissions OK. "We now set type directly from author's disks. Our equipment can read many CPM 5¼ formats, and can read IBM disks if the file is ASC II. We can do this for our own books, and we can save subsidy publishers 40-50% on their typesetting bills." Computer printout submissions acceptable. Reports in 1 week on queries; 3 weeks on mss. Book catalog for business size SAE with 39¢ postage.

Nonfiction: How-to, reference, technical, and textbook. "Motorcycle and aircraft technical books only." Accepts nonfiction translations. Publishes for enthusiasts. Submit complete ms. Reviews artwork/photos as part of ms package.

Recent Nonfiction Title: *A Guide to Autogyros,* by Crowe (construction, flight training, operation of autogyros).

Fiction: "Motorcycle or aircraft-related only." Accepts fiction translations. Immediate needs are "slim," but not non-existent. Submit complete ms.

Recent Fiction Title: *Motorcycle Summers,* by Gately (G-rated short stories about motorcycling).

Tips: "The type of book a writer has the best chance of selling to our firm is how-to fix motorcycles—specifically Harley-Davidson. We have a strong, established market for these books."

ART DIRECTION BOOK COMPANY, 10 E. 39th St., New York NY 10016. (212)889-6500. Editorial Director: Don Barron. Senior Editor: Loren Bliss. Publishes hardcover and paperback originals. Publishes 15-20 titles/year. Pays 10% royalty on retail price; offers average $1,000 advance. Publishes book an average of 1 year after acceptance. Photocopied submissions OK. Computer printout submissions acceptable; no dot-matrix. Reports in 3 months. Free book catalog.

Nonfiction: Commercial art, ad art how-to and textbooks. Query first with outline/synopsis and 1 sample chapter. "We are interested in books for the professional advertising art field—that is, books for art directors, designers, etc.; also entry level books for commercial and advertising art students in such fields as typography, photography, paste-up, illustration, clip-art, design, layout and graphic arts." Reviews artwork/photos as part of ms package.

Recent Nonfiction Title: *How To Prepare Roughs, Comps, and Mock-Ups,* by John Marqvand.

ASHER-GALLANT PRESS, (formerly Caddylak Publishing), Division of Caddylak Systems, Inc., 60 Shames Dr., Westbury NY 11590. (516)333-7440. Executive Vice President: Edward Werz. Publishes softcover and loose-leaf-format originals (sold mostly through direct marketing). Averages 15-20 titles/year; receives 150 submissions annually. 75% of books from first-time authors. 95% of books from unagented writers. "Many of our authors are first-time authors when they begin working with us, but write several subsequent books for us. Payment for each project is treated individually, but generally, the rights to smaller works (up to about 25,000 words) are purchased on a flat fee basis, and rights to larger works are purchased on a royalty basis." Advance varies by project. Publishes books an average of 6 months after acceptance. Simultaneous and photocopied submissions OK. Computer printout submissions acceptable; prefers letter-quality to dot-matrix. Ms returned only if requested. "We prefer to keep a writer's sample on file for possible future assignments." Reports negative results in 2 weeks on queries; 1 month on mss. Free book catalog.

Nonfiction: How-to and reference. Subjects include business (general) and management topics. "We plan to do 35 to 40 new titles during the next two years. The list will consist of individual business titles, more technical management reports, and longer, more comprehensive books that will be published in binder format. All subject matter must be appropriate to our broad audience of middle-level corporate managers. No sensational, jazzy nonfiction without solid research behind it." Submit outline/synopsis and sample chapters.

Recent Nonfiction Title: *Research Any Business Question—Fast and Professionally,* by Ronald Roel (business how-to).

Tips: "The deciding factors in whether or not we publish a certain book are: (1) we believe there will be a very sizeable demand for the book, (2) the outline we review is logically structured and very comprehensive, and (3) the sample chapters are concisely and clearly written and well-researched."

ASHTON-TATE PUBLISHING GROUP, Division Ashton-Tate; 10150 W. Jefferson Blvd., Culver City CA 90230. (213)204-5570. Editor: Bill Jordan. Publishes trade paperback originals. Averages 30 titles/year; receives 100 submissions annually. 60% of books from first-time authors; 100% of books from unagented writers. Pays royalty on cash received. Publishes book an average of 3½ months after acceptance. Simultaneous and photocopied submissions OK. Electronic submissions OK via IBM PC 5¼" disks DOS, but requires hard copy also. Computer printout submissions acceptable; prefers letter-quality to dot-matrix. Reports in 3 weeks on queries; 1 month on mss. Free book catalog; ms guidelines for SASE.

Nonfiction: Technical, microcomputer-related. Especially looking for microcomputer hardware and software topic areas for introductory through advanced readers. No non-computer related material. Submit outline/synopsis and sample chapters.

Tips: Audience is "specific software end-users, software application developers, and general audience/microcomputer enthusiasts. The writer has the best chance of selling us intermediate to advanced microcomputer technology books."

‡**ASSOCIATED BOOK PUBLISHERS, INC.**, Box 5657, Scottsdale AZ 85261-5657. (602)837-9388. Editor: Ivan Kapetanovic. Publishes hardcover and paperback originals and software. "Offer outright payment or standard minimum book contract. We have not made a practice of giving advances." Averages 3-4 titles/year. Will consider photocopied submissions. Computer printout submissions acceptable. Submit outline and 1 sample chapter, or submit complete ms. Reports in 3 weeks. "We are not responsible for unsolicited materials unless return postage is enclosed."
Nonfiction: "We would especially consider publication of books suitable for junior high and high school students, in the field of guidance, including occupational information, college entrance and orientation, personal and social problems and how to pass tests of all kinds. In addition to the categories listed below, we are interested in bibliographies in all subject areas and in textbooks for elementary through high school grades. Books published in following categories: economics, linguistics, dictionaries, education, children's books, cooking and nutrition, gardening, history, hobby and crafts, self-help and how-to, sociology and guidance. Accepts nonfiction translations. No strict length requirements." Reviews artwork/photos as part of ms package.
Recent Nonfiction Title: *Croatia and the Croatians*, by Prpic.

‡*ASSOCIATED FACULTY PRESS, INC.**, Rt. 100, Millwood NY 10546. (914)762-2200. President: Dr. Richard Koffler. Publishes hardcover originals and reprints. Averages 20-30 titles/year; receives 150 submissions annually. 30% of books from first-time authors; 95% of books from unagented writers. May subsidy publish, "but only after careful editorial review." Publishes book an average of 18 months after acceptance. Simultaneous submissions of proposal OK. Computer printout submissions acceptable; no dot-matrix. Reports in 1 month on queries; 3 months on mss. Book catalog for 9x12 SAE with 2 first class stamps.
Imprints: Kennikat (nonfiction reprints), Richard Koffler, president. National Universities Publications (nonfiction), Richard Koffler, president.
Nonfiction: Biography, reference, monographs, supplementary texts, and professional books on Americana; business and economics; health-related (not medicine); history; modern literary criticism; politics (public administration); sociology; and law and criminal justice. "We are rather backed up for at least one full year. Do not submit manuscript without first sending proposal." No trade books or academic books in fields not indicated above. Query or submit academic vita, table of contents and proposal.
Recent Nonfiction Title: *Unwelcome Guests*, by Jason Silverman (history).
Tips: "Our audience is college and university libraries, law libraries, scholars in fields listed above, and discriminating general readers. We are not trade publishers. In general, purely scholarly books are having a harder time of it."

DEAN ASTER PUBLISHING CO., Box 10752, Merrillville IN 46411. Editor-in-Chief: Anthony Philip. Associate Editor: Marianne Michael. Publishes hardcover, trade paperback and mass market paperback originals. Averages 6-9 titles/year. 10% of books from first-time authors ("we hope to increase this percentage"); 100% of books from unagented writers. Pays 5-15% royalty on retail price. Offers average $500 advance. Publishes book an average of 9 months after acceptance. Simultaneous submissions OK. Computer printout submissions acceptable; no dot-matrix. Reports in 6 weeks on queries; 2 months on mss. Book catalog $1; ms guidelines for SASE.
Nonfiction: How-to, illustrated book, reference, self-help, technical and textbook. Subjects include health (medical education); psychology (biofeedback, etc.); recreation (sports, athletic training); and science information. "We are particularly interested in medical or health education books written for the health care professional. Self-help books for the lay audience are also needed. We will consider academic texts, science information books, and books written for the sports athlete." No historical, music, art, cookbooks, political, or books of a humorous nature." Query. Reviews artwork/photos.
Recent Nonfiction Title: *Mind Over Fatter*, by Dr. Mary F. Asterita (self-help, weight management).
Fiction: Science fiction. "Although we have yet to publish fiction, we may consider good science fiction." Query.
Tips: "Our books are read by medical, science or psychology students, health care professionals, people interested in improving their health or outlook on life, and people who desire to learn more about modern science and technology. We are writing for a more educated audience. Our readers demand more information regarding the underlying anatomical and physiological reasons for the exercise routines, diets and rest requirements they read in print."

ATHENEUM CHILDREN'S BOOKS, Macmillan, Inc., 115 5th Ave., New York NY 10003. (212)614-1300. Editorial Director: Jonathan J. Lanman. Publishes hardcover originals. Averages 60 titles/year; receives 7,000-8,000 submissions annually. 8-12% of books from first-time authors; 50% of books from unagented writers. Pays 10-12½% royalty on retail price; offers average $2,000-3,000 advance. Publishes book an aver-

Close-up

Jonathan J. Lanman
Editorial Director
Atheneum Children's Books

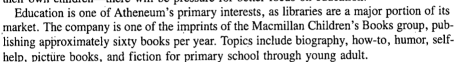

Jonathan Lanman sees an interesting future for children's books. "The growth in the juvenile population—the new baby boom—should affect the publishing we do over the next decade," Lanman says. "We already see this in the infant market.

"I also anticipate that—with a lot of young and well-educated parents out there concerned with the education of their own children—there will be pressure for better focus on education."

Education is one of Atheneum's primary interests, as libraries are a major portion of its market. The company is one of the imprints of the Macmillan Children's Books group, publishing approximately sixty books per year. Topics include biography, how-to, humor, self-help, picture books, and fiction for primary school through young adult.

Before coming to Atheneum, Lanman edited picture books and juvenile fiction and nonfiction for other publishers. His background includes "no specific training, except perhaps for some developmental psychology I studied in college. I have always been a reader and a writer and find those skills are what led me to publishing. Three years as a teacher also helped."

In summing up Atheneum's needs, Lanman emphasizes quality. "We simply look for good writing, original themes, and accurate portrayals of children's feelings, behavior and perceptions. Any other variables concern market trends at the time.

"What I'm most interested in right now would be humor—warm humor for kids. I think humor works best when it makes a point as well."

Lanman stresses the importance of writing for the market. "I think that it is a mistake to write for me. We publish for a market and the writer should know that market." He finds that many writers suffer from the misconception that writing a children's book is easier than writing an adult book.

He also cautions writers that the company's catalog is not a comprehensive guide to its publishing program. "The list is changing in directions that the catalog doesn't indicate, but the catalog shows the *kinds* of fiction and writers we are publishing. Writers still need to go to the children's section of a library or bookstore and read what is being written for children."

Lanman finds frustration in "the vast amount of material that we receive from authors who should be more honest with themselves about the quality of their work before submitting it."

Writers who wish to present a book project to Lanman should use a selling approach that is direct and professional. "No gimmicks or cuteness," he advises. "A writer should submit a straightforward and concise query letter (one page) giving information about the book and author." Writers with proposals should be patient about receiving a response; manuscript evaluation is sometimes delayed by more immediate tasks. "We are slow for a reason—we have many things to do at the same time."

A professional dedicated to his field, Lanman finds many rewards in his work. "The joys are in finding good new authors and watching their reputations grow."

—Michael A. Banks

age of 18 months after acceptance. Photocopied submissions OK. Computer printout submissions acceptable; prefers letter-quality to dot-matrix. Reports in 2 weeks on queries; 2 months on mss. Book catalog and ms guidelines for 9x12 SAE and 8 first class stamps.

Imprints: Argo Books (science fiction and fantasy), Marcia Marshall, editor.

Nonfiction: Biography, how-to, humor, illustrated book, juvenile (pre-school through young adult) and self-help, all for juveniles. Subjects include: Americana, animals, art, business and economics, cooking and foods, health, history, hobbies, music, nature, philosophy, photography, politics, psychology, recreation, religion, sociology, sports, and travel, all for young readers. "Do remember, most publishers plan their lists as much as two years in advance. So if a topic is 'hot' right now, it may be 'old hat' by the time we could bring it out. It's better to steer clear of fads. Some writers assume juvenile books are for 'practice' until you get good enough to write adult books. Not so. Books for young readers demand just as much 'professionalism' in writing as adult books. So save those 'practice' manuscripts for class, or polish them before sending them." Query, submit outline/synopsis and sample chapters, or complete ms. Reviews artwork/photos as part of ms package; prefers photocopies of artwork.

Recent Nonfiction Title: *Programming For Real*, by Harvey Lord (computer 'how-to').

Fiction: Adventure, ethnic, experimental, fantasy, gothic, historical, horror, humor, mainstream, mystery, romance, science fiction, suspense, and western, all in juvenile versions. "We have few specific needs except for books that are fresh, interesting and well-written. Again, fad topics are dangerous, as are works you haven't polished to the best of your ability. (The competition is fierce.) We've been inundated with dragon stories (misunderstood dragon befriends understanding child), unicorn stories (misunderstood child befriends understanding unicorn), and variations of 'Ignatz the Egg' (Everyone laughs at Ignatz the egg [giraffe/airplane/accountant] because he's square [short/purple/stupid] until he saves them from the eggbeater [lion/storm/I.R.S. man] and becomes a hero). Other things we don't need at this time are safety pamphlets, ABC books, and rhymed narratives. We have little need for children's poetry. In writing picture book texts, avoid the coy and 'cutesy.' " Query, submit outline/synopsis and sample chapters, or complete ms.

Recent Fiction Title: *Izzy, Willy Nilly*, by Cynthia Voigt (young adult problem novel).

Poetry: "At this time there is *very* little market for children's poetry. We don't anticipate needing any for the next year or two, especially rhymed narratives."

Tips: "Our books are aimed at children from pre-school age, up through high school. Our young adult novels and much of our science fiction and fantasy also cross over into adult markets. Government cut-backs to schools and city libraries have impacted heavily on publishers of quality books for children. We're having to cut down on the number of books we take on and, unfortunately, this usually hits new authors hardest."

ATHENEUM PUBLISHERS, 115 5th Ave., New York NY 10003. Editor-in-Chief: Thomas A. Stewart. Receives 10,000 submissions annually. 5% of books from first-time authors; 1% of books from unagented writers. Average print order for a writer's first book is 5,000. Publishes book an average of 1 year after acceptance. Simultaneous and photocopied submissions OK. Electronic submissions OK, but requires hard copy also. Computer printout submissions acceptable; prefers letter-quality to dot-matrix. Reports in 6 weeks.

Nonfiction: General trade material dealing with politics, psychology, history, cookbooks, sports, biographies and general interest. Length: 40,000 words minimum. Query or submit outline/synopsis and a sample chapter.

Recent Nonfiction Title: *At Mother's Request*, by Jonathan Coleman.

Tips: "We would prefer not to have artwork or photographs accompany unsolicited manuscripts."

ATHLETIC PRESS, Box 80250, Pasadena CA 91108. (213)283-3446. Editor-in-Chief: Donald Duke. Publishes paperback originals. Averages 3 titles/year. Pays 10% royalty; no advance. Publishes book an average of 1 year after acceptance. Query or submit complete ms. "Illustrations will be requested when we believe manuscript is publishable." Simultaneous and photocopied submissions OK. Computer printout submissions acceptable. Reports in 1 month. Free book catalog.

Nonfiction: Specializes in sports conditioning books.

ATLANTIC MONTHLY PRESS, 8 Arlington St., Boston MA 02116. (617)536-9500. New York Office: 420 Lexington Ave., New York NY 10170. (212)687-2424. Editor-in-Chief: Harold Evans. Executive Editor: Upton Birnie Brady. Editor-in-Chief, children's books: Melanie Kroupa. Senior Editors: Joyce Johnson and Edward Weeks. Associate Editors: C. Michael Curtis, Amy Meeker (children's books). Averages 50 titles/year; receives 3,000 submissions annually. 20% of books from first-time authors; 10% of books from unagented writers. "Advance and royalties depend on the nature of the book, the stature of the author, and the subject matter." Publishes book an average of 9 months after acceptance. Computer printout submissions acceptable; no dot-matrix. Include sample chapter with query, especially with fiction query.

Nonfiction: Publishes general nonfiction, biography, autobiography, science, philosophy, the arts, belles lettres, history and world affairs. Looks for "intelligence, coherence, organization, good writing (which comes first), neatness of presentation—and a covering letter." Length: 70,000-200,000 words. Reviews artwork/photos.

Recent Nonfiction Title: *The Moral Life of Children,* by Robert Coles.
Fiction: Publishes general fiction, juveniles and poetry. Length: 70,000-200,000 words.
Recent Fiction Title: *Soldiers in Hiding,* by Richard Wilsey.

AUGSBURG PUBLISHING HOUSE, 426 S. 5th St., Box 1209, Minneapolis MN 55440. (612)330-3432. Director, Book Department: Roland Seboldt. Publishes hardcover and paperback originals and paperback reprints. Publishes 45 titles/year; receives 5,000 submissions annually. 20% of books from first-time authors; 95% of books from unagented writers. Average print order for a writer's first book is 5,000. Pays 10-15% royalty on retail price; offers variable advance. Publishes book an average of 1 year after acceptance. Simultaneous and photocopied submissions OK. Computer printout submissions acceptable; no dot-matrix. Reports in 6 weeks.
Nonfiction: Health, psychology, religion, self-help and textbooks. "We are looking for manuscripts that apply scientific knowledge and Christian faith to the needs of people as individuals, in groups and in society;" also good contemporary stories with a Christian theme for the young readers in age categories 8-11, 12-14, and 15 and up." Query or submit outline/synopsis and a sample chapter or submit complete ms. Reviews artwork/photos.
Recent Nonfiction Title: *Bringing Out the Best in People,* by Alan Loy McGinnis.

‡AUTO BOOK PRESS, P.O. Bin 711, San Marcos CA 92069. (619)744-3582. Editorial Director: William Carroll. Publishes hardcover and paperback originals. Averages 3 titles/year; receives 24 submissions annually. 75% of books from first-time authors; 100% of books from unagented writers. Pays 15% royalty; offers variable advance. Publishes book an average of 1 year after acceptance. Simultaneous and photocopied submissions OK. Computer printout submissions OK; prefers letter-quality to dot-matrix. Reports in 2 weeks.
Nonfiction: Automotive material only: technical or definitive how-to. Query. Accepts outline/synopsis and 3 sample chapters.

AVALON BOOKS, Thomas Bouregy & Co., Inc., 401 Lafayette St., New York NY 10003. Editor: Rita Brenig. Publishes 60 titles/year. Pays $400 advance which is applied against sales of the first 3,500 copies of the book. Computer printout submissions acceptable; no dot-matrix. Reports in 15 weeks. Tip sheet for SASE.
Fiction: "We want well-plotted, fast-moving light romances, romance-mysteries, gothics, westerns, and nurse-romance books of about 50,000 words." Submit one-page synopsis or submit complete ms. No sample chapters or long outlines.
Recent Fiction Title: *Secret of Brackenwood,* by Juanita Tyree Osborne.
Tips: "We like writers to focus on the plot, drama, and characters, not the background."

*AVI PUBLISHING CO., 250 Post Rd. E., Box 831, Westport CT 06881. (203)226-0738. Editor-in-Chief: James R. Ice, Ph.D. Publishes hardcover and paperback originals. Publishes 30 titles/year; receives 100 + submissions annually. 50 + % of books from first-time authors; 90 + % of books from unagented writers. Subsidy publishes 10% of books. "Subsidy publishes symposia; subject matter within the areas of food, nutrition, agriculture and health, endorsed by appropriate professional organizations in the area of our specialty." Pays 10% royalty based on list price on the first 3,000 copies sold; offers average $5,000 advance (paid only on typing and art bills). Publishes book an average of 15 months after acceptance. Electronic submissions OK with permission, but requires hard copy also. Computer printout submissions acceptable; no dot-matrix. Reports in 1 month. Free book catalog and ms guidelines.
Nonfiction: Specializes in books on foods, agriculture, nutrition and health, scientific, technical, textbooks and reference works. Accepts nonfiction translations. Query or "submit a 500-word summary, a preface, a table of contents, estimated number of pages in manuscript, 1-2 sample chapters, when to be completed and a biographical sketch." Reviews artwork/photos as part of ms package.
Recent Nonfiction Title: *Site Engineering for Landscape Architects,* by Stum and Nathan.
Tips: "The writer has the best chance of selling our firm books on technology or science—areas in which our company specializes."

‡*AVIATION BOOK CO., 1640 Victory Blvd., Glendale CA 91201. (213)240-1771. Editor: Walter P. Winner. Publishes hardcover and paperback originals and reprints. Averages 5 titles/year; receives 25 submissions annually. 10% of books from first-time authors; 100% of books from unagented writers. Subsidy publishes 2% of books. Pays royalty on retail price. No advance. Query with outline. Publishes book an average of 1 year after acceptance. Computer printout submissions acceptable; prefers letter-quality to dot-matrix. Reports in 4 months. Free book catalog.
Nonfiction: Aviation books, primarily of a technical nature and pertaining to pilot training. Young adult level and up. Also aeronautical history. Asks of ms, "Does it fill a void in available books on subject?" or, "Is it better than available material?" Reviews artwork/photos as part of ms package.
Recent Nonfiction Title: *Instrument Flight Training Manual.*

AVON BOOKS, 1790 Broadway, New York NY 10019. Editor-in-Chief: Susanne Jaffee. Publishes paperback originals and paperback reprints. Averages 300 titles/year. Buys 10-20 unsolicited mss/year. Pay and advance are negotiable. Publishes ms an average of 2 years after acceptance. Simultaneous and photocopied submissions OK. Computer printout submissions acceptable; prefers letter-quality to dot matrix. Reports in 2 months. Book catalog for SASE.
Nonfiction: Biography, business/economics, health, history, hobbies, how-to, juveniles, politics, popular psychology, reference, self-help, sports, and war. No textbooks.
Recent Nonfiction Title: *Sylvia's Porter's Love and Money*, by Sylvia Porter.
Fiction: Adventure, fantasy, historical, mainstream, mystery, romance, science fiction, suspense and western. Submit outline/synopsis and first three sample chapters.
Recent Fiction Title: *A Heart So Wild*, by Johanna Lindsey.

AVON FLARE BOOKS, (formerly called *Flare Books*), Young Adult Imprint of Avon Books, a division of the Hearst Corp., 1790 Broadway, New York NY 10019. (212)399-1384. Senior Editor: Ellen Krieger. Publishes mass market paperback originals and reprints. 10-15% of books from first-time authors; 25% of books from unagented writers. Pays 6-8% royalty; offers average $2,000 advance. Publishes book an average of 15 months after acceptance. Simultaneous and photocopied submissions OK. Computer printout submissions acceptable; prefers letter-quality to dot-matrix. Reports in 10 weeks. Ms guidelines for SASE.
Nonfiction: General. Query or submit outline/synopsis and 6 sample chapters. "We are *very* selective with young adult nonfiction." Reviews artwork/photos.
Recent Nonfiction Title: *Battle Off Midway Island*, by Theodore Taylor.
Fiction: Adventure, ethnic, experimental, fantasy, humor, mainstream, mystery, romance, suspense and contemporary. "We are very selective with science fiction, fantasy and mystery." Mss appropriate to ages 12-18. Query with sample or submit complete ms.
Recent Fiction Title: *Downtown*, by Norma Fox Mazer.

‡**AYA PRESS**, Box 1153 Station F, Toronto, Ontario M4Y 2T8 Canada. Subsidiaries include Pencil Books. Publisher: Beverly Daurio. Publishes hardcover and trade paperback originals. Averages 4 titles/year; receives 300 submissions annually. 35% of books from first-time authors; 100% of books from unagented writers. "Only persons requesting subsidy publications are considered for subsidy publications through our subsidiary, Pencil Books." Pays 10% royalty on retail price. "Occasionally, different contracts are negotiated." No advance. Publishes book an average of 6 months after acceptance. Photocopied submissions OK. Computer printout submissions acceptable; no dot-matrix. Reports in 1 month on queries; 2 months on mss. Book catalog for #9 SAE with IRC.
Nonfiction: Illustrated book, juvenile and reference. Subjects include sociology (Canadian immigrant experience) and Canadian literature. Not currently interested in book mss that do not cover Canadian immigrant experience and Canadian children's experience. Submit outline/synopsis and sample chapters. Reviews artwork/photos. "We are just entering the nonfiction market."
Fiction: "Erotica, experimental, humor, mainstream and excellent writing which does not suit categorization. Also welcome is fiction about the Canadian immigrant experience." Formula fiction will not be considered. Submit outline/synopsis and sample chapters.
Recent Fiction Title: *The Mikveh Man*, by Sharon Drache (short stories).
Poetry: Needs "excellent work by proven writers or new poets with good credits." No rhyming poetry. Submit complete ms.
Recent Poetry Title: *Luna-verse*, by Catherine Ahearn (love/lyrical).
Tips: "Trends we have noticed in book publishing over the last few years include increasing specialization of markets. Special limited editions have done well, and so have our anthologies. More nonfiction is planned for the future. Our audience is upscale, educated and appreciates fine trade editions and eclectic, demanding writing."

BAEN PUBLISHING ENTERPRISES, (formerly Baen Enterprises), 260 Fifth Ave., New York NY 10001. (212)532-4111. Senior Editor: Elizabeth Mitchell. Publishes hardcover trade paperback and mass market paperback originals and mass market paperback reprints. Averages 65-90 titles/year; receives 1,000 submissions annually. 5% of books from first-time authors; 2% of books from unagented writers. Pays 6-12% royalty on cover price or makes outright purchase. Simultaneous and photocopied submissions OK. Computer printout submissions acceptable if letter-quality. Reports in 2 weeks on queries; 2 months on mss. Ms guidelines for SASE.
Nonfiction: Technical (computer). No high tech science; computer titles and futuristic topics such as space technology, artificial intelligence, etc. Submit outline/synopsis and sample chapters or complete ms.
Recent Nonfiction Title: *The Future of Flight*, by Leik Myrabo/Dean Ing (high tech).
Fiction: Fantasy and science fiction, high tech adventure. Submit outline/synopsis and sample chapters or complete ms.
Recent Fiction Title: *At Any Price*, by David Drake.

Tips: "Our audience includes those who are interested in *hard* science fiction and quality fantasy pieces that instruct as well as entertain."

*BAKER BOOK HOUSE COMPANY, Box 6287, Grand Rapids MI 49506. (616)676-9185. Editorial Director: Dan Van't Kerkhoff. Publishes hardcover and paperback originals, and paperback reprints. Averages 80 titles/year; receives 1,500 submissions annually. 20% of books from first-time authors; 80% of books from unagented writers. Average print order for a writer's first book is 5,000. Subsidy publishes 5% of books. Pays 10% royalty. Also buys booklet-length mss by outright purchase: $250-500. No advance. Publishes book an average of 8-16 months after acceptance. Simultaneous and photocopied submissions OK. Computer printout submissions acceptable "if legible"; prefers letter-quality to dot-matrix. Reports in 1 month. Book catalog for large SAE and $1.20 postage.
Nonfiction: Humor, juvenile, philosophy, psychology, religion, self-help and textbook. "All must be of religious nature." Submit outline/synopsis and 2-3 sample chapters (more, if chapters are brief) or submit complete ms. Reviews artwork/photos.
Recent Nonfiction Title: *Christian Excellence*, by Jon Johnston.

BAKER STREET PRODUCTIONS LTD., 502 Range St., Box 3610, Mankato MN 56001. (507)625-2482. Contact: Karyne Jacobsen. Publishes hardcover and trade paperback originals and software. Averages 8 titles/year; receives 100 submissions annually. 10% of books from first-time authors; 80% of books from unagented writers. Publishes book an average of 9 months after acceptance. Photocopied submissions OK. Computer printout submissions acceptable; prefers letter-quality to dot-matrix. Reports in 1 month on queries; 2 months on mss. Reviews artwork/photos.
Fiction: Adventure, fantasy, humor and mystery. Needs juvenile materials, grades 1-3. No science fiction. Submit outline/synopsis and sample chapters. "No manuscripts longer than 2,000 words." Reviews artwork/photos.
Recent Fiction Title: *Everything Is Special*, by Neese (guidance).

BALE BOOKS, Box 2727, New Orleans LA 70176. Editor-in-Chief: Don Bale Jr. Publishes hardcover and paperback originals and reprints. Averages 10 titles/year; receives 25 submissions annually. 50% of books from first-time authors; 90% of books from unagented writers. Average print order for a writer's first book is 1,000. Offers standard 10-12½-15% royalty contract on wholesale or retail price; sometimes purchases mss outright for $500. Offers no advance. Publishes book an average of 3 years after acceptance. "Most books are sold through publicity and ads in the coin newspapers." Will consider photocopied submissions. Computer printout submissions acceptable; no dot-matrix. "Send manuscript by registered or certified mail. Be sure copy of manuscript is retained." Book catalog for SAE and 39¢ postage.
Nonfiction: Numismatics. "Our specialty is coin and stock market investment books; especially coin investment books and coin price guides. We are open to any new ideas in the area of numismatics. The writer should write for a teenage through adult level. Lead the reader by the hand like a teacher, building chapter by chapter. Our books sometimes have a light, humorous treatment, but not necessarily." Looks for "good English, construction and content, and sales potential." Submit outline/synopsis and 3 sample chapters.
Recent Nonfiction Title: *Fabulous Investment Potential of Liberty Walking Half Dollars.*

BALLANTINE/DEL REY/FAWCETT BOOKS, Division of Random House, 201 E. 50th St., New York NY 10022. "Science fiction and fantasy should be sent to Owen Locke, executive editor. Proposals for trade books, poster books, calendars, etc., should be directed to Joelle Delbourgo, editor of trade books. Proposals including sample chapters for contemporary and historical fiction and romances should be sent to Ann La-Farge, senior editor of Ballantine or Barbara Dicks, senior editor of Fawcett." Publishes trade and mass market paperback originals and reprints. Royalty contract varies. Published 700 titles last year.
Nonfiction: General nonfiction. "Not interested in poetry; books under 50,000 words are too short for consideration. Since we are a mass market house, books which have a heavy regional flavor would be inappropriate for our list."
Fiction: General fiction, science fiction and fantasy.

BALLINGER PUBLISHING CO., 54 Church St., Harvard Square, Cambridge MA 02138. (617)492-0670. President: Carol Franco. Publishes hardcover and paperback originals. Averages 50 titles/year. Pays royalty by arrangement. Simultaneous and photocopied submissions OK. Computer printout submissions acceptable; prefers letter-quality to dot-matrix. Reports in 1 month. Free book catalog.
Nonfiction: Professional and reference books in economics, business, finance, high technology, and international relations. Submit outline/synopsis and sample chapters or submit complete ms.
Recent Nonfiction Title: *Nuclear Battlefields*, by William Arkin and Richard Fieldhouse.

BANKERS PUBLISHING CO., 210 South St., Boston MA 02111. (617)426-4495. Executive Editor: Jack R. Bruggeman. Publishes hardcover originals. Averages 7 titles/year; receives 20-30 submissions annually. 50%

of books from first-time authors; 100% of books from unagented writers. Average print order for a writer's first book is 2,000. Pays 10-15% royalty on both wholesale and retail price; buys some mss outright for negotiable fee. Publishes book an average of 8 months after acceptance. Computer printout submissions acceptable; prefers letter-quality to dot-matrix. Reports in 2 months. Book catalog and ms guidelines for 5½x8½ SAE and 2 first class stamps.

Nonfiction: How-to reference texts on banking only, for banking professionals. "Because of their nature, our books remain useful for many years (it is not unusual for a title to remain in print for 5-10 years). However, some of our technical titles are revised and updated frequently." Looks for "the ability of the author to communicate practical, how-to technical knowledge to the reader in an understanding way." Submit outline/synopsis and 2 sample chapters.

Recent Nonfiction Title: *Commercial Loan Officer's Handbook*, by Robert H. Behrens.

Tips: "As long as a book contains technical, necessary information about doing a particular banking job, it does well. We try to provide bankers with information and guidance not available anywhere else. Most of our writers are experienced bankers, but we are willing to consider a professional researcher/writer for some projects. We seek to work with new authors."

‡BANKS-BALDWIN LAW PUBLISHING CO., 1904 Ansel Rd., Cleveland OH 44106. (216)721-7373. Editor-in-Chief: P.J. Lucier. Publishes law books and services in a variety of formats. Averages approximately 50 titles/year; receives 5-10 submissions annually. 5% of books from first-time authors; 90% of books from unagented writers. "Most titles include material submitted by outside authors." Pays 10-15% royalty or fee. Offers advance not to exceed 25% of anticipated royalty or fee. Publishes book an average of 18 months after acceptance. Photocopied submissions OK. Electronic submissions OK; call for information, but requires hard copy also. Computer printout submissions acceptable; prefers letter-quality to dot-matrix. Reports in 3 weeks on queries; 6 weeks on submissions. Free book catalog; ms guidelines for SASE.

Nonfiction: Reference, law/legal. Query.

Recent Nonfiction Title: *Ohio Juvenile Law*, by Paul C. Giannelli and William Kurtz (handbook).

Tips: "We publish books for attorneys, government officials and professionals in allied fields. Trends in our field include more interest in handbooks, less in costly multi-volume sets; electronic publishing. Writer has the best chance of selling us a book on a hot new topic of law. Check citations and quotations carefully."

BANTAM BOOKS, INC., 666 5th Ave., New York NY 10103. Imprints include Skylark, For Young Readers, Sweet Dreams, Peacock Press, Loveswept, New Age Books, Spectra Windstone, and Bantam Classics. (212)765-6500. Chairman/CO-CEO: Lou Wolfe. President/COO/CO-CEO: Alberto Vitale. Vice President/Publisher/Editor-in-Chief: Linda Grey. Vice President and Editorial Director/Adult Fiction and Nonfiction Books: Steve Rubin. Publishes mass market, trade paperback, and hardcover books for adults, young adults (ages 12-17), and young readers (ages 8-12), fiction and nonfiction reprints and originals. Pays variable royalty and advance. Publisher does not accept queries or unsolicited manuscripts.

Nonfiction: Linda Cunningham, Executive Editor, Religious and Inspirational Books; Toni Burbank, Executive Editor (women's studies, school and college); Fred Klein, Vice President and Executive Editor/Media; Senior Editors: (cookbooks, mysteries, health); Linda Cunningham (business, finance); Deborah Futter (school and college, classics); Tobi Sanders (science); Nessa Rapoport (Bantam Jewish Bookshelf).

Fiction: Sol Skolnick—Trade and HC Association Publisher; Peter Guzzardi (sports and general fiction); Carolyn Nichols (Loveswept); Lou Aronica, Editor, Spectra Science Fiction and Fantasy; Kate Miciak, Administrative Editor (general fiction, mysteries); Elizabeth Barrett, Associate Editor, Loveswept. Young Adult titles: Betsy Gould (Associate Publisher for young readers); Judy Gitenstein, books for young readers. Nina Hoffman (Director of Subsidiary Rights); Linda Biagi (Manager of Subsidiary Rights); Kenzi Sugihara (Director Bantam Electronic Publishing); Alicia Condon, Senior Editor Loveswept. Also considers submissions to war series.

BARNES & NOBLE, Division of Harper & Row, 10 E. 53rd St., New York NY 10022. (212)207-7000. Director: Brad Miner. Editor: Jeanne Flagg. Publishes paperback originals and paperback reprints. Averages 40 titles/year. Pays standard paperback royalties for reprints; offers variable advance. Simultaneous and photocopied submissions OK. Computer printout submissions acceptable. Reports in 1 month.

Nonfiction: Education paperbacks including "College Outline Series" (summaries of college subjects) and Everyday Handbooks (self-teaching books on academic subjects, and skills and hobbies). Query or submit outline/synopsis and sample chapters. Looks for "an indication that the author knows the subject he is writing about and that he can present it clearly and logically."

BARRON'S EDUCATIONAL SERIES, INC., 113 Crossways Park Dr., Woodbury NY 11797. Publishes hardcover and paperback originals and software. Publishes 170 titles/year. 10% of books from first-time authors; 90% of books from unagented writers. Pays royalty, based on both wholesale and retail price. Publishes book an average of 9 months after acceptance. Simultaneous and photocopied submissions OK. Computer printout acceptable; prefers letter-quality to dot-matrix. Reports in 3 months. Book catalog $5. "Only writers with contracts receive guidelines."

Nonfiction: Adult education, art, cookbooks, foreign language, review books, guidance, pet books, travel, literary guides, juvenile, sports, test preparation materials and textbooks. Reviews artwork/photos as part of package. Query or submit outline/synopsis and 2-3 sample chapters. Accepts nonfiction translations.

Recent Nonfiction Title: *The Joy of Ice Cream*, by Matthew Klein; *The Five Senses*, children's series by J.M. Parramon and J.J. Puigi; *The Traveler's Dictionary*.

Tips: "The writer has the best chance of selling us a book that will fit into one of our series."

BEACON HILL PRESS OF KANSAS CITY, Box 527, Kansas City MO 64141. Book division of Nazarene Publishing House. Coordinator: Betty Fuhrman. Publishes hardcover and paperback originals. Averages 65-70 titles/year. Offers "standard contract (sometimes flat rate purchase). Advance on royalty is paid on first 1,000 copies at publication date. On standard contract, pays 10% on first 10,000 copies and 12% on subsequent copies at the end of each calendar year." Publishes book an average of 2 years after acceptance. Computer printout submissions acceptable; prefers letter-quality to dot-matrix. Reports in 4-8 months unless immediately returned. "Book Committee meets quarterly to select from the manuscripts which will be published."

Nonfiction: Inspirational, Bible-based. Doctrinally must conform to the evangelical, Wesleyan tradition. Conservative view of Bible. No autobiography, poetry, devotional collections, or children's picture books. Accent on holy living; encouragement in daily Christian life. Popular style books usually under 128 pages. Query. Textbooks "almost exclusively done on assignment." Full ms or outline/sample chapters. Length: 20,000-40,000 words.

Recent Nonfiction Title: *Mirror, Mirror . . . Please Lie*, by Pat Wellman.

BEACON PRESS, 25 Beacon St., Boston MA 02108. (617)742-2110. Director: Wendy J. Strothman. Publishes hardcover originals and paperback reprints. Averages 32 titles/year; receives 2500+ submissions annually. 10% of books from first-time authors; 80% of books from unagented writers. Average print order for a writer's first book is 3,000. Offers royalty on net retail price; advance varies. Publishes book an average of 1 year after acceptance. Simultaneous and photocopied submissions OK. Computer printout submissions acceptable; prefers letter-quality to dot-matrix. Return of materials not guaranteed without SASE. Reports in 2 months. Query or submit outline/synopsis and sample chapters to Nancy Lattanzio, editorial assistant.

Nonfiction: General nonfiction including works of original scholarship, religion, women's studies, philosophy, current affairs, literature communications, sociology, psychology, history, political science, art and some counseling.

Recent Nonfiction Title: *Image As Insight: Visual Understanding in Western Christianity and Secular Culture*, by Margaret R. Miles.

Tips: "No fiction or poetry submissions invited. No children's books. Authors should have academic affiliation."

BEAU LAC PUBLISHERS, Box 248, Chuluota FL 32766. Publishes hardcover and paperback originals.

Nonfiction: "Military subjects. Specialist in social side of service life." Query.

Recent Nonfiction Title: *Military Jargon*, by P.T. James.

BEAUFORT BOOKS, INC., 9 E. 40th St., New York NY 10016. (212)685-8588. Editor-in-Chief: Susan Suffes. Publishes hardcover and trade paperback originals. Averages 40-50 titles/year; receives 1,000 submissions annually. 10% of books from unagented writers. Pays 7½-15% royalty on retail price; offers variable advance. Publishes book an average of 1 year after acceptance. Simultaneous and photocopied submissions OK. Reports in 2 weeks on queries; 1 month on mss. Book catalog for 6x9 SAE and 2 first class stamps.

Nonfiction: Subjects include biography, health, business, sports, travel, history, music, and recreation. Query, or submit outline synopsis and 3 sample chapters or complete ms.

Recent Nonfiction Title: *Jagger*, by Carey Schofield.

Fiction: Mystery, thrillers, contemporary and literary novels. "No first novels, no science fiction." Accepts fiction translations from French. Query or submit complete ms.

Recent Fiction Title: *Deathwatch*, by Ellesten Trevor.

THE BENJAMIN COMPANY, INC., One Westchester Plaza, Elmsford NY 10523. (914)592-8088. President: Ted Benjamin. Publishes hardcover and paperback originals. Averages 20-30 titles/year. 90-100% of books from unagented writers. Publishes book an average of 6 months after acceptance. Buys mss by outright purchase. Offers advance. Simultaneous and photocopied submissions OK. Electronic submissions OK via IBM-PC, Hayes 1200 B, but requires hard copy also. Computer printout submissions acceptable; prefers letter-quality to dot-matrix. Reports in 2 months.

Nonfiction: Business/economics, cookbooks, cooking and foods, health, hobbies, how-to, self-help, sports and consumerism. "Ours is a very specialized kind of publishing—for clients (industrial and association) to use in promotional, PR, or educational programs. If an author has an idea for a book and close connections with a company that might be interested in using that book, we will be very interested in working together with the author to 'sell' the program and the idea of a special book for that company. Once published, our books do get trade distribution through a distributing publisher, so the author generally sees the book in regular book outlets as well as in the special programs undertaken by the sponsoring company. We do not encourage submission of manuscripts. We usually commission an author to write for us. The most helpful thing an author can do is to let us know what he or she has written, or what subjects he or she feels competent to write about. We will contact the author when our needs indicate that the author might be the right person to produce a needed manuscript." Query. Submit outline/synopsis and 1 sample chapter. Looks for "possibility of tie-in with sponsoring company or association."

Recent Nonfiction Title:*Do's and Taboos Around the World*, for Parker Pen.

BENNETT & MCKNIGHT PUBLISHING CO., Division of Glencoe Publishing Co., 809 W. Detweiler Dr., Peoria IL 61615. (309)691-4454. Vice President/Publisher: David M. Whiting. Publishes hardcover and paperback originals. Specializes in textbooks and related materials. Receives 25 submissions annually. 10% of books from first-time authors; 100% of books from unagented writers. Pays up to 10% royalty for textbooks "based on cash received, less for supplements"; no advance. Publishes book an average of 2 years after acceptance. Averages 50 titles/year. Query "with 1-2 sample chapters that represent much of the book; not a general introduction if the ms is mostly specific 'how-to' instructions." Photocopied submissions OK. Computer printout submissions acceptable. Reports in 1 month. Free book catalog and ms guidelines.

Nonfiction: Publishes textbooks and related items for home economics, industrial and technology education, career education, and art education, allied health occupations and vocational training in schools, junior high and above. Wants "content with good coverage of subject matter in a course in one of our fields; intelligent organization; and clear expression."

THE BERKLEY PUBLISHING GROUP, (publishers of Berkley/Berkley Trade Paperbacks/Jove/Charter/Second Chance at Love/Pacer; Ace Science Fiction), 200 Madison Ave., New York NY 10016. (212)686-9820. Vice President/Publisher: Roger Cooper. Editor-in-Chief: Nancy Coffey. Publishes paperback originals and reprints. Publishes approximately 900 titles/year. Pays 6-10% royalty on retail price; offers advance. Publishes book an average of 18 months after acceptance. "We don't accept unsolicited material."

Nonfiction: How-to, inspirational, family life, philosophy and nutrition.

Recent Nonfiction Title: *The One Minute Manager*.

Fiction: Adventure, historical, mainstream men's adventure, young adult, suspense, western, occult, romance and science fiction. Submit outline/synopsis and first 3 chapters (for Ace Science Fiction only).

Recent Fiction Title: *The Accidental Tourist*, by Anne Tyler.

Young Adult Fiction Title: *I Stay Near You*, by M.E. Kerr.

BETHANY HOUSE PUBLISHERS, 6820 Auto Club Rd., Minneapolis MN 55438. (612)944-2121. Editorial Director: Carol Johnson. Publishes hardcover and paperback originals and paperback reprints. "Contracts negotiable." Averages 50 titles/year; receives 1,200 submissions annually. 15% of books from first-time authors; 95% of books from unagented writers. Publishes book an average of 9-18 months after acceptance. Simultaneous and photocopied submissions OK. Electronic submissions OK; "no limitation regarding compatibility— we hire a transfer from other companies if necessary." Computer printout submissions acceptable. Reports in 1-2 months. Book catalog and ms guidelines for SASE.

Nonfiction: Publishes reference (lay-oriented); devotional (evangelical, charismatic); and personal growth books. Submit outline and 2-3 sample chapters. Looks for "provocative subject, quality writing style, authoritative presentation, unique approach, sound Christian truth." Reviews artwork/photos as part of ms package.

Recent Nonfiction Title: *The Land and People Jesus Knew*, by J. Robert Teringo (reference).

Fiction: Well-written stories with a Christian message. No poetry. Submit synopsis and 2-3 sample chapters to Nathan Lenseth, Assistant Editor. Guidelines available.

Recent Fiction Title: *The Stonewyeke Trilogy*, by Phillips and Pella.

Tips: "The writer has the best chance of selling our firm a book that will market well in the Christian bookstore. List other books in your query in this category (price, length, main thrust), and tell how this one is better and unique."

BETTER HOMES AND GARDENS BOOKS, 1716 Locust St., Des Moines IA 50336. Editor: Gerald Knox. Publishes hardcover originals and reprints. Publishes 30 titles/year. "Ordinarily we pay an outright fee for work (amount depending on the scope of the assignment). If the book is the work of one author, we sometimes offer royalties in addition to the fee." Will consider photocopied submissions. Reports in 6 weeks.

Nonfiction: "We publish nonfiction in many family and home service categories, including gardening, decorating and remodeling, sewing and crafts, money management, entertaining, handyman's topics, cooking and nutrition, and other subjects of home service value. Emphasis is on how-to and on stimulating people to action. We require concise, factual writing. Audience is primarily husbands and wives with home and family as their main center of interest. Style should be informative and lively with a straightforward approach. Stress the posi-

tive. Emphasis is entirely on reader service. We approach the general audience with a confident air, instilling in them a desire and the motivation to accomplish things. Food book areas that we have already dealt with in detail are currently overworked by writers submitting to us. We rely heavily on a staff of home economist editors for food books. We are interested in nonfood books that can serve mail order and book club requirements (to sell at least for $9.95 and up) as well as trade. Rarely is our first printing of a book less than 100,000 copies. Publisher recommends careful study of specific *Better Homes and Gardens* book titles before submitting material." Prefers outlines and 1 sample chapter, but will accept complete ms. Will consider photocopied submissions.
Tips: Queries/mss may be routed to other editors in the publishing group.

BETTERWAY PUBLICATIONS, INC., White Hall VA 22987. (804)823-5661. Senior Editor: Robert F. Hostage. Publishes hardcover and trade paperback originals. Averages 12-14 titles/year; receives 1,200 submissions annually. 50-60% of books from first-time authors; 90% of books from unagented writers. Pays 10-16% royalty on wholesale price; offers $500 advance. Publishes book an average of 8 months after acceptance. Simultaneous and (quality copies please) photocopied submissions OK. Electronic submissions OK (IBM compatible preferred). but requires hard copy also. Computer printout submissions acceptable; no dot-matrix. Reports in 6 weeks on queries; 2 months on mss. Book catalog and ms guidelines for 9x12 SAE with 56¢ postage.
Nonfiction: How-to, illustrated book, juvenile, reference, and self-help on business and economics, cooking and foods, health, hobbies, psychology, sociology, genealogy, small businesses, all aspects of ownership ("e.g., contracting your own home, securing the right mortgage loan, avoiding foreclosure of home, farm, or business."). "We are seeking to expand our list in small and home-based business guides or handbooks, crafts resource books, genealogy books (advanced how to), books that present career, lifestyle, family choices to women." No cookbooks. Submit outline/synopsis and sample chapters. Reviews artwork/photos.
Recent Nonfiction Title: *Temporary Employment—The Flexible Alternative*, by Demaris C. Smith (guide to temporary employment market).
Tips: "The audience we envision for our books is typically adults of both sexes who are looking for useful and practical books that will enhance their business and personal lives. More specifically, mothers with growing families looking for career and personal development options. If I were a writer trying to market a book today, I would determine that there was a market for the book I intended to write and that the market was not already saturated. For example, another general book on child abuse probably would not be salable."

*BINFORD & MORT PUBLISHING, 1202 N.W. 17th Ave., Portland OR 97209. (503)221-0866. Publisher: James Gardenier. Publishes hardcover and paperback originals and reprints. Receives 500 submissions annually. 60% of books from first-time authors; 90% of books from unagented writers. Average print order for a writer's first book is 5,000. Pays 10% royalty on retail price; offers variable advance (to established authors). Publishes about 10-12 titles annually. Occasionally does some subsidy publishing (10%), at author's request. Publishes book an average of 1 year after acceptance. Reports in 4 months. Computer printout submissions acceptable; prefers letter-quality to dot-matrix.
Nonfiction: Books about the Pacific Coast and the Northwest. Western Americana, biography, history, nature, recreation, reference, and travel. Query with sample chapters and SASE. Reviews artwork/photos as part of ms package.
Recent Nonfiction Title: *Wade Hampton Pipes Arts and Crafts Architect in Portland Oregon*, by Don Marshall.
Fiction: Low priority. No needs at this time.

JOHN F. BLAIR, PUBLISHER, 1406 Plaza Dr., Winston-Salem NC 27103. (919)768-1374. Editor-in-Chief: John F. Blair. Publishes hardcover originals, trade paperbacks and occasionally reprints; receives 1,000 submissions annually. 20-30% of books from first-time authors; 90% of books from unagented writers. Average print order for a writer's first book is 3,500. Royalty to be negotiated. Publishes book an average of 2 years after acceptance. Free book catalog. Submit synopsis/outline and first 3 chapters or complete ms. Electronic submissions OK via IBM PC, MultiMate word processing, but requires hard copy also. Computer printout submissions acceptable; no dot-matrix. Reports in 3 months. Book catalog and ms guidelines for large manila SAE and 56¢ postage.
Nonfiction: Especially interested in well-researched adult biography and history. Preference given to books dealing with Southeastern United States. Also interested in environment and Americana; query on other nonfiction topics. Looks for utility and significance. Reviews artwork/photos as part of ms package.
Recent Nonfiction Title: *Pennsylvania's Historic Restaurants and Their Recipes*, by Dawn O'Brien and Claire Walter.
Fiction: "We are most interested in serious novels of substance and imagination. Preference given to material related to Southeastern United States. No category fiction. Juveniles should be for ages 9-14; no picture books. We are accepting few poetry mss at this time."
Recent Fiction Title: *Southern Dreams and Trojan Women*, by Leo Snow.

‡BLUEJAY BOOKS INC., Suite 306, 1123 Broadway, New York NY 10010. (212)206-1538. Publisher: James Frenkel. Publishes hardcover and trade paperback originals, and trade paperback reprints. Averages 35

titles/year; receives 1,000 submissions annually. 5% of books from first-time authors; 1% of books from un-agented writers. Pays variable royalty on retail price. Advance varies. Publishes book an average of 1 year after acceptance. Computer printout submissions acceptable; prefers letter-quality to dot-matrix. Reports in 2 months on queries; 4 months on mss. Book catalog for 9x12 SAE with 2 first class stamps.
Nonfiction: Biography. All submissions must relate to science fiction/fantasy. Query.
Recent Nonfiction Title: *Faces of Science Fiction*, by Patti Perret (photos/biography/science fiction).
Fiction: Fantasy, mystery and science fiction. "Nothing but science fiction and fantasy of very high quality." Query or submit outline/synopsis and sample chapters.
Recent Fiction Title: *The Hounds of God*, by Judith Tarr (fantasy).

BOOKCRAFT, INC., 1848 W. 2300 South, Salt Lake City UT 84119. (801)972-6180. Editorial Manager: Cory H. Maxwell. Publishes (mainly hardcover) originals and reprints. Pays standard 10-12½-15% royalty on retail price: "we rarely give a royalty advance." Averages 30-35 titles/year; receives 400-500 submissions annually. 25% of books from first-time authors; 100% of books from unagented writers. Publishes book an average of 6 months after acceptance. Will consider photocopied submissions. Computer printout submissions acceptable; prefers letter-quality to dot-matrix. Reports in about 2-3 months. Will send general information to prospective authors on request. Query. "Include contents page with manuscript." Ms guidelines for SASE.
Nonfiction: "We publish for members of The Church of Jesus Christ of Latter-Day Saints (Mormons) and do not distribute to the national market. All our books are closely oriented to the faith and practices of the LDS church, and we will be glad to review such mss. Mss which have merely a general religious appeal are not acceptable. Ideal book lengths range from about 64 to 224 pages or so, depending on subject, presentation, and age level. We look for a fresh approach—rehashes of well-known concepts or doctrines not acceptable. Mss should be anecdotal unless truly scholarly or on a specialized subject. Outlook must be positive. We do not publish anti-Mormon works. We don't publish poetry, plays, personal philosophizings, family histories, or personal histories. We also publish short and moderate length books for Mormon youth, about ages 14 to 19, mostly nonfiction. These reflect LDS principles without being 'preachy'; must be motivational. 30,000-45,000 words is about the right length, though good longer mss are not entirely ruled out. This is a tough area to write in, and the mortality rate for such mss is high. We publish only 2 or 3 new juvenile titles annually."
Recent Nonfiction Title: *But for a Small Moment*, by Neal A. Maxwell.
Fiction: Must be closely oriented to LDS faith and practices.
Recent Fiction Title: *Circle of Fire*, by Herb Harker.

‡*BOOKMAKERS GUILD, INC., Suite 202, 1430 Florida Ave., Longmont CO 80501. (303)442-5774. Executive Editor: Normandi Ellis. Publishes hardcover and trade paperback originals, and hardcover and trade paperback reprints. Averages 8-10 titles/year; receives 50 submissions annually. 30% of books from first-time authors; 100% of books from unagented writers. Subsidy publishes 10% of books. Pays 10-15% royalty on net receipts. Offers average $500 advance. Publishes books an average of 18 months after acceptance. Photocopied submissions OK. Computer printout submissions acceptable; prefers letter-quality to dot-matrix. Reports in 2 weeks on queries; 2 months on mss after query, 4 months on ms without query. Book catalog free on request.
Nonfiction: How-to, juvenile, reference, self-help, textbook and social issues on business and economics (as relate to family); health; history (national and international); nature (general interest and professional); and psychology (focus on children and family). "We see a continuing focus on children and youth, especially books on child advocacy, behavior, education, development, and some children's literature. Potential growth areas are the natural sciences such as oceanography, earth science, botany. No cookbooks, local history, poetry, sci-fi, computers, fashion, sports or other topics ill-written and ill-conceived." Query or submit outline/synopsis and sample chapters. Sometimes reviews artwork/photos.
Fiction: Experimental and mainstream. "We are mostly looking for books for children, but are considering one or two adult titles." No sci-fi, erotica, confession, historical, gothic or romance. Query.
Tips: "Books that are sensitively written, well-researched, and on topics that are not already flooding the market have the best chance of selling to our firm. The best advice is to be unique and research *Books in Print* for marketability."

‡BOREALIS PRESS, LTD., 9 Ashburn Dr., Nepean, Ontario K2E 6N4 Canada. Editorial Director: Frank Tierney. Senior Editor: Glenn Clever. Publishes hardcover and paperback originals. Averages 4 titles/year; receives 400-500 submissions annually. 80% of books from first-time authors; 100% of books from unagented writers. Pays 10% royalty on retail price; no advance. Publishes book an average of 6 months after acceptance. "No multiple submissions or electronic printouts on paper more than 8½ inches wide." Computer printout submissions acceptable; prefers letter-quality to dot-matrix. Reports in 4 months. SAE and IRCs. Book catalog $1.
Nonfiction: "Only material Canadian in content." Query. Reviews artwork/photos as part of ms package. Looks for "style in tone and language, reader interest, and maturity of outlook."
Recent Nonfiction Title: *The Canadian Parliamentary Handbook 1983-84*, by John Bejermi.

Fiction: "Only material Canadian in content and dealing with significant aspects of the human situation." Query.
Recent Fiction Title: *The Trouble with Heroes and Other Stories*, by Guy Vanderhaeghe.
Tips: "Ensure that creative writing deals with consequential human affairs, not just action, sensation, or cutesy stuff."

THE BORGO PRESS, Box 2845, San Bernardino CA 92406. (714)884-5813. Publisher: Robert Reginald. Editor: Mary A. Burgess. Publishes hardcover and paperback originals. Averages 100+ titles/year; receives 200+ submissions annually. 5% of books from first-time authors; 10% of books from unagented writers. Pays royalty on retail price: "10% of gross, with a 12% escalator." No advance. Publishes book an average of 1-2 years after acceptance. "Virtually all of our sales are to the library market." "Will accept diskettes compatible with IBM PC using MS—Dos 2.1 with WordStar; requires hard copy also." Computer printout submissions acceptable; no dot-matrix. Reports in 2 months. Book catalog and writer's guidelines for SAE and 39¢ postage.
Nonfiction: Publishes literary critiques, bibliographies, historical research, film critiques, theatrical research, interview volumes, biographies, social studies, political science, and reference works for library and academic markets. Query with letter or outline/synopsis and 1 sample chapter. "All of our books, without exception, are published in open-ended, numbered, monographic series. Do not submit proposals until you have looked at our catalogs and publications. We are not a market for fiction, poetry, popular nonfiction, artwork, or anything else except scholarly monographs in the humanities and social sciences. We discard unsolicited manuscripts from outside of our subject fields which are not accompanied by SASEs." Sometimes reviews artwork/photos.
Recent Nonfiction Title: *Fidel by Fidel: An Interview with Fidel Castro*, by J.M. Elliot and Representative Mervyn Dymally.

*DON BOSCO PUBLICATIONS, 475 N. Ave., Box T, New Rochelle NY 10802. (914)576-0122. Subsidiaries include Salesiana Publishers. Editorial Director: John Malloy. Publishes hardcover and trade paperback originals. Averages 6-10 titles/year; receives 50 submissions annually. 15% of books from first-time authors; 100% of books from unagented writers. Average print order for a writer's first book is 3,000. Subsidy publishes 10% of books. "We judge the content of the manuscript and quality to be sure it fits the description of our house. We subsidy publish for nonprofit and religious societies." Pays 5-10% royalty on retail price; offers average $100 advance. Publishes book an average of 10 months after acceptance. Computer printout submissions acceptable; no dot-matrix. Reports in 2 weeks on queries; 2 months on mss. Free book catalog.
Nonfiction: Biography, juvenile and textbook on Roman Catholic religion and sports. "Biographies of outstanding Christian men and women of today. Sports for youngsters and young adults. We are a new publisher with wide experience in school marketing, especially in religious education field." Accepts nonfiction translations from Italian and Spanish. Query or submit outline/synopsis and 2 sample chapters. Occasionally reviews artwork/photos as part of ms package.
Recent Nonfiction Title: *The Falcon and the Dove*, by Peter Lappin.
Tips: Queries/mss may be routed to other editors in the publishing group.

THE BOSTON MILLS PRESS, 132 Main St., Erin Ontario N0B 1T0 Canada. (519)833-2407. President: John Denison. Publishes hardcover and trade paperback originals. Averages 16 titles/year; receives 100 submissions annually. 75% of books from first-time authors; 90% of books from unagented writers. Pays 6-10% royalty on retail price; no advance. Publishes book an average of 8 months after acceptance. Simultaneous and photocopied submissions OK. Electronic submissions OK if compatible with IBM PC (Volks writer), but requires hard copy also. Computer printout submissions acceptable. Reports in 2 weeks on queries; 4 weeks on mss. Free book catalog.
Nonfiction: Illustrated book. Subjects include history. "We're interested in anything to do with Canadian or American history—especially transportation. We like books with a small, strong market." No autobiographies. Query. Reviews artwork/photos.
Recent Nonfiction Title: *Next Stop Grand Central*, by Stan Fischler (railway history).
Tips: "We can't compete with the big boys so we stay with short-run specific market books that bigger firms can't handle. We've done well this way so we'll continue in the same vein. We tend to accept books from completed manuscripts."

THOMAS BOUREGY AND CO., INC., 401 Lafayette St., New York NY 10003. Editor: Rita Brenig. Imprint includes Avalon Books (fiction). Offers advance on publication date. Averages 60 titles/year. Reports in 15 weeks. Computer printout submissions acceptable; no dot-matrix.
Fiction: Romances, nurse/romances, westerns and gothic novels. Avoid sensationalist elements. Send one-page query with SASE. No sample chapters. Length: about 50,000 words.
Recent Fiction Title: *Bluegrass Nurse*, by Barbara Zelaya.

BRADBURY PRESS, (affiliate of Macmillan, Inc.), 866 3rd Ave. New York NY 10022. (212)702-9809. Publisher: Norma Jean Sawicki. Editor-in-Chief: Richard Jackson. Publishes hardcover originals for children and young adults. Averages 40 titles/year. Pays royalty and offers advance. No simultaneous submissions. Reports in 3 months.

Fiction: Picture books, concept books, photo essays and novels. Also "stories about real kids; special interest in realistic dialogue." No adult ms. No fantasy or religious material. Submit complete ms.

Recent Fiction Title: *The Moonlight Man*, by Paula Fox (novel).

Tips: "Blockbusters make it *possible* to take risks; we are interested in publishing new writers and illustrators."

‡*BRADSON PRESS, INC.,** 120 Longfellow St., Thousand Oaks CA 91360. (818)707-0471. President: Donn Delson. Publishes trade paperback originals and reprints. Averages 3 titles/year. Subsidy publishes 50% of books "depending on quality of work and market potential." Pays 5-12% royalty. Publishes book an average of 6 months after acceptance. Simultaneous and photocopied submissions OK. Computer printout submissions acceptable. Reports in 6 weeks. Free book catalog.

Nonfiction: Humor, juvenile, reference, self-help and technical covering health, hobbies, psychology, sociology, sports, entertainment and communications. "Self-help and how-to books are our primary focus—also interested in unique humorous concepts for mass market." No history, politics, religion. Submit outline/synopsis and sample chapters. Reviews artwork/photos as part of ms package.

Recent Nonfiction Title: *Motion Picture Distribution: An Accountant's Perspective*, by D. Leedy.

Fiction: Humor. No religious or western material. Submit outline/synopsis and sample chapters.

‡BRAEMAR BOOKS LTD.,** Box 4142, Station A, Victoria, British Columbia V8X 3X4 Canada. (604)382-2665. Managing Director: John A. Stuart. Averages 6-10 titles/year; receives 50-100 submissions annually. 80-90% of books from first-time authors; 100% of books from unagented writers. "We are primarily involved in trade paperback originals, but, to date, have experience with hard cover and mass market paperback originals, and trade paperback reprints." Pays 4-15% royalty. Offers negotiable advance. Publishes book an average of 1 year after acceptance. Simultaneous and photocopied submissions OK. Reports in 2 weeks on queries; 1 month on mss. Free book catalog.

Nonfiction: General trade books on Canadian history (including Scottish traditions in Canada), novels and works of ethical and social interest. "We are interested in subjects of broad ethical and social interest that will sell in the Canadian market and also find readership in the U.S. and other parts of the English-speaking world. We also plan to launch a Canadian novelist series, i.e., novels written by Canadians." Will not consider other types of material. Query.

Recent Nonfiction Title: *Barns of Western Canada*, by Bob Hainstock (illustrated survey).

Fiction: Adventure, ethnic, gothic, historical, humor, mainstream, mystery, religious, romance, suspense and western. "We are interested in novels written by Canadians, including those written by first-time novelists." Will not consider types of fiction not listed above. Query.

Tips: "While we plan to experiment with certain mass paperback titles (including a forthcoming book on abortion), we believe our current list caters, in large part, to people who are continually searching for Canadian materials. Although we are not interested in manuscripts outside our areas of interest, we are prepared to devote considerable time to polishing 'diamonds in the rough,' providing their authors are not adverse to media exposure."

BRANDEN PRESS, INC., 17 Station St., Box 843, Brookline Village MA 02147. (617)734-2045. President: Adolph Casó. Subsidiaries include International Pocket Library and Popular Technology, Four Seas, Brashear. Publishes hardcover and trade paperback originals, hardcover and trade paperback reprints and software. Averages 15 titles/year; receives 400 submissions annually. 80% of books from first-time authors; 90% of books from unagented writers. Average print order for a writer's first book is 3,000. Pays 5-10% royalty on wholesale price; offers $1,000 maximum advance. Publishes book an average of 10 months after acceptance. Electronic submissions OK if compatible with IBM PC, but requires hard copy also. Computer printout submissions acceptable; prefers letter-quality to dot-matrix. Inquiries only with SAE and 1 first class stamp. Reports in 1 week on queries; 2 months on mss. Book catalog for SASE.

Nonfiction: Biography, illustrated book, juvenile, reference, technical and textbook. Subjects include Americana, art, health, history, music, photography, politics, sociology and classics. Especially looking for "about 10 manuscripts on national and international subjects, including biographies of well-known individuals." No religion or philosophy. Query. Reviews artwork/photos as part of ms package.

Recent Nonfiction Title: *Matter of Survival*, by Chris Noel.

Fiction: Adventure (well-written, realistic); ethnic (histories, integration); historical (especially biographies); mainstream (emphasis on youth and immigrants); religious (historical-reconstructive); romance (novels with well-drawn characters); and books about computers and software. No science, mystery or pornography. Query.

Recent Fiction Title: *Merger*, by David Thomsen.

Poetry: No religious, humorous or autobiographical poetry books. Submit 5 poems.

Recent Poetry Title: *The Ruin Revived*, by Mark Rudman.

Tips: "Branden publishes only manuscripts determined to have a significant impact on modern society. Our audience is a well-read general public, professionals, college students, and some high school students. If I were a writer trying to market a book today, I would thoroughly investigate the number of potential readers interested in the content of my book."

GEORGE BRAZILLER, INC., 1 Park Ave., New York NY 10016. 25% of books from first-time authors; 10% of books from unagented writers. Average print order for a writer's first book is 3,000; receives 500 submissions annually. Offers standard 10-12½-15% royalty contract; offers variable advance depending on author's reputation and nature of book. Publishes book an average of 10 months after acceptance. Computer printout submissions acceptable; prefers letter-quality to dot-matrix. No unsolicited mss. Reports in 6 weeks.
Fiction and Nonfiction: Publishes general fiction and nonfiction; subjects include literature, art, philosophy and history. Accepts nonfiction and fiction." Query.
Recent Nonfiction Title: *The Affair: The Case of Alfred Dreyfus*, by Jean-Denis Bredin, translated by Jeffrey Mehlman.
Recent Fiction Title: *The Sea-Crossed Fisherman*, by Yashar Kemal.

*BRETHREN PRESS, 1451 Dundee Ave., Elgin IL 60120. (312)742-5100. Owned and managed by The Church of the Brethren General Board. Book Editor: David Eller. Publishes hardcover and trade paperback originals, and trade paperback reprints. Averages 10 titles/year; receives 150 queries/submissions annually. 30% of books from first-time authors; 90% of books from unagented writers. "We occasionally do 'shared risk' publications in which the author or other publishing partner shares financially in the start-up costs. This varies according to the manuscript; could be up to 50% or several thousand dollars. The publishing partner agrees to buy back unsold inventory after three years. This is an unusual arrangement, usually made only when a denominational program unit requires a book on a certain subject." Payment depends on target market. Typical contract: up to $1,000 advance against 10% net royalties for first 5,000 copies; 12% net on 5,001 copies and up. Publishes book an average of 1 year after acceptance. Simultaneous and photocopied submissions OK. Electronic submissions OK on IBM PC/DOS (inquire), but requires hard copy also. Computer printout submissions acceptable; prefers letter-quality to dot-matrix. Reports in 2 months on queries; 6 months (hopefully) on mss. Free book catalog.
Nonfiction: Subjects include business and economics, cooking and foods, health, history, philosophy, politics, psychology, religion and sociology. All titles should be from a faith perspective. Needs theology, doctrines, devotional, peace-related, simple living, family life and women's issues, "Plain People" heritage, and current and international events. No how-to books. Query or submit outline/synopsis and sample chapters. Reviews artwork/photos.
Recent Nonfiction Title: *The Idea of Disarmament*, by Alan Geyer.
Fiction: Religious. "The only fiction published in recent years were inspirational, with historical settings in 'Pennsylvania Dutch'/Plain People context." No romances. Query.
Tips: "We prefer timely issues with solid theological content, well-written for the average reader. Adhere to *Chicago Manual* style and *Church of the Brethren Handbook of Style*."

BREVET PRESS, INC., Box 1404, Sioux Falls SD 57101. Publisher: Donald P. Mackintosh. Managing Editor: Peter E. Reid. Publishes hardcover and paperback originals and reprints. Receives 40 submissions annually. 50% of books from first-time authors; 100% of books from unagented writers. Average print order for a writer's first book is 5,000. Pays 5% royalty; advance averages $1,000. Query; "after query, detailed instructions will follow if we are interested." Publishes book an average of 1 year after acceptance. Simultaneous and photocopied submissions OK. Computer printout submissions acceptable. Reports in 2 months. Free book catalog.
Nonfiction: Specializes in business management, history, place names, and historical marker series. Americana (A. Melton, editor); business (D.P. Mackintosh, editor); history (B. Mackintosh, editor); and technical books (Peter Reid, editor). Reviews artwork/photos. Send copies if photos/illustrations are to accompany ms.
Recent Nonfiction Title: *Challenge*, by R. Karolevitz (history).
Tips: "Write with market potential and literary excellence. Keep sexism out of the manuscripts by male authors."

*BRIARCLIFF PRESS PUBLISHERS, 11 Wimbledon Ct., Jericho NY 11753. Editorial Director: Trudy Settel. Senior Editor: J. Frieman. Publishes hardcover and paperback originals. Averages 5-7 titles/year; receives 250 submissions annually. 10% of books from first-time authors; 60% of books from unagented writers. Average print order for a writer's first book is 5,000. Subsidy publishes 20% of books. Pays $4,000-5,000 for outright purchase; offers average of $1,000 advance. Publishes book an average of 6 months after acceptance. Computer printout submissions acceptable; no dot-matrix. "We do not use unsolicited manuscripts. Ours are custom books prepared for businesses, and assignments are initiated by us."
Nonfiction: How-to, cookbooks, sports, travel, fitness/health, business and finance, diet, gardening and crafts. "We want our books to be designed to meet the needs of specific businesses." Accepts nonfiction trans-

lations from French, German and Italian. Query. Submit outline and 2 sample chapters. Reviews artwork/photos as part of ms package.
Recent Nonfiction Title: *Maytag Handbook of Good Cooking*, by Ann Arnott.

BRICK HOUSE PUBLISHING CO., 3 Main St., Andover MA 01810. (617)475-9568. Publisher: Robert Runck. Publishes hardcover and trade paperback originals. Averages 20 titles/year; receives 100 submissions annually. 20% of books from first-time authors; 100% of books from unagented writers. Pays 10-15% royalty on wholesale price. Offers average $1,000 advance. Publishes book an average of 6 months after acceptance. Simultaneous and photocopied submissions OK. Electronic submissions OK, but requires hard copy also. Computer printout submissions acceptable; prefers letter-quality to dot-matrix. Reports in 2 weeks on queries; 3 months on mss. Book catalog for SAE; ms guidelines for SASE.
Nonfiction: How-to, reference, technical and textbook. Subjects include business and consumer advice. "We are looking for writers to do books in the following areas: practical guidance and information for people running small businesses, consumer trade books on money and job topics, and college business textbooks." Query.
Recent Nonfiction Title: *How to Make Big Money Mowing Small Lawns*, by Robert Welcome (how-to).

BRIDGE PUBLISHING, INC., 2500 Hamilton Blvd., South Plainfield NJ 07080. (201)754-0745. Executive Editor: Stephen G. Dunham. Imprints include Logos (Pentecostal/Charismatic), Haven (Evangelical), and Open Scroll (Pentecostal/Charismatic and Evangelical). Contact Robert Oliver, assistant editor for imprint submissions. Publishes trade and mass-market paperback originals and reprints. Averages 25 titles/year; receives 1,000 submissions annually. 25% of books from first-time authors; 95% of books from unagented writers. Average print order for a writer's first book is 7,500. Pays negotiable royalty or makes outright purchase. Assigns projects to writers. Offers negotiable advance. Publishes book an average of 1 year after acceptance. Photocopied submissions OK. Computer printout submissions acceptable; prefers letter-quality to dot-matrix. Reports in 1 month o queries; 3 months on mss. Book catalog $1; ms guidelines for SASE.
Nonfiction: How-to, self-help and religious/Christian (nondenominational). Subjects include current events, health, religion, and personal testimony. Especially looking for books with spiritual emphasis. Query with outline/synopsis and at least 2 sample chapters or submit complete ms.
Recent Nonfiction Title: *Getting Them Sober Vol. 3*, by Toby Rice Drews.
Fiction: Religious and inspirational. Query.
Recent Fiction Title: *Rust on My Soul*, by Neil Wyrick (novel).
Tips: "A nonfiction book of general, current interest that approaches a subject from a fresh perspective has the best chance of selling to our firm. We don't want to duplicate existing work. Consult other Christians from a number of churches and backgrounds other than your own to get their points of view on your subject. Too many submissions to us are written from a narrow point of view."

‡BROADMAN PRESS, 127 9th Ave. N, Nashville TN 37234. Editorial Director: Harold S. Smith. Publishes hardcover and paperback originals (85%) and reprints (15%). Averages 90 titles/year. Pays 10% royalty on retail price; no advance. Photocopied submissions OK "only if they're sharp and clear." Computer printouts acceptable; prefers letter-quality to dot-matrix. Reports in 2 months.
Nonfiction: Religion. "We are open to freelance submissions in the children's and inspirational areas. Materials in both areas must be suited for a conservative Protestant readership. No poetry, biography, sermons, or anything outside the area of the Protestant tradition." Query, submit outline/synopsis and sample chapters, or submit complete ms. Reviews artwork/photos as part of ms package.
Fiction: Religious. "We publish almost no fiction—less than five titles per year. For our occasional publication we want not only a very good story, but also one that sets forth Christian values. Nothing that lacks a positive Christian emphasis; nothing that fails to sustain reader interest." Submit complete ms with synopsis.
Tips: "Bible study is very good for us, but our publishing is largely restricted in this area to works that we enlist on the basis of specific author qualifications. Preparation for the future and living with life's stresses and complexities are trends in the subject area."

‡BROADWAY PRESS, Suite 407, 120 Duane St., New York NY 10007. (212)693-0570. Publishers: Cathy Blaser and David Rodger. Publishes trade paperback originals. Averages 2-3 titles/year; receives 3-4 submissions annually. 50% of books from first-time authors; 25% of books from unagented writers. Pays negotiable royalty on wholesale price. Publishes book an average of 18 months after acceptance. Simultaneous and photocopied submissions OK. Computer printout submissions acceptable. Reports in 1 month on queries. Book catalog for #10 SAE with 39¢ postage.
Nonfiction: Reference and technical. Subjects include theatre and the performing arts. "We're looking for professionally oriented and authored books for technical theatre and the performing arts. Most of our books are in-house publications, but we will accept author's queries for titles fitting the above criteria." Submit outline/synopsis and sample chapters. All unsolicited mss are returned unopened.
Recent Nonfiction Titles: *The New York Theatrical Sourcebook*, by The Association of Theatrical Artists & Craftspeople (reference book for services and supplies).

‡**BRUNNER/MAZEL, PUBLISHERS,** Box 419, 1889 Palmer Ave., Larchmont NY 10538. (914)834-3920. Senior Editor: Ms. Ann Alhadeff. Publishes hardcover originals. Averages 25 titles/year; receives 400 submissions annually. Offers average $1,000 advance. Publishes book an average of 1 year after acceptance. Simultaneous submissions OK. Computer printout submissions acceptable; prefers letter-quality to dot-matrix. Simultaneous submissions OK. Reports in 1 week on queries; 2 weeks on mss. Free ms guidelines.
Nonfiction: Clinical psychology and psychiatry on health, psychology, social work, child development, psychiatry, hypnosis and family therapy. No submissions for a general audience. Submit outline/synopsis and sample chapters.
Recent Nonfiction Title: *Violence in the Home*, edited by Mary Lystad, Ph.D.

BUCKNELL UNIVERSITY PRESS, Lewisburg PA 17837. (717)524-3674. Distributed by Associated University Presses. Director: Mills F. Edgerton, Jr. Publishes hardcover originals. Averages 18-20 titles/year; receives 150 + submissions annually. 20% of books from first-time authors; 99% of books from unagented writers. Pays royalty. Publishes book an average of 2 years after acceptance. Photocopied submissions OK. Electronic submissions OK, but requires hard copy also. Computer printout submissions acceptable. Reports in 1 month on queries; 6 months on mss. Free book catalog.
Nonfiction: Subjects include scholarly art, history, literary criticism, music, philosophy, politics, psychology, religion and sociology. "In all fields, our criterion is scholarly presentation; manuscripts must be addressed to the scholarly community." Query. Reviews artwork/photos.
Recent Nonfiction Title: *Leaders in the Study of Animal Behavior*, by Donald A. Dewsbury.
Tips: "An original work of high-quality scholarship has the best chance of selling to us; we publish for the scholarly community."

*****BYLS PRESS,** Department of Bet Yoatz Library Services, 6247 N. Francisco Ave., Chicago IL 60659. (312)262-8959. President: Daniel D. Stuhlman. Publishes trade paperback originals. Averages 3 titles/year; receives 10-20 submissions annually. Subsidy publishes variable percentage of books. Pays 7½-15% on wholesale price; no advance. Photocopied submissions OK. Electronic submissions preferred, on North Star 5¼" SD, IBM-PC 5¼ disk, MS DOS, ASCII compatible or modem. Writers may submit via computer bulletin board. Computer printout submissions acceptable; prefers letter-quality to dot-matrix. Reports in 1 week on queries; reporting time on mss "depends on material." Free book catalog.
Nonfiction: How-to (for teachers), and juvenile. Subjects include baking and religion ("stories aimed at children for Jewish holidays"). "We're looking for children's books for Jewish holidays that can be made into computer personalized books. In particular we need books for Sukkot, Shabbat and Purim. We need titles for our teacher education series." Query; "no agents, authors only. Do not submit ideas without examining our books. Ask yourself if a book idea fits what we are looking for."
Recent Nonfiction Title: *My Own Hanukah Story*, by D. Stuhlman (children's).
Fiction: Religious (stories for Jewish children). No expository fiction. "All unsolicited manuscripts are returned only if return postage is included."

C Q PRESS, 1414 22nd St. NW, Washington DC 20037. (202)887-8642. Director: Joanne Daniels. Publishes hardcover and paperback originals. Receives 20-30 submissions annually. 90% of books from unagented writers. Pays standard college royalty on wholesale price; offers college text advance. Publishes book an average of 5 months after acceptance of final ms. Simultaneous and photocopied submissions OK. Computer printout submissions acceptable; no dot-matrix. Reports in 3 months. Free book catalog.
Nonfiction: College text. All levels of political science texts. "We are one of the most distinguished publishers in the area of political science textbooks." Submit outline and sample chapter.
Recent Nonfiction Title: *Rational Politics*, by Steven J. Brams.

CAMARO PUBLISHING CO., 90430 World Way Center, Los Angeles CA 90009. (213)837-7500. Editor-in-Chief: Garth W. Bishop. Publishes hardcover and paperback originals. Pays royalty on wholesale price. "Every contract is different. Many books are bought outright." Published 11 titles last year.
Nonfiction: Books on travel, food, wine, health and success. Query.
Recent Nonfiction Title: *All-American Heroes Yearbook*.

CAMBRIDGE, THE ADULT EDUCATION COMPANY, 888 7th Ave., New York NY 10106. (212)957-5300. Executive Editor: Jerry Long. Publishes paperback originals in adult education. Averages 25 titles/year;

Market conditions are constantly changing! If this is 1988 or later, buy the newest edition of Writer's Market at your favorite bookstore or order directly from Writer's Digest Books.

receives 20 submissions annually. 2% of books from first-time authors; 1% of books from unagented writers. Pays usually flat fee only; occasionally pays 6% royalty on institutional net price; offers small advance. Publishes book an average of 9 months after acceptance. Photocopied submissions OK. Electronic submissions OK via Apple Writer. Computer printout submissions acceptable; no dot-matrix. Reports in 1 month. Free book catalog.

Nonfiction: Basic skills—adult education only—emphasizing alternative programs. Vocational, pre-GED and GED. Best known for GED preparation material. Submit prospectus and sample lesson only. No phone calls. Looks for "marketability (how broad and how stable the market is for the program); understanding of adult students (learning styles and needs); thoroughness of design of program (will it require substantial editing? How does the design relate to current educational practice); and cost factors, possible production problems." Reviews artwork/photos as part of ms package.

Recent Nonfiction Title: *Snapshots: A Collection of Readings for Adults* (ABE reading program).

Tips: "The writer has the best chance of selling our firm adult education books dealing with a grade three to seven reading level—in Math, Social Studies, Science and English. We prefer a lot of exercises, a pretest and post-test, and an answer key."

CAMBRIDGE UNIVERSITY PRESS, 32 E. 57th St., New York NY 10022. Editorial Director: Colin Day. Publishes hardcover and paperback originals. Publishes 900 titles/year; receives 1,000 submissions annually. 50% of books from first-time authors; 99% of books from unagented writers. Pays 10% royalty on receipts; 8% on paperbacks; no advance. Publishes book an average of 1 year after acceptance. Electronic submissions OK via most IBM/IBM compatible/Apple microcomputer 5¼" disks; most dedicated W.P. systems; some tapes to prearranged specifications, but requires hard copy also. Computer printout submissions acceptable. Reports in 4 months.

Nonfiction: Anthropology, archeology, economics, life sciences, mathematics, psychology, physics, art history, upper-level textbooks, academic trade, scholarly monographs, biography, history, and music. Looking for academic excellence in all work submitted. Department Editors: Elizabeth Maguire (humanities); Susan Milmoe (psychology); Rufus Neal (physical sciences); Frank Smith (history, political science); Ellen Shaw (English as second language); Colin Day (economics); James DeMartino (life sciences); Jonathan Sinclair-Wilson (philosophy); Peter-John Leone (earth sciences); David Emblidge (religious studies). Query. Reviews artwork/photos.

Recent Nonfiction Title: *The Making of American Industrial Research*, by Leonard Reich.

CAMELOT BOOKS, Children's Book Imprint of Avon Books, a division of the Hearst Corp., 1790 Broadway, New York NY 10019. (212)399-1383. Senior Editor: Ellen Krieger. Publishes paperback originals and reprints. Averages 36 titles/year; receives 1,500-2,000 submissions annually. 10-15% of books from first-time authors; 25% of books from unagented writers. Pays 6-8% royalty on retail price; offers minimum advance $1,500. Publishes book an average of 15 months after acceptance. Simultaneous and photocopied submissions OK. Computer printout submissions acceptable; prefers letter-quality to dot-matrix. Reports in 10 weeks. Free book catalog; ms guidelines for 8x10 SAE and 98¢ postage.

Fiction: Subjects include adventure, fantasy, humor, mainstream, mystery, science fiction ("very selective with mystery and science fiction") and suspense. Submit entire ms or 3 sample chapters and outline.

Recent Fiction Title: *Morgan's Zoo*, by James Howe.

‡*CANTERBURY PRESS, Box 2151C, Berkeley CA 94702. (415)843-1860. Editors: Ian Faircloth and Norine Brogan. Publishes hardcover and trade paperback originals. Averages 3-4 titles/year; receives approximately 100 submissions annually. 75% of books from first-time authors; 90% of books from unagented writers. Currently does subsidy publish, "and would like to increase this area. We would consider the manuscript in question. If we liked it but were less certain of its marketability this would more likely qualify it for author participation." Pays 5-8% royalty on wholesale price. Offers average $500 advance. Publishes book an average of 4 months after acceptance. Simultaneous and photocopied submissions OK. Electronic submissions via disk or modem acceptable—"we are compatible with all systems"; but hard copy must accompany an electronic submission. Computer printout submissions acceptable; prefers letter-quality to dot-matrix. Reports in 1 month on queries; 2 months on manuscripts. Book catalog free on request.

Nonfiction: Subjects include philosophy, politics and sociology. "We need work which highlights social injustice, and political strategies to alleviate this. Studies on 'third world' peoples, people with disabilities, native Americans and other minority groups—works which evidence the plight of the underprivileged." Query; all unsolicited mss are returned unopened.

Recent Nonfiction Title: *Living Outside Inside*, by Susan Hannaford, (a social study on the plight of disabled people).

Fiction: Adventure, experimental, fantasy and humor. "We need fiction works of a high literary standard which offer a social, political and/or cultural insight. No predictable material which really has nothing to offer the type of reader we would like to attract." Query; all unsolicited mss are returned unopened.

Recent Fiction Title: *Gringos Do Go to Heaven*, by Marie Hanson, (contemporary novel).

Tips: "The audience we envision for our books is a mature adult audience that appreciates good literature, but realizes that we are in a developing society which can be influenced by that literature—an audience that appreciates innovative writing which may bring new ideas and important insights. If I were a writer trying to market a book today, I would remain confident in my work and persevere—there's always an opening somewhere."

CAROLINA BIOLOGICAL SUPPLY CO., 2700 York Rd., Burlington NC 27215. (919)584-0381. Head, Scientific Publications: Dr. Phillip L. Owens. Publishes paperback originals. Averages 15 titles/year; receives 30 submissions annually. 25% of books from first-time authors; 100% of books from unagented writers. Pays 10% royalty on sales. Publishes book an average of 1 year after acceptance. Simultaneous and photocopied submissions OK. Electronic submissions OK via Apple IIe, TMac, but requires hard copy also. Computer printout submissions acceptable; no dot-matrix. Reports in 2 weeks on queries.
Nonfiction: Self-help, technical, textbook on animals, health, nature, biology and science. "We will consider short (10,000 words) manuscripts of general interest to high school and college students on health, computers, biology, physics, astronomy, microscopes, etc. Longer manuscripts less favored but will be considered." Query first. Reviews photos/artwork as part of ms package.
Recent Nonfiction Title: *Space Medicine*, by Paul C. Rambaut.

‡CARPENTER PRESS, Route 4, Pomeroy OH 45769. (614)992-7520. Publisher: Robert Fox. Publishes trade paperback originals. Averages 0-4 titles/year; receives 200 submissions annually. 50% of books from first-time authors; 100% of books from unagented writers. Pays 10% minimum royalty on wholesale price. Publishes book 1-4 years after acceptance. Simultaneous and photocopied submissions OK. Computer printout submissions acceptable; no dot-matrix. Reports in 1 week on queries; 3 months on mss. Book catalog for business size SAE and 1 first class stamp.
Fiction: Experimental, fantasy, mainstream, and science fiction. "We are backlogged for at least two years and cannot consider new manuscripts for that time." No genre fiction. Query.
Recent Fiction Title: *Leviathan*, by Hugh Fox (novel).

CARROLL & GRAF PUBLISHERS, INC., 260 5th Ave., New York NY 10001. (212)889-8772. Contact: Kent Carroll. Publishes hardcover, trade and mass market paperback originals, and trade paperback, and mass market paperback reprints. Averages 100 titles/year; receives 1,000 submissions annually. 10% of books from unagented authors; 10% of books from unagented writers. Pays 6-10% royalty on retail price. Publishes book an average of 1 year after acceptance. Photocopied submissions OK. Computer printout submissions acceptable; prefers letter-quality to dot-matrix. Reports in 2 weeks on queries; 1 month on mss. Free book catalog.
Nonfiction: Biography and fiction. Query; all unsolicited mss are returned unopened. Reviews artwork/photos as part of ms package.
Fiction: Adventure, erotica, fantasy, humor, mainstream, mystery, and suspense. Query; all unsolicited mss are returned unopened.

CARSTENS PUBLICATIONS, INC., Hobby Book Division, Box 700, Newton NJ 07860. (201)383-3355. Publisher: Harold H. Carstens. Publishes paperback originals. Averages 5 titles/year. 100% of books from unagented writers. Pays 10% royalty on retail price; offers average advance. Publishes book an average of 2 years after acceptance. Electronic submissions OK if compatible with ASCII-5¼" floppy disk, TRS 80 or MSDOS modem. Computer printout submissions acceptable; prefers letter-quality to dot-matrix. Book catalog for SASE.
Nonfiction: Model railroading, toy trains, model aviation, railroads and model hobbies. "We have scheduled or planned titles on several railroads as well as model railroad and model airplane books. Authors must know their field intimately since our readers are active modelers. Our railroad books presently are primarily photographic essays on specific railroads. Writers cannot write about somebody else's hobby with authority. If they do, we can't use them." Query. Reviews artwork/photos as part of ms package.
Recent Nonfiction Title: *How to Build Model Railroad Structures* (how-to).
Tips: "No fiction. We need lots of good b&w photos. Material must be in model, hobby, railroad field only."

CATHOLIC TRUTH SOCIETY, 38/40 Eccleston Square, London SW1V 1PD England. (01)834-4392. Editorial Director: David Murphy. Publishes hardcover and paperback originals and reprints. Averages 80 titles/year; receives 300 submissions annually. An estimated 20% of books from first-time authors; 100% from unagented writers. Average print order for a writer's first book is 5,000. Pays in outright purchase of $50-400; no advance. Publishes book an average of 6 months after acceptance. Simultaneous and photocopied submissions OK. Computer printout submissions acceptable; prefers letter-quality to dot-matrix. Reports in 1 month. SAE with IRCs. "Do not send U.S. Mail stamps for return of manuscript." Free book catalog and ms guidelines.
Nonfiction: Books dealing with how to solve problems in personal relationships, parenthood, teen-age, widowhood, sickness and death, especially drawing on Christian and Catholic tradition for inspiration; simple accounts of points of interest in Catholic faith, for non-Catholic readership; and books of prayer and devotion.

Query, submit outline/synopsis and sample chapter, or submit complete ms. Reviews artwork/photos as part of ms package.

Recent Nonfiction Title: *The Teaching of the Catholic Church: a New Catechism of Christian Doctrine*, by Herbert McCabe, O.P.

Tips: "Catholic Truth Society publishes nothing but Roman Catholic books, because we are a charity for the purpose of publishing Roman Catholic books."

CATHOLIC UNIVERSITY OF AMERICA PRESS, 620 Michigan Ave. NE, Washington DC 20064. (202)635-5052. Director: Dr. David J. McGonagle. Marketing Manager: Cynthia Miller. Averages 10-15 titles/year; receives 100 submissions annually. 50% of books from first-time authors; 100% of books from unagented writers. Average print order for a writer's first book is 1,000. Pays variable royalty on net receipts. Publishes book an average of 1 year after acceptance. Electronic submissions OK, but requires hard copy also. Computer printout submissions acceptable; no dot-matrix. Reports in 2 months.

Nonfiction: Publishes history, biography, languages and literature, philosophy, religion, church-state relations, political theory and social studies. No unrevised doctoral dissertations. Length: 200,000-500,000 words. Query with sample chapter plus outline of entire work, along with curriculum vitae and list of previous publications. Reviews artwork/photos.

Recent Nonfiction Title: *The Grammar of Silence: A Reading of Marguerite de Navarre's Poetry*, by Robert D. Cottrell.

Tips: Freelancer has best chance of selling "scholarly monographs and works suitable for adoption as supplementary reading material in courses."

‡THE CAXTON PRINTERS, LTD., 312 Main St., Box 700, Caldwell ID 83605. (208)459-7421. Vice President: Gordon Gipson. Publishes hardcover and trade paperback originals. Averages 6-8 titles/year; receives 250 submissions annually. 50% of books from first-time authors; 60% of books from unagented writers. Audience includes Westerners, students, historians and researchers. Pays royalty; advance $500-2,000. Publishes book an average of 18 months after acceptance. Simultaneous and photocopied submissions OK. Computer printout submissions acceptable; no dot-matrix. Reports in 2 weeks on queries; 8 weeks on mss. Free book catalog.

Nonfiction: Coffee table, Americana and Western Americana. "We need good Western Americana, preferably copiously illustrated with unpublished photos." Query. Reviews artwork/photos as part of ms package.

Recent Nonfiction Title: *Pioneer Trails West*, edited by Don Worcester.

Tips: "Western Americana, especially the northwest (preferably with outstanding previously unpublished black-and-white photos), has the best chance of selling to our firm."

*CAY-BEL PUBLISHING COMPANY, Thompson-Lyford Bldg., 2nd Fl., 45 Center St., Brewer ME 04412. (207)989-3820. Editor-in-Chief: John E. Cayford. Imprints include C&H Publishing Co. Publishes hardcover and trade paperback originals, and hardcover and trade paperback reprints. Averages 8 titles/year; receives 350 submissions annually. 50% of books from first-time authors; 100% of books from unagented writers. Average print order for a writer's first book is 2,000-5,000. Subsidy publishes 5% of books when authors "want us to put their manuscript in a book form, to typeset it and print it, but want to handle their own sales." Pays 10-15% royalty on retail price. Publishes book an average of 6-8 months after acceptance. Simultaneous and photocopied submissions OK. Computer printout submissions acceptable; prefers letter-quality to dot-matrix. Reports in 2 weeks on queries; 1 month on mss. Free book catalog; ms guidelines for $1.

Nonfiction: Biography, cookbook, reference and maritime. Subjects include Americana, cooking and foods, history, religion, and vital records and genealogy. "Our book schedule is fairly well filled for the next year, but we will give very careful consideration to any book about a Maine personage or to a Maine history." No poetry or pornography. Query first, then submit complete ms. Reviews artwork/photos.

Recent Nonfiction Title: *The Sunrise Route, A History of Railroads in Washington County, Maine*, by Michael W. Zimmerman.

Fiction: "We have planned a series of books written by a Maine author in the 1920s, however these will be reprints and an in-house project."

Tips: "If the author's book deals with a phase of Maine's great history, regardless of how bad the writing is, we'll work with him or her so long as the subject matter is factual, and we can check it, which we do. No history book leaves this office without a member of the staff checking the sources. We have set in motion a planned series of booklets dealing with Maine personalities and historically-important Maine cities and towns. These booklets will average from 44 to 88 pages. Thus far we have researched the lives of more than 56 Mainers who have gone on to attain fame and fortune. These booklets will average a run of 10,000 copies and retail on the average for $2.95 to $3.95 each."

*CBP PRESS, Subsidiary of Christian Board of Publication, Box 179, St. Louis MO 63166. (314)371-6900. Editor: Herbert H. Lambert. Publishes trade paperback originals and trade paperback reprints. Averages 12 titles/year; receives 400 submissions annually. 50% of books from first-time authors; 100% of books from un-

agented writers. "We subsidy publish about one or two books in ten, and the subsidy usually comes from friends, foundations, or church agencies." An author should be subsidy published "when projected sales are under 3,000, and the book is needed." Pays 17% royalty on wholesale price; offers no advance. Publishes book an average of 1 year after acceptance. Simultaneous and photocopied submissions OK. Computer print-out submissions acceptable; prefers letter-quality to dot-matrix. Reports in 6 weeks. Free book catalog.
Nonfiction: Biography, how-to, humor, and self-help on religion. "We are looking for books of Bible theology spirituality, worship, and practical Christianity. These books may be primarily for clergy or laity of mainline Protestant and Roman Catholic groups." Submit outline/synopsis and sample chapters.
Recent Nonfiction Title: *Only By Grace*, by Tom S. Sampson.
Tips: "Deal with some current theme that has not been adequately discussed in other books. We look for books on personal devotions or lay Christianity that have a unique approach."

‡**CEDARSHOUSE PRESS**, 406 W. 28th St., Bryan TX 77801. (713)822-5615. Editor: Paul Christensen. Publishes hardcover originals and trade paperback reprints. Averages 4-8 titles/year. Pays 5-8% royalty on retail price. Photocopied submissions OK. Reports in 6 weeks on queries; 4 months on mss.
Nonfiction: Biography, reference, belles lettres on Americana, history, philosophy, politics, and travel. "Studies of neglected American authors, fiction, poetry, nonfiction; controversial historical subjects—race relations, leftist political systems in US, generation studies of Americans in 20th century, commentary on contemporary society, etc." Publishes for Southwestern readers interested in the lore and mythology of the region; readers of innovative and experimental fiction and verse; historical and critical writing appealing to writers, social observers, general interest audiences." No pop studies, slick prose, devotional or religious subjects, magazine writing, superficial surveys, trendy concepts, "coffee table" book writing, photo books, private journals and survival memoirs, etc. Query or submit outline/synopsis and 3 sample chapters.
Fiction: "Very low priority; no particular needs at this time except for distinguished mss of experimental prose." No conventional fiction of any type. Query.
Poetry: "Long poems of an experimental attitude; regional poetry stressing unique perception of land and people; Southwestern topics; books tightly ordered and innovative." Accepts poetry translations from French and Spanish. No conventional lyrics, collections of verse, theme books, confessional writing, memoirs, travelogues, scenic poems, anthologies. Submit 6-10 samples.
Recent Poetry Title: *Osiris at the Roller Derby*, by J. Edgar Simmons.
Tips: Queries/mss may be routed to other editors in the publishing group.

CELESTIAL ARTS, Box 7327, Berkeley CA 94707. (415)524-1801. Editorial Director: George Young. Editor: Paul Reed. Publishes paperback originals. Publishes 20 titles/year; receives 12,000 submissions annually. 50% of books from first-time authors; 90% of books from unagented writers. Average print order for a writer's first book is 5,000. Publishes book an average of 9 months after acceptance. Simultaneous and photocopied submissions OK. Electronic submissions OK via diskette only, not via modem—should be IBM PC compatible. Computer printout submissions acceptable; prefers letter-quality to dot-matrix. Reports in 3 months. Free book catalog.
Nonfiction: Publishes biography, cookbooks/cooking, health, psychology, new age philosophy, gay, and self-help. No poetry. "Submit 2-3 sample chapters and outline; no original copy. If return requested, include postage." Reviews artwork/photos.
Recent Nonfiction Title: *Two Hearts Are Better Than One*, by Bob Mandel.
Tips: "Celestial Arts is a subsidiary of *Ten Speed Press*, and the same guidelines apply. We do not want to see the same manuscripts submitted to both Ten Speed and Celestial."

‡**CHATHAM PRESS**, Box A, Old Greenwich CT 06870. Publishes hardcover and paperback originals, reprints and anthologies relating to New England and the Atlantic coastline. Averages 14 titles/year; receives 50 submissions annually. 30% of books from first-time authors; 75% of books from unagented writers. "Standard book contract does not always apply if the book is heavily illustrated. Average advance is low." Publishes book an average of 6 months after acceptance. Electronic submissions OK via IBM. Computer printout submissions acceptable; prefers letter-quality to dot-matrix. Query with outline and 3 sample chapters. Reports in 2 weeks. Free book catalog.
Nonfiction: Publishes mostly "regional history and natural history, involving mainly Northeast seaboard and the Carolinas, mostly illustrated, with emphasis on conservation and outdoor recreation." Accepts nonfiction translations from French and German. Reviews artwork/photos as part of ms package.
Recent Nonfiction Title: *A Beachcomber's Companion*, by Ted Wesemann.
Tips: "Illustrated New England-relevant titles have the best chance of selling to our firm."

‡**CHELSEA GREEN**, Box 283, Chelsea VT 05038. (802)685-3108. Editor: Ian Baldwin Jr. Publishes hardcover and trade paperback originals and reprints. Averages 6 titles/year; receives 100 submissions annually. 30% of books from first-time authors; 90% of books from unagented writers. Pays 10-15% net royalty. Offers average $1,000 advance. Publishes book an average of 9 months after acceptance. Simultaneous and photo-

copied submissions OK. Electronic submissions OK via MacIntosh, but requires hard copy also. Computer printout submissions acceptable. Free book catalog.

Nonfiction: Biography and illustrated books on art, history, nature, politics and travel. "We are looking for good biography." Query or submit outline/synopsis and sample chapters.

Recent Nonfiction Title: *The Upper Valley,* by Jerold Wikoff (regional history).

Fiction: Ethnic, regional, experimental and mainstream. "We are looking for strong regional fiction." Query or submit outline/synopsis and sample chapters.

Recent Fiction Title: *In a Pig's Eye,* by Karl Schwenke (regional humor).

‡**CHICAGO REVIEW PRESS,** 814 N. Franklin, Chicago IL 60610. (312)337-0747. Editor: Linda Matthews. Publishes hardcover and trade paperback originals. Averages 30 titles/year; receives 200+ submissions annually. 60% of books from first-time authors; 80% of books from unagented writers. Pays 10-15% royalty. Offers average $1,500 advance. Publishes book an average of 6 months after acceptance. Simultaneous and photocopied submissions OK. Electronic submissions OK if CPM compatible. Computer printout submissions acceptable; no dot-matrix. Reports in 1 month on queries; 3 months on mss. Book catalog free on request.

Nonfiction: Cookbook, how-to, humor, reference, self-help and guidebooks on cooking and foods, recreation, travel and popular science, study guides, and regional. Needs regional Chicago material and how-to, travel, popular science, family, cookbooks for the national audience. Query or submit outline/synopsis and sample chapters. Reviews artwork/photos.

Recent Nonfiction Title: *The Straight Dope,* by Cecil Adams (humor).

Tips: "The audience we envision for our books is adults and young people 15 and older, educated readers with special interests, do-it-yourselfers, travellers, students, and young professionals. A trend we have noticed is the comeback of the successful short-run title, study guides and practical information, and the popularization of technical subjects, and information."

‡**CHILDRENS PRESS,** 1224 W. Van Buren St., Chicago IL 60607. (312)666-4200. Editorial Director: Fran Dyra. Averages 80 titles/year; receives 2,000+ submissions annually. 5-10% of books from first-time authors; 100% of books from unagented writers. Pays in outright purchase or offers small advance against royalty. Publishes book an average of 1 year after acceptance. Simultaneous submissions OK. Computer printout submissions acceptable; prefers letter-quality to dot-matrix. Reports in 3 months.

Nonfiction: For supplementary use in elementary and junior high schools; picture books for early childhood and beginning readers; high-interest, easy reading material. Specific categories include social studies and science. Especially wants new biographies. Length: 50-10,000 words. For picture books, needs are very broad. They should be geared from preschool to grade 3. "We have a strong tendency to publish books in series. Odds are against a single book that couldn't, if sales warrant, develop into a series." Length: 50-1,000 words. Send outline with 1 sample chapter; complete ms for picture books. Accepts translations. Reviews artwork and photos as part of ms package, "but best to submit ms first." Do not send finished artwork with ms.

Recent Nonfiction Title: *People of Distinctions,* (biography series).

Fiction: For supplementary use in elementary and secondary schools. Length: 50-10,000 words. Picture books from preschool to grade 3. Length: 50-1,000 words. Send outline with sample chapters; complete ms for picture books. Do not send finished artwork with ms.

Tips: Submissions often "lack originality. Too often authors talk 'down' to young readers. First, it must be a good story, then it can have an educational or moral point. We're looking for writers in the science and technology areas. Nonfiction for middle grades (reading level 5th grade) has the best chance of selling to our firm."

‡**CHILTON BOOK CO.,** Chilton Way, Radnor PA 19089. Editorial Director: Alan F. Turner. Publishes hardcover and trade paperback originals. Publishes 90 titles/year. Pays royalty; average advance. Simultaneous and photocopied submissions OK. Electronic submissions OK, decided "case by case." Computer printout submissions acceptable. Reports in 3 weeks.

Nonfiction: Business/economics, crafts, how-to and technical. "We only want to see any manuscripts with informational value." Query or submit outline/synopsis and 2-3 sample chapters.

Recent Nonfiction Title: *Competitive Marketing Strategies.*

***CHINA BOOKS AND PERIODICALS, INC.,** 2929 24th St., San Francisco CA 94110. (415)282-2994. Editorial Director: Foster Stockwell. Publishes hardcover and trade paperback originals. Averages 6 titles/year; receives 40 submissions annually. 50% of books from first-time authors; 80% of books from unagented writers. Pays 2-10% royalty on retail price. Offers average $1,000 advance. Publishes book an average of 6 months after acceptance. Simultaneous and photocopied submissions OK. Electronic submissions OK, but requires hard copy also. Computer printout submissions acceptable; prefers letter-quality to dot-matrix. Reports in 2 weeks. Book catalog free on request.

Nonfiction: Biography, "coffee table" book, cookbook, how-to, juvenile and reference, all related to China. Query or submit outline/synopsis and sample chapters. Reviews artwork/photos as part of ms package.

Recent Nonfiction Title: *Two Years in the Melting Pot,* by Zongren (biography). Publishes only fiction sub-

jects related to China. Query or submit outline/synopsis and sample chapters.
Recent Fiction Title: *Milton and Matilda*, by Nancy Besst (children's story).
Tips: "Our audience includes tourists, art collectors and China scholars."

‡**CHOSEN BOOKS PUBLISHING CO., LTD.,** Imprint of Fleming H. Revell Co., 184 Central Ave., Old Tappan NJ 07675. (201)768-8060. Editor: Jane Campbell. Publishes hardcover and trade paperback originals. Averages 16 titles/year; receives 500 submissions annually. 15% of books from first-time authors; 98% of books from unagented writers. Pays royalty on retail price—7½% average on quality paper; 10% on hardcover. Publishes book an average of 9 months after acceptance. Simultaneous and photocopied submissions OK. Computer printout submissions acceptable; prefers letter-quality to dot-matrix. Reports in 2 months on queries; 3 months on mss. Book catalog not available; ms guidelines for SASE. Occasionally makes work-for-hire assignments.
Nonfiction: How-to, self-help, and 'teaching' or first-person narrative on religion. "We publish books reflecting the current acts of the Holy Spirit in the world—books with a charismatic Christian orientation, whether teaching or first-person narrative." No poetry. Submit outline/synopsis and sample chapters. Reviews artwork/photos as part of ms package.
Recent Nonfiction Title: *God Is a Matchmaker*, by Derek Prince (Bible-based teaching).
Tips: "Narratives don't do as well as 'teaching' books, which are what the Christian audience is looking for. Check out other Chosen titles to see the style of writing and subject matter we print. State the theme clearly in your proposal as well as your letter, and structure the manuscript around the theme."

‡**CHRISTIAN ED. PUBLISHERS,** Subsidiary of Success With Youth Publications, Box 261129, San Diego CA 92126. (619)578-4700. Subsidiaries include Rainbow Publishers. Editorial Director: Dr. Lon F. Ackelson. Trade paperback originals. Averages 20-30 titles/year; receives 100 submissions annually. 10% of books from first-time authors; 100% of books from unagented writers. Buys ms for $250 (2-3¢/word). No advances. Publishes book an average of 1 year after acceptance. Photocopied submissions OK. Computer printout submissions acceptable; no dot-matrix. Reports in 3 weeks on queries; 2-3 months on mss. Book catalog for 8x11 SAE and 3 first class stamps; ms guidelines for SASE.
Nonfiction: How-to, illustrated book, juvenile and reference on evangelical, non-denominational religion. Looks for nonfiction ms on parties, games, activities and devotionals for children and youth; program book articles for children's and youth's expressional training sessions. Just starting program for two's to three's, and a junior take-home feature. No topics that do not dovetail with our Christian education product line. No articles that are not directly tied to scriptural principles for life." Query or submit outline/synopsis and sample chapters. Reviews artwork/photos as part of ms package.
Recent Nonfiction Title: *Children's Sermons*, by William Martin (how-to).
Fiction: Adventure, mystery, and religious. Needs take-home papers for pre-school, primary and junior— brief stories, read-to-me stories, activity page items (puzzles, projects, etc.), and program books for children and youth (contemporary stories, adventure or mystery stories for juniors). Query or submit outline/synopsis and sample chapters.
Recent Fiction Title: *Bible Explorer For Juniors*, by Sandra Stone.
Tips: "Our audience is children and teens in thousands of churches nationwide, and their leaders. The types of books the writer has the best chance of selling to our firm are expressional training programs that are fresh, exciting and timely, and activities."

***THE CHRISTOPHER PUBLISHING HOUSE,** 106 Longwater Dr., Norwell MA 02061. (617)878-9336. Managing Editor: Susan Lukas. Publishes hardcover and trade paperback originals. Averages 20-30 titles/year; receives over 300-400 submissions annually. 30% of books from first-time authors; 100% of books from unagented writers. Subsidy publishes 50% of books based on subject matter and marketability. Pays 5-30% of royalty on wholesale price; offers no advance. Publishes book an average of 2 years after acceptance. Simultaneous and photocopied submissions OK. Electronic submissions OK; will arrange for online translation at time of transmission but requires hard copy also. Computer printout submissions acceptable; prefers letter-quality to dot-matrix. Reports in 1 month. Free book catalog; ms guidelines for SASE.
Nonfiction: Biography, how-to, reference, self-help, textbook and religious. Subjects include Americana, animals, art, business and economics, cooking and foods (nutrition), health, history, philosophy, politics, psychology, religion, sociology and travel. "We will be glad to review all nonfiction manuscripts, particularly college textbook and religious-oriented. Submit complete ms. Reviews artwork/photos.
Recent Nonfiction Title: *Women Priests and Other Fantasies*, by Rev. Vincent P. Miceli (religion).
Poetry: "We will review all forms of poetry." Submit complete ms.
Tips: "Our books are for a general audience, slanted toward college-educated readers. There are specific books targeted towards specific audiences when appropriate."

‡**CHRONICLE BOOKS,** Chronicle Books, 1 Hallidie Plaza, San Francisco CA 94102. (415)777-7240. Senior Editor: William LeBlond. Publishes hardcover and trade paperback originals. Averages 35 titles/year; receives

300 submissions annually. 20% of books from first-time authors; 70% of books from unagented writers. Pays 6-10% royalty on retail price. Offers average $3,000 advance. Publishes book an average of 1½ years after acceptance. Simultaneous and photocopied submissions OK. Computer printout submissions acceptable; prefers letter-quality to dot-matrix. Reports in 1 month on queries; 2 months on mss. Book catalog for 9x12 SAE with 3 first class stamps.

Nonfiction: "Coffee table" book, cookbook, and regional California on art, cooking and foods, nature, photography, recreation, and travel. Query or submit outline/synopsis and sample chapters. Reviews artwork/photos.

Recent Nonfiction Title: *Gifts of Age*, by Charlotte Painter and Pamela Valois (photographs and essays).

CITADEL PRESS, 120 Enterprise Ave., Secaucus NJ 07094. (212)736-0007. Editorial Director: Allan J. Wilson. Publishes hardcover originals and paperback reprints. Receives 800-1,000 submissions annually. 7% of books from first-time authors; 50% of books from unagented writers. Average print order for a writer's first book is $5,000. Pays 10% royalty on hardcover, 5-7% on paperback; offers average $3,000 advance. Publishes book an average of 2 months after acceptance. Simultaneous submissions OK. Computer printout submissions acceptable; no dot-matrix. Reports in 2 months. Catalog for $1.

Nonfiction: Biography, film, psychology, humor and history. Also seeks "off-beat material," but no "poetry, religion, politics." Accepts nonfiction and fiction translations. Query. Accepts outline/synopsis and 3 sample chapters. Reviews artwork/photos.

Recent Nonfiction Title: *Arrogant Aussie*, by Michael Leapman.

Tips: "We concentrate on biography, popular interest, and film, with limited fiction (no romance, religion, poetry, music)."

‡CLARION BOOKS, Ticknor & Fields: a Houghton Mifflin Company. 52 Vanderbilt Ave., New York NY 10017. Editor and Publisher: James C. Giblin. Senior Editor for Nonfiction: Ann Troy. Associate Editor: Dianne Hess. Publishes hardcover originals. Averages 30-32 titles/year. Pays 5-10% royalty on retail price; $1,000-3,000 advance, depending on whether project is a picture book or a longer work for older children. Photocopied submissions OK. No multiple submissions. Computer printout submissions acceptable; no dot-matrix. Reports in 2 months. Publishes book an average of 18 months after acceptance. Free book catalog.

Nonfiction: Americana, biography, holiday, humor, nature, photo essays and word play. Prefers books for younger children. Reviews artwork/photos as part of ms package. Query.

Recent Nonfiction Title: *Cowboys of the Wild West*, by Russell Freedman.

Fiction: Adventure, fantasy, humor, mystery, strong character studies, and suspense. "We would like to see more humorous contemporary stories that young people of 8-12 or 10-14 can identify with readily." Accepts fiction translations. Query on ms of more than 50 pages. Looks for "freshness, enthusiasm—in short, life" (fiction and nonfiction).

Recent Fiction Title: *Watermusic*, by Sarah Sargent (ages 9-12).

‡*ARTHUR H. CLARK CO., Box 230, Glendale CA 92109. (213)245-9119. Editorial Director: Robert A. Clark. Publishes hardcover originals. Averages 8 titles/year; receives 40 submissions annually. 40% of books from first-time authors; 100% of books from unagented writers. Subsidy publishes 10% of books based on whether they are "high-risk sales." Pays 10% minimum royalty on wholesale prices. Publishes book an average of 9 months after acceptance. Photocopied submissions OK. Computer printout submissions acceptable; prefers letter-quality to dot-matrix. Reports in 1 week on queries; 2 months on mss. Free book catalog.

Nonfiction: Biography, reference and historical nonfiction. Subjects include Americana and history. "We're looking for documentary source material in Western American history." Query or submit outline/synopsis and 3 sample chapters. Looks for "content, form, style." Reviews artwork/photos as part of ms package.

Recent Nonfiction Title: *The Custer Trail*, by John Carroll.

Tips: "Western Americana (nonfiction) has the best chance of selling to our firm."

*CLEANING CONSULTANT SERVICES, INC., 1512 Western Ave., Seattle WA 98101. (206)682-9748. President: William R. Griffin. Publishes trade paperback originals and reprints. Averages 4-6 titles/year; receives 15 submissions annually. 75% of books from first-time authors; 100% of books from unagented writers. Subsidy publishes 10% of books. "If they (authors) won't sell it and won't accept royalty contract, we offer our publishing services and often sell the book along with our books." Pays 5-15% royalty on retail price or outright purchase, $100-2,500, depending on negotiated agreement. Publishes book an average of 6-12 months

ALWAYS submit mss or queries with a stamped, self-addressed envelope (SASE) within your country or International Reply Coupons (IRCs) purchased from the post office for other countries.

after acceptance. Photocopied submissions OK. Computer printout submissions acceptable; prefers letter-quality to dot-matrix. SASE required if author asks for ms back. Reports in 6 weeks on queries; 3 months on mss. Free book catalog; ms guidelines for SASE.

Nonfiction: How-to, illustrated book, reference, self-help, technical, textbook and directories. Subjects include business, health, and cleaning and maintenance. Needs books on anything related to cleaning, maintenance, self-employment or entrepreneurship. Query or submit outline/synopsis and sample chapters or complete ms. Reviews artwork/photos.

Recent Nonfiction Title: *Food Service, Health Sanitation and Safety,* by Bruce Jackson (how-to).

Tips: "Our audience includes those involved in cleaning and maintenance service trades, opportunity seekers, schools, property managers, libraries—anyone who needs information on cleaning and maintenance. How-to and self-employment guides are doing well for us in today's market."

‡CLEVELAND STATE UNIVERSITY POETRY CENTER R.T. 1815, Cleveland State University, Cleveland OH 44115. (216)687-3986. Co-Editor: Leonard M. Trawick. Publishes trade paperback originals. Averages 5 titles/year; receives 400 queries, 200 mss annually. 60% of books from first-time authors; 100% of books from unagented writers. CSU poetry series pays 10% royalty plus 50 copies on wholesale price if sold by bookseller, on retail price if sold by CSU Poetry Center; Cleveland Poetry Series (Ohio poets only) pays 100 copies. No advance. Publishes book an average of 6 months after acceptance. Simultaneous and photocopied submissions OK. Computer printout submissions acceptable; prefers letter-quality to dot-matrix. Reports in 2 weeks on queries; 6 months on mss. Free book catalog; ms guidelines for SASE.

Poetry: "We expect to accept 4-5 book-length manuscripts in spring 1987 for publication in 1988. Manuscripts should be submitted in December-February 1987. We expect to have similar needs in following years." No light verse; "inspirational"; greeting card verse. ("This does not mean that we do not consider poetry with humor or philosophical/religious import.") Query—ask for guidelines. Submit only December-February. Reviews artwork/photos if applicable (i.e., concrete poetry).

Recent Poetry Title: *The Catastrophe of Rainbows,* by Martha Collins (serious, difficult).

Tips: "Our books are for serious readers of poetry, i.e. poets, critics, academics, students, people who read *Poetry, Field, American Poetry Review, Antaeus,* etc." Trends include "movement from 'confessional' poetry; greater attention to form and craftsmanship. Try to project an interesting, coherent personality; link poems so as to make coherent unity, not just a miscellaneous collection." Especially needs "poems with *mystery,* i.e., poems that reflect profound thought, but do not tell all—suggestive, tantalizing, enticing."

‡CLIFFS NOTES, INC., Box 80728, Lincoln NE 68501. (402)477-6971. Editor: Michele Spence. Publishes trade paperback originals. Averages 10 titles/year. 100% of books from unagented writers. Pays royalty on wholesale price. Buys some mss outright; "full payment on acceptance of ms." Publishes book an average of 1 year after acceptance. Computer printout submissions acceptable. Reports in 1 month. Free book catalog. "We provide specific guidelines when a project is assigned."

Nonfiction: Self-help, and textbook. "We publish self-help study aids directed to junior high through graduate school audience. Publications include *Cliffs Notes, Cliffs Test Preparation Guides,* and *Cliffs Teaching Portfolios,* and other study guides. Most authors are experienced teachers, usually with advanced degrees. *Teaching Portfolio* authors are experienced high school English teachers who can provide practical, proven classroom material designed for junior high and high school English teachers. Some books also appeal to a general lay audience." Query.

COACH HOUSE PRESS, INC., Box 458, Morton Grove IL 60053. (312)967-1777. Publisher/President: David Jewell. Publishes production script originals. Averages 3-8 titles/year; receives 150-200 submissions annually. 50% of books from first-time authors; 95% of books from unagented writers. Pays 10% royalty on receipts from book sales; 50% royalty on performance. Publishes book an average of 3-15 months after acceptance. Simultaneous and photocopied submissions OK. Electronic submissions OK on ASCII. Computer printout submissions acceptable; prefers letter-quality to dot-matrix. Reports in 1 month on queries; 3 months on mss. Free script catalog.

Nonfiction: Drama production guides and aids.

Recent Nonfiction Title: *Acting Up! An Innovative Guide to Creative Drama for Older Adults,* by Telander, Verson and Quinlan.

Fiction: Plays for children's theatre, one-act plays for high school contest and plays for senior adults. Query or submit complete ms.

Recent Fiction Title: *Blue Horses,* by Kathryn Schultz-Miller (playscript).

Tips: "Plays which sell best to today's producers respect children as intelligent, alert and informed, and *avoid* stereotyping any group as evil, stupid or immature. If I were a writer trying to market a book today, I would get a first-class production of my play, and then watch the audience react and adjust my play accordingly."

COLES PUBLISHING CO., LTD., 90 Ronson Dr., Rexdale, Ontario, Canada M9W 1C1. (416)243-3132. Manager of Publishing/Editorial Director: Helena Aalto. Publishes hardcover and paperback originals and reprints. Averages 25 titles/year; receives 100 submissions annually. 20% of books from first-time authors; 100% of books from unagented writers. Average print order for a writer's first books is 5,000. "We are a subsidiary company of 'Coles, the Book People,' a chain of 235 bookstores throughout Canada and America." Pays by outright purchase of $500-$2,500; advance averages $500. Publishes book an average of 8 months after acceptance. Buys Canadian rights only. Simultaneous and photocopied submissions OK. Reports in 1 month. SAE and International Reply Coupons. Book catalog $3.

Nonfiction: "We publish in the following areas: education, language, science, math, pet care, gardening, cookbooks, medicine and health, occult, business, reference, technical and do-it-yourself, crafts and hobbies, antiques, games, and sports. We also publish a complete line of literary study aids sold worldwide." No philosophy, religion, history or biography. Submit outline/synopsis and sample chapters.

Recent Nonfiction Title: *Street Proofing*.

Tips: "The writer has the best chance of selling us wide appeal, practical self-help books."

COLLECTOR BOOKS, Box 3009, Paducah KY 42001. Editor: Steve Quertermous. Publishes hardcover and paperback originals. Publishes 30-35 titles/year. 50% of books from first-time authors; 100% of books from unagented writers. Average print order for a writer's first book is 5,000. Pays 5% royalty on retail; no advance. Publishes book an average of 8 months after acceptance. Send prints or transparencies if illustrations are to accompany ms. Computer printout submissions acceptable; no dot-matrix. Reports in 1 month. Free book catalog.

Nonfiction: "We only publish books on antiques and collectibles. We require our authors to be very knowledgeable in their respective fields and have access to a large representative sampling of the particular subject concerned." Query. Accepts outline/synopsis and 2-3 sample chapters. Reviews artwork/photos as part of ms package.

Recent Nonfiction Title: *Character Toys*, by D. Longest.

COLLIER MACMILLAN CANADA, INC., 50 Gervais Dr., Don Mills, Ontario M3C 3K4 Canada. Publishes originals and reprints in hardcover and paperback. Published 15 titles last year; receives 500 submissions annually. 75% of books from first-time authors; 95% of books from unagented writers. Advance varies, depending on author's reputation and nature of book. Reports in 6 weeks. SAE with IRC. Publishes book an average of 9 months after acceptance.

Nonfiction: Vocational—technical, family studies, language arts, (for Canadian high school curricula). Query.

Tips: "Writers have the best chance of selling us young adult fiction and textbooks for grades 7 through 12 (controlled vocabulary)."

COLORADO ASSOCIATED UNIVERSITY PRESS, Box 480, 1344 Grandview Ave., University of Colorado, Boulder CO 80309. (303)492-7191. Editor: Frederick Rinehart. Publishes hardcover and paperback originals. Averages 10 titles/year; receives 350 submissions annually. 50% of books from first-time authors; 99% of books from unagented writers. Average print order for a writer's first book is 500-1,000. Pays 10-12½-15% royalty contract on wholesale or retail price; "no advances." Publishes book an average of 18 months after acceptance. Will consider photocopied submissions "if not sent simultaneously to another publisher." Electronic submissions OK via IBM PC, Apple (inquire first), but requires hard copy also. Computer printout submissions acceptable; prefer letter-quality to dot-matrix. Reports in 3 months. Free book catalog.

Nonfiction: Scholarly, regional and environmental subjects. Length: 250-500 pages. Query first with table of contents, preface or opening chapter. Reviews artwork/photos as part of ms package.

Recent Nonfiction Title: *Dr. Webb of Colorado Springs*, by Helen Clapesattle (medical science).

Tips: "Books should be solidly researched and from a reputable scholar, because we are a university press."

COLUMBIA PUBLISHING CO., INC., Frenchtown NJ 08825. (201)996-2141. Editorial Director: Bernard Rabb. Publishes hardcover originals. Receives 1,000 submissions annually. 30% of books from first-time authors; 100% of books from unagented writers. Average print order for a writer's first book is 3,000. Pays 10% royalty; offers average advance. Publishes book an average of 9 months after acceptance. Simultaneous and photocopied submissions OK. Electronic submissions OK on IBM PC or DOS 2.1. Computer printout submissions acceptable; no dot-matrix. Reports in 6 months or longer.

Nonfiction: Biography, theater, film, dance, classical music, political science, business, recreation, and nature/ecology. Accepts nonfiction and fiction translations from French and German. "We do not want spy novels, westerns, romances, science fiction, mysteries, fad books, religious titles or academic books not applicable to a lay audience." Submit complete ms. Reviews artwork/photos as part of ms package.

Recent Nonfiction Title: *New York and the China Trade*, by Howard.

Fiction: Alternative fiction. Literary novels—serious fiction only. Submit complete ms.

Recent Fiction Title: *Odyssey of Revenge*, by Diamond.

COMMUNICATION SKILL BUILDERS, INC., Box 42050, Tucson AZ 85733. (602)323-7500. Acquisitions/Editorial Manager: Ronald H. Weintraub. Publishes paperback originals, kits, games, software and audio cassettes. Averages 60 titles/year; receives 150 submissions annually. 50% of books from first-time authors; 100% of books from unagented writers. Pays negotiable royalty on wholesale or retail price. Publishes book an average of 9 months after acceptance. No simultaneous submissions; photocopied submissions OK. Electronic submissions OK, if IBM-PC compatible or telecommunicated through modem, but requires hard copy also. Computer printout submissions acceptable. Reports in 2 months. Free book catalog—Speech-Language/Special Education.

Nonfiction: Speech-Language/Special Education material: Articulation therapy, language remediation and development; hearing impaired; adult communicative disorders; physically handicapped/developmentally delayed; early childhood education; professional resources; assessment materials. Reviews artwork/photos as part of ms package. "If a material is illustrated, costs for the photographs or drawings are the responsibility of the author."

Recent Nonfiction Title: *All About Me.*

COMMUNICATIONS PRESS, INC., 1735 DeSales St. NW, Washington DC 20036. (202)639-8822. Production Coordinator: Patricia C. Thomas. Publishes hardcover, trade paperback, and professional/text paperback originals. Averages 6-10 titles/year. 95% of books from unagented writers. Pays royalty or honorarium; offers "nominal, if any" advance. Publishes book an average of 9 months after acceptance. Computer printout submissions acceptable; no dot-matrix. Reports in 1 month. Free book catalog.

Nonfiction: Reference, technical and textbook. Subjects include business and economics (communications); journalism and communications; performing arts; politics and sociology (science/technology, public affairs and communications). Submit outline/synopsis and 2 sample chapters. Reviews artwork/photos.

Recent Nonfiction Title: *Acting in the Million Dollar Minute: The Art and Business of Performing in TV Commercials,* by Tom Logan.

COMPCARE PUBLICATIONS, 2415 Annapolis Lane, Minneapolis MN 55441. Publisher: Arnold Keuning. Publishes hardcover and trade paperback originals. Averages 6-8 titles/year; receives 300 submissions annually. 75% of books from first-time authors; 60% of books from unagented writers. Average print order for a writer's first book is 7,500. Pays negotiable royalty; offers negotiable advance. Publishes book an average of 18 months after acceptance. Simultaneous and photocopied submissions OK. Computer printout submissions acceptable; prefers letter-quality to dot-matrix. Reports in 2 months. Free book catalog; ms guidelines for SASE.

Nonfiction: Personal growth books on alcoholism/chemical dependency, weight control, personal relationships including parenting and emotional health. "Prefer to hear from writers with credentials in the field they are writing about." Query. Reviews artwork/photos.

Recent Nonfiction Title: *The Hug Therapy Book,* by Kathleen Keating, drawings by Mimi Noland.

Tips: "Avoid material that is not new and not positive and problem-solving. Research must be documented well or the writer must have credentials in the field. Writing must be credible while still general-market readable."

COMPUBIBS, Subsidiary of Vantage Information Consultants, Inc., Box 22684, Lexington KY 40502. Acquisitions Editor: Herbert Regenstreif. Publishes trade paperback originals and software. Averages 8-10 titles/year; receives 25 submissions annually. 40% of books from first-time authors; 100% of books from unagented writers. Makes $100-300 outright purchase plus payment of flat rate/copy if minimum number is exceeded; offers no advance. Publishes ms an average of 4-6 months after acceptance. Photocopied submissions OK. Computer printout submissions acceptable; prefers letter-quality to dot-matrix. Reports in 1 month on queries; 6 weeks on mss.

Nonfiction: Reference and bibliographies. Subjects include business and economics, history, psychology, sports, computers and libraries. Query.

Recent Nonfiction Titles: *Anorexia and Bulimia: An Annotated Bibliography,* by I. Taler (reference book).

Tips: "Reference books for a general or professional audience have the best chance of selling to our firm. In completing a book for us, author must honor time provision. Our books are valuable in part because of their currency. If information becomes stale, some titles are less valuable."

COMPUTE! BOOKS, A Division of COMPUTE! Publications, Inc., A subsidiary of ABC Consumer Magazine, Inc. one of the ABC Publishing Companies, Box 5406, Greensboro NC 27403. (919)275-9809. Book editor: Stephen Levy. Publishes trade paperback originals and software. Averages 36-48 titles/year. Pays 15% of gross wholesale receipts as royalty on one-author books; pro rata (per page) share of 7½% of gross receipts, plus one-time fee as royalty on collections. Photocopied submissions OK. Publishes ms an average of 6 months after acceptance. Electronic submissions OK if prior arrangements made. Computer printout submissions acceptable (dot-matrix OK if clear). Reports in 3 months.

Nonfiction: Books on computers. "We publish books for the home computer user and are always looking for reference books, teaching books, and books of useful programs for small computers. Books must be aimed at the users of a *specific* computer with a specific and limited purpose in mind. For instance, our *Mapping the 64* covers Commodore 64 memory locations clearly and completely with general tips for using them but does not

attempt to provide any full-fledged programs. If you have unusual expertise or inside knowledge of a particular subject, then we might well be interested in a highly technical reference book on the order of *Atari BASIC Sourcebook*, but usually we try to aim our books at nontechnical users who are learning to use their computers in their own way and at their own pace. Writers should think of their audience as intelligent people who want their computers to improve their lives and the lives of their loved ones. We are also interested in entertainment programs and programming; home applications; educational programs; and books that teach programming at different levels—if a family or individual would find them useful and interesting." Submit outline and synopsis with sample chapters. "Writers who are known to us through articles in *COMPUTE! Magazine* and *COMPUTE!'s Gazette* already have our trust—we know they can come through with the right material—but we have often bought from writers we did not know, and from writers who had never published anything before."
Recent Nonfiction Title: *128 Machine Language for Beginners*, by Richard Mansfield.
Tips: "If I were trying to create a marketable computer book today, I would become intimately familiar with one computer, then define a specific area to explain to less-familiar computer users, and write a clear, concise outline of the book I meant to write, along with a sample chapter from the working section of the book (not the introduction). Then send that proposal to a publisher whose books you believe are excellent and who targets the same audience you are aiming at. Once the proposal was in the mail, I'd forget about it. Keep learning more about the computer and develop another book proposal. *Don't write a book without a go-ahead from a publisher*. The chances are too great that you will spend 6 months writing a book, only to discover that there are nine on the market with the same concept by the time your manuscript is ready to send out."

COMPUTER SCIENCE PRESS, INC., 1803 Research Blvd., Rockville MD 20850. (301)251-9050. President: Barbara B. Friedman. Editor-in-Chief: Dr. Arthur D. Friedman. Publishes hardcover and paperback originals and software. Averages 20 titles/year. 25% of books from first-time authors; 98% of books from unagented writers. Average print order for a writer's first book is 3,000. Pays royalty on net price; no advance. Publishes book an average of 6 months after acceptance. Simultaneous and photocopied submissions OK. Computer printout submissions acceptable. Reports ASAP. Free book catalog.
Nonfiction: "Technical books in all aspects of computer science, computer engineering, computer chess, electrical engineering, computers and math, and telecommunications. Both text and reference books. Will also consider public appeal 'trade' books in computer science, manuscripts and diskettes for computer education at all levels: elementary, secondary and college and professional." Also publishes bibliographies in computer science areas and the irregular periodicals *Journal of VLSI Systems & Computations* and *Journal of Telecommunication Networks*. Query or submit complete ms. "We prefer 3 copies of manuscripts." Looks for "technical accuracy of the material and the reason this approach is being taken. We would also like a covering letter stating what the author sees as the competition for this work and why this work is superior."
Recent Nonfiction Title: *Spread Spectrum Communication*, by Simon, Scholtz, Omura and Levitt.

CONCORDIA PUBLISHING HOUSE. Product Development Department, 3558 S. Jefferson Ave., St. Louis MO 63118. (314)664-7000. Produces religious material for preschool through adult audiences, for denominational (Lutheran), general Christian, and home use. "Writer must have demonstrated skills producing material for print and audio/visual. Initial query is preferred in view of existing production commitments and necessity to maintain a satisfactory product mix. We accept almost no freelance materials; none for curriculum. If accepted, the content must be explicitly Christian. Most writers are paid on a royalty basis. Do not send complete manuscripts or multiple submissions."
Tips: "Send a prospectus of unique project only—to be evaluated as to producibility, market, etc."

‡CONSUMER REPORTS BOOKS, Subsidiary of Consumers Union. Subsidiaries include *Consumer Reports* magazine and *Penny Power*, (magazine for children 8-14). 256 Washington St., Mt. Vernon NY 10550. (914)667-9400. Contact: Director, Consumer Reports Books. Publishes trade paperback originals, and trade paperback reprints. Averages 20-25 titles/year; receives 500 submissions annually. Most of books from unagented writers. Pays variable royalty on retail price; buys some mss outright. Publishes book an average of 3 months after acceptance. Simultaneous and photocopied submissions OK. Computer printout submissions acceptable; prefers letter-quality to dot-matrix. Reports in 1 month on queries; 2 months on mss. Free book listing.
Nonfiction: Cookbook, how-to, reference, self-help and technical, and how-to books for children. Subjects include business and economics, cooking and foods, health, music and consumer guidance. Submit outline/synopsis and 1-2 sample chapters.
Recent Nonfiction Title: *Guide to Appliances.*

‡COPLEY BOOKS, Subsidiary of The Copley Press, Inc., (Copley Newspapers), Box 957, La Jolla CA 92038. (619)454-1842, 454-0411. Manager: Jean I. Bradford. Publishes hardcover originals. Averages 1-2 titles/year; receives 60 submissions annually. 25% of books from first-time authors; 100% of books from unagented writers. Pays royalty; "individual agreement with author for each publication." Publishes book a minimum of 1 year after acceptance. Simultaneous and photocopied submissions OK. Computer printout submis-

sions acceptable; prefers letter-quality to dot-matrix. Reports in "a few weeks." Free book catalog.
Nonfiction: Well-researched, historical narratives of California (including Baja, California) and the Southwest. Will consider manuscripts which provide newly-discovered or little-known facts about this region's history and which present the material in a clear, interesting manner for the general reader. Subject matter must have broad enough appeal for reasonably large volume sales potential. Illustrations are important, so a list of available artwork should be submitted with query, outline/synopsis, and perhaps one or two sample chapters.
Recent Nonfiction Title: *A Cast of Hawks*, by Milton S. Gould (a tale of scandal and power politics in early San Francisco).

CORDOVAN PRESS, Division of Scripps-Howard Business Publications, 5314 Bingle Rd., Houston TX 77092. (713)688-8811. Publisher: Delton Simmons. Publishes hardcover and paperback originals and reprints. Averages 5 titles/year. Pays negotiable royalty. Publishes book an average of 1 year after acceptance. Computer printout submissions acceptable.
Nonfiction: Professional business and finance, and business self-help. Regional trade, on Western and Southwestern history, Texas and Southwestern travel and guidebooks. Query.

CORNELL MARITIME PRESS, INC., Box 456, Centreville MD 21617. Managing Editor: Willard A. Lockwood. Imprint includes Tidewater Publishers. Publishes original hardcover and quality paperbacks. Averages 10 titles/year; receives 150 submissions annually. 41% of books from first-time authors; 99% of books from unagented writers. Payment is negotiable but royalties do not exceed 10% for first 5,000 copies, 12½% for second 5,000 copies, 15% on all additional. Royalties for original paperbacks and regional titles are invariably lower. Revised editions revert to original royalty schedule. Publishes book an average of 10 months after acceptance. Electronic submissions OK via disk, but requires hard copy also. Computer printout submissions acceptable; prefers letter-quality to dot-matrix. Send queries first, accompanied by writing samples and outlines of book ideas. Reports in 1 month. Free book catalog and ms guidelines.
Nonfiction: Marine subjects (highly technical); manuals; and how-to books on maritime subjects. Tidewater Publishers imprint publishes books on regional history, folklore and wildlife of the Chesapeake Bay and the Delmarva Peninsula.
Recent Nonfiction Title: *Upgrading and Refurbishing the Older Fiberglass Sailboat.*

‡COUNCIL OAK BOOKS, LTD., 1428 S. St. Louis, Tulsa OK 74120. (918)587-6454. Editorial Director: Sally Dennison. Publishes hardcover originals and reprints. Averages 2-10 titles/year; receives approximately 100 submissions annually. 50% of books from first-time authors; 95% of books from unagented writers. Pays royalty on retail price. Simultaneous and photocopied submissions OK. Computer printout submissions acceptable; prefers letter-quality to dot-matrix. Reports in 1 month on queries; 3 months on mss. Free book catalog.
Nonfiction: Biography, memoir, cookbook, how-to, humor, illustrated book, self-help and textbook. Subjects include Americana, animals, art, business and economics, cooking and foods, health, history, hobbies, music, nature, philosophy, photography, politics, psychology, recreation, sociology sports and travel. Submit outline/synopsis and sample chapters or complete ms. Reviews artwork/photos.
Recent Nonfiction Title: *Cleora's Kitchens, 8 Decades of Great American Food*, by Cleora Butler (cookbook/memoir).
Fiction: Historical, humor and mainstream; novels. "Any *upscale* fiction. It must be intelligent, and have an honest heart. We would like to see good novellas." No standard genre fiction, religious or devotional. Submit outline/synopsis and sample chapters or complete ms.
Recent Fiction Title: *The Silver DeSoto*, by Patty Lou Floyd (novel).
Tips: "Non-genre fiction and upscale market nonfiction have the best chance of selling to us."

CRAFTSMAN BOOK CO. OF AMERICA, 6058 Corte Del Cedro, Box 6500, Carlsbad CA 92008. (619)438-7828. Editor-in-Chief: Laurence D. Jacobs. Publishes paperback originals and software. Averages 10 titles/year; receives 40 submissions annually. 90% of books from first-time authors; 99% of books from unagented writers. Average print order for a writer's first book is 5,000. Pays royalty of 12½% of gross revenues, regardless of quantity sold. "More than 60% of our sales are directly to the consumer, and since royalties are based on gross revenues the author's share is maximized." Publishes book an average of 15 months after acceptance. Will consider photocopied submissions. Computer printout submissions acceptable; prefers letter-quality to dot-matrix. Reports in 2 weeks. Free catalog and ms guidelines.
Nonfiction: "We publish practical references for professional builders and are aggressively seeking manuscripts related to construction, the building trades, civil engineering, construction cost estimating and construction management. Ours are how-to books for homeowners. Emphasis is on step-by-step instructions, illustrations, charts, reference data, checklists, forms, samples, cost estimates, estimating data, rules of thumb, and procedures that solve actual problems in the field or in the builder's office. Each book covers a limited subject fully, becomes the owner's primary reference on that subject, has a high utility-to-cost ratio, and helps the owner make a better living in his profession. We like to see ideas and queries for books in their early stages; we work with first-time authors, prefer an outline or query, and look for completeness in the coverage of

the topic, and clear, simple writing." Query or submit outline. Reviews artwork/photos as part of ms package.
Recent Nonfiction Title: *Paint Contractor's Manual*, by Dave Matis and Jobe H. Toole.

CREATIVE ARTS BOOK COMPANY, Donald S. Ellis, San Francisco; Black Lizard Books; Life and Health Books; Creative Arts Communications Books; 833 Bancroft Way, Berkeley CA 94710. (415)848-4777. Publisher: Donald S. Ellis. Senior Editor: Pennfield Jensen. Business Manager: Anne Fuller. Publishes hardcover and paperback originals and paperback reprints. Averages 18 titles/year; receives 800-1,000 submissions annually. 10% of books from first-time authors; 20% of books from unagented writers. Pays 5-15% royalty on retail price or buys some mss outright for $500-10,000. Offers minimum $500 advance. Publishes book an average of 12-18 months after acceptance. Simultaneous and photocopied submissions OK. Computer printout submissions acceptable. Reports in 3 weeks. Free book catalog.
Nonfiction: Alternative health and foods, cookbooks, how-to, biographies and essays, but open to anything *brilliant* (except poetry). Reviews artwork/photos as part of ms package.
Recent Nonfiction Title: *Just Being At the Piano*, by Mildred Chase.
Fiction: "Looking for serious literary fiction of broad appeal."
Recent Fiction Title: *Into the Light*, by Alex Hancock.

‡CRITIC'S CHOICE PAPERBACKS, Subsidiary of Lorevan Publishing, Inc., 31 E. 28th St., New York NY 10016. (212)685-1550. Editor-in-Chief: Norman Goldfind. Publishes mass market paperback originals and reprints. Averages 96 titles/year; receives 100 submissions annually. 1% of books from first-time authors; 5% of books from unagented writers. Pays 6-8% royalty on retail price. Offers average $1,000 advance. Publishes book an average of 18 months after acceptance. Computer printout submissions acceptable; no dot-matrix. Reports in 2 weeks on queries; 2 months on mss. Book catalog for #10 SAE with 37¢ postage.
Nonfiction: Humor.
Fiction: Adventure, historical, horror, mainstream, mystery, science fiction, suspense, western, spy/espionage, thriller, and action. Query or submit outline/synopsis and sample chapters; all unsolicited mss are returned unopened.

THE CROSSING PRESS, Box 640, Trumansburg NY 14886. Co-Publishers: Elaine Goldman Gill, John Gill. Publishes hardcover and trade paperback originals. Averages 14-15 titles/year; receives 500 submissions annually. 20% of books from first-time authors; 90% of books from unagented writers. Pays royalty. Publishes book an average of 18 months after acceptance. Simultaneous and photocopied submissions OK. Electronic submissions acceptable if IBM compatible, but requires hard copy also. Computer printout submissions acceptable. Reports in 2 months on queries; 3 months on mss. Free book catalog.
Nonfiction: Cookbook, how-to, literary and feminist. Subjects include cooking, health, gays and feminism. Accepts nonfiction, fiction and poetry translations. Submissions to be considered for the feminist series must be written by women. Submit outline and sample chapter. Reviews artwork/photos as part of ms package.
Recent Nonfiction Title: *Reclaiming Birth.*
Fiction: Feminism (good literary material). Submit outline and sample chapter.
Recent Fiction Title: *The Kitchen Man.*
Tips: "Simple intelligent query letters do best. No come-ons, no cutes. It helps if there are credentials. Authors should research the press first to see what sort of books it publishes."

CROSSWAY BOOKS, 9825 W. Roosevelt Rd., Westchester IL 60153. Subsidiary of Good News Publishers. Managing Editor: Ted Griffin. Publishes hardcover and trade paperback originals. Averages 25 titles/year; receives 3,500 submissions annually. 10% of books from first-time authors; 50% of books from unagented writers. Average print order for a writer's first book is 3,000. Pays negotiable royalty; offers negotiable advance. Publishes book an average of 1 year after acceptance. Computer printout submissions acceptable; prefers letter-quality to dot-matrix. Reports in 2 months. Book catalog and ms guidelines for 9x12 SAE and 90¢ postage.
Nonfiction: Subjects include issues on Christianity in contemporary culture, Christian doctrine, and church history. Accepts translations from European languages. "All books must be written out of Christian perspective or world view." No unsolicited ms. Query by letter first.
Recent Nonfiction Title: *Who Speaks for God?*, by Charles Colson.
Fiction: Mainstream; science fiction; fantasy (genuinely creative in the tradition of C.S. Lewis, J.R.R. Tolkien and Madeleine L'Engle); and juvenile age 6 and up to young adult. No formula romance. Query by mail first. "All fiction must be written from a genuine Christian perspective."
Recent Fiction Title: *Empyrion: The Search for Fierra and Empyrion: The Siege of Dome*, by Stephen R. Lawhead.
Tips: "The writer has the best chance of selling our firm a book which, through fiction or nonfiction, shows the practical relevance of biblical doctrine to contemporary issues and life."

CROWN PUBLISHERS, INC., 225 Park Ave. S., New York NY 10003. (212)254-1600. Imprints include Clarkson N. Potter, Arlington House, Harmony and Julian Press. Publishes hardcover and paperback origi-

nals. Publishes 250 titles/year. Simultaneous submissions OK. Reports in 2 months.
Nonfiction: Americana, animals, art, biography, cookbooks/cooking, health, history, hobbies, how-to, humor, juveniles, music, nature, philosophy, photography, politics, psychology, recreation, reference, science, self-help and sports. Query with letter only.

‡**HARRY CUFF PUBLICATIONS LIMITED**, 1 Dorset St., St. John's, Newfoundland A1B 1W8 Canada. (709)726-6590. Editor: Harry Cuff. Hardcover and trade paperback originals. Averages 15 titles/year; receives 50 submissions annually. 50% of books from first-time authors; 100% of books from unagented writers. Pays 10% royalty on retail price. No advance. Publishes book an average of 6 months after acceptance. Photocopied submissions OK. Computer printout submissions acceptable; no dot-matrix. Reports in 4 months on mss. Book catalog free on request.
Nonfiction: Biography, humor, illustrated book, juvenile, reference, technical, and textbook, all dealing with Newfoundland. Subjects include history, photography, politics and sociology. Query.
Recent Nonfiction Title: *A Tale of Two Cemeteries*, by Charles Rendell.
Fiction: Ethnic, historical, humor and mainstream. Needs fiction about Newfoundlanders or Newfoundland. "No erotica under any circumstances." Submit complete ms.
Recent Fiction Title: *Flavian's Fortune*, by Alastair Macdonald.
Tips: "We are currently dedicated to publishing Newfoundlanders. The writer has the best chance of selling our firm well-written memoirs or "rememberings" as we call them. There are many books of this genre, but few are well-written."

‡**DANCE HORIZONS**, 1801 E. 26th St., Brooklyn NY 11229. (212)627-0477. Editorial Director: A.J. Pischl. Publishes hardcover and paperback originals and paperback reprints. Averages 9 titles/year; receives 50-75 submissions annually. 75% of books from first-time authors; 100% of books from unagented writers. Pays 10% royalty on retail price; offers average $500 advance. Publishes book an average of 18 months after acceptance. Simultaneous and photocopied submissions OK. Computer printout submissions acceptable; no dot-matrix. Reports in 1 month. Free book catalog.
Nonfiction: "Anything dealing with dance." Query first. Reviews artwork/photos.
Recent Nonfiction Title: *Ballet: Bias & Belief*, by Lincoln Kirstein.

‡*JOHN DANIEL, PUBLISHER**, Box 21922, Santa Barbara CA 93121. (805)962-1780. Subsidiaries include Fithian Press. Independent book producer/packager. Publisher: John Daniel. Publishes trade paperback originals. Averages 12 titles/year; receives 50 submissions annually. 50% of books from first-time authors; 100% of books from unagented writers. Subsidy publishes 50% of titles. "If we like a book but don't feel its commercial possibilities justify a financial risk, we offer the Fithian Press contract: author pays major production costs in exchange for a 50%-of-net royalty." Pays 10-50% royalty on wholesale price. Publishes book an average of 6 months after acceptance. Simultaneous and photocopied submissions OK. Electronic submissions OK via IBM compatible systems, but requires hard copy also. Computer printout submissions acceptable. Reports in 6 weeks on queries; 2 months on mss. Book catalog free on request.
Nonfiction: Biography, cookbook, humor, self-help and photo-essay on Americana, cooking and foods, nature, philosophy and photography. "We'll look at anything, but are particularly interested in books whose literary merit is foremost—as opposed to books that simply supply information. No libelous, obscene, poorly written, or unintelligent manuscripts." Query or submit outline/synopsis and sample chapters. Reviews artwork/photos.
Recent Nonfiction Title: *Brief Cherishing A Napa Valley Harvest*, by Hildegarde Flanner (essays).
Fiction: Adventure, ethnic, experimental, fantasy, historical, humor, mainstream and mystery. "We do best with books by authors who have demonstrated a clear, honest, elegant style. No libelous, obscene, poorly written, or boring submissions." Query or submit outline/synopsis and sample chapters.
Recent Fiction Title: *In the Time of the Russias*, by Stella Zamvil (short stories/Judaica).
Poetry: "We're open to anything, but we're very cautious. Poetry's hard to sell." Submit complete ms.
Recent Poetry Title: *The Swans*, by Janet Lewis (Opera libretto).
Tips: "If I were a writer trying to market a book today, I would envision my specific audience and approach publishers who demonstrate that they can reach that audience. Writing is not always a lucrative profession; almost nobody makes a living off of royalties from small-press publishing houses. That's why the authors we deal with are dedicated to their art and proud of their books—but don't expect to appear on the Carson show. Small-press publishers have a hard time breaking into the bookstore market. We try, but we wouldn't be able to survive without a healthy direct-mail sale."

DANTE UNIVERSITY OF AMERICA PRESS, INC., Box 635, Weston MA 02193. Contact: Manuscripts Editor. Publishes hardcover originals and reprints, and trade paperback originals and reprints. Averages 3-5 titles/year; receives 50 submissions annually. 50% of books from first-time authors; 50% of books from unagented writers. Average print order for a writer's first book is 3,000. Pays royalty; offers negotiable advance. Publishes book an average of 10 months after acceptance. Simultaneous and photocopied submissions OK.

Electronic submissions OK on Altos 8000 or IBM compatible, but requires hard copy also. Computer printout submissions acceptable. Reports in 6 weeks on queries; 2 months on mss. Book catalog for business size SAE and 1 first class stamp.

Nonfiction: Biography, reference, reprints, and nonfiction and fiction translations from Italian and Latin. Subjects include general scholarly nonfiction, Renaissance thought and letter, Italian language and linguistics, Italian-American history and culture, and bilingual education. Query first. Reviews artwork/photos as part of ms package.

Recent Nonfiction Title: *The Inferno*, by Dante (new translation by Nicholas Kilmer; 34 modern illustrations by Benjamin Martinez).

Poetry: "There is a chance that we would use Renaissance poetry translations."

DARTNELL CORP., 4660 N. Ravenswood Ave., Chicago IL 60640. (312)561-4000. Editorial Director: Scott Pemberton. Averages 7 titles/year; receives 150-200 submissions annually. 50% of books from first-time authors; 99% of books from unagented writers. Average print order for a writer's first book is 2,000. Pays in royalties on sliding scale based usually on retail price. Publishes book an average of 1 year after acceptance. Electronic submissions OK on Penta, but requires hard copy also. Computer printout submissions acceptable; no dot-matrix. Reports in 1 month. Free ms guidelines for SASE.

Nonfiction: Publishes business manuals, reports and handbooks. Interested in new material on business skills and techniques in management, sales management, marketing, supervision, administration, advertising, etc. Submit outline and sample chapter.

Recent Nonfiction Title: *Successful Telemarketing*, by Peg Fisher.

DATA AND RESEARCH TECHNOLOGY CORP., D.A.R.T. Corp., 1102 McNeilly Ave., Pittsburgh PA 15216. Editor: K.K. McNulty. Publishes software. Receives 25-50 submissions annually. 80% of books from first-time authors; 100% of books from unagented writers. Average print order for a writer's first book is 2,500. Pays 10% royalty; buys some mss outright. Publishes ms an average of 6 months after acceptance. Electronic submissions OK via IBM-PC DOS, but requires hard copy also. Computer printout submissions acceptable; prefers letter-quality to dot-matrix. Reports in 3 weeks.

Nonfiction: Publishes the "Answers" (series of select bibliographies). Current and original bibliographies as reference sources for specific audiences like telecommunications managers, condominium owners, or people interested in computer applications, etc. "To be accepted for publication, the quality must meet the approval of any serious researcher or librarian. The references must include a brief abstract, title, publisher, pages, price. The bibliography should include not only books, but periodicals, tapes, any audiovisuals, videotapes and disks, trade associations, etc." Also looks at any authoritative, specific manuscripts in the field of bibliography. Query. Accepts outline/synopsis and 1 sample chapter. Reviews artwork/photos.

DATAMOST, INC., 21040 Nordhoff St., Chatsworth CA 91311. (818)709-1202. Managing Editor: Lorraine Coffey. Publishes trade paperback originals and software. Averages 20-30 titles/year; receives 250 submissions annually. 80% of books from first-time authors; 95% of books from unagented writers. Pays 6-10% royalty on wholesale price or retail price; offers negotiable advance. Publishes book an average of 3-6 months after acceptance. Simultaneous and photocopied submissions OK. Electronic submissions OK on Apple with standard DOS format. Computer printout submissions acceptable. Reports in 4 weeks on queries; 6 weeks on mss. Free book catalog; writer's guidelines for SASE.

Nonfiction: How-to, reference, technical and textbook. Subjects include hobbies and computers. "Our manuscript needs are based on the computer industry. We are always looking for books on the newest machine, software utility or hardware. Our books are aimed toward the home user (children and adults) with little or no computer knowledge." Query or submit outline/synopsis and sample chapters. Reviews artwork/photos.

Recent Nonfiction Title: *Apple Thesaurus*, by Aaron Filler (hardware/software reference).

Fiction: "We have not published any titles in this category, but we are always willing to review queries for possible submissions." We are currently exploring this area. Query or submit outline/synopsis and sample chapters.

Tips: "The freelancer has the best chance of selling us machine (computer) specific instructional books. We like to see *advanced* topic books, if they are written clearly. We want complete books. We stand behind our books, so if your book includes programming, test it before you send it. We try to act quickly when we receive a new manuscript or query. Although our books have always been computer-related, we are always willing to look at different types of manuscripts."

‡*MAY DAVENPORT, PUBLISHERS, 26313 Purissima Rd., Los Altos Hills CA 94022. (415)948-6499. Editor/Publisher: May Davenport. Imprint includes md Books (nonfiction and fiction). Hardcover and trade paperback originals. Averages 3-4 titles/year; receives 1,000-2,000 submissions annually. 95% of books from first-time authors; 95% of books from unagented writers. Subsidy publishes 20% of books. Pays 15% royalty on retail price; no advance. Publishes book an average of 1-3 years after acceptance. Reports in 3 weeks.

Nonfiction: Juvenile and textbook. Subjects include Americana, animals, art, music and nature. Our readers

are students in elementary and secondary public school districts, as well as correctional institutes of learning, etc." No "hack writing." Query.
Recent Nonfiction Title: *Erica, The Ecologist,* by Beverly S. Brown.
Fiction: Adventure, ethnic, fantasy. "We're overstocked with picture books and first readers; prefer closet-plays for the TV-oriented teenagers (one act). "Be entertaining while informing." No sex or violence. Query.
Recent Fiction Title: *Trust Me, Jennifer,* by Val Call.
Tips: "Make people laugh. Humor has a place, too."

HARLAN DAVIDSON, INC., 3110 N. Arlington Heights Rd., Arlington Heights IL 60004. (312)253-9720. Subsidiary includes The Forum Press, Inc. Editor-in-Chief: Maureen Gilgore Hewitt. Publishes hardcover and paperback originals. Averages 12 titles/year; receives 500 submissions annually. 5% of books from first-time authors; 100% of books from unagented writers. Pays royalty on net price. Publishes book an average of 9 months after acceptance. Computer printout submissions acceptable. Reports in 1 month on queries; 3 months on mss.
Nonfiction: Textbook. Subjects include business and economics, history, philosophy, politics, psychology, and sociology. Particularly looking for history mss. Submit outline/synopsis, sample chapters, and recent vita.
Recent Nonfiction Title: *A History of American Business,* by C. Joseph Pusateri (textbook).
Tips: "Books that do well for us are introductory, very clearly written, lively in style, and written by academics with solid credentials and institutional affiliations. Students today seem to respond best to material that gets to the point quickly, yet entertainingly. If I were a writer trying to market a book today, I would be persistent. Things often fail to move in publishing simply because too many things cry for attention at once. A quiet, polite, follow-up note (or two or three) can keep a project alive through to acceptance or redirection."

STEVE DAVIS PUBLISHING, Box 190831, Dallas TX 75219. Publisher: Steve Davis. Publishes hardcover and trade paperback originals. Averages 5 titles/year; receives several hundred submissions annually. 60% of books from first-time authors; 100% of books from unagented writers. Pays 10-15% royalty on net price. Publishes book an average of 1 year after acceptance. "Disk submissions compatible with PC-DOS or MS-DOS (and some CP/M formats), ASCII files OK, only *after* project is accepted from query; should be accompanied by hardcopy printout and should not use extensive special formatting codes." Computer printout submissions acceptable; query first and use fresh ribbon. "We expect manuscripts to be professionally proofed for style, grammar and spelling before submission." Reports in 3 weeks on queries *if interested.* Not responsible for unsolicited material. Does not publish fiction.
Nonfiction: Books on applications of personal computers, modern technology and communications, and current social issues. "We are very selective about our list. We look for material that is professionally prepared, takes a fresh approach to a timely topic, and offers the reader helpful information." No religious or occult topics, no sports, and no mass market material such as diet books, cookbooks, joke books, exercise books, etc. Query should include phone number, a description of the project and its potential market, an outline and a couple of sample pages. "We can only respond to projects that interest us."
Recent Nonfiction Title: *The Electric Mailbox: A User's Guide to Electronic Mail Services.*

DAW BOOKS, INC., 1633 Broadway, New York NY 10019. Editor: Betsy Wollheim. Publishes science fiction paperback originals and reprints. Publishes 62 titles/year. Pays 6% royalty; offers $2,500+ advance. Simultaneous submissions "returned at once, unread." Computer printout submissions acceptable; prefers letter-quality to dot-matrix. Reports in 6 weeks. Free book catalog.
Fiction: "We are interested in science fiction and fantasy novels only. We do not publish any other category of fiction. We are not seeking collections of short stories or ideas for anthologies. We do not want any nonfiction manuscripts." Submit complete ms.

JOHN DE GRAFF, INC., Distributed by International Marine Publishing Co., Camden ME 04843. Editorial: Clinton Corners NY 12514. (914)266-5800. President: John G. DeGraff. Publishes hardcover originals. Averages 2-3 titles/year; receives 30-40 submissions annually. 50% of books from first-time authors; 100% of books from unagented writers. Pays 10% royalty on retail price. Publishes book an average of 1 year after acceptance. Simultaneous and photocopied submissions OK. Computer printout submissions acceptable. Reports in 2 weeks on queries; 1 month on mss. Free book catalog.
Nonfiction: Nautical (pleasure boating). "Our books are for yachtsmen, boat builders and naval architects. We're interested in the how-to aspects rather than boating experiences." Submit complete ms. Reviews artwork/photos as part of ms package.
Recent Nonfiction Title: *Aground!!,* by James Minnoch.

‡DEL REY BOOKS, Subsidiary of Ballantine Books, 201 E. 50th St., New York NY 10022. (212)572-2677. Executive Editor: Owen Lock. Publishes hardcover, trade paperback and mass market originals (90%) and mass market paperback reprints (10%). Averages 80 titles/year; receives 1,000 submissions annually. 10% of books from first-time authors; 40% of books from unagented writers. Pays royalty on retail price. Offers competitive advance. Publishes book an average of 1 year after acceptance. Photocopied submissions OK. Computer printout submissions acceptable; prefers letter-quality to dot-matrix. Reports in 1 month on queries; 6 months on mss.

Fiction: Fantasy ("should have the practice of magic as an essential element of the plot") and science fiction ("well-plotted novels with good characterization, exotic locals, and detailed alien cultures. Novels should have a 'sense of wonder' and be designed to please readers"). Will need "144 original fiction manuscripts of science-fiction and fantasy suitable for publishing over the next two years. No flying-saucers, Atlantis, or occult novels." Submit complete ms.

Recent Fiction Title: *Killashandra*, by Anne McCaffran (original science-fiction hardcover).

Tips: "Del Rey is a reader's house. Our audience is anyone who wants to be pleased by a good entertaining novel. We do very well with original fantasy novels, in which magic is a central element, and with hard-science science-fiction novels. Pay particular attention to plotting and a satisfactory conclusion. It must be/feel believable. They're what the readers like."

DELACORTE PRESS, 245 E. 47th St., New York NY 10017. (212)605-3000. Editor-in-Chief: Jackie Farber. Publishes hardcover originals. Publishes 20 titles/year. Pays 10-12½-15% royalty; average advance. Publishes book an average of 2 years after acceptance. Simultaneous and photocopied submissions OK. Computer printout submissions acceptable; prefers letter-quality to dot-matrix. Reports in 2 months.

Fiction and Nonfiction: Query, outline or brief proposal, or complete ms accepted only through an agent; otherwise returned unopened. No mss for children's or young adult books accepted in this division.

Recent Nonfiction Title: *Enter Talking*, by Joan Rivers.

Recent Fiction Title: *Secrets*, by Danielle Steel.

‡DELL PUBLISHING CO., INC., 1 Dag Hammarskjold Plaza, New York NY 10017. Imprints include Dell, Delacorte Press, Delta Books, Dell Trade Paperbacks, Laurel, Delacorte Press Books for Young Readers, Candlelight Books, Yearling and Laurel Leaf. Publishes hardcover and paperback originals and reprints. Publishes 500 titles/year. Pays royalty on retail price. "General guidelines for unagented submissions. Please adhere strictly to the following procedure: 1) Do not send manuscript, sample chapters or art work; 2) Do not register, certify or insure your letter; 3) Send only a 4-page synopsis or outline with a cover letter stating previous work published or relevant experience." Simultaneous and photocopied submissions OK. Reports in 3 months.

Nonfiction: "Because Dell is comprised of several imprints, each with its own editorial department, we ask you to carefully review the following information and direct your submission to the appropriate department. Your envelope must be marked, Attention: (blank) Editorial Department—Proposal. Fill in the blank with one of the following: Delacorte: Publishes in hardcover. Looks for popular nonfiction (*SON*). Delta and Dell Trade: Publishes in trade paperback; rarely publishes original fiction; looks for useful, substantial guides (*Getting Work Experience*); entertaining, amusing nonfiction (*The Mom Book*); serious work in the area of modern society. Yearling and Laurel Leaf: Publishes in paperback and hardcover for children and young adults, grades 7-12. Purse: Publishes miniature paperbacks about 60 pages in length on topics of current consumer interest, e.g., diet, exercise, coin prices, etc."

Fiction: Refer to the above guidelines. Delacorte: Publishes top-notch commercial fiction in hardcover (e.g., *Secrets*). Dell: Publishes mass-market paperbacks; rarely publishes original nonfiction; looks for family sagas, historical romances, sexy modern romance, adventure and suspense, thrillers, occult/horror and war novels. Especially interested in submissions for our Candlelight Ecstasy Line.

DELMAR PUBLISHERS, INC., 2 Computer Dr., W., Box 15015, Albany NY 12212-5015. (518)459-1150. Vice President of Publishing: G.C. Spatz. Publishes hardcover and paperback textbooks and educational software. Averages 50 titles/year; receives 150 submissions annually. 35% of books from first-time authors; 100% of books from unagented writers. Average print order for a writer's first book is 5,000. Pays royalty on wholesale price. Publishes book an average of 3 years after acceptance. Electronic submissions acceptable on IBM PC or WordStar, but requires hard copy also. Computer printout submissions acceptable; no dot-matrix. Reports in 2 weeks on queries; 2 months on submissions. Free book catalog.

Nonfiction: Subjects include business and data processing, allied health/nursing, childcare, mathematics, agriculture/horticulture texts, and textbooks for most vocational and technical subjects. Books are used in secondary and postsecondary schools. Query and submit outline/synopsis and 2-3 sample chapters. Reviews artwork/photos as part of ms package.

Recent Nonfiction Title: *Fundamentals of CAD*, by Gary Bertdine.

Tips: Vocational textbooks have the best chance of selling for *Delmar Publishers*. Queries/mss may be routed to other editors in the publishing group.

DELTA BOOKS, Division of Dell Publishing Co., 1 Dag Hammarskjold Plaza, New York NY 10017. (212)605-3000. Editor-in-Chief: Jackie Farber. Publishes trade paperback reprints and originals. Averages 10 titles/year. Pays 6-7½% royalty; offers advance. Simultaneous and photocopied submissions OK. Computer

printout submissions acceptable; prefers letter-quality to dot-matrix. Reports in 2 months. Book catalog for 8½x11 SASE.
Nonfiction: Consciousness, health, how-to, humor, music, New Age, photography, politics, recreation, reference, science, self-help and sports. "We would like to see books on the arts, social history, social criticism and analysis, and child care. We do not want to see biography, philosophy, academic books, textbooks, juveniles, or poetry books." Query or submit outline/synopsis and sample chapters. Prefers submissions through agents.
Fiction: "We are looking for original, innovative and contemporary novels." Submit through an agent.

DEMBNER BOOKS, 80 8th Ave., New York NY 10011. (212)924-2525. Subsidiary of Red Dembner Enterprises, Corp. Associate Editor: Therese Eiben. Publishes hardcover and trade paperback originals, and hardcover and trade paperback reprints. Averages 10-15 titles/year; receives 500-750 submissions annually. 20% of books from first-time authors; 75% of books from unagented writers. Pays 10-15% royalty on hardcover; 6-7½% royalty on paperback, both on retail price. Offers average $1,000-5,000 advance. Publishes book an average of 1 year after acceptance. Simultaneous and legible photocopied submissions OK. Computer printout submissions acceptable; no dot-matrix. Reports in 2 weeks on queries; 10 weeks on mss. Book catalog available from W.W. Norton, 500 5th Ave., New York NY 10110; ms guidelines for SASE.
Nonfiction: How-to, reference, self-help and workbooks. Subjects include animals, health, film, history (popular), music, psychology, sports and social causes. "We want books written by knowledgeable authors that focus on a problem area (health/home/handicapped) and offer an insightful guidance toward solutions." No surveys or collections—books that do not focus on one specific, promotable topic. Also, no books on heavily published topics, such as weight loss and exercise programs. Query or submit outline/synopsis and sample chapters. Reviews artwork/photos.
Recent Nonfiction Title: *Coping with High Blood Pressure*, by Sandy Sorrentino, M.D., Ph.D., and Carl Hausman.
Fiction: Adventure, mystery, suspense, western and literary. "We look for genre fiction (mystery, suspense, etc.), that keeps pace with the times, deals with contemporary issues, and has three-dimensional characters. Occasionally we publish literary novels, but the writing must be of excellent quality." No indulgent, self-conscious fiction. Query or submit outline/synopsis and sample chapters.
Recent Fiction Title: *Let Sleeping Dogs Lie*, by John Riggs.
Tips: "Dembner Books has been publishing for eleven years. We take a great deal of pride in the books we publish. We are interested in serving a need as well as entertaining. We publish books worth reading and even worth keeping. Small hardcover houses such as ourselves are being very careful about the books they choose for publication primarily because secondary rights sales have dropped, and the money is less. Quality is of utmost importance."

T.S. DENISON & CO., INC., 9601 Newton Ave., S. Minneapolis MN 55431. Editor-in-Chief: W.E. Rosenfelt. Publishes teacher aid materials; receives 500 submissions annually. 90% of books from first-time authors; 100% of books from unagented writers. Average print order for a writer's first book is 500. Royalty varies; no advance. Publishes book an average of 1-2 years after acceptance. Photocopied submissions OK. Computer printout submissions acceptable; no dot-matrix. Reports in 1 month. Book catalog and ms guidelines for SASE.
Nonfiction: Specializes in preschool teaching aids. Send prints if photos are to accompany ms. Submit complete ms. Reviews artwork/photos as part of ms package.

DENLINGER'S PUBLISHERS, LTD., Box 76, Fairfax VA 22030. (703)631-1500. Publisher: William W. Denlinger. Publishes hardcover and trade paperback originals, hardcover and trade paperback reprints. Averages 12 titles/year; receives 250 submissions annually. 5% of books from first-time authors; 95% of books from unagented writers. Average print order for a writer's first book is 3,000. Pays variable royalty. No advance. Publishes book an average of 18 months after acceptance. Simultaneous and photocopied submissions OK. Electronic submissions OK via Zexox, but requires hard copy also. Computer printout submissions acceptable; prefers letter-quality to dot-matrix. Reports in 1 week on queries; 6 weeks on mss. Book catalog for SASE.
Nonfiction: How-to and technical books on dogs and Americana. Query. Reviews artwork/photos.
Recent Nonfiction Title: *Bird Dogs and Upland Game Birds*, by Jack Stuart.
Fiction: Southern historical.
Recent Fiction Title: *Mandingo*.

‡*DEVONSHIRE PUBLISHING CO., Box 7066, Chicago IL 60680. (312)242-3846. Vice President: Don Reynolds. Publishes hardcover and trade paperback originals. Averages 3 titles/year; receives 150 submissions annually. 75% of books from first-time authors; 75% of books from unagented writers. "Although we do not generally subsidy publish we will enter into 'cooperative publishing agreements' with an author if the subject matter is of such limited appeal that we doubt its profitability, or the author desires a more extravagant finished product than we planned to produce." Pays 10-15% royalty on retail price. "Royalty would be higher if author engaged in cooperative venture." Offers negotiable advance. Publishes book an average of 8 months after acceptance. Simultaneous and photocopied submissions OK. Computer printout submissions acceptable; prefers letter-quality to dot-matrix. Reports in 1 month on queries; 2 months on submissions.

Nonfiction: Illustrated book, reference, technical and textbook. Subjects include business and economics, history, hobbies, nature, psychology, religion and sociology. "We will be looking for books that have an impact on the reader. A history or religious book will have to be more than just a recitation of past events. Our books must have some relation to today's problems or situations." No works of personal philosophy or unverifiable speculation. Query and/or submit outline/synopsis and sample chapters.

Recent Nonfiction Title: *The Alexandria Letters*, by D.S. Kosinski (history/religious).

Fiction: Erotica, experimental, historical, horror, religious and science fiction. "All works must have some relevance to today's reader and be well written. We hope to produce one or two titles, but our main thrust will be in the nonfiction area. However, if a work is thought-provoking and/or controversial, we may give it priority. Query and/or submit outline/synopsis and sample chapters.

Tips: "Since we are a small publishing company (and new), we can aim for the smaller, more specialized market. We envision that the audience for our books will be well educated with a specific area of interest. Because we are new, we can afford to look at work that other publishers have passed over. Although we are not looking for works that are controversial just for the sake of controversy, we are looking for topics that go beyond the norm. If it is documented and has a strong basis or foundation, we will endeavor to publish it."

DHARMA PUBLISHING, 2425 Hillside Ave., Berkeley CA 94704. (415)548-5407. Manuscript Editor: Elizabeth Cook. Publishes hardcover and paperback originals. "Dharma Publishing is a small, non-profit company dedicated to preserving Tibetan cultural and religious heritage." Publishes 10 titles/year; receives 100 submissions annually. 100% of books from unagented writers. Average print order for a writer's first book is 3,000. Pays 5-7% royalty on retail price; no advance. Average length of time between acceptance of a manuscript and publication of the work varies widely. Electronic submissions OK on CPM, but requires hard copy also. Computer printout submissions acceptable. Reports in 2 months. Book catalog $4.95.

Nonfiction: Considers only translations of traditional Buddhist texts, research aids, and reference materials useful in the study of Buddhism. Does not publish original commentaries on Buddhist topics. Highest priority—translations from Sanskrit and/or Tibetan. Reviews artwork/photos.

DIAL BOOKS FOR YOUNG READERS, Division of E.P. Dutton, 2 Park Ave., New York NY 10016. (212)725-1818. Editor: Paula Wiseman. Imprints include Dial Easy-to-Read Books, Out-and-About Books, and Dial Very First Books. Publishes hardcover originals. Averages 50 titles/year; receives 20,000 submissions annually. 10% of books from first-time authors. Pays variable royalty and advance. Simultaneous and photocopied submissions OK, but not preferred. Computer printout submissions acceptable; no dot-matrix. Reports in 2 weeks on queries; 3 months on mss. Book catalog and ms guidelines for SASE.

Nonfiction: Juvenile picture books and young adult books. Especially looking for "quality picture books and well-researched young adult and middle-reader mss." Not interested in alphabet books, riddle and game books, and early concept books." Query with outline/synopsis and sample chapters. Reviews artwork/photos.

Recent Nonfiction Title: *Mountains*, by Clive Catchpole (picture book).

Fiction: Adventure, fantasy, historical, humor, mystery, romance (appropriate for young adults), and suspense. Especially looking for "lively and well written novels for middle grade and young adult children involving a convincing plot and believable characters. The subject matter or theme should not already be overworked in previously published books. The approach must not be demeaning to any minority group, nor should the roles of female characters (or others) be stereotyped, though we don't think books should be didactic, or in any way message-y." No "topics inappropriate for the juvenile, young adult, and middle grade audiences. No plays or poetry." Submit complete ms.

Recent Fiction Title: *Last One Home*, by Mary Pope Osborne.

Tips: "Our readers are anywhere from preschool age to teenage. Picture books must have strong plots, lots of action, unusual premises, or universal themes treated with freshness and originality. Humor works well in these books. A very well thought out and intelligently presented book has the best chance of selling. Genre isn't as much of a factor as presentation."

‡DIAMOND PRESS, Box 167, Maple Glen PA 19002. (215)345-6094. Marketing Director: Paul Johnson. Publishes trade paperback originals. Averages 2 titles/year ("looking for more"). Pays 5-20% royalty on retail price; will also buy outright or negotiate special contract. Negotiable advance. Publishes book an average of 6 months after acceptance. Simultaneous and photocopied submissions OK. Computer printout submissions acceptable; prefers letter-quality to dot-matrix. Reports in 3 weeks.

Nonfiction: Cookbook, how-to, self-help, technical, sports (specifically slow pitch softball), antiques, Americana, art, hobbies, and recreation. "We are specifically looking for areas unpublished by anyone else, and are particularly interested in antiques and slow pitch softball." Submit outline/synopsis and sample chapters. Reviews artwork/photos.

Recent Nonfiction Title: *The Strategy of Pitching Slow Pitch Softball*, by Michael Ivankovich.
Tips: "If I were a writer trying to market a book today, I would find an undeveloped field and position myself as a specialist. I would do this by writing as many books and articles in this field as possible."

DILLON PRESS, INC., 500 S. 3rd St., Minneapolis MN 55415. (612)333-2691. Editorial Director: Uva Dillon. Senior Editor: Tom Schneider. Juvenile Fiction Editor: Janet Mills. Nonfiction Editor: Jan Zelasko. Publishes hardcover originals. Averages 30-40 titles/year; receives 3,000 submissions annually. 50% of books from first-time authors; 90% of books from unagented writers. Average print order for a writer's first book is 3,000-5,000. Pays royalty and by outright purchase. Publishes book an average of 1 year after acceptance. Computer printout submissions acceptable; no dot-matrix. Reports in 6 weeks.
Nonfiction: "We are actively seeking mss for the juvenile educational market." Subjects include foreign countries, contemporary biographies for elementary and middle grade levels, unusual approaches to science topics for primary grade readers, wildlife, crafts/outdoor activities, and contemporary issues of interest and value to young people. Submit complete ms or outline and 1 sample chapter. No query letters. Reviews artwork/photos as part of ms package.
Recent Nonfiction Title: *Zimbabwe: A Treasure of Africa*, by Al Stark.
Fiction: "We are looking for fiction mss that appeal to fourth through ninth grade readers." Subjects include mysteries, adventure, fantasy, science fiction, contemporary problems, and girls' sports stories. Especially interested in historical fiction based on an actual event. No picture books.
Recent Fiction Title: *Mr. Z and the Time Clock*, by Bonnie Pryor.
Tips: "A well-written, lively, and interesting nonfiction/fiction manuscript on a subject with appeal to young people has the best chance of selling to our firm."

DIMENSION BOOKS, INC., Box 811, Denville NJ 07834-0811. (201)627-4334. Contact: Thomas P. Coffey. Publishes 25 titles/year; receives 450-500 submissions annually. 10% of books from first-time authors; 60% of books from unagented writers. Pays "regular royalty schedule" based on retail price; advance is negotiable. Publishes book an average of 3-5 months after acceptance. Computer printout submissions acceptable. Book catalog for SAE and 2 first class stamps. Reports in 1 week.
Nonfiction: Publishes general nonfiction including religion, principally Roman Catholic. Also psychology. Accepts nonfiction translations. Query. Accepts outline/synopsis and 3 sample chapters. Length: 40,000 words minimum. Reviews artwork/photos.
Recent Nonfiction Title: *The Enneagram: A Journey of Self-Discovery*, by Beesing, Nogosek, and O'Leary.

DODD, MEAD & CO., 79 Madison Ave., New York NY 10016. (212)685-6464. President: John Harden. Publisher: Lynne Lumsden. Senior Editors: Jerry Gross, Allen T. Klots, Margaret Norton, Cynthia Vartan and Mary Kennan. Managing Editor: Chris Fortunato. Averages 200 titles/year. Pays 10-15% royalty; advances vary, depending on the sales potential of the book. A contract for nonfiction books is offered on the basis of a query, a suggested outline and a sample chapter. Write for permission before sending mss. Adult fiction, the arts, current events, business, science and nature, self-help and how-to, holistic health and healing should be addressed to Editorial Department. Publishes book an average of 9 months after acceptance. Electronic submissions OK "only on exceptional occasions when submission can be used on equipment of our suppliers." Reports in 6 weeks.
Fiction and Nonfiction: Publishes book-length mss. Length: 60,000-100,000 words average. Looks for high quality; mysteries and romantic novels of suspense, biography, popular science, travel, yachting and other sports, music and other arts. Very rarely buys photographs or poetry. Publishes books for juveniles. Director of Children's Books: Jo Ann Daly. Length: 1,500-75,000 words.
Tips: "Freelance writers should be aware of trends toward nonfiction and the difficulty of publishing marginal or midlist fiction."

DOLL READER, Subsidiary of Hobby House Press, Inc., 900 Frederick St., Cumberland MD 21502. (301)759-3770. Subsidiaries include *Doll Reader* and *The Teddy Bear and Friends Magazine*. Publisher: Gary R. Ruddell. Publishes hardcover originals. Averages 18 titles/year. 20% of books from first-time authors; 90% of books from unagented writers. Pays royalty. Publishes book an average of 18 months after acceptance. Simultaneous and photocopied submissions OK. Computer printout submissions acceptable; prefers letter-quality to dot-matrix. Reports in 2 weeks. Free book catalog.
Nonfiction: Doll-related books. "We publish books pertaining to dolls and teddy bears as a collector's hobby; we also publish pattern books. The *Doll Reader* is published 8 times a year dealing with the hobby of doll collecting. We appeal to those people who are doll collectors, miniature collectors, as well as people who sew for dolls. Our magazine has a worldwide circulation of close to 50,000." Query or submit outline/synopsis. Reviews artwork/photos as part of ms package. *The Teddy Bear and Friends Magazine* is published bimonthly.
Recent Nonfiction Title: *6th Blue Book of Dolls and Values*, by Jan Foulke (price guide for dolls).

DORCHESTER PUBLISHING CO., INC., Suite 900, 6 E. 39th St., New York NY 10016. (212)725-8811. Editorial Director: Jane Thornton. Imprint includes Leisure Books. Publishes mass market paperback originals and reprints. Averages 144 titles/year; receives thousands of submissions annually. 50% of books from first-time authors; 60% of books from unagented writers. Pays royalty on retail price or makes outright purchase. Offers average $1,000 advance. Publishes book an average of 18 months after acceptance. Simultaneous and photocopied submissions OK. Computer printout submissions acceptable; no dot-matrix. Reports in 6 weeks on queries; up to 4 months on mss. Free book catalog; ms guidelines for SASE.
Nonfiction: "Our needs are minimal as we publish perhaps four nonfiction titles a year." Query.
Fiction: Historical (120,000+ words); horror (90,000-100,000+ words); mainstream (100,000+ words); mystery (50,000-60,000 words); historical romantic suspense (75,000-90,000 words). We are strongly backing the horror/occult, historical romance, contemporary women's fiction and short mystery." No sweet romance, science fiction, western, erotica or male adventure. Query or submit outline/synopsis and sample chapters.
Recent Fiction Title: *Satin and Steel*, by Catherine Hart (historical romance).
Tips: "Horror/occult and historical romance are our best sellers."

DOUBLEDAY & CO., INC., Dept. AA-M, 245 Park Ave., New York NY 10167. Publishes hardcover and paperback originals. Offers royalty on retail price; offers variable advance. Reports in 2½ months. "At present, Doubleday and Co. is *only* able to consider fiction for mystery/suspense, science fiction, and romance imprints." Send *copy* of complete manuscript (60,000-80,000 words) to Crime Club Editor, Science Fiction Editor, or Starlight Romance Editor as appropriate. Sufficient postage for return via fourth class mail must accompany manuscript.

DOUGLAS & MCINTYRE PUBLISHERS, 1615 Venables St., Vancouver, British Columbia V5L 2H1 Canada. (604)254-7191. Manuscript Editor: Shaun Oakey. Imprints include Groundwood Books. Publishes hardcover originals and trade paperback originals; and trade paperback reprints. Averages 50 titles/year; receives 600 submissions annually. 50% of books from first-time authors; 90% of books from unagented writers. Pays 8-15% royalty on retail price; offers average $500 advance. Simultaneous and photocopied submissions OK. Reports in 1 month on queries; 2 months on mss. Free book catalog.
Nonfiction: Biography, cookbook, illustrated book, juvenile and Canadian history. Subjects include Canadiana, art, business and economics, cooking and foods, history, and Canadian politics. No how-to; outdoor guides; or medical/health books. Query and submit outline/synopsis and sample chapters or complete ms.
Recent Nonfiction Title: *The World of Canadian Wine*, by John Schreiner.
Fiction: Ethnic, experimental, historical and literary/women's. "Will begin fiction list in fall '86; we will be interested only in literary works." No mass market-type material—romance, gothic, etc. Submit outline/synopsis and sample chapters or complete ms.
Tips: "For our fiction and general trade lists we prefer Canadian authors."

DOW JONES-IRWIN, (Business and Finance) 1818 Ridge Rd., Homewood IL 60430. (312)798-6000. Editor-in-Chief: Richard J. Staron. Publishes originals only. Averages 100 titles/year; receives 200 submissions annually. 20% of books from first-time authors; 75% of books from unagented writers. Royalty schedule and advance negotiable. Publishes book an average of 6 months after acceptance. Electronic submissions OK via Wordstar on IBM, but requires hard copy also. Computer printout submissions acceptable; prefers letter-quality to dot-matrix. Reports in 1 month.
Nonfiction: Business and financial subjects. Query with outline.
Recent Nonfiction Title: *Money Market: Myth, Reality and Practice*, by Marcia Stigum.
Tips: Queries/mss may be routed to other editors in the publishing group. "The writer has the best chance of selling our firm serious how-to books on all aspects of business."

DOWN EAST BOOKS, Subsidiary of Down East Enterprise, Inc., Box 679, Camden ME 04843. (207)594-9544. Editor: Karin Womer. Publishes hardcover and trade paperback originals and trade paperback reprints. Averages 10-16 titles/year; receives 400 submissions annually. 50% of books from first-time authors; 90% of books from unagented writers. Average print order for a writer's first book is 2,500. Pays 10-15% on receipts. Offers average $200 advance. Publishes book an average of 12 months after acceptance. Simultaneous and photocopied submissions OK. Computer printout submissions acceptable; prefers letter-quality to dot-matrix. Reports in 2 weeks on queries; 2 months on mss. Book catalog and ms guidelines for SASE.
Nonfiction: Biography, cookbooks, illustrated books, juvenile, reference and guidebooks. Subjects include Americana, art, cooking and foods, history, nature, traditional crafts and recreation. "Our books have a Maine or New England emphasis." Query. Reviews artwork/photos as part of ms package.
Recent Nonfiction Title: *Adventure: Queen of the Windjammers*, by Joseph Garland.
Fiction: "We publish no fiction except for an occasional juvenile title (average 1/year)."
Recent Fiction Title: *Crystal: The Story of a Real Baby Whale*, by Karen Smyth.

‡*DRAGON'S TEETH PRESS, El Dorado National Forest, Georgetown CA 95634. (916)333-4224. Editor: Cornel Lengyel. Publishes trade paperback originals and software. Averages 6 titles/year; receives 100+ submissions annually. 50% of books from first-time authors; 75% of books from unagented writers. Subsidy publishes 25% of books; applies "if book has high literary merit, but very limited market." Pays 10% royalty on retail price, or in copies. Publishes book an average of 1 year after acceptance. Simultaneous and photocopied submissions OK. Computer printout submissions acceptable. Reports in 2 weeks on queries; 1 month on mss. Book catalog for SAE with 63¢ postage.
Nonfiction: Music and philosophy. Publishes for 500 poets, or potential poets. Query or submit outline/synopsis and sample chapters. Reviews artwork/photos as part of ms package.
Poetry: "Highly original works of potential literary genius. No trite, trivial or trendy ego exhibitions." Submit 10 samples or the complete ms.
Recent Poetry Title: *The Thirteenth Labor*, by Ronald Belluomini.

THE DRAGONSBREATH PRESS, 10905 Bay Shore Dr., Sister Bay WI 54234. Editor: Fred Johnson. Publishes hardcover and trade paperback originals only in handmade limited edition form, no mass-market. "The Dragonsbreath Press is a small press producing handmade limited edition books including original artwork meant for collectors of fine art and books who appreciate letterpress printing. This audience accepts a handmade book as a work of art." Averages 1 title/year; receives 500 submissions annually. Payment conditions "to be arranged"; no advance. Simultaneous and photocopied submissions OK. Computer printout submissions acceptable; prefers letter-quality to dot-matrix. Reports in 2 months on queries; 3 months on mss.
Nonfiction: Biography, humor and illustrated books. Subjects include Americana, art, history and photography. "We're interested in anything suited to handmade book production—short biography, history, original artwork, photography." Query first; do not submit ms. Reviews artwork/photos as part of ms package.
Fiction: Adventure, erotica, experimental, fantasy, horror, humor, mystery and science fiction. "We are looking for short, well written stories which lend themselves to illustration and deserve to be made into fine, handmade books." *No long, novel length manuscripts* or *children's books*. Query first; do not submit ms.
Poetry: "We're looking for good readable poetry that is unique. No religious, sweet Hallmark style or divorce poems." Submit 3 samples with query; submit complete ms "only when requested."
Tips: "We are not currently reading any manuscripts. Please do not submit manuscripts unless they have been requested. Do not send novels. Our typical book would consist of one or two short stories, not a whole collection. Always include SASE if reply wanted."

DRAMA BOOK PUBLISHERS, 821 Broadway, New York NY 10003. (212)228-3400. Contact: Ralph Pine or Judith Holmes. Publishes hardcover and paperback originals and reprints. Averages 15 titles/year; receives 500 submissions annually. 70% of books from first-time authors; 90% of books from unagented writers. Royalty varies; advance varies; negotiable. Publishes book an average of 18 months after acceptance. Computer printout submissions acceptable; prefers letter-quality to dot-matrix. Reports in 1 to 2 months.
Nonfiction: Books—texts, guides, manuals, directories, reference—for and about performing arts theory and practice: acting, directing; voice, speech, movement, music, dance, mime; makeup, masks, wigs; costumes, sets, lighting, sound; design and execution; technical theatre, stagecraft, equipment; stage management; producing; arts management, all varieties; business and legal aspects; film, radio, television, cable, video; theory, criticism, reference; playwriting; theatre and performance history. Accepts nonfiction, drama and technical works in translations also. Query; accepts 1-3 sample chapters; no complete mss. Reviews artwork/photos as part of ms package.
Fiction: Professionally produced plays and musicals.

DUNDURN PRESS LTD., Box 245, Station F, Toronto, Ontario, M4Y 2L4 Canada. (416)461-1881. Publisher: Kirk Howard. Publishes hardcover, trade paperback and hardcover reprints. Averages 15 titles/year; receives 500 submissions annually. 45% of books from first-time authors; 100% of books from unagented writers. Average print order for a writer's first book is 3,000. Pays 10% royalty on retail price; 8% royalty on some paperback children's books. Publishes book an average of 1 year after acceptance. "Easy-to-read" photocopied submissions OK. Computer printout submissions acceptable; prefers letter-quality to dot-matrix.
Nonfiction: Biography, "coffee table" books, juvenile, literary and reference. Subjects include Canadiana, art, history, hobbies, Canadian history and literary criticism. Especially looking for Canadian biographies. No religious or soft science topics. Query with outline/synopsis and sample chapters. Reviews artwork/photos as part of ms package.
Recent Nonfiction Title: *Fragments of War: Stories from World War II*, (nonfiction).
Tips: "Publishers want more books written in better prose styles. If I were a writer trying to market a book today, I would visit book stores and watch what readers buy and what company publishes that type of book 'close' to my manuscript."

*DUQUESNE UNIVERSITY PRESS, 600 Forbes Ave., Pittsburgh PA 15282. (412)434-6610. Averages 9 titles/year; receives 400 submissions annually. 25% of books from first-time authors; 90% of books from un-

agented writers. Average print order for a writer's first book is 1,500. Subsidy publishes 20% of books. Pays 10% royalty on net sales; no advance. Publishes book an average of 1 year after acceptance. Electronic submissions OK but check with publisher; but requires hard copy also. Computer printout submissions acceptable; no dot-matrix. Query. Reports in 3 months. Free writer's guidelines.
Nonfiction: Scholarly books in the humanities, social sciences for academics, libraries, college bookstores and educated laypersons. Length: open. Looks for scholarship.
Recent Nonfiction Title: *Imaginative Thinking*, by Edward L. Murray.

‡DUSTBOOKS, Box 100, Paradise CA 95969. (916)877-6110. Publisher: Len Fulton. Publishes hardcover and paperback originals. Averages 7 titles/year. Offers 15% royalty. Offers average $500 advance. Simultaneous and photocopied submissions OK if so informed. Computer printout submissions acceptable. Reports in 1-2 months. Free book catalog.
Nonfiction: Technical. "DustBooks would like to see manuscripts dealing with microcomputers (software, hardware) and water (any aspect). Must be technically sound and well-written. We have at present no titles in these areas. These represent an expansion of our interests." Submit outline/synopsis and sample chapters.

E.P. DUTTON, 2 Park Ave., New York NY 10016. (212)725-1818. Publisher, Children's Books: Ann Durell. Averages 40 titles/year. 15% of books from first-time authors; 85% of books from unagented writers. Pays royalty on list price; offers variable advance. Considers unsolicited mss. Computer printout submissions acceptable; prefers letter-quality to dot-matrix. "Please send query letter first on all except picture book manuscripts."
Fiction: Picture books; Smart Cats (beginning readers); stories for ages 8-12; novels, including fantasy and science fiction for ages 12 and up. Reviews artwork/photos as part of ms package. Emphasis on good writing and quality for all ages.
Tips: Queries/mss may be routed to other editors in the publishing group.

EAKIN PUBLICATIONS, INC., Box 23066, Austin TX 78735. (512)288-1771. Imprints include Nortex. Editorial Director: Edwin M. Eakin. Publishes hardcover and paperback originals and reprints. Averages 40 titles/year; receives 350 submissions annually. 80% of books from first-time authors; 90% of books from unagented writers. Average print order for a writer's first book is 2,000. Pays 10-12-15% in royalty. Publishes book an average of 1 year after acceptance. Simultaneous and photocopied submissions OK. Electronic submissions OK via IBM, but requires hard copy also. Computer printout submissions acceptable; prefers letter-quality to dot-matrix. Reports in 3 months. Book catalog and ms guidelines for SASE.
Nonfiction: History, juvenile history, contemporary, and regional. Specifically needs biographies of well-known Texas people, current Texas politics and history for grades 3-9. Query first or submit outline/synopsis and sample chapters. Reviews artwork/photos.
Recent Nonfiction Title: *CLINT, Biography of Clint Murchison Sr.*
Fiction: Historical fiction for school market. Specifically need juveniles that relate to Texas. Query or submit outline/synopsis and sample chapters.
Recent Fiction Title: *Where the Pirates Are*, by Tom Townsend.

EAST-WOODS-PRESS, (Trade name of Fast & McMillan Publishers, Inc.), 429 East Blvd., Charlotte NC 28203. (704)334-0897. Editorial Director: Sally Hill McMillan. Publishes hardcover and paperback originals and hardcover and paperback reprints. Publishes 10-15 titles/year. Pays 5-12% royalty on retail price. Offers average $500 advance. "Submissions must be on hard copy. If accepted, we can work with disks to edit and produce." Computer printout submissions acceptable. Reports in 6 weeks on queries; 8 weeks on mss. Book catalog for 9x12 SAE and 2 first class stamps.
Nonfiction: "Coffee table" books, cookbooks, how-to, self-help and travel guides. No business or humor. "We are mainly interested in travel and the outdoors. Regional guidebooks are our specialty, but anything on travel and outdoors will be considered." Query. "A list of competitive books should be submitted, along with specific reasons why this manuscript should be published. Also, maps and art should be supplied by the author."
Recent Nonfiction Title: *Wildflower Folklore*, by Laura C. Martin.

*ECW PRESS, Subsidiaries include Emerson House, Poetry Canada Review, Essays on Canadian Writing, 307 Coxwell Ave., Toronto, Ontario M4L 3B5 Canada. (416)694-3348. President: Jack David. Imprints include ECW Press. Publishes hardcover and trade paperback originals. Publishes 12-15 titles/year; receives 120 submissions annually. 50% of books from first-time authors; 80% of books from unagented writers. Subsidy publishes (nonauthor) up to 5% of books. Pays 10% royalty on retail price. Simultaneous and photocopied submissions OK. Electronic submissions OK on CP/M, but requires hard copy also. Computer printout submissions acceptable; prefers letter-quality to dot-matrix. Reports in 2 weeks. Free book catalog.
Nonfiction: Reference and Canadian literary criticism. "ECW is interested in all literary criticism aimed at the undergraduate and graduate university market." Query. Reviews artwork/photos as part of ms package.
Recent Nonfiction Title: *North of America*, by James Doyle (literary criticism).

Tips: "The writer has the best chance of selling literary criticism to our firm because that's our specialty and the only thing that makes us money."

‡**EDEN PRESS**, 4626 St. Catherine St. W., Montreal, Quebec H32 153 Canada. (514)931-3910. Publisher: Pamela Chichinskas. Publishes hardcover and trade paperback originals. Averages 15-25 titles/year; receives 300 submissions annually. 50% of books from first-time authors; 45% of books from unagented writers. Pays royalty. Publishes book an average of 18 months after acceptance. Photocopied submissions OK. Electronic submissions acceptable, list of system's requirements available upon demand; but requires hard copy also. Computer printout submissions acceptable; prefers letter-quality to dot-matrix. Reports in 1 month on queries; 3 months on mss. Book catalog free on request.
Imprints: Eden Intrigue (fiction) and Eden Entertainment (fiction).
Nonfiction: Biography, how-to, illustrated book, reference, self-help, technical, medical, scientific. Subjects include business and economics, health, history, nature, philosophy, politics, psychology, recreation, religion, sociology, sports, and humor on any subject. "Books on investment and finance (written by qualified professionals only), biography, and lay-market health books written only by medical professionals." Query. Reviews artwork/photos.
Recent Nonfiction Title: *The Next Canadian Economy*, by Dian Cohen and Kristian Shannon (economics).
Fiction: Mystery, science fiction, suspense, and intrigue and spies. Submit outline/synopsis and sample chapters.

EDITS PUBLISHERS, Box 7234, San Diego CA 92107. (619)488-1666. Editorial Director: Robert R. Knapp. Publishes hardcover and paperback originals. Averages 4 titles/year. Pays variable royalty on retail price; no advance. Photocopied submissions OK. Reports in 2 months. Book catalog for SASE.
Nonfiction: "Edits publishes scientific and text books in social sciences, particularly counseling and guidance, psychology, statistics and education." Query or submit sample chapters.
Recent Nonfiction Title: *Actualizing Therapy*, by E. Shostrom (therapy text).

*****EDUCATION ASSOCIATES**, Division of The Daye Press, Inc., Box 8021, Athens GA 30603. (404)542-4244. Editor, Text Division: D. Keith Osborn. Publishes hardcover and trade paperback originals. Averages 2-6 titles/year; receives 150 submissions annually. 1% of books from first-time authors; 100% of books from unagented writers. Subsidy publishes 10% of books. "We may publish a textbook which has a very limited audience and is of unusual merit . . . but we still believe that the book will make a contribution to the educational field." Buys mss "on individual basis." Publishes book an average of 9 months after acceptance. Photocopied submissions OK. Computer printout submissions acceptable; no dot-matrix. Reports in 1 month on queries.
Nonfiction: How-to and textbook. Subjects include psychology and education. "Books in the fields of early childhood and middle school education. Do not wish basic textbooks. Rather, are interested in more specific areas of interest in above fields. We are more interested in small runs on topics of more limited nature than general texts." Query with one-page letter; do not send entire manuscript. If interested will request synopsis and sample chapters. No reply unless SAE is enclosed.
Recent Nonfiction Title: *Computer Mat*, by A.B. Wilson.
Tips: College textbooks—usually dealing with early childhood, middle school, or child development—have the best chance of selling to *Education Associates*.

*****WILLIAM B. EERDMANS PUBLISHING CO.**, Christian University Press, 255 Jefferson Ave. SE, Grand Rapids MI 49503. (616)459-4591. Editor-in-Chief: Jon Pott. Publishes hardcover and paperback originals and reprints. Averages 65-70 titles/year; receives 3,000-4,000 submissions annually. 25% of books from first-time authors; 95% of books from unagented writers. Average print order for a writer's first book is 4,000. Subsidy publishes 1% of books. Pays 7½-10% royalty on retail price; usually no advance. Publishes book an average of 1 year after acceptance. Simultaneous and photocopied submissions OK if noted. Computer printout submissions acceptable; no dot-matrix. Reports in 3 weeks for queries; 4 months for mss. Looks for "quality and relevance." Free book catalog.
Nonfiction: Reference, textbooks and tourists guidebooks. Subjects include history, philosophy, psychology, religion, sociology, regional history and geography. "Approximately 80% of our publications are religious—specifically Protestant—and largely of the more academic or theological variety (as opposed to the devotional, inspirational or celebrity-conversion type of book). Our history and social studies titles aim, similarly, at an academic audience; some of them are documentary histories. We prefer that writers take the time to notice if we have published anything at all in the same category as their manuscript before sending it to us." Accepts nonfiction translations. Query. Accepts outline/synopsis and 2-3 sample chapters. Reviews artwork/photos.
Recent Nonfiction Title: *Dispensations*, by Richard John Neuhaus.

‡*****EFFECTIVE LEARNING, INC.**, 7 N. MacQuesten Pkwy., Box 2212, Mt. Vernon NY 10551. (914)664-7944. Editor: William Brandon. Publishes hardcover and paperback originals and reprints. Averages 6-10 ti-

tles/year; receives 100 submissions annually. 10% of books from first-time authors; 100% of books from un-agented writers. Subsidy publishes 2% of books. Publishes book an average of 2 years after acceptance. Simultaneous submissions OK. Computer printout submissions acceptable; prefers letter-quality to dot-matrix. Query. Reports in 2 months. Free book catalog.

Nonfiction: Americana, biography, business, cookbooks, cooking and food, economics, genealogy, history, hobbies, how-to, Judaica, multimedia material, nature, philosophy, politics, reference, religious, scientific, self-help, sociology, technical, textbooks and travel. "All manuscripts should be sent to the editorial review committee."

Recent Nonfiction Title: *Escape From Jesus: One Man's Search For a Meaningful Judaism*, by Shlomoh Sherman (religion).

ENSLOW PUBLISHERS, Bloy St. and Ramsey Ave., Box 777, Hillside NJ 07205. (201)964-4116. Editor: Ridley Enslow. Publishes hardcover and paperback originals. Averages 30 titles/year. Pays 10-15% royalty on retail price or net price; offers $500-5,000 advance. Publishes book an average of 8 months after acceptance. Photocopied submissions OK. Computer printout submissions acceptable. Reports in 2 weeks. Free book catalog.

Nonfiction: Biography, business/economics, health, hobbies, how-to, juveniles, philosophy, psychology, recreation, reference, science, self-help, sociology, sports and technical. Accepts nonfiction translations. Submit outline/synopsis and 2 sample chapters. Reviews artwork/photos as part of ms package.

Recent Nonfiction Title: *Bioethics: Dilemmas in Modern Medicine*, by A. Weiss.

‡ENTELEK, Ward-Whidden House/The Hill, Box 1303, Portsmouth NH 03801. Editor-in-Chief: Albert E. Hickey. Publishes paperback originals. Offers royalty on retail price of 5% trade; 10% textbook. No advance. Averages 4-5 titles/year. Free catalog. Photocopied and simultaneous submissions OK. Submit outline and sample chapters or submit complete ms. Reports in 1 week.

Nonfiction: Publishes computer books and software of special interest to educators. Length: 3,000 words minimum.

ENTERPRISE PUBLISHING CO., INC., 725 Market St., Wilmington DE 19801. (302)654-0110. Publisher: T.N. Peterson. Editor: Ann Faccenda. Publishes hardcover and paperback originals, "with an increasing interest in newsletters and periodicals." Averages 8 titles/year; receives 150 submissions annually. 50% of books from first-time authors; 90% of books from unagented writers. Pays royalty on wholesale or retail price. Offers $1,000 average advance. Publishes book an average of 6 months after acceptance. Simultaneous and photocopied submissions OK, but "let us know." Electronic submissions OK, but requires hard copy also. Computer printout submissions acceptable; prefers letter-quality to dot-matrix. Catalog and writer's guidelines for SASE.

Nonfiction: "Subjects of interest to small business executives/entrepreneurs. They are highly independent and self-sufficient, and of an apolitical to conservative political leaning. They need practical information, as opposed to theoretical: self-help topics on business, including starting and managing a small enterprise, advertising, marketing, raising capital, public relations, tax avoidance and personal finance. Business/economics, legal self-help and business how-to." Queries only. All unsolicited mss are returned unopened. Reviews artwork/photos.

Recent Nonfiction Title: *Five Minute Phobia Cure*, by Roger Callahan.

*PAUL S. ERIKSSON, PUBLISHER, 208 Battell Bldg., Middlebury VT 05753. (802)388-7303; Summer: (802)247-8415. Publisher/Editor: Paul S. Eriksson. Associate Publisher/Co-Editor: Peggy Eriksson. Publishes hardcover and paperback trade originals and paperback trade reprints. Averages 5-10 titles/year; receives 1,500 submissions annually. 25% of books from first-time authors; 95% of books from unagented writers. Average print order for a writer's first book is 3,000-5,000. Subsidy publishes 5% of books. Pays 10-15% royalty on retail price; advance offered if necessary. "We have to like the book and probably the author." Publishes book an average of 6 months after acceptance. Photocopied submissions OK. Computer printout submissions acceptable; prefers letter-quality to dot-matrix. Reports in 3 weeks. Free book catalog.

Nonfiction: Americana, birds (ornithology), art, biography, business/economics, cookbooks/cooking/foods, health, history, hobbies, how-to, humor, music, nature, philosophy, photography, politics, psychology, recreation, self-help, sociology, sports and travel. Submit outline/synopsis and sample chapters.

Recent Nonfiction Title: *Most of My Patients Are Animals*, by Robert M. Miller, D.V.M. with an Introduction by James Herriot.

Fiction: Mainstream. Submit outline/synopsis and sample chapters.

Recent Fiction Title: *The Headmaster's Papers*, by Richard A. Hawley.

Tips: "We look for intelligence, excitement and salability. We prefer manuscripts written out of deep, personal knowledge or experience."

*ETC PUBLICATIONS, Drawer ETC, Palm Springs CA 92263. (619)325-5352. Editorial Director: LeeOna S. Hostrop. Senior Editor: Dr. Richard W. Hostrop. Publishes hardcover and paperback originals. Averages 12 titles/year; receives 100 submissions annually. 75% of books from first-time authors; 90% of books from un-agented writers. Average print order for a writer's first book is 2,500. Subsidy publishes 5-10% of books. Offers 5-15% royalty, based on wholesale and retail price. No advance. Publishes book an average of 1 year after acceptance. Simultaneous and photocopied submissions OK. Computer printout submissions acceptable; prefers letter-quality to dot-matrix. Reports in 3 weeks. Book catalog $2.

Nonfiction: Business management, educational management, gifted education, books for writers and text-books. Accepts nonfiction translations in above areas. Submit complete ms. Reviews artwork/photos as part of ms package.

Recent Nonfiction Title: *The Forbidden Apple—Sex in the Schools*, by Victor Ross and John Marlowe (education).

Tips: "ETC will seriously consider textbook manuscripts in any knowledge area in which the author can guarantee a first-year adoption of not less than 500 copies. Special consideration is given to those authors who are capable and willing to submit their completed work in camera-ready, typeset form."

EXANIMO PRESS, 23520 Hwy. 12, Segundo CO 81070. Editor: Dean Miller. Publishes hardcover and trade paperback originals. Averages 4-10 titles/year; receives 25 submissions annually. 90% of books from first-time authors; 100% of books from unagented writers. Average print order for a writer's first book is 5,000. Pays 10% minimum royalty on retail price; buys some mss outright for $500-1,500; no advance. Publishes ms 6-36 months after acceptance. Photocopied submissions OK. Computer printout submissions acceptable if legible; prefers letter-quality to dot-matrix. Reports in 1 month on queries; 2 weeks on mss. Book catalog for SAE and 1 first class stamp.

Nonfiction: How-to and technical. Subjects include prospecting; small mining; treasure hunting; self-employment; dowsing (water witching); and self- or family-improvement from a financial point of view. "We are concentrating on books that graphically tell how to get out of debt and into profitable self-employment. Our *Owlhooter's Manual—The Poor Man's Guide To Financial Independence* is the first of 25 scheduled volumes. Volume 2 deals with 'cottage industries' or profitable work at home. We want books that detail the conversion of hobbies or avocations into profitable businesses." Likes 8x10 pages, 40-104 pages. Prefers a profusely illustrated book, has in-house artist. Needs mss on flea-marketeering and garage/yard sales. No copy artistry or read-and-rewrites. Query. Submit outline and synopsis, 1 sample chapter and intended table of contents. Reviews artwork/photos as part of ms package.

Recent Nonfiction Title: *Coinshooter's Manual—How To Use Your Metal Detector Profitably.*

Tips: "How-to-do-it books covering individual or family survival in a declining economy have the best chance of selling to our firm. Converting hobbies into profitable small businesses is one example. Develop a reputation for technically accurate manuscripts and success will follow. We have found that many would-be authors with superb writing aptitude are not aware that their local libraries are usually crammed with technical reference data."

‡FABER & FABER, INC., Division of Faber & Faber, Ltd., London, England; 50 Cross St., Winchester MA 01890. (617)721-1427. Editor-in-Chief: Douglas W. Hardy. Publishes hardcover and trade paperback originals, and hardcover and trade paperback reprints. Averages 20 titles/year; receives 600 submissions annually. 10% of books from first-time authors; 25% of books from unagented writers. Pays 7½-10% royalty on wholesale or retail price; advance varies. Publishes book an average of 1 year after acceptance. Simultaneous and photocopied submissions OK. Computer printout submissions acceptable; prefers letter-quality to dot-matrix. Reports in 3 weeks on queries; 6 weeks on mss. Book catalog for 9x12 SAE and 5 first class stamps.

Nonfiction: Biography, "coffee table" book, how-to, humor, illustrated book, juvenile, self-help and business. Subjects include Americana, animals, art, health, history, hobbies, music, photography, politics, sociology and travel. Query. Reviews artwork/photos as part of ms package.

Recent Nonfiction Title: *Peacekeepers at War*, by Michael Petit.

Fiction: Ethnic, experimental, historical, mainstream, mystery and regional. No historical/family sagas. Query.

Recent Fiction Title: *Floral Street*, by Simon Burt.

Tips: "We are a growing publisher, and we acquire manuscripts and publish books with great care. Writers with books on very obscure topics should look elsewhere. We take journalists seriously as possible book authors; many of our titles are house-generated with a writer brought on later."

FACTS ON FILE, INC., 460 Park Ave. S., New York NY 10016. (212)683-2244. Executive Editor: Gerard Helferich. Publishes hardcover and trade paperback originals, and hardcover reprints. Averages 120 titles/year; receives approximately 1,000 submissions annually. 25% of books from unagented writers. Pays 6-15% royalty on retail price. Offers average $7,500 advance. Simultaneous and photocopied submissions OK. Electronic submissions OK, but requires hard copy also. "We have IBM PC with Wordstar and Multi-Mate. Almost any disk can be converted to a compatible form." Computer printout submissions acceptable; prefers letter-quality to dot-matrix. Reports in 2 weeks on queries; 1 month on mss. Book catalog free on request.

Nonfiction: Illustrated book, juvenile, reference, and other informational books on Americana, animals, art, business and economics, cooking and foods (no cookbooks), health, history, hobbies, music, nature, philosophy, psychology, recreation, religion and sports. "We need serious, informational books for a targeted audience. All our books must have strong library interest, but we also distribute books effectively to the book trade." No cookbooks, biographies, pop psychology, humor, do-it-yourself crafts or poetry. Query or submit outline/synopsis and sample chapters. Reviews artwork/photos.

Recent Nonfiction Title: *Vietnam War Almanac*, by Harry Summers (military/political reference).

Tips: "Our audience is libraries and schools, for our more reference-oriented books and libraries, schools and bookstores for our less reference-oriented informational titles."

FAIRCHILD BOOKS & VISUALS, Book Division, 7 E. 12th St., New York NY 10003. Manager: E.B. Gold. Publishes hardcover and paperback originals. Offers standard minimum book contract; no advance. Pays 10% of net sales distributed twice annually. Averages 12 titles/year; receives 100 submissions annually. 50% of books from first-time authors; 99% of books from unagented writers. Publishes book an average of 1 year after acceptance. Photocopied submissions OK. Computer printout submissions acceptable; prefers letter-quality to dot-matrix. Free book catalog; ms guidelines for SASE.

Nonfiction: Publishes business books and textbooks relating to fashion, electronics, marketing, retailing, career education, advertising, home economics and management. Length: Open. Query, giving subject matter, brief outline and at least 1 sample chapter. Reviews artwork/photos as part of ms package.

Recent Nonfiction Title: *Essential Terms of Fashion*, by Calasabetta.

Tips: "The writer has the best chance of selling our firm fashion, retailing or textile related books that can be used by both the trade and schools. If possible, the writer should let us know what courses would use the book."

FAIRLEIGH DICKINSON UNIVERSITY PRESS, 285 Madison Ave., Madison NJ 07940. (201)377-4050. Chairperson, Editorial Committee: Harry Keyishian. Publishes hardcover originals. Averages 35 titles/year; receives 300 submissions annually. 33% of books from first-time authors; 100% of books from unagented writers. Average print order for a writer's first book is 1,000. "Contract is arranged through Associated University Presses of Cranbury, New Jersey. We are a *selection* committee only." Publishes book an average of 18 months after acceptance. Computer printout submissions acceptable; prefers letter-quality to dot-matrix. Reports in 2 weeks on queries; 4 months on mss. Free book catalog.

Nonfiction: Reference and scholarly books. Subjects include art, business and economics, history, literary criticism, music, philosophy, politics, psychology, sociology and women's studies. Looking for scholarly books in all fields. No nonscholarly books. Query with outline/synopsis and sample chapters. Reviews artwork/photos as part of ms package.

Recent Nonfiction Title: *Transcendentalism and the Western Messenger: A History of the Magazine and its Contributors*, by Robert D. Habich.

Tips: "Research must be up to date. Poor reviews result when authors' bibliographies and notes don't reflect current research."

‡*FALCON PRESS, Subsidiary of J.W. Brown, 3660 N. 3rd St., Phoenix AZ 85012. (602)246-3546. Vice President: C. Hogan. Publishes hardcover and trade paperback originals, and hardcover and trade paperback reprints. Averages 12 titles/year; receives 60 submissions annually. 10-15% of books from first-time authors; 70% of books from unagented writers. Subsidy publishes 2% of books. Subsidy publishes if author is unknown or had poor performance on previous titles. Pays 4-10% royalty on retail price. Offers average $500 advance. Publishes book an average of 13 months after acceptance. Simultaneous and photocopied submissions OK. Computer printout submissions acceptable; prefers letter-quality to dot-matrix. Reports in 1 month. Book catalog for #10 SAE with 1 first class stamp.

Nonfiction: Biography, how-to, illustrated book, reference, self-help, technical and textbooks on business and economics, health, history, nature, philosophy, politics, psychology, religion, sociology, and metaphysics. Needs mss on psychology, sociology, new age, and the occult. Submit outline/synopsis and sample chapters. Reviews artwork/photos.

Recent Nonfiction Title: *Mysticism Psychology Oedipus*, by Israel Regardie (psychology).

Fiction: Adventure, confession, erotica, ethnic, experimental, fantasy, historical, horror, mainstream, mystery, religious, science fiction and suspense. Needs science-fiction, fantasy, and experimental mss. Submit outline/synopsis and sample chapters.

Recent Fiction Title: *The Quest*, by Marvin Spiegelman (fantasy).

Poetry: Will publish minimal poetry in the next two years. Submit samples.

Recent Poetry Title: *The Worlds Tragedy*, by Aleister Crowley (revelatory).

‡*FALCON PRESS PUBLISHING CO., INC., 27 Neill Ave., Box 731, Helena MT 59624. (406)442-6597. Publisher: Bill Schneider. Publishes hardcover and trade paperback originals. Averages 10-15 titles/year. Subsidy publishes 30% of books. Pays 8-15% royalty on net price or flat fee. Publishes book an average of 6 months after ms is in final form. Reports in 3 weeks on queries. Free book catalog.

Nonfiction: Coffee table book, how-to and self-help. Subjects include Americana, cooking and foods, health, history, hobbies, nature, photography, recreation, sports and travel. "We're primarily interested in ideas for recreational guidebooks and books on regional outdoor or geographic subjects—especially on Colorado and California." No fiction or poetry. Query only. Do not send ms.
Recent Nonfiction Title: *The Rivers of Colorado*, by Jeff Rennicke.

*THE FAMILY ALBUM, Rt. 1, Box 42, Glen Rock PA 17327. (717)235-2134. Contact: Ron Lieberman. Publishes hardcover originals and reprints and software. Averages 4 titles/year; receives 150 submissions annually. 30% of books from first-time authors; 100% of books from unagented writers. Average print order for a writer's first book is 1,000. Subsidy publishes 20% of books. Pays royalty on wholesale price. Publishes book an average of 10 months after acceptance. Simultaneous and photocopied submissions OK. Electronic submissions OK on 5¼ floppy disk—CP/M. Computer printout submissions acceptable; prefers letter-quality to dot-matrix. Reports in 2 months.
Nonfiction: "Significant works in the field of (nonfiction) bibliography. Worthy submissions in the field of Pennsylvania-history, biography, folk art and lore. We are also seeking materials relating to books, literacy, and national development. Special emphasis on Third World countries, and the role of printing in international development." No religious material. Submit outline/synopsis and sample chapters.

‡FARNSWORTH PUBLISHING CO., Subsidiary of Longman Financial Services Publishing Inc., 78 Randall Ave., Rockville Centre NY 11570. (516)536-8400. President: Lee Rosler. Publishes hardcover originals. "Standard royalty applies, but 5% is payable on mail order sales." Publishes 20 titles/year. Publishes book an average of 1 year after acceptance. Computer printout submissions accepted "for consideration"; prefers letter-quality to dot-matrix. Reports in 2 months.
Nonfiction: "Our books appeal to lawyers, accountants, life underwriters, financial planners and others in the financial services industry (subject matter may cover selling techniques, estate and financial planning, taxation, money management, etc.)." Submit outline/synopsis and 2 sample chapters.

FARRAR, STRAUS AND GIROUX, INC., 19 Union Sq. W., New York NY 10003. Children's Editor: Stephen Roxburgh. Publishes hardcover originals. Receives 2,000 submissions annually. Pays royalty; advance. Publishes book an average of 18 months after acceptance. Photocopied submissions OK. Computer printout submissions acceptable; prefers letter-quality to dot-matrix. Reports in 3 months. Catalog for SAE and 56¢ postage.
Nonfiction and Fiction: "We are primarily interested in fiction picture books and novels for children and young adults." Submit outline/synopsis and sample chapters. Reviews artwork/photos as part of ms package.
Recent Nonfiction Title: *Grace in the Wilderness*, by Aranka Siegal.
Recent Fiction Title: *The Treasure of Plunderell Manor*, by Bruce Clements.
Recent Picture Book Title: *Froggie Went A-Courting*, by Chris Conover.
Tips: Fiction of all types has the best chance of selling to this firm. Farrar, Straus and Giroux publishes a limited number of nonfiction titles.

THE FEMINIST PRESS, The City University of New York, 311 E. 94th St., New York NY 10128. (212)360-5790. Publisher: Florence Howe. Publishes paperback originals and reprints of literature. Averages 12-15 titles/year; receives 500+ submissions annually. 10% of books from first-time authors; 90% of books unagented submissions. Pays 10% royalty on net sales; no advance. Publishes book an average of 9 months after acceptance. Simultaneous and photocopied submissions OK. Computer printout submissions acceptable. Reports in 3 months. Query or submit outline/synopsis and sample chapters.
Nonfiction: Feminist books for a general trade and women's studies audience. "We publish biographies, reprints of lost feminist literature, women's history, bibliographies and educational materials. No material without a feminist viewpoint. No contemporary adult fiction, drama, poetry, or dissertation." Looks for "feminist perspective, interesting subject, potential use in women's studies classroom, sensitivity to issues of race and class, clear writing style, general grasp of subject." Sometimes reviews artwork/photos as part of ms package.
Recent Nonfiction Title: *The Cross Cultural Study of Women*, by Margot Duley-Morrow and Mary I. Edwards.
Tips: "Submit a proposal for an important feminist work that is sophisticated in its analysis, yet readably free of jargon. Both historical and contemporary subjects will be considered. We are especially interested in works that appeal to both a trade audience and a women's studies classroom market."

‡FIDDLEHEAD POETRY BOOKS & GOOSE LANE EDITIONS, 132 Saunders St., Fredericton, New Brunswick E3B 1N3 Canada. (506)454-8319. General Editor: Peter Thomas. Publishes hardcover and trade paperback originals. Averages 12 titles/year; receives 250 submissions annually. 33⅓% of books from first-time authors; 75-100% of books from unagented writers. Pays royalty on retail price, makes outright purchase or offers royalty or purchase with copies. "How authors are paid depends very much on situation." No advances. Publishes book 10 months after acceptance. Computer printout submissions acceptable. Reports in 3 weeks on queries; 2 months on mss. Book catalog free on request.

Imprints: Goose Lane Editions (nonfiction and fiction), Peter Thoma, general editor.

Nonfiction: Coffee table book and reference on Canadian and maritime provinces, history, photography, regional literature and linguistics. Submit outline/synopsis and sample chapters.

Recent Nonfiction Title: *When Rum Was King*, by B.J. Grant (popular history).

Fiction: Experimental, mainstream, and "first" novel authors. "Erotica, confession, or dull or immature fiction is not required. SASE absolutely necessary for return of manuscript." Submit outline/synopsis and sample chapters or complete ms.

Recent Fiction Title: *Paradise Siding*, by Allan Donaldson (short stories).

Poetry: Open to collections of poetry; modern/experimental preferable. Submit complete ms with SASE.

Recent Poetry Title: *Post-Sixties Nocturne*, by Pier Giorgio Di Cicco.

Tips: "No one will ever grow rich by publishing poetry. We have a much easier time marketing fiction and nonfiction but feel a cultural obligation as a small literary press."

‡FIREBRAND BOOKS, 141 The Commons, Ithaca NY 14850. (607)272-0000. Publisher: Nancy K. Bereano. Publishes hardcover and trade paperback originals and hardcover and trade paperback reprints. Averages 6-8 titles/year; receives 200-300 submissions annually. 50% of books from first-time authors; 75% of books from unagented writers. Pays 7-9% royalty on retail price, or makes outright purchase. Publishes book an average of 18 months after acceptance. Simultaneous and photocopied submissions OK "with notification." Computer printout submissions acceptable; prefers letter-quality to dot-matrix. Reports in 2 weeks on queries; 2 months on mss. Book catalog free on request.

Nonfiction: Criticism and essays. Subjects include feminism and lesbianism. Submit complete ms.

Recent Nonfiction Title: *My Mama's Dead Squirrel, Lesbian Essays on Southern Culture*, by Mab Segrest (collection of essays).

Fiction: Will consider all types of feminist and lesbian fiction.

Recent Fiction Title: *Moll Cutpurse*, by Ellen Galford (novel). Submit complete ms.

Recent Poetry Title: *Jonestown and Other Madness*, by Pat Parker.

Tips: "Our audience includes feminists, lesbians, ethnic audiences, and other progressive people."

FITZHENRY & WHITESIDE, LTD., 195 Allstate Parkway, Markham, Ontario L3R 4T8 Canada. (416)477-0030. Vice-President: Robert Read. Trade Editor: Helen Heller. Publishes hardcover and paperback originals and reprints. Royalty contract varies; advance negotiable. Publishes 50 titles/year, text and trade. Photocopied submissions OK. Reports in 1-3 months. Enclose return postage.

Nonfiction: "Especially interested in topics of interest to Canadians, and by Canadians." Textbooks for elementary and secondary schools, also biography, business, history, health, fine arts. Submit outline and sample chapters. Length: open.

Recent Title: *From Worst to First* (story of Toronto Blue Jays).

FLEET PRESS CORP., 160 5th Ave., New York NY 10010. (212)243-6100. Editor: Susan Nueckel. Publishes hardcover and paperback originals and reprints; receives 200 submissions annually. 10% of books from first-time authors; 25% of books from unagented writers. Royalty schedule and advance "varies." Publishes book an average of 15 months after acceptance. Computer printout submissions acceptable; no dot-matrix. Reports in 8 weeks. Free book catalog.

Nonfiction: History, biography, arts, religion, general nonfiction and sports. Length: 45,000 words. Publishes juveniles. Stresses social studies and minority subjects; for ages 8-15. Length: 25,000 words. Query with outline; no unsolicited mss. Reviews artwork/photos.

FLORA AND FAUNA PUBLICATIONS, Suite 100, 4300 NW 23rd Ave., Gainesville FL 32606. (904)371-9858. Publisher: Bernadette T. D'Allesandro. Book publisher/packager. Publishes hardcover and trade paperback originals. Averages 8-10 titles/year; receives 70 submissions annually. 50% of books from first-time authors; 100% of books from unagented writers. Average print order for a writer's first book is 500. Pays 15% royalty on list price; usually no advance because of high royalty. Publishes book an average of 1 year after acceptance. Photocopied submissions OK. Electronic submissions OK via DOS or CP/M. Computer printout submissions acceptable; prefers letter-quality to dot-matrix. Reports in 2 weeks on queries; 3 months on mss. Free book catalog; ms guidelines for SASE.

Nonfiction: Reference, technical, textbook and directories. Subjects include plants and animals (for amateur and professional biologists), and natural history. Looking for "books dealing with kinds of plants and animals, especially insects. No nature stories or 'Oh My' nature books." Query with outline/synopsis and 3 sample chapters. Reviews artwork/photos as part of ms package.

Recent Nonfiction Title: *Plants and Insects*, by P. Jolivet (natural history).

Tips: "Well-documented books, especially those that fit into one of our series, have the best chance of selling to our firm—biology, natural history, no garden books."

J. FLORES PUBLICATIONS, Box 14, Rosemead CA 91770. (818)287-2195. Editor: Eliezer Flores. Publishes trade paperback originals and reprints. Averages 10 titles/year. 99% of books from unagented writers. Pays 10-15% royalty on net sales; no advance. Publishes book an average of 8 months after acceptance. Simultaneous and photocopied submissions OK. Computer printout submissions acceptable; prefers letter-quality to dot-matrix. Reports in 1 month on queries; 6 weeks on mss. Free book catalog; ms guidelines for SAE and 1 first class stamp.
Nonfiction: How-to, illustrated book and self-help. "We need original nonfiction manuscripts on military science, weaponry, improvised weaponry, self-defense, survival, police science, the martial arts, guerrilla warfare and silencers. How-to manuscripts are given priority." No pre-World War II material. Query with outline and 2-3 sample chapters. Reviews artwork/photos. "Photos are accepted as part of the manuscript package and are strongly encouraged."
Recent Nonfiction Title: *Modern-Day Ninjutsu.*
Tips: "Trends include illustrated how-to books on a specific subject. Be thoroughly informed on your subject and technically accurate."

‡FLORICANTO PRESS, Hispanex (Hispanic Information Exchange), 604 William St., Oakland CA 94612. (415)893-8702. Associate Publisher: Claire Splan. Publishes hardcover and trade paperback originals. Averages 2-5 titles/year; receives 50-100 submissions annually. 90% of books from first-time authors; 90% of books from unagented writers. Pays 5-20% royalty on net receipts. Publishes book an average of 9 months after acceptance. Simultaneous and photocopied submissions OK. Electronic submissions OK via IBM-PC readable—ASCII, but requires hard copy also. Computer printout submissions acceptable; prefers letter-quality to dot-matrix. Reports in 2 months on queries; 3 months on mss. Ms guidelines for SASE.
Nonfiction: Juvenile and reference; must be Hispanic-related. "Our nonfiction book manuscript needs include reference works related to Hispanics in the United States—directories, bibliographies, studies—and Hispanic-related children's nonfiction." No submissions unrelated to Hispanics. Submit complete ms.
Recent Nonfiction Title: *Bilindex* (bilingual subject headings).
Fiction: Ethnic; Hispanic-related adult and children's fiction. No submissions unrelated to Hispanics. Submit complete ms.
Tips: "Our audience includes professionals serving Hispanics, and the Hispanic community."

‡FLORIDA TREND BOOK DIVISION, (formerly Trend House) Box 611, St. Petersburg FL 33731. (813)821-5800. Chairman: Eugene C. Patterson. President: Andrew Barnes. Publisher: Richard Edmonds. Publishes hardcover and paperback originals and reprints. Specializes in books on Florida—all categories. Pays royalty; no advance. Books are marketed through *Florida Trend* magazine. Publishes book an average of 8 months after acceptance. Computer printout submissions acceptable; no dot-matrix. Reports in 1 month.
Nonfiction: Business, economics, history, law, politics, reference, textbooks and travel. "All books pertain to Florida." Query. Reviews artwork/photos as part of ms package.

FODOR'S TRAVEL GUIDES, 2 Park Ave., New York NY 10016. (212)340-9800. Publisher: Richard T. Scott. Publishes paperback travel guides. Averages 120 titles/year.
Nonfiction: "We are the publishers of periodic travel guides—regions, countries, cities, and special tourist attractions. We do not solicit manuscripts on a royalty basis, but we are interested in travel writers and/or experts who will and can cover an area of the globe for Fodor's for a fee." Submit credentials and samples of work.
Recent Nonfiction Title: *Fodor's Fun in Paris.*

‡*FORDHAM UNIVERSITY PRESS, University Box L, Bronx NY 10458. (212)579-2320. Director: H.G. Fletcher. Averages 8 titles/year. Subsidy publishes 0-5% of books. Pays royalty on sales income. Send written queries only; do not send unsolicited manuscripts. Publishes book an average of 2 years after acceptance. Computer printout submissions acceptable; no dot-matrix. Reports in 1 week. Free book catalog.
Nonfiction: Humanities. "We would like the writer to use the *MLA Style Sheet*, latest edition. We do not want dissertations or fiction material."
Recent Nonfiction Title: *A Dependent People,* by Elaine Forman Crane.

FORMAN PUBLISHING INC., Suite 206, 11661 San Vicente Blvd., Los Angeles CA 90049. (213)820-8672. President: Len Forman. Publishes hardcover and mass market paperback originals. Averages 6 titles/year; receives 200 submissions annually. 100% of books from first-time authors; 100% of books from unagented writers. Average print order for a writer's first book is 10,000 (hardcover), 100,000 (softcover). Pays standard royalty. Publishes book an average of 1 year after acceptance. Photocopied submissions OK. Computer printout submissions acceptable; prefers letter-quality to dot-matrix. Reports in 1 month.
Nonfiction: Cookbook, how-to and self-help. Accepts nonfiction translations. Submit outline/synopsis and 3 sample chapters. Reviews artwork/photos.
Recent Nonfiction Title: *PMS Self-Help Book,* by Dr. Susan Lark.

THE FRASER INSTITUTE, 626 Bute St., Vancouver, British Columbia V6E 3M1 Canada. (604)688-0221. Assistant Director: Sally Pipes. Publishes trade paperback originals. Averages 7-10 titles/year; receives 30 submissions annually. Pays honorarium. Publishes book an average of 6 months after acceptance. Simultaneous and photocopied submissions OK. Electronic submissions OK via IBM PC or PC compatible, but requires hard copy also. Computer printout submissions acceptable; prefers letter-quality to dot-matrix. SAE and IRC. Reports in 6 weeks. Free book catalog; ms guidelines for SASE.
Nonfiction: Analysis, opinion, on economics, social issues and public policy. Subjects include business and economics, politics, religion and sociology. "We will consider submissions of high-quality work on economics, social issues, economics and religion, public policy, and government intervention in the economy." Submit complete ms.
Recent Nonfiction Title: *Focus: On Employment Equity*, by M. Walker and W. Block.
Tips: "Our books are read by well-educated consumers, concerned about their society and the way in which it is run and are adopted as required or recommended reading at colleges and universities in Canada, the U.S. and abroad. Our readers feel they have some power to improve society and view our books as a source of the information needed to take steps to change unproductive and inefficient ways of behavior into behavior which will benefit society. Recent trends to note in book publishing include affirmative action, banking, broadcasting, insurance, healthcare and religion. A writer has the best chance of selling us books on government, economics, finance, or social issues."

THE FREE PRESS, Division of the Macmillan Publishing Co., Inc., 866 3rd Ave., New York NY 10022. President/Publisher: Erwin A. Glikes. Averages 65 titles/year; receives 3,000 submissions annually. 15% of books from first-time authors; 50% of books from unagented writers. Royalty schedule varies. Publishes book an average of 11 months after acceptance. "Prefers camera-ready copy to machine-readable media." Computer printout submissions acceptable; prefers letter-quality to dot-matrix. Reports in 3 weeks.
Nonfiction: Professional books and textbooks. Publishes college texts, adult nonfiction, and professional books in the social sciences, humanities and business. Reviews artwork/photos as part of ms package "but we can accept no responsibility for photos or art." Looks for "identifiable target audience, evidence of writing ability." Accepts nonfiction translations. Send 1-3 sample chapters, outline, and query letter before submitting mss.

SAMUEL FRENCH, INC., 45 W. 25th St., New York NY 10010. (212)206-8990. Subsidiaries include Samuel French Ltd. (London); Samuel French (Canada) Ltd. (Toronto); Samuel French, Inc. (Hollywood); and Baker's Plays, (Boston). Editor: Lawrence Harbison. Publishes paperback acting editions of plays. Averages 80-90 titles/year; receives 1,200 submissions annually, mostly from unagented playwrights. 10% of books from first-time authors; 20% of books from unagented writers. Pays 10% book royalty on retail price. Pays 90% stock production royalty; 80% amateur production royalty. Offers variable advance. Publishes book an average of 6 months after acceptance. Simultaneous and photocopied submissions OK. Reports immediately on queries; from 6 weeks to 8 months on mss. Book catalog $1.25, postpaid; ms guidelines $3, postpaid.
Nonfiction: Acting editions of plays.
Tips: "Broadway and Off-Broadway hit plays, light comedies and mysteries have the best chance of selling to our firm. Our market is theater producers—both professional and amateur—and actors. Read as many plays as possible of recent vintage to keep apprised of today's market; write small-cast plays with good female roles; and be one hundred percent professional in approaching publishers and producers (see guidelines)."

C.J. FROMPOVICH PUBLICATIONS, RD 1, Chestnut Rd., Coopersburg PA 18036. (215)346-8461. Contact: Publisher. Publishes trade and mass market paperback originals. Averages 3 titles/year; receives 20 submissions annually. 100% of books from first-time authors; 100% of books from unagented writers. Pays 10% royalty on wholesale price. No advance. Publishes book an average of 9 months after acceptance. Computer printout submissions acceptable; prefers letter-quality to dot-matrix. Reports in 1 month. Book catalog for business size SAE and 1 first class stamp.
Nonfiction: Self-help, technical on natural nutrition. "We are a specialty house dealing in just those issues." Submit outline/synopsis and sample chapters.
Recent Nonfiction Title: *Contraception Naturally*, by Dr. Francis J. Trapani, D.C.

FRONT ROW EXPERIENCE, 540 Discovery Bay Blvd., Byron CA 94514. (415)634-5710. Editor: Frank Alexander. Publishes trade paperback originals. Averages 2-3 titles/year; receives 20 submissions annually. 90% of books from first-time authors; 100% of books from unagented writers. Average print order for a writer's first book is 500. Pays 5-10% royalty on net sales. Publishes book an average of 1 year after acceptance. Simultaneous and photocopied submissions OK. Computer printout submissions acceptable; no dot-matrix. "We return submissions but not without a SASE." Reports in 1 week on queries; 1 month on mss. Free book catalog.
Nonfiction: How-to, reference, curriculum guides for movement education, special education, educational games, and perceptual-motor development. Especially needs innovative curriculum guides. Publishes for elementary physical education directors, elementary, junior high, and preschool teachers, YMCA activity direc-

tors, occupational therapists, physical therapists, curriculum directors, and childhood development professionals in general. Accepts nonfiction translations from any language in subject areas we specialize in. No mss outside of movement education, special education, educational games, and perceptual-motor development. Reviews artwork/photos as part of ms package. Query. Submit outline/synopsis and 3 sample chapters.
Recent Nonfiction Title: *Poetry in Motion*, by Rae Pica.
Tips: "We accept *only* movement education, special education, perceptual-motor development and educational games manuscripts."

‡**GAMBLING TIMES**, 1018 N. Cole, Hollywood CA 90038. (213)466-5261. Marketing Director: Robert Ames. Publishes hardcover and softcover. Averages 12 titles/year; receives 200-250 submissions annually. 5-10% of books from first-time authors; 99% of books from unagented writers. Pays 9-11% royalty on retail price for hardcover; 4-6% on softcover. Publishes book an average of 9 months after acceptance. Simultaneous and photocopied submissions OK. Computer printout submissions acceptable; no dot-matrix. Reports in 3 months. Ms guidelines for SASE.
Nonfiction: How-to. "Straight gambling material related to gambling systems, betting methods, etc. Also interested in political, economic and legal issues surrounding gambling inside and outside the US." Submit sample chapters. Reviews artwork/photos. Gambling-related books only.
Tips: "Technical books on gambling strategy, odds etc., have the best chance of selling to our firm. (We have basic books on all areas of gambling.) You should play the game you write about. Don't invent strategies that are mathematically unsound."

GARBER COMMUNICATIONS, INC., (affiliates: Steinerbooks, Spiritual Fiction Publications, Spiritual Science Library, Rudolf Steiner Publications, Freedeeds Library, Biograf Publications), 5 Garber Hill Rd., Blauvelt NY 10913. (914)359-9292. Editor: Bernard J. Garber. Publishes hardcover and paperback originals and reprints. Averages 15 titles/year; receives 250 submissions annually. 10% of books from first-time authors; 100% of books from unagented writers. Average print order for a writer's first book is 500-1,000 copies. Pays 5-7% royalty on retail price; offers average $500 advance. Publishes book an average of 1 year after acceptance. Will consider photocopied submissions. Reports in 2 months. Free book catalog; ms guidelines for SAE and 25¢ postage.
Nonfiction: Spiritual sciences, occult, philosophical, metaphysical and ESP. These are for our Steiner Books division only. Serious nonfiction. Philosophy and Spiritual Sciences: Bernard J. Garber. Query with outline and first, middle and last chapters for nonfiction.
Recent Nonfiction Title: *Frederick Nietzsche*, by Rudolf Steiner.
Fiction: Patricia Abrams, editor, the new genre called Spiritual Fiction Publications. "We are now looking for original manuscripts or rewrites of classics in modern terms."
Recent Fiction Title: *Legend*, by Barry Maher.

GARDEN WAY PUBLISHING, Storey Communications, Inc., Schoolhouse Rd., Pownal VT 05261. (802)823-5811. Editor: Deborah Burns. Publishes hardcover and paperback originals. "We are looking at audio and video cassettes." Publishes 12 titles/year; receives 2,000 submissions annually. 50% of books from first-time authors; 75% of books from unagented writers. Average print order for a writer's first book is 7,500. Offers a flat fee arrangement varying with book's scope, or royalty, which usually pays author 8% of book's net price. Advances are negotiable, but usually range from $1,500 to $3,000. "We stress continued promotion of titles and sales over many years." Emphasizes direct mail sales and sales to specialty stores, plus sales to bookstores through Harper and Row. Publishes book 1 year after acceptance. Photocopied submissions OK. Computer printout submissions acceptable; no dot-matrix. Enclose return postage.
Nonfiction: Books on gardening (both vegetable and ornamental), cooking, nutrition, house building and remodeling, animals, country living, and country business. Emphasis should be on how-to. Length requirements are flexible. "The writer should remember the reader will buy his book to learn to do something, so that all information to accomplish this must be given. We are publishing specifically for the person who is concerned about natural resources and a deteriorating life style and wants to do something about it." Query with outline and 2-3 sample chapters. Reviews artwork/photos as part of ms package.
Recent Nonfiction Title: *A Garden of Wildflowers*, by Henry W. Art.
Tips: "We look for comprehensive, authoritative manuscripts. Authors should look at our other books to see how theirs would suit our line, and tell us who they feel the audience for their book would be."

GARLAND PUBLISHING, INC., 136 Madison Ave., New York NY 10016. (212)686-7492. Vice President: Gary Kuris. Publishes hardcover originals. Averages 150 titles/year. 99% of books from unagented writers. Pays 10-15% royalty on wholesale price. "Depending on marketability, authors may prepare camera-ready copy." Publishes book an average of 9 months after acceptance. Simultaneous and photocopied submissions OK. Computer printout submissions acceptable; prefers letter-quality to dot-matrix. Reports in 2 weeks on queries; 1 month on mss. Free book catalog; ms guidelines for SASE.
Nonfiction: Reference books for libraries. Humanities and social sciences. Accepts nonfiction translations.

"We're interested in reference books—encyclopedias, bibliographies, sourcebooks, indexes, etc.—in all fields." Submit outline/synopsis and 1-2 sample chapters. Reviews artwork/photos as part of ms package.
Recent Nonfiction Title: *Ulysses*, by James Joyce (a synoptic edition).

‡**GARLINGHOUSE COMPANY**, 320 SW 33rd St., Box 299, Topeka KS 66601. (913)267-2490. President: Whitney Garlinghouse. Publishes trade paperback originals. Averages 2-5 titles/year. Usually pays 6% royalty on retail price; sometimes offers advances of up to $1,500; buys some mss outright. Simultaneous and photocopied submissions OK. Computer printout submissions OK; prefers letter-quality to dot-matrix. Reports in 1 month.
Nonfiction: How-to relating to the home. Suitable subject areas include home building and design; underground homes and other innovative building techniques; home remodeling and repairs; solar energy; energy conservation in the home; home projects; furniture making and restoration; and home workshop aids. Principally interested in books that deal specifically with saving (or making) money. Accepts nonfiction translations. Submit outline/synopsis and 3 sample chapters. "List credentials with submissions."

GENERAL HALL, INC., 23-45 Corporal Kennedy St., Bayside NY 11360. (718)423-9397. Publisher: Ravi Mehra. Publishes hardcover and trade paperback originals for the college market. Averages 5-6 titles/year; receives 100-300 submissions annually. 10% of books from first-time authors; 100% of books from unagented writers. Pays 10-15% royalty. Publishes book an average of 10 months after acceptance. Simultaneous and photocopied submissions OK. Computer printout submissions acceptable; no dot-matrix. Reports in 6 weeks. Reviews artwork/photos.
Nonfiction: Reference and textbook. Subjects include Americana, blacks, business and economics, politics, psychology and sociology. Submit complete ms.
Recent Nonfiction Title: *The Future of Women*, by Rona M. Fields.

THE J. PAUL GETTY MUSEUM, Subsidiary of The J. Paul Getty Museum Trust, Box 2112, Santa Monica CA 90406. (213)459-2306. Editor: Sandra Knudsen Morgan. Publishes hardcover and trade paperback originals and reprints. Averages 10 titles/year; receives 50 submissions annually. 10% of books from first-time authors; 100% of books from unagented writers. Average print order for a writer's first book is 1,500. Pays 6-12% royalty on retail price; buys some mss outright; offers average $2,000 honorarium. Publishes book an average of 18 months after acceptance. Photocopied submissions OK. Electronic submissions OK via IMB PC or Displaywriter, but requires hard copy also. Computer printout submissions acceptable; prefers letter-quality to dot-matrix. Reports in 2 months. Book catalog and ms guidelines for SASE.
Nonfiction: Reference and scholarly on art and history. "Scholarly titles and well-researched general and children's titles on topics related to the museum's seven collections: Greek and Roman art and architecture (especially the Villa dei Papiri), illuminated manuscripts, drawings and paintings from the Renaissance through the nineteenth century, European sculpture decorative arts of the Regence through Napoleonic periods, and photographs." No nonEuropean art. Query. Reviews artwork/photos as part of ms package.
Recent Nonfiction Title: *Early Cycladic Sculpture*, by Pat Getz-Preziosi.
Tips: "Art history related to Museum collections has the best chance of selling to our firm."

THE C.R. GIBSON COMPANY, 32 Knight St., Norwalk CT 06856. (203)847-4543. Senior Editor: Jayne Bowman. Publishes hardcover originals. Averages 25 titles/year; receives 230 submissions annually. Pays royalty or outright purchase. Publishes book an average of 18 months after acceptance. Simultaneous and photocopied submissions OK. Reports in 3 weeks on queries; 2 months on mss. Free book catalog.
Nonfiction: Juvenile and gift books. Subject includes religion/inspiration. Query or submit outline/synopsis and sample chapter. Reviews artwork/photos.
Tips: "Religious inspirational books or books suitable for special occasion gift-giving have the best chance of selling to our firm."

GIFTED EDUCATION PRESS, The Reading Tutorium, 10201 Yuma Ct., Box 1586, Manassas VA 22110. (703)369-5017. Publisher: Maurice D. Fisher. Publishes mass market paperback originals. Averages 3-5 titles/year; receives 10 submissions annually. 100% of books from first-time authors; 100% of books from unagented writers. Pays royalty of $1 per book. Publishes book an average of 4 months after acceptance. Simultaneous and photocopied submissions OK. Computer printout submissions acceptable; prefers letter-quality to dot-matrix. Reports in 1 month on queries; 3 months on mss. Free book catalog.
Nonfiction: How-to. Subjects include philosophy, psychology, education of the gifted; and how to teach children to read. "Need books on how to educate gifted children—both theory and practice. Also, we are searching for books on using computers with the gifted, and how to teach children with learning problems to read. Need rigorous books on procedures, methods, and specific curriculum for the gifted." Query.
Recent Nonfiction Title: *Foundations of Humanities Education for Gifted Students*, by Michael Walters and James Lo Giudice.
Tips: "If I were a writer trying to market a book today, I would develop a detailed outline based upon intensive

study of my field of interest. Present creative ideas in a rigorous fashion. Be knowledgeable about and comfortable with ideas."

GINN AND CO., 191 Spring St., Lexington MA 02173. (617)863-7600. Senior Vice President, Publications: Mary Ansaldo. Averages 200 titles/year; receives 75-100 submissions annually. 50% of books from first-time authors; 95 + % of books from unagented writers. Royalty schedule: from 10% of net on a secondary book to 3% on elementary materials. "We are doing a significant number of books on a work-for-hire or fee basis." Publishes book an average of 15 months after acceptance. Electronic submissions OK, but requires hard copy also. Computer printout submissions acceptable. Reports in 2 to 6 weeks. Sample chapters, complete or partially complete mss will be considered. Enclose return postage.
Nonfiction: Publishers of textbooks and instructional materials for elementary schools. Ms guidelines for SASE.
Tips: Queries/mss may be routed to other editors in the publishing group.

THE GLOBE PEQUOT PRESS, INC., Old Chester Rd., Box Q, Chester CT 06412. (203)526-9571. Vice President/Publications Director: Linda Kennedy. Publishes hardcover and paperback originals and paperback reprints. Averages 15 titles/year; receives 2,000 submissions annually. 20% of books from first-time authors; 75% of books from unagented writers. Average print order for a writer's first book is 5,000-7,500. Offers 7½-10% royalty on net price; offers modest advances. Publishes book an average of 1 year after acceptance. Simultaneous and photocopied submissions OK. Computer printout submissions acceptable; prefers letter-quality to dot-matrix. Reports in 6 weeks. Book catalog for 9x12 SASE.
Nonfiction: Cookbooks (national preferred to regional), travel guidebooks (regional OK), Northeast-Americana, journalism/media, natural history, outdoor recreation. No doctoral theses, genealogies, or textbooks. Submit outline, table of contents, sample chapter(s), and resume/vita. Complete mss accepted. Reviews artwork/photos.
Recent Nonfiction Title: *Seafood As We Like It.*

‡GOLD EAGLE BOOKS, Subsidiary of Harlequin Enterprises Ltd., 225 Duncan Mill Rd., Don Mills, Ontario M3B 3K9 Canada. (416)445-5860. Executive Editor: Mark Howell. Publishes mass market paperback originals and reprints (50% each). Averages 54 titles/year; receives 1,100 submissions annually. 20% of books from first-time authors; 25% of books from unagented writers. Pays 4-8% royalty on retail price; offers average $5,000-10,000 advance. Publishes book an average of 1 year after acceptance. Photocopied submissions OK. Electronic submissions OK via IBM/Samna, but requires hard copy also. Computer printout submissions acceptable; no dot-matrix. Reports in 1 month on queries; 2 months on mss. Free book catalog; ms guidelines for SASE.
Fiction: Adventure, horror, mystery and suspense. "Gold Eagle is growing in 1986/87 to include one-off books published monthly in the categories of suspense, detective fiction, superior thrillers and sagas." No science fiction or fantasy.
Tips: "We like books that have an original, scary edge to them, strong on reader identification but likely to surprise. Although our readership is supposedly male, the range of commercial novels that interest us is wide, and we're looking for the best available, suspenseful stories told in a hard, realistic, contemporary style. We look for the identifiable difference. This must be evident in any encapsulated summary of a submitted book; such a summary should ideally be only a sentence long, a paragraph at the most."

‡GOLDEN BOOKS, Western Publishing Co., Inc., 850 3rd Ave., New York NY 10022. Publisher, Adult Books: Jonathan P. Latimer. Publisher, Children's Books: Doris Duenewald. Averages 200 titles/year; receives 1,000 submissions annually. 10-15% of books from first-time authors; 50% of books from unagented writers. Pays royalty; buys some mss outright. Publishes book an average of 3 months after acceptance. Computer printout submissions acceptable; prefers letter-quality to dot-matrix.
Nonfiction: Adult nonfiction, limited to cookbooks and nature guides. Children's books, including picturebooks, concept books, novelty books, and information books. Query before submitting ms. Looks for "completeness, an indication that the author knows his subject and audience." Reviews artwork/photos.
Fiction: Children's picturebooks and young fiction. Query before submitting ms.

GOLDEN WEST BOOKS, Box 80250, San Marino CA 91108. (213)283-3446. Editor-in-Chief: Donald Duke. Managing Editor: Vernice Dagosta. Publishes hardcover and paperback originals. Receives 50 submissions annually. 50% of books from first-time authors; 100% of books from unagented writers. Pays 10% royalty contract; no advance. Publishes book an average of 3 months after acceptance. Simultaneous and photocopied submissions OK. Computer printout submissions acceptable; prefers letter-quality to dot-matrix. Reports in 1 month. Free book catalog.
Nonfiction: Publishes selected Western Americana and transportation Americana. Query or submit complete ms. "Illustrations and photographs will be examined if we like manuscript."

GOLDEN WEST PUBLISHERS, 4113 N. Longview, Phoenix AZ 85014. (602)265-4392. Editor: Hal Mitchell. Publishes trade paperback originals. Averages 4 titles/year; receives 400-500 submissions annually. 50% of books from first-time authors; 100% of books from unagented writers. Average print order for a writer's first book is 5,000. Pays 6-10% royalty on retail price or makes outright purchase of $500-2,500. No advance. Publishes book an average of 6 months after acceptance. Simultaneous and photocopied submissions OK. Electronic submissions OK if compatible with Comp Edit, but requires hard copy also. Computer printout submissions acceptable; no dot-matrix. Reports in 2 weeks on queries; 1 month on mss. Book catalog for business size SAE and 1 first class stamp.

Nonfiction: Cookbooks, books on the Southwest and West. Subjects include cooking and foods. Query or submit outline/synopsis and sample chapters. Prefers query letter first. Reviews artwork/photos as part of ms package.

Recent Title: *Cowboy Slang*, by Edgar R. "Frosty" Potter.

‡GOVERNMENT INSTITUTES, INC., Suite 24, 966 Hungerford Dr., Rockville MD 20850. (301)251-9250. Director, Publications Department: G. David Williams. Publishes hardcover and softcover originals. Averages 24 titles/year; receives 20 submissions annually. 50% of books from first-time authors; 100% of books from unagented writers. Pays variable royalty or fee. No advance. Publishes book an average of 4 months after acceptance. Simultaneous and photocopied submissions OK. Computer printout submissions acceptable; prefers letter-quality to dot-matrix. Reports in 1 month on queries; 2 months on mss. Book catalog and ms guidelines free on request.

Nonfiction: Reference and technical. Subjects include environmental law and energy. Needs professional-level titles in environmental law and energy. Submit outline/synopsis and sample chapters. Reviews artwork/photos.

Recent Nonfiction Title: *Environmental Law Handbook, 8th Edition*, by J. Gordon Arbuckle, et al. (professional).

‡GRAFTON BOOKS, A Division of the Collins Publishing Company, 8 Grafton St., London, W1X 3LA, United Kingdom. 01-493-7070. Editorial Directors: John Boothe (trade books), Nick Austin (paperbacks). Publishes hardcover and trade paperback originals and mass market paperback reprints and originals. Averages 100 titles/year in hardback; receives 500 submissions annually. 2% of books from first-time writers; 5% of books from unagented writers. Pays 6-15% royalty on retail price. Advance varies. Simultaneous and photocopied submissions OK. Computer printout submissions acceptable; no dot-matrix. Reports in weeks. Free book catalog.

Nonfiction: Biography, cookbook, humor, illustrated book, reference, business and economics, cooking and foods, health, hobbies, nature, politics, psychology, recreation, religion, sports and travel. No do-it-yourself. Query, submit outline/synopsis and sample chapters, or complete ms. Reviews artwork/photos.

Recent Nonfiction Title: *FDR: A Biography*, by Ted Morgan (biography).

Fiction: (Hardcover) adventure, fantasy, historical, humor, mainstream, science fiction. (Paperback) same as above, plus suspense, war, and film tie-ins. No westerns, light romances or crime fiction. Query, submit outline/synopsis and sample chapters, or complete ms.

Recent Fiction Title: *Hold the Dream*, by Barbara Taylor Bradford (general novel).

Tips: "Strong female-oriented fiction in hardback. Paperback is equally oriented to male and female. Classless."

GRAPHIC ARTS CENTER PUBLISHING CO., 3019 NW Yeon Ave., Box 10306, Portland OR 97210. (503)226-2402. General Manager and Editor: Douglas Pfeiffer. Publishes hardcover originals. Averages 3-6 titles/year. Pays outright purchase averaging $3,000.

Nonfiction: "All titles are pictorials with text. Text usually runs separately from the pictorial treatment. Authors must be previously published and are selected to complement the pictorial essay." Query.

*GRAPHIC IMAGE PUBLICATIONS, Box 6417, Alexandria VA 22306. Publisher: Hurb Crow. Publishes trade and mass market paperback originals. Averages 5 titles/year. Subsidy publishes 15% of books based on "length of experience and success of prior works." Pays 5-15% royalty on wholesale price; advance negotiable. Publishes book an average of 6 months after acceptance. Query with outline/synopsis and 2 sample chapters to the attention of John Hunter, managing editor. Reports in 2 months. Simultaneous and photocopied submissions OK. Computer printout submissions acceptable; no dot-matrix.

Nonfiction: How-to and travel. "We publish for people with a desire to learn on their own; and for people who love to travel and to know about the areas they visit."

Recent Nonfiction Title: *Cabo San Lucas*, by Susan H. Crow.

Fiction: Romance novels.

Tips: "Be professional in your query, and let us know a little about yourself, be positive." Queries/mss may be routed to other editors in the publishing group.

GRAYWOLF PRESS, Box 75006, St. Paul MN 55175. (612)222-8342. Editor/Publisher: Scott Walker. Imprints include Graywolf Short Fiction Series. Publishes hardcover and trade paperback originals, and trade paperback reprints. Averages 10-16 titles/year; receives 500+ submissions annually. 25% of books from first-time authors; 40% of books from unagented writers. Pays 7-10% royalty on retail price. Publishes book an average of 9 months after acceptance. Photocopied submissions acceptable; prefers letter-quality to dot-matrix. Reports in 2 weeks on queries; 1 month on mss. Free book catalog.
Fiction: Short fiction collections. "Limited to direct solicitation only." Query through agent only.

GREAT OCEAN PUBLISHERS, 1823 N. Lincoln St., Arlington VA 22207. (703)525-0909. President: Mark Esterman. Publishes hardcover and trade paperback originals and hardcover reprints. Averages 3 titles/year; receives 350 submissions annually. 10% of books from first-time authors; 50% of books from unagented writers. Average print order for a writer's first book is 3,000-5,000. Pays 8-10% hardcover royalty; 6-8% paperback on retail price; occasionally offers advance. Publishes book an average of 1 year after acceptance. Simultaneous (if so indicated) and photocopied submissions OK. Computer printout submissions acceptable; prefers letter-quality to dot-matrix. Reports in 3 weeks.
Nonfiction: Biography, how-to, illustrated book, reference, self-help and technical. Subjects include art, business and economics, child care/development, health, history, music, philosophy, politics and religion. "Any subject is fine as long as it meets our standards of quality." Submit outline/synopsis and sample chapters. "SASE *must* be included with all material to be returned." Looks for "1) good writing, 2) clear evidence that manuscript is intended as a *book*, not a long collection of weakly organized small pieces, and 3) good organization—not to mention a worthwhile, interesting subject." Accepts nonfiction translations—query first. Reviews artwork/photos.
Recent Nonfiction Title: *Beethoven Remembered.*
Tips: "Nonfiction with a real theme and a mature knowledgeable point of view have the best chance of selling to Great Ocean. If you have to ask . . ."

‡GREEN HILL PUBLISHERS, INC./JAMESON BOOKS, 722 Columbus St., Ottawa IL 61350. (815)434-7905. (Distributed by Kampmann & Co.). Publisher: Jameson G. Campaigne. Senior Editor: Richard S. Wheeler. Publishes hardcover, trade paper and mass market paperback originals. Publishes 12-14 titles/year. .Pays 6-15% royalty. Advance averages $2,500. Simultaneous and "clean" photocopied submissions OK. Electronic submissions OK but query first; requires hard copy also. Computer printout submissions acceptable; prefers letter-quality to dot-matrix. Reports in 2 months on queries; 4 months on mss. Book catalog for 6x9 SASE.
Nonfiction: Biography (of major subjects), business and economics, history, politics, Chicago themes.
Recent Nonfiction Title: *Jesse Jackson and the Politics of Race* (biography and social commentary).
Fiction: Adventure, ethnic (American Indian), historical, mainstream, Western and business fiction, especially "mountain man, early fur trade stories." Query or submit complete ms.
Recent Fiction Title: *Carry the Wind*, by Terry Johnston (Western/historical).
Tips: "Concentrate on literacy, vocabulary, grammar, basic story telling and narrative skills."

‡GREEN TIGER PRESS, 1061 India St., San Diego CA 92101. (619)238-1001. Editor: Harold Darling. Imprints include Star & Elephant (nonfiction and fiction). Publishes hardcover and trade paperback originals and reprints. Averages 12 titles/year; receives 2,500+ submissions annually. 5% of books from first-time authors; 80% of books from unagented writers. Pays 10% maximum royalty on retail price. Publishes book an average of 1 year after acceptance. Simultaneous and photocopied submissions OK. Computer printout submissions acceptable; prefers letter-quality to dot-matrix. Reports in 4 weeks on queries; 4 months on mss. Book catalog for 6x9 SAE with 44¢ postage.
Nonfiction: Illustrated book and juvenile. Subjects include illustrations and fantasy.
Recent Nonfiction Title: *The World of Carl Larsson* (commentary on life and work of illustrator includes over 400 illustrations).
Fiction: Juvenile, fantasy, myth, art.
Recent Fiction Title: *The Teddy Bears' Picnic*, by Jimmy Kennedy.
Poetry: Submit 3 samples.
Recent Poetry Title: *Lost Wine*, by John Theobald (7 centuries of French/English lyric poetry).
Tips: "We look for manuscripts containing a romantic, visionary or imaginative quality, often with a mythic feeling where fantasy and reality co-exist. Since we are a visually-oriented house, we look for manuscripts whose texts readily conjure up visual imagery."

‡*WARREN H. GREEN, INC., 8356 Olive Blvd., St. Louis MO 63132. Editor: Warren H. Green. Imprints include Fireside Books. Publishes hardcover originals. Offers "10-20% sliding scale of royalties based on quantity distributed. All books are short run, highly specialized, with no advance." Subsidy publishes about 1% of books, e.g., "books in philosophy and those with many color plates." Averages 30 titles/year; receives 200+ submissions annually. 15% of books from first-time authors; 100% of books from unagented writers. "37% of total marketing is overseas." Will send a catalog to a writer on request. Publishes book an average of 10 months after acceptance. Will consider simultaneous and photocopied submissions. Computer printout submissions acceptable; no dot-matrix. Query or submit outline and sample chapters. "Publisher requires 300-500-word statement of scope, plan, and purpose of book, together with curriculum vitae of author." Reports in 60-90 days.

Nonfiction: Medical and scientific. "Specialty monographs for practicing physicians and medical researchers. Books of 160 pages upward. Illustrated as required by subject. Medical books are non-textbook type, usually specialties within specialties, and no general books for a given specialty. For example, separate books on each facet of radiology, and not one complete book on radiology. Authors must be authorities in their chosen fields and accepted as such by their peers. Books should be designed for all doctors in English speaking world engaged in full or part time activity discussed in book. We would like to increase publications in the fields of radiology, anesthesiology, pathology, psychiatry, surgery and orthopedic surgery, obstetrics and gynecology, and speech and hearing." Also interested in books on health, philosophy, psychology and sociology. Reviews artwork/photos as part of ms package.

Recent Nonfiction Title: *Labat's Regional Anesthesia*, by Dr. John Adrian.

GREENLEAF CLASSICS, INC., Box 20194, San Diego CA 92120. Managing Editor: Ralph Vaughan. Publishes paperback originals. Publishes 450 titles/year; receives 1,000-2,000 submissions annually. 15% of books from first-time authors; 90% of books from unagented writers. Pays by outright purchase about 3 months after acceptance. Publishes book an average of 9 months after acceptance. Computer printout submissions acceptable; no dot-matrix. Reports in 1-2 months. "No manuscripts will be returned unless accompanied by return postage." Ms guidelines for SASE.

Fiction: Specializes in adult erotic novels. "All stories must have a sexual theme. They must be contemporary novels dealing with the serious problems of everyday people. All plots are structured so that characters must get involved in erotic situations. Write from the female viewpoint (third person). Request our guidelines before beginning any project for us." Preferred length: 35,000 words. Send complete ms (preferred); or at least 3 sample chapters.

*GREENWOOD PRESS, Box 5007, Westport CT 06881. (203)226-3571. Executive Vice President: James Sabin. Averages 600 titles/year; receives 1,000-2,000 submissions annually. Subsidy publishes "less than 1%." 50% of books from first-time authors; 90% of books from unagented writers. Average print order for a writer's first book is 1,000-2,000. Pays negotiable royalty; offers negotiable advance. Publishes book an average of 1 year after acceptance. Simultaneous and photocopied submissions OK. "We encourage authors under contract to submit manuscripts on disk or mag tape. We accept from a range of different systems." Computer printout submissions acceptable; no dot-matrix. Reports in 6 weeks. Free book catalog. Guidelines issued upon contract signing.

Nonfiction: Reference (dictionaries and handbooks); professional books in business and law (the Quorum Books imprint); and scholarly books and advanced texts (Praeger Publishers). Query or submit prospectus, 1 sample chapter and vita. Reviews artwork/photos.

Recent Nonfiction Title: *Dictionary of Mexican-American History*, by Matt Meier and Feliciano Rivera.

Tips: "The writer has the best chance of selling our firm non-fiction references, and professional materials because of better market conditions. Once the author has signed a contract to write a book for us, the writing pitfall the author must avoid is writing a book significantly different from that placed under contract."

GROUPWORK TODAY, INC., Box 258, South Plainfield NJ 07080. Editor-in-Chief: Harry E. Moore, Jr. Publishes hardcover and paperback originals. Averages 4-6 titles/year; receives 20-30 submissions annually. 90% of books from first-time authors; 100% of books from unagented writers. Average print order for a writer's first book is 1,000. Offers $100 advance against royalties on receipt of contract and completion of ms ready for publication; 10% of gross receipts from sale of book. Publishes book an average of 6-8 months after acceptance. Computer printout submissions acceptable; no dot-matrix. Books are marketed by direct mail to Groupwork Agency executives and professionals (YMCA, YWCA, Scouts, Salvation Army, colleges, directors of organized camps, and libraries). "Also will answer specific questions from an author considering us as a publisher." No simultaneous submissions. Reports in 2 months. Book catalog for SAE with 50¢ in stamps. Ms guidelines for SASE.

Nonfiction: "We are publishers of books and materials for professionals and volunteers who work with people in groups. Titles are also used by colleges for texts and resources. Some of our materials are also suited to the needs of professionals who work with individuals. Groupwork agency management, finance, program development and personnel development are among the subjects of interest to us. Writers must be thoroughly familiar with 'people work' and have fresh insights to offer. New writers are most welcome here. Lengths are open but usually run 40,000-60,000 words." Readers are mainly social agency administrators and professional staff members. Groupwork materials are also read by volunteers serving in the social agencies. Mss are judged by experienced professionals in social agencies. The company is advised on policy direction by a council of advisors from national agencies and colleges across the nation. "We also are publishing our 'monogram' series to

deal with the most important problems with which social work agencies must deal today. We are also in the market for papers, 15-35 double-spaced pages, for a Management Workbook Series. Papers must deal with finance, program development, communication, organizational planning or some other subject directed to the problems of nonprofit, human services organizations. We pay a $35 advance against a 10% royalty on gross sales." Submit outline and 3 sample chapters for nonfiction. Reviews artwork/photos as part of ms package.
Recent Nonfiction Title: *Meaning Well is Not Enough: Perspectives on Volunteering*, by Jane Mallory Park.
Tips: "If a writer will send material only on which he or she has done as much work as possible to make a good outline, a sample chapter or two to indicate writing ability, and the idea is a contribution to our field, we will spend all kinds of time guiding the author to completion of the work."

‡GRUNWALD AND RADCLIFF PUBLISHERS, Subsidiary of Grunwald, Inc., Suite 344, 5049 Admiral Wright Rd., Virginia Beach VA 23462. (804)490-1132. President and Publisher: Stefan Von Rath-Grunwald, Ph.D. Publishes hardcover and trade paperback originals, and hardcover and trade paperback reprints. Averages 10 titles/year; receives 15 submissions annually. 80% of books from first-time authors; "many" from unagented writers. Pays 6-25% royalty on wholesale price. Offers average $2,000 advance. Publishes book an average of 1 year after acceptance. Simultaneous and photocopied submissions OK. Electronic submissions OK via Apple IIe and Lexatar VT 1303. Computer printout submissions acceptable; prefers letter-quality to dot-matrix. Reports in 1 month. Book catalog for 10x4 SAE with 1 first class stamp.
Imprints: Ben-Gurion Books and Media Productions (nonfiction and fiction), Reba A. Karp, editor. Pennsylvania Publishers (nonfiction), Jill Vaden, editor.
Nonfiction: Biography, "coffee table" book, cookbook, reference and textbook. Subjects include Americana, art, cooking and foods, health, history (pictorial) and religion. "We are looking for manuscripts in the areas indicated, which can also be converted into media productions (video, audio)." No highly technical texts, or topics not listed above. Query or submit outline/synopsis and sample chapters. Reviews artwork/photos as part of ms package.
Recent Nonfiction Title: *Kidney Patient's Wellness Diet—Tasty Recipes.*
Fiction: "*Only* Judaica, preferably Holocaust." Query. Has not yet published any fiction.

*GUERNICA EDITIONS, Box 633, Station N.D.G., Montreal, Quebec H4A 3R1 Canada. (514)481-5569. President/Editor: Antonio D'Alfonso. Publishes hardcover and trade paperback originals, hardcover and trade paperback reprints and software. Averages 10 titles/year; receives 1,000-2,000 submissions annually. 5% of books from first-time authors. Average print order for a writer's first book is 750-1,000. Subsidy publishes (non-author) 50% of titles. "Subsidy in Canada is received only when the author is established, Canadian-born and active in the country's cultural world. The others we subsidize ourselves." Pays 3-10% royalty on retail price. Makes outright purchase of $200-5,000. Offers 10¢/word advance for translators. Photocopied submissions OK. IRCs required. "American stamps are of no use to us in Canada." Reports in 1 month on queries; 6 weeks on mss. Free book catalog.
Nonfiction: Biography, humor, juvenile, reference and textbook. Subjects include art, history, music, philosophy, politics, psychology, recreation, religion and Canadiana.
Fiction: Ethnic, historical, mystery. "We wish to open up into the fiction world. No country is a country without its fiction writers. Canada is growing some fine fiction writers. We'd like to read you. No first novels." Query.
Poetry: "We wish to have writers in translation. Any writer who has translated Italian poetry is welcomed. Full books only. Not single poems by different authors, unless modern, and used as an anthology. First books will have no place in the next couple of years." Submit samples.
Recent Poetry Title: *French Poets of Today* (anthology).

GUIDANCE CENTRE, Faculty of Education, University of Toronto, 10 Alcorn Ave., Toronto, Ontario M4V 2Z8 Canada. (416)978-3210. Editorial Director: L. Miller. Coordinating Editor: Gethin James. Publishes hardcover and paperback originals. Averages 50 titles/year; receives 50 submissions annually. 5% of books from first-time authors; 5% of books from unagented writers. Pays in royalties. Publishes book an average of 6 months after acceptance. Electronic submissions OK via IBM PC, but requires hard copy also. Computer printout submissions acceptable; prefers letter-quality to dot-matrix. Reports in 1 month. Submissions returned "only if Canadian postage is sent." Free book catalog.
Nonfiction: "The Guidance Centre is interested in publications related to career planning and guidance and in measurement and evaluation. Also general education. No manuscripts which have confined their references and illustrations to United States material." Submit complete ms. Consult Chicago *Manual of Style*.
Recent Nonfiction Title: *Loneliness*, by Bulka.

*GULF PUBLISHING CO., Book Division, Box 2608, Houston TX 77001. (713)529-4301. Vice President: C.A. Umbach Jr. Editor-in-Chief: William J. Lowe. Imprints include Gulf (sci-tech and business/management) and Lone Star Books (regional Texas books). Publishes hardcover and large format paperback originals and software. Averages 40-50 titles/year; receives 300 submissions annually. 60% of books from first-time authors; 95% of books from unagented writers. Subsidy publishes 5% of books. Pays 10% royalty on net income; offers $300-2,000 advance. Publishes book an average of 10 months after acceptance. Simultaneous and photocopied submissions OK. Computer printout submissions OK; no dot-matrix. Reports in 2 months. Free book catalog; ms guidelines for SASE.

Nonfiction: Business, management, reference, regional trade, scientific and technical. Submit outline/synopsis and 1-2 sample chapters. Reviews artwork/photos as part of ms package.

Recent Nonfiction Title: *Managing for Productivity*, by John Belcher.

Tips: "Tell us the market, and how it can be reached at *reasonable* cost."

H.P. BOOKS, Subsidiary of Knight-Ridder Newspapers, Box 5367, Tucson AZ 85703. Publisher: Rick Bailey. Publishes hardcover and paperback originals. Averages 60-65 titles/year. Pays royalty on wholesale price; advance negotiable. Publishes ms an average of 9 months after acceptance. Simultaneous and photocopied submissions OK. "We delight in disk submissions but must be 8" diskette compatible with Wang VS 100 system or transfer directly to computer via telephone modem." Reports in 1 month. Free book catalog.

Nonfiction: Specializes in how-to books in several fields, all photo-illustrated. Cookbooks, cooking and foods, gardening, hobbies, how-to, leisure activities, photography, automotive, health, recreation, self-help, computer and technical books. Most books are 160 pages minimum; "word count varies with the format." Query only and state number and type of illustrations available. Submit introduction and 1 sample chapter. "We *require* author to supply photos and illustrations to our specifications."

Recent Nonfiction Title: *Complete Guide to Prescription and Non-Prescription Drugs*, by H. Winter Griffith, M.D.

*H.W.H. CREATIVE PRODUCTIONS, INC., 87-53 167th St., Jamaica NY 11432. (212)297-2208. President: Willis Hogan, Jr. Imprints include Phase One Graphic (nonfiction and fiction), Contact Maxine Bayliss about imprints. Publishes hardcover and trade paperback originals. Averages 5 titles/year; receives 400 submissions annually. 70% of books from first-time authors; 90% of books from unagented writers. Subsidy publishes 1% of books. Pays 10-15% royalty on wholesale price; offers average $200 advance. Publishes book an average of 18-24 months after acceptance. Photocopied submissions OK. Computer printout submissions acceptable; prefers letter-quality to dot-matrix. Reports in 1 month on queries; 2 months on mss.

Nonfiction: Biography, cookbook, humor, illustrated book and self-help. Subjects include Americana, animals, art, cooking and foods, health, hobbies, nature, photography (as a creative art form), recreation, travel and energy. Particularly interested in cookbooks, personalities, self portraits, new forms of energy, high technology. Submit outline/synopsis and sample chapters. Reviews artwork/photos.

Recent Nonfiction Title: *The African American Historical Card Collection.*

Fiction: Confession, ethnic, experimental, fantasy, humor, mainstream, romance, science fiction, suspense and plays. "Mindblowing science fiction, clean romance, experimental writing on any subject, children's stories." Submit outline/synopsis and sample chapters.

Recent Fiction Title: *The Native New Yorker.*

ROBERT HALE LIMITED, Clerkenwell House, 45/47 Clerkenwell Green, London EC1R 0HT England. (01)251-2661. Managing Director: John Hale. Chief Editor: Carmel Elwell. Publishes hardcover and trade paperback originals, and hardcover reprints. Averages 450 titles/year; receives 4,000 submissions annually. 10% of books from first-time authors; 30% of books from unagented writers. Pays royalty on retail price. Publishes book an average of 8 months after acceptance. Photocopied submissions OK. Computer printout submissions acceptable. Reports in 1 week on queries; 6 weeks on mss. Book catalog for $1 (postage). ("Send dollar bills or checks for postage and *not* postage stamps, postal coupons, money orders, etc.")

Nonfiction: Biography, "coffee table" book, cookbook, how-to, humor, illustrated book, reference and self-help. Subjects include animals, art, cooking and foods, health, history, hobbies, music, nature, photography, politics, recreation, religion, sports and travel. No autobiography of unknown persons, verse, philosophy, American history, education or technical material. Submit outline/synopsis and sample chapters.

Recent Nonfiction Title: *Ava*, by Roland Flamini (biography).

Fiction: Adventure, gothic, historical, mainstream, mystery, romance, suspense and western. "We are seeking anything between the lengths of 40,000 and 100,000 words for the adult reader." No Americana, confession, erotica, ethnic, experimental, fantasy, horror, humor, religious or science fiction. Submit outline/synopsis and sample chapters.

Recent Fiction Title: *The Shadow King*, by Roberta J. Dewa (historical).

ALEXANDER HAMILTON INSTITUTE, 1633 Broadway, New York NY 10019. (212)397-3580. Senior Editor: Rick Wolff. Publishes hardcover and paperback originals. Averages 18 titles/year; receives 200 + submissions annually. 40% of books from first-time authors; 90% of books from unagented writers. "We pay advance against negotiated royalty or straight fee (no royalty)." Offers average $2,000 advance. Publishes book an average of 10 months after acceptance. Simultaneous submissions OK. Computer printout submissions acceptable; no dot-matrix. Reports in 3 weeks on queries; 7 weeks on mss.

Nonfiction: How-to, reference and self-help. Subjects include business and economics and management. "Our needs are in the leading edge of business/management field. Since we publish only a specific type of book, we have very select needs. We want only 'how-to' books in the management area. We do *not* want traditional textbooks." Query or submit outline/synopsis and sample chapters. Reviews artwork/photos.
Recent Nonfiction Title: *Performance Appraisals: The Latest Legal Nightmare.*
Tips: "We sell exclusively by direct mail to managers and executives around the world. A writer must know his/her field and be able to teach its principles clearly and concisely."

‡HANCOCK HOUSE PUBLISHERS LTD., 1431 Harrison Ave., Blaine WA 98230. (604)538-1114. Publisher: David Hancock. Publishes hardcover and trade paperback originals, and hardcover and trade paperback reprints. Averages 12 titles/year; receives 400 submissions annually. 50% of books from first-time authors; 100% of books from unagented writers. Pays 10% maximum royalty on wholesale price. Simultaneous submissions OK. Publishes book an average of 6 months after acceptance. Computer printout submissions acceptable; prefers letter-quality to dot-matrix. Reports in 6 months. Book catalog free on request. Ms guidelines for SASE.
Nonfiction: Biography, cookbook, how-to and self-help. Subject include Americana; cooking and foods; history (Northwest coast Indians); nature; recreation (sports handbooks for teachers); sports; and investment guides. Query with outline/synopsis and sample chapters. Reviews artwork/photos.
Recent Nonfiction Title: *The Ships of British Columbia*, by Bannerman (history).

HANLEY & BELFUS, INC., 210 S. 13th St., Philadelphia PA 19107. (215)546-4995. President: John J. Hanley. Executive Vice President: Linda C. Belfus. Publishes hardcover and trade paperback originals. Averages 10 titles/year; receives 200 submissions annually. 50% of books from first-time authors; 100% of books from unagented writers. Pays 10% royalty on retail price. Publishes book an average of 9 months after acceptance. Simultaneous and photocopied submissions OK. Electronic submissions OK on Apple Macintosh PC, but requires hard copy also. Computer printout submissions acceptable; prefers letter-quality to dot-matrix. Reports in 1 week on queries; 2 weeks on mss. Free ms guidelines.
Nonfiction: Reference, textbook, medical manuals and atlases. Subjects include health. Especially looking for textbooks for medical students, nursing students and allied health students, and selected reference books for practicing doctors. Query or submit outline/synopsis and sample chapters. Reviews artwork/photos.

‡HARBOR HOUSE PUBLISHERS, 221 Water St., Boyne City MI 49712. (616)582-2814. Chairman: Jacques LesStrang. Publishes hardcover and trade paperback originals and hardcover and trade paperback reprints. Averages 6 titles/year. Pays 10-15% royalty on wholesale price. Advance varies. Photocopied submissions OK. Reports in 1 month. Book catalog free on request.
Nonfiction: "Coffee table" book, illustrated book, and maritime. Subjects include business and economics, cooking and foods, and Great Lakes subjects. "Our manuscript needs include pictorials of all kinds, books conceived within the Great Lakes region and maritime subjects." Submit outline/synopsis and sample chapters or complete ms.
Recent Nonfiction Title: *Caves and Caving*, by Lee Jackson (how-to).

HARLEQUIN BOOKS, Subsidiary of Torstar, 225 Duncan Mill Rd., Don Mills, Ontario M3B 3K9 Canada. (416)445-5860. Subsidiaries include Worldwide Library and Silhouette Books, editorial offices, 300 E. 42nd St., New York NY 10017. Vice President and Editorial Director: Star Helmer. Publishes mass market paperback originals. Averages 675 titles/year; receives 10,000 submissions annually. 10% of books from first-time authors; 20% of books from unagented writers. Pays 6-8% "escalating" royalty on retail price. Offers advance. Publishes book an average of 2 years after acceptance. Photocopied submissions OK. Computer printout submissions acceptable; prefers letter-quality to dot-matrix. Reports in 2 weeks on queries; 2 months on mss. Free ms guidelines.
Imprints: Harlequin Books of North America, 6 fiction series. Harlequin Romance. Presents. American Romance. Superromance. Intrigue and Temptation. Silhouette Books, 5 fiction series. Romance Desire. Special Edition. Intimate Moments.
Fiction: Gothic, regency, intrigue, traditional, short contemporary sensuals, long contemporary romances. "We're always looking for new authors." Query.
Tips: "Harlequin readership comprises a wide variety of ages, backgrounds, income and education levels. The audience is predominantly female. Because of the high competition in women's fiction, readers are becoming very discriminating. They look for a quality read. If I were a writer trying to market a book today, I would read as many recent romance books as possible in all series to get a feel for the scope, new trends, acceptable levels of sensuality, etc."

‡HARPER & ROW JUNIOR BOOKS GROUP, 10 E. 53rd St., New York NY 10022. (212)207-7044. Imprints include: Harper & Row Junior Books, including Charlotte Zolotow and Harper Carousel Books; T.Y. Crowell; Lippincott and Trophy Junior Books. Publisher: Elizabeth Gordon. Editors: Charlotte Zolotow, Nina

Ignatowitz, Marilyn Kriney, Barbara Fenton. Laura Geringer, Robert O. Warren, Antonia Q. Markiet. Publishes hardcover originals and paperback reprints—board books, picture books, easy-to-read, middle-grade, teenage, and young adult novels. Published 70 titles in 1986 (Harper, cloth); 72 titles (Harper-Trophy, paperback); 35 titles (Crowell); 20 titles (Lippincott); 48 titles (Harper Carousel). Query; submit complete ms; submit outline/synopsis and sample chapters; or submit through agent. Photocopied submissions OK. Computer printout submissions acceptable. "Please identify simultaneous submissions." Reports in 2-3 months. Pays average royalty of 10%. Royalties on picture books shared with illustrators. Offers advance. Book catalog for self-addressed label. Writers guidelines for SASE.
Nonfiction: Science, history, social studies, and sports. Reviews artwork/photos as part of ms package.
Fiction: Fantasy, animal, spy/adventure, science fiction, problem novels, contemporary. Needs picture books, easy-to-read, middle-grade, teenage and young adult novels.
Recent Titles: *Tales Mummies Tell*, by Patricia Lauber (Crowell); *Beware the Dragons*, written and illustrated by Sarah Wilson (Harper).
Tips: "Write from your own experience and the child you once were. Read widely in the field of adult and children's literature. Realize that writing for children is a difficult challenge."

HARPER & ROW PUBLISHERS, INC., 10 E. 53rd St., New York NY 10022. (212)207-7000. Imprints include Barnes & Noble; Harper & Row-San Francisco (religious books only); Perennial Library; and Torchbooks. Managing Editor: Katharine Kirkland. Publishes hardcover and paperback originals, and paperback reprints. Publishes 300 titles/year. Pays standard royalties; advances negotiable. No unsolicited queries or mss. Reports on solicited queries in 6 weeks.
Nonfiction: Americana, animals, art, biography, business/economics, cookbooks, health, history, how-to, humor, music, nature, philosophy, photography, poetry, politics, psychology, reference, religion, science, self-help, sociology, sports and travel. "No technical books."
Fiction: Adventure, fantasy, gothic, historical, mainstream, mystery, romance, science fiction, suspense, western and literary. "We look for a strong story line and exceptional literary talent."

‡HARROW AND HESTON, Stuyvesant Plaza, Box 3934, Albany NY 12203. (518)442-5223. Editor-in-Chief: Graeme Newman. Publishes hardcover and trade paperback originals and paperback reprints. Averages 4 titles/year; receives 10-20 submissions annually. 80% of books from first-time authors; 100% of books from unagented writers. Pays 10% royalty on wholesale price. Publishes book an average of 3 months after acceptance. Simultaneous and photocopied submissions OK. Electronic submissions OK via IBM PC or compatible—must be in ASCII files, but requires hard copy also. Computer printout submissions acceptable. Reports in 2 months on queries; 6 months on mss. Ms guidelines for SASE.
Nonfiction: Textbooks on sociology and criminal justices. Query.
Recent Nonfiction Title: *A Primer in Radical Criminology*, by Michael Lynch and W. Byron Groves.
Tips: "Submissions must be clearly written with no jargon, and directed to upper undergraduate or graduate criminal justice students, on central criminal justice topics."

THE HARVARD COMMON PRESS, 535 Albany St., Boston MA 02118. (617)423-5803. President: Bruce P. Shaw. Publishes hardcover and trade paperback originals and reprints. Averages 6 titles/year; receives "thousands" of submissions annually. 75% of books from first-time authors; 75% of books from unagented writers. Average print order for a writer's first book is 7,500. Pays royalty; offers average $1,000 advance. Publishes book an average of 9 months after acceptance. Simultaneous and photocopied submissions OK. Computer printout submissions acceptable; no dot-matrix. Reports in 1 month. Book catalog for 9x11½ SAE and 56¢ postage; ms guidelines for SASE.
Nonfiction: Travel, cookbook, how-to, reference and self-help. Subjects include Americana, business, cooking and foods, and travel. "We want strong, practical books that help people gain control over a particular area of their lives, whether it's family matters, business or financial matters, health, careers, food or travel. An increasing percentage of our list is made up of books about travel and travel guides; in this area we are looking for authors who are well traveled, and who can offer a different approach to the series guidebooks. We are open to good nonfiction proposals that show evidence of strong organization and writing, and clearly demonstrate a need in the marketplace. First-time authors are welcome." Accepts nonfiction translations. Submit outline/synopsis and 1-3 sample chapters. Reviews artwork/photos.
Recent Nonfiction Title: *The Nursing Mothers Companion*, by Kathleen Huggins.

HARVARD UNIVERSITY PRESS, 79 Garden St., Cambridge MA 02138. (617)495-2600. Director: Arthur J. Rosenthal. Editor-in-Chief: Maud Wilcox. Publishes hardcover and paperback originals and reprints. Publishes 120 titles/year. Publishes ms an average of 1 year after acceptance. Electronic submissions OK "at the discretion of our production department," but requires hard copy also. Computer printout submissions acceptable; no dot-matrix. Free book catalog and ms guidelines.
Nonfiction: "We publish only scholarly nonfiction." No fiction.

HARVEST HOUSE PUBLISHERS, 1075 Arrowsmith, Eugene OR 97402. (503)343-0123. Managing Editor: Eileen L. Mason. Acquisitions Editor: Joan Durham. Publishes hardcover, trade paperback and mass market originals and reprints. Averages 55-60 titles/year; receives 1,200+ submissions annually, 10% of books from first-time authors; 90% of books from unagented writers. Pays 14-18% royalty on wholesale price. Publishes book an average of 1 year after acceptance. Simultaneous and photocopied submissions OK. Computer print-out submissions acceptable; prefers letter-quality to dot-matrix. Reports in 10 weeks. Book catalog for 8½x11 SAE with 2 first class stamps; manuscript guidelines for SASE.
Nonfiction: Biography, how-to, illustrated book, juvenile, reference, self-help, textbook and gift books on Evangelical Christian religion. No cookbooks, theses, dissertations or music.
Recent Nonfiction Title: *The Seduction of Christianity*, by Dave Hunt and T.A. McMahon.
Fiction: Historical, mystery and religious. No romances or short stories. Query or submit outline/sysnopsis and sample chpaters.
Recent Fiction Title: *Bright Conquest*, by Ruth Livingston Hill (classic fiction).
Tips: Audience is women ages 25-40 and high school youth—evangelical Christians of all denominations.

HAYDEN BOOK CO., 10 Mulholland Dr., Hasbrouck Heights NJ 07604. (201)393-6000. Editorial Director: Michael Violano. Publishes hardcover and paperback originals and software. Averages 60 titles/year; receives 250 submissions annually. 15% of books from first-time authors; 90% of books from unagented writers. Average print order for a writer's first book is 5,000-20,000. Pays 12-15% royalty; offers advance. Publishes book an average of 5 months after acceptance. Simultaneous (if so identified) and photocopied submissions OK. Electronic submissions OK on 5¼" and 8" disks from microcomputer systems, but requires 3 hard copies also. Reports in 6 weeks. Free book catalog; ms guidelines for SASE.
Nonfiction: Publishes technician-level and engineering texts and references on microcomputers, digital electronics, electricity and robotics, computer science texts, books on programming, and applications for popular microcomputers.

HAZELDEN FOUNDATION, Dept. of Educational Materials, Box 176, Center City MN 55012. (612)257-4010. Managing Editor: Linda Peterson. Publishes hardcover and trade paperback originals and pamphlets. Predominantly direct mail. Averages 70 titles/year. Pays 7-9% royalty on retail price; buys some mss outright; offers $150-300+ advance. Publishes ms an average of 10 months after acceptance. Simultaneous and photocopied submissions OK. Computer printout submissions acceptable. "We immediately acknowledge receipt. A decision is usually made within 2 months."
Nonfiction: Reference, self-help, psychology, sociology and addictions. "We are seeking manuscripts of pamphlet or booklet length. The subject matter, ideally, will center around alcoholism, drug abuse or other addictions. The focus would be on the prevention, recovery from, or understanding of an addiction." Publishes for people recovering from an addiction and those close to them; people seeking information about alcoholism/drug abuse; and professionals who help such people. No personal stories or poetry. Submit outline/synopsis, introduction and 2 sample chapters.
Recent Nonfiction Title: *Of Course You're Angry*, by Gayle Rosellini and Mark Worden.

HEALTH PROFESSION DIVISION, McGraw-Hill Book Co., 1221 Avenue of the Americas, New York NY 10020. General Manager: Thomas Kothman. Publishes 60 titles/year. Pays on royalty basis.
Nonfiction: Textbooks, major reference books and continuing education materials in the field of medicine.
Recent Nonfiction Title: *Myology*, by Engle and Banker.

*HEART OF THE LAKES PUBLISHING, 2989 Lodi Rd., Interlaken NY 14847-0299. (607)532-4997. Contact: Walter Steesy. Publishes hardcover and trade paperback originals and hardcover and trade paperback reprints. Averages 10-15 titles/year; receives 10-15 submissions annually. 100% of books from unagented writers. Average print order for a writer's first book is 500-1,000. Subsidy publishes 50% of books, "depending on type of material and potential sales." Payment is "worked out individually." Publishes book an average of 1 year after acceptance. Simultaneous and photocopied submissions OK. Electronic submissions OK; contact in advance for information. Computer printouts acceptable. Reports in 1 week on queries; 2 weeks on mss. Current books flyer for business size SAE and 1 first class stamp; full catalog $3.
Nonfiction: New York state and New England history and genealogy. Query. Reviews artwork/photos.
Recent Nonfiction Title: *Peopling of Tompkins County*, by Carol Kammen.
Fiction: "Not looking for any, but will review any that deal with New York state historical subjects."

D.C. HEATH & CO., 125 Spring St., Lexington MA 02173. (617)862-6650. President: Loren Korte. College Division Editor-in-Chief: Bruce Zimmerli. General Manager Lexington Books: Robert D. Bovenschulte. College Division. Editor-in-Chief: Barbara Piercecchi. Vice President/General Manager—Electronics Publishing Division: Thomas Haver. Editor-in-Chief—School Division: Roger Rogalin. Publishes hardcover and paperback textbooks (grades kindergarten through college), professional scholarly, and software. Averages 300 titles/year. Offers standard royalty rates. Query. Publishes book an average of 1 year after acceptance. Electronic submissions OK if compatible with Wang and IBM. Computer printout submissions acceptable;prefers letter-quality to dot-matrix.

Textbooks: Texts at the college level in history, political science, chemistry, math, biology, physics, economics, modern languages, English, business, and computer science. Also publishes professional reference books: "Advanced-level research studies in the social sciences, library science, and in technical fields (Lexington Books)." Length varies.

Tips: Queries/mss may be routed to other editors in the publishing group.

HEINLE & HEINLE PUBLISHERS, INC., Subsidiary of Linguistics International, Inc., 20 Park Plaza, Boston MA 02216. (617)451-1940. President: Charles H. Heinle. Editor-in-Chief: Stanley Galek. Publishes books and software. Averages 15 titles/year; receives 50-60 submissions annually. 50% of books from first-time authors; 100% of books from unagented writers. Pays 6-15% royalty on net price; no advance. Publishes book an average of 18 months after acceptance. Electronic submissions OK via IBM, but requires hard copy also. Computer printout submissions acceptable; prefers letter-quality to dot-matrix. Reports immediately on queries; 2 weeks on mss. Free book catalog; ms guidelines for SASE.

Nonfiction: Textbook. "Foreign language and English as a second or foreign language text materials. Before writing the book, submit complete prospectus along with sample chapters, and specify market and competitive position of proposed text."

Recent Nonfiction Title: *Impression/Expression*, by Wolff von Schmidt, Gerhard P. Knapp and Mona Knapp.

Tips: "Introductory college foreign language textbooks have the best chance of selling to our firm."

HELIX PRESS, 4410 Hickey, Corpus Christi TX 78413. (512)852-8834. Editor: Aubrey R. McKinney. Publishes hardcover originals. Averages 3 titles/year. 100% of books from first-time authors; 100% of books from unagented writers. Pays 3-10% royalty on wholesale price. Publishes book an average of 6 months after acceptance. Simultaneous and photocopied submissions OK. Computer printout submissions acceptable; prefers letter-quality to dot-matrix. Reports in 1 month.

Nonfiction: Adult, science oriented. Subjects include physical science, natural science and cosmology, written for the layman. Emphasize the sciences—physical, natural (conservation, ecology, natural history), and field adventures. Query or submit outline/synopsis and sample chapters. Reviews artwork/photos.

Recent Nonfiction Title: *Back Through the Looking Glass*, by McKinney.

HENDRICKSON PUBLISHERS, INC., 137 Summit St., Box 3473, Peabody MA 01961-3473. (617)532-6546. Executive Editor: Dr. Ben Aker. Publishes hardcover and trade paperback originals, and hardcover and trade paperback reprints. Averages 6-12 titles/year; receives 85 submissions annually. 5% of books from first-time authors; 100% of books from unagented writers. Pays 5-15% royalty on wholesale and retail price. Average advance depends on project. Publishes book an average of 6 months after acceptance. Simultaneous (if so notified) and photocopied submissions OK. Computer printout submissions acceptable; prefers letter-quality to dot-matrix. Reports in 1 month on queries; 6 weeks on mss. Free book catalog. Ms guidelines for SASE.

Nonfiction: Religious. "We will consider any quality manuscripts within the area of religion, specifically related to Biblical studies and related fields. Popularly written manuscripts are not acceptable." Submit outline/synopsis and sample chapters or complete ms.

Recent Nonfiction Title: *The Spirit and the Church: Antiquity*, by Dr. Stanley Burgess.

‡HERALD PUBLISHING HOUSE, 3225 South Noland Rd., Box HH, Independence MO 64055. (816)252-5010. Subsidiaries include Independence Press. Editorial Director: Roger Yarrington. Publishes hardcover and trade paperback originals and hardcover and trade paperback reprints. Averages 30 titles/year; receives 700 submissions annually. 20% of books from first-time authors; 100% of books from unagented writers. Pays 5% maximum royalty on retail price. Offers average $400 advance. Publishes book an average of 14 months after acceptance. Computer printout submissions acceptable; no dot-matrix. Reports in 3 weeks on queries; 2 months on mss. Book catalog free on request.

Imprints: Herald Publishing House (nonfiction and fiction), Roger Yarrington, editorial director. Independence Press (nonfiction and fiction), Roger Yarrington, editorial director.

Nonfiction: Self-help and religious (RLDS Church) on Americana, history and religion. Herald House focus: history and doctrine of RLDS Church. Independence Press focus: regional studies (Midwest, Missouri). No submissions not related to RLDS Church (Herald House) or to Midwest regional studies (Independence Press). Query. Use *Chicago Manual of Style*. Reviews artwork/photos as part of ms package.

✝ The double dagger before a listing indicates that the listing is new in this edition. New markets are often the most receptive to freelance contributions.

Recent Nonfiction Title: *Ozark Almanac* (Independence Press), by A.E. Lucas (essays).
Tips: The audience for Herald Publishing House is members of the Reorganized Church of Jesus Christ of Latter Day Saints; for Independence Press, persons living in the Midwest or interested in the Midwest.

HERE'S LIFE PUBLISHERS, INC., Subsidiary of Campus Crusade for Christ, Box 1576, San Bernardino CA 92404. (714)886-7981. President and editorial director: Les Stobbe. Publishes hardcover and trade paperback originals and mass market paperback originals. Averages 30 titles/year; receives 400 submissions annually. 40% of books from first-time authors; 100% of books from unagented writers. Average print order for a writer's first book is 5,000. Pays 15% royalty on wholesale price. Offers $1,000-2,000 advance. Publishes book an average of 1 year after acceptance. Simultaneous and photocopied submissions OK. Electronic submissions OK if IBM compatible on disk; no special requirements on modem. Requires hard copy also. Computer printout submissions acceptable; no dot-matrix. Reports in 1 month on queries; 3 months on mss. Ms guidelines for SASE.
Nonfiction: Biography, how-to, illustrated book, reference and self-help. Needs "books in the areas of evangelism, Christian growth and family life; must reflect basic understanding of ministry and mission of Campus Crusade for Christ. No metaphysical or missionary biography." Query or submit outline/synopsis and sample chapters. Reviews artwork/photos.
Recent Nonfiction Title: *His Image . . . My Image*, by Josh McDowell.
Tips: "The writer has the best chance of selling our firm a sharply focused how-to book, that provides a Biblical approach to a felt need."

*HERITAGE BOOKS, INC., 3602 Maureen, Bowie MD 20715. (301)464-1159. Editorial Director: Laird C. Towle. Publishes hardcover and paperback originals and reprints. Averages 30 titles/year; receives 100 submissions annually. 25% of books from first-time authors; 100% of books from unagented writers. Subsidy publishes 5% or less of books. Pays 10% royalty on retail price; no advance. Publishes book an average of 9 months after acceptance. Simultaneous and photocopied submissions OK. Computer printout submissions acceptable; prefers letter-quality to dot-matrix. Reports in 1 month. Free book catalog.
Nonfiction: "We particularly desire nonfiction titles dealing with history and genealogy including how-to and reference works, as well as conventional histories and genealogies. The titles should be either of general interest or restricted to Eastern US. We prefer writers to query, submit an outline/synopsis, or submit a complete ms, in that order, depending on the stage the writer has reached in the preparation of his work." Reviews artwork/photos.
Recent Nonfiction Title: *Pioneers of Crawford County, Pennsylvania, 1788-1800*, edited by Robert D. Ilisevich.
Tips: "The quality of the book is of prime importance; next is its relevance to our fields of interest."

HEYDAY BOOKS, Box 9145, Berkeley CA 94709. (415)549-3564. Publisher: Malcolm Margolin. Publishes hardcover and trade paperback originals, trade paperback reprints. Averages 4-6 titles/year; receives 200 submissions annually. 50% of books from first-time authors; 100% of books from unagented writers. Pays 8-15% royalty on retail price; offers average $1,000 advance. Publishes book an average of 8 months after acceptance. Computer printout submissions acceptable; no dot-matrix. Reports in 1 week on queries; up to 5 weeks on mss. Book catalog for business size SASE and 1 first class stamp.
Nonfiction: How-to and reference. Subjects include Americana, history, nature and travel. "We publish books about native Americans, natural history, history, and recreation, with a strong California focus." Query. Reviews artwork/photos.
Recent Nonfiction Title: *Roads to Ride*, by Grant Peterson.
Fiction: Historical. Must have strong regional (California) focus. Query.
Recent Fiction Title: *Yamino-Kwiti*, by Donna Preble.
Tips: "Give good value, and avoid gimmicks. A useful, factual book about some aspect of California has the best chance of selling to our firm."

HOLIDAY HOUSE, INC., 18 E. 53rd St., New York NY 10022. (212)688-0085. Editorial Director: Margery Cuyler. Publishes hardcover originals. Averages 35-40 titles/year. Pays in royalties based on retail price; offers variable advance. Photocopied submissions OK. Computer printout submissions acceptable. Reports in 2 months.
Nonfiction and Fiction: General fiction and nonfiction for young readers—pre-school through high school. "It's better to submit the ms without art." Submit outline/synopsis and 3 sample chapters or complete ms. "No certified, insured or registered mail accepted."
Recent Nonfiction Title: *Ellis Island*, by Leonard Everett Fisher.
Recent Fiction Title: *The Summer of Mrs. Mac Gregor*, by Betty Renwright.

HOLLOWAY HOUSE PUBLISHING CO., 8060 Melrose Ave., Los Angeles CA 90046. (213)653-8060. Editorial Director: Raymond Friday Locke. Publishes paperback originals (95%) and reprints (5%). Averages 30 titles/year; receives 300-500 submissions annually. 50% of books from first-time authors; 80% of books from unagented writers. Average print order for a writer's first book is 15,000-20,000. Pays royalty based on retail price. Publishes book an average of 6 months after acceptance. Photocopied submissions OK. Electronic submissions OK on or compatible with IBM PC or WordStar, but requires hard copy also. Submit outline and 3 sample chapters. Reports in 6 weeks. Free book catalog and ms guidelines for SASE.

Nonfiction: Gambling and game books—from time to time publishes gambling books along the line of *How to Win, World's Greatest Winning Systems, Backgammon, How to Play and Win at Gin Rummy*, etc. Send query letter and/or outline with one sample chapter. Length: 60,000 words. Reviews artwork/photos as part of ms package.

Recent Nonfiction Title: *Eddie Murphy*, by Marianne Ruuth (biography).

Fiction: "Holloway House is the largest publisher of Black Experience literature. We are in the market for hard-hitting contemporary stories with easily identifiable characters and locations. Dialogue must be realistic. Some sex is acceptable but not essential (refer to writer's guidelines). Action, people and places must be thoroughly depicted and graphically presented." Black romance line newly launched—Holloway House Heartline Romances, designed to appeal to middle class black women paralleling other romance lines designed for white readers.

Recent Fiction Title: *Hot Snake Nights*, by Romare Duke.

HOUGHTON MIFFLIN CO., 2 Park St., Boston MA 02108. (617)725-5000. Editor-in-Chief: Nan A. Talese. Managing Editor: Linda Glick Conway. Hardcover and paperback originals and paperback reprints. Royalty of 6-7½% on retail price for paperbacks; 10-15% on sliding scale for standard fiction and nonfiction; advance varies widely. Publishes book an average of 18 months after acceptance. Publishes 110 titles/year. Simultaneous submissions and photocopied submissions OK. Computer printout submissions acceptable; no dot-matrix. "Proposals will not be returned without SASE." Reports in 6-8 weeks.

Nonfiction: Americana, natural history, animals, biography, cookbooks, health, history, how-to, politics, psychology and self-help. Query.

Recent Nonfiction Title: *House*, by Tracy Kidder.

Fiction: Historical, mainstream, literary, mystery, science fiction and suspense. Also publishes poetry. Query.

Recent Fiction Title: *The Handmaid's Tale*, by Margaret Atwood.

HOUGHTON MIFFLIN CO., Children's Trade Books, 2 Park St., Boston MA 02108. Contact: Editor. Publishes hardcover originals and trade paperback reprints (some simultaneous hard/soft). Averages 45-50 titles/year. Pays standard royalty; offers advance. Computer printout submissions acceptable; no dot-matrix; and no justified right margins. Reports in 1 month on queries; 2 months on mss. Free book catalog.

Nonfiction: Submit outline/synopsis and sample chapters. Reviews artwork/photos as part of ms package.

Fiction: Submit complete ms.

HOUNSLOW PRESS, A Division of Anthony R. Hawke Limited, 124 Parkview Ave., Willowdale, Ontario M2N 3Y5 Canada. (416)225-9176. President: Anthony Hawke. Publishes hardcover and trade paperback originals and reprints. Averages 6 titles/year; receives 500 submissions annually. 5% of books from first-time authors; 80% of books from unagented writers. Average print order for a writer's first book is 1,000. Pays 5-10% royalty on retail price; offers average $500 advance. Publishes book an average of 18 months after acceptance. Simultaneous and photocopied submissions OK. Reports in 2 weeks on queries; 1 month on mss. Free book catalog.

Nonfiction: Biography, "coffee table" book, cookbook, how-to, humor, illustrated book, juvenile, reference and self-help. Subjects include animals, art, business and economics, cooking and foods, health, history, hobbies, nature, philosophy, photography, politics, psychology, recreation, religion and travel. Publishes for a general audience. "We do well with cookbooks and photography books about Canadian themes." Query. Submit outline/synopsis and 4 sample chapters. Reviews artwork/photos.

Recent Nonfiction Title: *Eating for the Health of It—A New Look at Nutrition*, by Helen Bishop MacDonald.

Fiction: Adventure, humor and mainstream. Query.

Poetry: Query.

Recent Poetry Title: *Variorum*, by Doug Fetherling.

Tips: "Selp-help, humor, and controversial nonfiction sell the best in the retail market. We really want exceptional material from outstanding, talented writers—our standards are high."

*HOWELL-NORTH BOOKS, Subsidiary of Darwin Publications, 850 N. Hollywood Way, Burbank CA 91505. (818)848-0944. Editorial Director: Victoria Darwin. Publishes hardcover and trade paperback originals, and hardcover and trade paperback reprints. Averages 8 titles/year; receives 300 submissions annually. 50% of books from first-time authors; 95% of books from unagented writers. Subsidy publishes 10% of books. Pays 5-15% royalty on retail price. Publishes book an average of 18 months after acceptance. Computer printout submissions acceptable; prefers letter-quality to dot-matrix. Simultaneous and photocopied submissions OK. Reports within 2 weeks on queries; 6 weeks on mss. Free book catalog.

Nonfiction: Biography, "coffee table" book, and illustrated book. Subjects include Americana, history, hobbies, nature, recreation and travel (modes of transportation, specifically railroading). "We wish to broaden nonrailroad area; adventure, maritime and recreation will receive higher priority. Histories will not be considered unless they have a strong contemporary market." No personal travel guides, tips, etc., for Europe; autobiographies. Query strongly preferred or submit outline/synopsis and sample chapters. "Mss and queries will not be answered without SASE." Reviews artwork/photos.

Recent Nonfiction Title: *Rail City: Chicago, USA*, by George H. Douglas (history).

Tips: "Manuscript must be clean (good spelling, grammar, etc.) and research accurate. Problems in these areas cost time and money. Writer must be capable of following through with details as needed."

HUDSON HILLS PRESS, INC., Suite 1308, 230 5th Ave., New York NY 10001. (212)889-3090. President/Editorial Director: Paul Anbinder. Publishes hardcover and paperback originals. Averages 8 titles/year; receives 50-100 submissions annually. 15% of books from first-time authors; 90% of books from unagented writers. Average print order for a writer's first book is 3,000. Offers royalties of 5-8% on retail price. Average advance: $5,000. Publishes book an average of 1 year after acceptance. Simultaneous and photocopied submissions OK. Computer printout submissions acceptable; prefers letter-quality to dot-matrix. Reports in 1 month. Free book catalog.

Nonfiction: Art and photography. "We are only interested in publishing books about art, and photography and monographs." Query first, then submit outline/synopsis and sample chapters. Reviews artwork/photos.

Recent Nonfiction Title: *Arts of the North American Indian*.

‡HUMAN KINETICS PUBLISHERS, INC., Box 5076, Champaign IL 61820. (217)351-5076. Publisher: Rainer Martens. Publishes hardcover and trade paperback originals. Averages 80 titles/year; receives 300 submissions annually. 50% of books from first-time authors; 99% of books from unagented writers. Pays 10-15% royalty on wholesale price; offers average $500 advance. Publishes book an average of 9 months after acceptance. Simultaneous and photocopied submissions OK. Electronic submissions OK—all IBM, Apple (except MacIntosh) and C/PM, but requires hard copy also. Computer printout submissions acceptable; prefers letter-quality to dot-matrix. Reports in 2 months. Free book catalog and ms guidelines.

Imprints: Human Kinetics (nonfiction), Dr. Gwen Steigelman, editor. Leisure Press (nonfiction), Vic MacKenzie, editor. Life Enhancement Publications (nonfiction), Dr. Sue Wilmoth, editor.

Nonfiction: How-to, reference, self-help, technical and textbook. Subjects include health; recreation; sports, sport sciences and sports medicine; and physical education. Especially interested in books on wellness, including stress management, weight management, leisure management, and fitness; books on all aspects of sports technique or how-to books and coaching books; books which interpret the sport sciences and sports medicine, including sport physiology, sport psychology, sport pedagogy and sport biomechanics. No sport biographies, sport record or statistics books or regional books. Submit outline/synopsis and sample chapters. Reviews artwork/photos as part of ms package.

Recent Nonfiction Title: *Sport and Higher Education*, by Don Chu (reference).

Tips: "Books which accurately interpret the sport sciences and health research to coaches, athletes and fitness enthusiasts have the best chance of selling to us."

HUMANICS LIMITED, Suite 201, 1389 Peachtree St. NE, Atlanta GA 30309. (404)874-2176. President: Gary B. Wilson. Publishes softcover, educational and trade paperback originals. Averages 10 titles/year; receives 500 submissions annually. 20% of books from first-time authors; 100% of books from unagented writers. Average print order for a writer's first book is 5,000. Pays average 10% royalty on net sales; buys some mss outright. Publishes book an average of 9 months after acceptance. Computer printout submissions acceptable; prefers letter-quality to dot-matrix. Reports in 4 months. Free book catalog; ms guidelines for SASE.

Nonfiction: Self-help and teacher resource books. Subjects include health, psychology, sociology, education, business and New Age. Submit outline/synopsis and at least 3 sample chapters. Reviews artwork/photos as part of ms package.

Recent Nonfiction Title: *Tao of Leadership*, by John Heider (New Age).

Tips: "We are actively seeking authors with New Age material. We are not signing any new education contracts for the next two years."

*HUNTER HOUSE, INC., PUBLISHERS, Box 1302, Claremont CA 91711. General Manager: K.S. Rana. Publishes hardcover and trade paperback originals. Averages 12 titles/year; receives 200 submissions annually. 50% of books from first-time authors; 50% of books from unagented writers. Subsidy publishes 16% of books. "We determine whether an author should be subsidy published based upon subject matter, quality of the work, and if a subsidy is available." Pays 7½-12½% royalty on retail price. Offers $50 advance. Publishes book an average of 12-18 months after acceptance. Simultaneous and photocopied submissions OK. Electronic submissions OK on Osborne SSDD or transferrable formats. Computer printout submissions acceptable. Reports in 2 months on queries; 6 months on mss. Free book catalog.

Nonfiction: How-to, juvenile, and self-help. Subjects include health, psychology and "new science." Needs mss on "family and health, especially emerging areas in women's health, men's opening up and single parenting, older people, young adult, especially on health and intergenerational concerns." No evangelical, right-wrong political, Americana or esoteric. Query or submit outline/synopsis and sample chapters. Reviews artwork/photos.

Recent Nonfiction Title: *Tales of the Comet*, by Douglas Campbell and John Higgins (popular science).

Fiction: Erotica, and ethnic fiction, fantasy, and science fiction by women. Needs one or two historical/mythical/fantasy books by and for women. Query or submit outline/synopsis and sample chapters.

Recent Fiction Title: *On the Road to Baghdad*, by Güneli Gün.

Tips: "Manuscripts on family and health, or psychology for an aware public do well for us. Write simply, with established credentials and imagination. We respect writers and do not mistreat them. We ask for the same consideration."

HUNTINGTON HOUSE, INC., 1200 N. Market St., Shreveport LA 71107. (318)221-2767. President: Bill Keith. Publishes hardcover, trade paperback, and mass market paperback originals, trade paperback reprints and software. Averages 10-20 titles/year; receives 200 submissions annually. 50% of books from first-time authors; 20% of books from unagented writers. Average print order for a writer's first book is 10,000. Pays 10-15% royalty on wholesale and retail price, or $50; offers $100-2,500 advance. Publishes book an average of 6 months after acceptance. Simultaneous and photocopied submissions OK. Electronic submissions OK. Computer printout submissions acceptable. Reports in 2 months on queries; 3 months on mss. Free book catalog and ms guidelines.

Nonfiction: Biography, self-help and religious. "We publish self-help books and Christian growth books oriented to the Christian community." No New Age, occult, humanism or liberal theology. Query. Reviews artwork/photos.

Recent Nonfiction Title: *The Hidden Dangers of the Rainbow*, by Constance Cumbey.

Tips: "Write clear, crisp, exciting self-help or teaching manuscripts. Current Christian concerns books have the best chance of selling to our firm."

HURTIG PUBLISHERS LTD., 10560 105th St., Edmonton, Alberta T5H 2W7 Canada. (403)426-2359. Editor-in-Chief: Elizabeth Munroe. Hardcover and paperback originals and reprints. Averages 12 titles/year; receives 1,000 submissions annually. 15% of books from first-time authors; 90% of books from unagented writers. Typically pays 10% royalty on first 7,500 copies; 12% on next 7,500; 15% thereafter. Offers $500-1,000 advance on first book. Photocopied submissions OK. Computer printouts acceptable; "will read anything legible—must be hard copy printout." Prefers letter of inquiry first. Reports in 2-3 months. Free book catalog.

Nonfiction: Publishes biographies of well-known Canadians, Canadian history, humor, nature, topical Canadian politics and economics, reference (Canadian), and material about native Canadians "aimed at the nationalistic Canadian interested in politics, the North and energy policy." No poetry or original fiction. Query or submit outline/synopsis and 1-2 sample chapters; or submit complete ms. Very few unsolicited mss published. Looks for "suitability of topic to general publishing program; market interest in topic; qualifications of writer to treat that topic well; quality of writing." State availability of photos and/or illustrations to accompany ms.

Recent Nonfiction Title: *Pitseolak: A Canadian Tragedy*, by David F. Raine.

Tips: "Submissions must appeal to a very wide general audience, since the Canadian market is small."

IDEALS PUBLISHING CORP., Nelson Place at Elm Mill Pike, Box 14130, Nashville IN 37214-1000. Vice President of Publishing: Patricia Pingry. Publishes hardcover and paperback juvenile books, cookbooks, greeting booklets, and *Ideals* periodical. Pays on royalty and buy-out basis; offers advance only on assigned projects. Photocopied submissions OK. Reports in 4-6 weeks.

Nonfiction: Cookbooks. Length: 300 recipes.

Recent Nonfiction Title: *Wok Cookbook.*

Fiction: "Juveniles fall into one of 3 categories: seasonal (holiday theme), religious, or of some educational or moral value. They must stress the same traditional values as *Ideals* periodicals." Query. Length varies.

‡IMAGINE, INC., Box 9674, Pittsburgh PA 15226. (412)571-1430. President: R.V. Michelucci. Publishes trade paperback originals. Averages 3 titles/year; receives 10 submissions annually. 50% of books from first-time authors; 75% of books from unagented writers. Pays 6-10% royalty on retail price. Offers average $500 advance. Publishes book an average of 8 months after acceptance. Photocopied submissions OK. Computer printout submissions acceptable; no dot-matrix. Reports in 2 weeks on queries; 2 months on mss. Book catalog for #10 SAE with 1 first class stamp.

Nonfiction: "Coffee table" book, how-to, illustrated book and reference. Subjects include films, science fiction, fantasy and horror. Submit outline/synopsis and sample chapters or complete ms.

Recent Nonfiction Title: *The Complete Night of the Living Dead Filmbook*, by John Russo (film bio).

Fiction: Fantasy, horror, humor and science fiction.

Tips: "If I were a writer trying to market a book today, I would research my subject matter completely before sending a manuscript. Our audience is between ages 18-45 and interested in film, science fiction, fantasy and the horror genre."

INCENTIVE PUBLICATIONS, INC., 3835 Cleghorn Ave., Nashville TN 37215. (615)385-2934. Editor: Jennifer Goodman. Publishes paperback originals. Averages 15-20 titles/year; receives 350 submissions annually. 25% of books from first-time authors; 95% of books from unagented writers. Pays royalty or makes outright purchase. Publishes book an average of 1 year after acceptance. Photocopied submissions OK. Computer printout submissions acceptable; prefers letter-quality to dot-matrix. Reports in 2 weeks on queries; 3 weeks on mss. Free book catalog.
Nonfiction: Teacher resources and books on educational areas relating to children. Submit outline/synopsis and sample chapters. Reviews artwork/photos as part of ms package.
Recent Nonfiction Title: *The I'm Ready to Learn Series,* by Imogene Forte.

*INDIANA UNIVERSITY PRESS, 10th & Morton Sts., Bloomington IN 47405. (812)337-4203. Director: John Gallman. Publishes hardcover and paperback originals (75%) and paperback reprints (25%). Averages 90-100 titles/year. 30% of books from first-time authors. 98% from unagented writers. Average print order for a writer's first book is 1,500. Subsidy publishes (nonauthor) 10% of books. Pays maximum 10% royalty on retail price; offers occasional advance. Publishes book an average of 18 months after acceptance. Photocopied submissions OK. Electronic submissions OK if IBM compatible, but requires hard copy also. Computer printout submissions acceptable; no dot-matrix. Reports in 2 months. Free book catalog and ms guidelines.
Nonfiction: Scholarly books on humanities, history, philosophy, religion, Jewish studies, Black studies, translations, semiotics, public policy, film, music, linguistics, social sciences, regional materials, African studies, women's studies, and serious nonfiction for the general reader. Query or submit outline/synopsis and sample chapters. "Queries should include as much descriptive material as is necessary to convey scope and market appeal to us." Reviews artwork/photos.
Recent Nonfiction Title: *Semiotics and the Philosophy of Language,* by Umberto Eco.
Fiction: Query or submit outline/synopsis.

‡INDUSTRIAL PRESS INC., 200 Madison Ave., New York NY 10016. (212)889-6330. Director of Marketing: Woodrow Chapman. Publishes hardcover originals. Averages 3 titles/year; receives 15 submissions annually. 2% of books from first-time authors; 100% of books from unagented writers. Publishes book an average of 1 year after acceptance of finished ms. Electronic submissions OK if "compatible with composition material." Computer printout submissions acceptable; no dot-matrix. Reports in 1 month. Free book catalog.
Nonfiction: Reference and technical. Subjects include business and economics, science and engineering. "We envision professional engineers, plant managers, on-line industrial professionals responsible for equipment operation, professors teaching manufacturing, engineering, technology related courses as our audience." Especially looking for material on manufacturing technologies and titles on specific areas in manufacturing and industry. Computers in manufacturing are a priority. No energy-related books or how-to books. Query.
Recent Nonfiction Title: *Reliability for the Technologies,* by Leonard Doty.

INFORMATION RESOURCES PRESS, A Division of Herner and Company, Suite 700, 1700 N. Moore St., Arlington VA 22209. (703)558-8270. Vice President/Publisher: Ms. Gene P. Allen. Publishes hardcover originals. Averages 6 titles/year; receives 25 submissions annually. 80% of books from first-time authors; 100% of books from unagented writers. Pays 10-15% royalty on net cash receipts after returns and discounts. Publishes book an average of 1 year after acceptance. Simultaneous and photocopied submissions OK. Electronic submissions OK on Wang VS, but requires hard copy also. Reports in 2 weeks on queries; 2 months on mss. Free book catalog and ms guidelines.
Nonfiction: Reference, technical and textbook. Subjects include health and library and information science. Needs basic or introductory books on information science, library science, and health planning that lend themselves for use as textbooks. Preferably, the mss will have been developed from course notes. No works on narrow research topics (nonbasic or introductory works). Submit outline/synopsis and sample chapters or complete ms.
Recent Nonfiction Title: *Childhood Information Resources,* by Marda Woodbury (text, reference). Reviews artwork/photos.
Tips: "Our audience includes libraries (public, special, college and university); librarians, information scientists, college-level faculty; schools of library and information science; health planners, graduate-level students of health planning, and administrators; economists. Our marketing program is slanted toward library and information science and we can do a better job of marketing in these areas."

*INSTITUTE FOR THE STUDY OF HUMAN ISSUES, (ISHI Publications), 210 S. 13th St., Philadelphia PA 19107. (215)732-9729. Director of Publications: Betty Crapivinsky-Jutkowitz. Associate Director: Edward A. Jutkowitz. Managing Editor: Brad Fisher. Publishes hardcover and paperback originals and paperback reprints. Averages 18 titles/year; receives 150 submissions annually. 5-10% of books from first-time authors; 75% of books from unagented writers. Publishes 10% of books by partial subsidy. Pays 10-12½% royalty on wholesale price; no advance. Publishes book an average of 15 months after acceptance. Photocopied submissions OK. Electronic submissions OK via IBM PC-compatible 5¼" discs, but requires hard copy also. Computer printout submissions acceptable; no dot-matrix. Reports in 3 months. Book catalog and ms guidelines for SASE.

Nonfiction: Books on political science, history, anthropology, folklore, sociology, economics and drug studies, suitable for students and scholars in these fields. Accepts nonfiction translations. Submit outline/synopsis for initial consideration. Reviews artwork/photos as part of ms package.

Recent Nonfiction Title: *The President and Economic Policy*, edited by James Pfiffner.

Tips: "Latin American politics and current events, or Regional Americana are our strongest markets. Use up-to-date sources, documented controversies, good maps or photos, and a foreword by a well-known figure."

INTERCULTURAL PRESS, INC., Box 768, Yarmouth ME 04096. (207)846-5168. Contact: David S. Hoopes, Editor-in-Chief, 130 North Rd., Vershire VT 05079. (802)685-4448. Publishes hardcover and trade paperback originals. Averages 5-6 titles/year; receives 50-80 submissions annually. 50% of books from first-time authors; 95% of books from unagented writers. Pays royalty; occasionally offers small advance. Publishes book an average of 2 years after acceptance. Simultaneous and photocopied submissions OK. Electronic submissions OK, but requires hard copy also. Computer printout submissions acceptable; prefers letter-quality to dot-matrix. Reports in "several weeks" on queries; 2 months on mss. Free book catalog and ms guidelines.

Nonfiction: How-to, reference, self-help, textbook and theory. Subjects include business and economics, philosophy, politics, psychology, sociology, travel, or "any book with an international or domestic intercultural, multicultural or cross-cultural focus, i.e., a focus on the cultural factors in personal, social, political or economic relations. We want books with an international or domestic intercultural or multicultural focus, especially those on business operations (how to be effective in intercultural business activities) and education (textbooks for teaching intercultural subjects, for instance). Our books are published for educators in the intercultural field, business people who are engaged in international business, and anyone else who works in an international occupation or has had intercultural experience. No manuscripts that don't have an intercultural focus." Accepts nonfiction translations. Query "if there is any question of suitability (we can tell quickly from a good query)," or submit outline/synopsis. Do not submit mss unless invited.

Recent Nonfiction Title: *Good Neighbors: Communicating with the Mexicans* (self-help; theory).

*INTERGALACTIC PUBLISHING CO., Box 5013, Cherry Hill NJ 08034. (609)665-7577. Contact: Samuel W. Valenza, Jr. Intergalactic is now a subsidiary of Regal Communications Corporation, publishers of *Lottery Magazine*. Averages 3-10 titles/year; receives 10-20 submissions annually. 80% of books from first-time authors; 100% of books from unagented writers. Average print order for a writer's first book is 1,000-5,000. Subsidy publishes 30-40% of books. Publishes book an average of 1 year after acceptance. Electronic submissions OK via CP/M 2.0 Microsoft-Osborne, but requires hard copy also. Computer printout submissions acceptable; no dot-matrix.

Nonfiction: The publisher invites mss dealing with lottery in general and *systems of play* in particular. The company also produces and sells lottery and gaming related products and games, and invites submissions of ideas for same. Reviews artwork/photos.

Recent Nonfiction Title: *A History of: From Roman Times to Present*.

INTERNATIONAL MARINE PUBLISHING CO., 21 Elm St., Camden ME 04843. Editor-in-Chief: Jonathan Eaton. Publishes hardcover and paperback originals. Averages 18 titles/year; receives 500-700 submissions annually. 50% of books from first-time authors; 80% of books from unagented writers. Pays standard royalties, based on net price, with advances. Publishes book an average of 8 months after acceptance. Computer printout submissions acceptable; prefers letter-quality to dot-matrix. Reports in 6 weeks. Free book catalog; ms guidelines for SASE.

Nonfiction: "Mostly marine nonfiction but a wide range of subjects within that category: boatbuilding, boat design, yachting, seamanship, boat maintenance, maritime history, etc." All books are illustrated. "Material in all stages welcome. We prefer queries first with 2-3 sample chapters." Reviews artwork/photos as part of ms package.

Recent Nonfiction Title: *Cruising in Comfort*, by Jim Skoog.

Fiction: "Marine fiction of excellence will be considered."

Tips: "Freelance writers should be aware of the need for clarity, accuracy and interest."

‡INTERNATIONAL PUBLISHERS CO., INC., #1301, 381 Park Ave. S., New York NY 10016. (212)685-2864. President: Betty Smith. Publishes hardcover and trade paperback originals and trade paperback reprints. Averages 10-20 titles/year; receives 200 submissions annually. 15% of books from first-time authors. Pays 5% royalty on paperbacks; 10% royalty on cloth. No advance. Publishes book an average of 6 months after acceptance. Simultaneous and photocopied submissions OK. Computer printout submissions acceptable; prefers letter-quality to dot-matrix. Reports in 1 month on queries; 6 months on mss. Free book catalog. Ms guidelines $1 with SASE.

Nonfiction: Biography, reference and textbook. Subjects include Americana, economics, history, philosophy, politics, social sciences, and Marxist-Leninist classics. "Books on labor, black studies and women's studies based on Marxist science have high priority." Query or submit outline/synopsis and sample chapters. Reviews artwork/photos as part of ms package.

Recent Nonfiction Title: *May Day, A Short History, 1886-1986*, by Philip Foner.

Fiction: "We publish very little fiction. Query or submit outline/synopsis and sample chapters.

Poetry: "We rarely publish individual poets, usually anthologies."

Recent Poetry Title: *New and Old Voices of Wah' Kon-Tah*, editors Dodge and McCullough (contemporary native American Indian poetry).

INTERNATIONAL SELF-COUNSEL PRESS, LTD., 306 W. 25th St., North Vancouver, British Columbia V7N 2G1 Canada. (604)986-3366. President: Diana R. Douglas. Senior Editor: Pat Robertson. Publishes trade paperback originals. Averages 10-15 titles/year; receives 100 submissions annually. 50% of books from first-time authors; 100% of books from unagented writers. Average print order for a writer's first book is 4,000. Pays 10% royalty on wholesale price; no advance. Publishes book an average of 9 months after acceptance. Simultaneous and photocopied submissions OK. Computer printout submissions acceptable; prefers letter-quality to dot-matrix. Reports in 6 weeks. SASE (Canadian), IRCs. Free book catalog. Ms guidelines for SASE.

Nonfiction: Specializes in self-help and how-to books in law, business, reference, and psychology for lay person. Submit outline/synopsis and sample chapters. Follow Chicago *Manual of Style*.

Recent Nonfiction Title: *Photography and the Law*, by Christopher DuVernet.

INTERNATIONAL WEALTH SUCCESS, Box 186, Merrick NY 11566. (516)766-5850. Editor: Tyler G. Hicks. Averages 10 titles/year; receives 100+ submissions annually. 100% of books from first-time authors; 100% of books from unagented writers. Average print order for a writer's first book "varies from 500 and up, depending on the book." Pays 10% royalty on wholesale or retail price. Buys all rights. Usual advance is $1,000, but this varies, depending on author's reputation and nature of book. Publishes book 4 months after acceptance. Photocopied and dot-matrix submissions OK. Electronic submissions OK on Apple II or III, and IBM PC disks, but requires hard copy also. Computer printout submissions acceptable. Query. Reports in 1 month. Enclose return postage. Free book catalog and ms guidelines.

Nonfiction: *Self-Help and How-to:* "Techniques, methods, sources for building wealth. Highly personal, how-to-do-it with plenty of case histories. Books are aimed at the wealth builder and are highly sympathetic to his and her problems." Financing, business success, venture capital, etc. Length: 60,000-70,000 words. Reviews artwork/photos as part of ms package.

Recent Nonfiction Title: *How to Grow Rich in Real Estate*, by Nielsen.

Tips: "The writer has the best chance of selling our firm self-help moneymaking titles directed at small business ventures. Give good, real-life examples of the recommended techniques at work."

*THE INTERSTATE PRINTERS & PUBLISHERS, INC., 19 N. Jackson St., Box 50, Danville IL 61834. (217)446-0500. Acquisitions/Vice President-Editorial: Ronald L. McDaniel. Hardcover and paperback originals and software. Publishes about 50 titles/year. 50% of books from first-time authors; 100% of books from unagented writers. Subsidy publishes 5% of books. Usual royalty is 10%; no advance. Markets books by mail and exhibits. Publishes book an average of 9 months after acceptance. Computer printout submissions acceptable; prefers letter-quality to dot-matrix. Reports in 1-2 months. Free book catalog.

Nonfiction: Publishes high school and undergraduate college-level texts in vocational education (agriculture and agribusiness, trade and industrial education, home economics and business education). Also publishes professional references, texts, and supplementary materials in special education (including speech-language pathology, audiology, learning disabilities, neurological impairment). "We favor, but do not limit ourselves to, works that are designed for class—quantity rather than single-copy sale." Query or submit outline/synopsis and 2-3 sample chapters. Reviews artwork/photos as part of ms package.

Recent Nonfiction Title: *Sheep & Goat Science*, 5th ed.

Tips: "Freelance writers should be aware of strict adherence to the use of nonsexist language; fair and balanced representation of the sexes and of minorities in both text and illustrations; and discussion of computer applications wherever applicable. The writer has the best chance of selling an undergraduate college-level text. We are able to pinpoint the market for such a work."

INTERURBAN PRESS/TRANS ANGLO BOOKS, Box 6444, Glendale CA 91205. (213)240-9130. President: Mac Sebree. Publishes hardcover and trade paperback originals. Averages 10 titles/year; receives 50-75 submissions yearly. 35% of books from first-time authors; 99% of books from unagented writers. Average print order for a writer's first book is 2,000. Pays 5-10% royalty on retail price; offers no advance. Computer printout submissions acceptable. Reports in 2 weeks on queries; 2 months on mss. Free book catalog.

Nonfiction: Western Americana and transportation. Subjects include Americana, business and economics, history, hobbies and travel. "We are interested only in manuscripts about railroads, local transit, local history, and western American (gold mining, logging, early transportation, etc.). Also anything pertaining to preservation movement, nostalgia." Query. Reviews artwork/photos.
Recent Nonfiction Title: *Silver Short Line*, by Demoro/Wurm (history).
Tips: "We stick strictly to the topics already enumerated. Our audience is comprised of hobbyists in the rail transportation field ("railfans"); those interested in Western Americana (logging, mining, etc.); and students of transportation history, especially railroads and local rail transit (streetcars)."

*INTERVARSITY PRESS, Box 1400, Downers Grove IL 60515. (312)964-5700. Managing Editor: Andrew T. LePeau. Publishes hardcover and paperback originals. Averages 50 titles/year; receives 900 submissions annually. 15% of books from first-time authors; 95% of books from unagented writers. Subsidy publishes 8% of books. Pays 10% royalty on retail price; offers average $750 advance. Publishes book an average of 15 months after acceptance of final draft. "Indicate simultaneous submissions." Computer printout submissions acceptable; no dot-matrix. Reports in 4 months. Free book catalog; ms guidelines for SASE.
Nonfiction: "InterVarsity Press publishes books geared to the presentation of Biblical Christianity in its various relations to personal life, art, literature, sociology, psychology, philosophy, history and so forth. Though we are primarily publishers of trade books, we are cognizant of the textbook market at the college, university and seminary level within the general religious field. The audience for which the books are published is composed primarily of adult Christians. Stylistic treatment varies from topic to topic and from fairly simple popularizations to scholarly works primarily designed to be read by scholars." Accepts nonfiction translations. Query or submit outline/synopsis and 2 sample chapters.
Recent Nonfiction Title: *Sandy: A Heart for God*, by Leighton Ford.
Tips: "The writer has the best chance of selling our firm a book in that person's area of expertise, whether written at a popular or scholarly level. A journalistic approach is usually not sophisticated enough for us."

*IOWA STATE UNIVERSITY PRESS, 2121 S. State Ave., Ames IA 50010. (515)292-0140. Director: Richard Kinney. Managing Editor: Bill Silag. Hardcover and paperback originals. Averages 35 titles/year; receives 350 submissions annually. 98% of books from unagented writers. Average print order for a writer's first book is 2,000. Subsidy publishes (nonauthor) 10-50% of titles, based on sales potential of book and contribution to scholarship. Pays 10-12½-15% royalty on wholesale price; no advance. Publishes book an average of 1 year after acceptance. Simultaneous submissions OK, if advised; photocopied submissions OK. Electronic submissions OK, but requires hard copy also. Computer printout submissions acceptable; prefers letter-quality to dot-matrix. Reports in 4 months. Free book catalog; ms guidelines for SASE.
Nonfiction: Publishes biography, history, scientific/technical textbooks, the arts and sciences, statistics and mathematics, and medical and veterinary sciences. Accepts nonfiction translations. Submit outline/synopsis and several sample chapters, preferably not in sequence; must be double-spaced throughout. Looks for "unique approach to subject; clear, concise narrative; and effective integration of scholarly apparatus." Send contrasting b&w glossy prints to illustrate ms. Reviews artwork/photos.
Recent Nonfiction Title: *Gentlemen on the Prairie*, by Curt Harnack.
Tips: "The writer has the best chance of selling our firm scholarly monographs in veterinary medicine, engineering, etc."

‡IRON CROWN ENTERPRISES, Box 1605, Charlottesville VA 22902. (804)295-3918. Managing Editor: Terry K. Amthor. Publishes 8½x11" paperback and mass market paperback originals. Averages 20 titles/year; receives 20 submissions annually. 50% of books from first-time authors; 100% of books from unagented writers. Pays 2-4% royalty on wholesale price, or makes outright purchase for $1,000-2,000. Offers average $500 advance. Publishes book an average of 2-12 months after acceptance. Photocopied submissions OK. Computer printout submissions acceptable; prefers letter-quality to dot-matrix. Reports in 1 month on queries; 3 months on mss. Book catalog and ms guidelines for 4x9½ SAE.
Imprints: Questbooks (fiction), John Ruemmler, editor.
Fiction: Fantasy and science fiction fantasy role-playing supplements. Query.
Recent Fiction Title: *Riders of Rohan*, by Christian Gehman (fiction gamebook).
Tips: "Our basic audience is role-players, who are mostly aged 12-25. Iron Crown Enterprises publishes only a very specific sub-genre of fiction, namely fantasy role-playing supplements. We own the exclusive worldwide rights for such material based on J.R.R. Tolkien's *Hobbit* and *Lord of the Rings*. We also have a line of science-fiction supplements and are planning a line of fantasy books of our own. With our Questbooks we have a growing crossover into a general Fantasy readership. Questbooks, more similar to standard fiction, allows the reader to choose courses for the main character as he proceeds through alternative plotlines in the book. We are currently concentrating on a very specific market, and potential submissions must fall within stringent guidelines. Due to the complexity of our needs, please query. Extensive research is necessary."

ISHIYAKU EUROAMERICA, INC., Subsidiary of Ishiyaku Publishers, Inc., Tokyo, Japan: 11559 Rock Island Court, St. Louis MO 63043. (314)432-1933. President: Manuel L. Ponte. Publishes hardcover originals.

Averages 10 titles/year; receives 50 submissions annually. 75% of books from first-time authors; 100% of books from unagented writers. Average print order for a writer's first book is 3,000. Pays 10% minimum royalty on retail price or pays 35% of all foreign translation rights sales. Offers average $1,000 advance. Simultaneous submissions OK. Electronic submissions OK via IBM PC or Apple, but requires hard copy also. Computer printout submissions acceptable; no dot-matrix. Reports in 2 weeks on queries; 1 week on mss. Free book catalog; ms guidelines for SASE.

Nonfiction: Reference and medical/nursing textbooks. Subjects include health (medical and dental); psychology (nursing); and psychiatry. Especially looking for "all phases of nursing education, administration and clinical procedures." Query, or submit outline/synopsis and sample chapters or complete ms. Reviews artwork/photos.

Recent Nonfiction Title: *Ceramo-Metal Technology*, by Masahiro Kuwata (dental techniques atlas).

ISI PRESS, Subsidiary of Institute for Scientific Information, 3501 Market St., Philadelphia PA 19104. (215)386-0100. Director: Robert A. Day. Publishes hardcover and paperback originals. Averages 18 titles/ year; receives 75+ submissions annually. 10% of books from first-time authors; 90% of books from unagented writers. Pays 10% royalty on retail price; offers average $500 advance. Publishes book an average of 6 months after acceptance. Computer printout submissions acceptable; prefers letter-quality to dot-matrix. Reports in 1 week on queries; 6 weeks on mss.

Nonfiction: How-to and technical on communications. "We are developing a strong professional writing series. In general, we publish scholarly and professional books concerned with communications: writing, editing, publishing, etc." Query or submit outline/synopsis and 1 sample chapter.

Recent Nonfiction Title: *How to Write a Usable User Manual*, by Edmond H. Weiss.

*JALMAR PRESS, INC., 45 Hitching Post Dr., Bldg. 2, Rolling Hills Estates CA 90274-4297. (213)547-1240. Editor: Suzanne Mikesell. Publishes trade paperback originals. Averages 6 titles/year. Pays 5-15% on net sales. Subsidy publishes 50% of books. Publishes book an average of 18 months after acceptance. Simultaneous and photocopied submissions OK. Electronic submissions OK via WP disks; but requires hard copy also. Computer printout submissions acceptable. Reports in 1 month on queries; 3 months on mss. Free book catalog on request.

Nonfiction: Psychological, self-help, parenting and educational. Helpful, purposeful books for schools, families, adults and children, that assist positive mental health, self-esteem development. Right-brain/whole-brain materials. Peacemaking skills materials. No technical, academic-oriented manuscripts. Must be practical—reach a wide audience. Reviews artwork/photos as part of ms package. Query or submit outline/synopsis and 2 sample chapters or complete ms.

Recent Nonfiction Title: *Free Flight: Celebrating Your Right Brain*, by Barbara Meister Vitale.

JAMESTOWN PUBLISHERS, INC., Box 9168, Providence RI 02940. (401)351-1915 or 1-800-USA-READ. Senior Editor: Ted Knight. Publishes paperback and hardcover supplementary reading text/workbooks and software. Averages 25-30 titles/year; receives 100 + submissions annually. 10% of books from first-time authors; 100% of books from unagented writers. Average print order for a writer's first book is 10,000. Pays 10% royalty on retail price; buys some mss outright; offers variable advance. Publishes book an average of 1 year after acceptance. Computer printout submissions acceptable; prefers letter-quality to dot-matrix. Reports in 1 month. Free book catalog.

Nonfiction: Textbook. "Materials for improving reading and study skills for kindergarten through twelfth grade, college, and adult education." Submit outline/synopsis and sample chapters. Reviews artwork/photos as part of ms package.

Recent Nonfiction Title: *Heroes*, by Henry and Melissa Billings.

Fiction: "We occasionally use original fiction as the basis for comprehension exercises and drills." Submit outline/synopsis and sample chapters.

Tips: "We operate in a very clearly, narrowly defined subject area. The better a writer knows this field and the more familiar he or she is with our products, the better. Reading/study skills material paralleling our current skills breakdown, and exceptional and innovative/groundbreaking material in the same areas have the best chance of selling to our firm."

JH PRESS, Box 294, Village Station, New York NY 10014. (212)255-4713. Publisher: Terry Helbing. Publishes trade paperback originals. Averages 3 titles/year. Pays 6-10% royalty on retail price; offers average $100 advance. Publishes book an average of 9 months after acceptance. Simultaneous and photocopied submissions OK. Reports in 2 weeks. Free book catalog.

Nonfiction: Subjects include drama and theater. Studies of gay theater or gay plays. Query. Reviews artwork/photos as part of ms package.

Recent Nonfiction Title: *Gay Theatre Alliance Directory of Gay Plays*, by Terry Helbing.

Fiction: Drama and theater. Gay plays that have been produced but not previously published. Query.

Recent Fiction Title: *Last Summer at Bluefish Cove*, by Jane Chambers (play).

JOHNSON BOOKS/SPRING CREEK PRESS, 1880 S. 57th Ct., Boulder CO 80301. (303)443-1576. Editorial Director: Michael McNierney. Spring Creek Press: Scott Roederer. Publishes hardcover and paperback originals and reprints. Publishes 8-10 titles/year; receives 500 submissions annually. 30% of books from first-time authors; 100% of books from unagented writers. Average print order for a writer's first book is 5,000. Royalties vary. Publishes book an average of 1 year after acceptance. Good computer printout submissions acceptable; prefers letter-quality to dot-matrix. Reports in 1-2 months. Free book catalog; ms guidelines for SASE.
Nonfiction: General nonfiction, books on the West, environmental subjects, natural history, geology, archaeology, guidebooks, and outdoor recreation. "We are publishing a new series of books on fly-fishing under a separate imprint, Spring Creek Press." Accepts nonfiction translations. "We are primarily interested in books for the informed popular market, though we will consider vividly written scholarly works. As a small publisher, we are able to give every submission close personal attention." Query first or call. Accepts outline/synopsis and 3 sample chapters. Looks for "good writing, thorough research, professional presentation and appropriate style. Marketing suggestions from writers are helpful." Reviews artwork/photos.
Recent Nonfiction Title: *The Compleat Angler's Catalog*, by Scott Roederer.
Tips: Spring Creek Press imprint will publish series of books on fly-fishing.

JONATHAN DAVID PUBLISHERS, 68-22 Eliot Ave., Middle Village NY 11379. (718)456-8611. Editor-in-Chief: Alfred J. Kolatch. Publishes hardcover and paperback originals. Averages 25-30 titles/year; receives 600 submissions annually. 50% of books from first-time authors; 75% of books from unagented writers. Pays standard royalty. Publishes book an average of 1 year after acceptance. Computer printout submissions acceptable; no dot-matrix. Reports in 3 weeks.
Nonfiction: Adult nonfiction books for a general audience. Cookbooks, cooking and foods, how-to, baseball and football, reference, self-help, Judaica. Query.
Recent Nonfiction Title: *The Ultimate Baseball Trivia Book*, by Richard Vickroy and Herbert Ruth.

JUDSON PRESS, Valley Forge PA 19481. (215)768-2117. Senior Editor: Phyllis A. Frantz. Publishes hardcover and paperback originals. Averages 10-15 titles/year; receives 500 queries annually. Average print order for a writer's first book is 3,500. 10% royalty on retail price or flat fee. Publishes book an average of 9 months after acceptance. Computer printout submissions acceptable; no dot-matrix. Query with outline and 1 sample chapter. Reports in 6 months. Enclose return postage. Free book catalog; ms guidelines for SASE.
Nonfiction: Adult religious nonfiction of 30,000-80,000 words. "Our audience is mostly church members who seek to have a more fulfilling personal spiritual life and want to serve Christ in their churches and other relationships."
Recent Nonfiction Title: *Letters to a Retired Couple*, by David and Vera Mace.

‡KALMBACH PUBLISHING CO., 1027 N. 7th St., Milwaukee WI 53233. (414)272-2060. Books Editor: Bob Hayden. Publishes hardcover and paperback originals and paperback reprints. Averages 6 titles/year; receives 25 submissions annually. 85% of books from first-time authors; 100% of books from unagented writers. Offers 5-8% royalty on retail price. Average advance: $1,000. Publishes book an average of 18 months after acceptance. Computer printout submissions acceptable; prefers letter-quality to dot-matrix. Reports in 8 weeks. Free book catalog.
Nonfiction: Hobbies, how-to, and recreation. "Our book publishing effort is in railroading and hobby how-to-do-it titles *only.*" Query first. "I welcome telephone inquiries. They save me a lot of time, and they can save an author a lot of misconceptions and wasted work." In written query, want to see "a detailed outline of two or three pages and a complete sample chapter with photos, drawings, and how-to text." Reviews artwork/photos.
Recent Nonfiction Title: *The Historical Guide to North American Railroads*, by George H. Drury.
Tips: "Our books are about half text and half illustrations. Any author who wants to publish with us must be able to furnish good photographs and rough drawings before we'll consider contracting for his book."

KAR-BEN COPIES INC., 6800 Tildenwood Ln., Rockville MD 20852. (301)984-8733. President: Judy Groner. Publishes hardcover and trade paperback originals. Averages 8 titles/year; receives 150 submissions annually. 50% of books from first-time authors; 100% of books from unagented writers. Average print order for a writer's first book is 5,000. Pays 6-8% royalty on gross sales; makes negotiable outright purchase; offers average $1,000 advance. Publishes book an average of 1 year after acceptance. Computer printout submissions acceptable. Reports in 1 week on queries; 1 month on mss. Free book catalog; ms guidelines for SASE.
Nonfiction: Jewish juvenile. Subjects include religion and Jewish history texts. Especially looking for books on Jewish history, holidays, and customs for children—"early childhood and elementary." Query with outline/synopsis and sample chapters or submit complete ms. Reviews artwork/photos as part of ms package.
Recent Nonfiction Title: *The Yanor Torah*, by Erwin and Agnes Herman (true Holocaust adventure story).
Fiction: Adventure, fantasy, historical and religious (all Jewish juvenile). Especially looking for Jewish holiday and history-related fiction for young children. Submit outline/synopsis and sample chapters or complete ms.
Recent Fiction Title: *Hanukkah Cat*, by Chaya Burstein (juvenile fiction).

Tips: "We envision Jewish children and their families, and juveniles interested in learning about Jewish subjects, as our audience."

‡*WILLIAM KAUFMANN, INC., 95 1st St., Los Altos CA 94022. Editor-in-Chief: William Kaufmann. Hardcover and paperback originals and reprints. Subsidy publishes 10% of books. "Generally offers standard minimum book contract of 10-12½-15% but special requirements of book may call for lower royalties"; no advance. Averages 15 titles/year. Reports in 1-2 months. Free book catalog.
Nonfiction: "We specialize in not being specialized; we look primarily for originality and quality." Publishes Americana, art, biography, business, computer science, economics, history, how-to, humor, medicine and psychiatry, psychology, scientific, and textbooks. Does not want to see cookbooks, novels, poetry, inspirational/religious or erotica. Query. Discourages submission of unsolicited manuscripts.
Recent Nonfiction Title: *The High-Tech Career Book*, by Betsy A. Collard.

*KENT STATE UNIVERSITY PRESS, Kent State University, Kent OH 44242. (216)672-7913. Director: John T. Hubbell. Editor: Jeanne West. Publishes hardcover and paperback originals and some reprints. Averages 15-20 titles/year. Subsidy publishes 25% of books. Standard minimum book contract on net sales; rarely offers advance. "Always write a letter of inquiry before submitting manuscripts. We can publish only a limited number of titles each year and can frequently tell in advance whether or not we would be interested in a particular manuscript. This practice saves both our time and that of the author, not to mention postage costs. If interested we will ask for complete manuscript. Decisions based on in-house readings and two by outside scholars in the field of study." Computer printout submissions acceptable; prefers letter-quality. Reports in 6-10 weeks. Enclose return postage. Free book catalog.
Nonfiction: Especially interested in "scholarly works in history of high quality, particularly any titles of regional interest for Ohio. Also will consider scholarly biographies, literary studies, archeological research, the arts, and general nonfiction."
Recent Nonfiction Title: *"The Best School in the World": West Point, the Pre-Civil War Years, 1833-1866*, by James L. Morrison, Jr. (history).

‡MICHAEL KESEND PUBLISHING, LTD., 1025 5th Ave., New York NY 10028. (212)249-5150. Director: Michael Kesend. Publishes hardcover and trade paperback originals, and hardcover and trade paperback reprints. Averages 4-6 titles/year; receives 150 submissions annually. 50% of books from first-time authors; 50% of books from unagented writers. Pays 3-12½% royalty on wholesale price or retail price, or makes outright purchase for $500 minimum. Advance varies. Publishes book an average of 18 months after acceptance. Simultaneous and photocopied submissions OK. Computer printout submissions acceptable; prefers letter-quality to dot-matrix. Reports in 2 months on queries; 3 months on mss. Book catalog free on request.
Nonfiction: Biography, how-to, illustrated book, self-help and sports. Subjects include animals, health, history, hobbies, nature, sports, travel, the environment, and guides to several subjects. Needs sports, health self-help and environmental awareness guides. No photography mss. Submit outline/synopsis and sample chapters. Reviews artwork/photos.
Recent Nonfiction Title: *Butch Beard's Basic Basketball*, by Butch Beard (how to play and coach basketball).
Fiction: Adventure, erotica, ethnic, experimental, historical, humor, mystery, suspense and sports fiction. No science fiction or romance. Submit outline/synopsis and sample chapters.
Recent Fiction Title: *Asylum Piece*, by Anna Kavan (literary fiction).
Tips: "It helps a great deal to have a targeted audience, i.e., literary as for *Asylum Piece*. If I were a writer trying to market a book today, I would decide who my audience was and try to write towards them or at least meet them halfway."

KEY PORTER BOOKS LIMITED, 70 The Esplanade, Toronto, Ontario M5E 1R2 Canada. (416)862-7777. Editor-in-Chief: Phyllis Bruce. Publishes trade and paperback originals. Averages 30 titles/year; receives 200+ submissions annually. 5% of books from first-time authors; 30% of books from unagented writers. Pays in royalties or outright purchase. Advance varies widely. Publishes book 1-2 years after acceptance. Simultaneous and photocopied submissions OK. Free book catalog.
Nonfiction: Biography, "coffee table" book, cookbook, how-to, humor, illustrated book and self-help. Subjects include Americana, animals, art, business and economics, cooking and foods, health, history, hobbies, music, nature, photography, politics, recreation, sports and travel. No fiction or juvenile books. Submit outline/synopsis and sample chapters or complete ms. Reviews artwork/photos.
Recent Nonfiction Title: *Railway Country*, by Dudley Witney and Brian D. Johnson.
Tips: "Illustrated, general adult nonfiction with particular relevance to the international market has the best chance of selling to our firm."

B. KLEIN PUBLICATIONS, Box 8503, Coral Springs FL 33065. (305)752-1708. Editor-in-Chief: Bernard Klein. Hardcover and paperback originals. Specializes in directories, annuals, who's who type of books, bibli-

ography, business opportunity, reference books. Averages 15-20 titles/year. Pays 10% royalty on wholesale price, "but we're negotiable." Advance "depends on many factors." Markets books by direct mail and mail order. Simultaneous and photocopied submissions OK. Reports in 1-2 weeks. SASE. Book catalog for SASE.
Nonfiction: Business, hobbies, how-to, reference, self-help, directories and bibliographies. Query or submit outline/synopsis and sample chapters or complete ms.
Recent Nonfiction Title: *Mail Order Business Directory* 14th edition.

KNIGHTS PRESS, Box 454, Pound Ridge NY 10576. Publisher: Elizabeth G. Gershman. Publishes trade paperback originals. Averages 12-18 titles/year; receives 500 submissions annually. 50% of books from first-time authors; 75% of books from unagented writers. Pays 10 plus escalating royalty on retail price; offers average $500 advance. Publishes book an average of 1 year after acceptance. Photocopied submissions OK. Computer printout submissions acceptable; prefers letter-quality to dot-matrix. Reports in 1 month on queries; 3 months on mss. Book catalog and ms guidelines for business size SASE.
Fiction: Adventure, confession, erotica (very soft-core considered), ethnic, experimental, fantasy, gothic, historical, horror, humor, mystery, romance, science fiction, suspense and western. "We publish only gay men's fiction; must show a positive gay lifestyle or positive gay relationship." No young adult or children's; no pornography; no formula plots, especially no formula romances; or no hardcore S&M. Query a must. Submit outline/synopsis and sample chapters. Do not submit complete manuscript unless requested.
Recent Fiction Title: *The Secrets of Mabel Eastlake*, by Donald S. Olson.
Tips: "We are interested in well-written, well-plotted gay fiction. We are looking only for the highest quality gay literature."

ALFRED A. KNOPF, INC., 201 E. 50th St., New York NY 10022. (212)751-2600. Senior Editor: Ashbel Green. Children's Book Editor: Ms. Frances Foster. Publishes hardcover and paperback originals. Published 218 titles in 1985. 15% of books from first-time authors; 40% of books from unagented writers. Royalties and advance "vary." Publishes book an average of 10 months after acceptance. Simultaneous (if so informed) and photocopied submissions OK. Reports in 1 month. Book catalog for SASE.
Nonfiction: Book-length nonfiction, including books of scholarly merit. Preferred length: 40,000-150,000 words. "A good nonfiction writer should be able to follow the latest scholarship in any field of human knowledge, and fill in the abstractions of scholarship for the benefit of the general reader by means of good, concrete, sensory reporting." Query. Reviews artwork/photos.
Recent Nonfiction Title: *Distant Neighbors*, by A. Riding (current affairs).
Fiction: Publishes book-length fiction of literary merit by known or unknown writers. Length: 30,000-150,000 words. Submit complete ms.
Recent Fiction Title: *The Lonely Silver Rain*, by J.D. MacDonald.

KNOWLEDGE INDUSTRY PUBLICATIONS, INC., 701 Westchester Ave., White Plains, NY 10604. (914)328-9157. Vice President/Publisher: Barbara Miller. Publishes hardcover and paperback originals. Averages 30 titles/year; receives 80-90 submissions annually. 50% of books from first-time authors; 100% of books from unagented writers. Average print order for a writer's first book is 2,500. Offers 5-10% royalty on wholesale price; also buys mss by outright purchase for minimum $500. Offers negotiable advance. Publishes book an average of 6 months after acceptance. Photocopied submissions OK. Electronic submissions OK via IBM, but requires hard copy also. Computer printout submissions acceptable; no dot-matrix. Reports in 2 weeks. Free book catalog; ms guidelines for SASE.
Nonfiction: Business and economics. Especially needs "communication and information technologies, TV and video, library and information science, information management." Query first, then submit outline/synopsis and sample chapters. Reviews artwork/photos as part of ms package.
Recent Nonfiction Title: *Electronic Publishing Plus*.

JOHN KNOX PRESS, 341 Ponce de Leon Ave. NE, Atlanta GA 30365. (404)873-1549. Editorial Director: Walter C. Sutton. Acquisitions Editor: John G. Gibbs. Averages 24 nonfiction titles/year. Pays royalty on income received; no advances. 20% of books from first-time authors; 100% of books from unagented writers. Publishes book an average of 9-12 months after acceptance. Electronic submissions OK on Wang VS 90. Computer printout submissions acceptable. Free catalog and "Guidelines for a Book Proposal" on request with SASE.
Nonfiction: "We publish textbooks, resource books for ministry, and books to encourage Christian faith, in subject areas including biblical studies, theology, ethics, psychology, counseling, worship, and the relationship of science and technology to faith." Query or submit outline/synopsis and sample chapters.

KARL KRAMER VERLAG GMBH & CO., Rotebuhlstrasse 40, D-7000, Stuttgart, Germany. 49-711-62-08-93. President/Editorial Director: Karl H. Kramer. Publishes hardcover and paperback originals. Averages 15 titles/year; receives 29 submissions annually. 90% of books from first-time authors; 95% of books from unagented writers. Pays 10% minimum royalty; offers $500-$1,000 advance. Publishes book an average of 2

years after acceptance. Electronic submissions OK via Linotronic, but requires hard copy also. Computer printout submissions acceptable; prefers letter-quality to dot-matrix. Reports in 2 months. Free book catalog.
Nonfiction: Architecture. Submit outline/synopsis and sample chapters or complete ms. Reviews artwork/photos.
Recent Nonfiction Title: *Space and Form*, by Juergen Joedicke.

ROBERT E. KRIEGER PUBLISHING CO. INC., Box 9542, Melbourne FL 32902-9542. (305)724-9542. Executive Assistant: Ann M. Krieger. Publishes hardcover and paperback originals and reprints. Averages 120 titles/year; receives 50-60 submissions annually. 10% of books from first-time authors; 100% of books from unagented writers. Pays royalty on net realized price. Publishes book an average of 8 months after acceptance. Computer printout submissions acceptable; prefers letter-quality to dot-matrix. Reports in 1 month. Free book catalog.
Nonfiction: College reference, technical, and textbook. Subjects include business and economics, history, music, philosophy, psychology, recreation, religion, sociology, sports, chemistry, physics, engineering and medical. Reviews artwork/photos.
Recent Nonfiction Title: *Public History: An Introduction*, edited by Barbara J. Howe and Emory Kemp.

LACE PUBLICATIONS INC., Box 10037, Denver CO 80210-0037. (303)778-7702. Managing Editor: Artemis OakGrove. Publishes trade paperback originals and reprints. Receives 100 submissions annually. Average print order for a writer's first book is 2,000. Pays royalty. "Each project is negotiated on an individual basis. We will eventually offer advances. Lace no longer accepts unsolicited queries, manuscripts, poetry or short stories." Publishes book an average of 15 months after acceptance.
Fiction: Entertainment for lesbians.
Recent Fiction Title: *A Third Story*, by Carole Taylor.

DAVID S. LAKE PUBLISHERS, 19 Davis Dr., Belmont CA 94002. (415)592-7810. Editorial Director: Carol Haggerty. Editorial and Marketing Director: Ina Tabibian (Fearon Teacher Aid). Averages 100-120 titles/year. Pays royalty or fee outright. Photocopied submissions OK. Computer printout submissions acceptable; prefers letter-quality to dot-matrix. Reports in 1 month. Free book catalog.
Nonfiction: Educational. Query or submit outline/synopsis.
Recent Nonfiction Title: *Reinforcing Reference Skills*.
Fiction: "We are looking for easy-to-read fiction suitable for middle school and up. We prefer the major characters to be young adults or adults. Solid plotting is essential." Length: 20,000 words maximum. Submit complete ms.
Recent Fiction Title: *Vanished*, (a mystery double fastback).

LAKE VIEW PRESS, Box 578279, Chicago IL 60657. (312)935-2694. Director: Paul Elitzik. Publishes hardcover and paperback originals. Averages 6 titles/year; receives 100 submissions annually. 10% of books from first-time authors; 100% of books from unagented writers. Average print order for a writer's first book is 3,000. Pays 8-10% royalty on retail price. No advance. Publishes book an average of 1 year after acceptance. Computer printout submissions acceptable; no dot-matrix. Do not send insured. Reports in 2 months. Catalog for SAE with 2 first class stamps.
Nonfiction: Films, Middle East, Afro-American, labor, women, and Asia. Accepts nonfiction translations. "Our audience interest is scholarly books on current affairs, politics and the contemporary cultural scene." Submit outline, and author biography.
Recent Nonfiction Title: *Solidarity Forever: An Oral History of the IWW*, by Stewart Bird, Dan Georgahas and Deborah Shaffer.

LAKEWOOD BOOKS, 4 Park Ave., New York NY 10016. Editorial Director: Donald Wigal, Ph.D. Publishes only 64-page "Impulse" originals. "We are not a trade book publisher." Publishes up to 38 titles/year; receives 100 submissions annually. 95% of books from unagented writers. Average print order for a writer's first book is 10,000. Pays on a "qualified" work-for-hire basis. "Few exceptions." Publishes book an average of 1 year after acceptance. Simultaneous and photocopied submissions OK. Electronic submissions OK via PC-DOS 3.1 or earlier, but requires hard copy also. Computer printout submissions acceptable; prefers letter-quality to old dot-matrix. Reports in 2 months. Ms guidelines for SASE.
Nonfiction: "Our books are apparently bought by women who have families, or are attracted to a rather middle-of-the-road life style. Our titles are mainly self-help (exercise, diet) and informational (finances, how-to). We avoid controversial topics. Nonfiction which ties in with specific products welcomed by query (e.g., '100 Tips on Using Brand X in the Garden')." No fiction, poetry, astrology, puzzle, cookbook or sport titles needed at present. Query. Author should have "an awareness of our format (limitations and potential), and sensitivity to the mass market. Concise overview best." Reviews artwork/photos.
Recent Nonfiction Title: *Shape Up Hips and Thighs*.
Tips: "The rare writer who understands the Impulse buyer will not submit books to us that are more fitting for

the trade book publisher. Nearly *all* the submissions we receive are inappropriate for our Impulse market. We have published about two hundred titles and only two have been results of over the transom submissions."

*PETER LANG PUBLISHING, INC., 62 W. 45th St., New York NY 10036. (212)302-6740. Subsidy of Verlag Peter Lang AG, Bern, Switzerland. Editor-in-Chief: Jay Wilson. Publishes hardcover and trade paperback originals, and hardcover and trade paperback reprints. Averages 120 titles/year; receives 600 submissions annually. 75% of books from first-time authors; 98% of books from unagented writers. Subsidiary publishes 50% of books. All subsidies are guaranteed repayment plus profit (if edition sells out) in contract. Subsidy published if ms is highly specialized and author relatively unknown. Pays 10-30% royalty on net price. Translators get flat fee plus percentage of royalties. No advance. Publishes book an average of 1 year after acceptance. Photocopied submissions OK. Computer printout submissions acceptable; prefers letter-quality to dot-matrix. Reports in 2 months on queries; 4 months on mss. Free book catalog and ms guidelines.
Nonfiction: Biography, reference, textbook and scholarly monograph. Subjects include Americana, art, business and economics, health, history, music, philosophy, politics, psychology, religion, sociology and biography. All books are scholarly monographs, textbooks, reference books, reprints of historic texts, critical editions or translations. "We are expanding and are receptive to any scholarly project in the humanities and social sciences." No mss shorter than 200 pages; college textbooks. Submit complete ms.
Recent Nonfiction Title: *People of the High Country*, by Gary Wright (archaeology).
Fiction: Critical editions and English translations of classics in any language. "We publish primarily nonfiction." Submit outline/synopsis and complete ms.
Recent Fiction Title: *Summer Tales*, by Johann Beer (short story collection).
Poetry: Scholarly critical editions only. Submit complete ms.
Recent Poetry Title: *The Poetry of Dino Frescobaldi*, by Joseph Alessia.
Tips: "Besides our commitment to specialist academic monographs, we are one of the few U.S. publishers who publish books in most of the modern languages."

LARSON PUBLICATIONS, INC., 4936 Route 414, Burdett NY 14818. (607)546-9342. Director: Paul Cash. Publishes hardcover and trade paperback originals and hardcover and trade paperback reprints. Averages 4-5 titles/year. Average print order for a writer's first book is 3,000-4,000. Pays 10% minimum royalty of cash received, flexible maximum on wholesale price. Reports "as soon as possible—no full-time reader." Will not consider unsolicited manuscripts.
Nonfiction: Subjects include alternative education, health, parenting, philosophy and religion. Query only; do not send complete ms.
Recent Nonfiction Title: *The Notebooks of Paul Brunton: Perspectives*, by Paul Brunton (philosophy/spiritual).
Fiction: Fantasy, mystical allegory, religious and science fiction. "We are just beginning to explore this area." No mss unrelated to spiritual self-discovery. Query only; do not send unsolicited ms.
Tips: "Our audience is independent, spiritually-minded, all ages."

LEARNING ENDEAVORS, 1616 3rd St. N, St. Cloud MN 56301. (612)432-0710. Editor: W.E. Bach. Publishes hardcover and trade paperback originals and mass market paperback originals. Averages 1-3 titles/year; receives 25 submissions annually. 50% of books from first-time authors; 100% of books from unagented writers. Pays 10% maximum royalty on wholesale price. Publishes manuscript an average of 1 year after acceptance. Photocopied submissions OK. Computer printout submissions acceptable. Reports in 3 weeks on queries; 2 months on mss.
Nonfiction: Education and special education textbooks. "We publish material which is used by the teacher of students with learning difficulties. Books should be usable in the classroom and pointed toward a single or multiple grades." Query.
Recent Nonfiction Title: *Study Skills: Learning Made Easier*, by Swiderski/Zettel (study guide).
Tips: "We need a workbook for junior and senior high school students with learning difficulties, with accurate and easy guidelines for use."

LEARNING PUBLICATIONS, INC., Box 1326, Holmes Beach FL 33509. (813)778-5524. Publisher: Edsel Erickson. Publishes hardcover and trade paperback originals. Averages 15 titles/year; receives 500 w submissions annually. 75% of books from first-time authors; 90% of books from unagented writers. Average print order for a writer's first book is 1-2,000. Pays 5% royalty on income received from sales. No advance. Publishes book an average of 18 months after acceptance. Photocopied submissions OK. Electronic submissions OK via IBM compatible, but requires hard copy also. Computer printout submissions acceptable; prefers letter-quality to dot-matrix. Reports in 3 weeks on queries; 3 months on mss. Free book catalog; ms guidelines for SASE.
Nonfiction: How-to (for professionals); self-help (for general public); technical; textbooks on art, psychology, sociology; and reference books for counselors, teachers and school administrators. Books to help parents of children with reading problems and special needs (impaired, gifted, etc.), or art activity books for teachers. Query with outline/synopsis and sample chapters.

Recent Nonfiction Title: *Relapse Prevention Workbook: For Recovering Alcoholics and Drug Dependent Persons*, by Dennis C. Daley.

LEE'S BOOKS FOR YOUNG READERS, 813 West Ave., Box 111, O'Neil Professional Bldg., Wellington TX 79095. (806)447-5445. Independent book producer/packager. Publisher: Lee Templeton. Publishes hardcover originals. Averages 8 titles/year; receives 60 submissions annually. 20% of books from first-time authors; 100% of books from unagented writers. Average print order for a writer's first book is 1,000. Pays 10% minimum royalty on wholesale price. No advance. Publishes book an average of 1 year after acceptance. Computer printout submissions acceptable; no dot-matrix. Free book catalog.
Nonfiction: Biography. "Our books are nonfiction history of young heroes. All our books are written for 'reluctant' readers in junior high school market (10-14 age group), to be sold to junior (middle) school libraries. We will consider queries about young American heroes, male or female, that historians overlooked." Reviews artwork/photos. All unsolicited mss are returned unopened.
Recent Nonfiction Title: *Columbus' Cabin Boy.*
Tips: "Tell a beautiful story about a young person (under age 19) who performed a heroic deed that affected history. The only books we publish are nonfiction—about 'Young Heroes of America,' preferably under 200 pages, with good illustrations and pictures."

‡HAL LEONARD PUBLISHING CORP., 8112 W. Bluemound Rd., Box 13819, Milwaukee WI 53213. (414)774-3630. Managing Editor: Glenda Herro. Publishes hardcover and trade paperback originals. Averages 20 titles/year; receives 25 submissions annually. 95% of books from unagented writers. Pays 5-10% royalty on wholesale or retail price; offers average $5,000 advance. Publishes book an average of 1 year after acceptance. Simultaneous and photocopied submissions OK. Reports in 2 months on queries; 3 months on mss. Free book catalog.
Imprints: Robus Books (nonfiction), Glenda Herro, managing editor.
Nonfiction: Biography, "coffee table" book, how-to, humor, illustrated book, juvenile, reference and technical. "The majority of our titles are music or entertainment-industry related." Especially interested in "subject matter related to pop and rock music, Broadway theatre, film and television personalities, and general interest material in the music and entertainment industry." Query. Reviews artwork/photos.
Recent Nonfiction Title: *Lyrics by Oscar Hammerstein II*, edited by Wm. Hammerstein.
Tips: "Our books are for all age groups interested in music and entertainment. Robus Books (rock photo biographies) are geared to the juvenile and young adult markets."

LEXIKOS, 4079 19th Ave., San Francisco CA 94132. (415)584-1085. Editor: Mike Witter. Publishes hardcover and trade paperback originals and trade paperback reprints. Averages 5-7 (growing each season) titles/year; receives 200 submissions annually. 50% of books from first-time authors; 90% of books from unagented writers. Average print order for a writer's first book is 5,000. Royalties vary from 8-12½% according to book sold. "Authors asked to accept lower royalty on high discount (50% plus) sales." Offers average $1,000 advance. Publishes book an average of 10 months after acceptance. Simultaneous and photocopied submissions OK. Computer printout submissions acceptable. Reports in 1 month. Book catalog for 6x9 SAE and 2 first class stamps.
Nonfiction: "Coffee table" book, illustrated book. Subjects include regional, outdoors, oral histories, Americana, history and nature. Especially looking for 50,000-word "city and regional histories, anecdotal in style for a general audience; books of regional interest about *places*; adventure and wilderness books; annotated reprints of books of Americana; Americana in general." No health, sex, European travel, diet, broad humor, fiction, quickie books (we stress backlist vitality), religion, children's or nutrition. Submit outline/synopsis and sample chapters. Reviews artwork/photos.
Recent Nonfiction Title: *The Making of Golden Gate Park—The Early Years: 1865-1906*, by Ray Clary.
Tips: "A regional interest or history book has the best chance of selling to Lexikos. Submit a short, cogent proposal; follow up with letter queries. Give the publisher reason to believe you will help him *sell* the book (identify the market, point out the availability of mailing lists, distinguish your book from the competition). Avoid grandiose claims."

LIBERTY PUBLISHING COMPANY, INC., 50 Scott Adam Rd., Cockeysville MD 21030. (301)667-6680. Publisher: Jeffrey B. Little. Imprints include Liberty Personal Counsel Library, J. Little, publisher. Publishes hardcover and mostly trade paperback originals and software. Averages 10-15 titles/year; receives 500 submissions annually. 10% of books from first-time authors; 95% of books from unagented writers. Average print order for a writer's first book is 4,000-6,000. Pays 6-12% royalty on wholesale or retail price; buys some mss outright for $500-1,500; offers average $400 advance. Publishes book an average of 6-12 months after acceptance. Computer printout submissions acceptable; prefers letter-quality to dot-matrix. Reports in 3 weeks on queries; 1-2 months on mss. "Exclusive distribution arrangements with self-publishers possible."
Nonfiction: Biography, cookbook, how-to, illustrated book and self-help. Subjects include Americana, business and economics, cooking and foods, history, hobbies, photography (b&w only), recreation, sports, travel;

educational, parent guides and computer software. Accepts nonfiction translations. "How-to or self-help books dealing with concrete advice written by people qualified to address the subject. Extensive graphic possibilities preferred. No self-improvement books dealing with psychology and mind improvement. No poetry, please." Query with author biography or submit outline/synopsis and 3 sample chapters. Reviews artwork/photos as part of ms package.

Recent Nonfiction Title: *Understanding Wall Street*, by J. Little (business guide for the layman investor).

Tips: Freelancer has best chance of selling business and how-to. "Know your competition and tell us why your book is better."

*LIBRA PUBLISHERS, INC., Suite 330, 4901 Moreno Blvd., San Diego CA 92117. (619)581-9449. Contact: William Kroll. Publishes hardcover and paperback originals. Specializes in the behavioral sciences. Averages 15 titles/year; receives 300 submissions annually. 60% of books from first-time authors; 85% of books from unagented writers. 10-15% royalty on retail price; no advance. "We will also offer our services to authors who wish to publish their own works. The services include editing, proofreading, production, artwork, copyrighting, and assistance in promotion and distribution." Publishes book an average of 8 months after acceptance. Computer printout submissions acceptable; prefers letter-quality to dot-matrix. Reports in 2 weeks. Free book catalog.

Nonfiction: Mss in all subject areas will be given consideration, but main interest is in the behavioral sciences. Prefers complete manuscript but will consider outline/synopsis and 3 sample chapters. Reviews artwork/photos as part of ms package.

Recent Nonfiction Title: *Surviving Adolescence*, by Robbie Louise Taylor.

‡LIBRARY RESEARCH ASSOCIATES, INC., Subsidiaries include Empire State Fiction, RD #5, Box 41, Dunderberg Rd., Monroe NY 10950. (914)783-1144. President: Matilda A. Gocek. Publishes hardcover and trade paperback originals. Averages 4 titles/year; receives about 30 submissions annually. 100% of books from first-time authors; 100% of books from unagented writers. Pays 10% maximum royalty on retail price. Offers 20 copies of the book as advance. Publishes book an average of 14 months after acceptance. Photocopied submissions OK. Computer printout submissions acceptable; no dot-matrix. Reports in 3 weeks on queries; 3 months on mss. Book catalog free on request.

Imprints: Empire State Fiction (fiction), Patricia E. Clyne, senior editor.

Nonfiction: Biography, "coffee table" book, how-to, reference, technical and American history. Subjects include Americana, art, business and economics, history, philosophy, politics and travel. "Our nonfiction book manuscript needs for the next year or two will include books about American artists, graphics and photography, historical research of some facet of American history, and definitive works about current or past economics or politics." No astrology, occult, sex, adult humor or gay rights. Submit outline/synopsis and sample chapters.

Recent Nonfiction Title: *Electron Microscopy: 41 Exercises*, by Betty Ruth Jones, Ph.D. (college and advanced text).

Fiction: Send fiction to Empire State Fiction, Patricia E. Clyne, senior editor. Adventure (based in an authentic NY location); historical (particularly in or about New York state); mystery; and suspense. "I try to publish at least three novels per year. Characterization is so important! The development of people and plot must read well. The realism of world events (war, terrorism, catastrophes) is turning readers to a more innocent world of reading for entertainment with less shock value. Free speech (free *everything*!) is reviving old values. Explicit sex, extreme violence, vile language in any form will not be considered." Submit outline/synopsis and sample chapters.

Recent Fiction Title: *The Tenth Men*, by Allen G. Eastby (American Revolution in Hudson Valley, New York).

Tips: "Our audience is adult, over age 30, literate and knowledgeable in business or professions. The writer has the best chance of selling our firm historical fiction or nonfiction and scientific texts. If I were a writer trying to market a book today, I would try to write about people in a warm human situation—the foibles, the loss of self, the unsung heroism—angels with feet of clay."

LIBRARIES UNLIMITED, Box 263, Littleton CO 80160. (303)770-1220. Editor-in-Chief: Bohdan S. Wynar. Publishes hardcover and paperback originals and hardcover reprints. Averages 30-40 titles/year; receives 100-200 submissions annually. 10-20% of books from first-time authors. Average print order for a writer's first book is 2,000. 10% royalty on net sales; advance averages $500. Publishes book an average of 1 year after acceptance. Marketed by direct mail to 40,000 libraries and schools in this country and abroad. Reports in 2 months. Free book catalog and ms guidelines.

Nonfiction: Publishes reference and library science text books. Looks for professional experience. Query or submit outline/synopsis and sample chapters. All prospective authors are required to fill out an author questionnaire. Query if photos/illustrations are to accompany ms.

Recent Nonfiction Title: *Creative Writing*, by Phillips and Steiner.

LIGUORI PUBLICATIONS, Book and Pamphlet Dept., 1 Liguori Dr., Liguori MO 63057. (314)464-2500. Editor-in-Chief: Rev. Christopher Farrell, C.SS.R. Managing Editor: Thomas Artz, C.SS.R. Publishes paperback originals. Specializes in Catholic-Christian religious materials. Averages 30 titles/year; receives about 200 submissions annually. About 40% of books from first-time authors; 95% of books from unagented writers. Average print order for a writer's first book is 10,000-16,000. Pays royalty on books; flat fee on pamphlets and teacher's guides. Publishes book an average of 8 months after acceptance. Electronic submissions on TRS-80 Model III in a 1.3 system/1.0 version OK "if sent with computer printout." Computer printout submissions acceptable; no dot-matrix. Query or submit outline/synopsis and 1 sample chapter; "never submit total book." Reports in 3-5 weeks. SASE. Book catalog and ms guidelines for SASE.
Nonfiction: Publishes doctrinal, inspirational, biblical, self-help and educational materials. Looks for "thought and language that speak to basic practical religious concerns of contemporary Catholic Christians."
Recent Nonfiction Title: *Faith and Doubt Today.*
Tips: "Simply written and short self-help/educational material that is easily understood and can relate to the 'ordinary' Catholic has the best chance of selling to our firm."

LINCH PUBLISHING, INC., Box 75, Orlando FL 32802. (305)647-3025. Vice President: David L. Kellogg. Editor: Pauline Wylie. Publishes hardcover and trade paperback originals. Receives 100 submissions annually. 50% of books from first-time authors; 50% of books from unagented writers. Pays 8-12% royalty on wholesale price. Rarely pays advances. Publishes book an average of 6 months after acceptance. Simultaneous and photocopied submissions OK. Computer printout submissions acceptable; prefers letter-quality to dot-matrix. Reports in 6 weeks. Book catalog for $1 and regular size SAE with 39¢ postage.
Nonfiction: Specializes in books on estate planning and legal how-to books which must be applicable in all 50 states. "We are interested in a record keeping book for heirs, how to get through probate and settle an estate, and minimizing federal estate and/or state inheritance taxes." Query editor by phone before submitting mss. "We could have already accepted a manuscript and be in the process of publishing one of the above."
Recent Nonfiction Title: *Ask an Attorney.*
Tips: Currently interest is mainly estate planning.

LITTLE, BROWN AND CO., INC., 34 Beacon St., Boston MA 02108. Contact: Editorial Department, Trade Division. Publishes hardcover and paperback originals and paperback reprints. Averages 100+ titles/year. "Royalty and advance agreements vary from book to book and are discussed with the author at the time an offer is made. Submissions only from authors who have had a book published or have been published in professional or literary journals, newspapers or magazines." Computer printout submissions acceptable; prefers letter-quality to dot-matrix. Reports in 3 months for queries/proposals.
Nonfiction: "Some how-to books, distinctive cookbooks, biographies, history, science and sports." Query or submit outline/synopsis and sample chapters. Reviews artwork/photos as part of ms package.
Recent Nonfiction Title: *Ansel Adams; an Autobiography.*
Fiction: Contemporary popular fiction as well as fiction of literary distinction. "Our poetry list is extremely limited; those collections of poems that we do publish are usually the work of poets who have gained recognition through publication in literary reviews and various periodicals." Query or submit outline/synopsis and sample chapters.
Recent Fiction Title: *The LeBaron Secret,* by Stephen Birmingham.

*LLEWELLYN PUBLICATIONS, Subsidiary of Chester-Kent, Inc., Box 64383-WM86, St. Paul MN 55164-0383. (612)291-1970. President: Carl L. Weschcke. Publishes hardcover and trade paperback originals and reprints and software. Averages 12-15 titles/year; receives 300 submissions annually. 50% of books from first-time authors; 95% of books from unagented writers. Subsidy publishes 10% or less of books; "generally the subsidized book is well-written and makes a valuable contribution to the subject area, but we feel the market potential to be too small for our investment in publication, or the book is too expensive or too slow in turnover." Pays 10-15% royalty. Publishes book an average of 1 year after acceptance. Simultaneous and photocopied submissions OK. Computer printout submissions acceptable; no dot-matrix. Reports in 3 months. Book catalog $2; ms guidelines for $1 and SASE.
Nonfiction: "Coffee table" book, how-to, reference, self-help and textbook. Subjects include astrology and occultism. Especially looking for self-help through astrology and occultism, with the emphasis on practicality, readability, and wide market. No pseudo or "pop" approaches to the subjects; no "satanism." Submit outline/synopsis and sample chapters. Reviews artwork/photos.
Recent Nonfiction Title: *The Llewellyn Guide to Magical States of Consciousness,* by Denning and Phillips (Qabalah and meditation).
Tips: " 'Real' self-help or how-to books (tapes and software also) dealing with aspects of astrology, magic, psychic development, spiritual development, lunar gardening, past life regression, hypnosis and self-hypnosis, etc. have the best chance of selling to our firm. The writer should show that he or she understands the market as well as the subject area—so that the book is written to fulfill a marketable need."

LODESTAR BOOKS, Division of E. P. Dutton, 2 Park Ave., New York NY 10016. (212)725-1818. Editorial Director: Virginia Buckley. Editor: Rosemary Brosnan. Hardcover originals. Publishes juveniles, young adults, fiction and nonfiction; no picture books. Averages 20 titles/year; receives 800 submissions annually. 10-20% of books from first-time authors; 25-30% of books from unagented writers. Average print order for a writer's first book is 4,000-5,000. Pays royalty on invoice list price; advance offered. Publishes book an average of 18 months after acceptance. Photocopied submissions OK. Electronic submissions OK, but requires hard copy also. Computer printout submissions acceptable; prefers letter-quality to dot-matrix. Reports in 2-4 months. Ms guidelines for SASE.
Nonfiction: Query or submit outline/synopsis and 2-3 sample chapters including "theme, chapter-by-chapter outline, and 1 or 2 completed chapters." State availability of photos and/or illustrations. Queries/mss may be routed to other editors in the publishing group. Reviews artwork/photos as part of ms package.
Fiction: Publishes only for young adults and juveniles: adventure, fantasy, humorous, contemporary, mystery, science fiction, suspense and western books. Submit complete ms.
Tips: "A young adult novel that is literary, fast-paced, well-constructed (as opposed to a commercial novel) and well-written nonfiction on contemporary issues have the best chance of selling to our firm.

LOIRY PUBLISHING HOUSE, Suite 301, 226 W. Pensacola St., Tallahassee FL 32301. (904)681-0019. Executive Editor: Carol J. Loiry. Publishes hardcover and trade paperback originals. Pays 10% royalty. Pays 15% royalty after 15,000 copies sold. Negotiable advance. Simultaneous and photocopied submissions OK. Reports in 1 month.
Nonfiction: How-to, self-help, expose, political, biography, and supplemental high school and college textbook. "Loiry Publishing House is rapidly expanding and looking for high-quality manuscripts with a market that can be identified and reached. We published 15 titles in 1986 and will be publishing 25 titles or more in 1987. We have full access to national media and distribution. Authors will be much more satisfied with the way we treat them than the way big New York publishers would treat them. We have several areas of special publishing emphasis: Human Relations: personal growth, stress management, overall wellness, effective parenting, dating, sexuality, and race relations; Achievement: new ways on how to achieve success; Children and Youth: the conditions of, importance of, policies affecting, advocacy for, and activism of (looking for manuscripts on child abuse, missing children, children in poverty, latchkey children, and school improvement, emphasizing solutions and how they can be attained); Politics: what is really going on in politics and government (looking for manuscripts on the impact of U.S. foreign policy, especially in Central America, and manuscripts on the impact of the Reagan Administration on American life); and Empowerment: new strategies on how individuals can make a difference. We do not usually publish children's books, only books for adults on issues affecting children. Arrogant authors need not contact us." Query.
Recent Nonfiction Title: *Habit Breakthrough*, by Mitch Bobrow, M.S.W.

‡LOMOND PUBLICATIONS, INC., Box 88, Mt. Airy MD 21771. (301)829-1496. Publisher: Lowell H. Hattery. Publishes hardcover originals. Averages 3-10 titles/year; receives 30 submissions annually. 50% of books from first-time authors; 100% of books from unagented writers. Pays 10% royalty on net price or makes outright purchase. No advance. Publishes book an average of 6-18 months after acceptance. Simultaneous submissions OK. Computer printout submissions acceptable. Reports in 1 month. Free book catalog.
Nonfiction: Technical, professional and scholarly. Subjects include business and economics, politics, sociology, public policy, technological change and management. Query or submit complete ms.
Tips: "We publish for the scholarly, professional, and well-informed lay readers of all countries. We publish only English titles, but many are subsequently reprinted and translated in other languages. A writer's best bet with us is an interdisciplinary approach to management, technology or public policy."

‡*LONE STAR PUBLISHERS, INC., Box 9774, Austin TX 78766. (512)255-2333. Editorial Director: A.J. Lerager. Publishes hardcover and paperback originals. Averages 3 titles/year. Subsidy publishes approximately 1 title/year based on "the subject matter, the author's reputation, the potential market, the capital investment, etc." Pays 12½-15% royalty on wholesale or retail price; no advance. Simultaneous and photocopied submissions OK. Computer printout submissions acceptable. Reports in 3 weeks. Free book catalog.
Nonfiction: College textbooks. No poetry. Query.
Recent Nonfiction Title: *Principles of International Accounting*, by Samuel Fox and Norlin G. Reuschhoff.

‡LONGMAN FINANCIAL SERVICES PUBLISHING, (formerly Longman Group U.S.A.), 500 N. Dearborn, Chicago IL 60610. (312)836-0466. Sponsoring Editor, Real Estate Professional Books, Real Estate Textbooks: Bobbye Middendorf. Acquisitions Editor, Financial Services Professional Books and Financial Services Textbooks: Ivy Lester. Associate Publisher Subscription Services: Sheila Frank. Imprints include Real Estate Education Co., Farnsworth Publishing R&R Newkirk, Educational Methods, Inc. and Longman Financial Services Publishing. Publishes hardcover and paperback originals and subscription products for real estate, insurance and financial planning professionals (includes standard and client newsletters and loose leaf services). Averages 50 titles/year; receives 100 submissions annually. 60% of books from first-time authors; 99% of books from unagented writers. Average print order for a writer's first book is 500-3,000. Pays 5-15% royalty; no advance. Publishes book an average of 1 year after acceptance. Simultaneous and photocopied submissions OK. Computer printout submissions acceptable; prefers letter-quality to dot-matrix. Reports in 2 months. Free book catalog and ms guidelines.

Nonfiction: "Publishes books for real estate professionals and other financial services professionals (banking, financial planning, insurance, securities). Any topics appropriate for this market are of interest." Submit outline and 1-3 sample chapters (but not the first chapter) or complete ms. Reviews artwork/photos as part of ms package.

Recent Nonfiction Title: *Investments; A Practical Approach* (text book).

Tips: "We seek well-targeted books and proposals for course works, and professional how-to and reference books in all segments of the financial services industry. The writer must know the market, and, more importantly, the competitive books. Once a proposal is signed, authors often lose their market focus. We recommend close, careful attention be paid to a detailed chapter-by-chapter outline."

LONGMAN, INC., 95 Church St., White Plains NY 10601. (914)993-5000. President: Bruce S. Butterfield. Publishes hardcover and paperback originals. Publishes 200 titles/year. Pays variable royalty; offers variable advance. Photocopied submissions OK. Reports in 6 weeks.

Nonfiction: Textbooks only (elementary/high school, college and professional): world history, political science, economics, communications; social sciences, education, English, Latin, foreign languages, English as a second language. No trade, art or juvenile.

LOOMPANICS UNLIMITED, Box 1197, Port Townsend WA 98368. Book Editor: Michael Hoy. Publishes trade paperback originals. Publishes 12 titles/year; receives 50 submissions annually. 40% of books from first-time authors; 100% of books from unagented writers. Average print order for a writer's first book is 1,000. Pays 7½-20% royalty on wholesale or retail price; or makes outright purchase of $100-1,200. Offers average $500 advance. Publishes book an average of 10 months after acceptance. Simultaneous and photocopied submissions OK. Computer printout submissions acceptable; prefers letter-quality to dot-matrix. Reports in 6 weeks. Free book catalog.

Nonfiction: How-to, reference and self-help. Subjects include business and economics, philosophy, politics, travel, and "beat the system" books. "We are looking for how-to books in the fields of espionage, investigation, the underground economy, police methods, how to beat the system, crime and criminal techniques. No cookbooks, inspirational, travel, or cutesy-wutesy stuff." Query, or submit outline/synopsis and sample chapters. Reviews artwork/photos.

Recent Nonfiction Title: *Methods of Disguise*, by John Sample (how-to).

Tips: "Our audience is young males looking for hard-to-find information on alternatives to 'The System.' "

*LORIEN HOUSE, Box 1112, Black Mountain NC 28711. Editor: David A. Wilson. Publishes trade paperback originals. Averages 2-4 titles/year; receives 100 submissions annually. 50% of books from first-time authors; 100% of books from unagented writers. Average print order for a writer's first book is 1,000. Subsidy publishes up to 25% of books. "Rather than subsidy, we do a co-op publishing, sharing costs with the author." Pays 15% royalty on retail price. No advance. Publishes book an average of 18 months after acceptance. Computer printout submissions acceptable; prefers letter-quality to dot-matrix. Reports in 1 week on queries. Book catalog 50¢; ms guidelines for SASE.

Nonfiction: How-to, technical and literary. Subjects include history (American); nature (wild foods, ecology); and philosophy (metaphysics). "We are open to any subject as long as it is well done and treated as a literary and technical piece at the same time." No photo essays or children's books. Query. Reviews artwork/photos as part of ms package.

Recent Nonfiction Title: *Arthur: The King of Light*, by Allen Artos (history/metaphysics).

Fiction: Science fiction/fantasy on dragons. Query.

Recent Fiction Title: *Dragon Study*, by David A. Wilson (fact/fantasy).

Poetry: Co-op only. Query. "I need to be very selective and can do at maximum one title per year."

Recent Poetry Title: *Sonnets for a New Age*, by William Walters (poetry/metaphysics).

Tips: "The writer has the best chance of selling our firm nonfiction, because it sells best. How-to would be best within the category of nonfiction."

LOTHROP, LEE & SHEPARD BOOKS, Division of William Morrow Company, 105 Madison Ave., New York NY 10016. (212)889-3050. Editor-in-Chief: Dorothy Briley. Hardcover original children's books only. Royalty and advance vary according to type of book. Averages 60 titles/year; receives 4,000 submissions annually. Less than 2% of books from first-time authors; 25% of books from unagented writers. Average print order for a writer's first book is 6,000. State availability of photos to accompany ms. Publishes book an average of 2 years after acceptance. Photocopied submissions OK, but originals preferred. No simultaneous submissions. Computer printout submissions acceptable; no dot-matrix. Responds in 6 weeks. Book catalog for SAE.

Fiction and Nonfiction: Publishes picture books, general nonfiction, and novels. Submit outline/synopsis

and sample chapters for nonfiction. Juvenile fiction emphasis is on novels for the 8-12 age group. Submit complete ms for fiction. Looks for "organization, clarity, creativity, literary style."
Recent Title: *Commodore Perry in the Land of the Shogun*, by Rhoda Blumberg.
Tips: "Trends in book publishing that freelance writers should be aware of include the demand for books for children under age three and the shrinking market for young adult books, especially novels."

LOTUS PRESS, INC., Box 21607, Detroit MI 48221. (313)861-1280. Editor/Publisher: Naomi Madgett. Imprint includes Penway Books. Publishes hardcover and trade paperback originals. Averages 4-7 titles/year; receives 900-1,000 submissions annually. 30% of books from first-time authors; 100% of books from unagented writers. Pays in copies. "Authors are given 25 free copies and may (but are not required to) order additional copies at a discount. It is the best we can do." Publishes book an average of 20 months after acceptance. Photocopied submissions OK. Computer printout submissions acceptable; prefers letter-quality to dot-matrix. Reports in 6 weeks. Free book catalog and ms guidelines; SASE appreciated.
Poetry: "We publish poetry exclusively, except for the one textbook under the Penway imprint. We are already committed for the next two years. We are most committed to the consideration of black poets." No amateur variety poetry; poetry imitative of other poets' styles and attitudes; or poetry which has a vocabulary in poor taste. "We do not want to see *any* nonfiction." Submit 3-5 poems. Reviews artwork/photos.
Recent Poetry Title: *Now Is the Thing to Praise*, by Dolores Kendrick (lyric).
Tips: "Our audience is college-educated, black and white, poetry lovers; those who appreciate the possibilities of language. Poetry is the only genre we publish. The author must view his/her work as art."

LOUISIANA STATE UNIVERSITY PRESS, Baton Rouge LA 70803. (504)388-6618. Associate/Executive Editor: Beverly Jarrett. Director: L.E. Phillabaum. Averages 60 titles/year; receives 200-300 submissions annually. Approximately 80% of books from first-time authors; 85% of books from unagented writers. Average print order for a writer's first book is 1,000-1,500. Pays royalty on wholesale price; no advance. Publishes book an average of 2 years after acceptance. Photocopied submissions OK. Electronic submissions OK, varied capacity, but requires hard copy also. Computer printout submissions acceptable; no dot-matrix. Reports in 1 month on queries; 1-6 months on mss. Free book catalog; ms guidelines for SASE.
Nonfiction: "We would like to have manuscripts on humanities and social sciences, with special emphasis on Southern history and literature; Southern studies; French studies; political philosophy; and music, especially jazz." Query.
Recent Nonfiction Title: *The History of Southern Literature*, edited by Louis D. Rubin, Jr., et al.
Tips: "The writer has the best chance of selling us scholarly books in Southern studies, because we are a university press."

*LOYOLA UNIVERSITY PRESS, 3441 N. Ashland Ave., Chicago IL 60657. (312)281-1818. Editorial Director: George A. Lane. Imprints include Campion Books. Publishes hardcover and trade paperback originals, and hardcover and trade paperback reprints. Receives 100 submissions annually. 40% of books from first-time authors; 95% of books from unagented writers. Subsidy publishes 5% of books. Pays 5-10% royalty on wholesale price; offers no advance. Publishes book an average of 1 year after acceptance. Simultaneous and photocopied submissions acceptable. Electronic submissions OK on TRS-80 5" disks, Models 3&4 and CompuScan OCR, but requires hard copy also. Computer printout submissions acceptable; prefers letter-quality to dot-matrix. Reports in 1 month on queries; 1 month on mss. Book catalog for 7x10 SAE.
Nonfiction: Biography and textbook. Subjects include art (religious); history (church); and religion. The four subject areas of Campion Books include Jesuitica (Jesuit history, biography and spirituality); Literature-Theology interface (books dealing with theological or religious aspects of literary works or authors); contemporary Catholic concerns (books on morality, spirituality, family life, pastoral ministry, prayer, worship, etc.); and Chicago/art (books dealing with the city of Chicago from historical, artistic, architectural, or ethnic perspectives, but with religious emphases). Query before submitting ms. Reviews artwork/photos.
Recent Nonfiction Title: *Hollywood and The Catholic Church*, by Les and Barbara Keyser.
Tips: "Our audience is principally the college-educated reader with religious, theological interest."

‡McCLELLAND AND BANTAM LTD., (Seal Books), #601, 60 St. Clair Ave. E., Toronto, Ontario M4T 1N5 Canada. (416)922-4970. Vice President/Publisher: Janet Turnbull. Publishes trade paperback and mass market paperback originals and mass market paperback reprints. Averages 24 titles/year; receives 1,000 submissions annually. 10% of books from first-time authors; 80% of books from unagented writers. "All authors published by this firm must be Canadian citizens, residents of Canada, or their subject matter must be (in part) of Canadian content." Pays royalty on retail price; offers average $4,000 (Canadian) advance. Publishes book an average of 1 year after acceptance. Simultaneous submissions OK. Computer printout submissions acceptable; prefers letter-quality to dot-matrix. SASE or SAE, IRC. Reports in 6 weeks.
Nonfiction: How-to and self-help. Subjects include Canadiana, health, nature, politics and sports. Submit outline/synopsis and sample chapters.
Recent Nonfiction Title: *Heart Attacks*, by Dr. Khan.

Fiction: Adventure, historical, horror, mainstream, mystery, romance and suspense. Submit outline/synopsis and sample chapters.
Recent Fiction Title: *Dance of Shiva*, by William Deverell.
Tips: "Nonfiction backlist (how-to) or genre fiction have the best chance of selling to our firm."

MARGARET K. McELDERRY BOOKS, Macmillan Publishing Co., Inc., 115 Fifth Ave., New York NY 10003. Editor: Margaret K. McElderry. Publishes hardcover originals. Publishes 20-25 titles/year; receives 1,200-1,300 submissions annually. 8% of books from first-time authors; 45% of books from unagented writers. The average print order is 6,000-7,500 for a writer's first teen book; 7,500-10,000 for a writer's first picture book. Pays royalty on retail price. Publishes book an average of 1½ years after acceptance. Reports in 6 weeks. Computer printout submissions acceptable; no dot-matrix. Ms guidelines for SASE.
Nonfiction and Fiction: Quality material for preschoolers to 16-year-olds. Looks for "originality of ideas, clarity and felicity of expression, well-organized plot (fiction) or exposition (nonfiction) quality." Reviews artwork/photos as part of ms package.
Recent Title: *Jonah and the Great Fish*, by Warwick Hutton.
Tips: "There is not a particular 'type' of book that we are interested in above others; rather, we look for superior quality in both writing and illustration." Freelance writers should be aware of the swing away from teen-age problem novels to books for young readers.

McFARLAND & COMPANY, INC., PUBLISHERS, Box 611, Jefferson NC 28640. (919)246-4460. President: Robert Franklin. Business Manager: Rhonda Herman. Editor: Virginia Hege. Publishes hardcover and "quality" paperback originals; a non-"trade" publisher. Averages 55 titles/year; receives 700 submissions annually. 70% of books from first-time authors; 98% of books from unagented writers. Average print order for a writer's first book is 1,000. Pays 10-12½% royalty on gross receipts; no advance. Publishes book an average of 15 months after acceptance. Computer printout submissions acceptable; prefers letter-quality to dot-matrix. Reports in 2 weeks.
Nonfiction: Reference books and scholarly, technical and professional monographs. Subjects include Americana, art, business, chess, drama/theatre, health, cinema/radio/TV (very strong here), history, literature, librarianship (very strong here), music, parapsychology, religion, sociology, sports/recreation, women's studies, and world affairs. "We will consider *any* scholarly book—with authorial maturity and competent grasp of subject." Reference books are particularly wanted—fresh material (i.e., not in head-to-head competition with an established title). "We don't like manuscripts of fewer than 200 double-spaced typed pages. Our market consists mainly of libraries. Our film books make it into book clubs frequently." No memoirs, poetry, children's books, devotional/inspirational works or personal essays. Query or submit outline/synopsis and sample chapters. Reviews artwork/photos as part of ms package.
Recent Nonfiction Title: *Sports Quotations*, by Andrew J. Maikovich (reference).
Tips: "We do *not* accept novels or fiction of any kind. Don't worry about writing skills—we have editors. What we want is well-organized *knowledge* of an area in which there is not good information coverage at present, plus reliability so we don't feel we have to check absolutely everything."

McGRAW-HILL BOOK CO., College Division, 1221 Avenue of the Americas, New York NY 10020. (212)512-2000. Publisher, Social Sciences: Philip Butcher. Publisher, Business and Economics: Joseph Marcelle. Publishes hardcover and softcover technical material and software for the college market.
Nonfiction: The College Division publishes textbooks. The writer must know the college curriculum and course structure. Also publishes scientific texts and reference books in business and economics, computers, engineering, social sciences, physical sciences, nursing, and mathematics. Material should be scientifically and factually accurate. Most, but not all, books should be designed for existing courses offered in various disciplines of study. Books should have superior presentations and be more up-to-date than existing textbooks.

DAVID McKAY CO., INC., 2 Park Ave., New York NY 10016. Publisher: Richard T. Scott. Publishes hardcover and paperback originals. Averages 5 titles/year. "No unsolicited manuscripts or proposals considered or acknowledged."

MACMILLAN OF CANADA, Suite 685, 146 Front St. W., Toronto, Ontario M5J 1G2 Canada. Publisher: Linda McKnight. Managing Editor: Maggie MacDonald. Subsidiary Rights Manager: Anne Holloway. Publishes hardcover originals and paperback reprints. Averages 25 titles/year; receives 3,000 submissions annually. 10% of books from first-time authors; 50% of books from unagented writers. 10% royalty on retail price. Publishes book an average of 1 year after acceptance. Computer printout submissions acceptable; prefers letter-quality to dot-matrix. Reports in 10 weeks. SAE and IRCs. Book catalog for SAE and IRCs.
Nonfiction: "We publish Canadian authors on all sorts of subjects and books of all sorts that are about Canada. Biography, history, art, current affairs, how-to and juveniles. Particularly looking for good topical nonfiction." Submit translations. Accepts outline/synopsis and 3 to 5 sample chapters "depending on length of total manuscript." Reviews artwork/photos as part of ms package.

Recent Nonfiction Title: *Smart Cooking*, by Anne Lindsey.
Fiction: Query.
Recent Fiction Title: *Bred in the Bone*, by Robertson Davies.

MACMILLAN PUBLISHING COMPANY, Children's Book Department, 866 3rd Ave., New York NY 10022. Publishes hardcover and paperback originals and reprints. Averages 130 titles/year. Will consider juvenile submissions only. Fiction and nonfiction. Enclose return postage.

MADRONA PUBLISHERS, INC., Box 22667, Seattle WA 98122. (206)325-3973. President: Daniel J. Levant. Editorial Director: Sara Levant. Publishes hardcover and paperback originals and paperback reprints. Averages 8 titles/year; receives 1,000 submissions annually. 80% of books from first-time authors; 95% of books from unagented writers. Average print order for a writer's first book is 5,000. Pays 15-17½% royalty on net sales; offers $1,000 average advance. Publishes book an average of 1 year after acceptance. Computer printout submissions acceptable; prefers letter-quality to dot-matrix. Reports in 2 months.
Nonfiction: Americana, biography, cooking and foods, health, history, hobbies, how-to, humor, photography, politics, psychology, recreation, self-help and travel. Query, submit outline/synopsis and at least 2 sample chapters or complete ms. Accepts nonfiction and fiction translations. Reviews artwork/photos (if appropriate) as part of ms package.
Recent Nonfiction Title: *Speaking Out, Fighting Back*, by Sister Vera Gallagher.
Tips: "*Good* popular psychology on subjects of current interest—family, alcoholism, parenting, social problems, etc.—has the best chance of selling to our firm."

THE MAIN STREET PRESS, William Case House, Pittstown NJ 08867. (201)735-9424. Editorial Director: Martin Greif. Publishes hardcover and trade paperback originals. Averages 20 titles/year; receives 250 submissions annually. 10% of books from first-time authors; 100% of books from unagented writers. Pays 3-15% royalty on wholesale or retail price; offers average $4,000 advance. Publishes book an average of 1 year after acceptance. Simultaneous and photocopied submissions OK. Computer printout submissions acceptable; prefers letter-quality to dot-matrix. Reports in 2 months on queries; 3 months on mss. Reviews artwork/photos. Book catalog $1.50.
Nonfiction: Coffee table book, how-to, illustrated book and reference. Subjects include Americana, art, hobbies, gardening, film, architecture, popular culture and design. "We publish *heavily illustrated* books on almost all subjects; we publish *only* illustrated books." Especially needs how-to quilting books. "We do not want to consider any nonfiction book with fewer than 75 illustrations." Query or submit outline/synopsis and sample chapters.
Recent Nonfiction Title: *Quilting for Beginners*, by Agnes Frank (quilting).
Tips: "Our books are for the "carriage trade.""

MARATHON INTERNATIONAL PUBLISHING COMPANY, INC., Dept. WM, Box 33008, Louisville KY 40232. (502)245-1566. President: Jim Wortham. Publishes hardcover originals, and trade paperback originals, trade paperback reprints. Averages 10 titles/year. Pays 10% royalty on wholesale. Publishes book an average of 10 months after acceptance. Simultaneous and photocopied submissions OK. Computer printout submissions acceptable. Reports in 1 week on queries; 2 weeks on mss. Book catalog for 6x9 SAE and 4 first class stamps.
Nonfiction: Cookbooks, how-to, self-help. Subjects include business and economics, and offbeat humor. Especially needs how-to make extra money-type mss; self-improvement; how a person can be happier and more prosperous. No biography or textbooks. Query. Reviews artwork/photos as part of ms package.
Recent Nonfiction Title: *How to Make Money in Penny Stocks*, by Jim Scott (financial).

*MAVERICK PUBLICATIONS, Drawer 5007, Bend OR 97708. (503)382-6978. Book publisher and independent book producer/packager. Publisher: Ken Asher. Publishes hardcover and trade paperback originals. Averages 15 titles/year; receives 200 submissions annually. "Like every other publisher, the number of books we can publish is limited. We would like to suggest to any writer who has a timely manuscript and is having trouble getting it published to consider publishing it themselves. We will be glad to discuss this alternative with anyone who might be interested." 40% of books from first-time authors; 95% of books from unagented writers. Pays 15% royalty on net selling price. Publishes book an average of 6 months after acceptance. Simultaneous and photocopied submissions OK. Computer printout submissions acceptable; prefers letter-quality to dot-matrix. Reports in 2 weeks on queries; 3 weeks on mss. Book catalog on request.
Nonfiction: Biography, cookbook, illustrated book, self-help and technical. Subjects include Americana, cooking and foods, health, history, hobbies, music and travel. Query. Reviews artwork/photos.
Recent Nonfiction Title: *Edmund Halley and his Comet*, by Louis Baldwin (biography).
Fiction: Adventure, historical, mystery and science fantasy. "We have no specific needs, but prefer stories based on facts." Submit outline/synopsis and sample chapters.
Recent Fiction Title: *The Wizard of Ekotronix*, by Michael O'Reilly (science-fantasy).

Tips: "Book publishing trends include direct marketing by independent publishers of quality material to an intelligent public. A timely, well-researched exposé of national or at least regional importance has the best chance of selling to our firm."

‡MAZDA PUBLISHERS, 1203 Flint St., Cincinnati OH 45215. (513)621-0077. Editor-in-Chief/Publisher: Ahmad Jabbari. Publishes hardcover and trade paperback originals and trade paperback reprints. Averages 6 titles/year; receives approximately 25 submissions annually. 90% of books from first-time authors; 100% of books from unagented writers. Pays royalty on wholesale price; no advance. Publishes book an average of 4 months after acceptance. Photocopied submissions OK. Electronic submissions OK via IBM, Wang, etc., but requires hard copy also. Computer printout submissions acceptable; prefers letter-quality to dot-matrix. Reports in 2 weeks on queries; 6 weeks on mss. Free book catalog; ms guidelines for SASE.
Nonfiction: Cookbook, juvenile, reference, textbook, scholarly books. Subjects include art, business and economics, cooking and foods, history, politics, sociology, and social sciences in general. "Our primary objective is to publish scholarly books and other informational books about the Middle East and North Africa. All subject areas will be considered with priority given to the scholarly books." Query with outline/synopsis and sample chapters. Reviews artwork/photos.
Recent Nonfiction Title: *Arabic-Speaking Immigrants in the United States and Canada.*
Poetry: Translations and scholarly presentation of poetry from the poets of the Middle Eastern countries only. Submit 5 poems.
Recent Poetry Title: *The Homely Touch: Folk Poetry of Old India* (translated from Sanscrit).
Tips: "We publish books for an academic audience and laymen."

MCN PRESS, Box 702073, Tulsa OK 74170. (918)743-6048. Publisher: Jack Britton. Publishes hardcover and trade paperback originals. Averages 5-7 titles/year; receives 30-35 submissions annually. 75% of books from first-time authors; 75% of books from unagented writers. Pays 10% royalty on wholesale or retail price; offers no advance. Publishes book an average of 6 months after acceptance. Computer printout submissions acceptable; prefers letter-quality to dot-matrix. Reports in 10 weeks. Free book catalog. Ms guidelines for SASE.
Nonfiction: Biography, illustrated book and reference. Subjects include history and hobbies. "Our audience includes collectors, military personnel and military fans." Submit outline/synopsis and sample chapters or complete ms.
Recent Nonfiction Title: *Medals, Military and Civilian of U.S.*, by Borthick and Britton (reference).

MEDICAL ECONOMICS BOOKS, Division of Medical Economics Co., 680 Kinderkamack Rd., Oradell NJ 07649. Acquisitions Editor: Thomas Bentz. Publishes hardcover, paperback, and spiral bound originals. Company also publishes magazines and references for doctors, nurses, pharmacists and laboratorians. Averages 36 titles/year; receives 100 submissions annually. 95% of books from unagented writers. Pays by individual arrangement. Publishes book an average of 11 months after acceptance. Simultaneous and photocopied submissions OK. Electronic submissions OK via IBM (Atex), but requires hard copy also. Computer printout submissions acceptable; prefers letter-quality to dot-matrix. Reports in 6 weeks. Free book catalog; ms guidelines for SASE. Tests freelancers for rewriting, editing, and proofreading assignments.
Nonfiction: Clinical and practice—financial management references, handbooks, and manuals. Medical—primary care—all fields; obstetrics and gynecology, laboratory medicine and management. Critical care nursing. Submit table of contents and prospectus. Reviews artwork/photos as part of ms package.
Recent Nonfiction Title: *Guide to Interpreting 12-Lead ECGs*, by J. Marcus Wharton, M.D. and Nora Goldschlager, M.D.
Tips: "Books addressed to and written by, MDs and health-care managers and financial professionals have the best chance of selling to our firm." Queries/mss may be routed to other editors in the publishing group.

MEMPHIS STATE UNIVERSITY PRESS, Memphis State University, Memphis TN 38152. (901)454-2752. Editor-in-Chief: J. Ralph Randolph. Publishes hardcover and paperback originals. Averages 5 titles/year; receives 50 submissions annually. 50% of books from first-time authors; 100% of books from unagented writers. Each contract is subject to negotiation. Publishes book an average of 12 months after acceptance. Will consider photocopied submissions. Computer printout submissions acceptable; prefers letter-quality to dot-matrix. Query. Accepts outline/synopsis and 2 sample chapters. Reports in 6 months. Free book catalog.
Nonfiction: Regional emphasis. "We publish scholarly and trade nonfiction, books in the humanities, social sciences, and regional material. Interested in nonfiction material within the lower Mississippi River Valley. Tennessee history, and regional folklore." Reviews artwork/photos.
Recent Nonfiction Title: *Home Place*, by Robert Drake (growing up in west Tennessee).
Tips: Considering new material on a very limited basis until 1987.

MENASHA RIDGE PRESS, INC., Box 59257, Birmingham AL 35259. (205)991-0373. Publisher: R.W. Sehlinger. Publishes hardcover and trade paperback originals. Averages 10-15 titles/year; receives 600-800 submissions annually. 50% of books from first-time authors; 90% of books from unagented writers. Average print order for a writer's first book is 4,000. Pays 10% royalty on wholesale price or purchases outright; offers average $1,000 advance. Publishes book an average of 8 months after acceptance. Simultaneous and photo-copied submissions OK. Electronic submissions OK on IBM PC/300 or 1200 Baud; sometimes requires hard copy. Computer printout submissions acceptable; prefers letter-quality to dot-matrix. Reports in 1 month. Ms guidelines for SASE.

Nonfiction: How-to, reference, self-help, consumer, outdoor recreation, travel guides and small business. Subjects include business and economics, health, hobbies, recreation, sports, travel and consumer advice. No biography or religious copies. Submit outline/synopsis and sample chapters. Reviews artwork/photos.

Recent Nonfiction Title: *Shipwrecks: Diving the North Carolina Coast*, by Farb (scuba diving/history).

Tips: Audience: age 25-60, 14-18 years' education, white collar and professional, $30,000 median income, 75% male, 75% east of Mississippi River.

*MERCURY HOUSE INC., Suite 700, 300 Montgomery St., San Francisco CA 94104. (415)433-7042. President: William M. Brinton. Executive Editor: Alev Lytle. Publishes hardcover originals. Averages 10-15 titles/year; receives 500 submissions annually. 20% of books come from first-time authors; 10% of books from un-agented writers. Average print order for a writer's first book is 5,000. Subsidy publishes "only if there is a good market and author has something unique to say, and can say it well." Pays standard royalties; advances negotiable. "Will consider negotiating with author who pays a percentage of cost of printing, publishing, selling book—a tax-oriented transaction." Publishes books an average of 9 months after acceptance. Simultaneous and photocopied submissions OK only if publisher is informed prior to arrangement. Computer printout submissions acceptable in letter-quality type only; no dot-matrix. Reports in 4 weeks on queries; 6 weeks on mss.

Nonfiction: Original and unusual adult nonfiction, on a limited basis. Query with outline/synopsis and sample chapters. All unsolicited mss are returned unopened. SASE for both sample chapters and complete ms.

Recent Nonfiction Title: *The Psychic Detectives.*

Fiction: Original adult fiction, translations, reprints. Query with outline/synopsis and sample chapters. All unsolicited mss are returned unopened. SASE for both sample chapters and complete ms.

Recent Fiction Title: *The Alaska Deception.*

Tips: "Our audience is adult. The editorial process is highly rigorous. Mercury House uses electronic marketing of its titles through computer users, as well as traditional distribution channels."

MERIWETHER PUBLISHING LTD., 885 Elkton Dr., Colorado Springs CO 80907. (303)594-4422. Editor/President: Arthur L. Zapel. Publishes trade paperback originals and reprints. Averages 25-30 titles/year; receives 1,100 submissions annually. 80% of books from first-time authors; 95% of books from unagented writers. Pays 10% royalty on wholesale or retail prices or outright purchase. Publishes books an average of 7 months after acceptance. Simultaneous and photocopied submissions OK. Reports in 3 weeks on queries; 1 month on mss. Book catalog for 8½x11 SAE and $1 postage. Ms guidelines for $1 or SASE.

Nonfiction: How-to, self-help, textbook and one-act plays. Subjects include religion, speech, drama and English. "We specialize in books dealing with the communication arts: drama, speech, theatre, English, etc. We also publish how-to books for youth activities. Books of plays are our specialty." No cookbooks, philosophy, sociology, etc. Query. Reviews artwork/photos. "We occasionally make work-for-hire assignments; usu-ally only with writers we have published before."

Recent Nonfiction Title: *Original Auditions for Actors*, by Eddie Lawrence.

Fiction: Religious plays or comedy one-act plays or comedy musicals.

Tips: "We are primarily play publishers but we also publish how-to books relating to speech, drama and youth activities, and nonfiction religious books. A writer should be sure that he/she has a fresh idea—a unique theme or concept. We look for writers who are ahead of the trends."

MERRILL PUBLISHING CO., a Bell & Howell Co., 1300 Alum Creek Dr., Columbus OH 43216. (614)890-1111. Publishes hardcover and paperback originals and software. Averages 400 titles/year; receives 200 submissions annually. 50% of books from first-time authors; the majority of books from unagented writers. Publishes book an average of 1 year after acceptance. "Royalties and contract terms vary with the nature of the material. They are very competitive within each market area. Some projects are handled on an outright purchase basis." Will accept simultaneous submissions if notified. Electronic submissions OK on various systems; hard copy suggested. Computer printout submissions acceptable; prefers letter-quality to dot-matrix. Submit outline/synopsis and 3 sample chapters. Reports in 1-3 months.

Education Division: Editor-in-Chief: Ann Turpie. Publishes texts, workbooks, software, and other supplementary materials for elementary, junior high and high schools in the subject areas of language arts and literature, mathematics, science, health, and social studies (no juvenile stories or novels). Bilingual materials (Spanish) are also published for mathematics and science. Reviews artwork/photos.

College Division: Editor-in-Chief, Education, Special Education and Humanities, Business, Mathematics, Science and Technology: Franklin Lewis. Publishes college texts and related materials. Reviews artwork/photos.

*MEYERBOOKS, PUBLISHER, Box 427, Glenwood IL 60425. (312)757-4950. Publisher: David Meyer. Publishes hardcover and trade paperback originals and hardcover and trade paperback reprints. Averages 3 titles/year; receives 25 submissions annually. 50% of books from first-time authors; 100% of books from unagented writers. Is willing to subsidy publish. "Subject matter and intended audience determine whether an author should be subsidy published. If we cannot correctly identify the market for the subject, but the author can, we consider this kind of project suitable for subsidy treatment." Pays 5-10% royalty, on wholesale price or retail price. Makes outright purchase for minimum $500. Offers average $250 advance. Publishes book an average of 15 months after acceptance. Simultaneous and photocopied submissions OK. Computer printout submissions acceptable; prefers letter-quality to dot-matrix. Reports in 1 month on queries; 6 months on mss. Book catalog for #10 SASE and 1 first class stamp.
Nonfiction: History, reference and self-help. Subjects include Americana, cooking and foods, health (natural healing), history (theatre), hobbies (magic) and nature. "We publish books for limited, specialized markets." Books have been contracted on an anecdotal reminiscences of a rare book dealer, a theatrical autobiography, and a history of Mormon printing in Navoo, Illinois. "No technical books, esoteric subjects, or books which might be better published by large New York publishers." Query or submit outline/synopsis and sample chapters. Reviews artwork/photos.
Recent Nonfiction Title: *American Folk Medicine*, by Clarence Meyer (health).
Tips: "Choose carefully the subject you intend to spend a year or more of your time and effort in completing. Consider whether your book project realistically has an audience sufficient enough to warrant publication and satisfactory sales. You might convince yourself that a slapdash manuscript or an obscure subject will be of interest to people, but you must convince more than yourself—you must convince a publisher."

THE MGI MANAGEMENT INSTITUTE, INC., 378 Halstead Ave., Harrison NY 10528. (914)835-5790. President: Dr. Henry Oppenheimer. Averages 15 titles/year; receives 3-4 submissions annually. 50% of books from first-time authors; 100% of those books from unagented writers. Pays 3-5% royalty on retail price of correspondence course (price is usually in $100 range) or 10-15% for conventional book. Publishes book an average of 6 months after acceptance. Electronic submissions OK on IBM PC, Wordstar, but requires hard copy also. Computer printout submissions acceptable. Reports in 2 weeks. Free book catalog.
Nonfiction: How-to, technical and correspondence courses. Subjects include business and economics, electrical engineering, computer, and manufacturing-related topics. Needs correspondence courses in manufacturing management, computers, artificial intelligence and marketing professional services. Reviews artwork/photos.
Recent Nonfiction Title: *Expert Systems*, by Dr. Kamran Parsaye (correspondence course).
Tips: "We are interested in textbooks also if specific market can be identified. Our audience includes graduate engineers and architects, manufacturing supervisors and managers, and real estate investors."

MICROTREND, BOOKS, Slawson Communications, Inc., 3719 6th Ave., San Diego CA 92103. (619)291-9126. Publishes trade paperback originals and software. Averages 12 titles/year; receives 100 submissions annually. 10% of books from first-time authors; 20% of books from unagented writers. Average print order for a writer's first book is 5,000-50,000. Pays 10-20% royalty on wholesale price. Offers variable advance. Publishes book an average of 6 months after acceptance. Simultaneous and photocopied submissions OK. Computer printout submissions acceptable; prefers letter-quality to dot-matrix. Reports in 2 weeks on queries; 1 month on mss. Ms guidelines for SASE.
Nonfiction: How-to, self-help, and technical—only microcomputer subjects. Query. Reviews artwork/photos as part of ms package.
Recent Nonfiction Title: *LOGO Handbook*, by Guy Stone.

MILLER BOOKS, 2908 W. Valley Blvd., Alhambra CA 91803. (818)284-7607. Subsidiaries include *San Gabriel Valley Magazine*, Miller Press and Miller Electric. Publisher: Joseph Miller. Publishes hardcover and trade paperback originals, hardcover reprints and software. Averages 4 titles/year. Pays 10-15% royalty on retail price; buys some mss outright. Simultaneous and photocopied submissions OK. Computer printout submissions acceptable. Reports in 2 weeks on queries; 2 months on mss. Free book catalog.
Nonfiction: Cookbook, how-to, self-help, textbook and remedial textbooks. Subjects include Americana, animals, cooking and foods, history, philosophy and politics. "Remedial manuscripts are needed in most fields." No erotica. Submit complete ms. Reviews artwork/photos as part of ms package. "Please don't send letters. Let us see your work."
Recent Nonfiction Title: *Every Feeling is Desire*, by James Smith, M.D.
Fiction: Adventure, historical, humor, mystery and western. No erotica; "no returns on erotic material." Submit complete ms.
Recent Fiction Title: *The Magic Story*, by F.V.R. Dey (positive thinking).
Tips: "Write something good about people, places and our country. Avoid the negative—it doesn't sell."

‡MIT PRESS, 28 Carleton St., Cambridge MA 02142. (617)253-1693. Acquisitions Coordinator: Cristina Sanmartin. Averages 100 titles/year. "Subsidies are sometimes provided by cultural agencies but not by author." Pays 8-10% royalty on wholesale or retail price; $500-1,000 advance. Publishes book an average of 18 months after acceptance. Electronic submissions OK "if compatible with our computer graphics equipment," but requires hard copy also. Computer printout submissions acceptable; prefers letter-quality to dot-matrix. Reports in 6 weeks. Free book catalog.

Nonfiction: Computer science/artificial intelligence, civil engineering/transportation, neuroscience, linguistics/psychology/philosophy, architecture, design, visual communication, economics, physics, math, and history of science and technology. "Our books must reflect a certain level of technological sophistication. We do not want fiction, poetry, literary criticism, education, pure philosophy, European history before 1920, belles-lettres, drama, personal philosophies, or children's books." Submit outline/synopsis, academic resume and sample chapters.

Recent Nonfiction Title: *Computers and Communications: A Vision of C & C*, by Koji Kobayashi.

‡MODERN LANGUAGE ASSOCIATION OF AMERICA, 10 Astor Pl., New York NY 10003. (212)475-9500. Director of Book Publications: Walter S. Achtert. Publishes hardcover and trade paperback originals. Averages 20 titles/year; receives 100 submissions annually. 100% of books from unagented writers. Pays 5-15% royalty on net proceeds. Offers average $100 advance. Publishes book an average of 11 months after acceptance. Photocopied submissions OK. Electronic submissions acceptable; prefers letter-quality to dot-matrix. Reports in 3 weeks on queries; 3 months on mss. Book catalog free on request.

Nonfiction: Reference and professional. Subjects include language and literature. Needs mss on current issues in research and teaching of language and literature. No critical monographs. Query or submit outline/synopsis and sample chapters.

Recent Nonfiction Title: *Helping Students Write Well*, by Barbara E. Fassler Walvoord.

‡MONITOR BOOK CO., INC., 9441 Wilshire Blvd., Beverly Hills CA 90212. (213)271-5558. Editor-in-Chief: Alan F. Pater. Hardcover originals. Pays 10% minimum royalty or by outright purchase, depending on circumstances; no advance. Send prints if photos and/or illustrations are to accompany ms. Reports in 4 months. Book catalog for SASE.

Nonfiction: Americana, biographies (only of well-known personalities), law and reference books.

Recent Nonfiction Title: *What They Said in 1985* (yearbook of world opinion).

MOREHOUSE-BARLOW CO., INC., 78 Danbury Rd., Wilton CT 06897. Editorial Director: Stephen S. Wilburn. Publishes hardcover and paperback originals. Averages 20 titles/year; receives 500 submissions annually. 40% of books from first-time authors; 100% of books from unagented writers. Pays 10% royalty on retail price. Publishes book an average of 8 months after acceptance. Computer printout submissions acceptable; no dot-matrix.

Nonfiction: Specializes in Anglican religious publishing. Theology, ethics, church history, pastoral counseling, liturgy and religious education. Accepts outline/synopsis and 2-4 sample chapters. No poetry or drama. Reviews artwork/photos as part of ms package.

Recent Nonfiction Title: *The Killing, Suffering, Sex, and Other Paradoxes.*

‡MORGAN AND MORGAN, INC., 145 Palisade St., Dobbs Ferry NY 10522. (914)693-0023. President: Douglas Morgan. Publishes hardcover and trade paperback originals (80%) and hardcover and trade paperback reprints (20%). Averages 5 titles/year; receives 300 submissions annually. 50% of books from first-time authors; 95% of books from unagented writers. (Editor's note: Morgan & Morgan Inc., does not subsidy publish, but Morgan Press, an affiliated company, subsidy publishes 100% of books.) Pays 5-10% royalty on net price; makes outright purchase, $100-5,000; or pays 20-35% retail price per book sold. Offers average $500 advance. Publishes book an average of 1 year after acceptance. Photocopied submissions OK (if original is provided upon ms acceptance). Electronic submissions OK via IBM System 34/Mergenthaler CRtronic 300, but requires hard copy also. Computer printout submissions acceptable; prefers letter-quality to dot-matrix. Reports in 2 months. Free book catalog.

Nonfiction: "Coffee table" book; photography how-to, illustrated book, juvenile, reference, technical and textbook; and Tarot-related. "We are looking for manuscripts on photography for the professional or educated layman and manuscripts on the Tarot for the layman. Both types should cover aspects on which there is little information available." Query or submit outline/synopsis and sample chapters. Reviews artwork/photos.

Recent Nonfiction Title: *How to Shoot a Movie and Video Story*, by Arthur Gaskill and David Englander (how-to).

Tips: "Our audience is interested in photography (with emphasis on technical facets) or Tarot."

WILLIAM MORROW AND CO., 105 Madison Ave., New York NY 10016. Publisher: Sherry W. Arden. Imprints include Greenwillow Books (juveniles), Susan Hirschman, editor. Lothrop, Lee and Shepard (juveniles), Dorothy Briley, editor. Morrow Junior Books (juveniles), David Reuther, editor. Quill (trade paperback), Allison Brown-Cerier, Managing Editor. Affiliates include Hearst Books (trade). Editorial Director: Joan Nagy. Hearst Marine Books (nautical). Beech Tree Books, James D. Landis, Publisher. Receives 10,000

submissions annually. 30% of books from first-time authors; 5% of books from unagented writers. Payment is on standard royalty basis. Publishes book an average of 1-2 years after acceptance. Computer printout submissions acceptable; prefers letter-quality to dot-matrix. Query letter on all books. No unsolicited mss or proposals. Mss and proposals should be submitted through a literary agent.
Nonfiction and Fiction: Publishes adult fiction, nonfiction, history, biography, arts, religion, poetry, how-to books and cookbooks. Length: 50,000-100,000 words. Query only; mss and proposals should be submitted only through an agent.
Recent Fiction Title: *Lie Down With Lions*, by Ken Follett.

MORROW JUNIOR BOOKS, 105 Madison Ave., New York NY 10016. (212)889-3050. Editor-in-Chief: David L. Reuther. Senior Editor: Andrea Curley. Publishes hardcover originals. Publishes 50 titles/year. All contracts negotiated separately; offers variable advance. Computer printout submissions acceptable; prefers letter-quality to dot-matrix. Reports in 6 weeks. Free book catalog.
Nonfiction: Juveniles (trade books). No textbooks. Query. Reviews artwork/photos as part of ms package.
Fiction: Juveniles (trade books).

MOSAIC PRESS MINIATURE BOOKS, 358 Oliver Rd., Cincinnati OH 45215. (513)761-5977. Publisher: Miriam Irwin. Publishes hardcover originals. Averages 4 titles/year; receives 150-200 submissions annually. 49% of books from first-time authors. Average print order for a writer's first book is 2,000. Buys mss outright for $50. Publishes book an average of 30 months after acceptance. Computer printout submissions acceptable; no dot-matrix. Reports in 2 weeks; "but our production, if manuscript is accepted, often takes 2 or 3 years." Book catalog $3.
Nonfiction: Biography, cookbook, humor, illustrated book and satire. Subjects include Americana, animals, art, business and economics, cooking and foods, health, history, hobbies, music, nature, sports and travel. Interested in "beautifully written, delightful text. If factual, it must be extremely correct and authoritative. Our books are intended to delight, both in their miniature size, beautiful bindings and excellent writing." No occult, pornography, science fiction, fantasy, haiku, or how-to. Query or submit outline/synopsis and sample chapters or complete ms. Reviews artwork/photos as part of ms package.
Recent Nonfiction Title: *Colonial Lighthouses*, by Margaret Hassert.
Tips: Factual—freelancer has best chance of selling a factual ms; "I want a book to tell me something I don't know."

MOTORBOOKS INTERNATIONAL PUBLISHERS & WHOLESALERS, INC., Box 2, Osceola WI 54020. Director of Publications: Tim Parker. Senior Editor: Barbara K. Harold. Hardcover and paperback originals. Averages 10-12 titles/year. 100% of books from unagented writers. Offers 7-15% royalty on wholesale or retail price. Offers average $1,500 advance. Publishes book an average of 7-10 months after acceptance. Simultaneous and photocopied submissions OK. Electronic submissions OK, but requires hard copy also. Computer printout submissions acceptable; prefers letter-quality to dot-matrix. Reports in 3 months. Free book catalog; ms guidelines for SASE.
Nonfiction: Publishes biography, history, how-to, photography, and motor sports as they relate to cars, trucks, motorcycles, motor sports and aviation (domestic and foreign). No repair manuals. Submit outline/synopsis, 1-2 sample chapters and sample of illustrations. "State qualifications for doing book." Reviews artwork/photos as part of ms package. Accepts nonfiction translations from German/Italian.
Recent Nonfiction Title: *The Harley-Davidson Motor Company*, by David Wright.
Tips: "Trends in book publishing that freelance writers should be aware of include higher trade discounts resulting in less total royalties."

***MOUNTAIN PRESS PUBLISHING CO.**, 1600 North Ave. W, Missoula MT 59806. Publisher: David P. Flaccus. Hardcover and paperback originals (90%) and reprints (10%). Averages 12 titles/year; receives 150 submissions annually. 50% of books from first-time authors; 95% of books from unagented writers. Average print order for a writer's first book is 3,000-5,000. Royalty of 12% of net amount received; no advance. Subsidy publishes less than 5% of books. "Top-quality work in very limited market only." Publishes book an average of 6-12 months after acceptance. Computer printout submissions acceptable; prefers letter-quality to dot-matrix. Reports in 1 month. Free book catalog.
Nonfiction: Publishes history (western Americana); hobbies; how-to (angling, hunting); nature (geology, habitat and conservation); outdoor recreation (backpacking, fishing, etc.); technical (wood design and technology); and textbooks. Looks for "target audience, organization, quality of writing and style compatibility with current list and goals." Accepts nonfiction translations. State availability of photos and/or illustrations to accompany ms. Reviews artwork/photos as part of ms package.
Recent Nonfiction Title: *Mammals of the Northern Rockies* (regional full color guide to mammals).
Tips: "Demonstrate to us the need for the book—what makes your book different from others already in print. Assess the market size and suggest ways and means of contacting that market."

THE MOUNTAINEERS BOOKS, 306-2nd Ave W., Seattle WA 98119. (206)285-2665. Manager: Donna DeShazo. Publishes hardcover and trade paperback originals (85%) and reprints (15%). Averages 10-15 titles/year; receives 150-250 submissions annually. 25% of books from first-time authors; 98% of books from un-agented writers. Average print order for a writer's first book is 2,000-5,000. Offers 17½% royalty based on net sales. Offers advance on occasion. Publishes book an average of 1 year after acceptance. Dot-matrix submissions are acceptable with new ribbon and double spaced. Reports in 6-8 weeks. Free book catalog and ms guidelines for 9x12 SAE with 39¢ postage.
Nonfiction: Recreation, non-competitive sports, and outdoor how-to books. "We specialize only in books dealing with mountaineering, hiking, backpacking, skiing, snowshoeing, canoeing, bicycling, etc. These can be either how-to-do-it, where-to-do-it (guidebooks), or accounts of mountain-related experiences." Does *not* want to see "anything dealing with hunting, fishing or motorized travel." Submit outline/synopsis and mini-mum of 2 sample chapters. Accepts nonfiction translations. Looks for "expert knowledge, good organization."
Recent Nonfiction Title: *Trekking in Nepal*, by Stephen Bezruchka (guidebook).
Fiction: "We might consider an exceptionally well-done book-length manuscript on mountaineering." Does *not* want poetry or mystery. Query first.
Tips: "The type of book the writer has the best chance of selling our firm is an authoritative guidebook (*in our field*) to a specific area not otherwise covered; a first-person narrative of outdoor adventure otherwise undupli-cated in print."

JOHN MUIR PUBLICATIONS, Box 613, Santa Fe NM 87504. (505)982-4078. Project Co-ordinator: Richard Harris. Publishes trade paperback originals. Averages 10 titles/year; receives 500 submissions annually. 10% of books from first-time authors; 90% of books from unagented writers. Average print order for a writer's first book is 7,500-10,000. Pays 7-9% royalty; offers variable advance. Publishes book an average of 1 year after acceptance. Simultaneous and photocopied submissions OK. Electronic submissions OK with IBM PC com-patibility, but requires hard copy also. Computer printout submissions acceptable; no dot-matrix. Reports in 1 month on queries; 2 months on mss. Free book catalog.
Nonfiction: How-to, illustrated book, general nonfiction. Subjects include automobile repair manuals, gen-eral nonfiction, and travel. "We are interested in manuscripts written with warmth, wit, humor and accuracy. The topic of such a submission is open. We're particularly interested in manuscripts pertaining to automobile repair and maintenance. We don't publish theory books or political treatises or books like 'The History of Ten-nis Memorabilia'; topics must either have a practical application or be of current interest." Submit outline/syn-opsis and at least 3 sample chapters. Reviews artwork/photos as part of ms package.
Recent Nonfiction Title: *Road & Track's Used Car Classics*, edited by Peter Bohr.
Tips: "*Please* take a look at our books before submitting a manuscript. It is friendliness and humor that set our books apart. Also we often get queries for 'the children's book editor' or 'the poetry editor' when a bit of re-search would reveal we publish neither children's nor poetry books. The writer has the best chance of selling our firm travel or automotive-related books or subjects promoting self-sufficiency."

MULTNOMAH PRESS, 10209 SE Division St., Portland OR 97266. (503)257-0526. Editorial Manager: Rodney L. Morris. Publishes hardcover and trade paperback originals, and trade paperback reprints. Averages 40 titles/year; receives 500 submissions annually. 30% of books from first-time authors; 100% of books from unagented writers. Pays royalty on wholesale price. Publishes books an average of 9 months after acceptance. Photocopied submissions OK. Electronic submissions OK on MSDOS or PCDOS compatible, but requires hard copy also. Computer printout submissions acceptable; no dot-matrix. Reports in 6 weeks on queries; 10 weeks on mss. Free book catalog; ms guidelines for SASE.
Nonfiction: "Coffee table" book and self-help. Subjects include religion. "We publish issue-related books linking social/ethical concerns and Christianity; books addressing the needs of women from a Christian point of view; books addressing the needs of the traditional family in today's society; and books explaining Christian theology in a very popular way to a lay audience." No daily devotional, personal experience, Scripture/photo combinations or poetry. Submit outline/synopsis and sample chapters. Reviews artwork/photos.
Recent Nonfiction Title: *Imagination: Embracing a Theology of Wonder*, by Cheryl Forbes (Christian so-cial-ethical).
Tips: "We are looking for well-developed, researched and documented books addressing a critical issue from a theologically conservative point of view. We have a reputation for tackling tough issues from a Biblical view; we need to continue to deserve that reputation. Avoid being too scholarly or detached. Although we like well-researched books, we do direct our books to a popular market, not just to professors of theology."

MUSEUM OF NEW MEXICO PRESS, Box 2087, Santa Fe NM 87503. (505)827-6454. Director: James Maf-chir. Editor-in-Chief: Sarah Nestor. Hardcover and paperback originals (90%) and reprints (10%). Averages 4-6 titles/year; receives 100 submissions annually. 50% of books from first-time authors; 75% of books from un-agented writers. Average print order for a writer's first book is 2,000-5,000. Royalty of 10% of list after first

1,000 copies; no advance. Publishes book an average of 1 year after acceptance. Computer printout submissions acceptable; no dot-matrix. Reports in 1-2 months. Free book catalog.
Nonfiction: "We publish both popular and scholarly books on regional anthropology, history, fine and folk arts; geography, natural history, the Americas and the Southwest; regional cookbooks; art, biography (regional and Southwest); music; nature; reference, scientific and technical." Accepts nonfiction translations. Prints preferred for illustrations; transparencies best for color. Sources of photos or illustrations should be indicated for each. Query or submit outline/synopsis and sample chapters to Sarah Nestor, Editor-in-Chief. Mss should be typed double-spaced, follow Chicago *Manual of Style*, and be accompanied by information about the author's credentials and professional background. Reviews artwork/photos as part of ms package.

MUSEUM OF NORTHERN ARIZONA PRESS, Box 720, Rt. 4, Flagstaff AZ 86001. (602)774-5211. Publisher: Diana Clark Lubick. Publishes hardcover and trade paperback originals. Averages 6-8 titles/year; receives 35 submissions annually. 10% of books from first-time authors; 100% of books from unagented writers. Pays one-time fee on acceptance of ms. No advance. Publishes book an average of 1 year after acceptance. Queries only. Electronic submissions OK via IBM PC or Macintosh. Computer printout submissions acceptable; prefers letter-quality to dot-matrix. Reports in 1 month. Free book catalog; ms guidelines for SASE.
Nonfiction: Coffee table book, reference, technical. Subjects include Southwest, art, nature, science. Especially needs manuscripts on the Colorado Plateau that are written for a well-educated general audience." Query or submit outline/synopsis and 3-4 sample chapters. Accepts artwork/photos.
Recent Nonfiction Title: *Images on Stone* (rock art).

MUSIC SALES CORP., 24 E. 22nd St., New York NY 10010. (212)254-2100. Imprints include Acorn, Amsco, Ariel, Consolidated, Embassy, Oak, Yorktown, Music Sales Ltd., London; Wise Pub., Ashdown Ltd., and Music Sales, Australia. Editor-in-Chief: Eugene Weintraub. President (NY office): Barry Edwards. Production Manager: Daniel R. Earley. Publishes paperback originals and reprints. Averages 100 titles/year; receives 75 submissions annually. 33% of books from first-time authors; 99% of books from unagented writers. Standard publishing contracts. Publishes book an average of 6 months after acceptance. Simultaneous and photocopied submissions OK. Computer printout submissions acceptable; no dot-matrix.
Nonfiction: Instructional music books; also technical, theory, reference and pop music personalities. Music Sales Corporation publishes and distributes a complete line of quality music instruction books for every musician from beginner to professional. Reviews artwork/photos.
Recent Nonfiction Title: *The Complete Keyboard Player*, (series of books from beginner to advanced), by Kenneth Baker.
Tips: "An accurate, well-written manuscript on electronic, hi-tech equipment used by musicians has the best chance of selling to our firm. Use concise, easy-to-understand 'layman's' language to communicate complex or abstract electronic music processes and theory."

MUSTANG PUBLISHING CO., Box 9327, New Haven CT 06533. (203)624-5485. President: Rollin Riggs. Publishes hardcover and trade paperback originals. Averages 6 titles/year; receives 1,000 submissions annually. 50% of books from first-time authors; 100% of books from unagented writers. Pays 7-10% royalty on retail price. Publishes book an average of 1 year after acceptance. Simultaneous and photocopied submissions OK. No electronic submissions. Computer printout submissions acceptable; prefers letter-quality to dot-matrix. Reports in 1 month. Book catalog available from our distributor: Kampmann & Company, 9 E. 40th St., New York NY 10016.
Nonfiction: How-to, humor and self-help. Subjects include Americana, hobbies, recreation, sports and travel. "Our needs are very general—humor, travel, how-to, nonfiction, etc.—for the 18 to 35-year-old market." Query or submit outline/synopsis and sample chapters.
Recent Nonfiction Title: *Beer Games II: The Exploitative Sequel*, by Griscom, Rand, Johnston, and Balay.
Tips: "If it's clever, interesting and marketable, I'll take a look at it."

THE NAIAD PRESS, INC., Box 10543, Tallahassee FL 32302. (904)539-9322. Editorial Director: Barbara Grier. Publishes paperback originals. Averages 12 titles/year; receives 255 submissions annually. 20% of books from first-time authors; 99% of books from unagented writers. Average print order for a writer's first book is 12,000. Pays 15% royalty on wholesale or retail price; no advance. Publishes book an average of 1 year after acceptance. Reports in 2 months. Book catalog and ms guidelines for SAE and 39¢ postage..
Fiction: "We publish lesbian fiction, preferably lesbian/feminist fiction. We are not impressed with the 'oh woe' school and prefer realistic (i.e., happy) novels. We emphasize fiction and are now heavily reading manuscripts in that area. We are working in a lot of genre fiction—mysteries, science fiction, short stories, fantasy—all with lesbian themes, of course." Query.
Recent Fiction Title: *An Emergence of Green*, by Katherine V. Forrest.

THE NATIONAL GALLERY OF CANADA, Publications Division, 75 Alberta St., R-330, Ottawa, Ontario K1A 0M8 Canada. (613)990-0540. Head: Peter L. Smith. Publishes hardcover and paperback originals. Aver-

ages 15 titles/year. Subsidy publishes (non-author) 100% of books. Pays in outright purchase of $1,500-2,500; offers average $700 advance. Photocopied submissions OK. Reports in 3 months. Free sales catalog.
Nonfiction: "In general, we publish only *solicited* manuscripts on art, particularly Canadian art, and must publish them in English and French. Exhibition catalogs are commissioned, but we are open (upon approval by Curatorial general editors) to manuscripts for the various series, monographic and otherwise, that we publish. All manuscripts should be directed to our Editorial Coordinator, who doubles as manuscript editor. Since we publish translations into French, authors have access to French Canada and the rest of Francophonia. Because our titles are distributed by the University of Chicago Press, authors have the attention of European as well as American markets."
Recent Nonfiction Title: *Vatican Splendor: Masterpieces of Baroque Art*, by Catherine Johnston, Gyde Sheperd and Marc Worsdale.

NATIONAL PRESS, INC., 7508 Wisconsin Ave., Bethesda MD 20814. (301)657-1616. Publisher: Joel D. Joseph. Publishes hardcover and trade paperback originals, and hardcover and trade paperback reprints and software. Averages 10-12 titles/year. 50% of books from first-time authors; 80% of books from unagented writers. Pays 5-10% royalty on retail price. Offers variable advance. Publishes book an average of 9 months after acceptance. Computer printout submissions acceptable; prefers letter-quality to dot-matrix. Simultaneous and photocopied submissions OK. Reports in 1 month. Free book catalog.
Nonfiction: Consumer guides, cookbook, how-to, humor, illustrated book, juvenile, reference and self-help. Subjects include Americana, animals, business and economics, cooking and foods, health, recreation, sports and travel. Query and/or submit outline/synopsis and sample chapters.
Recent Nonfiction Title: *How to Watch Ice Hockey*, by Bernie Wolfe.

‡NATIONAL PUBLISHERS OF THE BLACK HILLS, INC., 137 E. Main St., Elmscord NY 10523. Editorial Director: Ellen Schneid Coleman. Publishes trade and text paperback originals and software. Averages 10 titles/year. Pays negotiable royalty; offers negotiable advance. Publishes book an average of 9 months after acceptance. Computer printout submissions acceptable. Reports in 3 weeks on queries; 5 weeks on mss.
Nonfiction: Technical, business and economics texts, medical administrative assisting, computer science texts, travel, and general texts aimed at the post-secondary school market. Immediate needs include basic electronics texts, algebra and remedial math. Query or submit outline/synopsis and 3 sample chapters, or complete ms. Reviews artwork/photos as part of ms package.
Recent Nonfiction Title: *Your Job, Your Future*, by Carolyn Hettich.

NATIONAL TEXTBOOK CO., 4255 W. Touhy Ave., Lincolnwood IL 60646. (312)679-5500. Editorial Director: Leonard I. Fiddle. Publishes softcover originals for education and trade market, and software. Averages 20-30 titles/year; receives 200+ submissions annually. 10% of books from first-time authors; 80% of books from unagented writers. Mss purchased on either royalty or buy-out basis. Publishes book an average of 6-12 months after acceptance. Computer printout submissions acceptable; no dot-matrix. Enclose return postage. Book catalog and writer's guidelines for SAE and 2 first class stamps. Send sample chapter and outline or table of contents. Reports in 4 months.
Nonfiction: Textbook. Major emphasis being given to foreign language and language arts areas, especially secondary level material. Judith Clayton, Language Arts Editor. Michael Ross, Foreign language and ESL. Barbara Wood Donner, Career Guidance. Harry Briggs, Business Books.
Recent Nonfiction Title: *Building Real Life English Skills*, by Penn and Starkey (survival reading and writing).

NATUREGRAPH PUBLISHERS, INC., Box 1075, Happy Camp CA 96039. (916)493-5353. Editor: Barbara Brown. Quality trade books. Averages 5 titles/year; receives 200 submissions annually. 75% of books from first-time authors; 100% of books from unagented writers. Average print order for a writer's first book is 2,500. "We offer 10% of wholesale; 12½% after 10,000 copies are sold. To speed things up, queries should include summary, detailed outline, comparison to related books, 2 sample chapters, availability and samples of any photos or illustrations, and author background. Send manuscript only on request." Publishes book an average of 18 months after acceptance. Photocopied submissions OK. Computer printout submissions acceptable; prefers letter-quality to dot-matrix. Reports in 2 months. Free book catalog; ms guidelines for SASE.
Nonfiction: Primarily publishes nonfiction for the layman in 7 general areas: natural history (biology, geology, ecology, astronomy); American Indian (historical and contemporary); outdoor living (backpacking, wild edibles, etc.); land and gardening (modern homesteading); crafts and how-to; holistic health (natural foods and healing arts); and PRISM Editions (Baha'i and other new age approaches to harmonious living). All material must be well-grounded; author must be professional, and in command of effective style. Our natural history and American Indian lines can be geared for educational markets." Reviews artwork/photos.
Recent Nonfiction Title: *Oaks of North America*, by Miller and Lamb.

NAVAL INSTITUTE PRESS, Annapolis MD 21402. Acquisitions Editor: Deborah Guberti. Press Director: Thomas F. Epley. Averages 30 titles/year; receives 200 submissions annually. 80% of books from first-time au-

thors; 99% of books from unagented writers. Average print order for a writer's first book is 3,000. Pays 14-18-21% royalty based on net sales; modest advance. Publishes book an average of 10 months after acceptance. Computer printout submissions acceptable; no dot-matrix. Reports in 2 weeks on queries; 6 weeks on other submissions. Free book catalog; ms guidelines for SASE.
Nonfiction: "We are interested only in naval and maritime subjects: tactics, strategy, navigation, naval history, biographies of naval leaders and naval aviation." Reviews artwork/photos as part of ms package.
Fiction: Limited, very high quality fiction on naval and maritime themes.
Recent Title: *The Hunt for Red October*, by Tom Clancy.

NC PRESS, 31 Portland St., Toronto, Ontario M5V 2V9 Canada. (416)593-6284. Editorial Director: Caroline Walker. Publishes hardcover and paperback originals and reprints and a full line of children's books. Averages 10-15 titles/year; receives 500 submissions annually. 50% of books from first-time authors; 80% of books from unagented writers. Average print order for a writer's first book is 2,500. Pays royalty on list under 50% discount. Computer printout submissions acceptable. Include IRCs with submissions. Ms guidelines for SASE.
Nonfiction: "We generally publish books of social/political relevance either on contemporary topics of concern (current events, ecology, etc.), or historical studies and popular health books. We publish primarily Canadiana. We cannot publish a U.S. author without U.S. co-publisher." Submit outline/synopsis and 1-2 sample chapters.
Recent Nonfiction Title: *Choice Cooking*, by The Canadian Diabetes Association.

THOMAS NELSON PUBLISHERS, Nelson Place at Elm Hill Pike, Nashville TN 37214. (615)889-9000. Editorial Director: Bruce A. Nygren. Publishes hardcover and paperback originals and reprints. Averages 75 titles/year. Pays royalty or by outright purchase; sometimes in advance. Publishes book an average of 1 year after acceptance. Computer printout submissions acceptable. Reports in 2 months. Book catalog for SASE.
Nonfiction: Adult trade and reference books on religion, as well as children's (must be orthodox Christian in theology). Accepts outline/synopsis and 3 sample chapters. Reviews artwork/photos as part of ms package.
Recent Nonfiction Title: *The Road Unseen*, by Peter and Barbara Jenkins.

NELSON-HALL PUBLISHERS, 111 N. Canal St., Chicago IL 60606. (312)930-9446. Editorial Director: Harold Wise, Ph.D. Publishes hardcover and paperback originals. Averages 105 titles/year. Pays 15% maximum royalty on retail price; offers average advance. Photocopied submissions OK. Reports in 1 month. Free book catalog.
Nonfiction: Textbooks and general scholarly books in the social sciences. Query.
Recent Nonfiction Title: *Sociology: the Science of Human Organization*, by Jonathan H. Turner.

NEW AMERICAN LIBRARY, 1633 Broadway, New York NY 10019. (212)397-8000. Imprints include Signet, Mentor, Signet Classics, Plume, Meridian, D.A.W Books, and NAL Books. Publisher: Elaine Koster. Editor-in-Chief: Maureen Baron. Editor-in-Chief/Trade Books: Arnold Dolin. Editor-in-Chief/Hardcover: Michaela Hamilton. Publishes hardcover and paperback originals and hardcover reprints. Publishes 350 titles/year. Royalty is "variable"; offers "substantial" advance. Query letters *only*. Replies in 1 month. Free book catalog.
Tips: Queries may be routed to other editors in the publishing group.

THE NEW ENGLAND PRESS, INC., Box 575, Shelburne VT 05482. (802)863-2520/985-2569. President: Alfred Rosa. Publishes hardcover and trade paperback originals and trade paperback reprints. Averages 6-10 titles/year; receives 200+ submissions annually. 50% of books from first-time authors; 75% of books from unagented writers. Pays 10-15% royalty on wholesale price. Publishes ms an average of 1 year after acceptance. Photocopied submissions OK. Computer printout submissions acceptable; no dot-matrix. Reports in 2 weeks on queries; 1 month on mss. Free book catalog; ms guidelines for SASE.
Nonfiction: Biography, cookbook, how-to, humor and illustrated book. Subjects include Americana (Vermontiana and New England); cooking and foods, history (New England orientation); and essays (New England orientation). No juvenile or psychology. Query or submit outline/synopsis chapters. Reviews artwork/photos.
Recent Nonfiction Title: *Vermont Saints & Sinners*, by Lee Dana Goodman (historical Vermontiana—geniuses, nincompoops, and other curiosities).
Fiction: Historical (New England orientation), and humor. No novels. Query.
Recent Fiction Title: *The Joys of Cheap Wine*, by Henry Billings (humor).
Tips: "As a small but emerging company we attempt to emphasize personalized service and establishing a good rapport with our authors. Although we are small, we do believe in advertising—TV included in our regional area."

NEW LEAF PRESS, INC., Box 311, Green Forest AR 72638. Editor-in-Chief: Harriett Dudley. Hardcover and paperback originals. Specializes in charismatic books. Publishes 15 titles/year; receives 236 submissions annually. 15% of books from first-time authors; 90% of books from unagented writers. Average print order for a

writer's first book is 10,000. Pays 10% royalty on first 10,000 copies, paid once a year; no advance. Send photos and illustrations to accompany ms. Publishes book an average of 10 months after acceptance. Simultaneous and photocopied submissions OK. Electronic submissions OK via 128 Commodore, but requires hard copy also. Computer printout submissions acceptable. Reports in 3 months. Free book catalog and ms guidelines for SASE. Reviews artwork/photos.
Nonfiction: Biography and self-help. Charismatic books; life stories, and how to live the Christian life. Length: 100-400 pages. Submit complete ms.
Recent Nonfiction Title: *Peaceful Storm*, by Charles F. Robertson.
Tips: "Biographies, nonfiction, and Bible-based fiction have the best chance of selling to our firm. Honest and real-life experience help make a book or query one we can't put down."

NEW READERS PRESS, Publishing division of Laubach Literacy International, Box 131, Syracuse NY 13210. Senior Editor: Wendy Stein. Reading, writing and ESL; Senior Editor: Mary Ann Lapinski, Math, Social Studies and Science. Publishes paperback originals. Averages 30 titles/year; receives 200 submissions annually. 40% of books by first-time authors; 100% of books by unagented writers. Average print order for a writer's first book is 5,000. "Most of our sales are to high school classes for slower learners, special education, and adult basic education programs, with some sales to volunteer literacy programs, private human-services agencies, prisons, and libraries with outreach programs for poor readers." Pays royalty on retail price, or by outright purchase. "Rate varies according to type of publication and length of manuscript." Advance is "different in each case, but does not exceed projected royalty for first year." Publishes book an average of 1 year after acceptance. Photocopied submissions OK. Electronic submissions OK if IBM-PC compatible, but requires hard copy also. Computer printout submissions acceptable; prefers letter-quality to dot-matrix. Reports in 2 months. Free book catalog.
Nonfiction: "Our audience is adults and older teenagers with limited reading skills (6th grade level and below). We publish basic education materials in reading and writing, math, social studies, health, science, and English-as-a-second-language for double illiterates. We are particularly interested in materials that fulfill curriculum requirements in these areas. Manuscripts must be not only easy to read (3rd-6th grade level) but mature in tone and concepts. We are not interested in biography, poetry, or anything at all written for children." Accepts outline/synopsis and 1-3 sample chapters "depending on how representative of the total they are." Reviews artwork/photos as part of ms package.
Recent Nonfiction Title: *Economics: It's Your Business*, by Henry Billings.
Fiction: Short novels (12,000-15,000 words) at third grade reading level on themes of interest to adults and older teenagers.

‡NEW SOCIETY PUBLISHERS, 4722 Baltimore Ave., Philadelphia PA 19143. (215)726-6543. Collectively managed. Publishes hardcover and trade paperback originals and reprints. Averages 18 titles/year; receives 200 submissions annually. 80% of books from first-time authors; 95% of books from unagented writers. Pays 10-12½% royalty on net receipts. Offers average $500 advance. Publishes book an average of 18 months after acceptance. Photocopied submissions OK. Computer printout submissions acceptable; prefers letter-quality to dot-matrix. Reports in 1 month on queries; 3 months on mss. Book catalog free on request; ms guidelines for SASE.
Nonfiction: Biography, humor, illustrated book, social self-help and books on nonviolent action (case studies). Subjects include history, philosophy, politics, psychology, religion, sociology, feminism, ecology, worker self-management, group dynamics and peace issues. No books about the damage which will be done by nuclear war. Query *only*; "all unsolicited mss are thrown in trash." Reviews artwork/photos as part of ms package.
Recent Nonfiction Title: *This Way Daybreak Comes: Women's Values and the Future*, by Annie Cheathant (women's studies, illustrated).
Tips: "Trees are more scarce and more valuable than books. I'd like to see more writers refrain until they really have something to say, and are clear about whom they wish to say it."

NEW YORK ZOETROPE, INC., 80 E. 11th St., New York NY 10003. (212)420-0590. Contact: James Monaco. Publishes hardcover and trade paperback originals, hardcover and trade paperback reprints and software. Averages 25-50 titles/year; receives 25-50 submissions annually. 25% of books from first-time authors; 75% of books from unagented writers. Pays 10-20% royalty on wholesale prices or makes outright purchase of $500-1,000. Offers average $200 advance. Publishes book an average of 9 months after acceptance. Simultaneous and photocopied submissions OK. Electronic submissions OK via 1200 Baud standard communication parameters, but requires hard copy also. Computer printout submissions acceptable; prefers letter-quality to dot-matrix. Reports in 2 weeks on queries; 2 months on mss.
Nonfiction: "Coffee table" book, reference, technical and textbook. Subjects include business and economics, travel and media. Interested especially in film and computer subjects. No fiction. Query.
Recent Nonfiction Title: *Making Ghostbusters: The Annotated Screenplay*.
Tips: "Film- or media-oriented (academic and popular) and movie tie-ins have the best chance of selling to our firm. Media books are our strongest line."

NEWCASTLE PUBLISHING CO., INC., 13419 Saticoy, North Hollywood CA 91605. (213)873-3191. Editor-in-Chief: Alfred Saunders. Publishes trade paperback originals and reprints. Averages 8 titles/year; receives 300 submissions annually. 70% of books from first-time authors; 95% of books from unagented writers. Average print order for a writer's first book is 3,000-5,000. Pays 5-10% royalty on retail price; no advance. Publishes book an average of 8 months after acceptance. Simultaneous and photocopied submissions OK. Computer printout submissions acceptable; prefers letter-quality to dot-matrix. Reports in 3 weeks on queries; 6 weeks on mss. Free book catalog; ms guidelines for SASE.
Nonfiction: How-to, self-help, metaphysical and New Age. Subjects include health (physical fitness, diet and nutrition), psychology and religion. "Our audience is made up of college students and college-age nonstudents; also, adults ages 25 and up." No biography, travel, children's books, poetry, cookbooks or fiction. Query or submit outline/synopsis and sample chapters. Looks for "something to grab the reader so that he/she will readily remember that passage."
Recent Nonfiction Title: *Tarot for Your Self*, by Mary K. Greer(occult/self-help).
Tips: "Check the shelves in the larger bookstores on the subject of the manuscript being submitted. A book on life extension, holistic health, or stress management has the best chance of selling to our firm."

NIMBUS PUBLISHING LIMITED, Subsidiary of H.H. Marshall Ltd., Box 9301, Station A, Halifax, Nova Scotia B3K 5N5 Canada. (902)454-8381. Contact: Elizabeth Eve. Imprints include: Petheric Press (nonfiction and fiction). Publishes hardcover and trade paperback originals and trade paperback reprints. Averages 10 titles/year; receives 60 submissions annually. 50% of books from first-time authors; 100% of books from unagented writers. Average print order for a writer's first book is 3,000. Pays 4-10% royalty on retail price. Publishes book an average of 2 years after acceptance. Photocopied submissions OK. Electronic submissions OK, but requires hard copy also. Computer printout submissions acceptable. IRCs. Reports in 2 months on queries; 4 months on mss. Free book catalog.
Nonfiction: Biography, "coffee table" books, cookbooks, how-to, humor, illustrated books, juvenile and books of regional interest. Subjects include art, cooking and foods, history, nature, travel and regional. "We do some specialized publishing, otherwise, our audience is the tourist and trade market in Nova Scotia." Query or submit outline/synopsis and a minimum of 1 sample chapter. Reviews artwork/photos as part of ms package.
Recent Nonfiction Title: *An Atlantic Album, Photographs of the Atlantic Provinces before 1920.*
Tips: "Titles of regional interest, withj potential for national or international sales have the best chance of selling to our firm."

NITTY GRITTY COOKBOOKS, 447 E. Channel Rd., Box 2008, Benicia CA 94510. (707)746-0800. President: Earl Goldman. Publishes trade and mass market paperback originals. Averages 4 titles/year; receives 200 submissions annually. 50% of books from first-time authors; 100% of books from unagented writers. Pays negotiable royalty. Offers average $500 advance. Publishes book an average of 6 months after acceptance. Simultaneous and photocopied submissions OK. Computer printout submissions acceptable. Reports in 2 weeks. Free book catalog and ms guidelines.
Nonfiction: Books on cooking and foods. "We publish cookbooks only." Query or submit outline/synopsis and sample chapters.

NORTH LIGHT, Imprint of Writer's Digest Books, 9933 Alliance Rd., Cincinnati OH 45242. (513)984-0717. Editorial Director: David Lewis. Publishes hardcover and trade paperback originals. Averages 20-25 titles/year. Pays 10% royalty on net receipts. Offers $3,000 advance. Simultaneous submissions and photographs of artwork OK. Reports in 3 weeks on queries; 2 months on mss. Free book catalog.
Nonfiction: How-to art and graphic arts instruction books. Interested in books on watercolor painting, oil painting, basic drawing, pen and ink, airbrush, markers, basic design, color, illustration techniques, layout and typography. Does not want coffee table art books with no how-to art instruction. Query or submit outline/synopsis and examples of artwork.
Recent Nonfiction Title: *Exploring Color*, by Nita Leland (art instruction-all levels).

‡NORTH POINT PRESS, 850 Talbot Ave., Berkeley CA 94706. (415)527-6260. Contact: Kathleen Moses. Publishes hardcover and trade paperback originals, and trade paperback reprints. Averages 30 titles/year; receives 4,000 submissions annually. 5% of books from first-time authors; 40% of books from unagented writers. Photocopied submissions OK. Publishes book an average of 10 months after acceptance. Computer printout submissions acceptable; no dot-matrix. Reports in 3 months. Material not accompanied by return postage will not be returned. Free book catalog; ms guidelines for SASE.
Nonfiction: Biography. Subjects include cooking and foods (not cookbooks); history; nature; philosophy; sociology (cultural anthropology); and travel (literary travel). No heavily illustrated books, children's books, how-tos, technical, academic, cookbooks, or "western"-genre biographies. Query.
Recent Nonfiction Title: *Between Meals, An Appetite for Paris*, by A.J. Liebling (memoir).
Fiction: Serious literature and fiction in translation. No genre or children's fiction. Query.
Recent Fiction Title: *Ghost Dance*, by Carole Maso (novel).

Poetry: No unsolicited poetry manuscripts.
Recent Poetry Title: *Collected Poems*, by Wendell Berry.

*****NORTHEASTERN UNIVERSITY PRESS**, 17 Cushing Hall, Northeastern University, 360 Huntingon Ave., Boston MA 02115. (617)437-2783. Editorial Director: Deborah Kops. Editor: Nancy Waring. Publishes hardcover originals, and hardcover and paperback reprints. Averages 12 titles/year; receives 150 submissions annually. 80% of books from first-time authors; 100% of books from unagented writers. Average print order for a writer's first book is 1,500. Subsidy publishes (non-author) 0-5% of books. Pays 7-10% royalty on wholesale price. Publishes book an average of 9 months after acceptance. Computer printout submissions acceptable; no dot-matrix. Reports in 1 month on queries; 3 months on mss.
Nonfiction: Biography, reference and scholarly. Subjects include history, music, politics, criminal justice, literary criticism, women's studies, New England regional and scholarly material. "We are looking for scholarly works of high quality, particularly in the fields of American history, criminal justice, literary criticism, French literature, music and women's studies. Our books are read by scholars, students, and a limited trade audience." Submit outline/synopsis and 2-3 sample chapters. Reviews artwork/photos as part of ms package.
Recent Nonfiction Title: *Restitution: The Land Claims of the Mashpee, Passamaquoddy and Penobscot Indians*, by Paul Brodeur.
Poetry: One title per year—the winner of the Samuel French Morse Poetry Prize.
Recent Poetry Title: *Rain*, by William Carpenter.
Tips: "Scholarly books have the best chance of selling to Northeastern—we're a university press. For *Writer's Market* readers, regional books are a good bet."

NORTHERN ILLINOIS UNIVERSITY PRESS, DeKalb IL 60115. (815)753-1826/753-1075. Director: Mary L. Lincoln. Pays 10-15% royalty on wholesale price. Free catalog.
Nonfiction: "The NIU Press publishes mainly history, political science, literary criticism and regional studies. It does not consider collections of previously published articles, essays, etc., nor do we consider unsolicited poetry." Accepts nonfiction translations. Query with outline/synopsis and 1-3 sample chapters.
Recent Nonfiction Title: *Chicago Divided: The Making of a Black Mayor*, by Paul Kleppner.

NORTHLAND PRESS, Box N, Flagstaff AZ 86002. (602)774-5251. Hardcover and paperback originals and reprints. Advance varies. Averages 20 titles/year; receives 300 submissions annually. 10% of books from first-time authors; 95% of books from unagented writers. Pays royalty on wholesale price. Publishes book an average of 8 months after acceptance. Computer printout submissions acceptable; prefers letter-quality to dot-matrix. Simultaneous and photocopied submissions OK. Reports in 2 months. Free book catalog. Ms guidelines for SASE.
Nonfiction: Publishes western Americana, Indian arts and culture, Southwestern natural and human history and fine photography with a western orientation. Query. "Submit a proposal including an outline of the book, a sample chapter, the introduction or preface and sample illustrations. Include an inventory of items sent." Looks for "clearly developed treatment of subject, appropriate for a sophisticated general adult reader; tightly constructed presentation; an outline of author's background; pertinent research reference. Author should include assessment of intended audience (potential buyers and market) and other books published on same subject-matter." Transparencies and contact sheet required for photos and/or illustrations to accompany ms.
Recent Nonfiction Title: *The Goldwaters of Arizona*, by Dean Smith.
Tips: "Any project benefits by a clear, technically accurate presentation and a unique point of view. We are generally not interested in material that has been covered at length in other publications."

NORTHWOODS PRESS, Box 88, Thomaston ME 04861. An affiliate of The Conservatory of American Letters. (207)354-6550. Editor-in-Chief: R.W. Olmsted. Publishes hardcover and trade paperback originals. Averages 20 titles/year; receives 1,000 submissions annually. 100% of books from unagented writers. Average print order for a writer's first book is 500-1,000. Pays 10% royalty on amount received by publisher. Offers no advance. Publishes book an average of 9 months after acceptance. Simultaneous submissions OK; photocopied submissions on plain bond only. Electronic submissions OK if compatible with Compugraphic Editwriter 7300, Sanyo computer (1160) TI 99/4A. "We are working on disc to disc phone transfer from any personal computer directly to typesetter." Computer printout submissions acceptable. Reports in 3 weeks. Book catalog for 6x9 SAE and 1 first class stamp; ms guidelines for SASE.
Poetry: Good, serious work. No "Edgar A. Guest type poetry, no versy stuff that rhymes and no 'typewriter' poetry."
Recent Poetry Title: *Answers To A Bowing Moon*, by Ann Zoller.

*****NORTHWORD**, Box 5634, Madison WI 53705. (608)231-2355. Editor: Jill Weber Dean. Publishes trade paperback originals and trade paperback reprints. Averages 2-3 titles/year; receives approximately 100 submissions annually. 10-15% of books from first time authors; 40-50% unagented submissions. "We have done very little subsidy publishing and don't seek more. We have done two projects where a university engaged our serv-

ices to produce a book and paid for production costs. *Rarely*, we receive a manuscript that deserves to be published but shows no potential for commercial success." Pays 15% royalty on wholesale price. Offers average $250 advance. Publishes book an average of 1 year after acceptance. Electronic submissions OK—modem: 1200 or 300 Baud; disk: MSDOS formatted dual-density, double-sided, soft-sectored, 362 K as ASCII text or Wang word processing documents. Requires hard copy also. Computer printout submissions acceptable; prefers letter-quality to dot-matrix. Simultaneous submissions OK *only* if we are so informed. "It takes me forever to reply to most submissions. I do not object to polite periodic reminders, however." Average report time 12-18 months. Free book catalog.
Nonfiction: Subjects include history, nature, recreation, and travel. "We publish *only* titles of *genuine* focus and appeal for the geographical area centered on Wisconsin and the neighboring states (especially Minnesota and Michigan). We are always looking for guidebooks of various types to our region—travel, recreation, sporting activities, historical sights, natural landmarks, etc." No religion. Submit outline/synopsis and sample chapters. Reviews artwork/photos as part of ms package.
Recent Nonfiction Title: *Fire & Ice*, by Davenport and Wells (historic disaster epics).
Tips: "In general, our audience is a literate, curious, fairly well-educated group interested in enjoying life in our region to the fullest. We are a tiny but serious firm, and what little publishing we do, we do well."

W.W. NORTON CO., INC., 500 5th Ave., New York NY 10110. (212)354-5500. Managing Editor: Sterling Lawrence. Publishes 213 titles/year; receives 5,000 submissions annually. Often publishes new and unagented authors. Royalty varies on retail price; advance varies. Publishes book an average of 1 year after acceptance. Photocopied and simultaneous submissions OK. Computer printout submissions acceptable. Submit outline and/or 2-3 sample chapters for fiction and nonfiction. Return of material not guaranteed without SASE. Reports in 1 month. Ms guidelines for SASE.
Nonfiction and Fiction: "General, adult fiction and nonfiction of all kinds on nearly all subjects and of the highest quality possible within the limits of each particular book." Last year there were 56 book club rights sales; 30 mass paperback reprint sales; and "innumerable serializations, second serial, syndication, translations, etc." Looks for "clear, intelligent, creative writing on original subjects or with original characters."
Recent Nonfiction Title: *Jane Brody's Good Food Book*, by Jane E. Brody.
Recent Fiction Title: *American Falls*, by John Calvin Batchelor.
Tips: "Long novels are too expensive—keep them under 350 (manuscript) pages."

NOYES DATA CORP., (including Noyes Press and Noyes Publications), Noyes Bldg., Park Ridge NJ 07656. Publishes hardcover originals. Averages 60 titles/year. Pays 10%-12% royalty on retail price; advance varies, depending on author's reputation and nature of book. Query Editorial Department. Reports in 2 weeks. Enclose return postage. Free book catalog.
Nonfiction: (Noyes Press) "Art, classical studies, archeology, and history. Material directed to the intelligent adult and the academic market." Technical: (Noyes Publications) Publishes practical industrial processing science—technical, economic books pertaining to chemistry, chemical engineering, food, textiles, energy, electronics, pollution control—primarily of interest to the business executive. Length: 50,000-250,000 words.

OAK TREE PUBLICATIONS, Suite 202, 9601 Aero Dr., San Diego CA 92123. (619)560-5163. Editor: Beth Ingram. Publishes hardcover and trade paperback originals. Averages 20 titles/year; receives 5,000 submissions annually. 50% of books from first-time authors; 50% of books from unagented writers. Pays royalty on wholesale price. Advance varies. Publishes book an average of 1 year after acceptance. Simultaneous and photocopied submissions OK. Computer printout submissions acceptable; prefers letter-quality to dot-matrix. Reports in 1 month. Book catalog free on request; ms guidelines for SASE.
Fiction: Mass market children's books. Needs 32-page picture books for 3-8 year olds and series, suitable for mass market (highly illustratable). No juvenile or young adult fiction. Submit complete ms. Reviews artwork/photos as part of ms package.
Recent Fiction Title: *Make Believe and Me Series*, by Barbara Alexander (children's picture book).
Tips: "If I were a writer trying to market a book today, I would research publishers carefully and be persistent in submitting manuscripts. Our audience is young readers and to-be-read-to children."

OCCUPATIONAL AWARENESS, Box 948, Los Alamitos CA 90720. Editor-in-Chief: Edith Ericksen. Publishes originals and software. Averages 10 titles/year. Offers standard contract. Average advance $1,500.

ALWAYS submit mss or queries with a stamped, self-addressed envelope (SASE) within your country or International Reply Coupons (IRCs) purchased from the post office for other countries.

Publishes book an average of 1 year after acceptance. Photocopied submissions OK. Electronic submissions OK, but requires hard copy also. Computer printout submissions acceptable.

Nonfiction: Materials on behavior/adjustment (no TA), textbooks, workbooks, kits, career guidance, relating careers to curricula, special education and tests. Submit outline and 3 sample chapters for professional books and textbooks. Reviews artwork/photos as part of ms package.

OCTAMERON ASSOCIATES, 820 Fontaine St., Alexandria VA 22302. (703)823-1882. Editorial Director: Karen Stokstad. Publishes trade paperback originals. Averages 15 titles/year; receives 100 submissions annually. 10% of books from first-time authors; 100% of books from unagented writers. Average print order for a writer's first book is 8,000-10,000. Pays 7½% royalty on retail price. Publishes book an average of 6 months after acceptance. Simultaneous submissions OK. Electronic submissions OK via IBM PC, Microsoft and Word software, but requires hard copy also. Computer printout submissions acceptable; prefers letter-quality to dot-matrix. Reports in 2 weeks. Free book catalog.

Nonfiction: Reference, career and post-secondary education subjects. Travel guides. Especially interested in "paying-for-college and college admission guides." Query. Submit outline/synopsis and 2 sample chapters. Reviews artwork/photos as part of ms package.

Recent Nonfiction Title: *Do It-Write*, by G. Gary Ripple.

ODDO PUBLISHING, INC., Box 68, Beauregard Blvd., Fayetteville GA 30214. (404)461-7627. Managing Editor: Genevieve Oddo. Publishes hardcover and paperback originals; receives 300 + submissions annually. 25% of books from first-time authors; 100% of books from unagented writers. Average print order for a writer's first book is 3,500. Scripts are usually purchased outright. "We judge all scripts independently." Royalty considered for special scripts only. Publishes book an average of 2-3 years after acceptance. Computer printout submissions acceptable; no dot-matrix. Reports in 4 months. Book catalog $1.07. "Manuscript will not be returned without SASE."

Nonfiction: Publishes juvenile books in language arts, workbooks in math, writing (English), photophonics, science (space and oceanography), and social studies for schools, libraries, and trade. Interested in children's supplementary readers in the areas of language arts, math, science, social studies, etc. "Texts run from 1,500 to 3,500 words. Ecology, space, patriotism, oceanography and pollution are subjects of interest. Manuscripts must be easy to read, general, and not set to outdated themes. They must lend themselves to full color illustration. No stories of grandmother long ago. No love angle, permissive language, or immoral words or statements." Submit complete ms, typed clearly. Reviews artwork/photos as part of ms package.

Recent Nonfiction Title: *Bobby Bear and The Band.*

Tips: "We feel it is important to produce books that will make children feel good."

OHIO STATE UNIVERSITY PRESS, 1050 Carmack Rd., Columbus OH 43210. (614)422-6930. Director: Peter J. Givler. Pays royalty on wholesale or retail price. Averages 20 titles/year. Query letter preferred with outline and sample chapters. Reports in 2 months. Ms held longer with author's permission. Enclose return postage.

Nonfiction: Publishes history, biography, science, philosophy, the arts, political science, law, literature, economics, education, sociology, anthropology, geography, and general scholarly nonfiction. No length limitations.

Recent NonfictionTitle: *Paintings from Books: Art and Literature in Britain, 1760-1900*, by Richard D. Altick.

Tips: Publishes some poetry and fiction.

OHIO UNIVERSITY PRESS, Scott Quad, Ohio University, Athens OH 45701. (614)594-5505. Imprints include Ohio University Press and Swallow Press. Acting Director: Holly Panich. Publishes hardcover and paperback originals and reprints. Averages 25-30 titles/year. Pays in royalties starting at 1,500 copies based on wholesale or retail price. No advance. Photocopied submissions OK. Reports in 3-5 months. Free book catalog.

Nonfiction: "General scholarly nonfiction with particular emphasis on 19th century literature and culture. Also history, social sciences, philosophy, business, western regional works and miscellaneous categories." Query.

Recent Nonfiction Title: *Forms of Feelings in Victorian Fiction*, by Barbara Hardy.

‡101 PRODUCTIONS, 834 Mission St., San Francisco CA 94103. (415)495-6040. Editor-in-Chief: Jacqueline Killeen. Publishes paperback originals. Offers standard minimum book contract on retail prices. Averages 12 titles/year; receives 200 submissions annually. 10% of books from first-time authors; 90% of books from unagented writers. Publishes book an average of 1 year after acceptance. Photocopied submissions OK. "We are equipped to edit and typeset from electronic disks, providing the software is compatible with Wordstar"; requires hard copy also. Computer printout submissions acceptable; prefers letter-quality to dot-matrix. No unsolicited mss will be read. Free book catalog.

Nonfiction: Mostly how-to: cookbooks, home, gardening, outdoors, and travel. Heavy emphasis on graphics and illustrations. Query. Reviews artwork/photos as part of ms package. Most books are 192 pages.
Recent Nonfiction Title: *Bread and Breakfast.*

OPEN COURT PUBLISHING CO., Box 599, LaSalle IL 61301. Publisher: M. Blouke Carus. Director, General Books: Dr. Andre Carus. Averages 30 titles/year; receives 500 + submissions annually. 20% of books from first-time authors; 90% of books from unagented writers. Royalty contracts negotiable for each book. Publishes book an average of 9 months after acceptance. Electronic submission OK via IBM or compatible PC, PC-XT, PC-AT, but requires hard copy also. Computer printout submissions acceptable; prefers letter-quality to dot-matrix. Enclose return postage.
Nonfiction: Philosophy, psychology, science and history of science, mathematics, comparative religion, education, Orientalia, and related scholarly topics. Accepts nonfiction translations from German and French. "This is a publishing house run as an intellectual enterprise, to reflect the concerns of its staff and as a service to the world of learning." Query or submit outline/synopsis and 2-3 sample chapters. Reviews artwork/photos as part of ms package.
Recent Nonfiction Title: *Wittgenstein*, by W.W. Bartley, III.
Tips: "We are a scholarly publisher, with our list centering mainly on philosophy, with psychology, religion, economics, and science."

OPTIMUM PUBLISHING INTERNATIONAL INC., 2335 Sherbrooke St. West, West Montreal, Quebec H3H 1G6 Canada. (514)932-0776. Managing Director and Editor-in-Chief: Michael S. Baxendale. Hardcover and paperback originals and reprints. Averages 21 titles/year; receives 1,000 w submissions annually. 10% of books from first-time authors; 50% of books from unagented writers. Pays royalty or fee negotiated with author or agent depending on project involved. Publishes in both official Canadian languages (English and French). Publishes book an average of 1 year after acceptance. Photocopied submissions OK. Electronic submissions OK, but query first; requires hard copy also. Computer printout submissions acceptable; no dot-matrix. Reports in 6 weeks. SAE and IRCs.
Nonfiction: Biography, child care, cookbooks, cooking and foods, gardening, government and politics, history, natural history, how-to, health, nature, crafts, photography, art, self-help, crime, sports, and travel books. Query or submit outline/synopsis and sample chapters. Reviews artwork/photos.
Recent Nonfiction Title: *Creative Parenting*, by William Leons, M.D.

ORBIS BOOKS, Maryknoll NY 10545. (914)941-7590. Editor-in-Chief: John Eagleson. Publishes paperback originals. Publishes 35 titles/year. 7-8½-10% royalty on retail prices; offers averages $1,000 advance. Query with outline, 2 sample chapters, and prospectus. Electronic submissions OK. Reports in 6 weeks. Enclose return postage.
Nonfiction: "Religious developments in Asia, Africa and Latin America. Christian missions. Justice and peace. Christianity and world religions."
Recent Nonfiction Title: *We Drink from Our Own Wells*, by Gustavo Gutierrez.

OREGON STATE UNIVERSITY PRESS, 101 Waldo Hall, Corvallis OR 97331. (503)754-3166. Hardcover and paperback originals. Averages 5 titles/year; receives 100 submissions annually. 75% of books from first-time authors; 100% of books from unagented writers. Average print order for a writer's first book is 3,000. Pays royalty on wholesale price. No advance. Publishes book an average of 1 year after acceptance. Electronic submissions OK; query first; requires hard copy also. Computer printout submissions acceptable; no dot-matrix. Reports in 1 month. Book catalog for SASE.
Nonfiction: Publishes scholarly books in history, biography, geography, literature, social science, marine and freshwater sciences, life sciences, geology, education, and bibliography, with strong emphasis on Pacific or Northwestern topics. Submit outline/synopsis and sample chapters.
Recent Nonfiction Title: *Regionalism and the Pacific Northwest*, edited by William G. Robbins, Robert J. Frank, and Richard E. Ross.

‡ORTHO INFORMATION SERVICES, Chevron Chemical Co., 575 Market St., San Francisco CA 94105. (415)894-0277. Editorial Director: Robert J. Dolezal. Publishes hardcover and trade paperback originals and reprints. Averages 30 titles/year; receives 100+ submissions annually. 10% of books from first-time authors; 20% of books from unagented writers. Makes outright purchase. Publishes book an average of 2 years after acceptance. Simultaneous submissions OK. Electronic submissions OK via IBM-PC format/XyWrite, but requires hard copy also. Computer printout submissions acceptable; prefers letter-quality to dot-matrix. Reports in 3 weeks on queries; 1 month on mss. Book catalog for 9x12 SASE.
Imprints: California Culinary Academy (nonfiction), Sally Smith, project editor. Academy Cookbooks.
Nonfiction: Cookbook, how-to, illustrated book and reference. Subjects include cooking and foods, hobbies, nature, gardening and home repair. "All our projects are internally generated from project proposals—assignment of author, photographers, some illustration from project outline, including outside submissions." No an-

ecdotal/biographical, gardening, how-to, cooking or previously covered topics. Query. All unsolicited mss are returned unopened.
Recent Nonfiction Title: *Upholstery*, by Karin Shakery (how to).

ORYX PRESS, 2214 N. Central Ave., Phoenix AZ 85004. (602)254-6156. President/Editorial Director: Phyllis B. Steckler. Publishes hardcover and paperback originals. Averages 40 titles/year; receives 300 submissions annually. 40% of books from first-time authors; 100% of books from unagented writers. Average print order for a writer's first book is 1,000. Pays 10-15% royalty on net receipts; no advance. Publishes book an average of 9 months after acceptance. Electronic submissions OK on IBM compatible, 1600 BPI ASC II format, but requires hard copy also. Computer printout submissions acceptable; prefers letter-quality to dot-matrix. Reports in 2 months. Free book catalog and ms guidelines.
Nonfiction: Bibliographies, directories, general reference, library and information science, business reference, health care, gerontology, automation, and agriculture monographs. Publishes nonfiction for public, college and university, junior college, school and special libraries; agriculture specialists, health care deliverers; and managers. Query or submit outline/synopsis and 1 sample chapter, or complete ms. Queries/mss may be routed to other editors in the publishing group.
Recent Nonfiction Title: *Librarian in Search of a Publisher: How to Get Published*, by Brian Alley and Jennifer Cargill.

OTTENHEIMER PUBLISHERS, INC., 300 Reisterstown Rd., Baltimore MD 21208. (301)484-2100. Book Packager. President: Allan T. Hirsh Jr. Vice-President; Allan T. Hirsh III. Managing Editor: Emeline Kroiz. Publishes hardcover and paperback originals. Publishes 250 titles/year; receives 500 submissions annually. Less than 1% of books from first-time authors; 100% of books from unagented writers. Average print order for a writer's first book is 15,000. Negotiates royalty and advance. Publishes book an average of 6 months after acceptance. Photocopied submissions OK. Computer printout submissions acceptable; prefers letter-quality to dot-matrix. Reports in 1 month.
Nonfiction: Cookbooks, reference, gardening, home repair and decorating, automotive and medical for the layperson. Submit outline/synopsis and sample chapters or complete ms. Reviews artwork/photos as part of ms package.
Tips: "We're looking nonfiction adult books in the how-to information area, for mass market—we're a packager."

OUR SUNDAY VISITOR, INC., 200 Noll Plaza, Huntington IN 46750. (219)356-8400. Director: Robert Lockwood. Publishes paperback originals and reprints. Averages 20-30 titles a year; receives 75 submissions annually. 10% of books from first-time authors; 90% of books from unagented writers. Pays variable royalty on net receipts; offers average $500 advance. Publishes book an average of 1 year after acceptance. Electronic submissions OK via IBM; requires hard copy also. Computer printout submissions acceptable; prefers letter-quality to dot-matrix. Reports in 1 month on most queries and submissions. Author's guide and catalog for SASE.
Nonfiction: Catholic viewpoints on current issues, reference and guidance, Bibles and devotional books, and Catholic heritage books. Prefers to see well-developed proposals as first submission with "annotated outline, three sample chapters, and definition of intended market." Reviews artwork/photos as part of ms package.
Recent Nonfiction Title: *Strange Gods: Contemporary Religious Cults in America*, by William Whalen.
Tips: "Solid devotional books that are not first person; well-researched church histories or lives of the saints; and self-help for those over 55 have the best chance of selling to our firm. Make it solidly Catholic, unique, without pious platitudes."

OUTBOOKS INC., 217 Kimball Ave., Golden CO 80401. Contact: William R. Jones. Publishes trade paperback originals and reprints. Averages 10 titles/year. Pays 5% royalty on retail price. Computer printout submissions acceptable. Reports in 1 month on queries only. Book catalog for $1.
Nonfiction: Regional books on Americana, history, nature, recreation and travel. Publishes for "lay enthusiasts in American history, outdoors, and natural history, ecology, and conservation." Query only; send no ms until requested.
Recent Nonfiction Title: *Evidence and the Custer Enigma*, by Jerome A. Greene.

THE OVERLOOK PRESS, Distributed by Viking/Penguin, 12 W. 21st St., New York NY 10010. (212)337-5200. Contact: Editorial department. Imprints include Tusk Books. Publishes hardcover and trade paperback originals and hardcover reprints. Averages 25 titles/year; receives 300 submissions annually. Pays 3-15% royalty on wholesale price. Submissions accepted only through literary agents. Reports in 2 months. Free book catalog.
Nonfiction: How-to and reference. Subjects include Americana, business and economics, history, nature, recreation, sports, and travel. No pornography.

Fiction: Adventure, ethnic, fantasy/science fiction, historical, mainstream, mystery/suspense. "We tend not to publish commercial fiction."
Recent Fiction Title: *Sunrising*, by David Cook.
Poetry: "We like to publish poets who have a strong following—those who read in New York City regularly or publish in periodicals regularly." No poetry from unpublished authors. Submit complete ms.
Recent Poetry Title: *To An Idea*, by David Shapiro.
Tips: "We are a very small company. If authors want a very quick decision, they should go to another company first and come back to us. We try to be as prompt as possible, but it sometimes takes over 3 months for us to get to a final decision."

OWL CREEK PRESS, 1620 N. 45th St., Seattle WA 98103. Editor: Rich Ives. Publishes hardcover, trade paperback and mass market paperback originals, and mass market paperback reprints. Averages 5-10 titles/year; receives 2,000 submissions annually. 50% of books from first-time authors; 95% of books from unagented writers. Pays 10-20% royalty on wholesale price (cash or equivalent in copies). If paid in copies, royalty is advanced. Photocopied submissions OK. Computer printout submissions acceptable; prefers letter-quality to dot-matrix. Reports in 2 months. Book catalog for standard size SAE and 1 first class stamp.
Nonfiction: Photography. "Our selections are made solely on the basis of lasting artistic quality." No cookbooks, how-to, juvenile, self-help, technical or reference. Submit outline/synopsis and sample chapters.
Fiction: "We seek writing of lasting artistic merit in all areas. Writing genre is irrelevant, although we avoid easy approaches and formula work. We are not interested in writing that attempts to fulfill genre requirements or comply with preconceived notions of mass market appeal. If it's work of lasting quality we will try to find and build a market for it." Submit outline/synopsis and sample chapters.
Poetry: "We publish both full-length and chapbook titles. Selections are based solely on the lasting quality of the manuscripts. No manuscripts where genre category or preconceived ideas of mass market appeal dominate the work." Submit complete ms, unsolicited through contests only.
Recent Poetry Title: *Small Mercies*, by Elizabeth Weber.
Tips: "We attempt to reach the reader with a somewhat discerning taste first. Future plans include further expansion into fiction and translated titles (both poetry and fiction) as well as maintaining a continued series of both full-length and chapbook poetry originals. We are nonprofit, dedicated to the promotion of literary art."

P.P.I. PUBLISHING, 835 E. Congress Park, Box 335, Dayton OH 45459. (513)433-2709. Vice President: Kim Brooks. Publishes mass market paperback originals (booklets). Averages 45-50 titles/year; receives 250 submissions annually. 45% of books from first-time authors; 100% of books from unagented writers. Average print order for a writer's first book is 1,000. Pays 10% royalty on retail selling price to customer (some customer discounts). Publishes book an average of 3 months after acceptance. Simultaneous and photocopied submissions OK. Computer printout submissions acceptable but not preferable; no dot-matrix. Reports in 3 weeks on queries; 10 weeks on mss. Book catalog with or without guidelines for SAE and 2 first class stamps; ms guidelines only for SAE and 1 first class stamp.
Nonfiction: Juvenile and teens, and self-help. Subjects include health and sociology. "We publish nonfiction booklets of 15,000 words or larger for junior and senior high schools, libraries, colleges, universities and other specialized markets such as social service organizations. Our main subjects include controversial issues and items in the news. Topics that students are preparing for research papers or debates are of particular interest. We keep our markets informed on what's happening today in the world, in the home, in schools, and for the future. Some recent topics that were published include how to deal with freshman stress for the college student, euthanasia, prescription drug abuse, teens and drinking and driving, food irradiation, teenage suicide, the Klan, television, etc. We are especially looking for 15,000-word manuscripts or larger on current events. We're not interested in how-to, technical material, travel or cookbooks." Submit outline/synopsis, sample chapters or complete ms. "For new authors we prefer outlines or queries to save them time and trouble." Reviews artwork/photos as part of ms package on a limited basis.
Recent Nonfiction Titles: *Teenage Drinking and Driving: A Deadly Duo*, by Elaine Fantle Shimberg.
Tips: "Find out how today's event and news affect students and people in general, and what the future outlook is for social issues, world issues and family. One of our largest markets is high schools."

‡PACIFIC BOOKS, PUBLISHERS, Box 558, Palo Alto CA 94302. (415)856-0550. Editor: Henry Ponleithner. Averages 8 titles/year. Royalty schedule varies with book. No advance. Send complete ms. Computer printout submissions OK "if clean, typewriter-quality." Reports "promptly." Will send catalog on request.
Nonfiction: General interest, professional, technical and scholarly nonfiction trade books. Specialties include western Americana and Hawaiiana. Looks for "well-written, documented material of interest to a significant audience." Also considers text and reference books; high school and college. Accepts artwork/photos and translations.
Recent Nonfiction Title: *The Issei: Portrait of a Pioneer*, edited by Eileen Sunada Sarasohn (history).

PACIFIC PRESS PUBLISHING ASSOCIATION, Book Division, Seventh-day Adventist Church, Box 7000, Boise ID 83707. (208)465-2576. Vice President of Editorial Development: Humberto M. Rasi. Publishes hardcover and trade paperback originals and hardcover and trade paperback reprints. Averages 50 titles/year; receives 800 submissions annually. Up to 50% of books from first-time authors; 100% of books from un-agented writers. Pays 5-7% royalty on retail price. Offers average $300 advance. Publishes books an average of 6 months after acceptance. Photocopied submissions OK. Electronic submissions OK ("We have an Alter-text disk reader and can read all major systems."); requires hard copy also. Computer printout submissions acceptable; prefers letter-quality to dot-matrix. Reports in 1 month on queries; 2 months on mss. Ms guidelines for SASE.

Nonfiction: Biography, cookbook (vegetarian), how-to, juvenile, self-help and textbook. Subjects include cooking and foods (vegetarian only), health, nature, religion, and family living. "We are an exclusively religious publisher. We are looking for practical, how-to-oriented manuscripts on religion, health, and family life that speak to human needs, interests and problems from a Biblical perspective. We can't use anything totally secular or written from other than a Christian perspective." Query or submit outline/synopsis and sample chapters. Reviews artwork/photos as part of ms package.

Recent Nonfiction Title: *God Cares,* by Mervyn Maxwell (devotional/expository study of the Book of Revelation).

Tips: "Our primary audiences are members of our own denomination (Seventh-day Adventist), the general Christian reading market, and the secular or nonreligious reader. Books that are doing well for us are those that relate the Biblical message to practical human concerns and those that focus more on the experiential rather than theoretical aspects of Christianity."

PADRE PRODUCTIONS, Box 1275, San Luis Obispo CA 93406. Editor-in-Chief: Lachlan P. MacDonald. Publishes hardcover and paperback originals and reprints. Pays minimum 6% royalty. Offers $200-1,000 advance. Averages 6-10 titles/year; receives 400 submissions annually. 50% of books from first-time authors; 90% of books from unagented writers. Publishes book an average of 3-4 years after acceptance. Average print order for a writer's first book is 3,000. State availability of photos and/or illustrations or include contact sheet or stat. Simultaneous submissions OK. Electronic submissions OK via all formats. Computer printout submissions acceptable; prefers letter-quality to dot-matrix. Reports in 6 months. Mss and queries without SASE are not answered. Book catalog and ms guidelines for SASE.

Nonfiction: Subjects include Americana (antiques); art; business and economics (opportunities) hobby (collectibles); cookbook; history (California); how-to; money and finances (investments for the layman); marine life and maritime; nature (with illustrations); photography; publishing; recreation; reference; self-help; and travel. Query or submit outline and 2-3 sample chapters. "Include ample packaging; type all material; don't send slides unless asked." Reviews artwork/photos as part of ms package.

Recent Nonfiction Title: *Dangerous Marine Animals of the Pacific Coast,* by Christina Parsons.

Fiction and Poetry: Subjects include (in order of preference): fantasy, contemporary and juvenile. Juveniles for ages 8-14 years, (about 160 pages with strong illustrative possibilities). Submit sample chapters and outline.

Tips: "The writer has the best chance of selling our firm manuscripts with illustrations as local area guide."

THE PAGURIAN CORPORATION LIMITED, 13 Hazelton Ave., Toronto, Ontario M5R 2E1 Canada. (416)968-0255. Editor-in-Chief: Christopher Ondaatje. Publishes paperback and hardcover originals and reprints. Averages 2 titles/year. Offers negotiable royalty contract. Advance negotiable. Publishes book an average of 6 months after acceptance. Photocopied submissions OK. Computer printout submissions acceptable; prefers letter-quality to dot-matrix. Submit 2-page outline, synopsis or chapter headings and contents. Reports "immediately." SAE with IRC.

Nonfiction: Publishes general interest trade and art books. Will consider fine arts, outdoor and cookbook. Length: 40,000-70,000 words. Reviews artwork/photos as part of ms package.

Tips: "We are publishing *fewer* books, and all are Canadian art or art history themes."

PALADIN PRESS, Box 1307, Boulder CO 80306. (303)443-7250. President/Publisher: Peder C. Lund. General Manager: Kim R. Hood. Editorial Director: Rose-Marle Strasburg. Publishes hardcover and paperback originals and paperback reprints. Averages 30 titles/year; receives 700-800 submissions annually. 50% of books from first-time authors; 100% of books from unagented writers. Pays 10-12-15% royalty on net sales. Publishes book an average of 1 year after acceptance. Simultaneous and photocopied submissions OK. Computer printout submissions acceptable. Reports in 1 month. Free book catalog.

Nonfiction: "Paladin Press primarily publishes original manuscripts on martial arts, military science, weap-

Market conditions are constantly changing! If this is 1988 or later, buy the newest edition of Writer's Market *at your favorite bookstore or order directly from* Writer's Digest Books.

onry, self-defense, survival, police science, guerrilla warfare, fieldcraft and humor. How-to manuscripts are given priority. Manuals on building weapons, when technically accurate and clearly presented, are encouraged. If applicable, send sample photographs and line drawings with complete outline and sample chapters." Query or submit outline/synopsis and sample chapters. Reviews artwork/photos as part of ms package.
Recent Nonfiction Title: *Flimflam Man: How Con Games Work,* by M. Allen Henderson.
Tips: "We need concise, instructive material aimed at our market and accompanied by sharp, relevant illustrations and photos. As we are primarily a publisher of 'how-to' books, a manuscript which has step-by-step instructions, written in a clear and concise manner (but not strictly outline form) is desirable."

‡PANDORA PRESS, Imprint of Routledge and Kegan Paul, 29 W. 35th St., New York NY 10001. (212)244-3336. Editor: Philippa Parewster. Publishes hardcover and trade paperback originals and trade paperback reprints. Averages 30 titles/year; receives 600 submissions annually. 40% of books from first-time authors; 70% of books from unagented writers. Pays 7½-15% royalty on retail price; offers average $3,500 advance. Publishes book an average of 1 year after acceptance. Simultaneous and photocopied submissions OK. Computer printout submissions acceptable. Reports in 2 months on queries; 3 months on mss. Book catalog free on request; ms guidelines for SASE.
Nonfiction: Biography, reference, self-help, technical, textbook and general interest and scholarly women's studies. Subjects include art, health, history, philosophy, photography, politics, religion, sociology, sports and feminist theory. "Pandora is a specifically feminist press which addresses a range of interests both within and arising out of the women's movement in the U.S., in the U.K. and internationally. Manuscripts across the whole range of disciplines in women's studies (history, sociology, literary theory, etc.), self-help, and reference will be considered." No mss that do not fit these categories. Query or submit outline/synopsis and sample chapters. Reviews artwork/photos as part of ms package.
Recent Nonfiction Title: *The Dora Russell Reader,* by Dora Russell (journalism, social commentary).
Fiction: Adventure, ethnic, experimental, historical, humor and reprints of 13th, 19th, and early 20th century novels that have been out of print but are outstanding works. Query or submit outline/synopsis and sample chapters.
Recent Fiction Titles: *Plum Bun: A Novel Without a Moral,* by Jessie Fauset (reprint of a 1929 black woman's novel).
Tips: "The writer has the best chance of selling our firm challenging accessible feminist works in a range of areas; that is the audience Pandora tries to reach and the contribution the Press makes, in the best traditions of the feminist movement. The books which are most successful address an important contemporary social issue and/or uncover a new area of interest to women. And the fiction is to entertain; above all."

PANJANDRUM BOOKS, Suite 1, 11321 Iowa Ave., Los Angeles CA 90025. (213)477-8771. Subsidiaries include Panjandrum Books Inc. Editor/Publisher: Dennis Koran. Publishes hardcover and trade paperback originals. Averages 4-5 titles/year. Pays 7-10% royalty on retail price. Computer printout submissions acceptable. Reports in 2 weeks on queries; 2 months on mss. Book catalog for 7x10 SAE and 2 first class stamps.
Nonfiction: Biography, cookbook, how-to, juvenile and reference. Subjects include cooking health, hobbies, music, philosophy, theater and drama, herbs, vegetarianism, and childhood sexuality. "We're looking for manuscripts of cookbooks, health books, music (how-to) and drama, and are open to queries on other subjects." No religious or humorous. Query or submit outline/synopsis and sample chapters.
Recent Nonfiction Title: *Alfred Jarry: The Man with the Axe,* by Lennon (literary biography).
Fiction: Avant-garde, experimental, surreal and translations of European literature (not previously translated into English). Query with sample chapter.
Recent Fiction Title: *Fighting Men,* by Manus (post-Vietnam novel).
Poetry: Submit maximum 5 poems.
Recent Poetry Title: *Visions of the Fathers of Lascaux,* by Eshleman.

PANTHEON BOOKS, Division of Random House, Inc., 201 E. 50th St., New York NY 10022. Averages 90 titles/year. Pays royalty on invoice price (retail price minus freight pass-through, usually 50¢). Publishes book an average of 1 year after acceptance (longer if ms not written/completed when contract is signed). Address queries to Adult Editorial Department (28th Floor). "We prefer to work with experienced writers who have already published at least one book or several articles. In addition to a description of the book, queries must include a brief market study detailing how the book proposed will be different from other books available on the subject." Computer printout submissions acceptable; prefers letter-quality to dot-matrix.
Nonfiction: Emphasis on Asia, international politics, radical social theory, history, medicine, women's studies, and law. Recreational guides and practical how-to books as well. Query letters only. No mss accepted. Publishes some juveniles. Address queries to Juvenile Editorial Department (6th floor).
Recent Nonfiction Title: *The Abandonment of the Jews,* by David S. Wyman.
Fiction: Publishes fewer than 5 novels each year, primarily mysteries and foreign fiction in translation. Queries on fiction not accepted.

‡**PARA RESEARCH, INC.**, 85 Eastern Ave., Gloucester MA 01930. (617)283-3438. Managing Editor: Julie Lockhart. Publishes trade paperback originals. Averages 4-5 titles/year; receives 200-250 submissions annually. 50% of books from first-time authors; 100% of books from unagented writers. Pays royalty on wholesale price; offers variable advance. Publishes book an average of 18 months after acceptance. Simultaneous and photocopied submissions OK. Computer printout submissions acceptable; prefers letter-quality to dot-matrix. Reports in 2 weeks on queries; 1 month on mss. Free book catalog; ms guidelines for SASE.

Nonfiction: How-to, reference and self-help. Subjects include health, philosophy, psychology, sociology, astrology and metaphysics. "We are looking for well-written, original books on all types of metaphysical subjects. Books that empower the reader or show him/her ways to develop personal skills are prefered. New approaches, techniques, or concepts are best. No 'channeled' books, no personal accounts that don't have direct relevance to the general audience, no moralistic, fatalistic, sexist, or strictly philosophical books." Query or submit outline/synopsis and sample chapters.

Recent Nonfiction Title: *Win-Win Negotiations for Couples*, by Charlotte Whitney (how-to/self-help).

Tips: "Our audience is somewhat knowledgeable in metaphysical fields; well-read; progressive; people who are interested in taking an active part in improving their lives; those who are seeking answers outside the conventional arenas. Well-written, originally researched books on astrology/metaphysics have the best chance of selling to our firm. Expertise in the field(s) is not enough. No Sun-sign material. We prefer more advanced work. We still get a lot of submissions without SASE. Please be sure to enclose this. Don't send us the entire manuscript unless we request it. Please keep manuscripts between 80,000 and 110,000 words."

‡***PARAGON HOUSE PUBLISHERS**, 2 Hammarskjold Plaza, New York NY 10017. (212)223-6433. Editor-in-Chief: Ken Stuart. Publishes hardcover and trade paperback originals and reprints. Averages 50 titles/year; receives 1,000 submissions annually. 10-20% of nonfiction from first-time authors; 50% of books from unagented writers. Subsidy publishes 2% of books/year. Whether an author is subsidy published is determined by "how much subsidy there is, as well as how much market." Pays 7-15% royalty on retail price. Offers $0-5,000 advance "when appropriate." Simultaneous and photocopied submissions acceptable; no dot-matrix. Reports in 2 weeks on queries; 6 weeks on mss. Book catalog free on request.

Nonfiction: Biography, illustrated book, reference and textbook. Subjects include Americana, history, music, philosophy, politics, religion, and literature. Especially needs history, biography and serious nonfiction. No self help, diet, gardening, crafts, occult or humor. Query or submit outline/synopsis and sample chapters. Reviews artwork/photos as part of ms package.

Recent Nonfiction Title: *Women in Soviet Prisons*, by Helene Celmina (autobiography).

Fiction: Experimental, classic modern and contemporary reprints, "serious fiction" and translations. "No writers without established reputations; no new writers." Especially needs translations of classic modern and contemporary writers from other cultures, and paperback reprints of modern and contemporary English language classics. Query or submit outline/synopsis and sample chapters.

Recent Fiction Title: *Stories of Life and Death*, by Juan Ramon Jiminez (short stories).

Poetry: Selected poems from established poets and reprints of modern classics. No new writers or unestablished writers. Submit approximately 10 samples.

Recent Poetry Title: *The Poet's Craft*, by Bill Packard (interviews with Auden, Ginsberg, Ashbery, etc.)

Tips: "We are looking for books that fall between the cracks, such as books which are too mid-list for trade houses and not scholarly enough for university presses."

‡**PARENTING PRESS, INC.**, 7744 31st Ave. NE, Seattle WA 98115. (206)527-2900. Editor: Shari Steelsmith. Publishes hardcover and trade paperback originals. Averages 10 titles/year; receives 50 submissions annually. 80% of books from first-time authors; 100% of books from unagented writers. Pays 8-10% royalty on retail price. Offers average $150 advance. Publishes book an average of 9 months after acceptance. Simultaneous and photocopied submissions OK. Computer printout submissions acceptable; no dot-matrix. Reports in 3 weeks on queries; 6 weeks on mss. Free book catalog and ms guidelines.

Nonfiction: Illustrated book, juvenile, self-help and parenting. "We need books that build competence in parents and children and improve the quality of family life. No 'should' books—we instead like to see manuscripts that provide a variety of ways to do things—not just one 'right' way." Submit outline/synopsis and sample chapters or complete ms. Reviews artwork/photos as part of ms package.

Recent Nonfiction Titles: *Kids Can Cooperate*, by Elizabeth Crary (parenting).

Tips: "Our audience is thinking adults who are looking for ways to improve the quality of family life. The writer has the best chance of selling our firm a book that provides alternatives in child guidance and child-rearing issues. We are 'alternative' oriented. Books on child guidance are doing well for us. Make certain there is a wide enough need for the book before writing, and field test it yourself. I would say field testing the manuscript with parents and children improves it immensely."

PAULIST PRESS, 997 Macarthur Blvd., Mahwah NJ 07430. (201)825-7300. Publisher: Rev. Kevin A. Lynch. Managing Editor: Donald Brophy. Publishes hardcover and paperback originals and paperback reprints. Averages 100 titles/year; receives 500 submissions annually. 5-8% of books from first-time authors; 95% of books from unagented writers. Pays royalty on retail price. Occasionally offers advance. Publishes book an average of 8 months after acceptance. Photocopied submissions OK. Electronic submissions OK, but requires hard copy also. Computer printout submissions acceptable; prefers letter-quality to dot-matrix. Reports in 1 month.

Nonfiction: Philosophy, religion, self-help and textbooks (religious). Accepts nonfiction translations from German, French and Spanish. "We would like to see theology (Catholic and ecumenical Christian), popular spirituality, liturgy, and religious education texts." Submit outline/synopsis and 2 sample chapters. Reviews artwork/photos as part of ms package.

Recent Nonfiction Title: *The Ground Is Holy, the Sanctuary Movement in the U.S.*, by Ignatius Bau

‡PBC INTERNATIONAL INC., Subsidiaries include Pisces Books and The Photographic Book Company, 1 School St., Glen Cove NY 11542. (516)676-2727. Editorial Director: H. Taylor. Publishes hardcover and trade paperback originals. Averages 10 titles/year; receives 100-200 submissions annually. Most of books from first-time authors and unagented writers, done on assignment. Pays royalty and/or flat fees. Simultaneous and photocopied submissions OK. Computer printout submissions acceptable; prefers letter-quality to dot-matrix.

Imprints: Library of Applied Design (nonfiction), H. Taylor, editorial director. Pisces Books (nonfiction), H. Taylor, editorial director.

Nonfiction: Subjects include marine animals, commercial art, nature (marine only), underwater photography, and skin diving. Library of Applied Design needs books that show the best in current design trends in all fields. Pisces Books needs books for snorklers and skin divers, on marine life, travel, diver safety, etc. No submissions not covered in the above listed topics. Query with outline/synopsis and sample chapters. Reviews artwork/photos as part of ms package.

Recent Nonfiction Title: *The Best of Store Designs*, by the National Retail Merchants Association (full-color design reference).

PEACHTREE PUBLISHERS, LTD., 494 Armour Circle NE, Atlanta GA 30324. (404)876-8761. Executive Editor: Chuck Perry. Publishes hardcover and trade paperback originals. Averages 18-20 titles/year; receives up to 1,000 submissions annually. 75% of books from first-time authors; 95% of books from unagented writers. Average print order for a writer's first book is 5,000-10,000. Publishes book an average of 1 year after acceptance. Computer printout submissions acceptable; prefers letter-quality to dot-matrix. Reports in 1 week on queries; 3 months on mss. Free book catalog; ms guidelines for SASE.

Nonfiction: Cookbook and humor. Subjects include cooking and foods, history, recreation and travel. No business, technical, reference, art and photography, juvenile or animals. Submit outline/synopsis and sample chapters. Reviews artwork/photos as part of ms package.

Recent Nonfiction Title: *The Calling*, by Sterling Watson.

Fiction: Historical, humor and mainstream. "We are particularly interested in fiction with a Southern feel." No fantasy, juvenile, science fiction or romance. Submit outline/synopsis and sample chapters.

Recent Fiction Title: *The Marriage Map*, by Maxine Rock.

Tips: "We're looking for mainstream fiction and nonfiction of Southern interest; although our books are sold throughout the United States, our principal market is the Southeastern region—Virginia to Texas."

‡PELICAN PUBLISHING COMPANY, 1101 Monroe St., Box 189, Gretna LA 70053. (504)368-1175. Assistant Editor: Karen T. Leathem. Publishes hardcover, trade paperback and mass market paperback originals and reprints. Averages 40 titles/year; receives 1,800 submissions annually. 30% of books from first-time authors; 97% of books from unagented writers. Pays royalty on wholesale price. Publishes book an average of 18 months after acceptance. Photocopied submissions OK. Computer printout submissions acceptable; no dot-matrix. Reports in 3 weeks on queries; 4 months on mss.

Nonfiction: Biography, "coffee table" book (limited), cookbook, how-to, humor, illustrated book, juvenile, self-help, motivational, inspirational, and Scottish." Subjects include Americana (especially Southern regional, Ozarks, Texas); business and economics(popular how-to and motivational); cooking and food; health; history; music (American artforms: jazz, blues, Cajun, R&B); politics (special interest in conservative viewpoint); recreation; religion (for popular audience mostly, but will consider others); and travel. *Travel*: Regional and international (especially areas in Pacific). *Motivational*: with business slant. *Inspirational*: authors must be someone with potential for large audience. *Cookbooks*: "We look for authors with strong connection with restaurant industry or cooking circles, i.e. someone who can promote successfully." *How-to*: will consider broad range. Query. Reviews artwork/photos as part of ms package.

Recent Nonfiction Title: *Mackie Shilstone's Feelin' Good About Fitness*, by Mackie Shilstone (health and fitness).

Fiction: Historical, humor, mainstream, Southern, juvenile and young adult. "Fiction needs are *very* limited. One novel is probably the maximum we would publish in the next year or two. We are most interested in Southern novels. We are also looking for good mainstream juvenile/young adult works." No romance, science fiction, fantasy, gothic, mystery, erotica, confession, horror; no sex or violence. Submit outline/synopsis and sample chapters.

Recent Fiction Title: *Henry Hamilton, Graduate Ghost*, by Marilyn Redmond (juvenile novel).
Tips: "We do extremely well with travel, motivational, cookbooks, and children's titles. We will continue to build in these areas. The writer must have a clear sense of the market and this includes knowledge of the competition."

‡THE PENKEVILL PUBLISHING COMPANY, Box 212, Greenwood FL 32443. (904)569-2811. Director: Stephen H. Goode. Publishes hardcover originals. Averages 10 titles/year; receives approximately 20 submissions annually. 40% of books from first-time authors; 100% of books from unagented writers. Pays 10-15% royalty on wholesale price. Publishes book an average of 15 months after acceptance. Simultaneous and photocopied submissions OK. Computer printout submissions acceptable; prefers letter-quality to dot-matrix. Reports in 2 weeks on queries; 6 weeks on submissions. Free book catalog.
Nonfiction: Reference, textbook and scholarly/critical. Subjects include history (19th, 20th Century American and European; Civil War and current interest); psychology; sociology (of current interest, divorce, terrorism); and literature and the arts and humanities. "Substantively, there are three areas of current interest: 1. Scholarly & critical works in the arts and humanities from the Renaissance forward; 2. 19th and 20th century American & Continental history, such as the American Civil War (e.g. Wheeler's Last Raid or a collection of essays on the literature, film, and art arising from the Vietnam war); 3. modern social currents, such as divorce, terrorism, the [Jewish] Holocaust, etc. (e.g., an annual bibliography and survey of divorce in America; an annual bibliography of terrorism, etc.). On another level, we are interested in the following genres: diaries, correspondence, histories of movements, biographies, critical and scholarly editions, sources (e.g. Faulkner's library); and in the following kinds of reference works; bibliographies, preferably annotated, checklists; dictionaries (of authors' works, such as a Proust dictionary), etc." Query.
Recent Nonfiction Title: *Romanticism & Ideology, Essays and Addresses, 1971-1980*, by Morse Peckham (scholarly-critical).
Tips: "The type of book a writer has the best chance of selling to us is something unique in modern letters; that is, that hasn't been done before—such as the *Poetry of Jane Welch and Thomas Carlyle* (a forthcoming title); the sources of Melville [either externally (his personal library) or internally (an examination of references in his works) arrived at]; or an index to the magazines that are members of the CCLM (a forthcoming annual title that indexes 350 + literary magazines that are members of the Council of Literary Magazines), etc."

PENTAGRAM, Fathom Press, Box 379, Markesan WI 53946. Editor/publisher/printer: Michael Tarachow. Publishes trade paperback originals. Averages 0-5 titles/year; receives a varying number of submissions annually. 50% of books from first-time authors; 100% of books from unagented writers. Payment varies. Publishes book an average of 2 years after acceptance. Photocopied submissions OK; no simultaneous submissions. Computer printout submissions acceptable; prefers letter-quality to dot-matrix. Reports in 1 week. Always query with SASE before sending ms. Free book catalog.
Poetry and Essays: Query with SASE before sending mss. May review artwork/photos as part of ms package.
Recent Poetry Title: *Blossoms and Bones*, by Christopher Buckley.
Tips: "Pentagram publishes books by letterpress; handset metal type on mould-made and/or hand-made papers. We are looking for readers who experience books with their five—or more—senses."

*PEREGRINE SMITH BOOKS, Gibbs M. Smith Inc., Box 667, Layton UT 84041. (801)544-9800. Editorial Director: James Thomas. Publishes hardcover and paperback originals and reprints. Subsidy publishes 5% of books. Receives 1,000 + submissions annually. 41% of books from first-time authors; 75% of books from unagented writers. Average print order for a writer's first book is 5,000. Pays 10% royalty on wholesale price. Offers average $1,000 advance. Publishes book an average of 1 year after acceptance. Photocopied submissions OK. Reports in 3 months. Book catalog 56¢.
Nonfiction: "Subjects include western American history, natural history, American architecture, photography, art history and fine arts. "We consider biographical, historical, descriptive and analytical studies in all of the above. Much emphasis is also placed on pictorial content." Submit complete ms. Accepts nonfiction translations from French. Consult Chicago *Manual of Style*. Reviews artwork/photos as part of ms package.
Recent Nonfiction Title: *Lawrence in Oaxaca: A Search for the Novelist in Mexico*, by Ross Parmenter.
Fiction: "We publish contemporary literary fiction. No unsolicited manuscripts accepted." Looks for "style, readable, intelligent, careful writing. Must be geared to a competitive commercial market." Accepts fiction translations from French.
Tips: "Write seriously. If fiction, no potboilers, bestseller movie tie-in type hype books and no science fiction. If nonfiction, only serious, well-researched critical, historical or craft-related topics."

PETERSON'S GUIDES, INC., Box 2123, Princeton NJ 08540. (609)924-5338. Publisher/President: Peter W. Hegener. Executive Vice President and Editorial Director: Karen C. Hegener. Publishes paperback originals and software (for the educational/guidance market. Averages 25-30 titles/year. Receives 150-200 submissions annually. 50% of books from first-time authors; 90% from unagented writers. Average print order for a writer's

first books is 5,000-12,000. Pays 5-10% royalty on net sales; offers advance. Publishes book an average of 9 months after acceptance. Photocopied submissions OK. Computer printout submissions acceptable; prefers letter-quality to dot-matrix. Reports in 3 months. Free catalog.
Nonfiction: Educational and career reference and guidance works for professionals, libraries, and trade. Submit complete ms or detailed outline and sample chapters. Looks for "appropriateness of contents to our market, accuracy of information and use of reliable information sources, and writing style suitable for audience." Reviews artwork/photos as part of ms package.
Recent Nonfiction Title: *SAT Success*, by Joan Carris.

PETROCELLI BOOKS, INC., Research Park, 251 Wall St., Princeton NJ 08540. (609)924-5851. Editorial Director: O.R. Petrocelli. Senior Editor: Rick Batlan. Publishes hardcover and paperback originals. Publishes 20 titles/year. Offers 12½-18% royalties. No advance. Simultaneous and photocopied submissions OK. Computer printout submissions acceptable; prefers letter-quality to dot-matrix. Reports in 1 month. Free book catalog.
Nonfiction: Business/economics, reference, technical, and textbooks. Submit outline/synopsis and 1-2 sample chapters.
Recent Nonfiction Title: *Applications in Artificial Intelligence*, edited by Stephen J. Andriole.

PHAROS BOOKS, (formerly World Almanac Publications), 200 Park Ave., New York NY 10166. (212)692-3824. Editor-in-Chief: Hana Umlauf Lane. Senior Acquisitions Editor: Beverly Jane Lee. Publisher of *The World Almanac*. Publishes hardcover and trade paperback originals. Averages 30 titles/year. Pays 5-15% on retail price. Publishes book an average of 1 year after acceptance. Computer printout submissions acceptable; prefers letter-quality to dot-matrix. Reports in 3 weeks. Free book catalog.
Nonfiction: "We look for books under four imprints: Pharos Books for nonfiction with strong consumer interest; World Almanac for innovative reference books; Topper for humor books; and Sparkler for fine children's books. We expect at least a synopsis/outline and sample chapters, and would like to see the completed manuscript." Reviews artwork/photos as part of ms package.

PHILOMEL BOOKS, Division of The Putnam Publishing Group, 51 Madison Ave., New York NY 10010. (212)689-9200. Editor-in-Chief: Patricia Lee Gauch. Editor: Victoria Rock. Publishes quality hardcover originals. Publishes 12-20 titles/year; receives 2,600 submissions annually. 15% of books from first-time authors; 30% of books from unagented writers. Pays standard royalty. Advance negotiable. Publishes book an average of 1-2 years after acceptance. Computer printout submissions acceptable; prefers letter-quality to dot-matrix. Reports in 1 month on queries. Request book catalog from marketing department of Putnam Publishing Group.
Nonfiction: Young adult and children's picture books. No alphabet books or workbooks. Query first. Looks for quality writing, unique ideas, particulary fine regional fiction and picture books; writing quality; suitability to our market."
Recent Nonfiction Title: *Anno's Hat Tricks*, by A. Nozaki and M. Anno.
Fiction: Young adult and children's books on any topic. Query to department.
Recent Fiction Title: *A White Romance*, by Virginia Hamilton.
Tips: "We are interested in the beauty of language—books written with a child's vision that celebrate human spirit."

PICKWICK PUBLICATIONS, 4137 Timberlane Dr., Allison Park PA 15101. Editorial Director: Dikran Y. Hadidian. Publishes paperback originals and reprints. Averages 3-6 titles/year; receives 10 submissions annually. 50% of books from first-time authors; 90% of books from unagented writers. Publishes book an average of 18-24 months after acceptance. Photocopied submissions OK. Computer printout submissions acceptable. Reports in 4 months. Free book catalog.
Nonfiction: Religious and scholarly mss in Biblical archeology, Biblical studies, church history and theology. Also reprints of outstanding out-of-print titles and original texts and translations. Accepts nonfiction translations from French or German. No popular religious material. Query. Accepts outline/synopsis and 2 sample chapters. Consult *MLA Style Sheet* or Turabian's *A Manual for Writers*.
Recent Nonfiction Title: *Coleridge as Poet & Religious Thinker*, by David Jasper.

PILOT BOOKS, 103 Cooper St., Babylon NY 11702. (516)422-2225. Publishes paperback originals. Averages 20-30 titles/year; receives 300-400 submissions annually. 20% of books from first-time authors; 90% of books from unagented writers. Average print order for a writer's first book is 3,000. Offers standard royalty contract based on wholesale or retail price. Usual advance is $250, but this varies, depending on author's reputation and nature of book. Publishes book an average of 8 months after acceptance. Computer printout submissions acceptable; prefers letter-quality to dot-matrix. Reports in 1 month.
Nonfiction: Financial, business, travel, career, personal guides and training manuals. "Our training manuals are utilized by America's major corporations as well as the government." Directories and books on travel and moneymaking opportunities. Wants "clear, concise treatment of subject matter." Length: 8,000-30,000

words. Send outline. Reviews artwork/photos as part of ms package.
Recent Nonfiction Title: *Directory of Low Cost Vacations with A Difference*, by J. Crawford.

PINEAPPLE PRESS, INC., Box 314, Englewood FL 33533. (813)475-2238. Editor: June Cussen. Publishes hardcover and trade paperback originals. Averages 6-8 titles/year; receives 600 submissions annually. 20% of books from first-time authors; 80% of books from unagented writers. Pays 6½-15% royalty on retail price. Seldom offers advance. Publishes book an average of 6 months after acceptance. Simultaneous and photocopied submissions OK. Electronic submissions OK via disk or modem; query first. Hard copy must accompany an electronic submission. Computer printout submissions acceptable; no dot-matrix. Reports in 1 month on queries; 6 weeks on mss. Book catalog for SAE and 39¢ postage.
Nonfiction: Biography, how-to, reference, nature and young adult. Subjects include animals, cooking and foods, history and nature. "We will consider all nonfiction topics, but not those heavily illustrated. We are seeking quality nonfiction on diverse topics for the library and book trade markets." No heavily illustrated submissions, pop psychology, or autobiographies. Query or submit outline/synopsis and sample chapters.
Recent Nonfiction Title: *Cry of the Panther*, by James P. McMullen (personal account of tracking panthers).
Fiction: Experimental, historical and mainstream. No romance, science fiction, or children's (below the young adult level). Query or submit outline/synopsis and sample chapters.
Recent Fiction Title: *Orlok*, by Don Dandrea (historical fiction).
Tips: "If I were a writer trying to market a book today, I would learn everything I could about book publishing and book publicity and agree to actively participate in promoting my book."

‡PLATT & MUNK PUBLISHERS, Division of Grosset & Dunlap, 51 Madison Ave., New York NY 10010. Editor-in-Chief: Bernette G. Ford. Publishes hardcover and paperback originals. Averages 10-20 titles/year; receives more than 10,000 submissions annually. Pays $1,000-2,000 in outright purchase; advance negotiable. Publishes book an average of 18 months after acceptance. Simultaneous and photocopied submissions OK. Reports in 10 weeks.
Nonfiction: Juveniles. Submit proposal or query first. "Nature, science, and light technology are of interest." Looks for "new ways of looking at the world of children."
Recent Nonfiction Title: *How Big Is a Brachiosaurus?*, by Susan Carroll.
Fiction: Juveniles, picture books for 3-7 age group and some higher. Also interested in anthologies and collections with a fresh approach.
Recent Fiction Title: *The Easy-to-Read Little Engine That Could*, by Watty Piper.
Tips: "Nonfiction that is particularly topical or of wide interest in the mass market; a new concept for novelty format for preschoolers; and very well-written fiction on topics that appeal to parents of preschoolers have the best chance of selling to our firm. We want something new—a proposal for a new series for the ordinary picture book. You have a better chance if you have new ideas."

PLAYERS PRESS, INC., Box 1132, Studio City CA 91604. (818)789-4980. Vice President, Editorial: Robert W. Gordon. Publishes hardcover and trade paperback originals, and trade paperback reprints. Averages 15-25 titles/year; receives 75-300 submissions annually. 10% of books from first-time authors; 90% of books from unagented writers. Pays royalty on retail price. Publishes book an average of 20 months after acceptance. Simultaneous and photocopied submissions OK. Reports in 4 months. Book catalog for 6x9 SAE and 39¢ postage.
Nonfiction: Juvenile and theatrical drama/entertainment industry. Subjects include the performing arts. Needs quality plays and musicals, adult or juvenile. Submit complete ms. Reviews artwork/photos as part of ms package.
Fiction: Adventure, confession, ethnic, experimental, fantasy, historical, horror, humor, mainstream, mystery, religious, romance, science fiction, suspense and western. Submit complete ms.
Recent Fiction Title: *Love Garden*, by James Sunwall (comedy).
Tips: "Plays, entertainment industry texts and children's story books have the best chance of selling to our firm."

‡PLURIBUS PRESS, INC., Division of Teach'em, Inc., 160 E. Illinois St., Chicago IL 60611. Associate Editor: Ellen Slezak. Publishes hardcover and trade paperback originals. Averages 15 titles/year. Pays royalty. Simultaneous and photocopied submissions (if so advised) OK. Will consider computer printout submissions. Reports in 1 month.
Nonfiction: How-to, self-help, technical and textbooks. Subjects include business and economics, health, psychology, sports, management "for adult professionals interested in improving the quality of their work and home life. In particular we want material that shows how to or is in self-help, technical, or textbook form with emphasis on health and education administration. Will consider proposals in the following areas: business/management, psychology, and sports. We will consider humorous treatment. No fiction, poetry, art, nature, history, juvenile, politics, religion, travel, biography or autobiography considered." Query or submit outline/synopsis and 3 sample chapters.

POCKET BOOKS, 1230 Avenue of the Americas, New York NY 10020. Imprints include Washington Square Press (high-quality mass market), and Poseidon Press (hardcover fiction and nonfiction). Publishes paperback originals and reprints, mass market and trade paperbacks. Averages 300 titles/year; receives 750 submissions annually. 15% of books from first-time authors; 5% of books from unagented writers. Pays royalty on retail price. Publishes book an average of 1 year after acceptance. Computer printout submissions acceptable; prefers letter-quality to dot-matrix. Query only. No unsolicited mss.
Nonfiction: History, biography, reference and general nonfiction.
Recent Nonfiction Title: *Challengers: The Inspiring Life Stories of the Seven Brave Astronauts of Shuttle Mission 51-L,* by the staff of *The Washington Post.*
Fiction: Adult, (mysteries, science fiction, romance, westerns).
Recent Fiction Title: *The Color Purple,* by Alice Walker.

PORTER SARGENT PUBLISHERS, INC., 11 Beacon St., Boston MA 02108. (617)523-1670. Publishes hardcover and paperback originals, reprints, translations and antholigies. Averages 3 titles/year. Pays royalty on retail price. "Each contract is dealt with on an individual basis with the author." Send query with brief description, table of contents, sample chapter and information regarding author's background. Computer printout submissions acceptable. Enclose return postage. Looks for "originality and clear and concise treatment and availability of subject." Free book catalog.
Nonfiction: Reference, special education and academic nonfiction. "Handbook Series and Special Education Series offer standard, definitive reference works in private education and writings and texts in special education. The Extending Horizons Series is an outspoken, unconventional series which presents topics of importance in contemporary affairs and the social sciences." This series is particularly directed to the college adoption market. Accepts nonfiction translations from French and Spanish. Contact: Peter M. Casey.
Recent Nonfiction Title: *Workplace Democracy and Social Change,* by Frank Lindenfeld and Joyce Rothschild-Whitt, editors (political science).

POSEIDON PRESS, Division of Pocket Books, 1230 Avenue of the Americas, New York NY 10020. (212)246-2121. Vice President/Publisher: Ann E. Patty. Publishes hardcover and trade paperback originals. Averages 10-12 titles/year; receives 1,000 submissions annually. 20% of books from first-time authors; none from unagented writers. Pays 10-15% royalty on hardcover retail price. Publishes book an average of 9 months after acceptance. Computer printout submissions acceptable; no dot-matrix. Does not accept unsolicited material.
Nonfiction: Biography, cookbook, reference and self-help. Subjects include business and economics, health, history, psychology and sociology. No religious/inspirational or humor.
Fiction: Literary, historical, contemporary and mainstream.

POTENTIALS DEVELOPMENT FOR HEALTH & AGING SERVICES, 775 Main St., Buffalo NY 14203. (716)842-2658. Publishes paperback originals. Averages 6 titles/year; receives 30-40 submissions annually. 90% of books from first-time authors; 100% of books from unagented writers. Average print order for a writer's first book is 1,500. Pays 5% royalty on sales. Publishes book an average of 1 year after acceptance. Computer printout submissions acceptable; no dot-matrix. Reports in 6 weeks. Free book catalog and ms guidelines for SASE.
Nonfiction: "We seek material of interest to those working with elderly people in the community and in institutional settings. We need tested, innovative and practical ideas." Query or submit outline/synopsis and 3 sample chapters to J.A. Elkins. Looks for "suitable subject matter, writing style and organization." Reviews artwork/photos as part of ms package.
Recent Nonfiction Title: *Fragrance Projects for Sensory Stimulation,* by P. Gwinnup.
Tips: "The writer has the best chance of selling us materials of interest to those working with elderly people in nursing homes, senior and retirement centers. Our major market is activity directors. Give us good reasons why activity directors would want or need the material submitted."

CLARKSON N. POTTER, INC., 225 Park Ave., New York NY 10003. (212)254-1600. Vice President/Editorial Director: Carol Southern. Managing Director: Michael Fragnito. Publishes hardcover and trade paperback originals. Averages 55 titles/year; receives 1,500 submissions annually. 18% of books from first-time authors, but many of these first-time authors are well-known and have had media coverage. Buys no unagented submissions. Pays 10% royalty on hardcover; 5-7½% on paperback; 5-7% on illustrated hardcover, varying escalations; advance depends on type of book and reputation or experience of author. No unagented mss can be considered. Photocopied submissions OK. Computer printout submissions acceptable. Reports in 1 month. Free book catalog.
Nonfiction: Publishes art, autobiography, biography, cooking and foods, how-to, humor, juvenile, nature, photography, self-help, style and annotated literature. Accepts nonfiction translations. "Manuscripts must be cleanly typed on 8½x11 nonerasable bond; double-spaced. Chicago *Manual of Style* is preferred." Query or

submit outline/synopsis and sample chapters. Reviews artwork/photos as part of ms package.
Recent Nonfiction Title: *Italian Style*, by Catharine Sabino.
Fiction: Will consider "quality fiction."
Recent Fiction Title: *Bad Manners*, by Maggie Paley.

THE PRAIRIE PUBLISHING COMPANY, Box 264, Postal Station C, Winnipeg, Manitoba R3M 3S7 Canada. (204)885-6496. Publisher: Ralph Watkins. Publishes trade paperback originals. Averages 4 titles/year; receives 25 submissions annually. 4% of books from first-time authors; 85% of books from unagented writers. Average print order for a writer's first book is 2,000. Pays 10% royalty on retail price. Photocopied submissions OK. Computer printout submissions acceptable; no dot-matrix. Reports in several weeks. Free book catalog; ms guidelines for SASE. Reviews artwork/photos as part of ms package.
Nonfiction: Biography and cookbook. Subjects include cooking and foods. "We would look at any submissions."
Recent Nonfiction Title: *My Name Is Marie Anne Gabaury*, by Mary Jordan.

PRAKKEN PUBLICATIONS, INC., Box 8623, Ann Arbor MI 48107. (313)769-1211. Publisher/executive editor: Alan H. Jones. Publishes hardcover and trade paperback originals. Averages 3 titles/year; receives 10 submissions annually. 50% of books from first-time authors; 100% of books from unagented writers. Pays 10% royalty on net price. Publishes book an average of 6 months after acceptance. Simultaneous and photocopied submissions OK. Computer printout submissions acceptable; prefers letter-quality to dot-matrix. Reports in 2 weeks on queries; 1 month on mss. Free book catalog.
Nonfiction: General education, vocational and technical education. "We are interested in manuscripts with broad appeal in any of the specific subject areas of the industrial arts, vocational-technical education, and in the general education field." Submit outline/synopsis and sample chapters. Reviews artwork/photos as part of ms package.
Recent Nonfiction Title: *Basic Mathematics*, by A.L. Hambley (textbook).

‡PRECEDENT PUBLISHING, INC., 737 N. LaSalle St., Chicago IL 60610. (312)944-2525. President: Michael Gross. Publishes hardcover originals and reprints. Averages 10 titles/year; receives 1,000 submissions annually. 50% of books from first-time authors; 100% of books from unagented writers. Pays 7½-10% royalty on wholesale price. No advance. Publishes book an average of 6 months after acceptance. Electronic submissions OK via IBM, but requires hard copy also. Computer printout submissions acceptable. Simultaneous submissions OK. Reports in 1 month on queries. Book catalog free on request.
Nonfiction: Biography and reference. Needs scholarly, semi-academic mss. No how-to books. Query.
Recent Nonfiction Title: *Envelopes of Sound*, by Ron Grele (history).

PRENTICE-HALL, Books for Young Readers (A Division of Simon & Schuster), 1230 Ave. of the Americas, New York NY 10020. Editorial Director: Grace Clarke. Manuscripts Editor: Rose Lopez. Publishes hardcover and paperback originals and paperback reprints. Publishes 30 hardcovers/year, 15 paperbacks/year. Pays royalty. Offers advance. Reports in 6 weeks. Book catalog for SASE.
Nonfiction: All subjects, all age groups but special interest in topical science and technology, art, social sciences, history (any unusual approaches), humor (no jokes or riddles but funny fiction), music (keen interest in basic approaches, no biographies), sociology (8-12), and sports (6-9), puzzle and participation (6-8). Query. Accepts outline/synopsis and 5-6 sample chapters from published writers; entire ms from unpublished writers. Prefers to see portfolio separate from ms except when illustrator is making the submission or when clarity requires that ms be accompanied by photos or rough illustrations.
Recent Nonfiction Title: *The Marvelous Music Machine: A Story of the Piano*, by Mary Blocksma, illustrated by Mischa Richter.
Fiction: Gothic, humor, mainstream and mystery. Submit outline/synopsis and sample chapters.
Recent Fiction Title: *Texas Trail to Calamity*, by Robert Quackenbush (detective mystery, ages 6-9).
Picture Books: Accent on humor.
Recent Picture Book: *A Weekend in the Country*, by Lee Lorenz.

‡PRENTICE-HALL CANADA, INC., College Division, 1870 Birchmount Road, Scarborough, Ontario M1P 2J7 Canada. (416)293-3621. Executive Editor: Cliff Newman. Publishes hardcover and paperback originals and software; receives 200-300 submissions annually. 30-40% of books from first-time authors; 100% of books from unagented writers. Pays 10-15% royalty on net price. Publishes book an average of 14 months after acceptance. Electronic submissions OK via IBM PC disk, but requires hard copy also. Computer printout submissions acceptable; prefers letter-quality to dot-matrix.
Nonfiction: The College Division publishes textbooks suitable for the community college and large university market. Most submissions should be designed for existing courses in all disciplines of study. Will consider software in most disciplines, especially business and sciences. Canadian content is important. The division also publishes books in computer science, technology and mathematics.

Recent Nonfiction Title: *Contemporary Business Mathematics with Canadian Applications*, by Hummelbrunner.

PRENTICE-HALL CANADA, INC., Educational Book Division, 1870 Birchmount Road, Scarborough, Ontario M1P 2J7 Canada. (416)293-3621. Executive Editor: Rob Greenaway.
Nonfiction: Publishes texts, workbooks, and instructional media including computer courseware for elementary, junior high and high schools. Subjects include business, computer studies, geography, history, language arts, mathematics, science, social studies, technology, and French as a second language.

PRENTICE-HALL CANADA, INC., Trade Division, 1870 Birchmount Road, Scarborough, Ontario M1P 2J7 Canada. (416)293-3621. Acquisitions Editor: Iris Skeoch. Publishes hardcover and trade paperback originals and software. Averages 15 titles/year; receives 300-350 submissions annually. 40% of books from first-time authors; 40% of books from unagented writers. Negotiates royalty and advance. Publishes book an average of 9 months after acceptance. Electronic submissions OK, but requires hard copy also. Computer printout submissions acceptable; prefers letter-quality to dot-matrix. SAE and IRCs. Reports in 10 weeks. Ms guidelines for SASE.
Nonfiction: Subjects of Canadian and international interest; art, politics and current affairs, business, travel, health and food. Send sample chapters or outlines. Reviews artwork/photos as part of ms package.
Recent Nonfiction Title: *Across The Table*, by Cynthia Wine and Mary Pratt.
Tips: Needs general interest non-fiction books on topical subjects. "Present a clear, concise thesis, well-argued with a thorough knowledge of existing works."

PRENTICE-HALL, INC., Business & Professional Books Division, Gulf & Western, Inc., Sylvan Ave., Englewood Cliffs NJ 07632. (201)592-2000. Vice President: Ted Nardin. Publishes hardcover and trade paperback originals. Averages 150 titles/year; receives 1,000+ submissions annually. 50% of books from first-time authors; 95% of books from unagented writers. Pays royalty: 5% on cash received on *mail order*, or 10-15% on all *trade* sales. Offers $3,000-5,000 advance. Publishes book an average of 8 months after acceptance. Simultaneous and photocopied submissions OK. Electronic submissions OK, but requires hard copy also. Computer printout submissions acceptable; prefers letter-quality to dot-matrix. Reports in 3 weeks. Free book catalog; writer's guidelines for SASE.
Nonfiction: How-to, reference, self-help and technical. Subjects include business and economics, recreation, sports, real estate, law, accounting, computers and education. Needs business, professional, technical and educational references, for sale primarily via direct mail. Query or submit outline/synopsis and sample chapters. Reviews artwork/photos as part of ms package
Recent Nonfiction Title: *The Marketing Plan Workbook*, by J.C. Makens.
Tips: "We seek high-level, practical references that command high prices and that can be sold to targeted markets via direct mail."

THE PRESERVATION PRESS, National Trust for Historic Preservation, 1785 Massachusetts Ave. NW, Washington DC 20036. Editor: Diane Maddex. Publishes nonfiction books and periodicals on historic preservation (saving and reusing the "built environment"). Averages 6 titles/year; receives 30+ submissions annually. 40% of books from first-time authors; 50% of books from unagented writers. Books are often commissioned by the publisher. Publishes book an average of 2 years after acceptance. Electronic submissions OK via IBM, but requires hard copy also. Computer printout submissions acceptable; no dot-matrix.
Nonfiction: Subject matter encompasses architecture and architectural history, building restoration and historic preservation. No local history. Query. Looks for "relevance to national preservation-oriented audience; educational or instructional value; depth; uniqueness; need in field." Reviews artwork/photos as part of ms package.
Recent Nonfiction Title: *What Style Is It? A Guide to American Architecture*.
Tips: "The writer has the best chance of selling our firm a book clearly related to our mission—historic preservation— that covers new ideas and is unique and practical. If it fills a clear need, we will know immediately."

PRESIDIO PRESS, 31 Pamaron Way, Novato CA 94947. (415)883-1373. Editor-in-Chief: Adele Horwitz. Senior Editor: Joan Griffin. Publishes hardcover and paperback originals. Receives 50 submissions annually. 90% of books from first-time authors; 95% of books from unagented writers. Pays 15% royalty on net price. Offers nominal advance. Publishes book an average of 10 months after acceptance. Photocopied submissions OK. Electronic submissions OK, but requires hard copy also. Reports in 3 months. Free book catalog.
Nonfiction: Military history. No scholarly. Fiction with military background considered. Accepts nonfiction translations. Query or submit outline/synopsis and 3 sample chapters. Reviews artwork/photos as part of ms package.
Recent Nonfiction Title: *The Rise and Fall of an American Army: U.S. Ground Forces, Vietnam, 1965-1973*, by Shelby L. Stanton.
Tips: "Have the proper experience or qualifications for the subject."

PRESS GANG PUBLISHERS, 603 Powell St., Vancouver, British Columbia V6A 1H2 Canada. (604)253-2537. Publishes trade paperback originals. Averages 2 titles/year. 50% of books from first-time authors; 90% of books from unagented writers. Pays royalty. Offers no advance. Publishes book an average of 18 months after acceptance. Simultaneous and photocopied submissions OK. Computer printout submissions acceptable; prefers letter-quality to dot-matrix. Reports in 1 month on queries; 2 months on mss. Book catalog for business size SAE and 50¢ (Canadian funds).
Nonfiction: Women's politics. "We are a feminist press, interested in analytical and historical work." No mss without relevance to women's liberation. Preference given to Canadian mss. Submit outline/synopsis and sample chapters. Reviews artwork/photos as part of ms package.
Recent Nonficton Title: *Still Sane*, by Persimmon Blackbridge and Sheila Gilhool.
Fiction: Short stories, novels (by/about women), and nonsexist children's books. No mss without relevance to women's liberation. Submit complete ms.

PRICE/STERN/SLOAN INC., PUBLISHERS, 410 N. La Cienega Blvd., Los Angeles CA 90048. Imprints include Serendipity Books, Bugg Books, Wee Sing Books, Troubador Press and Laughter Library. Associate Editor: Claudia Sloan. Publishes trade paperback originals. Averages 100-120 titles/year; receives 6,000+ submissions annually. 20% of books from first-time authors; 60% of books from unagented writers. Pays royalty on wholesale price, or by outright purchase. Offers small or no advance. Publishes book an average of 1 year after acceptance. Computer printout submissions acceptable; no dot-matrix. Reports in 3 months. Ms guidelines for SASE.
Nonfiction: Subjects include humor self-help (limited), and satire (limited). Juveniles. Query *only*. "Most titles are unique in concept as well as execution and are geared for the so-called gift market." Reviews artwork/photos as part of ms package.
Tips: "Humor and satire were the basis of the company's early product and are still the mainstream of the company."

PRINCETON ARCHITECTURAL PRESS, 40 Witherspoon St., Princeton NJ 08540. (609)924-7911. Associate Editor: Juliana Mastroserio. Publishes hardcover and trade paperback originals and hardcover reprints. Averages 8 titles/year; receives 20 submissions annually. 50% of books from first-time authors; 100% of books from unagented writers. Pays 6-12% royalty on wholesale price. Simultaneous and photocopied submissions OK. Electronic submissions OK on IBM and Altos compatibles, but requires hard copy also. Computer printout submissions acceptable; no dot-matrix. Reports in 1 month. Free book catalog.
Nonfiction: "Coffee table" book, illustrated book and textbook. Subjects include art, history and architecture. Needs texts on architecture, landscape architecture, architectural monographs, and texts to accompany a possible reprint, architectural history and urban design. Submit outline/synopsis and sample chapters or complete ms. Reviews artwork/photos as part of ms package.
Recent Nonfiction Title: *The Danteum*, by Thomas Schumacher (architectural history).
Tips: "Our audience is architects, designers, urban planners, architectural theorists, and architectural-urban design historians. Also many academicians and practitioners. In architecture, write about postmodern thought; in design, focus on historical precedent."

*PRINCETON UNIVERSITY PRESS, 41 William St., Princeton NJ 08540. (609)452-4900. Editor-in-Chief: Sanford G Thatcher. Publishes hardcover and trade paperback originals and reprints. Averages 140 titles/year; receives 5,000 submissions annually. 50% of books from first-time authors; 99% of books from unagented writers. Average print order for writer's first book is 1,250. Subsidy assists (non-author) 50% of books, "when we don't break even on the first printing." Pays 10% maximum royalty on retail price. Rarely offers advance. Publishes book an average of 1 year after acceptance. Simultaneous submissions OK, if notified; photocopied submissions OK. Electronic submissions OK on Penta with Telemedia interface, compatible with Radio Shack TRS-80, IBM PC, and Wang. Requires hard copy also. Computer printout submissions acceptable; no dot-matrix. Reports in 2 weeks on queries; 1 month on mss "if unsuitable" or 6 months "if suitable and put through entire review process." Ms guidelines for SASE.
Nonfiction: Biography, reference and technical. Subjects include art history, literary criticism, history, philosophy, religion, political science, economics, anthropology, sociology and science.
Recent Nonfiction Title: *Churchill and Roosevelt: The Complete Correspondence*, edited by Warren F. Kimball.
Poetry: Poetry submissions (original and in translation) are judged in competition. Write to Robert Brown. Submit complete ms.
Tips: "A work of original scholarship that significantly contributes to the advance of knowledge in its field via new data or new interpretations, or both, has the best chance of selling. We do not often offer advance contracts; most books we accept are already completed."

PRINTEMPS BOOKS, INC., Box 746, Wilmette IL 60091. (312)251-5418. Secretary/Treasurer: Beatrice Penovich. Publishes trade paperback originals. Averages 3 titles/year. Pays royalty or makes outright pur-

chase, "to be agreed upon." Offers no advance. Reports in 1 month on mss.
Fiction: Adventure, ethnic, fantasy, humor, mystery, suspense, and children's stories (short). "Our aim is to both entertain and educate students who have less than average reading skills. We envision publication of a collection of stories suitable for high school students who have a very limited vocabulary." Publishes for school systems and over-the-counter purchases. Submit complete ms.

PROMETHEUS BOOKS, INC., 700 E. Amherst St., Buffalo NY 14215. (716)837-2475. President/Editor-in-Chief: Paul Kurtz. Vice President/Director of Advertising and Promotion: Victor Gulotta. Publishes hardcover and trade paperback originals. Averages 40 titles/year; receives 3,000 + submissions annually. 10-20% of books from first-time authors; 75% from unagented writers. Pays 5-10% royalty on wholesale price; offers negotiable advance. Publishes book an average of 1 year after acceptance. Computer printout submissions acceptable; no dot-matrix. Reports in 2 months. Free book catalog.
Nonfiction and Fiction: Textbook and trade. Subjects include philosophy, science, the paranormal, psychology, religion, sociology, medical ethics, biography, literature and criticism. "Prometheus is an independent publishing house with a commitment to maximizing the availability of books of high scholarly merit and popular interest. We welcome manuscript proposals suitable to our publishing program, which focuses on the humanities and social and natural sciences. One area of specialization in which we have experienced tremendous growth is scientific criticism of 'paranormal phenomena.' We also are interested in examining proposals for competitive college texts, both primary and supplementary." Accepts nonfiction translations. Submission of popular trade nonfiction is also encouraged. Submit outline/synopsis and/or "at least the first few" chapters. Reviews artwork/photos as part of ms package.
Recent Title: *Storm Over Biology*, by Bernard Davis.

PRUETT PUBLISHING CO., 2928 Pearl, Boulder CO 80301. Managing Editor: Gerald Keenan. Averages 20 titles/year; receives 200 submissions annually. 50% of books from first-time authors; 100% of books from unagented writers. Average print order for a writer's first book is 2,000-3,000. Pays royalty on wholesale price. "Most books that we publish are aimed at special interest groups. As a small publisher, we feel most comfortable in dealing with a segment of the market that is very clearly identifiable, and one we know we can reach with our resources." Publishes book an average of 10 months after acceptance. Legible photocopies acceptable. Any disk submissions would have to interface with present typesetting system, but requires hard copy also. Computer printout submissions acceptable; no dot-matrix. Reports in 1 month. Free catalog on request; ms guidelines for SASE.
Nonfiction: Publishes general adult nonfiction and textbooks. Subjects include pictorial railroad histories, outdoor activities related to the Intermountain West, and some western Americana. Textbooks with a regional (intermountain) aspect for preschool through college level. "Like most small publishers, we try to emphasize quality from start to finish, because, for the most part, our titles are going to a specialized market that is very quality conscious. We also feel that one of our strong points is the personal involvement ('touch') so often absent in a much larger organization." Accepts outline/synopsis and 3 sample chapters. Mss must conform to the Chicago *Manual of Style*. Reviews artwork/photos as part of ms package.
Recent Nonfiction Title: *Letter from Honeyhill*, by Wahl.

PSG PUBLISHING CO., INC., 545 Great Rd., Littleton MA 01460. (617)48-8971. President/Publisher: Frank Paparello. Publishes hardcover and paperback originals. Receives 100 submissions annually. 50% of books from first-time authors; 100% of books from unagented writers. Pays royalty on net revenues. Specializes in publishing medical and dental books, newsletters and journals for the professional and student markets. Pays 10-15% royalty. Publishes book an average of 8 months after acceptance. Simultaneous submissions OK. Electonic submissions OK via IBM PC, but requires hard copy also. Computer printout submissions acceptable; prefers letter-quality to dot-matrix. Reports in 1 month. Free book catalog and ms guidelines.
Nonfiction: Medical and dental books, newsletter and journals. Request proposal form. Query or submit complete ms. Reviews artwork photos as part of ms package.
Recent Nonfiction Title: *Sports Injuries*, by Paul Vinger, M.D.
Tips: "Books on clinical medicine for practicing professionals have the best chance of selling to our firm." Queries/mss may be routed to other editors in the publishing group.

PURDUE UNIVERSITY PRESS, South Campus Courts, D., West Lafayette IN 47907. (317)494-2035. Director: William J. Whalen. Managing Editor: Verna Emery. Publishes hardcover and paperback originals. Specializes in scholarly books from all areas of academic endeavor. Averages 7-8 titles/year; receives 200 submissions annually. 20% of books from first-time authors; 100% of books from unagented writers. Pays 10% royalty on list price. Offers no advance. Publishes book an average of 1 year after acceptance. Photocopied submissions OK "if author will verify that it does not mean simultaneous submission elsewhere." Computer printout submissions acceptable; no dot-matrix. Reports in 4 months. Free book catalog. Prepare ms according to Chicago *Manual of Style*.
Nonfiction: Publishes agriculture, Americana, art (but no color plates), biography, communication, econom-

ics, engineering, history, horticulture, literature, philosophy, political science, psychology, science, sociology, and literary criticism. "Works of scholarship only." Submit complete ms only. Reviews artwork/photos as part of ms package.
Recent Nonfiction Title: *Hoosier Home Remedies*, by Varro E. Tyler.
Tips: "A book that fills a need in a scholarly field and/or contributes to one of our specialty areas—biography, theory of biography, south central European history, literature, philosophy, interdisciplinary studies, regional interest—has the best chance of selling to our firm. In writing and researching a book, the writer should present new information in an engaging style. In a query, the author should clearly define the book's intended audience and *raison d'etre*. These things help us justify publishing a book and give us confidence that we can find a tangible market for it."

Q.E.D. INFORMATION SCIENCES, INC., 170 Linden St., Box 181, Wellesley MA 02181. (617)237-5656. Manager of Publishing/Software: Jerry Murphy. Publishes computer books and software for MIS professionals. Averages 20 titles/year. Pays 10-15% royalty on net receipts. Publishes book an average of 6 months after acceptance. Electronic submissions OK on IBM PC. Computer printout submissions OK. Preliminary reports in 1 week on queries; 3 weeks on mss. Free book catalog.
Nonfiction: Technical. Subjects include computers, personal computing, and database technology. "Our books are read by data processing managers and technicians." Submit outline/synopsis and 2 sample chapters. Reviews artwork/photos as part of ms package.
Recent Nonfiction Title: *Data Dictionary: Concepts and Uses*, by R. Perkinson.

QUARTET BOOKS INC., Subsidiary of The Namara Group. Suite 2005, 215 S. Park Ave., New York NY 10003. (212)254-2277. Director: Marilyn Warnick. Editor: Catherine Norden. Subsidiaries include The Women's Press and Namara Publications and Robin Clark. Publishes hardcover and trade paperback originals and reprints. Averages 40 titles/year in US, 200 in UK. 20% of books from first-time authors; 15% of books from unagented writers. Pays 6-12% royalty; offers average $2,000 advance. Publishes book an average of 10 months after acceptance. Simultaneous submissions OK. Reports in 3 weeks on queries; 6 weeks on mss. Book catalog for 7x9 SAE and 2 first class stamps.
Nonfiction: Biography, "coffee table" book, and illustrated book. Subjects include animals, business and economics, history, jazz, philosophy, photography, politics, psychology, sociology and Middle Eastern politics, culture and society. Especially looking for "well-written, thoroughly researched books on most serious topics and on people who will be of interest to both the English and American reader. No cookery, health, do-it-yourself, keep-fit, astrology, World War II experiences, or anything sexist or racist. Submit outline/synopsis and sample chapters. Reviews artwork/photos as part of ms package.
Recent Nonfiction Title: *The Transformation of Spain.*
Fiction: Submit through agent only. Adventure, erotica (only if very literary), mainstream, crime, and feminist. No romances, science fiction, westerns, horror, or any genre books other than crime.
Recent Fiction Title: *Distant View of a Minaret*, by Alisa Risaat.
Tips: "If I were a writer trying to market a book today, I would try to come up with something fresh rather than imitating current bestsellers. We are looking for titles that can be published by our sister company, Quartet Books Ltd. in London, as well as by the U.S. company, so the books must appeal to both markets."

QUE CORPORATION, 7999 Knue Rd., Indianapolis IN 46250. (317)842-7162. Executive Editor/Acquisitions: Pegg Kennedy. Publishes tutorial and application books on popular business software, and trade paperback originals, hardware and software products guides, software for books on computer spreadsheets, and software. Published approximately 35 titles in 1986; receives 700 submissions annually. 80% of books from first-time authors; 100% of books from unagented writers. Pays 8-15% escalating royalty on wholesale price. Publishes book an average of 4 months after acceptance. Simultaneous (if so advised) and photocopied submissions OK. Requires hard copy. Computer printout submissions acceptable; prefers letter-quality to dot-matrix. Reports in 1 month. Free book catalog.
Nonfiction: How-to, technical, and reference books relating to microcomputers; textbooks on business use of microcomputers; software user's guides and tutorials; operating systems user's guides; computer programming language reference works; books on microcomputer systems, spreadsheet software business applications, word processing, data base management, time management, popular computer programs for the home, computer graphics and game programs, networking, communications, languages, educational uses of microcomputers, computer-assisted instruction in education and business and course-authoring applications. "We will consider books on most subjects relating to microcomputers." Query, submit outline/synopsis and sample chapters, or send complete ms. Reviews artwork/photos as part of ms package.
Recent Nonfiction Title: *Using Paradox*, by George Chou, Ph.D.

QUILL, An imprint of William Morrow and Co., Inc., Subsidiary of The Hearst Corporation, 105 Madison Ave., New York NY 10016. (212)889-3050. Managing Editor: Alison Brown Cerier. Publishes trade paperback originals and reprints. Averages 50 titles/year; receives over 2,000 submissions annually. 40% of books

Close-up

Alison Brown Cerier
Managing Editor
Quill

"Make me want to read more," Alison Brown Cerier says when asked what kind of query letters are likely to receive a positive response. "I see so many proposals that I've got to be grabbed right away."

Cerier receives 25 to 30 unsolicited proposals a week for the paperback trade and nonfiction books she handles at Quill, a division of William Morrow & Company, Inc. Of these 25-30, she generally asks to see more—an outline or sample chapter—from only one writer each week. And after reading through the outlines and sample chapters, she'll ultimately ask only a small number of writers for completed manuscripts. "Often what I saw in the proposal isn't there in life," she says.

Most of the books that Cerier accepts are agented, and she urges writers to find themselves a compatible agent. "A good agent helps far beyond negotiating the contract," she says. For one thing, agents are often invaluable in helping the writer shape the initial proposal. An agent might help a writer rewrite a proposal several times before it is submitted to a publisher. Cerier says when she is impressed by an unagented proposal that does not meet Quill's own needs, she will sometimes suggest the writer get in touch with a particular agent.

According to Cerier, poor research often hampers a writer's credibility. Writers who query with the comment that no one has ever written a book about natural childbirth, for example, have obviously not done their homework. And a writer with a proposal for a book about bowling who says there are 40 million bowlers in the U.S., so this book will sell 40 million copies, is just not thinking clearly.

A good proposal, Cerier says, starts with a one-sentence "sales-handle," a description of the book that tells why a bookseller and eventually a reader will want it. The query letter could also include a sentence on the writer's credentials, a few "teaser lines," and a tie-in to a current trend. "It's wonderful when a writer compares the book to others we've published," Cerier says, "as I'll have experience with these titles, and I'll know the writer has looked at the types of books we publish."

In addition to advising writers to find a good agent, Cerier suggests that writers try to break into the trade-book market by publishing elsewhere first. "One way I find new writers is by reading magazines," she says. In addition, she states that book producers (once called book packagers) also offer an outlet for a beginning writer.

On occasion, Cerier works with authors who are not writers by profession, but experts on a subject she feels is likely to interest the general public. Cerier says she's often surprised at how quickly these new writers learn to edit their own work to make it suitable for publication. "I've found that if I edit the first chapter," she says, "writers often catch on and improve quickly, so I don't have to do as much work." The most important aspect of good nonfiction writing, of course, is an interesting and original *subject.*   *—Laurie Henry*

Editor's note: As we went to press, we learned that Cerier had become editor at Doubleday. Doug Stumps was named Quill's new managing editor.

from first-time authors; 5% of books from unagented writers. Pays royalty on retail price. Offers variable advance. Publishes ms an average of 1 year after acceptance. Simultaneous and photocopied submissions OK. Computer printout submissions acceptable; prefers letter-quality to dot-matrix. No unsolicited mss or proposals; mss and proposals should be submitted through a literary agent. Reports in 1 month.
Nonfiction: Biography and trade books. Subjects include cooking and foods, history, music, psychology, science, and puzzles and games. Needs nonfiction trade paperbacks with enduring importance; books that have backlist potential and appeal to educated people with broad intellectual curiosities. No fiction, poetry, fitness, diet, how-to, self-help or humor. Query.
Recent Nonfiction Title: *Everything Is Somewhere: the Geography Quiz book,* by Jack McClintoch and David Helgren.

‡**QUINLAN PRESS,** Subsidiary of Addison C. Getchell & Son, Inc. and Quinlan Publishing, 131 Beverly St., Boston MA 02114. (617)227-4870/1-800-551-2500. Independent book producer/packager. Executive Editor: Sandra E. Bielawa. Publishes hardcover and trade paperback originals. Averages 15-20 titles/year; receives 100 submissions annually. 75% of books from first-time authors; 90% of books from unagented writers. Pays 7-12% royalty on retail price; buys one ms outright for $1,000-5,000. Offers average $500 advance. Publishes book 1 year after acceptance. Simultaneous submissions OK. Computer printout submissions acceptable. Reports in 5 weeks on queries; 2 months on mss.
Nonfiction: Biography, humor, illustrated book and self-help. Subjects include Americana, animals, history, hobbies, music, photography, politics, recreation, religion, sociology and sports. "We are interested in publishing any nonfiction book we feel is consumable by the population in general. Nothing too esoteric." Submit outline/synopsis and sample chapters.
Recent Nonfiction Title: *A Cop's Cop,* by Ed Connolly and Chris Harding.
Fiction: "We do not publish fiction at this time, but are willing to consider humorous or adventure-type novels."
Tips: Trends in book publishing over the last few years have included novelty items, for example our trivia series, which have been well-received as the reading public looks for a light-hearted approach to learning. For the future what we're looking toward is more nonfiction, and alternative portrayals of both stories and instructive material. Our audience is those with an interest in reading works depicting true-life experiences which are not necessarily sensational, but rather realistic and entertaining in their own right. As a publisher of many first-time authors, books stand a very good chance if their content is true-to-life and, in some way, the first of their kind."

RAINBOW BOOKS, Box 1069, Moore Haven FL 33471. (813)946-0293. Associate: B. Lampe. Publishes hardcover and trade paperback originals. Averages 8-10 titles/year; receives 600 submissions annually. 70% of books from first-time authors; 68% of books from unagented writers. Publishes book an average of 8 months after acceptance. Reports in 1 week. Queries only. Book catalog $1.
Nonfiction: Reference and resource books plus some well-targeted how-to.
Recent Nonfiction Title: *Astros: A Do-It-Yourself Astrology Guidebook,* by Patricia Lewis.

RAINTREE PUBLISHERS INC., 310 W. Wisconsin Ave., Milwaukee WI 53202. (414)273-0873. Editor-in-Chief: Russell Bennet. Publishes hardcover originals. Usually makes outright purchase. Simultaneous and photocopied submissions OK. Computer printout submissions acceptable; prefers letter-quality to dot-matrix. Reports in approximately 2 months.
Nonfiction: Juvenile and reference. Subjects include animals, health, history, nature, photography and science. "We publish school and library books in series." Query with outline/synopsis and sample chapters.
Fiction: Adventure, historical and science fiction. Query with outline/synopsis and sample chapters.

‡**RANDALL HOUSE PUBLICATIONS,** Box 17306, Nashville TN 37217. (615)361-1221. Editor-in-Chief: H.D. Harrison. 25% of books from first-time authors; 95% of books from unagented writers. Pays royalties. Publishes book an average of 9 months after acceptance. Simultaneous submissions OK. Computer printout submissions acceptable; prefers letter-quality to dot-matrix. Reports in 6 weeks on mss. Free book catalog; ms guidelines for SASE.
Nonfiction: Religion. Submit complete ms.
Fiction: Religious. No fiction teaching a moral. Submit complete ms.
Tips: "True life experience from conservative Christian viewpoint and Biblical analysis/exergesis from Arminian Baptist perspective have the best chance of selling to our firm."

REFERENCE SERVICE PRESS, Suite 310, 3540 Wilshire Blvd., Los Angeles CA 90010. (213)251-3743. President: Dr. Gail Schlachter. Publishes hardcover and paperback originals. Averages 10-20 titles/year; receives 30-50 submissions annually. 90% of books from unagented writers. Average print order for a writer's first book is 1,000. Pays 10-20% royalty on net price, depending upon form of submission. Publishes book an average of 9 months after acceptance. Photocopied submissions OK. Electronic submissions OK via IBM, but requires hard copy also. Computer printout submissions acceptable; prefers letter-quality to dot-matrix. Reports in 45 days. Ms guidelines for SASE.

Nonfiction: Reference works (directories, dictionaries, handbooks, guides, bibliographies, encyclopedias, almanacs, serials, etc.) in any subject area and monographs on topics of interest to reference librarians. Query or submit outline/prospectus and 2-3 sample chapters. Reviews artwork/photos as part of ms package.

Recent Nonfiction Title: *Financial Aids for the Disabled and Their Dependents, 1986-87*, by Gail A. Schlachter.

REGENTS PUBLISHING CO., INC., 2 Park Ave., New York NY 10016. Acquisitions: Irwin Harris. 5% of books from first-time authors; 100% of books from unagented writers. Average print order for a writer's first book is 10,000. Computerized Instruction Editor: David Tillyer. Publishes English as a second language textbooks, computer-assisted instruction programs for the same market, and software. Averages 50 titles/year; receives 250 submissions annually. Publishes book an average of 1 year after acceptance. Electronic submissions OK on Apple IIE or IBM PC, but requires hard copy also. Computer printout submissions acceptable; no dot-matrix.

Nonfiction: Textbooks. Publishes ESL/EFL and Spanish language textbooks for all ages. Produces ESP materials for business, science, language arts, etc. Prefers complete proposals, including description of target market, comparison with similar materials already on the market, description of age/grade/difficulty level, as well as table of contents and at least 3 sample units.

Recent Nonfiction Title: *Spectrum* (an adult notional/functional ESL series).

Tips: Freelance writers should be aware of English as second language trends and market needs in education.

REGNERY/GATEWAY, INC., 950 N. Shore Drive, Lake Bluff IL 60044. President: Clyde P. Peters. Chairman: Henry Regnery. Publishes hardcover and paperback originals and paperback reprints. Averages 6-12 titles/year. Pays royalty. Simultaneous and photocopied submissions OK. Computer printout submissions acceptable. "Responds only to submissions in which there is interest." Free book catalog.

Nonfiction: Biography, economics, history, philosophy, politics, psychology, religion, science, sociology and education (teaching). Accepts nonfiction translations. "We are looking for books on current affairs—of either political, legal, social, environmental, educational or historical interest. Books heavy on sex and obscene brutality should not be submitted. No fiction, verse or children's literature." Queries preferred. Additional information if requested. No unsolicited mss accepted. Looks for "a novel approach to the subject, expertise of the author, clean, respectable writing, salability of the proposed work."

Recent Nonfiction Title: *Rice Paddy Grunt*, by John Brown.

RELIGIOUS EDUCATION PRESS, 1531 Wellington Rd., Birmingham AL 35209. (205)879-4040. Editor: James Michael Lee. Publishes trade paperback originals. Averages 5 titles/year; receives 80 submissions annually. 40% of books from first-time authors; 100% of books from unagented writers. Pays 10% royalty on actual selling price. "Many of our books are work for hire. We do not have a subsidy option." Offers no advance. Photocopied submissions OK. Information on request for electronic submissions. Computer printout submissions OK; no dot-matrix. Reports in 3 weeks on queries; 2 months on mss. Free book catalog.

Nonfiction: Technical and textbook. Scholarly subjects on religion and religious education. "We publish serious, significant and scholarly books on religious education and pastoral ministry." No mss under 200 pages, books on Biblical interpretation, or "popular" books. Query. Reviews artwork/photos as part of ms package.

Recent Nonfiction Title: *The Spiritualism of the Religious Educator*, by Lee (religion/psychology).

Tips: "Write clearly, reason exactly and connectively, and meet deadlines."

‡RENAISSANCE HOUSE PUBLISHERS, Box 177, 541 Oak St., Frederick CO 80530. (303)833-2030. Subsidiary of Jende-Hagan, Inc. Editor: Eleanor Ayer. Publishes hardcover and trade paperback originals and trade paperback reprints. Averages 6 titles/year; receives 100-150 submissions annually. 60% of books from first-time authors; 75% of books from unagented writers. Pays 10-15% royalty on wholesale price. Offers average advance of 10% of anticipated first printing royalties. May consider work for hire for experts in specific fields of interest. Publishes book an average of 18 months after acceptance. Simultaneous and photocopied submissions OK. Electronic submissions OK; "we have some flexibility; please query." Computer printout submissions acceptable; prefers letter-quality to dot-matrix. Reports in 1 month on queries; 2 months on mss. Book catalog free on request.

Nonfiction: Biography and general interest nonfiction. Subjects include Americana, history, hobbies and naturalist philosophy. Needs mss on history, "especially concerning the American Westward movement. History told from the perspective of a common person living in uncommon times. History that ties the past with the present. History for the lay reader. No personal reminiscences, general traditional philosophy, children's books, general cookbooks, books on topics totally unrelated to subject areas specified above." Submit outline/synopsis and sample chapters. Reviews artwork/photos as part of ms package.

Recent Nonfiction Title: *People of the Moonshell: A Western River Journal*, by Nancy M. Peterson (Western Americana).

Tips: "If I were a writer trying to market a book today, I would be persistent; be *certain* that my book was extremely compatible with a publisher's line before approaching that house; ask for recommendations or referrals with every rejection; try more than once at houses where I felt my book was especially compatible; be certain that the publisher who accepts my manuscript has an adequate marketing network to sell the number of books that I want to see sold. Query the house on details of its marketing program."

*RESOURCE PUBLICATIONS, INC., Suite 290, 160 E. Virginia St., San Jose CA 95112. Editorial Director: Kenneth E. Guentert. Publishes paperback originals. Publishes 10 titles/year; receives 100-200 submissions annually. 30% of books from first-time authors; 99% of books from unagented writers. Average print order of a writer's first book is 1,500. Subsidy publishes 10% of books. "If the author can present and defend a personal publicity effort or otherwise demonstrate demand and the work is in our field, we will consider it." Pays 8% royalty; offers no advance. Publishes book an average of 18 months after acceptance. Photocopied submissions (with written assurance that work is not being submitted simultaneously) OK. Electronic submissions OK if CP/M 8" single density disks, but requires hard copy also. Computer printout submissions acceptable; prefers letter-quality to dot-matrix. Reports in 2 months.
Nonfiction: "We look for creative source books for the religious education, worship, religious art, and architecture fields. How-to books, especially for contemporary religious art forms, are of particular interest (dance, mime, drama, choral reading, singing, music, musicianship, bannermaking, statuary, or any visual art form). No heavy theoretical, philosophical, or theological tomes. Nothing utterly unrelated or unrelatable to the religious market as described above. Query or submit outline/synopsis and sample chapters. "Prepare a clear outline of the work and an ambitious schedule of public appearances to help make it known and present both as a proposal to the publisher. With our company a work that can be serialized or systematically excerpted in our periodicals is always given special attention." Accepts translations. Reviews artwork/photos as part of ms package.
Recent Nonfiction Title: *Banners Without Words*, by Jill Knuth (how-to).
Fiction: "Light works providing examples of good expression through the religious art forms. Any collected short works in the areas of drama, dance, song, stories, anecdotes or good visual art." Query or submit outline/synopsis and sample chapters.
Recent Fiction Title: *Balloons! Candy! Toys!*, by Daryl Olszewski (stories).
Tips: "Books that provide readers with practical, usable suggestions and ideas pertaining to worship, education and the religious arts has the best chance of selling to our firm.

FLEMING H. REVELL CO., Central Ave., Old Tappan NJ 07675. Imprints include Power Books and Spire. Vice President/Editor-in-Chief: Gary A. Sledge. Managing Editor: Norma F. Chimento. Publishes hardcover and paperback originals and reprints. Averages 80 titles/year; receives 1,000 submissions annually. 10% of books from first-time authors; 95% of books from unagented writers. Pays royalty on retail price; sometimes offers advance. Publishes book an average of 1 year after acceptance. Computer printout submissions acceptable; prefers letter-quality to dot-matrix. No unsolicited mss. Book catalog and ms guidelines for SASE.
Nonfiction: Religion and inspirational. "All books must appeal to Protestant-evangelical readers." Query. Reviews artwork/photos as part of ms package.
Recent Nonfiction Title: *Forgive Me*, by Cathleen Crowell Webb, with Marie Chapian.
Fiction: Protestant-evangelical religion and inspiration. Query.
Recent Fiction Title: *No Other Choice*, by Lissa Halls Johnson.
Tips: "The writer has the best chance of selling our firm Christian books from an area of personal expertise."

REVIEW AND HERALD PUBLISHING ASSOCIATION, 55 West Oak Ridge Dr., Hagerstown MD 21740. Acquisition Editor: Penny Wheeler. Publishes hardcover and paperback originals and software. Specializes in religious-oriented books. Averages 30-40 titles/year; receives 300 submissions annually. 15% of books from first-time authors; 100% of books from unagented writers. Average print order for a writer's first book is 5,000-7,500. Pays 5-10% royalty on retail price; offers average $100 advance. Publishes book an average of 1 year after acceptance. Computer printout submissions acceptable; prefers letter-quality to dot-matrix. Reports in 4 months. Free brochure; ms guidelines for SASE.
Nonfiction: Juveniles (religious-oriented only), nature, and religious, all 20,000-60,000 words; 128 pages average. Query or submit outline/synopsis and 2-3 sample chapters. Prefers to do own illustrating. Looks for "literary style, constructive tone, factual accuracy, compatibility with Adventist theology and life style, and length of manuscript." Reviews artwork/photos as part of ms package.
Recent Nonfiction Title: *Who Said Life Is Fair*, by Jerry A. Gladson.
Tips: "Familiarize yourself with Adventist theology because Review and Herald Publishing Association is owned and operated by the Seventh-day Adventist Church. We are accepting fewer but better-written manuscripts."

REYMONT ASSOCIATES, 6556 Sweet Maple Lane, Boca Raton FL 33433. Editor-in-Chief: D.J. Scherer. Managing Editor: Felicia Scherer. Publishes paperback originals. Receives 30 submissions annually. 20% of

books from first-time authors; 100% of books from unagented writers. Average print order for a writer's first book is 1,000. Pays 10-12-15% royalty on wholesale price; no advance. Publishes book an average of 3 months after acceptance. Computer printout submissions acceptable. Reports in 2 weeks. Book catalog for SASE.
Nonfiction: Publishes business reports, how-to, unique directories, and bibliographies. " 'Net' writing; no rhetoric. Aim for 7,500-10,000 words." Submit outline/synopsis and 2 sample chapters. Reviews artwork/photos as part of ms package.
Recent Nonfiction Title: *How to Make Money with Pen & Ink Drawings.*
Tips: Trends in book publishing that freelance writers should be aware of include "the need for sharply focused single-subject reports of 7,000-8,000 words in length."

THE RIVERDALE COMPANY, INC., PUBLISHERS, Suite 102, 5506 Kenilworth Ave., Riverdale MD 20737. (301)864-2029. President: John Adams. Editor: Mary Power. Publishes hardcover originals. Averages 16-18 titles/year; receives 50 submissions annually. 20% of books from first-time authors; 100% of books from unagented writers. Pays 0-15% royalty on wholesale price. Publishes book an average of 8 months after acceptance. Computer printout submissions acceptable; prefers letter-quality to dot-matrix. Reports in 1 week on queries; 2 months on mss. Free book catalog.
Nonfiction: "We publish technical and social science books for scholars, students, policymakers; and tour, restaurant and recreational guides for the mass market." Subjects include economics, history, humanities, politics, psychology, sociology and travel. Especially needs social science and travel mss on South Asia or Africa. Will consider college text proposals in economics and Third World studies; travel guides of any sort. Query. Accepts outline/synopsis and 2-3 sample chapters.

‡ROCKY TOP PUBLICATIONS, Subsidiary of Rocky Top Supply, Box 33, Stamford NY 12167. (607)652-2567. President/Publisher: Joseph D. Jennings. Publishes hardcover and paperback originals. Averages 4 titles/year. 70% of books from first-time authors; 95% of books from unagented writers. Pays 4-10% royalty (may vary) on wholesale price. Publishes book an average of 6 months after acceptance. Photocopied submissions OK. Computer printout submissions acceptable; prefers letter-quality to dot-matrix. Reports in 2 weeks on queries; 4 months on mss. Ms guidelines for SASE; free book catalog.
Nonfiction: How-to, reference, self-help and technical. Subjects include animal health; health; hobbies (crafts); medical; nature; philosophy (Thoreau or environmental only); and science. "We are actively looking for expose-type material on science, medicine and health—well written and researched only." No autobiographies, biographies, business "get rich quick" or fad books. Submit outline/synopsis and sample chapters or complete ms. Reviews artwork/photos as part of ms package.
Recent Nonfiction Title: *New Age Medical Pharmacology*, by J. Gooze (herbal guide).
Tips: "Our readers range from self-sufficiency people, to medical and health professionals, environmentalists, and gardeners. Scientific, medical, health, pharmaceutical, and environmental (conservation, naturalist) books have the best chance of selling to us."

RODALE PRESS, Prevention Health Books Div., 33 E. Minor St., Emmaus PA 18049. (215)968-5171. Senior Editors: Carol Keough and Debora Tkac. Publishes hardcover and trade paperback originals and reprints. Averages 20 titles/year; receives 100 submissions annually. 10% of books from first-time authors; 1% of books from unagented writers. Pays royalty on retail price: 10-15% trade hardcover; 7½ trade paperback; or 2% major mail order. Offers average $7,500 advance. Publishes book an average of 1 year after acceptance. Simultaneous and photocopied submissions OK. Will discuss electronic submissions with author, but requires hard copy also. Computer printout submissions acceptable; prefers letter-quality to dot-matrix. Reports in 1 month. Free book catalog.
Nonfiction: Cookbook, how-to, reference, self-help—all health books. Subjects include health, psychology and fitness. Especially interested in "how-to books on health care with practical, self-help information by doctors and other health professionals, or a careful author using primary medical studies." No technical, textbook, non-health related books. Query with outline/synopsis and sample chapters. Reviews artwork/photos.
Recent Nonfiction Title: *The Mollen Method*, by Dr. Art Mollen (diet, fitness).
Tips: "Our audience is over 50 years of age, health conscious, mostly women. Writers have the best chance of selling us health books in their field of expertise. They must have the ability to turn technical information into friendly, easy-to-understand copy."

*RONIN PUBLISHING INC., Box 1035, Berkeley CA 94701. (415)540-6278. Publisher: Sebastian Orfal. Publishes originals and trade paperback reprints. Averages 4 titles/year; receives 150-300 submissions annually. 25% of books from first-time authors. Pays 10-20% royalty on wholesale price; if co-published with author, royalties are negotiable. Offers $500 advance (sometimes). Publishes book an average of 6 months after acceptance. Electronic submissions OK via IBM-PC, MAC, Northstar, but requires hard copy also.
Nonfiction: How-to (business), humor, and illustrated book. Subjects include business and economics, health, nutrition and psychology (business). "We are primarily interested in management psychology how-to." Query.

Recent Nonfiction Title: *Beating Job Burnout,* (3rd ed.), by B. Potter.
Fiction: Humor. Primarily interested in illustrated humor. Query or submit outline/synopsis and sample chapters.
Recent Fiction Title: *Computer Comics,* by Orlafi.

THE ROSEN PUBLISHING GROUP, 29 E. 21st St., New York NY 10010. (212)777-3017. President: Roger Rosen. Imprints include Pelion Press (music titles). Publishes hardcover originals. Entire firm averages 46 titles/year; young adult division averages 35 titles/year. 45% of books from first-time authors; 80% of books from unagented writers. Pays royalty or makes outright purchase. Publishes book an average of 9 months after acceptance. Simultaneous and photocopied submissions OK. Computer printout submissions acceptable; prefers letter-quality to dot-matrix. Reports in 1 month. Free book catalog; ms guidelines for SASE.
Nonfiction: Young adult, reference, self-help and textbook. Subjects include art, health (coping), and music. "Our books are geared to the young adult audience whom we reach via school and public libraries. Most of the books we publish are related to career guidance and personal adjustment. We also publish material on the theater, music and art, as well as journalism for schools. Interested in supplementary material for enrichment of school curriculum." Mss in the young adult nonfiction areas include of vocational guidance, personal and social adjustment, journalism and theatre. For Pelion Press, mss on classical music, emphasis on opera and singing." Query or submit outline/synopsis and sample chapters. Reviews artwork/photos as part of ms package.
Recent Nonfiction Title: *Coping with Academic Anxiety,* by Ottens.
Tips: "The writer has the best chance of selling our firm a book on vocational guidance or personal social adjustment."

ROSS BOOKS, Box 4340, Berkeley CA 94704. President: Franz Ross. Publishes hardcover and paperback originals, paperback reprints, and software. Averages 7-10 titles/year; receives 200 submissions annually. 90% of books from first-time authors; 99% of books from unagented writers. Average print order for a writer's first book is 5,000-10,000. Offers 8-12% royalty on net price. Offers average advance of 2% of the first print run. Publishes book an average of 1 year after acceptance. Simultaneous and photocopied submissions OK. Electronic submissions OK on TRS 80 model L/6 or IBM PC. Computer printout submissions acceptable; prefers letter-quality to dot-matrix. Reports in 1 month. Free book catalog.
Nonfiction: Popular how-to on science, general how-to. No political or children's books. Accepts nonfiction translations. Submit outline/synopsis and 2 sample chapters with SASE. Reviews artwork/photos as part of ms package.
Recent Nonfiction Title: *300 Years at the Keyboard.*

*ROSSEL BOOKS, 44 Dunbow Dr., Chappaqua NY 10514. (914)238-8954. President: Seymour Rossel. Publishes hardcover originals, trade paperback originals, reprints and software. Averages 6-8 titles/year; receives 150-200 submissions annually. 15% of books from first-time authors; 90% of books from unagented writers. Average print order for a writer's first book is 2,500. "We subsidy publish only books which have been sponsored by foundations, organizations, etc." Pays royalty on wholesale or retail price. Offers negotiable advance. Publishes book an average of 1 year after acceptance. Photocopied submissions OK. Electronic submissions OK on IBM PC, DOS compatible. Computer printout submissions acceptable; prefers letter-quality to dot-matrix. Reports in 2 weeks on queries; 1 month on mss. Book catalog for business size SAE and 39¢ postage.
Nonfiction: Jewish cookbook, how-to, illustrated book, juvenile, reference, textbook, and Judaica in all fields—art, cooking and foods, history, philosophy, photography, politics, psychology, religion, sociology and travel. "We currently seek juvenile nonfiction manuscripts on Jewish subjects; adult manuscripts on being Jewish in America, Jews on the frontier, interesting anecdotal histories with Jewish content, and collections of American Jewish photos. We do not publish adult Jewish fiction." Submit outline/synopsis and sample chapters. Reviews artwork/photos as part of ms package.
Recent Nonfiction Title: *Torah From Our Sage,* by J. Nevsner (commentary on Jewish classic, Pirke Avot).
Fiction: Juvenile Jewish adventure, ethnic, historical, mystery, religious, romance and science fiction. No adult fiction. Submit outline synopsis and sample chapters.
Tips: "Within the next year, Rossel Books will be initiating a new publishing imprint, Longhorn Books. Longhorn will seek to do Texas-oriented material for the Texas regional marketplace. We would be glad to see submissions for this new imprint as well."

‡ROUNDTABLE PUBLISHING, INC., 933 Pico Blvd., Santa Monica CA 90405. (213)450-9777. Senior Editor: Shirley Pescia. Publishes hardcover and trade paperback originals. Averages 5-15 titles/year; receives 100+ submissions annually. 25% of books from first-time authors; 10% of books from unagented writers. Pays royalty on retail price. Publishes book an average of 18 months after acceptance. Simultaneous and photocopied submissions OK. Computer printout submissions acceptable; prefers letter-quality to dot-matrix. Reports in 1 month on queries; 2 months on mss. Free book catalog.
Nonfiction: Biography, how-to, humor, juvenile and self-help. Subjects include art, motion pictures and TV,

business and economics, health, politics and psychology. Especially interested in celebrity biographies, motion picture and TV related books, juvenile, how-to or self-help. No cookbooks, history or textbooks. Submit outline/synopsis and sample chapters or complete ms. Reviews artwork/photos as part of ms package.
Recent Nonfiction Title: *Same Song Separate Voices*, Lennon Sisters (autobiography).
Fiction: Adventure, erotica, fantasy, gothic, historical, mainstream, mystery, romance, science fiction and suspense. Averages 1 book/year. No pornography. Submit complete ms.
Recent Fiction Title: *Seldom Sung Songs*, by Ray Locke (Southern setting).
Tips: "Our books are for a mainstream audience—children and adult. Writers have the best chance of selling us biographies."

ROUTLEDGE & KEGAN PAUL, INC., Imprint of Methuen, Inc., 29 W. 35th St., New York NY 10001. (617)742-5863. U.S. Editor: Stratford Caldecott. Eight subject editors in the U.K. Editorial Director: Malcolm Campbell. Imprints include Ark, Arkana and Pandora Press. Pandora Press publishes both fiction and nonfiction and deals with topics of interest to women. Arkana publishes primarily books on popular religious topics, especially Eastern religions and occult. Publishes hardcover and trade paperback originals and reprints. Averages 200 titles/year; receives 5,000+ submissions annually. 10% of books from first-time authors; 50-70% of books from unagented writers. Pays 7½-10% royalty on retail price; offers average $1,000 advance. Publishes book an average of 1 year after acceptance. Inquire about electronic submissions. Simultaneous and photocopied submissions OK. Computer printout submissions acceptable; prefers letter-quality to dot-matrix. Reports in 3 weeks on queries; 6 weeks on mss. Book catalog 73¢; ms guidelines for SASE.
Nonfiction: Academic monograph and textbook. Subjects include biography, illustrated book, reference, self-help, social sciences, philosophy, history, travel, psychology, women's studies, mind/body/spirit, education, geography, economics and literary criticism. No Biblical prophecies. Monograph length: 100,000 words maximum. Query and/or submit outline/synopsis and sample chapters.
Recent Nonfiction Title: *Rough Guide to Greece*, by Mark Ellingham (travel).
Fiction: Routledge & Kegan Paul no longer publishes fiction. Fiction appears only under its imprint, Pandora Press.

ROWMAN & LITTLEFIELD, PUBLISHERS, Division of Littlefield Adams & Co., 81 Adams Dr., Totowa NJ 07512. Managing Director: Arthur Hamparian. Publishes hardcover and paperback originals and reprints. Receives 500 submissions annually. 50% of books from first-time authors; 100% of books from unagented writers. Pays 5-12½% royalty on net sales; offers no advance. Publishes book an average of 9 months after acceptance. Electronic submissions OK, but requires hard copy also. Computer printout submissions acceptable; prefers letter-quality to dot-matrix. Simultaneous submissions OK. Reports in 2 months. Free book catalog; ms guidelines for SASE.
Nonfiction: Technical and textbooks. Subjects include art, business/economics, health, philosophy, politics, reference, science and sociology. "We publish scholarly studies in these fields with special emphasis on international studies (development, Third World, trade, finance, agricultural), labor economics and agricultural science, economics and philosophy. Our authors are typically academics writing for other professionals, for government bodies and other organizations which utilize primary research." Submit outline/synopsis and sample chapters.
Recent Nonfiction Title: *Nuclear Weapons and the Future of Humanity*, edited by Avner Cohen and Steven Lee.

‡ROXBURY PUBLISHING CO., Box 491044, Los Angeles CA 90049. (213)458-3493. Executive Editor: Claude Teweles. Publishes hardcover and paperback originals and reprints. Averages 20 titles/year. Pays royalty; offers negotiable advance. Simultaneous, photocopied and computer printout submissions OK. Reports in 1 month.
Nonfiction: College-level textbooks only. Subjects include business and economics, humanities, philosophy, psychology, social sciences and sociology. Query, submit outline/synopsis and sample chapters, or submit complete ms.
Recent Nonfiction Title: *Decision Making in Business*, edited by Jack Maroun.

ROYAL PUBLISHING CO., Subsidiary of ROMC (Recipes of the Month Club), Box 5027, Beverly Hills CA 90210. (213)550-7170. President: Mrs. Harold Klein. Publishes hardcover, trade, and mass market paperback originals. Averages 4 titles/year; receives 400-500 submissions annually. 50% of books from first-time authors; 50% of books from unagented writers. Pays 8-12% royalty on retail price; buys some mss outright. Publishes book an average of 1 year after acceptance. Photocopied submissions OK. Electronic submissions OK, but requires hard copy also. Computer printout submissions acceptable; prefers letter-quality to dot-matrix. Free book catalog.
Nonfiction: Cookbook. "We especially need cookbooks, diet, food history and specialty cookbooks." Submit complete ms. Reviews artwork/photos as part of ms package.
Recent Nonfiction Title: *Wining and Dining*, by Riess.

RPM PRESS, INC., Box 157, Verndale MN 56481. Publisher: David A. Hietala. Publishes trade paperback originals, and audio-cassette training programs (with workbook) and selected software. Averages 18-24 titles/year; receives 75-150 submissions annually. 75% of books from first-time authors; 100% of books from un-agented writers. Average print order for a writer's first book is 1,000-5,000. Pays 5-15% royalty on retail price or makes outright purchases of $200-1,500. Offers average advance to established authors of $500. Publishes book/training program an average of 6-9 months after acceptance. Simultaneous and photocopied submissions okay. Electronic submissions OK; prefers IBM-PC-readable diskettes in ASC II files—and hard copy also. Computer printout submissions OK; no dot-matrix. Reports in 5 weeks on queries; 2 months on mss (usually sooner for both). Book catalog for 9x12 SAE and with 4 oz. postage.

Nonfiction: How-to, reference, technical, and audio-cassette training programs on business, applied management, finance, program development, client programming, and engineering geared toward managing the nonprofit workcenter (for the handicapped). "We are looking for how-to books and audio-tape training programs that tell how to set up new business ventures; improve present management practice in this specialized setting; how-to training programs on setting up quality assurance programs, marketing rehabilitation services, or developing innovative types of service delivery mechanisms. People who buy our books and training programs are managers and concerned professionals looking to improve the management practice of their nonprofit business enterprises or programs, so we obviously like to hear from writers who have spent some time in the management of these business and service organizations (or who can speak assertively as if they had). We realize that few writers have the hard-won experience that we are looking for—that's why we offer *extensive* editorial assistance to the few authors we end up working with. If you want to work with us, please note the sort of marketplace we're serving and the type of material we seek. We receive hundreds of query letters each year that are outside our area of specific interest. We have no upper limit on the number of books we publish annually—our limit is based on the number of on-target manuscripts we have available. We are entirely receptive to hearing all ideas and are interested in working with new or established authors who, once they establish themselves with us, are willing to work with us on a long-term basis. We would also like to identify software developers that would like to freelance with us on projects in this market—IBM and Apple II only." Query.

Recent Nonfiction Title: *Basic Management*, by P. McCray.

‡*RUSSICA PUBLISHERS, INC., 799 Broadway, New York NY 10003. (212)473-7480. Contact: David A. Daskal. Publishes trade paperback originals and reprints. Averages 15 titles/year. Subsidy publishes 50% of books. Pays 10-15% royalty on retail price. Photocopied submissions OK. Reports in 2 weeks. Free book catalog.

Nonfiction: Biography and humor. Subjects include history. "We're looking for biographies of prominent Russians or Slavs written in English. All other mss must be in Russian only."

Recent Nonfiction Title: *Uncensored Russian Limericks*, by V. Kozlovsky (folklore).

Fiction: Adventure, erotica, ethnic, horror, humor, mystery and suspense. "Russian language manuscripts only." Submit complete ms.

Recent Fiction Title: *Poetry*, by Marina Tsvetaeva.

Poetry: Modern Russian poetry. Submit complete ms.

Recent Poetry Title: *Roman Elegies*, by Joseph Brodsky.

RYND COMMUNICATIONS, National Health Publishing, National Law Publishing, 99 Painters Mill Rd., Owings Mills MD 21117. (301)363-6400. Acquisitions Editor: Elanore Lampner. Publishes hardcover originals. Averages 10-15 titles/year and quarterly subscription service. Receives 60 submissions annually. 30% of books from first-time authors; 100% of books from unagented writers. Pays 10-12% royalty on retail price. Offers average $250 advance. Publishes book an average of 1 year after acceptance. Electronic submissions OK on IBM compatible. Computer printout submissions acceptable; prefers letter-quality to dot-matrix. Reports in 2 weeks on queries; 10 weeks on mss. Free book catalog.

Nonfiction: Reference, technical and textbook. Subjects include business and economics (health-related); health (administration); and health law. Needs textbooks in hospital and nurse management and administration; alternative health care delivery systems; medical ethics and liability; health care marketing and economics. Nothing clinical; prefers works that can be used as both references and textbooks; no trade books. Query or submit outline/synopsis and sample chapters.

Recent Nonfiction Title: *Power and Politics in Nursing Administration*, by Dorothy del Bueno, Ed.D., R.N. and Cynthia M. Freund, Ph.D., R.N.(reference text).

Tips: "We are a growing house devoted to health care. We welcome new authors, whether or not they have already published; we look for academic and experience background and a clear writing style."

S. C. E.-EDITIONS L'ETINCELLE, Suite 206, 4920 Blvd. de Maisonneuve W. Westmount, Montreal, Quebec H3Z 1N1 Canada. (514)488-9531. President: Robert Davies. Publishes trade paperback originals in French translation. Averages 12 titles/year; receives 200 submissions annually. 10% of books from first-time authors; 80% of books from unagented writers. Average print order for a writer's first book is 4,000. Pays 8-12% royalty on retail price; offers average $1,000 advance. Publishes book an average of 1 year after acceptance. Simultaneous and photocopied submissions OK. Electronic submissions OK via ASCII and EBCDIC, but requires hard copy also. Computer printout submissions acceptable. Reports in 2 months on queries; 3 months on mss. Free book catalog.

Imprints: L'Etincelle (nonfiction and fiction). Memoire Vive (microcomputer books).

Nonfiction: Biography, cookbook, how-to, humor, reference and self-help. Subjects include animals, business and economics, cooking and foods, health, history, hobbies, microcomputers, nature, philosophy, politics, psychology, recreation, sociology, sports and travel. Accepts nonfiction translations. "We are looking for about five translatable works of nonfiction, in any popular field. Our audience includes French-speaking readers in all major markets in the world." No topics of interest only to Americans. Query or submit outline/synopsis and 3 sample chapters. Reviews artwork/photos or part of ms package.

Recent Nonfiction Title: *Lay Bare the Heart, Relaxation Techniques for Children.*

ST. ANTHONY MESSENGER PRESS, 1615 Republic St., Cincinnati OH 45210. Editor-in-Chief: The Rev. Norman Perry, O.F.M. Publishes paperback originals. Averages 12 titles/year; receives 250 submissions annually. 10% of books from first-time authors; 100% of books from unagented writers. Pays 6-8% royalty on retail price; offers average $600 advance. Publishes book an average of 8 months after acceptance. Books are sold in bulk to groups (study clubs, high school or college classes) and in bookstores. Photocopied submissions OK if they are not simultaneous submissions to other publishers. Electronic submissions OK, but requires hard copy also. Computer printout submissions acceptable; no dot-matrix. Free catalog.

Nonfiction: Religion. "We try to reach the Catholic market with topics near the heart of the ordinary Catholic's belief. We want to offer insight and inspiration and thus give people support in living a Christian life in a pluralistic society. We are not interested in an academic or abstract approach. Our emphasis is on popular writing with examples, specifics, color and anecdotes." Length: 25,000-40,000 words. Query or submit outline and 2 sample chapters. Reviews artwork photos as part of ms package.

Recent Nonfiction Title: *Fundamentalism: What Every Catholic Needs to Know*, by Anthony E. Gilles.

Tips: "The book cannot be the place for the author to think through a subject. The author has to think through the subject first and then tell the reader what is important to know. Style uses anecdotes, examples, illustrations, human interest, 'colorful' quotes, fiction techniques of suspense, dialogue, characterization, etc. Address practical problems, deal in concrete situations, free of technical terms and professional jargon."

‡ST. BEDE'S PUBLICATIONS, Box 545, Petersham MA 01366. (617)724-3407. Editorial Director: Sr. Mary Joseph, OSB. Publishes hardcover originals, trade paperback originals and reprints. Averages 6-8 titles/year; receives 30 submissions annually. 30-40% of books from first-time authors; 90% of books from unagented writers. Subsidy publishes 10% of books. "Whether an author is subsidy published depends upon the subject and audience we think we can reach." Pays 5-10% royalty on wholesale price or retail price. No advance. Publishes book an average of 2 years after acceptance. Simultaneous and photocopied submissions OK. Accepts electronic submissions via disk or modem. "We can take any PC disk and make it into a typesetting disk"; also requires hard copy. Computer printout submissions acceptable; no dot-matrix. Reports in 2 weeks on queries; 3 months on mss. Free book catalog; ms guidelines for SASE.

Nonfiction: Textbook (theology), religion, prayer, spirituality, hagiography, theology, philosophy, church history and related lives of saints fields. "We are always looking for excellent books on prayer, sprituality liturgy, church or monastic history. Theology and philosophy are important also. We publish English translations of foreign works in these fields if we think they are excellent and worth translating." No submissions unrelated to religion, theology, spirituality, etc. Query or submit outline/synopsis and sample chapters.

Recent Nonfiction Title: *Process Theology*, by Illtyd Trethowan, OSB (philosophy/theology).

Fiction: Historical (only if religious) and religious. "Generally we don't do fiction—but we are willing to look over a manuscript if it fits into our categories." No fiction submissions unrelated to religion. Query or submit outline/synopsis and sample chapters.

Tips: "For our theology/philosophy titles our audience is scholars, colleges and universities, seminaries, etc. For our other titles (i.e. prayer, spirituality, lives of saints, etc.) the audience is above-average readers interested in furthering their knowledge in these areas. Theology seems to be swinging back to studying more conservative lines. We're finding a lot of excellent books being published in France and are getting the rights to translate these. Also, there's great, general interest in prayer and spirituality so we try to publish really excellent titles in these areas, too. New material, or newly translated material, gets priority."

ST. LUKE'S PRESS, Mid-Memphis Tower, 1407 Union, Memphis TN 38104. (901)357-5441. Subsidiaries include Raccoon Books, Inc. (literary nonprofit), and American Blake Foundation (scholarly nonprofit). Consulting Editor: Roger Easson, Ph.D. Averages 8-10 titles/year; receives 3,000 submissions annually. 50% of books from unagented writers. Average print order for a writer's first book is 5,000. Pays 10% minimum royalty on invoice; offers average $100-200 advance. Publishes book an average of 2 years after acceptance. Electronic submissions OK on TRS 80, but requires hard copy also. Computer printout submissions acceptable. Reports in 3 months. Book catalog $1.

Nonfiction: Biography. Accepts translations. Submit story line and 3 sample chapters. Reviews artwork/ photos as part of ms package.
Recent Nonfiction Title: *Absolutely, Positively Overnight,* by Robert Sigafoos.
Fiction: Submit story line and 3 sample chapters.
Recent Fiction Title: *Covenant at Coldwater,* by John Osier.

‡**ST. MARTIN'S PRESS,** 175 5th Ave., New York NY 10010. Averages 900 titles/year; receives 3,000 submissions annually. 15-20% of books from first-time authors; 30% of books from unagented writers. Electronic submissions OK, but requires hard copy also. Computer printout submissions acceptable; prefers letter-quality to dot-matrix. Reports "promptly."
Nonfiction and Fiction: General and textbook. Publishes general fiction and nonfiction; major interest in adult fiction and nonfiction, history, self-help, political science, popular science, biography, scholarly, popular reference, etc. Query. Reviews artwork/photos as part of ms package. "It takes very persuasive credentials to prompt us to commission a book or outline."
Recent Title: *Isak Dinesen,* by Judith Thurmon.
Tips: "We do almost every kind of book there is—trade, textbooks, reference and children's books. Crime fiction has the best chance of selling to our firm—over fifteen percent of all the trade books we published are this category."

***ST. VLADIMIR'S SEMINARY PRESS,** 575 Scarsdale Rd., Crestwood NY 10707. (914)961-8313. Managing Editor: Theodore Brail. Publishes hardcover and trade paperback originals and reprints. Averages 15 titles/ year. Subsidy publishes 20% of books. Market considerations determine whether an author should be subsidy published. Pays 7% royalty on retail price. Simultaneous and photocopied submissions OK. Computer printout submissions acceptable; prefers letter-quality to dot-matrix. Reports in 3 months on queries; 6 months on mss. Free book catalog and ms guidelines.
Nonfiction: Religion dealing with Eastern Orthodox theology. Query. Reviews artwork/photos as part of ms package.
Recent Nonfiction Title: *The Sacrament of Love,* by Paul Evdokimov (theology of marriage).
Tips: "We have an interest in books that stand on firm theological ground; careful writing and scholarship are basic."

‡**SANDLAPPER PUBLISHING, INC.,** Box 1932, Orangeburg SC 29116. (803)531-1658. Acquisitions: Allison L. Stein. Publishes hardcover and trade paperback originals and reprints. Averages 6 titles/year; receives 200 submissions annually. 80% of books from first-time authors; 90% of books from unagented writers. Pays 15% maximum royalty on wholesale price. Publishes book an average of 18 months after acceptance. Photocopied submissions OK; simultaneous submissions OK if informed ("please inform us of other offers"). Computer printout submissions acceptable; no dot-matrix. Reports in 1 month on queries; 6 months on mss. Book catalog and ms guidelines for 9x12 SASE with 73¢ postage.
Nonfiction: Biography, "coffee table" book, cookbook, humor, illustrated book, juvenile, reference and textbook. Subjects are limited to South Carolina history, culture and cuisine. "We are looking for manuscripts that show a new facet of the rich heritage of our state, by both South Carolinians and residents of other states. If it is not related to South Carolina, we don't want to see it. I refuse to read self-help books, children's books about divorce, kidnapping, etc., and we are not looking at any 'growing up poor and Southern' manuscripts at this time. Absolutely no religious manuscripts." Query or submit outline/synopsis and sample chapters "if you're not sure it's what we're looking for, otherwise complete ms." Reviews artwork/photos as part of ms package.
Recent Nonfiction Title: *Reminiscences of Sea Island Heritage,* by Ronald Daise (oral history of former slaves of St. Helena Island, South Carolina).
Fiction: Does not need fiction submissions at this time, "but I will look at good strong fiction by South Carolinians and/or about South Carolina. Also, good, strong juvenile fiction about South Carolina history, and fiction showing new facets of our state and its heritage. No romance, no horror, no science fiction, no religious fiction, etc." Query or submit outline/synopis and sample chapters.
Recent Fiction Title: *Stranded!,* by Idella Bodie (children's mystery adventure set on resort spot).
Tips: "Our readers are South Carolinians, visitors to the state's tourist spots, and friends and family that live out-of-state. We are rapidly becoming the regional publisher for South Carolina. We are a very small publishing house, limited in our needs and our market, limited in our manpower. We often need several months to evaluate the numerous submissions, so please be patient. And, better yet, if your manuscript isn't about South Carolina, please send it somewhere else. Give a confident presentation, but don't be a pushy author."

‡**SANTA BARBARA PRESS,** 1129 State St., Santa Barbara CA 93101. (805)966-2060. Editor-in-Chief: George Erikson. Publishes hardcover and trade paperback originals, and trade paperback reprints. Averages 12 titles/year; receives 75 submissions annually. 50% of books from first-time authors; 50% of books from unagented writers. Pays 5-10% royalty. Offers maximum $1,000 advance. Publishes book an average of 1 year

after acceptance. Simultaneous submissions OK. Electronic submissions OK on 5¼" floppy disk. Computer printout submissions acceptable; no dot-matrix. Reports in 3 weeks on queries; 3 months on mss. Book catalog for 4x9 SAE with 2 first class stamps.

Nonfiction: Biography, how-to and self-help. Subjects include philosophy, religion, sociology, sports and travel. "Our nonfiction book manuscript needs include biography and autobiographies." No humor, juvenile or cookbooks. Query.

Recent Nonfiction Title: *Beautiful Bad Girl: The Vicki Morgan Story*, by Gordon Basichis (biography).

SAYBROOK PUBLISHING CO., Suite 4, 4223 Cole Ave., Dallas TX 75205. (214)521-2375. President: Cynthia Giles. Publishes hardcover and trade paperback originals and reprints. Averages 6 titles/year; receives 700 submissions annually. 25% of books from first-time authors; 50% of books from unagented writers. Average print order for a writer's first book is 5,000. Pays 6-12% royalty on retail price. Publishes book an average of 9 months after acceptance. Simultaneous and photocopied submissions OK. Electronic submissions OK via IBM PC, but requires hard copy also. Computer printout submissions acceptable; prefers letter-quality to dot-matrix. Reports in 3 months. Ms guidelines for SASE.

Nonfiction: Biography, juvenile, and literary human science. Subjects include Americana, art, business and economics, health, nature, philosophy, politics, psychology, religion, sociology, women's studies and environmental studies. "Especially interested in scholarly studies in the human sciences which are also exciting, marketable dramatic literature written for substantial sales in the trade." Submit outline/synopsis and sample chapters. Reviews artwork/photos as part of ms package.

Recent Nonfiction Title: *My Quest for Beauty*, by Rollo May.

Fiction: "We look for books in almost any fiction category—including mystery, science fiction, adventure and comedy—which genuinely entertain, but do much more. We are particularly interested in books which relate to current events and concerns, with vivid, memorable characters dealing with significant issues."

Recent Fiction Title: *Pasaquina*, by Erin O'Shaughnessy.

Tips: "Our books are for the intelligent, curious, general reader. Seek to tell the truth about human beings by any means. The times in which we live demand it. There are enough readers who hunger for it. Think. Then think again. Keep thinking. And also cherish the reader. If your submission is important and you can convince us that you are determined to do the very best work you are capable of, we will work with you all the way for as long as it takes."

SCARECROW PRESS, INC., 52 Liberty St., Metuchen NJ 08840. Editor in Chief: Norman Horrocks. Senior Editor: Barbara Lee. Publishes hardcover originals. Averages 110 titles/year; receives 600-700 submissions annually. 70% of books from first-time authors; 100% of books from unagented writers. Average print order for a writer's first book is 1,000. Pays 10% royalty on list price of first 1,500 copies; 15% of list price thereafter. Offers no advance. Publishes book 10-12 months after receipt of ms. Photocopied submissions OK. Electronic submissions OK via IBM compatible system, but requires hard copy also. Computer printout submissions acceptable; no dot-matrix. Reports in 2 weeks. Free book catalog.

Nonfiction: Books about music. Needs reference books and meticulously prepared annotated bibliographies, indexes, women's studies and movies. Query. Occasionally reviews artwork/photos as part of ms package.

SCHIRMER BOOKS, Macmillan Publishing Co., Inc., 866 3rd Ave., New York NY 10022. Senior Editor: Maribeth Anderson Payne. Publishes hardcover and paperback originals, paperback reprints and some software. Averages 20 books/year; receives 250 submissions annually. 40% of books from first-time authors; 95% of books from unagented writers. Average print order for a writer's first book is 3,000-5,000. Pays royalty on wholesale or retail price; offers small advance. Submit photos and/or illustrations "if central to the book, not if decorative or tangential." Publishes book an average of 1 year after acceptance. Electronic submissions OK, requirements "determined on a per project basis"; but requires hard copy also. Computer printout submissions acceptable; prefers letter-quality to dot-matrix. Reports in 2 months. Book catalog and ms guidelines for SASE.

Nonfiction: Publishes college texts, biographies, scholarly, reference and how-to on the performing arts specializing in music, also dance and theatre. Needs texts or scholarly mss for college or scholarly audience. Submit outline/synopsis and sample chapters and current vita. Reviews artwork/photos as part of ms package.

Recent Nonfiction Title: *Schoenberg and His Circle: A Viennese Portrait*, by Joan Allen Smith.

Tips: "The writer has the best chance of selling our firm a music book with a clearly defined, reachable audience, either scholarly or trade. Must be an exceptionally well-written work of original scholarship prepared by an expert in that particular field who has a thorough understanding of correct manuscript style and attention to detail (see the Chicago *Manual of Style*)."

‡SCHOLASTIC, INC., 730 Broadway, New York NY 10003. (212)505-3000. Editor: Ann Reit. Imprints include Wildfire and Sunfire. Publishes trade paperback originals and software. Averages 36 titles/year. pays 6% royalty on retail price. Computer printout submissions acceptable; no dot-matrix. Reports in 3 months. Ms guidelines for business size SASE.

Fiction: Romance (Wildlife line), and historical romance (Sunfire). Wildfire books should be 40,000-45,000 words, for girls ages 12-15 who are average to good readers. Query. Request ms guidelines and follow carefully before submitting outline and 3 sample chapters.

Tips: Queries/mss may be routed to other editors in the publishing group.

‡SCHOLIUM INTERNATIONAL, INC., 265 Great Neck Rd., Great Neck NY 11021. Editor-in-Chief: Arthur L. Candido. Publishes hardcover and paperback originals. Averages 19 titles/year. Standard minimum book contract of 10%. Photocopied submissions OK. No computer printout or disk submissions. Reports in 2 weeks. Free book catalog.

Nonfiction: Subjects include science and technology, cyrogenics, electronics, aviation, medicine, physics, etc. "We also publish books in other areas whenever it is felt the manuscript has good sales and reception potential. Query. Contact us prior to sending ms, outlining subject, number of pages and other pertinent information which would enable us to make a decision as to whether we would want to review the manuscript. If interested, we will contact author; if we do not respond, we are not interested in reviewing complete manuscript."

‡*ABNER SCHRAM LTD., 36 Park St., Montclair NJ 07042. (201)744-7755. President: Frances Schram. Executive Editor: Spencer Carr. Publishes hardcover and paperback originals. Averages 33 titles/year. Subsidy publishes 3-4% books. Offers 7½-10% royalty; very limited advance. Simultaneous and photocopied submissions OK. Reports in 2 months. Book catalog for 8x10½ SASE.

Nonfiction: "Our main thrust is art and art history." Also interested in the slight outer periphery of art history and wants some idea of photos that could illustrate the book. Query first.

Recent Nonfiction Title: *Drawings from Venice*, by Pignetti and Romancelli.

CHARLES SCRIBNER'S SONS, Children's Books Department, 115 5th Ave., New York NY 10003. (212)486-4035. Editorial Director, Children's Books: Clare Costello. Publishes hardcover originals, and paperback reprints of own titles. Averages 40 titles/year. Pays royalty on retail price; offers advance. Publishes book an average of 1 year after acceptance. Computer printout submissions acceptable. Free book catalog.

Nonfiction: Subjects include animals, art, biography, health, hobbies, humor, nature, photography, recreation, science and sports. Query. Reviews artwork/photos as part of ms package.

Recent Nonfiction Title: *Wolfman*, by Lawrence Pringle.

Fiction: Adventure, fantasy, historical, humor, mainstream, mystery, science fiction and suspense. Submit outline/synopsis and sample chapters.

Recent Fiction Title: *The Wild Children*, by Felice Holmen.

SECOND CHANCE AT LOVE, 200 Madison Ave., New York NY 10016. (212)686-9820. Subsidiary of Berkley Publishing Group. Senior Editor: Ellen Edwards. Publishes mass market paperback original category romances. Averages 72 titles/year; receives 1,200 submissions annually. 10% of books from first-time authors; 15% of books from unagented writers. Pays 2-6% royalty. Photocopied submissions OK. Computer printout submissions acceptable; prefers letter-quality to dot-matrix. Reports in 6 weeks. Ms guidelines for SASE.

Fiction: Contemporary romance. Accepts 3 sample chapters and detailed chapter-by-chapter outline, but prefers complete ms from unpublished writers. Query and request ms guidelines.

Recent Fiction Title: *Dillon's Promise*, by Cinda Richards.

SECOND CHANCE PRESS/PERMANENT PRESS, Rd. A2, Noyac Rd., Sag Harbor NY 11963. (516)725-1101. Editor: Judith Shepard. Publishes hardcover and trade paperback originals, hardcover trade paperback, and mass market paperback reprints. "Second Chance Press devotes itself exclusively to re-publishing fine books that are out of print and deserve continued recognition." Averages 12 titles/year; receives 700 submissions annually. 25% of books from first-time authors; 75% of books from unagented writers. Average print order for a writer's first book is 2,000. Pays 10% maximum royalty on wholesale price; offers average $200 advance. Publishes book an average of 18 months after acceptance. Simultaneous and photocopied submissions OK. Computer printout submissions acceptable; prefers letter-quality to dot-matrix. Reports in 2 weeks on queries; 3 months on mss.

Nonfiction: Biography, and current events. Subjects include Americana, history, philosophy, politics, psychology and religion. No scientific and technical material or academic studies. Query.

Recent Nonfiction Title: *Kal Flight 007: The Hidden Story*, by Oliver Clubb.

Fiction: Adventure, confession, ethnic, experimental, fantasy, historical, humor, mainstream, mystery, and suspense. Especially looking for fiction with a unique point of view—"original and arresting", suitable for college literature classes. No mass market romance. Query.

Recent Fiction Title: *Hermanos*, by William Herrick.

SELF-COUNSEL PRESS, INC., 306 W. 25th St., North Vancouver, British Columbia V7N 2G1 Canada. Subsidiary of International Self-Counsel Press, Ltd., 1303 N. Northgate Way, Seattle WA 98133. (206)522-8383. Senior Editor: Patricia Robertson. Publishes trade paperback originals. Averages 15 new titles/year; receives

200 submissions annually. 30% of books from first-time authors; 95% of books from unagented writers. Average print order for a writer's first book is 5,000. Pays 10% royalty on wholesale price. Publishes book an average of 9 months after acceptance. Computer printout submissions acceptable; no dot-matrix. Reports in 6 weeks on queries; 2 months on mss. Free book catalog and ms guidelines.
Nonfiction: How-to and reference on law, business and finance; do-it-yourself and self-help law books for lay people. New line of psychology self-help books. "Emphasis is on clear, practical step-by-step approach to subject; not interested in general theory or personal experience approach." Query or submit outline/synopsis and sample chapters.
Recent Nonfiction Title: *Conquering Compulsive Eating,* by Alice Katz.

SERVANT PUBLICATIONS, 840 Airport Blvd., Box 8617, Ann Arbor MI 48107. (313)761-8505. Editor: Ann Spangler. Publishes hardcover, trade and mass market paperback originals and trade paperback reprints. Averages 25 titles/year. 5% of books from first-time authors; 95% of books from unagented writers. Pays 10% royalty on retail price. Publishes book an average of 1 year after acceptance. Computer printout submissions acceptable. Reports in 2 months. Free book catalog.
Nonfiction: Subjects include religion. "We're looking for practical Christian teaching, scripture, current problems facing the Christian church, and inspiration." No heterodox or non-Christian approaches. Query or submit brief outline/synopsis and 1 sample chapter. All unsolicited mss are returned unopened. Reviews artwork/photos as part of ms package.
Recent Nonfiction Title: *A Lamp for My Feet,* by Elisabeth Elliot.

*SEVEN LOCKS PRESS, INC., Box 27, Cabin John MD 20818. (202)362-4714. Publisher: Calvin Kytle. Publishes hardcover and trade paperback originals, and hardcover and trade paperback reprints. Averages 6 titles/year; receives 100 submissions annually. 50% of books from first-time authors; 50% of books from unagented writers. Subsidy publishes 50% of books. Whether an author will be subsidy published depends on the "type of manuscript and cost of production." Pays 10% royalty of gross sales. Simultaneous and photocopied submissions OK. Computer printout submissions acceptable; no dot-matrix. Reports in 1 month on queries; 3 months on mss. Free book catalog.
Nonfiction: Biography, reference and textbook. Subjects include Americana, business and economics, history, international relations, nature, politics, religion and sociology. Especially needs "books that promise to enlighten public policy; also, books of regional interest that are entertaining. Query or submit outline/synopsis and sample chapters. Reviews artwork/photos as part of ms package.
Recent Nonfiction Title: *The Hundred Percent Challenge,* edited by Charles Smith (international affairs).
Tips: "Literate, intelligent, socially conscious men and women are our readers."

SEVEN SEAS PRESS, 2 Dean Ave., Newport RI 02840. (401)847-1683. Editor: James Gilbert. Publishes hardcover and paperback originals. Averages 12 titles/year; receives 350 submissions annually. 50% of books from first-time authors; 90% of books from unagented writers. Average print order for a writer's first book is 3,000. Pays 8-12½% on gross receipts. Offers average $1,500 advance. Publishes book an average of 14 months after acceptance. Computer printout submissions acceptable; prefers letter-quality to dot-matrix. Reports in 1 month.
Nonfiction: "Coffee table" book, cookbook, how-to, humor, illustrated book, reference and technical. "All our titles are in the nautical/marine field. We specialize in informative books that help cruising sailors, in particular, enjoy their sport." Also publishes a line of nonfiction nautical high adventure books. Query or submit outline/synopsis and sample chapters. Reviews artwork/photos as part of ms package.
Recent Nonfiction Title: *The Handbook For Non-Macho Sailors,* by Katy Burke (boating).

‡SHAMELESS HUSSY PRESS, Box 3092, Berkeley CA 94703. (415)547-1062. Editor: L. Bosserman. Publishes trade paperback originals and reprints. Averages 3 titles/year; receives 160 submissions annually. 85% of books from first-time authors; 100% of books from unagented writers. Pays 10% royalty on net profits and 100 copies. Publishes book an average of 3 years after acceptance. Simultaneous and photocopied submissions OK. Computer printout submissions acceptable; prefers letter-quality to dot-matrix. Reports in 6 months. Free book catalog.
Nonfiction: Biography, illustrated book and juvenile. Subjects include Americana, history, psychology and sociology. Needs feminist interviews and biographies. No pornography or anything oppressive to anyone. Submit outline/synopsis and sample chapters. Reviews artwork/photos as part of ms package.
Recent Nonfiction Title: *15 Past 70,* by James Maas (interviews).
Fiction: Adventure, confession, ethnic, experimental, historical, humor and religious. Submit outline/synopsis and sample chapters.
Recent Fiction Title: *Lavinia,* by George Sand (novel).
Poetry: Feminist, mystical, and other. No pornography or oppressive poetry. Submit 5-10 samples.
Recent Poetry Title: *Strawberries,* by Barbara Noda (love poems).

HAROLD SHAW PUBLISHERS, 388 Gundersen Dr., Box 567, Wheaton IL 60189. (312)665-6700. Editor: Ramona C. Cramer. Publishes hardcover and paperback originals and paperback reprints. Averages 24 titles/year; receives 2,000 submissions annually. 5% of books from first-time authors; 90% of books from unagented writers. Average print order for a writer's first book is 5,000-7,500. Offers 5-10% royalty on retail price. Offers average $300 advance (only with established authors). Publishes book an average of 2 years after acceptance. Electronic submissions OK via MS-DOS (IBM), but requires hard copy also. Computer printout submissions acceptable; no dot-matrix. Reports in 4-6 weeks. Book catalog for SAE and 3 first class stamps. Ms guidelines for SASE.
Nonfiction: How-to, juveniles, poetry, literary, religion and self-help. Especially needs "manuscripts dealing with the needs of Christians in today's changing world that give practical help and challenge for living out their Christian faith. HSP publishes only for the *Christian* market. No fiction is accepted and very little poetry—we publish only one volume of poetry evey other year. We do not want to see poetry unless the poet is already established and has a wide reading audience. Manuscripts must be high in quality and creativity." Query first, then submit outline/synopsis and 2-3 sample chapters.
Recent Nonfiction Title: *Joy Unspeakable*, by Martyn Lloyd-Jones.
Tips: "Trends in book publishing that freelance writers should be aware of include the need to use nonsexist language without going to extremes."

SHINING STAR PUBLICATIONS, Subsidiary of Good Apple Inc., Box 1329, Jacksonville OR 97530. (503)899-7121. Editor: Becky Daniel. Averages 12 titles/year; receives 100 submissions annually. 50% of books from first-time authors; 100% of books from unagented writers. Makes outright purchase. No advance. Publishes book an average of 1 year after acceptance. Photocopied submissions OK. Computer printout submissions acceptable. Reports in 1 month. Book catalog for 9x12 SAE and 2 first class stamps to Donna Borst, Shining Star, Box 299, Carthage IL 62321. Ms guidelines for SASE.
Nonfiction: Workbooks on Christian religion. Submit complete ms.
Recent Nonfiction Title: *Life of Jesus Series*, by Rebecca Daniel (workbook).
Fiction: Religious (Bible-based stories). Submit complete ms.
Tips: "Submissions should be single spaced with art suggestions."

‡THE SHOE STRING PRESS, (Archon Books, Linnet Books, Library Professional Publications), 925 Sherman Ave., Hamden CT 06514. (203)248-6307. Distributor for the Connecticut Academy of Arts and Sciences. President: James Thorpe III. Publishes 50 titles/year; receives 500 submissions annually. 30% of books from first-time authors; 90% of books from unagented writers. Royalty on net; no advance. Publishes book an average of 1 year after acceptance. Electronic submissions OK, but requires hard copy also. Computer printout submissions acceptable; prefers letter-quality to dot-matrix. Reports in 6 weeks.
Nonfiction: Publishes scholarly books: history, biography, literary criticism, reference, geography, bibliography, military history, information science, library science, education and general adult nonfiction. Accepts nonfiction translations. Preferred length: 40,000-130,000 words, though there is no set limit. Query with table of contents and 2-3 sample chapters. Reviews artwork/photos as part of ms package.
Recent Nonfiction Title: *Pursuing Innocent Pleasures: The Gardening World of Alexander Pope*, by Peter Martin.
Tips: Queries/mss may be routed to other editors in the publishing group.

SIERRA CLUB BOOKS, 730 Polk St., San Francisco CA 94109. (415)776-2211. Editor-in-Chief: Daniel Moses. Publishes hardcover and paperback originals and reprints. Averages 20 titles/year; receives 500+ submissions annually. 50% of books from unagented writers. Pays 7-12½% royalty on retail price. Offers average $5,000 advance. Publishes book an average of 12-18 months after acceptance. Computer printout submissions acceptable. Reports in 2 months. Free book catalog.
Nonfiction: Animals health; history (natural); how-to (outdoors); juveniles; nature; philosophy; photography; recreation (outdoors, nonmechanical); science; sports (outdoors); and travel (by foot or bicycle). "The Sierra Club was founded to help people to explore, enjoy and preserve the nation's forests, waters, wildlife and wilderness. The books program looks to publish quality trade books about the outdoors and the protection of natural resources. Specifically, we are interested in undeveloped land (not philosophical but informational), nuclear power, self-sufficiency, natural history, politics and the environment, and juvenile books with an ecological theme." Does *not* want "personal, lyrical, philosophical books on the great outdoors; proposals for large color photographic books without substantial text; how-to books on building things outdoors; books on motorized travel; or any but the most professional studies of animals." Query first, submit outline/synopsis and sample chapters. Reviews artwork/photos ("duplicates, not originals") as part of ms package.
Recent Nonfiction Title: *A Killing Rain: The Global Threat of Acid Precipitation*, by Thomas Pawlick.
Fiction: Adventure, historical, mainstream and science fiction. "We do very little fiction, but will consider a fiction manuscript if its theme fits our philosophical aims: the enjoyment and protection of the environment." Does *not* want "any manuscript with animals or plants that talk; apocalyptic plots." Query first, submit outline/synopsis and sample chapters, or submit complete ms.

SILHOUETTE BOOKS, 300 E. 42nd St., New York NY 10017. (212)682-6080. Editor-in-Chief: Karen Solem. Publishes mass market paperback originals. Averages 312 titles/year; receives 4,000 submissions annually. 10% of books from first-time authors; 25% of books from unagented writers. Pays royalty. Publishes book an average of 1 year after acceptance. Computer printout submissions acceptable; no dot-matrix. No unsolicited mss. Send query letter; 2 page synopsis and SASE to head of imprint. Ms guidelines for SASE.
Imprints: Silhouette Romances (contemporary adult romances), Tara Hughes, Senior Editor; 53,000-58,000 words. Silhouette Special Editions (contemporary adult romances), Roz Noonan, senior editor; 75,000-80,000 words. Silhouette Desires (contemporary adult romances), Isabel Swift, editor; 55,000-65,000 words. Silhouette Intimate Moments (contemporary adult romances), Leslie Wainger, senior editor; 80,000-85,000 words. Silhouette First Loves (contemporary young adult romances), Nancy Jackson, senior editor; 45,000-50,000 words.
Fiction: Romance (contemporary romance for adults and young adults). "We are interested in seeing submissions for all our lines. No manuscripts other than contemporary romances of the type outlined above." Mss should "follow our general format, yet have an individuality and life of its own that will make it stand out in the readers' minds."
Recent Fiction Title: *Sarah's Child*, by Linda Howard.
Tips: "The contemporary romance market is constantly changing and developing, so when you read for research, read the latest books and those that have been recommended to you by those knowledgable in the genre."

SIMON & SCHUSTER, Trade Books Division, 1230 Avenue of the Americas, New York NY 10020. "If we accept a book for publication, business arrangements are worked out with the author or his agent and a contract is drawn up. The specific terms vary according to the type of book and other considerations. Royalty rates are more or less standard among publishers. All unsolicited manuscripts will be returned unread. Only manuscripts submitted by agents or recommended to us by friends or actively solicited by us will be considered. In such cases, our requirements are as follows: All manuscripts submitted for consideration should be marked to the attention of a specific editor. It usually takes at least three weeks for the author to be notified of a decision—often longer. Sufficient postage for return by first-class registered mail, or instructions for return by express collect, in case of rejection, should be included. Manuscripts must be typewritten, double-spaced, on one side of the sheet only. We suggest margins of about one and one half inches all around and the standard 8"x11" typewriter paper." Computer printout submissions acceptable; prefers letter-quality to dot-matrix.
Nonfiction and Fiction: "Simon and Schuster publishes books of general adult fiction, history, biography, science, philosophy, the arts and popular culture, running 50,000 words or more. Our program does not, however, include school textbooks, extremely technical or highly specialized works, or, as a general rule, poetry or plays. Exceptions have been made, of course, for extraordinary manuscripts of great distinction or significance."
Tips: Queries/mss may be routed to other editors in the publishing group.

*SLAVICA PUBLISHERS, INC., Box 14388, Columbus OH 43214. (614)268-4002. President/Editor: Charles E. Gribble. Publishes hardcover and paperback originals, reprints and software. Averages 20 titles/year; receives 100 submissions annually. 80%+ of books from first-time authors; 100% of books from unagented writers. Subsidy publishes 33-50% of books. "All manuscripts are read for quality; if they pass that test, then we talk about money. We *never* accept full subsidies on a book, and we *never* publish anything that has not passed the scrutiny of expert readers. Most subsidies are very small (usually in the range of $200-800)." Offers 10-15% royalty on retail price; "for some books, royalties do not begin until specified number has been sold." Publishes book an average of 1 year after acceptance. "Only in exceptional circumstances will we consider simultaneous submissions, and only if we are informed of it. We strongly prefer good photocopied submissions rather than the original." Electronic submissions OK on any CP/M or MSDOS 5¼, but requires hard copy also. Computer printout submissions acceptable; prefers letter-qualtiy to dot-matrix. Query first. Reports in 1 week to 4 months (more in some cases). Free book catalog.
Nonfiction: Biography, history, reference, textbooks, travel, language study, literature, folklore and literary criticism. "We publish books dealing with almost any aspect of the peoples, languages, literatures, history and cultures of Eastern Europe and the Soviet Union, as well as general linguistics and Balkan studies. We do not publish original fiction and in general do not publish books dealing with areas of the world other than Eastern Europe, the USSR and the Balkans (except for linguistics, which may deal with any area)." Accepts nonfiction translations from Eastern European languages. Query first. Looks for authors of scholarly books and textbooks who know their fields and write clearly. Reviews artwork/photos as part of ms package.
Recent Nonfiction Title: *Tyrant and Victim in Dostoevsky*, by Gary Cox.
Tips: "A large percentage of our authors are academics, but we would be happy to hear from other authors as well. We need books dealing with our areas; we get too many submissions that are in the wrong fields. Very few of our books sell well enough to make the author much money, since the field in which we work is so small. The few that do make money are normally textbooks."

SOS PUBLICATIONS, 4223-25 W. Jefferson Blvd., Los Angeles CA 90016. (213)730-1815. Publisher: Paul Bradley. Publishes mini-bound originals and re-prints. Averages 4 titles/month; receives 800-1,000 submissions annually. 40% of books from first-time authors; 40% of books from unagented writers. Average print order for a writer's first book is 30,000. Pays 6-15% royalty on net selling price. Publishes book an average of 9 months after acceptance. Photocopied submissions OK. Computer printout submissions acceptable; no dot-matrix. SASE which will *enclose* the manuscript *must* accompany submission. Any queries *must* also include SASE. "Due to both the large number of manuscripts we receive and our limited reading staff, we report as soon as possible—but allow approximately 4-5 months." Book catalog for 8½x11 SAE with 39¢ postage.
Imprints: Private Library Collection (fiction).
Fiction: Carla O. Glover, fiction editor. Mystery, adventure, romance and suspense. "Our Private Library Collection consists of the Mini-Bound, a hardcover book the size of a mass-market paperback. It showcases original titles, illustrations and new authors. There are four categories: the novel, mystery, romance, and adventure. Two further categories are anticipated: Science fiction and westerns. Don't send any science fiction or western *before* the winter of 1987. It is suggested to query first when that time of year arrives." Especially needs main stream mss. No horror or occult. Send complete ms.
Recent Fiction Title: *The Wind of Change*, by Judith Hagar (romance).
Tips: "Well-written romance and mystery does well for us, but we need mainstream. There is no particular style that we *must* have, but our reviewer's list includes *The New York Times*. Study the *New York Times* trends to review. If I were a writer trying to market a book today I would follow guidelines *exactly*. I would *not* call an editor. I would not take a rejection personally."

THE SOURCEVIEW PRESS, Subsidiary of The SourceView Corp., 835 Castro St., Martinez CA 94553. (415)228-6228. Editor: Michael Dean. Publishes trade paperback originals and software. Averages 2-5 titles/year; 100 software titles/year. Pays 6-9% royalty on wholesale price. Reports in 2 weeks on mss; does not respond to queries.
Nonfiction: Reference and technical. Computer software only. Needs books on computer languages, disk operating systems, theory of writing software, etc. No how-to books in application areas geared to specific software. Submit outline/synopsis and sample chapters or complete ms; prefers agented submissions.
Tips: "Our audience includes college-educated managerial persons with day-to-day involvement with microcomputers."

SOUTH END PRESS, 116 St. Botolph, Boston MA 02115. (617)266-0629. Publishes trade paperback and hardcover originals and trade paperback reprints. Averages 15 nonfiction titles/year; receives 900 submissions annually. 50% of books from first-time authors; 90% of books from unagented writers. Pays 10% royalty on net price. Publishes book an average of 6 months after acceptance. Simultaneous submissions OK. Computer printout submissions acceptable. Reports in 2 months. Free book catalog.
Nonfiction: Subjects include politics, economics, feminism, social change, radical cultural criticism, explorations of race, class, and sex oppression and liberation. No conservative political themes. Submit outline/synopsis and 1-2 sample chapter(s).

SOUTHERN ILLINOIS UNIVERSITY PRESS, Box 3697, Carbondale IL 62901. (618)453-2281. Director: Kenney Withers. Averages 50 titles/year; receives 500 submissions annually. 50% of books from first-time authors; 99% of books from unagented writers. Pays 10-12½% royalty on net price. Publishes book an average of 1 year after acceptance. Computer printout submissions acceptable; no dot-matrix. Reports in 6 weeks. Free book catalog.
Nonfiction: "We are interested in scholarly nonfiction on the humanities, social sciences and contemporary affairs material. No dissertations or collections of previously published articles." Accepts nonfiction translations from French, German, Scandinavian and Hebrew. Query.
Recent Nonfiction Title: *Thomas Pynchon*, by Cowart (literary criticism).

‡SPARROW PRESS, Subsidiaries include Sparrow Poverty Pamphlets and Vagrom Chap Books, 103 Waldron St., West Lafayette IN 47906. (317)743-1991. Editor/Publisher: Felix Stefanile. Publishes trade paperback originals. Averages 3 pamphlets and 1-3 chapbooks/year; receives 1,200 submissions annually. 25% of books from first-time authors; 100% of books from unagented writers. Pays $25 advance on royalties, 20% of profits after cost is recovered. No simultaneous submissions. Publishes book an average of 10 months after acceptance. Reports in 1 month on queries; 6 weeks on mss. Book catalog and ms guidelines for SASE. Sample pamphlet $2.
Imprints: Sparrow Poverty Pamphlets (poetry), Felix Stefanile, editor/publisher. Vagrom Chap Books (poetry, by invitation), Felix Stefanile, editor/publisher.
Poetry: "We need the best poetry we can find. We plan at least three volumes a year. We are not interested in seeing any humor, or religious verse. We don't want prose poems. We do not want cut-up prose confessional poems." 28 page typescript only, one poem/page. "If we want to see more, we'll ask." *No* queries answered without SASE. Send complete ms.

Recent Poetry Title: *A Dream of Plum Blossoms*, by Norbert Krapf (traditional free verse).
Tips: "Our readers are contemporary-minded fellow poets, creative writing students, serious readers and teachers. Poetry is becoming more formal again, more literate. The better poets write out of their hearts, and find their own genuine, if not too large, following. On the other hand, one of our poets has gone through three printings."

SPINSTERS/AUNT LUTE BOOKS, Box 410687, San Francisco CA 94141. Editor/Publisher: Sherilyn Thomas and Joan Pinkvoss. Publishes trade paperback originals and reprints. Averages 7-10 titles/year; receives 250 submissions annually. 50% of books from first-time authors; 90% of books from unagented writers. Pays 8-12% royalty on retail price. Publishes book an average of 1 year after acceptance. Photocopied submissions OK. Computer printout submissions acceptable; prefers letter-quality to dot-matrix. Reports in 3 weeks on queries; 2 months on mss. Free book catalog. Ms guidelines for SASE.
Nonfiction: Self-help and feminist analysis for positive change. Subjects include health, history, philosophy, politics, psychology, sociology, feminism and lesbianism. "We would like to see an incisive and clear work on an issue of import in the lesbian and feminist communities. No sexist, racist or homophobic work—in general, work based on oppression of any people is not wanted." Submit outline/synopsis and sample chapters. Reviews artwork/photos as part of ms package.
Recent Nonfiction Title: *Call Me Woman*, by Ellen Kuzwayo (autobiography).
Fiction: Ethnic, women's, lesbian. Submit outline/synopsis and sample chapters.
Recent Fiction Title: *The Woman Who Owned The Shadows*, by Paula Gunn Allen (native American novel).
Poetry: Minimal. Submit complete ms.
Recent Poetry Title: *We Say We Love Each Other*, by Minnie Bruce Pratt (Southern lesbian).

ST PUBLICATIONS, Book Division, 407 Gilbert Ave., Cincinnati OH 45202. (513)421-4050. Book Division Coordinator: Carole Singleton. Publishes hardcover and trade paperback originals and hardcover reprints. Averages 3-5 titles/year; receives 15-20 submissions annually. 50% of books from first-time authors; 100% of books from unagented writers. Pays royalty on wholesale price: 15% from initial sales of book, or 20% (after recovery of production costs). Publishes book an average of 9 months after acceptance. Photocopied submissions OK. Computer printout submissions acceptable. Reports in 6 weeks on queries; 2 months on mss. Free book catalog; ms guidelines for SASE.
Nonfiction: How-to, reference, technical and textbook. Subjects include art (collections of copyright-free artwork suitable for sign, display or screen printing industries). "We need technical how-to books for professionals in three specific industries: the sign industry, including outdoor advertising, electric and commercial signs; the screen printing industry, including the printing of paper products, fabrics, ceramics, glass and electronic circuits; and the visual merchandising and store design industry. We are not interested in submissions that do not relate specifically to those three fields." Submit outline/synopsis and sample chapters. Reviews artwork/photos as part of ms package.
Recent Nonfiction Title: *Mastering Layout*, by Mike Stevens (how-to on sign painting and design).
Tips: "The writer has the best chance of selling our firm how-to books related to our industries: signs, screen printing, and visual merchandising. These are the fields our marketing and distribution channels are geared to. Request copies of, and thoroughly absorb the information presented in, our trade magazines (*Signs of the Times, Visual Merchandising*, and *Screen Printing*). Our books are permanent packages of this type of information."

STACKPOLE BOOKS, Box 1831, Harrisburg PA 17105. Editorial Director: Chet Fish. Publishes hardcover and paperback originals. Publishes approximately 50 titles/year. "Proposals should begin as a one-page letter, leading to chapter outline only on request. If author is unknown to Stackpole, supply credentials." Publishes book an average of 9 months after acceptance. Computer printout submissions acceptable; prefers letter-quality to dot-matrix. Ms guidelines for SASE.
Nonfiction: Outdoor-related subject areas—firearms, fishing, hunting, wildlife, outdoor skills, military guides, decoy carving/woodcarving, and space exploration. Reviews artwork/photos as part of ms package.

STANDARD PUBLISHING, 8121 Hamilton Ave., Cincinnati OH 45231. (513)931-4050. Publisher/Vice President: Ralph M. Small. Publishes hardcover and paperback originals and reprints. Specializes in religious books. Averages 75 titles/year; receives 2,500 submissions annually. 25% of books from first-time authors; 90% of books from unagented writers. Average print order for a writer's first book is 7,500. Pays 10% royalty on wholesale price "for substantial books. Lump sum for smaller books." Offers $200-1,500 advance. Publishes book an average of 1 year after acceptance. Electronic submissions OK (except on Apple); requires hard copy also. Computer printout submissions acceptable; no dot-matrix. Reports in 2-3 months. Ms guidelines for SASE.
Nonfiction: Publishes how-to; crafts (to be used in Christian education); juveniles; reference; Christian education; quiz; puzzle and religious books; and college textbooks (religious). All mss must pertain to religion. Query or submit outline/synopsis and 2-3 sample chapters. Reviews artwork/photos as part of ms package.

Recent Nonfiction Title: *Child Abuse: What You Can Do About It*, by Jeannette Lockerbie.
Fiction: Religious, devotional books.
Recent Fiction Title: *In Another Land, a Jennifer Book*, by Jerry Jenkins.
Tips: "Children's book, Christian education, activity books, and helps for Christian parents and church leaders are the types of books writers have the best chance of selling to our firm."

*STANFORD UNIVERSITY PRESS, Stanford CA 94305. (415)497-9434. Editor: William W. Carver. Averages 55 titles/year; receives 900 submissions annually. 40% of books from first-time authors, 95% of books from unagented writers. Subsidy publishes (non-author) 75% of books. Pays up to 15% royalty; sometimes offers advance. Publishes book an average of 14 months after acceptance. Photocopied submissions OK. Electronic submissions by agreement only; requires hard copy also. Computer printout submissions acceptable; no dot-matrix. Reports in 3 weeks on queries; 5 weeks on mss. Free book catalog.
Nonfiction: Scholarly books in the humanities; social sciences and natural sciences; European history; history and culture of China, Japan and Latin America; biology and taxonomy; anthropology, linguistics, and psychology; archaeology and geology; literature, criticism, and literary theory; political science and sociology; and classical studies. Also high-level textbooks and books for a more general audience. Query. Reviews artwork/photos as part of ms package.
Recent Nonfiction Title: *The Letters of Anthony Trollope*, edited by N. John Hall.
Tips: "We are interested in seeing syntheses, upper division texts, handbooks, and general interest. The writer has the best chance of selling a work of original scholarship with an argument of some importance and an appeal to a broad audience."

‡STATE HISTORICAL SOCIETY OF WISCONSIN, 816 State St., Madison WI 53706. (608)262-9604. Editorial Director: Paul H. Hass. Senior Editor: William C. Marten. Publishes hardcover and paperback originals and hardcover reprints. Publishes 2 titles/year. Pays 10% royalty; no advance. Photocopied submissions OK. Reports in 2 months. Free book catalog.
Nonfiction: "Research and interpretation in history of the American Middle West—broadly construed as the Mississippi Valley. Must be thoroughly documented, but on topics of sufficient interest to attract the layman as well as the scholar. 150,000-200,000 words of text, exclusive of footnotes and other back matter. No extremely narrowly focused monographs on non-Wisconsin subjects."
Recent Nonfiction Title: *Old Abe the War Eagle*, by Richard Zeitlin.

STEIN AND DAY PUBLISHERS, Scarborough House, Briarcliff Manor NY 10510. Averages 100 titles/year. Offers standard royalty contract.
Nonfiction & Fiction: Publishes general adult fiction and nonfiction books; no juvenile or college. All types of nonfiction except technical. Quality fiction. No unsolicited mss without querying first. Nonfiction, send outline or summary and sample chapter. *Must* furnish SASE with all fiction and nonfiction queries. Minimum length: 65,000 words.
Recent Nonfiction Title: *The Specialist*, by Gayle Rivers.
Recent Fiction Title: *Kara Kush*, by Indries Shah.

STEMMER HOUSE PUBLISHERS, INC., 2627 Caves Rd., Owings Mills MD 21117. (301)363-3690. President: Barbara Holdridge. Publishes hardcover originals. Averages 25 titles/year; receives 500+ submissions annually. 10% of books from first-time authors; 90% of books from unagented writers. Average print order for a writer's first book is 4,000-10,000. Pays royalty on wholesale price. Publishes book an average of 6 months after acceptance. Computer printout submissions acceptable; no dot-matrix. Reports in 2 weeks on queries; 3 months on mss. Book catalog for 9x12 SAE and 56¢ postage.
Nonfiction: Biography, cookbook, illustrated book, juvenile and design books. Subjects include Americana, animals, art, cooking and foods, history and nature. Especially looking for "quality biography, history, and art and design." No humor. Query or submit outline/synopsis and sample chapters.
Recent Nonfiction Title: *An Italic Calligraphy Handbook*, by Mary Leister (natural history).
Fiction: Adventure, ethnic, historical, mainstream and philosophical. "We want only manuscripts of sustained literary merit. No popular-type manuscripts written to be instant bestsellers." Query.
Recent Fiction Title: *The Fringe of Heaven*, by Margaret Sutherland (contemporary novel).
Tips: "If I were a writer trying to market a book today, I would not imitate current genres on the bestseller lists, but strike out with a subject of intense interest to me." Freelancer has best chance of selling a book with a universal theme, either for adults or children, exceptionally well written, and marketable internationally. "Our goal is a list of perennial sellers of which we can be proud."

✚ *The double dagger before a listing indicates that the listing is new in this edition. New markets are often the most receptive to freelance contributions.*

STERLING PUBLISHING, 2 Park Ave., New York NY 10016. (212)532-7160. Acquisitions Manager: Sheila Anne Barry. Publishes hardcover and paperback originals and reprints. Averages 80 titles/year. Pays royalty; offers advance. Publishes book an average of 8 months after acceptance. Computer printout submissions acceptable; prefers letter-quality to dot-matrix. Reports in 6 weeks.
Nonfiction: Alternative lifestyle, fiber arts, games and puzzles, health how-to and medicine, business, foods, hobbies, how-to, children's humor, occult, pets, photography, recreation, reference, self-help, sports, theatre (how-to), technical, collecting, wine and woodworking. Query or submit complete chapter list, detailed outline/synopsis and 2 sample chapters with photos if necessary. Reviews artwork/photos as part of ms package.
Recent Nonfiction Title: *Windows on the World Complete Wine Course*, by Kevin Zraly.

‡STILLPOINT PUBLISHING, INC., Subsidiary of Dutton/New American Library, Box 640 Meetinghouse Rd., Walpole NH 03608. (603)756-3508. Editorial Assistant: Jean Etter. Publishes hardcover originals and trade paperback originals and reprints. Averages 6-10 titles/year; receives 750 submissions annually. 60% of books from first-time authors; 15% of books from unagented writers. Pays 7.5-15% royalty on retail price. No advances. Publishes book an average of 1 year after acceptance. Simultaneous and photocopied submissions OK. Electronic submissions OK via Cross Talk software, but requires hard copy also. Reports in 2 weeks on queries; 2 months on mss. Call (800)847-4014 for free book catalog.
Imprints: Angelfood (fiction), Jean Etter, editorial assistant.
Nonfiction: Cookbook, juvenile, self-help, and books on spirituality and the metaphysical. Subjects include cooking and foods, health, philosophy, psychology, religion, sports and channeled material. "We are looking for eight to ten books dealing with spirituality and life transformation, whether the transformation is through sports, meditation, or a near-death experience or being in contact with higher dimensions of being." No submissions that do not deal with spirituality. Also interested in acquisitions and out of print titles. Submit complete ms.
Recent Nonfiction Title: *Why Me?*, by Patricia Norris, Ph.D. and Garrett Porter (health).
Fiction: Non-secular religion, and science fiction dealing with what mankind might become. "We are looking for two to three good books that show mankind's evolving spirituality. No submissions not dealing with mankind's quest for spirituality and transformation." Submit complete ms.
Recent Fiction Title: *The Moebius Seed*, by Steven Rosen, Ph.D. (science fiction).
Tips: "If I were a writer trying to market a book today, I would try to match my book to the proper publisher. We have a very specific market and appreciate hearing from authors who write books concerning how mankind is changing spiritually and what we might be heading towards. We've noticed a trend to trade paperbacks. We do well with channeled material—information that comes through from the non-physical realm. Books of the caliber of Jane Roberts and *Agartha* by Meredith Young are coming to us to be published. Our audience is interested in the spiritual quality of their lives, and the integration of mind, body and spirit."

STIPES PUBLISHING CO., 10-12 Chester St., Champaign IL 61820. (217)356-8391. Contact: Robert Watts. Publishes hardcover and paper originals. Averages 25 titles/year; receives 150 submissions annually. 50% of books from first-time authors; 100% of books from unagented writers. Pays 15% maximum royalty on retail price. Publishes book an average of 4 months after acceptance. Computer printout submissions acceptable; prefers letter-quality to dot-matrix. Reports in 2 weeks on queries; 2 months on mss.
Nonfiction: Technical (some areas), textbooks on business and economics, music, chemistry, agriculture/horticulture, and recreation and physical education. "All of our books in the trade area are books that also have a college text market." No "books unrelated to educational fields taught at the college level." Submit outline/synopsis and 1 sample chapter.
Recent Nonfiction Title: *Keyboard Fundamentals*, by James Lyke and Denise Edwards (college text and adult beginners).

STOEGER PUBLISHING COMPANY, 55 Ruta Court, S. Hackensack NJ 07606. (201)440-2700. Subsidiary includes Stoeger Industries. Publisher: Robert E. Weise. Publishes trade paperback originals. Averages 12-15 titles/year. Royalty varies, depending on ms. Simultaneous and photocopied submissions OK. Reports in 1 month on queries; 3 months on mss. Free book catalog.
Nonfiction: Cookbook, how-to and self-help. Subjects include sports, outdoor sports, cooking and foods, and hobbies. Especially looking for how-to books relating to hunting, fishing, or other outdoor sports. Submit outline/synopsis and sample chapters.
Recent Nonfiction Title: *Advanced Muzzleloading*, by Toby Bridges.

STONE WALL PRESS, INC., 1241 30th St., NW, Washington DC 20007. President/Publisher: Henry Wheelwright. Publishes hardcover and trade paperback originals. Averages 2-5 titles/year; receives 50 submissions annually. 75% of books from first-time authors; 95% of books from unagented writers. Average print order for a writer's first book is 3,000-4,000. Pays standard royalty; offers minimal advance. Publishes book an average of 6 months after acceptance. Computer printout submissions acceptable; no dot-matrix. Reports in 2 weeks. Book catalog for business size SAE and 1 first class stamp.

Nonfiction: How-to and environmental/outdoor. "Unique, practical, illustrated how-to outdoor books (nature, camping, fishing, hiking, hunting, etc.) and environmental books for the general public." Query. Looks for "concise, sharp writing style with humorous touches; a rough table of contents for an idea of the direction of the book, a new approach or topic which hasn't been done recently." Accepts outline/synopsis and several sample chapters. Reviews artwork/photos as part of ms package.

Recent Nonfiction Title: *Fly Fishing for Salmon*, by Neil Graesser.

STONEYDALE PRESS PUBLISHING CO., 304 Main St., Stevensville MT 59870. (406)777-2729. Publisher: Dale A. Burk. Publishes hardcover and trade paperback originals. Averages 4-6 titles/year; receives 100-125 submissions annually. 20% of books from first-time authors; 100% of books from unagented writers. Pays 10-12% royalty on actual price or makes outright purchase. Offers average $500 advance. Publishes book an average of 14 months after acceptance. Electronic submissions OK on CPM, but requires hard copy also. Computer printout submissions acceptable. Reports in 1 month. Book catalog for SAE and $1 postage.

Nonfiction: Biography, "coffee table" book and how-to. Subjects include Americana, art, history, nature, recreation, travel and Montana topics. Emphasis is on hunting and fishing. "We're looking for good outdoor recreation book ideas for our area (northern Rocky Mountains, Pacific Northwest); historical ideas from the same region not over done in the past. Also open to 'coffee table' format books, if we can be convinced a market exists for a specific idea." Query. Reviews artwork/photos as part of ms package.

Recent Nonfiction Title: *Young People's Guide to Yellowstone National Park*, by Robin Tawney.

STRAWBERRY HILL PRESS, 2594 15th Ave., San Francisco CA 94127. President: Jean-Louis Brindamour, Ph.D. Senior Editors: Donna L. Osgood, Joseph Lubow, Carolyn Soto, Robin Witkin. Publishes paperback originals. Publishes 12 titles/year; receives over 5,000 submissions annually. 90% of books written by first-time authors; 98% of books from unagented writers. Average print order for a writer's first book is 5,000. "We are a small house, proud of what we do, and intending to stay relatively small (that does not mean that we will do a less-than-professional job in marketing our books, however). The author-publisher relationship is vital, from the moment the contract is signed until there are no more books to sell, and we operate on that premise. We do no hardcovers, and, for the moment at least, our format is limited strictly to 6x9 quality paperbacks. We seldom print fewer than 5,000 copies in a first printing, with reprintings also never falling below that same figure." Pays 10% royalty on wholesale price; no advance. Publishes book an average of 2 years after acceptance. Photocopied submissions OK. Electronic submissions OK on TRS 80 Model III or Kaypro system. Computer printout submissions acceptable; no dot-matrix. Reports in 2 months. Book catalog for SAE and 2 first class stamps.

Nonfiction: Self-help, inspiration (not religion), biography/autobiography, cookbooks, health and nutrition, aging, diet, popular philosophy, metaphysics, alternative life style; Third World, minority histories, oral history and popular medicine. Accepts nonfiction and fiction translations. No religion, sports, craft books, photography or fine art material. Submit outline/synopsis and 1 sample chapter.

Recent Nonfiction Title: *Living Up the Street*, by Gary Soto.

Recent Fiction Title: *Dowry of Death*, by Melvin A. Casberg, M.D.

*LYLE STUART, INC., 120 Enterprise Ave., Secaucus NJ 07094. (201)866-0490, (212)736-1141. Subsidiaries include Citadel Press and University Books. President: Lyle Stuart. Publisher: Carole Stuart. Editor-in-Chief: Mario Satori. Publishes hardcover and trade paperback originals, and trade paperback reprints. Averages 100 titles/year; receives 1,500-2,000 submissions annually. 70% of books from first-time authors; 60% of books from unagented writers. Subsidy publishes 5% of books. Pays 10-12% royalty on retail price; offers "low advance." Publishes book an average of 10 months after acceptance.

Nonfiction: Biography, "coffee table" book, how-to, humor, illustrated book and self-help. Subjects include Americana, art, business and economics, health, history, music and politics. "The percentage of acceptable over-the-transom manuscripts has been so low during the years that we are no longer reading unsolicited material." Reviews artwork/photos as part of ms package.

Recent Nonfiction Title: *The Elegant Inn*.

Recent Fiction Title: *The Blue Bicycle*.

Tips: "The writer has the best chance of selling us a book that is controversial—and professionally written."

STUDIO PRESS, (formerly Lightbooks), Box 1268, Twain Harte CA 95383. (209)533-4222. Publisher: Paul Castle. Publishes hardcover and paperback originals. Averages 3-5 titles/year; receives 10-15 submissions annually. 100% of books from first-time authors; 100% of books from unagented writers. Average print order for a writer's first book is 2,000-3,000. Pays 10-15% royalty on wholesale or retail price; no advance. Publishes book an average of 3-6 months after acceptance. Simultaneous and photocopied submissions OK. Computer printout submissions acceptable; prefers letter-quality to dot-matrix. Reports in 1 month.

Nonfiction: Photography. "We are always interested in good manuscripts on technique and/or the business of

photography. We especially want manuscripts on *marketing* one's photography. We don't want manuscripts on art criticism of photography, collections of art photos, basic photo teaching books, or anything other than books on the technique and/or business of photography. Query; if the idea is good, we'll ask for outline/synopsis and sample chapters." Reviews artwork/photos as part of ms package. "Artwork/photos are essential to acceptance."
Recent Nonfiction Title: *The Boudoir Portrait*, by Bob and Carla Calkins.
Tips: "We need more anecdotes and word illustrations to amplify the writer's points. We particularly look for skilled photographers who are doing something very well and can communicate their expertise to others. We are willing to work with such individuals on extensive re-write and editing, if what they have to say is valuable."

SUCCESS PUBLISHING, 8084 Nashua Dr., Lake Park FL 33410. (305)626-4643. President: Allan H. Smith. Publishes trade paperback originals. Averages 8-10 titles/year; receives 50 submissions annually. 50% of books from first-time authors; 65% of books from unagented writers. Pays variable royalty on wholesale price (10% minimum) or makes minimum outright purchase of $1,000. Publishes book an average of 4 months after acceptance. Simultaneous submissions OK. Computer printout submissions acceptable; prefers letter-quality to dot-matrix. Reports in 1 month on queries; 6 weeks on mss. Book catalog for SAE and 1 first class stamp.
Nonfiction: How-to, juvenile, self-help and craft. Subjects include business and economics and hobbies. Especially looking for mss interesting to home-based business people; middle school and high school children, and those interested in sewing and crafts. No poetry, cult, religious or technical books. Query and/or submit outline/synopsis and sample chapters.
Recent Nonfiction Title: *Sewing for Profits*, by Judith and Allan Smith.

‡SHERWOOD SUGDEN & COMPANY, PUBLISHERS, 1117 8th St., La Salle IL 61301. (815)223-1231. Publisher: Sherwood Sugden. Publishes hardcover and trade paperback originals and reprints. Averages 8 titles/year. Pays 4-12% royalty. Simultaneous and photocopied submissions OK. Computer printout submissions acceptable. Reports in 3 weeks on queries; 3 months on mss. Book catalog for business size SAE.
Nonfiction: Subjects include history, philosophy, politics, religion (Christian, especially Roman Catholic), and literary criticism. "We're looking for lucid presentations and defenses of orthodox Roman Catholic doctrine, Church history and lives of the Saints aimed at the average intelligent reader. (Possibly one or two scholarly works of the same sort as well.) Works of criticism of British or American authors: perhaps a biography or two; also a work in elementary syllogistic logic. The audience for our books ranges from the bright high school student with a curiosity about ideas through the mature general reader. Certain of our titles (perhaps 30% of our annual output) will appeal chiefly to the advanced student or scholar in the relevant disciplines." Submit outline/synopsis and 1 sample chapter.
Recent Nonfiction Title: *Why Hawthorne Was Melancholy* (Vol. III in the trilogy, *The Prophetic Poet and the Spirit of the Age*), by Marion Montgomery.

THE SUNSTONE PRESS, Box 2321, Santa Fe NM 87504-2321. (505)988-4418. Editor-in-Chief: James C. Smith Jr. Publishes paperback originals; few hardcover originals. Averages 16 titles/year; receives 400 submissions annually. 70% of books from first-time authors; 100% of books from unagented writers. Average print order for writer's first book is 2,000-5,000. Pays royalty on wholesale price. Publishes book an average of 1 year after acceptance. Computer printout submissions acceptable, prefers letter-quality to dot-matrix. Reports in 2 months.
Nonfiction: How-to series craft books. Books on the history and architecture of the Southwest. Looks for "strong regional appeal (Southwestern)." Reviews artwork/photos as part of ms package.
Recent Nonfiction Title: *Hovels, Haciendas, and House Calls*, by Dorothy Simpson Beimer (biography).
Fiction: Publishes "for readers who use the subject matter to elevate their impressions of our world, our immediate society, families and friends." No explicit sex or language.
Recent Fiction Title: *Dead Kachina Man*, by Teresa Van Etten.
Poetry: Traditional or free verse. Poetry book not exceeding 64 pages. Prefers Southwestern theme.
Recent Poetry Title: *Weathered*, by Linda Monacelli Johnson.

‡SUSANN PUBLICATIONS, INC., 3110 N. Fitzhugh, Dallas TX 75204. (214)528-8940. Publisher: Susan Goldstein. Publishes paperback originals. Averages 3 titles/year; receives 100 submissions annually. 95% of books from first-time authors; 100% of books from unagented writers. Offers 10-15% royalty on retail price. No advance. Publishes book an average of 1 year after acceptance. Simultaneous and photocopied submissions OK. Reports in 1 month.
Nonfiction: Cookbooks, cooking and foods, health, how-to, humor, and self-help. "We are interested in how-to books which specifically help us toward self-improvement and fitness. We are a female-owned company. We do not want to see sexist, chauvinistic or anti-woman material." Query first "always." Reviews artwork/photos as part of ms package.

Recent Nonfiction Title: *The Underground Shopper Series: Dallas/Fort Worth, New York City, Houston, Austin/San Antonio.*
Tips: "Take some time with your query letter. Mistakes are very unappealing. Include biographical information (limit to one paragraph) with an eye to what is promotable about yourself. We also act as a literary agent."

‡*ALAN SUTTON PUBLISHING LIMITED**, 30 Brunswick Rd., Gloucester, GL1 1JJ England. (0452)419575. Publishing Director: Peter Clifford. Publishes hardcover, trade paperback, and mass market paperback originals and reprints. Averages 100 titles/year; receives 300 submissions annually. 25% of books from first-time authors; 50% of books from unagented writers. Subsidy publishes 10% of books. Subsidy publishes if "in our opinion a book is worthy of publication but requires investment considerably in excess of its shorter term earning capacity, a subvention may make publication viable." Pays 3-8% royalty on retail price, or makes outright purchase of $700-1,400. Offers average $500 advance. Publishes book an average of 9 months after acceptance. Simultaneous and photocopied submissions OK. Computer printout submissions acceptable; prefers letter-quality to dot-matrix. Reports in 1 month on queries; 2 months on mss. Book catalog free on request.
Nonfiction: Biography, coffee table book, humor, illustrated book, juvenile (only a few titles), and reference. Subjects include history; nature; animals, art photography (old photographs); travel; archaeology; topography; and journals. "We have a very wide-ranging requirement for quality illustrated and unillustrated nonfiction particulary in the history field." No textbooks, etc. Query or submit outline/synopsis and sample chapters. Reviews artwork/photos as part of ms package.
Recent Nonfiction Title: *The Battle of Bosworth*, by Michael Bennett (history).
Fiction: Reprints and new editions of classic fiction. Needs "good editions (with or without new introductions) of classic and literary fiction. We consider very little contemporary fiction." Query or submit outline/synopsis and sample chapters.
Recent Fiction Title: *Fortune of the Rougons*, by Emile Zola (translation in small paperback format).
Tips: "The writer has the best chance of selling our firm a book which takes a new approach or angle and which is, in the broadest sense of the term, allied to the historical field (one of our main selling areas). We look for accuracy, economy of style and thorough research, producing a book which will be respected by the academic world yet readable and compelling to the interested layman."

SYBEX, INC., 2344 6th St., Berkeley CA 94710. (415)848-8233. Editor-in-Chief: Dr. Rudolph S. Langer. Acquisitions Editor: Chuck Ackerman. Publishes paperback originals. Offers averages 60 titles/year. Royalty rates vary. Offers average $2,500 advance. Publishes book an average of 3 months after acceptance. Simultaneous and photocopied submissions OK. "We prefer hard copy for proposal evaluations and encourage our authors to submit WordStar diskettes upon completion of their manuscripts." WordStar word processor diskettes preferred. Computer printout submissions acceptable. Reports in 2 months. Free book catalog.
Nonfiction: Computer and electronics. "Manuscripts most publishable in the field of personal computers, personal computer applications, microprocessors, hardware, programming, languages, applications, and telecommunications." Submit outline/synopsis and 2-3 sample chapters. Accepts nonfiction translations from French or German. Looks for "clear writing; technical accuracy; logical presentation of material; and good selection of material, such that the most important aspects of the subject matter are thoroughly covered; well-focused subject matter; and well-thought-out organization that helps the reader understand the material. And marketability." Reviews artwork/photos as part of ms package.
Recent Nonfiction Title: *Mastering Symphony.*
Tips: Queries/mss may be routed to other editors in the publishing group.

‡*SYMMES SYSTEMS**, Box 8101, Atlanta GA 30306. Editor-in-Chief: E. C. Symmes. Publishes hardcover and paperback originals. 50% of books from first-time authors; 100% of books from unagented writers. Pays 10% royalty on wholesale price. "Contracts are usually written for the individual title and may have different terms." No advance. Subsidy publishes 40% of books. Publishes book an average of 14 months after acceptance. Will consider photocopied and simultaneous submissions. Computer printout submissions acceptable; no dot-matrix. Acknowledges receipt of submission in 10 days; evaluates within 1 month. Query.
Nonfiction: Nature. "Our books have mostly been in the art of bonsai (miniature trees). We are publishing quality information for laypersons (hobbyists). Most of the titles introduce information that is totally new for the hobbyist." Text must be topical, showing state-of-the-art. All books so far have been illustrated with photos and/or drawings. Would like to see more material on self-help business subjects; also photography and collecting photographica. Length: open. Reviews artwork/photos as part of ms package.
Recent Nonfiction Title: *The Physician's Guide to Nutritional Therapy*, by Anderson.

SYRACUSE UNIVERSITY PRESS, 1600 Jamesville Ave., Syracuse NY 13210. (315)423-2596. Director: Luther Wilson. Averages 25 titles/year; receives 350 submissions annually. 40% of books from first-time authors; 95% of books from unagented writers. Pays royalty on net sales. Publishes book an average of 10 months after acceptance. Simultaneous and photocopied submissions OK "if we are informed." Computer printout submissions acceptable. Reports in 2 weeks on queries; "longer on submissions." Free book catalog. Ms guidelines for SASE.

Nonfiction: "The best opportunities in our nonfiction program for freelance writers are of books on New York state. We have published regional books by people with limited formal education, but authors were thoroughly acquainted with their subjects, and they wrote simply and directly about them. Provide precise descriptions about subjects, along with background description of project. The author must make a case for the importance of his or her subject." Query. Accepts outline/synopsis and at least 2 sample chapters. Reviews artwork/photos as part of ms package.

Recent Nonfiction Title: *Marietta Holley: Life With "Josiah Allen's Wife"*, by Kate Winter.

T.F.H. PUBLICATIONS, INC., 211 W. Sylvania Ave., Neptune City NJ 07753. (201)988-8400. Independent book producer/packager. Managing Editor: Neal Pronek. Publishes hardcover originals. Averages 40 titles/year; receives 200 submissions annually. 80% of books from first-time authors; 95% of books from unagented writers. Royalty varies, depending on type of book, etc. Also makes outright purchases of $10 per page. Offers advance of ½ of total based upon estimation of total pages in final printed work. Publishes book an average of 1 year after acceptance. Simultaneous and photocopied submissions OK. Electronic submissions OK if compatible with three major DOS's, Editwriters and Multimate. Computer printout submissions acceptable; prefers letter-quality to dot-matrix. Reports in 3 weeks. Book catalog free on request.

Nonfiction: "Coffee table" book, how-to, illustrated book, reference, technical and textbook. Subjects include animals. "Our nonfiction book manuscript needs are for books that deal with specific guidelines for people who own or are interested in purchasing a particular breed of animal. No books exclusively devoted to personal experiences with a particular pet, for example, *My Pet Sam*." Submit outline/synopsis and sample chapters. Reviews artwork/photos as part of ms package.

Recent Nonfiction Titles: *The Rottweiler*, by Richard F. Stratton.

Tips: "Our audience is any and everyone who owns a pet. We do well with books that have a lot of photographs, and those that offer good sound advice for caring for a particular breed."

T.L. ENTERPRISES, INC., Book Division, 29901 Agoura Rd., Agoura CA 91301. (818)991-4980. Editor-in-Chief: Michael Schneider. Manager: Rena Copperman. Publishes trade and mass market paperback originals. Averages 2 titles/year. Pays 5-10% royalty on retail price. Publishes book an average of 1 year after acceptance. Computer printout submissions acceptable; no dot-matrix. SASE if you need materials returned. Reports in 1 month.

Nonfiction: How-to, reference, technical and travel/touring related to owning a recreational vehicle. Subjects include cooking and foods, hobbies, nature, recreation and travel. "We *do* read all queries, and we will mail test titles of promise; test winners will receive an immediate home. At present, our book market consists primarily of RV owners, plus motorcycle and bicycle touring enthusiasts and photographers. For now, our book audience is our magazine audience—the million or more people who read *Trailer Life*, *MotorHome*, *Rider*, Bicycle Rider, and Darkroom Photography, et al—together with the 450,000 families who belong to our Good Sam (RV owners) Club." Query with outline/synopsis. Reviews artwork/photos as part of ms package.

Recent Nonfiction Title: *RVing America's Backroads*, by Bob Longsdorf.

‡T&T CLARK LTD., 59 George St., Edinburgh, EH2 2LQ Scotland. (031)225-703. Editorial Director: Geoffrey Green. Publishes hardcover and paperback originals and reprints. Averages 50 titles/year; receives 100 submissions annually. 10% of books from first-time authors; 99% of books from unagented writers. Pays 5-10% royalty based on wholesale or retail price. May offer 500 pounds advance. Simultaneous and photocopied submissions OK. Electronic submissions OK, prefers hard copy also. Computer printout submissions acceptable. Reports in 1 month. Free book catalog.

Nonfiction: Religion, law, philosophy, and history. Accepts translations. Top level academic. Query first. Review artwork/photos as part of ms package.

Recent Nonfiction Title: *A History of Christian Doctrine*, by H. Cunliffe-Jones (religion/theology/history student textbook).

TAB BOOKS, INC., Blue Ridge Summit PA 17214. (717)794-2191. Vice President: Ray Collins. Publishes hardcover and paperback originals and reprints. Publishes 200 titles per year; receives 400 submissions annually. 50% of books from first-time authors; 85% of books from unagented writers. Average print order for writer's first book is 10,000. Pays variable royalty; buys some mss outright for a negotiable fee. Offers advance. Photocopied submissions OK (except for art). Electronic submissions OK on IBM PC, WordStar. Computer printout submissions acceptable; prefers letter-quality to dot-matrix. Reports in 6 weeks. Free book catalog and ms guidelines.

Nonfiction: TAB publishes titles in such fields as computer hardware, computer software, business, solar and alternate energy, marine line, aviation, automotive, music technology, consumer medicine, electronics, electrical and electronics repair, amateur radio, shortwave listening, model railroading, toys, hobbies, drawing, animals and animal power, practical skills with projects, building furniture, basic how-to for the house,

building large structures, calculators, robotics, telephones, model radio control, TV servicing, audio, recording, hi-fi and stereo, electronic music, electric motors, electrical wiring, electronic test equipment, video programming, CATV, MATV and CCTV, broadcasting, photography and film, appliance servicing and repair, advertising, antiques and restoration, bicycles, crafts, farmsteading, hobby electronics, home construction, license study guides, mathematics, metalworking, reference books, schematics and manuals, small gasoline engines, two-way radio and CB, and woodworking. Accepts nonfiction translations. Reviews artwork/photos as part of ms package.
Tips: "How-to or aviation books have the best chance of selling to our firm."

TAPLINGER PUBLISHING CO., INC., 132 W. 22nd, New York NY 10011. (212)741-0801. Editors: Ms. Bobs Pinkerton and Roy E. Thomas. Publishes hardcover originals. Publishes 75 titles/year. 2% of books from first-time authors; 1% of books from unagented writers. Average print order for a writer's first book is 3,000-5,000. Pays standard royalty; offers variable advance. Publishes book an average of 1 year after acceptance. Simultaneous and photocopied submissions OK. Computer printout submissions acceptable; no dot-matrix. Reports in 10 weeks.
Imprints: Crescendo (music).
Nonfiction: Art, biography, calligraphy, history, theatre, general trade and belles-lettres. No juveniles. Query.
Fiction: Serious contemporary quality fiction. Accepts fiction translations. No juveniles.

‡TAYLOR PUBLISHING COMPANY, Subsidiary of Insilco, 1550 W. Mockingbird Ln., Dallas TX 75235. (214)637-2800. Editorial Assistant: Dominique Gioia. Publishes hardcover originals. Averages 24 titles/year; receives 250 submissions annually. 50% of books from first-time authors; 50% of books from unagented writers. Pays 5-15% royalty; buys some mss outright. No advances. Publishes book 1 year after acceptance. Simultaneous and photocopied submissions OK. Computer printout submissions acceptable. Reports in 6 weeks on queries; 2 months on unsolicited mss. Book catalog free on request; ms guidelines for business size SASE.
Nonfiction: Biography, "coffee table" book, cookbook and how-to. Subjects include Americana, business and economics, nature, photography, politics, sports and travel. Submit outline/synopsis and sample chapters. Reviews artwork/photos as part of ms package.
Recent Nonfiction Title: *Kentucky Bred*, by Dan White.
Fiction: Ethnic, experimental, historical, and suspense. Submit outline/synopsis and sample chapters.
Tips: "The writer has the best chance of selling regional books to our firm."

*TEACHERS COLLEGE PRESS, 1234 Amsterdam Ave., New York NY 10027. (212)678-3929. Director: Carole P. Saltz. Publishes hardcover and paperback originals and reprints. Averages 50 titles/year. Subsidy publishes (non-author) 10% of books. Pays royalty. Publishes book an average of 1 year after acceptance. Reports in 1 year. Free book catalog.
Nonfiction: "This university press concentrates on books in the field of education in the broadest sense, from early childhood to higher education: good classroom practices, teacher training, special education, innovative trends and issues, administration and supervision, film, continuing and adult education, all areas of the curriculum, comparative education, computers, guidance and counseling and the politics, economics, nursing, philosophy, sociology and history of education. The press also issues classroom materials for students at all levels, with a strong emphasis on reading and writing." Submit outline/synopsis and sample chapters.
Recent Nonfiction Title: *Reading Without Nonsense*, 2nd edition, by Frank Smith.

TEMPLE UNIVERSITY PRESS, Broad and Oxford Sts., Philadelphia PA 19122. (215)787-8787. Editor-in-Chief: Michael Ames. Publishes 35 titles/year. Pays royalty of up to 10% on wholesale price. Publishes book an average of 9 months after acceptance. Electronic submissions OK, but requires hard copy also. Computer printout submissions acceptable. Reports in 3 months. Free book catalog.
Nonfiction: American history, sociology, women's studies, health care, philosophy, public policy and regional (Philadelphia area). "All books should be scholarly. Authors are generally connected with a university. No memoirs, fiction or poetry." Uses Chicago *Manual of Style*. Reviews artwork/photos as part of ms package. Query.
Recent Nonfiction Title: *Democratic Vistas: Post Offices and Public Art in the New Deal*, by Marlene Park and Gerald Markowitz.

TEN SPEED PRESS, Box 7123, Berkeley CA 94707. Publisher: P. Wood. Editors: G. Young and P. Reed. Publishes trade paperback originals and reprints. Averages 20 titles/year; receives 12,000 submissions annually. 50% of books from first-time authors; 90% of books from unagented writers. Average print order for a writer's first book is 5,000-7,000. Offers standard royalties. Offers advance. Publishes book an average of 8 months after acceptance. Computer printout submissions acceptable; prefers letter-quality to dot-matrix. Reports in 1 month. Free book catalog.
Imprints: Celestial Arts.

Nonfiction: Americana, gardening, careers, cookbooks, business, cooking and foods, life guidance, history, humor, nature, self-help, how-to, hobbies, recreation and travel. Subjects range from bicycle books to business. "We will consider any first-rate nonfiction material that we feel will have a long shelf life and be a credit to our list." No set requirements. Submit outline and sample chapters. Reviews artwork/photos as part of ms package.
Tips: "Do not send duplicate submissions to our subsidiary, Celestial Arts."

‡TENSLEEP PUBLICATIONS, Video Resources, Inc., Rm. 524, Citizens Building, Box 925, Aberdeen SD 57401. (605)226-0488. Publisher: Ken Melius (nonfiction). Juvenile Editor: Victoria Peterson. Publishes hardcover and trade paperback originals. Averages 3-5 titles/year; receives 200 submissions annually. 95% of books from first-time authors; 100% of books from unagented writers. Pays 6-12% royalty on retail price. Offers $1,000 advance. Publishes book an average of 8 months after acceptance. Simultaneous and photocopied submissions OK. Computer printout submissions acceptable. Reports in 3 weeks on queries; 2 months on mss. Book catalog free on request; free ms guidelines.
Nonfiction: How-to, juvenile, reference and self-help. Subjects include business and economics, cooking and foods, hobbies, nature, recreation, travel and juvenile (preschool to age 9). "We are seeking works especially on time management and the concept of time. We need a unique approach to the concept of time as a commodity, how time can be used effectively, how it can be wasted—and the effects. Also seeking specific reference books for specific types of businesses." No music, art and religion. Query or submit outline/synopsis and sample chapters. Reviews artwork/photos as part of ms package.
Recent Nonfiction Title: *Kids and Cars*, by Ellyce Field and Susan Shlom (travel/how-to).
Fiction: Juvenile, preschool to age 9. "We need well written, creative manuscripts with engaging characters that lend themselves to serial possibilities. No 'cutesie', poorly conceived manuscripts that talk down to children." Query or submit complete ms.
Tips: "We envision an audience in need of specific information about certain business activities or practices, information about travel and recreation. Cookbooks should appeal to a broad cross-section of the public. We seek books with a two to three year shelf life. Books aimed at specific, easily identifiable audiences seem to be a trend. Travel books continue to do well in today's market. In the future, we need unique, informative books written for a certain market whether it be business, travel or recreation markets. Juvenile books should not only be unique but should reflect current interests of children."

TEXAS CHRISTIAN UNIVERSITY PRESS, Box 30783, TCU, Fort Worth TX 76129. (817)921-7822. Director: Keith Gregory. Editor: Judy Alter. Publishes hardcover originals, some reprints. Averages 12 titles/year; receives 100 submissions annually. 10% of books from first-time authors; 75% of books from unagented writers. Pays royalty. Publishes book an average of 16 months after acceptance. Computer printout submissions acceptable; no dot-matrix. Reports "as soon as possible."
Nonfiction: American studies, Texana, theology, literature and criticism, and young adult regional fiction. "We are looking for good scholarly monographs, other serious scholarly work and regional titles of significance." Query. Reviews artwork/photos as part of ms package.
Recent Nonfiction Title: *Warning: Writer at Work, The Best Collectibles of Larry L. King*.
Recent Fiction Title: *The Times It Never Rained*, by Kelton (reprint).
Tips: "Regional and/or Texana-nonfiction or fiction—and scholarly studies in religion, sports and rhetoric have the best chance of breaking into our firm."

TEXAS MONTHLY PRESS, INC., Subsidiary of Mediatex Communications Corp., Box 1569, Austin TX 78767. (512)476-7085. Editorial Director: Scott Lubeck. Publishes hardcover and trade paperback originals, and trade paperback reprints. Averages 20-28 titles/year; receives 400 submissions annually. 60% of books from first-time authors; 85% of books from unagented writers. Pays royalty; offers advance. Publishes book an average of 1 year after acceptance. Simultaneous and photocopied submissions OK. Electronic submissions OK on IBM, CPM, but requires hard copy also. Computer printout submissions acceptable. Reports in 2 weeks on queries; 2 months on mss. Free book catalog.
Nonfiction: Biography, "coffee table" book, cookbook, humor, guidebook, illustrated book and reference. Subjects include Texana, art, business and economics, cooking and foods, history, nature, photography, politics, recreation, sports and travel. Texas-related subjects only. "Especially interested in biographies of distinguished Texans in all fields." Query or submit outline/synopsis and 3 sample chapters. Reviews artwork/photos as part of ms package.
Recent Nonfiction Title: *Rio Grande: Mountains to the Sea*, by Jim Bones.
Fiction: Ethnic, mainstream. "All stories must be set in the South or Southwest." No experimental, erotica, confession, gothic, romance or poetry. Query or submit outline/synopsis and 3 sample chapters. No unsolicited mss.
Recent Fiction Title: *Deer in Water*, by Jan Reid.

TEXAS WESTERN PRESS, The University of Texas at El Paso, El Paso TX 79968. (915)747-5688. Director/Editor: Dale L. Walker. Publishes hardcover and paperback originals. Publishes 7-8 titles/year. "This is a uni-

versity press, 33 years old; we do offer a standard 10% royalty contract on our hardcover books and on some of our paperbacks as well. We try to treat our authors professionally, produce handsome, long-lived books and aim for quality, rather than quantity of titles carrying our imprint." Reports in 1-3 months. Free book catalog, author guidelines. Will consider photocopied submissions; require letter-outline and not complete ms.
Nonfiction: Scholarly books. Historic and cultural accounts of the Southwest (West Texas, New Mexico, northern Mexico and Arizona). Some literary works, occasional scientific titles. "Our *Southwestern Studies* use manuscripts of up to 30,000 words. Our hardback books range from 30,000 words up. The writer should use good exposition in his work. Most of our work requires documentation. We favor a scholarly, but not overly pedantic, style. We specialize in superior book design." Query. Follow *Chicago Manual of Style*.
Recent Nonfiction Title: *War, Revolution and the Ku Klux Klan*, by Shawn Lay.

‡**THEATRE ARTS BOOKS**, 153 Waverly Place, New York NY 10014. (212)675-1815. Director: George Zournas. Publishes trade paperback originals. Averages 3 titles/year; receives 100 submissions annually. 100% of books from unagented writers. Pays royalty. No advance. Publishes ms an average of 2 years after acceptance. Photocopied submissions OK. Computer printout submissions acceptable; no dot-matrix. "Report time varies—2-3 weeks in slow seasons, 3 months in busy seasons." Use *Chicago Manual of Style* for ms guidelines.
Nonfiction: Drama and theatre. Subject include acting, directing, lighting, costume, dance, staging, etc. "We publish only books of broad general interest to actors, directors and theatre technicians, especially books that could be useful in college classrooms. Most of our authors have had long experience in professional theatre. Topics that are very narrowly focused (a costume book on women's shoes in the eighteenth century, for example) would not be acceptable. We no longer publish original plays." Query with outline, synopsis and author's qualifications.
Recent Nonfiction Title: *Training for the Theatre*, by Michel Saint-Denis.

***THE THEOSOPHICAL PUBLISHING HOUSE**, Subsidiary of The Theosophical Society in America, 306 W. Geneva Rd., Wheaton IL 60189. (312)665-0123. Senior Editor: Shirley Nicholson. Publishes trade paperback originals. Averages 12 titles/year; receives 750-1,000 submissions annually. 50-60% of books from first-time authors; 95% of books from unagented writers. Average print order for a writer's first book is 5,000. Subsidy publishes 10% of books based on "author need and quality and theme of manuscript." Pays 10-12% royalty on retail price; offers average $1,500 advance. Publishes book an average of 8 months after acceptance. Simultaneous and photocopied submissions OK. Computer printout submissions acceptable; prefers letter-quality to dot-matrix. Reports in 2 weeks on queries, 2 months on mss. Free book catalog; ms guidelines for SASE.
Imprint: Quest (nonfiction).
Nonfiction: Subjects include self-development, self-help, philosophy (holistic), psychology (transpersonal), Eastern and Western religions, comparative religion, holistic implications in science, health and healing, yoga, meditation and astrology. "TPH seeks works which are compatible with the theosophical philosophy. Our audience includes the 'new age' consciousness community seekers in all religions, general public, professors, and health professionals. No submissions which do not fit the needs outlined above." Accepts nonfiction translations. Query or submit outline/synopsis and sample chapters. Reviews artwork/photos as part of ms package.
Recent Nonfiction Title: *Spiritual Aspects of Male/Female Relations*, by Scott Miners.
Tips: "The writer has the best chance of selling our firm a book which illustrates a connection between spiritually-oriented philosophy or viewpoint and some field of current interest."

THISTLEDOWN PRESS, 668 E. Place, Saskatoon, Saskatchewan S7J 2Z5 Canada. (306)477-0556. Editor-in-Chief: Paddy O' Rourke. Publishes hardcover and trade paperback originals by resident Canadian authors *only*. Averages 8 titles/year; receives 150 submissions annually. 50% of books from first-time authors; 100% of books from unagented writers. Average print order for a writer's first (poetry) book is 750 or (fiction) 1,000. Pays standard royalty on retail price. Publishes book an average of 18-24 months after acceptance. Computer printout submissions acceptable; no dot-matrix. Reports in 2 weeks on queries; 2 months on poetry mss; 3 months on fiction mss. Free book catalog; ms guidelines for SASE.
Fiction: Literary. Interested in fiction mss from resident Canadian authors only. Minimum of 30,000 words.
Recent Fiction Title: *The Need of Wanting Always*, by Gertrude Story (literary—short stories).
Poetry: "The author should make him/herself familiar with our publishing program before deciding whether or not her/his work is appropriate." No poetry by people *not* citizens and residents of Canada. Submit complete ms. Minimum of 60 pages. Prefers poetry mss that have had some previous exposure in literary magazines.
Recent Poetry Title: *Man at Stellaco River*, by Andrea Wreggott (contemporary Canadian).
Tips: "We prefer a book that has literary integrity and a distinct voice."

THOMAS PUBLICATIONS, Subsidiary of Thomas Graphics, Inc., Box 33244, Austin TX 78764. (512)832-0355. Contact: Ralph D. Thomas. Publishes trade paperback originals and trade paperback reprints. Averages 8-10 titles/year; receives 20-30 submissions annually. 90% of books from first-time authors; 90% of books from unagented writers. Pays 10-15% royalty on wholesale or retail price, or makes outright purchase of $500-

2,000. Publishes book an average of 1 year after acceptance. Simultaneous and photocopied submissions OK. Computer printout submissions acceptable; no dot-matrix. Reports in 2 weeks on queries; 1 month on mss. Book catalog $1.

Nonfiction: How-to, reference and textbook. Subjects include sociology and investigation and investigative techniques. "We are looking for hardcore investigative methods books, manuals on how to make more dollars in private investigation, private investigative marketing techniques, and specialties in the investigative professions." Query or submit outline/synopsis and sample chapters. Reviews artwork/photos as part of ms package.

Recent Nonfiction Title: *How to Find Anyone Anywhere*, by Ralph Thomas (investigation).

Tips: "Our audience includes private investigators, those wanting to break into investigation, related trades such as auto repossessors, private process servers, news reporters, and related security trades."

THORNDIKE PRESS, One Mile Rd., Box 159, Thorndike ME 04986. (207)948-2962. Senior Editor: Timothy A. Loeb. Publishes hardcover and paperback originals and reprints. Averages 136 titles/year; receives 500 submissions annually. 10% of books from first-time authors; 90% of books from unagented writers. Average print order for writer's first book is 2,000. Offers 6-10% of list; or makes outright purchase for $500-2,000. Offers average $1,000 advance. Publishes book an average of 18 months after acceptance. Electronic submissions OK on IBM PC compatible disks. Computer printout submissions acceptable; prefers letter-quality to dot-matrix. Unsolicited submissions not accompanied with SASE with proper postage will not be returned. Reports in 2 months. Book catalog for SAE and 54¢ postage.

Nonfiction: Biography, animals, outdoors how- and where-to, nature, and all subjects of New England regional interest. Especially needs "manuscripts relating to the wilderness and oudoor recreation (hunting, fishing, etc.) in the Northeast U.S." *No* poetry, young adult, adventure suspense, cookbooks, science fiction, erotica, history, romance, crafts, drama, computer, engineering, religion, Gothic, mass market titles or children's books. Submit outline/synopsis and 2-3 sample chapters. Reviews artwork/photos as part of ms package.

Recent Nonfiction Title: *Trout and Salmon Fishing in Northern New England*, by Al Raychard.

Fiction: Humor (New England), and serious regional fiction (Maine and New England). "We will always consider exceptional manuscripts in our areas of interest, but 90% of the submissions we receive are not appropriate to our line. We prefer short works." No young adult or children's books; no poetry. Submit outline/synopsis and 2-3 sample chapters.

Recent Fiction Title: *Beer and Skittles*, by B.J. Morison (mystery).

Tips: "I wish authors who have been turned down repeatedly would not send such oft-rejected material here in hope that 'well, maybe . . .' As a small publisher, we are probably *more* selective, not less, than the big houses, simply because we have fewer slots per year to fill. What we *are* looking for, and seek queries on, is New England nature and outdoors guidebooks that take a how-to and/or where-to-go approach to a specific activity, as well as New England regional biography, humor, and serious (or 'literary') general fiction."

THORSONS PUBLISHERS, LTD, Denington Estate, Wellingborough, Northamptonshire NN8 2RQ England. Editor-in-Chief: J.R. Hardaker. Publishes hardcover and paperback originals and reprints. Pays 7½-10% royalty. Publishes book an average of 9 months after acceptance. Photocopied submissions OK. Computer printout submissions acceptable; prefers letter-quality to dot-matrix. SAE with IRCs. Reports in 1 month. Free book catalog.

Nonfiction: Natural health and healing, natural food and vegetarian cookery, alternative medicine, hypnotism and hypnotherapy, practical psychology, inspiration, mind training, personal improvement, self-help themes, books for women, special diets, animal rights, public speaking topics, and yoga and related disciplines. Submit outline/synopsis and 3 sample chapters. Reviews artwork/photos as part of ms package.

Tips: Queries/mss may be routed to other editors in the publishing group.

THREE CONTINENTS PRESS, 1336 Connecticut Ave. NW, Washington DC 20009. Publisher/Editor-in-Chief: Donald E. Herdeck. General Editor: Norman Ware. Publishes hardcover and paperback originals and reprints. Receives 200 submissions annually. 15% of books from first-time authors; 100% of books from unagented writers. Average print order for a writer's first book is 1,000. Pays 10% royalty; advance "only on delivery of complete manuscript which is found acceptable; usually $300." Photocopied (preferred) and simultaneous submissions OK. State availability of photos/illustrations. Computer printout submissions acceptable; prefers letter-quality to dot-matrix. Reports in 6 months. Free book catalog.

Nonfiction and Fiction: Specializes in African, Caribbean and Middle Eastern (Arabic and Persian) literature and criticism and translation, Third World literature and history. Scholarly, well-prepared mss; creative writing. Fiction, poetry, criticism, history and translations of creative writing. "We search for books which will make clear the complexity and value of African literature and culture, including bilingual texts (African language/English translations) of previously unpublished authors from less well-known areas of Africa. We are always interested in genuine contributions to understanding African and Caribbean culture." Length: 50,000-125,000 words. Query. "Please do not submit manuscript unless we ask for it." Reviews artwork/photos as part of ms package.

Recent Nonfiction Title: *So Spoke the Uncle,* by Jean Price-Mars.
Recent Fiction Title: *Tales from the Cameroon,* René Philombe, Trans. by Richard Bjornson.
Tips:"We need a *polished* translation, or original prose or poetry by non-Western authors *only.*"

THRESHOLD BOOKS, R.D. 3, Box 1350, Putney VT 05346. (802)387-4586/254-8300. Director: Edmund Helminski. Publishes hardcover and trade paperback originals. Averages 2-3 titles/year; receives 600 submissions annually. 20% of books from first-time authors; 75% of books from unagented writers. Pays 7-15% royalty on wholesale price. Publishes book an average of 10 months after acceptance. Simultaneous and photocopied submissions OK. Computer printout submissions acceptable. Reports in 3 weeks on queries; 2 months on mss. Free book catalog.
Nonfiction: Biography, literary and philosophical. Subjects include philosophy, spirituality, psychology, religion, and literary translation. Needs philosophy, history of religion, the arts, Sufism, and mysticism. Query.
Recent Nonfiction Title: *Steps to Freedom.*
Fiction: Philosophical/international, Third World. Query.
Poetry: "We will consider translations of the great poets, of any culture or era." Submit complete ms.
Recent Poetry Title: *Open Secret Versions of Rumi,* by Barks and Moyne (13th century Persian).
Tips: "Books with spiritual significance and quality writing have the best chance of selling to our firm."

THUNDER'S MOUTH PRESS, Box 780, New York NY 10025. (212)595-2025. Publisher: Neil Ortenberg. Publishes hardcover and trade paperback originals and reprints. Averages 6 titles/year; receives 1,000 submissions annually. 75% of books from unagented writers. Average print order for a writer's first book is 2,000. Pays 5-10% royalty on retail price; offers average $200 advance. Publishes book an average of 8 months after acceptance. Reports in 3 weeks on queries; 2 months on mss. Book catalog for SAE and 22¢ postage.
Nonfiction: Biography, cookbook, how-to and self-help. Subjects include cooking and foods, history, philosophy, politics and sociology. Publishes for "college students, academics, politically left of center, ethnic, social activists, women, etc. We basically do poetry and fiction now, but intend to start doing nonfiction over the next few years. How-to books, or biographies, history books, cookbooks would be fine." No cat books. Query or submit outline/synopsis and sample chapters.
Fiction: Erotica, ethnic, experimental, historical, humor, science fiction and political. "We are interested in doing anywhere from 3-5 novels per year, particularly highly literary or socially relevant novels." No romance. Query or submit outline/synopsis and sample chapters.
Recent Fiction Title: *The Red Menace,* by Michael Anania.
Poetry: "We intend to publish 3-5 books of poetry per year." No elitist, rhymes or religious poetry." Submit complete ms.
Recent Poetry Title: *Echoes Inside the Labyrinth,* by Tom McGrath.

TIMBER PRESS, 9999 S.W. Wilshire, Portland OR 97225. (503)292-0745. Editor: Richard Abel. Publishes hardcover and paperback originals. Publishes 20 titles/year; receives 300-400 submissions annually. 90% of books from first-time authors; 100% of books from unagented writers. Pays 10-20% royalty; sometimes offers advance to cover costs of artwork and final ms completion. Publishes book an average of 9 months after acceptance. Electronic submissions OK on most micros and word processors using disks, but requires hard copy also. Computer printout submissions acceptable; prefers letter-quality to dot-matrix. Reports in 2 months. Free book catalog; ms guidelines for SASE.
Nonfiction: Arts and crafts, natural history, Northwest regional material, forestry and horticulture. Accepts nonfiction translations from German. Query or submit outline/synopsis and 3-4 sample chapters. Reviews artwork/photos as part of ms package.
Recent Nonfiction Title: *Complete Book of Roses,* by Krussmann (horticulture).
Tips: "The writer has the best chance of selling our firm good books on botany, horticulture, forestry, agriculture and serious music."

TIME-LIFE BOOKS INC., 777 Duke St., Alexandria VA 22314. (703)838-7000. Editor: George Constable. Publishes hardcover originals. Averages 40 titles/year. "We have no minimum or maximum fee because our needs vary tremendously. An advance, as such, is not offered. Author is paid as he completes part of contracted work." Books are almost entirely staff-generated and staff-produced, and distribution is primarily through mail order sale. Query to the Director of Corporate Development.
Nonfiction: "General interest books. Most books tend to be heavily illustrated (by staff), with text written by assigned authors. We very rarely accept mss or book ideas submitted from outside our staff." Length: open.
Recent Nonfiction Title: *Time Frame.*

TIMES BOOKS, Division of Random House, Inc., 201 East 50 St., New York NY 10022. (212)872-8110. Editorial Director: Jonathan B. Segal. Senior Editors: Kathleen Moloney, Elisabeth Scharlatt and Hugh O'Neill. Publishes hardcover and paperback originals and reprints. Publishes 45 titles/year. Pays royalty; average advance. Publishes book an average of 1 year after acceptance. Computer printout submissions acceptable.

Nonfiction: Business/economics, science and medicine, history, biography, women's issues, the family, cookbooks, current affairs, cooking, self-help and sports. Accepts only solicited manuscripts. Reviews artwork/photos as part of ms package.
Recent Nonfiction Title: *Final Harvest*, by Andrew H. Malcolm.

*TOMPSON & RUTTER INC., Box 297, Grantham NH 03753. (603)863-4392. President: Frances T. Rutter. Publishes trade paperback originals. Averages 3 titles/year; receives 35-40 submissions annually. 20% of books from first-time authors; 100% of books from unagented writers. Average print order for a writer's first book is 1,000-1,500. Subsidy publishes 5% of books. Pays average 10% royalty on wholesale price. No advance. Publishes book an average of 1 year after acceptance. Simultaneous submissions OK. Computer printout submissions acceptable; no dot-matrix. Reports in 1 month. Included in Shoe String Press catalog.
Nonfiction: Local history and New England folklore. Query with 1-page sample of published writing. Reviews artwork/photos as part of ms package.
Recent Nonfiction Title: *New Hampshire, Crosscurrents in Its Development*, by Nancy C. Heffernan and Ann Page Stecker.

TOR BOOKS, 9th Floor, 49 W. 24th St., New York NY 10010. (212)564-0150. Editor-in-Chief: Beth Meacham. Publishes mass market hardcover and trade paperback originals and reprints. Averages 72 books/year. Pays 6-8% royalty; offers negotiable advance.
Fiction: Horror, science fiction, occult, chillers, suspense, espionage, historical, and fantasy. Prefers agented mss or proposals.
Recent Fiction Title: *Santiago*, by Mike Resnik.
Tips: "We're pretty broad in the occult, horror and fantasy but more straightforward in science fiction and thrillers, tending to stay with certain authors and certain types of work."

TRANS-CANADA PRESS, Division of the Cardamon Corp., 161 Davenport Rd., Toronto, Ontario M5R 1J1 Canada. (416)968-2714. General Manager: Liz Scott. Publishes hardcover and trade paperback originals. Averages 5 titles/year. Publishes book an average of 3 months after acceptance. Simultaneous submissions OK. Electronic submissions OK via Xerox 820, 860, but requires hard copy also. Computer printout submissions acceptable; prefers letter-quality to dot-matrix. Reports in 1 month.
Nonfiction: Biography. Subjects include business management, economics, and biographical information (who's who). Needs mss on food business/management only. Query.
Recent Nonfiction Title: *Who's Who in Canadian Business*.

‡TRANSNATIONAL PUBLISHERS, INC., Box 7282, Ardsley-on-Hudson NY 10503. (914)693-0089. Publisher: Ms. Heike Fenton. Publishes hardcover originals. Averages 10-15 titles/year; receives 50 submissions annually. 10% of books from first-time authors; 100% of books from unagented writers. Pays 5-10% royalty. Publishes book an average of 6 months after acceptance. Simultaneous and photocopied submissions OK. Computer printout submissios acceptable. Reports in 2 weeks on queries; 1 month on mss. Book and ms guidelines free on request.
Nonfiction: Reference, textbook and books for professionals. Subjects include politics, international law, criminal law, human rights, women's studies and political theory. Needs scholarly works in the area of International law and politics. No submissions on topics other than those listed above. Submit outline/synopsis and sample chapters.
Recent Nonfiction Title: *Apathy in America*, by Stephen E. Bennett (political science).
Tips: "The audience for our books includes law libraries, public libraries, universities, government personnel, military personnel, college students and women's rights groups."

‡TRAVEL KEYS, Box 160691, Sacramento CA 95816. (916)452-5200. Publisher: Peter B. Manston. Publishes hardcover and trade paperback originals. Averages 3 titles/year; receives 8 submissions annually. 50% of books from first-time authors; 75% of books from unagented writers. Pays 6-15% royalty ("rarely, we mostly use work for hire"); or makes outright purchase for $500 minimum. Offers minimum $500 advance. Publishes book an average of 1 year after acceptance. Simultaneous and photocopied submissions OK. Electronic submissions OK via ASCII, but requires hard copy also. Reports in 1 month. Book catalog for #10 SAE with 1 first class stamp.
Nonfiction: How-to on travel. "We need carefully researched, practical travel manuscripts. No science or technical submissions." Submit outline/synopsis and sample chapters. Reviews artwork/photos as part of ms package.
Recent Nonfiction Titles: *Manston's Travel Key Europe*, by Manston.
Tips: "Most of our titles, so far, are staff written. Our audience is travelers looking for easily accessible, down-to-earth, practical information. If I were a writer trying to market a book today, I would research well, double-check facts and (if possible) find a good agent."

TROUBADOR PRESS, A division of Price/Stern/Sloan, Publishers, Inc., Suite 205, 1 Sutter St., San Francisco CA 94104. (415)397-3716. Editorial Director: Malcolm K. Whyte. Publishes paperback originals. Averages 4 titles/year; receives 300 submissions annually. 90% of books from unagented writers. Average print order for a writer's first book is 10,000. Pays royalty. Offers average $500 advance. Publishes book an average of 6 months after acceptance. Computer printout submissions acceptable; prefers letter-quality to dot-matrix. Reports in 1 month. Book catalog and ms guidelines for SASE.
Nonfiction: "Troubador Press publishes mainly, but is not limited to, children's activity books: coloring, cutout, mazes, games, paper dolls, etc. All titles feature original art and exceptional graphics. Interested in expanding on themes of 80 current titles. We like books which have the potential to develop into series." Query or submit outline/synopsis and 2-3 sample chapters with conciseness and clarity of a good idea. Reviews artwork as part of ms package.
Recent Nonfiction Title: *Dinosaur Action Set*, by M.K. Whyte, illustrated by Don Smith.
Tips: "We continue to publish new authors along with established writers/artists and licensed properties. We feel the mix is good and healthy." Queries/mss may be routed to other editors in the publishing group.

*CHARLES E. TUTTLE CO., INC., Publishers & Booksellers, Suido 1-chome, 2-6, Bunkyo-ku, Tokyo, Japan 112. Publishes originals and reprints. "Handles all matters of editing, production and administration including royalties, rights and permissions." Averages 30 titles/year. Subsidy publishes 30% of books. Pays $500 against 10% royalty on retail price; advance varies. Send complete mss or queries accompanied by outlines or sample chapters and biographical data to Tokyo. U.S. and Canada distributors: Publishers and Booksellers, Drawer F, 26-30 Main St., Rutland VT 05701. Publishes book an average of 2 years after acceptance. Computer printout submissions acceptable; no dot-matrix. Reports in 6 weeks. Book catalog $1.
Nonfiction: Specializes in publishing books about Oriental art, culture, language and sociology as well as history, literature, cookery, sport, martial arts, and children's books which relate to Asia, the Hawaiian Islands, Australia and the Pacific areas. Also interested in Americana, especially antique collecting, architecture, genealogy and Canadiana. No poetry and fiction except that of Oriental themes. Accepts translations. Normal book length only. Looks for "subject matter related to Asia, particularly Japan; authority of the author; balance and logical order in the structure of the manuscript; presentation—minimum of spelling/grammatical errors, double-spaced typing." Reviews artwork/photos as part of ms package.
Recent Nonfiction Title: *The Japanese Art of Stone Appreciation: Suseki and Its Use with Bonsai*, by V.T. Covello and Y. Yoshimura.

TWAYNE PUBLISHERS, A division of G.K. Hall & Co., 70 Lincoln St., Boston MA 02111. (617)423-3990. Publishes hardcover and paperback originals. Publishes 120 titles/year; receives 1,000 submissions annually. 5% of books from first-time authors; 10% of books from unagented writers. Average print order for a writer's first book is 1,000. Pays royalty. Query only with SASE, outline and 2 sample chapters. Reports in 5 weeks. No unsolicited mss—query first.
Nonfiction: Publishes scholarly books and volumes in and out of series for the general reader. Literary criticism, biography, history; women's studies, art history, current affairs and science.
Recent Nonfiction Title: *Mothers and Sons*, by Carole Klein.
Tips: Queries may be routed to other editors in the publishing group. Unsolicited mss will not be read.

TWENTY-THIRD PUBLICATIONS, INC., 185 Willow St., Box 180, Mystic CT 06355. (203)536-2611. Acquisitions: Patricia Kluepfel. Publishes trade paperback originals. Averages 30 titles/year; receives 250 submissions annually. 25% of books from first-time authors; 90% of books from unagented writers. Average print order for a writer's first book is 5,000. Pays average 10% royalty on net receipts. Publishes book an average of 15 months after acceptance. Reports in 3 weeks. Book catalog for 9x12 SAE and 2 first class stamps.
Nonfiction: Religious education and adult education (Roman Catholic). "Our audience is teachers, mainstream and educators." Query.
Recent Nonfiction Title: *Morality of Capital Punishment*, by R. Endres.

*TYNDALE HOUSE PUBLISHERS, INC., 336 Gundersen Dr., Wheaton IL 60187. (312)668-8300. Editor-in-Chief/Acquisitions: Wendell Hawley. Publishes hardcover and trade paperback originals and hardcover and mass paperback reprints. Averages 100 titles/year; receives 3,000 submissions annually. 15% of books from first-time authors; 99% of books from unagented writers. Average print order for a writer's first book is 7,000-10,000. Subsidy publishes 2% of books. Pays 10% royalty; offers negotiable advance. Publishes book an average of 18 months after acceptance. Computer printout submissions acceptable; no dot-matrix. Reports in 6 weeks. Free book catalog; ms guidelines for SASE.
Nonfiction: Religious books only: personal experience, family living, marriage, Bible reference works and commentaries, Christian living, devotional, inspirational, church and social issues, Bible prophecy, theology and doctrine, counseling and Christian psychology, Christian apologetics and church history. Submit table of contents, chapter summary, preface, first 2 chapters and 1 later chapter.
Fiction: Biblical novels. Submit outline/synopsis and sample chapters.

ULTRALIGHT PUBLICATIONS, INC., Box 234, Hammelstown PA 17036. (717)566-0468. Editor: Michael A. Markowski. Imprints includes Aviation Publishers and Medical Information Systems. Publishes hardcover and trade paperback originals. Averages 8 titles/year; receives 30 submissions annually. 50% of books from first-time authors; 100% of books from unagented writers. Average print order for a writer's first book is 5,000. Pays 10-15% royalty on wholesale price; buys some mss outright. Offers average $1,000 advance. Publishes book an average of 6 months after accetpance. Simultaneous and photocopied submissions OK. Computer printout submissions acceptable; no dot-matrix. Reports in 3 weeks on queries; 2 months on mss. Book catalog and ms guidelines for SASE.
Nonfiction: How-to, technical on hobbies (model airplanes) and aviation. Publishes for "aviation buffs, dreamers and enthusiasts. We are looking for titles in the homebuilt, ultralight, sport and general aviation fields. We are interested in how-to, technical and reference books of short to medium length that will serve recognized and emerging aviation needs." Also interested in automotive historical, reference and how-to; popular health, medical, and fitness for the general public. Self-help, motivation and success are also areas of interest. Query or submit outline/synopsis and 3 sample chapters. Reviews artwork/photos as part of ms package.
Recent Nonfiction Title: *Composite Construction*, by Lambie (how-to).

UMI RESEARCH PRESS, University Microfilms, Inc., Bell & Howell, 300 N. Zeeb Road, Ann Arbor MI 48106. Contact: Acquisitions Editor. Publishes hardcover originals and revised dissertations. Averages 85 titles/year; receives 200 submissions annually. 80% of books from first-time authors. Average print order for a writer's first book is 500. Pays 5% royalty on net sales. Offers average $100 advance. Publishes book an average of 9 months after acceptance. Photocopied submissions OK. Electronic submissions OK on most systems, but requires hard copy also. Computer printout submissions acceptable "if good quality." Ms guidelines available.
Nonfiction: Scholarly and professional research and critical studies. Subjects include architecture; cinema (theory and aesthetics); art; theatre (history and theory); business and economics; musicology; computer science; photography (theory); material culture; cultural anthropology; psychology (clinical); religion; urban planning and history; and literary criticism. Especially looking for "scholarly works, original conclusions resulting from careful academic research. Primarily aimed at graduate, post-graduate and professional level. Academics, research librarians, art and music communities, business and computer science professionals are our audience." No mass market books. Query.
Recent Nonfiction Title: *The Museum World of Henry James*, by Adeline Tintner.
Tips: "Send letters of inquiry to appropriate publishers *before* devoting hours to a manuscript. Get feedback at the outline/prospectus stage."

UNIVELT, INC., Box 28130, San Diego CA 92128. (619)746-4005. Editorial Director: H. Jacobs. Publishes hardcover originals. Averages 8 titles/year; receives 20 submissions annually. 5% of books from first-time authors; 5% of books from unagented writers. Average print order for a writer's first book is 1,000-2,000. Pays 10% royalty on actual sales; no advance. Publishes book an average of 4 months after acceptance. Computer printout submissions acceptable; prefers letter-quality to dot-matrix. Reports in 1 month. Book catalog and ms guidelines for SASE.
Nonfiction: Publishes in the field of aerospace, especially astronautics and technical communications, but including application of aerospace technology to Earth's problems. Submit outline/synopsis and 1-2 sample chapters. Reviews artwork/photos as part of ms package.
Recent Nonfiction Title: *Handbook of Soviet Manned Space Flight.*
Tips: "Writers have the best chance of selling manuscripts on the history of astronautics (we have a history series) and astronautcis/space/light subjects. We publish for the American Astronautical Society." Queries/mss may be routed to other editors in the publishing group.

*UNIVERSE BOOKS, 381 Park Ave. S, New York NY 10016. (212)685-7400. Editorial Director: Louis Barron: Publishes hardcover and paperback originals and reprints. Averages 45 titles/year; receives 1,000 submissions annually. 15% of books from first-time authors; 75% of books from unagented writers. Average print order for a writer's first book is 3,000-4,000. Offers 10-15% royalty on retail price (hardbound books). "On a few extra-illustrated art books and on special studies with a limited market we may pay a smaller royalty." Offers $1,000-4,000 advance . "If a book makes a genuine contribution to knowledge but is a commercial risk, we might perhaps accept a subsidy from a foundation or other organization, but not directly from the author." Publishes book an average of 9 months after acceptance. Simultaneous and photocopied submissions OK. Computer printout submissions acceptable; no dot-matrix. "Will not return material without postage-paid SAE." Reports in 2 weeks. Book catalog for 4 first-class stamps (no SASE).
Nonfiction: Animals, art, economics, history, linguistics, nature, performing arts, politics, reference and science. Universe also pays secondary attention to biography, health and how-to. Also uses "monographs on specific animal, bird or plant species; social histories of specific types of artifacts or social institutions; art histories of specific types of artifacts or symbols. We publish books in the following categories: antiques, crafts and collectibles, art, architecture and design, history, life, physical and agricultural sciences, ballet, music,

contemporary problems, and social sciences (especially books on survival, appropriate technology, and the limits to growth). We do not publish fiction, poetry, cookbooks, criticism or belles lettres." Accepts nonfiction French and German translations. Submit outline/synopsis and 2-3 sample chapters. Reviews artwork/photos as part of ms package.
Recent Nonfiction Title: *A Century of Modern Painting.*

UNIVERSITY OF ALABAMA PRESS, Box 2877, University AL 35486. Director: Malcolm MacDonald. Publishes hardcover originals. Averages 40 titles/year; receives 200 submissions annually. 80% of books from first-time authors; 100% of books from unagented writers. "Pays maximum 10% royalty on wholesale price; no advance." Publishes book an average of 16 months after acceptance. Computer printout submissions acceptable. Free book catalog; ms guidelines for SASE.
Nonfiction: Biography, history, music, philosophy, politics, religion and sociology. Considers upon merit almost any subject of scholarly interest, but specializes in linguistics and philology, political science and public administration, literary criticism and biography, philosophy and history. Accepts nonfiction translations. Reviews artwork/photos as part of ms package.
Recent Nonfiction Title: *Black Eagle: General Daniel "Chappie", James, Jr.* (biography).

THE UNIVERSITY OF ALBERTA PRESS, 141 Athabasca Hall, Edmonton, Alberta T6G 2E8 Canada. (403)432-3662. Director: Norma Gutteridge. Publishes hardcover and trade paperback originals, and trade paperback reprints. Averages 10 titles/year; receives 200-300 submissions annually. 60% of books from first-time authors; 100% of books from unagented writers. Average print order for a writer's first book is 1,500. Pays 10% royalty on retail price. Publishes book an average of 1 year after acceptance. Electronic submissions OK on IBM Compatible, but requires hard copy also. Computer printout submissions acceptable; no dot-matrix. Reports in 1 week on queries; 3 months on mss. Free book catalog and ms guidelines.
Imprint: Pica Pica Press.
Nonfiction: Biography, how-to, reference, technical textbook, and scholarly. Subjects include art, history, nature, philosophy, politics, and sociology. Especially looking for "biographies of Canadians in public life, and works analyzing Canada's political history and public policy, particularly in international affairs. No pioneer reminiscences, literary criticism (unless in Canadian literature), reports of narrowly focused studies, unrevised theses." Submit complete ms. Reviews artwork/photos as part of ms package.
Recent Nonfiction Title: *Canada and the Arab World*, by Tarig Ismael (Canadian international affairs).
Tips: "We are interested in original research making a significant contribution to knowledge in the subject."

UNIVERSITY OF ARIZONA PRESS, 1615 E. Speedway, Tucson AZ 85719. (602)621-1441. Director: Stephen Cox. Publishes hardcover and paperback originals and reprints. Averages 40 titles/year; receives 300-400 submissions annually. 40% of books from first-time authors; 90% of books from unagented writers. Average print order for a writer's first book is 1,500. Royalty terms vary; usual starting point is after sale of first 1,000 copies. Publishes book an average of 1 year after acceptance. Photocopied submissions OK. Electronic submissions OK on IBM PC with WordStar, but requires hard copy also. Computer printout submissions acceptable; no dot-matrix. Reports in three months. Free catalog; ms guidelines for SASE.
Nonfiction: Serious books about the American West, Mexico and natural history, and about subjects strongly identified with the universities in Arizona—anthropology, philosophy, arid lands studies, space sciences, Asian studies, Southwest Indians, Mexico and creative nonfiction. Query and submit outline and sample chapters. Reviews artwork/photos as part of ms package.
Recent Nonfiction Title: *Gathering the Desert*, by Gary Paul Nabhan.
Tips: "Study our list, and compare the project being queried with past publications. Call to find out if submission is worthwhile. A book targeted to our list and that anticipates, in some way, the future shape of that list and ventures into new territory has the best chance of selling to our firm."

‡THE UNIVERSITY OF ARKANSAS PRESS, University of Arkansas, McIlroy House, Fayetteville AR 72701. (501)575-3246. Director: Miller Williams. Publishes hardcover and trade paperback originals and reprints. Averages 12 titles/year; receives 4,000 submissions annually. 30% of books from first-time authors; 99% of books from unagented writers. Pays 10% royalty on wholesale price. Publishes book an average of 18-24 months after acceptance. Simultaneous and photocopied submissions OK. Electronic submissions OK on CPT disk *only*; requires hard copy also. Computer printout submissions acceptable; no dot-matrix. Responds in 2 weeks on queries; 1 month on mss. Free book catalog; ms guidelines for SASE.
Nonfiction: Biography, illustrated book. Subjects include Americana, art, history, music, and sociology. Specifically needs biographies of regional and historical subjects. Submit outline/synopsis and sample chapters.
Recent Nonfiction Title: *Myth, Media and the Southern Mind*, by Stephen Smith (sociology).
Fiction: Mainstream. Will publish one or two collections of short stories in the next year or two. No erotica, juvenile, confession, horror, romance, western or other novels or full-length fiction. Submit outline/synopsis and sample chapters.

Recent Fiction Title: *Oxbridge Blues*, by Frederic Raphail (short fiction).
Tips: "We expect to see more and more utilization of university presses for first works of new writers, and collections of out-of-print works of literary value. We try to reach a wide segment of academia, as well as the general reading public."

‡UNIVERSITY OF CALIFORNIA PRESS, 2120 Berkeley Way, Berkeley CA 94720. Director: James H. Clark. Assistant Director: Lynne E. Withey. Los Angeles office: Suite 613, 10995 Le Conte Ave., UCLA, Los Angeles CA 94995. New York office: Room 513, 50 E. 42 St., New York NY 10017. London office: University Presses of California, Chicago, Harvard and MIT, 126 Buckingham Palace Rd., London SW1W 9SD England. Publishes hardcover and paperback originals and reprints. "On books likely to do more than return their costs, a standard royalty contract beginning at 10% is paid; on paperbacks it is less." Published 200 titles last year. Queries are always advisable, accompanied by outlines or sample material. Accepts nonfiction translations. Send to Berkeley address. Reports vary, depending on the subject. Enclose return postage.
Nonfiction: "Most of our publications are hardcover nonfiction written by scholars." Publishes scholarly books including art, literary studies, social sciences, natural sciences and some high-level popularizations. No length preferences.
Fiction and Poetry: Publishes fiction and poetry only in translation, usually in bilingual editions.

UNIVERSITY OF ILLINOIS PRESS, 54 E. Gregory, Champaign IL 61820. (217)333-0950. Director/Editor: Richard L. Wentworth. Publishes hardcover and trade paperback originals, and hardcover and trade paperback reprints. Averages 70-80 titles/year. 50% of books from first-time authors; 95% of books from unagented writers. Pays 0-15% royalty on net sales; offers average $1,000-1,500 advance (rarely). Publishes book an average of 1 year after acceptance. Simultaneous and photocopied submissions OK. Electronic submissions OK via IBM-PC, but requires hard copy also. Computer printout submissions acceptable; no dot-matrix. Reports in 1 week on queries; 4 months on mss. Free book catalog; ms guidelines for SASE.
Nonfiction: Biography, reference and scholarly books. Subjects include Americana, business and economics, history (especially American history), music (especially American music), politics, sociology, sports and literature. Always looking for "solid scholarly books in American history, especially social history; books on American popular music, and books in the broad area of American studies." Query with outline/synopsis.
Recent Nonfiction Title: *Bluegrass: A History*, by Neil V. Rosenberg (Music in American Life Series).
Fiction: Ethnic, experimental and mainstream. "We publish four collections of stories by individual writers each year. We do not publish novels." Query.
Recent Fiction Title: *Getting to Know the Weather*, by Pamela Painter (short stories).
Tips: "Serious scholarly books that are broad enough and well-written enough to appeal to non-specialists are doing well for us in today's market. Writers of nonfiction whose primary goal is to earn money (rather than get promoted in an academic positon) are advised to try at least a dozen commercial publishers before thinking about offering the work to a university press."

UNIVERSITY OF IOWA PRESS, Westlawn, Iowa City IA 52242. (319)353-3181. Director: Paul Zimmer. Publishes hardcover and paperback originals. Averages 20-25 titles/year; receives 300-400 submissions annually. 30% of books from first-time authors; 95% of books from unagented writers. Average print order for a writer's first book is 1,200-1,500. Pays 7-10% royalty on retail price. "We market mostly by direct mailing of fliers to groups with special interests in our titles and by advertising in trade and scholarly publications." Publishes book an average of 1 year after acceptance. Electronic submissions OK for tape, but requires hard copy also. Readable computer printout submissions acceptable. Reports in 4 months. Free book catalog and ms guidelines.
Nonfiction: Publishes anthropology, archaeology, British and American literary studies, history (Victorian, U.S., German, medieval, Latin American), natural history and scientific books. Currently Publishes the Iowa School of Letters Award for Short Fiction. Looks for "evidence of original research; reliable sources; clarity of organization, complete development of theme with documentation and supportive footnotes and/or bibliography; and a substantive contribution to knowledge in the field treated." Query or submit outline/synopsis. Use Chicago *Manual of Style*. Reviews artwork/photos as part of ms package.
Recent Nonfiction Title: *The Politics of Language: Liberalism as Word and Symbol*, by Ronald Rotunda.

UNIVERSITY OF MASSACHUSETTS PRESS, Box 429, Amherst MA 01004. (413)545-2217. Director: Bruce Wilcox. Acquisitions Editor: Richard Martin. Publishes hardcover and paperback originals, reprints and imports. Averages 25-30 titles/year; receives 600 submissions annually; 20% of books from first-time authors; 90% of books from unagented writers. Average print order for a writer's first book is 1,500. Royalties depend on character of book; if offered, generally at 10% of net income. Advance rarely offered. No author subsidies accepted. Publishes book an average of 11 months after acceptance. Electronic submissions OK, but requires hard copy also. Computer printout submissions acceptable; prefers letter-quality to dot-matrix. Preliminary report in 1 month. Free book catalog.
Nonfiction: Publishes Afro-American studies, art and architecture, biography, criticism, history, natural his-

tory, philosophy, poetry, psychology, public policy, sociology and women's studies in original and reprint editions. Accepts nonfiction translations. Submit outline/synopsis and 1-2 sample chapters. Reviews artwork/photos as part of ms package.

Recent Nonfiction Title: *Wood, Brick, and Stone: The North American Settlement Landscape*, by Allen G. Noble (architectural history).

Tips: "As members of AAUP, we sometimes route (queries/mss) to other university presses."

UNIVERSITY OF MISSOURI PRESS, 200 Lewis Hall, Columbia MO 65211. (314)882-7641. Director: Edward D. King. Associate Director: Susan McGregor Denny. Publishes hardcover and paperback originals and paperback reprints. Averages 30 titles/year; receives 300 submissions annually. 40% of books from first-time authors; 100% of books from unagented writers. Average print order for a writer's first book is 1,000. Pays up to 10% royalty on net receipts; no advance. Publishes book an average of 1 year after acceptance. Photocopied submissions OK. Electronic submissions OK on IBM PCxt, but requires hard copy also. Computer printout submissions acceptable; prefers letter-quality to dot-matrix. Reports in 6 months. Free book catalog; ms guidelines for SASE.

Nonfiction: Scholarly publisher interested in history, literary criticism, political science, social science, music, art, art history, and original poetry. Also regional books about Missouri and the Midwest. No mathematics or hard sciences. Query or submit outline/synopsis and sample chapters. Consult *Chicago Manual of Style*.

Fiction: "Fiction, poetry and drama manuscripts are taken into submission only in February and March of odd-numbered years. We publish original short fiction in the Breakthrough Series, not to exceed 35,000 words. May be short story collection or novella. We also publish poetry and drama in the same series. No limitations on subject matter." Query.

Recent Fiction Title: *Off in Zimbabwe*, by Rod Kessler (stories).

UNIVERSITY OF NEVADA PRESS, Reno NV 89557. (702)784-6573. Director: John F. Stetter. Editor: Nicholas M. Cady. Publishes hardcover and paperback originals and reprints. Averages 12 titles/year; receives 200 submissions annually. 20% of books from first-time authors; 100% of books from unagented writers. Average print order for a writer's first book is 3,000. Pays 10% royalty on retail price. Publishes book an average of 2 years after acceptance. Computer printout submissions acceptable; no dot-matrix. Preliminary reports in 2 months. Free book catalog and ms guidelines.

Nonfiction: Specifically needs regional history and natural history, anthropology, biographies and Basque studies. "We are the first university press to sustain a sound series on Basque studies—New World and Old World." No juvenile books. Submit complete ms. Reviews artwork/photos as part of ms package.

Recent Nonfiction Title: *Birds of the Great Basin: A Natural History*, by Fred A. Ryser, Jr.

*UNIVERSITY OF NEW MEXICO PRESS, Journalism 220, Albuquerque NM 87131. (505)277-2346. Director: Elizabeth C. Hadas. Publishes hardcover and trade paperback originals and reprints. Averages 50 titles/year. 40% of books from first-time authors; 90% of books from unagented writers. Average print order for writer's first books is 1,500. Subsidy publishes 1% of books "depending upon nature of manuscript." Pays maximum 10% royalty on wholesale price. Publishes book an average of 18 months after acceptance. Electronic submissions OK, but requires hard copy also. Computer printout submissions acceptable; prefers letter-quality to dot-matrix. Reports in 2 weeks on queries; 6 months on mss. Free book catalog.

Nonfiction: Scholarly and regional books covering Americana, art, history, nature and photography. Query. Reviews artwork/photos as part of ms package.

Recent Nonfiction Title: *Bourbons and Brandy: Imperial Reform in Eighteenth-Century Arequipa*.

Fiction: "No original fiction. Any fiction manuscripts will be returned unread if accompanied by SASE. Otherwise, they will be discarded."

THE UNIVERSITY OF NORTH CAROLINA PRESS, Box 2288, Chapel Hill NC 27514. (919)966-3561. Editor-in-Chief: Iris Tillman Hill. Publishes hardcover and paperback originals. Specializes in scholarly books and regional trade books. Averages 50 titles/year. 70% of books from first-time scholarly authors; 90% of books from unagented writers. Royalty schedule "varies." Occasional advances. Send prints to illustrate ms "only if they are a major part of the book." Photocopied submissions OK. Electronic submissions OK, but requires hard copy also. Computer printout submissions acceptable; no dot-matrix. Publishes book an average of 1 year after acceptance. Reports in 5 months. Free book catalog; ms guidelines for SASE.

Nonfiction: "Our major fields are American history and Southern studies." Also, scholarly books in legal history, literary studies, classics, oral history, political science, urban studies, religious studies, historical sociology and Latin American studies. Special focus on general interest books on the lore, crafts, and natural history of the Soutwest. Submit outline/synopsis and sample chapters. Must follow *Chicago Manual of Style*. Looks for "intellectual excellence and clear writing. We do *not* publish poetry or original fiction." Reviews artwork/photos.

Recent Nonfiction Title: *Bill Neal's Southern Cooking*, by Bill Neal.

Tips: "We are primarily academic book publishers and we are looking for impressive original research and good writing."

UNIVERSITY OF OKLAHOMA PRESS, 1005 Asp Ave., Norman OK 73019. (405)325-5111. Editor-in-Chief: John Drayton. Publishes hardcover and paperback originals; and reprints. Averages 50 titles/year. Pays royalty comparable to those paid by other publishers for comparable books. Publishes book an average of 12-18 months after acceptance. Electronic submissions OK, but requires hard copy also. Computer printout submissions acceptable; prefers letter-quality to dot-matrix. Reports in 4 months. Book catalog $1.
Nonfiction: Publishes American Indian studies, Western U.S. history and classical studies. No poetry and fiction. Query, including outline, 1-2 sample chapters and author resume. Chicago *Manual of Style* for ms guidelines. Reviews artwork/photos as part of ms package.
Recent Nonfiction Title: *Thomas De Quincey: Bicentenary Studies*, edited by Robert Lance Synder.

*UNIVERSITY OF PENNSYLVANIA PRESS, Blockley Hall, 418 Service Dr., Philadelphia PA 19104. (215)898-6261. Director: Thomas M. Rotell. Publishes hardcover and paperback originals and reprints. Averages 50 titles/year; receives 600 submissions annually. 10-20% of books from first-time authors; 99% of books from unagented writers. Subsidy publishes (non-author) less than 1% of books. Subsidy publishing is determined by: evaluation obtained by the press from outside specialists; work approved by Faculty Editorial Committee; subsidy approved by funding organization. Royalty determined on book-by-book basis. Publishes book an average of 9 months after acceptance. State availability of photos and/or illustrations to accompany ms, with copies of illustrations. Photocopied submissions OK. Electronic submissions OK via IBM, Apple Macintosh, but requires hard copy also. Computer printout submissions acceptable; prefers letter-quality to dot-matrix. Reports in 3 months. Free book catalog; ms guidelines for SASE.
Nonfiction: Publishes Americana, biography, business, economics, history, medicine, biological sciences, computer science, physical sciences, law, anthropology, folklore and literary criticism. "Serious books that serve the scholar and the professional." Follow the Chicago *Manual of Style*. Query with outline and letter describing project.
Recent Nonfiction Title: *Passing the Time in Ballymenone*, by Henry Glassie.
Tips: Queries/mss may be routed to other editors in the publishing group.

THE UNIVERSITY OF TENNESSEE PRESS, 293 Communications Bldg., Knoxville TN 37996. Contact: Acquisitions Editor. Averages 30 titles/year; receives 750 submissions annually. 50% of books from first-time authors; 99% of books from unagented writers. Average print order for a writer's first book is 1,250. Pays negotiable royalty on retail price. Publishes book an average of 10 months after acceptance. Photocopied submissions OK. "We can only review hard copy." Computer printout submissions acceptable; no dot-matrix. Reports in 2 week on queries; "in 1 month on submissions we have encouraged." Book catalog 75¢; ms guidelines for SASE.
Nonfiction: American history, political science, religious studies, sports studies, literary criticism, Black studies, women's studies, Caribbean, anthropology, folklore and regional studies. Prefers "scholarly treatment and a readable style. Authors usually have Ph.D.s." Submit outline/synopsis, author vita, and 2 sample chapters. No fiction, poetry or plays. Reviews artwork/photos as part of ms package.
Recent Nonfiction Title: *Nightly Horrors: Crisis Coverage in Television Network News*, by Dan Nimmo and James E. Combs.
Tips: "Our market is in several groups: scholars; educated readers with special interests in given scholarly subjects; and the general educated public interested in Tennessee, Appalachia and the South. Not all our books appeal to all these groups, of course, but any given book must appeal to at least one of them."

UNIVERSITY OF TEXAS PRESS, Box 7819, Austin TX 78713. Managing Editor: Barbara Spielman. Averages 60 titles/year; receives 1,000 submissions annually. 50% of books from first-time authors; 99% of books from unagented writers. Average print order for a writer's first book is 1,000. Pays royalty usually based on net income; occasionally offers advance. Publishes book an average of 18 months after acceptance. Electronic submissions OK, but requires hard copy also. Computer printout submissions acceptable; no dot-matrix. Reports in 2 months. Free book catalog and writer's guidelines.
Nonfiction: General scholarly subjects: astronomy, natural history, economics, Latin American and Middle Eastern studies, native Americans, classics, films, medical, biology, contemporary architecture, archeology, Chicano studies, physics, health, sciences, international relations, linguistics, photography, twentieth-century and women's literature. Also uses specialty titles related to Texas and the Southwest, national trade titles, and regional trade titles. Accepts nonfiction and fiction translations (generally Latin American fiction). Query or submit outline/synopsis and 2 sample chapters. Reviews artwork/photos as part of ms package.
Recent Nonfiction Title: *Peppers: The Domesticated Capsicums*, by Jean Andrews.
Tips: "It's difficult to make a manuscript over 400 double-spaced pages into a feasible book. Authors should take special care to edit out extraneous material." Looks for sharply focused, in-depth treatments of important topics.

UNIVERSITY OF UTAH PRESS, University of Utah, 101 University Services Bldg., Salt Lake City UT 84112. (801)581-6771. Director: Stephen H. Hess. Publishes hardcover and paperback originals and reprints.

Averages 18 titles/year; receives 500 submissions annually. 30% of books from first-time authors. Average print order for writer's first book is 1,000. Pays 10% royalty on net sales on first 2,000 copies sold; 12% on 2,001 to 4,000 copies sold; 15% thereafter. Publishes book an average of 18 months after acceptance. Computer printout submissions acceptable; no dot-matrix. Reports in 10 weeks. Free book catalog; ms guidelines for SASE.

Nonfiction: Scholarly books on Western history, philosophy, anthropology, Mesoamerican studies, folklore, and Middle Eastern studies. Accepts nonfiction translations. Popular, well-written, carefully researched regional studies for Bonneville Books Series. Query with outline and 3 sample chapters. Author should specify page length in query. Reviews artwork/photos as part of ms package.

Recent Nonfiction Title: *Goodbye to Poplarhaven: Recollections of a Utah Boyhood*, by Edward A. Geary.

UNIVERSITY OF WISCONSIN PRESS, 114 N. Murray St., Madison WI 53715. (608)262-4928 (telex: 265452). Director: Allen N. Fitchen. Acquisitions Editors: Barbara J. Hanrahan and Gordon Lester-Massman. Publishes hardcover and paperback originals, reprints and translations. Averages 50 titles/year. Pays standard royalties on retail price. Reports in 3 months.

Nonfiction: Publishes general nonfiction based on scholarly research. Looks for "originality, significance, quality of the research represented, literary quality, and breadth of interest to the educated community at large." Accepts nonfiction translations. Follow Chicago *Manual of Style*. Send complete ms.

Recent Nonfiction Title: *The Rhetoric of Economics*, by Donald N. McCloskey.

UNIVERSITY PRESS OF AMERICA, 4720 Boston Way, Lanham MD 20706. (301)459-3366. Publisher: James E. Lyons. Publishes hardcover and paperback originals and reprints. Averages 450 titles/year. Pays 5-15% royalty on wholesale price; occasional advance. No computer printout submissions. Reports in 6 weeks. Free book catalog.

Nonfiction: Scholarly monographs, college, and graduate level textbooks in history, economics, business, psychology, political science, African studies, Black studies, philosophy, religion, sociology, music, art, literature, drama and education. No juvenile, elementary or high school material. Submit outline.

Recent Nonfiction Title: *Vietnam as History*, by Peter Braestrup.

UNIVERSITY PRESS OF KANSAS, 329 Carruth, Lawrence KS 66045. (913)864-4154. Editor: Fred Woodward. Hardcover and paperback originals. Averages 20 titles/year; receives 500-600 submissions annually. 25% of books from first-time authors; 95% of books from unagented writers. Royalties negotiable; no advance. Markets books by advertising and direct mail, chiefly to libraries and scholars. "State availability of illustrations if they add significantly to the manuscript." Publishes book an average of 10 months after acceptance. Computer printout submissions acceptable; no dot-matrix. Reports in 4 months. Free book catalog; ms guidelines for SASE.

Nonfiction: Publishes biography, history, sociology, philosophy, politics, regional subjects (Kansas, Great Plains, Midwest); and scholarly. Reviews artwork/photos as part of ms package. Query.

Recent Nonfiction Title: *Norus Ordo Seclorum: The Intellectual Origins of the Constitution*, (history).

‡UNIVERSITY PRESS OF KENTUCKY, 102 Lafferty Hall, Lexington KY 40506-0024. (606)257-2951. Associate Director: Jerome Crouch. Publishes hardcover originals and hardcover and trade paperback reprints. Averages 35 titles/year; receives 200 submissions annually. 25-50% of books from first-time authors; 98% of books from unagented writers. Pays 10-15% royalty on wholesale price. "As a nonprofit press, we generally exclude the first 1,000 copies from royalty payment." No advance. Publishes ms an average of 1 year after acceptance. Photocopied submissions OK if clearly legible. Computer printout submissions acceptable; prefers letter-quality to dot-matrix. Reports in 1 month on queries; 3 months on mss. Free book catalog.

Nonfiction: Biography, reference and monographs. Subjects include Americana, history, politics and sociology. "We are a scholarly publisher, publishing chiefly for an academic and professional audience. Strong areas are history, literature, political science, folklore, anthropology, and sociology. Our books are expected to advance knowledge in their fields in some measure. We would be interested in the treatment of timely topics in the fields indicated, treatments that would be solid and substantial but that would be readable and capable of appealing to a general public." No "textbooks; genealogical material; lightweight popular treatments; how-to books; and generally books not related to our major areas of interest." Query. Reviews artwork/photos, but generally does not publish books with extensive number of photos.

Recent Nonfiction Title: *OPEC: The Failing Giant*, by Mohammed E. Ahrari (economic and political analysis).

Tips: "Most of our authors are drawn from our primary academic and professional audience. We are probably not a good market for the usual freelance writer, unless his work fits into our special requirements. Moreover, we do not pay advances and income from our books is minimal; so we cannot offer much financial reward to a freelance writer."

UNIVERSITY PRESS OF MISSISSIPPI, 3825 Ridgewood Rd., Jackson MS 39211. (601)982-6205. Director: Barney McKee. Acquisitions Editor: Seetha Srinivasan. Publishes hardcover and paperback originals and reprints. Averages 20 titles/year; receives 150 submissions annually. 50% of books from first-time authors; 100% of books from unagented writers. Customarily pays 10% net royalty. No advance. Publishes book an average of 9 months after acceptance. Computer printout submissions acceptable. Reports in 2 months. Free book catalog.

Nonfiction: Americana, biography, history, politics, sociology, literary criticism. Especially needs regional studies and literary studies, particularly mss on William Faulkner and Eudora Welty. Submit outline/synopsis and sample chapters and curriculum vita. Reviews artwork/photos as part of ms package.

Recent Nonfiction Title: *Conversations with Walker Percy*, ed. by Lewis A. Lawson and Victor A. Kramer.

*UNIVERSITY PRESS OF VIRGINIA, Box 3608, University Station, Charlottesville VA 22903. (804)924-3468. Editor-in-Chief: Walker Cowen. Publishes hardcover and paperback originals and reprints. Averages 45 titles/year; receives 250 submissions annually. 70% of books from first-time authors; 100% of books from unagented writers. Average print order for a writer's first book is 1,000. Royalty on retail depends on the market for the book; sometimes none is made. "We subsidy publish 30% of our books (10% author-subsidized), based on cost versus probable market." Publishes book an average of 10 months after acceptance. Computer printout submissions acceptable; no dot-matrix. Returns rejected material within a week. Reports on acceptances in 2 months. Free catalog; ms guidelines for SASE.

Nonfiction: Publishes Americana, business, history, law, medicine and psychiatry, politics, reference, scientific, bibliography, and decorative arts books. "Write a letter to the director, describing content of the manuscript, plus length. Also specify if maps, tables, illustrations, etc., are included." No educational, sociological or psychological mss. Reviews artwork/photos as part of ms package.

Recent Nonfiction Title: *The Lyrical Left: Randolph Bourne, Alfred Stieglitz, and the Origins of Cultural Radicalism in America*, by Edward Abrahams.

‡VALLEY OF THE SUN PUBLISHING COMPANY, Subsidiary of The Sutphen Corporation, Box 2010, Malibu CA 90265. Contact: Sharon Boyd. Publishes trade paperback originals. Averages 6-12 titles/year; receives 100 submissions annually. 50% of books from first-time authors; 100% of books from unagented writers. Pays variable royalty, "usually 8% of what we receive—80% of our books are sold directly to the consumer via mail order program"; averages $1,000 advance. Publishes book an average of 6 months after acceptance. Simultaneous and photocopied submissions OK. Computer printout submissions acceptable; prefers letter-quality to dot-matrix. Reports in 6 weeks on submissions. Book catalog for 9x12 SAE with 85¢ postage.

Nonfiction: Metaphysical, primarily reincarnation. "We are interested primarily in books about reincarnation from *very* knowledgeable writers. Must be documented material and offer something new on the subject. We will consider other metaphysical subjects, but this material usually comes from those who actually work in the field. No 'channeled' material—we won't even consider it. No general reincarnation information explaining how it all works." Submit complete ms. Reviews artwork/photos as part of ms package.

Recent Nonfiction Title: *A Veil Too Thin*, by Betty Riley (documented case of reincarnation out of control and affecting present life).

‡ALFRED VAN DER MARCK EDITIONS, Suite 1301, 1133 Broadway, New York NY 10010. (212)645-5150. Editorial Director: Robert Walter. Publishes hardcover and paperback originals and reprints. Averages 10-20 titles/year; receives 250 submissions annually. 50% of books from first-time authors; 20% of books from unagented writers. Pays 3-15% royalty on wholesale or retail price. Offers average $5,000 advance. Publishes book an average of 1 year after acceptance. Simultaneous and photocopied submissions OK. Electronic submissions OK, but requires hard copy also. Computer printout submissions acceptable; prefers letter-quality to dot-matrix. Reports in 1 month on queries; 2 months on mss. Book catalog free on request.

Nonfiction: Biography, coffee table book, how-to illustrated book, and self-help. Subjects include Americana (pre-Columbus); art (contemporary); health (natural healing); history (prehistory and cultural history); music (dance and drama); photography; religion (comparative religion and mythology); and travel (photojournalistic accounts). Needs mss on "interesting conceptual projects on the cutting edge of contemporary cultural activities, as well as timeless reference works. No conventional illustrated books, 'how-I-spent-a-year-of-my-life' photography." Query or submit outline/synopsis and sample chapters. Submit complete ms through agents only. Reviews artwork/photos as part of ms package.

Recent Nonfiction Title: *Historical Atlas of World Mythology, Vol. 1*, by Joseph Campbell (mythology/reference).

Poetry: Seminal collections and anthologies *only*. Submit query.

Recent Poetry Title: *Shaking the Pumpkin: Traditional Poetry of the Indian North Americas*, by Jerome Rothenberg.

Tips: "The audience for our books is a general audience with interest in contemporary and timeless culture."

VANCE BIBLIOGRAPHIES, 112 N. Charter, Box 229, Monticello IL 61856. (217)762-3831. Publisher: Judith Vance. Publishes trade paperback originals. Averages 480 titles/year, 240/imprints; receives 500 submissions annually. 10% of bibliographies from first-time authors; 100% of bibliographies from unagented writers.

Average print order for a writer's first bibliography is 250. Pays $100 honorarium and 10-20 author's copies. Publishes bibliography an average of 4 months after acceptance. Photocopied submissions OK. Computer printout submissions acceptable; prefers letter-quality to dot-matrix. Reports in 1 week on queries; 2 weeks on mss. Free book catalog; ms guidelines for SASE.

Imprints: Architecture Series (bibliography). Public Administration Series (bibliography). Judith Vance, publisher.

Nonfiction: Bibliographies on public administration and/or architecture and related subject areas. Publishes for "graduate students and professionals in the field; primary customers are libraries." Query or submit complete ms.

Recent Nonfiction Title: *Housing from Redundant Buildings: A Select Bibliography,* by V.J. Nurcombe.

‡**VANGUARD PRESS, INC.,** 424 Madison Ave., New York NY 10017. Editor-in-Chief: Bernice S. Woll. Publishes hardcover originals. Averages 20 titles/year; receives 15,000 submissions annually. 10% of books from first-time authors; 10% of books from unagented writers. Offers 7½-15% royalty on retail price; pays variable advance. Simultaneous and photocopied submissions OK. Computer printout submissions acceptable; prefers letter-quality to dot-matrix. Reports in 2 months.

Nonfiction: Animals; art; biography (especially of musicians, artists and political figures); business (management, making money, how-to); cookbooks (gourmet and diet books); cooking and foods; history (scholarly, but written with flair); hobbies (crafts, especially sewing); how-to; humor; juveniles (folk stories, nature and art topics); music (no scores, but anything pertaining to the field—also, jazz); nature (ecology and nature adventure); philosophy; poetry; politics (current issues); psychology; religion in literature and society (no tracts); current sociology studies; sports; travel; juvenile science; and literary criticism. "No textbooks, coffee table books, reference books or technical material." Query or submit outline/synopsis and sample chapters.

Recent Nonfiction Title: *History of Anti-Semitism, Vol. IV,* by Leon Poliakor.

Fiction: Believable adventure, experimental, humor, mystery, modern suspense and "good-literature." No confessions, erotica or gothics. Query or submit outline/synopsis and sample chapters.

Recent Fiction Title: *A Certain Mr. Takahashi,* by Ann Ireland.

VEHICULE PRESS, Box 125, Place du Parc Station, Montreal, Quebec H2W 2M9 Canada. (514)844-6073. President/Publisher: Simon Dardick. Managing Editor: Margaret Christakos. Publishes trade paperback originals by Canadian authors *only.* Average 8 titles/year; receives 250 submissions annually. 20% of books from first-time authors; 95% of books from unagented writers. Pays 10-15% royalty on retail price; offers $200-500 advance. Publishes book an average of 1 year after acceptance. Photocopied submissions OK. Electronic submissions OK via CPM, WordStar or Philips Micom, but requires hard copy also. Computer printout submissions acceptable; prefers letter-quality to dot-matrix. SAE with IRC. "We would appreciate receiving an IRC rather than U.S. postage stamps which we cannot use." Reports in 2 weeks on queries; 2 months on mss. Free book catalog.

Imprints: Signal Editions (poetry). Dossier Quebec (history, memoirs).

Nonfiction: Biography and memoir. Subjects include Canadiana, history, politics, social history and literature. Especially looking for Canadian social history. Query. Reviews artwork/photos as part of ms package.

Recent Nonfiction Title: *The Life of a Document: A Global Approach to Archives and Records Management,* by Carol Couture and J-Y Rousseau.

Fiction: Short stories only. Query.

Recent Fiction Title: *Voyage to the Other Extreme,* by Marilu Mallet (short stories).

Poetry: Contact Michael Harris, editor. Looking for Canadian authors only. Submit complete ms.

Recent Poetry Title: *Veiled Countries,* by Marie-Claire Blais.

Tips: "We are only interested in Canadian authors."

‡*VESTA PUBLICATIONS, LTD.,** Box 1641, Cornwall, Ontario K6H 5V6 Canada. (613)932-2135. Editor-in-Chief: Stephen Gill. Paperback and hardcover originals. 10% minimum royalty on wholesale price. Subsidy publishes 5% of books. "We ask a writer to subsidize a part of the cost of printing; normally, it is 50%. We do so when we find that the book does not have a wide market, as in the case of university theses and the author's first collection of poems. The writer gets 25 free copies and 10% royalty on paperback editions." No advance. Publishes 16 titles/year; receives 350 submissions annually. 80% of books from first-time authors; 100% of books from unagented writers. Simultaneous submissions OK if so informed. Photocopied submissions OK. Electronic submissions OK via Kaypro. Computer printout submissions acceptable; prefers letter-quality to dot-matrix. Reports in 1 week on queries; 1 month on mss. SAE with IRCs. Free book catalog.

Nonfiction: Publishes Americana, art, biography, cookbooks, cooking and foods, history, philosophy, poetry, politics, reference, and religious. Accepts nonfiction translations. Query or submit complete ms. Reviews artwork/photos. Looks for knowledge of the language and subject. "Query letters and mss should be accompanied by synopsis of the book and biographical notes." State availability of photos and/or illustrations to accompany ms.

Recent Nonfiction Title: *Famine,* by Edward Pike.

Close-up

Nan Graham
Senior Editor
Viking Penguin, Inc.

When writers try to understand why their manuscripts have been rejected or their queries unanswered, they sometimes cling to stubborn misconceptions. "Editors don't have any feelings," they tell themselves. "Editors don't do anything but send rejection letters and take long lunches."

Nan Graham responded good-naturedly when we asked her about such accusations. "We editors have a lot of authors who would like more of us than we can give. An author has one book; we have dozens. We don't so much forget the human side—that it is a writer's work of two years or ten—as we find ourselves incapable of meeting all the demands at once."

Those demands go far beyond most writers' perceptions. Graham gave an insider's view of the usual stages a manuscript passes through at Viking. First Graham and another member of the editorial staff must read and recommend the manuscript. Then they make a compelling presentation at an editorial meeting. Third, Graham and her assistant must prepare a more-or-less realistic assessment of the book's sales potential—a profit and loss statement—before an offer is made.

But that's just the beginning of the editor's involvement. "If you really care about a book . . . you've got to shepherd it not just through editing and production but through sales and marketing," Graham says. "Sometimes your support departments—subsidiary rights, publicity, marketing—need a steady dose of your own enthusiasm and imagination. From the beginning, you must decide whether a manuscript will sustain your interest and enthusiasm—love, if possible—throughout that process."

Graham began her publishing career as an editorial assistant at Ballantine and was on the editorial staff at Pantheon for five years before joining Viking in 1984. She was named senior editor in 1986. We asked Graham to describe a few books that have affected her deeply.

"In 1981 I edited a journal, *Daybook*, by an artist named Ann Truitt. In it she talks about her life as a woman, an artist and a mother. It is the first book I edited that engaged every part of me and taught me what my role as editor could be."

Graham also mentioned *Berlin Wild, A Novel* by Elly Welt as "one of the most compelling stories I have read." The novel is about good and evil, seen through the eyes of a half-Jewish, half-Aryan anesthesiologist remembering his youth in Berlin in the 1940's. "I had always been suspicious and slightly uncomfortable about Holocaust fiction. But I realized that *Berlin Wild* was not a Holocaust novel. It is ambitious, uncompromised, and extraordinarily moving.

Graham's enthusiasm for excellent manuscripts is apparent, but she admits to occasional frustration. "I get impatient when I think a writer isn't working as hard as he or she could; when a writer seems to have given up; when he or she has forgotten that the book should be as good as it can possibly be. But above all, the writer must have something to say."

Graham's expectations may be high, but they're no higher than writers should expect . . . from any editor . . . or from themselves.

Becky Hall Williams

VGM CAREER HORIZONS, (Division of National Textbook Co.), 4255 W. Touhy Ave., Lincolnwood IL 60646-1975. (312)679-4210. Editorial Director: Leonard Fiddle. Senior Editor: Barbara Wood Donner. Publishes hardcover and paperback originals and software. Averages 20-30 titles/year; receives 150-200 submissions annually. 10% of books from first-time authors; 95% of books from unagented writers. Pays royalty or makes outright purchase. Advance varies. Publishes book an average of 1 year after acceptance. Simultaneous and photocopied submissions OK. Accepts electronic submissions but requirements for compatibility must be discussed; hard copy must accompany an electronic submission. Computer printout submissions OK, prefers letter-quality to dot-matrix. Reports in 6 weeks. Book catalog and ms guidelines for SASE. .
Nonfiction: Textbook and general trade on careers and jobs. Nonfiction book manuscript needs are for careers in agriculture, biotechnology, sales and marketing, liberal arts, information technology, etc. Query or submit outline/synopsis and sample chapters. Reviews artwork/photos as part of ms package.
Recent Nonfiction Title: *Careers in Business,* by Stair and Domkowski.
Tips: "Our audience is job seekers, career planners, job changers, and students and adults in education and trade markets."

‡VIKING PENGUIN, INC., 40 W. 23rd St., New York NY 10010. Imprints include Viking; Penguin; Viking Kestrel; Puffin; Stephen Greene Press; Frederick Warne; and Elisabeth Sifton Books. All unsolicited material is returned unopened; proposals through agents only.

*VOLCANO PRESS, INC., 330 Ellis St., San Francisco CA 94102. (415)664-5600. President: Ruth Gottstein. Publishes trade paperback originals. Averages 4 titles/year; receives 100 submissions annually. 90% of books from first-time authors; 95% of books from unagented writers. Average print order for a writer's first book is 5,000. Publishes some mss by author participation (co-venture). Pays royalty; buys some mss outright. Publishes book an average of 18 months after acceptance. Simultaneous and photocopied submissions OK if so stated. Computer printout submissions acceptable; no dot-matrix. Reports in 3 months. Book catalog for business size SAE and 1 first class stamp.
Nonfiction: Women and social change. Subjects include business and economics, health, history, philosophy, politics, psychology, sociology and travel. Query or submit outline/synopsis (1/2page description) and sample chapters. "No telephone solicitations." Send correctly stamped self-addressed bag for ms return. Reviews artwork/photos as part of ms package.
Recent Nonfiction Title: *Menopause, Naturally,* by Sadja Greenwood, M.D.
Tips: "We prefer books originating in experience(s) rather than someone's doctoral thesis. Books on topics which are emerging in the social and economic scene, as related to women, and books with heavy emphasis on women's health, as broadly defined, have the best chance of selling to our firm."

J. WESTON WALCH, PUBLISHER, Box 658, Portland ME 04104. (207)772-2846. Managing Editor: Richard S. Kimball. Editor: Jane Carter. Computer Editor: Robert Crepeau. Publishes paperback originals and software. Averages 120 titles/year; receives 300 submissions annually. 10% of books from first-time authors; 95% of books from unagented writers. Average print order for a writer's first book is 700. Offers 10-15% royalty on gross receipts; buys some titles by outright purchase for $100-2,500. No advance. Publishes book an average of 18 months after acceptance. Electronic submissions OK on most microcomputers, Apple preferred, but requires hard copy also. Computer-printout submissions acceptable; prefers letter-quality to dot-matrix. Reports in 3 weeks. Book catalog $1.05. Ms guidelines for SASE.
Nonfiction: Subjects include art, business, computer education, economics, English, foreign language, government, health, history, mathematics, music, psychology, recreation, science, social science, sociology, special education and sports. "We publish only supplementary educational material for sale to secondary schools throughout the U.S. and Canada. Formats include books, posters, ditto master sets, visual master sets (masters for making transparencies), cassettes, filmstrips, microcomputer courseware and mixed packages. Most titles are assigned by us, though we occasionally accept an author's unsolicited submission. We have a great need for author/artist teams or for authors who can write at third- to tenth-grade levels. We do *not* want basic texts, anthologies or industrial arts titles. Most of our authors—but not all—have secondary teaching experience. I cannot stress too much the advantages that an author/artist team would have in approaching us and probably other publishers." Query first. Looks for "sense of organization, writing ability, knowledge of subject, skill of communicating with intended audience." Reviews artwork/photos as part of ms package.
Recent Nonfiction Title: *Cultural Conflict: Case Studies in a World of Change,* by Edward Lerner.

WALKER AND CO., 720 5th Ave., New York NY 10019. Contact: Submissions Editor. Hardcover and paperback originals and reprints. Averages 150 titles/year; receives 3,500 submissions annually. 50% of books from first-time authors; 50% of books from unagented writers. Pays 10-12-15% royalty on retail price or makes outright purchase. Advance averages $1,000-2,500 "but could be higher or lower." Photocopied submissions OK. Free book catalog. Do not telephone submissions editions.
Nonfiction: Publishes Americana, art, biography, business, histories, how-to, juveniles, science and history, medicine and psychiatry, music, nature, sports, parenting, psychology, recreation, reference, popular science,

and self-help books. Query or submit outline/synopsis and sample chapter. Reviews artwork/photos as part of ms package (photographs).
Recent NonfictionTitle: *Asimov's Guide to Halley's Comet* (science).
Fiction: Mystery, romantic suspense, regency romance, historical romance, western, action adventure/espionage, science fiction and fantasy.
Recent Fiction Title: *Blunt Darts*, by Jeremiah Healy.

WALLACE—HOMESTEAD BOOK CO., American Broadcasting Company, Inc., 580 WatersEdge, Lombard IL 60148. (312)953-1100. General Manager: William N. Topaz. Publishes hardcover and trade paperback originals. Averages 30 titles/year; receives 300 submissions annually. 50% of books from first-time authors; 95% of books from unagented writers. Pays royalty on net price. Publishes book an average of 8 months after receipt of acceptable manuscript and materials. "Consult with production manager about electronic submissions." Computer printout submissions acceptable; prefers letter-quality to dot-matrix. Simultaneous and photocopied submissions OK. Reports in 1 month. Free book catalog and ms guidelines.
Nonfiction: Cookbook, how-to and reference. Subjects include Americana, art, business and economics, cooking and food, hobbies and crafts, photography, needlecraft, antiques and collectibles. Especially looking for mss on antiques, collectibles, memorabilia, quilting, cookbooks, and other specialty areas. No school or textbook material. Submit outline/synopsis and sample chapters. Reviews artwork/photos as part of ms package.
Recent Nonfiction Title: *Kitchen Casanova*, by D.L. wilson (cooking).
Tips: "Our books are intended for an adult nontechnical audience."

WESTERN MARINE ENTERPRISES INC., Box Q, Ventura CA 93002. (805)644-6043. Editor: William Berssen. Publishes hardcover and trade paperback originals. Averages 6 titles/year. Pays 15% royalty on net price. Offers no advance. Computer printout submissions acceptable; prefers letter-quality to dot-matrix. Reports in 3 week.
Nonfiction: Boating. "We specialize in boating books—mainly how-to and when-to." No "simple narrative accounts of how someone sailed a boat from here to there." First-time book authors should submit complete ms.
Recent Nonfiction Title: *Cruising Guide to California's Channel Islands*, by Brian M. Fagan (sail and powerboat guide).

WESTERN PRODUCER PRAIRIE BOOKS, Box 2500, Saskatoon, Saskatchewan S7K 2C4 Canada. Manager: Rob Sanders. Publishes hardcover and paperback originals and reprints. Specializes in historical nonfiction, natural history, and young adult novels with emphasis on Western Canadian region. Averages 17 titles/year; receives 400-500 submissions annually. 20% of books from first-time authors; 80% of books from unagented writers. Average print order for a writer's first book is 400. Pays negotiable royalty on list price. Publishes book an average of 1 year after acceptance. Submit contact sheets or prints if illustrations are to accompany ms. Electronic submissions OK via disk, but requires hard copy also. Computer printout submissions acceptable; no dot-matrix. Reports in 4 months. SAE with IRC. Free book catalog; ms guidelines for SASE (Canada), IRC.
Nonfiction: Publishes history, nature, photography, biography, reference, agriculture, economics, politics and cookbooks. Accepts nonfiction and fiction translations. Submit outline, synopsis and 2-3 sample chapters. Reviews artwork/photos as part of ms package.
Recent Nonfiction Title: *The Wonder of Canadian Birch*, by Candace Savage.

WESTERN TANAGER PRESS, 1111 Pacific Ave., Santa Cruz CA 95060. (408)425-1111. Publisher: Hal Morris. Publishes hardcover and trade paperback originals and reprints. Averages 3 titles/year; receives 50-100 submissions annually. 25% of books from first-time authors; 100% of books from unagented writers. Average print order for a writer's first book is 2,000. Publishes book an average of 6 months after acceptance. Computer printout submissions acceptable; prefers letter-quality to dot-matrix.
Nonfiction: Biography and history. "We are looking for works of local and regional history dealing with California. This includes biography, natural history, art and politics. Also interested in travel, hiking, biking guides and touring books." Query. Looks for "a well-written, well-thought-out project with a specific audience in mind." Reviews artwork/photos as part of ms package.

WESTERNLORE PRESS, Box 35305, Tucson AZ 85740. Editor: Lynn R. Bailey. Publishes 6-12 titles/year. Pays standard royalties on retail price "except in special cases." Query. Reports in 2 months. Enclose return postage with query.
Nonfiction: Publishes Western Americana of a scholarly and semischolarly nature: anthropology, history, biography, historic sites, restoration, and ethnohistory pertaining to the greater American West. Re-publication of rare and out-of-print books. Length: 25,000-100,000 words.

*WHITAKER HOUSE, Pittsburgh and Colfax Sts., Springdale PA 15144. (412)274-4440. Managing Editor: Donna C. Arthur. Paperback originals and reprints. Averages 30-35 titles/year; receives 75-100 submissions annually. 100% of books from unagented authors. Subsidy publishes (non-author) 25% of books. "We publish only Christian books." Royalty negotiated based on the net price of the book. Publishes book an average of 8 months after acceptance. "We market books in Christian book stores and in rack-jobbing locations such as supermarkets and drug stores." Electronic submissions OK via IBM Display Writer; requires hard copy also. Computer printout submissions acceptable; prefers letter-quality to dot-matrix. Query. Unsolicited mss returned. Ms guidelines for SASE.
Nonfiction: Publishes mostly how-to books ("how to move on in your Christian walk"; 90,000 words); and religious ("don't want heavy theology"; 90,000 words). Looking for teaching books with illustrations, anecdotes, and personal experiences used throughout, typed, double-spaced, about 300 pages in length. "Please note that we want teaching books that give the author's life experiences as well as solid Christian teaching." Looks for "well-written informative work that *follows our specifications*." Accepts outline/synopsis and 2-3 sample chapters.
Recent Nonfiction Title: *Imperfect Mates/Perfect Marriage*, by Diane Hampton.
Tips: "The writer has the best chance of selling our firm a book that has been ghostwritten for a well-known Christian personality."

THE WHITSTON PUBLISHING CO., Box 958, Troy NY 12181. (518)283-4363. Editorial Director: Jean Goode. Publishes hardcover originals. Averages 20 titles/year; receives 100 submissions annually. 50% of books from first-time authors; 100% of books from unagented writers. Pays 10-12-15% royalty on wholesale price; no advance. Publishes book an average of 30 months after acceptance. Computer printout submissions acceptable; no dot-matrix. Reports in 1 year.
Nonfiction: "We publish scholarly and critical books in the arts, humanities and some of the social sciences. We also publish reference books, bibliographies, indexes, checklists and monographs. We do not want author bibliographies in general unless they are unusual and unusually scholarly. We are, however, much interested in catalogs and inventories of library collections of individuals, such as the catalog of the Evelyn Waugh Collection at the Humanities Research Center, the University of Texas at Austin; and collections of interest to the specific scholarly community, such as surveys of early Black newspapers in libraries in the U.S., etc." Accepts poetry translations from French and Spanish. Query or submit complete ms. Reviews artwork/photos as part of ms package.
Recent Nonfiction Title: *Marcel Duchamp: Eros C'est la Vie*, by A. Marquis (biography).

WILDERNESS PRESS, 2440 Bancroft Way, Berkeley CA 94704. (415)843-8080. Editorial Director: Thomas Winnett. Publishes paperback originals. Averages 4 titles/year; receives 150 submissions annually. 20% of books from first-time authors; 95% of books from unagented writers. Average print order for a writer's first book is 5,000. Pays 8-10% royalty on retail price; offers average $500 advance. Publishes book an average of 6 months after acceptance. Computer printout submissions acceptable; prefers letter-quality to dot-matrix. Reports in 2 weeks. Book catalog for SASE.
Nonfiction: "We publish books about the outdoors. Most of our books are trail guides for hikers and backpackers, but we also publish how-to books about the outdoors and perhaps will publish personal adventures. The manuscript must be accurate. The author must thoroughly research an area in person. If he is writing a trail guide, he must walk all the trails in the area his book is about. The outlook must be strongly conservationist. The style must be appropriate for a highly literate audience." Query, submit outline/synopsis and sample chapters, or submit complete ms demonstrating "accuracy, literacy, and popularity of subject area." Reviews artwork/photos as part of ms package.
Recent Nonfiction Title: *Place Names of Sierra Nevada*, by Peter Browning.

WILLIAMSON PUBLISHING CO., Box 185, Church Hill Rd., Charlotte VT 05445. (802)425-2102. Editorial Director: Susan Williamson. Publishes trade paperback originals. Averages 10-12 titles/year; receives 250 submissions annually. 50% of books from first-time authors; 80% of books from unagented writers. Average first print order for a writer's first book is 5,000-10,000. Pays 10-12% royalty on sales dollars received or makes outright purchase if favored by author. Advance negotiable. Publishes book an average of 1 year after acceptance. Simultaneous and photocopied submissions OK. Computer submissions acceptable; prefers letter-quality to dot-matrix. Reports in 1 month on queries; 3 months on mss. Book catalog for SAE and 2 first class stamps.
Nonfiction: How-to, cookbook, illustrated book and self-help. Subjects include travel, landscaping, gardening, building, animals, business, education, cooking and foods, health, hobbies, nature and children. "Our areas of concentration are people-oriented business books, cookbooks, travel books, gardening, small-scale livestock raising, family housing (all aspects), health and education." No children's books, photography, politics, religion, history, art or biography. Query with outline/synopsis and sample chapters. Reviews photos as part of ms package.
Recent Nonfiction Title: *The Camper's Companion to Northern Europe*, by Dennis and Tina Juffe.

Tips: "In our specialized area, the more solid how-to information (written from experience) on subjects important in people's lives, the better."

WILSHIRE BOOK CO., 12015 Sherman Rd., North Hollywood CA 91605. (213)875-1711. Editorial Director: Melvin Powers. Publishes paperback originals and reprints. Publishes 50 titles/year; receives 6,000 submissions annually. 25% of books from first-time authors; 75% of books from unagented writers. Average print order for a writer's first book is 5,000. Pays standard royalty; offers variable advance. Computer printout submissions acceptable; no dot-matrix. Reports in 2 weeks. Book catalog for SASE.
Nonfiction: Health, hobbies, how-to, psychology, recreation, self-help, entrepreneurship, how to make money, and mail order. "We are always looking for self-help and psychological books such as *Psycho-Cybernetics* and *Guide to Rational Living*. We need manuscripts teaching mail order, entrepreneur techniques, how to make money and advertising. We publish 70 horse books. All that I need is the concept of the book to determine if the project is viable. I welcome phone calls to discuss manuscripts with authors." Reviews artwork/photos as part of ms package.
Recent Nonfiction Title: *How to Self-Publish Your Book and Have the Fun and Excitement of Being a Best-Selling Author*, by Melvin Powers.

‡*B.L. WINCH & ASSOCIATES, 45 Hitching Post Dr., Bldg. 2, Rolling Hills Estates CA 90274. (213)539-6430. Editorial Director: B.L. Winch. Production Editor: J. Lovelady. Senior Editor: Suzanne Mikesell. Publishes paperback originals and reprints. Averages 4-8 titles/year; receives 500-1,000 submissions annually. 20% of books from first-time authors; 90% of books from unagented writers. Subsidy publishes 5-20% of books. Offers 5-15% royalty on net receipts. Publishes book an average of 18 months after acceptance. Simultaneous and photocopied submissions OK. Electronics submissions acceptable via IBM; but requires hard copy also. Computer printout submissions acceptable. Reports in 3 months. Free book catalog.
Nonfiction: Parent-oriented enabling self-help materials (infant to teen), effective curriculum guidebooks and strategies, classroom management guidebooks, and right brain learning materials. Reviews artwork/photos as part of ms package. "Prefer completed ms."
Recent Nonfiction Title: *Project Self-Esteem: A Parent Involvement Program for Elementary-Age Children*, by Sandy McDaniel and Peggy Bielen.

WINCHESTER PRESS, Imprint of New Century Publishers, Inc., 220 Old New Brunswick Rd., Piscataway NJ 08854. Consulting Editor: Robert Elman. Publishes hardcover and paperback originals. Averages 10-15 titles/year; receives 300 submissions annually. 20% of books from first-time authors; 80% of books from unagented writers. Pays 10-12½-15% royalty on retail price. Publishes book an average of 9 months after acceptance. "Submit sample photos and some idea of total number projected for final book." Simultaneous and photocopied submissions OK. Reports in 3 months. Free book catalog.
Nonfiction: Main interest is in leisure activities, outdoor sports, crafts and related subjects. Subjects include recreation (outdoor); sports (hunting, fishing, etc.); and technical (firearms, fishing tackle, etc.). Looks for "good organization, defined audience potential, original and accurate information and good photographs." Submit outline/synopsis and sample chapters. Reviews artwork/photos as part of ms package.
Recent Nonfiction Title: *The Orivs Book of Upland Bird Shooting*, by Geoffrey Norman.
Tips: "The writing of leisure-activities books—particularly how-to books—has vastly improved in recent years. Manuscripts must now be better written and must reflect new ideas and new information if they are to be considered for publication by Winchester Press. Recreational equipment and opportunities have expanded, and writers must also be up-to-date journalists."

WINDSOR BOOKS, Subisidary of Windsor Marketing Corp., Box 280, Brightwaters NY 11718. (516)666-4631. Managing Editor: Stephen Schmidt. Publishes hardcover and trade paperback originals, reprints, and very specific software. Averages 8 titles/year; receives approximately 20 submissions annually. 60% of books from first-time authors; 90% of books from unagented writers. Pays 10% royalty on retail price; 5% on whole-sale price (50% of total cost); offers variable advance. Publishes book an average of 9 months after acceptance. Simultaneous and photocopied submissions OK. Computer printout submissions acceptable; prefers letter-quality to dot-matrix. Reports in 2 weeks on queries; 3 weeks on mss. Free book catalog and ms guidelines.
Nonfiction: How-to and technical. Subjects include business and economics (investing in stocks and commodities). Interested in books on strategies, methods for investing in the stock market, options market, and commodity markets. Query or submit outline/synopsis and sample chapters. Reviews artwork/photos as part of ms package.
Recent Nonfiction Title: *How to Triple Your Money Every Year with Stock Index Futures*, by George Angell (hardcover).
Tips: "Our books are for serious investors; we sell through direct mail to our mailing list and other financial lists. Writers must keep their work original; this market tends to have a great deal of information overlap among publications."

‡**WINDSOR PUBLICATIONS**, 8900 Quartz Ave., Box 9071, Northridge CA 91328. Senior Publications Editor: Lin Schonberger. Receives 50 submissions annually. 25% of books from first-time authors; 100% of books from unagented writers. "We publish pictorial civic publications, business directories, and relocation guides for chambers of commerce, boards of realtors, etc. Our audience is anyone considering relocating or visiting another part of the country, and our publications document in pictures and words every aspect of a city or area. Writers and photographers work on assignment only, after having demonstrated ability through samples. Publications are annual or biennial, vary in size and are titled with the name of a city. Circulation is controlled. Writers and writer/photographers with strong interview, reporting and travel writing experience are especially sought." Publishes book an average of 10 months after acceptance.
Nonfiction: "All mss assigned. Unsolicited manuscripts and/or photos not wanted." Queries, stating writing and/or photography experience and including tearsheets, are welcome. Length: 3,000-10,000 words. Pays $500-2,400 on acceptance for all rights. Photography for each publication usually assigned to photographer on per-day rate plus expenses. Also purchases stock, speculative and existing photos on one-time use basis if they pertain to future publications. 35mm and larger color transparencies, b&w contact sheets and negatives or b&w prints (5x7 to 8x10) are acceptable; no color prints. Fully descriptive captions required.

‡***WINE APPRECIATION GUILD LTD.**, Vintage Image, Wine Advisory Board, 155 Connecticut St., San Francisco CA 94107. (514)864-1202. Director: Maurice Sullivan. Publishes hardcover and trade paperback originals, trade paperback reprints, and software. Averages 26 titles/year; receives 30-40 submissions annually. 30% of books from first-time authors; 100% of books from unagented writers. Subsidy publishes 6% of books. Pays 5-15% royalty on wholesale price or makes outright purchase; offers average $1,000 advance. Publishes book an average of 18 months after acceptance. Simultaneous and photocopied submissions OK. Electronic submissions OK via IBM PC etc., but requires hard copy also. Reports in 2 months. Book catalog for $2.
Imprints: Vintage Image and Wine Advisory Board (nonfiction).
Nonfiction: Cookbook and how-to—wine related. Subjects include wine, cooking and foods and travel. Must be wine-related. Submit outline/synopsis and sample chapters. Reviews artwork/photos as part of ms package.
Recent Nonfiction Title: *Wine of Bordeaux*, by Edmand Penning-Roswell.
Tips: "Our books are read by wine enthusiasts—from neophytes to professionals, and wine industry and food industry people. We are interested in anything of a topical and timely nature connected with wine, by a knowledgeable author. We do not deal with agents of any type. We prefer to get to know the author as a person and to work closely with him/her."

WINGBOW PRESS, Subsidiary of Bookpeople, 2929 Fifth St., Berkeley CA 94710. (415)549-3030. Editor: Randy Fingland. Publishes hardcover and trade paperback originals and trade paperback reprints. Averages 3-4 titles/year; receives 500 submissions annually. 20% of books from first-time authors; 100% of books from unagented writers. Average print order for a writer's first book is 7,500. Pays 7-10% royalty on retail price; offers average $500 advance. Publishes book an average of 18 months after acceptance. Electronic submissions OK on IBM and Epson, but requires hard copy also. Computer printout submissions acceptable. Reports in 3 weeks on queries; 9 weeks on mss. Free book catalog.
Nonfiction: How-to, reference, psychology and sociology. Especially needs regional guides to San Francisco Bay area. Query or submit outline/synopsis and 1-5 sample chapters. Reviews artwork/photos as part of ms package.
Recent Nonfiction Title: *Working Inside Out: Tools for Change*, by Margo Adair (psychology/women's spirituality).
Tips: "We are not currently seeking poetry or original fiction. The writer has the best chance of selling regional guidebooks, psychology/health/self-sustenance, and women's books. That's where our marketing strength lies. We usually want to see a completed manuscript before signing a contract; if not, manuscript must be readable, grammatical, and author must be willing to be edited."

WINGRA WOODS PRESS, Box 9601, Madison WI 53715. Acquisitions Editor: M.G. Mahoney. Book packager. Publishes trade paperback originals. Averages 6-10 titles/year; receives 200+ submissions annually. 50% of books from first-time authors; 50% of books from unagented writers. Pays 10-12% royalty on retail price. Publishes book an average of 18 months after acceptance. Simultaneous and photocopied submissions OK. Computer printout submissions acceptable. Reports in 6 weeks.
Nonfiction: Cookbook, how-to, juvenile, self-help. Subjects include Americana, popular history and science, animals, art, and nature. Especially looking for popularized book-length treatments of specialized knowledge; interested in proposals from academics and professionals. Query with outline/synopsis. Do not send complete ms. Reviews artwork/photos as part of ms package.
Recent Nonfiction Title: *The Christmas Cat.*

*WINSTON-DEREK PUBLISHERS, Pennywell Dr., Box 90883, Nashville TN 37209. (615)329-1319/356-7384. Publisher: James W. Peebles. Pubishes hardcover, trade, and mass market paperback originals. Averages 35-40 titles/year; receives 2,500+ submissions annually. 60% of books from first-time authors; 80% of books from unagented authors. Average print order for writer's first book is 3,000-5,000. "We will co-publish exceptional works of quality and style only when we reach our quota in our trade book division." Pays 10-15% of the net amount received on sales. Advance varies. Simultaneous and photocopied submissions OK. Computer printout submissions acceptable; prefers letter-quality to dot-matrix. Queries and mss without SASE will be discarded. Reports in 1 month on queries; 2 months on mss.
Nonfiction: Biography (current or historically famous) and behavioral science and health (especially interested in mss of this category for teenagers and young adults). Subjects include Americana; theology; philosophy (nontechnical with contemporary format); religion (noncultist); and inspirational. Length: 50,000-60,000 words or less. Submit outline and first 2 or 4 chapters. Reviews artwork/photos as part of manuscript package. No political or technical material.
Recent Nonfiction Title: *God Loves the Arabs, Too*, by Louis Hamada.
Fiction: Ethnic (non-defamatory); religious (theologically sound); suspense (highly plotted); and Americana (minorities and whites in positive relationships). Length: 50,000 words or less. "We can use fiction with a semi-historical plot; it must be based or centered around actual facts and events—Americana, religion, gothic and science fiction. We are looking for juvenile books on relevant aspects of growing up and understanding life's situations. No funny animals talking." Children's/juvenile books must be of high quality. Submit complete ms for children and juvenile books with illustrations, which are optional.
Recent Fiction Title: *Beyond the Strawberry Patch*, by Rose S. Bell.
Poetry: Should be inspirational and with meaning. Poetry dealing with secular life should be of excellent quality. "We will accept unusual poetry books of exceptional quality and taste. We do not publish avant-garde type poetry." Submit complete ms. No single poems.
Recent Poetry Title: *A Carousel of Poetry*, by Alyce Lunsford.
Tips: "We do not publish material that advocates violence or is derogative of other cultures or beliefs. Outstanding biographies are quite successful, as are books dealing with the simplicity of man and his relationship with his environs. Our imprint Scythe Books for children needs material for adolescents within the 9-13 age group. These manuscripts should help young people with motivation for learning and succeeding at an early age, goal setting and character building. Biographies of famous women and men as role models are always welcomed. Stories must have a new twist and be provocative."

‡ALAN WOFSY FINE ARTS, Box 2210, San Francisco CA 94126. Publishes hardcover and paperback originals and hardcover reprints. Subsidy publishes 15% of books. Specializes in art reference books, specifically catalogs of graphic artists; bibliographies related to fine presses and the art of the book. Pays negotiable fee on retail price; offers advance. Publishes 5 titles annually. Reports in 1 month. Free book catalog.
Nonfiction: Publishes reference books on art. Seeking catalogues of (i.e., reference books on) collectibles. Query. Reviews artwork/photos as part of ms package.

‡WOODLANDS BOOKS, (formerly Biworld Publishers, Inc.), 500 N. 1030 W. Lindon UT. (801)785-8100. Vice President: Al Lisonbee. Publishes hardcover and trade paperback originals. Averages 12-20 titles/year; receives 200 submissions annually. 10% of books from first-time authors; 100% of books from unagented writers. Pays 8-12% royalty on net price; no advance. Publishes book an average of 1 year after acceptance. Reports in 2 weeks on queries; 1 month on mss. Free book catalog.
Nonfiction: Cookbook, how-to, reference, self-help and textbook. Subjects include cooking and foods, health and nature. "We're looking for reputable, professionally-done, well-researched manuscripts dealing in health, natural medicine, etc." Submit outline/synopsis and sample chapters or complete ms. Reviews artwork/photos as part of ms package.
Recent Nonfiction Title: *Healing Energies*, by Stephen Shepard.
Tips: "The health field is just now dawning. Health-related books of quality research are in demand."

*WOODSONG GRAPHICS, INC., Box 238, New Hope PA 18938. (215)794-8321. Editor: Ellen P. Bordner. Publishes hardcover and trade paperback originals. Averages 6 titles/year; receives 2,500-3,000 submissions annually. 40-60% of books from first-time authors; 100% of books from unagented writers. Average print order for writer's first book is 2,500-5,000. Will occasionally consider subsidy publishing based on "quality of material, motivation of author in distributing his work, and cost factors (which depend on the type of material involved), plus our own feelings on its marketability." Subsidy publishes 15% of books. Pays royalty on net price; offers average $100 advance. Publishes book an average of 1 year after acceptance. Simultaneous submissions OK. Computer printout submissions acceptable; prefers letter-quality to dot-matrix. Reports in 1 month on queries; reports on full mss *can* take several months, depending on the amount of material already in the house. "We do everything possible to facilitate replies, but we have a small staff and want to give every manuscript a thoughtful reading." Book catalog for SAE and 1 first class stamp.
Nonfiction: Biography, cookbook, how-to, humor, illustrated book, juvenile, reference, and self-help. Sub-

jects include cooking and foods, hobbies, philosophy and psychology. "We're happy to look at anything of good quality, but we're not equipped to handle lavish color spreads at this time. Our needs are very open, and we're interested in seeing any subject, provided it's handled with competence and style. Good writing from unknowns is also welcome." No pornography; only minimal interest in technical manuals of any kind. Query or submit outline/synopsis and at least 2 sample chapters. Reviews artwork/photos as part of ms package.

Recent Nonfiction Title: *The Shadow Hill Book of Squares, Bars & Brownies*, by Susan Ashley.

Fiction: Adventure, experimental, fantasy, gothic, historical, humor, mainstream, mystery, romance, science fiction, suspense and western. "In fiction, we are simply looking for books that provide enjoyment. We want well-developed characters, creative plots, and good writing style." No pornography or "sick" material. Submit outline/synopsis and sample chapters.

Poetry: "We are unable to take on any new poetry manuscripts for the time being."

Tips: "Good nonfiction with an identified target audience and a definite slant has the best chance of selling to our firm. We rarely contract in advance of seeing the completed manuscript."

WORD BEAT PRESS, Box 10509, Tallahassee FL 32302-2509. Editor: Allen Woodman. Publishes trade paperback originals and reprints. Averages 3-5 titles/year; receives 500 submissions annually. 50% of books from first-time authors; 80% of books from unagented writers. Average print order for a writer's first book is 500-1,000. Pays 10% royalty on wholesale price. Offers average $100 advance. Publishes book an average of 1 year after acceptance. Computer printout submissions acceptable; prefers letter-quality to dot-matrix. Reports in 5 weeks on queries; 3 months on mss. Book catalog for legal size SAE and 1 first class stamp.

Nonfiction: "We will look at any book that would be of interest to fiction writers, how-to, self-help, reference, and other books about writing." Reviews artwork/photos as part of ms package. Query first.

Fiction: Short story collections and novellas; "open to fine writing in any category." Query first.

Tips: "We hold annual fiction book competitions judged by nationally recognized writers. Past judges have included George Plimpton, Eve Shelnutt, Janet Burroway and Joy Williams. Send SASE for details. Writers have the best chance of selling short story collections and books of interest to professional writers."

WORD BOOKS PUBLISHER, Division of Word Inc., subsidiary of ABC, 4800 W. Waco Dr., Waco TX 76703. (817)772-7650. Managing Editor: Al Bryant. Publishes hardcover and trade paperback originals, and hardcover, trade paperback, and mass market paperback reprints. Averages 50 titles/year; receives 2,000 submissons annually. 15% of books from first-time authors; 98% of books from unagented writers. Pays 7½-15% royalty on retail price; offers average $2,000 advance. Publishes book an average of 1 year after acceptance. Photocopied submissions OK. Electronic submissions OK. Computer printout submissions acceptable; no dot-matrix. Reports in 1 month on queries; 2 months on mss. Free book catalog; ms guidelines for SASE.

Nonfiction: Biography, "coffee table" book, cookbook, how-to, reference, self-help, and textbook. Subjects include health, history (church and Bible), philosophy, politics, psychology, religion, sociology, and sports. Especially looking for "religious books that help modern-day Christians cope with the stress of life in the 20th century. We welcome queries on all types of books." Query with outline/synopsis and sample chapters. Reviews artwork/photos as part of ms package.

Recent Nonfiction Title: *The Be Happy Attitudes*, by Robert Schuller.

Fiction: Religious, romance and science fiction. No non-religious fiction. Submit outline/synopsis and sample chapters.

Tips: "Nonfiction has the best chance of selling to our firm, since 90% of our books are nonfiction."

‡**WORKMAN PUBLISHING COMPANY, INC.**, 1 W. 39th St., New York NY 10018. (212)398-9160. Publishes hardcover and trade paperback originals and hardcover and trade paperback reprints and calendars. Averages 25 titles/year (and 25 calendars). Pays royalty. Simultaneous and photocopied submissions OK. Reports in 6 months. Book catalog free on request.

Nonfiction: "Coffee table" book, cookbook, how-to, humor, illustrated book, juvenile, and self-help. Subjects include Americana, art, cooking and foods, health, history, hobbies, nature, photography, recreation, religion, sports, travel and humor. Query or submit outline/synopsis and sample chapters.

Recent Nonfiction Titles: *The Pentagon Catalog*, by Cerp and Beard (humor).

WORLD NATURAL HISTORY PUBLICATIONS, Division of Plexus Publishing, Inc., 143 Old Marlton Pike, Medford NJ 08055. (609)654-6500. Editorial Director: Thomas Hogan. Publishes hardcover and paperback originals. Averages 4 titles/year; receives 10-20 submissons annually. 70% of books from first-time authors; 90% of books from unagented writers. Pays 10-20% royalty on wholesale price; buys some booklets outright for $250-1,000. Offers $500-1,000 advance. Simultaneous and photocopied submissions OK. Computer printout submissions acceptable; prefers letter-quality to dot-matrix. Reports in 2 months. Book catalog for SASE.

Nonfiction: Animals, biography (of naturalists), nature and reference. "We are looking for manuscripts of about 300-400 pages for our series *Introduction to ...* which concentrates on some group of plants or animals and is designed for high school and undergraduate college use and for amateur naturalists. We will consider any book on a nature/biology subject, particularly those of a reference (permanent) nature. No philosophy or psychology; no gardening; generally not interested in travel, but will consider travel that gives sound ecological information." Also interested in mss of about 20-40 pages in length.for feature articles in *Biology Digest* (guidelines for these available with SASE). Always query. Reviews artwork/photos as part of ms package.

Recent Nonfiction Title: *Working for Life: Careers in Biology.*

Tips: "Write a book that is absolutely accurate and that has been reviewed by specialists to eliminate misstatement of fact."

‡*WRIGHT PUBLISHING COMPANY, INC., Suite 303, 1422 W. Peachtree St., Atlanta GA 30309. (404)876-1900. Editor-in-Chief: Yvonne Bowman Wright. Publishes hardcover, trade paperback, and mass market paperback originals and reprints. Averages 10 titles/year; receives 500 submissions annually. 75% of books from first-time authors; 95% of books from unagented writers. Subsidy publishes 50% of books. "We determine whether an author should be subsidy published based on the book's potential marketability and the author's financial resources." Pays 12-17% royalty on wholesale price, makes outright purchase of $2,000 maximum, or author pays for production. Offers average 20% advance. Publishes book an average of 10 months after acceptance. Computer printout submissions acceptable; no dot-matrix. Reports in 2 months on queries; 2 months on mss.

Nonfiction: Biography, cookbook, how-to, humor, illustrated book, juvenile, self-help, technical, and textbook. Subjects include business and economics, cooking and foods, health, and sports. "We are especially interested in technical, business, economics, juvenile, sports, health and beauty, and cookbooks. Also, biographies and/or autobiographies." Submit outline/synopsis and sample chapters or complete ms. Reviews artwork/photos as part of ms package.

Recent Nonfiction Title: *Living Thoughts*, by Ernest Manor.

Fiction: Adventure, confession, erotica, ethnic, fantasy, horror, humor, mainstream, mystery, romance, science fiction, and suspense. Submit outline/synopsis and sample chapters or complete ms.

WRITER'S DIGEST BOOKS, 9933 Alliance Rd., Cincinnati OH 45242. Editorial Director: David Lewis (general interest books). Acquisitions Editor: Jean Fredette (writing books). Publishes hardcover and paperback originals (nonfiction only). Averages 45 titles/year. Pays advance and 10% royalty on net receipts. Simultaneous (if so advised) and photocopied submissions OK. Computer printout submissions OK; prefers letter-quality to dot-matrix. Publishes book an average of 1 year after acceptance. Enclose return postage. Book catalog for SASE.

Nonfiction: Writing, photography, music, and other creative pursuits, as well as general-interest subjects. "We're seeking up-to-date, how-to treatments by authors who can write from successful experience. Should be well-researched, yet lively and readable. Query or submit outline/synopsis and sample chapters. Be prepared to explain how the proposed book differs from existing books on the subject. We are also very interested in republishing self-published nonfiction books and good instructional or reference books that have gone out of print before their time. No fiction or poetry. Send sample copy, sales record, and reviews if available." Reviews artwork/photos as part of ms package.

Recent Nonfiction Title: *Waking Up Dry*, by Dr. Martin Scharf.

YANKEE BOOKS, Subsidiary of Yankee Publishing Inc., Main St., Dublin NH 03444. (603)563-8111. Editor: Clarissa M. Silitch. Publishes trade paperback and hardcover originals. Averages 8-10 titles/year. 50% of books from first-time authors; 50% of books from unagented writers. Average print order for a writer's first book is 5,000-10,000. Pays royalty with $1,000-5,000 advance. Publishes book an average of 18 months after acceptance. Electronic submissions OK if compatible with IBM PC, DD, DS, but requires hard copy also. Computer printout submissions acceptable; prefers letter-quality to dot-matrix. Reports in 1 month on queries; 6 weeks on mss. Free book catalog.

Nonfiction: Cookbooks, how-to, country matters, nature, subjects related in one way or another to New England: nostalgia, Americana antiques, cooking, crafts, house and home, gardening, the outdoors, essays, folklore and popular history, photographs, today and old-time, travel in the Northeast U.S., the sea, boats, sailors, et al. No scholarly history, even slightly off-color humor, highly technical works, or biographies of persons not strikingly interesting. Query or submit outline/synopsis and sample chapters or complete ms. Reviews artwork/photos as part of ms package.

Recent Nonfiction Title: *The Loon, Voice of the Wilderness*, by Joan Dunning.

YORK PRESS LTD., Box 1172, Fredericton, New Brunswick E3B 5C8 Canada. (506)458-8748. General Manager/Editor: Dr. S. Elkhadem. Publishes trade paperback originals. Averages 8 titles/year; receives 25 submissions annually. 10% of books from first-time authors; 100% of books from unagented writers. Pays 5-10% royalty on wholesale price. Publishes book an average of 6 months after acceptance. Photocopied submissions OK. Computer printout submissions acceptable; prefers letter-quality to dot-matrix. Reports in 1 week on queries; 1 month on ms. Free book catalog; ms guidelines $1.50.

Nonfiction: Reference, textbook and scholarly. Especially needs literary criticism, comparative literature and linguistics. Query.

Recent Nonfiction Title: *Franz Kafka: Life, Work, and Criticism,* by K.J. Fickert.

Tips: "If I were a writer trying to market a book today, I would spend a considerable amount of time examining the needs of a publisher *before* sending my manuscript to him. Scholarly books are the only kind we publish. The writer must adhere to our style manual and follow our guidelines exactly."

YOURDON PRESS, Subsidiary of Yourdon Inc., 1501 Broadway, New York NY 10036. (212)391-2828. Acquisitions Editor: Dan Mausner. Publishes trade paperback originals. Averages 10 titles/year; receives 25 submissions annually. 50% of books from first-time authors; 100% of books from unagented writers. Pays 15% royalty on net receipts. Publishes book an average of 6 months after acceptance. Electronic submissions OK, straight ASCII files on IBM disk for upload to UNIX typesetter, but requires hard copy also. Computer printout submissions acceptable. Reports in 1 month on queries; 2 months on mss. Free book catalog.

Nonfiction: Technical. Subjects in the area of development of computer systems. Especially interested in following topics: structured programming, software engineering, project management, information modeling and data base design, planning in data processing departments; information centers, prototyping and fourth generation languages. No highly esoteric, academic mss. Query or submit outline/synopsis and sample chapters. Reviews artwork/photos as part of ms package.

Recent Nonfiction Title: *Structure Development for Real-Time Systems,* by Stephen Mellor.

Tips: "Our books are read by programmers, systems analysts, data processing managers, information systems managers, and business executives. Highly readable, sophisticated, and practical books in our subject areas have the best chance of selling to us. Mention existing titles in the field and explain how your proposal goes beyond them or occupies a special niche."

ZEBRA BOOKS, Subsidiary of Norfolk Publishing Co., 475 Park Ave., S., New York NY 10016. (212)889-2299. Editorial Director: Leslie Gelbman. Publishes mass market paperback originals and reprints. Averages 150 titles/year; receives thousands of submissions annually. 50% of books from first-time authors; 50% of books from unagented writers. Pays royalty on retail price or makes outright purchase. Publishes book an average of 12-18 months after acceptance. Simultaneous and photocopied submissions OK. Computer printout submissions acceptable; no dot-matrix. Reports in 3 months on queries; 4 months on mss. Book catalog for business size SAE and 39¢ postage.

Nonfiction: Biography, how-to, humor and self-help. Subjects include health, history and psychology. "We are open to many areas, especially self-help, stress, money management, child-rearing, health, war (WWII, Vietnam), and celebrity biographies." No nature, art, music, photography, religion or philosophy. Query or submit outline/synopsis and sample chapters.

Recent Nonfiction Title: *Iacocca,* by David Abodahn.

Fiction: Adventure, men's action, confession, erotica, gothic, historical, horror, humor, mainstream, medical novels, romance and suspense. Tip sheet on historical romances, gothics, family sagas, adult romances and women's contemporary fiction is available. No poetry or short story collections. Query with synopsis and several sample chapters. SASE is a must.

Recent Fiction Title: *Destiny's Temptress,* by Janelle Taylor.

THE ZONDERVAN CORP., 1415 Lake Drive, SE, Grand Rapids MI 49506. (616)698-6900. Executive Editor: Cheryl Forbes. Publishes hardcover and trade and mass paperback originals and trade and mass market paperback reprints. Averages 100 titles/year; receives 3,500 submissions annually, 30% of books from first-time authors; 98% of books from unagented writers. Average print order for a writer's first book is 5,000. Pays royalty of 14% of the net amount received on sales of cloth and softcover trade editions and 12% of net amount received on sales of mass market paperbacks. Offers variable advance. Electronic submissions OK on IBM compatible and Wang. Computer printout submissions are acceptable; prefers letter-quality to dot-matrix. The author should separate the perforated pages. Reports in 3 months on queries. Book catalog for 9x12 SAE and $1.22 postage. Ms guidelines for SASE.

Nonfiction: Biography, "coffee table" book, how-to, humor, illustrated book, reference, devotional and gift, self-help, youth books, Bible study, inspirational romance, history, books for charsismatics; textbooks on philosophy, psychology, religion and sociology. All from religious perspective (evangelical). Immediate needs include "books that take a fresh approach to issues and problems in the evangelical community; that offer new insights into solving personal and interpersonal problems; and that encourage readers to mature spiritually." No mss written from an occult point of view. Query or submit outline/synopsis and 2 sample chapters.

Recent Nonfiction Title: *Festival,* by Gladis De Pree.

Fiction: Books that deal realistically and creatively with relevant social and religious issues. No mss for new children's books or poetry. Query or submit outline/synopsis and 2 sample chapters.

Recent Fiction Title: *Captain, My Captain,* by Deborah Meroff.

Subsidy Publishers

The following publishers produce more than fifty percent of their books on a subsidy basis. What they charge and what they offer to each writer varies, so you'll want to judge each publisher on its own merit. Because subsidy publishing can cost you several thousand dollars, make sure the number of books, the deadlines, and services offered by a publisher are detailed in *your* contract. If you are willing to pay to have your book published, you should be willing to hire an attorney to review the contract. This step prevents misunderstandings between you and your prospective publisher. *Don't ever agree to terms you don't understand.* For more information on subsidy publishing, consult the Book Publishers introduction in this book.

Aegina Press and University Editions
   4937 Humphrey Rd., Huntington WV 25704
Brunswick Publishing Company
   Box 555, Lawrenceville VA 23868
Camden House, Inc.
   Drawer 2025, Columbia SC 29202
Dawn Sign Press
   Suite 516, 2490 Channing Way, Berkeley CA 94704
Eastview Editions
   Box 783, Westfield NJ 07091
EMC Publishing
   EMC Corporation, 300 York Ave., St. Paul MN 55101
ESPress, Inc.
   Box 55482, Washington DC 20011
The Golden Quill Press
   Avery Rd., Francestown NH 03043
Moon Publications
   Box 1696, Chico CA 95927
Morgan Press,
   affiliated with Morgan & Morgan, Inc., 145 Paliside St., Dobbs Ferry NY 10522

New Vision Books
   1005 Pruit Dr., Redondo Beach CA 90278
Nichols Publishing Co.
   Box 96, New York NY 10024
R & E Publishers, Inc.
   Box 2008, Saratoga CA 95070
Peter Randall Publisher
   500 Market St., Box 4726, Portsmouth·NH 03801
Howard W. Sams and Co., Inc.
   4300 W 62nd St., Indianapolis IN 46268
Vantage Press
   516 W. 34th St., New York NY 10001
Wimmer Brothers Books
   Box 18408, 4210 B.F. Goodrich Blvd., Memphis TN 38118
Wordware Publishing, Inc.
   Suite 101, 1506 Capital Ave., Plano TX 75074
Writers Publishing Service Co.
   1512 Western Ave., Seattle WA 98101

66 *All beginning writers are uncertain about the quality of their work. Exposure to the raw writing of others through copy editing assignments or manuscript reviewing gives one a perspective on the level of one's own writing. This can also be accomplished by attending adult education classes on writing that enable beginning writers to critique each other's work.* **99**

John H. Lavin

Book Publishers
Subject Index

Nonfiction

This index will help you find publishers that consider books on specific subjects—the subjects you choose to write about. Remember that a publisher may be listed here under a general subject category like Art and Architecture, while the company publishes *only* art history or how-to books. Be sure to consult each company's detailed individual listing, its book catalog and several of its books before you send your query or manuscript.

Agriculture/Horticulture. AVI; Delmar; Interstate; Oryx; Purdue; Rowman & Littlefield; Stipes; Tab; Timber; Universe; Univ. Press of America; Western Producer.

Alternative Lifestyles. And/Or; Celestial; Naturegraph; New Society; Newcastle; South End; Sterling; Strawberry Hill; Theosophical; Thorsons; Thunder's Mouth.

Americana. Angel; Arbor House; Associated Faculty; Atheneum Children's; Binford & Mort; Blair; Branden; Brevet; Caxton; Cay-Bel; Cedarshouse; Christopher; Clarion; Arthur H. Clark; Copley; Council Oak; Daniel; Davenport; Denlinger's; Diamond; Douglas & McIntyre; Down East; Dragonsbreath; Eriksson; Faber & Faber; Falcon Press Pub.; General Hall; Globe Pequot; Golden West Books; Green Tiger; Grunwald and Radcliff; H. W. H.; Hancock; Harper & Row; Harvard Common; Herald; Heyday; Houghton Mifflin; Hounslow; Howell-North; International Publishers; Interurban; Jonathan David; Kaufmann; Key Porter; Lang; Lexikos; Liberty; Library Research; McFarland & Co.; Madrona; Main St.; Maverick; Meyerbooks; Miller; Monitor; Mosaic; Mustang; National Press; New England; Northland; Outbooks; Overlook; Pacific; Padre; Paragon; Pineapple; Purdue; Quinlan; Rainbow; Renaissance; Saybrook; Second Chance/Permanent; Seven Locks; Shameless Hussy; Stemmer; Sterling; Stoneydale; Stuart; Taylor; Ten Speed; Texas Christian Univ.; Thorndike; Tuttle; Univ. of Arkansas; Univ. of Illinois; Univ. of New Mexico; Univ. of North Carolina; Univ. of Pennsylvania; Univ. Press of Kentucky; Univ. Press of Mississippi; Univ. Press of Virginia; Van der Marck; Vesta; Walker; Wallace-Homestead; Westernlore; Wingra; Winston-Derek; Yankee.

Animals. Alaska Nature; Angel; Atheneum Children's; Barron's; Carolina; Christopher; Coles; Council Oak; Davenport; Dembner; Denlinger's; Dial; Dillon; Eriksson; Faber & Faber; Flora and Fauna; Garden Way; H.W.H.; Hale; Harper & Row; Houghton Mifflin; Iowa State; Kesend; Key Porter; Miller; Mosaic; National Press; Pineapple; Quartet; Quinlan; Raintree; Rocky Top; S.C.E.; Scribner's; Sierra Club; Stemmer; Sterling; T.F.H.; Tab; Thorndike; Thorsons; Universe; Univ. of Arizona; Vanguard; Williamson; Wingra; World Natural History.

Anthropology/Archaeology. Cambridge Univ.; Inst. for Study of Human Issues; Johnson; Kent State; Museum of New Mexico; North Point; Northland; Noyes; Ohio State; Pickwick; Princeton Univ.; Santa Barbara; Stanford; Sutton; UMI; Univ. of Arizona; Univ. of Iowa; Univ. of Nevada; Univ. of Pennsylvania; Univ. Tennessee; Univ. of Texas; Univ. of Utah; Univ. Press of Kentucky; Westernlore.

Art & Architecture. Abrams; Arbor House; Art Direction; Atheneum Children's; Barron's; Beacon; Bennett & McNight; Branden; Braziller; Bucknell; Chelsea Green; Christopher; Chronicle; Copley; Council Oak; Davenport; Delta; Dharma; Diamond; Douglas & McIntyre; Down East; Dragonsbreath; Dundurn; Effective Learning; Faber & Faber; Fairleigh Dickinson; Fitzhenry & Whiteside; Fleet; Getty; Great Ocean; Green Tiger; Grunwald and Radcliff; Guernica; H.P.; H.W.H.; Hale; Harper & Row; Hounslow; Hudson Hills; International Publishers; Intervarsity; Iowa State; Kaufmann; Kent State; Key Porter; Kramer; Lang; Learning Pub.; Library Research; Loyola; McFarland & Co.; MacMillan of Canada; Main St.; Mazda; MIT; Morrow; Mosaic; Museum of New Mexico; Museum of Northern Arizona; National Gallery of Canada; Nimbus; North Light; Northland; Noyes; Ohio State; Optimum; Padre; Pagurian; Pandora; PBC; Penkevill; Pineapple; Potter; Prentice-Hall; Prentice-Hall Canada; Preservation; Princeton Architectural; Princeton Univ.; Purdue; Resource; Rosen; Roundtable; Rowman & Littlefield; Saybrook; Schram; Scribner's; Simon & Schuster; ST; Stemmer; Sterling; Stoneydale; Stuart; Sunstone; Tab; Taplinger; Texas Monthly; Theatre Arts; Timber; Troubador; Tuttle; Twayne; UMI; Universe; Univ. of Alabama; Univ. of Alberta; Univ. of Arkansas; Univ. of California; Univ. of Massachusetts; Univ. of Missouri; Univ. of New Mexico; Univ. of Texas; Univ. Press of America; Univ. Press of Virginia; Van der Marck; Vanguard; Vesta; Walch; Walker; Wallace-Homestead; Western Tanager; Whitson; Williamson; Wingra; Wofsy; Writer's Digest.

Astrology/Psychic Phenomena. ACS; Brunner/Mazel; Coles; Garber; Larson; Llewellyn; McFarland & Co.; Morgan & Morgan; Newcastle; Para Research; Prometheus; Sterling; Theosophical; Valley of the Sun.

Autobiographies. Arbor House; Atlantic Monthly; Potter.

Bibliographies. Associated Book; Compubibs; Computer Science; Data and Research Technology; Family Album; Feminist; Garland; Klein; Oregon State; Oryx; Reymont; Scarecrow; Shoe String; Univ. Press of Virginia; Vance; Whitson.

Biography. Academy Chicago; Addison-Wesley; Adler & Adler; Alaska Nature; Alaska Northwest; American Atheist; Ancestry; Angel; Associated Faculty; Atheneum; Atheneum Children's; Atlantic Monthly; Avon; Beaufort; Binford & Mort; Blair; Bluejay; Borgo; Bosco; Branden; Brethren; Cambridge Univ.; Carroll & Graf; Catholic Univ.; Cay-Bel; CBP; Cedarshouse; Celestial; Chelsea Green; China; Christopher; Citadel; Clarion; Arthur H. Clark; Columbia; Copley; Council Oak; Creative Arts; Cuff; Daniel; Dante; Dharma; Dillon; Dorchester; Douglas & McIntyre; Down East; Dragonsbreath; Dundurn; Eden; Effective Learning; Enslow; Eriksson; Faber & Faber; Falcon; Family Album; Feminist; Fitzhenry & Whiteside; Fleet; Grafton; Great Ocean; Green Hill; Grunwald and Radcliff; Guernica; H.W.H.; Hale; Hancock; Harper & Row; Harvest; Here's Life; Houghton Mifflin; Hounslow; Howell-North; Huntington; Hurtig; International Publishers; Iowa State; Kent State; Kesend; Key Porter; Lang; Lee's; Leonard; Liberty; Library Research; Little, Brown & Co.; Loiry; Loyola; MacMillan of Canada; Madrona; Maverick; MCN; Monitor; Morrow; Mosaic; Motorbooks; Museum of New Mexico; Naval Inst.; New England; New Leaf; New Society; Nimbus; North Point; Northeastern Univ.; Ohio State; Optimum; Oregon State; Our Sunday Visitor; Pacific Press; Pandora; Panjandrum; Paragon; Pelican; Pineapple; Pocket; Poseidon; Potter; Prairie; Precedent; Princeton Univ.; Prometheus; Purdue; Quartet; Quill; Quinlan; Regnery/Gateway; Renaissance; Roundtable; Routledge & Kegan Paul; Russica; S.C.E.; St. Luke's; St. Martin's; Sandlapper; Santa Barbara; Saybrook; Schirmer; Scribner's; Second Chance/Permanent; Seven Locks; Shameless Hussy; Shoe String; Simon & Schuster; Slavica; Stemmer; Stoneydale; Stuart; Sutton; Taplinger; Taylor; Texas Monthly; Thorndike; Threshold; Thunder's Mouth; Trans-Canada; Twayne; Universe; Univ. of Alabama; Univ. of Alberta; Univ. of Arkansas; Univ. of Illinois; Univ. of Massachusetts; Univ. of Nevada; Univ. of Pennsylvania; Univ. Press of Kansas; Univ. Press of Kentucky; Univ. Press of Mississippi; Van der Marck; Vanguard; Vehicule; Vesta; Walker; Western Producer; Western Tanager; Westernlore; Winston-Derek; Woodsong; Word Books; World Natural History; Wright; Yankee; Zebra; Zondervan.

Business & Economics. Addison-Wesley; Adler & Adler; Allen & Unwin; Allen; Almar; American Council for the Arts; Arbor House; ARCsoft; Asher-Gallant; Associated Book; Associated Faculty; Atheneum Children's; Avon; Ballinger; Bankers; Bantam; Beaufort; Benjamin; Betterway; Bookmakers; Brethren; Brevet; Briarcliff; Brick; Cambridge Univ.; Chilton; Christopher; Cleaning Consultant; Coles; Columbia; Communications; Compubibs; Consumer Reports; Cordovan; Council Oak; Dartnell; Davidson; Delmar; Devonshire; Douglas & McIntyre; Dow Jones-Irwin; Eden; Effective Learning; Enslow; Enterprise; Eriksson; ETC; Exanimo; Fairchild; Fairleigh Dickinson; Falcon; Farnsworth; Fitzhenry & Whiteside; Florida Trend; Fraser; Free; General Hall; Grafton; Great Ocean; Green Hill; Greenwood; Gulf; Hamilton; Harbor; Harper & Row; Harvard Common; Heath; Hounslow; Humanics; Industrial; Inst. for Study of Human Issues; Intercultural; International Publishers; International Self-Counsel; International Wealth Success; Interurban; Kaufmann; Key Porter; Klein; Knowledge Industry; Krieger; Lang; Liberty; Library Research; Linch; Lomond; Longman, Inc.; Loompanics; McFarland & Co.; McGraw-Hill; Marathon; Mazda; Menasha Ridge; Mercury; Merrill; MGI; MIT; Mosaic; National Press; National Pub. of Black Hills; National Textbook; New York Zoetrope; Noyes; Ohio Univ.; Oryx; Overlook; Padre; Pelican; Petrocelli; Pilot; Pluribus; Poseidon; Prentice-Hall Canada; Prentice-Hall; Princeton Univ.; Purdue; Quartet; Regnery/Gateway; Reymont; Riverdale; Ronin; Roundtable; Routledge & Kegan Paul; Rowman & Littlefield; Roxbury; RPM; Rynd; S.C.E.; Saybrook; Self-Counsel; Seven Locks; South End; Stanford; Sterling; Stipes; Stuart; Tab; Ten Speed; Tensleep; Texas Monthly; Times; Trans-Canada; UMI; Universe; Univ. of Illinois; Univ. of Pennsylvania; Univ. of Texas; Univ. Press of America; Univ. Press of Virginia; Vanguard; Volcano; Walch; Walker; Wallace-Homestead; Western Prairie; Willamson; Wilshire; Windsor; Wright.

Career Guidance. Almar; Associated Book; Bennett & McNight; Chatham; Collier MacMillan; Fairchild; Guidance; Interstate; McFarland & Co.; National Textbook; Occupational Awareness; Octameron; Peterson's; Pilot; Rosen; Ten Speed; VGM Career; Writer's Digest.

Coffee Table Books. Appalachian Mountain; China; Chronicle; Down East; Dundurn; Eden; Fiddlehead; Grunwald and Radcliff; Hale; Harbor; Hounslow; Howell-North; Imagine; Key Porter; Leonard; Library Research; Llewellyn; Main St.; Morgan & Morgan; Multnomah; Museum of Northern Arizona; Nimbus; Pelican; Princeton Architectural; Quartet; Sandlapper; Seven Seas; Stoneydale; Stuart; Sutton; T.F.H.; Taylor; Texas Monthly; Van der Marck; Zondervan.

Communications. Beacon; Bradson; Communication Skill; Communications; Drama; ISI; Knowledge Industry; Longman, Inc.; Meriwether; New York Zoetrope; Purdue; Thorsons; Univelt; Word Beat; Writer's Digest.

Community/Public Affairs. Communications; Groupwork Today; Indiana Univ.; MacMillan of Canada; Temple Univ.; UMI; Univ. of Massachusetts.

Computers/Electronics. American Federation of Information Processing Societies; ARCsoft; Ashton-Tate; Baen; Carolina; Chilton; Compubibs; Compute!; Computer Science; Datamost; Davis; Delmar; Dust-Books; Entelek; Fairchild; Graphic Image; Hayden; Heath; Kaufmann; McGraw-Hill; Microtrend; MIT;

National Pub. of Black Hills; New York Zoetrope; Noyes; Prentice-Hall Canada; Prentice-Hall; Q.E.D.; Que; S.C.E.; Sourceview; Sybex; Tab; UMI; Univ. of Pennsylvania; VGM Career; Walch; Yourdon.

Consumer Affairs. Almar; Consumer Reports; Dell; Menasha Ridge.

Cooking, Foods & Nutrition. Aglow; Alaska Northwest; Angel; Applezaba; Arbor House; Associated Book; Atheneum; Atheneum Children's; AVI; Bantam; Barron's; Benjamin; Berkley; Better Homes & Gardens; Betterway; Brethren; Briarcliff; BYLS; Camaro; Cay-Bel; Celestial; Chicago Review; China; Christopher; Chronicle; Coles; Consumer Reports; Council Oak; Creative Arts; Crossing; Daniel; Diamond; Douglas & McIntyre; Down East; Effective Learning; Eriksson; Falcon Press Pub.; Forman; Frompovich; Garden Way; Globe Pequot; Golden West Pub.; Grafton; Grunwald and Radcliff; H.P.; H.W.H.; Hale; Hancock; Harbor; Harper & Row; Harvard Common; Houghton Mifflin; Hounslow; Humanics; Ideals; Jonathan David; Key Porter; Liberty; Little, Brown & Co.; LoneStar; Madrona; Main St.; Marathon; Maverick; Mazda; Meyerbooks; Miller; Morrow; Mosaic; Museum of New Mexico; National Press; New England; Nimbus; Nitty Gritty; North Point; 101 Prod.; Optimum; Ortho; Ottenheimer; Pacific Press; Padre; Pagurian; Panjandrum; Peachtree; Pelican; Pineapple; Poseidon; Potter; Prairie; Prentice-Hall Canada; Quill; Rodale; Ronin; Royal; S.C.E.; Sandlapper; Seven Seas; Stackpole; Stemmer; Sterling; Stillpoint; Stipes; Stoeger; Strawberry Hill; Susann; Taylor; Ten Speed; Tensleep; Texas Monthly; Thorsons; Thunder's Mouth; Times; Tuttle; Univ. Press of Virginia; Vanguard; Vesta; Wallace-Homestead; Western Producer; Williamson; Wine Appreciation; Wingra; Woodland; Woodsong; Word Books; Wright; Yankee.

Counseling. Accelerated Development; Barron's; Beacon; Consumer Reports; Edits; Groupwork; Interstate; Knox; Learning Pub.; Morehouse-Barlow; Occupational Awareness; Tyndale.

Crafts. Associated Book, Better Homes & Gardens; Briarcliff; Chilton; Collector; Dillon; Doll; Front Row; Naturegraph; Optimum; Rocky Top; Stackpole; Standard; Success; Sunstone; Timber; Universe; Vanguard; Wallace-Homestead; Winchester; Yankee.

Education(al). Accelerated Development; Acropolis; Addison-Wesley; Adler & Adler; American Catholic; Associated Book; Bantam; Barnes & Noble; Barron's; BYLS; Cambridge; CBP; Cliffs Notes; Coles; Collier MacMillan; Communicaton Skill; Dante; Denison; Eakin; Edits; Education Assoc.; Entelek; ETC; Feminist; Gifted Education; Guidance; Heritage; Humanics; Incentive; Intercultural; Interstate; Jalmar; Jamestown; Lake; Larson; Learning Endeavors; Learning Pub; Liberty; Liguori; Longman, Inc.; Merrill; MGI; Morehouse-Barlow; National Pub. of Black Hills; National Textbook; Naturegraph; New Readers; Occupational Awareness; Octameron; Oddo; Ohio State; Open Court; Oregon State; Oryx; P.P.I.; Peterson's; Pilot; Porter; Sargent; Prakken; Prentice-Hall; Que; Regents; Regnery/Gateway; Religious Ed.; Resource; Riverdale; Rosen; Routledge & Kegan Paul; Shoe String; Stanford; Teachers College; Theatre Arts; Twenty-Third; Univ. Press of America; VGM Career; Walch; Whitaker; Williamson.

Ethnic. Borealis; BYLS; China; Dante; Dharma; Firebrand; Fleet; Floricanto; General Hall; Guernica; Heart of the Lakes; Holloway; Indiana Univ.; Inst. for Study of Human Resources; International Publishers; Kar-Ben Copies; Museum of New Mexico; Museum of Northern Arizona; Naturegraph; Northland; Open Court; Pelican; Riverdale; Russica; Slavica; South End; Stanford; Strawberry Hill; Texas Western; Three Continents; Thunder's Mouth; Tuttle; Univ. of Arizona; Univ. of Massachusetts; Univ. of Nevada; Univ. of Oklahoma; Univ. of Pennsylvania; Univ. of Tennessee; Univ. of Texas; Univ. of Utah; Univ. Press of America; Westernlore; Yankee.

Fashion & Beauty. Acropolis; Fairchild; Volcano.

Feminism. Crossing; Feminist; Firebrand; Pandora; Press Gang; Shameless Hussy; South End; Spinsters; Thorsons.

Film/Cinema/Stage. Atlantic Monthly; Borgo; Bradson; Broadway; Citadel; Coach House; Columbia; Communications; Drama; French; Indiana Univ.; JH; Lake View; McFarland & Co.; Main St.; Panjandrum; Penkevill; Roundtable; Scarecrow; Schirmer; Sterling; Taplinger; UMI; Universe; Univ. of Texas; Univ. Press of America.

Games & Entertainment. Coles; Dell; Gambling Times; H.P.; Holloway; Intergalactic; Leonard; McFarland & Co.; Quill; Standard; Sterling; Troubador.

Gardening/Plants. Associated Book; Better Homes & Gardens; Briarcliff; Coles; Delmar; Garden Way; H.P.; Main St. Naturegraph; 101 Prod.; Optimum; Ortho; Ottenheimer; Panjandrum; Symmes; Ten Speed; Timber; Transnational; Universe; Yankee.

Gay/Lesbian. Alyson; Crossing; Firebrand; JH; Spinsters.

General Nonfiction. Academy Chicago; Adler & Adler; American Atheist; American Psychiatric; Atlantic Monthly; Avon Flare; Ballantine; Beacon; Braemar; Braziller; Delacorte; Dell; Fleet; Heath; Johnson; Kent State; Learning Pub.; Morrow; Muir; New American; Norton; Oddo; Ohio Univ.; Pacific; Pagurian; Pandora; Pharos; Pineapple; Pocket; Prentice-Hall Canada; Pruett; Quinlan; St. Martin's; Shoe String; Stein & Day; Taplinger; Time-Life; University of Wisconsin; Viking Penguin.

Government & Politics. Addison-Wesley; Adler & Adler; Allen & Unwin; American Atheist; Angel; Arbor House; Associated Faculty; Atheneum; Atheneum Children's; Avon; Beacon; Borgo; Branden; Brethren; Bucknell; CQ; Canterbury; Cedarshouse; Chelsea Green; Christopher; Columbia; Communications; Council Oak; Cuff; Davidson; Delta; Douglas & McIntyre; Eakin; Eden; Effective Learning; Eriksson; Faber & Faber; Farleigh Dickinson; Falcon; Florida Trend; Fraser; General Hall; Government Institutes; Grafton; Great Ocean; Green Hill; Guernica; Hale; Harper & Row; Harrow and Heston; Harvard Common; Heath; Houghton Mifflin; Hounslow; Hurtig; Inst. for Study of Human Issues; Intercultural; International Publishers; Key Porter; Lake View; Lang; Library Research; Loiry; Lomond; Longman, Inc.; Loompanics; Louisiana State; McClelland and Bantam; Madrona; Mazda; Mercury; Miller; NC; New Society; Northeastern Univ.; Northern Illinois Univ.; Ohio State; P.P.I.; Pandora; Pantheon; Paragon; Pelican; Prentice-Hall Canada; Press Gang; Princeton Univ.; Purdue; Quartet; Quinlan; Rainbow; Regnery/Gateway; Riverdale; Roundtable; Rowman & Littlefield; S.C.E.; St. Martin's; Saybrook; Second Chance/Permanent; Seven Locks; South End; Spinsters; Stanford; Stuart; Sugden; T&T Clark; Taylor; Texas Monthly; Thunder's Mouth; Transnational; Universe; Univ of Alabama; Univ. of Alberta; Univ. of Illinois; Univ. of Massachusetts; Univ. of North Carolina; Univ. of Pennsylvania; Univ. of Tennessee; Univ. Press of America; Univ. Press of Kansas; Univ. Press of Kentucky; Univ. Press of Mississippi; Univ. Press of Virginia; Vanguard; Vehicule; Vesta; Volcano; Walch; Western Producer; Western Tanager; Word Books.

Health & Medicine. Acropolis; ACS; Addison-Wesley; Adler & Adler; Almar; American Psychiatric; And/Or; Angel; Arbor House; Associated Faculty; Aster; Atheneum Children's; Augsburg; AVI; Avon; Bantam; Beaufort; Benjamin; Better Homes & Gardens; Betterway; Bookmakers; Bradson; Branden; Brethren; Briarcliff; Bridge; Brunner/Mazel; Camaro; Cambridge Univ.; Carolina; Celestial; Christopher; Cleaning Consultant; Coles; Compcare; Consumer Reports; Copley; Council Oak; Creative Arts; Crossing; Delmar; Delta; Eden; Enslow; Eriksson; Faber & Faber; Falcon; Falcon Press Pub.; Fitzhenry & Whiteside; Golden West Pub.; Grafton; Great Ocean; Warren H. Green; Grunwald and Radcliff; H.P.; H.W.H.; Hale; Hanley & Belfus; Harper & Row; Harvard Common; Hazelden; Health Profession; Houghton Mifflin; Hounslow; Human Kinetics; Humanics; Hunter; Information Resources; Iowa State; Ishiyaku Euroamerica; Kaufmann; Kesend; Key Porter; Krieger; Lang; McClelland and Bantam; McFarland & Co.; McGraw-Hill; Madrona; Maverick; Medical Economics; Menasha Ridge; Meyerbooks; Mosaic; National Press; National Pub. of Black Hills; Naturegraph; NC; New Leaf; Newcastle; Optimum; Oryx; Ottenheimer; P.P.I.; Pacific Press; Pandora; Panjandrum; Pantheon; Para Research; Pineapple; Pluribus; Poseidon; Potentials Development; Prentice-Hall; Prentice-Hall Canada; Prometheus; PSG; Raintree; Rocky Top; Rodale; Ronin; Rosen; Roundtable; Rowman & Littlefield; Rynd; S.C.E.; Saybrook; Scholium; Scribner's; Sierra Club; Spinsters; Sterling; Stillpoint; Strawberry Hill; Stuart; Susann; Tab; Temple Univ.; Theosophical; Thorsons; Times; Ultralight; Universe; Univ. of Pennsylvania; Univ. of Texas; Univ. Press of Virginia; Van der Marck; Volcano; Walch; Walker; Williamson; Wilshire; Winston-Derek; Woodland; Word Books; Wright; Zebra.

History. Academy Chicago; Alaska Northwest; Allen & Unwin; Ancestry; Angel; Appalachian Mountain; Arbor House; Associated Book; Associated Faculty; Atheneum; Atheneum Children's; Atlantic Monthly; Avon; Beacon; Beaufort; Betterway; Binford & Mort; Blair; Bookmakers; Borgo; Boston Mills; Braemar; Branden; Braziller; Brethren; Brevet; Bucknell; Cambridge Univ.; Catholic Univ.; Cay-Bel; Cedarshouse; Chelsea Green; Christopher; Citadel; Arthur H. Clark; T & T Clark; Compubibs; Cordovan; Council Oak; Crossway; Cuff; Davidson; Devonshire; Dharma; Dial; Dillon; Douglas & McIntyre; Down East; Dragonsbreath; Dundurn; Eakin; Eden; Eerdmans; Effective Learning; Eriksson; Faber & Faber; Fairleigh Dickinson; Falcon; Falcon Press Pub.; Farrar, Straus and Giroux; Fiddlehead; Fitzhenry & Whiteside; Fleet; Flores; Florida Trend; Getty; Globe; Golden West Pub.; Grafton; Great Ocean; Green Hill; Grunwald and Radcliff; Guernica; Hale; Hancock; Harper & Row Jr.; Harper & Row; Harvard Common; Heart of the Lakes; Heath; Herald; Heritage; Heyday; Houghton Mifflin; Hounslow; Howell-North; Hurtig; Indiana Univ.; Inst. for Study of Human Issues; International Marine; International Publishers; Interurban; Intervarsity; Iowa State; Johnson; Kar-Ben Copies; Kaufmann; Kent State; Kesend; Key Porter; Krieger; Lang; Lee's; Lexikos; Liberty; Library Research; Little, Brown & Co.; Longman, Inc.; Lorien; Louisiana State; Loyola; McFarland & Co.; MacMillan of Canada; Madrona; Maverick; Mazda; MCN; Memphis State; Meyerbooks; Miller; Morrow; Mosaic; Mountain; Museum of New Mexico; Museum of Northern Arizona; Naturegraph; Naval Inst.; NC; New England; New Leaf; New Society; Nimbus; North Point; Northeastern Univ.; Northern Illinois Univ.; Northword; Noyes; Ohio State; Ohio Univ.; Open Court; Optimum; Oregon State; Our Sunday Visitor; Outbooks; Overlook; Padre; Paladin; Pandora; Pantheon; Paragon; Peachtree; Penkevill; Pickwick; Pineapple; Pocket; Poseidon; Prentice-Hall; Prentice-Hall Canada; Preservation; Presidio; Press Gang; Princeton Architectural; Princeton Univ.; Purdue; Quartet; Quill; Quinlan; Rainbow; Raintree; Regnery/Gateway; Renaissance; Riverdale; Routhledge & Kegan Paul; Russia; S.C.E.; St. Bede's; St. Martin's; Second Chance/Permanent; Seven Locks; Shameless Hussy; Shoe String; Simon & Schuster; Slavica; Spinsters; State Historical Society of Wisconsin; Stemmer; Stoneydale; Strawberry Hill; Stuart; Sugden; Sunstone; Sutton; T&T Clark; Taplinger; Temple Univ.; Ten Speed; Texas Christian Univ.; Texas Monthly; Texas Western; Three Continents; Thunder's Mouth; Times; Tompson & Rutter; Tuttle; Twayne; Universe; Univ. of Alabama; Univ. of Alberta; Univ. of Arkansas; Univ. of Illinois; Univ. of Iowa; Univ. of Massachusetts; Univ. of Missouri; Univ. of Nevada; Univ. of New Mexico; Univ. of North Carolina; Univ. of Oklahoma; Univ. of Pennsylvania; Univ. of Tennessee; Univ. of Utah; Univ. Press of America; Univ. Press of Kansas; Univ. Press of Kentucky; Univ. Press of Mississippi; Univ. Press of Virginia; Van der Marck; Vanguard; Vehicule; Vesta; Volcano; Walch; Walker; Western Producer; Western Tanager; Westernlore; Wingra; Word Books; Yankee; Zebra; Zondervan.

Hobby. Almar; Ancestry; Angel; ARCsoft; Associated Book; Atheneum Children's; Avon; Bale; Barnes & Noble; Benjamin; Betterway; Bradson; Carstens; Coles; Collector; Council Oak; Datamost; Devonshire; Diamond; Doll; Dundurn; Effective Learning; Enslow; Eriksson; Faber & Faber; Falcon Press Pub.; Grafton; H.P.; H.W.H.; Hale; Harvard Common; Hounslow; Howell-North; Interurban; Kalmbach; Kesend; Key Porter; Klein; Liberty; Madrona; Main St.; Maverick; MCN; Menasha Ridge; Meyerbooks; Mosaic; Mountain; Mustang; Ortho; Padre; Panjandrum; Pineapple; Quinlan; Renaissance; S.C.E.; St. Martin's; Scribner's; Sterling; Stoeger; Success; Symmes; Tab; Ten Speed; Tensleep; Ultralight; Vanguard; Wallace-Homestead; Williamson; Wilshire; Woodsong.

Home/Family Life. Addison-Wesley; Bennett & McNight; Berkley; Better Homes & Gardens; Brunner/Mazel; Catholic Truth; Collier MacMillan; Compcare; Delmar; Delta; Fairchild; Garlinghouse; Golden; Great Ocean; Here's Life; Humanics; Interstate; Knox; Lakewood; 101 Prod.; Optimum; Ortho; Ottenheimer; Pacific Press; Parenting; Rosen; Shaw; Sterling; Times; Tyndale; Whitaker; Williamson; Winch; Zebra.

How-To. AASLH; Acropolis; Addison-Wesley; Albatross; Allen; Almar; American Council for the Arts; Amphoto; Ancestry; Andrews, McMeel & Parker; Angel; Appalachian Mountain; Arbor House; ARCsoft; Arman; Art Direction; Asher-Gallant; Aster; Atheneum Children's; Barnes & Noble; Benjamin; Berkley; Betterway; Bookmakers; Briarcliff; Brick; Bridge; BYLS; Cay-Bel; CBP; Chicago Review; Chilton; China; Chosen; Christian Ed.; Christopher; Cleaning Consultant; Compcare; Consumer Reports; Cornell Maritime; Council Oak; Creative Arts; Datamost; Davis; De Graff; Dell; Delta; Dembner; Denlinger's; Diamond; Dundurn; Eden; Effective Learning; Enslow; Ericksson; ETC; Exanimo; Faber & Faber; Falcon; Falcon Press Pub.; Flores; Forman; Front Row; Gambling Times; Garlinghouse; Gifted Education; Golden; Golden West Pub.; Graphic Image; Great Ocean; H.P.; Hale; Hamilton; Hancock; Harper & Row; Harvard Common; Harvest; Here's Life; Heritage; Heyday; Houghton Mifflin; Human Kinetics; Hunter; Imagine; Intercultural; International Self-Counsel; International Wealth Success; ISI; Johnson; Jonathan David; Kalmbach; Kaufmann; Kesend; Key Porter; Klein; Larson; Learning Pub.; Leonard; Liberty; Library Research; Linch; Little, Brown & Co.; Llewellyn; Loiry; Lone Star; Loompanics; Lorien; McClelland and Bantam; MacMillan of Canada; Madrona; Main St.; Marathon; Menasha Ridge; Meriwether; MGI; Miller; Morrow; Motorbooks; Mountain; Mountaineers; Muir; Music Sales; Mustang; National Press; Naturegraph; New England; Newcastle; Nimbus; North Light; 101 Prod.; Optimum; Ortho; Overlook; Pacific Press; Padre; Paladin; Panjandrum; Pantheon; Para Research; Pelican; Pineapple; Pluribus; Potter; Prentice-Hall; Que; Quinlan; Rainbow; Resource; Reymont; Rocky Top; Rodale; Ronin; Ross; Roundtable; RPM; S.C.E.; Santa Barbara; Schirmer; Self-Counsel; Seven Seas; Shaw; Sierra Club; ST; Standard; Sterling; Stoeger; Stone Wall; Stoneydale; Stuart; Success; Sunstone; Susann; T.F.H.; T.L.; Tab; Taylor; Ten Speed; Tensleep; Thomas; Thorndike; Thunder's Mouth; Ultralight; Universe; Univ. of Alberta; Van der Marck; Vanguard; Walker; Wallace-Homestead; Western Marine; Wilderness; Williamson; Wilshire; Windsor; Wine Appreciation; Wingbow; Wingra; Woodland; Woodsong; Word Beat; Word Books; Wright; Writer's Digest; Yankee; Zebra; Zondervan.

Humanities. American Council for the Arts; Duquesne; Fordham; Free; Garland; Indiana Univ.; Louisiana State; Penkevill; Prometheus; Riverdale; Roxbury; Saybrook; Southern Illnois Univ.; Stanford; Whitson.

Humor. American Atheist; Andrews, McMeel & Parker; Angel; Applezaba; Atheneum Children's; Baker; Bradson; Celestial; Chicago Review; Citadel; Clarion; Council Oak; Critic's Choice; Cuff; Daniel; Davenport; Delta; Dorchester; Dragonsbreath; Eriksson; Faber & Faber; Farrar, Straus and Giroux; Grafton; Guernica; H.W.H.; Hale; Harper & Row; Harvard Common; Hounslow; Hurtig; Kaufmann; Key Porter; Leonard; Madrona; Marathon; Mosaic; Mustang; National Press; New England; New Society; Nimbus; Paladin; Peachtree; Pelican; Pharos; Potter; Prentice-Hall; Price/Stern/Sloan; Quinlan; Rainbow; Rocky Top; Ronin; Roundtable; Russica; S.C.E.; Sandlapper; Scribner's; Seven Seas; Sterling; Stuart; Susann; Sutton; Ten Speed; Texas Monthly; Thorndike; Vanguard; Woodsong; Wright; Zebra; Zondervan.

Illustrated Book. Addison-Wesley; Appalachian Mountain; Aster; Atheneum Children's; Aya; Betterway; Boston Mills; Branden; Chelsea Green; Christian Ed.; Cleaning Consultant; Council Oak; Cuff; Devonshire; Douglas & McIntyre; Down East; Dragonsbreath; Eden; Falcon; Flores; Grafton; Hale; Harbor; Harvest; Here's Life; Howell-North; Imagine; Kesend; Key Porter; Leonard; Liberty; Main St.; Maverick; MCN; Monitor; Morgan & Morgan; Muir; National Press; New England; New Society; Nimbus; Northland; Oddo; 101 Prod.; Optimum; Ortho; Paragon; Parenting; Pelican; Princeton Architectural; Pruett; Quartet; Quinlan; Ronin; Routledge & Kegan Paul; Sandlapper; Schram; Seven Seas; Shameless Hussy; Stemmer; Stuart; Sutton; T.F.H.; Texas Monthly; Univ. of Arkansas; Univ. Press of Virginia; Van der Marck; Williamson; Wright; Zondervan.

Juvenile. Abingdon; Alaska Nature; Alaska Northwest; Associated Book; Atheneum Children's; Augsburg; Avon; Baker; Bantam; Betterway; Bookcraft; Bookmakers; Bosco; Bradson; Branden; Brethren; Broadman; BYLS; Cay-Bel; Childrens; China; Christian Ed.; Clarion; Concordia; Cuff; Davenport; Dell; Denison; Dial; Dillon; Douglas & McIntyre; Down East; Dundurn; Enslow; Faber & Faber; Farrar, Straus and Giroux; Feminist; Fleet; Floricanto; Gibson; Golden; Green Tiger; Guernica; Harper & Row Jr.; Harvest; Holiday; Houghton Mifflin; Hounslow; Humanics; Incentive; Kar-Ben Copies; Lee's; Leonard; Lodestar; Lothrop, Lee & Shepard; McElderry; MacMillan of Canada; MacMillan; Mazda; Morgan & Morgan; Morrow Jr.; National Press; Nelson; Nimbus; Oddo; P.P.I.; Pacific Press; Panjandrum; Pantheon; Parenting; Pelican; Philomel; Platt & Munk; Potter; Prentice-Hall; Raintree; Review and Herald; Roundtable; Sandlapper; Saybrook; Scribner's; Shameless Hussy; Shaw; Sierra Club; Standard; Stemmer; Sterling; Stillpoint; Success; Sutton; Tensleep; Troubador; Tuttle; Vanguard; Viking Penguin; Walker; Williamson; Wingra; Woodland; Woodsong; Wright; Zondervan.

Labor & Management. Abbott, Langer & Assoc.; Dartnell; Groupwork Today; International Publishers; Interstate; Lomond; MIT; New Society; Pluribus; Ronin; Rowman & Littlefield; RPM.

Language & Literature. Allen & Unwin; Associated Book; Aya; Bantam; Barron's; Beacon; Brandon; Braziller; Cambridge; Catholic Univ.; Coles; Communication Skill; Crossing; Dante; Fiddlehead; Fitzhenry & Whiteside; Heath; Heinle & Heinle; Indiana Univ.; Intervarsity; Kent State; Longman, Inc.; Lorien; Louisiana State; McFarland & Co.; Meriwether; Merrill; MIT; Modern Language Assoc.; National Textbook; New Readers; Noyes; Oddo; Ohio State; Oregon State; Paragon; Penkevill; Prentice-Hall Canada; Prometheus; Purdue; Regents; Rosen; Slavica; Stanford; Taplinger; Texas Christian Univ.; Three Continents;

Threshold; Tuttle; Universe; Univ. of Alabama; Univ. of California; Univ. of Illinois; Univ. of Iowa; Univ. of North Carolina; Univ. of Texas; Univ. Press of America; Univ. Press of Kentucky; Univ. Press of Mississippi; Vanguard; Vehicule; Walch; York.

Literary Criticism. Allen & Unwin; Associated Faculty; Borgo; Dundurn; ECW; Fairleigh Dickinson; Northern Illinois Univ.; Princeton Univ.; Prometheus; Purdue; Routledge & Kegan Paul; Shoe String; Slavica; Stanford; Sugden; Texas Christian Univ.; Texas Western; Twayne; UMI; Univ. of Alabama; Univ. of Massachusetts; Univ. of Missouri; Univ. of Pennsylvania; Univ. of Tennessee; Univ. Press of Mississippi; Vanguard; Whitson; York.

Marine Subjects. Cay-Bel; Cornell Maritime; Harbor; International Marine; Naval Inst.; Oddo; Oregon State; Padre; PBC; Seven Seas; Tab; Western Marine; Yankee.

Military. Avon; Beau Lac; MCN; Naval Inst.; Paladin; Presidio; Shoe String; Stackpole.

Money & Finance. Acropolis; Addison-Wesley; Almar; Bale; Ballinger; Bankers; Bantam; Benjamin; Better Homes & Gardens; Cordovan; Dow Jones-Irwin; Enterprise; Farnsworth; International Self-Counsel; International Wealth Success; Lakewood; Linch; Longman Financial; Marathon; Medical Economics; Padre; Pilot; Prentice-Hall; RPM.

Music & Dance. American Catholic; Atheneum Children's; Beaufort; Branden; Bucknell; Cambridge Univ.; Columbia; Communications; Concordia; Consumer Reports; Council Oak; Dance Horizons; Davenport; Delta; Dragon's Teeth; Drama; Eriksson; Faber & Faber; Fairleigh Dickinson; Fleet; Grafton; Great Ocean; Guernica; Hale; Harper & Row; Harvard Common; International Publishers; Key Porter; Krieger; Lang; Leonard; Louisiana State; McFarland & Co.; Maverick; Morrow; Mosaic; Museum of New Mexico; Music Sales; Northeastern Univ.; Ohio State; Panjandrum; Paragon; Pelican; Penkevill; Prentice-Hall; Quill; Quinlan; Resource; Rosen; Scarecrow; Schirmer; Simon & Schuster; Stipes; Stuart; Tab; Theatre Arts; UMI; Universe; Univ. of Alabama; Univ. of Arkansas; Univ. of Illinois; Univ. of Missouri; Univ. Press of America; Van der Marck; Vanguard; Walch; Walker; Whitson; Writer's Digest.

Nature & Environment. Abrams; Addison-Wesley; Alaska Nature; Alaska Northwest; Angel; Appalachian Mountain; Atheneum Children's; Binford & Mort; Blair; Bookmakers; Carolina; Chatham; Chelsea Green; Chronicle; Clarion; Colorado Assoc. Univ.; Columbia; Council Oak; Daniel; Davenport; Devonshire; Dial; Dillon; Down East; DustBooks; East Woods; Eden; Effective Learning; Eriksson; Falcon; Falcon Press Pub.; Flora And Fauna; Garden Way; Garlinghouse; Government Institutes; Grafton; Guernica; H.W.H.; Hale; Hancock; Harper & Row; Harvard Common; Helix; Heyday; Houghton Mifflin; Hounslow; Howell-North; Hurtig; Johnson; Kaufmann; Kesend; Key Porter; Krieger; Lexikos; Lorien; McClelland and Bantam; Meyerbooks; Mosaic; Mountain; Museum of New Mexico; Museum of Northern Arizona; Naturegraph; New Society; Nimbus; North Point; Northland; Northward; Noyes; Oddo; Optimum; Oregon State; Ortho; Outbooks; Overlook; Pacific Press; Padre; Pagurian; Paladin; PBC; Pineapple; Platt & Munk; Potter; Purdue; Raintree; Regnery/Gateway; Review and Herald; Rocky Top; S.C.E.; Saybrook; Scribner's; Seven Locks; Sierra Club; Stackpole; Stanford; Stemmer; Stoeger; Stone Wall; Stoneydale; Sutton; Symmes; T.F.H.; Taylor; Ten Speed; Tensleep; Texas Monthly; Thorndike; Timber; Universe; Univ. of Alberta; Univ. of Massachusetts; Univ. of Nevada; Univ. New Mexico; Univ. of North Carolina; Univ. of Texas; Vanguard; Walker; Western Producer; Western Tanager; Wilderness; Williamson; Wingra; Woodland; World Natural History; Yankee.

Philosophy. Alba House; Allen & Unwin; American Atheist; And/Or; Angel; Arbor House; Atheneum Children's; Atlantic Monthly; Baker; Beacon; Berkley; Braziller; Brethren; Bucknell; Canterbury; Catholic Univ.; Cedarshouse; Celestial; Christopher; T & T Clark; Council Oak; Daniel; Dante; Davidson; Dharma; Dragon's Teeth; Eden; Eerdmans; Effective Learning; Enslow; Eriksson; Faber & Faber; Fairleigh Dickinson; Falcon; Farrar, Straus and Giroux; Garber; Gifted Education; Great Ocean; Guernica; Harper & Row; Hounslow; Indiana Univ.; Intercultural; International Publishers; Intervarsity; Krieger; Lang; Larson; Library Research; Loompanics; Lorien; Louisiana State; Miller; New Society; North Point; Ohio State; Ohio Univ.; Open Court; Pandora; Panjandrum; Para Research; Paragon; Paulist; Princeton Univ.; Prometheus; Purdue; Quartet; Regnery/Gateway; Renaissance; Rocky Top; Routledge & Kegan Paul; Rowman & Littlefield; Roxbury; S.C.E.; St. Bede's; Saybrook; Second Chance/Permanent; Sierra Club; Simon & Schuster; South End; Spinster; Stillpoint; Strawberry Hill; Sugden; T&T Clark; Temple Univ.; Theosophical; Threshold; Thunder's Mouth; Univ. of Alabama; Univ. of Alberta; Univ. of Arizona; Univ. of Massachusetts; Univ. of Pennsylvania; Univ. of Utah; Univ. Press of America; Univ. Press of Kansas; Vanguard; Vesta; Volcano; Winston-Derek; Woodsong; Word Books.

Photography. Addison-Wesley; Alaska Nature; Amphoto; Angel; Appalachian Mountain; ARCsoft; Art Direction; Atheneum Children's; Branden; Chronicle; Council Oak; Cuff; Daniel; Delta; Dharma; Diamond; Down East; Dragonsbreath; Eriksson; Faber & Faber; Falcon Press Pub.; Fiddlehead; Graphic Image; Guernica; H.P.; H.W.H.; Hale; Harper & Row; Hounslow; Hudson Hills; Key Porter; Liberty; Madrona; Morgan & Morgan; Motorbooks; Optimum; Owl Creek; Padre; Pandora; PBC; Potter; Quartet; Quinlan; Raintree; Scribner's; Sierra Club; Sterling; Studio; Sutton; Taylor; Texas Monthly; UMI; Univ. of New Mexico; Univ. of Texas; Van der Marck; Wallace-Homestead; Western Producer; Writer's Digest; Yankee.

Psychology. Accelerated Development; ACS; Addison-Wesley; Adler & Adler; Affirmation; Alba House; American Psychiatric; Angel; Arbor House; Aster; Atheneum; Atheneum Children's; Augsburg; Avon; Baker; Beacon; Betterway; Bookmakers; Bradson; Brethren; Brunner/Mazel; Bucknell; Cambridge Univ.; Celestial; Christopher; Citadel; Compubibs; Council Oak; Davidson; Delta; Dembner; Devonshire; Dharma; Dimension; Eden; Edits; Education Assoc.; Eerdmans; Enslow; Eriksson; Fairleigh Dickinson; Falcon; Farrar, Straus and Giroux; General Hall; Gifted Education; Grafton; Guernica; Harper & Row; Harvard Common; Hazelden; Houghton Mifflin; Hounslow; Humanics; Hunter; Intercultural; International Publishers; Intervarsity; Ishiyaku Euroamerica; Jalmar; Kaufmann; Knox; Krieger; Lang; Learning Pub.; Libra; Madrona; MIT; New Society; Newcastle; Occupational Awareness; Open Court; Panjandrum; Para Research; Pelican; Penkevill; Pluribus; Poseidon; Prometheus; Purdue; Quartet; Quill; Rainbow; Regnery/ Gateway; Riverdale; Rodale; Ronin; Rosen; Roundtable; Routledge & Kegan Paul; Roxbury; S.C.E.; Saybrook; Second Chance/Permanent; Self-Counsel; Shameless Hussy; Spinsters; Stanford; Stillpoint; Theosophical; Threshold; Ultralight; UMI; Univ. of Massachusetts; Univ. of Pennsylvania; Univ. Press of America; Univ. Press of Virginia; Vanguard; Volcano; Walch; Walker; Wilshire; Winch; Wingbow; Winston-Derek; Woodsong; Word Books; Zebra; Zondervan.

Real Estate. Longman Financial; Prentice-Hall.

Recreation. Abrams; Addison-Wesley; Alaska Nature; American Council for the Arts; Angel; Appalachian Mountain; Arbor House; Aster; Atheneum Children's; Beaufort; Binford & Mort; Celestial; Chicago Review; Chronicle; Columbia; Council Oak; De Graff; Delta; Diamond; Dillon; Down East; East Woods; Eden; Enslow; Ericksson; Falcon Press Pub.; Globe Pequot; Grafton; Guernica; H.P.; H.W.H.; Hale; Hancock; Harvard Common; Hounslow; Howell-North; Human Kinetics; International Marine; Johnson; Jonathan David; Kaufmann; Key Porter; Liberty; McFarland & Co.; Madrona; Menasha Ridge; Mountain; Mountaineers; Mustang; National Press; Northword; Outbooks; Overlook; Padre; Pantheon; PBC; Peachtree; Pelican; Prentice-Hall; Quinlan; S.C.E.; Scribner's; Sierra Club; Stackpole; Sterling; Stipes; Stoneydale; Ten Speed; Tensleep; Texas Monthly; Thorndike; Walch; Walker; Wilderness; Williamson; Winchester.

Reference. AASLH; Abbott, Langer & Assoc.; Accelerated Development; Acropolis; Adler & Adler; Albatross; Allen & Unwin; American Atheist; American Council for the Arts; American Federation of Information Processing Societies; American Psychiatric; Ancestry; Andrews, McMeel & Parker; Appalachian Mountain; ARCsoft; Arman; Asher-Gallant; Associated Faculty; Aster; AVI; Aya; Ballinger; Bankers; Banks-Baldwin; Bethany; Betterway; Binford & Mort; Bookmakers; Borgo; Bradson; Branden; Brick; Broadway; Cay-Bel; Cedarshouse; Chicago Review; China; Christian Ed.; Christopher; Arthur H. Clark; Cleaning Consultant; Coles; Communications; Compubibs; Compute!; Computer Science; Consumer Reports; Craftsman; Cuff; Dante; Datamost; Davis; Delta; Dembner; Devonshire; Down East; Drama; Dundurn; ECW; Eden; Edits; Eerdmans; Effective Learning; Enslow; ETC; Fairleigh Dickinson; Falcon; Fiddlehead; Flora and Fauna; Floricanto; Florida Trend; Free; Front Row; Garland; General Hall; Getty; Government Institutes; Grafton; Great Ocean; Greenwood; Grunwald and Radcliff; Guernica; Gulf; Hale; Hamilton; Hancock; Hanley & Belfus; Harper & Row; Harvard Common; Harvest; Hayden; Hazelden; Health Profession; Heath; Here's Life; Heritage; Heyday; Human Kinetics; Hurtig; Imagine; Industrial; Information Resources; Intercultural; International Publishers; Ishiyaku Euroamerica; Jonathan David; Kalmbach; Klein; Knox; Krieger; Lang; Learning Pub.; Leonard; Library Research; Libraries Unlimited; Llewellyn; Loompanics; McFarland & Co.; McGraw-Hill; Main St.; Mazda; MCN; Medical Economics; Menasha Ridge; Meyerbooks; Modern Language Assoc.; Monitor; Morgan & Morgan; Museum of New Mexico; Museum of Northern Arizona; National Press; Nelson; New York Zoetrope; North Light; Northeastern; Octameron; Oregon State; Ortho; Oryx; Ottenheimer; Our Sunday Visitor; Overlook; Pacific; Padre; Pandora; Panjandrum; Para Research; Paragon; Penkevill; Peterson's; Petrocelli; Pharos; Pineapple; Pocket; Porter Sargent; Poseidon; Precedent; Prentice-Hall; Princeton Univ.; Que; Rainbow; Raintree; Reference Service; Reymont; Riverdale; Rocky Top; Rodale; Rosen; Routledge & Kegan Paul; Rowman & Littlefield; RPM; Rynd; S.C.E.; St.Martin's; Sandlapper; Scarecrow; Schirmer; Self-Counsel; Seven Locks; Seven Seas; Shoe String; Slavica; Sourceview; ST; Standard; Sterling; Sutton; T.F.H.; T.L.; Tab; Tensleep; Texas Monthly; Thomas; Transnational; Ultralight; Universe; Univ. of Alberta; Univ. of Illinois; Univ. Press of Kentucky; Univ. Press of Virginia; Vesta; Walker; Wallace-Homestead; Western Producer; Western Tanager; Winch; Windsor; Wingbow; Wofsy; Woodland; Woodsong; Word Beat; Word Books; World Natural History; Writer's Digest; Yankee; York; Zondervan.

Regional. Alaska Northwest; Ancestry; Appalachian Mountain; Aya; Binford & Mort; Blair; Borealis; Braemar; Caxton; Cay-Bel; Chatham; Chicago Review; Chronicle; Collier MacMillan; Colorado Assoc. Univ.; Copley; Cordovan; Douglas & McIntyre; Down East; Dundurn; Eakin; East Woods; Eerdmans; Family Album; Fiddlehead; Fitzhenry & Whiteside; Florida Trend; Globe Pequot; Golden West Books; Golden West Pub.; Graphic Arts Center; Guernica; Gulf; Hancock; Harbor; Heart of the Lakes; Herald; Heritage; Hurtig; Indiana Univ.; Interurban; Johnson; Kent State; Lexikos; Louisiana State; Memphis State; Mountain; Mountaineers; Museum of New Mexico; Museum of Northern Arizona; National Gallery of Canada; New England; Nimbus; Northeastern Univ.; Northern Illinois Univ.; Northland; Northword; Ohio Univ.; Oregon State; Outbooks; Pacific; Pantheon; Pelican; Pineapple; Prentice-Hall Canada; Press Gang; Pruett; Quartet; Sandlapper; State Historical Society of Wisconsin; Stoneydale; Sunstone; Syracuse Univ.; Temple Univ.; Texas Christian Univ.; Texas Monthly; Texas Western; Thorndike; Timber; Tompson & Rutter; Tuttle; Univ. of Arizona; Univ. of Arkansas; Univ. of Missouri; Univ. of Nevada; Univ. of New Mexico; Univ. of North Carolina; Univ. of Tennessee; Univ. of Utah; Univ. Press of Kansas; Univ. Press of Mississippi; Vehicule; Western Tanager; Westernlore; Wingbow; Yankee.

Religion. Abingdon; Accent Books; Affirmation; Aglow; Alba House; Alban Institute; American Atheist; American Catholic; Angel; Atheneum Children's; Augsburg; Baker; Bantam; Beacon Hill; Beacon; Bethany; Bookcraft; Bosco; Brethren; Bridge; Broadman; Bucknell; BYLS; Catholic Truth; Catholic Univ.; Cay-Bel; CBP; Chosen; Christian Ed.; Christopher; Concordia; Crossway; Devonshire; Dharma; Dimension; Eden; Eerdmans; Effective Learning; Falcon; Fleet; Fraser; Gibson; Grafton; Great Ocean; Grunwald and Radcliff; Guernica; Hale; Harvest; Hendrickson; Herald; Here's Life; Hounslow; Huntington; Indiana

Univ.; Intervarsity; Jonathan David; Judson; Kar-Ben Copies; Knox; Krieger; Lang; Larson; Liguori; Loyola; McFarland & Co.; Meriwether; Morehouse-Barlow; Morrow; Multnomah; Nelson; New Leaf; New Society; Newcastle; Open Court; Orbis; Our Sunday Visitor; Pacific Press; Pandora; Paragon; Paulist; Pelican; Pickwick; Princeton Univ.; Prometheus; Quinlan; Randall; Regnery/Gateway; Religious Ed.; Resource; Revell; Review and Herald; St. Anthony Messenger; St. Bede's; St. Vladimir's; Santa Barbara; Saybrook; Second Chance/Permanent; Servant; Seven Locks; Shaw; Shining Star; Standard; Stillpoint; Sugden; T&T Clark; Texas Christian Univ.; Theosophical; Threshold; Twenty-Third; Tyndale; UMI; Univ. of Alabama; Univ. of North Carolina; Univ. of Tennessee; Univ. Press of America; Van der Marck; Vanguard; Vesta; Whitaker; Winston-Derek; Word Books; Zondervan.

Scholarly. Associated Faculty; Bucknell; Cambridge Univ.; Catholic Univ.; Chicago Review; Colorado Assoc. Univ.; Dante; Duquesne; Fairleigh Dickinson; Fordham; Getty; Warren H. Green; Greenwood; Harvard Univ.; Indiana Univ.; ISI; Kent State; Knopf; Lomond; McFarland & Co.; Mazda; Memphis State; MIT; Nelson-Hall; Northeastern Univ.; Northern Illinois Univ.; Noyes; Ohio State; Ohio Univ.; Open Court; Oregon State; Pacific; Pandora; Penkevill; Pickwick; Precedent; Purdue; Religious; Routledge & Kegan Paul; Rowman & Littlefield; St. Martin's; Saybrook; Schirmer; Scholium; Shoe String; Southern Illinois Univ.; Stanford; Sugden; Temple Univ.; Texas Christian Univ.; Texas Western; Three Continents; Twayne; UMI; Univ. of Alabama; Univ. of Alberta; Univ. of Arizona; Univ. of California; Univ. of Illinois; Univ. of Iowa; Univ. of Massachusetts; Univ. of Missouri; Univ. of Nevada; Univ. of New Mexico; Univ. of North Carolina; Univ. of Oklahoma; Univ. of Pennsylvania; Univ. of Tennessee; Univ. of Texas; Univ. of Utah; Univ. of Wisconsin; Univ. Press of America; Univ. Press of Kansas; Univ. Press of Mississippi; Univ. Press of Virginia; Westernlore; Whitson; Wingra; York.

Science & Technology. Abrams; Addison-Wesley; Adler & Adler; Allen & Unwin; Almar; American Astronautical Society; And/Or; Aster; Atlantic Monthly; Ballinger; Bantam; Bennett & McNight; Cambridge Univ.; Carolina; Childrens; Coles; Collier MacMillan; Computer Science; Davis; Delmar; Delta; Diamond; Dillon; Eden; Effective Learning; Enslow; Farrar, Straus and Giroux; Fitzhenry and Whiteside; Warren H. Green; Gulf; H.W.H.; Harper & Row Jr.; Harper & Row; Hayden; Heath; Helix; Industrial; Iowa State; Johnson; Kaufmann; Knowledge Industry; Knox; Krieger; Little, Brown & Co.; Lomond; McGraw-Hill; Medical Economics; Merrill; MGI; MIT; Museum of New Mexico; Museum of Northern Arizona; Naturegraph; New Readers; Oddo; Ohio State; Open Court; Oregon State; Oryx; Platt & Munk; Prentice-Hall; Prentice-Hall Canada; Princeton Univ.; Prometheus; Purdue; Quill; Rainbow; Raintree; Regnery/Gateway; Riverdale; Rocky Top; Ross; Rowman & Littlefield; St. Martin's; Scholium; Scribner's; Sierra Club; Simon & Schuster; Tab; Texas Western; Times; Transnational; Twayne; Univelt; Universe; Univ. of California; Univ. of Iowa; Univ. of Pennsylvania; Univ. of Texas; Univ. Press of Virginia; Vanguard; Walch; Walker; Wingra.

Self-help. AASLH; Acropolis; ACS; Addison-Wesley; Affirmation; Aglow; Alaska Nature; Allen; Almar; American Psychiatric; Angel; Arbor House; Associated Book; Aster; Atheneum Children's; Augsburg; Avon; Baker; Benjamin; Bethany; Betterway; Bookmakers; Bradson; Brethren; Bridge; Carolina; CBP; Chicago Review; Chosen; Christopher; Cleaning Consultant; Cliffs Notes; Compcare; Consumer Reports; Council Oak; Daniel; Delta; Dembner; Dharma; Diamond; Eden; Effective Learning; Enslow; Eriksson; Exanimo; Faber & Faber; Falcon; Falcon Press Pub.; Flores; Forman; Frompovich; Golden West Pub.; Grafton; Great Ocean; Gulf; H.P.; H.W.H.; Hale; Hamilton; Hancock; Harper & Row; Harvard Common; Harvest; Hazelden; Herald; Here's Life; Houghton Mifflin; Hounslow; Human Kinetics; Humanics; Huntington; Intercultural; International Self-Counsel; Internatonal Wealth Success; Jalmar; Jonathan David; Kesend; Key Porter; Klein; Lakewood; Larson; Learning Pub.; Liberty; Liguori; Llewellyn; Lone Star; Loompanics; McClelland and Bantam; Madrona; Marathon; Maverick; Menasha Ridge; Meriwether; Meyerbooks; Muir; Multnomah; Mustang; National Press; New Leaf; New Society; Newcastle; Octameron; Optimum; Our Sunday Visitor; P.P.I.; Pacific Press; Padre; Pandora; Para Research; Parenting; Paulist; Pelican; Pluribus; Posiedon; Potter; Prentice-Hall; Price/Stern/Sloan; Rainbow; Rocky Top; Rodale; Rosen; Roundtable; Routledge & Kegan Pual; S.C.E.; St. Martin's; Santa Barbara; Self-Counsel; Shaw; Spinsters; Sterling; Stillpoint; Stoeger; Strawberry Hill; Success; Susann; Ten Speed; Tensleep; Thorsons; Thunder's Mouth; Times; Van der Marck; Walker; Whitaker; Williamson; Wilshire; Winch; Wingra; Woodland; Woodsong; Word Beat; Word Books; Wright; Yankee; Zebra; Zondervan.

Social Sciences. Catholic Univ.; Chicago Review; Delta; Duquesne; Edits; Fitzhenry & Whiteside; Fleet; Free; Garland; Groupwork Today; Harper & Row Jr.; Heath; Indiana Univ.; Iowa State; McGraw-Hill; Mazda; Memphis State; Naturegraph; NC; Nelson-Hall; New Readers; New Society; Oddo; Ohio Univ.; Oregon State; Prentice-Hall; Prentice-Hall Canada; Riverdale; Routledge & Kegan Paul; Roxbury; Shoe String; Southern Illinois Univ.; Stanford; Sutton; Transnational; Univ. of Alabama; Univ. of California; Univ. of Missouri; Walch; Whitson.

Sociology. Addison-Wesley; Adler & Adler; Alba House; Allen & Unwin; American Council for the Arts; American Psychiatric; Angel; Associated Book; Associated Faculty; Atheneum Children's; Beacon; Betterway; Bradson; Braemar; Branden; Brethren; Brunner/Mazel; Bucknell; Canterbury; Christopher; Communications; Council Oak; Davidson; Dembner; Devonshire; Eden; Eerdmans; Effective Learning; Enslow; Eriksson; Faber & Faber; Fairleigh Dickinson; Falcon; Farrar, Straus and Giroux; Firebrand; Fraser; General Hall; Harper & Row; Harrow and Heston; Harvard Common; Hazelden; Humanics; Inst. for Study of Human Issues; Intercultural; International Publishers; Intervarsity; Krieger; Lang; Learning Pub.; Lomond; Longman, Inc.; McFarland & Co.; Mazda; New Society; North Point; Ohio State; P.P.I.; Pandora; Pantheon; Para Research; Penkevill; Poseidon; Prentice-Hall; Princeton Univ.; Prometheus; Purdue; Quartet; Quinlan; Rainbow; Regnery/Gateway; Riverdale; Rowman & Littlefield; Roxbury; S.C.E.; Santa

Barbara; Saybrook; Seven Locks; Shameless Hussy; Spinsters; Stanford; Temple Univ.; Thomas; Thunder's Mouth; Tuttle; Univ. of Alabama; Univ. of Alberta; Univ. of Arkansas; Univ. of Illinois; Univ. of Massachusetts; Univ. of North Carolina; Univ. Press of Kansas; Univ. Press of Kentucky; Univ. Press of Mississippi; Vanguard; Vehicule; Volcano; Walch; Wingbow; Wordbooks; Zondervan.

Sports. Addison-Wesley; Appalachian Mountain; Arbor House; Atheneum; Atheneum Children's; Athletic; Avon; Barron's; Beaufort; Benjamin; Bosco; Bradson; Briarcliff; Coles; Compubibs; Council Oak; Delta; Dembner; Diamond; Eden; Enslow; Eriksson; Falcon Press Pub.; Fleet; Grafton; Green Hill; Hale; Hancock; Harper & Row Jr.; Harper & Row; Harvard Common; Human Kinetics; Johnson; Jonathan David; Kaufmann; Kesend; Key Porter; Krieger; Lang; Lexikos; Liberty; Little, Brown & Co.; Lone Star; McClelland and Bantam; McFarland & Co.; Menasha Ridge; Mosaic; Motorbooks; Mountain; Mountaineers; Mustang; National Press; Optimum; Overlook; Pandora; PBC; Pineapple; Pluribus; Prentice-Hall; Quinlan; S.C.E.; Santa Barbara; Scribner's; Sierra Club; Stackpole; Sterling; Stillpoint; Stoeger; Stone Wall; Taylor; Texas Monthly; Times; Tuttle; Ultralight; Univ. of Illinois; Univ. of Tennessee; Vanguard; Walch; Walker; Western Marine; Western Tanager; Wilderness; Winchester; Word Books; Wright.

Technical. AASLH. Allen & Unwin; Almar; American Council for the Arts; American Federation of Information Processing Societies; American Psychiatric; Amphoto; ARCsoft; Arman; Aster; Auto; AVI; Aviation; Baen; Branden; Brevet; Brick; Broadway; Carolina; Chilton; Cleaning Consultant; Coles; Compute!; Cornell Maritime; Craftsman; Cuff; Datamost; Davis; Devonshire; Eden; Effective Learning; Enslow; ETC; Faber & Faber; Falcon; Flora and Fauna; Flores; Frompovich; Govenment Institutes; Great Ocean; H.P.; Heath; Human Kinetics; Industrial; Information Resources; Iowa State; ISI; Krieger; Leonard; Library Research; Lomond; Lorien; McGraw-Hill; Maverick; MGI; Modern Language Assoc.; Morgan & Morgan; Mountain; Museum of New Mexico; Museum of Northern Arizona; National Pub. of Black Hills; New York Zoetrope; Noyes; Ohio State; Oregon State; Pacific; Pandora; Petrocelli; Pluribus; Prakken; Prentice-Hall Canada; Prentice-Hall; Princeton Univ.; Q.E.D.; Que; Religious Ed.; Renaissance; Rowman & Littlefield; RPM; Rynd; Seven Seas; Sourceview; ST; Sterling; Stipes; T.F.H.; T.L.; Tab; Theatre Arts; Ultralight; Univelt; Univ. of Alberta; Univ. of Arizona; Univ. Press of Virginia; Winchester; Windsor; Wright; Writer's Digest; Yourdon.

Textbook. AASLH; Abingdon; Accelerated Development; Alba House; Allen & Unwin; American Psychiatric; ARCsoft; Arman; Art Direction; Asher-Gallant; Associated Faculty; Aster; Augsburg; AVI; Baker; Barron's; Bennett & McKnight; Bookmakers; Bosco; Branden; Brethren; Brick; Cambridge Univ.; Carolina; Christopher; Cleaning Consultant; Cliffs Notes; Collier MacMillan; Communications; Computer Science; Council Oak; Cuff; Datamost; Davenport; Davidson; Delmar; Devonshire; Down East; Edits; Education Assoc.; Eerdmans; Effective Learning; ETC; Fairchild; Falcon; Fitzhenry & Whiteside; Flora and Fauna; Florida Trend; Free; General Hall; Ginn; Grunwald and Radcliff; Guernica; Hanley & Belfus; Harrow and Heston; Harvest; Hayden; Health Profession; Heath; Heinle & Heinle; Human Kinetics; Humanics; Information Resources; International Publishers; Interstate; Iowa State; Jamestown; Kaufmann; Knox; Krieger; Lang; Learning Endeavors; Learning Pub.; Libraries Unlimited; Llewellyn; Loiry; Lone Star; Longman, Inc.; Lotus; Loyola; McGraw-Hill; Mazda; Meriwether; Merrill; Miller; Morgan & Morgan; Mountain; National Pub. of Black Hills; National Textbook; Nelson-Hall; New York Zoetrope; Occupational Awareness; Oddo; Pacific; Pacific Press; Pandora; Paragon; Penkeville; Petrocelli; Pluribus; Porter Sargent; Potentials Development; Prakken; Prentice-Hall Canada; Princeton Architectural; Prometheus; Pruett; Regents; Religious Ed.; Rosen; Routledge & Kegan Paul; Rowman & Littlefield; Roxbury; Rynd; St. Bede's; St. Martin's; Sandlapper; Schirmer; Seven Locks; Slavica; ST; Stanford; Stipes; T.F.H.; Teachers College; Thomas; Transnational; Univ. of Alberta; Univ. Press of America; VGM Career; Walch; Word Books; Wright; York; Zondervan.

Translations. Dante; Dharma; Dimension; ETC; Forman; Garland; Hunter; Iowa State; Lake View; Lang; Museum of New Mexico; North Point; Norton; Paragon; Paulist; Pickwick; Porter Sargent; Regnery/Gateway; Ross; S.C.E.; St. Bede's; St. Luke's; Shoe String; Slavica; Tab; Three Continents; Threshold; Timber; Tuttle; Universe; Western Producer.

Transportation. American Astronautical Society; Auto; Aviation; De Graff; Golden West Books; H.P.; International Marine; Kalmbach; MIT; Motorbooks; Muir; Ottenheimer; Pruett; Rosen; Scholium; T.L.; Tab; Ultralight.

Travel. Academy Chicago; Adler & Adler; Alaska Northwest; Almar; American Council for the Arts; And/Or; Appalachian Mountain; Atheneum Children's; Barron's; Beaufort; Binford & Mort; Briarcliff; Camaro; Cedarshouse; Chelsea Green; Chicago Review; Christopher; Chronicle; Council Oak; East Woods; Eerdmans; Effective Learning; Eriksson; Faber & Faber; Falcon Press Pub.; Florida Trend; Fodor's; Globe Pequot; Golden West Pub.; Grafton; Graphic Image; H.W.H.; Hale; Harper & Row; Harvard Common; Heyday; Hounslow; Howell-North; Intercultural; Interurban; Kesend; Key Porter; Lexikos; Liberty; Library Research; Loompanics; Madrona; Main St.; Maverick; Menasha Ridge; Mosaic; Muir; Mustang; National Press; National Pub. of Black Hills; New York Zoetrope; Nimbus; North Point; Northword; Octameron; 101 Prod.; Optimum; Outbooks; Overlook; Padre; PBC; Peachtree; Pelican; Pilot; Pineapple; Prentice-Hall Canada; Riverdale; Routledge & Kegan Paul; S.C.E.; Santa Barbara; Sierra Club; Slavica; Stoneydale; Sutton; T.L.; Taylor; Ten Speed; Tensleep; Texas Monthly; Travel Keys; Van der Marck; Vanguard; Walker; Western Marine; Western Tanager; Wine Appreciation; Yankee.

Women's Issues/Studies. Bantam; Beacon; Feminist; Firebrand; Indiana Univ.; International Publishers; New Society; Northeastern Univ.; Pandora; Pantheon; Routledge & Kegan Paul; Saybrook; Scarecrow; South End; Susann; Temple Univ.; Thorsons; Thunder's Mouth; Times; Univ. of Massachusetts; Univ. of Tennessee; Univ. of Texas; Volcano.

World Affairs. Adler & Adler; Atlantic Monthly; Ballinger; Beacon; Family Album; Intercultural; Lake View; NC; New Society; Orbis; P.P.I.; Pandora; Pantheon; Prentice-Hall Canada; Regnery/Gateway; Rowman & Littlefield; Second Chance/Permanent; Seven Locks; Southern Illinois Univ.; Stanford; Strawberry Hill; Transnational; Twayne; Univ. of Texas.
Young Adult. Dell; Dial; Farrar, Straus and Giroux; Harper & Row Jr.; Holiday; Lodestar; Nelson; P.P.I.; Philomel; Pineapple; Rosen; Success; Texas Christian Univ.; Winston-Derek.

Fiction

This subject index for fiction will help you pinpoint fiction markets without having to scan all the book publishers' listings. As with the nonfiction markets, read the complete individual listings for each publisher for advice on what types of fiction the company buys. For more detailed advice and additional fiction markets that offer a royalty or copies as payment, consult *Fiction Writer's Market* (Writer's Digest Books).

Adventure. Alaska Nature; Angel; Arbor House; Arman; Atheneum Children's; Avon; Avon Flare; Baker St.; Berkley; Braemar; Branden; Camelot; Canterbury; Carroll & Graf; Christian Ed.; Clarion; Critic's Choice; Daniel; Davenport; Dell; Dembner; Dial; Dragonsbreath; Falcon; Farrar, Straus and Giroux; Gold Eagle; Grafton; Green Hill; Green Tiger; Hale; Harper & Row Jr.; Harper & Row; Hounslow; Kar-Ben Copies; Kesend; Lace; Library Research; Lodestar; Lothrop, Lee & Shepard; McClelland and Bantam; Maverick; Miller; Mountaineers; Overlook; Pandora; Players; Printemps; Quartet; Quinlan; Raintree; Rossel; Roundtable; Russica; Saybrook; Scribner's; Second Chance/Permanent; Shameless Hussy; Sierra Club; SOS; Stemmer; Vanguard; Walker; Woodsong; Wright; Zebra.
Confession. Falcon; H.W.H.; Players; Second Chance/Permanent; Shameless Hussy; Wright; Zebra.
Erotica. Aya; Carroll & Graf; Devonshire; Dragonsbreath; Falcon; Graphic Image; Greenleaf; Guernica; Hunter; Kesend; Lace; Quartet; Roundtable; Russica; Thunder's Mouth; Wright; Zebra.
Ethnic. Atheneum Children's; Avon Flare; Borealis; Braemar; Branden; China; Cuff; Daniel; Davenport; Faber & Faber; Falcon; Floricanto; Green Hill; Grunwald and Radcliff; Guernica; H.W.H.; Hunter; Kesend; Lace; Overlook; Pandora; Players; Printemps; Rossel; Russica; Second Chance/Permanent; Shameless Hussy; Stemmer; Taylor; Texas Monthly; Three Continents; Threshold; Thunder's Mouth; Univ. of Illinois; Winston-Derek; Wright.
Experimental. Applezaba; Atheneum Children's; Avon Flare; Aya; Bookmakers; Canterbury; Carpenter; Daniel; Devonshire; Dragonsbreath; Faber & Faber; Falcon; Fiddlehead; Green Tiger; H.W.H.; Kesend; Pandora; Panjandrum; Paragon; Pineapple; Players; Second Chance/Permanent; Shameless Hussy; Taylor; Thunder's Mouth; Univ. of Illinois; Woodsong.
Fantasy. Ace; Angel; Arbor House; Atheneum Children's; Avon; Avon Flare; Baen; Baker St.; Ballantine; Bantam; Bluejay; Camelot; Canterbury; Carpenter; Carroll & Graf; Clarion; Crossway; Daniel; Davenport; Daw; Del Rey; Dial; Dragonsbreath; Falcon; Farrar, Straus and Giroux; Grafton; Green Tiger; H.W.H.; Harper & Row Jr.; Harper & Row; Hunter; Imagine; Iron Crown; Kar-Ben Copies; Lace; Larson; Lodestar; Lothrop, Lee & Shepard; Maverick; Overlook; Padre; Panjandrum; Players; Printemps; Roundtable; Scribner's; Second Chance/Permanent; Tor; Woodsong; Wright.
Feminist. Crossing; Firebrand; Press Gang; Quartet; Shameless Hussy.
Gay/Lesbian. Alyson; Firebrand; JH; Knights; Naiad.
General Fiction. Atlantic Monthly.
Gothic. Atheneum Children's; Avalon Bethany; Bouregy; Braemar; Hale; Harlequin; Harper & Row; Lace; Prentice-Hall; Roundtable; Woodsong; Zebra.
Historical. Alaska Nature; Atheneum Children's; Avon; Berkley; Braemar; Branden; Braziller; Critic's Choice; Cuff; Daniel; Dell; Denlinger's; Devonshire; Dial; Dorchester; Dundurn; Eakin; Faber & Faber; Falcon; Farrar, Straus and Giroux; Grafton; Guernica; Hale; Harper & Row; Heyday; Houghton Mifflin; Kar-Ben Copies; Kesend; Lace; Library Research; Lothrop, Lee & Shepard; McClelland and Bantam; Maverick; Miller; New England; Overlook; Pandora; Peachtree; Pineapple; Players; Poseidon; Raintree; Rossel; Roundtable; Sandlapper; Scholastic; Scribner's; Second Chance/Permanent; Shameless Hussy; Sierra Club; Stemmer; Taylor; Thunder's Mouth; Tor; Woodsong; Zebra.
Horror. Atheneum Children's; Devonshire; Dorchester; Dragonsbreath; Falcon; Gold Eagle; Grafton; Imagine; McClelland and Bantam; Players; Russica; Tor; Wright; Zebra.
Humor. Angel; Applezaba; Atheneum Children's; Avon Flare; Aya; Baker St.; Bradson; Braemar; Camelot; Canterbury; Carroll & Graf; Clarion; Cuff; Daniel; Davenport; Dial; Dragonsbreath; Falcon; Farrar, Straus and Giroux; Grafton; H.W.H.; Hounslow; Imagine; Kesend; Lace; Lodestar; Lothrop, Lee & Shepard; Meriwether; Miller; New England; Pandora; Peachtree; Pelican; Players; Prentice-Hall; Printemps; Quinlan; Ronin; Russica; Saybrook; Scribner's; Second Chance/Permanent; Shameless Hussy; Thorndike; Thunder's Mouth; Vanguard; Woodsong; Wright; Zebra.

Juvenile. Abingdon; Atheneum Children's; Atlantic Monthly; Baker; Bantam; Blair; Bradbury; BYLS; Childrens; Clarion; Crossway; Dial; Dillon; Down East; Dutton; Eakin; Farrar, Straus and Giroux; Floricanto; Green Tiger; H.W.H.; Harper & Row Jr.; Holiday; Houghton Mifflin; Ideals; Kar-Ben Copies; Lodestar; Lothrop, Lee & Shepard; McElderry; MacMillan; Morrow Jr.; Padre; Pelican; Pharos; Philomel; Platt & Munk; Prentice-Hall; Press Gang; Printemps; Rossel; Sandlapper; Scribner's; Tensleep; Winston-Derek.

Literary. Beaufort; Columbia; Creative Arts; Dembner; Douglas & McIntyre; Harper & Row; Knopf; Lang; Little, Brown & Co.; Poseidon; Stemmer; Taplinger; Thistledown.

Mainstream/Contemporary. Academy Chicago; Adler & Adler; Angel; Applezaba; Atheneum Children's; Avon; Avon Flare; Aya; Beaufort; Berkley; Blair; Bookmakers; Braemar; Branden; Braziller; Camelot; Carpenter; Carroll & Graf; Critic's Choice; Crossway; Cuff; Daniel; Delacorte; Dell; Delta; Dillon; Dorchester; Faber & Faber; Falcon; Farrar, Straus and Giroux; Fiddlehead; Grafton; Green Hill; H.W.H.; Hale; Harper & Row Jr.; Harper & Row; Houghton Mifflin; Hounslow; Jamestown; Little, Brown & Co.; McClelland and Bantam; Morrow; New American; North Point; Norton; Ohio State; Overlook; Owl Creek; Padre; Paragon; Peachtree; Pelican; Pineapple; Players; Poseidon; Potter; Prentice-Hall; Quartet; Roundtable; St. Martin's; Saybrook; Scribner's; Second Chance/Permanent; Sierra Club; Simon & Schuster; Stein and Day; Stemmer; Texas Monthly; Univ. of Arkansas; Univ. of Illinois; Univ. of Missouri; Viking Penguin; Woodsong; Wright; Zebra.

Military/War. Bantam; Dell; Grafton.

Mystery. Academy Chicago; Atheneum Children's; Avalon; Avon; Avon Flare; Baker St.; Bantam; Beaufort; Bluejay; Braemar; Camelot; Carroll & Graf; Christian Ed.; Clarion; Critic's Choice; Daniel; Davenport; Dembner; Dial; Dillon; Dorchester; Doubleday; Dragonsbreath; Faber & Faber; Falcon; Farrar, Straus and Giroux; Gold Eagle; Guernica; Hale; Harper & Row; Houghton Mifflin; Kesend; Library Research; Lodestar; Lothrop, Lee & Shepard; McClelland and Bantam; Maverick; Miller; Overlook; Players; Pocket; Prentice-Hall; Printemps; Rossel; Roundtable; Russica; Saybrook; Scribner's; Second Chance/Permanent; SOS; Vanguard; Walker; Woodsong; Wright.

Occult. Berkley; Dell; Garber; Tor.

Picture books. Bradbury; Childrens; Christian Ed.; Concordia; Dial; Dutton; Golden; Harper & Row Jr.; Oak Tree; Platt & Munk; Prentice-Hall.

Plays. Coach House; Drama; French; H.W.H.; JH; Meriwether; Univ. of Missouri.

Poetry. Ahsahta; Atlantic Monthly; Branden; Braziller; Cedarshouse; Christopher; Cleveland State Univ. Poetry Center; Dragon's Teeth; Dragonsbreath; Green Tiger; Guernica; Houghton Mifflin; Hounslow; Lang; Lotus; Marathon; Morrow; Northeastern Univ.; Northwoods; Ohio State; Overlook; Owl Creek; Padre; Pentagram; Princeton Univ.; St. Luke's; Shaw; Sparrow; Sunstone; Thistledown; Three Continents; Threshold; Thunder's Mouth; Univ. of Massachusetts; Univ. of Missouri; Van der Marck; Vanguard; Vesta; Woodsong.

Regional. Aya; Cay-Bel; Dundurn; Faber & Faber; Library Research; Peachtree; Pelican; St. Luke's; Sandlapper; Sunstone; Texas Christian Univ.; Thistledown; Thorndike; Vehicule; Winston-Derek.

Religious. Aglow; Baker; Bookcraft; Braemar; Branden; Brethren; Bridge; Broadman; BYLS; Christian Ed.; Concordia; Devonshire; Falcon; Ideals; Kar-Ben Copies; Larson; Players; Randall; Resource; Revell; Rossel; St. Bede's; Shameless Hussy; Shining Star; Standard; Stillpoint; Tyndale; Winston-Derek; Word Books.

Romances. Alaska Nature; Arbor House; Atheneum Children's; Avalon; Avon; Avon Flare; Berkley; Bethany; Bouregy; Braemar; Branden; Dell; Dial; Doubleday; Farrar, Straus and Giroux; Grafton; Graphic Image; H.W.H.; Hale; Harlequin; Harper & Row; Holloway; Lace; McClelland and Bantam; Meriwether; Players; Pocket; Rossel; Roundtable; Scholastic; Second Chance at Love; Silhouette; SOS; Walker; Woodsong; Word Books; Wright; Zebra.

Science Fiction. Ace; Arbor House; Aster; Atheneum Children's; Avon; Avon Flare; Baen; Ballantine; Bantam; Berkley; Bluejay; Camelot; Carpenter; Critic's Choice; Crossway; Daw; Del Rey; Devonshire; Dillon; Doubleday; Dragonsbreath; Falcon; Farrar, Straus and Giroux; Grafton; Guernica; H.W.H.; Harper & Row Jr.; Harper & Row; Houghton Mifflin; Hunter; Imagine; Iron Crown; Lace; Larson; Lodestar; Lothrop, Lee & Shepard; Overlook; Players; Pocket; Raintree; Rossel; Roundtable; Saybrook; Scribner's; Sierra Club; Stillpoint; Thunder's Mouth; Tor; Woodsong; Word Books; Wright.

Short Story Collections. Applezaba; Aya; Graywolf.

Spiritual. Garber; Larson; Stemmer; Stillpoint; Threshold.

Sports. Bantam; Dillon; Kesend.

Suspense. Alaska Nature; Arbor House; Atheneum Children's; Avon; Avon Flare; Berkley; Braemar; Camelot; Carroll & Graf; Clarion; Critic's Choice; Davenport; Dell; Dembner; Dial; Dorchester; Doubleday; Falcon; Farrar, Straus and Giroux; Gold Eagle; Grafton; Guernica; H.W.H.; Hale; Harlequin; Harper & Row; Houghton Mifflin; Kesend; Library Research; Lodestar; Lothrop, Lee & Shepard; McClelland and Bantam; Mercury; Overlook; Players; Printemps; Roundtable; Russica; Scribner's; Second Chance/Permanent; Taylor; Tor; Walker; Winston-Derek; Woodsong; Wright; Zebra.

Western. Atheneum Children's; Avalon; Avon; Berkley; Bouregy; Braemar; Critic's Choice; Dembner; Farrar, Straus and Giroux; Green Hill; Hale; Harper & Row; Lace; Lodestar; Miller; Players; Pocket; Walker; Woodsong.

Young Adult. Atheneum Children's; Avon Flare; Bantam; Berkley; Bethany; Bradbury; Branden; Crossway; Dial; Farrar, Straus and Giroux; Harper & Row Jr.; Holiday; Lake; Lodestar; McElderry; New Readers; Pelican; Philomel; Scholastic; Silhouette.

Consumer Publications

If you're a beginning writer, you'll be amazed at the number of magazines listed in *Writer's Market*: familiar magazines, yes, but also magazines you've never seen, never heard of and would never have *imagined*. You'll enjoy getting acquainted with the tremendous variety of freelance opportunities described in the individual listings.

Consumer publications—covered in this section—are the magazines you, your family and friends buy at the newsstand or with subscriptions. People read them for information and entertainment. Consumer magazines are often slanted toward a special interest (hobbies, sports, house and garden) or a particular age group (children, teens, retirement). Look at the Table of Contents again to see how they're categorized. Be sure to read the brief introductions at the beginning of each category section for suggestions on related markets.

Whether you're a beginner or an experienced freelancer, you should know that consumer magazines—like book publishers—are in a state of transition. They're changing their titles, their editors, their focuses and their formats. New magazines are started every day, but magazines depend on income from subscribers and advertisers to keep them going; when that income drops, they cease publication.

To keep pace with such changes, make regular trips to your local bookstore, newsstand or library. Read magazines like *Writer's Digest*, *Folio* and other publications that report on magazines; you'll learn about changes that have occurred since this edition of *Writer's Market* went to press. Examine the publications you think you'd like to write for. If you can't locate a recent issue of a magazine that interests you, write for a sample copy.

You'll also want to stay ahead of the trends that affect editors' choices. In general, you can expect to see some of the following:

● Greater specialization is apparent in many types of magazines. For example, some fitness magazines are narrowing their content to focus on weightlifting or "staying young." We're seeing more of a regional emphasis, especially in business publications. Some magazines, once geared toward "homeowners," now focus on "first-time homeowners who have recently purchased a house or condominium for more than $70,000."

● How-to magazines (and how-to articles in general interest magazines) continue to be very popular. Readers want more than entertainment for the purchase price of their magazines. Writers who can describe complicated projects in clear and simple prose will have an advantage in today's market.

● Economic trends can affect the editorial slant of magazines. You'll find that some are "going upscale" with articles on exotic travel, gourmet cooking and art collecting. At other magazines, there's a new "country" orientation that has more to do with lifestyle than life on a farm.

● Conservative politics and religion are bringing new magazines to life, as well as changing the image of a few formerly liberal publications. Both will be looking for writers who can slant articles to this growing audience.

● Investigative journalism seems to be declining. Magazine publishers know about rising insurance costs; they prefer to avoid the threat of libel.

● Fiction in consumer magazines is unpredictable. You'll find more, shorter stories in some publications, while others are discontinuing fiction altogether. *Writer's Market* includes listings for fiction in genre magazines (science fiction, mystery and romance); men's, women's, juvenile and teen magazines; literary and "little" magazines and general interest publications. Scan other categories, too—and investigate *Fiction Writer's Market* (Writer's Digest Books) for more complete information.

● An increasing *visual* emphasis is apparent in many magazines. Some people blame (or credit) TV and *USA Today* for this trend, citing readers' short attention spans and their dependence on pictures instead of words. Shorter articles, brief items in groups, and greater reliance on graphics are common. Writers who can provide photographs with their manuscripts will have an advantage.

● New types of magazines are emerging, too. Regional, foreign or demographic editions of a single magazine can be produced with slightly altered content. "Poster" magazines for schools and universities are popular, while electronic magazines on computer data bases remain in the early stages of development.

As you think about magazine trends and the types of articles you plan to write, try to consider as many options as possible. Don't overspecialize; today's trend may become tomorrow's forgotten fad. You can diversify the topics you write about, just as many large corporations diversify to reduce their dependence on one product. Expand your knowledge on a variety of subjects; the result will be more marketing opportunities and a greater depth in your writing.

You can also increase the value of your ideas by expanding the number of publications you write for. An easy way to accomplish this is by revising or changing the slant of one article to make it suitable for a second or third magazine. Suppose you've interviewed a politician from your home town; she has a large family and pilots her own plane. The information from one interview could be developed into articles for a number of magazines—regional, general interest, family and child care, aviation or women's. See the Trade, Technical and Professional Journals section of *Writer's Market* for suggestions on writing for those publications. Successful freelancers have to discover—and develop—their ideas.

Remember to follow the requirements of the magazines listed in *Writer's Market*. If an editor specifically requests queries—and most of them do—don't be foolish and send a complete manuscript. As you read the listings, look for those that accept simultaneous submissions and previously published material. You may be able to sell one article to two or more magazines.

Before writing on any subject, ask yourself: How can I make this story appeal to the editor and readers of this particular magazine? How will my treatment of this topic affect readers' lives? With those answers in mind, you'll be well on your way to writing better—and more marketable—material.

Animal

Editors at animal publications want material that *helps* animal owners and trainers. "The article has to address the readers, presenting information that is either of interest or value to 'pet' people, or exceptionally entertaining," points out one editor. Animal magazine editors get too many gruesome stories about animals, "first pets" and "talking animals." The publications in this section deal with pets, racing and show horses, other pleasure animals and wildlife. Magazines about animals bred and raised for the market are classified in the Farm category. Publications about horse racing can be found in the Sports section.

AMERICAN FARRIERS JOURNAL, The Laux Company Publishers, Inc., Box 700, Ayer MA 01432. (617)772-4890. Editor: Horst D. Dornbusch. Published 7 times/year. Magazine covering horseshoeing, horse health related to legs and feet of horses and metalworking for a professional audience of full-time horseshoers, veterinarians and horse trainers. Circ. 4,000. Pays on publication. Byline given. Buys all rights. Submit material 3 months in advance. Computer printout submissions acceptable; dot-matrix submission accepted only

when double-spaced. Reports in 4 weeks on queries; 2 weeks on mss. Sample copy $7; writer's guidelines for SAE and 1 first class stamp.
Nonfiction: Book excerpts, general interest, historical/nostalgic, how-to, interview/profile, new product, personal experience, photo feature and technical. Buys 50 mss/year. Send complete ms. Length:.800-3,000 words. Pays $50-450.
Photos: Send photos with ms. Reviews b&w contact sheets, b&w negatives, 35mm color transparencies, and 8x10 b&w or color prints. Captions and identification of subjects required. Buys one-time rights.

ANIMAL KINGDOM, New York Zoological Park, Bronx NY 10460. (212)220-5121. Editor: Eugene J. Walter Jr. "We are backlogged with submissions and prefer not to receive unsolicited submissions at this time."

‡APPALOOSA WORLD, Appaloosa World Magazine, Inc., Box 1035, Daytona Beach FL 32029. (904)767-6284. Editor: Gerald A. Matacale. 50% freelance written. A monthly magazine highlighting Appaloosa breed show news, results and events. Features training and breeding articles as well as the breed's leading personalities and horses. Circ. 40,112. Pays on acceptance. Byline given. Offers 100% kill fee. Buys first rights and second serial (reprint) rights, and makes work-for-hire assignments. Photocopied and previously published submissions OK. Computer printout submissions acceptable; prefers letter-quality to dot-matrix. Reports in 1 week. Sample copy $5; free writer's guidelines.
Nonfiction: How-to (horse or rider training) and interview/profile (on assignment only). No articles written for children, or horse lovers as opposed to horse owners. Buys 50-100 mss/year. Query with published clips. Length: 1,000-5,000 words. Pays $8/double-spaced pica typewritten page. Pays expenses of writers on assignment.
Photos: Send photos with submission. Reviews 4x5 or larger prints. Offers $5/photo. Captions required. Buys one-time rights.
Tips: "Best approach is a telephone call to the editor."

ARABIAN HORSE TIMES, Adams Corp., Rt. 3, Waseca MN 56093. (507)835-3204. Editor: Marian Studer-Johnson. Managing Editor: Linda White. 20% freelance written. Works with a small number of new/unpublished writers each year. Monthly magazine about Arabian horses. Editorial format includes hard news (veterinary, new products, book reports, etc.), lifestyle and personality pieces, and bloodline studies. Circ. 19,000. Pays on publication. Publishes ms an average of 6 months after acceptance. Byline given. Offers 33% kill fee. Buys first serial rights. Submit seasonal/holiday material 3 months in advance. Simultaneous queries OK. Computer printout submissions acceptable; prefers letter-quality to dot-matrix. Reports in 3 weeks on queries; 6 weeks on mss. Free sample copy and writer's guidelines.
Nonfiction: General interest, how-to, interview/profile, new product and photo feature. Buys at least 12 mss/year. Query with published clips. Length: 1,000-5,000 words. Pays $75-350. Sometimes pays expenses of writers on assignments.
Photos: Prefers 5x7 color prints. Payment depends on circumstances. Captions and identification of subjects required. Buys one-time rights.
Fiction: Will look at anything about horses except erotica. Buys 1-2 mss/year. Send complete ms. Length: 1,500-5,000 words. Pays $75-250.
Poetry: Horse-related poetry only. Buys 1-2 poems/year. Submit maximum of 1 poem. Pays $25.
Fillers: Buys 12/year. Length: 100-500 words. Pays $10-75.
Tips: "As our periodical is specific to Arabian horses, we are interested in anyone who can write well and tightly about them. Send us something timely. Also, narrow your topic to a specific horse, incident, person or problem. 'Why I Love Arabians' will not work."

BIRD TALK, Dedicated to Better Care for Pet Birds, Fancy Publications, Box 6050, Mission Viejo CA 92690. (714)240-6001. Editor: Linda W. Lewis. Managing Editor: Karyn New. 85% freelance written. Works with a small number of new/unpublished writers each year. Monthly magazine covering the care and training of cage birds for men and women who own any number of pet or exotic birds. Circ. 70,000. Pays latter part of month in which article appears. Publishes ms an average of 4 months after acceptance. Byline given. Buys first North American serial rights. Submit seasonal/holiday material 5 months in advance. Photocopied and previously published submissions OK. Computer printout submissions acceptable; prefers letter-quality to dot-matrix. Reports in 3 weeks on queries; 8 weeks on mss. Sample copy $3; writer's guidelines for 9x12 SAE and 1 first class stamp.
Nonfiction: General interest (anything to do with pet birds); historical/nostalgic (of bird breeds, owners, cages); how-to (build cages, aviaries, playpens and groom, feed, breed, tame); humor; interview/profile (of bird and bird owners); new product; how-to (live with birds—compatible pets, lifestyle, apartment adaptability, etc.); personal experience (with your own bird); photo feature (humorous or informative); travel (with pet birds or to see exotic birds); and articles giving medical information, legal information, and description of breeds. No juvenile or material on wild birds not pertinent to pet care; everything should relate to *pet* birds. Buys 150 mss/year. Query or send complete ms. Length: 500-3,000 words. Pays 3-5¢/word.

Photos: State availability of photos. Reviews b&w contact sheets. Pays $75-150 for color transparencies; $15 minimum for 8x10 b&w prints. Model release and identification of subjects required. Buys one-time rights.
Columns/Departments: Editorial (opinion on a phase of owning pet birds) and Small Talk (short news item of general interest to bird owners). Buys 20 mss/year. Send complete ms. Length: 300-1,200 words. Pays 3¢/word and up.
Fiction: "Only fiction with pet birds as primary focus of interest." Adventure, fantasy, historical, humorous, mystery, suspense. No juvenile, and no birds talking unless it's their trained vocabulary. Buys 6 mss/year. Send complete ms. Length: 2,000-3,000 words. Pays 3¢/word and up.
Tips: "Send grammatical, clean copy on a human-interest story about a pet bird or about a medical or health-related topic. We also need how-tos on feather crafts; cage cover making; aviary, perch and cage building; and planting plants in aviaries safe and good for birds. Keep health, nutrition, lack of stress in mind regarding pet birds. Study back issues to learn our style."

CAT FANCY, Fancy Publications, Inc., Box 6050, Mission Viejo CA 92690. (714)240-6001. Editor: Linda W. Lewis. 80-90% freelance written. Monthly magazine for men and women of all ages interested in all phases of cat ownership. 80 pages. Circ. 150,000. Pays after publication. Publishes ms an average of 6 months after acceptance. Buys first American serial rights. Byline given. Submit seasonal/holiday material 4 months in advance. Computer printout submissions acceptable. Reports in 6 weeks. Sample copy $3; writer's guidelines for SASE.
Nonfiction: Historical, medical, how-to, humor, informational, personal experience, photo feature and technical. Buys 5 mss/issue. Query or send complete ms. Length: 500-3,000 words. Pays 3-5¢/word.
Photos: Photos purchased with or without accompanying ms. Pays $10 minimum for 8x10 b&w glossy prints; $50-150 for 35mm or 2¼x2¼ color transparencies. Send prints and transparencies. Model release required.
Fiction: Adventure, fantasy, historical and humorous. Nothing written with cats speaking. Buys 1 ms/issue. Send complete ms. Length: 500-3,000 words. Pays 5¢/word.
Fillers: Newsworthy or unusual; items with photo and cartoons. Buys 10 fillers/year. Length: 100-500 words. Pays $20-35.
Tips: "We receive more filler-type articles than we can use. It's the well-researched, hard information article we need."

CATS MAGAZINE, Cats Magazine Inc., Box 37, Port Orange FL 32029. (904)788-2770. Editor: Linda J. Walton. 50% freelance written. A monthly magazine for cat lovers, veterinarians, breeders and show enthusiasts. Circ. 120,000. Pays on publication. Byline given. Buys one-time rights. Submit seasonal/holiday material 7 months in advance. Reports in 1 month on queries; 3 months on manuscripts (sometimes longer depending on the backlog.) Free sample copy and writer's guidelines.
Nonfiction: Book excerpts; general interest (concerning cats); how-to (care for cats); humor; interview/profile (on cat owning personalities); new product; personal experience; photo feature; and technical (veterinarian writers). No talking cats. Buys 36 mss/year. Send complete ms. Length 800-2,500 words. Pays $25-300.
Photos: Send photos with submission. Reviews transparencies. Offers $5-25/photo. Identification of subjects required. Buys one-time rights.
Fiction: Fantasy, historical, mystery, science fiction, slice-of-life vignettes and suspense. "We rarely use fiction, but are not adverse to using it if the cat theme is handled in smooth, believable manner. All fiction must involve a cat or relationship of cat and humans, etc." No talking cats. Buys 4-6 mss/year. Send complete ms. Length: 800-2,500 words. Pays $25-300.
Poetry: Avant-garde, free verse, haiku, light verse and traditional. Length: 4-64 lines. Pays 50¢/line.
Tips: "Fiction and articles are the freelancer's best bet. Writers must at least like cats. Writers who obviously don't, miss the mark."

THE CHRONICLE OF THE HORSE, The Chronicle of the Horse, Inc., Box 46, Middleburg VA 22117. (703)687-6341. Editor: John Strassburger. Managing Editor: Nancy Comer. 80% freelance written. Weekly magazine about horses. "We cover English riding sports, including horse showing, grand prix jumping competitions, steeplechase racing, foxhunting, dressage, endurance riding and combined training. We are the official publication for the national governing bodies of many of the above sports. We feature news of the above sports, and we also publish how-to articles on equitation and horse care, and interviews with leaders in the various fields." Circ. 21,000. Pays for features on acceptance; news and other items on publication. Publishes ms an average of 3 months after acceptance. Byline given. Offers negotiable kill fee. Buys first North American rights and makes work-for-hire assignments. Submit seasonal/holiday material 3 months in advance. Computer printout submissions acceptable only if double spaced, 8½x11 format; dot-matrix OK. Simultaneous queries and photocopied submissions OK. Reports in 2 weeks. Sample copy $2; free writer's guidelines.
Nonfiction: General interest; historical/nostalgic (history of breeds, use of horses in other countries and times, art, etc); how-to (trailer, train, design a course, save money, etc.); humor (centered on living with horses or horse people); interview/profile (of nationally known horsemen or the very unusual); technical (horse care, articles on feeding, injuries, care of foals, shoeing, etc.); and news (of major competitions, clear assignment

with us first). Special issues include Steeplechasing; Grand Prix Jumping; Combined Training; Dressage; Hunt Roster; Junior and Pony; and Christmas. No Q&A interviews, clinic reports, Western riding articles, personal experience, or wild horses. Buys 300 mss/year. Query or send complete ms. Length: 300-1,225 words. Pays $25-200.

Photos: State availability of photos. Reviews 5x7 b&w prints. Pays $10-15. Identification of subjects required. Buys one-time rights.

Columns/Departments: Dressage, Combined Training, Horse Show, Horse Care, Polo, Racing, Racing over Fences, Young Entry (about young riders, geared for youth), Horses and Humanities, and Hunting. Query or send complete ms. Length: 300-1,225 words. Pays $25-200.

Poetry: Light verse and traditional. No free verse. Buys 100 mss/year. Length: 5-30 lines. Pays $15.

Fillers: Anecdotes, short humor, newsbreaks and cartoons. Buys 250 mss/year. Length: 50-175 lines. Pays $10-25.

Tips: "Get our guidelines. Our readers are sophisticated, competitive horsemen. Articles need to go beyond common knowledge. Freelancers often attempt too broad or too basic a subject. We welcome well-written news stories on major events, but clear the assignment with us."

DOG FANCY, Fancy Publications, Inc., Box 6050, Mission Viejo CA 92690. (714)240-6001. Editor: Linda Lewis. Managing Editor: Moira Anderson. 75% freelance written. Eager to work with/unpublished writers. "We'd like to see a balance of both new and established writers." Monthly magazine for men and women of all ages interested in all phases of dog ownership. Circ. 100,000. Pays after publication. Publishes ms an average of 9 months after acceptance. Buys first American serial rights. Byline given. Submit seasonal/holiday material 4 months in advance. Computer printout submissions acceptable; prefers letter-quality to dot-matrix. Sample copy $3; writer's guidelines for SASE.

Nonfiction: Historical, medical, how-to, humor, informational, interview, personal experience, photo feature, profile and technical. "We're planning one or two *major* features covering significant events in the dog world. We'll be looking for (and paying more for) high quality writing/photo packages on topics outside of our normal range of features. Interested writers should query with topics." Buys 5 mss/issue. Query or send complete ms. Length: 500-3,000 words. Pays 5¢/word. Sometimes pays the expenses of writers on assignment.

Photos: Photos purchased with or without accompanying ms. Pays $10 minimum for 8x10 b&w glossy prints; $50-150 for 35mm or 2¼x2¼ color transparencies. Send prints and transparencies. Model release required.

Fiction: Adventure, fantasy, historical and humorous. Buys 5 mss/year. Send complete ms. Length: 500-3,000 words. Pays 5¢/word.

Fillers: "Need short, punchy photo fillers and cartoons." Buys 10 fillers/year. Pays $20-35.

Tips: "We're looking for the unique experience that communicates something about the dog/owner relationship—with the dog as the focus of the story, not the owner. Articles that provide hard information (medical, etc.) through a personal experience are appreciated. Note that we write for a lay audience (non-technical), but we do assume a certain level of intelligence: no talking down to people. If you've never seen the type of article you're writing in *Dog Fancy*, don't expect to."

HORSE AND HORSEMAN, Box HH, Capistrano Beach CA 92624. Editor: Mark Thiffault. 30% freelance written. Works with a small number of new/unpublished writers each year. For owners of pleasure horses; with main interest in show/pleasure riding, but covers all phases and types of horsemanship. Monthly magazine. Circ. 96,000. Buys all rights. Byline given. Buys 40-50 mss/year. Pays on acceptance. Publishes ms an average of 6 months after acceptance. Sample copy $2; writer's guidelines for SASE. Submit special material (horse and tack care; veterinary medicine pieces in winter and spring issues) 3 months in advance. Computer printout submissions acceptable; prefers letter-quality to dot-matrix. Reports in 1 month. Query or submit complete ms.

Nonfiction: Training tips, do-it-yourself pieces, grooming and feeding, stable management, tack maintenance, sports, personalities, rodeo and general horse-related features. Emphasis must be on informing, rather than merely entertaining. Aimed primarily at the beginner, but with information for experienced horsemen. Subject matter must have thorough, in-depth appraisal. Interested in more Western (show) riding/training copy, plus special horse areas like Tennessee Walkers and other gaited breeds. More factual breed histories. Uses informational, how-to, personal experience, interview, profile, humor, historical, nostalgia, successful business operations, technical articles. Length: 2,500 words average. Pays $75-200.

Photos: B&w photos (4x5 and larger) purchased with or without mss. Pays $4-10 when purchased without ms. Uses original color transparencies (35mm and larger). No duplicates. Pays $100 for cover use. Payment for inside editorial color is negotiated.

HORSE & RIDER MAGAZINE, Rich Publishing, Inc., 41919 Moreno Rd., Temecula CA 92390. (714)676-5712. Editor: Ray Rich. Managing Editor: Judy Kizler. 90% freelance written. Monthly magazine for horse owners, riders, breeders and trainers. "Our readers look to us for articles that deal with every aspect of horse care, conditioning, training and performance. We therefore emphasize practical information and prefer subject matter the reader can apply to enjoying his horse. This includes interviews with successful trainers and breeders, veterinarians, competitive riders, and other experts." Circ. 105,789. Pays prior to publication. Publishes ms an average of 3 months after acceptance. Buys all rights. Submit seasonal/holiday material 3 months in advance. Computer printout submissions acceptable; prefers letter-quality to dot-matrix. Reports in 1 week on queries. Sample copy $2; free writer's guidelines.

Nonfiction: Historical/nostalgic (Old West); how-to (training horses); humor (cowboy-type); interview/profile (trainer); new product; and personal experience (riding). "We also publish annuals: *Horse Women, Horse Action, Horse Care, Horse Lover's, All-Western Yearbook.*" Buys 220 mss/year. Query or send complete ms. Length: 500-2,500 words. Pays $100-360.

Photos: Laurie Guidero, photo editor. State availability of photos or send photos with query or ms. Pays $10-25 for 8x10 b&w prints; $50-100 for 8x10 color prints. Captions and identification of subjects required. Buys one-time rights.

Columns/Departments: Dan Cotterman, column/department editor. Buys 48 mss/year (regular contributors).

Tips: "Organizing and presenting an informative, entertaining article usually requires considerable effort. Good composition demands at least one rewrite during which the writer trims and polishes what will exist as the finished product. Have your article tech-checked by the trainer or veterinarian you have interviewed. This is best done before typing the final copy to send to us."

HORSE ILLUSTRATED, Fancy Publications, Inc., Box 6050, Mission Viejo CA 92690. (714)240-6001. Editor: Jill-Marie Jones. 90% freelance written. Monthly magazine for men and women of all ages interested in all phases of horse ownership. Circ. 50,000. Pays after publication. Publishes ms an average of 4 months after acceptance. Buys first North American serial rights. Submit seasonal/holiday material 4 months in advance. Computer printout submissions acceptable. Sample copy $3; free writer's guidelines.

Nonfiction: Medical, how-to, humor, informational, interview, photo feature, profile, technical and sport. Buys 5 mss/issue. Length: 500-2,500 words. Pays 3-5¢/word.

Photos: Photos purchased with or without accompanying ms. Pays $10 minimum for 8x10 b&w glossy prints; $50-150 for 35mm 2¼x2¼ color transparencies. Send prints and transparencies. Model release required.

Fiction: Adventure and humor. Buys 5 mss/year. Send complete ms. Length: 500-2,000 words. Pays 3-5¢/word.

Fillers: Newsworthy or unusual items with photo and cartoons. Buys 10/year. Pays $20-35.

Tips: "We believe very strongly in working with new/young journalists with talent, and support them by giving them more and more assignments. The most annoying aspect of working with freelance writers is not meeting deadlines. Writers often don't realize editors/publishers have unforgiving timetables; and if a writer misses a deadline even once, we are very gun shy about using him/her again."

HORSEMEN'S YANKEE PEDLAR NEWSPAPER, 785 Southbridge St., Auburn MA 01501. (617)832-9638. Publisher: Nancy L. Khoury. Associate Editors: Suzy Lucine, Katharine Stoudt. 40% freelance written. "All-breed monthly newspaper for horse enthusiasts of all ages and incomes, from one-horse owners to large commercial stables. Covers region from New Jersey to Maine." Circ. 12,000. Pays on publication. Buys all rights for one year. Submit seasonal/holiday material 3 months in advance of issue date. Computer printout submissions acceptable; prefers letter-quality to dot-matrix. Publishes ms an average of 5 months after acceptance. Reports in 1 month. Sample copy $1.75.

Nonfiction: Humor, educational and interview about horses and the people involved with them. Pays $2/published inch. Buys 50 mss/year. Submit complete ms or outline. Length: 1,500 words maximum.

Photos: Purchased with ms. Captions and photo credit required. Buys 3 cover photos/year; pays $25. Submit b&w prints. Pays $5.

Columns/Departments: Area news column. Buys 85-95/year. Length: 1,200-1,400 words. Pays 75¢/column inch. Query.

Tips: "Query with outline of angle of story, approximate length and date when story will be submitted. Stories should be people oriented and horse focused. Send newsworthy, timely pieces, such as stories that are applicable to the season, for example: foaling in the spring or how to keep a horse healthy through the winter. We like to see how-tos, features about special horse people and anything that has to do with the preservation of horses and their rights as creatures deserving a chance to survive."

HORSEPLAY, Box 545, Gaithersburg MD 20877. (301)840-1866. Editor: Cordelia Doucet. 50% freelance written. Prefers to work with published/established writer; works with a small number of new/unpublished writers each year. Monthly magazine covering horses and English horse sports for a readership interested in horses, show jumping, dressage, combined training, hunting, and driving. 60-80 pages. Circ. 47,500. Pays end of publication month. Buys all rights, first North American serial rights, and second serial (reprint) rights. Offers kill fee. Byline given. Submit all material at least 2 months in advance. Computer printout submissions acceptable; no dot-matrix. Reports within 3 weeks. Sample copy $2.95; free writer's and photographer's guidelines.

Nonfiction: Instruction (various aspects of horsemanship, course designing, stable management, putting on horse shows, etc.); competitions; interview; photo feature; profile and technical. Length: 1,000-3,000 words. Pays 9¢/word, all rights; 8¢/word, first North American serial rights; 7¢/word, second rights. Sometimes pays the expenses of writers on assignment.

Photos: Cathy Heard, art director. Purchased on assignment. Write captions on separate paper attached to photo. Query or send contact sheet, prints or transparencies. Pays $10-20 for 8x10 b&w glossy prints; $175 for color transparencies for cover; $45 for inside color.

Tips: Don't send fiction, western riding, or racing articles.

HORSES ALL, Box 550, Nanton Alberta T0L 1R0 Canada. (403)646-2271. Editor: Jacki French. 30% freelance written. Eager to work with new/unpublished writers. Monthly tabloid for horse owners, 75% rural, 25% urban. Circ. 11,200. Pays on publication. Publishes ms an average of 6 months after acceptance. Buys one-time rights. Phone queries OK. Submit seasonal material 3 months in advance. Simultaneous, photocopied (if clear), and previously published submissions OK. Computer printout submissions acceptable. Reports on queries in 5 weeks; on mss in 6 weeks. Sample copy $2.

Nonfiction: Interview, humor and personal experience. Query. Pays $20-100. Pays expenses of writers on assignment.

Photos: State availability of photos. Captions required.

Columns/Departments: Length: 1-2 columns. Query. Open to suggestions for new columns/departments. Send query to Doug French.

Fiction: Historical and western. Query. Pays $20-100.

Tips: "We use more short articles. The most frequent mistakes made by writers in completing an article assignment for us are poor research, wrong terminology, and poor (terrible) writing style."

HORSES WEST, Horses West, Inc., Box 1590, Boulder CO 80306-1590. (303)499-7662. Editor-in-Chief: Jaymee Brandt. 75% freelance written. Monthly tabloid covering regional and national news and current information on the training, showing, feeding and care of horses. "*Horses West* is an all-breed regional newspaper serving the Rocky Mountain states. Our readers are primarily exhibitors, horse breeders, horse owners and advertisers in the horse industry." Circ. 12,000. Pays within 30 days after publication. Publishes ms an average of 1 month after acceptance. Byline given. Offers 20% kill fee. Buys all rights, first rights (primary), and second serial (reprint) rights. Submit seasonal/holiday material 4 months in advance. Simultaneous queries, and simultaneous, photocopied, and previously published submissions OK. Electronic submissions acceptable via IBM PC or clone generated, MS DOS operating system, 300 or 1200 baud; requires hard copy also. Computer printout submissions acceptable; prefers letter-quality to dot-matrix. Reports in 3 months. Sample copy for $1, 9x12 SAE and 6 first class stamps; writer's guidelines for business size SAE and 1 first class stamp.

Nonfiction: Book excerpts (from horse training and care books); exposé (controversial topics in the horse industry); general interest (regional and national news on well-known events and/or horses and personalities; horsekeeping and stable management; showing techniques; breeding programs); historical/nostalgic (relating to horses); how-to; humor (cartoons, short anecdotes relating to horses); interview/profile (all-discipline, successful trainers and exhibitors—highlighting techniques, methods or practical approaches to solving a horse problem); opinion (on happenings in the horse world); personal experience (human-interest stories: working-student training, well-known horses, national/regional); photo feature (how-to, training, human interest, humorous, the unusual); technical (riding, training, updates on veterinary treatments; horsekeeping, stable management; tack and equipment—explain use); helpful hints on time-saving horse care techniques—any of value to horse owners. Also, articles relating to horse racing and profiles of famous race horses. Buys 20-30 mss/year. Query. Length: 500-3,000 words. Pays $1-2/column inch for first rights, less for previously published material. Sometimes pays the expenses of writers on assignment.

Photos: State availability of photos with query. Reviews 5x7 and 8x10 b&w and color glossy prints. Payment for photos included in payment for ms. Captions, model releases and identification of subjects required.

Fiction: Adventure, fantasy, historical, humorous, mainstream, mystery, novel excerpts, science fiction and suspense. "No tear-jerkers." Buys 2-3 mss/year. Query. Length: 1,000-2,500 words. "We will serialize top-quality stories of more than 3,000 words." Pays $1-2/column inch, less for previously published material.

Poetry: Free verse, light verse and traditional. "No greeting-card-level poetry." Submit maximum 5 poems. Length: 28 lines maximum. Pays $5.

Fillers: Clippings, jokes, gags, anecdotes, short humor and newsbreaks. Buys 12-20/year. Length: 100-1,000 words. Pays $5-10.

Tips: "We are looking for skillfully written articles in a feature-style, photojournalistic format. Interviews, how-to, general interest, humor/cartoons and regional/national news—all on the subject of all-breed training, showing, feeding, breeding and care of horses—are the areas most open to freelancers."

‡LONE STAR HORSE REPORT, Box 14767, Fort Worth TX 76117. (817)834-3951. Editor: Henry L. King. 15-20% freelance written. Monthly magazine on horses and horse people in and around Dallas/Ft. Worth metroplex. Circ. 6,364. Pays on publication. Publishes ms an average of 2 months after acceptance. Byline given. Buys first rights and second serial (reprint) rights to material originally published elsewhere. Submit seasonal/

holiday material 2 months in advance. Photocopied and previously published submissions OK. Computer printout submissions acceptable. Reports in 2 weeks on queries; 4 weeks on mss. Sample copy $1; free writer's guidelines.

Nonfiction: How-to (how a specific horseman trains horses for specific events); interview/profile (horsemen living in trade area); photo feature (horses, farms, arenas, facilities, people in trade area). Buys 30-40 mss/year. Query with published clips or send complete ms. Length: 200-2,000 words. Pays $15-60.

Photos: State availability of photos. Pays $5 for 5x7 b&w prints. Buys one-time rights.

Tips: "We need reports of specific horse-related events in north Texas area such as trail rides, rodeos, play days, shows, etc., and also feature articles on horse farms, outstanding horses and/or horsemen. Emphasis on local events as opposed to events which would attract national coverage is a trend that writers should be aware of."

THE MORGAN HORSE, American Morgan Horse Association, Box 1, Westmoreland NY 13490. (315)735-7522. Editor: James Blonquist. 60% freelance written. Monthly breed journal covering the training, showing, and vet care of Morgan horses. Circ. 10,000. Pays on publication. Publishes ms an average of 3 months after acceptance. Byline given. Rights vary with submission. Submit seasonal/holiday material 3 months in advance. Simultaneous queries and simultaneous, photocopied, and previously published submissions OK (subject to editor's discretion). Computer print out submissions acceptable; prefers letter-quality to dot-matrix. Reports in 3 months. Sample copy $3; writer's guidelines for business size SAE and 1 first class stamp.

Nonfiction: How-to (trailering, driving, training, etc.); human interest (if highly unusual); interview/profile (of respected Morgan personalities); veterinary articles. Special issues include Morgan Grand National, Stallion, Mare, Gelding, Foal, International. No articles dealing with half-bred Morgans. "We have few fillers we can print but always seem to receive more than our share of them." Buys 15-20 mss/year. Query with clips of published work. Length: 500-3,000 words. Pays 5¢/word and up. Sometimes pays the expenses of writers on assignment.

Photos: Send photos with ms. Pays $5 minimum for 8x10 b&w prints, $20 for color. Captions, model release and identification of subjects required.

Tips: "We like to see completed manuscripts from new writers and welcome articles on veterinary breakthroughs and training. We do develop a stable and encourage new contributors to grow into our group after proving themselves with a few articles."

‡NATIONAL SHOW HORSE NEWS, National Show Horse Registry, Suite 237, 10401 Linn Station Rd., Louisville KY 40223. (502)423-1902. Editor: Terry Kerns. Managing Editor: Steve Hauser. 50% freelance written. Works with a small number of new/unpublished writers each year. A magazine covering "all aspects of the horse industry as it applies to National Show Horse." Circ. 5,000. Pays on acceptance. Publishes ms an average of 3 months after acceptance. Byline given. Buys one-time rights. Electronic submissions OK via systems compatible with MacIntosh system, but requires hard copy also. Computer printout submissions acceptable; prefers letter-quality to dot-matrix. Reports within 2 weeks. Free sample copy and writer's guidelines.

Nonfiction: How-to (training the English style show horse); interview/profile (of successful breeders/exhibitors or persons involved in the field—artist, photographers, etc.); and photo feature (must tie directly to some aspect of National Show Horse World). "All material must be related to horses. We are not interested in material unless it relates to National Show Horses or parent breeds (Arabian/Saddlebred)." Buys 50 mss/year. Query. Length: 500-3,000 words. Pays $50-150.

Photos: Sue Winnell, photo editor. State availability of photos with query letter or ms. Receives transparencies and prints. Pays $10. Captions and identification of subjects required. Buys one-time rights.

Tips: "Become familiar with the goals and purposes of the registry and then develop a feature on a breeder/exhibitor/event in your local area. We have a growing need for material from sections of the country we cannot easily cover from our home offices. Our greatest need is for major articles that we can develop into three-to-six page spreads."

‡PACIFIC COAST JOURNAL, Pacific Coast Quarter Horse Association, Gate 12, Cal-Expo, Box 25482. Sacramento CA 95825. (916)924-7265. Editor: Jill L. Scopinich. 20% freelance written. A monthly magazine covering Cutting and Quarter Horses on the Pacific Coast published by and for members of two equine groups which concentrate on Cutting and Quarter Horses. "It is more technical than most equine publications and our readers are extremely knowledgable on the subject." Circ. 8,000. Pays on acceptance. Byline given. Offers 50% kill fee. Buys first rights and second serial (reprint) rights. Simultaneous, photocopied and previously published submissions OK. Computer printout submissions acceptable; no dot-matrix. Reports in 3 months. Sample copy for 9x12 SAE with 5 first class stamps. Writer's guidelines for #10 SAE with 1 first class stamp.

Nonfiction: How to train Quarter or Cutting Horses, make or care for tack, trailers, etc. No articles that are aimed at newcomers to the horse industry, or that are about other breeds. Buys 36 mss/year. Send complete ms. Length: 750-3,000 words. Pays $100-300 for assigned articles; $50-175 for unsolicited articles; will trade advertising if writer requests. Sometimes pays expenses of writers on assignment.

Photos: Send photos with submission. Reviews contact sheets, transparencies, and 5x7 prints. Offers no additional payment for photos accepted with ms unless negotiated in advance. Captions, model releases, and identification of subjects required. Buys one-time rights.

Columns/Departments: Bookshelf (reviews of books written by professionals concerning the Quarter or Cutting Horse industries). Buys 12 mss/year. Send complete ms. Length: 300-500 words. Pays $35-50.

Fillers: Anecdotes, facts and short humor. Buys 24/year. Length: 50-100 words. Pays $20-40.

Tips: "Send examples of your work that have been published in other equine magazines, or send a cover letter explaining your expertise in the field you are writing about. It is important to our readers that our writers are knowledgable in the fields of Cutting and Quarter Horses. At all times remember that our readers are well-educated in the industry and the majority are professionals, so never speak 'down' to them."

PAINT HORSE JOURNAL, American Paint Horse Association, Box 18519, Fort Worth TX 76118. (817)439-3400. Editor: Bill Shepard. 10% freelance written. Works with a small number of new/unpublished writers each year. For people who raise, breed and show Paint horses. Monthly magazine. Circ. 12,000. Pays on acceptance. Publishes ms an average of 3 months after acceptance. Buys first North American serial rights. Pays negotiable kill fee. Byline given. Phone queries OK, but prefers written query. Submit seasonal/holiday material 3 months in advance. Photocopied and previously published submissions OK. Computer printout submissions acceptable; prefers letter-quality to dot-matrix. Reports in 1 month. Sample copy, $1; writer's guidelines for SAE and 1 first class stamp.

Nonfiction: General interest (personality pieces on well-known owners of Paints); historical (Paint horses in the past—particular horses and the breed in general); how-to (train and show horses); and photo feature (Paint horses). Buys 4-5 mss/issue. Send complete ms. Pays $50-250. Sometimes pays the expenses of writers on assignment.

Photos: Send photos with ms. Offers no additional payment for photos accepted with accompanying ms. Uses 3x5 or larger b&w glossy prints; 35mm or larger color transparencies. Captions required.

Tips: "*PHJ* needs breeder-trainer articles from areas throughout U.S. and Canada. Photos with copy are almost always essential. Well-written first person articles welcome. Submit well-written items that show a definite understanding of the horse business. Use proper equine terminology and proper grounding in ability to communicate thoughts."

PURE-BRED DOGS AMERICAN KENNEL GAZETTE, American Kennel Club, Inc., 51 Madison Ave., New York NY 10010. (212)696-8332. Editor: Ms. Pat Beresford. 40% freelance written. Official publication of the American Kennel Club, a monthly magazine covering pure-bred dogs. "Reaches breeders, exhibitors and owners of pure-bred dogs. All articles published must be related to the pure-bred·dog fancy—dog showing, judging, breeding, health and medicine, grooming, training, and the dog in art or literature." Circ. 50,000. Pays on publication. Publishes ms an average of 12-18 months after acceptance. Byline given. Buys first North American serial rights. Submit seasonal/holiday material 8 months in advance. Reports in 1 month. Free sample copy and writer's guidelines.

Nonfiction: General interest, how-to, photo feature, technical, medical, and must relate to the canine. Buys about 25 mss/year. Send complete ms. Length: 750-3,000 words. Pays $50-250 and up "depending on article."

Photos: Send photos with accompanying query or ms. Reviews 8x10 b&w and color prints or slides. Pay depends on entire article. Model release and identification of subjects required.

Tips: "We simply like to have complete outlines of manuscripts on any ideas submitted. If we like the work or see potential, we will contact the writer. Only editorial features section is open to freelancers. We like to see in-depth coverage of dogs with good photo illustrations."

PURRRRR! THE NEWSLETTER FOR CAT LOVERS, The Meow Company, Suite 187, 89 Massachusetts Ave., Boston MA 02115. Editor: Carol Page. 90% freelance written. Works with a small number of new/unpublished writers each year. A bimonthly newsletter for the average cat owner, *not* breeders. "The publication is designed to amuse while providing cat lovers with information about the care, feeding and enjoyment of house cats." Circ. 2,000+. Pays on publication. Publishes ms an average of 1 year after acceptance. Byline given. Buys first serial rights and second serial (reprint) rights. Submit seasonal/holiday material 6 months in advance. Photocopied and previously published submissions OK unless it's been published in a competing publication, such as *Cats* and *Cat Fancy*. Computer printout submissions acceptable; no dot-matrix. Reports in 2 weeks. Sample copy $2; writer's guidelines for business size SAE and 1 first class stamp.

Nonfiction: General interest; historical; how-to; literary cat lovers (have featured Colette, Mark Twain and May Sarton); humor; interview/profile; new product; travel, off-beat unusual. "We want a humorous slant wherever possible; writing should be tight and professional. Avoid the first person." Special Christmas issue. No shaggy cat stories, sentimental stories, "I taught Fluffy to roll over" cutsie material. Absolutely no fiction or poetry. Buys 50/mss year. Query with published clips, or send complete ms. *Do not call*. Length: 250-1,500 words. Pays: $15-100.

Photos: Avoid "cute" photos. State availability of photos. Pays $5-10 for 5x8 b&w prints. Buys one-time rights.

Fillers: Clippings, anecdotes, short humor and newsbreaks. Buys 20/year. Length: 25-75 words. Pays $5.
Tips: "An articulate query letter, accompanied by clips, is the best way to get an assignment. Following the basic rules of freelancing such as sending a SASE, will win you favor with this editor. I'm amazed at how many people try to get away with not doing it."

THE QUARTER HORSE JOURNAL, Box 32470, Amarillo TX 79120. (806)376-4811. Editor-in-Chief: Audie Rackley. 20% freelance written. Prefers to work with published/established writers. Official publication of the American Quarter Horse Association. Monthly magazine. Circ. 77,000. Pays on acceptance. Publishes ms an average of 3 months after acceptance. Buys first North American serial rights. Submit seasonal/holiday material 2 months in advance. Computer printout submissions acceptable; prefers letter-quality to dot-matrix. Reports in 2 weeks. Free sample copy and writer's guidelines for 2 first class stamps.
Nonfiction: Historical ("those that retain our western heritage"); how-to (fitting, grooming, showing, or anything that relates to owning, showing, or breeding); informational (educational clinics, current news); interview (feature-type stories—must be about established horses or people who have made a contribution to the business); new product; personal opinion; and technical (equine updates, new surgery procedures, etc.). Buys 30 mss/year. Length: 800-2,500 words. Pays $50-250.
Photos: Purchased with accompanying ms. Captions required. Send prints or transparencies. Uses 5x7 or 8x10 b&w glossy prints; 2¼x2¼ or 4x5 color transparencies. Offers no additional payment for photos accepted with accompanying ms.
Tips: "Writers must have a knowledge of the horse business. We will be purchasing more material on Quarter Horse racing."

THE THOROUGHBRED REVIEW, (incorporating *The Canadian Horse*), *Journal of Thoroughbred Racing and Breeding in Canada,* Canadian Thoroughbred Publishing Co. Ltd., 225 Industrial Parkway S, Box 670, Aurora, Ontario L4G 4J9 Canada. (416)727-7546. Editor-in-Chief: Susan Jane Arstey. Consulting Editor: Susan Rhodemyre. For thoroughbred horsemen. Monthly magazine. Circ. 5,500. Pays on publication. Buys all rights. Query first, "with a letter that demonstrates your knowledge of and familiarity with our magazine." Enclose SAE and International Reply Coupons.
Nonfiction: Material on Thoroughbred racing and breeding. Pays approximately 15¢/word.

THE WESTERN HORSEMAN, Box 7980, Colorado Springs CO 80933. Editor: Randy Witte. 40% freelance written. Works with a small number of new/unpublished writers each year. Monthly magazine covering western horsemanship. Circ. 156,357. Pays on acceptance. Publishes ms an average of 5 months after acceptance. Buys first serial rights. Byline given. Computer printout submissions acceptable; prefers letter-quality to dot-matrix. Submit seasonal/holiday material 3 months in advance. Reports in 3 weeks. Sample copy $1.95.
Nonfiction: How-to (horse training, care of horses, tips, etc.); and informational (on rodeos, ranch life, historical articles of the West emphasizing horses). Length: 1,500 words. Payment begins at $175; "sometimes higher by special arrangement."
Photos: Send photos with ms. Offers no additional payment for photos. Uses 5x7 or 8x10 b&w glossy prints and 35mm transparencies. Captions required.
Tips: "Submit clean copy with professional quality photos. Stay away from generalities. Writing style should show a deep interest in horses coupled with a wide knowledge of the subject."

Art

Art magazines vary as much as the types of media or artwork. Some of them want step-by-step art instruction articles; others need articles on exhibiting and selling artwork. Listed here are publications of and about art, art history, and specific art forms written for art patrons and artists. Publications addressing the business and management concerns of the art industry are listed in the Art, Design, and Collectibles category of the Trade Journals section.

THE AMERICAN ART JOURNAL, Kennedy Galleries, Inc., 40 W. 57th St., 5th Floor, New York NY 10019. (212)541-9600. Editor-in-Chief: Jane Van N. Turano. Prefers to work with published/ established writers; works with a small number of new/unpublished writers each year. Scholarly magazine of American art history of the 17th, 18th, 19th and 20th centuries, including painting, sculpture, architecture, decorative arts, etc., for people with a serious interest in American art, and who are already knowledgable about the subject. Readers are scholars, curators, collectors, students of American art, or persons who have a strong interest in Americana. Quarterly magazine; 96 pages. Circ. 2,000. Pays on acceptance. Publishes ms an average of 6 months after acceptance. Buys all rights, but will reassign rights to a writer. Byline given. Photocopied submissions OK. Computer printout submissions acceptable but with reluctance. Reports in 2 months. Sample copy $8.

Nonfiction: "All articles are about some phase or aspect of American art history." No how-to articles or reviews of exhibitions. No book reviews or opinion pieces. No human interest approaches to artists' lives. No articles written in a casual or "folksy" style. *Writing style must be formal and serious.* Buys 25-30 mss/year. Submit complete ms "with good cover letter." No queries. Length: 2,500-8,000 words. Pays $300-400.

Photos: Purchased with accompanying ms. Captions required. Uses b&w only. Offers no additional payment for photos accepted with accompanying ms.

Tips: "Articles *must be* scholarly, thoroughly documented, well-researched, well-written, and illustrated. Whenever possible, all manuscripts must be accompanied by b&w photographs which have been integrated into the text by the use of numbers."

ART TIMES, Cultural and Creative News, Box 730, Mount Marion NY 12456. (914)246-5170. Editor: Raymond J. Steiner. 10% (just fiction and poetry) freelance written. Will work with published/established writers; works with a small number of new/unpublished writers each year; and eager to work with new/unpublished writers. Monthly tabloid covering the arts (visual, theatre, dance, etc.). "*Art Times* covers the art fields and is distributed in locations most frequented by those enjoying the arts. Our 15,000 copies are distributed throughout three upstate New York counties rich in the arts as well as in most of the galleries in Soho, 57th Street and Madison Avenue in the metropolitan area; locations include theatres, galleries, museums, cultural centers and the like. Our readers are mostly over 40, affluent, art-conscious and sophisticated." Circ. 15,000. Pays on publication. Publishes ms an average of 6 months after acceptance. Byline given. Not copyrighted. Buys first serial rights. Submit seasonal/holiday material 6 months in advance. Simultaneous queries, and simultaneous and photocopied submissions OK. Reports in 1 month on queries; 3 months on mss. Sample copy for SAE and 3 first class stamps; writer's guidelines for business size envelope and 1 first class stamp.

Fiction: "We're looking for short fiction that aspires to be *literary.* No excessive violence, sexist, off-beat, erotic, sports, or juvenile fiction." Buys 8-10 mss/year. Send complete ms. Length: 1,500 maximum. Pays $15 maximum (honorarium).

Poetry: Poet's Niche. Avant-garde, free verse, haiku, light verse, and traditional. "We prefer well-crafted 'literary' poems. No excessively sentimental poetry." Buys 30-35 poems/year. Submit maximum 6 poems. Length: 20 lines maximum. Offers contributor copies.

Tips: "Be familiar with *Art Times* and its special audience. *Art Times* has literary leanings with articles written by a staff of scholars knowledgable in their respective fields. Our readers expect quality. Although an 'arts' publication, we observe no restrictions (other than noted) in accepting fiction/poetry other than a concern for quality writing—subjects can cover anything and not specifically arts."

THE ARTIST'S MAGAZINE, F&W Publishing Co., 9933 Alliance Rd., Cincinnati OH 45242. Editor: Michael Ward. 80% freelance written. Monthly magazine covering art instruction. "Ours is a highly visual approach to teaching the serious amateur artist techniques that will help him improve his skills and market his work. The style should be crisp and immediately engaging." Circ. 165,000. Pays on acceptance. Publishes ms an average of 6 months after acceptance. Byline given. Offers 20% kill fee. Buys first North American serial rights and second serial (reprint) rights. Simultaneous queries; and photocopied and previously published submissions OK "as long as noted as such." Computer printout submissions acceptable; prefers letter-quality to dot-matrix. Reports in 1 month. Sample copy $2.50 with 9x12 SAE; free writer's guidelines.

Nonfiction: Book excerpts; how-to (every aspect of technique for painting, drawing and business of art; use new product or media); and inspirational (how an artist may have succeeded through hard work, determination, etc.). No unillustrated articles; no seasonal/holiday material. Buys 60 mss/year. Query. Length: 500-2,500 words. Pays $50-350. Sometimes pays expenses of writers on assignment.

Photos: "Photos are required with every sort of article and are essential in any instructional piece." Reviews 35mm color slides or 4x5 transparencies. Payment is for the "package" of slide, text and captions. Captions required. Buys one-time rights.

Columns/Departments: Book reviews; The Artist's Life (brief items about art and artists); and P.S. (1-page humorous look at art). Buys 100 mss/year. Send complete ms. Length: 200 words for book reviews; 400-600 words for The Artist's Life; 300-400 words for P.S. Pays $30 for book reviews; $50-100 for The Artist's Life; and $50-100 for P.S.

Tips: "Look at several issues carefully and read the author's guidelines carefully. We require professional quality slides and/or transparencies to accompany article."

‡ARTVIEWS, Visual Arts Ontario, 439 Wellington St. W, Toronto, Ontario M5V 1E7 Canada. (416)591-8883. Editor: Rachel Rafelman. Quarterly magazine "exploring the current visual arts scene—issues, events, major exhibitions—particularly as they pertain to Ontario's art community." Circ. 8,000. Pays on acceptance.

Byline given. Offers 25% kill fee. Buys one-time rights. Simultaneous queries and previously published submissions OK. Reports in 2 weeks on queries; 5 weeks on mss. Free sample copy and writer's guidelines.
Nonfiction: Interview/profile, opinion, photo feature, art issues. No exhibition reviews. Buys 8 mss/year. Query with published clips if available. Length: 500-1,500 words. Pays $50-150.
Photos: State availability of photos. Pays $10-25 for 8x10 b&w prints. Captions and identification of subjects required.
Fillers: Newsbreaks, art, cartoons. Buys variable number of mss/year. Length: 200-500 words. Pays $5-25.

‡CREATIVE CRAFTERS JOURNAL, The Magazine of America's Original Fine Artists, Photographers and Craftspeople, Creative Crafters Publishing, 488-A River Mountain Rd., Lebanon VA 24266. (703)873-7402. Editor: Steve McCay. 15% freelance written. A quarterly magazine covering art, craft and photography. Audience is art patrons—collectors, investors, art directors, buyers for stores. "Most stories are profiles of contemporary artistic talents who market their wares directly to the public—our readers." Circ. 10,000. Pays on publication. Publishes ms an average of 6 months after acceptance. Byline given. Buys first rights. Submit seasonal/holiday material 6 months in advance. Computer printout submissions acceptable; prefers letter-quality to dot-matrix. Reports in 6 weeks. Sample copy $3.50; writer's guidelines for legal size SASE.
Nonfiction: Humor, inspirational, interview/profile, personal experience and photo feature. Special Christmas Craft Portfolio—8-12 feature artists—crafts and wares that make good Christmas gifts and are for sale via mail order. Needs to see slides for jurying by June 1. No how-to-make specific craft, pattern, etc. Buys 8 mss/year. Query with or without published clips. Length: 1,000-2,500 words. Pays $50 for assigned articles; pays $25 for unsolicited articles. "Whenever article is autobiographical we pay 20 copies of issue and one year subscription."
Photos: Send photos with submission. Reviews 35mm slides and 4x5 transparencies. Offers no additional payment for photos accepted with ms. Captions required. Buys one-time rights.
Columns/Departments: Book Reviews (art books of interest to art patrons); and Exhibition Review (of open/competitive art shows and gallery shows of combined works). Buys 8 mss/year. Query with published clips. Length: 500-2,000 words. Pays $5-10.
Poetry: Light verse and traditional. Must have slant on the art world/community. Buys 4 poems/year. Submit maximum 3 poems. Length: 50 lines maximum. Pays $5-10.
Fillers: Anecdotes, facts, gags to be illustrated by cartoonist, newsbreaks and short humor. Must have appeal to art patrons. Length: 100-500 words. Pays $5-25.
Tips: "Superior quality photos are a must. We feature creative talents of the arts community—primarily those willing to sell their wares direct to a retail market via mail order. We like to see slides of art work first. Mostly we use autobiorgaphical or first-person self portrait/profiles. We'd like to have a feature collector each issue with photos of the collection—be it art, pottery, metal, fiber, wood, etc.—with details on the pieces collected, philosophy of collectors, tips on displaying a collection. We provide a media for fine artists, photographers and craftspeople to reach their market."

‡DESIGN FOR ARTS IN EDUCATION MAGAZINE, Heldref Publications, 4000 Albemarle St. NW, Washington DC 20016. (202)362-6445. Publisher: Cornelius W. Vahle. Managing Editor: Mary Singer. 100% freelance written. Eager to work with new/unpublished writers. "For policymakers, teachers, art specialists, administrators, and parents who work with children in education." Bimonthly magazine. Publishes ms an average of 2 months after acceptance. Byline given. Computer printout submissions acceptable; prefers letter-quality to dot-matrix. Reports in 8-10 weeks. Sample copy $3. Editorial guidelines for SASE.
Nonfiction: Articles should be 2,000-6,000 words in length. Format follows *Chicago Manual of Style*.
Tips: "The purpose of *Design for Arts in Education* is to discuss major policy issues concerning K-12 education in the various arts. The magazine's editorial philosophy involves a commitment to present a broad range of policy views and questions of concern to the arts education field. The magazine is intended as a journal of ideas, rather than a chronical of events. It is intended as a forum for debate rather than a platform for advocacy. It seeks to broaden and deepen perspective, rather than to confirm previous belief."

‡EXHIBIT, Magazine of Art, Allied Publications, 1776 Lake Worth Rd., Lake Worth FL 33460. (305)582-2099. Editor: Mark Adams. 20% freelance written. A bimonthly magazine distributed to "patrons of private galleries, framing shops and art supply stores through the mail and over-the-counter. Its fourteen pages consist of news briefs and feature articles on current major museum exhibits, featured artists and art appreciation." Circ. 30,000. Pays on acceptance. Publishes ms an average of 4 months after acceptance. Byline given. Buys

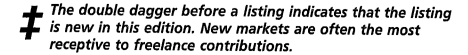

The double dagger before a listing indicates that the listing is new in this edition. New markets are often the most receptive to freelance contributions.

first rights, one-time rights, second serial (reprint) rights, and sometimes makes work-for-hire assignments. Submit seasonal/holiday material 8 months in advance. Simultaneous, photocopied, and previously published submissions OK. Computer printout submissions acceptable. Reports in 1 month. Sample copy and writers guidelines for 9x12 SAE with 50¢ postage.
Nonfiction: General interest (on art appreciation); historical/nostalgic; biographical; interview/profile (on an artist, photos a must); and photofeature (color or b&w). No how-to pieces. Buys 6-12 mss/year. Query with or without published clips, or send complete ms. Length: 500-800 words. Pays 5¢/word or $25 maximum; may pay with copies or premiums rather than cash, if writer requests.
Photos: Send photos with submission. Reviews transparencies and b&w prints. Offers $5 minimum/photo. Captions and identification of subjects required. Buys one-time rights.
Tips: Freelancers have the best chance of selling *Exhibit* "short nonfiction—articles and essays offering perspectives on artists and their styles and techniques, and general art appreciation."

‡**GLASS**, Box 23383, Portland OR 97223. Editor: Jim Wilson. 20% freelance written. Works with a small number of new/unpublished writers each year. A fine arts quarterly publication that showcases all aspects of glass art as well as artists, collectors, museum exhibits, etc. Appeals to artists, hobbyists, museums, galleries, collectors and anyone else interested in looking at glass art. Circ. 30,000. Pays 1 month after publication. Publishes ms an average of 6 months after acceptance. Computer printout submissions acceptable; prefers letter-quality to dot-matrix. Free writer's guidelines.
Nonfiction: "This magazine showcases glass as a fine art, showing only the best. We are looking for artists' profiles, exhibit reviews, special features. Writing for this publication requires considerable knowledge about the medium." Pays $400 maximum.

‡**GLASS STUDIO**, Box 23383, Portland OR 97223. Contact: Editor. 65% freelance written. Prefers to work with published/established writers. A monthly magazine for artists, craftspeople, and hobbyists working in blown glass, stained glass, conceptual glass, as well as collectors, museum curators, gallery and shop owners, students in the arts, and anyone else interested in glass art. Circ. 30,000. Computer printout submissions acceptable; prefers letter-quality to dot-matrix. Pays 1 month after publication. Sample copy $2; writer's guidelines for SASE.
Nonfiction: "We are looking for technical articles, how-to articles from people who know what they're talking about. Also, features on artists, glass companies, and unusual stories related to glass art. Remember, you are writing for a specific audience that either works with glass or collects it." Pays $200 maximum.
Photos: No additional payment for photos used with mss.

METALSMITH, Society of North American Goldsmiths, 6707 N. Santa Monica Blvd., Milwaukee WI 53217-3940. Editor: Sarah Bodine. Editorial address: 1 Penn Lyle Rd., Princeton Jct. NJ 08550. Quarterly magazine covering craft metalwork and metal arts for people who work in metal and those interested in the field, including museum curators, collectors and teachers. The magazine covers all aspects of the craft including historical and technical articles, business and marketing advice and exhibition reviews. Circ. 5,000. Pays on publication. Byline given. Buys first North American serial rights. Submit seasonal/holiday material 6 months in advance. Photocopied and previously published submissions (foreign) OK. Computer printout submissions acceptable; prefers letter-quality to dot-matrix. Reports in 1 month on queries; 6 weeks on mss.
Nonfiction: Expose (metals, markets, theft); historical/nostalgic; how-to (advanced-level metalsmithing techniques); humor; inspirational; interview/profile; opinion (regular column); personal experience; photo feature; technical (research); and travel (*Metalsmith*'s Guides to Cities). Special issue features Annual Summer Program Listing. Buys 15 mss/year. Query with clips of published work and indicate "experience in the field or related fields." Length: 1,000-3,500 words. Pays $25-400/article.
Columns/Departments: Exhibition Reviews; Issues; Galleries; Marketing and Business Advice; Metalsmith's Guides to Cities and Regions and Book Reviews. Buys 20 mss/year. Query with clips of published work. Length: 250-3,000 words. Pays $25-100/article.
Tips: "The discovery of new talent is a priority—queries about innovative work which has not received much publicity are welcome. Almost all our writing is done by freelancers. Those knowledgable in the field and who have previous experience in writing analysis and criticism are most sought after. *Metalsmith* is looking to build a stable of crafts writers and so far have found these few and far between. Those who have both a feeling for metalwork of all kinds and a sharp pencil are sought. Articles must have substance, thematic unity and depth. We are not looking for pretty pictures of metalwork, but analysis, presentation of new or undiscovered talent and historical documentation. A few lines of explanation of a story idea are therefore helpful."

‡**METROPOLIS, The Architecture and Design Magazine of New York**, Bellerophon Publications, 177 E 87th St., New York NY 10128. (212)722-5050. Editor: Susan S. Szenasy. Managing Editor: Claude Lubroth. 60% freelance written. A monthly (except bimonthly January/February and July/August) magazine for consumers interested in architecture and design. Circ. 15,110. Pays on acceptance. Publishes ms an average of 3-6 months after acceptance. Byline given. Buys first rights or makes work-for-hire assignments. Submit cal-

endar material 6 weeks in advance. Photocopied submissions OK. Computer printout submissions acceptable; prefers letter-quality to dot-matrix. Reports in 2 weeks on queries; 1 month on mss. Sample copy $3.50 including postage.

Nonfiction: Book excerpts; essays (design, residential interiors); historical (New York); opinion (design architecture); and profile (only well-known international figures in USA). No profiles on individuals or individual architectural practices, technical information, information from public relations firms, fine arts, or things outside of New York area. Buys approximately 30 mss/year. Query with published clips. Length: 1,500-3,000 words. Pays $350-500.

Photos: State availability, or send photos with submission. Reviews contact sheets, 35mm or 4x5 transparencies, or 8x10 b&w prints. Payment offered for certain photos. Captions required. Buys one-time rights.

Columns/Departments: Insites (Manhattan miscellany: information on design and architecture around New York), 100-600 words; In Print (book review essays), 600-750 words. Buys approximately 10 mss/year. Query with published clips. Pays $50-100.

Tips: "Keep in mind that we are *only* interested in the consumer end of architecture and design. Send query with examples of photos explaining how you see illustrations working with article. Also, be patient and don't expect an immediate answer after submission of query."

THE ORIGINAL ART REPORT, Box 1641, Chicago IL 60690. Editor and Publisher: Frank Salantrie. 1% freelance written. Emphasizes "visual art conditions from the visual artists' and general public's perspectives." Newsletter; 6-8 pages. Pays on publication. Reports in 4 weeks. Sample copy $1.25 and 1 first class stamp.

Nonfiction: Expose (art galleries, government agencies ripping off artists, or ignoring them); historical (perspective pieces relating to now); humor (whenever possible); informational (material that is unavailable in other art publications); inspirational (acts and ideas of courage); interview (with artists, other experts; serious material); personal opinion; technical (brief items to recall traditional methods of producing art); travel (places in the world where artists are welcome and honored); philosophical, economic, aesthetic, and artistic. "No vanity profiles of artists, arts organizations, and arts promoters' operations." Buys 4-5 mss/year. Query or submit complete ms. Length: 1,000 words maximum. Pays 1¢/word.

Columns/Departments: New column: In Back of the Individual Artist. "Artists express their views about non-art topics. After all, artists are in this world, too"; WOW (Worth One Wow), Worth Repeating, and Worth Repeating Again. "Basically, these are reprint items with introduction to give context and source, including complete name and address of publication. Looking for insightful, succinct commentary." Submit complete ms. Length: 500 words maximum. Pays ½¢/word.

Tips: "I get excited when ideas address substantive problems of individual artists in the art condition and as they affect the general population. Send original material that is direct and to the point, opinionated and knowledgable. Write in a factual style with clarity. No straight educational or historical stuff. All material must be original or unique." Recent article example: "A Gathering of the Clan" (vol. 8, no. 3). Send SASE with 1 first class stamp for sample copy.

PROFESSIONAL STAINED GLASS, (formerly *Glass Craft News*), Edge Publishing Group, Room 701, 270 Lafayette St., New York NY 10012. (212)966-6694. Editor: Albert Lewis. Monthly magazine covering stained glass. "Our readers are stained glass professionals, retailers and hobbyists. We are interested in articles that are useful to them, rather than merely interesting." Circ. 12,700. Pays on publication. Byline given. Offers $25 kill fee. Buys first North American serial rights. Simultaneous queries, and simultaneous, photocopied and previously published submissions OK. Computer printout submissions acceptable. Reports in 2 weeks on queries; 1 month on mss. Sample copy for 9x12 SAE and $1 postage; writer's guidelines for 4x9½ SAE and 1 first class stamp.

Nonfiction: How-to (anything related to stained glass); interview/profile (of stained glass craftsmen); new product; and technical. "We like articles on techniques, features on individuals who are doing interesting work in glass (with emphasis on the technical aspects of their work), and marketing tips. We also want articles on subjects other than glass, which would be of use to hobbyists, e.g., cabinetmaking, lighting techniques and glass photography. We are not interested in nonpractical articles, such as stories about church windows or Louis Tiffany." Buys 30 mss/year. Query. Length: 750-2,000 words. Pays $50-200.

Photos: State availability of photos. Pays $5-25 for color contact sheets, transparencies and 8x10 prints. Identification of subjects required. Buys one-time rights.

Tips: "Freelancers should have a reasonable understanding of the crafts field, particularly stained glass. We get too many articles from people who are not familiar with their subject."

SOUTHWEST ART, Box 13037, Houston TX 77219. (713)850-0990. Editor: Susan Hallsten McGarry. 80% freelance written. Emphasizes art—paintings, sculpture and fine art photography. Monthly. Pays on tenth of the month of publication. Publishes ms an average of 8 months after acceptance. Buys all rights to ms (not artwork). Photocopied submissions OK. Computer printout submissions acceptable; no dot-matrix. Reports in 4 months. Sample copy $6.

Nonfiction: Informational, interview, personal opinion and profile. "We publish articles about artists and art trends, concentrating on a geographical area west of the Mississippi River. Articles should explore the artist's personality, philosophy, media and techniques, and means by which they convey ideas." Buys 100 mss/year. Must submit 20 color prints/transparencies along with a full outline biography of the artist. If artist is accepted, article length is 1,800-2,000 words minimum. Pays on sliding scale to $300. Sometimes pays the expenses of writers on assignment.

Tips: The writer has a better chance of breaking in at *Southwest Art* with short, lesser-paying articles and fillers (rather than with major features) because "short pieces, skillfully handled, are an excellent gauge of feature writing potential. Submit both published and unpublished samples of your writing. An indication of how quickly you work and your availability on short notice is helpful."

‡SPLASH, Art and Contemporary Culture, Crandall Enterprises, Inc., 458A N. Tamiami Trail, Osprey FL 33559. (813)966-5137. Editor: Jordan Crandall. Managing Editor: Lisa D. Black. 75% freelance written. A bimonthly magazine covering the arts, "but we are eclectic. *Splash* is devoted to art and contemporary culture. Our audience is generally well-educated and interested in the arts. There is no special slant, per se, but we dare to be controversial and are decidedly progressive in our thinking." Circ. 5,000. Pays 30 days after publication. Publishes ms an average of 4 months after acceptance. Byline sometimes given. Buys first rights. Submit seasonal/holiday material 4 months in advance. Simultaneous and photocopied submissions OK. Reports in 2 weeks on queries; 1 month on mss. Sample copy $3; free writer's guidelines.

Nonfiction: Essays; exposé; general interest; historical/nostalgic; humor; interview/profile; opinion; personal experience; photo feature; religious; travel; and reviews (art, music, film, books, dance). Does not want anything in a strictly journalistic mode—no newspaper-type mss will be considered. Buys 50-60 mss/year. Query with or without published clips, or send complete ms. Length: 250-2,000 words. Pays $50-350. Sometimes pays expenses of writers on assignment, but generally does not assign freelance writers.

Photos: State availability or send photos with submission. Reviews b&w glossy prints, any size. Offers $5-25/photo. Captions, model releases and identification of subjects required. Buys one-time rights; photo essays, first time rights only.

Columns/Departments: Expo (reviews on *all* the arts—local as well as national), 500-750 words; Opine (educated opinions on politics, art, relgion, current issues), 750-1,250 words; Arena (short, sophisticated humor), 250-500 words, Studio (introduction to new and/or emerging talents in all the arts), 500-1,000 words. Buys 25 mss/year. Query with published clips. Length: 250-1,250 words. Pays $50-250.

Fiction: "We use *very little* fiction at present." Confession, experimental, fantasy, novel excerpts and slice-of-life vignettes. "No lengthy stories (no book-size texts)—the shorter the fiction, and the more avant garde, the better the chances are that we will use it." Buys 5 mss/year. Query with published clips. Length: 250-1,000 words. Pays $50-350.

Poetry: "We use very little poetry at present." No traditional, Victorian-type verse; "the shorter and more avant garde, the better." Buys 5 poems/year. Submit maximum 10 poems. Length: 5-75 lines. Pays $15-75.

Fillers: Anecdotes, facts, and short humor. Buys 10/year. Length: 150-500 words. Pays $15-75.

Tips: "Our style is progressive, avant garde. In a word, our magazine is *style-oriented* and decidedly *not* journalistic. If a manuscript is approached aesthetically as opposed to journalistically it has a much better chance of being published. Sample writings ought to be sent and perhaps a cover letter stating interests, etc. All areas are open to freelancers. Reviews must be topical, interesting, insightful and succinct. The interviews we do are generally with accomplished, well-known people in all fields—art, literature, politics, entertainment. As above, we require progressive writers and not journalists."

‡WESTART, Box 6868, Auburn CA 95604. (916)885-0969. Editor-in-Chief: Martha Garcia. Emphasizes art for practicing artists and artist/craftsmen; students of art and art patrons. Semimonthly tabloid; 20 pages. Circ. 7,500. Pays on publication. Buys all rights. Byline given. Phone queries OK. Photocopied submissions OK. Sample copy 50¢; free writer's guidelines.

Nonfiction: Informational; photo feature and profile. No hobbies. Buys 6-8 mss/year. Query or submit complete ms. Length: 700-800 words. Pays 50¢/column inch.

Photos: Purchased with or without accompanying ms. Send b&w prints. Pays 50¢/column inch.

Tips: "We publish information which is current—that is, we will use a review of an exhibition only if exhibition is still open on date of publication. Therefore, reviewer must be familiar with our printing deadlines and news deadlines."

WOMEN ARTISTS NEWS, Midmarch Associates, Box 3304 Grand Central Station, New York NY 10163. Editor: Rena Hansen. 70-90% freelance written. Works with small number of new/unpublished writers each year; eager to work with new/unpublished writers. Bimonthly magazine for "artists and art historians, museum and gallery personnel, students, teachers, crafts personnel, art critics and writers." Circ. 5,000. Buys first serial rights only when funds are available. "Token payment as funding permits." Publishes ms an average of 2 months after acceptance. Byline given. Submit seasonal material 2 months in advance. Computer printout submissions acceptable; no dot-matrix. Reports in 1 month. Sample copy $2.50.

Nonfiction: Features, informational, historical, interview, opinion, personal experience, photo feature and technical. Query or submit complete ms. Length: 500-2,500 words.
Photos: Used with or without accompanying ms. Query or submit contact sheet or prints. Pays $5 for 5x7 b&w prints when money is available. Captions required.

Association, Club
and Fraternal

Association publications enable writers to write for national audiences while covering a local story of national interest. If your town has a Kiwanis, Lions, or Rotary Club chapter, one of its projects might merit a story in the club's magazine. Some association magazines circulate worldwide. These publications link members who live continents from one another or in the same town. They keep members, friends and institutions informed of the ideals, objectives, projects, and activities of the sponsoring club. Club-financed magazines that carry material not directly related to the group's activities (for example, *The American Legion Magazine* in the General Interest section) are classified by their subject matter in the Consumer and Trade Journals sections of this book.

BFG TODAY, The BFGoodrich Company, 500 S. Main St., Akron OH 44318. (216)374-2633. Editor: Denise Bowler. 25% freelance written. Quarterly magazine for employees and retirees of the BFGoodrich Company, manufacturer of chemicals, plastics, tires and engineered products. "*BFG Today* seeks to help readers understand how the company operates and how internal issues and trends affect it." Circ. 40,000. Pays on acceptance. Publishes ms an average of 3 months after acceptance. Byline given. Makes work-for-hire assignments. Submit seasonal/holiday material 6 months in advance. No simultaneous queries, or simultaneous, photocopied or previously published submissions. Computer printout submissions acceptable; prefers letter-quality to dot-matrix. Reports in 1 month. Free copy and sample guidelines.
Nonfiction: General interest, how-to, humor, interview/profile, new product and technical. Buys 8 mss/year. Query with published clips. Length: 600-2,500 words. Pays $300 minimum. Pays expenses of writers on assignment.
Tips: "Query the magazine with business, industry or how-to story ideas that will be of interest to our readers. Include samples of published writing, preferably previously published in other corporate magazines."

CALIFORNIA HIGHWAY PATROLMAN, California Association of Highway Patrolmen, 2030 V St., Sacramento CA 95818. (916)452-6751. Editor: Carol Perri. 80% freelance written. Prefers to work with published/established writers; works with a small number of new/unpublished writers each year; eager to work with new/unpublished writers. Monthly magazine. Circ. 20,000. Pays on publication. Publishes ms an average of 6 months after acceptance. Buys one-time rights. Submit seasonal/holiday material 6 months in advance. Computer printout submissions acceptable. Reports in 3 months. Free sample copy and writer's guidelines.
Nonfiction: Publishes articles on transportation safety, driver education, consumer interest, California history, humor and general interest. "Topics can include autos, boats, bicycles, motorcycles, snowmobiles, recreational vehicles and pedestrian safety. We are also in the market for California travel pieces and articles on early California. We are *not* a technical journal for teachers and traffic safety experts, but rather a general interest publication geared toward the layman." Pays 2½¢/word.
Photos: "Illustrated articles always receive preference." Pays $2.50/b&w photo. Captions required.
Tips: "If a writer feels the article idea, length and style are consistent with our magazine, submit the manuscript for me to determine if I agree. We are looking for articles for specific holidays."

CATHOLIC FORESTER, Catholic Order of Foresters, 425 W. Shuman Blvd., Naperville IL 60566. (312)983-4920. Editor: Barbara Cunningham. 35% freelance written. Prefers to work with published/established writers; works with a small number of new/unpublished writers each year; eager to work with new/unpublished writers. A bimonthly magazine of short, general interest articles and fiction for members of the Order, which is a fraternal insurance company. Family type audience, middle class. Circ. 150,000. Pays on acceptance. Publishes ms an average of 6 months after acceptance. Byline given. Buys one-time rights, second serial (reprint) rights, and simultaneous rights. Submit seasonal/holiday material 6 months in advance. Simultaneous, photocopied, and previously published submissions OK. Computer printout submissions acceptable; no dot-matrix. Reports in 6 weeks on ms. Sample copy for 8½x11 SAE and 73¢ postage; free writer's guidelines.

Nonfiction: General interest; historical/nostalgic; how-to (carpentry, cooking, repairs, etc.) humor; inspirational; interview/profile; new product; opinion; personal experience; photo feature; technical (depends on subject); and travel. "Short feature articles of interest to the all-American type are most open to freelancers." No blatant sex nor anything too violent. Send complete ms. Length: 1,000-3,000 words. Pays 5¢/word; more for excellent ms.

Photos: Prefers something of unusual interest or story-telling. State availability of photos, or send photos with query or ms. Reviews any size b&w and color prints. Payment to be determined. Captions, model releases, and identification of subjects required. Buys one-time rights.

Columns/Departments: Needs unusual items on what is going on in the world; new, interesting products, discoveries or happenings. Send complete ms. Length: 1,000 words. Payment to be determined.

Fiction: Adventure, historical, humorous, mainstream, mystery, religious (Catholic), romance, suspense and western. No sex or extreme violence. Length: up to 3,000 words. Pays 5¢/word; more for excellent ms.

Poetry: Free verse, Haiku, light verse, traditional. Submit maximum 5 poems. Payment to be determined.

Fillers: Cartoons, jokes, anecdotes, short humor. Length: 300-500 words. Payment to be determined.

CBIA NEWS, Journal of the Connecticut Business and Industry Association, CBIA Service Corp., 370 Asylum St., Hartford CT 06103. (203)547-1661. Editor: Mara Braverman. 30% freelance written. A monthly tabloid (except combined July/August issue) covering business in Connecticut for approximately 6,500 member companies. Half of the *News* is about the association and written in-house. Other half is about how to run your business better; interesting businesspeople in Connecticut, and business trends here. These are sometimes written by freelancers. Circ. 7,200. Pays on acceptance. Publishes ms an average of 5 months after acceptance. Byline given. Offers 20% kill fee. Buys variable rights; can be negotiable. Photocopied and previously published submissions OK if not published in competing publication. Computer printout submissions acceptable; prefers letter-quality to dot-matrix. Reports in 2 weeks. Free sample copy.

Nonfiction: Book excerpts, how-to (how to run your business better in some specific way); interview/profile (must be a Connecticut person). Buys approximately 20 mss/year. Query with published clips. Length and payment vary with the subject.

Photos: State availability of photos with query or ms. Reviews b&w contact sheets. Pays negotiable rate. Model release and identification of subjects required.

Tips: "Write to me including resume and clips. They do *not* have to be from business publications. If I'm interested, I'll contact you and describe fees, rules, etc."

CHARIOT, Ben Hur Life Association, Box 312, Crawfordsville IN 47933. (317)362-4500. Editor: Loren Harrington. 15-20% freelance written. A quarterly magazine covering fraternal activities of membership plus general interest items. Circ. 11,000. Usually pays on acceptance, sometimes on publication. Publishes ms an average of 6 months after acceptance. Byline and brief biography given. Not copyrighted. Buys variable rights. Submit seasonal/holiday material 10 months in advance. Simultaneous queries, and simultaneous and photocopied submissions OK. Computer printout submissions acceptable; prefers letter-quality to dot-matrix. Reports in 2 weeks on queries; 1 month on mss. Sample copy for 9x12 SAE and 4 first class stamps—for *serious* inquiries only; writer's guidelines for business size SASE and 2 first class stamps.

Nonfiction: General interest, historical and how-to. "Absolutely *nothing* of a smutty, sexually-oriented, gay, etc. nature. Only items of benefit to our readers and/or family would be considered." Query with or without published clips, or send complete ms. Length: 300-3,500 words. Pays 3-20¢/word. Sometimes pays the expenses of writers on assignment.

Photos: State availability of photos with query letter or ms. "We would like to have quality photo with query. We will return if rejected." Reviews b&w and color contact sheets and b&w and color prints. Payment for photos included in payment for mss. Captions, model release and identification of subjects required. Buys one-time rights.

Columns/Departments: Columns are editorial or insurance-related. "Would consider a query piece, but it would have to be extremely applicable."

Fiction: Especially interested in "really good, *short*, fiction. It must have theme of helping another person or benefitting a worthy cause. Absolutely *nothing* of a smutty, sexually-oriented, gay, etc. nature. Only stories of benefit to our readers and/or family would be considered." Query with or without published clips or send complete ms. Length: 300-2,500 words. Pays 3-20¢/word.

Fillers: No fillers considered at present—will take a look at cartoons.

Tips: "Our requirements are very tightly edited and professionally written with a wide appeal to our particular audience, self-help volunteer and charity. Those items that we can give our local units to encourage their fraternal participation and projects would be considered more than any other single submitted features."

CLUB COSTA MAGAZINE, (formerly *Vacation Times and Business Travel*), Club Costa Corp. dba Airline Discount Club-International, Box 616, Parker CO 80134. (303)841-4337. Editor: Richard A. Bodner. 65% freelance written. Prefers to work with published/ established writers; works with a small number of new/un-published writers each year. A quarterly magazine available only to club members covering discounted accom-modations, travel and other savings available through ADC-I. "We offer airline employee 'discount' prices to our members on a variety of accommodations, flights, car rentals and activities. Our format features money-saving tips for vacation and destination features for the areas in which we have properties available. Readers are mature adults with above average incomes." Circ. 2,000 + . Pays on acceptance. Publishes ms an average of 6 months after acceptance. Byline given. Buys one-time rights, simultaneous rights and second serial (re-print) rights. Submit seasonal/holiday material 6 months in advance. Simultaneous, photocopied, and previ-ously published submissions OK. Computer printout submissions acceptable; prefers letter-quality to dot-ma-trix. Reports in 3 weeks. Sample copy $3; writer's guidelines 25¢.
Nonfiction: Historical/nostalgic, how-to, personal experience and travel. "Articles should relate to saving money while on vacation, features about destination, activites, background/history of area(s), bargain pur-chases, how to plan a vacation, tips for the business traveler, and others of interest to the vacationer. Do not send articles that are unrelated to areas in which we have properties available. No articles about camping, hunt-ing, fishing." Buys 15-20 mss/year. Send complete ms. Length: 300-1,200 words. Pays $25-125. Photos are required with most articles.
Photos: Brad Margritz, photo editor. State availability of photos. Pays $5-15 for b&w slides and 3x4 prints. Captions and model release required. Buys one-time rights.
Tips: "We require accuracy and tight copy. Writers will see that most articles we publish are devoid of 'fluff' and puffery. Our purpose is to inform—most articles have a sidebar where appropriate."

THE ELKS MAGAZINE, 425 W. Diversey, Chicago IL 60614. Executive Editor: William J. Ballee. 50% freelance written. Emphasizes general interest with family appeal. Magazine published 10 times/year. 48 pages. Circ. 1,600,000. Pays on acceptance. Buys first North American serial rights. Computer printout sub-missions acceptable; no dot-matrix. Reports in 6 weeks. Sample copy and writer's guidelines for 9x12 SASE.
Nonfiction: Articles of information, business, contemporary life problems and situations, nostalgia, or just interesting topics, ranging from medicine, science, and history, to sports. "The articles should not just be a re-hash of existing material. They must be fresh, thought provoking, well researched and documented." No fic-tion, travel or political articles, fillers or verse. Buys 2-3 mss/issue. Query; no phone queries. Length: 1,500-3,000 words. Pays from $100.
Tips: "Requirements are clearly stated in our guidelines. Loose, wordy pieces are not accepted. A submission, following a query letter go-ahead, should include several b&w prints if the piece lends itself to illustration. We offer no additional payment for photos accepted with manuscripts."

‡FEDCO REPORTER, A Publication Exclusively for FEDCO Members, 9300 Santa Fe Springs Rd., San-ta Fe Springs CA 90670. (213)946-2511. Editor: Michele A. Brunmier. 90% freelance written. A monthly cat-alog/magazine for FEDCO department store members, covering FEDCO merchandise and including "articles designed to help members improve their homes, lower their cost of living, develop new skills, and learn about new trends." Circ. 1,800,000. Pays on acceptance. Publishes ms an average of 3 months after acceptance. By-line given. Offers $50 kill fee. Buys first rights. Computer printout submissions acceptable. Reports in 6 weeks. Sample copy for 9x12 SASE; writer's guidelines for SASE.
Nonfiction: General interest, historical, interview/profile. No first person narrative. Buys 50 mss/year. Que-ry with published clips. Length: 300-1,000 words. Pays $50-350.
Photos: State availability of photos. Reviews b&w and color slides. No payment, byline only.
Fillers: Historical anecdotes or everyday information.
Tips: "We will publish excellent writing that is well-researched regardless of prior writings. The entire editori-al content of our publication is based on freelance submissions. Articles should be of topical interest to con-sumers. California historicals are also very popular."

4-H LEADER—the national magazine for 4-H, 7100 Connecticut Ave., Chevy Chase MD 20815. (301)961-2896. Editor: Suzanne C. Harting. 20% freelance written. Monthly magazine for "volunteers of a wide range of ages who lead 4-H clubs; most with college education whose primary reason for reading us is their interest in working with kids in informal youth education projects, ranging from aerospace to sewing, and almost anything in between." Circ. 70,000. Pays on acceptance. Publishes ms an average of 3 months after ac-ceptance. Buys first serial rights or one-time rights. Submit seasonal material 1 year in advance. Reports in 1 month. Free sample copy and writer's guidelines.
Nonfiction: Education and child psychology from authorities, written in light, easy-to-read fashion with spe-cific suggestions on how the layman can apply principles in volunteer work with youth; how-to pieces about genuinely new and interesting crafts of any kind. "Craft articles must be fresh in style and ideas, and tell how to make something worthwhile—almost anything that tells about kids having fun and learning outside the class-room, including how they became interested, most effective programs, etc., always with enough detail and ex-

amples, so reader can repeat project or program with his or her group, merely by reading the article. Speak directly to our readers without preaching. Tell them in a conversational manner how they might work better with kids to help them have fun and learn at the same time. Use lots of genuine examples (although names and dates are not important) to illustrate points. Use contractions when applicable. Write in a concise, interesting way. Our readers have other jobs and not a lot of time to spend with us. Will not print personal reminiscences, stories on 'How this 4-H club made good' or about state or county fair winners. Length: 3-8 pages, typewritten, double-spaced. Payment up to $200, depending on quality and accompanying photos or illustrations.
Photos: State availability of photos. "Photos must be genuinely candid, of excellent technical quality and preferably shot in 'available light' or in that style; must show young people or adults and young people having fun learning something. How-to photos or drawings must supplement instructional texts. Photos do not necessarily have to include people. Photos are usually purchased with accompanying ms, with no additional payment. Captions required. If we use an excellent single photo, we generally pay $25 and up."
Tips: "We are very specialized, and unless a writer has been published in our magazine before, he more than likely doesn't have a clue to what we can use. When a query comes about a specific topic, we often can suggest angles that make it usable. There will be more emphasis on interpersonal skills, techniques for working with kids, more focus on the family. Write for a sample copy. I judge a writer's technical skills by the grammar and syntax of his query letter; I seldom ask for a manuscript I think will require extensive reorganization or heavy editing."

KIWANIS, 3636 Woodview Trace, Indianapolis IN 46268. Executive Editor: Chuck Jonak. 50% of feature articles freelance written. Magazine published 10 times/year for business and professional men and their families. Circ. 300,000. Pays on acceptance. Buys first North American serial rights. Pays 20-40% kill fee. Publishes ms an average of 3 months after acceptance. Byline given. Computer printout submissions acceptable; no dot-matrix. Reports within 2 months. Sample copy and writer's guidelines for 9x12 SAE and 75¢ postage.
Nonfiction: Articles about social and civic betterment, business, science, education, religion, family, sports, health, recreation, etc. Emphasis on objectivity, intelligent analysis and thorough research of contemporary problems. Positive tone preferred. Concise, lively writing, absence of cliches, and impartial presentation of controversy required. When applicable, information and quotation from international sources are required. Avoid writing strictly to a U.S. audience. Especially needs articles on business and professional topics that will directly assist the readers in their own businesses (generally independent retailers and companies of less than 25 employees) or careers. "We have an increasing need for articles of international interest and those that will enlighten our readers about the health needs and safety of children." Length: 2,500-3,000 words. Pays $400-1,000. "No fiction, personal essays, fillers or verse of any kind. A light or humorous approach welcomed where subject is appropriate and all other requirements are observed." Sometimes pays the expenses of writers on assignment.
Photos: "We accept photos submitted with manuscripts, but we do not pay extra for them; they are considered part of the price of the manuscript. Our rate for a manuscript with good photos is higher than for one without." Model release and identification of subjects required. Buys one-time rights.
Tips: "Feature section is open to freelancers. First, obtain writer's guidelines and sample copy. Study for general style and content. Present well-researched, smoothly written manuscript that contains a 'human quality' with the use of anecdotes, practical examples, quotation, etc. When querying, present detailed outline of proposed manuscript's focus, direction, and editorial intent. Indicate expert sources to be used for attribution, as well as article's tone and length."

THE LION, 300 22nd St., Oak Brook IL 60570. (312)986-1700. Editor-in-Chief: Roy Schaetzel. Senior Editor: Robert Kleinfelder. 35% freelance written. Works with a small number of new/unpublished writers each year. Covers service club organization for Lions Club members and their families. Monthly magazine; 56 pages. Circ. 670,000. Pays on acceptance. Publishes ms an average of 5 months after acceptance. Buys all rights. Byline given. Phone queries OK. Photocopied submissions OK. Computer printout submissions acceptable; no dot-matrix. Reports in 2 weeks. Free sample copy and writer's guidelines.
Nonfiction: Informational (stories of interest to civic-minded men) and photo feature (must be of a Lions Club service project). No travel, biography, or personal experiences. No sensationalism. Prefers anecdotes in articles. Buys 4 mss/issue. Query. Length: 500-2,200. Pays $50-400. Sometimes pays the expenses of writers on assignment.
Photos: Purchased with or without accompanying ms or on assignment. Captions required. Query for photos. B&w and color glossies at least 5x7 or 35mm color slides. Total purchase price for ms includes payment for photos, accepted with ms. "Be sure photos are clear and as candid as possible."
Tips: "Incomplete details on how the Lions involved actually carried out a project and poor quality photos are the most frequent mistakes made by writers in completing an article assignment for us."

THE MODERN WOODMEN, 1701 1st Ave., Rock Island IL 61201. (309)786-6481. Editor: Gloria Bergh. "Our publication is for families who are members of Modern Woodmen of America. Modern Woodmen is a fraternal life insurance society, and most of our members live in smaller communities or rural areas throughout the United States. Various age groups read the magazine." 10% freelance written. Quarterly magazine, 24 pages. Circ. 350,000. Not copyrighted. Pays on acceptance. Publishes ms an average of 6 months after acceptance. Buys second serial (reprint) rights to material published elsewhere. Photocopied and simultaneous submissions OK. Computer printout submissions acceptable. Reports in one month if SASE included. Sample copy and guidelines for SAE and 2 first class stamps.

Nonfiction: For children and adults. We seek lucid style and rich content.

Photos: B&w and color photos purchased with ms. Captions optional. Payment varies with quality and need. Buys 6-8 mss/year. $50 minimum. Length: 1,000-1,200 words.

Fiction: Most of the fiction we publish is for children and teens. We stress plot and characterization. A moral is a pleasant addition but not required.

Tips: "We want articles that appeal to young families, emphasize family interaction, community involvement, family life. We also consider educational, historical and patriotic articles. We don't want religious articles or teen romances. Focus on people, whether the article is about families or is educational, historical or patriotic."

THE OPTIMIST MAGAZINE, Optimist International, 4494 Lindell Blvd., St. Louis MO 63108. (314)371-6000. Editor: Dennis R. Osterwisch. Assistant Editor: Martha Padberg. 10% freelance written. Eager to work with new/unpublished writers. Monthly magazine about the work of Optimist clubs and members for the 155,000 members of the Optimist clubs in the United States and Canada. Circ. 155,000. Pays on acceptance. Publishes ms an average of 4 months after acceptance. Buys first North American serial rights. Submit seasonal material 3 months in advance. Photocopied and previously published submissions OK. Computer printout submissions acceptable; prefers letter-quality to dot-matrix. Reports in 1 week. Sample copy and writer's guidelines for SAE and 4 first class stamps.

Nonfiction: "We want articles about the activities of local Optimist clubs. These volunteer community-service clubs are constantly involved in projects, aimed primarily at helping young people. With over 4,000 Optimist clubs in the U.S. and Canada, writers should have ample resources. Some large metropolitan areas boast several dozen clubs. We are also interested in feature articles on individual club members who have in some way distinguished themselves, either in their club work or their personal lives. Good photos for all articles are a plus, and can mean a bigger check. We are no longer a market for general-interest articles." Buys 2-3 mss/issue. Query. "Submit a letter that conveys your ability to turn out a well-written article and tells exactly what the scope of the article will be and whether photos are available." Length: 1,000-1,500 words. Pays $150 and up.

Photos: State availability of photos. Payment negotiated. Captions preferred. Buys all rights. "No mug shots or people lined up against the wall shaking hands. We're always looking for good color photos relating to Optimist activities that could be used on our front cover. Colors must be sharp and the composition must be suitable to fit an 8½x11 cover."

Tips: "Find out what the Optimist clubs in your area are doing, then find out if we'd be interested in an article on a specific club project. All of our clubs are eager to talk about what they're doing. Just ask them and you'll probably have an article idea."

PERSPECTIVE. Pioneer Clubs, Division of Pioneer Ministries, Inc., Box 788, Wheaton IL 60189-0788. (312)293-1600. Editor: Lorraine Mulligan Davis. 5% freelance written. Works with a small number of new/unpublished writers each year. "All subscribers are volunteer leaders of clubs for girls and boys in grades 1-12. Clubs are sponsored by evangelical churches throughout North America." Quarterly magazine; 32 pages. Circ. 24,000. Pays on acceptance. Publishes ms an average of 9 months after acceptance. Buys first North American serial rights and second serial (reprint) rights to material originally published elsewhere. Submit seasonal/holiday material 9 months in advance. Simultaneous submissions OK. Computer printout submissions acceptable if double-spaced; no dot-matrix. Reports in 6 weeks. Writer's packet $1.50; includes writer's guidelines and sample magazine.

Nonfiction: How-to (projects for clubs, crafts, cooking, service);informational (relationships, human development, mission education, outdoor activities); inspirational (Bible studies, adult leading youths); interview (Christian education leaders); personal experience (of club leaders). Buys 4-10 mss/year; 3 unsolicited/year. Byline given. Query. Length: 200-1,500 words. Pays $10-60. Pays expenses of writers on assignment. .

Columns/Departments: Storehouse (craft, game, activity, outdoor activity suggestions—all related to club projects for any age between grades 1-12). Buys 4-6 mss/year. Submit complete ms. Length: 150-250 words. Pays $8-20.

Tips: "We only assign major features to writers who have proven previously that they know us and our constituency. Submit articles directly related to club work, practical in nature, i.e., ideas for leader training in communication, Bible knowledge, teaching skills. They must have practical application. We want substance—not ephemeral ideas. In addition to a summary of the article idea and evidence that the writer has knowledge of the subject, we want evidence that the author understands our purpose and philosophy. We're doing more and more inhouse writing—less purchasing of any freelance."

‡PORTS O' CALL. Box 530, Santa Rosa CA 95402. (707)542-0898. Editor: William A. Breniman. Newsbook of the Society of Wireless Pioneers. Society members are mostly early-day wireless "brass-pounders"

who sent code signals from ships or manned shore stations handling wireless or radio traffic. Biannually. Not copyrighted. Pays on acceptance. No computer printout or disk submissions. Reports on submissions "within 30 days (depending on workload)."
Nonfiction: Articles about early-day wireless as used in ship-shore and high power operation; radar, electronic aids, SOS calls, etc. Early-day ships, records, etc. "Writers should remember that our members have gone to sea for years and would be critical of material that is not authentic. We are not interested in any aspect of amateur radio. We are interested in authentic articles dealing with ships (since about 1910)." Oddities about the sea and weather as it affects shipping. Buys 45 unsolicited mss/year. Query. Length: 500-2,000 words. Pays 1-5¢/word.
Photos: Fred B. Rosebury, department editor. Purchased with mss. Unusual shots of sea or ships. Wireless pioneers. Prefers b&w, "4x5 would be the most preferable size but it really doesn't make too much difference as long as the photos are sharp and the subject interests us." Fine if veloxed, but not necessary. Pays $2.50-10; "according to our appraisal of our interest." Ship photos of various nations, including postcard size, if clear, 25¢-$1 each.
Poetry: Ships, marine slant (not military), shipping, weather, wireless. No restrictions. Pays $1-$2.50 each.
Tips: "Material will also be considered for our *Ports O' Call* biannual and *Sparks Journal*, a quarterly tabloid newsletter. *Sparks* (published yearly) takes most of the contents used in *Port O'.Call*, published now every 2 years in encyclopedic format and content. *The Sparks Journal*, published quarterly in tabloid form carries much of the early days, first hand history of wireless (episodes and experiences). Also, *Wireless Almanac* contains much nautical data relating to radio and wireless used at sea."

‡RECREATION NEWS, Official Publication of the League of Federal Recreation Associations, Inc., Icarus Publishers, Inc., Box 32335, Washington DC 20007. (202)965-6960. Editor: Annette Licitra. 50% freelance written. Works with a small number of new/unpublished writers each year. A monthly guide to leisure activities for federal workers covering outdoor recreation, federal issues, money, travel, fitness & health, and indoor pastimes. Circ. 104,000. Pays on publication. Publishes ms an average of 3 months after acceptance. Byline given. Offers 20% kill fee on 4th assignment (first 3 on speculation). Buys one-time rights, all rights, first rights and second serial (reprint) rights. Submit seasonal/holiday material 5 months in advance. Simultaneous queries, simultaneous, photocopied, and previously published submissions OK. Computer printout submissions acceptable. Reports in 3 weeks on queries; 1 month on mss. Free sample copy and writer's guidelines.
Nonfiction: Richard Koman, articles editor. Book excerpts (on recreation, travel); exposé (relating to federal workers); general interest (on recreation, outdoors); historical/nostalgic (Washington-related); how-to (on leisure-time hobbies); humor (on working, home life); interview/profile (with an expert on fitness, sports); opinion (on federal worker issues); and personal experience (with family life, life in Washington). Special issues feature skiing (December) and federal worker health care (November). No inhouse propaganda from government agencies. Buys 45 mss/year. Query with clips of published work. Length: 500-3,000 words. Pays $50-300. Sometimes pays the expenses of writers on assignment.
Photos: Kathy Velis, photo editor. State availability of photos with query letter or ms. Reviews contact sheets, transparencies, and 5x7 b&w prints. Pays $25-40/b&w photo ordered from contact sheet, $50-75 for color. Captions and identification of subjects required.
Columns/Departments: Richard Koman, columns, departments editor. Books (recreation, outdoors, hobbies, travel); food (unconventional outdoor); money (personal finance); Reflections (column on home life, work); health. Buys 15-20 mss/year. Query with clips of published work or send complete ms (on speculation only). Length: 500-1,200 words. Pays $50-75.
Tips: "Our writers generally have a few years of professional writing experience and their work runs to the lively and conversational. We're growing. We'll need more manuscripts in a wider range of recreational topics, including the off-beat. The areas of our publication most open to freelancers are general articles, and the Reflections column. Reflections is introspective, while main pieces are action-oriented."

REVIEW, A Publication of North American Benefit Association, North American Benefit Association, 1338 Military St., Box 5020, Port Huron MI 48061-5020. (313)985-5191, ext. 77. Editor: Virginia E. Farmer. Associate Editor: Patricia Pfeifer. 10-15% freelance written. Quarterly trade journal on insurance/fraternal deeds. Family magazine. Circ. 35,000. Pays on acceptance. Publishes ms an average of 2 years after acceptance. Byline given. Not copyrighted. Buys one-time rights, simultaneous rights, and second serial (reprint) rights. Submit seasonal/holiday material 6 months in advance. Simultaneous, photocopied and previously published submissions OK. Computer printout submissions acceptable; no dot-matrix. Reports in 6 weeks. Sample copy for SAE.
Nonfiction: General interest, historical/nostalgic, how-to (improve; self-help); humor; inspirational; personal experience; and photo feature. No political/controversial. Buys 4-10 mss/year. Send complete ms. Length: 600-1,500 words. Pays 3-5¢/word.
Photos: Prefers ms with photos if available. Send photos with ms. Reviews 5x7 or 8x10 b&w prints. Pays $10-15. Model release and identification of subjects required. Buys one-time rights.

Fiction: Adventure, humorous and mainstream. Buys 2-4 mss/year. Send complete ms. Length: 600-1,500 words. Pays 3-5¢/word.
Tips: "We like articles with accompanying photos; articles that warm the heart; stories with gentle, happy humor. Give background of writer as to education and credits. Manuscripts and art material will be carefully considered, but received only with understanding that North American Benefit Association shall not be responsible for loss or injury."

THE ROTARIAN, Official Magazine of Rotary International, 1600 Ridge Ave., Evanston IL 60201. (312)328-0100. Editor: Willmon L. White. 50% freelance written. For Rotarian business and professional men and their families; for schools, libraries, hospitals, etc. Monthly. Circ. 502,000. Usually buys all rights. Pays on acceptance. Query preferred. Computer printout submissions acceptable; prefers letter-quality to dot-matrix. Reports in 1 month. Sample copy for SAE and 7 first class stamps; writer's guidelines for SAE and first class stamp.
Nonfiction: "The field for freelance articles is in the general interest category. These run the gamut from guidelines for daily living to such concerns as world hunger, the nuclear arms race, and preservation of environment. Recent articles have dealt with the age of video, worldwide status of the elderly, and employee drug abuse and prevention. Articles should appeal to an international audience and should in some way help Rotarians help other people. An article may increase a reader's understanding of world affairs, thereby making him a better world citizen. It may educate him in civic matters, thus helping him improve his town. It may help him to become a better employer, or a better human being. We are interested in articles on unusual Rotary club projects or really unusual Rotarians. We carry debates and symposiums, but are careful to show more than one point of view. We present arguments for effective politics and business ethics, but avoid expose and muckraking. Controversy is welcome if it gets our readers to think but does not offend minority, ethnic or religious groups. In short, the rationale of the organization is one of hope and encouragement and belief in the power of individuals talking and working together." Query preferred. Length: 1,000-2,000 words. Payment varies. Rarely pays the expenses of writers on assignment.
Photos: Purchased with mss or with captions only. Prefers 2¼x2¼ or larger color transparencies, but also uses 35mm. B&w prints and photo essays. Vertical shots preferred to horizontal. Scenes of international interest. Color cover.

‡**THE SAMPLE CASE**, The Order of United Commercial Travelers of America, 632 N. Park St., Box 159019, Columbus OH 43215. (614)228-3276. Editor: William J. Purpura. Bimonthly magazine covering news for members of the United Commercial Travelers. Emphasizes fraternalism for its officers and active membership. Circ. 180,000. Pays on publication. Buys one-time rights. Submit seasonal/holiday material 6 months in advance. Simultaneous queries and submissions OK. Reports in 3 months. Free sample copy and writer's guidelines.
Nonfiction: Articles on travel destination (cities and regions in the U.S. and Canada); food/cuisine; health/fitness/safety; hobbies/entertainment; fraternal/civic activities; business finance/insurance.
Photos: David Knapp, art director. State availability of photos with ms. Pays minimum $20 for 5x7 b&w or larger prints; $30 for 35mm or larger color transparencies used inside (more for cover). Captions required.

THE SERTOMAN, Sertoma International, 1912 E. Meyer Blvd., Kansas City MO 64132. (816)333-8300. Editor: M. Megan Fitzsimmons. 1% freelance written. Quarterly magazine with "service to mankind" as its motto edited for business and professionals. Circ. 35,000. Pays on acceptance. Publishes ms an average of 3 months after acceptance. Byline given. Buys one-time rights. Submit seasonal material 3 months in advance. Simultaneous, photocopied and previously published submissions OK. Computer printout submissions acceptable. Reports in 2 weeks. Free sample copy.
Nonfiction: "We're especially interested in articles on speech and hearing, Sertoma's international sponsorship and local Sertoma Clubs across the U.S., Canada and Mexico." Query with clips of previously published work. Length: 500-2,000 words. Pays $25-100.
Photos: Pays $5 minimum/5x7 b&w glossy prints. Captions and model release required. Buys one-time rights.

‡**THE SONS OF NORWAY VIKING**, Sons of Norway, 1455 W. Lake St., Minneapolis MN 55408: (612)827-3611. Editor: Gaelyn Beal. 10% freelance written. Works with a small number of new/unpublished writers each year. A monthly magazine for the Sons of Norway, a fraternal and cultural organization, covering Norwegian culture, heritage, history, Norwegian-American topics, modern Norwegian society, genealogy and travel. "Our audience is Norwegian-Americans (middle-aged or older) with strong interest in their heritage and anything Norwegian. Many have traveled to Norway." Circ. 77,000. Pays on publication. Publishes ms an average of 8 months after acceptance. Byline given. Offers $50 kill fee. Buys first North American serial rights and second serial (reprint) rights. Submit seasonal/holiday material 4 months in advance. Photocopied and previously published submissions OK. Computer printout submissions acceptable; prefers letter-quality to dot-matrix. Reports in 1 month on queries; 6 weeks on mss. Free sample copy on request.

Nonfiction: General interest, historical/nostalgic, humor, interview/profile, and travel—all having a Norwegian angle. "Articles should not be personal impressions nor a colorless spewing of facts, but well-researched and conveyed in a warm and audience-involving manner. Does it entertain *and* inform?" Buys 10 mss/year. Query or send complete ms. Length: 1,500-3,000 words. Pays $75-250.
Photos: Reviews transparencies and prints. Pays $10-20/photo; pays $100 for cover color photo. Identification of subjects required. Buys one-time rights.
Tips: "Show familiarity with Norwegian culture and subject matter. Our readers are somewhat knowledgeable about Norway and quick to note misstatements. Articles about modern Norway are most open to freelancers—the society, industries—but historical periods also okay. Call before a scheduled trip to Norway to discuss subjects to research or interview while there. The *Viking* will purchase more articles because more editorial pages have been added."

‡TEEN TIMES, Future Homemakers of America, 1910 Association Dr., Reston VA 22091. (703)476-4900. Editor: Deb Olcott Taylor. 5% freelance written. A quarterly nonprofit student organization national newsletter covering FHA/HERO chapters and teen concerns. "Our feature articles present current facts related to teen concerns and focus on how teens can make a difference by tackling those concerns." Circ. 325,000. Pays on publication. Publishes ms an average of 6 months after acceptance. Byline given. Buys all rights. Submit seasonal/holiday 6 months in advance. Simultaneous, photocopied and previously published submissions OK. Computer printout submissions acceptable; prefers letter-quality to dot-matrix. Reports in 2 months. Sample copy $1 with 9x12 SAE and 39¢ postage; writer's guidelines for #10 SAE with 22¢ postage.
Nonfiction: How-to (teens: careers, community action, handling crises); and interview/profile (former members, current members). No cooking, sewing, sports, craft, grooming or etiquette. Buys 1-2 mss/year. Query. Length: 500-750 words. Pays $85-125.
Photos: State availability of photos with submission. Reviews contact sheets. Captions and model releases required. Buys one-time rights.
Tips: "Contact local junior or senior high school home economics department to make contact with a local Future Homemakers of America chapter; focus on subject of concern to today's teens. Typically each issue includes a feature article on a teen concern area with examples, facts, advice from experts and ideas/examples of members making a difference in this area. Write so teens can relate."

THE TOASTMASTER, Box 10400, Santa Ana CA 92711. (714)542-6793. Editor-in-Chief: Tamara Nunn. "We are backlogged with submissions and prefer not to receive unsolicited submissions at this time."

WOODMEN OF THE WORLD MAGAZINE, 1700 Farnam St., Omaha NE 68102. (402)342-1890, ext. 302. Editor: Leland A. Larson. 20% freelance written. Works with a small number of new/unpublished writers each year. Published by Woodmen of the World Life Insurance Society for "people of all ages in all walks of life. We have both adult and child readers from all types of American families." Monthly. Circ. 467,000. Not copyrighted. Buys 20 mss/year. Pays on acceptance. Byline given. Buys one-time rights. Publishes ms an average of 2 months after acceptance. Will consider photocopied and simultaneous submissions. Computer printout submissions acceptable; prefers letter-quality to dot-matrix. Submit seasonal material 3 months in advance. Reports in 5 weeks. Free sample copy.
Nonfiction: "General interest articles which appeal to the American family—travel, history, art, new products, how-to, sports, hobbies, food, home decorating, family expenses, etc. Because we are a fraternal benefit society operating under a lodge system, we often carry stories on how a number of people can enjoy social or recreational activities as a group. No special approach required. We want more 'consumer type' articles, humor, historical articles, think pieces, nostalgia, photo articles." Buys 15-24 unsolicited mss/year. Submit complete ms. Length: 2,000 words or less. Pays $10 minimum, 5¢/word depending on count.
Photos: Purchased with or without mss; captions optional "but suggested." Uses 8x10 glossy prints, 4x5 transparencies ("and possibly down to 35mm"). Payment "depends on use." For b&w photos, pays $25 for cover, $10 for inside. Color prices vary according to use and quality. Minimum of $25 for inside use; up to $150 for covers.
Fiction: Humorous and historical short stories. Length: 1,500 words or less. Pays "$10 minimum or 5¢/word, depending on count."

❝ A good query letter isn't necessarily an end in itself, but an entré to a relationship. But be straightforward and clear, not cute or clever. I'm a busy editor and I am not amused by cute. ❞

Gay L. Totten, Purdue Alumnus

_____ Astrology and Psychic

Some writers explore life from an astrological or psychic perspective. If you want to write for these publications, be sure to read them first. Each has an individual personality and approach to these phenomena. The following publications regard astrology, psychic phenomena, ESP experiences, and related subjects as sciences or as objects of serious study.

DOORWAYS TO THE MIND, Aries Productions, Inc., Box 29396, Sappington MO 63126. Editor: Beverly C. Jaegers. Managing Editor: G. Weingart. 80-90% freelance written. Quarterly magazine covering mind development, PSI, practical ESP, stock-prediction and Wall Street; working with ESP predictions; contests, dowsing and pendulum work. For a general audience interested in mental development and self-help/ESP using Russian/U.S. methods. Pays on publication. Publishes ms an average of 6 months after acceptance. Byline given. Buys second serial (reprint) rights and all rights. Not copyrighted. Buys one-time rights. Submit seasonal/holiday material 4 months in advance. Simultaneous queries, and simultaneous, photocopied, and previously published submissions OK. Computer printout submissions acceptable; prefers letter-quality to dot-matrix. Reports in 6 weeks. Sample copy for $1 with 6x9 SAE and 69¢ postage; writer's guidelines for business-size SAE and 2 first class stamps.
Nonfiction: Michael Christopher, articles editor. Book excerpts, general interest, inspirational, interview/profile, opinion. Not interested in articles on witchcraft, the occult, UFOs, space creatures or space vehicles, etc. Buys 10-15 mss/year. Send complete ms. Length: 1,000-2,500 words. Pays $10 minimum.
Columns/Departments: Michael Christopher, column/department editor. News & Notes, Book Reviews. Buys 10-12 mss/year. Send complete ms. Length: 200-350 words. Pays $5 minimum.
Poetry: Light verse, traditional. Buys 3-4 poems/year. Submit maximum 5 poems. Pays in 5 contributor copies.
Fillers: Newsbreaks. Buys variable number/year. Length: 200-550 words. Pays $2 minimum.
Tips: "Write realistically; avoid wordiness and overuse of 'I'. Research and include helpful data on ESP development, mind control, and psychic research, dowsing and pendulum, special studies such as graphoanalysis, astrology, archeology, and crime detection with ESP."

FATE, Clark Publishing Co., 500 Hyacinth Place, Highland Park IL 60035. Editor: Mary Margaret Fuller. 70% freelance written. Monthly. Buys all rights; occasionally North American serial rights only. Byline given. Pays on publication. Query. Reports in 2 months.
Nonfiction and Fillers: Personal psychic experiences, 300-500 words. Pays $10. New frontiers of science, and ancient civilizations, 2,000-3,000 words; also parapsychology, occultism, witchcraft, magic, spiritual healing miracles, flying saucers, etc. Must include complete authenticating details. Prefers interesting accounts of single events rather than roundups. "We very frequently accept manuscripts from new writers; the majority are individuals' first-person accounts of their own psychic experience. We do need to have all details, where, when, why, who and what, included for complete documentation." Pays minimum of 5¢/word. Fillers should be fully authenticated. Length: 100-300 words.
Photos: Buys good glossy prints with mss. Pays $5-10.

‡HOROSCOPE GUIDE, Box 70, West Springfield MA 01090. Editor: Susan Gaetz. 75% freelance written. Prefers to work with published/established writers; works with a small number of new/unpublished writers each year. For persons interested in astrology as it touches their daily lives; all ages. Monthly. Circ. 50,000. Publishes ms an average of 3 months after acceptance. Pays on publication. Buys all rights. Byline given. Buys 40 mss/year. Submit seasonal material 5 months in advance. Computer printout submissions acceptable; no dot-matrix. Submit complete ms. Sample copy for $1.50.
Nonfiction, Poetry and Fillers: Wants anything of good interest to the average astrology buff, preferably not so technical as to require more than basic knowledge of birth sign by reader. Mss should be light, readable, entertaining and sometimes humorous. Not as detailed and technical as other astrology magazines, "with the astro-writer doing the interpreting without long-winded reference to his methods at every juncture. We are less reverent of astrological red tape." Wants mss about man-woman relationships, preferably in entertaining and occasionally humorous fashion. No textbook-type material. Does not want to see a teacher's type of approach to the subject. Length: 900-4,000 words. Pays 2-3¢/word. Buys traditional forms of poetry. Length: 4-16 lines. Pays $2-$8. Sometimes pays the expenses of writers on assignment.

Tips: "Best way to break in with us is with some lively Sun-sign type piece involving some area of man-woman relationships—love, sex, marriage, divorce, differing views on money, religion, child-raising, in-laws, vacations, politics, lifestyles, etc."

‡INNER LIGHT, Enlightment in the New Age, Global Communications, 316 5th Ave., New York NY 10001. (212)685-4080. Editor: Timothy Beckley. Managing Editor: Diane Tessman. 50% freelance written. A quarterly magazine with an "upbeat approach showing how metaphysical/New Age studies can assist readers in leading better, more prosperous lives and educating them to the fact that there are other dimensions they can tap into to make this really better." Circ. 50,000. Pays on publication. Publishes ms an averag of 3 months after acceptance. Byline given. Buys first North American serial rights and second serial (reprint) rights. Simultaneous queries, photocopied and previously published submissions OK. Reports in 1 month. Sample copy $1.25.
Nonfiction: How-to, inspirational, interview/profile and personal experience. "No rehashing of material that has been in print." Buys 25 mss/year. Send complete ms. Length: 1,800-2,500 words. Pays $50 maximum.
Photos: Send photos with accompanying query or ms. Reviews b&w prints. Pays $5-10. Identification of subjects required. Buys one-time rights.
Fillers: Revelations, (letters about personal experiences). Pays $5.

METAPSYCHOLOGY, The Journal of Discarnate Intelligence, Box 30022, Philadelphia PA 19103. Editor: Tam Mossman. 80% freelance written. Eager to work with new/unpublished writers. Quarterly journal/review on channeling—transmission of spirit writings and messages through Ouija board, automatic writing, trance, etc. For those interested in Jane Roberts' Seth books and other wisdom from spirit entities. Estab. 1985. Circ. 2,500. Pays on publication. Publishes ms an average of 4 months after acceptance. Byline given. Buys all rights for Q & A section and first serial rights. Submit seasonal/holiday material 6 months in advance. Simultaneous queries. and simultaneous and photocopied submissions OK. Computer printout submissions acceptable; no dot-matrix. Reports in 1 week on queries; 2-3 weeks on mss. Sample copy $5; free writer's guidelines (included in sample issue).
Nonfiction: Book excerpts (first serial); channeled essays; how-to (only by trance psychics); encounters with spirits; interview/profile (of trance psychics); personal experience; and use of mind for personal evolution. "No self-aggrandizement, religious treatises, articles with a religious axe to grind (pro or con), personal opinion pieces, or pointless voyages into autobiographical thickets." Buys 25 mss/year, most are channeled material. Query with clips of channeled material. Length: 2,000 words. "We serialize book-length pieces but query first. Don't send book-length mss we have not asked to see." Pays 3¢/word, depending on length, quality.
Photos: Photos used only on cover. "We do not want unsolicited photos/art."
Columns/Departments: Questions and Answers—trance psychics should write for guidelines. Book reviews—write, with previous review clips. Psychometrists should write in if their impressions are particularly vivid and accurate. Buys 100+ mss/year. Query with published clips. Length: 100-5,000 words. Pays 3¢/word.
Tips: "First, read a sample copy of *Metapsychology*. If your material, or writing, or insight, is up to our standards, then you have an excellent chance of getting published—especially if you channel spirit messages yourself. Few other publications accept trance material at all. Interviews with 'professional' channelers would be welcome. Interviews with spirit guides would be preferred, however. We also want interviews with psychiatrists and psychologists who are supportive of channeling."

NEW REALITIES, Suite 408, 680 Beach St., San Francisco CA 94109. (415)776-2600. Editor: James Bolen. 20% freelance written. For general public interested in total wellness, personal growth and in holistic approach to living. Straightforward, entertaining material on new environments, the healing arts, new spirituality, consciousness research, and the frontiers of human potential and the mind. Bimonthly. Pays on publication. Publishes manuscript an average of 6 months after acceptance. Reports in 6 weeks. Computer printout submissions acceptable.
Nonfiction: "Documented articles on mental, physical and spiritual holistic dimensions of humankind. Balanced reporting, no editorializing. No personal experiences as such. Accepts profiles of leaders in the field. Must have documented evidence about holistic leaders, healers, researchers. Short bibliography for further reading." Query. Length: 1,500-3,500 words. Pays $75-250. Accepts photos. Sometimes pays the expenses of writers on assignment.
Tips: "The writer may have a better chance of breaking in at our publication with short articles and fillers since this gives us the opportunity to become familiar with their writing style. The most frequent mistakes made by writers in completing an article for us are incomplete research, subjective reporting, facts not documented, and poor grammatic structure."

PREDICTION, The Magazine for Astrology and the Occult, Link House Magazines Ltd., Link House, Dingwall Ave., Croydon, CR9 2TA, England. 01-686-2599. Editor: Jo Logan. 90% freelance written. Monthly magazine. Circ. 35,000. Pays on acceptance. Publishes ms an average of 6 months after acceptance. Byline

given. Buys first British serial rights. Computer printout submissions acceptable; no dot-matrix. SAE and IRCs. Reports in 1 month. Free sample copy.
Nonfiction: New product (within confines of magazine); personal experience (of an occult nature only); and technical (astrology, tarot, palmistry, alternative medicine, etc.). Buys 50 mss/year. Send complete ms. Length: 1,000-2,000 words. Pays £20-80. Sometimes pays the expenses of writers on assignment.
Columns/Departments: Astrology. Buys 12 mss/year. Length: 750 words. Pays £20.
Fillers: Clippings, anecdotes and newsbreaks.
Tips: "Feature articles with an occult slant and astrological profiles (with charts) of personalities living or dead are most open to freelancers. We prefer first-hand material from practitioners and/or observers."

THE UNEXPLAINED, The Unknown Visited and Explained, (formerly *Mysteries of Life*), National Publishing, Box 8042, Van Nuys CA 91409. (818)366-1090. Editor: Hank Krastman. 90% freelance written. Eager to work with new/unpublished writers. Quarterly magazine of unusual places (Egypt, India, Tibet, South America) and the occult, astrology, mystic. Circ. 30,000. Pays on publication. Publishes ms an average of 3 months after acceptance. Byline given. Buys all rights. Submit seasonal/holiday material 3 months in advance. Simultaneous queries, and simultaneous and photocopied submissions OK. Computer printout submissions acceptable; prefers letter-quality to dot-matrix. Reports in 2 weeks. Sample copy for 8½x11 SASE.
Nonfiction: General interest, how-to, photo feature, and travel. Buys 40 mss/year. Send complete ms. Length: open. Pays 3-5¢/word. Sometimes pays the expenses of writers on assignment.
Photos: Cherry Krastman, photo editor. Send photos with query or ms. Reviews 8½x11 b&w prints. Pays $5-10. Captions, model release and identification of subjects required. Buys all rights.
Tips: "We need good researched articles with photos, drawings or witnesses."

— Automotive and Motorcycle

Economy, luxury, and just-for-fun vehicles of all makes and models are showcased in these magazines. Publications in this section detail the maintenance, operation, performance, racing and judging of automobiles and recreational vehicles. Publications that treat vehicles as means of transportation or shelter instead of as a hobby or sport are classified in the Travel, Camping, and Trailer category. Journals for teamsters, service station operators, and auto and motorcycle dealers will be found in the Auto and Truck classification of the Trade Journals section.

AMERICAN MOTORCYCLIST, American Motorcyclist Association, Box 6114, Westerville OH 43081-6114. (614)891-2425. Executive Editor: Greg Harrison. For "enthusiastic motorcyclists, investing considerable time and money in the sport. We emphasize the motorcyclist, not the vehicle." Monthly magazine. Circ. 134,000. Pays on publication. Rights purchased vary with author and material. Pays 25-50% kill fee. Byline given. Query. Submit seasonal/holiday material 4 months in advance. Reports in 1 month. Sample copy $1.25.
Nonfiction: How-to (different and/or unusual ways to use a motorcycle or have fun on one); historical (the heritage of motorcycling, particularly as it relates to the AMA); interviews (with interesting personalities in the world of motorcycling); photo feature (quality work on any aspect of motorcycling); and technical or how-to articles. No product evaluations or stories on motorcycling events not sanctioned by the AMA. Buys 20-25 mss/year. Query. Length: 500 words minimum. Pays minimum $3/published column inch.
Photos: Purchased with or without accompanying ms, or on assignment. Captions required. Query. Pays $15 minimum per photo published.
Tips: "Accuracy and reliability are prime factors in our work with freelancers. We emphasize the rider, not the motorcycle itself. It's always best to query us first and the further in advance the better to allow for scheduling."

AUTOMOBILE QUARTERLY, 221 Nassau St., Princeton NJ 08542. (609)924-7555. Editor-in-Chief: L. Scott Bailey. Emphasizes automobiles and automobile history. Quarterly hardbound magazine; 112 pages. Circ. 26,000. Pays on acceptance. Buys all rights. Pays expenses as kill fee. Byline given. Reports in 3 weeks. Sample copy $13.95.

Nonfiction: Authoritative articles relating to the automobile and automobile history. Historical, interview and nostalgia. Buys 5 mss/issue. Query. Length: 2,000-20,000 words. Pays $200-800.
Photos: Purchased on assignment. Captions required. Query. Uses 8x10 b&w glossy prints and 4x5 color transparencies. "Payment varies with assignment and is negotiated prior to assignment."
Tips: "Familiarity with the magazine is a *must*."

‡BMX PLUS MAGAZINE, Daisy/Hi-Torque Publishing Co., Inc., 10600 Sepulveda Blvd., Mission Hills CA 91345. (714)545-6012. Editor: John Ker. Monthly magazine covering the sport of bicycle motocross for a youthful readership (95% male, aged 8-25). 5% freelance written. Circ. 90,000. Pays on publication. Byline given. Buys one-time rights. Submit seasonal/holiday material 3 months in advance. Simultaneous queries and submissions OK. Computer printout submissions acceptable. Reports in 2 months. Publishes ms an average of 3 months after acceptance. Sample copy $2; writer's guidelines for business size SAE and 1 first class stamp.
Nonfiction: Historical/nostaglic, how-to, humor, interview/profile, new product, photo feature, technical, travel. "No articles for a general audience; our readers are BMX fanatics." Buys 20 mss/year. Send complete ms. Length: 500-1,500 words. Pays $30-250.
Photos: "Photography is the key to our magazine. Send us some exciting and/or unusual photos of hot riders in action." Send photos with ms. Pays $25 for color photo published; $10 for b&w photos. Reviews 35mm color transparencies and b&w negatives and 8x10 prints. Captions and identification of subjects required.
Tips: "The sport of BMX is very young. The opportunities for talented writers and photographers in this field are wide open. Send us a good interview or race story with photos. Race coverage is the area that's easiest to break into. It must be a *big* race, preferably national or international in scope. Submit story within one week of completion of race."

‡BRITISH CAR & BIKE, 2D Studio, Box 1045, Canoga Park CA 91304. (818)710-1234. Editor: Dave Destler. 40% freelance written. A quarterly magazine covering British cars and British motorcycles. "We focus upon the cars and motorcycles built in Britain, the people who built them, drive them, ride them, love them. Writers must be among the aforementioned. Written by enthusiasts for enthusiasts." Estab. 1985. Circ. 20,000. Pays on publication. Publishes ms an average of 3 months after acceptance. Byline given. Buys all rights. Submit seasonal/holiday material 4 months in advance. Photocopied submissions OK. Electronic submissions OK via Apple compatible. Computer printout submissions acceptable. Reports in 1 month. Sample copy $3.50; writer's guidelines for SAE with 1 first class stamp.
Nonfiction: Historical/nostalgic: how-to (on repair or restoration of a specific model or range of models, new technique or process); humor (based upon a realistic nonfiction situation); interview/profile (famous racer, designer, engineer, etc.); photo feature and technical. "No submissions so specific as to appeal or relate to a very narrow range of readers; no submissions so general as to be out-of-place in a specialty publication." Buys 30 mss/year. Send complete ms. "Include SASE if submission is to be returned." Length: 750-4,500 words. Pays $2-5/column inch for assigned articles; pays $2-3/column inch for unsolicited articles. Sometimes pays writers with contributor copies or other premiums rather than cash on prior arrangement.
Photos: Send photos with submission. Reviews transparencies and prints. Offers $5-20/photo. Captions and identification of subjects required. Buys all rights.
Columns/Departments: Update (newsworthy briefs of interest, not too timely for quarterly publication), approximately 50-175 words; Collector's Corner (British car or bike oriented collectibles, such as stamps, models, hood ornaments, old literature, etc.—writer must be expert), approximately 1,000 words; Club Scene (specific club profile, including history, activities, membership information, functions, etc. or general club interest such as starting a new club or running one better—should be officer or active member of club). Buys 20 mss/year. Send complete ms. Pays $10-50.
Tips: "Thorough familiarity of subject is essential. *British Car & Bike* is read by experts and enthusiasts who can see right through superficial research. Facts are important, and must be accurate. Writers should ask themselves 'I know I'm interested in this story, but will most of *British Car & Bike*'s readers appreciate it?' Club scene and Update are areas most open to freelancers."

CAR AND DRIVER, 2002 Hogback Rd., Ann Arbor MI 48104. (313)994-0055. Editor: Don Sherman. For auto enthusiasts; college-educated, professional, median 24-35 years of age. Monthly magazine; 160 pages. Circ. 900,000. Pays on acceptance. Rights purchased vary with author and material. Buys all rights or first North American serial rights. Buys 10-12 unsolicited mss/year. Submit seasonal material 4 months in advance. Reports in 2 months.
Nonfiction: Non-anecdotal articles about the more sophisticated treatment of autos and motor racing. Exciting, interesting cars. Automotive road tests, informational articles on cars and equipment; some satire and humor. Personalities, past and present, in the automotive industry and automotive sports. "Treat readers as intellectual equals. Emphasis on people as well as hardware." Informational, how-to, humor, historical, think articles, and nostalgia. Query with clips of previously published work. Length: 750-2,000 words. Pays $200-1,500. Also buys mini-features for FYI department. Length: about 500 words. Pays $100-500.
Photos: B&w photos purchased with accompanying mss with no additional payment.

Tips: "It is best to start off with an interesting query and to stay away from nuts-and-bolts stuff since that will be handled in-house or by an acknowledged expert. Our goal is to be absolutely without flaw in our presentation of automotive facts, but we strive to be every bit as entertaining as we are informative."

CAR COLLECTOR/CAR CLASSICS, Classic Publishing, Inc., Suite 144, 8601 Dunwoody Pl., Atlanta GA 30338. Editor: Donald R. Peterson. 90% freelance written. Works with a small number of new/unpublished writers each year. For people interested in all facets of collecting classic, milestone, antique, special interest and sports cars; also mascots, models, restoration, garaging, license plates and memorabilia. Monthly magazine; 76 pages. Circ. 45,000. Pays on publication. Publishes ms an average of 4 months after acceptance. Buys first serial rights. Submit seasonal/holiday material 4 months in advance. Photocopied submissions OK. Computer printout submissions acceptable; no dot-matrix. Reports in 2 months. Sample copy for $2; writer's guidelines for SAE and 1 first class stamp.
Nonfiction: General interest, historical, how-to, humor, inspirational, interview, nostalgia, personal opinion, profile, photo feature, technical and travel. Buys 75-100 mss/year. Query with clips of published work. Buys 24-36 unsolicited mss/year. Length: 300-2,500 words. Pays 5¢/word minimum. Sometimes pays the expenses of writers on assignment.
Photos: "We have a continuing need for high-quality color positives (e.g., 2¼ or 35mm) *with* copy." State availability of photos with ms. Offers additional payment for photos with accompanying mss. Uses b&w glossy prints; color transparencies. Pays a minimum of $75 for cover and centerfold color; $10 for inside color; $5 for inside b&w. Captions and model release required.
Columns/Departments: "Rarely add a new columnist but we are open to suggestions." Buys 36/year. Query with clips of published work. Length: 2,000 maximum; prefer 1,000-2,000 words. Pays 5¢/word minimum.
Tips: "The most frequent mistakes are made by writers who are writing to a 'Sunday supplement' audience rather than to a sophisticated audience of car collectors and submitting stories that are often too basic and assume no car knowledge at all on the part of the reader."

CAR CRAFT, Petersen Publishing Co., 8490 Sunset Blvd., Los Angeles CA 90069. (213)657-5100, ext. 345. Editor: Jeff Smith. For men and women, 18-34, "enthusiastic owners of 1949 and newer muscle cars." Monthly magazine; 132 pages. Circ. 400,000. Study past issues before making submissions or story suggestions. Pays generally on publication, on acceptance under special circumstances. Buys all rights. Buys 2-10 mss/year. Computer printout submissions acceptable. Query.
Nonfiction: How-to articles ranging from the basics to fairly sophisticated automotive modifications. Drag racing feature stories and some general car features on modified late model automobiles. Especially interested in do-it-yourself automotive tips, suspension modifications, mileage improvers and even shop tips and homemade tools. Length: open. Pays $100-200/page.
Photos: Photos purchased with or without accompanying text. Captions suggested, but optional. Reviews 8x10 b&w glossy prints; 35mm or 2¼x2¼ color. Pays $30 for b&w, color negotiable. "Pay rate higher for complete story, i.e., photos, captions, headline, subtitle: the works, ready to go."

CORVETTE FEVER, Prospect Publishing Co., Inc., Box 44620, Ft. Washington MD 20744. (301)839-2221. Publisher: Patricia E. Stivers. 40% freelance written. Bimonthly magazine; 64-84 pages. Circ. 35,000. Pays on publication. Publishes ms an average of 4 months after acceptance. Buys first and second serial (reprint) rights. Byline given. Phone queries OK. Submit seasonal/holiday material 4 months in advance. Photocopied submissions OK. Reports in 1 month. Sample copy and writer's guidelines $2.
Nonfiction: General interest (event coverage, personal experience); historical (special or unusual Corvette historical topics); how-to (technical and mechanical articles, photos are a must); humor (Corvette-related humor); interview (with important Corvette persons, race drivers, technical persons, club officials, etc.); nostalgia (relating to early Corvette car and development); personal experiences (related to Corvette car use and experiences); profile (prominent and well-known Corvette personalities wanted for interviews and articles); photo feature (centerspread in color of Corvette and female Vette owner; photo essays on renovation, customizing and show cars); technical (any aspect of Corvette improvement or custom articles); and travel (relating to Corvette use and adventure). Buys 4-6 mss/issue. Query or send complete ms. Length: 500-2,500 words. Pays $40-300.
Photos: Send photos with ms. Pays $5 for 5x7 b&w glossy prints; $10 for color contact sheets and transparencies. Captions preferred; model release required.
Columns/Departments: Innovative Ideas, In Print, Model Shop, Pit Stop, and Tech Vette. Buys 3 mss/issue. Send complete ms. Length: 300-800 words. Pays $24-200.
Fiction: "Any type of story as long as it is related to the Corvette." Buys 1-2 mss/issue. Send complete ms. Length: 500-2,500 words. Pays $40-200.
Fillers: Clippings, jokes, gags, anecdotes, short humor and newsbreaks. Buys 2-3/issue. Length: 25-150 words. Pays $2-15.

‡**CORVETTE NEWS**, c/o GM Photographic, 30005 Van Dyke Ave., Warren MI 48090. Managing Editor: Kari Plyer. 100% freelance written. For Corvette owners worldwide. Quarterly magazine. Circ. 150,000. Buys all

rights. Pays on publication. Publishes ms an average of 4 months after acceptance. Electronic submissions OK but requirements "need to be discussed with the writer;" requires hard copy also. Computer printout submissions acceptable. Free sample copy and editorial guidelines.

Nonfiction: "Articles must be of interest to audience. Subjects considered include: technical articles dealing with restorations, engines, paint, body work, suspension, parts searches, etc.; competition, 'Vettes vs. 'Vettes, or 'Vettes vs. others; profiles of Corvette owners/drivers; general interest articles, such as the unusual history of a particular early model Corvette, and perhaps its restoration; one owner's do-it-yourself engine repair procedures, maintenance procedures, Corvettes in unusual service, hobbies involving Corvettes, sports involving Corvettes; celebrity owner profiles; special Corvette events such as races, drags, rallies, concours, gymkhanas, slaloms; travel, in USA or abroad, via Corvette. No articles negative to cars in general and Corvette in particular or articles not connected, in some way, to Corvette. Send an approximately 100-word query on the proposed article and add a statement about how you are prepared to supplement it with drawings or photographs." Length: 1,200-3,600 words. Query. Pays $100/published page. Sometimes pays the expenses of writers on assignment.

Photos: Color transparencies are preferred when submitted with ms; 35mm smallest format accepted.

Tips: "We are always looking for new ideas, new writing approaches. But the writer must have a solid knowledge about Corvette—either owns one, has driven one, or comes in contact with people who do own the car. We need writers who have an ability to translate very technical subjects into readable prose."

CYCLE, CBS, 780-A Lakefield Rd., Westlake Village CA 91361. (818)889-4360. Editor: Phil Schilling. Managing Editor: Allyn Fleming. 20% freelance written. Monthly magazine covering motorcycles for motorcycle owners (mostly men). Circ. 400,000. Pays on publication. Publishes ms an average of 4 months after acceptance. Byline given. Buys first North American serial rights. Submit seasonal/holiday queries 4 months in advance. Simultaneous queries and photocopied submissions OK. Computer printout submissions acceptable. Reports in 2 months.

Nonfiction: Investigative, historical, interview/profile (of racing personalities or others in the industry); photo feature; technical (theory or practice); travel (long-distance trips anywhere in the world); and reports on racing. Query "with references." Length: 2,000-4,000 words. Pays $400-700.

Photos: Pays $40-150 for b&w prints; $50-250 for 35mm color transparencies. Model releases and identification of subjects required. Buys one-time rights.

THE EJAG MAGAZINE, EJAG Publications, Box J, Carlisle MA 01741. (617)369-5531. Editor: Lori R. Toepel. 50-55% freelance written. Monthly magazine covering "everything about Jaguar and Daimler autos for readers ranging from corporate presidents to local car-fixers to Sunday mechanics—all Jaguar-Daimler fans." Circ. 30,000. Pays on acceptance. Publishes ms 3-4 months after acceptance. Byline given. Offers $10-25 kill fee. Buys all rights unless otherwise negotiated. Submit seasonal/holiday material 3 months in advance. Computer printout submissions acceptable "if easily readable"; prefers letter-quality to dot-matrix. Reports in 1 month. Free sample copy and writer's guidelines.

Nonfiction: General interest (on auto field in general); historical/nostalgic (on Jaguars of previous eras, in U.S. and abroad); how-to (do it yourself pieces in depth for maintenance, repair, restoration); interview/profile (of Jag owners, racers, factory people, collectors); new product (anything applicable to Jaguars); personal experience; photo feature (on beautiful Jaguars, technical procedures, restorations); technical (do-it-yourself or general tech background). "No club news or club meets (we have direct lines to these). No technical articles that sound like manuals." Buys 25 or more unsolicited mss/year. Query. Length: 1,200-5,000 words. "Longer articles accepted—for splitting into installments." Pays 5-8¢/word for general topics, 10-15¢/word for technical and do-it-yourself. Sometimes pays the expenses of writers on assignment.

Photos: State availability of photos. Pays $5 maximum for 35mm, 3x3 color transparencies and 3x5 and 5x7 b&w prints. Caption, model release and identification of subjects (if possible) required. Buys all rights unless otherwise negotiated.

Fillers: "We buy many fillers so they are always welcomed."

Tips: "We welcome unpublished writers *but* you must know the subject. We enjoy working with the 'veterans' and the newcomers."

‡ENTHUSIAST, Harley-Davidson Motor Co., Inc., Box 653, Milwaukee WI 53202. (414)935-4524. Editor: Buzz Buzzelli. A magazine published 3 times annually covering Harley-Davidson motorcycles and people. Circ. 239,000. Pays on acceptance. Byline given. Buys one-time rights. Submit seasonal/holiday material 3 months in advance. Simultaneous queries, and simultaneous, photocopied, and previously published submissions OK. Computer printout submissions acceptable. Reports in 2 months. Free sample copy and writer's guidelines.

Nonfiction: Historical/nostalgic; humor; personal experience; photo feature (color—touring, travel); and travel (with 4-color—must feature Harley Davidson product). No opinion articles. Buys 6 mss/year. Length: 1,500-2,000 words. Pays $100-300.

Photos: State availability or send photos with ms. Reviews b&w prints. Buys one-time rights.

Tips: "We want clear, concise, accurate information; light, up-beat style. Touring features with insightful themes are most open to freelancers. Avoid the 'Then We Woke Up, Then We Ate, Then We Brushed Our Teeth' stuff."

FOUR WHEELER MAGAZINE, 6728 Eton Ave., Canoga Park CA 91303. (818)992-4777. Publisher: Dave Cohen. Features Editor: Bruce W. Smith. 20% freelance written. Works with a small number of new/unpublished writers each year. Emphasizes four-wheel-drive vehicles, competition and travel/adventure. Monthly magazine; 164 pages. Circ. 205,000. Pays on publication. Publishes ms an average of 4 months after acceptance. Buys all rights. Submit seasonal/holiday material at least 4 months in advance. Electronic submissions OK via 5¼" CP/M (Kaypro 2x), but requires hard copy also. Computer printout submissions acceptable; prefers letter-quality to dot-matrix. Sample copy for SASE.
Nonfiction: 4WD competition and travel/adventure articles, technical, how-to's, and vehicle features about unique four-wheel drives. "We like the adventure stories that bring four wheeling to life in word and photo: mud-running deserted logging roads, exploring remote, isolated trails, or hunting/fishing where the 4x4 is a necessity for success." See features by Bruce Smith, Gary Wescott, Don Biggs and Dick Stansfield for examples. Query with photos before sending complete ms. Length: 1,200-2,000 words; average 4-5 pages when published. Pays $100/page minimum for complete package. Sometimes pays the expenses of writers on assignment.
Photos: Requires professional quality color slides and b&w prints for every article. Captions required. Prefers Kodachrome 64 or Fujichrome 50 in 35mm or 2¼ formats. "Action shots a must for all vehicle features and travel articles."
Tips: "Show us you know how to use a camera as well as the written word. The easiest way for a new writer/photographer to break into our magazine is to read several issues of the magazine, then query with a short vehicle feature that will show his or her potential as a creative writer/photographer."

FRIENDS MAGAZINE, Ceco Communications, Inc., 30400 Van Dyke Blvd., Warren MI 48093. (313)575-9400. Executive Editor: Herman Duerr. "*Friends* is a magazine for Chevrolet owners; Chevrolet products are the 'hook' to all of our stories." 75-85% freelance written. Prefers to work with published/established writers. Monthly magazine; 32 pages. Circ. 1,000,000. Pays on acceptance. Publishes ms an average of 6 months after acceptance. Buys first rights in most cases. Computer printout submissions acceptable. Submit seasonal/holiday material 6 months in advance. Simultaneous and photocopied submissions OK. Reports in 1 month. Free sample copy and writer's guidelines.
Nonfiction: Travel (by automobile; U.S. only); celebrity profiles (of Chevrolet owners); unusual use of Chevrolet products; humor (auto-related); entertainment (programs and events sponsored by Chevrolet); and photo features (strong Chevrolet-tied photo essays). We're looking for freelancers who can focus and produce lively copy and write a story that will interest or excite the general reader. Query by mail only. Releases required for all persons named or quoted in story. Sometimes pays expenses on assignment.
Photos: State availability of photos. Pays $200/page. Transparencies only. "About the only time we'll consider black and white is when the article is an early historical piece." Captions and model release required.
Tips: "Writing style must be 'people' oriented with plenty of quotes and conversational tone. Avoid 'dry' narrative."

HOT BIKE, McMullen Publishing Co., 2145 W. Le Palme, Anaheim CA 92632. (714)635-9040. Editor: Paul Garson. 20-50% freelance written. Prefers to work with published/established writers; works with a small number of new/unpublished writers each year; eager to work with new/unpublished writers. Monthly magazine that is a serious, tech-oriented, high performance motorcycle publication with emphasis on Harley-Davidson motorcycles, plus coverage of race events, classics and exotics. Circ. 80,000. Pays on publication. Publishes ms an average of 3 months after acceptance. Byline given. Buys one-time rights. Submit seasonal/holiday material 3 months in advance. Photocopied submissions OK. Computer printout submissions acceptable; no dot-matrix. Reports in 2 weeks. Sample copy $1.25; writer's guidelines for SAE with 1 first class stamp.
Nonfiction: Historical/nostalgic (classic bikes and events); how-to (tech article, high performance engine, suspension, etc.); interview/profile (top racers and builders); new products (for new product section); photo feature (high-performance street and track machine); and travel (unusual touring articles). Exclusives on hot new performance bikes, mostly Harley-Davidson. Also, European Harley coverage, but not "old-style choppers." Buys 40 mss/year. Send complete ms. Length: 500-3,000 words. Pays $50-300. Sometimes pays the expenses of writers on assignment.
Photos: "For cover consideration, a female model helps—no nudes—keep it sexy but tasteful. Photos should be dramatic if they are race oriented." Pays $20-50 for b&w contact sheets, negatives and prints (5x7 or 8x10); $30-100 for color transparencies (35mm or 2¼). Captions, model releases and identification of subjects required.
Tips: "Have a hot subject, hot photos, clear and concise writing. Bad photos ruin most freelance submissions. Read the magazine and study format style and subject matter. We are always willing to give you new writers a chance."

KEEPIN' TRACK OF VETTES, Box 48, Spring Valley NY 10977. (914)425-2649. Editor: Shelli Finkel. 70% freelance written. Works with a small number of new/unpublished writers each year. Monthly magazine; 60-68 pages. For Corvette owners and enthusiasts. Circ. 38,000. Pays on publication. Publishes ms an average of 3 months after acceptance. Buys all rights. Byline given. Submit seasonal/holiday material 3 months in advance. Computer printout submissions acceptable; prefers letter-quality to dot-matrix. Reports in 1 month. Free sample copy and writer's guidelines.
Nonfiction: Expose (telling of Corvette problems with parts, etc.); historical (any and all aspects of Corvette developments); how-to (restorations, engine work, suspension, race, swapmeets); humor; informational; interview (query); nostalgia; personal experience; personal opinion; photo feature; profile (query); technical; and travel. Buys 8-10 mss/issue. Query or submit complete ms. Pays $50-200. Sometimes pays the expenses of writers on assignment.
Photos: Send photo with ms. Pays $10-35 for b&w contact sheets or negatives; $10-50 for 35mm color transparencies; offers no additional payment for photos with accompanying ms.
Tips: The writer "must have more than a passing knowledge of Corvettes specifically and automobiles in general."

MOTOR TREND, Petersen Publishing Co., 8490 Sunset Blvd., Los Angeles CA 90069. (213)854-2222. Executive Editor: Jack Nerad. 15-20% freelance written. Prefers to work with published/established writers. For automotive enthusiasts and general interest consumers. Monthly. Circ. 750,000. Publishes ms an average of 3 months after acceptance. Buys all rights. "Fact-filled query suggested for all freelancers." Computer printout submissions acceptable; prefers letter-quality to dot-matrix. Reports in 30 days.
Nonfiction: Automotive and related subjects that have national appeal. Emphasis on domestic and imported cars, roadtests, driving impressions, auto classics, auto, travel, racing, and high-performance features for the enthusiast. Packed with facts. Freelancers should confine queries to feature material; road tests and related activity handled inhouse. Sometimes pays the expenses of writers on assignment.
Photos: Buys photos, particularly of prototype cars and assorted automotive matter. Pays $25-250 for b&w glossy prints or color transparencies.
Fillers: Automotive newsbreaks, humorous short takes, automotive cartoons, featurettes. 500 words maximum.

‡MOTORCYCLE BUYERS' GUIDE, CRV Publishing Canada Ltd., Suite 202, 2077 Dundas St. E., Mississauga, Ontario, L4X 1M2, Canada. Editorial Director: Reg Fife. An annual motorcycling magazine. Circ. 100,000. Pays on publication. Byline given. Buys first rights. Submit seasonal/holiday material 4 months in advance. Reports in 2 months. Free sample copy and writer's guidelines.
Nonfiction: Query. Length: 1,000-3,000 words. Pays variable rates.
Photos: State availability of photos. Reviews color transparencies and prints. Captions required. Buys onetime rights.

‡MUSTANG MONTHLY, Dobbs Publications, Inc., Box 6320, Lakeland FL 33807. (813)646-5743. Editor: Jim Smart. Managing Editor: Donald Farr. 40% freelance written. A monthly magazine covering the 1964½ through 1973 Ford Mustang, some '79-86. "We focus on stock and original Mustangs as they came from the factory. Our average audience makes over $30,000 annually, and is 35 years of age." Circ. 50,000. Pays on publication. Publishes ms an average of 6 months after acceptance. Byline given. Buys all rights. Submit seasonal/holiday material 3 months in advance. Simultaneous submissions OK. Computer printout submissions acceptable; prefers letter-quality to dot-matrix. Reports in 6 weeks on manuscripts. Free sample copy and writers guidelines.
Nonfiction: General interest, historical/nostalgic, how-to, humor, interview/profile, new product, opinion, photo feature and technical. No fiction or personal experiences written first person. Buys 50 mss/year. Query with or without published clips, or send complete ms. "Freelancers should write for editorial requirement package *first*." Length: 2,500 words maximum. Pays $275 maximum. Pays the expenses of writers on assignment.
Photos: Send photos with submission. Reviews contact sheets, negatives and transparencies. No color prints. Offers $100 maximum/photo (color cover $150, b&w $10 each). Captions, model releases, and identification of subjects required.
Columns/Departments: Horse Sense (general interest on Mustangs). Buys 12 mss/year. Query with published clips. Length: 800 words maximum depending on published word count. Pays $275 maximum.
Fillers: Facts and short humor. Buys 30/year. Length: 1,000 words maximum. Pays $275 maximum depending on published word count.
Tips: *Mustang Monthly* is looking for features and how-to.

NISSAN DISCOVERY, The Magazine for Nissan Owners, Donnelley Marketing, Box 4617, N. Hollywood CA 91607. (213)877-4406. Editor: Wayne Thoms. 65% freelance written. Prefers to work with published/established writers. Bimonthly magazine for Nissan owners and their families. Circ. 500,000. Pays on acceptance. Publishes ms an average of 4 months after acceptance. Byline given. Not copyrighted. Buys first North American serial rights. Submit seasonal/holiday material 5 months in advance. Photocopied and previously published submissions OK. Computer printout submissions acceptable; no dot-matrix. Reports in 1 month. Sample copy $1.50 in cash or stamps, 9x12 SAE, and 80¢ postage; writer's guidelines for business-size SAE and 22¢ postage.

Nonfiction: Historical/nostalgic, humor, photo feature, travel. "We need general family interest material with heavy emphasis on outstanding color photos: travel, humor, food, lifestyle, sports, entertainment." Buys 25 mss/year. Query. Length: 1,300-1,800 words. Pays $300-1,000. Sometimes pays the expenses of writers on assignment.

Photos: State availability of photos. Reviews 2¼" and 35mm color transparencies. No b&w photos. "Payment usually is part of story package—all negotiated." Captions and identification of subjects required. Buys one-time rights.

Tips: "A freelancer can best break in to our publication by submitting a brief idea query with specific information on color slides available. Offer a package of copy and art."

NORTHEAST RIDING, Northeast Riding Inc., 209 Whitney St., Hartford CT 06105. (203)236-6604. Editor: Patricia Fahy. 70% freelance written. Monthly magazine "to entertain and inform the road and street motorcyclists of the Northeast, who ride for recreation and commuting. Area events, good roads to ride, and club activities are featured along with information on camping, service, safety, and political issues affecting riding in the area." Circ. 20,000. "Payment is negotiable prior to acceptance. Payment made on publication." Publishes ms an average of 3 months after acceptance. Byline given. Buys first rights. Submit seasonal/holiday material 6 months in advance. Simultaneous queries, and simultaneous, photocopied, and previously published submissions OK. Computer printout submissions acceptable. Reports in 2 weeks. Sample copy for 9x12 SAE and 90¢ postage.

Nonfiction: General interest (places to ride); historical/nostalgic (on vintage bikes); interview/profile (unusual biker); new product (accessories); opinion (legislation); personal experience (riding/touring); photo feature (motorcycles with people); technical (repair/service/testing); travel (mostly New England); and articles on safety. Buying very small amount of material; most is donated. No material on dirt bikes, enduros, or trials. Send complete ms. Length: 500-2,000 words. Payment is minimal. Sometimes pays the expenses of writers on assignment.

Photos: Send photos with query or manuscript. Reviews 4x5 b&w prints. Captions required. Buys one-time rights.

Columns/Departments: Safety, Legal, Technical, Favorite Ride. Send complete ms. Length 500-1,000 words. Payment is negotiable prior to acceptance. Payment made on publication.

Tips: "Submit ms and photos ready to use. Articles must be of interest to Northeastern motorcyclists, and photos should include motorcycles *and* people. The Favorite Ride department is most open to freelancers. Write about New England locations, specific description of route. Include at least one b&w photo of area *with* motorcycle."

OFF-ROAD MAG, Argus Publishing, Suite 316, 12301 Wilshire Blvd., Los Angeles CA 90025. (213)820-3601. Editor: Rick Sieman. Monthly magazine covering off-pavement vehicles, particularly 4-wheel drive, utility, and pickup trucks; and off-road racing and rallying vehicles. Readers are owners and people who aspire to own off-road vehicles, as well as those who intend to modify engines and other components for off-road use. Circ. 120,000. Pays on publication. Byline given. Buys all rights, "but may reassign rights upon request." Submit seasonal/holiday material 4 months in advance. Computer prinout submissions acceptable; prefers letter-quality to dot-matrix. SASE. Reports in 1 month. Writer's guidelines for business size SAE and 1 first class stamp.

Nonfiction: Technical (modification); travel (and adventure in the continental U.S.); off-road groups; and land-closures. "The key to writing for us is technical expertise. You must be knowledgeable on the subject." Buys 50 mss/year. Send complete ms and photos or diagrams. Length: 1,500-3,000 words. Pays $125-400.

POPULAR CARS, The Complete Street Machine Magazine, McMullen Publishing, Inc., 2145 W. La Palma, Anaheim CA 92801-1785. (714)635-9040. Editor: Brian Hatano. 25% freelance written. Prefers to work with published/established automotive writers. Monthly magazine on contemporary, high performance, domestic automobiles. "Our main emphasis is on 'street machines' (owner-modified cars) and 60's and 70's 'muscle' cars and related subjects." Circ. 85,000. Pays on publication. Publishes ms an average of 4 months after acceptance. Byline given. Kill fee negotiated in advance. Buys first serial rights. Submit material 3 months in advance. Computer printout submissions acceptable; prefers letter-quality to dot-matrix. Reports in 3 weeks on queries; 1 month on mss. Sample copy $2.50; free photographer's guidelines.

Nonfiction: Historical/nostalgic (60's, 70's muscle cars); how-to (street performance and drag racing); interview/profile (of people associated with automotive performance subjects); new product (new cars—2 page maximum, performance cars *only*); photo feature (on people's street machines); technical (street performance); and drag race and street machine event coverage. Special issues on Ford '64-'70 Mustangs, Corvettes, '55-57,

Chevys, Pro Streeters. No new car tests. Buys 36-40 mss/year. Query with published clips. Length: 435-1,175 words. Pays $75-300.

Photos: Reviews 35mm color transparencies and 5x7 b&w prints. Pays $20-75 for transparencies; $0-20 for prints. Captions, model release, and identification of subjects required. Buys all rights.

Tips: "A freelancer can best break into our publication by a query, submission of past work, good quality manuscripts, reputation, and good 'car features'."

‡**RIDER**, 29901 Agoura Rd., Agoura CA 91301. Editor: Tash Matsuoka. 60% freelance written. For owners and prospective buyers of motorcycles to be used for touring, sport riding, and commuting. Monthly magazine; 100-160 pages. Buys all rights. Pays on publication. Sample copy $2. Free writer's guidelines. Query first. Submit seasonal material 3 months in advance. Photocopied submissions OK. Computer printout submissions acceptable; no dot-matrix. Reports in 1 month.

Nonfiction: Articles directly related to motorcycle touring, camping, commuting and sport riding including travel, human interest, safety, novelty, do-it-yourself and technical. "Articles which portray the unique thrill of motorcycling." Should be written in clean, contemporary style aimed at a sharp, knowledgeable reader. Buys informational how-to, personal experience, profile, historical, nostalgia and personal opinion. Length is flexible. Pays $100 for Favorite Ride feature and $150-450 for major articles.

Photos: Offers no additional payment for photos purchased with ms. Captions required. "Quality photographs are critical. Graphics are emphasized in *Rider*, and we must have photos with good visual impact."

ROAD KING MAGAZINE, Box 250, Park Forest IL 60466. Editor-in-Chief: George Friend. 10% freelance written. Eager to work with new/unpublished writers each year. Truck driver leisure reading publication. Quarterly magazine; 72 pages. Circ. 224,000. Pays on acceptance. Publishes ms an average of 2 months after acceptance. Usually buys all rights; sometimes buys first serial rights. Byline given "always on fiction—if requested on nonfiction—copyright mentioned only if requested." Submit seasonal/holiday material 3 months in advance. Simultaneous and photocopied submissions OK. Sample copy for 7x10 SAE with 73¢ postage or get free sample copy at any Union 76 truck stop.

Nonfiction: Trucker slant or general interest, humor, and photo feature. No articles on violence or sex. Name and quote release required. No queries. Submit complete ms. Length: 500-1,200 words. Pays $50-400.

Photos: Submit photos with accompanying ms. No additional payment for b&w contact sheets or 2¼x2¼ color transparencies. Captions preferred. Buys first rights. Model release required.

Fiction: Adventure, historical, humorous, mystery, rescue-type suspense and western. Especially about truckers. No stories on sex and violence. "We're looking for quality writing." Buys 4 mss/year. Submit complete ms. Length: approximately 1,200 words. Pays up to $400. Writer should quote selling price with submission.

Fillers: Jokes, gags, anecdotes and short humor about truckers. Buys 20-25/year. Length: 50-500 words. Pays $5-100.

Tips: No collect phone calls or postcard requests. "We don't appreciate letters we have to answer. Do not submit manuscripts or art or photos using registered mail, certified mail or insured mail. Publisher will not accept such materials from the post office. Publisher will not discuss refusal with writer. Nothing personal, just legal. Do not write and ask if we would like such and such article or outline. We buy only from original and complete manuscript submitted on speculation. Do not ask for writer's guidelines. See above and/or get copy of magazine and be familiar with our format before submitting anything. We are a trucker publication whose readers are often family members and sometimes Bible Belt. We refrain from violence, sex, nudity, etc. Never phone for free copy as we will not handle such phone calls."

STOCK CAR RACING MAGAZINE, Box 715, Ipswich MA 01938. Editor: Dick Berggren. 75% freelance written. Eager to work with new/unpublished writers. For stock car racing fans and competitors. Monthly magazine; 100 pages. Circ. 400,000. Pays on publication. Publishes ms an average of 3 months after acceptance. Buys all rights. Byline given. Computer printout submissions acceptable; prefers letter-quality to dot-matrix. Reports in 6 weeks.

Nonfiction: "Uses nonfiction on stock car drivers, cars, and races. We are interested in the story behind the story in stock car racing. We want interesting profiles and colorful, nationally interesting features. We are looking for more technical articles, particularly in the area of street stocks and limited sportsman." Query. Buys 50-60 mss/year. Length: 100-6,000 words. Pays up to $350.

Photos: State availability of photos. Pays $20 for 8x10 b&w photos; up to $250 for 35mm or larger color transparencies. Captions required.

Tips: "We get more queries than stories. We just don't get as much material as we want to buy. We have more room for stories than ever before. We are an excellent market with 12 issues per year."

3 WHEELING MAGAZINE, The Original All Terrain Vehicle Magazine, Wright Publishing Co., 2949 Century Pl., Box 2260, Costa Mesa CA 92626. (714)979-2560. Editor: Bruce Simurda. Managing Editor: Rick Busenkell. 5% freelance written. Works with a small number of new/unpublished writers each year. Monthly magazine covering all terrain vehicles. Circ. 75,000. Pays on publication. Publishes ms an average of 3 months after acceptance. Byline given. Buys all rights. Submit seasonal/holiday material 3 months in advance. Simultaneous queries and simultaneous submissions OK. Computer printout submissions acceptable; no dot-matrix. Reports in 1 month. Sample copy for 9x12 SAE and 5 first class stamps.

Nonfiction: General interest, how-to, new product, personal experience, technical and travel. Especially interested in articles on specific off-road riding areas. Buys 10 mss/year. Query. Length: 600-900 words. Pays $60-90. Sometimes pays the expenses of writers on assignment.

Photos: State availability of photos. Reviews b&w contact sheets and 35mm color transparencies. Captions, model releases and identification of subjects required.

Columns/Departments: All freelance columns on contract basis only. Buys 36 mss/year. Query. Length: 600-650 words. Pays $60-90.

‡TRUCKIN', McMullen Publishing, Inc., 2145 W. LaPalma Ave., Anaheim CA 92801. (714)635-9040. Editor: Steve Stillwell. 10% freelance written. A monthly magazine covering street custom pickups, vans and mini-trucks. Circ. 115,000. Pays on publication. Publishes ms an average of 9 months after acceptance. Byline given. Buys all rights. Submit seasonal/holiday material 4 months in advance. Computer printout submissions acceptable; prefers letter-quality to dot-matrix. Reports in 1 month. Sample copy $3; free writer's guidelines.

Nonfiction: General interest; historical/nostalgic; how-to (installations and modifications); humor; new product; photo feature (of pickups, vans and mini-trucks—old and new); and event coverage (truck-ins, some races etc.) Buys 24-36 mss/year. Send complete ms. Length: Prefers 1-2 double-spaced, typed pages for features; other negotiable depending on article content. Pay varies depending on type and length of article.

Photos: Send photos with submission. Reviews contact sheets and transparencies. Pay varies with type of article. Model releases required. Buys all rights.

Fillers: Will consider any submitted.

Tips: "Calling or writing to verify our interest in a proposed article is helpful to both our staff and the writer. Technical articles, features and event coverage are most open to freelancers."

VOLKSWAGEN'S WORLD, Volkswagen of America, 888 W. Big Beaver Rd., Box 3951, Troy MI 48099. Editor: Ed Rabinowitz. Magazine published 5 times/year for Volkswagen owners in the United States. Circ. 250,000. Pays on acceptance. Buys all rights. Byline given. Computer printout submissions acceptable. Reports in 6 weeks. Free writer's guidelines.

Nonfiction: "Interesting stories on people using Volkswagens; useful owner modifications of the vehicle; travel pieces with the emphasis on people, not places; Volkswagenmania stories, personality pieces, inspirational and true adventure articles. The style should be light. Our approach is subtle, however, and we try to avoid obvious product puffery, since *Volkswagen's World* is not an advertising medium. We prefer a first-person, people-oriented handling. No basic travelogues; stay away from Beetle stories. With all story ideas, please query first. All unsolicited manuscripts will be returned unopened. Though queries should be no longer than 2 pages, they ought to include a working title, a short, general summary of the article, and an outline of the specific points to be covered. We strongly advise writers to read at least 2 past issues before working on a story." Buys 10-12 mss/year. Length: 1,000 words maximum; "shorter pieces, some as short as 450 words, often receive closer attention." Pays $150 per printed page for photographs and text; otherwise, a portion of that amount, depending on the space allotted. Most stories go 2 pages; some run 3 or 4.

Photos: Submit photo samples with query. Photos purchased with ms; captions required. "We prefer color transparencies, 35mm or larger. All photos should carry the photographer's name and address. If the photographer is not the author, both names should appear on the first page of the text. Where possible, we would like a selection of at least 40 transparencies. It is recommended that at least one show the principal character or author. Quality photography can often sell a story that might be otherwise rejected. Every picture should be identified or explained." Model releases required. Pays $350 maximum for front cover photo.

Fillers: "Short, humorous anecdotes about Volkswagens." Pays $15.

Tips: "Style of the publication and its content are being structured toward more upscale, affluent buyer. VW drivers are not the same as those who used to drive the Beetle."

VW & PORSCHE, Argus Publishers, Suite 316, 12301 Wilshire Blvd., Los Angeles CA 90025. (213)820-3601. Editor: C. Van Tune. 60% freelance written. Bimonthly magazine covering VW, Porsche and Audi cars for owners. Circ. 75,000. Pays one month before publication. Publishes ms an average of 6 months after acceptance. Byline given. Kill fee varies. Buys all rights. Submit seasonal/holiday material 4 months in advance. Computer printout submissions acceptable; prefers letter quality to dot-matrix. Reports in 2 weeks on queries. Free sample copy.

Nonfiction: How-to (restore, maintain or tune-up); Special, modified or restored VWs and Porsches. Buys 30-35 mss/year. Query. Length: 1,000-2,500 words. Pays $75-100/printed page. "More if color pictures are used." Sometimes pays the expenses of writers on assignment.

Photos: "We require crisp, well-lit b&w and color prints and slides; great variety in angles and settings."

State availability of photos. Reviews 8x10 glossy prints. Identification and/or signed release of subjects required.
Tips: "All of our articles deal with VWs, Porsches and Audis in a technical light, therefore a strong technical knowledge is critical; short articles used may occasionally be humorous, not so 'techy.'"

Aviation

Airline deregulation is one trend that affects the type of material that aviation magazine editors buy. "Competition (resulting from deregulation) means that commercial air travel is forever changing," said one editor. "That's what the readers want to know about." Editors at aviation magazines sometimes find unsolicited material too elementary for their audiences who *know* commercial aviation. Professional and private pilots, and aviation enthusiasts read the publications in this section. Magazines intended for passengers of commercial airlines are grouped in the In-Flight category. Technical aviation and space journals and publications for airport operators, aircraft dealers and others in aviation businesses are listed under Aviation and Space in the Trade Journals section.

AERO, Fancy Publications, Box 6050, Mission Viego CA 92690. (714)240-6001. Editor: Dennis Shattuck. Managing Editor: Merry MacTavish. 50% freelance written. For owners of private aircraft. "We take a unique, but limited view within our field." Circ. 75,000. Buys first North American serial rights. Buys about 30-50 mss/year. Pays after publication. Sample copy $3; writer's guidelines for SASE. Will consider photocopied submissions if guaranteed original. Reports in 2 months. Query.
Nonfiction: Material on aircraft products, developments in aviation, specific airplane test reports, travel by aircraft, development and use of airports. All must be related to general aviation field. Length: 1,000-4,000 words. Pays $75-250.
Photos: Pays $15 for 8x10 b&w glossy prints purchased with mss or on assignment. Pays $150 for color transparencies used on cover.
Columns/Departments: Weather flying, instrument flight refresher, new products.
Tips: "Freelancer must know the subject about which he is writing; use good grammar; know the publication for which he's writing; remember that we try to relate to the middle segment of the business/pleasure flying public. We see too many 'first flight' type of articles. Our market is more sophisticated than that. Most writers do not do enough research on their subject. Would like to see more material on business-related flying, more on people involved in flying."

‡AIR & SPACE MAGAZINE, Smithsonian Institution, Room 3401, National Air and Space Museum, 7th and Independence S.W., Washington DC 20560. (202)357-4414. Editor: George Larson. Managing Editor: Philip Hayward. 80% freelance written. A bimonthly magazine covering aviation and aerospace for a non-technical audience. "Features are slanted to a technically curious, but not necessarily technically knowledgeable audience. We are looking for unique angles to aviation/aerospace stories, history, events, personalities, current and future technologies, that emphasize the human-interest aspect." Estab. 1985. Circ. 200,000. Pays half on acceptance, half on publication. Publishes ms an average of 3 months after acceptance. Byline given. Offers variable kill fee. Buys first North American serial rights. Photocopied submissions OK. Accepts electronic submissions via disk or modem, query for details; hard copy also required. Reports in 1 month. Sample copy for $3.50 plus $2.09 postage; free writer's guidelines.
Nonfiction: Essays; general interest (on aviation/aerospace) historical/nostalgic; humor; interview/profile; photo feature; and technical. No pilot reports on aircraft. Query with published clips. Pays $1,200-2,000. Sometimes pays the expenses of writers on assignment.
Photos: State availability of photos with submission. Reviews contact sheets and 35 mm transparencies. Payment rates follow the guidelines of the American Society of Magazine Photographers. Model releases and identification of subjects required. Buys one-time rights.

AOPA PILOT, 421 Aviation Way, Frederick MD 21701. (301)695-2350. Editor: Edward G. Tripp. 15% freelance written. Prefers to work with published/established writers; works with a small number of new/unpublished writers each year; eager to work with new/unpublished writers. For aircraft owners, pilots, and the complete spectrum of the general aviation industry. Official magazine of the Aircraft Owners and Pilots Association. Monthly. Circ. 260,000. Pays on acceptance. Publishes ms an average of 3 months after acceptance. Buys first North American serial rights. Reports in 2 months. No computer disk submissions. Computer printout submissions acceptable; prefers letter-quality to dot-matrix. Sample copy $2.
Nonfiction: Factual articles up to 2,500 words that will inform, educate and entertain pilots and aircraft owners ranging from the student to the seasoned professional. These pieces should be generously illustrated with good quality photos, diagrams or sketches. Quality and accuracy essential. Topics covered include maintenance, operating technique, reports on new and used aircraft, avionics and other aviation equipment, places to fly (travel), governmental policies (local, state and federal) relating to general aviation. Additional features on weather in relation to flying, legal aspects of aviation, flight education, pilot fitness, and aviation history are used occasionally. No commonplace first-solo or fly-in/local-event stories. Query. Pays $400 maximum. Sometimes pays the expenses of writers on assignment.
Photos: Pays $25 minimum for each photo or sketch used. Original b&w negatives or color slides should be made available.

AVIATION/USA, Randall Publishing Company, Box 2029, Tuscaloosa AL 35403. (205)349-2990. Editor: Claude Duncan. 25-50% freelance written. Eager to work with new/unpublished writers. Weekly tabloid on general aviation (small planes, not jets). "Most of our readers are private pilots who like to read about other pilots, their planes, equipment and adventures." Estab. 1985. Circ. 10,000. Pays on acceptance. Publishes ms an average of 1 month or less after acceptance. Byline given. Offers 100% kill fee. Not copyrighted. Buys first serial rights, one-time rights, second serial (reprint) rights and simultaneous rights. Simultaneous and previously published (updated) submissions OK. Computer printout submissions acceptable; prefers letter-quality to dot-matrix. Reports in 2 weeks. Free sample copy and writer's guidelines.
Nonfiction: General interest (with general aviation angle); historical/nostalgic (except combat stories); how-to (overcome flight problems); humor (with pilot angle); interview/profile (with general aviation angle); personal experience (with pilots); technical (planes); travel (related to small planes); and small local airports. Buys 100 mss/year. Send complete ms. Length: 250-1,000 words. Pays $10-50 sometimes. Pays expenses of writers on assignment.
Photos: Send photos with query or ms. Prefers b&w or color prints; commercially processed OK if sharp. Pays $5.
Tips: "We encourage multiple submissions. Submitting art with copy gives a definite edge. Nothing is too local if it's interesting."

FLIGHT REPORTS, Peter Katz Productions, Inc., 1280 Saw Mill River Rd., Yonkers NY 10710. (914)423-6000. Editor: Mary Hunt. Managing Editor: Peter J. Katz. 50% freelance written. Monthly travel magazine for pilots and aircraft owners. Pays on publication. Byline given. Buys all rights. Submit seasonal/holiday material 2 months in advance. Reports in 2 weeks. Sample copy $1.
Nonfiction: Destination reports include what to do, where to stay, and airport facilities for domestic travel and Canada only. No foreign travel. Buys variable number of mss/year. Query. Length: 750-1,500 words. Pays $25-50.
Photos: State availability of photos. Pays $5 for 3½x5½ b&w and color prints. Captions required.
Tips: "Pilot's license and cross country flying experience is helpful. Some aviation background is required."

FLYING, CBS Magazine, 1 Park Ave., New York NY 10016. (212)503-4000. Editor-in-Chief: Richard L. Collins. Editorial Coordinator: Mary McDonnell. 5% freelance written. For private and commercial pilots involved with, or interested in, the use of general-aviation aircraft (not airline or military) for business and pleasure. Monthly magazine; 116 pages. Circ. 370,000. Pays on acceptance. Buys one-time rights. Submit seasonal/holiday material 4 months in advance of issue date. Reports in 3 weeks.
Nonfiction: How-to (piloting and other aviation techniques); and technical (aviation-related). No articles on "My Trip" travel accounts, or historical features. Buys about 12 mss/year. Submit complete ms. Length: 750-3,500 words. Pays $50-1,000.
Columns/Departments: "I Learned About Flying From That" personal experience. Pays $100 minimum.
Tips: "New ideas and approaches are a must. Tone must be correct for knowledgeable pilots rather than the non-flying public. Facts must be absolutely accurate."

FREQUENT FLYER, Dun & Bradstreet, 888 7th Ave., New York NY 10106. Editor: Coleman A. Lollar. 75% freelance written. Monthly magazine covering business travel (airlines/airports/aviation) for mostly male high-level business executive readership. Circ. 350,000. Pays on acceptance. Publishes ms an average of 6 months after acceptance. Byline given. Offers $75 kill fee. Buys all rights. Submit seasonal/holiday material 6

Close-up

George Larson
Editor
Air & Space

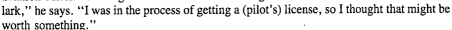

For George Larson, combining his hobby of flying and his profession as a writer was "just a happy accident."

Larson had worked on *Medical World News* and *Scholastic Magazine*, in addition to writing for "a large number of other magazines." But he was working as a musician and flying as a hobby when he answered a blind ad for an aviation editor. "I thought I would answer the thing as a lark," he says. "I was in the process of getting a (pilot's) license, so I thought that might be worth something."

Apparently it was; Larson got the job at *Flying Magazine*, then moved on to *Business and Commercial Aviation* before becoming editor of *Air & Space*. The first issue of this new Smithsonian Institution bimonthly magazine was published in the spring of 1986.

At *Air & Space* the goal isn't to provide technical information for pilots, but to provide information about aviation and space for the general reader. "The idea was to occupy a niche that was empty before," Larson says. "This magazine explores the ways in which people relate to aviation and space activities. It's a magazine that seeks to discover."

As a pilot with 1,500 hours of air time, Larson understands all the technical language and jargon, but says, "I find myself trying to forget that and keep the reader's view foremost. At *Air & Space*, my 15 years of magazine editing and writing are far more important than the specialized experience of flying."

Larson admits it's difficult not to think in technical terms. "I rely on other people to let me know when I start thinking too technically," he says. "Most of our readers are not pilots and don't understand or care about the 'insider' chatter that often excludes them from reading about space and aviation activities."

Instead, Larson's magazine concentrates on "the human interest focus" of space and aviation. It tempers the technical focus of many aviation publications by sympathizing with a "kind of public sense of romance" with space. "We serve that romance with information," he says.

In conjunction with the human interest focus, Larson also looks for "the unusual point of view" when considering articles and proposals for *Air & Space*.

Subjects of articles "may not necessarily be all that novel," he says, "but the perspective is different from that of other publications covering insiders, trade people and pilots. You have to be like a cameraman looking for a new angle."

He echoes the advice given by editors of all types of publications. "Convey a sense of freshness in the way the subject will be handled," Larson counsels writers. "That's really all we ask."

—Glenda Tennant

months in advance. Computer printout submissions acceptable; no dot-matrix. Reports in 2 months on queries; 1 month on mss. Free sample copy and writer's guidelines.

Nonfiction: Book excerpts, expose, new product, technical, travel, and news reporting, in particular on airports/aircraft/airlines/hotel/credit card/car rental. Not interested in queries on stress or anything written in the first person; no profiles, humor or interviews. "*FF* reports on travel as part of an executive's job. We do not assume that he enjoys travel, and neither should the freelancer." Buys 100 mss/year. Query with published clips. Length: 800-3,000 words. Pays $100-500. Sometimes pays the expenses of writers on assignment.

Photos: Eve Cohen, articles editor. "We accept both b&w and color contact sheets, transparencies and prints; rates negotiable." Buys one-time rights.

Tips: "We publish very little destination material, preferring articles about how deregulation, airport developments, etc., have affected air services to a destination, rather than descriptive articles. We avoid all travel articles that sound promotional. We publish general business/economic features when they directly relate to the reader as a *mobile* businessman (portable computers, foreign banking, credit card/traveler's check development, etc.). We do not report on other business topics. We like service articles, but not in the usual 'how-to' format: our readers travel too much (average of almost 50 roundtrips a year) to be told how to pack a bag, or how to stay in touch with the office. In service articles, we prefer a review of how frequent travelers handle certain situations rather than how they *should* handle them. Unrequested manuscripts will probably not be read. Give us a good, solid story idea. If accepted, expect a fairly detailed assignment from us. We rewrite heavily. Overly sensitive authors may want to avoid us."

GENERAL AVIATION NEWS, Box 110918, Carrollton TX 75006. (214)446-2502. Editor: D.E. Murphy. 10-20% freelance written. Works with a small number of new/unpublished writers each year. For pilots, aircraft owners, aviation buffs, aircraft dealers, and related business people. Biweekly tabloid; 24-36 pages. Circ. 30,000. Pays on publication. Publishes ms an average of 1 month after acceptance. Buys all rights. Byline on all features and most news stories. Phone queries OK. Submit seasonal/holiday material 1 month in advance. Simultaneous submissions okay if prior arrangements made with editor. Computer printout submissions acceptable. Sample copy $1. Proposal or rejection within 1 month.

Nonfiction: General aviation stories of interest to nationwide audience of persons connected to aviation. Articles on any aspect of aviation will be considered provided they are of interest to those in the general aviation community. "We are a *general aviation* (no airlines, no military) publication. Historical people, events or aircraft which have more than local appeal are good bets." Buys 10-20 unsolicited mss/year. Length: about 1,000 words maximum. Pays up to $50 per published article, less for shorter articles. Sometimes pays expenses of writers on assignment.

Photos: Send photo material with accompanying mss. Pays $5 for b&w or color prints. Captions required. Buys all rights.

Tips: "Writers should read *GAN* before sending mss; also recommend that writers read other aviation publications/periodicals, to have a grasp of current trends and attitudes in the general aviation world. Follow the advice in the front of *Writer's Market*. *GAN* is a good place for beginning freelancers to try their hand."

KITPLANES, "Featuring Fast-Build Aircraft for the Home Craftsman." Fancy Publications, Box 6050, Mission Viejo CA 92690. (714)240-6001. Editor: Dennis Shattuck. Managing Editor: Joe O'Leary. 60% freelance written. Monthly magazine covering self-construction of private aircraft for pilots and builders. Circ. 45,000. Pays on publication. Publishes ms an average of 6 months after acceptance. Byline given. Offers negotiable kill fee. Buys first North American serial rights. Submit seasonal/holiday material 6 months in advance. Computer printout submissions acceptable; dot-matrix must be caps and lower case printing. Reports in 2 weeks on queries; 6 weeks on mss. Sample copy $3; writer's guidelines for business size SAE.

Nonfiction: How-to, interview/profile, new product, personal experience, photo feature technical general interest. "We are looking for articles on specific construction techniques, the use of tools, both hand and power, in aircraft building, the relative merits of various materials, conversions of engines from automobiles for aviation use, installation of instruments and electronics." No general-interest aviation articles, or "My First Solo" type of articles. Buys 80 mss/year. Query. Length: 500-5,000 words. Pays $100-400.

Photos: Send photos with query or ms or state availability of photos. Pays $10-75 for b&w prints; $20-150 for color transparencies and color prints. Captions and identification of subjects required. Buys one-time rights.

Tips: "*Kitplanes* contains very specific information—a writer must be extremely knowledgeable in the field. Major features are entrusted only to known writers. I cannot emphasize enough that articles must be directed at the individual aircraft constructor. We will not accept or even consider articles about personal experiences in flight."

PRIVATE PILOT, Fancy Communications Corp., Box 6050, Mission Viejo CA 92690. (714)240-6001. Editor: Dennis Shattuck. Managing Editor: April E. Hay. 60% freelance written. For owner/pilots of private aircraft, for student pilots and others aspiring to attain additional ratings and experience. "We take a unique, but limited view within our field." Circ. 85,000. Buys first North American serial rights. Buys about 60-90 mss/year. Pays on publication. Sample copy $3; writer's guidelines for SASE. Will consider photocopied submissions if guaranteed original. No simultaneous submissions. Computer printout submissions acceptable "if double spaced and have upper and lower case letters." Reports in 2 months. Query.

Nonfiction: Material on techniques of flying, developments in aviation, product and specific airplane test reports, travel by aircraft, development and use of airports. All must be related to general aviation field. No personal experience articles. Length: 1,000-4,000 words. Pays $75-300.

Photos: Pays $15 for 8x10 b&w glossy prints purchased with mss or on assignment. Pays $150 for color transparencies used on cover.

Columns/Departments: Business flying, homebuilt/experimental aircraft, pilot's logbook. Length: 1,000 words. Pays $50-125.

Tips: "Freelancer must know the subject about which he is writing; use good grammar; know the publication for which he's writing; remember that we try to relate to the middle segment of the business/pleasure flying public. We see too many 'first flight' type of articles. Our market is more sophisticated than that. Most writers do not do enough research on their subject. Would like to see more material on business-related flying, more on people involved in flying."

‡SPACE WORLD, 203W, 600 Maryland Ave. SW, Washington DC 20024. (202)484-1111. Editor: Tony Reichhardt. Managing Editor: Helga Onan. 80% freelance written. Prefers to work with published/established writers; eager to work with new/unpublished writers. A monthly magazine covering the space program. "We publish non-technical, lively articles about all aspects of international space programs from shuttle missions to planetary probes to plans for the future." Circ. 20,000. Pays on publication. Publishes ms an average of 3 months after acceptance. Byline given. Buys first North American serial rights. Simultaneous and photocopied submissions OK. Electronic submissions OK via IBM PC computer (Word Perfect Software), Hayes Smartcom 2 Modem, 300 or 1200 baud, but requires hard copy also. Computer printout submissions acceptable; prefers letter-quality. Reports in 2 weeks on queries; 1 month on mss. Sample copy for 9x12 SAE with 2 first class stamps; free writer's guidelines.

Nonfiction: Essays, expose, general interest, historical/nostalgic, how-to, humor, interview/profile, new product, opinion, personal experience, photo feature and technical. No very technical articles. Query with published clips, or send complete ms. Length: 1,000-2,500 words. Pays $150 maximum. "Our circulation should go up, due to a new membership recruitment campaign. Pay for articles may rise as well."

Photos: Send photos with submission. Reviews 5x7 prints. Offers no additional payment for photos accepted with ms. Captions required.

Tips: "We're looking for behind-the-scenes, authoritative and accurate articles that aren't overly technical. We cover the whole wide range of space activities—the human side as well as the science. Assume that you are writing for a curious, intelligent person."

SPORT FLYER, Ultralight Flyer, Inc., Box 98786, Tacoma WA 98498-0786. (206)588-1743. Editor: Bruce Williams. 50% freelance written. Prefers to work with published/established writers; will work with new/unpublished writers. Monthly tabloid covering sport and recreational aviation nationwide. "Provides coverage of aviation news, activities, regulations and politics of sport aviation from ballooning, soaring and hang gliding to aerobatics, skydiving, homebuilt aircraft and ultralight aviation, with emphasis on timely features of interest to active participants knowledgeable about their niche of aviation." Circ. 10,000. Pays 1 month after publication. Publishes ms an average of 1 month after acceptance. Byline given. Buys one-time rights and first North American serial rights, on occasion second serial (reprint) rights. Submit seasonal/holiday material 3 months in advance. Simultaneous queries, photocopied and previously published submissions from noncompetitive publications OK, but must be identified. Computer printout submissions acceptable. Inquire about electronic submissions. Reports in 2 weeks on queries; 1 month on mss. Sample copy $2; writer's guidelines and style guidelines for business size SASE.

Nonfiction: Features of current interest about sport aviation—developments in technology and regulations, competitions, fly-ins and other activities. Short features on new products and services, safety, flying technique and maintenance. Query first on historical, nostalgic features and profiles/interviews. Buys 20 mss/year. Query or send complete ms with SASE. Length 500-2,000 words. Pays $3/printed column inch maximum. Sometimes pays the expenses of writers on assignment.

Photos: "Good pics a must." Send photos (b&w or color prints preferred) with ms. All photos must have complete captions and carry photographer's ID. Pays $10/b&w photo used. Query on color slides.

Tips: "We're trying to provide more in-depth coverage of news and events from all the activities we feature. Our readers are knowledgeable about their activities, and our writers should have equal expertise. We always are looking for features on places to fly and interviews or features about people involved in sport aviation. We're looking for articles about good places to fly, features about major competitions in each of the activities we cover and inside news from sanctioning organizations and associations. Travel features must include information on what to do once you've arrived, with addresses from which readers can get more information. Get direct quotations from the principals involved in news features. We want current, first-hand information."

WESTERN FLYER, N.W. Flyer, Inc., Box 98786, Tacoma WA 98498-0786. (206)588-1743. Editor: Bruce Williams. 30% freelance written. Prefers to work with published/established writers; works with a small number of new/unpublished writers each year; and will work with new/unpublished writers. Biweekly tabloid covering general aviation. Provides "coverage of aviation news, activities, regulations and politics of general and sport aviation with emphasis on timely features of interest to pilots and aircraft owners." Circ. 20,000. Pays 1 month after publication. Publishes ms an average of 1 month after acceptane. Byline given. Buys one-time rights and first North American seral rights, on occasion second serial (reprint) rights. Submit seasonal/holiday material 2 months in advance. Simultaneous queries, photocopied and previously published submissions from noncompetitive publications OK but must be identified. Computer printout submissions acceptable. Inquire about electronic submissions. Reports in 2 weeks on queries; 1 month on mss. Sample copy $2; writer's guidelines, style guidelines for business size SASE.

Nonfiction: Features of current interest about aviation businesses, developments at airports, new products and services, safety, flying technique and maintenance. "Good medium-length reports on current events—controversies at airports, problems with air traffic control, FAA, etc. We want solid news coverage of breaking stories." Query first on historical, nostalgic features and profiles/interviews. Many special sections through-out the year, send SASE for list. Buys 100 mss/year. Query or send complete ms. Length: 500-2,000 words. Pays $3/printed column inch maximum. Sometimes pays the expenses of writers on assignment.

Photos: "Good pics a must." Send photos (b&w or color prints preferred) with ms. All photos must have complete captions and carry photographer's ID. Pays $10/b&w photo used. Query on color slides.

Tips: "We always are looking for features on places to fly and interviews or features about people and businesses using airplanes in unusual ways. Travel features must include information on what to do once you've arrived, with addresses from which readers can get more information. Get direct quotations from the principals involved in the story. We want current, first-hand information."

WINGS MAGAZINE, Division of Corvus Publishing Group, Ltd., Suite 158, 1224 53rd Ave. NE, Calgary Alberta T2E 7E2 Canada. Publisher: Paul Skinner. "We are backlogged with submissions and prefer not to receive unsolicited submissions at this time."

——— Business and Finance

General interest business publications give executives and consumers information from different perspectives—from local reports to national overviews. National and regional publications are listed below in separate categories. These publications cover business trends, computers in business, and the general theory and practice of business and financial management. Magazines that have a technical slant are classified in the Trade Journals section under the Business Management, Finance, Industrial Operation and Management, or Management and Supervision categories.

National

‡ACROSS THE BOARD MAGAZINE, The Conference Board, 845 3rd Ave., New York NY 10022. (212)759-0900. Editor: Howard Muson. 75% freelance written. A monthly magazine except a combined July/August issue, oriented toward general issues of interest to business executives. Circ. 35,000. Pays on publication. Publishes ms an average of 3 months after acceptance. Byline given. Offers $100 kill fee. Buys first North American serial rights and second serial (reprint) rights. Submit seasonal/holiday material 3 months in advance. Simultaneous and photocopied submissions OK. Sample copy for 8½x11 SAE with 2 first class stamps; writer's guidelines for business size SAE with 1 first class stamp.

Nonfiction: Book excerpts, essays, general interest, humor, interview/profile and opinion. No how-to articles, articles about bold, new products designed to revolutionize the industry, or articles written for a technical or specialized audience. Buys 35-40 mss/year. Query with or without published clips, or send complete ms. Length: 250-4,000 words. Pays $50-1,000; may pay with subscription if author requests a complimentary subscription in lieu of payment. Sometimes pays the expenses of writers on assignment.

Photos: Send photos with submission. Reviews contact sheets and negatives. Buys one-time rights.

Columns/Departments: Commentary, 250-2,000 words; Capitol Debate, 250-2,000 words; and Books, 1,500 words. Buys 25-30 mss/year. Send complete ms.
Fillers: Susan Maier, fillers editor. Anecdotes, facts, short humor and quizzes. Buys very few.

BETTER BUSINESS, National Minority Business Council, Inc., 235 E. 42nd St., New York NY 10017. (214)573-2385. Editor: John F. Robinson. 50% freelance written. Quarterly magazine covering small/minority business. Circ. 9,200. Pays on publication. Publishes ms an average of 2 months after acceptance. Byline given. Buys first North American serial rights and all rights. Submit seasonal material 1 month in advance. Computer printout submissions acceptable; prefers letter-quality to dot-matrix. Sample copy $3 and 9x12 SAE with $1.50 postage; free writer's guidelines.
Nonfiction: Interview/profile, technical. Buys 10 mss/year. Query with clips. Length: 3,000-5,000 words. Pays $200-250.
Photos: State availability of photos. Reviews b&w prints. Captions required. Buys all rights.

‡BUSINESS AGE, The Magazine for Small Business, Business Trends Communications Corp., Box 11597, Milwaukee WI 53211. (414)332-7507. Editor: Margaret A. Brickner. Associate Editor: Katherine L. Steinbach. 25% freelance written. Bimonthly magazine for owners/managers of businesses with 1-100 employees. Articles should emphasize useful information for effective business operation. Estab. 1985. Circ. 100,000. Pays on acceptance. Publishes ms an average of 3 months after acceptance. Byline given. Buys first North American serial rights. Computer printout submissions acceptable; prefers letter-quality to dot-matrix. Reports in 3 weeks on queries; 1 month on mss. Writer's guidelines for business-size SAE with 1 first class stamp.
Nonfiction: How-to (finance, accounting, marketing, management, business law, personnel management, customer relations, planning, taxes, international businesses); interview/profile (successful businesses and small business advocates). All articles should have clear application to small business. Query or send complete ms. State availability of photos. Length: 1,500-2,000 words. Pays $100 minimum.
Tips: "Keep in mind that small business owners want to increase profits and productivity. Emphasize the how-to and tailor your piece to benefit the reader."

‡BUSINESS WEEK, 1221 Avenue of the Americas, New York NY 10020. Does not use freelance material.

COMMODITY JOURNAL, American Association of Commodity Traders, 10 Park St., Concord NH 03301. Editor: Arthur N. Economou. For investors interested in commodity trading based on cash and spot-deferred markets, financial instruments and foreign currencies. Bimonthly tabloid. Circ. 220,000. Pays on publication. Buys all rights. Byline given. Written queries OK. Reports in 4 months. Free sample copy and writer's guidelines.
Nonfiction: Technical (commodity and foreign currency trading, investing and hedging; commodity markets and foreign currency trends; written intelligibly for investors). "We are not interested in articles concerning the conventional futures market, except insofar as the spot or cash-based markets provide a better alternative." Buys 2 mss/issue. Query. Length: 1,000-2,000 words. Pays 10¢/word.

D&B REPORTS, The Dun & Bradstreet Magazine for Small Business Management, Dun & Bradstreet, 299 Park Ave., 24th Floor, New York NY 10171. (212)593-6723. Editor: Patricia W. Hamilton. 10% freelance written. A bimonthly magazine for small business. "Articles should contain useful information that managers of small businesses can apply to their own companies. *D&B Reports* focuses on companies with $10 million in annual sales and under." Circ. 76,000. Pays on acceptance. Publishes ms an average of 2-3 months after acceptance. Byline given. Buys all rights. Computer printout subissions acceptable; prefers letter-quality to dot-matrix. Reports in 3 weeks on manuscripts. Free sample copy and writer's guidelines.
Nonfiction: How-to (on management); and interview/profile (of successful entrepreneurs). Buys 5 mss/year. Query. Length: 1,500-2,500 words. Pays $500 minimum.
Photos: State availability of photos with submission. Identification of subjects required. Buys one-time rights.
Tips: "The area of our publication most open to freelancers is profiles of innovative companies and managers."

THE EXECUTIVE FEMALE, NAFE, 1041 Third Ave., New York NY 10021. (212)371-0740. Editor: Susan Strecker. Managing Editor: Mary E. Terzella. 30% freelance written. Emphasizes "upbeat and useful career and financial information for the upwardly mobile female." 30% freelance written. Bimonthly magazine; 60 pages. Circ. 150,000. Byline given. Pays on publication. Publishes ms an average of 6 months after acceptance. Submit seasonal/holiday material 6 months in advance. Buys first rights, first North American serial rights, one-time rights, all rights, simultaneous rights and second serial (reprint) rights to material originally published elsewhere. Simultaneous and photocopied submissions OK. Computer printout submissions acceptable; no dot-matrix. Reports in 3 months. Sample copy $2.50; free writer's guidelines.

Nonfiction: "Articles on any aspect of career advancement and financial planning are welcomed." Sample topics: managerial work issues, investment, coping with inflation, trends in the work place, money-saving ideas, financial planning, trouble shooting, business communication, time and stress management, and career goal setting and advancement. No negative or radical material. Written queries only. Length: 1,000-2,500 words. Pays $50-$100 minimum. Sometimes pays the expenses of writers on assignment.

Columns/Departments: Profiles (interviews with successful women in a wide range of fields, preferably nontraditional areas for women); Entrepreneur's Corner (successful female business owners with unique ideas); Horizons (career planning, personal and professional perspectives and goal-setting); More Money (specific financial issues, social security, tax planning); and Your Executive Style (tips on health and lifestyle). Department length: 800-1,200 words. Pays $25-50 minimum.

FACT, The Money Management Magazine, 305 E. 46th St., New York NY 10017. Editor-in-Chief: Daniel M. Kehrer. 25% freelance written. Monthly personal money management and investment magazine for sophisticated readers. Circ. 70,000. Pays on acceptance. Publishes ms an average of 2 months after acceptance. Byline given. Offers 25% kill fee. Buys first rights, nonexclusive (reprint) rights and second serial (reprint) rights. Simultaneous queries OK. Computer printout submissions acceptable; prefers letter-quality to dot-matrix. Reports in 6 months. Free sample copy.

Nonfiction: General interest (specific money management topics); how-to (invest in specific areas); and new product. No business articles; no "how-to-balance your checkbook" articles. Writers must be knowledgeable and use lots of sidebars and tables. Buys 25-35 mss/year. Query with published clips. Length: 1,000-2,500 words. Pays $50-250.

Columns/Departments: Stocks, mutual funds, precious metals, bonds, real estate, collectibles, taxes, insurance, cash management and banking. Buys 10-20 mss/year. Query with published clips. Length: 1,500-1,800 words. Pays $50-250.

Tips: "Show writing credentials and expertise on a specific subject. Try something fresh. Read the magazine. Our readers are sophisticated about investments and money management."

FORBES, 60 5th Ave., New York NY 10011. (212)620-2200. Managing Editor: Sheldon Zalaznick. "We occasionally buy freelance material. When a writer of some standing (or whose work is at least known to us) is going abroad or into an area where we don't have regular staff or bureau coverage, we have given assignments or sometimes helped on travel expenses." Pays negotiable kill fee. Byline usually given.

‡HOME BUSINESS NEWS, The Magazine for Home-based Entreprenuers, 12221 Beaver Pike, Jackson OH 45640. (614)988-2331. Editor: Ed Simpson. 60% freelance written. Eager to work with new/unpublished writers. A bimonthly magazine covering home-based businesses and marketing. Pays on publication. Publishes ms an average of 4 months after acceptance. Byline sometimes given. Buys first North American serial rights and second serial (reprint) rights. Submit seasonal/holiday material 4 months in advance. Simultaneous, photocopied and previously published submissions OK. Electronic submissions OK via IBM PC, MS-DOS and WordStar, but requires hard copy also. Computer printout submissions acceptable; prefers letter-quality to dot-matrix. Reports in 1 week on queries; 3 weeks on mss. Sample copy $2; writer's guidelines for SASE with 1 first class stamp.

Nonfiction: Book excerpts, inspirational, interview/profile (of home business owners), new products, personal experience, computer-based home businesses and mail order success stories. Buys 15-20 mss/year. Query with published clips. Length: 800-3,000 words. Pays $20-100; will pay with ad space if agreed upon.

Photos: State availability of photos with submission. Offers no additional payment for photos accepted with ms. Captions and identification of subjects required. Buys one-time rights.

Columns/Departments: Home Business Profiles (profiles of home business owners), 2,000 words. Buys 10 mss/year. Query with published clips. Pays $20-100.

Fillers: Facts and newsbreaks. Buys 10/year. Length: 50-300 words. Pays $5-10.

‡HOME WORK DIGEST and DIRECTORY and SOURCEBOOK, EJP Publishing Company, 3012 N. Santa Rita Ave., Tucson AZ 85719. (602)628-7678. Editor: Ethel Jackson Price. 80% freelance written. Eager to work with new/unpublished writers. A monthly newsletter and annual directories which are slanted to cottage industries and other home-based businesses. Estab. 1985. Newsletter circ. 1,712. Pays on publication for newsletter; on acceptance for directory. Publishes ms an average of 6 months after acceptance. Byline given. Buys first North American serial rights. Submit seasonal/holiday material 6 months in advance. Computer printout submissions acceptable; no dot-matrix. Reports in 6 weeks on mss. Sample newsletter $2; directory $6.

Nonfiction: All submissions must relate to cottage industries or other home based businesses. "We'll consider just about anything but we do *not* want articles favorable to establishment or patronization of a business that is illegal, pornographic, etc." Send complete ms. Length: 250-1,500 words. Pays $50-500.

Photos: "We do not customarily purchase photos; however, in some cases, they might be acceptable in the directory and sourcebook." State availability of photos with query letter or manuscript. 5x7 or 8x10 b&w

prints. No color or transparencies. Pays $5-25/photo. Model releases and identification of subjects required. Buys one-time rights "but would have to negotiate each purchase individually."

Fillers: Frances G. Smith, fillers editor. Clippings, anecdotes, short humor and newsbreaks. Buys varying number of fillers/year. Length: 50-250 words. Pays $5-50.

Tips: "Make sure that when facts are quoted adequate research has been done."

INC MAGAZINE, The Magazine for Growing Companies, INC Publishing Corp., 38 Commercial Wharf, Boston MA 02110. (617)227-4700. Editor: George Gendron. Executive Editor: Bo Burlingham. Managing Editor: Sara P. Noble. 10% freelance written. Prefers to work with published/established writers. A monthly business magazine for chief executive officers and managers of growing companies up to $100 million in sales. Circ. 600,000. Pays on acceptance. Publishes ms an average of 2 months after acceptance. Byline given. Offers 33% kill fee. Buys first North American serial rights. Submit seasonal/holiday material 3 months in advance. Electronic submissions OK via ASCII, 300 or 1200 BPS Hayes Smart modem, but requires hard copy also. Computer printout submissions acceptable; prefers letter-quality to dot-matrix. Reports in 6 weeks on queries; 1 month on mss.

Nonfiction: Interview/profile and opinion. Buys 8 mss/year. Query with published clips. Length: 1,000-4,000 words. Pays $150-2,500. Pays expenses of writers on assignment.

Columns/Departments: Insider, Hands On, Management Columns. Buys 10 mss/year. Query with published clips. Length: 350-1,200 words. Pays $150-800.

Tips: "We are cutting back on freelance submissions in general, tending to working with those freelancers with whom we presently have a working relationship."

‡**THE INTERNATIONAL ADVISOR**, WMP Publishing Company, Suite 103, 2211 Lee Road, Winter Park FL 32789. (305)628-5300. Editor: Dennis Hardaker. Managing Editor: Linda R. Bevan. 50% freelance written. A monthly newsletter on global diversification in investments. This monthly investment advisory publication selects, analyzes, and recommends the most promising world stocks and monitors the world's stock markets, offering its readers the chance to participate in these gains. Pays on publication. Publishes ms an average of 2 months after acceptance. Byline given. Buys all rights. Photocopied submissions OK. Computer printout submissions acceptable. Reports in 2 weeks. Free sample copy and writer's guidelines.

Nonfiction: Opinion and technical on market analyses, stock recommendations, investment trends, etc. No politically liberal submissions. Buys 40 mss/year. Send complete ms. Length: 1,200-6,000 words. Pays $120-1,200. Sometimes pays expenses of writers on assignment.

Tips: "All articles should be as timely as deadlines permit, and must draw obvious conclusions."

‡**INVESTigate, The Journal of Investment Protection**, Investment Publishing Group, Suite 103, 2211 Lee Rd., Winter Park FL 32789. (305)628-5300. Associate Editor: Mike Ketcher. Managing Editor: Jerry Schomp. 40% freelance written. A monthly newsletter on investment fraud and protection of assets. Circ. 25,000. Pays on publication. Publishes ms an average of 2 months after acceptance. Byline given. Buys all rights. Photocopied submissions OK. Computer printout submissions acceptable. Reports in 2 weeks. Free sample copy and writer's guidelines.

Nonfiction: Exposé (investment industry, related areas) and how-to (protect assets; rights of investors, etc.). Buys 40 mss/year. Query with published clips. Length: 1,200-6,000 words. Pays $120-1,200. Sometimes pays expenses of writers on assignment.

Tips: "*INVESTigate* is a financial newsletter, with its focus on alerting subscribers to dishonesty, misrepresentation, bad deals, and even criminal fraud in the investment area, and then educating and directing them toward worthwhile opportunities."

‡**THE NCFE MOTIVATOR**, National Center for Financial Education, Inc. (NCFE), Suite 560 West, 25 Van Ness Ave., San Francisco CA 94102. (415)621-6961. Editor: Paul Richard. 40% freelance written. Works with published/established writers (50%) and a small number of new/unpublished writers (30%); eager to work with new/unpublished writers (20%). A monthly newsletter covering financial education/information. "This is not a publication for the sophisticated investor, but rather for novices, beginners, those who hope to become investors, as well as high school students." Circ. 1,500 + (estimated total after client reprint is 35,000). Pays on publication. Publishes ms an average of 3 months after acceptance. Byline given. Buys all rights. Submit seasonal/holiday material 4 months in advance. Simultaneous, photocopied and previously published submissions OK. Computer printout submissions acceptable; prefers letter-quality to dot-matrix. Reports in 3 weeks on queries; 6 weeks on mss. Sample copy for #10 SAE with 2 first class stamps; writer's guidelines for #10 SAE with 1 first class stamp.

Nonfiction: How-to (finance, credit, debt, savings, insurance, banking, wills) and interview/profile. Buys 20-30 mss/year. Query with published clips. Length: 500-1,200 words. Pays $25-100 for assigned articles; pays $15-70 for unsolicited articles. Sometimes pays the expenses of writers on assignment.

Photos: State availability of photos with submission. Reviews contact sheets. Offers no additional payment for photos accepted with ms. Captions and identification of subjects required.

Fillers: Facts and newsbreaks. Buys 25 +/year. Length: 100-500 words. Pays $10-50.

SYLVIA PORTER'S PERSONAL FINANCE MAGAZINE, 380 Lexington Ave., New York NY 10017. (212)557-9100. Editor: Patricia Estess. Executive Editor: Elana Lore. Managing Editor: Greg Daugherty. 75% freelance written. Prefers to work with published/established writers. Monthly (10 issues/year). Pays on acceptance. Publishes ms an average of 3 months after acceptance. Byline given. Offers 20% kill fee. Buys a combination of all rights and second serial (reprint) rights. Submit seasonal/holiday material 4 months in advance. No simultaneous queries. No simultaneous, photocopied or previously published submissions. Computer printout submissions acceptable; no dot-matrix. Electronic submissions OK, "we're compatible with just about every system." Reports in 2 months. Free sample copy; writer's guidelines for SAE and 1 first class stamp.
Nonfiction: General interest (financial). Only articles dealing with personal finance; no financially technical articles. "Send a cover letter with original ideas or slants about personal finance articles you'd like to do for us, accompanied by clippings of your previously published work. The features section is most open to freelancers. We will be covering topics such as financial planning, saving, investing, real estate, taxes, in each issue." Length: 1,000-1,500 words. Pays negotiable rates. Sometimes pays the expenses of writers on assignment.

TECHNICAL ANALYSIS OF STOCKS AND COMMODITIES, The Trader's Magazine, 9131 California Ave. SW, Box 46518, Seattle WA 98146-0518. (206)938-0570. Editor: Jack K. Hutson. 75% freelance written. Eager to work with new/unpublished writers. Magazine covers methods of investing and trading stocks, bonds and commodities (futures), options, mutual funds, and precious metals. Circ. 15,000. Pays on publication. Publishes ms an average of 3 months after acceptance. Byline given. Offers 50% kill fee. Buys all rights, however, second serial (reprint) rights are allowed the author provided copyright credit is given." Photocopied and previously published submissions OK. Electronic submissions via phone 300/1200 baud or Apple II/IBM PC computer disk, but requires hard copy-also. Computer printout submissions acceptable; prefers letter-quality to dot-matrix. Reports in 3 weeks on queries; 1 month on mss. Sample copy $5; detailed writer's guidelines for business size SAE and 1 first class stamp.
Nonfiction: Reviews (new software or hardware that can make a trader's life easier; comparative reviews of software books, services, etc.); how-to (make a trade); technical (trading and software aids to trading); utilities (charting or computer programs, surveys, statistics, or information to help the trader study or interpret market movements); humor (unusual incidents of market occurrences, cartoons). No newsletter-type, buy-sell recommendations. The article subject must relate to a technical analysis charting or numerical technique used to trade securities or futures. Buys 80 mss/year. Query with published clips if available or send complete ms. Length: 1,500-4,000 words. Pays $100-500. (Applies per inch base rate and premium rate—write for information). Sometimes pays expenses of writers on assignment.
Photos: Christine M. Napier, photo editor. State availability of photos. Pays $10-100 for 5x7 b&w glossy prints or color slides. Captions, model release and identification of subjects required. Buys one-time rights.
Columns/Departments: Buys 10 mss/year. Query. Length: 800-1,600 words. Pays $50-200.
Fillers: Melissa J. Hughes, fillers editor. Jokes. Must relate to trading stocks, bonds, options or commodities. Buys 50/year. Length: 100-500 words. Pays $10-50.
Tips: "Describe how to use technical analysis chart or computer work in day-to-day trading of stocks, bonds, mutual funds, options or commodities. A blow-by-blow account of how a trade was made, including the trader's thought processes, is, to our subscribers, the very best received story. One of our prime considerations is to instruct in a manner that the layperson can comprehend. We are not hyper-critical of writing style. The completeness and accuracy of submitted material is of the utmost consideration. Write for detailed writer's guidelines."

TRAVEL SMART FOR BUSINESS, Communications House, 40 Beechdale Rd., Dobbs Ferry NY 10522. (914)693-8300. Editor/Publisher: H.J. Teison. Managing Editor: L.M. Lane. 20% freelance written. Monthly newsletter covering travel and information on keeping travel costs down for business travelers and business travel managers. Circ. 2,000. Pays on publication. Publishes ms an average of 6 weeks after acceptance. No byline given. "Writers are listed as contributors." Buys first North American serial rights. Computer printout submissions acceptable; prefers letter-quality to dot-matrix. Reports in 6 weeks. Sample copy for business size SAE, and 2 first class stamps; writer's guidelines free for business size SAE and 1 first class stamp.
Nonfiction: "Inside" travel facts for companies that travel; how-to (pick a meeting site, save money on travel); reviews of facilities and restaurants; analysis of specific trends in travel affecting business travelers. No general travel information, backgrounders, or non-business-oriented articles. "We're looking for value-oriented, concise, factual articles." Buys 20 mss/year. Query with clips of published work. Length: 250-1,500 words. Pays $20-150.
Tips: "We are primarily staff written, with a few regular writers. Know the travel business or have business travel experience. People with a specific area of experience or expertise have the inside track."

WEEKDAY, Enterprise Publications, Suite 3417, 20 N. Wacker Dr., Chicago IL 60606. For the average employee in business and industry. Circ. 30,000. Buys all rights. Byline given. Pays on acceptance.
Nonfiction and Photos: Uses articles slanted toward the average person, with the purpose of increasing his

understanding of the business world and helping him be more successful in it. Also uses articles on "How to Get Along With Other People," and informative articles on meeting everyday problems—consumer buying, legal problems, community affairs, real estate, education, human relations, etc. Length: approximately 1,000 words maximum. Pays $20-50. Uses b&w human interest photos.

‡WORLD MARKET PERSPECTIVE, WMP Publishing Company, Suite 103, 2211 Lee Rd., Winter Park FL 32789. (305)628-5300. Editor: Jerry Schump. Associate Editor: Joyce Morris. 60% freelance written. A monthly newsletter covering research in economic science and world markets. Circ. 25,000. Pays on publication. Byline given. Buys all rights. Photocopied submissions OK. Computer printout submissions acceptable. Reports in 2 weeks. Free sample copy and writer's guidelines.
Nonfiction: Opinion and technical on market analysis, stock recommendations, investment trends, etc. No politically liberal submissions. Buys 40 mss/year. Send complete ms. Length: 1,200-6,000 words. Pays $120-1,200.
Tips: "*World Market Perspective* studies the global markets for specific and general economic trends and analyzes them so that our subscribers can use the information to make better investment decisions. We follow the Austria school of economics, and prefer that articles reflect this viewpoint. However, we occasionally print material of a different viewpoint if we feel it is of interest to our readership."

Regional

‡AKRON BUSINESS REPORTER, Akron Business Reporter Company, 8870 Darrow Rd., Twinsburg OH 44087. (216)650-0861. Publisher: Bruce David. Editor: John Dages. 20% freelance written. A monthly tabloid featuring business news, business features and columns for the Akron and Summit County business community. Estab. 1985. Circ. 12,000. Pays on publication. Publishes ms an average of 1-2 months after acceptance. Byline given. Offers 50% kill fee. Buys first North American serial rights, one time rights, second serial (reprint) rights and simultaneous rights. Submit seasonal/holiday material 2 months in advance. Simultaneous, photocopied, and previously published submissions OK. Computer printout submissions acceptable; prefers letter-quality to dot-matrix. Reports in 2 weeks. Sample copy $1; free writer's guidelines.
Nonfiction: General interest, how-to, interview/profile, new product, business, success stories and marketing ideas for small to medium-sized businesses. Special issues cover business/industrial real estate, retailing polymers, women/minorities in business and robotics. No humor, exposés or religion. Buys 12-24 mss/year. Query with published clips. Length: 1,000-1,500 words. Pays $2/column inch.
Photos: State availability of photos with submission. Reviews 5x7 prints. Offers $25 maximum/photo. Identification of subjects required. Buys one-time rights.
Tips: "We appreciate the use of the Associated Press Stylebook."

‡ARIZONA TREND, Magazine of Business and Finance, Trend Magazines, Inc., Suite 710, 3003 N. Central Ave., Phoenix AZ 85012. (602)230-1117. Editor: James M. Kiser. Managing Editor: John Craddock. A monthly regional business magazine. Estab. 1986. Circ. 20,000. Pays on acceptance. Byline given. Offers variable kill fee. Buys first North American serial rights. Computer printout submissions acceptable; no dot-matrix. Reports in 2 weeks on queries; 1 week on mss. Sample copy $2.25 with 9x12 SAE and 7 first class stamps.
Nonfiction: Essays, interview/profile, and new product. Query. Length: 2,000-3,000 words. Pays $300-800. Pays the expenses of writers on assignment.
Photos: State availability of photos with submission. Reviews transparencies. Offers $50 minimum/photo. Captions and identification of subjects required. Buys one-time rights.

BOULDER BUSINESS REPORT, Boulder Business Report, 2141 14th St., Boulder CO 80302. (303)440-4952. Editor: Suzanne Gripman. 50% freelance written. Prefers to work with published/established writers; works with a small number of new/unpublished writers each year. Monthly newspaper covering Boulder area business issues. Offers "news tailored to a monthly theme and read primarily by Boulder, Colorado businesspeople and by some investors nationwide. Philosophy: Descriptive, well-written prose of educational value." Circ. 7,000. Pays on publication. Publishes ms an average of 1 month after acceptance. Byline given. Offers 10% kill fee. Buys one-time rights and second serial (reprint) rights. Simultaneous queries and photocopied submissions OK. Electronic submissions OK via Apple III. Computer printout submissions acceptable; prefers letter-quality to dot-matrix. Reports in 1 month on queries; 2 weeks on mss. Sample copy $1.75.
Nonfiction: Book excerpts, interview/profile, new product, photo feature of company, examination of competition in a particular line of business. "All our issues are written around a monthly theme. No articles are accepted in which the subject has not been pursued in depth and both sides of an issue presented in a writing style with flair." Buys 48 mss/year. Query with published clips. Length: 250-2,000 words. Pays $25-200.
Photos: State availability of photos with query letter. Reviews b&w contact sheets; prefers "people

portraits." Pays $10 maximum for b&w contact sheet. Identification of subjects required. Buys one-time rights and reprint rights.
Tips: "It would be difficult to write for this publication if a freelancer was unable to localize a subject. In-depth articles are written by assignment. The freelancer located in the Boulder, Colorado area has an excellent chance here."

‡**BUSINESS ATLANTA,** Communication Channels Inc., 6255 Barfield Rd., Atlanta GA 30328. (404)256-9800. Editor: Luann Nelson. 80% freelance written. A monthly magazine covering Atlanta and Georgia. Circ. 25,000. Pays on publication. Publishes ms an average of 3 months after acceptance. Byline given. Offers 10% kill fee. Buys first North American serial rights and second serial (reprint) rights. Submit seasonal/holiday material 4 months in advance. Reports in 6 months on queries; 3 months on manuscripts. Sample copy $2.
Nonfiction: Humor and interview/profile. No product related material or case studies. Buys 150 mss/year. Query with published clips. Length: 1,000-4,000 words. Pays $250-800. Sometimes pays the expenses of writers on assignment. Buys one-time rights and reprint rights.
Columns/Departments: Southern Stocks (review of publicly traded Atlanta-based company); Profile (interview with local business person); Enterprise (analysis of a local business); and Marketing (analysis of a local business's marketing approach), all 1,500-1,800 words. Buys 85 mss/year. Query with published clips. Pays $300-350.
Tips: "We do not use writers from outside the state of Georgia except in very rare cases. The back-of the-book departments are most open to new writers. Our intial assignments are made on speculation only."

‡**THE BUSINESS TIMES, For Connecticut Executives,** The Business Times, Inc., 544 Tolland St., East Hartford CT 06108. (203)289-9341. Editor: Mark Isaacs. 20% freelance written. A monthly tabloid covering general business news, information and feature articles for upper-level executives in Connecticut. Circ. 25,000. Pays on publication. Publishes ms an average of 3 months after acceptance. Byline given. Buys all rights in Connecticut. Simultaneous, photocopied and previously published submissions OK. Reports in 1 month. Sample copy $1.75.
Nonfiction: Interview/profile and opinion. No humor, product information, or highly technical articles; no articles on selling, or anything aimed at "middle management." Buys 3-5 mss/year. Query with published clips. Length: 500-1,400 words; prefers 600-1,000 words. Pays $50-300 for assigned articles; pays $30-200 for unsolicited articles.
Photos: State availability of photos with submission. Reviews contact sheets. Offers $10-30/photo. Identification of subjects required. Buys one-time rights.
Columns/Departments: Viewpoint (any area of controversy in business, finance and sometimes, economic issues) and Management (articles useful to upper-level management to improve productivity, etc.). Buys 3-5 mss/year. Query with published clips and/or send complete ms. Length: 500-800 words. Pays $30-75.
Tips: "We are geographically-oriented to Connecticut-based businesses, so the most important thing is that the story appeal to our audience. Writers outside of the area might consider concentrating on an area of interest (national legislation or issue, for example) that has a Connecticut tie-in or might impact in a unique way on Connecticut business. Also, we prefer articles with very specific examples to support arguments. Most open to freelancers is our op-ed or Viewpoint section, for which we almost always look for new, fresh articles on controversial subjects related to business from a free market perspective. This does not require Connecticut tie-in."

BUSINESS TO BUSINESS, Tallahassee's Business Magazine, Business to Business, Inc., Box 6085, Tallahassee FL 32314. (904)222-7072. Editor: Howard Libin. 80% freelance written. Works with a small number of new/unpublished writers each year. Monthly tabloid covering business in the North Florida-South Georgia Big Bend region. Circ. 16,000. Pays on acceptance. Publishes ms an average of 2 months after acceptance. Byline given "generally." Buys all serial rights. "We purchase rights depending on the article, author and costs." Submit seasonal/holiday material 4 months in advance. Photocopied and previously published submissions OK. Computer printout submissions acceptable; prefers letter-quality to dot-matrix. Reports in 2 weeks on queries; 3 weeks on mss. Sample copy and writer's guidelines for 9x12 SAE and 5 first class stamps.
Nonfiction: Book excerpts (reviews of business related books—*Megatrends, Positioning*); In Search of Excellence (topics of interest to business-minded people); historical/nostalgic (only pertaining to the Big Bend); how-to (select the right typewriter, adding machine, secretary, phone system, insurance plan); new products; technical (articles on finance marketing, investment, advertising and real estate as it applies to small business). "We also solicit articles on controversial topics relating to business and government." Special "inserts" planned: advertising, office of the future, consulting, taxes. "No really basic material. Writers must assume that readers have some idea of business vocabulary. No new business profiles, or material without local handle." After Work section contains a wide array of "lifestyle" pieces—health, food, hobbies, travel,

recreation, etc. Buys 50-100 mss/year. Query with published clips if available. Length: 500-2,000 words. Pays $25-300. "Articles with photos and/or artwork pay more."

Photos: State availability of photos. Pays $5-20 for b&w contact sheet and b&w prints. Identification of subjects required.

Columns/Departments: "Shorts accepted on all aspects of doing business. Each story should tackle one topic and guide reader from question to conclusion. General appeal for all trades and industries." Buys 50-75 mss/year. Query with published clips if available. Length: 500-1,000 words. Pays $25-100.

Tips: "Send a query with past writing sample included. If it seems that a writer is capable of putting together an interesting 500-800 word piece dealing with small business operation, we're willing to give him/her a try. Meeting deadlines determines writer's future with us. We're open to short department pieces on management, finance, marketing, investments, real estate. Articles must be tightly written—direct and to the point; keep it casual, but put in the facts."

BUSINESS VIEW OF SW FLORIDA, Florida Business Publications Inc., Box 9859, Naples FL 33941. (813)263-7525. Editor: Meg Andrew. 100% freelance written. Prefers to work with published/established writers. A monthly magazine covering business trends and issues in southwest Florida. Circ. 14,200. Pays on publication (occasionally on acceptance). Publishes ms an average of 6 months after acceptance. Byline given. Buys all rights (reassigned to writer within 3 months of publication) or makes work-for-hire assignments. Simultaneous, photocopied and previously published submissions OK. Computer printout submissions acceptable; prefers letter-quality to dot-matrix. Reports in 2 months. Sample copy $2 with 8½x11 SAE and 5 first class stamps; free writer's guidelines.

Nonfiction: Book excerpts (business); how-to (management); humor (business); interview/profile (regional); and technical. "No jokes, puzzles, or whimsy, unless it pertains directly to business." Buys 24-36 mss/year. Query with published clips. Length: 100-3,000 words. Pays $15-350 for assigned articles; pays $15-200 for unsolicited articles. Sometimes pays the expenses of writers on assignment.

Photos: State availability of photos with submission. Reviews contact sheets and 5x7 prints. Offers $25-35/photo. Buys one-time rights.

Columns/Departments: Personal Finance (general investment opportunities), Management, Computers (software information that helps business people—"High level material—stay away from ABC computer level"). Buys 12-20 mss/year. Send complete ms. Length: 750-1,200 words. Pays $25-100.

Fillers: Facts and newsbreaks. Buys 36/year. Length: 75-200 words. Pays $15-25.

Tips: "Our readers like specific answers to specific problems. Do not send generalized how-to articles that do not offer concrete solutions to management problems. Our readers are busy; so be concise and upbeat in style. Profiles of southwest Florida business leaders are most open to freelance writers. These are short (500 words) articles that present local, interesting personalities. How-to articles in the areas of management, personal finance, retailing, accounting, investing, computers, personnel, and stress management are also open."

CRAIN'S CLEVELAND BUSINESS, 140 Public Square, Cleveland OH 44114. (216)522-1383. Editor: Brian Tucker. Weekly tabloid about business in the 7 county area surrounding Cleveland and Akron for upper income executives, professionals and entrepreneurs. Circ. 26,000. Average issue includes 2-3 freelance news or feature articles. Pays on publication. Byline given. Buys first North American serial rights. Phone queries OK. Reports in 3 weeks.

Nonfiction: "We are interested in business and political events and their impact on the Cleveland area business community." Query. Length: 500-1,200 words. Pays $5/column inch for news stories; $3/column inch for special section features.

Photos: State availability of photos. Reviews 5x7 b&w glossy prints. Pays $10/photo used. Captions required. Buys one-time rights.

THE FINANCIAL POST, Maclean Hunter, Ltd., 777 Bay St., Toronto, Ontario, M5W 1A7 Canada. Editor-in-Chief: Neville J. Nankivell. Executive Editor: Dalton S. Robertson. Managing Editor: Anne Bower. Copy and Design Editor: Christopher Watson. 10% freelance written. Emphasizes Canadian business, investment/finance and public affairs. Weekly newspaper. Circ. 200,000. Pays on publication. Buys one-time rights. Pays 50% kill fee. Byline given. Reports in 3 weeks. Sample copy $1.

Nonfiction: Useful news and information for executives, managers and investors in Canada. Buys 3 mss/issue. Query. Length: 700-800 words. Pays 15-25¢/word.

Photos: State availability of photos with query. Pays $25-50 for 8x10 b&w glossy prints. Captions required. Buys one-time rights.

‡FLORIDA TREND, Magazine of Florida Business and Finance, Box 611, St. Petersburg FL 33731. (813)821-5800. Editor: Rick Edmonds. Managing Editor: Jeffrey Tucker. A monthly magazine covering business and economics for Florida business people or investors. Circ. 42,000. Pays on acceptance. Byline given. Offers 25% kill fee. Buys first North American serial rights. Computer printout submissions acceptable. Reports in 1 month. Sample copy $2.25.

Nonfiction: Business and finance. Buys 15-20 mss/year. Query with or without published clips. Length: 1,200-2,500 words. Pays $500-900.

ILLINOIS BUSINESS, Crain Communications, Inc., 740 N. Rush, Chicago IL 60611. (312)280-3163. Editor: Joe Cappo. Managing Editor: Alan Rosenthal. 90% freelance written. Quarterly business publication for company presidents, owners, board chairmen, state officials. Circ. 25,000. Pays on acceptance. (All articles are on a work-for-hire basis.) Publishes ms an average of 3 months after acceptance. Computer printout submissions acceptable. Reports in 1 month.
Nonfiction: "Anything to do with Illinois business and economics." Buys 64 mss/year. (All articles are commissioned.) Query with published clips. Length: 2,500 words maximum. Pays $300 and up; average feature-length article pays $1,000. Sometimes pays the expenses of writers on assignment.
Tips: "Read our publication before submitting a query. All material must be about Illinois business. The magazine is seeking Illinois writers and photographers who can cover Illinois business subjects."

INDIANA BUSINESS, 1200 Waterway Blvd., Indianapolis IN 46202. (317)844-8627. Editor: Joan S. Marie. Monthly magazine. 35% freelance written. Pays 30 days after publication. Rights negotiable. Computer printout double-space submissions acceptable; prefers letter-quality to dot-matrix. Publishes ms an average of 3 months after acceptance. Sample copy $1.75.
Nonfiction: "All articles must relate to Indiana business and must be of interest to a broad range of business and professional people." Especially interested in articles on agribusiness, international affairs as they affect Indiana business, executive health issues, new science and technology projects happening in Indiana. "We would like to hear about business success stories but only as they pertain to current issues, trends, (i.e., a real estate company that has made it big because they got in on the Economic Development Bonds and invested in renovation property)." Buys 15-20 mss/year. Query or send complete ms. Pay negotiable. Sometimes pays expenses of writers on assignment.
Photos: State availability of photos. Pay negotiable for b&w or color photos. Captions and model release required.
Tips: "A query letter must show that the author is familiar with our publication. It should also be concise but catchy. Be willing to submit samples and/or articles on speculation. We are very interested in articles that flow well—business-like, but not dry. Also, the more timely, the better. Be specific about a person, product, company, new program, etc. Stay away from generalizations. The magazine has 3 special sections: Agribusiness, International Affairs, Management."

KANSAS BUSINESS NEWS, Kansas Business Publishing Co., Inc., Suite 124, 3601 S.W. 29th, Topeka KS 66614. (913)293-3010. Editor: Dan Bearth. 30% freelance written. Monthly magazine about Kansas business for the business owner, executives and professionals who want to know what is going on in the state that will affect the way they do business, their profits, labor requirements, etc. All submissions must relate to local business conditions. Circ. 15,000. Pays on publication. Publishes ms an average of 6 months after acceptance. Buys all rights. Phone queries OK. Submit seasonal material 3 months in advance. Simultaneous and previously published submissions OK. Computer printout submissions acceptable.
Nonfiction: How-to, humor, interview, profile, and technical. Query only. Pays $25-250. Sometimes pays expenses of writers on assignment.
Photos: Marsh Galloway, editor. State availability of photos or send photos with ms. Reviews b&w contact sheets and negatives. Offers no additional payment for photos accepted with ms. Captions preferred; model release required. Buys all rights.
Columns/Departments: Management, Government, Personnel Management, Taxes, Telecommunications, Small Business, Computers and Technology, Insurance, Labor Relations and Personal Finance. Query only. Pays $25 minimum.

MEMPHIS BUSINESS JOURNAL, Mid-South Communications, Inc., Suite 322, 4515 Poplar St., Memphis TN 38117. (901)685-2411. Editor: Barney DuBois. 20% freelance written. Works with a small number of new/unpublished writers each year. Weekly tabloid covering industry, trade, agribusiness and finance in west Tennessee, north Mississippi, east Arkansas, and the Missouri Bootheel. "Articles should be timely and relevant to business in our region." Circ. 10,400. Pays on acceptance. Publishes ms an average of 2 weeks after acceptance. Byline given. Pays $50 kill fee. Buys one-time rights, second serial (reprint) rights, and makes work-for-hire assignments. Submit seasonal/holiday material 2 months in advance. Publishes ms an average of 2 weeks after acceptance. Simultaneous queries and submissions OK. Computer printout submissions acceptable; prefers letter-quality to dot-matrix. Reports in 2 weeks. Free sample copy.
Nonfiction: Exposé, historical/nostalgic, interview/profile, business features and trends. "All must relate to business in our area." Buys 130 mss/year. Query with or without clips of published work or send complete ms. Length: 750-2,000 words. Pays $80-200. Sometimes pays the expenses of writers on assignment.
Photos: State availability of photos or send photos with ms. Pays $25-50 for 5x7 b&w prints. Identification of subjects required. Buys one-time rights.

Tips: "We are interested in news—and this means we can accept short, hard-hitting work more quickly. We also welcome freelancers who can do features and articles on business in the smaller cities of our region. We are a weekly, so our stories need to be timely."

MINNESOTA BUSINESS JOURNAL, For Decisionmakers of Growing Companies, Dorn Communications, 7831 E. Bush Lake, Minneapolis MN 55435. (612)835-6855. Editor: Donald R. Nelson. Managing Editor: Terry Fiedler. 75% freelance written. Prefers to work with published/established writers. A monthly regional business magazine covering general business and Minnesota companies with revenue of less than $25 million per year for managers of small, growing, Minnesota-based companies. Circ. 26,000. Pays on publication. Publishes ms an average of 3 months after acceptance. Byline given. Offers kill fee of 25% of agreed-upon price. Not copyrighted. Buys first serial rights and makes work-for-hire assignments. Simultaneous queries and simultaneous submissions OK. Computer printout submissions acceptable; prefers letter-quality to dot-matrix. Reports in 2 weeks on queries; 1 month on mss. Free sample copy.

Nonfiction: How-to (anything related to running a company efficiently, often written within the context of a company profile); and interview/profile (Minnesota business leaders, company profiles with how-to slant). "Articles all feature a how-to slant, how to manage people, how to cut costs, how to solve family business problems, how to arrange financing, etc. We are especially interested in articles that deal with managerial or operational problems, and how they are solved. We also focus on the financing and growth of entrepreneurial ventures." Buys 36 mss/year. Query with published clips. Length: 1,500-3,500 words. Pays $50-700. Pays the expenses of writers on assignment.

Tips: Accepts queries and submissions only from Minnesota-based writers. "We cover only Minnesota-based companies (no subsidiaries, franchises, or distributorships). Focus is on entreprenurial ventures, especially in high-tech areas. We are not a Chamber of Commerce newsletter, but a magazine about (not necessarily pro-) business. If you believe that business stories can be entertaining and dramatic, and you're a solid reporter, you can probably write for us."

‡NEVADA BUSINESS JOURNAL, Nevada's Only State-wide Business Magazine, H&M Publications, Suite 270, 2375 E. Tropicana, Las Vegas NV 89109. (702)454-1669. Editor: Henry C. Holcomb. Managing Editor: Jeffrey Hunter. 90% freelance written. A monthly magazine covering business in Nevada. Estab. 1986. Circ. 15,000. Pays on acceptance. Publishes ms an average of 2 months after acceptance. Byline given. Offers $75 kill fee. Buys all rights. Submit seasonal/holiday material 3 months in advance. Photocopied submissions OK. Computer printout submissions acceptable; prefers letter-quality to dot-matrix. Reports in 1 week. Free sample copy and writer's guidelines.

Nonfiction: Essays; General interest (business); how-to (execute specific business activities); interview/profile; photo feature; and technical. No expose, humor, religious or travel. Buys 108 mss/year. Query with or without published clips. Length: 2,000-3,000 words. Pays $150-300. Sometimes pays expenses of writers on assignment; always pays telephone expenses.

Photos: Send photos with submission. Reviews 35mm or 2¼x2¼ transparencies and 5x7 or 8x10 prints. Offers no additional payment for photos accepted with ms. Captions and identification of subjects required. Rights purchased depend on assignment.

Tips: Company, executive and industry profiles are most open to freelancers.

‡NEW BUSINESS MAGAZINE, Clubhouse Publishing, Box 3312, Sarasota FL 33581. (813)366-8225. Editor: Dan Denton. Managing Editor: Pam Daniel. A bimonthly business publication for business people in Sarasota and Manatee counties. "*New Business* provides a review and digest of local business events; profiles, commentary, perspective, and reporting on people, trends, and issues in area business. Reporting of local business from an intelligent, questioning perspective is the key to our stories; we're not interested in puff pieces or in very general how-to." Circ. 10,000. Pays on publication. Byline given. Offers variable kill fee. Buys first North American serial rights or second serial (reprint) rights. Previously published submissions sometimes OK. Computer printout submissions acceptable; prefers letter-quality to dot-matrix. Reports in 1 month on queries; 6 weeks on manuscripts. Sample copy $3.

Nonfiction: Humor (short essays with a business slant); interview/profile; new product (if local); and opinion. "No general business articles about national trends-we're very local." Buys 25 mss/year. Query with or without published clips. Length 350-3,000 words. Pays $50-400 for assigned articles; pays $50-150 for unsolicited articles. Sometimes pays the expenses of writers on assignment.

Photos: State availability of photos with submission. Offers $25 minimum/photo. Buys one-time rights.

Columns/Department: Backtalk (humor about business trends and attitudes), 500-800 words; and Comment (essays with a strong point of view about local business events or trends), 800-1,300 words. Buys 6 mss/year. Query with or without published clips or send complete ms. Pays $50-100.

‡NEW JERSEY BUSINESS, 50 Park Place, Newark NJ 07102. (201)623-8359. Executive Editor: James Prior. Emphasizes business in the state of New Jersey. Monthly magazine. Pays on acceptance. Buys all rights. Simultaneous and previously published work OK. Reports in 3 weeks. Sample copy $1.

Nonfiction: "All freelance articles are upon assignment, and they deal with business and industry either directly or more infrequently, indirectly pertaining to New Jersey." Buys 6 mss/year. Query or send clips of published work. Pays $150-200.
Photos: Send photos with ms. Captions preferred.

‡**NEW ORLEANS BUSINESS**, Cox Enterprises, Inc., 401 Whitney Ave., Box 354, Gretna LA 70054. (504)362-4310. Editor: Lan Sluder. 15% freelance written. A weekly tabloid covering business news in New Orleans and the Gulf south. "We're edited for the high-income (average reader makes $91,300) executive and professional." Circ. 20,000. Pays on publication. Publishes ms an average of 1 month after acceptance. Byline given. Buys one-time rights. Submit seasonal/holiday material 2 months in advance. Simultaneous, photocopied, and previously published submissions OK. Reports in 2 weeks. Sample copy for 9x12 SAE with 5 first class stamps; free writer's guidelines.
Nonfiction: Book excerpts, how-to and interview/profile. Buys 100 mss/year. Query with or without published clips, or send complete ms. Length: 500-2,500 words. Pays $50-300 for assigned articles; pays $50-200 for unsolicited articles. Sometimes pays the expenses of writers on assignment.
Photos: State availability of photos with submission. Reviews contact sheets. Offers $5-25/photo. Captions, model releases, and identification of subjects required. Buys one-time rights.
Columns/Departments: Buys 5 mss/year. Query with or without published clips or send complete ms. Length: 500-1,500 words. Pays $50-200.
Tips: "The area of our publication most open to freelancers is how-to—good nuts and bolts basics on running a business better, managing better, making more money, etc. Should be well-researched, not personal opinion."

‡**OFFICE GUIDE TO MIAMI, A Guide to Office Space, Products & Services** , Office Guide to Miami, Inc., Suite 325, 5775 Blue Lagoon Drive, Miami FL 33126. (305)261-9700. Editor: Louise Hinton. Managing Editor: Linda Walters. 10% freelance written. A quarterly business magazine (relocation guide) covering finance, computers, communications and other office related topics. "We are geared to impart quick, concise information to today's business community. Our thrust is commercial real estate; our style entertaining as well as informative." Circ. 17,000/ Pays on publication. Publishes ms an average of 2 months after acceptance. Byline sometimes given. Offers negotiable kill fee. Buys all rights. Submit seasonal/holiday material 2 months in advance. Simultaneous, photocopied, and previously published submissions OK. Electronic submissions OK; has a New Altos system—will advise. Computer printout submissions acceptable; no dot-matrix. Reports in 2 weeks on queries; 3 weeks on manuscripts. Sample copy for 9x12 SAE with 2 first class stamps; free writer's guidelines.
Nonfiction: General interest, interview/profile, new product and technical, all business related. "Puff is not acceptable, nor are vague or abstract reference articles." Buys 10 mss/year. Query with or without published clips, or send complete ms. Length: 750-2,500 words. Pays $75-300. Sometimes pays the expenses of writers on assignment.
Photos: Send photos with submission. Reviews 3x5 transparencies and prints. Offers no additional payment for photos accepted with ms. Identification of subjects required. Buys one-time rights.

OHIO BUSINESS, Business Journal Publishing Co., 425 Hanna Bldg., Cleveland OH 44115. (216)621-1644. Editor: Robert W. Gardner. Managing Editor: Michael E. Moore. 10% freelance written. Prefers to work with published/established writers. A monthly magazine covering general business topics. "*Ohio Business* serves the state of Ohio. Readers are business executives in the state engaged in manufacturing, agriculture, mining, construction, transportation, communications, utilities, retail and wholesale trade, services, and government." Circ. 35,000. Pays for features on acceptance; news on publication. Publishes ms an average of 4 months after acceptance. Byline sometimes given. Kill fee can be negotiated. Buys first serial rights; depends on projects. Submit seasonal/holiday material 3-4 months in advance. Simultaneous queries, and simultaneous, photocopied, and previously published submissions OK. Computer printout submissions acceptable; prefers letter-quality to dot-matrix. Reports in 2 weeks on queries; 1 month on mss. Sample copy $2; writer's guidelines for SAE and 1 first class stamp.
Nonfiction: Book excerpts, general interest, how-to, interview/profile, opinion and personal experience. "In all cases, write with an Ohio executive in mind. Stories should give readers useful information on business within the state, trends in management, ways to manage better, or other developments which would affect them in their professional careers." Buys 14-20 mss/year. Query with published clips. Length: 100-2,500 words. Pays $25 minimum. Sometimes pays expenses of writers on assignment.

ALWAYS submit mss or queries with a stamped, self-addressed envelope (SASE) within your country or International Reply Coupons (IRCs) purchased from the post office for other countries.

Photos: State availability of photos. Reviews b&w and color transparencies and prints. Captions and identification of subjects required. Buys variable rights.

Columns/Departments: News; People (features Ohio business execs); High-Tech (leading edge Ohio products and companies); Made in Ohio (unusual Ohio product/services). Query with published clips. Length 100-600 words. Pays $50 minimum.

Tips: "Features are most open to freelancers. Come up with new ideas or information for our readers: Ohio executives in manufacturing and service industries. Writers should be aware of the trend toward specialization in magazine publishing with strong emphasis on people in coverage."

‡ORANGE COUNTY BUSINESS JOURNAL, Scott Publishing, 1112 E. Chestnut, Santa Ana CA 92701. (714)835-9692. Editor: Vickora Clepper. 10% freelance written. A biweekly tabloid covering Orange County, California business. "We address top-level business executives." Circ. 20,000. Pays on publication. Publishes ms an average of 2 months after acceptance. Byline given. Buys first rights. Computer printout submissions acceptable; prefers letter-quality to dot-matrix. Reports in 3 weeks on queries. Free sample copy.

Nonfiction: How-to (business), interview/profile, and opinion. All submissions must be business-oriented. Buys 24 mss/year. Query. Length: 750-1,500 words. Pays $50-150. Sometimes pays the expenses of writers on assignment.

Photos: State availability of photos with submission. Reviews contact sheets. Offers $5/photo. Captions and identification of subjects required. Buys one-time rights.

Columns/Departments: Commentary (general interest business events), 750-1,000 words. Buys 8 mss/year. Query. Pays $50.

OREGON BUSINESS, MIF Publications, Suite 404, 208 SW Stark, Portland OR 97204. (503)223-0304. Editor: Robert Hill. 50% freelance written. Monthly magazine covering business in Oregon. Circ. 20,000. Pays on publication. Publishes ms an average of 4 months after acceptance. Byline given. Buys first rights. Submit seasonal/holiday material 3 months in advance. Photocopied and previously published submissions OK. Computer printout submissions acceptable; prefers letter-quality to dot-matrix. Reports in 1 month. Sample copy for business size SAE and $1.05 postage.

Nonfiction: General interest (real estate, business, investing, small business); interview/profile (business leaders); and new products. Special issues include tourism, world trade, finance. "We need articles on real estate or small business in Oregon, outside the Portland area." Buys 24 mss/year. Query with published clips. Length: 900-2,000 words. Pays 10¢/word minimum; $200 maximum. Sometimes pays expenses of writers on assignment.

PHOENIX BUSINESS JOURNAL, Scripps Howard Business Journals, Suite 100, 1817 N. 3rd St., Phoenix AZ 85004. (602)271-4712. Editor: Chambers Williams. 5% freelance written. Weekly tabloid covering business economics for CEOs and top corporate managers. Circ. 15,000. Pays on publication. Publishes ms an average of 3 weeks after acceptance. Byline given. Buys all rights. Submit seasonal/holiday material 1 month in advance. Computer printout submissions acceptable. Reports in 2 weeks. Sample copy free.

Nonfiction: Interview/profile (of entrepreneurs); and "news affecting all types of Phoenix area corporations, large and small. Our audience is all local." Buys 250 mss/year. Length: open. Pays average flat rate of $75/20 column inches.

‡PROFIT, Making it in Broward, Ft. Lauderdale/Broward County Chamber of Commerce, 208 SE 3rd Ave., Ft. Lauderdale FL 33301. (305)463-4500. Editor: Mary C. Brooks. 60% freelance written. A bimonthly magazine covering business subjects for Broward County, Florida. Circ. 15,000. Pays on publication. Publishes ms an average of 4 months after acceptance. Byline given. Buys first rights. Free sample copy.

Nonfiction: On local business. Buys 25 mss/year. Query with published clips. Length: 800-1,500 words. Pays $75-500 for assigned articles.

Photos: Send photos with submission. Reviews 35mm transparencies and 8x10 prints. Offers no additional payment for photos accepted with ms. Captions, model releases, and identification of subjects required.

REGARDIES: THE MAGAZINE OF WASHINGTON BUSINESS, 1010 Wisconsin Ave., NW, Washington DC 20007. (202)342-0410. Editor: Brian Kelly. 80% freelance written. Works with a small number of new/unpublished writers each year. Monthly magazine covering business and general features in the Washington DC metropolitan area for Washington business executives. Circ. 60,000. Pays within 30 days after publication. Publishes ms an average of 2 months after acceptance. Byline given. Pays variable kill fee. Buys first serial rights and second serial (reprint) rights. Computer printout submissions acceptable; prefers letter-quality to dot-matrix. Submit seasonal/holiday material 3 months in advance. Reports in 3 weeks.

Nonfiction: Profiles (of business leaders), investigative reporting, real estate, advertising, politics, lifestyle, media, retailing, communications, labor issues, and financial issues—all on the Washington business scene. "If it isn't the kind of story that could just as easily run in a city magazine or a national magazine like *Harper's*, *Atlantic*, *Esquire*, etc., I don't want to see it." Also buys book mss for excerpt. No how-to. Narrative

nonfiction only. Buys 90 mss/year. Length: 4,000 words average. Buys 5-6/issue. Pays negotiable rate. Pays the expenses of writers on assignment.
Columns/Departments: Length: 1,500 words average. Buys 8-12/issue. Pays negotiable rates.
Tips: "The most frequent mistake writers make is not including enough information and data about business, which with public companies is easy enough to find. This results in flawed analysis and a willingness to accept the 'official line.' "

SUCCESSFUL EXECUTIVE, (formerly *Executive*), Southam Communications Ltd., 1450 Don Mills Rd., Don Mills, Ontario M3B 2X7 Canada. (416)445-6641. Publisher: G. Wallace Wood. Editor: Patricia Anderson. Published 10 times/year. Magazine covering business issues for the ambitious, career-minded executive. Articles cover business, management, and lifestyle issues of concern to middle and senior executives in the public and private sectors. Circ. approximately 50,000, mostly Ontario. Pays on acceptance. Byline given. Buys first rights. Free sample copy.
Nonfiction: Query with clips of published work.
Fillers: Interested in business-oriented cartoons.

TIDEWATER VIRGINIAN, Suite A, 711 W. 21st, Norfolk VA 23517. Executive Editor: Marilyn Goldman. 80% freelance written. Prefers to work with published/established writers. Published by two Tidewater area chambers of commerce. Monthly magazine for business management people. Circ. 15,000. Buys first serial rights and second serial (reprint) rights to material originally published elsewhere. Byline given. Buys 60 mss/year. Pays on publication. Publishes ms an average of 2 months after acceptance. Sample copy $1.95. Photocopied and simultaneous submissions OK. Computer printout submissions acceptable; prefers letter-quality to dot-matrix. Reports in 3 weeks. Query or submit complete ms.
Nonfiction: Articles dealing with business and industry in Virginia, primarily the surrounding area of southeastern Virginia (Tidewater area). Profiles, successful business operations, new product, merchandising techniques and business articles. Length: 500-2,500 words. Pays $25-150. Sometimes pays the expenses of writers on assignment.
Tips: "Send in writing samples and call for an interview."

TUCSON BUSINESS DIGEST,, 3520 S. Dodge, Tucson AZ 85717. (602)571-1744. Editor: Dave Tedlock. Bimonthly magazine for businessmen. Circ. 18,000. Pays on publication. Byline negotiated. Buys first North American rights. Photocopied and electronic submissions OK; "Please query with SASE. We will forward access numbers and codes." Computer printout submissions acceptable. Reports in 1 month. Sample copy $5.
Nonfiction: "Articles should be relative to Tucson business: trends, analysis, success, etc." Buys 40 mss/year. Send query. Length: 500-2,000 words. Pays $25-175.
Photos: Send photos with ms. Reviews b&w and color contact sheets and color prints. Model release and identification of subjects required.
Tips: Tucson writers and Tucson business oriented stories only. No fiction, fillers or poetry.

‡VERMONT BUSINESS MAGAZINE, Manning Publications, Inc., Brattleboro Professional Center, Box 6120, Brattleboro VT 05301. (802)257-4100. Editor: Robert W. Lawson. 80% freelance written. A monthly tabloid covering business in Vermont. Circ. 13,000. Pays on publication. Publishes ms an average of 1 month after acceptance. Byline given. Offers $50-full payment kill fee. Not copyrighted. Buys one-time rights. Submit seasonal/holiday material 3 months in advance. Simultaneous submissions OK. Electronic submissions OK via IBM PC disk or 300/1200 modem. Computer printout submissions acceptable. Free sample copy.
Nonfiction: Interview/profile, new product, technical and business trends and issues. Buys 300 mss/year. Query with published clips. Length: 800-1,200 words. Pays $50-75. Pays the expenses of writers on assignment.
Photos: Send photos with submission. Reviews contact sheets. Offers $5-10/photo. Identification of subjects required.
Tips: "Read daily papers and look for business angles for a follow-up article. We're always looking for issue and trend articles rather than company or businessman profiles, although we do use the latter as well."

WASHINGTON BUSINESS JOURNAL, Scripps Howard Business Journals, 8321 Old Courthouse Rd., Vienna VA 22180. (703)442-4900. Editor: Susan E. Currier. 10-20% freelance written. Works with a small number of new/unpublished writers each year. Weekly tabloid covering business in the District of Columbia, suburban Maryland and Northern Virginia areas for business persons in middle management as well as chief executive officers. Circ. 20,000. Pays on publication. Publishes ms an average of 1 month after acceptance. Byline given. Not copyrighted. Buys all rights. Computer printout submissions acceptable; no dot-matrix. Sample copy $1.
Nonfiction: Interview/profile (of a local figure—public or small entrepreneur); new product (inventions or patents from area people); business. Special issues are published frequently. Editorial calendar available on

request. No generic or *national* business topics. Query with published clips or submit complete ms. Length: 600-1,800 words. Pays $3.50-$4.50/column inch. Sometimes pays the expenses of writers on assignment.
Photos: State availability or send photos with ms. Pays negotiable rates for 8x10 b&w prints. Identification of subjects required.
Tips: "Queries should have decent writing samples attached. Manuscripts should be well researched, well written and thorough. Neatness and quality of presentation is a plus, as is accurate spelling and grammar. *WBJ* is interested in all business topics including: technology, real estate, accounting, associations, science, education, government, etc. Information sources should be high level and subject should be timely. Accompanying sidebars, photographs and graphs are also well received."

WESTERN INVESTOR, Western States Investment Information, Willamette Publishing, Inc., Suite 1115, 400 SW 6th Ave., Portland OR 97204. (503)222-0577. Editor/Publisher: S.P. Pratt. Managing Editor: Donna Walker. 5% freelance written. Quarterly magazine for the investment community of the 13 western states. For stock brokers, corporate officers, financial analysts, trust officers, CPAs, investors, etc. Circ. 16,000. Pays on publication. Publishes ms an average of 6 months after acceptance. Byline given. Buys one time and second serial (reprint) rights and makes work-for-hire assignments. Simultaneous queries and simultaneous, photocopied and previously published submissions OK. Computer submissions acceptable; prefers letter-quality to dot-matrix. Sample copy $1.50 with SAE and $1.24 postage.
Nonfiction: General business interest ("trends, people, public, listed in our instrument data section"). "Each issue carries a particular industry theme." Query. Length: 200-2,000 words. Pays $50 minimum.
Photos: State availability of photos. Pays $10 minimum for 5x7 (or larger) b&w prints. Buys one-time rights.
Tips: "All editorial copy must pertain or directly relate to companies and/or industry groups included in our listed companies. Send us a one-page introduction including your financial writing background, story ideas, availability for assignment work, credits, etc. What we want at this point is a good working file of authors to draw from; let us know your special areas of interest and expertise. Newspaper business page writers would be good candidates. If you live and work in the west, so much the better."

WESTERN NEW YORK MAGAZINE, Buffalo Area Chamber of Commerce, 107 Delaware Ave., Buffalo NY 14202. (716)849-6689. Editor: J. Patrick Donlon. 10% freelance written. Monthly magazine of the Buffalo-Niagara Falls area. "Tells the story of Buffalo and Western New York, with special emphasis on business and industry and secondary emphasis on quality of life subjects." Circ. 8,000. Pays on acceptance. Publishes ms an average of 3 months after acceptance. Byline given. Offers $150 kill fee. Not copyrighted. Buys all rights. Submit seasonal/holiday material 3 months in advance. Simultaneous queries OK. Computer printout submissions acceptable; no dot-matrix. Reports in 1 month. Sample copy for $2, 9x12 SAE and 3 first class stamps; writer's guidelines for business size SAE and 1 first class stamp.
Nonfiction: General interest (business, finance, commerce); historical/nostalgic (Buffalo, Niagara Falls); how-to (business management); interview/profile (community leader); and Western New York industry, quality of life. "Broad-based items preferred over single firm or organization. Submit articles that provide insight into business operations, marketing, finance, promotion, and nuts-and-bolts approach to small business management. No nationwide or even New York statewide articles or pieces on specific companies, products, services." Buys 30 mss/year. Query with published clips. Length: 1,000-2,500 words. Pays $150-300. Sometimes pays the expenses of writers on assignment.
Photos: Pamela Mills, art director. State availability of photos. Reviews contact sheet. Pays $10-25 for 5x7 b&w prints.

__ *Career, College and Alumni*

To help students prepare for the job market, many of these magazines are looking for practical career information that readers can use. Some publications also cover issues and relationships. Three types of magazines are listed in this section: university publications written for students, alumni, and friends of a specific institution; publications about college life; and publications on career and job opportunities.

‡**ALABAMA ALUMNI MAGAZINE,** University of Alabama, Box 1928, Colonial Dr., University AL 35486. (205)348-1548. Editor: James M. Kenny. Managing Editor: Julie L. Griffin. 20% freelance written. A quarterly alumni magazine. "We present a positive but factual look at the University of Alabama and its faculty, staff, students and alumni. Our audience consists of alumni and supporters of the University of Alabama. We also

publish *Alabama Alumni News*." Circ. 20,000. Pays on acceptance. Publishes ms an average of 2 months after acceptance. Byline given. Not copyrighted. Buys first rights. Submit seasonal/holiday material 4 months in advance. Photocopied submissions OK. Electronic submissions OK via IBM XT; prefers hard copy accompany electronic submissions. Reports in 1 week on queries; 2 weeks on mss. Free writer's guidelines.

Nonfiction: Alumni (general interest), historical/nostalgic about university, and interview/profile. "We want only articles about the university, its alumni and students." Buys 8 mss/year. Query by mail or phone. Length: 400-4,000 words. Pays $20-300. Sometimes pays the expenses of writers on assignment.

Photos: State availability of photos with submission. Reviews prints. Payment offered on photos (depends on situation). Captions, model releases, and identification of subjects required. Buys one-time rights.

Columns/Departments: Who's Who (profiles of Alabama alumni), 600-1,200 words; Games (sports, especially shorties), 100-1,200 words; and Quest (university research), 600-1,200 words. Buys up to 8 mss/year. Query. Pays $5-50.

Tips: "Let us know when you come across a story idea connected with the University of Alabama , which is in Tuscaloosa—*not* Birmingham. We want freelancers to be our extension into the world at large, so we're interested in any workable ideas. Just make sure it has some connection with the right school. A freelancer could break in most easily by writing a suitable department article. We are especially looking for interesting profiles of alumni. It would be very easy to make a quick five or ten bucks by sending in a short notice on some athlete connected with this school (seen Joe Namath out jogging lately?). Similarly, do you know a professor/scientist with a 'Bama connection?"

‡ALABAMA ALUMNI NEWS, University of Alabama, Box 1928, Colonial Dr., University AL 35486. (205)348-1548. Editor: James M. Kenny. Managing Editor: Julie L. Griffin. 20% freelance written. A quarterly alumni tabloid. "We present a positive but factual look look at the University of Alabama and its faculty, staff, students and alumni. Our audience consists of alumni and supporters of the University of Alabama. We also publish *Alabama Alumni Magazine.*" Circ. 90,000. Pays on acceptance. Pubishes ms an average of 2 months after acceptance. Byline given. Not copyrighted. Buys first rights. Submit seasonal/holiday material 3 months in advance. Photocopied submissions OK. Electronic submissions OK via IBM XT; prefers hard copy accompany electronic submissions. Reports in 1 week on queries; 2 weeks on mss. Free writer's guidelines.

Nonfiction: Book excerpts, general interest, historical/nostalgic and interview/profile. No articles not about the University of Alabama, its alumni and students. Buys 8 mss/year. Query or phone. Open to beginning freelancers. Length: 400-4,000 words. Pays $20-300. Sometimes pays the expenses of writers on assignment.

Photos: State availability of photos with submissions. Payment depends on situation. Captions, model releases, and identification of subjects required. Buys one-time rights.

Columns/Departments: Alumni Profiles (profiles of Alabama alumni—photos must be included with the profile), 600-1,500 words. Buys up to 8 mss/year. Query. Pays $25-50.

Tips: "Alumni profiles of short or feature length will be read by one of the publications staff. We will accept any kind—sports, business, political, and even personal interest. "We would be, however, particularly interested in articles with a current news interest. Let us know when you come across a story idea connected with the University of Alabama (in Tuscaloosa, not UAB or UAH in Birmingham or Huntsville, respectively). We are particularly interested in alumni who live in other areas of the country—a listing of which may be obtained from alumni directories."

ALCALDE, Box 7278, Austin TX 78713. (512)476-6271. Editor: Ernestine Wheelock. 20% freelance written. Works with a small number of new/unpublished writers each year. Bimonthly magazine. Circ. 48,000. Pays on publication. Publishes ms an average of 6 months after acceptance. Buys all rights. Submit seasonal/holiday material 5 months in advance. Electronic submissions OK via Xerox 860 disk or Macintosh disk, but requires hard copy also. Computer printout submissions acceptable; prefers letter-quality to dot-matrix. Reports in 1 month.

Nonfiction: General interest; historical (University of Texas, research, and faculty profile); humor (humorous University of Texas incidents or profiles that include background data); interviews (University of Texas subjects); nostalgia (University of Texas traditions); profile (students, faculty or alumni); and technical (University of Texas research on a subject or product). No subjects lacking taste or quality, or not connected with the University of Texas. Buys 12 mss/year. Query. Length: 1,000-2,400 words. Pays according to importance of article.

THE BLACK COLLEGIAN, The National Magazine of Black College Students, Black Collegiate Services, Inc., 1240 S. Broad St., New Orleans LA 70125. (504)821-5694. Editor: James Borders. 40% freelance written. Magazine for black college students and recent graduates with an interest in black cultural awareness, sports, news, personalities, history, trends, current events and job opportunities. Published bimonthly during school year; (4 times/year). 160 pages. Circ. 190,000. Buys one-time rights. Byline given. Pays on publication. Offers ⅓ kill fee. Photocopied, previously published and simultaneous submissions OK. Computer printout submissions acceptable. Submit seasonal and special material 2 months in advance of issue date (Careers in Sciences, August; Computers/Grad School, November; Engineering and Travel/Summer Programs, January;

Finance and Jobs, March; Medicine, May). Reports in 3 weeks on queries; 1 month on mss. Sample copy for 9x12 SAE and 3 first class stamps; writer's guidelines for #10 SAE and 1 first class stamp.

Nonfiction: Material on careers, sports, black history, news analysis. Articles on problems and opportunities confronting black college students and recent graduates. Book excerpts, expose, general interest, historical/nostalgic, how-to (develop employability), opinion, personal experience, profile, inspirational, humor. Buys 40 mss/year (6 unsolicited). Query with published clips or send complete ms. Length: 500-2,500 words. Pays $25-350.

Photos: State availability of photos with query or ms, or send photos with query or ms. B&w photos or color transparencies purchased with or without mss. 8x10 b&w prints preferred. Captions, model releases and identification of subjects required. Pays $35/b&w; $50/color.

Tips: "Career features area is most open to freelancers."

CAMPUS VOICE, The National College Magazine, 13-30 Corporation, 505 Market St., Knoxville TN 37902. (615)521-0646. Executive Editor: Keith Bellows. Senior Editor: Suzanne Harper. Managing Editor: Barbara Penland. 80% freelance published. Bimonthly magazine. "The purpose of *Campus Voice* is to define and reflect the college experience of the '80s; to mirror the college culture; and to be jingoistic about college just as a city or regional magazine is jingoistic about its community." Circ. 1.2 million. Pays on acceptance. Publishes ms an average of 3 months after acceptance. Byline given. Offers 33⅓% kill fee. Buys first North American serial rights. Submit seasonal/holiday material 6 months in advance. Computer printout submissions acceptable; no dot-matrix. Reports in 3 weeks. Sample copy $2, 10x12 SAE and 6 first class stamps. Writer's guidelines for business size SAE, and 1 first class stamp.

Nonfiction: Book excerpts, expose, general interest, how-to (careers/academics with news angles), humor, interview/profile, personal experience, photo feature and travel. No inspirational, obvious college-oriented, ideas. Buys 100 mss/year. Query with published clips. Length: 750-4,000 words. Pays $500-5,000. Pays expenses of writers on assignment.

Tips: "Don't think of our readers as students—they're 18-to-24-year-olds with sophisticated tastes. If you pitch a college-based idea make it original. Area most open to freelancers is Campus Beat. Be relevant, off-beat, original. Look for news/entertainment ideas with a twist."

‡CARNEGIE-MELLON MAGAZINE, Carnegie-Mellon University, Pittsburgh PA 15213. (412)578-2900. Editor: Ann Curran. Alumni publication issued fall, winter, spring, summer covering university activities, alumni profiles, etc. Circ. 41,000. Pays on acceptance. Byline given. Not copyrighted. Reports in 1 month.

Nonfiction: Book reviews (faculty alumni); general interest; humor; interview/profile; photo feature. "We use general interest stories linked to CMU activities and research." No unsolicited mss. Buys 5 features and 5-10 alumni profiles/year. Query with published clips. Length: 2,500-6,000 words. Pays $250 or negotiable rate.

Poetry: Avant-garde or traditional. No previously published poetry. No payment.

Tips: "Consideration is given to professional writers among alumni."

COLLEGIATE CAREER WOMAN, For Career Minded Women, Equal Opportunity Publications, Inc., 44 Broadway, Greenlawn NY 11740. (516)261-8917. Editor: Anne Kelly. 80% freelance written. Magazine published 3 times/year (fall, winter, spring) covering career-guidance for college women. Strives "to aid women in developing career abilities to the fullest potential; improve job hunting skills; present career opportunities; provide personal resources; help cope with discrimination." Audience is 92% college juniors and seniors; 8% working graduates. Circ. 10,500. Controlled circulation, distributed through college guidance and placement offices. Publishes ms 3 months-1 year after acceptance. Pays on publication. Byline given. Buys first North American serial rights. Simultaneous queries and submissions OK. Computer printout submissions acceptable. Free sample copy and writer's guidelines.

Nonfiction: "We want career-related articles describing for a college-educated woman the how-tos of obtaining a professional position and advancing her career." Looks for practical features detailing self-evaluation techniques, the job-search process, and advice for succeeding on the job. Emphasizes role-model profiles of successful career women. Needs manuscripts presenting information on professions offering opportunities to young women—especially the growth professions of the future. Special issues emphasize career opportunities for women in fields such as health care, communications, sales, marketing, banking, insurance, finance, science, engineering, and computers, as well as opportunities in government, military and defense. Query first. Sometimes pays the expenses of writers on assignment.

Photos: Send with mss. Prefers 35mm color slides, but will accept b&w prints. Captions, model releases and identification of subjects required. Buys all rights.

Tips: Articles should focus on career-guidance, role model, and industry prospects for women and should have a "snappy, down-to-earth writing style."

THE COMPUTER & ELECTRONICS GRADUATE, The Entry-Level Career & Information Technology Magazine for CS, Systems, and EE Graduates, Equal Opportunity Publications, Inc., 44 Broadway, Greenlawn NY 11740. (516)261-8917. Editor: James Schneider. A quarterly career-guidance magazine for computer science/systems and electrical/electronics engineering students and professionals. "We strive to aid our readers in developing career abilities to the fullest potential; improve job-hunting skills; present career opportunities; provide personal resources." Circ. 26,000 (controlled circulation, distributed through college guidance and placement offices). Pays on publication. Byline given. Buys first North American serial rights. Deadline: fall, July 1; winter, Oct. 5; spring, Jan. 15; summer, April 15. Simultaneous queries and simultaneous, photocopied, and previously published submissions OK. Computer printout submissions acceptable; no dot-matrix. Reports in 1 month. Sample copy and writer's guidelines for 8½x11 SAE and 60¢ postage.

Nonfiction: Book excerpts (on job search techniques, role models, success stories, employment helps); general interest (on special concerns to computer science/systems, and electrical/electronics engineering students and professionals); how-to (on self-evaluation, job-finding skills, adjustment, coping with the real world); humor (student or career related); interview/profile (of successful computer science/systems and electrical/electronics engineering students and professionals); new product (new career opportunities); personal experience (student and career experiences); technical (on career fields offering opportunities); travel on overseas job opportunities; and coverage of other reader interests. Special issues include careers in industry and government in computer science, computer systems, electrical engineering, software systems, robotics, artificial intelligence, as well as opportunities in the military and in defense. No sensitive or highly technical material. Buys 20-25 mss/year. Query. Length: 1,250-3,000 words. Pays 10¢/word.

Photos: Anne Kelly, photo editor. State availability of photos or send photos with query or mss. Prefers 35mm color slides, but will accept b&w. Captions and identification of subjects required.

Tips: "Articles should focus on career-guidance, role model, and industry prospects for computer science, computer systems and electrical and electronics engineering students and professionals."

EQUAL OPPORTUNITY, The Nation's Only Multi-Ethnic Recruitment Magazine for Black, Hispanic, Native American & Asian American College Grads, Equal Opportunity Publications, Inc., 44 Broadway, Greenlawn NY 11740. (516)261-8917. Editor: James Schneider. 50% freelance written. Prefers to work with published/established writers. Magazine published 3 times/year (fall, winter, spring) covering career-guidance for minorities. "Our audience is 90% college juniors and seniors, 10% working graduates. An understanding of educational and career problems of minorities is essential." Circ. 15,000. Controlled circulation, distributed through college guidance and placement offices. Pays on publication. Publishes ms an average of 1 month after acceptance. Byline given. Buys first North American serial rights. Deadline dates: fall, Aug. 5; winter, Nov. 3; spring, Feb. 8. Simultaneous queries, and simultaneous, photocopied and previously published submissions OK. Computer printout submissions acceptable; no dot-matrix. Free sample copy and writer's guidelines for SAE and 3 first class stamps.

Nonfiction: Book excerpts and articles (on job search techniques, role models); general interest (on specific minority concerns); how-to (on job-hunting skills, personal finance, better living, coping with discrimination); humor (student or career related); interview/profile (minority role models); new product (new career opportunities); opinion (problems of minorities); personal experience (professional and student study and career experiences); technical (on career fields offering opportunities for minorities); travel (on overseas job opportunities); and coverage of Black, Hispanic, Native American and Asian American interests. Special issues include career opportunities for minorities in industry and government in fields such as banking, insurance, finance, communications, sales, marketing, engineering and computers, as well as careers in the government, military and defense. Query or send complete ms. Length: 1,250-3,000 words. Sometimes pays the expenses of writers on assignment.

Photos: Prefers 35mm color slides and b&w. Captions, and identification of subjects required. Buys first North American serial rights.

Tips: "Articles must be geared toward questions and answers faced by minority and women students."

GENERATION, The Student Magazine, Sub Board One, Inc., University of Buffalo, Box G Harriman, 3545 Main St. SUNYAB, Buffalo NY 14214. (716)831-2842. Editor: Andrew Galarneau. Supervising Editor: Gregory Colao. 75% freelance written. Eager to work with new/unpublished writers. A weekly student-oriented news, literary and feature magazine covering student issues and concerns with an emphasis on humor. Circ. 15,000. Pays on publication. Publishes ms an average of 2 months after acceptance. Byline given. Negotiable kill fee. Buys one-time rights. Submit seasonal/holiday material 3 months in advance. Simultaneous, photocopied, and previously published submissions OK. Computer printout submissions acceptable; prefers letter-quality to dot-matrix. Reports in 2 months. Sample copy for 8x11 SAE with 5 first class stamps.

Nonfiction: Essays, expose, general interest, how-to and humor. Nothing overly complex, technological or etymological. Buys 15 mss/year. Query with or without published clips, or send complete ms. Length: 400-4,000 words. Pays $20-$500 for agented articles; pays $10-300 for unsolicited articles. Will pay with copies or other permission if the writer requests. Sometimes pays the expenses of writers on assignment.

Photos: State availability of photos with submission. Reviews contact sheets. Offers $5-15/photo. Identification of subjects required. Buys one-time rights.

Columns/Departments: Buys 4 mss/year. Send complete ms. Length: 400-1,500 words. Pays $10-45.

Fiction: Rita Hilgendoff, fiction editor. Adventure, experimental, fantasy, horror, humorous, mystery, science fiction, slice-of-life and suspense. Buys 10 mss/year. Send complete ms. Length: 100-5,000 words. Pays $20-500.

Poetry: Brian Lambkin, poetry editor. Free verse, haiku, and light verse. Nothing with funny punctuation. Buys 20 poems/year. Submit maximum 5 poems. Length: 4-50 lines. Pays $5-45.

Fillers: Amy Robinson, fillers editor. Anecdotes, facts, gags to be illustrated by cartoonist and short humor. Buys 50/year. Length: 30-120 words. Pays $2-10.

Tips: "We look for the odd, the exciting, the thought-provoking. Most of our copy is written by people with less than two years of formal writing experience. We intend to cover topics at the University of Buffalo more ·closely this year."

HIS Magazine, Box 1450, Downers Grove IL 60515. (312)964-5700. Editor: Verne Becker. 80% freelance written. Issued monthly from October-April for college students, with "a Christian approach to the needs and issues they face." Pays on acceptance. Publishes ms an average of 1 year after acceptance. Buys first rights and second (reprint) rights to material originally published elsewhere. Reports in 3 months. Computer printout submissions acceptable; prefers letter-quality to dot-matrix.

Nonfiction and Fiction: "Articles dealing with practical aspects of Christian living on campus, relating contemporary issues to Biblical principles. Should show relationship between Christianity and various fields of study, Christian doctrine, or missions." Submit complete ms. Buys 55 unsolicited mss/year. Recent article example. "Clash of the Roommates: What to Do When You're Stuck in a Bad Situation." Length: 2,000 words maximum. Pays $50-200.

Poetry: Pays $20-50.

Tips: "Direct your principles and illustrations at college students. Avoid preachiness and attacks on various Christian ministries or groups; share your insights on a peer basis."

THE JOHNS HOPKINS MAGAZINE, The Johns Hopkins University, 203 Whitehead Hall, Baltimore MD 21218. (301)338-7645. Editor: Elise Hancock. Associate Editor: Edward C. Ernst. A bimonthly alumni general interest magazine with features on those subjects interesting Hopkins grads, i.e., medicine, literature, etc. Circ. 85,000. Pays on acceptance. Byline given. Buys one-time rights and first rights. Submit seasonal/holiday material 6 months in advance. Electronic submissions OK if compatible with DEC Mate (Digital) word processors. Computer printout submissions acceptable. Reports in 3 months. Sample copy for $1.50, 9x12 SAE, and 90¢ postage.

Nonfiction: General interest, how-to, humor, and photo feature, all *Hopkins related stories*—medical, music, physics, arts and sciences, engineering, continuing education, astronomy. Also interview/profile (alumni of Hopkins), and personal experience (if related to Hopkins). Buys approximately 9 mss/year. Query with published clips. Length: 5,000 words maximum. Pays $75-1,500.

Photos: State availability of photos. Reviews b&w contact sheets. Model releases and identification of subjects required. Buys one-time rights.

Fillers: Cartoons.

Tips: As well as having a specific tie to Hopkins, contributions must be general enough (non-technical) to appeal to wide audience, yet at a level which is apropos for university graduates. (Humor and personal insights help too.) The whole magazine is open to freelancers. Trends in alumni magazines are toward color, so promise of exciting color spreads lends the article to publication. Readers like brain twisters or thought provoking ethical issues or articles on new techniques in their field.

MAKING IT!, Careers Newsmagazine, Rm. 2J, 250 W. 94th St., New York NY 10025. (212)222-3338. Editor: Karen Rubin. "We are backlogged with submissions and prefer not to receive unsolicited submissions at this time."

MISSISSIPPI STATE UNIVERSITY ALUMNUS, Mississippi State University, Alumni Association, Editorial Office, Box 5328, Mississippi State MS 39762. (601)325-3442. Editor: Linsey H. Wright. 10% freelance written ("but welcome more"). Emphasizes articles about Mississippi State graduates and former students. For well-educated and affluent audience. Quarterly magazine; 36 pages. Circ. 15,650. Pays on publication. Publishes ms an average of 6 months after acceptance. Buys one-time rights. Pays 25% kill fee. Byline given. Phone queries OK. Submit seasonal/holiday material 3 months in advance. Simultaneous, photocopied and previously published submissions OK. Publishes ms an average of 6 months after acceptance. Computer printout submissions acceptable; prefers letter-quality to dot-matrix. Reports in 1 month. Free sample copy.

Nonfiction: Historical, humor (with strong MSU flavor; nothing risque), informational, inspirational, interview (with MSU grads), nostalgia (early days at MSU), personal experience, profile and travel (by MSU grads, but must be of wide interest to other grads). Buys 5-6 mss/year ("but welcome more submissions.") Send complete ms. Length: 500-2,000 words. Pays $50-150 (including photos, if used).

Photos: Offers no additional payment for photos purchased with accompanying ms. Captions required. Uses 5x7 and 8x10 b&w photos and color transparencies of any size.

Columns/Departments: Statesmen, "a section of the *Alumnus* that features briefs about alumni achievements and professional or business advancement. We do not use engagements, marriages or births. There is no payment for Statesmen briefs.''

Tips: ''All stories *must* be about Mississippi State University or its alumni. We welcome articles about MSU grads in interesting occupations and have used stories on off-shore drillers, miners, horse trainers, etc. We also want profiles on prominent MSU alumni and have carried pieces on Senator John C. Stennis, comedian Jerry Clower, professional football players and coaches, and Eugene Butler, former editor-in-chief of *Progressive Farmer* magazine. We feature four alumni in each issue, alumni who have risen to prominence in their fields or who are engaged in unusual occupations or who are involved in unusual hobbies. We're using more short features (500-700 words) to vary the length of our articles in each issue. We pay $50-75 for these, including 1 b&w photo.''

‡**MODERN SECRETARY,** Allied Publications, 1776 Lake Worth Rd., Lake Worth FL 33460. (305)582-2099. Editor: Mark Adams. 50% freelance written. A monthly magazine sold to businesses nationwide for distribution to their customers as a promotion/public relations tool. ''*Modern Secretary* serves a predominantly female readership in secretarial/clerical and office management positions.'' Circ. 50,000. Pays on acceptance. Publishes ms an average of 3 months after acceptance. Byline given (except for fillers). Buys first rights, one-time rights, second serial (reprint) rights, and makes some work-for-hire assignments. Submit seasonal/holiday material 8 months in advance. Simultaneous, photocopied, and previously published submissions OK. Computer printout submissions acceptable; prefers letter-quality to dot-matrix. Reports in 1 month. Sample copy and writer's guidelines for 9x12 SAE with 50¢ postage.

Nonfiction: Book excerpts (office practice); essays (humor/opinion); general interest (business); historical/nostalgic (on the job); how-to (on improving office methods and communication skills; most rejected ''for stating the obvious''); humor; inspirational (self-motivation, leadership and work values); interview/profile (with photos); new-product (with photos); opinion; personal experience (on the job); photo feature; technical (for lay readers, such as ''coping with your PC''); and travel (for business people). ''We look for short, sharp copy that makes a point. We don't have the page space for long articles.'' Buys 40-50 mss/year. Query with or without published clips. Length: 500-800 words (average). Pays 5¢/word minimum, $25 maximum. May pay with premiums rather than cash if writer requests.

Photos: Send photos with submission. Reviews prints. Offers $5 minimum/photo. Captions and identification of subjects required. Buys one-time rights.

Tips: Needs ''essays offering fresh perspectives on business practices and office life, as well as related lifestyles themes (young singles, working mothers, etc.), self-evaluation and improvement, human relations, communication, career advancement, and office humor and ancedotes.''

NATIONAL FORUM: THE PHI KAPPA PHI JOURNAL, The Honor Society of Phi Kappa Phi, 216 Petrie Hall, Auburn University AL 36849. Editor: Stephen W. White. Managing Editor: Betty Barrett. 20% freelance written. Prefers to work with published/established writers. Quarterly interdisciplinary, scholarly journal. ''We are an interdisciplinary journal that publishes crisp, nontechnical analyses of issues of social and scientific concern as well as scholarly treatments of different aspects of culture.'' Circ. 112,000. Pays on publication. Publishes ms an average of 6 months after acceptance. Byline given. Buys first serial rights. Submit seasonal/holiday material 6 months in advance. Electronic submissions acceptable; can accept 5¼'' diskettes compatible with Lanier No-Problem Shared System. Telecommunications capabilities if author has compatible equipment/software. Computer printout submissions acceptable; no dot-matrix. Reports in 6 weeks on queries; 2 months on mss. Sample copy $1.65; free writer's guidelines.

Nonfiction: General interest, interview/profile and opinion. Especially wants essays on contemporary American culture characterized by truth, affirmation, vitality and beauty. No how-to or biographical articles. Each issue is devoted to the exploration of a particular theme. Upcoming theme issues: ''The Human Brain'' ''Curricular Reform,'' ''News and the Media.'' Recent article example: ''Science, Society and the International Education Gap.'' Query with clips of published work. Buys 5 unsolicited mss/year. Length: 1,500-2,000 words. Pays $50-200.

Photos: State availability of photos. Identification of subjects required. Buys one-time rights.

Columns/Departments: Educational Dilemmas of the 80s and Book Review Section. Buys 8 mss/year for Educational Dilemmas, 40 book reviews. Length: Book reviews—400-800 words. Educational Dilemmas—1,500-1,800 words. Pays $15-25 for book reviews; $50/printed page, Educational Dilemmas.

Fiction: Humorous and short stories. No obscenity or excessive profanity. Buys 2-4 mss/year. Length: 1,500-1,800 words. Pays $50/printed page.

Poetry: Free verse, haiku, light verse, traditional. No love poetry. Buys 20 mss/year. Submit 5 poems maximum. Prefers shorter poems.

NOTRE DAME MAGAZINE, University of Notre Dame, Room 415, Administration Bldg., Notre Dame IN 46556. (219)239-5335. Editor: Walton R. Collins. Managing Editor: Kerry Temple. 75% freelance written. Quarterly magazine covering news of Notre Dame and education and issues affecting the Roman Catholic Church. ''We are interested in the moral, ethical and spiritual issues of the day and how Christians live in to-

day's world. We are universal in scope and Catholic in viewpoint and serve Notre Dame students, alumni, friends and constituencies." Circ. 102,000. Pays on acceptance. Publishes ms an average of 6 months after acceptance. Byline given. Kill fee negotiable. Buys first rights. Simultaneous queries OK. Electronic submissions OK with IBM, Phillips on Apple Micro compatability, but requires hard copy also. Computer printout submissions acceptable; prefers letter-quality to dot-matrix. Reports in 3 weeks. Free sample copy.
Nonfiction: Opinion, personal experience, religion. "All articles must be of interest to Christian/Catholic readers who are well educated and active in their communities." Buys 35 mss/year. Query with clips of published work. Length: 600-2,000 words. Pays $500-1,500. Sometimes pays the expenses of writers on assignment.
Photos: State availability of photos. Reviews b&w contact sheets, color transparencies, and 8x10 prints. Model releases and identification of subjects required. Buys one-time rights.

PRINCETON ALUMNI WEEKLY, Princeton University Press, 41 William St., Princeton NJ 08540. (609)452-4885. Editor: Charles L. Creesy. Managing Editor: Margaret M. Keenan. 50% freelance written. Eager to work with new/unpublished writers. Biweekly (during the academic year) magazine covering Princeton University and higher education for Princeton alumni, students, faculty, staff and friends. "We assume familiarity with and interest in the university." Circ. 51,000 Pays on publication. Publishes ms an average of 3 months after acceptance. Byline given. Offers $100 kill fee. Buys first serial rights and one-time rights. Submit seasonal/holiday material 2 months in advance. Simultaneous queries or photocopied submissions OK. Electronic submissions OK but requirements must be clarified with publisher—"too complex to summarize here." Computer printout submissions acceptable; prefers letter-quality to dot-matrix. Sample copy for 9x12 SAE and 71¢ postage.
Nonfiction: Book excerpts, general interest, historical/nostalgic, interview/profile, opinion, personal experience, photo feature. "Connection to Princeton essential. Remember, it's for an upscale educated audience." Special issue on education and economics (February). Buys 20 mss/year. Query with clips of published work. Length: 1,000-6,000 words. Pays $100-600. Pays expenses of writers on assignment.
Photos: State availability of photos. Pays $25-50 for 8x10 b&w prints; $50-100 for color transparencies. Reviews (for ordering purposes) b&w contact sheet. Captions and identification of subjects required.
Columns/Departments: "Columnists must have a Princeton connection (alumnus, student, etc.)." Buys 50 mss/year. Query with clips of published work. Length: 750-1,500 words. Pays $75-150.

THE PURDUE ALUMNUS, Purdue Alumni Association, Purdue Memorial Union 160, West Lafayette IN 47907. (317)494-5184. Editor: Gay L. Totten. 25% freelance written. Magazine published 9 times/year (except February, June, August) covering subjects of interest to Purdue University alumni. Circ. 66,000. Pays on publication. Publishes ms an average of 2 months after acceptance. Byline given. Buys first rights and makes work-for-hire assignments. Submit seasonal/holiday material 3 months in advance. Simultaneous queries, and simultaneous, photocopied, and previously published submissions OK. Computer printout submissions acceptable; prefers letter-quality to dot-matrix. Reports in 1 week on queries; 2 weeks on mss. Free sample copy.
Nonfiction: Book excerpts, general interest, historical/nostalgic, humor, interview/profile, personal experience. Focus is on campus news, issues, opinions of interest to 66,000 members of the Alumni Association. Feature style, primarily university-oriented. Issues relevant to education. Buys 12-20 mss/year. Length: 1,500-2,500 words maximum. Pays $25-250. Sometimes pays expenses of writers on assignment.
Photos: State availability of photos. Reviews b&w contact sheet or 5x7 prints.
Tips: "We're always anxious for new material, and depend rather heavily on freelancers. We prefer to work by assignment, and appreciate query with ideas, possibly writing samples. We don't pay much, but we do credit and have a well-educated, worldwide audience."

SCORECARD, Falsoft, Inc., 9509 US Highway 42, Box 385, Prospect KY 40059. (502)228-4492. Editor: John Crawley. Assistant Editor: Garry Jones. 50% freelance written. Prefers to work with published/established writers. A weekly tabloid sports fan magazine covering University of Louisville sports only. Circ. 3,000. Pays on publication. Publishes ms an average of 1 month after acceptance. Byline given. Buys first rights. Submit seasonal/holiday material 1 month in advance. Previously published submissions OK "rarely." Computer printout submissions acceptable; prefers letter-quality to dot-matrix. Reports in 2 weeks. Sample copy for $1 and SAE.
Nonfiction: Assigned to contributing editors. Buys 100 mss/year. Query with published clips. Length: 750-1,500 words. Pays $20-50. Sometimes pays expenses of writers on assignment.
Photos: State availability of photos.
Columns/Departments: Notes Page (tidbits relevant to University of Louisville sports program or former players or teams). Buys 25 mss/year. Length: Approximately 100 words. Pay undetermined.
Tips: "Be very familiar with history and tradition of University of Louisville sports program. Contact us with story ideas. Know subject."

THE STUDENT, 127 9th Ave. N., Nashville TN 37234. Contact: Editor. 30% freelance written. Works with a small number of new/unpublished writers each year. Publication of National Student Ministries of the Southern

Baptist Convention. For college students; focusing on freshman and sophomore levels. Published 12 times during the school year. Circ. 25,000. Buys all rights. Payment on acceptance. Publishes ms an average of 10 months after acceptance. Mss should be double spaced on white paper with 50-space line, 25 lines/page. Reports usually in 6 weeks. Computer printout submissions acceptable; no dot-matrix. Free sample copy and guidelines.

Nonfiction: Contemporary questions, problems, and issues facing college students viewed from a Christian perspective to develop high moral and ethical values. Cultivating interpersonal relationships, developing self-esteem, dealing with the academic struggle, coping with rejection, learning how to love, developing a personal relationship with Jesus Christ. Prefers complete ms rather than query. Length: 700 words maximum. Pays 5¢/word after editing with reserved right to edit accepted material.

Fiction: Satire and parody on college life, humorous episodes; emphasize clean fun and the ability to grow and be uplifted through humor. Contemporary fiction involving student life, on campus as well as off. Length: 1,000 words. Pays 4¢/word.

WPI JOURNAL, Worcester Polytechnic Institute, 100 Institute Rd., Worcester MA 01609. Editor: Kenneth McDonnell. 75% freelance written. A quarterly alumni magazine covering science and engineering/education/business personalities for 16,000 alumni, primarily engineers, scientists, managers; parents of students, national media. Circ. 22,500. Pays on publication. Publishes ms an average of 3 months after acceptance. Byline given. Buys one-time rights. Submit seasonal/holiday material 3 months in advance. Simultaneous queries, and simultaneous, photocopied and previously published submissions OK. Electronic submissions OK via disk compatible with DEC or NBI, but requires hard copy also. Computer printout submissions acceptable; prefers letter-quality to dot-matrix. Reports in 2 weeks on queries; 1 month on mss.

Nonfiction: Book excerpts; exposé (education, engineering, science); general interest; historical/nostalgic; how-to (financial, business-oriented); humor; interview/profile (people in engineering, science); personal experience; photo feature; and technical (with personal orientation). Query with published clips. Length: 1,000-4,000 words. Pays negotiable rate. Sometimes pays the expenses of writers on assignment.

Photos: State availability of photos with query or ms. Reviews b&w contact sheets. Pays negotiable rate. Captions required.

Fillers: Cartoons. Buys 4/year. Pays $75-100.

Tips: "Submit outline of story and/or ms of story idea or published work. Features are most open to freelancers."

Cartoon and Comic Books

Cartoonists and comic book artists turn to these publications to learn about the craft of cartooning. Comic book firms looking for writers are also listed in this section. For publications specifically on humor, see the Humor category. Cartoonists and syndicates that buy gaglines can be found in the Gag Writing section in the back of the book.

CARTOON WORLD, Box 30367, Dept. WM, Lincoln NE 68503. Editor: George Hartman. 25% freelance written. Works with published/established writers and a small number of new/unpublished writers each year. "Monthly newsletter for professional and amateur cartoonists who are serious and want to utilize new cartoon markets in each issue." Buys only from paid subscribers. Circ. 150-300. Pays on acceptance. Byline given. Buys second (reprint) rights to material originally published elsewhere. Not copyrighted. Submit seasonal/holiday material 3 months in advance. Simultaneous submissions OK. Publishes ms an average of 3 months after acceptance. Computer printout submissions acceptable; no dot-matrix. Reports in 1 month. Sample copy $5.

Nonfiction: "We want only positive articles about the business of cartooning and gag writing." Buys 10 mss/year. Query. Length: 1,000 words. Pays $5/page.

ECLIPSE COMICS, Box 199, Guerneville CA 95446. (707)869-9401. Publisher: Dean Mullaney. Editor-in-Chief: Catherine Yronwode. 100% freelance written. Works with a small number of new/unpublished writers each year. Publishers of various four-color comic books. *Eclipse* publishes comic books with high-quality paper and color reproduction, geared toward the discriminating comic book fan; and sold through the "direct sales" specialty store market. Circ. varies (35,000-85,000). Pays on acceptance (net 30 days). Publishes ms an average of 3 months after acceptance. Byline given. Buys first North American serial rights, second serial (reprint) rights with additional payment, and first option on collection and non-exclusive rights to sell material to South American and European markets (with additional payments). Simultaneous queries, and simultaneous and photocopied submissions OK. Computer printout submissions acceptable; no dot-matrix. Reports in 1 month. Sample copy $1.75, writer's guidelines for business-size SAE and 1 first class stamp.

Fiction: "All of our comics are fictional." Adventure, fantasy, mystery, romance, science fiction, horror, western. "No sexually explicit material, please." Buys approximately 150 mss/year (mostly from established comics writers). Send sample science fiction or horror script or plot synopsis. Length: 8-11 pages. Pays $30 minimum/page.

Tips: "At the present time we are publishing as many adventure and super-heroic series as our schedule permits. Because all of our comics are 'creator-owned,' we do not buy fill-in plots or scripts for these books. We do have two comics open to new writers, however. These are *Alien Encounters*, a bimonthly science fiction anthology, and *Tales of Terrors*, a bimonthly horror anthology. The stories in these titles vary from 1-page fillers to short stories of 8 or more pages each, with a maximum length of 11 pages. Plot synopsis of less than a page can be submitted; we will select promising concepts for development into full script submissions. All full script submissions should be written in comic book or 'screenplay' form for artists to illustrate. Science fiction themes we need include outer-space, ufos, alien invasions, time travel, inter-dimensional travel, nuclear holocaust aftermath, future-science exploration, robots, cyborgs, end-of-world, etc. Horror themes we need include vampires, werewolves, zombies, walking dead, monsters in the sewers, revenge from beyond the grave, 'murder will out' stories, and assorted slimy, creepy, gooey, demonic and horrific stuff. 85% of the stories in these anthologies have downbeat twist endings of the kind popularized by O. Henry and the EC comic books of the 1950s. The other 15% start off in that mold but lead to an unexpected upbeat resolution. Our special needs at the moment are for moody, romantic, character-oriented pieces with overtones of humanism, morality, political opinion, philosophical speculation, and/or social commentary. Comic book adaptations (by the original authors) of previously published science fiction and horror short stories are definitely encouraged."

FIRST COMICS, INC., includes *American Flagg!*, *Jon Sable*, *Grimjack*, *Nexus*, *Dreadstar*, *The Enchanted Apples of Oz*, *Elric*, 435 N. LaSalle St., Chicago IL 60610. (312)670-6770. Managing Editor: Richard Oliver. 100% freelance written. Comic book magazines published monthly, bimonthly, one-shot and trade paperbacks. "Our average reader is between ages 18 and 30 years, college educated, male." Circ. 4,000,000. Pays between acceptance and publication. Publishes ms an average of 9 months after acceptance. Byline given. Buys negotiable rights. Submit seasonal/holiday material 9 months in advance. Simultaneous queries OK. Electronic submissions OK via Apple compatible, but requires hard copy also. Computer printout submissions acceptable; prefers letter-qualty to dot-matrix. "We only respond to new writer queries—brief, with SASE." Reports in 6 months.

Fiction: In comic art format, subjects include adventure, experimental, fantasy, historical, humorous, mystery, science fiction and suspense. Query. Payment negotiable. Sometimes pays the expenses of writers on assignment.

Tips: Writer has a better chance of breaking in with short, lesser-paying articles and fillers. "We make regular on-going assignments, generally to the creators of the features."

MARVEL COMICS, 387 Park Ave. S., New York NY 10016. (212)576-9200. Editor-in-Chief: James Shooter. 98% freelance written. Publishes 40 comics and magazines per month, 6-12 graphic novels per year, and specials, storybooks, industrials, and paperbacks for all ages. 7 million copies sold/month. Pays a flat fee for most projects, or an advance and incentive, or royalty. Pays on acceptance. Publishes manuscript an average of 6 months after acceptance. Byline given. Rights purchased depend upon format and material. Submit seasonal/holiday material 8 months in advance.

Fiction: Comic plots and scripts. Adventure, fantasy, horror, humorous, romance, science fiction and western. No "noncomics." Buys 600-800 mss/year. Submit brief plot synopses *only*. Do not send scripts, short stories or long outlines. A plot synopsis should be less than two typed pages. Send two synopses at most. "Using Marvel characters is best." Sometimes pays the expenses of writers on assignment.

Tips: "Marvel Comics wants new talent. We want to maintain our leadership of the graphic storytelling medium, and grow."

> **66** **Send us a query; it's better to ask what you might think is a stupid question than to do what an editor knows is a stupid thing. 99**
>
> *Patrick Lucien Price*, AMAZING Stories

Child Care and Parental Guidance

Most people learn how to care for their children from their own parents, but research and new options are changing generation-ago practices. Today many career-oriented couples are starting families. Parents in the '80s are hearing terms that their parents didn't—single-parent households, gifted children, bonding, etc. Readers want information on new research—on pregnancy, infancy, childhood, and family—written for people who care for children. Child care magazines address these and other issues. Other markets that buy articles about child care and the family are included in the Education, Religious, and Women's sections of this book.

AMERICAN BABY MAGAZINE, For Expectant and New Parents, 575 Lexington Ave., New York NY 10022. (212)752-0775. Editor: Judith Nolte. Managing Editor: Phyllis Evans. 70% freelance written. Prefers to work with published/established writers; works with a small number of new/unpublished writers each year. A monthly magazine covering pregnancy, child care, and parenting. "Our readership is composed of women in late pregnancy and early new motherhood. Most readers are first-time parents, some have older children. A simple, straightforward, clear approach is mandatory." Circ. 1,000,000. Pays on acceptance. Publishes ms an average of 3 months after acceptance. Byline given. Buys first North American serial rights. Submit seasonal holiday material 5-6 months in advance. Simultaneous, photocopied and previously published submissions OK. Computer printout submissions acceptable; prefers letter-quality to dot-matrix. Reports in 3 weeks on queries; 2 months on mss. Sample copy for 9x12 SAE with $1.10 postage. Writer's guidelines for SASE.
Nonfiction: Book excerpts, essays, how-to (on some aspect of pregnancy or child care), humor, opinion and personal experience. "No 'hearts and flowers' or fantasy pieces." Buys 60 mss/year. Query with or without published clips, or send complete ms. Length: 1,000-2,500 words. Pays $200-600 for assigned articles; pays $100-400 for unsolicited articles. Pays the expenses of writers on assignment.
Photos: State availability of photos with submission. Reviews transparencies and prints. Model release and identification of subjects required. Buys one-time rights.
Columns/Departments: My Own Experience (should discuss personal experience in pregnancy and/or something that is universal, but offers new insight or advice), 1,500 words; and One View (an opinion essay on some aspect of pregnancy, birth, or parenting), 1,000 words. Buys 25 mss/year. Send complete ms. Pays $100-250.
Tips: "Articles should either give 'how to' information on some aspect of pregnancy or child care, cover some common problem of child raising, along with solutions, or give advice to the mother on some psychological or practical subject."

THE CRIB SHEET, A Family Magazine, Caronn Publications, 14109 NE 76th St., Vancouver WA 98662. (206)892-3037. Editor: Karen La Clergue. 95% freelance written. Eager to work with new/unpublished writers. Monthly magazine on birthing and newborn news. Circ. 5,000. Pays within two weeks after publication. Publishes ms an average of 6 months after acceptance. Byline given. Offers $5 kill fee. Not copyrighted. Buys simultaneous rights, first serial rights, and second serial (reprint) rights. Submit seasonal/holiday material 3 months in advance. Simultaneous, photocopied, and previously published submissions OK. Computer printout submissions acceptable; prefers letter-quality to dot-matrix. Reports in 5 weeks. Sample copy for 2 first class stamps; writer's guidelines for SAE and 1 first class stamp.
Nonfiction: Book excerpts; general interest (anything of interest to women—especially those with young children); how-to (handcrafted items, etc); humor (as it pertains to family life, birthing, rearing children); personal experience (birthing/coaching, rearing children, teaching, etc.); photo feature (family life—on the farm, in the city, etc.); travel (what to do when traveling with infants and young children with/without entertainment, etc.); and medical advances in natal and prenatal. Buys 20-50 mss/year. Send complete ms. Length: 500-1,500. Pays $2.50-5.
Photos: Send photos with query or ms. Reviews b&w and color prints, but color is printed as b&w. Pays $1. Captions required. Buys one-time rights.
Fiction: Adventure, fantasy (especially read aloud for young children); historical; mystery; romance; science

fiction; serialized novels; suspense; and all types of children's fiction—also artwork for children up to 8 years of age. All material should be family-oriented—no erotica or excessive language. Buys 10-20 mss/year. Send complete ms. Length: 500-1,500 words. Pays $2.50-5.
Poetry: Buys 5-15/year. Submit maximum 10 poems. Length: open. Pays $2.50.

‡**THE EXCEPTIONAL PARENT, Children with Disabilities/Practical Information,** Psy/Ed Corp., 605 Commonwealth Ave., Boston MA 02215. (617)536-8961. Editor: Maxwell Schleifer. Managing Editor: Ellen Herman. 30% freelance written. Magazine published 8 times/year covering issues of concern to parents of disabled children. "Our editorial goal is to provide practical guidance and help to those interested in the growth and development of people with disabilities. We bring together people with different perspectives to present the most comprehensive view of the individual, to generate new solutions to old problems, to create visions." Circ. 35,000. Pays on publication. Byline given. Buys all rights. Submit seasonal/holiday material 3 months in advance. Simultaneous, photocopied and previously published submissions OK. Computer printout submissions acceptable; prefers letter-quality to dot-matrix. Reports in 6 months maximum. Sample copy for $3; free writer's guidelines.
Nonfiction: Book excerpts; essays; how-to (adapt toys, fix wheelchairs, etc.); inspirational (family stories); new product; personal experience; and travel. Buys 40 mss/year. Send complete ms. Length: 500-5,000 words. Pays $25-75.
Photos: Send photos with submission. Reviews 3x5 or larger prints. Offers no additional payment for photos accepted with ms. Model releases required. Buys one-time rights.
Tips: "We welcome articles by parents, disabled individuals, professionals, and anyone else—including children."

EXPECTING, 685 3rd Ave., New York NY 10017. Editor: Evelyn A. Podsiadlo. Assistant Editor: Grace Lang. Issued quarterly for expectant mothers. Circ. 1,200,000. Buys all rights. Byline given. Pays on acceptance. Reports in 1 month. Free writer's guidelines.
Nonfiction: Prenatal development, layette and nursery planning, budgeting, health, fashion, husband-wife relationships, naming the baby, minor discomforts, childbirth, expectant fathers, working while pregnant, etc. Length: 800-1,600 words. Pays $200-300 for feature articles.
Fillers: Short humor and interesting or unusual happenings during pregnancy or at the hospital; maximum 100 words, $10 on publication; submissions to "Happenings" are not returned.
Poetry: Occasionally buys subject-related poetry; all forms. Length: 12-64 lines. Pays $10-30.

GIFTED CHILDREN MONTHLY, For the Parents of Children with Great Promise, Box 115, Sewell NJ 08080. (609)582-0277. Editor: Dr. James Alvino. Managing Editor: Robert Baum. 50% freelance written. Monthly newsletter covering parenting and education of gifted children for parents. Circ. 50,000. Pays on acceptance. Publishes ms an average of 6 months after acceptance. Buys all rights and first rights. Submit seasonal/holiday material 4 months in advance. Simultaneous queries, and simultaneous, photocopied, and previously published submissions OK. Computer printout submissions acceptable; prefers letter-quality to dot-matrix. Reports in 1 month on queries; 2 months on mss. Sample copy and writer's guidelines for 9x12 SAE and 51¢ postage.
Nonfiction: Book excerpts; personal accounts; how-to (on parenting of gifted kids); research into practice; outstanding programs; interview/profile; and opinion. Also puzzles, brainteasers and ideas for children's Spin-Off section. "Our Special Reports and Idea Place sections are most accessible to freelancers." Query with clips of published work or send complete ms. Buys 36 unsolicited mss/year. Length: Idea Place 500-750 words; Special Reports 1,000-2,500 words. Pays $10-200.
Tips: "We look forward to working with both new and veteran writers who have something new to say to the parents of gifted and talented children. It is helpful if freelancers provide copies of research papers to back up the article."

GROWING PARENT, Dunn & Hargitt, Inc., 22 N. 2nd St., Box 1100, Lafayette IN 47902. (317)423-2624. Editor: Nancy Kleckner. 40-50% freelance written. Works with a small number of new/unpublished writers each year. "We do receive a lot of unsolicited submissions but have had excellent results in working with some unpublished writers. So, we're always happy to look at material and hope to find one or two jewels each year." A monthly newsletter which focuses on parents—the issues, problems, and choices they face as their children grow. "We want to look at the parent as an adult and help encourage his or her growth not only as a parent but as an individual." Pays on acceptance. Publishes ms an average of 6 months after acceptance. Byline given. Buys first North American serial rights; maintains exclusive rights for three months. Submit seasonal/holiday material 6 months in advance. Photocopied submissions and previously published submissions OK. Computer printout submissions acceptable; prefers letter-quality to dot-matrix. Reports in 2 weeks. Sample copy and writer's guidelines for 9x6 SAE with 37¢ postage.
Nonfiction: "We are looking for informational articles written in an easy-to-read, concise style. We would like to see articles that help parents deal with the stresses they face in everyday life—positive, upbeat, how-to-

cope suggestions. We rarely use humorous pieces, fiction or personal experience articles. Writers should keep in mind that most of our readers have children under three years of age." Buys 15-20 mss/year. Query. Length: 1,500-2,000 words; will look at shorter pieces. 8-10¢/word (depends on article).

Tips: "Submit a very specific query letter with samples."

‡HOME EDUCATION MAGAZINE, Box 218, Tonasket WA 98855. Editor: Mark J. Hegener. Managing Editor: Helen E. Hegener. 80% freelance written. Eager to work with new/unpublished writers each year. A monthly magazine covering home-based education. "We feature articles which address the concerns of parents who want to take a direct involvement in the education of their children—concerns such as socialization, how to find curriculums and materials, testing and evaluation, how to tell when your child is ready to begin reading, what to do when home schooling is illegal in your state, teaching advanced subjects, etc." Circ. 2,500. Pays on publication. Publishes ms an average of 2 months after acceptance. Byline given. Buys first North American serial rights, first rights, one-time rights, second serial (reprint) rights, simultaneous rights, all rights, and makes work-for-hire assignments. Submit seasonal/holiday material 3 months in advance. Simultanous, photocopied and previously published submissions OK. Electronic submissions via CPM. "We use Kaypro II's", but requires hard copy also. Computer printout submissions acceptable; prefers letter-quality. Reports in 1 month. Sample copy $2; free writer's guidelines.

Nonfiction: Book excerpts, essays, how-to (related to home schooling), humor, inspirational, interview/profile, personal experience, photo feature, religious and technical. "No off-color submissions. We are a family publication." Buys 40-50 mss/year. Query with or without published clips, or send complete ms. Length: 250-2,500 words. Pays $5/500 words; 1 year subscription in addition to payment if desired.

Photos: Send photos with submission. Reviews 5x7, 35mm prints and b&w snapshots. Offers $5/photo; $10/photo used on the cover. Identification of subjects required. Buys one-time rights.

Columns/Departments: Kid's Pages (activities of interest to children), and Resources and Reviews (reviews of products of interest to home educators). Buys 20-30 mss/year. Send complete ms. Length: 100-250 words. Pays $5-25.

Poetry: Free verse, haiku, light verse and traditional. Buys 10-12 poems/year. Length: 4-40 lines. Pays $5-20.

Tips: "Articles are most open to freelancers; but know what you're talking about. We would like to see interviews with homeschool leaders; how-to articles (that don't preach, just present options); articles on computers, testing, accountability, working with the public schools, socialization, learning disabilities, resources, support groups, legislation and humor. We need answers to the questions that home schoolers ask."

HOME LIFE, Sunday School Board, 127 9th Ave. N., Nashville TN 37234. (615)251-2271. Editor-in-Chief: Reuben Herring. 40-50% freelance written. Eager to work with new/unpublished writers. Emphasizes Christian family life. For married adults of all ages, but especially newlyweds and middle-aged marrieds. Monthly magazine; 64 pages. Circ. 800,000. Pays on acceptance. Publishes ms an average of 18 months after acceptance. Buys first serial rights, first North American serial rights and all rights. Byline given. Phone queries OK, but written queries preferred. Submit seasonal/holiday material 1 year in advance. Computer printout submissions acceptable; prefers letter-quality to dot-matrix. Reports in 6 weeks. Sample copy 75¢; free writer's guidelines.

Nonfiction: How-to (good articles on marriage and family life); informational (about some current family-related issue of national significance such as "Television and the Christian Family" or "Whatever Happened to Family Worship?"); personal experience (informed articles by people who have solved marriage and family problems in healthy, constructive ways); marriage and family life with a masculine slant. "No column material. We are not interested in material that will not in some way enrich Christian marriage or family life." Buys 150-200 mss/year. Query or submit complete ms. Length: 600-2,400 words. Pays 4¢/word.

Fiction: "Fiction should be family-related and should show a strong moral about how families face and solve problems constructively." Buys 12-20 mss/year. Submit complete ms. Length: 1,000-2,400 words. Pays 5¢/word.

Tips: "Study the magazine to see our unique slant on Christian family life. We prefer a life-centered case study approach, rather than theoretical essays on family life. Our top priority is marriage enrichment material."

KIDS KIDS KIDS, The Santa Clara Newspaper for Parents, Kids Kids Kids Publications, Inc., Box 2277, Saratoga CA 95070. Editor: Lynn Berado. 80% freelance written. Prefers to work with locally-based published/established writers. Monthly tabloid of resource information for parents and teachers. Circ 50,000. Pays on publication. Publishes ms an average of 3 months after acceptance. Byline given. Buys one-time rights. Submit seasonal/holiday material 3 months in advance. Simultaneous, photocopied, and previously published submissions OK. Electronic submissions OK on IBM. Computer printout submissions acceptable. Sample copy and writer's guidelines for legal size SAE and $1.50 postage.

Nonfiction: Book excerpts (related to our interest group); expose (health, psychology); historical/nostalgic ("History of Diapers"); how-to (related to kids/parenting); humor; interview/profile; photo feature; and travel (with kids, family). Special issues include Music (February); Art (March); Kid's Birthdays (April); Summer

Camps (May); Family Fun (June); Pregnancy and Childbirth (July); Fashion (August); Health (September); and Mental Health (October). No opinion or religious articles. Buys 36-50 mss/year. Query or send complete ms. Length: 150-1,500 words. Pays $10-50. Sometimes pays expenses of writers on assignment.
Photos: State availability of photos. Prefers b&w contact sheets and/or 3x5 b&w prints. Pays $5-20. Model release required. Buys one-time rights.
Columns/Departments: Child Care, Family Travel, Birthday Party Ideas, Baby Page, Toddler Page, Kids Activity Page. Buys 36 mss/year. Send complete ms. Length: 800-1,000 words. Pays $5-25.
Fiction: Humorous.
Tips: "Submit new, fresh information concisely written and accurately researched."

L.A. PARENT, The Magazine for Parents in Southern California, Pony Publications, Box 65795, Los Angeles CA 90065. (818)240-PONY. Editor: Jack Bierman. Managing Editor: Judith Pfeffer. 80% freelance written. Prefers to work with published/established writers, and will work with a small number of new/unpublished writers each year. Monthly tabloid covering parenting. Circ. 75,000. Pays on publication. Publishes ms an average of 4 months after acceptance. Byline given. Buys all rights. Submit seasonal/holiday material 3 months in advance. Simultaneous queries and previously published submissions OK. Computer printout submissions acceptable. Reports in 1 month. Sample copy $2; free writer's guidelines.
Nonfiction: Steve Linder, articles editor. General interest, how-to. "We focus on southern California activities for families, and do round-up pieces, i.e., a guide to private schools, fishing spots." Buys 60-75 mss/year. Query with clips of published work. Length: 700-1,200 words. Pays $100 plus expenses.
Tips: "If you can write for a 'city magazine' in tone and accuracy you may write for us. The 'Baby Boom' has created a need for more generic parenting material."

LIVING WITH CHILDREN, Baptist Sunday School Board, 127 9th Ave. N., Nashville TN 37234. (615)251-2229. Editor: SuAnne Bottoms. 50% freelance written. Quarterly magazine covering parenting issues for parents of elementary-age children (ages 6 through 11). "Written and designed from a Christian perspective." Circ. 50,000. Pays on acceptance. Publishes ms an average of 2 years after acceptance. Byline given. "We generally buy all rights to mss; first serial rights on a limited basis. First and reprint rights may be negotiated at a lower rate of pay." Submit seasonal/holiday material 1 year in advance. Previously published submissions (on limited basis) OK. Computer printout submissions acceptable; no dot-matrix. Reports in 1 month on queries; 2 months on mss. Sample copy for 9x12 manila SASE; free writer's guidelines.
Nonfiction: How-to (parent), humor, inspirational, personal experience, and articles on child development. No highly technical material or articles containing more than 15-20 lines quoted material. Buys 60 mss/year. Query or send complete ms (queries preferred). Length: 800-1,800 words (1,450 words preferred). Pays 5¢/word.
Photos: "Submission of photos with mss is strongly discouraged."
Fiction: Humorous (parent/child relationships); and religious. "We have very limited need for fiction." Buys maximum of 4 mss/year. Length: 800-1,450 words. Pays 5¢/word.
Poetry: Light verse and inspirational. "We have limited need for poetry and buy only all rights." Buys 15 poems/year. Submit maximum 3 poems. Length: 4-30 lines. Pays $1.75 (for 1-7 lines) plus $1 for each additional line; pays $4.50 for 8 lines and more plus 65¢ each additional line.
Fillers: Jokes, anecdotes and short humor. Buys 15/year. Length: 100-400 words. Pays $5 minimum, 5¢/word.
Tips: "Articles must deal with an issue of interest to parents. A mistake some writers make in articles for us is failing to write from a uniquely Christian perspective; that is very necessary for our periodicals. Material should be 850, 1,450, or 1,800 words in length. All sections, particularly articles, are open to freelance writers. Only regular features are assigned."

LIVING WITH PRESCHOOLERS, Baptist Sunday School Board, 127 9th Ave. N., Nashville TN 37234. (615)251-2229. Editor: SuAnne Bottoms. 50% freelance written. Quarterly magazine covering parenting issues for parents of preschoolers (infants through 5-year-olds). The magazine is "written and designed from a Christian perspective." Circ. 152,000. Pays on acceptance. Publishes manuscript an average of 2 years after acceptance. Byline given. "We generally buy all rights to manuscripts. First and reprint rights may be negotiated at a lower rate of pay." Submit seasonal/holiday material 2 years in advance. Previously published submissions (on limited basis) OK. Computer printout submissions acceptable; no dot-matrix. Reports in 1 month on queries; 2 months on mss. Sample copy for 9x12 manila SASE; free writer's guidelines.
Nonfiction: How-to (parent), humor, inspirational, personal experience, and articles on child development. No highly technical material or articles containing more than 15-20 lines quoted material. Buys 60 mss/year. Query or send complete ms (queries preferred). Length: 800-1,800 words (1,450 words preferred). Pays 5¢/word for manuscripts offered on all-rights basis.
Photos: "Submission of photos with mss is strongly discouraged."
Fiction: Humorous (parent/child relationships); and religious. "We have very limited need for fiction." Buys maximum of 4 mss/year. Length: 800-1,450 words. Pays 5¢/word.

Poetry: Light verse and inspirational. "We have limited need for poetry and buy only all rights." Buys 15 poems/year. Submit maximum 3 poems. Length: 4-30 lines. Pays $1.75 (for 1-7 lines) plus $1 for each additional line; pays $4.50 for 8 lines and more plus 65¢ each additional line.

Fillers: Jokes, anecdotes and short humor. Buys 15/year. Length: 100-400 words. Pays $5 minimum, 5¢/word maximum.

Tips: "Articles must deal with an issue of interest to parents. A mistake some writers make in writing an article for us is failing to write from a uniquely Christian perspective; that is very necessary for our periodicals. Material should be 850, 1,450, or 1,800 words in length. All sections, particularly articles, are open to freelance writers. Only regular features are assigned."

NETWORK, The Paper for Parents, National Committee for Citizens in Education, 410 Wilde Lake Village Green, Columbia MD 21044. (301)997-9300. Editor: Chrissie Bamber. 10% freelance written. Works with a small number of new/unpublished writers each year. Tabloid published 8 times during the school year covering parent/citizen involvement in public schools. Circ. 6,000. Pays on publication. Publishes ms an average of 6 months after acceptance. Byline given. Buys first serial rights, first North American serial rights, one-time rights, second serial (reprint) rights, simultaneous rights, all rights and makes work-for-hire assignments. Submit seasonal/holiday material 3 months in advance. Simultaneous queries and photocopied submissions OK. Computer printout submissions acceptable. Reports in 6 weeks. Free sample copy; writer's guidelines for #10 SAE and 39¢ postage.

Nonfiction: Book excerpts (elementary and secondary public education); exposé (of school systems which attempt to reduce public access); how-to (improve schools through parent/citizen participation); humor (related to public school issues); opinion (school-related issues); personal experience (school-related issues). "It is our intention to provide balanced coverage of current developments and continuing issues and to place the facts about schools in a perspective useful to parents. No highly technical or scholarly articles about education; no child rearing articles or personal opinion not backed by research or concrete examples." Buys 4-6 mss/year. Query with clips of published work or send complete ms. Length: 1,000-1,500 words. Pays $25-100. Sometimes pays the expenses of writers on assignment.

Tips: "Readers want articles of substance with information they can use and act on, not headlines which promise much but deliver only the most shallow analysis of the subject. Information is first, style second. A high personal commitment to public schools and preferably first-hand experience is the greatest asset. A clear and simple writing style, easily understood by a wide range of lay readers is a must."

‡THE PARENT'S GUIDE, To child care and education in Bucks and Montgomery Counties, The Renters Guide, 460A Grape St., Warminster PA 18974. (215)674-2120. Editor: Mary A. Oat. 85% freelance written. A monthly newsletter covering child care and education. "Our audience is composed mainly of working parents (mostly white-collar) of children aged 0 to 8 years." Estab. 1985. Circ. 1,200. Pays on publication. Publishes ms an average of 2 months after acceptance. Byline given. Buys one-time rights. Submit seasonal/holiday material 2 months in advance. Simultaneous, photocopied, and previously published submissions OK. Computer printout submissions acceptable; prefers letter-quality to dot-matrix. Reports in 2 weeks. Sample copy for 9x12 SAE with 56¢ postage; free writer's guidelines.

Nonfiction: Essays (on themes of interest to parents); how-to (what parents can "do" with their children); humor, new product, opinion, personal experience, and articles on any subject of interest to parents of children up to age 8. Buys 60 mss/year. Send complete ms. Length: 500-1,500 words. Pays 2¢/word; pays in copies for opinion pieces.

Photos: Send photos with submissions (only if very important to article). Reviews 8x10 prints. Offers $2/photo. Captions required. Buys one-time rights.

Columns/Departments: Open to new ideas. Buys 12 mss/year. Query with column idea and send sample of proposed column. Length: 500-1,500 words. Pays 2¢/word.

Fiction: Humorous and slice-of-life-vignettes, dealing with any aspect of family life. No need for other types of fiction. Buys 6 mss/year. Send complete ms. Length: 500-1,500 words. Pays 2¢/word.

Poetry: Light verse. "Nothing morose, please." Buys 12 poems/year. Submit maximum 5 poems. Length: 4-36 lines. Pays 2¢/word.

Fillers: Anecdotes, facts, newsbreaks and short humor. Length: 50-250 words. Pays 2¢/word.

Tips: "Although our publication is local to Montgomery and Bucks Counties, Pennsylvania, we will accept submissions from anywhere as long as the subject is of universal interest to parents of children aged 0 to 8 years. We are an excellent market for new writers because we are more interested in the submission itself rather than the writer's resume."

PARENTS MAGAZINE, 685 3rd Ave., New York NY 10017. Editor: Elizabeth Crow. 25% freelance written. Monthly. Circ. 1,670,000. Pays on acceptance. Publishes ms an average of 8 months after acceptance. Usually buys first serial rights or first North American serial rights; sometimes buys all rights. Byline given "except for Almanac." Pays $100-350 kill fee. Computer printout submissions acceptable; prefers letter-quality to dot-matrix. Reports in approximately 6 weeks.

Nonfiction: "We are interested in well-documented articles on the development and behavior of preschool, school-age, and adolescent children and their parents; good, practical guides to the routines of baby care; articles that offer professional insights into family and marriage relationships; reports of new trends and significant research findings in education and in mental and physical health; and articles encouraging informed citizen action on matters of social concern. Especially need articles on women's issues, pregnancy, birth, baby care and early childhood. We prefer a warm, colloquial style of writing, one which avoids the extremes of either slang or technical jargon. Anecdotes and examples should be used to illustrate points which can then be summed up by straight exposition." Query. Length: 2,500 words maximum. Payment varies; pays $400 minimum; $50 minimum for Almanac items. Sometimes pays the expenses of writers on assignment.

Fillers: Anecdotes for "Parents Exchange," illustrative of parental problem-solving with children and teenagers. Pays $20 on publication.

PEDIATRICS FOR PARENTS, The Newsletter for Caring Parents, Pediatrics for Parents, Inc., 176 Mt. Hope Ave., Bangor ME 04401. (207)942-6212. Editor: Richard J. Sagall, M.D. 20% freelance written. Monthly newsletter covering medical aspects of raising children and educating parents about children's health. Circ. 2,800. Pays on publication. Publishes ms an average of 2 months after acceptance. Byline given. Buys first North American serial rights, first and second rights to the same material, and second (reprint) rights to material originally published elsewhere. Rights always include right to publish article in our books on "Best of . `. ." series. Submit seasonal/holiday material 6 months in advance. Simultaneous queries, and simultaneous, photocopied and previously published submissions OK. Electronic submissions OK compatible with Apple-PFS or Appleworks. Computer printout submissions acceptable. Reports in 1 month on queries; 6 weeks on mss. Sample copy for $2; writer's guidelines for business size SAE and 1 first class stamp.

Nonfiction: Book reviews; how-to (feed healthy kids, exercise, practice wellness, etc.); new product; technical (explaining medical concepts in shirtsleeve language). No general parenting articles. Query with published clips or submit complete ms. Length: 25-1,000 words. Pays 2-5¢/edited word.

Columns/Departments: Book reviews; Please Send Me (material available to parents for free or at nominal cost); Pedia-Tricks (medically-oriented parenting tips that work). Send complete ms. Pays $15-250. Pays 2¢/edited word.

Tips: "We are dedicated to taking the mystery out of medicine for young parents. Therefore, we write in clear and understandable language (but not simplistic language) to help people understand and deal intelligently with complex disease processes, treatments, prevention, wellness, etc. Our articles must be well researched and documented. Detailed references must always be attached to any article for documentation, but not for publication. We strongly urge freelancers to read one or two issues before writing."

SEATTLE'S CHILD, Box 22578, Seattle WA 98122. (206)322-2594. Editor: Ann Bergman. Managing Editor: Eleanor Weston. 80% freelance written. Eager to work with new/unpublished writers. Monthly tabloid of articles related to being a parent of children age 12 and under. Directed to parents and professionals involved with children 12 and under. Circ. 10,000. Pays on publication. Publishes ms an average of 2 months after acceptance. Byline given. Offers 50% kill fee. Buys first North American serial rights or all rights. Submit seasonal/ holiday material 6 months in advance. Simultaneous queries, and simultaneous and photocopied submissions OK. Electronic submissions OK via IBM PC, 1200 baud, but requires hard copy also. Computer printout submissions acceptable. Reports in 6 weeks on queries; 4 weeks on mss. Sample copy $1.50; writer's guidelines for business size SAE and 1 first class stamp.

Nonfiction: Needs reports on political issues affecting families. Expose, general interest, historical/nostalgic, how-to, humor, interview/profile, new product, opinion, personal experience, travel, record, tape and book reviews, and educational and political reviews. Articles must relate to parents and parenting. Buys 120 mss/year. Send complete ms (preferred) or query with published clips. Length: 400-2,500 words. Pays $25-500. Sometimes pays the expenses of writers on assignment.

Photos: Robert Cole, photo editor. Send photos with query or ms. Reviews 5x7 b&w prints. Pays $25-125. Model release required. Buys one-time rights or all rights.

Fillers: Gags. Buys 500/year. Length: 50-250 words. Pays 20¢/word.

Tips: "We prefer concise, critical writing and discourage overly sentimental pieces. Don't talk down to the audience. Consider that the audience is well-educated, sophisticated and well-read."

STEP-LIFE, The Problems & Joys of Step-parenting & Remarriage, Wall Publications, 901 Ivy Ct., Eaton OH 45320. (513)456-6611. Editor: Carla Wall. Bimonthly newsletter on step-parenting and remarriage. Estab. 1985. Circ. 500. Pays on publication. Publishes ms an average of 6 months after acceptance. Byline given. Buys first North American serial rights and second serial (reprint) rights. Submit seasonal/holiday material 4 months in advance. Simultaneous queries OK. Computer printout submissions acceptable; prefers letter-quality to dot-matrix. Reports in 2 weeks on queries; 2 months on mss. Sample copy $1 with SASE.

Nonfiction: How-to, humor, inspirational, interview/profile, opinion, and personal experience—anything on step-parenting and remarriage subjects. "No 'how we made it as a family.' We need fresh slants and good ideas." Buys 6-8 mss/year. Query. Length: 500-2,500 words. Pays 1-3¢/word.

Columns/Departments: Deena Sharpe, column/department editor. Between You and Me (on remarriages). Query. Length: 1,000-1,500 words. Pays 2-5¢/word.

Fiction: July/August issue is fiction edition. Humorous, mainstream and slice-of-life vignettes; stories focused on remarriage or step-parenting only. Buys 1-3 mss/year. Query. Length: 2,000 words maximum. Pays 1-4¢/word.

Fillers: Clippings, anecdotes, facts, jokes, gags, anecdotes, short humor and newsbreaks. Buys 6/year. Length: 50-1,000 words. Pays $1-5.

Tips: "We are backlogged with submissions and prefer not to receive unsolicited submissions at this time. Query with SASE. Don't phone editors unless you are advised to do so. We are accepting fillers."

TWINS, The Magazine for Parents of Multiples, TWINS Magazine, Inc., Box 12045, Overland Park KS 66212. (913)722-1090. Editor: Barbara C. Unell. 100% freelance written. Works with a small number of new/unpublished writers each year. A bimonthly magazine covering parenting of multiples. Circ. 30,000. Pays on publication. Publishes ms an average of 6 months after acceptance. Byline given. Buys all rights. Submit seasonal/holiday material 10 months in advance. Simultaneous, photocopied and previously published submissions OK. Computer printout submissions acceptable; prefers letter-quality to dot-matrix. Reports in 6 weeks on queries; 2 months on mss. Sample copy $3.50 plus $1.50 postage and handling; writer's guidelines for #10 SAE with 1 first class stamp.

Nonfiction: Book excerpts, general interest, how-to, humor, interview/profile, personal experience and photo feature. "No articles which substitute the word 'twin' for 'child'—those that simply apply the same research to twins that applies to singletons without any facts backing up the reason to do so." Buys 150 mss/year. Query with or without published clips, or send complete ms. Length: 1,250-3,000 words. Payment varies; sometimes pays in contributor copies or premiums instead of cash. Sometimes pays the expenses of writers on assignment.

Photos: Send photos with submission. Reviews contact sheets, 4x5 transparencies, and all size prints. Captions, model releases, and identification of subjects required. Buys all rights.

Columns/Departments: Resources, Supertwins, Prematurity, Family Health, Twice as Funny, Double Focus (series from pregnancy through adolescence), A Parent's Perspective (first-person accounts of beliefs about a certain aspect of parenting multiples) and Caring for You (ways parents can feel as good as can be as people, not just parents). Buys 70 mss/year. Query with published clips. Length: 1,250-2,000 words. Payment varies.

Fillers: Anecdotes and short humor. Length: 75-750 words. Payment varies.

Tips: "Features and columns are both open to freelancers. Columnists write for *Twins* on a continuous basis, so the column becomes their column. We are looking for a wide variety of the latest, well-researched practical information. There is no other magazine of this type directed to this market."

Consumer Service and Business Opportunity

Readers of these publications want to get the most for their money. Some magazines are geared to persons wanting to invest earnings or start a new business; others show readers how to make economical purchases. For some publications, entrepreneurship is an important topic. Publications for business executives and consumers interested in business topics are listed under Business and Finance. Those on how to run specific businesses are classified by category in Trade, Technical and Professional Journals.

BUSINESS TODAY, Meridian Publishing Inc., Box 10010, Ogden UT 84409. (801)394-9446. Editor: Robin Walker. 65% freelance written. Monthly magazine covering all aspects of business. Particularly interested in profiles of business personalities. Pays on acceptance. Publishes ms an average of 8 months after acceptance. Byline given. Buys first rights, second serial (reprint) rights and nonexclusive reprint rights. Computer printout submissions acceptable; prefers letter-quality to dot-matrix. Reports in 6 weeks. Sample copy for $1

and 9x12 SAE; writer's guidelines for legal-size SAE and 1 first class stamp. All requests for samples and guidelines should be addressed Attn: Editorial Assistant.
Nonfiction: General interest articles about employee relations, management principles, advertising methods and financial planning. Articles covering up-to-date practical business information are welcome. Cover stories are often profiles of people who have expertise and success in a specific aspect of business. Buys 40 mss/year. Query. Length: 1,000-1,400 words. Pays 15¢/word for first rights plus non-exclusive reprint rights. Payment for second rights is negotiable..
Photos: State availability of photos or send photos with query. Reviews 35mm or longer transparencies and 5x7 prints. Pays $35 for inside photo; pays $50 for cover photo. Captions, model releases and identification of subjects required.
Tips: "The key is a well-written query letter that: 1) demonstrates that the subject of the article is tried-and-true and has national appeal 2) shows that the article will have a clear, focused theme 3) outlines the availability (from writer or a photographer or a PR source) of top-quality color photos 4) gives evidence that the writer/photographer is a professional, even if a beginner."

CATALOG SHOPPER MAGAZINE, EGW International Corp., #8, 1300 Galaxy Way, Concord CA 94520. (415)671-9852. Editor: Debra Wittenberg. Quarterly magazine covering mail-order catalogs in over 40 categories. "Our magazine provides a unique way to shop at home from catalogs in over 40 categories. Included are many hard-to-find items. It is designed to help our readers by satisfying their hobby needs and making their lives more interesting through knowledge of the variety of specialty catalogs available to them." Circ. 15,000. Pays on publication. Publishes ms an average of 3 months after acceptance. Buys first North American serial rights. Submit seasonal/holiday material 6 months in advance. Simultaneous queries and photocopied submissions OK. Computer printout submissions acceptable; prefers letter-quality to dot-matrix. Reports in 2 weeks on queries; 8 weeks on mss. Sample copy $1.50; writer's guidelines for SAE.
Columns/Departments: Doing It Yourself, My Hobby, Life At A Glance, For Better Health, Investment Sidelights, Discovery & Science and High Tech Tidbits. Length: 250 words maximum for each original contribution. Maximum length 50 words for our Questions To Ponder and for jokes, ancedotes, short humor, puzzle or light verse in Take It Easy. Maximum length 100 words in our Point Of Interest for items including traveling, scenery, historical sites. Contributions to our Culinary Delights should list all ingredients and measurements. Choose a recipe that has an interesting story to go with it. Pays 4¢ a word.
Photos: Seeks colorful outdoor, seasonal photographs for magazine cover. Should be either 35mm negative color slide or 4x5 transparency. Prefers vertical photos. Will return material if requested; enclose SAE and adequate postage. When submitting work, include a brief note about yourself and the place where the picture was taken. This will be edited as a "cover photo" note if your photo is published. Pays $50 upon publication.

CONSUMER ACTION NEWS, 1579 Lexington Ave., Springfield OH 45505. (513)325-2001. Editor: Victor Pence. 50% freelance written. Eager to work with new/unpublished writers. A monthly newsletter circulated in the state of Ohio for readers who are interested in knowing how to handle any type consumer complaint. "We handle consumer complaints and publish results in newsletter." Circ. 5,000. Pays on acceptance. Publishes ms an average of 2 months after acceptance. Byline given. Copyrighted. Buys one-time rights. Submit seasonal/holiday material minimum 2 months in advance. Simultaneous queries, and simultaneous, photocopied, and previously published submissions OK. Computer printout submissions acceptable; prefers letter-quality to dot-matrix. Reports in 3 weeks. Sample copy for #10 SAE and 22¢ postage.
Nonfiction: Exposé (material has to be documented or supported with some type of evidence that is legally sound); general interest (could include experiences with a company—must name company, etc.); how-to (anything that could help consumers get better use from the products they buy. For example: a new slant on car care, repairing washer/drier, etc. Has to be very different, not the type of thing found in *Popular Mechanics*, etc.). No material that is not consumer "protection" oriented. Interviews no longer accepted. Send complete ms. Length: 2,000 words maximum. Pays $10-100. For material suitable for booklets of 10-30 pages, pays flat rate or percentage of sales, may consider combination of both. Sometimes pays the expenses of writers on assignment.
Columns/Departments: "We will consider ideas." Send complete ms. Pays $10-100.
Tips: "Every area is open to freelancers. Our type of publication is new in that we print complaints of consumers and name names of the companies involved. We give credit where it is due—good or bad."

CONSUMERS DIGEST MAGAZINE, Consumers Digest, Inc., 5705 N. Lincoln Ave., Chicago IL 60659. (312)275-3590. Editor: Robin C. Nelson. 75% freelance written. Prefers to work with published/established writers. Emphasizes anything of consumer interest. Monthly magazine. Circ. 1,000,000. Pays on acceptance. Publishes ms an average of 3 months after acceptance. Buys all rights. Computer printout submissions acceptable. Reports in 1 month. Free guidelines for SAE and 1 first class stamp to published writers only.
Nonfiction: Product-testing, evaluating; general interest (on advice to consumers, service, health, home, business, investments, insurance and money management); new products and travel. Query. Length: 1,200-3,000 words. Also buys shorter, more topical pieces (300-800 words) for Consumer Scope, Health

Digest. Fees negotiable. First-time contributors usually are paid 25¢/word. Expenses paid.
Tips: "Send short query with samples of published work. Assignments are made upon acceptance of comprehensive outline."

CONSUMERS' RESEARCH, 517 2nd St. NE, Washington DC 20002. Editor: Maureen Bozell. 70% freelance written. Prefers to work with published/established writers. Monthly. Byline given "except when the article as written requires extensive editing, improvement or amplification." Buys first serial rights, second serial (reprint) rights and all rights. Query. Publishes ms an average of 3 months after acceptance. Computer printout submissions acceptable; no dot-matrix. Sample copy for SAE and 4 first class stamps.
Nonfiction: Articles of practical interest to consumers concerned with tests and expert judgment of goods and services they buy. Must be accurate and well-supported by professional knowledge of subject matter of articles. "We are interested in articles that give information to consumers about past and current topics affecting them. The field is wide and includes products, home-improvement pieces, finance, health care, and consumer trend." Pays approximately $100/page.
Tips: "Any writer for *Consumer's Research* should make sure that an article is written knowledgeably, that it is filled with checked and rechecked facts, and that it is written well."

ECONOMIC FACTS, The National Research Bureau, Inc., 424 N. 3rd St., Burlington IA 52601. Editor: Rhonda Wilson. Editorial Supervisor: Doris J. Ruschill. Magazine for industrial workers of all ages. 25% freelance written. Works with a small number of new/unpublished writers each year. Published 4 times/year. Pays on publication. Buys all rights. Byline given. Submit seasonal/holiday material 7 months in advance of issue date. Previously published submissions OK. Publishes ms an average of 1 year after acceptance. Computer printout submissions acceptable; prefers letter-quality to dot-matrix. Reports in 1 week. Free writer's guidelines.
Nonfiction: General interest (private enterprise, government data, graphs, taxes and health care). Buys 3-5 mss/year. Query with outline of article. Length: 400-600 words. Pays 4¢/word.

ENTREPRENEUR MAGAZINE, 2311 Pontius Ave., Los Angeles CA 90064. (213)478-0437. Publisher: Wellington Ewen. 40% freelance written. For a readership looking for profitable opportunities in small businesses, as owners, franchisees. Monthly magazine with "tips and tactics on running a small business." Circ. 200,000. Pays 60 days after acceptance. Publishes ms an average of 3 months after acceptance. Buys all rights. Byline given. Submit seasonal/holiday material 5 months in advance of issue date. Photocopied submissions OK. Computer printout submissions acceptable; no dot-matrix. Reports in 2 months. Sample copy $3; free writer's guidelines.
Nonfiction: How-to (in-depth start-up details on 'hot' business opportunities like tanning parlors or computer stores). Buys 50 mss/year. Query with clips of published work. Length: 1,200-2,000 words. Payment varies.
Photos: "We need good b&w glossy prints or color transparencies to illustrate articles." Offers additional payment for photos accepted with ms. Uses 8x10 b&w glossy prints or standard color transparencies. Captions preferred. Buys all rights. Model release required.
Columns/Departments: New Products; New Ideas; Promo Gimmicks. Query. Length: 200-500 words. Pays $25-100.
Tips: "It's rewarding to find a freelancer who reads the magazine *before* he/she submits a query—and who turns in a piece that's exactly what you've told him/her you want—especially if it doesn't have to be rewritten several times. We get so many queries with the wrong 'angle.' I can't stress enough the importance of reading and understanding our magazine and who our audience is before you write. We're looking for writers who can perceive the difference between *Entrepreneur* and 'other' business magazines."

FDA CONSUMER, 5600 Fishers Lane, Rockville MD 20857. (301)443-3220. Editor: William M. Rados. 10% freelance written. Prefers to work with published/established writers. Monthly magazine. For "all consumers of products regulated by the Food and Drug Administration." A federal government publication. December/January and July/August issues combined. Circ. 15,000. Pays after acceptance. Publishes ms an average of 3 months after acceptance. Byline given. Not copyrighted. Pays 50% kill fee. "All purchases automatically become part of public domain." Buys 9-10 freelance mss a year. "We cannot be responsible for any work by writer not agreed upon by prior contract." Electronic submissions OK via Lanier. Computer printout submissions acceptable; prefers letter-quality to dot-matrix.
Nonfiction: "Articles of an educational nature concerning purchase and use of *FDA regulated* products and specific FDA programs and actions to protect the consumer's health and pocketbook. Authoritative and official agency viewpoints emanating from agency policy and actions in administrating the Food, Drug and Cosmetic Act and a number of other statutes. All articles subject to clearance by the appropriate FDA experts as well as acceptance by the editor. Articles based on health topics with the proviso that the subjects be connected to food, drugs, medicine, medical devices, and other products regulated by FDA. All articles based on prior arrangement by contract." Query. Length: 2,000-2,500 words. Pays $1,200 average. Sometimes pays the expenses of writers on assignment.

Photos: B&w photos are purchased on assignment only.
Tips: "Besides reading the feature articles in *FDA Consumer*, a writer can best determine whether his/her style and expertise suits our needs by submitting a query letter, resume and sample clips for our review."

INCOME OPPORTUNITIES, 380 Lexington Ave., New York NY 10017. Editor: Stephen Wagner. Associate Editor: Paula Nichols. 90% freelance written. Works with a small number of new/unpublished writers each year. Monthly magazine. For all who are seeking business opportunities, full- or part-time. Publishes magazine an average of 5 months after acceptance. Buys all rights. Two special directory issues contain articles on selling techniques, mail order, import/export, franchising and business ideas. Computer printout submissions acceptable. Reports in 2 weeks.
Nonfiction and Photos: Regularly covered are such subjects as mail order, direct selling, franchising, party plans, selling techniques and the marketing of handcrafted or homecrafted products. Wanted are ideas for the aspiring entrepreneur; examples of successful business methods that might be duplicated. No material that is purely inspirational. Buys 50-60 mss/year. Query with outline of article development. Length: 800 words for a short; 2,000-3,000 words for a major article. "Payment rates vary according to length and quality of the submission." Sometimes pays expenses of writers on assignment.
Tips: "Study recent issues of the magazine. Best bets for newcomers: Interview-based report on a successful small business venture."

MONEY MAKER, Your Guide to Financial Security & Wealth, Consumers Digest, Inc., 5705 N. Lincoln Ave., Chicago IL 60659. (312)275-3590. Editor: John Manos. 75% freelance written. Works with a small number of new/unpublished writers each year. Bimonthly magazine covering investment markets for unsophisticated investors. "Instructions for neophyte investors to increase their capital." Circ. 300,000. Pays on acceptance. Publishes ms an average of 3 months after acceptance. Byline given. Offers 50% kill fee. Buys all rights. Simultaneous queries and photocopied submissions OK. Computer printout submissions OK. Reports in 6 weeks on queries; 3 months on mss. Free sample copy and writer's guidelines.
Nonfiction: How-to (on investment areas); analysis of specific markets. "Indicate your areas of financial expertise." Buys 60 mss/year. Query with clips of published work if available. Length: 1,000-3,000 words. Pays $250-900. Pays the expenses of writers on assignment.
Tips: "We could use more queries that focus on personal financial planning and budgeting, with an emphasis on using real individuals as examples."

PUBLIC CITIZEN, Public Citizen, Inc., Box 19404, Washington DC 20036. Editor: Elliott Negin. 25% freelance written. Prefers to work with published/established writers. Bimonthly magazine covering consumer issues for "contributors to Public Citizen, a consortium of five consumer groups established by Ralph Nader in the public interest: Congress Watch, the Health Research Group, the Critical Mass Energy Project, the Litigation Group, and the Tax Reform Group. Our readers have joined Public Citizen because they believe the consumer should have a voice in the products he or she buys, the quality of our environment, good government, and citizen rights in our democracy." Circ. 50,000. Pays on publication. Publishes ms an average of 3 months after acceptance. Byline given. Buys first North American serial rights, second serial (reprint) rights and simultaneous rights. Submit seasonal/holiday material 3 months in advance. Electronic submissions OK via CPM or MS DOS, but requires hard copy also. Computer printout submissions acceptable; prefers letter-quality to dot-matrix. Reports in 1 month on queries; 2 months on mss. Publishes ms an average of 3 months after acceptance. Sample copy available.
Nonfiction: Exposé (of government waste and inaction and corporate wrongdoing); general interest (features on how consumer groups are helping themselves); how-to (start consumer groups such as co-ops, etc.); interview/profile (of business or consumer leaders, or of government officials in positions that affect consumers); and photo feature (dealing with consumer power). "We are looking for stories that go to the heart of an issue and explain how it affects individuals. Articles must be in-depth investigations that expose poor business practices or bad government or that call attention to positive accomplishments. Send us stories that consumers will feel they learned something important from or that they can gain inspiration from to continue the fight for consumer rights. All facts are double checked by our fact-checkers." No "fillers, jokes or puzzles." Query or send complete ms. Length: 500-10,000 words. Pays $750 maximum/article. Sometimes pays the expenses of writers on assignment.
Photos: State availability of photos. Reviews 5x7 b&w prints. "Photos are paid for with payment for ms." Captions required. Buys one-time rights.
Columns/Departments: Reliable Sources ("book reviews"). Query or send complete ms—"no clips." Length: 500-1,000 words. Pays $125 maximum/article.
Tips: No first-person articles, political rhetoric, or "mood" pieces; *Public Citizen* is a highly factual advocacy magazine. Knowledge of the public interest movement, consumer issues, and Washington politics is a plus.

‡**SUPER SHOPPER,** A.G.H. Publishing, 2911 S. Industrial Rd., Las Vegas NV 89109. (702)733-8080. Editor: Howard Bernard. 3-4% freelance written. A bimonthly magazine covering supermarket shopping/use of

coupons for value-conscious readers who are young middle-income families. Circ. 466,000. Pays 30 days from publication. Publishes ms an average of 2 months after acceptance. Byline given. Buys first rights or second serial (reprint) rights. Submit seasonal/holiday material 4 months in advance minimum. Simultaneous, photo- copied and previously published submissions are acceptable when "legible, meet criteria and when previously published on regional basis only." Computer printout submissions acceptable; prefers letter-quality to dot-matrix. Reports in 4 months. Sample copy for 6x9 SAE with 2 first class stamps; writer's guidelines for #10 SAE with 1 first class stamp.

Nonfiction: Book excerpts (when used to credit, emphasize, verify subject(s); proof of authorization for publication required); general interest (consumer awareness: discoveries/developments); how-to (save time and money; do-it-yourself: household repairs, gift ideas, etc.); new product (when includes: free samples, advice, toll free number and/or booklets, recipes, etc.). "Specifically, we are interested in articles on refunding, saving sense, health and good nutrition. Articles must be well written with good taste so as not to offend our readers and advertisers." Holiday issue: Thanksgiving/Christmas. Buys 8-12 mss/year. Send complete ms. Length: 700-1,500 words. Sometimes pays the expenses of writers on assignment.

Photos: Send photos with submission. "All articles should have accompanying color photos/illustrations whenever possible." Reviews 2x2 transparencies and 5x8 (color only) prints. Offers $10-25. Captions, model releases and identification of subjects required.

Columns/Departments: Family Health (exercise/nutrition information: tips to fitness/good health—should be enjoyable, interesting, new and refreshing; vitamin news/organic gardening information as it relates to health; other can include, environmental health, i.e., indoor-outdoor pollution), 700 words approximately. Buys 6 mss/year. Send complete ms. Pays $50-100.

Tips: "Each article received that is accompanied by a one paragraph synopsis of the subject matter may get a quicker review. Writer should always consider the timeliness of the subject matter in each article, i.e.; special events, holidays, etc. And of course, seasonality. Photos and/or illustrations get attention. Family Health article content should be thoroughly researched information and verifiable. The general interest, how-tos and new products will probably be the most available to the freelancer."

‡**SWEEPSTAKES MAGAZINE,** AGH Publishing, 2929 S. Industrial Rd., Las Vegas NV 89109. (702)733-8080. Managing Editor: Robert Morris. 3% freelance written. Eager to work with new/unpublished writers. A monthly magazine devoted to the hobby of entering sweepstakes and contests. Audience age group 16-90. Circ. 400,000. Pays on publication. Publishes ms an average of 3 months after acceptance. Byline given. Buys first rights. Submit seasonal/holiday material 4 months in advance. Simultaneous and photocopied submissions OK. Computer printout submissions acceptable; prefers letter-quality to dot-matrix. Reports in 2 months. Free sample copy; writer's guidelines for SAE and 2 first class stamps.

Nonfiction: How-to, humor, interview/profile and personal experience. "All should lean toward winning! Our readers are looking for the quickest, easiest and most 'sure fire' way to win that 'Big One.' We are looking for information concerning shortcuts to entering, tips on winning, interviews with large prize winners, profiles on large winners, kinds of contests to avoid, best chance contests and sweepstakes and the like." Buys 6 mss/year. Send complete ms. Length: 700-1,500 words. Pays $100 maximum. Sometimes pays the expenses of writers on assignment.

Columns/Departments: Buys 4 mss/year. Query with clips of published work. Length: 700-1,500 words. Pays $100 maximum.

Fillers: Clippings, jokes, anecdotes, short humor and newsbreaks. Length: 25-100 words. Pays variable rate.

Tips: Feature stories or fillers pertaining to the winning of contests and sweepstakes are most open to freelancers.

TOWERS CLUB, USA NEWSLETTER, The Original Information-By-Mail, Direct-Marketing Newsletter, TOWERS Club Press, Box 2038, Vancouver WA 98668. (206)574-3084. Editor: Jerry Buchanan. 5-10% freelance written. Works with a small number of new/unpublished writers each year. Newsletter published 10 times/year (not published in August or December) covering entrepreneurism (especially selling useful information by mail). Circ. 5,000. Pays on publication. Publishes ms an average of 2 months after acceptance. Byline given. Buys one-time rights. Submit seasonal/holiday material 10 weeks in advance. Simultaneous, photocopied, and previously published submissions OK. Computer printout submissions or 7" diskettes with TRS-80 Scriptsit software OK. Reports in 2 weeks. Sample copy for $3 and 39¢ postage.

Nonfiction: Exposé (of mail order fraud); how-to (personal experience in self-publishing and marketing); book reviews of brand new, self-published non-fiction how-to-do-it books (must include name and address of author). "Welcomes well-written articles of successful self publishing/marketing ventures. Must be current, and preferably written by the person who actually did the work and reaped the rewards. There's very little we will not consider, *if* it pertains to unique money-making enterprises that can be operated from the home." Buys 10 mss/year. Send complete ms. Length: 500-1,000 words. Pays $10-35. Pays extra for b&w photo and bonus for excellence in longer manuscript.

Tips: "The most frequent mistake made by writers in completing an article for us is that they think they can simply rewrite a newspaper article and be accepted. That is only the start. We want them to find the article about a successful self-publishing enterprise, and then go out and interview the principles for a more detailed how-to article, including names and addresses. We prefer that writer actually interview a successful self-publisher. Articles should include how idea first came to subject, how they implemented and financed and promoted the project. How long it took to show a profit and some of the stumbling blocks they overcame. How many persons participated in the production and promotion. How much money was invested (approximately) and other pertinent how-to elements of the story. Glossy photos of principles at work in their offices will help sell article. B&w only."

VENTURE, The Magazine for Entrepreneurs, Venture Magazine, Inc., 1st Floor, 521 5th Ave., New York NY 10175. (212)682-7373. Editor: Jeannie Mandelker. Monthly magazine about entrepreneurs for people owning their own businesses, starting new businesses or investing in entrepreneurial businesses.
Nonfiction: "We use current news on venture capital and entrepreneurs by assignment only." No unsolicited material. Query.

Detective and Crime

Fans of detective stories want to read accounts of actual espionage and criminal cases. Most of the following magazines buy nonfiction; a few buy both nonfiction and fiction. Markets specializing in criminal *fiction* are listed in Mystery publications.

DETECTIVE CASES, Detective Files Group, 1440 St. Catherine St. W., Montreal, Quebec H3G 1S2 Canada. Editor-in-Chief: Dominick A. Merle. Bimonthly magazine. See *Detective Files*.

DETECTIVE DRAGNET, Detective Files Group, 1440 St. Catherine St. W., Montreal, Quebec H3G 1S2 Canada. Editor-in-Chief: Dominick A. Merle. Bimonthly magazine; 72 pages. See *Detective Files*.

DETECTIVE FILES, Detective Files Group, 1440 St. Catherine St. W., Montreal, Quebec H3G 1S2 Canada. Editor-in-Chief: Dominick A. Merle. 100% freelance written. Bimonthly magazine; 72 pages. Pays on acceptance. Publishes ms an average of 3 months after acceptance. Buys all rights. Photocopied submissions OK. Include international reply coupons. Reports in 1 month. Free sample copy and writer's guidelines.
Nonfiction: True crime stories. "Do a thorough job; don't double-sell (sell the same article to more than one market); and deliver, and you can have a steady market. Neatness, clarity and pace will help you make the sale." Query. Length: 3,500-6,000 words. Pays $200-350.
Photos: Purchased with accompanying ms; no additional payment.

ESPIONAGE MAGAZINE, Leo II Publications, Ltd., Box 1184, Teaneck NJ 07666. (201)836-9177. Editor: Jackie Lewis. 90% freelance written. A bimonthly magazine "totally devoted to spy stories of international intrigue, suspense, blackmail, confused loyalties, deception, and other things immoral. Fiction and nonfiction stories by top writers in the world of espionage." Pays on publication. Publishes ms usually many months after acceptance. Byline given. Buys all rights, first North American serial rights and second serial (reprint) rights. Photocopied and previously published submissions OK. Computer printout submissions acceptable; no dot-matrix. Reports in about 1 month. Sample copy $3, 6x9 SAE, and 90¢ postage; writer's guidelines for business size SAE and 1 first class stamp.
Nonfiction: Spy oriented only: book excerpts, exposé, historical/nostalgic, interview/profile and personal experience. Anything relating to spy stories. Buys approximately 10 mss/year. Send complete ms. Length: 1,000-10,000 words. Pays 5-6¢/word depending on amount of editing needed. Sometimes pays the expenses of writers on assignment.
Fiction: Spy oriented only: adventure, condensed novels, confession, fantasy, historical, humorous, mystery; excerpts from published novels, romance, science fiction, suspense and western. Anything relating to intrigue, international suspense about spies. Buys 100 mss/year. Send complete ms. Length: 1,000-10,000 words. Pays 5-6¢/word depending on the amount of editing needed.
Fillers: Spy oriented only: anecdotes. Length: 20-100 words. Pays $5. Also games, crossword puzzles. Pays from $10-20.

Tips: "We are interested in any writer of fiction or nonfiction who writes spy stories. We will not accept explicit sex or gratuitous gore." First person stories are preferred, but stories from any perspective will be considered. Heroes can be any age, gender, nationality, or walk of life. "Send no subject however unless it is spy oriented."

FRONT PAGE DETECTIVE, INSIDE DETECTIVE, Official Detective Group, R.G.H. Publishing Corp., 20th Floor, 460 W. 34th St., New York NY 10001. (212)947-6500. Editor-in-Chief: Art Crockett. Editor of Front Page and Inside: Rose Mandelsberg.
Nonfiction: The focus of these two publications is similar to the others in the Official Detective Group. "We now use post-trial stories; rarely are pre-trial ones published." Byline given. For further details, see *Official Detective*.

HEADQUARTERS DETECTIVE, Detective Files Group, 1440 St. Catherine St. W., Montreal, Quebec H3G 1S2 Canada. Editor-in-Chief: Dominick A. Merle. Bimonthly magazine; 72 pages. See *Detective Files*.

MASTER DETECTIVE, Official Detective Group, R.G.H. Publishing Corp., 460 W. 34th St., New York NY 10001. Editor-in-Chief: Art Crockett. Managing Editor: Christos K. Ziros. 100% freelance written. Bimonthly. Circ. 350,000. Buys 9 mss/issue. See *Official Detective*.

OFFICIAL DETECTIVE, Official Detective Group, R.G.H. Publishing Corp., 460 W. 34th St., New York NY 10001. (212)947-6500. Editor-in-Chief: Art Crockett. Managing Editor: Christos Mirtsopoulos. 100% freelance written. Monthly magazine "for detective story or police buffs whose tastes run to *true*, rather than fictional crime/mysteries." Circ. 500,000. Pays on acceptance. Buys all rights. Byline given. Reports in 2 weeks.
Nonfiction: "Only *fact* detective stories. We are actively trying to develop new writers, and we'll work closely with those who show promise and can take the discipline required by our material. It's not difficult to write, but it demands meticulous attention to facts, truth, clarity, detail. Queries are essential with us, but I'd say the quickest rejection goes to the writer who sends in a story on a case that should never have been written for us because it lacks the most important ingredient, namely solid, superlative detective work. We also dislike pieces with multiple defendants, unless all have been convicted." Buys 150 mss/year. Query. Length: 5,000-6,000 words. Pays $250.
Photos: Purchased with accompanying mss. Captions required. Send prints for inside use; transparencies for covers. Pays $12.50 minimum for 4 x 5 b&w glossy prints. Pays $200 minimum for 2¼x2¼ or 35mm transparencies. Model release required for color photos used on cover.
Tips: Send a detailed query on the case to be submitted. Include: locale; victim's name; type of crime; suspect's name; status of the case (indictment, trial concluded, disposition, etc.); amount and quality of detective work; dates; and availability and number of pictures. "We're always impressed by details of the writer's credentials."

STARTLING DETECTIVE, Detective Files Group, 1440 St. Catherine St. W., Montreal, Quebec H3G 1S2 Canada. Editor-in-Chief: Dominick A. Merle. Bimonthly magazine; 72 pages. See *Detective Files*.

TRUE DETECTIVE, Official Detective Group, R.G.H. Publishing Corp., 460 W. 34th St., New York NY 10001. (212)947-6500. Editor-in-Chief: Art Crockett. Managing Editor: Christos Mirtsopoulos. Monthly. Circ. 500,000. Buys 10 mss/issue. Byline given. See *Official Detective*.

TRUE POLICE CASES, Detective Files Group, 1440 St. Catherine St. W., Montreal, Quebec H3G 1S2 Canada. Editor-in-Chief: Dominick A. Merle. Bimonthly magazine; 72 pages. Buys all rights. See *Detective Files*.

Ethnic/Minority

Traditions are kept alive, and new ones become established because of ethnic publications. Some ethnic magazines seek material that unites people of all races. "We solicit material that points out the similarity in the lives of all of us regardless of ethnic or racial background," said one editor. "Without mutual respect, we believe mankind is doomed." Ideas, interests and concerns of nationalities and religions are voiced by publications in this category. General interest lifestyle magazines for these groups are also included. Additional markets for writing with an ethnic orientation are located in the following sections: Career, College, and Alumni; Juvenile; Men's; Women's and Religious.

AIM MAGAZINE, AIM Publishing Company, 7308 S. Eberhart Ave., Chicago IL 60619. (312)874-6184. Editor: Ruth Apilado. Managing Editor: Dr. Myron Apilado. 75% freelance written. Eager to work with new/unpublished writers. Quarterly magazine on social betterment that promotes racial harmony and peace for high school, college and general audience. Circ. 10,000. Pays on publication. Publishes ms an average of 3 months after acceptance. Offers 60% of contract as kill fee. Not copyrighted. Buys one-time rights. Submit seasonal/holiday material 6 months in advance. Simultaneous queries, and simultaneous and photocopied submissions OK. Computer printout submissions acceptable; no dot-matrix. Reports in 6 weeks on queries. Writer's guidelines for $3., 8½x11 SAE and 65¢ postage.
Nonfiction: Exposé (education); general interest (social significance); historical/nostalgic (Black or Indian); how-to (help create a more equitable society); and profile (one who is making social contributions to community); and book reviews, reviews of plays "that reflect our ethnic/minority orientation." No religious material. Buys 16 mss/year. Send complete ms. Length: 500-800 words. Pays $25-35. Sometimes pays the expenses of writers on assignment.
Photos: Reviews b&w prints. Captions and identification of subjects required.
Fiction: Ethnic, historical, mainstream, and suspense. Fiction that teaches the brotherhood of man. Buys 20 mss/year. Send complete ms. Length: 1,000-1,500 words. Pays $25-35.
Poetry: Avant-garde, free verse, light verse. No "preachy" poetry. Buys 20 poems/year. Submit maximum 5 poems. Length: 15-30 lines. Pays $3-5.
Fillers: Jokes, anecdotes and newsbreaks. Buys 30/year. Length: 50-100 words. Pays $5.
Tips: "Interview anyone of any age who unselfishly is making an unusual contribution to the lives of less fortunate individuals. Include photo and background of person. We look at the nation of the world as part of one family. Short stories and historical pieces about blacks and Indians are the areas most open to freelancers. Subject matter of submission is of paramount concern for us rather than writing style. Articles and stories showing the similarity in the lives of people with different racial backgrounds are desired."

THE AMERICAN CITIZEN ITALIAN PRESS, 8262 Hascall St., Omaha NE 68124. (402)391-2012. Editor: Gene Failla. Managing Editor: Victor A. Failla. 20% freelance written. Quarterly newspaper of Italian-American news/stories. Circ. 5,600. Pays on publication. Publishes ms an average of 3 months after acceptance. By-line given. Not copyrighted. Buys first North American serial rights. Submit seasonal/holiday material 2 months in advance. Previously published submissions OK. Computer printout submissions acceptable; prefers letter-quality to dot-matrix. Reports in 1 month. Free sample copy.
Nonfiction: Book excerpts, general interest, historical/nostalgic, opinion and photo feature. Query with published clips. Length: 400-600 words. Pays $15-20. Sometimes pays the expenses of writers on assignment.
Photos: State availability of photos. Reviews b&w prints. Pays $5. Captions and identification of subjects required. Buys all rights.
Columns/Departments: Query.
Fiction: Query. Pays $15-20.
Poetry: Traditional. Buys 4-5/year. Submit maximum 2 poems. Pays $5-10.
Tips: Human interest stories are the most open to freelancers.

AMERICAN DANE, The Danish Brotherhood in America, 3717 Harney St., Box 31748, Omaha NE 68131. (402)341-5049. Editor: Jerome L. Christensen. Managing Editor: Pamela K. Dorau. 50% freelance written. Prefers to work with published/ established writers; works with a small number of new/unpublished writers each year. The monthly magazine of the Danish Brotherhood in America. All articles must have Danish ethnic flavor. Circ. 10,000. Pays on publication. Publishes ms an average of 1 year after acceptance. Byline given. Not copyrighted. Buys first rights. Submit seasonal/holiday material 1 year in advance. Photocopied submissions OK. Computer printout submissions acceptable; prefers letter-quality to dot-matrix. Reports in 2 weeks on queries. Sample copy $1 with 9½x4 SAE and 55¢ postage; writer's guidelines for 9½x4 SAE with 1 first class stamp.
Nonfiction: Historical, humor, inspirational, personal experience, photo feature and travel, all with a Danish flavor. Buys 12 mss/year. Query. Length: 1,500 words maximum. Pays $50 maximum for unsolicited articles.
Photos: Send photos with submission. Reviews prints. Offers no additional payment for photos accepted with ms. Captions and identification of subjects required. Buys one-time rights.
Fiction: Adventure, historical, humorous, mystery, romance and suspense, all with a Danish flavor. Buys 6-12 mss/year. Query with published clips. Length: 1,500 words maximum. Pays $50 maximum.
Poetry: Traditional. Buys 1-6 poems/year. Submit maximum 6 poems. Pays $35 maximum.

Fillers: Anecdotes and short humor. Buys 0-12/year. Length: 300 words maximum. Pays $15 maximum.
Tips: "Feature articles are most open to freelancers."

AN GAEL, Irish Traditional Culture Alive in America Today, The Irish Arts Center, 553 W. 51st St., New York NY 10019. (212)757-3318. Editor: Kevin McEneaney. 50% freelance written. Works with a small number of new/unpublished writers each year. Quarterly magazine covering the heritage of the Irish people with emphasis on the Irish-American experience. Material in the Irish language, as well as English is welcome. Written for all those who want to maintain or actively pursue Irish arts, history and language. Circ. 5,000. Pays on acceptance. Publishes ms an average of 6 months after acceptance. Byline given. Submit seasonal/holiday material 6 months in advance. Photocopied submissions OK. Computer printout submissions acceptable; prefers letter-quality to dot-matrix. Reports in 1 month.
Nonfiction: Humor, photo feature. Articles include periodic features on Irish language; history and drama; traditional music, dance and visual arts; Irish-American community profiles; fiction and poetry in both English and Irish; interviews with and profiles of cultural figures; and reviews of cultural activities, drama, books, films and records. Buys 30 mss/year. Send complete ms. Length: 1,000-1,500 words. Pays $10.
Photos: Descriptive of traditional Irish subject matter. Reviews 8x10 b&w glossy prints. Identification of subject required. Buys one-time rights.

‡ATTENZIONE, The Italian Lifestyle Magazine, Adam Publications, Inc., 152 Madison Ave., New York NY 10016. (212)683-9000. Editor: Lois Spritzer. 75% freelance written. Prefers to work with published/established writers; eager to work with new/unpublished writers. A monthly magazine which "celebrates the Italian lifestyle in design, fashion, travel, food, and addresses an audience of Italian Americans *and* Italophiles." Circ. 115,000. Pays 60 days after publication. Publishes ms an average of 3 months after acceptance. Byline given. Offers 25% kill fee. Buys first North American serial rights. Submit seasonal/holiday material 4 months in advance. Computer printout submissions acceptable; prefers letter-quality to dot-matrix. Reports in 2 months. Sample copy $3.50 with SASE; free writer's guidelines.
Nonfiction: Book excerpts, essays, general interest, historical/nostalgic, humor, interview/profile, photo feature and travel. Special issues include Food (December); Travel (April, October); Fashion (March, September). No family recollections. Query with or without published clips. Length: 1,500-3,000 words. Pays $200-500 for assigned articles; pays $150-350 for unsolicited articles. Sometimes pays the expenses of writers on assignment.
Photos: State availability of photos with submission. Offers no additional payment for photos accepted with ms. Identification of subjects required. Buys one-time rights.
Columns/Departments: Mary Ann Fusco, column/department editor. Media, Insight, and Report From Italy (all should have Italian-American link, e.g., how ethnic stereotyping can be fought; new scientific advances in Italy, etc.). Buys 5 mss/year. Query. Length: 1,500-2,000 words. Pays $150-300.
Tips: "*Attenzione* prefers a well-written query and published clips to unsolicited manuscripts. All queries are answered if accompanied by a SASE. Travel articles and interviews are most open to freelancers. We are always looking for an unusual slant even if it is an often covered subject, e.g., where the literati gather in Milan."

BALTIMORE JEWISH TIMES, 2104 N. Charles St., Baltimore MD 21218. (301)752-3504. Editor: Gary Rosenblatt. 25% freelance written. Weekly magazine covering subjects of interest to Jewish readers. "*Baltimore Jewish Times* reaches 20,000 Baltimore-area Jewish homes, as well as several thousand elsewhere in the U.S. and Canada; almost anything of interest to that audience is of interest to us. This includes reportage, general interest articles, personal opinion, and personal experience pieces about every kind of Jewish subject from narrowly religious issues to popular sociology; from the Mideast to the streets of Brooklyn, to the suburbs of Baltimore. We run articles of special interest to purely secular Jews as well as to highly observant ones. We are Orthodox, Conservative, and Reform all at once. We are spiritual and mundane. We are establishment and we are alternative culture." Circ. 20,000. Pays on publication. Publishes ms an average of 2 months after acceptance. Byline given. Buys one-time rights. Submit seasonal/holiday material 2 months in advance. Simultaneous queries, and photocopied and previously published submissions OK. Computer printout submissions acceptable; prefers letter-quality to dot-matrix. "We will not return submissions without SASE." Reports in 6 weeks. Sample copy $2.
Nonfiction: Barbara Pash, editorial assistant. Book excerpts, exposé, general interest, historical/nostalgic, humor, interview/profile, opinion, personal experience and photo feature. "We are inundated with Israel personal experience and Holocaust-related articles, so submissions on these subjects must be of particularly high quality." Buys 100 mss/year. "Established writers query; others send complete manuscript." Length: 1,200-6,000 words. Pays $25-150.
Photos: Kim Muller-Thym, graphics editor. Send photos with ms. Pays $10-35 for 8x10 b&w prints.
Fiction: Barbara Pash, editorial assistant. "We'll occasionally run a high-quality short story with a Jewish theme." Buys 6 mss/year. Send complete ms. Length: 1,200-6,000 words. Pays $25-150.

‡BLACK FAMILY, Black Family Publications, Inc., Box 1049, Herndon VA 22070-1046. (703)620-9836. Editor: Frank C. Kent. Managing Editor: Evelyn Ivery. 90% freelance written. A bimonthly magazine (monthly in October 1986) for and about black families. "This is a total family magazine. Submissions must be positive, promoting traditional family living. Stories about people who succeed against the odds are especially desirable." Circ. 250,000. Pays on publication. Publishes ms an average of 4 months after acceptance. Byline given. Offers 50% kill fee. Buys first rights; second serial (reprint) rights, all rights, and makes work-for-hire assignments. Submit seasonal/holiday material 4 months in advance. Simultaneous submissions OK. Computer printout submissions acceptable; prefers letter-quality to dot-matrix. Reports in 1 month. Sample copy for 9x12 SAE with $1.50 postage; writer's guidelines for #10 SAE with 1 first class stamp.

Nonfiction: Address to attention: nonfiction. General interest, historical/nostalgic, how-to, humor, inspirational, interview/profile, opinion (from scholars or well known blacks), personal experience, photo feature, religious and travel. Special issues include Holiday issue (Nov), Xmas (Dec), Bladk History (Feb), Martin Luther King's Birthday (Jan) and Travel (June). No material which does not promote stable family life (i.e. swinging singles, etc.). Buys 25 mss/year. Send complete ms. Length: 750-3,500 words. Pays $150-300 for assigned articles; pays $300 maximum for unsolicited articles. Pays expenses of writers on assignment.

Photos: State availability of photos with submission "on assignments, we will supply the photographer or make arrangements with writers." Offers no additional payment for photos accepted with ms. Captions, model releases and identification of subjects required.

Columns/Departments: Outstanding People (Black Americans who are doing exciting things in their communities. Especially senior citizens). Also Kids Games and About Black History. 500 words plus photo(s). Buys 12 mss/year. Query with published clips. Pays $25-50.

Fiction: Humorous and slice-of-life vignettes. "No erotica, horror, etc. We look for articles which would be published in *Readers Digest*." Buys 12 mss/year. Send complete ms only. Length: 2,500-5,000 words. Pays $250 flat fee if accepted.

Poetry: Avant-garde, free verse, light verse and traditional. "We are open. Just remember we are a family magazine." Buys varying number of poems/year. "No set number of poems per submission. Use common sense or it won't be read." Length: 8 lines minimum.

Tips: "Use *Reader's Digest*, *Woman's Day*, *LHJ*, etc. as guides—only slant stories for interest to black families."

B'NAI B'RITH JEWISH MONTHLY, B'nai B'rith International, 1640 Rhode Island Ave., N.W., Washington DC 20036. (202)857-6645. Editor: Marc Silver. 75% freelance written. A monthly magazine covering Jewish issues. "We have a Jewish family audience. Our magazine covers the Jewish World: politics, lifestyles, culture, religion and history." Circ. 200,000. Pays on publication. Publishes ms an average of 3 months after acceptance. Byline given. Offers 25% kill fee. Buys first North American serial rights. Submit seasonal/holiday material 6 months in advance. Computer printout submissions acceptable. Reports in 2 weeks on queries; 1 month on manuscripts. Free writer's guidelines.

Nonfiction: Book excerpts, essays, exposé, general interest, historical/nostalgic, how-to, humor, inspirational, interview/profile, new product, opinion, personal experience, photo feature, religious and travel. No immigrant reminiscences. Buys 35 mss/year. Query with published clips. Length: 300-5,000 words. Pays 10-25¢/word. Sometimes pays the expenses of writers on assignment.

Photos: State availability of photos with submission. Reviews contact sheets and transparencies. Offers $25-75/photo. Captions, model releases, and identification of subjects required. Buys one-time rights.

Columns/Departments: Arts (reviews, interviews with writers, artists, filmmakers, etc.), 300-1,000 words; Kol-Bo (humorous and offbeat material), 200-600 words; and Up Front (brief political items), 300-500 words. Buys 25 mss/year. Query with published clips. Pays $30-100.

CONGRESS MONTHLY, American Jewish Congress, 15 E. 84th St., New York NY 10028. (212)879-4500. Editor: Maier Deshell. 90% freelance written. Magazine published 7 times/year covering topics of concern to the American Jewish community representing a wide range of views. Distributed mainly to the members of the American Jewish Congress; readers are intellectual, Jewish, involved. Circ. 35,000. Pays on publication. Publishes ms an average of 3 months after acceptance. Byline given. Buys one-time rights. Submit seasonal/holiday material 2 months in advance. No photocopied or previously published submissions. Computer printout submissions acceptable; no dot-matrix. Reports in 2 months.

Nonfiction: General interest ("current topical issues geared toward our audience"). No technical material. Send complete ms. Length: 2,000 words maximum. Pays $100-150/article.

Photos: State availability of photos. Reviews b&w prints. "Photos are paid for with payment for ms."

Columns/Departments: Book, film, art and music reviews. Send complete ms. Length: 1,000 words maximum. Pays $100-150/article.

EBONY MAGAZINE, 820 S. Michigan Ave., Chicago IL 60605. Editor: John H. Johnson. Managing Editor: Charles L. Sanders. 10% freelance written. For Black readers of the U.S., Africa, and the Caribbean. Monthly. Circ. 1,800,000. Buys first North American serial rights and all rights. Buys about 10 mss/year. "We are now fully staffed, buying few manuscripts." Pays on publication. Publishes ms an average of 3 months after acceptance. Submit seasonal material 2 months in advance. Query. Reports in 1 month.

Nonfiction: Achievement and human interest stories about, or of concern to, Black readers. Interviews, profiles and humor pieces are bought. Length: 1,500 words maximum. "Study magazine and needs carefully. Perhaps one out of 50 submissions interests us. Most are totally irrelevant to our needs and are simply returned." Pays $200 minimum. Sometimes pays the expenses of writers on assignment.

Photos: Purchased with mss, and with captions only. Buys 8x10 glossy prints, color transparencies, 35mm color. Submit negatives and contact sheets when possible. Offers no additional payment for photos accepted with mss.

ESSENCE, 1500 Broadway, New York NY 10036. (212)730-4260. Editor-in-Chief: Susan L. Taylor. Editor: Audrey Edwards. Executive Editor: Cheryl Everette. Senior Editor: Elaine C. Ray. Emphasizes Black women. Monthly magazine; 150 pages. Circ. 950,000. Pays on acceptance. Makes assignments on work-for-hire basis. 3 month lead time. Pays 25% kill fee. Byline given. Submit seasonal/holiday material 6 months in advance. Computer printout submissions acceptable. Reports in 2 months. Sample copy $1.50; free writer's guidelines.

Features: "We're looking for articles that inspire and inform Black women. Our readers are interested and aware; the topics we include in each issue are provocative. Every article should move the *Essence* woman emotionally and intellectually. We welcome queries from good writers on a wide range of topics: general interest, health and fitness, historical, how-to, humor, self-help, relationships, work, personality interview, personal experience, political issues, and personal opinion." Buys 200 mss/year. Query. Length: 1,500-3,000 words. Pays $500 minimum.

Photos: Folayemi Debra Wilson, art director. State availability of photos with query. Pays $100 for b&w page; $300 for color page. Captions and model release required.

Columns/Departments: Query department editors: Contemporary Living (home, food, lifestyle, consumer information); Curtia James, Contemporary Living, editor; Arts & Entertainment: Pamela Johnson; Health & Fitness: Marjorie Whigham; Careers; Janine Coveney; Travel: Elaine C. Ray. Query. Length: About 1,000 words. Pays $100 minimum. "We are now accepting short poetry."

Tips: "We're looking for quality fiction; more self-improvement pieces, 'relationship' articles, career information and issues important to Black women."

FRIDAY (OF THE JEWISH EXPONENT), 226 S. 16th St., Philadelphia PA 19102. (215)893-5745. Editor: Jane Biberman. 98% freelance written. Monthly literary supplement for the Jewish community of Greater Philadelphia. Circ. 100,000. Pays after publication. Publishes ms an average of 6 months after acceptance. Byline given. Pays 25% kill fee. Buys first serial rights. Submit seasonal/holiday material 3 months in advance. Photocopied submissions OK. Computer printout submissions acceptable. Reports in 3 weeks. Sample copy and writer's guidelines for SASE.

Nonfiction: "We're interested only in articles on Jewish themes, whether they be historical, thought pieces, Jewish travel or photographic essays. Topical themes are appreciated." Buys 25 unsolicited mss/year. Length: 6-20 double-spaced pages. Pays $75 minimum.

Fiction: Short stories on Jewish themes. Length: 6-20 double-spaced pages. Pays $75 minimum.

Poetry: Traditional forms, blank verse, free verse, avant-garde and light verse; must relate to Jewish theme. Length varies. Pays $15 minimum.

GREATER PHOENIX JEWISH NEWS, Phoenix Jewish News, Inc., Box 26590, Phoenix AZ 85068. (602)870-9470. Executive Editor: Flo Eckstein. Managing Editor: Leni Reiss. 20% freelance written. Prefers to work with published/ established writers. Weekly tabloid covering subjects of interest to Jewish readers. Circ. 7,000. Pays on publication. Publishes ms an average of 3 months after acceptance. Byline given. Submit seasonal/holiday material 3 months in advance. Simultaneous queries, and simultaneous, photocopied, and previously published submissions OK. Computer printout submissions acceptable; prefers letter-quality to dot-matrix. (Must be easy to read, with upper and lower case.) Reports in 1 month. Sample copy $1.50; writer's guidelines for SAE and 1 first class stamp.

Nonfiction: General interest, issue analysis, interview/profile, opinion, personal experience, photo feature and travel. Special sections include Fashion and Health, House and Home, Back to School; Summer Camps; Party Planning; Bridal; Travel; Business and Finance; and Jewish Holidays. Buys 25 mss/year. Query with published clips or send complete ms. Length: 1,000-2,500 words. Pays $15-75 for simultaneous rights; $1.50/column inch for first serial rights. Sometimes pays the expenses of writers on assignment.

Photos: Send photos with query or ms. Pays $10 for 8x10 b&w prints. Captions required.

Tips: "We look for fresh, contemporary approaches to traditional subjects of interest to our Jewish readers. Our newspaper reaches across the religious, political, social and economic spectrum of Jewish residents in this burgeoning southwestern metropolitan area. We look for fairly short (maximum 1,500 words) pieces of a serious nature, written with clarity and balance. We stay away from cute stories as well as ponderous submissions."

HADASSAH MAGAZINE, 50 W. 58th St., New York NY 10019. Executive editor: Alan M. Tigay. 60% freelance written. Monthly, except combined issues (June-July and August-September). Circ. 370,000. Buys first rights (with travel articles, we buy all rights). Computer printout submissions acceptable; prefers letter-quality to dot-matrix. Reports in 6 weeks.
Nonfiction: Primarly concerned with Israel, Jewish communities around the world, and American civic affairs. Buys 10 unsolicited mss/year. Length: 1,500-2,000 words. Pays $200-400, less for reviews. Sometimes pays the expenses of writers on assignment.
Photos: "We buy photos only to illustrate articles, with the exception of outstanding color from Israel which we use on our covers. We pay $175 and up for a suitable cover photo. Offers $50/photo for inside b&w."
Fiction: Contact: Zelda Shluker. Short stories with strong plots and positive Jewish values. No personal memoirs, "schmaltzy" fiction, or women's magazine fiction. Length: 3,000 words maximum. Pays $300 minimum.
Tips: Of special interest are "strong fiction with a Jewish orientation; unusual experiences, with Jewish communities around the world-or specifically Israel."

THE HIGHLANDER, Angus J. Ray Associates, Inc., Box 397, Barrington IL 60011. (312)382-1035. Editor: Angus J. Ray. Managing Editor: Ethyl Kennedy Ray. 20% freelance written. Works with a small number of new/unpublished writers each year. Bimonthly magazine covering Scottish history, clans, genealogy, travel/history, and Scottish/American activities. Circ. 35,000. Pays on acceptance. Publishes ms an average of 6 months after acceptance. Byline given. Buys first North American serial rights and second serial (reprint) rights to material originally published elsewhere. Submit seasonal/holiday material 6 months in advance. Photocopied and previously published submissions OK. Computer printout submissions acceptable; no dot-matrix. Reports in 1 month. Sample copy and writer's guidelines free.
Nonfiction: Historical/nostalgic. "No fiction; no articles unrelated to Scotland." Buys 20 mss/year. Query. Length: 750-2,000 words. Sometimes pays $75-125. Pays the expenses of writers on assignment.
Photos: State availability of photos. Pays $5-10 for 8x10 b&w prints. Reviews b&w contact sheets. Identification of subjects required. Buys one-time rights.
Tips: "Submit something that has appeared elsewhere."

INSIDE, The Jewish Exponent Magazine, Federation of Jewish Agencies of Greater Philadelphia, 226 S. 16th St., Philadelphia PA 19102. (215)893-5700. Editor: Jane Biberman. Managing Editor: Robert Leiter. 95% freelance written (by assignment). Works with published/established writers and a small number of new/unpublished writers each year. Quarterly Jewish community magazine—for a 25 years and older general interest Jewish readership. Circ. 100,000. Pays on acceptance. Publishes ms an average of 2 months after acceptance. Byline given. Offers 20% kill fee. Buys one-time rights. Submit seasonal/holiday material 3 months in advance. Simultaneous queries OK. Computer printout submissions acceptable; no dot-matrix. Reports in 2 weeks on queries; 3 weeks on mss. Sample copy $3.50; free writer's guidelines.
Nonfiction: Book excerpts, general interest, historical/nostalgic, humor, interview/profile. Philadelphia angle desirable. No personal religious experiences or trips to Israel. Buys 6 mss/year. Query. Length: 1,500-3,000 words. Pays $200-700. Sometimes pays the expenses of writers on assignment.
Fiction: Short Stories. Query.
Photos: State availability of photos. Reviews color and b&w transparencies. Identification of subjects required.
Tips: "Personalities—very well known—and serious issues of concern to Jewish community needed." Query.

‡IRISH AMERICA MAGAZINE, Irish Voice Inc., Box 5141, Grand Central Station, New York NY 10163. (212)725-2993. Editor: Niall O'Dowd. Managing Editor: Patricia Harty. Circ. 35,000. 20% freelance written. A monthly magazine for Irish Americans covering business, politics, etc. "*Irish America Magazine* is aimed at the 40.7 million Irish Americans. Articles must have an Irish slant or connection and can be as diverse as the takeover bid at ABC, to an Island in the Caribbean that has St. Patrick's Day as a national holiday." Pays 1 month after publication. Publishes ms an average of 2 months after acceptance. Byline given. Buys one-time rights. Submit seasonal/holiday material 3 months in advance. Simultaneous and previously published submissions OK. Electronic submissions OK via Apple MacIntosh. Computer printout submissions acceptable; no dot-matrix. Reports in 2 months. Sample copy $2.50 with 9x11 SAE and $1.41 postage.
Nonfiction: Joseph McCann, articles editor. Book excerpts, essays, exposé, general interest, historical/nostalgic, humor, inspirational, interview/profile, new product, photo feature, religious, technical and travel. "No articles which would not be applicable to the Irish American reader, for example, seal hunting in Africa." Buys 24 mss/year. Send complete ms. Length: 1,000-2,500 words. Pays 8-20¢/word. Sometimes pays expenses of writers on assignment.
Photos: State availability of photos with submission. Reviews 8x10 transparencies and any size prints. Offers no additional payment for photos accepted with ms. Identification of subjects required.
Columns/Departments: Leo Fitzpatrick, column/department editor. Blazes Boylan ("Snippets" of news,

business, entertainment, etc.), 200-500 words; Business (Irish American company, president, takeover, etc.), 1,000-2,500 words; Music (Irish traditional, entertainer profiles.), 1,000-2,500 words; Books (reviews), 500-2,500 words; and Sports. Buys 25 mss/year. Send complete ms. Pays 8-20¢/word.

Fiction: Nuala McCreedy, fiction editor. Ethnic, historical, humorous and novel excerpts. No erotica or science fiction. Buys 10 mss/year. Send complete ms. Length: 1,000-3,000 words. Pays 8-20¢/word.

Poetry: Kevin McEneaney, poetry editor. Free verse and traditional. No avant-garde. Buys 10 poems/year. Submit maximum 2 poems. Length: 10-40 lines. Pays 8-20¢/word.

Fillers: Frank Barry, fillers editor. Facts, gags to be illustrated by cartoonist, newsbreaks and short humor. Buys 20/year. Length: 100-300 words. Pays 8-20¢/word.

Tips: "The area of our publication most open to freelancers is general interest articles from around the country and articles on business, politics, entertainment, festivals, concerts, novel reviews."

‡**THE ITALIAN TIMES OF MARYLAND,** Italian-American Publications, Inc., Box 20241, Baltimore MD 21284-2024. (301)337-0596. Publisher: Stephen J. Ferrandi. Managing Editor: Jodi Barke. 55% freelance written. Eager to work with new/unpublished writers. Monthly magazine covering anything of interest to Italian-Americans. Estab. 1985. Circ. 32,574. Pays on publication. Publishes ms an average of 3 months after acceptance. Byline given. Buys first rights, one-time rights, or second serial (reprint) rights. Submit seasonal/holiday material 5 months in advance. Simultaneous and previously published submissions OK. Computer printout submissions acceptable; no dot-matrix. Reports in 6 weeks on queries; 1 month on mss. Sample copy $1.

Nonfiction: Essays, exposé, general interest, historical/nostalgic, humor, interview/profile, opinion, personal experience, travel and young Italian-American success stories. Special issues include Italian Easter; all Italy issue with personal experiences, travel hints, food and wine featured (August); and Italian Christmas. Buys 15 mss/year. Send complete ms. Length: 100-10,000 words. Pays $2-100; mainly pays in copies "if new author with only average writing skills but good idea." Sometimes pays the expenses of writers on assignment.

Photos: Send photos with submission. Reviews 8x10 prints. Captions and identification of subjects required.

Fiction: Ethnic, humorous and slice-of-life vignettes. All fiction submissions must have an Italian or Italian-American theme. Buys 8 mss/year. Send complete ms. Length: 3,750 words maximum. Pays $2-50.

Poetry: F. Joseph Sebastian, poetry editor. Free verse, haiku, light verse and traditional. No mafia or organized crime poetry or anything that is anti-Italian. Buys 6 poems/year. Length: 50 lines maximum. Pays $2-25.

Fillers: Anecdotes, facts, newsbreaks and short humor. Buys 100/year. Length: 750 words maximum. Pays $2-25.

Tips: "We encourage good writers who haven't been published to send a manuscript for consideration. Stories and articles should be fast paced, easily digested and worth reading a second time. We welcome phone calls to answer any questions (9-5). We publish mostly freelance general interest and cover stories."

‡**JET,** 820 S. Michigan Ave., Chicago IL 60605. Executive Editor/Associate Publisher: Robert E. Johnson. For black readers interested in current news and trends. Weekly. Circ. 800,000. Primarily staff-written.

Nonfiction: Articles on topics of current, timely interest to black readers. News items and features: religion, education. African affairs, civil rights, politics and entertainment. Length: varies. Payment negotiated.

Photos: S.P. Flanagan, senior staff editor. Photo essays. Payment negotiable. Prefers b&w photos.

JEWISH NEWS, Suite 240, 20300 Civic Center Dr., Southfield MI 48076. (313)354-6060. Editor: Gary Rosenblatt. News Editor: Alan Hitsky. A weekly tabloid covering news and features of Jewish interest. Circ. 17,000. Pays on publication. Byline given. No kill fee "unless stipulated beforehand." Buys first North American serial rights. Simultaneous queries and photocopied submissions OK. Computer printout submissions acceptable; prefers letter-quality to dot-matrix. Reports in 2 weeks on queries; 1 month on mss. Sample copy for $1 and SASE.

❝ *I find that there are two necessary components which renew my resolve to continue writing after completing a project. The first requisite is rest—sufficient rest to restore physical energy and mental faculties. The second requirement is to constantly amass new ideas; notes for plots, research material which will implement them.* **❞**

Robert Bloch

Nonfiction: Book excerpts, humor, and interview/profile. Buys 10-20 mss/year. Query with or without published clips, or send complete ms. Length: 500-2,500 words. Pays $40-125.
Fiction: Ethnic. Buys 1-2 mss/year. Send complete ms. Length: 500-2,500 words. Pays $40-125.

‡**KOREAN CULTURE**, Korean Cultural Service, 5505 Wilshire Blvd., Los Angeles CA 90036. (213)936-7141. Editor: Steven Douglas Halasey. 10% freelance written. A quarterly magazine covering historical and modern culture of Korea. "An illustrated academic journal, it is distributed free of charge world-wide to both institutions and individuals. Readers include scholars and educated lay persons." Circ. 11,000. Pays on publication. Publishes ms an average of 9 months after acceptance. Byline given. Makes work-for-hire assignments. Submit seasonal/holiday material 6 months in advance. Computer printout submissions acceptable; prefers letter-quality to dot-matrix. Reports in 2 weeks on queries; 2 months on mss. Free sample copy and writer's guidelines.
Nonfiction: Essays, historical/nostalgic, interview/profile, photo feature, religious and travel. Annual tour guide, published in March issue: information on annual events in Korea required; sidebars on specific events required. No personal experience travelogues; technically complex submissions in linguistics, sociology, or political science; unresearched materials of any type. Buys 4 mss/year. Query with or without published clips, or send complete ms. Length: 3,000 minimum. Pays $100-250.
Photos: Send photos with submission. Reviews transparencies and prints. Offers no additional payment for photos accepted with ms. Captions and identification of subjects required. Buys all rights.
Columns/Departments: Review (publications, cultural events, films, exhibitions may be considered). Reviews should be well researched, and should place the item reviewed into the larger context of Korean culture. Buys 2 mss/year. Query with published clips. Length: approximately 3,000 words. Pays $100-250.
Tips: "*Korean Culture* is designed to educate the Western audience to the unique qualities of Korea. Specialists in Korean studies, or those with a sophisticated grounding in Korean affairs, will therefore have the best chance of submitting acceptable typescripts. Specialists in other fields (e.g., film, sports, travel, international trade) should be prepared to research their topic thoroughly prior to submission. Reviews of a variety of cultural events are needed most frequently; these are sometimes scattered across the United States and abroad, wherever a sizable Korean community exists. Some of these may be of interest to *Korean Culture*, but authors should inquire in advance, and obtain specific advice about the best method of approach for the topic."

LECTOR, The Hispanic Review Journal, Hispanic Information Exchange, Box 4273, Berkeley CA 94704. (415)893-8702. Editor: Roberto Cabello-Argandona. Managing Editor: John Frank. 90% freelance written. Eager to work with new/unpublished writers. A bimonthly magazine of Hispanic cultural articles and English reviews of books in Spanish. "We desire cultural articles, particularly of Hispanic arts and literature, written for a popular level (as opposed to an academic level). Articles are to be nonsexist, nonracist." Circ. 3,000. Pays on publication. Publishes ms an average of 6 months after acceptance. Byline given. Offers $50 kill fee. Buys first rights or makes work-for-hire assignments. Photocopied submissions OK; previously published submissions sometimes accepted. Electronic submissions OK via IBM PC, DOS 2.1, but requires hard copy also. Computer printout submissions acceptable; prefers letter-quality to dot-matrix. Reports in 3 weeks. Sample copy $3; writer's guidelines for SASE.
Nonfiction: Interview/profile, photo feature and articles on art, literature and Latino small presses. Some short fiction, poetry, political. No personal experience, religious or how-to. Buys 25 mss/year. "No unsolicited manuscripts; query us first." Length: 2,000-3,500 words. Pays $150-250 for assigned articles; pays $100-150 for unsolicited articles. "Writers, along with payment, always get five copies of magazine."
Photos: Send photos with submission. Reviews contact sheets. Captions required. Buys one-time rights.
Columns/Departments: Publisher's Corner (covers publishing houses in Latin America or U.S. [Latin]), 2,000-2,500; Perspective (cultural articles dealing with aspect of Hispanic art/lit), 2,500-3,500; Events in Profile (occasional column covering particular event in Chicano Studies), 1,500-2,000; Feature Review (in-depth review of particularly important published work), 2,500-3,000. Author's Corner (interview with recently published author), 1,500-2,000, and Inquiry (literary criticism) 2,000-2,500. Buys 15 mss/year. Query with published clips. Pays $100-250.
Tips: "In 1987 our articles will reflect a bigger emphasis on literature, and some exceptionally good short fiction and poetry by Latin American and U.S. Hispanic writers will be published."

MAINSTREAM AMERICA MAGAZINE, The Hemill Company, Inc., 2714 W. Vernon Ave., Los Angeles CA 90008. (213)290-1322. Editor: Diane Clark. Managing Editor: Adriene Diane L. Corbin. 90% freelance written. A monthly Black magazine for upwardly mobile professionals, businessmen, etc. Circ. 50,000. Pays on publication. Publishes ms an average of 4 months after acceptance. Byline given. Buys all rights. Submit seasonal/holiday material 3 months in advance. Simultaneous queries and submissions OK. Computer printout submissions acceptable; prefers letter-quality to dot-matrix. Reports in 1 month on queries; 2 months on mss. Free writer's guidelines.
Nonfiction: Expose (government, education, business as it impacts on Black Americans); general interest; historical/nostalgic; how-to (succeed in business, career, how to become a successful entrepreneur); inspira-

tional; interview/profile; personal experience (in business, corporate, career). "Features should be upbeat as an example for those striving toward success: political, Black enterprise, positive self image, education, etc." Buys 200 mss/year. Query with or without published clips, or send complete ms. Length: 500-2,000 words. Pays 6-8¢/word. Sometimes pays the expenses of writers on assignment.

Photos: State availability of photos or send photos with query or ms. Pays $10-15 for 8x10 b&w prints. Captions, model releases, and identification of subjects required. Buys one-time rights.

Tips: "The most frequent writer mistakes are failure to meet deadlines and lack of investigative detail; also far too many articles are too long. Read the magazine, follow format, and note subjects of interest. We're receptive to all well written material from known and unknown writers."

MALINI, Pan-Asian Journal for the Literati, Box 195, Claremont CA 91711. (714)625-2914. Editor: Chitra Chakraborty. Quarterly ethnic literary magazine covering Pan-Asian (India to Japan including some Pacific islands) literature and culture. 30% freelance written; 10-25% of material published is poetry. Byline given. Buys all rights. Publishes ms an average of 6 months after acceptance. Submit seasonal/holiday material 4 months in advance. Computer printout submissions acceptable; no dot-matrix. SASE. Reports in 1 month. Sample copy $1.39; writer's guidelines for legal-size SAE and 1 first class stamp.

Nonfiction: Book excerpts, expose, general interest, historical/nostalgic, humor and personal experience. Does not want to see anything that does not concern Pan-Asian group. Buys 6-10 mss/year. Query. Length: 750-1,200 words. Pays $35-100 (on acceptance).

Fiction: Ethnic. Buys 2-3 mss/year. Query. Length: 750-1,200 words. Pays $25-100 (on acceptance).

Poetry: Avant-garde, free verse, haiku, light verse, traditional and translations. No monologues or profanity. First-time typed, original submissions only. Buys 18-20 poems/year. Submit maximum 6 poems. Poetry submissions should be single-spaced within stanzas, double-spaced between stanzas, with a cover letter stating that the poems are indeed first-time submissions to *Malini*. Length: 3-33 lines. Pays $10-100 (on acceptance). Buys all rights.

Tips: "Anybody with ethnic awareness or sensitivity and literary talent can write for us. Ordering a sample copy will be of tremendous help to prospective contributors since there is no other magazine like *Malini* in the United States. Please do not send stories or articles without querying first. All submissions must include a cover letter indicating the status of the submission, i.e., whether they are first-time submissions or not." Submissions related to ethnic communities other than Pan-Asian groups specified above will not be accepted.

MIDSTREAM, A Monthly Jewish Review, 515 Park Ave., New York NY 10022. Editor: Joel Carmichael. 90% freelance written. Works with a small number of new/unpublished writers each year. Monthly. Circ. 14,000. Buys first North American serial rights. Byline given. Pays after publication. Publishes ms an average of 6 months after acceptance. Computer printout submissions acceptable; no dot-matrix. Reports in 2 months.

Nonfiction: "Articles offering a critical interpretation of the past, searching examination of the present, and affording a medium for independent opinion and creative cultural expression: Articles on the political and social scene in Israel, on Jews in Russia and the U.S.; generally it helps to have a Zionist orientation. If you're going abroad, we would like to see what you might have to report on a Jewish community abroad." Buys historical and think pieces, primarily of Jewish and related content. Pays 5¢/word.

Fiction: Primarily of Jewish and related content. Pays 5¢/word.

Tips: "A book review would be the best way to start. Send us a sample review or a clip, let us know your area of interest, suggest books you would like to review. The author should briefly outline the subject and theme of his article and give a brief account of his background or credentials in this field. Since we are a monthly, we look for critical analysis rather than a 'journalistic' approach."

MOMENT, Jewish Educational Ventures, 462 Boylston, Boston MA 02116. (617)536-6252. Editor: Leonard Fein. Managing Editor: Nechama Katz. 30% freelance written. Monthly (except January/February & July/August, when bimonthly). Magazine on Jewish affairs. "*Moment* is a lively, liberal, independent magazine of Jewish affairs." Circ. 25,000. Pays on publication. Publishes ms an average of 3 months after acceptance. Byline given. Offers 25% kill fee. Buys first North American serial rights. Submit seasonal/holiday material 3 months in advance. Photocopied submissions OK. Electronic submissions OK via Decmate II WPS. Computer printout submissions acceptable. Reports in 6 weeks on queries; 2 months on mss. Sample copy $3.50; free writer's guidelines.

Nonfiction: Book excerpts, historical and personal experience. "We are looking for high-quality journalism presenting critical thinking and reportage about the range of issues facing today's intelligent, liberal American Jew. We are looking for freelancers who can help us enrich the quality of Jewish discussion and debate." Buys 30 mss/year. Query with published clips or send complete ms. Pays $100-400. Sometimes pays the expenses of writers on assignment.

Photos: State availability of photos. Reviews b&w prints. Pays $35. Captions required. Buys one-time rights.

Fiction: Ethnic (only very well-written stories exploring the questions of Jewish industry and Jewish history); and religious (Jewish). "We have an over-abundance of Holocaust-related and 'grandmother' stories. We use

very little fiction, so would encourage only the very highest quality submissions." Buys 3 mss/year. Query with published clips. Length: 2,500-5,000 words. Pays $100-400 words.
Tips: "A detailed query letter, with clips, will help us respond to article ideas."

PALM BEACH JEWISH WORLD, Jewish World Publishing Corporation, Box 33433, West Palm Beach FL 33402. (305)833-8331. Editor: Martin Pomerance. Features Editor: Molly Staub. 30% freelance written. A weekly newspaper covering Jewish-oriented material. "All articles must have a strong Jewish slant. Our readers are all ages, all levels of affluence and all degrees of Jewish commitment. News stories are staff-written; however, we'll look at national features as well as those strongly focused on South Florida." Circ. 31,000. Publishes ms an average of 1 month after acceptance. Byline given. Offers $25 kill fee. Buys first North American serial rights. Submit seasonal/holiday material 3 months in advance. Simultaneous submissions OK if publisher is in another state. Electronic submissions OK via Hayes U.S. Robotics, 1200 baud, 1 stop bit, full duplex. Computer printout submissions acceptable; prefers letter-quality to dot-matrix. Reports in 1 month on queries; 2 months on mss. Sample copy and writer's guidelines for SAE and $1.24 postage.
Nonfiction: Exposé, general interest, historical/nostalgic, humor, inspirational, interview/profile, new product, photo feature, religious, travel and consumer. Special issues on religious holidays. "No amateurish compositions such as 'What Israel Means to Me' or 'How I Hated to put My Mother in an Old Age Home.' " Buys 120 mss/year. Query with or without published clips, or send complete ms (prefers query and clips). Length: 2,000 words maximum. Pays $50-200. ·
Photos: Send photos with submission. Reviews prints. Offers $7.50-10/photo. Captions and identification of subjects required. Buys one-time rights.
Columns/Departments: Travel (strong Jewish focus) and Entertainment (insightful) interviews of well-known personalities about influence of their Jewish heritage). Busy 15-20 mss/year. Query with published clips and SASE. Length: 1,000-2,000 words. Pays $50-100.
Tips: "I am definitely interested in travel articles, since I run a major travel feature weekly. I'm interested in both national and international destinations. Your best chance is with the more exotic spots, since I get inundated with pieces on Israel and western Europe. My primary requirement is that all articles have a strong Jewish slant. The story could be pegged to a Jewish personality who helped influence a geographic area (perhaps by developing a resort or kosher restaurant), or even a contemporary Jewish person noted in business or the arts. I prefer the stories to lead with the Jewish connection; then you can go into the tourist attractions."

PRESENT TENSE: The Magazine of World Jewish Affairs, 165 E. 56th St., New York NY 10022. (212)751-4000. Editor: Murray Polner. 95% freelance written. Prefers to work with published/established writers. For college-educated, Jewish-oriented audience interested in Jewish life throughout the world. Quarterly magazine. Circ. 45,000. Buys all rights. Byline given. Buys 60 mss/year. Pays on publication. Publishes ms an average of 6 months after acceptance. Computer printout submissions acceptable. Sample copy $4.50. Reports in 2 months. Query.
Nonfiction: Quality reportage of contemporary events (a la *Harper's, New Yorker*, etc.). Personal journalism, reportage, profiles and photo essays. Length: 3,000 words maximum. Pays $150-250. Sometimes pays the expenses of writers on assignment.
Tips: "Read our magazine."

RECONSTRUCTIONIST, 270 W. 89th St., New York NY 10024. (212)496-2960. Editor: Dr. Jacob Staub. 50% freelance written. Eager to work with new/unpublished writers. A general Jewish religious and cultural magazine. Monthly. Circ. 8,500. Buys first serial rights. Pays on publication. Publishes ms of 12-18 months after acceptance. Computer printout submissions acceptable; prefers letter-quality to dot-matrix. Free sample copy.
Nonfiction: Publishes literary criticism, reports from Israel and other lands where Jews live, and material of educational or communal interest. Query. Buys 35 mss/year. Preferred length is 2,000-3,000 words. Pays $36.
Fiction: Uses a small amount of fiction as fillers.
Poetry: Used as fillers.

‡THE UKRAINIAN WEEKLY, Ukrainian National Association, 30 Montgomery St., Jersey City NJ 07302. (201)434-0237. Editor: Roma Hadzewycz. 30% freelance written. A weekly tabloid covering news and issues of concern to Ukrainian community. Circ. 7,000. Pays on publication. Byline given. Buys first North American serial rights, second serial (reprint) rights or makes work-for-hire assignments. Submit seasonal/holiday material 1 month in advance. Reports in 1 month. Free sample copy and writer's guidelines.
Nonfiction: Book excerpts, essays, exposé, general interest, historical/nostalgic, interview/profile, opinion, personal experience, photo feature and news events. Special issues include Easter, Christmas, anniversary of Helsinki Accords, anniversary of Ukrainian Helsinki monitoring group. Buys 80 mss/year. Query with published clips. Length: 500-2,000 words. Pays $45-100 for assigned articles. Pays $25-100 for unsolicited articles. Sometimes pays the expenses of writers on assignment.

Photos: Send photos with submission. Reviews contact sheets, negatives and 3x5, 5x7 or 8x10 prints. Offers no additional payment for photos accepted with ms.
Columns/Departments: News & Views (commentary on news events), 500-1,000 words. Buys 10 mss/year. Query. Pays $25-50.
Tips: "Become acquainted with the Ukrainian community in the U.S. and Canada. The area of our publication most open to freelancers is community news—coverage of local events."

Food and Drink

Writers with a taste for fine wines and foods will want to shop for publications in this market. Magazines appealing to gourmets are classified here. Journals aimed at food processing, manufacturing, and retailing will be found in Trade Journals. Magazines covering nutrition for the general public are listed in the Health and Fitness category, while many magazines in the Lifestyle, General Interest and Women's categories also buy articles on these topics.

‡**BON APPETIT, America's Food and Entertaining Magazine.** Knapp Communications Corporation, 5900 Wilshire Blvd., Los Angeles CA 90036. (213)937-1025. Editor: William J. Garry. 70% freelance written. Monthly magazine. "Our articles are written in the first person voice and are directed toward the active cook. Emphasis on recipes intended for use by the dedicated amateur cook." Circ. 1,300,000. Pays on acceptance. Publishes ms an average of 6 months after acceptance. Byline given. Buys first North American serial rights and all rights. Submit seasonal/holiday material 6 months in advance. Computer printout submissions acceptable; no dot-matrix. Reports in 1 month. Free writer's guidelines.
Nonfiction: Barbara Fairchild, senior editor. How-to (cooking) and travel. No articles which are not food related. Buys 120 mss/year. Query with published clips. Length: 1,000-3,000 words. Pays $600-2,000. Sometimes pays the expenses of writers on assignment.
Photos: State availability of photos with submission. Reviews 35mm transparencies. Offers $175-550/photo. Captions, model releases and identification of subjects required. Buys one-time rights.
Columns/Departments: Laurie Glenn Buckle, column/department editor. Bon Voyage: travel articles featuring a specific city which cover, in a lively manner, interesting sights and landmarks and, especially, local restaurants and foods of note. Will need recipes from these restaurants. Buys 12 mss/year. Query. Length: 1,000-2,000 words. Pays $600-1,200.

COOK'S, The Magazine of Cooking in America. Pennington Publishing. 2710 North Ave., Bridgeport CT 06604. (203)366-4155. Editor: Judith Hill. Managing Editor: Sheila O'Meara Lowenstein. 50% freelance written. Prefers to work with published/established writers. A bimonthly magazine covering food and cooking in America. "*Cook's* publishes lively informative articles that describe food and restaurant trends in the U.S. or that describe hand-on cooking techniques. Almost all of our articles include recipes." Circ. 165,000. Pays on publication. Publishes ms an average of 8 months after acceptance. Byline given. 50% kill fee. Buys all rights. Submit seasonal/holiday material 10 months in advance. Photocopied submissions OK. Computer printout submissions acceptable; prefers letter-quality to dot-matrix. Reports in 2 months. Sample copy for 10"x13" SAE with $1.18 postage; writer's guidelines for #10 SAE with 1 first class stamp.
Nonfiction: Mary Caldwell, articles editor. Food and cooking. No travel, personal experience or nostalgia pieces, history of food and cuisine, or recipes using prepared ingredients (e.g., canned soups, "instant" foods, mixes, etc.). Buys 25-30 mss/year. Query with clips and sample original recipes. Length: 500-3,000 words plus recipes. Pays $75-375. Rarely pays expenses of writers on assignment.
Columns/Departments: Mary Caldwell, articles editor. Peak Produce (article plus 8-10 recipes focusing on a specific seasonal ingredient or type of ingredient), 500-1,000 words plus recipes; and Science of Cooking (how a particular aspect of cooking works), 1,500-2,500 words plus 1-2 recipes if appropriate. Buys about 9 mss/year. Query with published clips or unpublished writing sample. Length: 500-2,500 words. Pays $250-300.

‡**VINTAGE, The Magazine of Food, Wine and Gracious Living.** Wine News, Inc., Suite 370, E. 76th St., New York NY 10021. Editor: Philip Seldon. 80% freelance written. A monthly magazine covering food,

wine, travel, etc. Circ. 100,000. Pays on publication. Byline given. Buys all rights. Submit seasonal/holiday material 6 months in advance. Simultaneous, photocopied and previously published submissions OK. Computer printout submissions acceptable; prefers letter-quality to dot-matrix. Reports in 1 month. Sample copy $2 with 9x12 SAE; writer's guidelines for #10 SAE with 1 first class stamp.

Nonfiction: Book excerpts, exposé, how-to, interview/profile, new product, personal experience, photo feature and travel, all food and wine related. Buys 10-12 mss/year. Query with published clips, or send complete ms. Length: 750-4,000 words. Pays $100-500 for assigned articles; $50-250 for unsolicited articles. May pay in wine.

Photos: State availability of photos with submission or send photos with submission. Reviews contact sheets or transparencies. Offers no additional payment for photos accepted with ms. Captions, model releases and identification of subjects required. Buys one-time rights.

Fiction: Historical, humorous, mystery, slice-of-life vignettes and suspense, all food and wine related. Buys 10-12 mss/year. Query with published clips or send compelte ms. Length: 500-4,000 words.

‡**WINE & SPIRITS BUYING GUIDE**, Winestate Publications, Inc., Box 1548, Princeton NJ 08542. (609)921-2196. Editor: Joshua Greene. 60% freelance written. A bimonthly magazine covering wine and spirits tasting. Circ. 52,000. Pays on publication. Publishes ms an average of 3 months after acceptance. Byline given. Buys first North American serial rights. Computer printout submissions acceptable; prefers letter-quality to dot-matrix. Sample copy for 9x12 SAE with $1.07 postage; writer's guidelines for letter-size SAE with 1 first class stamp.

Nonfiction: Interview/profile (of a winemaker, importer, or wine personality) and travel (to wine related areas, vineyards, wineries, distilleries, etc.). Only wine or spirits related submissions. Buys 25 mss/year. Query with published clips. Length: 1,000-2,000 words. Pays $200-250 for assigned articles; pays $100-150 for unsolicited articles. Sometimes pays the expenses of writers on assignment.

Photos: Send photos with submission. Offers $25/photo. Model releases and identification of subjects required. Buys one-time rights.

‡**THE WINE SPECTATOR**, M. Shanken Communications, Inc., Opera Plaza Suite 2040, 601 Van Ness Ave., San Francisco CA 94102. (415)673-2040. Editor/Publisher: Marvin R. Shanken. 35-40% freelance written. Prefers to work with published/established writers. Twice monthly consumer newspaper covering wine. Circ. 58,000. Byline given. Buys first rights. Submit seasonal/holiday material 3 months in advance. Electronic submissions acceptable via 300 or 1200 baud, 7 bits, 1 stop bit, no parity preferred. Computer printout submissions acceptable "as long as they are legible." Reports in 3 weeks. Publishes ms an average of 3 months after acceptance. Sample copy $1.25; free writer's guidelines.

Nonfiction: General interest (news about wine or wine events); humor; interview/profile (of wine; vintners, wineries); opinion; and photo feature. No "winery promotional pieces or articles by writers who lack sufficient knowledge to write below just surface data." Query with clips of published work. Length: 800-1,200 words average. Pays $100/base; more for regular contributors.

Photos: Send photos with ms. Pays $25 minimum for b&w contact sheets and 5x7 prints. Identification of subjects required. Buys one-time rights.

Tips: "A solid knowledge of wine is a must. Query letters help, detailing the story idea; many freelance writers do not understand what a query letter is and how important it is to selling an article. New, refreshing ideas which have not been covered before stand a good chance of acceptance. *The Wine Spectator* is a consumer-oriented *newspaper* but we are interested in some trade stories; brevity is essential."

WINE TIDINGS, Kylix Media Inc., 5165 Sherbrooke St. W., 414, Montreal, Quebec H4A 1T6 Canada. (514)481-5892. Publisher: Judy Rochester. Editor: Barbara Leslie. 90% freelance written. Magazine published 8 times/year primarily for men with incomes of over $50,000. "Covers anything happening on the wine scene in Canada." Circ. 28,000. Pays on publication. Publishes ms an average of 3 months after acceptance. Byline given. Buys all rights. Submit seasonal/holiday material 3 months in advance. Computer printout submissions acceptable; prefers letter-quality to dot-matrix. Reports in 1 month.

Nonfiction: General interest; historical; humor; interview/profile; new product (and developments in the Canadian and U.S. wine industries); opinion; personal experience; photo feature; and travel (to wine-producing countries). "All must pertain to wine or wine-related topics and should reflect author's basic knowledge of and interest in wine." Buys 20-30 mss/year. Send complete ms. Length: 500-2,000 words. Pays $25-200.

Photos: State availability of photos. Pays $10-100 for color prints; $10 for b&w prints. Identification of subjects required. Buys one-time rights.

WINE WORLD MAGAZINE, Suite 116, 6308 Woodman Ave., Van Nuys CA 91401. (818)785-6050. Editor-Publisher: Dee Sindt. For the wine-loving public (adults of all ages) who wish to learn more about wine. Quarterly magazine; 48 pages. Buys first North American serial rights. Buys about 50 mss/year. Pays on publication. No photocopied submissions. Simultaneous submissions OK "if spelled out." Send $2 for sample copy and writer's guidelines,

Nonfiction: "Wine-oriented material written with an in-depth knowledge of the subject, designed to meet the needs of the novice and connoisseur alike. Wine technology advancements, wine history, profiles of vintners the world over. Educational articles only. No first-person accounts. Must be objective, informative reporting on economic trends, new technological developments in vinification, vine hybridizing, and vineyard care. New wineries and new marketing trends. We restrict our editorial content to wine, and wine-oriented material. Will accept restaurant articles—good wine lists. No more basic wine information. No articles from instant wine experts. Authors must be qualified in this highly technical field." Query. Length: 750-2,000 words. Pays $50-100.

‡WOMEN'S CIRCLE HOME COOKING, Box 198, Henniker NH 03242. Editor: Susan Hankins Andrews. 95% freelance written. Eager to work with new/unpublished writers. For women (and some men) of all ages who really enjoy cooking. "Our readers collect and exchange recipes. They are neither food faddists nor gourmets, but practical women and men trying to serve attractive and nutritious meals. Many work fulltime, and most are on limited budgets." Monthly magazine; 72 pages. Circ. 225,000. Pays on publication. Publishes ms an average of 6 months after acceptance. Buys all rights. Submit seasonal/holiday material 6 months in advance. Computer printout submissions acceptable; prefers letter-quality to dot-matrix. Reports in 2 months. Sample copy for large SASE.

Nonfiction: Exposé, historical, how-to, informational, inspirational, nostalgia, photo feature and travel. "We like a little humor with our food, for the sake of digestion. Keep articles light. Stress economy and efficiency. Remember that at least half our readers must cook after working a fulltime job. Draw on personal experience to write an informative article on some aspect of cooking. We're a reader participation magazine. We don't go in for fad diets, or strange combinations of food which claim to cure anything." No medical advice or sick or gross humor. Buys 48 mss/year. Query. Length: 50-1,000 words. Pays 2-5¢/word.

Photos: State availability of photos. Pays $5 for 4x5 b&w or color sharp glossy prints; $35 minimum for 35 mm, 2¼x2¼ and 4x5 transparencies used on cover.

Fiction: Humorous fiction related to cooking and foods. Length: 1,200 words maximum. Pays 2-5¢/word.

Poetry: Light verse related to cooking and foods. Length: 30 lines. Pays $5/verse.

Fillers: Short humorous fillers. Length: 100 words. Pays 2-5¢/word. Cartoons related to cooking and dining. $20/cartoon.

Tips: Good articles discuss some aspect of cooking and provide several recipes.

ZYMURGY, Journal of the American Homebrewers Association, American Homebrewers Association, Box 287, Boulder CO 80306. (303)447-0816. Editor: Charles N. Papazian. Managing Editor: Kathy McClurg. 10% freelance written. Quarterly magazine on homebrewing. Circ. 7,000. Pays on publication. Publishes ms an average of 6 months after acceptance. Buys first serial rights, first North American serial rights, and simultaneous rights. Submit seasonal/holiday material 5 months in advance. Simultaneous queries, and simultaneous, photocopied, and previously published submissions OK. Computer printout submissions acceptable; prefers letter-quality to dot-matrix. Sample copy $4; free writer's guidelines.

Nonfiction: General interest (beer); historical (breweries); interview/profile (brewers); photo-feature; and travel (breweries). Query. Length: 750-2,000 words. Pays $25-75.

Photos: Reviews b&w contact sheets and 8x10 b&w prints. Captions, model releases, and identification of subjects required.

Fiction: Beer brewing. Buys 1-2 mss/year. Query. Length: 750-2,000 words. Pays negotiable rates.

Games and Puzzles

If you like to play games—and are serious about them and can explain or create them—the following publications need you. Crossword fans will also find markets here. These publications are written by and for game enthusiasts interested in both traditional games and word puzzles and newer roleplaying adventure and computer and video games. Additional home video game publications are listed in the Theatre, Movie, TV and Entertainment section. Other puzzle markets may be found in the Juvenile section.

CHESS LIFE, United States Chess Federation, 186 Route 9W, New Windsor NY 12550. (914)562-8350. Editor: Larry Parr. 15% freelance written. Works with a small number of new/unpublished writers each year.

Monthly magazine covering the chess world. Circ. 60,000. Pays variable fee. Byline given. Offers kill fee. Buys first or negotiable rights. Submit seasonal/holiday material 8 months in advance. Simultaneous queries, and simultaneous, photocopied and previously published submissions OK. Computer printout submissions acceptable. Reports in 1 month. Publishes ms an average of 5 months after acceptance. Free sample copy and writer's guidelines.
Nonfiction: General interest, historical, interview/profile, and technical—all must have some relation to chess. No "stories about personal experiences with chess." Buys 30-40 mss/year. Query with samples "if new to publication." Length: 3,000 words maximum. Sometimes pays the expenses of writers on assignment.
Photos: Reviews b&w contact sheet and prints, and color prints and slides. Captions, model release and identification of subjects required. Buys all or negotiable rights.
Fiction: "Chess-related, high quality." Buys 1-2 mss/year. Pays variable fee.
Tips: "Articles must be written from an informed point of view—not from view of the curious amateur. Most of our writers are specialized in that they have sound credentials as chessplayers. Freelancers in major population areas (except New York and Los Angeles, which we already have covered) who are interested in short personality profiles and perhaps news reporting have the best opportunities. We're looking for more personality pieces on chessplayers around the country; not just the stars, but local masters, talented youths, and dedicated volunteers. Freelancers interested in such pieces might let us know of their interest and their range. Could be we know of an interesting story in their territory that needs covering."

DRAGON ® MAGAZINE, Monthly Adventure Role-Playing Aid, TSR, Inc., Box 756, 201 Sheridan Springs Rd., Lake Geneva WI 53147. (414)248-8044. Editor: Kim Mohan. 90% freelance written. Monthly magazine of fantasy and science-fiction role-playing games. "Most of our readers are intelligent, imaginative and under the age of 18." Circ. 110,000. Pays on publication; pays on acceptance for fiction only. Publishes ms an average of 6 months after acceptance. Byline given. Offers 75% kill fee. Buys first rights for fiction; all rights for most articles. Submit seasonal/holiday material 8 months in advance. Photocopied submissions OK. Computer printout submissions acceptable; prefers letter-quality to dot-matrix. Reports in 1 month on queries; 2 months on submissions. Sample copy $3.50; writer's guidelines for SASE.
Nonfiction: Articles on the hobby of gaming and fantasy role-playing. No general articles on gaming hobby; "our article needs are *very* specialized. Writers should be experienced in gaming hobby and role-playing. No strong sexual overtones or graphic depictions of violence." Buys 120 mss/year. Query. Length: 1,000-8,000 words. Pays $75-600 for assigned articles; pays $50-400 for unsolicited articles.
Fiction: Patrick Price, fiction editor. Adventure, fantasy, science fiction, and suspense. "No strong sexual overtones or graphic depictions of violence." Buys 8-12 mss/year. Send complete ms. Length: 2,000-8,000 words. Pays $100-500.
Tips: "*Dragon Magazine* and the related publications of Dragon Publishing are *not* periodicals that the 'average reader' appreciates or understands. A writer must *be* a reader, and must share the serious interest in gaming our readers possess."

GAMES, Playboy Enterprises, Inc., 1350 Ave. of the Americas, New York NY 10019. Editor: Wayne Schnittberger. 50% freelance written. Monthly magazine featuring games, puzzles, mazes and brainteasers for people 18-49 interested in verbal and visual puzzles, trivia quizzes and original games. Circ. 650,000. Average issue includes 5-7 feature puzzles, paper and pencil games and fillers, bylined columns and 1-2 contests. Pays on publication. Publishes ms an average of 6 months after acceptance. Byline given. Offers 25% kill fee. Buys all rights, first rights, first and second rights to the same material, and second (reprint) rights to material originally published elsewhere. Submit seasonal material 6 months in advance. Book reprints considered. Computer printout submissions acceptable; no dot-matrix. Reports in 6 weeks. Free writer's guidelines with SASE.
Nonfiction: "We are looking for visual puzzles, rebuses, brainteasers and logic puzzles. We also want newsbreaks, new games, inventions, and news items of interest to game players." Buys 4-6 mss/issue. Query. Length: 500-2,000 words. Usually pays $110/published page.
Columns/Departments: Wild Cards (25-200 words, short brainteasers, 25-100 wordplay, number games, anecdotes and quotes on games). Buys 6-10 mss/issue. Send complete ms. Length: 25-200 words. Pays $10-100.
Fillers: Will Shortz, editor. Crosswords, cryptograms and word games. Pays $25-100.

GIANT CROSSWORDS, Scrambl-Gram, Inc., Puzzle Buffs International, 1772 State Road, Cuyahoga Falls OH 44223. (216)923-2397. Editors: C.J. Elum and C.R. Elum. Managing Editor: Carol L. Elum. 40% freelance written. Crossword puzzle and word game magazines issued quarterly. Pays on acceptance. Publishes ms an average of 10 days after acceptance. No byline given. Buys all rights. Simultaneous queries OK. Reports in several weeks. "We furnish master grids and clue sheets and offer a 'how-to-make-crosswords' book for $6."
Nonfiction: Crosswords only. Query. Pays according to size of puzzle and/or clues.

THE GRENADIER MAGAZINE, The Independent War Game Review, J. Tibbetts & Son, Purveyors, 3833 Lake Shore Ave., Oakland CA 94610. (415)763-0928. Senior Editor: S.A. Jefferis-Tibbetts. 20% freelance written. Eager to work with new/unpublished writers. Bimonthly magazine covering military simulation and history. Circ. 6,000. Pays on publication. Publishes ms an average of 5 months after acceptance. Byline given. Buys all rights. Submit seasonal/holiday material 4 months in advance. Computer printout submissions acceptable; prefers letter-quality to dot-matrix. Reports in 2 weeks. Sample copy $3; writer's guidelines for legal size SAE and 1 first class stamp.
Nonfiction: Historical/nostalgic, how-to, new product, opinion and technical. Buys 36 mss/year. Query. Length: 5,000-12,500 words. Pays $25-100.
Photos: John T. Lamont, photo editor. Send photos with query. Pays $15 minimum for b&w contact sheets and for 8x10 b&w prints. Captions, model releases, and identification of subjects required.
Columns/Departments: Donald Harrison, column/department editor. Solitaire Gaming, Short Reviews of new products, Book Reviews, and Computer Reviews. Buys 108 mss/year. Send complete ms. Length: 150-500 words. Pays $5-15.
Tips: "We are increasing our emphasis on computer products."

OFFICIAL CROSSWORD PUZZLES, DELL CROSSWORD PUZZLES, POCKET CROSSWORD PUZZLES, DELL WORD SEARCH PUZZLES, OFFICIAL WORD SEARCH PUZZLES, DELL PENCIL PUZZLES & WORD GAMES, OFFICIAL PENCIL PUZZLES & WORD GAMES, DELL CROSSWORD SPECIAL, DELL CROSSWORDS AND VARIETY PUZZLES, DELL CROSSWORD YEARBOOK, OFFICIAL CROSSWORD YEARBOOK, DELL CROSSWORD ANNUAL, FAST 'N' FUN CROSSWORDS AND VARIETY PUZZLES, DELL CROSSWORD SUPER SPECIAL, DELL CROSSWORD EXTRAVAGANZA, DELL CHALLENGER CROSSWORDS, DELL PENCIL PUZZLES & WORD GAMES YEARBOOK, BEST OF DELL, Dell Puzzle Publications, 245 E. 47th St., New York NY 10017. Editor: Rosalind Moore. For "all ages from 8 to 80—people whose interests are puzzles, both crosswords and variety features." 95% freelance written. Buys all rights. Computer printout submissions acceptable; prefers letter-quality over dot-matrix.
Puzzles: "We publish puzzles of all kinds, but the market here is limited to those who are able to construct quality pieces that can compete with the real professionals . See our magazines; they are the best guide to our needs. We publish quality puzzles which are well-conceived and well-edited, with appeal to solvers of all ages and in almost every walk of life. We are the world's leading name in puzzle publications and are distributed in many countries around the world in addition to the continental U.S. However, no foreign language puzzles. Our market for regular crosswords and Anacrostics is very small, since long-time contributors supply most of the needs in those areas. However, we are always willing to see material of unusual quality, or with a new or original approach. We are in the market for expert-level 21x21 crosswords on a par with those appearing in the Sunday *New York Times*. Since most of our publications feature variety puzzles in addition to the usual features, we are especially interested in seeing picture features, and new and unusual puzzle features of all kinds. Do not send us remakes of features we are now using. Send only one sample, please, and make sure your name and address are on each page submitted. Nothing without an answer will be considered. Do not expect an immediate reply. Prices vary with the feature, but ours are comparable with the highest in the general puzzle field."

‡POKER-CHIPS, Official Publication of the International Home & Private Poker Player's Association, Scotty Barclay Poker Products, Rt. 2, Box 2845, Manistique MI 49854. (906)341-5468. Editor: Tony Wuehle. Works with a small number of new/unpublished writers each year. A quarterly tabloid covering recreational poker. "We are a publication for the serious home and private club poker player. Our readers are not professionals, but they do know and understand poker." Circ. 2,000. Pays on publication. Publishes ms an average of 4 months after acceptance. Byline given. Buys first rights. Photocopied submissions OK. Computer printout submissions acceptable; prefers letter-quality to dot-matrix. Reports in 2 weeks on queries; 1 month on mss. Sample copy $1.
Nonfiction: Essays; how-to (play various poker games well); new product (related to poker); and news of home and private poker groups. "No bad beat poker stories." Buys 4 mss/year. Query with or without published clips, or send complete ms. Length: 400-1,000 words. Pays $10-40 for articles; pays in copies for news of clubs.
Photos: Send photos with submission. Reviews 5x7 b&w prints. Offers no additional payment for photos accepted with ms. Captions, model releases, and identification of subjects required. Buys one-time rights. "We will probably use photos of club members only."

Market conditions are constantly changing! If this is 1988 or later, buy the newest edition of Writer's Market at your favorite bookstore or order directly from Writer's Digest Books.

Fillers: Anecdotes, facts and short humor. Length: 25-100 words. Pays in copies at this time.
Tips: "Articles on experience in tournament play, whether it be in a private or public game, are probably most open to freelancers. We will probably be interested in court decisions regarding poker games and possibly the poker games which are spread at the Native American casinos."

General Interest

General interest magazines need writers who can address many audiences at one time, but they don't need generalities. When a single story touches teens and senior citizens, wealthy readers and the unemployed, that's general interest. Some general interest publications, however, appeal to an audience of one general (but slightly varying) lifestyle, such as *Connoisseur* or *Grit*. Each magazine develops a "personality"—one that a writer should study before sending material to an editor. Other markets for general interest material in these Consumer categories: Ethnic/Minority, In-Flight, Lifestyles, Men's, Regional, and Women's.

THE AMERICAN LEGION MAGAZINE, Box 1055, Indianapolis IN 46206. (317)635-8411. Editor: Michael D. La Bonne. Monthly. 95% freelance written. Circ. 2,600,000. Buys first North American serial rights. Computer printout submissions acceptable; prefers letter-quality to dot-matrix. Reports on submissions "promptly." Publishes ms an average of 6 months after acceptance. Byline given. Pays on acceptance.
Nonfiction: Query first, but will consider unsolicited mss. "Prefer an outline query. Relate your article's thesis or purpose, tell why you are qualified to write it, the approach you will take and any authorities you intend to interview. War remembrance pieces of a personal nature (vs. historic in perspective) should be in ms form." Uses current world affairs, topics of contemporary interest, little-known happenings in American history, 20th century war-remembrance pieces, and 750-word commentaries on contemporary problems and points of view. No personality profiles, or regional topics. Buys 60 mss/year. Length: 1,800 words maximum. Pays $100-1,500.
Photos: On assignment.
Fillers: Short, tasteful jokes and humorous anecdotes. Pays $12.50-15.
Tips: Query should include author's qualifications for writing a technical or complex article. Also include thesis, length, outline and conclusion. "Send a thorough query. Submit material that is suitable for us, showing that you have read several issues. Attach a few clips of previously published material. *The American Legion Magazine* considers itself '*the* magazine for a strong America.' Any query reflective of this theme (which includes strong economy, educational system, moral fiber, infrastructure and armed forces) will be given priority."

‡THE BEST REPORT, "Exploring the World of Quality," Best Publications, Inc., Suite 4210, 350 Fifth Ave., New York NY 10118. (212)239-4400. Publisher: Norman Aronson. 50% freelance written. Works with a small number of new/unpublished writers each year. Monthly newsletter that "establishes qualitative hierarchies in goods, services, experiences." Circ. over 100,000. Pays on publication. Publishes ms an average of 3 months after acceptance. No byline given. Offers negotiable kill fee; usually 25%. Buys all rights, second (reprint) rights to material originally published elsewhere, and makes work-for-hire assignments. Submit seasonal/holiday material 3 months in advance. Simultaneous queries OK. Electronic submissions OK via IBM PC-Xywrite II, but requires hard copy also. Computer printout submissions acceptable. Reports in 3 weeks on queries. Free sample copy and writer's guidelines.
Nonfiction: Book excerpts, how-to (buying guides, travel guides), new product, and travel. Buys 100+ mss/year. Query. Features length: 1,000 words (generally). Pays average 30¢/word. Sometimes pays the expenses of writers on assignment.
Tips: "We want authoritative, documented reporting on 'bests' in any field of consumer-oriented quality. Short (250-500 words) items on goods, services of interest to high-income ($100,000-plus) audience are most open to freelancers."

A BETTER LIFE FOR YOU, The National Research Bureau, Inc., 424 N. 3rd St., Burlington IA 52601. (319)752-5415. Editor: Rhonda Wilson. Editorial Supervisor: Doris J. Ruschill. 75% freelance written. Works with a small number of new/unpublished writers each year. For industrial workers of all ages. Quarterly maga-

zine. Pays on publication. Publishes ms an average of 1 year after acceptance. Buys all rights. Submit seasonal/holiday material 7 months in advance of issue date. Previously published submissions OK. Computer printout submissions acceptable; prefers letter-quality to dot-matrix. Reports in 3 weeks. Free writer's guidelines.
Nonfiction: General interest (steps to better health, on-the-job attitudes); and how-to (perform better on the job, do home repair jobs, and keep up maintenance on a car). Buys 10-12 mss/year. Query or send outline. Length: 400-600 words. Pays 4¢/word.
Tips: "Writers have a better chance of breaking in at our publication with short articles and fillers because all of our articles are short."

CAPPER'S WEEKLY, Stauffer Communications, Inc., 616 Jefferson St., Topeka KS 66607. (913)295-1108. Editor: Dorothy Harvey. 25% freelance written. Emphasizes home and family for readers who live in small towns and on farms. Biweekly tabloid. Circ. 415,000. Pays for poetry on acceptance; articles on publication. Buys first serial rights only. Submit seasonal/holiday material 2 months in advance. Reports in 1 month; 8 months for serialized novels. Sample copy 55¢.
Nonfiction: Historical (local museums, etc.), inspirational, nostalgia, travel (local slants) and people stories (accomplishments, collections, etc.). Buys 35 mss/year. Submit complete ms. Length: 700 words maximum. Pays $1/inch.
Photos: Purchased with accompanying ms. Submit prints. Pays $5-10 for 8x10 or 5x7 b&w glossy prints. Total purchase price for ms includes payment for photos. Limited market for color photos (35mm color slides); pays $25 each.
Columns/Departments: Heart of the Home (homemakers' letters, recipes, hints), and Hometown Heartbeat (descriptive). Submit complete ms. Length: 300 words maximum. Pays $2-10.
Fiction: "We have begun to buy some fiction pieces—longer than short stories, shorter than novels." Mystery, adventure and romance mss. No explicit sex, violence or profanity. Buys 4-5 mss/year. Query. Pays $150-200.
Poetry: Free verse, haiku, light verse, traditional, nature and inspiration. "The poems that appear in *Capper's* are not too difficult to read. They're easy to grasp. We're looking for everyday events, and down-to-earth themes." Buys 4-5/issue. Limit submissions to batches of 5-6. Length: 4-16 lines. Pays $3-5.
Tips: "Study a few issues of our publication. Most rejections are for material that is too long, unsuitable or out of character for our paper (too sexy, too much profanity, etc.). On occasion, we must cut material to fit column space."

CHANGING TIMES, The Kiplinger Magazine, 1729 H St. NW, Washington DC 20006. Editor: Marjorie White. Less than 5% freelance written. Prefers to work with published/established writers. For general, adult audience interested in consumer information. Monthly. Circ. 1,350,000. Buys all rights. Reports in 1 month. Computer printout submissions acceptable. Pays on acceptance. Publishes ms an average of 3 months after acceptance. Thorough documentation required.
Nonfiction: "Most material is staff-written, but we accept some freelance." Query with clips of published work. No bylines. Sometimes pays the expenses of writers on assignment.

‡THE CHRISTIAN SCIENCE MONITOR, 1 Norway St., Boston MA 02115. (617)262-2300, ext. 2303. Contact: Submissions. International newspaper issued daily except Saturdays, Sundays and holidays in North America; weekly international edition. Special issues: travel, winter vacation and international travel, summer vacation, autumn vacation, and others. March and September: fashion. Circ. 160,000. Buys all newspaper rights for 3 months following publication. Buys limited number of mss, "top quality only." Publishes original (exclusive) material only. Pays on acceptance or publication, "depending on department." Submit seasonal material 2 months in advance. Reports in 4 weeks. Submit complete original ms or letter of inquiry. Writer's guidelines available.
Nonfiction: Roderick Nordell, feature editor. In-depth features and essays. Please query by mail before sending mss. "Style should be bright but not cute, concise but thoroughly researched. Try to humanize news or feature writing so reader identifies with it. Avoid sensationalism, crime and disaster. Accent constructive, solution-oriented treatment of subjects. Home Forum page buys essays of 400-900 words. Pays $70-140. Education, arts, real estate, travel, living, garden, books, sports, food, furnishings, and science pages will consider articles not usually more than 800 words appropriate to respective subjects." Pays $75-100.
Poetry: Traditional, blank and free verse. Seeks poetry of high quality and of all lengths up to 75 lines. Pays $25 average.

‡COLLAGE, Collage, Inc., 1200 S. Willis Ave., Wheeling IL 60090. (312)541-9290. Editor: Harriet Hirsch. Managing Editor: Emil G. Hirsch. 90% freelance written. Prefers to work with published/established writers; works with a small number of new/unpublished writers each year. Quarterly general interest magazine. Circ. 25,000. Pays on publication. Publishes ms an average of 2 months after acceptance. Byline given. Buys first North American serial rights. Submit seasonal/holiday material 2 months in advance. Simultaneous submissions OK. Computer printout submissions acceptable; no dot-matrix. Reports in 2 months. Sample copy for 9x12 SAE with 4 first class stamps.

Nonfiction: New discoveries in medicine or health care, general interest, historical/nostalgic, interview/profile, new product, opinion, travel and physical fitness. No controversial material. Buys 28 mss/year. Send complete ms. Length: 750-2,200 words. Pays $25-50. Sometimes pays the expenses of writers on assignment.

Photos: State availability of photos or send photos with submission. Reviews transparencies and prints. Pays $5-25/photo. Captions and model releases required. "We may be going to 4-color pictures on the inside of magazine—to improve appearance."

Columns/Departments: Restaurants Around the World (travel article with emphasis on foods of the region). Buys 4 mss/year. Send complete ms. Length: 750-1,500 words. Pays $25-50.

Fiction: Science fiction. No romance. Buys 1 ms/year. Query with published clips. Length: 750-1,500. Pays $25 minimum.

Poetry: Free verse. Buys 2 poems/year. Pays $25 minimum.

COMMENTARY, 165 E. 56th St., New York NY 10022. (212)751-4000. Editor: Norman Podhoretz. Monthly magazine. Circ. 50,000. Byline given. "All of our material is done freelance, though much of it is commissioned." Pays on publication. Query, or submit complete ms. Reports in 1 month.

Nonfiction: Brenda Brown, editor. Thoughtful essays on political, social and cultural themes; general, as well as with special Jewish content. Length: 3,000 to 7,000 words. Pays approximately $100/printed page.

Fiction: Marion Magid, editor. Uses some mainstream fiction. Length: varies. Pays $100/printed page.

‡THE CONNOISSEUR, The Hearst Corp., 224 W. 57th St., New York NY 10019. (212)262-5595. Editor-in-Chief: Thomas Hoving. Executive Editor: Philip Herrera. Managing Editor: Leslie Smith. 90% freelance written. Monthly magazine of the arts—fine, decorative and performing. "*Connoisseur* is written and designed for people who value excellence. It is informed by lively scholarship, a keen critical eye, and a civilized sense of fun. It covers a wide range of subjects and provides our audience with first-hand access to our topics and pertinent service data." Circ. 270,000. Pays on acceptance. Offers 15% kill fee. Buys first English language rights. Submit seasonal/holiday material 3 months in advance. Computer printout submissions acceptable; prefers letter-quality to dot-matrix. Reports in 1 month. For back issues phone (212)262-8485 or write 250 W. 55th St., New York NY 10019.

Nonfiction: Travel; the arts—fine, decorative, performing; food; wine; architecture; fashion and jewelry. Buys 120 mss/year. Query with published clips. Length: 350-2,500 words. Pays $100-2,000. Pays expenses of writers on assignment.

Photos: Linda Ferrer, photo editor. Captions, model releases and identification of subjects required. Buys one-time rights.

Columns/Departments: Connoisseur's World, and Private Line. Buys 50 mss/year. Query with published clips. Length: 1,500-2,000 words. Pays $500-750.

Tips: "A freelancer can best break in to our publication with a strong, original proposal backed by good clips. Be aware of what we *have been doing*—read the magazine. Connoisseur's World—short, timely proposals that are miniature magazine features—is the area most open to freelancers."

DIALOGUE, The Magazine for the Visually Impaired, Dialogue Publications, Inc., 3100 Oak Park Ave., Berwyn IL 60402. (312)749-1908. Editor: Nolan Crabb. 50% freelance written. Works with published/established writers and a small number of new/unpublished writers each year. Quarterly magazine of issues, topics and opportunities related to the visually impaired. Pays on acceptance. Publishes ms an average of 6 months after acceptance. Byline given. Buys all rights "with generous reprint rights." Submit seasonal/holiday material 6 months in advance. Photocopied submissions OK. Computer printout submissions acceptable; no dot-matrix. Reports in 2 weeks on queries; 1 month on mss. Free sample copy to visually impaired writers. Writer's guidelines in print for business size SAE and 1 first class stamp; send a 60-minute cassette for guidelines on tape.

Nonfiction: "Writers should indicate nature and severity of visual handicap." How-to (cope with various aspects of blindness); humor; interview/profile; new product (of interest to visually impaired); opinion; personal experience; technical (adaptations for use without sight); travel (personal experiences of visually impaired travelers); and first person articles about careers in which individual blind persons have succeeded. No "aren't blind people wonderful" articles; articles that are slanted towards sighted general audience. Buys 60 mss/year. Query with published clips or submit complete ms. Length: 3,000 words maximum. Prefers shorter lengths but will use longer articles if subject warrants. Pays $10-50. Sometimes pays the expenses of writers on assignment.

Photos: Dan Finch, photo editor. Photographs of paintings, sculpture and pottery by visually handicapped artists; and photos taken by visually impaired persons. State availability or send photos with ms. Pays $10-20 for 3½x4¾ b&w prints. Identification of subjects required. Buys one-time rights.

Columns/Departments: ABAPITA ("Ain't Blindness a Pain in the Anatomy")—short anecdotes relating to blindness; Recipe Round-Up; Around the House (household hints); Vox Pop (see magazine); Puzzle Box (see magazine and guidelines); book reviews of books written by visually impaired authors; Beyond the Armchair (travel personal experience); and Backscratcher (a column of questions, answers, hints). Buys 80 mss/year. Send complete ms. Payment varies.

Fiction: "Writers should state nature and severity of visual handicap." Bonnie Miller, fiction editor. Adventure, fantasy, historical, humorous, mainstream, mystery, science fiction, and suspense. No plotless fiction or stories with unbelievable characters; no horror; no explicit sex and no vulgar language. Buys 12 mss/year. Send complete ms. Length: 3,000 words maximum; shorter lengths preferred. Pays $10-50.

Poetry: "Writers should indicate nature and severity of visual impairment." Bonnie Miller, poetry editor. Free verse, haiku, and traditional. No religious poetry or any poetry with more than 20 lines. Buys 30 poems/year. Submit maximum 3 poems. Length: 20 lines maximum. Pays in contributor's copies.

Fillers: Jokes, anecdotes, and short humor. Buys few mss/year. Length: 100 words maximum. Payment varies.

Tips: "*Dialogue* cannot consider manuscripts from authors with 20/20 vision or those who can read regular print with ordinary glasses. Any person unable to read ordinary print who has helpful information to share with others in this category will find a ready market. We believe that blind people are capable, competent, responsible citizens, and the material we publish reflects this view. This is not to say we never sound a negative note, but criticism should be constructive. The writer sometimes has a better chance of breaking in at our publication with short articles and fillers. We are interested in material that is written for a general-interest magazine with visually impaired readers. As we move into a cassette version, we must tighten our format, this means fewer articles used, therefore they must be of the highest quality. We are *not* interested in scholarly journal-type articles; 'amazing blind people I have known,' articles written by sighted writers; articles and fiction that exceed our 3,000-word maximum length; and material that is too regional to appeal to an international audience. No manuscript can be considered without a statement of visual impairment, nor can it be returned without a SASE."

EQUINOX: THE MAGAZINE OF CANADIAN DISCOVERY, Equinox Publishing, 7 Queen Victoria Dr., Camden East, Ontario K0K 1J0 Canada. (613)378-6651. Editor: Barry Estabrook. Managing Editor: Bart Robinson. Executive Editor: Frank B. Edwards. Bimonthly magazine. "We publish in-depth profiles of people, places and wildlife to show readers the real stories behind subjects of general interest in the fields of science and geography." Circ. 150,000. Pays on acceptance. Byline given. Offers 50% kill fee. Buys first North American serial rights only. Submit seasonal queries 1 year in advance. SAE, IRCs. Computer printout submissions acceptable; prefers letter-quality to dot-matrix. Reports in 6 weeks. Sample copy $5; free writer's guidelines.

Nonfiction: Book excerpts (occasionally), geography, science and art. No travel articles. Buys 40 mss/year. Query. "Our biggest need is for science stories. We do not touch unsolicited feature manuscripts." Length: 5,000-10,000 words. Pays $1,500-negotiated.

Photos: Send photos with ms. Reviews color transparencies—must be of professional quality; no prints or negatives. Captions and identification of subjects required.

Columns/Departments: Nexus, current science that isn't covered by daily media. Habitat, Canadian environmental stories not covered by daily media. "Our most urgent need." Buys 80/year. Query with clips of published work. Length: 200-300 words. Pays $200.

Tips: "Submit Habitat and Nexus ideas to us—the 'only' route to a feature is through these departments if writers are untried."

FORD TIMES, 1 Illinois Center, Suite 1700, 111 E. Wacker Dr., Chicago IL 60601. Editor: Thomas A. Kindre. 85% freelance written. Works with a small number of new/unpublished writers each year. "General-interest magazine designed to attract all ages." Monthly. Circ. 1,200,000. Pays on acceptance. Publishes ms an average of 8 months after acceptance. Buys first rights only. Pays kill fee. Byline given. Submit seasonal material 6 months in advance. Computer printout submissions acceptable; prefers letter-quality to dot-matrix. Reports in 1 month. Free sample copy and writer's guidelines.

Nonfiction: "Almost anything relating to contemporary American life that is upbeat and positive. Topics include lifestyle trends, profiles, insights into big cities and small towns, the arts, the outdoors and sports. We are especially interested in subjects that appeal to readers in the 18-35 age group. We strive to be colorful, lively and, above all, interesting. We try to avoid subjects that have appeared in other publications or in our own." Buys 100 mss/year. Length: 1,500 words maximum. Query required unless previous contributor. Pays $500 minimum for full-length articles. Sometimes pays the expenses of writers on assignment.

Photos: "Speculative submission of high-quality color transparencies and b&w photos with mss is welcomed. We need bright, graphically strong photos showing people. We need releases for people whose identity is readily apparent in photos."

40+WOMEN, (formerly *40+*), 40+, Inc., Box 98120, Tacoma WA 98498. (206)582-1988. Publisher and Editor-in-Chief: Lynn Miranda. Executive Editors: Carmen Edwards, Ila Russell. 40% freelance written. Prefers to work with published/established writers; works with a small number of new/unpublished writers each year. Monthly magazine on matters of interest to women 40-65 years of age covering entire spectrum of careers including homemakers. "We deal realistically with issues and topics of interest to women 40 years of age and above. All models used in the magazine are 40 or above. Most contributors are 40 or more." Circ. 200,000. Pays on publication. Publishes ms an average of 6 months after acceptance. Byline given. Offers 50% kill fee. Buys first North American serial rights. Submit seasonal/holiday material 6 months in advance. Simultaneous queries OK. Computer printout submissions acceptable; prefers letter-quality to dot-matrix. Reports in 1 month on queries; 2 months on mss. Sample copy $1.50, and 88¢ postage. Writer's guidelines for SAE and 1 first class stamp.

Nonfiction: Book review (assignments only—query welcome); general interest (geared to 40+); humor (short); interview/profile (women 40+; unusual occupations—women of special interest); and travel. Also food, resources, nutrition, family relationships, fashion, little-known facts/updates/40+ trivia, the 40+ male point of view, first-person articles by readers having strong opinions on events, beliefs and feelings relevant to the 40+ experience. No arts and crafts, sewing, decorating, radical feminist or parenting (unless applicable to 40+). Buys 80 mss/year. Query with published clips or send complete ms. Length: 700-3,000 words. Pays $100-400; $25-35 for shorts. Sometimes pays the expenses of writers on assignment.

Photos: Send photos with ms. Reviews b&w contact sheets; 35mm, 2¼ or 5x5 color transparencies. Pays $25-35 for b&w; $35-150 for color. Captions and model releases required. Buys one-time rights and occasionally all rights.

Columns/Departments: Medical; careers; money matters; nutrition; leisure. Buys 24 mss/year. Query first. Length: 800-1,500 words. Pays $100-200.

Fiction: Prefers short-short and light fiction; humorous and romance (with 40+ character). No erotica, pornography, true confessions or retirement. Buys 24 mss/year. Send complete ms. Length: 1,000-2,000 words. Pays $200-300.

Poetry: Light verse and humorous. Buys 2-3/issue. Submit maximum 5 poems. Length: 20 lines maximum. Pays $25-35.

Fillers: Humor and cartoons (with 40+ character—not dumpy). Buys 5-7/year. Length: 1-2 lines. Pays standard rates for humor; pays $35 for cartoons.

Tips: "Areas most open to freelancers include humor, travel, unique places of interest to women and couple travelers and fiction. Viewpoint section entitled 'My turn' accepts first-person articles by readers having strong opinions on events, beliefs relevant to the 40+ experience (1,000-2,100 words). Address a group that is active—not ready for retirement. We'll be buying more freelance material because the magazine will be growing."

FRIENDLY EXCHANGE, Meredith Publishing Service, Locust at 17th, Des Moines IA 50336. (612)690-7383. Editor: Adele Malott. 85% freelance written. Quarterly magazine "designed to encourage the sharing or exchange of ideas, information and fun among its readers, for young, traditional families between the ages of 19 and 39 who live in the area west of the Mississippi River and north of the Ohio. For policyholders of the Farmers Insurance Group of companies." Circ. 4.5 million. Pays on acceptance. Publishes ms an average of 5 months after acceptance. Offers 25% kill fee. Buys all rights. Submit seasonal/holiday material 1 year in advance. Simultaneous queries and photocopied submissions OK. Computer printout submissions acceptable. Reports in 2 months. Sample copy for 9x12 SAE and five first-class stamps; writer's guidelines for business size SAE and 1 first class stamp.

Nonfiction: General interest (family activities, sports and health, car care); historical/nostalgic (heritage and culture); family finance; family travel (domestic); community and family lifestyle. "Whenever possible, a story should be told through the experiences of actual people or families in such a way that our readers will want to share experiences they have had with similar activities or interests. No product-publicity material." Buys 10 unsolicited mss/year. Query. Length: 1,000-2,000 words. Pays $400-800/article, plus agreed-upon expenses.

Photos: Peggy Fisher, art director. Send photos with ms. Pays $150-400 for 35mm color transparencies; and $50 for 8x10 b&w prints. Pays on publication.

Columns/Departments: All columns and departments rely on reader-generated ideas, recipes, household hints, etc. Study articles, "Family Skiing Fun" (Winter 1985) and "Drinking, Driving & Death" (Spring 1986)."

Tips: "The most frequent mistake made by writers is not listening to the editor closely enough or not reading the assignment letter carefully enough, so they fail to write the article the editor wants. Examples: Domestic travel means within the United States, not Mexico, Hong Kong or Europe. Family activities does not mean Club Med."

FUTURIFIC MAGAZINE, 280 Madison Ave., New York NY 10016. (212)684-4913. Editor-in-Chief: Balint Szent-Miklosy. 75% freelance written. Monthly. "*Futurific, Inc.* is an independent, nonprofit organization set up in 1976 to study the future, and *Futurific Magazine* is its monthly report on findings. We report on what is coming in all areas of life from international affairs to the arts and sciences. Readership cuts across all income levels and includes government, corporate and religious people." Circ. 10,000. Pays on publication. Publishes ms an average of 1 month after acceptance. Byline given in most cases. Buys one-time rights and will negotiate reprints. Computer printout submissions OK. Reports within 1 month. Sample copy for $2.

Nonfiction: All subjects must deal with the future: book excerpts, exposé, general interest, how to forecast

the future—seriously, humor, interview/profile, new product, photo feature and technical. No historical, opinion or gloom and doom. Send complete ms. Length: 5,000 words maximum. Payment negotiable.
Photos: Send photos with ms. Reviews b&w prints. Pay negotiable. Identification of subjects required.
Columns/Departments: Medical breakthroughs, new products, inventions, book, movie and theatre reviews, etc. "Anything that is new or about to be new." Send complete ms. Length: 5,000 words maximum.
Poetry: Avant-garde, free verse, haiku, light verse and traditional. "Must deal with the future. No gloom and doom or sad poetry." Buys 6/year. Submit unlimited number of poems. Length: open. Pays in copies.
Fillers: Clippings, jokes, gags, anecdotes, short humor, and newsbreaks. "Must deal with the future." Length: open. Pays in copies.
Tips: "We seek to maintain a light-hearted, professional look at forecasting. Be upbeat and show a loving expectation for the marvels of human achievement. Take any subject or concern you find in regular news magazines and extrapolate as to what the future will be. Use imagination. Get involved in the excitement of the international developments, social interaction, etc."

GOOD READING, for Everyone, Henrichs Publications, Inc., Box 40, Sunshine Park, Litchfield IL 62056. (217)324-3425. Editor: Peggy Kuethe. Managing Editor: Garth Henrichs. 80% freelance written. Eager to work with new/unpublished writers each year. A monthly general interest magazine with articles and stories based on a wide range of current or factual subjects. Circ. 7,500. Pays on acceptance. Publishes ms an average of 6 months after acceptance. Byline given. Buys first North American serial rights. Submit seasonal/holiday material 5 months in advance. Photocopied submissions OK. Computer printout submissions acceptable; prefers letter-quality to dot-matrix. Reports in 2 months. Sample copy 50¢; writer's guidelines for #10 SAE with 1 first class stamp.
Nonfiction: General interest, historical/nostalgic, humor, photo feature and travel. Also stories about annual festivals, new products, people who make a difference. "No material that deals with the sordid side of life, nothing about alcohol, smoking, drugs, gambling. Nothing that deals with the cost of travel, or that is too technical." Send complete ms. Length: 100-1,000 words. Pays $20-100 for unsolicited articles.
Photos: Send photos with submission. Reviews contact sheets and 3x5, 5x7, or 8x10 prints. Offers no additional payment for photos accepted with ms. Identification of subjects required. Buys one-time rights.
Columns/Departments: Youth Today (directed at young readers), 100 words maximum. Buys 6-9 mss/year. Send complete ms. Pays $10-50.
Poetry: Light verse. No limit to number of poems submitted at one time. Length: 4-16 lines. Pays in copies.
Fillers: Anecdotes, facts and short humor. Length: 50-150 words. Pays $10-30.
Tips: "The tone of *Good Reading* is wholesome, the articles are short. Keep writing informal but grammatically correct. *Good Reading* is general interest and directed at the entire family—so we accept only material that would be of interest to nearly every age group."

GRIT, Stauffer Communications, Inc., 208 W. 3rd St., Williamsport PA 17701. (717)326-1771. Editor: Naomi L. Woolever. 33% freelance written. Works with a small number of new/unpublished writers each year. For a general readership of all ages in small town and rural America. Tabloid newspaper. Weekly. Circ. 600,000. Buys first and second rights to the same material. Byline given. Buys 1,000-1,500 mss/year. Pays on acceptance for freelance material; on publication for reader participation feature material. Publishes ms an average of 2 months after acceptance. Computer printout submissions acceptable; no dot-matrix. Reports in 1 month. Sample copy $1; free writer's guidelines.
Nonfiction: Alvin Elmer, news editor. "We want mss about six basic areas of interest: people, religion, jobs (how individuals feel about their work), recreation, spirit of community (tradition or nostalgia that binds residents of a town together), and necessities (stories about people and how they cope—food, shelter, etc.) Also want sociological pieces about rural transportation and health problems or how a town deals effectively with vandalism or crime. Also first-person articles of 300 words or less about a person's narrowest escape, funniest moment, a turning point in life, or recollections of something from the past, i.e., a flood, a fire, or some other dramatic happening that the person experienced." Want good Easter, Christmas and holiday material. Mss should show some person or group involved in an unusual and/or uplifting way. "We lean heavily toward human interest, whatever the subject. Writing should be simple and down-to-earth." No "articles promoting alcoholic beverages, immoral behavior, narcotics, or unpatriotic acts." Query or submit complete ms. Length: 500 words maximum. Pays 12¢/word for first or exclusive rights; 6¢/word for second or reprint rights.
Photos: Photos purchased with or without ms. Looks for photos "outstanding in composition and technical quality." Captions required. No "deep shadows on (photo) subjects." Prefers 8x10 prints (*no* negatives or contact prints) for b&w, but will consider 5x7. Transparencies only for color. Pays $25 for b&w photos accompanying ms; $100 for front cover color photos.
Poetry: Joanne Decker, poetry editor. Buys traditional forms of poetry and light verse. "We want poems on seasonal, human interest and humorous topics. We'd also like to see poems about the holidays." Length: preferably 20 lines maximum. Pays $6 for 4 lines and under, plus 50¢/line for each additional line.
Tips: "The freelancer would do well to write for a copy of our Guidelines for Freelancers. We are planning an editorial calendar geared to gardening, travel, home improvement, home technology, canning, sports and fit-

ness and money management. Everything is spelled out there about how-tos, submission methods, etc. All manuscripts should include in upper right-hand corner of first page the number of words and whether it's first or second rights."

HARPER'S MAGAZINE, 666 Broadway, 11th Floor, New York NY 10012. (212)614-6500. Editor: Lewis H. Lapham. 40% freelance written. For well-educated, socially concerned, widely read men and women who value ideas and good writing. Monthly. Circ. 152,000. Rights purchased vary with author and material. Pays negotiable kill fee. Pays on acceptance. Computer printout submissions acceptable. Reports in 2 weeks. Publishes ms an average of 3 months after acceptance. Sample copy $2.50.
Nonfiction: "For writers working with agents or who will query first only, our requirements are: public affairs, literary, international and local reporting, and humor." No interviews. Complete mss and queries must include SASEs. No unsolicited poems will be accepted. Publishes one major article per issue. Length: 4,000-6,000 words. Publishes one major essay per issue. Length: 4,000-6,000 words. "These should be construed as topical essays on all manner of subjects (politics, the arts, crime, business, etc.) to which the author can bring the force of passionately informed statement." Generally pays 50¢-$1/word.
Photos: Deborah Rust, art director. Occasionally purchased with mss; others by assignment. Pays $50-500.

HEALTH & WEALTH, Allied Publications, 1776 Lake Worth Road, Lake Worth FL 33460. Editor: Mark Adams. A bimonthly of equal entertainment features with more specialized selections relating to personal health and finance. Circ. 75,000. Buys simultaneous rights, first rights, and second serial (reprint) rights. Submit seasonal material 6 months in advance. Simultaneous, photocopied and previously published submissions OK. Reports 3 months on mss. Sample copy $1 SAE; Writer's guidelines for SAE.
Nonfiction: General interest, humor, motivational, interviewed profile (must include subject's pictures), personal experience, photo feature, travel, lifestyle, fashion, and technical (for lay reader). Buys 50-100 mss/year. Send complete ms. Length: 400-1,000 words. Pays 5¢/published word or $25 maximum.
Fiction: Prefers humor. Buys up to 10 mss/year. Length 400-1,000 words. Pays 5¢/word or $25 maximum.
Photos: Send photos or state availability with ms. Pays 5$ for 8x10 b&w glossy prints or color transparencies. Captions preferred; indentification of subjects required. Buys one-time rights.
Cartoons: Buys few. Pays $10.
Tips: "Type manuscript, double-space and *keep a copy* (we sometimes lose them). Edit yourself ruthlessly for grammar, spelling, punctuation and style. Is your story unique? No queries—we simply can't answer them. We receive thousands of manuscripts a year, so no SASE, no answer, and no apologies. Follow the rules, be *very* patient and keep trying. We want to publish you."

IDEALS MAGAZINE, Box 141000, Ideals Publishing, Nelson Place at Elm Hill Pike, Nashville TN 37214. (615)889-9000. Editor: Ramona Richards. 95% freelance written. A magazine published eight times a year. "Our readers are generally women over 50. The magazine is mainly light poetry and short articles with a nostalgic theme. The eight issues are seasonally oriented, as well as being thematic." Pays on publication. Publishes ms an average of 1 year after acceptance. Byline given. Buys one-time North American serial and subsidiary rights. Submit seasonal/holiday material 8 months in advance. Simultaneous, photocopied, and previously published submissions OK. Computer printout submissions acceptable; prefers letter-quality to dot-matrix. Reports in 3 months. Writer's guidelines for #12 SAE with 1 first class stamp.
Nonfiction: Essays, historical/nostalgic, how-to (crafts), humor, inspirational and personal experience. "No down-beat articles or social concerns." Buys 40 mss/year. Query with or without published clips, or send complete ms. Length: 400-800 words. Pays $40-80.
Photos: Send photos with submission. Reviews transparencies and b&w prints. Offers no additional payment for photos accepted with ms. Captions, model release, and identification of subjects required. Buys one-time rights.
Fiction: Slice-of-life vignettes. Buys 2 mss/year. Query. Length: 400-800 words. Pays $40-80.
Poetry: Light verse and traditional. "No erotica or depressing poetry." Buys 250 poems/year. Submit maximum 15 poems. Pays $10.
Tips: "Poetry is the area of our publication most open to freelancers. It must be oriented around a season or theme. The basic subject of *Ideals* is nostalgia, and poetry must be optimistic (how hard work builds character—not how bad the Depression was.)"

KNOWLEDGE, Official Publication of the World Olympiads of Knowledge, RSC Publishers, 3863 Southwest Loop 820, S 100, Ft. Worth TX 76133-2076. (817)292-4272. Editor: Dr. O.A. Battista. Managing Editor: N.L. Matous. 90% freelance written. For lay and professional audiences of all occupations. Quarterly magazine; 60 pages. Circ. 1,500. Pays on publication. Publishes ms an average of 6 months after acceptance. Buys all rights. "We will reassign rights to a writer after a given period." Byline given. Submit seasonal/holiday material 6 months in advance. Computer printout submissions acceptable; prefers letter-quality to dot-matrix. Reports in 1 month. Sample copy $5.
Nonfiction: Informational—original new knowledge that will prove mentally or physically beneficial to all

readers. Buys 30 unsolicited mss/year. Query. Length: 1,500-2,000 words maximum. Pays $100 minimum. Sometimes pays the expenses of writers on assignment.

Columns/Departments: Journal section uses maverick and speculative ideas that other magazines will not publish and reference. Payment is made, on publication, at the following minimum rates: *Why Don't They*, $50; *Salutes*, $25; *New Vignettes*, $25; *Quotes To Ponder*, $10; and *Facts*, $5.

Tips: "The editors of *Knowledge* welcome submissions from contributors. Manuscripts and art material will be carefully considered but received *only* with the unequivocal understanding that the magazine will not be responsible for loss or injury. Material from a published source should have the publication's name, date, and page number. Submissions cannot be acknowledged and will be returned only when accompanied by a SAE having adequate postage."

LEFTHANDER MAGAZINE, Lefthander International, Box 8249, Topeka KS 66608. (913)234-2177. Managing Editor: Suzan Menendez. 80% freelance written. Eager to work with new/unpublished writers. Bimonthly. "Our readers are lefthanded people of all ages and interests in 50 U.S. states and 10 foreign countries. The one thing they have in common is an interest in lefthandedness." Circ. 22,000. Pays on publication. Publishes ms an average of 4 months after acceptance. Byline usually given. Offers 25% kill fee. Rights negotiable. Submit seasonal/holiday material 6 months in advance. Simultaneous queries OK. Computer printout submissions acceptable; prefers letter-quality to dot-matrix. Reports on queries in 4 weeks. Sample copy for 8½x11 SAE and $2. Writer's guidelines for legal size SAE and 1 first class stamp.

Nonfiction: Interviews with famous lefthanders; features about lefthanders with interesting talents and occupations; how-to features (sports, crafts, hobbies for lefties); research on handedness and brain dominance; exposé on discrimination against lefthanders in the work world; features on occupations and careers attracting lefties; education features relating to ambidextrous right brain teaching methods. Length: Buys 50-60 mss/year. 750-1,000 words for features. Buys 8-12 personal experience shorts/year. Query with SASE. Length 450-700 words. Pays $25. Pays expenses of writer on assignment.

Photos: State availability of photos for features. Pays $10-15 for b&w, good contrast b&w glossies. Rights negotiable.

Fiction: Lefty Jr., 4-page insert published 3 times/year. Children's short stories dealing with lefthandedness. Length: 500-750 words. Pays $35-50.

Fillers: Trivia, cartoons, word games for children's insert, interesting and unusual facts. Send on speculation. Buys 25-50/year. Pays $5-20.

Tips: "All material must have a lefthanded hook. We prefer quick, practical, self-help and self-awareness types of editorial content; keep it brief, light, and of general interest. More of our space is devoted to shorter pieces. A good short piece gives us enough evidence of writer's style, which we like to have before assigning full-length features. The most frequent mistakes made by writers in completing an article assignment for us are submitting incoherent material written by researchers who don't know how to write for a general-interest magazine, material that does not have lefthanded slant or does not fit our editorial guidelines and including material with themes that have been worked to death or been dealt with previously."

LIFE, Time & Life Bldg., Rockefeller Center, New York NY 10020. (212)586-1212. Managing Editor: Judith Daniels. Articles Editor: Dean Valentine. Monthly general-interest picture magazine for people of all ages, backgrounds and interests. Circ. 1.5 million. Average issue includes one short and one long text piece. Pays on acceptance. Byline given. Offers $500 kill fee. Buys first North American serial rights. Submit seasonal material 4 months in advance. Simultaneous and photocopied submissions OK. Computer printout submissions acceptable; prefers letter-quality to dot-matrix. Reports in 6 weeks on queries; immediately on mss.

Nonfiction: "We've done articles on anything in the world of interest to the general reader and on people of importance. It's extremely difficult to break in since we buy so few articles. Most of the magazine is pictures. We're looking for very high quality writing. We select writers who we think match the subject they are writing about." Buys 1-2 mss/issue. Query with clips of previously published work. Length: 2,000-6,000 words. Pays $3,000 minimum.

MACLEAN'S, Maclean Hunter Bldg., 777 Bay St., 7th, Toronto, Ontario M5W 1A7 Canada. (416)596-5386. Contact: Section Editors (listed in masthead). For news-oriented audience. Weekly newsmagazine; 90 pages. Circ. 650,000. Frequently buys first North American serial rights. Pays on acceptance. "Query with 200- or 300-word outline before sending material." Reports in 2 weeks. Electronic submissions OK. Computer printout submissions acceptable. SAE and IRCs.

Nonfiction: "We have the conventional newsmagazine departments (Canada, world, business, people, plus science, medicine, law, art, music, etc.) with roughly the same treatment as other newsmagazines. We specialize in subjects that are primarily of Canadian interest, and there is now more emphasis on international—particularly US—news. Most material is now written by staffers or retainer freelancers, but we are open to suggestions from abroad, especially in world, business and departments (like medicine, lifestyles, etc.). Freelancers should write for a free copy of the magazine and study the approach." Length: 400-3,500 words. Pays $300-1,500.

‡**NATIONAL ENQUIRER**, Lantana FL 33464. Editor: Iain Calder. Weekly tabloid. Circ. 4,550,000. Pays on acceptance at executive level, or negotiable kill fee. Query. "Story idea must be accepted first. We're no longer accepting unsolicited mss and all spec material will be returned unread."

Nonfiction: Any subject appealing to a mass audience. Requires fresh slant on topical news stories, waste of taxpayers' money by government, the entire field of the occult, how-to articles, rags to riches success stories, medical firsts, scientific breakthroughs, human drama, adventure and personality profiles. "The best way to understand our requirements is to study the paper." Pays $375-600 for most completed features, plus separate lead fees; more with photos. "Payments in excess of $2,000 are not unusual; we will pay more for really top, circulation-boosting blockbusters."

Photos: Uses single or series b&w and color photos that must be attention-grabbing. Wide range; anything from animal photos to great action photos. "We'll bid against any other magazine for once-in-lifetime pictures."

Poetry: Jim Allan, assistant editor. Short poems, most of them humorous and traditional rhyming verse. "We want poetry with a message or reflection on the human condition or everyday life." Avoid sending obscure or "arty" poetry or poems for art's sake. Will consider philosophical poems. Submit seasonal/holiday material at least 2 months in advance. Send SASE and social security number with all submissions. Pays $20 after publication.

‡**NATIONAL EXAMINER**, Globe Communications, Inc., 5401 N.W. Broken Sound Blvd., Boca Raton FL 33431. (305)997-7733. Editor: Bill Burt. Associate Editor: Cliff Linedecker. 15% freelance written. "We are a weekly supermarket tabloid that covers celebrity news, human interest features, medical breakthroughs, astrology, UFOs and the supernatural. Nonfiction stories should be well researched and documented, concise and fun to read." Circ. 1,000,000 +. Pays on acceptance. Publishes ms an average of 1 month after acceptance. Byline given. Buys first North American serial rights. Submit seasonal/holiday material 2 months in advance. Photocopied submissions OK. Computer printout submissions acceptable; prefers letter-quality to dot-matrix.

Nonfiction: Historical/nostalgic; interview/profile (of celebrities); photo feature (color preferred); and the supernatural. No fillers or political material. Buys 200 mss/year. Query with published clips. Length: 250-750 words. Pays $25-300.

Photos: Send photos with submission. Reviews contact sheets, 35mm transparencies, and 8x10 prints. Offers $35-100/photo. Captions and identification of subjects required. Buys one-time rights.

Columns/Departments: Phil Brennan, Spinechillers editor. Spinechillers (first-person personal occult experiences) 250-300 words. Buys 52 mss/year. Send complete ms. Pays $25.

Tips: "Send us a well crafted, carefully documented story. The areas of our publication most open to freelancers are celebrity interviews and color photo spreads featuring celebrities or general subjects."

NATIONAL GEOGRAPHIC MAGAZINE, 17th and M Sts. NW, Washington DC 20036. Editor: Wilbur E. Garrett. For members of the National Geographic Society. Monthly. Circ. more than 10,000,000. Query.

Nonfiction: *National Geographic* publishes first-person, general interest, heavy illustrated articles on science, natural history, exploration and geographical regions. Almost half the articles are staff-written. Of the freelance writers assigned, most are experts in their fields; the remainder are established professionals. Fewer than one percent of unsolicited queries result in assignments. Query (500 words) by letter, not by phone, to Senior Assistant Editor (Contract Writers). Do not send manuscripts. Before querying, study recent issues and check a *Geographic Index* at a library since the magazine seldom returns to regions or subjects covered within the past ten years.

Photos: Photographers should query in care of the Illustration Division.

NEW AGE JOURNAL, Rising Star Associates, 342 Western Ave., Brighton MA 02135. (617)787-2005. Editor: Ruth Sullivan. Editorial Manager: Elizabeth Vulich. 95% freelance written. Works with a small number of new/unpublished writers each year. A monthly magazine emphasizing "personal fulfillment and social change. The audience we reach is college-educated, social-service/hi-tech oriented, 25-45 years of age, concerned about social values, humanitarianism and balance in personal life." Pays half on acceptance, half on publication. Publishes ms an average of 5 months after acceptance. Byline given. Offers 25% kill fee. Buys first North American serial rights and reprint rights. Submit seasonal/material 5 months in advance. Simultaneous and photocopied submissions OK. Computer printout submissions are acceptable provided they are double-spaced "and dark enough." No dot-matrix. Reports in 1 month on queries. Sample copy $2.50; writers' guidelines for letter-size SAE with 1 first class stamp.

Nonfiction: Jean Callahan, articles editor. Book excerpts, exposé, general interest, how-to (travel on business, select a computer, reclaim land, plant a garden, behavior, trend pieces), humor, inspirational, interview/profile, new product and personal experience. Buys 120 mss/year. Query with published clips. Length: 500-4,000 words. Pays $50-3,000 for assigned articles; pays $50-1,500 for unsolicited articles. Pays the expenses of writers on assignment.

Photos: State availability of photos with submission. Offers no additional payment for photos accepted with ms. Model releases and identification of subjects required. Buys one-time rights.

Columns/Departments: Food; Body/Mind; Reflections; First Person; and Sci-Tech. Buys 180 mss/year. Query with published clips. Length: 100-1,500 words. Pays $100-800.

Tips: "Submit short, specific news items to the Upfront department. Query first with clips. A query is one to two paragraphs—if you need more space than that to *present* the idea, then you don't have a clear grip on it. The next open area is columns: First Person and Reflections often take first-time contributors. Read the magazine and get a sense of type of writing run in these two columns."

THE NEW YORKER, 25 W. 43rd St., New York NY 10036. Editor: William Shawn. Weekly. Circ. over 500,000. Reports in 2 months. Pays on acceptance. Computer printout submissions acceptable; prefers letter-quality to dot-matrix.

Nonfiction, Fiction, Poetry, and Fillers: Long fact pieces are usually staff-written. So is "Talk of the Town," although ideas for this department are bought. Pays good rates. Uses fiction, both serious and light. About 90% of the fillers come from contributors with or without taglines (extra pay if the tagline is used).

OPENERS, America's Library Newspaper, American Library Association, 50 E. Huron St., Chicago IL 60611. (312)944-6780. Editor: Ann M. Cunniff. Managing Editor: Deborah G. Robertson. 80% freelance written. Quarterly tabloid covering "what's great to read," about books, fitness and sports, art, music, TV and radio, movies, health, etc., as they relate/tie into the library. No first-person articles or tomes on the importance of reading and libraries. Distributed free. Circ. 250,000. Pays on publication. Publishes ms an average of 6 months after acceptance. Byline given. Buys all rights. Submit seasonal/holiday material 3 months in advance. Simultaneous queries, and simultaneous and photocopied submissions OK. Computer printout submissions acceptable; prefers letter-quality to dot-matrix. Reports in 2 months. Sample copy for 9x12 SAE.

Nonfiction: General interest, how-to and humor-relating to reading or books. "Send us an outline first." Buys 25 + mss/year. Query with published clips. Length: 200-800 words. Pays $25-100.

PARADE, Parade Publications, Inc., 750 3rd Ave., New York NY 10017. (212)573-7000. Editor: Walter Anderson. Weekly magazine for a general interest audience. 90% freelance written. Prefers to work with published/established writers. Circ. 30 million. Pays on acceptance. Publishes ms an average of 3 months after acceptance. Kill fee varies in amount. Buys first North American serial rights. Computer printout submissions acceptable. Reports in 5 weeks on queries. Writer's guidelines for 4x9 SAE and 1 first class stamp.

Nonfiction: General interest (on health, trends, social issues, business or anything of interest to a broad general audience); interview/profile (of news figures, celebrities and people of national significance); and "provocative topical pieces of news value." Spot news events are not accepted, as *Parade* has a 6-week lead time. No fiction, fashion, travel, poetry, quizzes, or fillers. Address queries to Articles Editor. Length: 800-1,500 words. Pays $1,000 minimum. Pays expenses of writers on assignment.

Tips: "Send a well-researched, well-written query targeted to our market. Please, no phone queries. We're interested in well-written exclusive manuscripts on topics of news interest. The most frequent mistake made by writers in completing an article for us is not adhering to the suggestions made by the editor when the article was assigned."

PEOPLE IN ACTION, Meridian Publishing Company, Inc., Box-10010, Ogden UT 84409. (801)394-9446. Editor: Marjorie Rice. 65% freelance written. A monthly inhouse magazine featuring personality profiles. Circ. 55,000. Pays on acceptance. Publishes ms an average of 8 months after acceptance. Byline given. Buys first rights, second serial (reprint) rights and non-exclusive reprint rights. Simultaneous, photocopied and previously published submissions OK. Computer printout submissions acceptable. Reports in 6 weeks. Publishes ms an average of 6 months after acceptance. Sample copy for $1 and 9x12 SAE; writer's guidelines for SAE and 1 first class stamp. All requests for samples and guidelines should be addressed Attn: Editorial Assistant.

Nonfiction: General interest personality profiles. Cover stories focus on nationally noted individuals in the fine arts, literature, entertainment, communications, business, sports, education, health, science and technology. The lives of those featured most exemplify positive values; overcoming obstacles, helping others, advancing culture, creating solutions. Buys 40 mss/year. Query. Length: 1,000-1,400 words. Pays 15¢/word for first rights plus non-exclusive reprint rights. Payment for second rights is negotiable.

Photos: State availability of photos or send photos with query. Pays $35/inside photo, $50/cover photo; uses glossy color prints and transparencies (slide to 8x10). Captions, model releases and identification of subjects required.

Columns/Departments: Regular column features: a 700-word profile of a gourmet chef, first-class restaurant manager, food or nutrition expert, or a celebrity who is also a top-notch cook; a recipe and 1-2 good color transparencies are essential. Buys $10 mss/year. Query. Pays 15¢/word.

Tips: "The key is a well-written query letter that: 1) demonstrates that the subject of the article has national appeal 2) shows that a profile of the person interviewed will have a clear, focused theme 3) outlines the availability (from the writer or a photographer or a PR source) of top-quality color photos 4) gives evidence that the writer/photographer is a professional, even if a beginner."

Close-up

Larry Smith
Managing Editor
Parade

Is the proposal interesting enough to entice 55 million readers? It must be if it is going to appear in *Parade* magazine. The magazine, distributed in Sunday newspapers, reaches about one-third of the adult reading audience in the United States.

"Most writers are not used to thinking in terms as large as *Parade*'s," says managing editor Larry Smith. "And the reader response is astounding because the audience is so vast."

An article that appears in *Parade* could appear in a newspaper, Smith says, "but most newspaper articles could not appear in *Parade*." He explains the difference: "By and large, news reporters' material is dictated by what happened yesterday or what's happening today. We have a six-week lead time. We anticipate things, but we don't rely on current events, so we have to find other ways to make the magazine interesting."

His recommendations for those breaking in at *Parade* are good advice for any writer. First, study the publication and work to develop good proposals. Smith says, "We have any number of people who are happy to interview Bob Hope for us. It's a plum assignment." But a new writer "has to come up with his own ideas and an interesting way to present them," he says. "We have discovered a writer, a guy in his mid-20s with tremendous energy, who is just bombarding us with good ideas. He studied the magazine at length."

Smith says his own background includes "a wealth of hard times" and almost 20 years of work on six newspapers, starting with *The Wyoming Eagle* in Cheyenne and ending with *The New York Times*. He is the author of a novel, *The Original*.

He contends that persistence paid off for him and will pay off for other writers. "Most people give up after two or three times if they're rejected. It's true with any goal, but it's really true with writing: If you don't quit something *can* happen, but if you quit, you know nothing is going to happen."

Writing, Smith says, "is about commitment in a very spiritual sense. Not in a religious sense, necessarily, but in a spiritual sense." Along with commitment, a writer should "never assume—just because your article or your idea is rejected—that it isn't publishable," he says. "There are a lot of reasons for rejection that have nothing to do with quality. Maybe we recently had an article about the same thing you propose. It doesn't mean we don't like it; we've just used it already."

Although Smith says writers need to be "inordinately tough-minded," he cautions them against being cynical. "People who choose to be cynical are afraid to believe in life's possibilities," he says.

—Glenda Tennant

READER'S DIGEST, Pleasantville NY 10570. Monthly. Circ. 16.5 million. Publishes general interest articles "as varied as all human experience." The *Digest* does not read or return unsolicited mss. Address proposals and tear sheets of published articles to the Editors. Considers only previously published articles; pays $900/*Digest* page for World Digest rights. (Usually split 50/50 between original publisher and writer.) Tear sheets of submitted article must include name of original publisher and date of publication.
Columns/Departments: "Original contributions become the property of *Reader's Digest* upon acceptance and payment. Life-in-these-United States contributions must be true, unpublished stories from one's own experience, revealing adult human nature, and providing appealing or humorous sidelights on the American scene. Length: 300 words maximum. Pays $300 on publication. True and unpublished stories are also solicited for Humor in Uniform, Campus Comedy and All in a Day's Work. Length: 300 words maximum. Pays $300 on publication. Towards More Picturesque Speech—the first contributor of each item used in this department is paid $40 for original material, $35 for reprints. Contributions should be dated, and the source must be given. For items used in Laughter, the Best Medicine, Personal Glimpses, Quotable Quotes, and elsewhere in the magazine payment is as follows; to the *first* contributor of each from a published source, $35. For original material, $20 per *Digest* two-column line, with a minimum payment of $50. Send complete anecdotes to excerpt editor."

READERS NUTSHELL, Allied Publications, 1776 Lake Worth Road, Lake Worth FL 33460. Editor: Mark Adams. 30% freelance written. Bimonthly magazine for customers of insurance agents. Insurance-related material; general interest. Circ. 75,000. Buys simultaneous rights, first serial rights, and second serial (reprint) rights. Submit seasonal material 6 months in advance. Simultaneous, photocopied, and previously published submissions OK. Computer printout submissions acceptable; prefers letter-quality to dot-matrix. Reports in 3 weeks on "holding" mss; in 3 months on mss. Sample copy $1 and SAE; writer's guidelines for SAE.
Nonfiction: Insurance-related, general interest (non-controversial home, family, and safety articles); humor; and interview (of famous people). Buys 50-100 mss/year. Send complete ms. Length: 400-1,000 words. Pays 5¢/published word or $25 maximum.
Fiction: Prefers humor. Length: 400-1,000 words. Pays 5¢/word or $25 maximum.
Photos: Send photos with ms. Pays $5 for 8x10 b&w glossy prints or color transparencies. Captions and identification of subjects required.
Fillers: Cartoons. Buys few. Pays $10.
Tips: "Type manuscript, double-spaced, and *keep a copy*. Edit yourself ruthlessly for grammar, etc. Make story unique. No queries. No SASE, no answer. Be patient and keep trying. We want to publish you."

READERS REVIEW, The National Research Bureau, Inc., 424 N. 3rd St., Burlington IA 52601. Editor: Rhonda Wilson. Editorial Supervisor: Doris J. Ruschill. 75% freelance written. Works with a small number of new/unpublished writers each year. "For industrial workers of all ages." Quarterly magazine. Pays on publication. Publishes ms an average of 1 year after acceptance. Buys all rights. Previously published submissions OK. Computer printout submissions acceptable; prefers letter-quality to dot-matrix. Submit seasonal/holiday material 7 months in advance of issue date. Reports in 3 weeks. Free writer's guidelines.
Nonfiction: General interest (steps to better health, attitudes on the job); how-to (perform better on the job, do home repairs, car maintenance); and travel. No articles on car repair, stress and tension. Buys 10-12 mss/year. Query with outline. Length: 400-600 words. Pays 4¢/word.
Tips: "Writers have a better chance of breaking in at our publication with short articles and fillers because all of our articles are short." Submit complete ms.

THE SATURDAY EVENING POST, The Saturday Evening Post Society, 1100 Waterway Blvd., Indianapolis, IN 46202. (317)636-8881. Editor: Cory SerVass, M.D. Managing Editor: Ted Kreiter. 40% freelance written. A family-oriented magazine published 9 times/year covering preventive medicine and health care. Circ. 700,000. Pays on publication. Byline given. Buys all rights. Submit seasonal/holiday material at least 3 months in advance. Simultaneous, photocopied and previously published submissions OK. Computer printout submissions acceptable. Reports in 1 month on queries; 6 weeks on mss. Writer's guidelines for business size SAE and 1 first class stamp.
Nonfiction: Barbara Potter, articles editor. General interest, health, interview/profile, religious. "No political articles, or articles containing sexual innuendo or hypersophistication." Buys 40-60 mss/year. Query with published clips. Length: 750-2,500 words. Pays $100 minimum. Sometimes pays the expenses of writers on assignment.
Photos: State availability of photos with submission. Reviews negatives and transparencies. Model releases and identification of subjects required. Buys one-time rights or all rights. Payment and rights negotiable.
Columns/Departments: Money Talk and Gardening/Home Improvement (new in '86), Travel (tourism-oriented). "See recent issues for topics and slant." Query with published clips. Length: 750-1,000 words. Pays $150 minimum.
Fiction: Rebecca Whitney, fiction editor. Adventure, historical, humorous, and mainstream. "Anything ex-

cept humor has only a *remote* chance." Buys approximately 2 mss/year. Send complete ms. Length: 2,500 words. Pays $150 minimum.
Fillers: Jack Gramling, Post Scripts editor. Anecdotes, short humor and light verse. Buys 200 + /year. Length: 300 words maximum. Pays $15.
Tips: The areas most open to freelancers are "Post Scripts—no cute kiddy sayings; keep submissions up-to-date—no put downs of hippies, etc.' when submitting, let the editor make up his own mind whether your material is humorous—and Travel—no first person—it's egocentric, thus boring; select mainstream locales; and have lots of pictures or know where to find them."

SATURDAY REVIEW, Saturday Review Publishing Co., Suite 460, 214 Massachusetts Ave. NE, Washington DC 20002. (202)547-1106. Editor: Frank Gannon. Bimonthly magazine covering literature and the arts for highly literate audience. Circ. 200,000. Pays within 30 days of publication. Byline given. Submit seasonal/holiday material 6 months in advance. Reports in 3 weeks. Sample copy for $2.50 and magazine size SASE.
Nonfiction: Book excerpts; interview/profile (with artists and writers); and coverage of cultural or artistic event. Buys 30 mss/year. Send complete ms. Length: 800-3,000 words. Pays $350-1,500. Briefings: 300-500 words. Pays $50-150.
Photos: Model release and identification of subjects required.
Tips: "We'll have more and shorter reviews of books and films and other departments as appropriate. Features should involve a profile of an important artist or writer—preferably one who has just produced or is about to produce an important work. Avoid the obvious and the overdone; we don't want to do the same people everyone else is doing."

SELECTED READING, The National Research Bureau, Inc., 424 N. 3rd St., Burlington IA 52601. Editor: Rhonda Wilson. Editorial Supervisor: Doris J. Ruschill. 75% freelance written. Works with a small number of new/unpublished writers each year. For industrial workers of all ages. Quarterly magazine. Pays on publication. Publishes ms an average of 1 year after acceptance. Buys all rights. Previously published submissions OK. Computer printout submissions acceptable; prefers letter-quality to dot-matrix. Submit seasonal/holiday material 6-7 months in advance of issue date. Reports in 3 weeks. Free writer's guidelines.
Nonfiction: General interest (economics, health, safety, working relationships); how-to; and travel (out-of-the way places). No material on car repair. Buys 10-12 mss/year. Query. A short outline or synopsis is best. Lists of titles are no help. Length: 400-600 words. Pays 4¢/word.
Tips: "Writers have a better chance of breaking in at our publication with short articles and fillers because all of our articles are short."

‡SEVEN, The Lifestyle Magazine of Caesars, Caesars World, Inc., Suite 2600, 1801 Century Park E., Los Angeles CA 90067. (213)552-2711. Editor: Stewart Weiner. Managing Editor: Nancy Gottesman. 100% freelance written. Works with a small number of new/unpublished writers each year. A bimonthly magazine covering attractions and events at Caesars World properties. Circ. 130,000. Pays on acceptance. Publishes ms an average of 1 month after acceptance. Byline given. Offers 25% kill fee. Buys first North American serial rights. Submit seasonal/holiday material 6 months in advance. Simultaneous submissions OK. Computer printout submissions acceptable; prefers letter-quality to dot-matrix. Reports in 6 weeks on queries. Sample copy for 6 first class stamps.
Nonfiction: Book excerpts, essays, historical/nostalgic, how-to, humor, interview/profile, new product and photo feature. Buys 20 mss/year. Query with published clips. No unsolicited ms. Length: 150-2,000 words. Sometimes pays $500-1,000. Sometimes pays the expenses of writers on assignment.
Photos: State availability of photos with submission. Offers $100-500/photo. Captions, model releases, and identification of subjects required. Buys one-time rights.
Columns/Departments: Gaming (how-to, historical, fiction), and Caesars People (celebrities interviewed or profiled) both 500-2,000 words. Query with or without published clips. Length: 500-2,000 words. Pays $500-1,000.
Fiction: Slice-of-life vignettes. No fiction without a reference to gaming or Caesars. Buys 3 mss/year. Query with published clips. Length: 500-2,000 words. Pays $500-1,000.
Fillers: Buys 10/year. Length: 25-150 words. Pays $75-100.
Tips: "Writers should have an interest in gaming and in the attractions and events associated with Caesars properties."

SHERATON, The Magazine for Sheraton Hotels in the Middle East and North Africa, Age Communications Ltd., Parkway House, Sheen Lane, London SW14 8LS England. Editor: Joseph Yogerst. Assistant Editor: Jules MacMahon. 80% freelance written. Eager to work with new/unpublished writers. A bimonthly magazine for Sheraton guests and employees covering a wide variety of subjects. Circ. 17,000. Pays on publication. Publishes ms 6 months after acceptance. Buys all rights. Submit seasonal/holiday material at least 4 months in advance. Simultaneous queries, and photocopied or previously published submissions OK. Computer printout submissions acceptable; prefers letter-quality to dot-matrix. SAE with IRC. Reports in 2 months.

Nonfiction: General interest articles for Sheraton guests and employees, roughly broken down into half Middle Eastern and half European/American. "The majority of readers are male, 25-50 years of age, with an annual income of $40-60,000." Regular features on Middle East and North African travel (cities or countries where there is a Sheraton hotel); luxury motoring (Rolls Royce, Cadillac, Mercedes etc.); innovation and technology (ranging from cellular phones to captive breeding to contemporary uses of neon); enterprise (profiles of famous entrepreneurs, businessmen, industrialists, artists); jewelry and antiques (corporate profiles of famous manufacturers or designers, or articles about a specific type of item or material, i.e. gold, diamonds, antique clocks etc.); sports and recreation (interviews with famous sports stars, how-to articles, photo essays on specific sports, etc.); Middle Eastern history and culture; celebrity interviews (i.e. film stars, musicians, artists, writers, etc.). Length: 1,500-2,000 words. Pays £80 Sterling (estimated $120) mss per 1,000 words. Query or send complete ms. Buys 30 mss/year.
Photos: State availability of photos. Captions required. Pays minimum of £20 for 35mm or larger format color transparencies. Buys first Middle East rights.
Tips: "We publish articles on anything that might be of interest to a top-level businessman, technician, engineer, and other professional who pays regular visits to the Middle East and North Africa."

SIGNATURE, The magazine of preferred literature. 641 Lexington Ave., New York NY 10022. Editor: Barbara Coats. 95% freelance written. Monthly. Circ. 815,000. Pays on acceptance. Publishes ms an average of 4 months after acceptance. Buys first rights only. Buys 175 mss/year. Submit seasonal material at least 5 months in advance. Computer printout submissions acceptable; prefers letter-quality to dot-matrix. Query. SASE. Free writer's guidelines.
Nonfiction: Buys virtually all nonfiction from freelance writers. Front-of-the-book pieces deal with photography, sports, fitness, arts, health, fashion, and business travel. Length: Generally 1,200-1,500 words. Pays $700-900. "While travel and travel-related pieces are the major portion of the so-called 'well' or central part of the book, we will entertain any feature-length piece that relates to the art of living well or at least living interestingly. That could include such pieces as 'In Search of the Ultimate Deli' to 'Traveling in the State Department plane with the Secretary of State.' Writing is of high quality and while celebrated bylines are sought and used, the market is open to any writer of talent and style. Writers who join the 'stable' are used with frequency." Feature length: 2,000-3,000 words. Pays $1,200 and up.
Photos: "Photographers are assigned to major pieces and often accompany the writer on assignment. In almost no cases are writers expected to take their own photographs. Quality standard in pictures is high and highly selective. Photography rates on request to the art director."
Tips: "While we are heavy on travel in all its phases—that is, far out Ladakh and Yemen and near at hand, e.g., Hemingway's Venice—we do try to embrace the many facets that make up the art of living well. So we are involved with good food, cuisine trends, sport in all forms, the arts, the stage and films and such concomitant subjects as fitness and finance."

SMITHSONIAN MAGAZINE, 900 Jefferson Drive, Washington DC 20560. Articles Editor: Marlane A. Liddell. 90% freelance written. Prefers to work with published/established writers. For "associate members of the Smithsonian Institution; 85% with college education." Monthly. Circ. 2 million. Buys first North American serial rights. Payment for each article to be negotiated depending on our needs and the article's length and excellence. Pays on acceptance. Publishes ms an average of 6 months after acceptance. Submit seasonal material 3 months in advance. Computer printout submissions acceptable; no dot-matrix. Reports in 6 weeks. Query.
Nonfiction: "Our mandate from the Smithsonian Institution says we are to be interested in the same things which now interest or should interest the Institution: cultural and fine arts, history, natural sciences, hard sciences, etc." Length: 750-4,500 words. Payment negotiable. Pays expenses of writers on assignment.
Photos: Purchased with or without ms and on assignment. Captions required. Pays $350/full color page.

‡SPECIAL CATEGORY, Brennan Partners, Inc., Suite 1042, 485 5th Ave., New York NY 10017. (212)867-9291. Editor: Peter J. Brennan. Managing Editor: Richard J. Anobile. 100% freelance written. "*Special* supplements run in all types of publications. The frequency depends upon the sponsor. Topics range from industrial developments to support of culture." Pays an advance, plus part on acceptance, and final on publication. Publishes ms an average of 6 weeks after acceptance. Byline given. Offers $2,400 cancellation fee. Buys all rights. Electronic submissions OK on TRS 80 Model I, IBM PC compatible, and CPM, but requires hard copy also. Computer printout submissions acceptable, prefers letter quality to dot-matrix. Writer's guidelines for 10x13 SAE with 4 first class stamps.
Nonfiction: General interest, how-to, new product, technical and travel. "Our business is one-shot nonfiction specials for many publications." Buys 6 mss/year. Query. "We do not want *any* unsolicited manuscripts. We assign all work." Length: 1,500 words minimum. Pays $2,400 minimum for solicited mss. Pays the expenses of writers on assignment.
Photos: State availability of photos with submission. Reviews contact sheets, transparencies and prints. Offers no additional payment for photos accepted with ms. Captions, model releases, and identification of subjects required. Buys one-time rights.

Columns/Departments: Query. Length: 800-2,000 words. Pays $300-1,000.
Tips: "Read the special supplements we have produced. In particular, read our guidelines and comply with the requirements. Show evidence that you can handle complex topics in depth."

THE STAR, 660 White Plains Rd., Tarrytown NY 10591. (914)332-5000. Editor: Leslie Hinton. Executive Editor: Phil Bunton. 40% freelance written. Prefers to work with published/established writers. "For every family; all the family—kids, teenagers, young parents and grandparents." Weekly magazine 56 pages. Circ. 3.5 million. Publishes ms an average of 1 month after acceptance. Buys first North American serial rights, occasional second serial book rights. Electronic submissions OK via Atex 7000/IBM compatible—300 or 1200 baud, 8 data bits, 1 stop bit, no parity. Computer printout submissions acceptable; prefers letter-quality to dot-matrix. Pays expenses of writers on assignment.
Nonfiction: Richard Kaplan, managing editor. Exposé (government waste, consumer, education, anything affecting family); general interest (human interest, consumerism, informational, family and women's interest); how-to (psychological, practical on all subjects affecting readers); interview (celebrity or human interest); new product; photo feature; profile (celebrity or national figure); health; medical; and diet. No first-person articles. Query or submit complete ms. Length: 500-1,000 words. Pays $50-1,500.
Photos: Alistair Duncan, photo editor. State availability of photos with query or ms. Pays $25-100 for 8x10 b&w glossy prints, contact sheets or negatives; $150-1,000 for 35mm color transparencies. Captions required. Buys one-time, or all rights.

SUNSHINE MAGAZINE, Henry F. Henrichs Publications, Box 40, Sunshine Park, Litchfield IL 62056. (217)324-3425. Editor: Peggy Kuethe. Managing Editor: Garth Henrichs. 95% freelance written. Eager to work with new/unpublished writers. A monthly magazine. "Primarily human interest and inspirational in its appeal, *Sunshine Magazine* provides worthwhile reading for all the family." Circ. 70,000. Pays on acceptance. Publishes ms an average of 6 months after acceptance. Byline given. Buys first North American serial rights or one-time rights. Submit seasonal/holiday material 6 months in advance. Photocopied submissions OK. Computer printout submissions acceptable; prefers letter-quality to dot-matrix. Reports in 2 months. Sample copy 50¢; writer's guidelines for #10 SAE with 1 first class stamp.
Nonfiction: Essays, historical/nostalgic, inspirational and personal experience. No material dealing with specifically religious matters or that is depressing in nature (divorce, drug abuse, alcohol abuse, death, violence, child abuse). Send complete ms. Length: 200-1,250. Pays $10-100.
Columns/Departments: Extraordinary Experience (personal experience), 500 words; Let's Reminisce (reminiscent, notalgia), 500 words; Guidelines (inspirational); 200 words; and Favorite Meditation (inspirational essay), 200 words. Buys 85-90 mss/year. Send complete ms. Pays $15-50.
Fiction: Inspirational and human interest. Buys 75-80 mss/year. Send complete ms.
Poetry: Light verse and traditional. No avant-garde, free verse or haiku. Buys 12-15 poems/year. No limit to the number of poems submitted at one time. Length: 4-16 lines. Pays $15-80, or may pay in copies.
Fillers: Anecdotes and short humor. Buys 1-5/year. Length: 50-150 words. Pays $10-20.
Tips: "Make a note that *Sunshine* is not religious—but it is inspirational. After reading a sample copy, you should know that we do not accept material that is very different from what we've been doing for over 60 years. Don't send a manuscript that is longer than specified or that is 'different' from anything else we've published—that's not what we're looking for. The whole magazine is written primarily by freelancers. We are just as eager to publish new writers as they are to get published."

TOWN AND COUNTRY, 1700 Broadway, New York NY 10019. (212)903-5000. Managing Editor: Jean Barkhorn. For upper-income Americans. Monthly. Pays on acceptance. Not a large market for freelancers. Always query first.
Nonfiction: Frank Zachary, department editor. "We're always trying to find ideas that can be developed into good articles that will make appealing cover lines." Wants provocative and controversial pieces. Length: 1,500-2,000 words. Pay varies. Also buys shorter pieces for which pay varies.

WEBB TRAVELER MAGAZINE, (formerly *Easy Living Magazine*), The Webb Co., 1999 Shepard Rd., St. Paul MN 55116. (612)690-7228. Editor: George Ashfield. 90% freelance written. Quarterly magazine emphasizing money management, consumer and American and foreign travel and food articles for a high-income audience 30-60 years of age. Pays on acceptance. Buys one-time rights and nonexclusive reprint rights. Submit seasonal/holiday material 1 year in advance. Photocopied submissions OK. Computer printout submissions acceptable. Reports on queries and mss in 6 weeks. Publishes ms an average of 4 months after acceptance. Free sample copy and writer's guidelines. Nonfiction only. No first person or personal experience. Query. Length: 1,000-2,000 words. Pays $200-600.
Photos: Contact Julie Hally at (612)690-7396 for current rates.

WHAT MAKES PEOPLE SUCCESSFUL, The National Research Bureau, Inc., 424 N. 3rd St., Burlington IA 52601. Editor: Rhonda Wilson. Editorial Supervisor: Doris J. Ruschill. 75% freelance written. Works with a

small number of new/unpublished writers each year. For industrial workers of all ages. Published quarterly. Pays on publication. Publishes ms an average of 1 year after acceptance. Buys all rights. Previously published submissions OK. Computer printout submissions acceptable; prefers letter-quality to dot-matrix. Submit seasonal/holiday material 8 months in advance of issue date. Reports in 3 weeks. Free writer's guidelines.
Nonfiction: How-to (be successful); general interest (personality, employee morale, guides to successful living, biographies of successful persons, etc.); experience; and opinion. No material on health. Buys 3-4 mss/issue. Query with outline. Length: 400-600 words. Pays 4¢/word.
Tips: Short articles and fillers (rather than major features) have a better chance of acceptance because all articles are short.

Health and Fitness

Each of the following magazines has its own prescription for health and fitness. Whether it's nutrition, exercise or both, writers must understand this prescription and make "dry facts" come alive. "Almost any medical subject is right for us, but we find very few people who can make the subject enticing to readers," says the managing editor of *Health*. "This is often a problem in the health and medical area." The magazines listed here specialize in covering health-and-fitness-related topics for a general audience. Magazines covering health topics from a medical perspective are listed in the Medical category of Trade Journals. Also see the Sports/Miscellaneous section where publications dealing with health and particular sports may be listed. And remember, nearly every general interest publication is a potential market for a health article.

ACCENT ON LIVING, Box 700, Bloomington IL 61702. (309)378-2961. Editor: Betty Garee. 80% freelance written. Eager to work with new/unpublished writers. For physically disabled persons and rehabilitation professionals. Quarterly magazine; 128 pages. Circ. 18,000. Buys first rights and second (reprint) rights to material originally published elsewhere. Byline usually given. Buys 50-60 unsolicited mss/year. Pays on publication. Publishes ms an average of 6 months after acceptance. Photocopied submissions OK. Computer printout submissions acceptable; prefers letter-quality to dot-matrix. Reports in 2 weeks. Sample copy $2; writer's guidelines for SAE and 1 first class stamp.
Nonfiction: Betty Garee, editor. Articles about new devices that would make a disabled person with limited physical mobility more independent; should include description, availability, and photos. Medical breakthroughs for disabled people. Intelligent discussion articles on acceptance of physically disabled persons in normal living situations; topics may be architectural barriers, housing, transportation, educational or job opportunities, organizations, or other areas. How-to articles concerning everyday living giving specific, helpful information so the reader can carry out the idea himself/herself. News articles about active disabled persons or groups. Good strong interviews. Vacations, accessible places to go, sports, organizations, humorous incidents, self improvement, and sexual or personal adjustment—all related to physically handicapped persons. No religious-type articles. "We are looking for upbeat material." Length: 250-1,000 words. Pays 10¢/word for article as it appears in magazine (after editing and/or condensing by staff). Query. Sometimes pays the expenses of writers on assignment.
Photos: Pays $5 minimum for b&w photos purchased with accompanying captions. Amount will depend on quality of photos and subject matter.
Tips: "Ask a friend who is disabled to read your article before sending it to *Accent*. Make sure that he/she understands your major points and the sequence or procedure."

AMERICAN HEALTH MAGAZINE, Fitness of Body and Mind, 80 Fifth Ave., New York NY 10011. (212)242-2460. Editor-in-Chief: T. George Harris. Editor: Joel Gurin. 70% freelance written. Prefers to work with published/established writers. 10 issues/year. General interest magazine that covers both scientific and "lifestyle" aspects of health, including laboratory research, clinical advances, fitness, holistic healing and nutrition. Circ. 850,000. Pays on acceptance. Publishes ms an average of 6 months after acceptance. Byline given. Offers 25% kill fee. Buys first North American serial rights, plus other rights that are "negotiable; in some cases." Computer printout submissions acceptable. Reports in 2 months. Sample copy for $2; writer's guidelines for 4x9 SAE and 1 first class stamp.

Nonfiction: Mail to Editorial/Features. Book excerpts; how-to; humor (if anyone can be funny, yes); interview/profile (health or fitness related); photo feature (any solid feature or news item relating to health); and technical. No mechanical research reports or fad weight loss plans. "Stories should be written clearly, without jargon. Information should be new, authoritative and helpful to readers." Buys 40-50 mss/year. Query with 2 clips of published work. "Absolutely *no* complete ms." Length: 1,000-3,000 words. Pays $500-2,000 upon acceptance. Pays the expenses of writers on assignment.

Photos: Mail to Editorial/Photo. Send photos with query. Pays $100-600 for 35mm transparencies and 8x10 prints "depending on use." Captions and identification of subjects required. Buys one-time rights.

Columns/Departments: Mail to Editorial/News. Medical News (technological update). Fitness Report, Nutrition News, Tooth Report, Mind/Body News, Family Report, and Skin, Scent and Hair. Other news sections included from time to time. Buys 300-400 mss/year. Query with clips of published work. Prefers 2 pages—500 words. Pays $150-250 upon acceptance.

Fillers: Mail to Editorial/Fillers. Anecdotes and newsbreaks. Buys 30/year. Length: 20-50 words. Pays $10-25.

Tips: "*American Health* has no full-time staff writers; we have chosen to rely on outside contributors for almost all our articles. The magazine needs good ideas, and good articles, from professional journalists, health educators, researchers and clinicians. Queries should be short (no longer than a page), snappy and to the point. Think short; think news. Give us a good angle and a paragraph of background. Queries only. We do not take responsibility for materials not accompanied by SASE."

BEAUTY DIGEST, For Health & Fitness, Mass Media Associates, 126 5th Ave., New York NY 10011. (212)255-0440. Editor: Diane Robbins. Managing Editor: Lorraine De Pasque. 25% freelance written. Bimonthly magazine on beauty, health, fitness, diet and emotional self-help. "All articles must be geared to making reader feel better about herself. Audiences are women 25-40 concerned with self-improvement, both physically and emotionally. Our publication is supportive and accepting." Circ. 250,000. Pays on acceptance. Publishes ms an average of 3 months after acceptance. Byline given. Offers 50% kill fee. Buys one-time rights and second serial (reprint) rights; makes work-for-hire assignments. Submit seasonal/holiday material 4 months in advance. Simultaneous, photocopied, and previously published submissions OK. Reports in 2 months.

Nonfiction: Book excerpts, how-to and personal experience. Special issues include fashion and women's health. No work-oriented, child-care, crafts or recipes. Buys 20 mss/year. Send complete ms. Length: 1,500-3,500 words. Pays $50-100. Sometimes pays the expenses of writers on assignment.

Columns/Departments: I Made Myself Over, 1,200 words with photos of before and after. Buys 6 mss/year. Send complete ms. Length: 1,200 words. Pays $100.

Tips: "Send previously published work as 25% of our magazine is reprints."

BESTWAYS MAGAZINE, Box 2028, Carson City NV 89702. Editor/Publisher: Barbara Bassett. 40% freelance written. Works with a small number of new/unpublished writers each year. Emphasizes health, diet and nutrition. Monthly magazine: 64 pages. Circ. 300,000. Pays on publication. Publishes ms an average of 6 months after acceptance. Byline given. Buys first North American serial rights. Submit seasonal/holiday material 6 months in advance. Computer printout submissions acceptable; prefers letter-quality to dot-matrix. Reports in 6 weeks. Writer's guidelines for SASE.

Nonfiction: General interest (nutrition, physical fitness, preventive medicine, supplements, natural foods); how-to (diet and exercise); and technical (vitamins, minerals, weight control and nutrition). "No direct or implied endorsements of refined flours, grains or sugar, tobacco, alcohol, caffeine, drugs or patent medicines." Buys 4 mss/issue. Query. Length: 1,500 words. Pays 10¢/word. Sometimes pays the expenses of writers on assignment.

Photos: State availability of photos with query. Pays $7.50 for 4x5 b&w glossy prints; $15 for 2¼x2¼ color transparencies. Captions preferred. Buys all rights. Model releases required.

BETTER HEALTH & LIVING, (formerly *Bruce Jenner's Better Health & Living*), Decathlon Corp., 800 2nd Ave., New York NY 10017. (212)986-9026. Editor: Julie Davis. Managing Editor: Laura L. Vitale. 80% freelance written. Bimonthly magazine on fitness, health and lifestyle. The magazine focuses on "how to make the most of your lifestyle in a healthy way and still enjoy yourself. Moderation is the key." Estab. 1985. Circ. 250,000. Publishes ms an average of 4 months after acceptance. Byline given. Offers 25% kill fee. Buys first North American serial rights. Submit seasonal/holiday materal 4 months in advance. Exclusive queries and submissions preferred. Reports in 1-2 months. Sample copy $2.50 with SAE and $1.75 postage.

Nonfiction: Book excerpts, general interest, interview/profile, new product, opinion, personal experience, photo feature and travel. No technical writing. Buys 50 mss/year. Query with published clips. Length: 500-5,000 words. Pays $200-1,000. Sometimes pays the expenses of writers on assignment.

Photos: May Sugano-Koto, art director. State availability of photos. Reviews 35mm b&w and color transparencies. Fees depend upon usage. Model releases and identification of subjects required. Buys one-time rights.
Columns/Departments: Better Living—items on beauty/grooming, stress management, fitness, lifestyle, illustrated health news; Healthwire—hard news items on health, fitness, medicine; Kidshape; Fitworks—new tools, gadgets, videos, books (highly photographed); Fitness to Go—away from home fitness. Buys 200 mss/year. Query with published clips. Length: 100-500 words. Pays $25-200.
Tips: "Send query with clips after familiarizing yourself with format. Submissions should be both male/female oriented. Healthwire and Better Living columns are most open to freelancers."

‡**DAZZLE**, The Webb Company (for Delta Dental Plans Foundation), 1999 Shepard Rd., St. Paul MN 55116. (612)690-7200. Editor: Gayle Bonneville. 95% freelance written. Works with a small number of new/unpublished writers each year. A quarterly company-sponsored magazine for the general public covering dentistry and dental and general health for the layperson. Circ. 75,000. Pays on acceptance. Publishes ms an average of 3 months after acceptance. Byline given. Offers 25% kill fee. Buys limited rights in work-for-hire. Submit seasonal/holiday material at least 6 months in advance. Simultaneous, photocopied, and previously published submissions OK, "but original, first-time articles preferred." Electronic submissions OK via ASCII file, MS DOS. Computer printout submissions acceptable; prefers letter-quality to dot-matrix. Reports in 1 month. Sample copy 6x9 SAE with 56¢ postage; free writer's guidelines with SAE.
Nonfiction: General health, nutrition and dental health. Also, book excerpts, essays, historical/nostalgic, humor, interview/profile and new product—if dental related. No opinion, technical dental or medical stories, stories negative to dentistry, religious or personal experience. Buys 24 mss/year. Query with published clips. Length: 500-1,400 words. Pays $250-500. Pays certain expenses of writers on assignment.
Photos: State availability of photos with submission. Reviews 35mm or 2¼ transparencies. Pays variable rate for photos. Buys one-time rights.
Columns/Departments: Tongue in Cheek (lighthearted look at dentistry, dental history, dental trivia), 500 words; and Commentary (essay on dentistry; witty, entertaining), 700 words. Buys 8 mss/year. Query with published clips. Length: 500-700 words. Pays $150-350.
Tips: "Feature stories are most open to freelancers."

‡**DIABETES SELF-MANAGEMENT**, Pharmaceutical Communications, Inc., 42-15 Crescent St., Long Island City NY 11101. (718)937-4283. Co-Editors: James Hazlett and Robert S. Dinsmoor. 20% freelance written. A bimonthly magazine. "We educate diabetics in the day-to-day and long-term aspects of their diabetes in a positive, upbeat way. We stress taking charge of the management of their diabetes." Circ. 265,000. Pays on acceptance. Publishes ms an average of 4 months after acceptance. Byline given. Offers 20% kill fee. Buys all rights and makes work-for-hire assignments. Submit seasonal/holiday material 6 months in advance. Reports in 6 weeks on queries. Sample copy $2 with 9x12 SAE and 6 first class stamps; free writer's guidelines.
Nonfiction: How-to (self-management, nutrition, exercise, pharmacology and self-help for persons with diabetes). No personal experiences, profiles, research breakthroughs or exposés. Buys 8 mss/year. Query with published clips. Length: 1,000-3,000 words. Pays $400-600 for assigned articles.

FRUITION, The Plan, Box 872-WM, Santa Cruz CA 95061. (408)458-3365. Biannual newsletter covering healthful living/creation of public food tree nurseries and relative social and horticultural matters. 15% freelance written. Eager to work with new/unpublished writers. Circ. 300. Payment method negotiable. Publishes ms an average of 4 months after acceptance. Byline given. Offers negotiable kill fee. Buys one-time rights. Simultaneous queries, photocopied and previously published submissions OK. Electronic submissions OK via MacIntosh 3½ mini disk qd ss. Computer printout submissions acceptable. Reports in 2-4 weeks. Sample copy $2; writer's guidelines for SAE and 39¢ postage.
Nonfiction: General interest, historical/nostalgic, how-to, inspirational, interview/profile, personal experience, photo feature—all must relate to public access—food trees, foraging fruit and nuts, and related social and horticultural matters. No articles "involving gardening with chemicals, or cloning plants. No articles on health with references to using therapies or medicines." Buys 4-6 mss/year. Length: 750-3,000 words. Pays negotiable fee. Sometimes pays the expenses of writers on assignment.
Photos: E. Eagle, photo editor. State availability of photos. Pays negotiable fee for b&w contact sheet and 5x5 or larger prints. Identification of subjects required. Buys one-time rights.
Poetry: E. Eagle, poetry editor. Avant-garde, free verse, haiku, light verse and traditional. Buys 4-6/year. Submit maximum 6 poems. Length: 2 lines-750 words. Pays negotiable fee.
Fillers: Clippings, short humor and newsbreaks. Buys 2-6/year. Length: 125-400 words. Pays negotiable fee.
Tips: "Get a copy of *Fruition* to see what we publish. The most frequent mistake made by writers is that material submitted does not relate to our publication."

‡**HEALTH MAGAZINE, Getting the Best from Yourself**, Family Media, Inc., 3 Park Ave., New York NY 10016. (212)340-9262. Editor: Hank Herman. Managing Editor: Leanne Kleinmann. 75% freelance written. A monthly magazine covering women's health issues. "*Health* is a service magazine that reaches a most-

ly-subscription audience of women in their twenties and thirties. We run pieces on medicine, health, nutrition, dieting, fitness, beauty, food and psychology/emotions." Circ. 1,000,000. Pays on acceptance. Publishes ms an average of 4 months after acceptance. Byline given. Offers 20% kill fee. Buys first North American serial rights. Submit seasonal/holiday material 4 months in advance. Computer printout submissions acceptable; prefers letter-quality to dot-matrix. Reports in 1 month. Free writer's guidelines.
Nonfiction: Exposé, general interest, humor, interview/profile, new product, and personal experience. Buys 325 mss/year. Query with published clips. Length: 250-2,500 words. Pays $150-1,300. Pays the expenses of writers on assignment.
Photos: State availability of photos with submission. Reviews transparencies.
Columns/Departments: Poundwise (weight loss related articles), 750 words; and Nutrition (food-related stories, nutritional benefits), 1,500 words. Buys 36 mss/year. Query with published clips. Length: 750-1,500 words. Pays $650-850.
Tips: "A freelancer's best first query to *Health* would be suggestions for our Breakthroughs section, the news briefs at the front of the book. Larger article queries should be well-researched and backed up by clips."

HEALTH PLEX MAGAZINE, The Magazine for Healthier Living, Methodist Hospital/Childrens Hospital, 8303 Dodge St., Omaha NE 68114. (402)390-4528. Managing Editor: Gini Goldsmith. 80% freelance written. Prefers to work with published/established writers. Most articles are written on assignment. Quarterly magazine on health information and medical subjects. Focuses on current health care topics, wellness-related articles, etc. Circ. 50,000. Pays on acceptance. Publishes ms an average of 3 months after acceptance. Byline given. Buys all rights and first serial rights; makes work-for-hire assignments. Submit seasonal/holiday material 3 months in advance. Photocopied submissions OK. Computer printout submissions acceptable; prefers letter-quality to dot-matrix. Reports in 1 month. Free sample copy.
Nonfiction: Only health/wellness articles. Buys 24 mss/year. Query with published clips or send complete ms. Length: 1,000-3,000 words. Pays $50-200. Sometimes pays the expenses of writers on assignment.
Photos: State availability of photos. Reviews b&w contact sheets and color transparencies. Pays $100-250. Model release required. Buys all rights.
Columns/Departments: Feelin' Good (wellness articles) and Health Updates (short topics on current health topics, new technology, etc).
Tips: "This is a corporate publication so all articles must have a broad consumer appeal and not be on an obscure medical topic. Since most articles are written on assignment, it is preferable to send a topic query or a submission of published articles for writing style selection."

‡IMC JOURNAL, The Health Publication of International Medical Center, International Medical Center, Suite 333, 1515 N.W. 167th St., Miami FL 33169. (305)623-1091. Editor: Marcia J. Maze. 40% freelance written. A magazine covering health maintenance, preventive medicine and fulfilled living. "We publish easy to read, human interest articles covering positive attitudes on aging and health; and articles slanted to inspire the reader to change their habits or lifestyles for the better." Circ. 170,000. Pays on publication. Publishes ms an average of 2 months after acceptance. Byline given. Buys first rights and second serial (reprint) rights. Submit seasonal/holiday material 4 months in advance. Photocopied submissions OK. Computer printout submissions acceptable; prefers letter-quality to dot-matrix. Reports in 1 month. Free sample copy.
Nonfiction: Historical/nostalgic (on medicine); interview/profile; personal experience; travel; and health and medicine. Buys 15 mss/year. Query with published clips. Length: 500-2,500 words. Pays $75-450 for assigned articles.
Photos: State availability of photos with submission. Reviews contact sheets and transparencies. Offers $25-55/photo. Captions required. Buys one-time rights.
Columns/Departments: Travel (health-related cruises, adventures), Diet and Nutrition (recipes, tips for dieting and personal experience), Fitness and Exercise (tips for keeping active, personal experience). Buys 10 mss/year. Query with published clips. Length: 500-1,500 words. Pays $75-200.
Tips: "A writer must exhibit a sensitivity and understanding towards aging and living a full life. Send a cover letter first, preferably with five article ideas, and you will be contacted within one month. The area of our publication most open to freelancers is travel—how to travel and what to see, where to stay, what to eat once you get there—particularly pertaining to the older population."

LET'S LIVE MAGAZINE, Oxford Industries, Inc., 444 N. Larchmont Blvd., Box 74908, Los Angeles CA 90004. (213)469-3901. Editor: Keith Stepro. Emphasizes nutrition. 90% freelance written. Works with a small number of new/unpublished writers each year. Monthly magazine; 96 pages. Circ. 135,000. Pays on publication. Publishes ms an average of 3 months after acceptance. Buys first North American serial rights. Byline given. Submit seasonal/holiday material 4 months in advance. Computer printout submissions acceptable; no dot-matrix. Reports in 3 weeks on queries; 6 weeks on mss. Sample copy $2.25; writer's guidelines for SAE and 1 first class stamp.
Nonfiction: General interest (effects of vitamins, minerals and nutrients in improvement of health or afflictions); historical (documentation of experiments or treatment establishing value of nutrients as boon to health);

how-to (acquire strength and vitality, improve health of adults and/or children and prepare tasty health-food meals); inspirational (first-person accounts of triumph over disease through substitution of natural foods and nutritional supplements for drugs and surgery); interview (benefits of research in establishing prevention as key to good health); advertised new product (120-180 words plus 5x7 or glossy of product); personal opinion (views of orthomolecular doctors or their patients on value of health foods toward maintaining good health); and profile (background and/or medical history of preventive medicine, M.D.s or Ph.D.s, in advancement of nutrition). "We do not want kookie first-person accounts of experiences with drugs or junk foods, faddist healers or unorthodox treatments..Manuscripts must be well-researched, reliably documented, and written in a clear, readable style." Buys 10-15 mss/issue. Query with published clips. Length: 750-1,600 words. Pays $50-150. Sometimes pays expenses of writers on assignment.

Photos: State availability of photos with ms. Pays $17.50 for 8x10 b&w glossy prints; $35 for 8x10 color prints and 35mm color transparencies; and $150 for good cover shot. Captions and model releases required.

Columns/Departments: My Story and Interviews (750-1,200 words). Buys 1-2/issue. Query. Pays $50-250. Last Word (700-800 words on some health aspect not usually appropriate for feature-length coverage). Pays $75-150.

Tips: "We want writers with experience in researching nonsurgical medical subjects, interviewing experts with the ability to simplify technical and clinical information for the layman. A captivating lead and structural flow are essential. The most frequent mistakes made by writers are in writing articles that are too technical; in poor style; written for the wrong audience (publication not thoroughly studied) or have unreliable documentation or overzealous faith in the topic reflected by flimsy research and inappropriate tone."

LISTEN MAGAZINE, 6830 Laurel St. NW, Washington DC 20012. (202)722-6726. Editor: Gary B. Swanson. 50% freelance written. Specializes in drug prevention, presenting positive alternatives to various drug dependencies. "*Listen* is used in many high school classes, in addition to use by professionals: medical personnel, counselors, law enforcement officers, educators, youth workers, etc." Monthly magazine, 32 pages. Circ. 100,000. Buys all rights unless otherwise arranged with the author. Byline given. Pays on acceptance. Publishes ms an average of 5 months after acceptance. Computer printout submissions acceptable; prefers letter-quality to dot-matrix. Reports in 4 weeks. SASE. Sample copy $1; send large manila SASE; free writer's guidelines.

Nonfiction: Seeks articles that deal with causes of drug use such as poor self-concept, family relations, social skills or peer pressure. Especially interested in youth-slanted articles or personality interviews encouraging nonalcoholic and nondrug ways of life. Teenage point of view is essential. Popularized medical, legal and educational articles. Also seeks narratives which portray teens dealing with youth conflicts, especially those related to the use of or temptation to use harmful substances. Growth of the main character should be shown. "We don't want typical alcoholic story/skid-row bum, AA stories. We are also being inundated with drunk-driving accident stories. Unless yours is unique, consider another topic." Buys 75-100 unsolicited mss/year. Query. Length: 500-1,500 words. Pays 4-7¢/word.

Photos: Purchased with accompanying ms. Captions required. Color photos preferred, but b&w acceptable.

Poetry: Blank verse and free verse only. Seeks image-invoking, easily illustrated poems of 5-15 lines to combine with photo or illustration to make a poster. Pays $15 maximum.

Fillers: Word square/general puzzles are also considered. Pays $15.

Tips: "True stories are good, especially if they have a unique angle. Other authoritative articles need a fresh approach. In query, briefly summarize article idea and logic of why you feel it's good."

‡MUSCLE & FITNESS. Weider Health & Fitness, 21100 Erwin St., Woodland Hills CA 91367. (818)884-6800. Editor: Bill Reynolds. Associate Publisher: Ben Pesta. 20% freelance written. Prefers to work with published/established writers; works with a small number of new/unpublished writers each year. Monthly magazine covering bodybuilding/physical fitness for fitness-minded men/women. Circ. 500,000. Pays 1 month after acceptance. Byline given. Buys all rights. Photocopied and, occasionally, previously published submissions (such as excerpts) OK. Computer printout submissions acceptable. Reports in 6 weeks.

Nonfiction: Book excerpts (occasionally, if within our philosophy); how-to (only within our philosophy); inspirational; and interview/profile. No article on unknown bodybuilder; unauthoritative pieces. No humor, astrology or erotica. Buys 150 mss/year. Query with clips or send outline proposal. Length: 2,500 words. Pays $250-negotiable/major feature. Sometimes pay expenses of writers on assignment.

Photos: Mandy Tanny, photo editor. Send proof sheets or transparencies. Pays negotiable rate for contact sheets, 60mm and 35mm transparencies, 8x10 prints. Captions, model releases and identification of subjects required. Buys all rights. "We seldom use black and white and are interested only in photos of top bodybuilders or well-known athletes."

Columns/Departments: See an issue of the magazine. Buys 60/year. Query with clips of published work or send outline proposal. Length: 500-700 words. Pays $100-150.

Tips: "The specialized nature of our coverage requires authoritative scientific knowledge for nonpersonality articles. Personality articles require prior approval and photo access. We prefer to base assignments on detailed outline proposals."

MUSCLE MAG INTERNATIONAL. 52 Bramsteele Rd.. Unit 2. Brampton. Ontario L6W 3M5 Canada. Editor: Robert Kennedy. 80% freelance written. "We do not care if a writer is known or unknown: published or unpublished. We simply want good instructional articles on bodybuilding." For 16 to 40-year-old men and women interested in physical fitness and overall body improvement. Monthly magazine; 100 pages. Circ. 140,000. Buys all rights. Pays on acceptance. Publishes ms an average of 4 months after acceptance. Byline given. Buys 80 mss/year. Sample copy $3. Computer printout submissions acceptable; no dot-matrix. Reports in 1 month. Submit complete ms. IRCs.
Nonfiction: Articles on ideal physical proportions and importance of supplements in the diet, training for muscle size. Should be helpful and instructional and appeal to young men and women who want to live life in a vigorous and healthy style. "We would like to see articles for the physical culturist on new muscle building techniques or an article on fitness testing." Informational, how-to. personal experience, interview, profile, inspirational. humor, historical. exposé, nostalgia, personal opinion, photo, spot news, new product, and merchandising technique articles. Length: 1.200-1.600 words. Pays 10¢/word. Sometimes pays the expenses of writers on assignment.
Columns/Departments: Nutrition Talk (eating for top results) and Shaping Up (improving fitness and stamina). Length: 1,300 words. Pays 10¢/word.
Photos: B&w and color photos are purchased with or without ms. Pays $10 for 8x10 glossy exercise photos: $10 for 8x10 b&w posing shots. Pays $100-200 for color cover and $15 for color used inside magazine (transparencies). More for "special" work.
Fillers: Newsbreaks, puzzles, quotes of the champs. Length: open. Pays $5 minimum.
Tips: "The best way to break in is to seek out the muscle-building 'stars' and do in-depth interviews with biography in mind. Color training picture support essential. Writers have to make their articles informative in that readers can apply them to help gain bodybuilding success."

‡NEW BODY, The Magazine of Health & Fitness. GCR Publishing Group, Inc., 888 7th Ave., New York NY 10106. (212)541-7100. Editor: Norman Zeitchick. Managing Editor: Sandra Kosherick. 75% freelance written. Eager to work with new/unpublished writers. A bimonthly magazine covering fitness and health for young. middle-class women. Circ. 125,000. Pays on publication. Publishes ms an average of 6 months after acceptance. Byline given. Offers negotiable kill fee. Buys first North American serial rights. Submit seasonal/holiday material 6 months in advance. Simultaneous and photocopied submissions OK. Computer printout submissions acceptable. Reports in 2 months. Sample copy and writer's guidelines for SASE.
Nonfiction: Book excerpts, exposé (investigational health issues); general interest; how-to (exercise, health); photo feature (exercise, food, fashion); and travel (spas, health clubs, exercise vacations). "We are interested in specific methods or programs of exercises designed by professionals to accomplish specific purposes." No articles on "How I do exercises." Buys 75 mss/year. Query with published clips. Length: 1,000-4,000 words. Pays $200-750 for assigned articles; $100-400 for unsolicited articles; sometimes pays travel and/or accomodations in lieu of fee. Sometimes pays the expenses of writers on assignment.
Photos: Reviews contact sheets, transparencies and prints. Model releases and identification of subjects required. Buys one-time rights.
Tips: "Make a clean statement of what article is about, what it would cover—not why the article is important. We're interested in new ideas, new trends or new ways of looking at old topics."

‡NONTOXIC & NATURAL NEWS. Nontoxic Lifestyle, Inc.. Box 475, Inverness CA 94937. (415)663-1312. Editor: Debra Lynn Dadd. 40% freelance written. A bimonthly magazine covering natural products and healthy living. Circ. 5,000. Pays on publication. Publishes ms an average of 2 months after acceptance. Byline given. Offers 25% kill fee. Buys first North American serial rights and second serial (reprint) rights. Submit seasonal/holiday material 3 months in advance. Photocopied and previously published submissions OK. Electronic submissions acceptable via Macintosh disks. Computer printout submissions acceptable; prefers letter-quality to dot-matrix. Reports in 3 weeks. Sample copy $2; writer's guidelines for #10 SASE.
Nonfiction: Book excerpts, exposé, general interest, how-to, interview/profile, new product, personal experience and technical. "Writers should have a good grasp on our subject matter, which is specifically natural products/living and nontoxic lifestyles." No "poorly researched articles." Buys 20 mss/year. Query or send complete ms. Length: 1,000-3,500 words. Pays $50-100 for assigned articles; pays $25-50 for unsolicited articles. Sometimes pays the expenses of writers on assignment.
Photos: Send photos with submission. Reviews 3x5 prints. Offers no additional payment for photos accepted with ms. Captions, model releases and identification of subjects required. Buys one-time rights.
Columns/Departments: Resources (sources for natural products/services, etc.); Product Updates (new natural products); Natural Living (healthy lifestyles); and Book Reviews. Buys 15 mss/year. Query or send complete ms. Length: 750-1,500 words. Pays $35-50.
Fillers: Anecdotes, cartoons, facts, newsbreaks and short humor. Buys 15/year. Length: 100-250 words. Pays $15-20.
Tips: "A freelancer's best approach is to write about a personal experience with natural, chemical-free products. All areas of the publication, except the editorial, are open to freelancers. We encourage freelance submissions, and work with the writer to obtain the best possible material."

NUTRITION FORUM, George F. Stickley Co., 210 West Washington Sq., Philadelphia PA 19106. (215)922-7126. Editor: Stephen Barrett, M.D. 50% freelance written. Works with a small number of new/unpublished writers each year. Monthly newsletter. "*Nutrition Forum* is an 8-page newsletter written for nutrition and health educators and intelligent laypersons. It reports on legal and political developments related to nutrition; practical applications of nutrition research; and nutrition fads, fallacies and quackery, including investigative reports." Circ. 1,000. Pays on publication. Publishes ms an average of 3 months after acceptance. Byline given. Buys first North American serial rights. Submit seasonal/holiday material 3 months in advance. Simultaneous queries and photocopied submissions OK. Computer printout submissions acceptable. Reports in 1 week. Free sample copy; writer's guidelines for 4x9½ SAE and 1 first class stamp.
Nonfiction: Exposé (of fads and illegal practices); interview/profile (of prominent nutritionists); and personal experience (of victims or investigators of quackery). Buys 36 mss/year. Query or send complete ms. Length: 400-3,000 words. Pays $40-300 or $6/published column inch (about 10¢/word). Sometimes pays expenses of writers on assignment.
Columns/Departments: Book reviews, 100-1,500 words.
Fillers: Newsbreak. "We carry several hundred per year. Most are developed in-house, but we are willing to use ones from freelancers." Length: 50-200 words. Pays $10-20.
Tips: An area most open to freelancers is undercover investigations of lawbreakers, or promoters of quackery. Everything sent will be read. All correspondence concerning articles should be sent to Stephen Barrett, M.D., Box 1747, Allentown PA 18105)—*not to the publisher.*"

OSTOMY QUARTERLY, United Ostomy Association, Inc., 2001 W. Beverly Blvd., Los Angeles CA 90057. (213)413-5510. Editor: Kathy Pape, M.S. 20% freelance written. Eager to work with new/unpublished writers. Quarterly magazine on ostomy surgery and living with ostomies. "The *OQ* is the official publication of UOA and should cover topics of interest to patients who underwent abdominal ostomy surgery (ileostomy, colostomy, urostomy). Most articles should be 'up-beat' in feeling; also, we cover new surgical techniques in ostomy surgery." Circ. 50,000. Pays on publication. Publishes ms an average of 6 months after acceptance. Byline given. Buys first North American serial rights; makes work-for-hire assignments. Submit seasonal/holiday material 3 months in advance. Simultaneous queries and photocopied submissions OK. Computer printout submissions acceptable; prefers letter-quality to dot-matrix. Print must be dark and readable. Reports in 3 months. Sample copy $2.50; free writer's guidelines and editorial calendar.
Nonfiction: General interest (parenting, psychology); humor (coping humorously with problems with ostomies); interview/profile (important MDs in gastroenterology, urology); personal experience (living with abdominal ostomies); technical (new surgical techniques in ostomy); and travel (with ostomies). No testimonials from members, "How I overcame . . . with ostomy and life is great now." Buys 6 mss/year. Query. Length: 800-2,400 words. Usually asks for pages of copy. Pays $50-150 maximum. Sometimes pays the expenses of writers on assignment but no more than $150 total (expenses plus fee) per article will be paid. No kill fee offered.
Photos: Reviews b&w and color transparencies. "We like to use photographs with articles, but price for article includes use of photos. We return photos on request." Captions and model releases required.
Columns/Departments: Book reviews (on ostomy care, living with ostomies); Ostomy World (any news items relating to ostomy, enterostomal therapy, medical); Q&A (answers medical questions from members); nutrition; financial; psychology. Primarily staff-written.
Tips: "We will be looking mainly for articles from freelancers about ostomy management, ostomy advances, people important to ostomates. Send different topics and ideas than we have published for 23 years. Be willing to attend free meeting of UOA chapter to get "flavor" of group. UOA is a nonprofit association which accounts for the fees offered. The *OQ* might be re-evaluated in terms of focus. The association might want to expand its focus to include the medical professionals who relate to people with ostomies (discharge planners, visiting nurses, ET nurses, pharmacists, etc.)"

‡RUNNING THROUGH TEXAS, Running Through Texas Inc., Suite 130, 2512 S. IH-35, Austin TX 78704. (512)440-0881. Editor: Robert M. McCorkle. 15% freelance written. "We are backlogged with submissions and prefer not to receive unsolicited submissions at this time."

‡RX BEING WELL, Biomedical Information Corp., 800 Second Ave., New York NY 10017. (212)599-3400. Editor: Mark Deitch. 50% freelance written. A bimonthly magazine covering health and medicine. "We publish authoritative health and medical information reaching readers primarily in physicians' waiting rooms. Articles are usually written with a physician coauthor." Circ. 350,000. Pays on acceptance. Publishes ms an average of 4-6 months after acceptance. Byline given. Offers ⅓ kill fee. Buys all rights. Reports in 1 month. Sample copy and writer's guidelines for 9x12 SASE.
Nonfiction: Health and medical. No personal experience ("My Gall Bladder Operation") or speculative therapies ("Ginseng Cures Heart Disease"). Buys 40-50 mss/year. Query with or without published clips, or send complete ms. Length: 1,000-2,000 words. Pays $500 minimum for assigned articles. Pays the expenses of writers on assignment within reasonable limits.

Tips: "Our editorial aim is health/medical education: providing authoritative (not trendy or speculative) information on disease treatment and prevention, nutrition, sports medicine, pre- and post-natal care, psychological health, and related topics."

SHAPE, Merging Mind and Body Fitness, Weider Enterprises, 21100 Erwin St., Woodland Hills CA 91367. (818)884-6800. Editor: Christine MacIntyre. 10% freelance written. Works with a small number of new/unpublished writers each year. Monthly magazine covering women's health and fitness. Circ. 560,000. Pays on publication. Publishes ms an average of 9 months after acceptance. Offers 1/3 kill fee. Buys all rights and reprint rights. Submit seasonal/holiday material 8 months in advance. Computer printout submissions acceptable; no dot-matrix. Reports in 2 months.
Nonfiction: Book excerpts; exposé (health, fitness related); how-to (get fit); interview/profile (of fit women); travel (spas). "We use health and fitness articles written by professionals in their specific fields. No articles which haven't been queried first." Query with clips of published work. Length: 500-2,000 words. Pays negotiable fee.

SLIMMER, Ritter/Geller Communications, Suite 3000, 3420 Ocean Park Blvd., Santa Monica CA 90405. (213)450-0900. Editor: Lori Berger. Managing Editor: Karre Slafkin. 75% freelance written. A bimonthly magazine. "We are a fitness lifestyle publication presenting articles and features on health, beauty, fashion, nutrition, diet and exercise in the hopes of presenting a head-to-toe approach to fitness. We attempt to excite the complacent woman about fitness and the idea of improving herself." Circ. 250,000. Pays on publication. Byline given. Offers 15-20% kill fee. Not copyrighted. Buys first rights, one-time rights and second serial (reprint) rights. Submit seasonal holiday material 6 months in advance. Photocopied submissions OK. Sample copy for 8½x11 SAE with 3 first class stamps; free writer's guidelines.
Nonfiction: Book excerpts (health, fitness, nutrition, celebrity workout books); exposé (such as the real Herbalife story); general interest; how-to (exercise, beauty, nutrition, etc.); inspirational ("How I lost 200 pounds"; "How I overcame chocolate craving"); interview/profile (celebrities relating beauty, fashion, fitness); personal experience (on makeovers, etc.); photo feature (on fashion, beauty, celebrities) and travel (spas, resorts, health retreats, bicycling paths, etc.). "No basic or general stories on aerobics, jogging, swimming—sports or ideas that we have obviously covered from a general nature many times over." Query with or without published clips or send complete ms. Length: 2,000-4,000 words. Pays $150-600 for assigned articles. Sometimes pays the expenses of writers on assignment.
Photos: State availability of photos with submission. Captions required.
Columns/Departments: Personal Best (beauty and fashion); Food for Thought (nutrition); Mind and Body (psychological side of fitness, diets, etc.); Body Works (how the body works); Fitness Forum (compendium of fitness, health, beauty, nutrition features); and Last Words (humorous first person perspective on fitness). Query. Length: 850-1,500. Pays $150-250.
Fillers: Facts and newsbreaks. Buys few fillers. Length 50-200 words. Pays $25-100.
Tips: "Find a new angle on an obvious story. Be creative. Look for authorities to quote in the article. Be persistent. Stories must be full of information and presented in thought-provoking manner."

‡SPORTS FITNESS, Sports Fitness, Inc., 21100 Erwin St., Woodland Hills CA 91367. (818)884-6800. Editor-in-Chief: Frederick Hatfield, Ph.D. Executive Editor: Kelly Garrett. 70% freelance written. A monthly magazine covering sports and fitness. "We emphasize state-of-the-art training and conditioning information as used by professional or world-class amateur athletes, with application for the average fitness enthusiast or weekend athlete. Authors are often Ph.D.s or M.D.s" Estab. 1985. Pays on acceptance. Byline given. 20% kill fee. Buys all rights. Submit seasonal/holiday material 4 months in advance. Computer printout submissions acceptable; prefers letter-quality to dot-matrix. Reports in 1 month. Sample copy for 8½x11 SASE; free writer's guidelines.
Nonfiction: How-to, inspirational and interview/profile. No fiction, poetry, or gossip. Buys 100 mss/year. Query with published clips. Length: 750-3,000 words. Pays $50-350 for assigned articles; pays $50-300 for unsolicited articles. Sometimes pays the expenses of writers on assignment.
Photos: State availability of photos with submission. Reviews transparencies. Offers no additional payment for photos accepted with ms. Identification of subjects required. Buys variable rights.
Columns/Departments: Young Athlete (topics in youth sports); Training Table (nutrition and supplements for sports training); Sports Medicine (treatment and prevention of sports injuries); and Lifetime Sports (news and tips on "weekend warrior" sports and fitness activities). Buys 30-40 mss/year. Query with or without published clips. Length: 750-1,200 words. Pays $50-200.

‡SUPERFIT, Rodale Press, Inc., 33 E. Minor St., Emmaus PA 18049. (215)967-5171. Editor: Gretchen Reynolds. Editorial Coordinator: Joann Williams. Approximately 50% freelance written. A quarterly magazine covering health and fitness. Emphasizes high performance, total fitness for life. Circ. 130,000. Pays on acceptance. Publishes ms an average of 5 months after acceptance. Byline given. Offers 25% kill fee. Buys one-time rights or all rights. Submit seasonal/holiday material 6 months in advance. Computer printout submis-

sions acceptable; prefers letter-quality to dot-matrix. Reports in 10 weeks on queries; 2 months on mss.
Nonfiction: Exposé; how-to (fitness related); interview/profile (sports/fitness); new product (fitness products); and travel (adventure/fitness). Buys 40-50 mss/year. Query with or without published clips, or send complete ms. Length: 800-2,500 words. Pays $150-1,000 for assigned articles; pays $100-800 for unsolicited articles. Sometimes pays expenses of writers on assignment.
Photos: State availability or send photos with submission. Reviews transparencies and prints. Offers $50 minimum/photo. Identification of subjects required. Buys one-time rights or all rights.
Columns/Departments: Fitnotes (short informative/newsy blurbs on health and fitness), 250-500 words; Voice (opinion column addressing controversy in health and fitness, 1,500 words; Travels (first-person account or perception of an adventure or experience/related to fitness); 1,500 words; Coach Approach (a coach or expert in health and fitness explains an interesting or unique method of training—how to), 1,500 words; Money (money related problems/issues in health and fitness e.g., health club contracts, decreased insurance costs from better health), 1,500 words; Mind Games (mental part of health and fitness and sports—psychology of fitness), 1,500 words. Pays $100-1,000. Locker Talk (tips from readers) 200-500 words. Pays $25. Query or send complete ms.
Editor's Note: As we went to press, we learned from associate editor Nelson Pena that Rodale Press' *Superfit* is ceasing publication with its Fall 1986 issue.

‡**TOTAL HEALTH, Body, Mind and Spirit,** Trio Publications, Suite 300, 6001 Topanga Cyn Blvd., Woodland Hills CA 91367. (818)887-6484. Editor: Robert L. Smith. Managing Editor: Rosemary Hofer. Prefers to work with published/established writers. 80% freelance written. A bimonthly magazine covering fitness, diet (weight loss), nutrition and mental health—"a family magazine about wholeness." Circ. 70,000. Pays on publication. Publishes ms an average of 3 months after acceptance. Byline given. Buys first rights. Submit seasonal/holiday material 4 months in advance. Photocopied submissions OK. Computer printout submissions acceptable. Reports in 1 month. Sample copy $1 with SAE; writer's guidelines for SAE.
Nonfiction: Exposé; how-to (pertaining to health and fitness); and religious (Judeo-Christian). Especially needs articles on skin and body care and power of positive thinking articles. No personal experience articles. Buys 48 mss/year. Send complete ms. Length: 2,000-3,000 words. Pays $50. Sometimes pays the expenses of writers on assignment.
Photos: State availability of photos with submission. Offers no additional payment for photos accepted with ms. Captions, model releases and identification of subjects required.
Columns/Departments: Query with or without published clips. Length: 1,000 words maximum. Pays $50 maximum.
Tips: "Feature length articles are most open to freelancers."

VIBRANT LIFE, A Christian Guide for Total Health, Review and Herald Publishing Assn., 55 W. Oak Ridge Dr., Hagerstown MD 21740. (301)791-7000. Editor: Ralph Blodgett. 95% freelance written. Enjoys working with published/established writers; works with a small number of new/unpublished writers each year; eager to work with new/unpublished writers. Bimonthly magazine covering family and health articles (especially with a Christian slant). Circ. 50,000. Pays on acceptance. "The average length of time between acceptance of a freelance-written manuscript and publication of the material depends upon the topics; some immediately used; others up to 2 years." Byline always given. Offers 25% kill fee. Buys first serial rights, first North American serial rights, or sometimes second serial (reprint) rights. Computer printout submissions acceptable; no dot-matrix. Submit seasonal/holiday material 6 months in advance. Photocopied (if clear) submissions OK. Reports in 2 months. Sample copy $1; free writer's guidelines.
Nonfiction: How-to (get out of debt, save time, have a better life); inspirational (articles showing how faith or trust in God helps people live better lives or have a happier family); and interview/profile (with personalities on the family, marriage, health or church). "We seek practical articles promoting a happier home, better health, and a more fulfilled life. We especially like articles designed to enrich husband/wife and parent/child relationships, features on breakthroughs in medicine, and most aspects of health (physical, mental, emotional, and spiritual). Recently published articles include "Six Keys to a Stronger Marriage," "Why Is Life So Unfair?" and "Can Exercise Improve Mental Function?." Buys 90-100 mss/year. Send complete ms. Length: 750-2,800 words. Pays $125-450. Pays the expenses of writers on assignment.
Photos: Send photos with ms. Needs 35mm transparencies. Not interested in b&w photos.
Tips: "*Vibrant Life* is published for the typical man/woman on the street, age 20-50. Therefore articles must be written in an interesting, easy-to-read style. Information must be reliable; no faddism. We are more conservative than other magazines in our field. Request a sample copy, and study the magazine and writer's guidelines."

‡**VIM AND VIGOR,** Vim and Vigor Inc., Suite 105, 2040 W. Bethany Home Rd., Phoenix AZ 85015. (602)246-5575. Editor: Preston V. McMurry, Jr. Managing Editor: Leo Calderella. 30% freelance written. A quarterly magazine covering health and fitness for various regions. "We publish stories about people and their

health care concerns and triumphs. Must contain accurate medical data which can pass our medical review board. While stories have the personal slant, they must include the universal aspects of the medical topic. We have a controlled circulation to top-income homeowners in each region." Estab. 1985. Circ. 97,000. Pays on publication. Publishes ms an average of 2 months after acceptance. Byline given. Offers $100 kill fee. Buys all rights. Submit seasonal/holiday material 5 months in advance. Photocopied submissions OK. Computer print-out submissions acceptable; prefers letter-quality to dot-matrix. Reports in 3 weeks on queries; 1 month on mss. Sample copy for 9x12 SAE with $1.24 postage; writer's guidelines for # SAE with 1 first class stamp.

Nonfiction: Personal experience (health and fitness), and medical and fitness. "No 'popular' medicine. We must pass our articles through a tough medical review board." Buys 10-12 mss/year. Query with published clips. Length: 1,200-1,500 words. Pays $250-350 for assigned articles. Sometimes pays the expenses of writers on assignment.

Photos: State availability of photos with submissions. Reviews transparencies. Offers no additional payment for photos accepted with ms if by writer; negotiates payment for photos by outside photographer. Model releases and identification of subjects required. Buys all rights.

Tips: "You must present the latest accurate medical facts available on a given topic in a way that will be understood by and interesting to the intelligent lay reader. You must present the human side, by interviewing patients who successfully handled a medical problem. You must present the professional side by interviewing doctors and other medical professionals (not Ph.Ds or psychotherapists)."

‡WALKWAYS, Update on Walkers and Walking. The WalkWays Center, #427, 733 15th St., NW, Washington DC 20005. (202)737-9555. Editor: Arnold Sagalyn. Managing Editor: Marsha L. Wallen. 50% freelance written. A newsletter on walking published monthly except February, May, August and November. Estab. 1985. Circ. 4,000. Pays on publication. Publishes ms an average of 1 month after acceptance. Byline given. Offers 50% kill fee. Buys first North American serial rights. Submit seasonal/holiday material 6 months in advance. Simultaneous and photocopied submissions OK. Reports in 2 weeks. Sample copy $1.50 with #10 SASE.

Nonfiction: Essays, how-to, humor, interview/profile, opinion, personal experience and travel. "No general travelogues, how walking is a religious experience, or narrow-scope articles about a type of walking with no examples of where it can be done in other places." Buys 8 mss/year. Send complete ms. Length: 200-750 words. Pays $10-50.

Photos: State availability of photos with submissions. Photos should include people walking or some other activity; should not be just scenery. Reviews contact sheet, 35mm transparencies, and 5x7 and 8x10 prints. Offers $10/photo. Captions required. Buys one-time rights.

Columns/Departments: Health notes, 350 words maximum, with art or photo; Networking (an information sharing department on specific subjects to familiarize readers, such as Volksmarching, race walking, how to form walking club), 350 words maximum, with art or photo; and Footloose (a walk or series of walks in special places with how-to information and sidebar information on how to get there, best time, best places to see, who was leader, etc.), 750 words maximum, with art or photo. Buys 32 mss/year. Send complete ms. Offers $10/photo.

Fiction: Humorous. Send complete ms. Length: 200 words maximum. Pays $10-20.

Poetry: Free verse, light verse and traditional. "No avant-garde about end of the world—depressing stuff." Submit maximum 3 poems. Length: 30 lines maximum. Pays $10.

Fillers: Facts and short humor. Length: 30-50 words. Pays $5.

Tips: "We need writers who can concentrate more on the walk and less about the scenery and extraneous details, although they are appreciated. If writing about a walking trips or experience, give details on how to get there, costs, etc., plus *other* places you can do similar walks. We like to approach themes versus single event or experiences, if possible and applicable."

WEIGHT WATCHERS MAGAZINE. 360 Lexington Ave., New York NY 10017. (212)370-0644. Editor-in-Chief: Lee Haiken. Articles Editor: Nelly Edmondson. 50% freelance written. Works with a small number of new/unpublished writers each year. Monthly publication for those interested in weight loss and weight maintenance through sensible eating and health/nutrition guidance. Circ. 859,000. Buys first North American serial rights only. Buys 18-30 unsolicited mss/year. Pays on acceptance. Publishes ms an average of 6 months after acceptance. Computer printout submissions acceptable; prefers letter-quality to dot-matrix. Reports in 1 month. Sample copy and writer's guidelines $1.75.

Nonfiction: Subject matter should be related to food, fitness, health or weight loss, but not specific diets or recipes. Would like to see researched articles related to the psychological aspects of weight loss and control and suggestions for making the battle easier. Inspirational success stories of weight loss following the Weight Watchers Program or other *sensible* weight-loss regimens also accepted. "We want to do more in-depth nutrition, psychology, and health pieces. Writers should interview top experts." Send queries with SASE. No full-length mss; send feature ideas, as well as before-and-after weight loss story ideas dealing either with celebrities or 'real people'. Length: 1,500 words maximum. Pays $200-600. Sometimes pays the expenses of writers on assignment.

Tips: "It's rewarding giving freelancers the rough shape of how an article should look and seeing where they go with it. It's frustrating working with writers who don't pay enough attention to revisions that have been requested and who send back second drafts with a few changes. We rarely use fillers. Writers can break in if their writing is lively, tightly constructed, and shows an understanding of our audience."

WHOLE LIFE, Journal for Personal and Planetary Health, Whole Life Enterprises, Inc., Suite 600, 89 5th Ave., New York NY 10003. (212)741-7274. Editor and Publisher: Marc Medoff. 50% freelance written. Works with a small number of new/unpublished writers each year. Tabloid covering holistic health, environment, and including some material on world peace. Circ. 58,000. Pays 40-60 days after publication. Publishes ms 2-8 months after acceptance. Byline given. Offers 25% kill fee. Buys first North American serial rights, all rights, and second serial (reprint) rights, and makes work-for-hire assignments; depends on topic and author. Submit seasonal/holiday material 4 months in advance. Simultaneous queries, and simultaneous, photocopied, and previously published submissions OK. Computer printout submissions acceptable; no dot-matrix. Reports in 2 months. Writer's guidelines for SASE.
Nonfiction: Book excerpts (health, environment, community activism); general interest (health sciences, holistic health, environment, alternative economics and politics); how-to (exercise, relaxation, fitness, appropriate technology, outdoors); interview/profile (on assignment); and new product (health, music, spiritual, psychological. natural diet). No undocumented opinion or narrative. Buys 80-100 mss/year. Query with published clips and resume. Length: 1,150-3,000 words. Pays $25-300. Sometimes pays expenses of writers on assignment.
Photos: Reviews b&w contact sheets, any size b&w and color transparencies and any size prints. Model releases and identification of subjects required. Buys one-time rights.
Columns/Departments: Films, Recipes, Herbs & Health, Resources, Whole Health Network, Living Lightly (appropriate technology), Peacefronts, News Views, Whole Life Person, Music, In the Market, Animal Rights—Human Wrongs, Whole Life Experience, Healthy Travel, Restaurant Review, Alternative Fitness, Whole Foods in the News, Whole Frauds in the News, People and Food. Buys 80-100 mss/year. Query with published clips and resume. Length: 150-1,000 words. Pays $25-80.

WHOLISTIC LIVING NEWS, Association for Wholistic Living. Box 16346, San Diego CA 92116. (619)280-0317. Editor: Judith Horton. 50% freelance written. Works with a small number of new/unpublished writers each year. Bimonthly newspaper covering the wholistic field from a wholistic perspective. Circ. 70,000. Pays on publication. Publishes ms an average of 8 months after acceptance. Byline given. Not copyrighted. Buys first serial rights and second serial (reprint) rights to material originally published elsewhere. Submit seasonal/holiday material 6 months in advance. Simultaneous queries, and simultaneous, photocopied, and previously published submissions OK. Computer printout submissions acceptable; prefers letter-quality to dot-matrix. Reports in 1 month on queries; 2 months on mss. Sample copy $1.50; free writer's guidelines.
Nonfiction: General interest (wholistic or new age overviews of a general topic); and how-to (taking responsibility for yourself—healthwise). No profiles, individual companies or personal experience. Buys 100 mss/year. Query with published clips. Length: 200-1,500 words. Pays $10-45. Sometimes pays the expenses of writers on assignment.
Photos: Send photos with query. Pays $7.50 for 5x7 b&w prints. Model releases and identification of subjects required.
Tips: "Study the newspaper—the style is different from a daily. The articles generally provide helpful information on how to feel your best (mentally, spiritually, physically). Any of the sections are open to freelancers: Creative Living, Health & Fitness, Arts, Nutrition and Network (recent events and upcoming ones). One of the main aspects of the paper is to promote the concept of a wholistic lifestyle and help people integrate it into their lives by taking simple steps on a daily basis."

THE YOGA JOURNAL, California Yoga Teachers Association, 2054 University Ave., Berkeley CA 94704. (415)841-9200. Editor: Stephan Bodian. 75% freelance written. Bimonthly magazine covering yoga, holistic health, conscious living, spiritual practices, and nutrition. "We reach a middle-class, educated audience interested in self-improvement and higher consciousness." Circ. 30,000. Pays on publication. Byline given. Offers $35 kill fee. Buys first North American serial rights only. Submit seasonal/holiday material 4 months in advance. Simultaneous queries and photocopied submissions OK. Reports in 6 weeks on queries; 2 months on mss. Publishes ms an average of 6 months after acceptance. Sample copy $2.50; free writer's guidelines.
Nonfiction: Book excerpts; how-to (exercise, yoga, massage, etc.); inspirational (yoga or related); interview/profile; opinion; personal experience; photo feature; and travel (if about yoga). "Yoga is our main concern, but our principal features in each issue highlight other new age personalities and endeavors. Nothing too far-out and mystical: Prefer stories about Americans incorporating yoga, meditation, etc., into their normal lives." Buys 40 mss/year. Query. Length: 750-3,500 words. Pays $35-150.
Photos: Diane McCarney, art director. Send photos with ms. Pays $100-150 for color transparencies; $10-15 for 8x10 b&w prints. Model release (for cover only) and identification of subjects required. Buys one-time rights.

Columns/Departments: Forum; Food (vegetarian, text and recipes); Health; Music (reviews of new age music); and Book Reviews. Buys 12-15 mss/year. Pays $10-25.
Tips: "We always read submissions. We are very open to freelance material and want to encourage writers to submit to our magazine. We're looking for out-of-state contributors, particularly in the Midwest and east coast."

‡YOUR HEALTH, Meridian Publishing Inc., Box 10010, Ogden UT 84409. (801)394-9446. Editor: Frank J. Cook. 65% freelance written. A monthly in-house magazine covering personal health, customized with special imprint titles for various businesses, organizations and associations. "Articles should be timeless, noncontroversial, upscale and positive, and the subject matter should have national appeal." Estab. 1985. Circ. 40,000. Pays on acceptance. Publishes ms an average of 8 months after acceptance. Byline given. Buys first rights, second serial (reprint) rights, and non-exclusive reprint rights. Simultaneous, photocopied, and previously published submissions OK. Computer printout submissions acceptable; prefers letter-quality to dot-matrix. Reports in 6 weeks. Sample copy $1 with 9x12 SAE; writer's guidelines for business size SAE with 1 first class stamp. (All requests for samples and guidelines should be addressed to—Attention: Editorial Assistant.)
Nonfiction: General interest stories about individual's health care needs, including preventative approaches to good health. Topics include advances in medical technology, common maladies and treatments, fitness and nutrition, hospital and home medical care, and personality profiles of both health care professionals and exceptional people coping with disability or illness. "We almost never use a first person narrative. No articles about chiropractic, podiatry or lay midwifery articles. Although we provide a forum for so call natural/holistic health maintenance ideas, many such articles are too general and unsubstantiated." Buys 40 mss/year. Query. Length: 1,000-1,400 words. Pays 15¢/word for first rights plus non-exclusive reprint rights. Payment for second rights is negotiable. Authors retain the right to resell material after it is printed by *Your Health*.
Photos: Send photos or state availability with submission. Reviews 35mm and 2¼x2¼ transparencies and 5x7 or 8x10 prints. Offers $35/inside photo and $50/cover photo. Captions, model releases and identification of subjects required.
Tips: "The key for the freelancer is a well-written query letter that demonstrates that the subject of the article has national appeal; establishes that any medical claims are based on interviews with experts and/or reliable documented sources; shows that the articles will have a clear, focused theme; outlines the availability (from the writer or photographer or a PR source) of top-quality color photos; and gives evidence that the writer/photographer is a professional, even if a beginner. The best way to get started as a contributer to *Your Health* is to prove that you can submit a well-focused article, based on facts, written cleanly per AP style, along with a variety of beautiful color transparencies to illustrate the story."

History

History repeats itself without being repetitive as editors of history magazines look for fresh accounts of past events. Some publications cover an era of a region; others deal with historic preservation. Listed here are magazines and others written for historical collectors, genealogy enthusiasts, historic preservationists and researchers. The Hobby and Craft category lists antique and other history markets.

AMERICAN HERITAGE, 10 Rockefeller Plaza, New York NY 10020. Editor: Byron Dobell. 70% freelance written. Bimonthly. Circ. 150,000. Usually buys first North American or all rights. Byline given. Buys 30 uncommissioned mss/year. Pays on acceptance. Publishes ms an average of 1 year after acceptance. Before submitting, "check our 28-year index to see whether we have already treated the subject." Submit seasonal material 1 year in advance. Electronic submissions acceptable ("any disk—to be converted by us in house"). Computer printout submissions acceptable; prefers letter-quality to dot-matrix. Reports in 1 month. Query. Writer's guidelines for SAE and 1 first class stamp.
Nonfiction: Wants "historical articles by scholars or journalists intended for intelligent lay readers rather than for professional historians." Emphasis is on authenticity, accuracy and verve. "Interesting documents, photographs and drawings are always welcome." Style should stress "readability and accuracy." Length: 1,500-5,000 words. Sometimes pays the expenses of writers on assignment.

Tips: "We have over the years published quite a few 'firsts' from young writers whose historical knowledge, research methods and writing skills met our standards. The scope and ambition of a new writer tell us a lot about his or her future usefulness to us. A major article gives us a better idea of the writer's value. Everything depends on the quality of the material. We don't really care whether the author is 20 and unknown, or 80 and famous, or vice versa."

AMERICAN HISTORY ILLUSTRATED, Box 8200, Harrisburg PA 17105. (717)657-9555. Editor: Ed Holm. 75% freelance written. Eager to work with new/unpublished writers. "A magazine of cultural, social, military and political history published for a general audience." Monthly except July/August. Circ. 125,000+. Pays on acceptance. Publishes ms 5-15 months after acceptance. Byline given. Buys all rights. Computer printout submissions acceptable; no dot-matrix. Reports in 10 weeks on queries; 16 weeks on mss. Writer's guidelines on request for business size SAE and 1 first class stamp; sample copy $3 (amount includes 3rd class postage) or $2.50 and SAE with 4 first class stamps.
Nonfiction: Regular features include American Profiles (biographies of noteworthy historical figures); Pages from an American Album (brief profiles of interesting personalities); Artifacts (stories behind historical objects); Portfolio (pictorial features on artists, photographers and graphic subjects); Digging Up History (coverage of recent archaeological and historical discoveries); and Testaments to the Past (living history articles on restored historical sites). "Material is presented on a popular rather than a scholarly level." Writers are encouraged to query before submitting ms. "Query letters should be limited to a concise 1-2 page proposal defining your article with an emphasis on its unique qualities." Buys 60 mss/year. Length: 1,000-3,000 words depending on type of article. Pays $100-450.
Photos: Occasionally buys 8x10 glossy prints with mss; welcomes suggestions for illustrations. Pays for the reproduced color illustrations that the author provides.
Tips: "Key prerequisites for publication are thorough research and accurate presentation, precise English usage and sound organization, a lively style, and a high level of human interest."

AMERICAN WEST, 3033 N. Campbell Ave., Tucson AZ 85719. Managing Editor: Mae Reid-Bills. Editor: Thomas W. Pew Jr. "We are backlogged with submissions and prefer not to receive unsolicited submissions at this time."

‡ANCESTRY NEWSLETTER, Ancestry, Inc., Box 476, Salt Lake City UT 84110. (801)531-1790. Editor: Scott R. Woodruff. Managing Editor: Robert J. Welsh. 95% freelance written. Eager to work with new/unpublished writers. A bimonthly newsletter covering genealogy and family history. "We publish practical, instructional, and informative pieces specifically applicable to the field of genealogy. Our audience is the active genealogist, both hobbyist and professional." Circ. 8,000. Pays on publication. Publishes ms an average of 4 months after acceptance. Byline given. Buys first North American serial rights or all rights. Submit seasonal/holiday material 4 months in advance. Simultaneous and photocopied submissions OK. Computer printout submissions acceptable; prefers letter-quality to dot-matrix. Reports in 2 weeks on queries; 1 month on mss. Free sample copy; writer's guidelines for SASE.
Nonfiction: General interest (genealogical); historical; how-to (genealogical research techniques); instructional; and photo feature (genealogically related). No unpublished or published family histories, genealogies; the "story of my great-grandmother," etc.' or personal experiences. Buys 18-20 mss/year. Send complete ms. Length: 400-2,000 words. Pays $50-100.
Photos: Send photos with submission. Reviews contact sheets and 5x7 prints. Offers no additional payment for photos accepted with ms. Identification of subjects required. Buys one-time rights.
Tips: "You don't have to be famous, but you must know something about genealogy. Our readers crave any information which might assist them in their ancestral quest."

THE ARTILLERYMAN, Century Publications, Inc., 3 Church St., Winchester MA 01890. (617)729-8100. 60% freelance written. Editor: C. Peter Jorgensen. Quarterly magazine covering antique artillery, fortifications, and crew-served weapons 1750 to 1900 for competition shooters, collectors and living history reenactors using muzzleloading artillery; "emphasis on Revolutionary War and Civil War but includes everyone interested in pre-1900 artillery and fortifications, preservation, construction of replicas, etc." Circ. 3,100. Pays on publication. Publishes ms an average of 3 months after acceptance. Byline given. Not copyrighted. Buys one-time rights. Simultaneous queries, and simultaneous, photocopied and previously published submissions OK. Computer printout submissions acceptable; prefers letter-quality to dot-matrix. Reports in 3 weeks. Free sample copy and writer's guidelines.
Nonfiction: Historical/nostalgic; how-to (reproduce ordnance equipment/sights/implements/tools/accessories, etc.); interview/profile; new product; opinion (must be accompanied by detailed background of writer and include references); personal experience; photo feature; technical (must have footnotes); and travel (where to find interesting antique cannon). Interested in "artillery *only*, for sophisticated readers. Not interested in other weapons, battles in general." Buys 24-30 mss/year. Send complete ms. Length: 300 words minimum. Pays $20-60.

Photos: Send photos with ms. Pays $5 for 5x7 and larger b&w prints. Captions and identification of subjects required.
Tips: "We regularly use freelance contributions for Places-to-Visit, Cannon Safety, The Workshop and Unit Profiles departments. Also need pieces on unusual cannon or cannon with a known and unique history. To judge whether writing style and/or expertise will suit our needs, writers should ask themselves if they could knowledgeably talk artillery with an expert. Subject matter is of more concern than writer's background."

BACKWOODSMAN MAGAZINE, The Publication for 20th Century Frontiersmen, Route 8, Box 579, Livingston TX 77351. Editor: Charlie Richie. 50% freelance written. Works with a small number of new/unpublished writers each year. Bimonthly magazine covering buckskinning, 19th century crafts, muzzleloading, homesteading and trapping. Circ. 5,000. Pays after publication. Publishes ms an average of 4 months after acceptance. Byline given. Buys first North American serial rights. Computer printout submissions acceptable; prefers letter-quality to dot-matrix. Reports in 2 weeks on queries. Sample copy $2.
Nonfiction: Historical/nostalgic (1780 to 1900); how-to (19th Century crafts, muzzle loading); inspirational (wilderness survival); interview/profile (real-life backwoodsmen); new product (buckskinning field); and travel (American historical). "We want 19th century craft how-tos—mostly the simple kinds of everyday woodslore-type crafts." Buys 30-40 mss/year. Send complete ms. Length: 3-4 double-spaced pages. Pays $20 maximum.
Photos: "We prefer that at least one b&w photo or illustration be submitted with ms."
Tips: "We publish articles by real backwoodsmen and prefer that the writer just be himself and not Hemingway."

BLUE & GRAY MAGAZINE, "For Those Who Still Hear the Guns," Blue & Gray Enterprises, Inc., 130 Galloway Rd. Galloway, OH 43119. (614)870-1861. Editor: David E. Roth. 65% freelance written. Bimonthly magazine on the Civil War period and current Civil War-related activities. "Our philosophy is color, quality and broad-based reporting. Included in this 'broad-based' reporting is the full range of Civil War-related topics. such as pure history articles, living history, relic hunting, collectibles, wargaming, book reviews, new discoveries. and tour guides of historical sites. Our distribution is international in scope and appeals to both a popular and scholarly market." Circ. 13,000 (with a 5% growth per issue). Pays on acceptance. Publishes ms an average of 6 months after acceptance. Byline given. Usually buys all rights; occasionally buys first serial rights or one-time rights. Submit seasonal/holiday material 6 months in advance. Computer printout submissions acceptable. Reporting time varies with query/manuscripts. Writer's guidelines for SAE with 1 first class stamp.
Nonfiction: Book excerpts (history); exposé (history); historical/nostalgic; how-to (history, living history, relic hunting, etc.); interview/profile (Civil War descendant); opinion (history); personal experience (history, re-enacting, relic hunting, etc.); photo feature (history); technical (history, re-enacting, relic hunting, etc.); travel (Civil War sites); or article on Civil War history. Query with or without published clips or send complete ms. Length: 1,000-6,000 words. Pays $25-350.
Photos: State availability of photos, or send photos with query or mss. Captions and identification of subjects required. Buys non-exclusive rights for continued use.
Columns/Departments: Book Reviews, Living History, Wargaming, Relic Hunting, Controversy, Profile, etc. Query with or without published clips, or send complete ms. Length: 1,000-4,000 words. Pays $25-250.
Tips: "Submit an appropriate Civil War-related ms with sources listed (footnotes preferred), and photos or photo suggestions. All areas of our publication are open to freelancers except Tour Guides which is somewhat restricted because of already firm commitments."

BRITISH HERITAGE, Historical Times, Inc., 2245 Kohn Rd., Box 8200, Harrisburg PA 17105. (717)657-9555. Editor: Gail Huganir. "We are backlogged with submissions and prefer not to receive unsolicited submissions at the time."

CANADIAN WEST, Box 3399, Langley, British Columbia V3A 4R7 Canada. (604)576-6561. Editor-in-Chief: Damian Inwood. 80-100% freelance written. Works with a small number of new/unpublished writers each year. Emphasizes pioneer history, primarily of British Columbia, Alberta and the Yukon. Quarterly magazine; 48 pages. Circ. 5,000. Pays on publication. Publishes ms an average of 3 months after acceptance. Buys first North American serial rights. Phone queries OK. Electronic submissions acceptable via IBM compatible disks, but requires hard copy also. Computer printout submissions acceptable; prefers letter-quality to dot-matrix. Previously published submissions OK. Reports in 2 months. Sample copy and writer's guidelines for $1.50.
Nonfiction: How-to (related to gold panning and dredging); historical (pioneers, shipwrecks, massacres, battles, exploration, logging, Indians, ghost towns, mining camps, gold rushes and railroads). No American locale articles. Buys 28 mss/year. Submit complete ms. Length: 2,000-3,500 words. Pays $100-300.
Photos: All mss must include photos or other artwork. Submit photos with ms. Payment included in price of article. Captions preferred. "Photographs are kept for future reference with the right to re-use. However, we do not forbid other uses, generally, as these are historical prints from archives."
Columns/Departments: Open to suggestions for new columns/departments.

‡CHICAGO HISTORY, The Magazine of the Chicago Historical Society, Chicago Historical Society, Clark St. at North Ave., Chicago IL 60614. (312)642-4600. Editor: Russell Lewis. Assistant Editor: Meg Walter. Editorial Assistant: Aleta Zak. 100% freelance written. A quarterly magazine covering Chicago history: cultural, political, economic, social, architectural. Circ. 5,500. Pays on publication. Byline given. Buys all rights. Submit seasonal/holiday material 9 months in advance. Photocopied submissions OK. Electronic submissions OK if IBM compatible, but requires hard copy also. Computer printout submissions acceptable. Reports in 6 weeks. Sample copy $3.75; free writer's guidelines.
Nonfiction: Book excerpts, essays, historical/nostalgic, interview/profile and photo feature. Articles to be "analytical, informative, and directed at a popular audience with a special interest in history." No "cute" articles. Buys 16-20 mss/year. Query; send complete ms. Length: approximately 4,500 words. Pays $250.
Photos: State availability of photos with submission and submit photocopies. Would prefer no originals. Offers no additional payment for photos accepted with ms. Identification of subjects required.
Columns/Departments: Book Reviews (Chicago and/or urban history), 500-750 words; and Review Essays (author reviews, comparatively, a compilation of several books on same topic—Chicago and/or urban history), 2,500 words. Buys 20 mss/year. Query; send complete ms. Pays $75-100 "but book review authors receive only one copy of book, no cash."
Tips: "Freelancer can best break in by 1) calling to discuss an article idea with editor; 2) submitting a detailed outline of proposed article. All sections of *Chicago History* are open to freelancers, but we suggest that authors do not undertake to write articles for the magazine unless they have considerable knowledge of the subject and are willing to research it in some detail. We require a footnoted manuscript, although we do not publish the notes."

CIVIL WAR TIMES ILLUSTRATED, 2245 Kohn Rd., Box 8200, Harrisburg PA 17105. (717)657-9555. Editor: John E. Stanchak. 90% freelance written. Works with a small number of new/unpublished each year. Magazine published monthly except July and August. Circ. 120,000. Pays on acceptance. Publishes ms an average of 1 year after acceptance. Buys all rights, first rights or one-time rights, or makes work-for-hire assignments. Submit seasonal/holiday material 1 year in advance. Computer printout submissions acceptable; prefers letter-quality to dot-matrix. Reports in 2 weeks on queries; 3 months on mss. Sample copy $3; free writer's guidelines.
Nonfiction: Profile, photo feature, and Civil War historical material. "Positively no fiction or poetry." Buys 20 mss/year. Length: 2,500-5,000 words. Query. Pays $75-450. Sometimes pays the expenses of writers on assignment.
Photos: Jeanne Collins, art director. State availability. Pays $5-50 for 8x10 b&w glossy prints and copies of Civil War photos: $400-500 for 4-color cover photos; and $100-250 for color photos for interior use.
Tips: "We're very open to new submissions. Querying us after reading several back issues, then submitting illustration and art possibilities along with the query letter is the best 'in.' Never base the narrative solely on family stories or accounts. Submissions must be written in a popular style but based on solid academic research. Manuscripts are required to have marginal source annotations."

EL PALACIO, THE MAGAZINE OF THE MUSEUM OF NEW MEXICO, Museum of New Mexico Press, Box 2087, Santa Fe NM 87504. (505)827-6794. Editor-in-Chief: Malinda Elliott. 15% freelance written. Prefers to work with published/established writers. Emphasizes the collections of the Museum of New Mexico and anthropology, ethnology, history, folk and fine arts, Southwestern culture, and natural history as these topics pertain to the Museum of New Mexico and the Southwest. Triannual magazine; 48 pages. Circ. 2,500. Pays on publication. "We hope to attract professional writers who can translate scholarly and complex information into material that will fascinate and inform a general educated readership." Acquires first North American serial rights. Byline given. Phone queries OK. Submit seasonal/holiday queries 1 year in advance. Photocopied and computer printout submissions OK. Electronic submissions OK via IBM compatible; all submissions must be saved in ASCII on a 5½ IBM compatible personal computer disk, but requires hard copy also. Computer printout submissions acceptable; no dot-matrix. Reports in 6 weeks. Sample copy $4; free writer's guidelines.
Nonfiction: Historical (on Southwest; substantive but readable—not too technical); folk art; archeology (Southwest); photo essay; anthropology; material culture of the Southwest. Buys 3-4 unsolicited mss/year. Recent articles documented Hispanic arts and crafts contained in the Museum; vanishing Hispanic art; Museum exhibits; paintings of famous Southwestern painters. "Other articles that have been very successful are a photo-essay on Chaco Canyon and other archeological spots of interest in the state and an article on Indian baskets and their function in Indian life." Query with credentials. Length: 1,750-4,000 words. Pays $50 honorarium minimum. Sometimes pays the expenses of writers on assignment.
Photos: Photos often purchased with accompanying ms, some on assignment. Prefers b&w prints. Informative captions required. Pays "on contract" for 5x7 (or larger) b&w photos and 5x7 or 8½x11 prints or 35mm color transparencies. Send prints and transparencies. Total purchase price for ms includes payment for photos.
Columns/Departments: New Acquisitions; Curator's Choice; Photo Essay, Books (reviews of interest to *El Palacio* readers), Museum Highlights (highlights a museum exhibit or event).
Tips: "*El Palacio* magazine offers a unique opportunity for writers with technical ability to have their work

published and seen by influential professionals as well as avidly interested lay readers. The magazine is highly regarded in its field. The writer should have strong writing skills, an understanding of the Southwest and of the field written about. Be able to communicate technical concepts to the educated reader. We like to have a bibliography, list of sources, or suggested reading list with nearly every submission."

MILITARY HISTORY, Empire Press, 105 Loudoun St. SW, Leesburg VA 22075. (703)771-9400. Editorial Director: Carl Gnam. 95% freelance written. "We'll work with anyone, established or not, who can provide the goods and convince us as to its accuracy." Bimonthly magazine covering all military history of the world. "We strive to give the general reader accurate, highly readable, often narrative popular history, richly accompanied by period art." Pays on publication. Publishes ms 6 months-1 year after acceptance. Byline given. Buys first North American serial rights. Submit anniversary material 6-12 months in advance. Photocopied submissions OK. Computer printout submissions acceptable; no dot-matrix. Reports in 1 month on queries; 2-4 months on mss. Sample copy $3; writer's guidelines for SAE with 1 first class stamp.
Nonfiction: Advance book excerpts; historical; interview (military figures of commanding interest); personal experience (only occasionally). Buys 18 mss, plus 6 interviews/year. Query with published clips. "To propose an article, submit a short, self-explanatory query summarizing the story proposed, its highlights and/or significance. State also your own expertise, access to sources or proposed means of developing the pertinent information." Length: 4,000 words. Pays $400.
Columns/Departments: Espionage, weaponry, personality, travel (with military history of the place) and books—all relating to military history. Buys 24 mss/year. Query with published clips. Length: 2,000 words. Pays $200.
Tips: "We would like journalistically 'pure' submissions that adhere to basics, such as full name at first reference, same with rank, and definition of prior or related events, issues cited as context or obscure military 'hardware.' Read the magazine, discover our style, and avoid subjects already covered. Pick stories with strong art possibilities (*real* art and photos), send photocopies, tell us where to order the art. Avoid historical overview, focus upon an event with appropriate and accurate context. Provide bibliography. Tell the story in popular but elegant style."

OLD WEST, Western Periodicals, Inc., Box 2107, Stillwater OK 74076. (405)743-3370. Quarterly magazine. Byline given. See *True West*.

‡PERSIMMON HILL, 1700 NE 63rd St., Oklahoma City OK 73111. Editor: Willard H. Porter. 80% freelance written. Works with a small number of new/unpublished writers each year. For an audience interested in Western art, Western history, ranching and rodeo, historians, artists, ranchers, art galleries, schools, and libraries. Publication of the National Cowboy Hall of Fame and Western Heritage Center. Quarterly. Circ. 15,000. Buys all rights. Byline given. Buys 12-14 mss/year. Pays on publication. Sample copy $3. Reporting time on mss accepted for publication varies. Returns rejected material immediately. Computer printout submissions acceptable: no dot-matrix.
Nonfiction: Historical and contemporary articles on famous Western figures connected with pioneering the American West, Western art, rodeo, cowboys, etc. (or biographies of such people), stories of Western flora and animal life, and environmental subjects. Only thoroughly researched and historically authentic material is considered. May have a humorous approach to subject. Not interested in articles that reappraise, or in any way put the West and its personalities in an unfavorable light. No "broad, sweeping, superficial pieces; i.e., the California Gold Rush or rehashed pieces on Billy the Kid, etc." Length: 2,000-3,000 words. Query. Pays $100-200: special work negotiated. Sometimes pays the expenses of writers on assignment.
Photos: B&w glossy prints or color transparencies purchased with or without ms, or on assignment. Pays according to quality and importance for b&w and color. Suggested captions appreciated.

PRESERVATION NEWS, National Trust for Historic Preservation, 1785 Massachusetts Ave. NW, Washington DC 20016. (202)673-4075. Editor: Arnold M. Berke. 10% freelance written. Prefers to work with published/established writers. A monthly tabloid covering preservation of historic buildings in the U.S. "We cover efforts and controversies involving historic buildings and districts. Most entries are news stories, features or essays." Circ. 175,000. Pays on acceptance. Publishes ms an average of 1 month after acceptance. Byline given. Offers variable kill fee. Not copyrighted. Buys one-time rights. Simultaneous queries, and photocopied and previously published submissions OK. Computer printout submissions acceptable. Reports in 1 month on queries. Sample copy $1 and $1 postage; writer's guidelines for SAE and 1 first class stamp.
Nonfiction: Historical/nostalgic, humor, interview/profile, opinion, personal experience, photo feature and travel. Buys 12 mss/year. Query with published clips. Length: 500-1,000 words. Pays $75-200. Sometimes pays the expenses of writers on assignment.
Photos: State availability of photos with query or ms. Reviews b&w contact sheet. Pays $25-100. Identification of subjects required.
Columns/Departments: "We seek an urban affairs reporter who can give a new slant on development conflict throughout the United States." Buys 6 mss/year. Query with published clips. Length: 600-1,000 words. Pays $75-200.

Tips: "The writer has a better chance of breaking in at our publication with short articles and fillers because we like to try them out first. Don't submit dull articles that lack compelling details."

‡TIMELINE, Ohio Historical Society, 1985 Velma Ave., Columbus OH 43211. (614)466-1500. Editor: Christopher S. Duckworth. 90% freelance written. A bimonthly magazine covering history, natural history, archaeology, and fine and decorative arts. Circ. 11,000. Pays on acceptance. Byline given. Offers $75 minimum kill fee. Buys first North American serial rights or all rights. Submit seasonal/holiday material 6 months in advance. Photocopied submissions OK. Electronic submissions OK on PC/DOS, but requires hard copy also. Computer printout submissions acceptable; no dot-matrix. Reports in 3 weeks on queries; 6 weeks on mss. Sample copy $4; free writer's guidelines.
Nonfiction: Book excerpts, essays, historical, profile (of individuals) and photo feature. Buys 22 mss/year. Query. Length: 500-6,000 words. Pays $100-900.
Photos: State availability of photos with submission. Will not consider submissions without ideas for illustration. Reviews contact sheets, transparencies, and 8x10 prints. Captions, model releases, and identification of subjects required. Buys one-time rights.
Tips: "We want crisply written, authoritative narratives for the intelligent lay reader. An Ohio slant may strengthen a submission, but it is not indispensable. Contributors must know enough about their subject to explain it clearly and in an interesting fashion. We use high-quality illustration with all features. If appropriate illustration is unavailable, we can't use the feature. The writer who sends illustration ideas with a manuscript has an advantage, but an often-published illustration won't attract us."

TRUE WEST, Western Periodicals, Inc., Box 2107, Stillwater OK 74076. (405)743-3370. Editor: John Joerschke. 100% freelance written. Works with a small number of new/unpublished writers each year. Magazine on Western American history before 1920. "We want reliable research on significant historical topics written in lively prose for an informed general audience." Circ. 100,000. Pays on acceptance. Publishes ms an average of 4 months after acceptance. Byline given. Buys first North American serial rights. Submit seasonal/holiday material 6 months in advance. Simultaneous queries OK. Computer printout submissions acceptable; prefers letter-quality to dot-matrix. Reports in 1 month on queries; 6 weeks on mss. Sample copy for $1; writer's guidelines for #10 SAE and 1 first class stamp.
Nonfiction: Historical/nostalgic, how-to, photo feature, travel, and western movies. "We do not want rehashes of worn-out stories, historical fiction, or history written in a fictional style. Buys 200 mss/year. Query. Length: 500-4,500 words. Pays $25-350.
Photos: Send photos with accompanying query or manuscript. Pays $10 for b&w prints. Identification of subjects required. Buys one-time rights.
Columns/Departments: Marcia Simpson, assistant editor. Western Roundup—200-300 word short articles on historically oriented places to go and things to do in the West with one b&w print. Buys 12-16/year. Send complete ms. Pays $35.
Tips: "Do original research on fresh topics. Stay away from controversial subjects unless you are truly knowledgeable in the field. Read our magazines and follow our writers' guidelines. A freelancer is most likely to break in with us by submitting thoroughly researched, lively prose on relatively obscure topics. First person accounts rarely fill our needs."

VIRGINIA CAVALCADE, Virginia State Library, Richmond VA 23219. (804)786-2312. Primarily for readers with an interest in Virginia history. 90% freelance written. "Both established and new writers are invited to submit articles." Quarterly magazine; 48 pages. Circ. 12,000. Buys all rights. Byline given. Buys 12-15 mss/year. Pays on acceptance. Publishes ms an average of 10 months after acceptance. Rarely considers simultaneous submissions. Submit seasonal material 15-18 months in advance. Reports in 1-3 months. Query. Computer printout submissions acceptable; prefers letter-quality to dot-matrix. Sample copy $2; free writer's guidelines.
Nonfiction: "We welcome readable and factually accurate articles that are relevant to some phase of Virginia history. Art, architecture, literature, education, business, technology and transportation are all acceptable subjects, as well as political and military affairs. Articles must be based on thorough, scholarly research. We require footnotes but do not publish them. Any period from the age of exploration to the mid-20th century, and any geographical section or area of the state may be represented. Must deal with subjects that will appeal to a broad readership, rather than to a very restricted group or locality. Articles must be suitable for illustration, although it is not necessary that the author provide the pictures. If the author does have pertinent illustrations or knows their location, the editor appreciates information concerning them." Length: 3,500-4,500 words. Pays $100.
Photos: Uses 8x10 b&w glossy prints; color transparencies should be at least 4x5.
Tips: "*Cavalcade* employs a narrative, anecdotal style. Too many submissions are written for an academic audience or are simply not sufficiently gripping."

‡YE OLDE NEWES, Stapleton Investments, Box 1508, Lufkin TX 75902-1508. (409)639-1314. Editor: Libby Stapleton. Managing Editor: C. Stapleton. 50% freelance written. Eager to work with new/unpublished

writers. Semiannual magazine about the Renaissance (1300 AD-1650 AD). Circ. 66,000. Pays on acceptance. Byline given. Buys non-exclusive, unlimited rights. Simultaneous queries, and simultaneous, photocopied, and previously published submissions OK. Computer printout submissions acceptable. Reports in 1 month on queries; 4 weeks on mss. Sample copy $3; writer's guidelines for business size SAE and 20¢ postage.
Nonfiction: Historical or how-to articles about crafts and trades of the period. All material must be appropriate to the medieval or Renaissance period. Query with or without published clips. Send complete ms. Length: 500-3,000 words. Pays $35.
Tips: "Query only on material relevant to the Renaissance. All queries and mss are given prompt attention. Having been published previously is not considered. We are interested in articles about artists and craftspeople who perform medieval crafts or entertainment and how-to articles about the period (recipes, crafts, etc.). Send postcard for acceptance/reject. Do not send original manuscript, as it will not be returned."

Hobby and Craft

If you use your writing skill to describe a hobby or craft you know, editors will be eager to get your manuscripts. Craftspeople always need new ideas. As for collectors, they need to know what is most valuable and why. Antique magazine editors, for instance, want the latest research. Collectors, do-it-yourselfers, and craftspeople look to these magazines for inspiration and information. Publications covering antiques and miniatures are also listed here. Publications for electronics and radio hobbyists are included in the Science classification.

AMERICAN BOOK COLLECTOR, Box 867, Ossining, NY 10562-0867. (914)941-0409. Editor: Bernard McTigue. 50% freelance written. Eager to work with new/unpublished writers. Monthly magazine on book collecting from the 15th century to the present for individuals, rare book dealers, librarians, and others interested in books and bibliomania. Circ. 3,500. Pays on publication. Publishes ms an average of 6 months after acceptance. Submit seasonal material 3 months in advance. Photocopied and previously published submissions OK. Electronic submissions OK if IBM PC, but requires hard copy also. Computer printout submissions acceptable; prefers letter-quality to dot-matrix. Reports in 6 weeks. Sample copy and writer's guidelines for $5.
Nonfiction: General interest (some facet of book collecting: category of books; taste and technique; artist; printer; binder); interview (prominent book collectors; producers of contemporary fine and limited editions; scholars; librarians); and reviews of exhibitions. Buys 20-30 unsolicited mss/year. "We absolutely require queries with clips of previously published work." Query should include precise description of proposed article accompanied by description of author's background plus indication of extent of illustrations. Length: 1,500-4,500 words. Pays 5¢/word. Sometimes pays the expenses of writers on assignment.
Photos: State availability of photos. Prefers b&w glossy prints of any size. Offers no additional payment for photos accompanying ms. Captions and model release required. Buys one-time rights.
Columns/Departments: Contact editor. Reviews of books on book collecting, and gallery exhibitions.
Tips: "We look for knowledgeable writing. A purely journalistic (i.e., learned while writing) approach is unlikely to be of value. We're now monthly—which means we need *twice* the material we needed in 1985."

AMERICAN CLAY EXCHANGE, Page One Publications, Box 2674, La Mesa CA 92041. (619)697-5922. Editor: Susan N. Cox. Biweekly newsletter on subjects relating to American made pottery—old or new—with an emphasis on antiques and collectibles for collectors, buyers and sellers of American made pottery, earthenware, china, dinnerware, etc. Pays on acceptance. Byline given. Buys all rights; will consider first serial rights." Submit seasonal/holiday material 4 months in advance. Computer printout submissions acceptable; no dot-matrix. Reports in 1 month on queries; 2 months on mss. Sample copy $1.50; free writer's guidelines.
Nonfiction: Book reviews (on books pertaining to American made pottery, china, earthenware); historical/nostalgic (on museums and historical societies in the U.S. if they handle pottery, etc.); how-to (identify pieces, clean, find them); and interview/profile (if artist is up-and-coming). No "I found a piece of pottery for 10¢ at a flea market" types. Buys 40-50 mss/year. Query or send complete ms. Length: 1,000 words maximum. Pays $125 maximum.
Photos: Send photos with ms. Pays $5 for b&w prints. Captions required. Does not accept color slides. Buys all rights: "will consider one-time rights."

Tips: "Know the subject being written about, including marks and values of pieces found. Telling a reader what 'marks' are on pieces is most essential. The best bet is to write a short (200-300 word) article with a few photos and marks. We are a small company willing to work with writers who have good, salable ideas and know our product. Any article that deals effectively with a little-known company or artist during the 1900-1950 era is most sought after. We have added a section devoted to dinnerware, mostly from the 1900-1950 era—same guidelines."

AMERICANA, 29 W. 38th St., New York NY 10018. (212)398-1550. Editor: Michael Durham. "We are backlogged with submissions and prefer not to receive unsolicited submissions at this time.

THE ANTIQUARIAN, Box 798, Huntington NY 11743. (516)271-8990. Editor-in-Chief: Marguerite Cantine. Managing Editor: Elizabeth Kilpatrick. Emphasizes antiques and 19th-century or earlier art. Monthly tabloid. 10% freelance written. Circ. 15,000. Pays on publication. Publishes ms an average of 2 months after acceptance. Buys all rights. Pays 10% kill fee. Byline given. Submit seasonal/holiday material 3 months in advance. Computer printout submissions acceptable; prefers letter-quality to dot-matrix. Reports in 6 weeks. Sample copy for 12x15½ SASE with $1.25 postage attached. No checks.
Nonfiction: How-to (refinish furniture, repair glass, restore old houses, restore paintings, rebind books, resilver glass, etc.); general interest (relations of buyers and dealers at antique shows/sales, auction reports); historical (data, personal and otherwise, on famous people in the arts and antiques field); interview; photo feature (auctions, must have caption on item including selling price); profile (wants articles around movie stars and actors who collect antiques; query); and travel (historical sites of interest in New York, New Jersey, Connecticut, Pennsylvania and Delaware). Wants concise articles, accurate research; no material on art deco, collectibles, anything made after 1900, cutesy things to 'remake' from antiques, or flea markets and crafts shows. Buys 6 mss/year. Submit complete ms. Length: 200-2,000 words. Pays 3¢/word.
Photos: Pays 50¢-$1 for 3½x5 glossy b&w prints. Captions required. Buys all rights. Model releases required.
Tips: "Don't write an article unless you *love* this field. Write as though you were carrying on a nice conversation with your mother. No pretentions. No superiority. It's frustrating when freelancers don't read, follow instructions, or send an SASE, call the office and *demand* answers to questions, or act unprofessionally. But once in a blue moon they do get a totally fresh idea."

ANTIQUE MONTHLY, Boone, Inc., Drawer 2, Tuscaloosa AL 35402. (205)345-0272. Editor/Publisher: Gray D. Boone. Senior Editor: Mandy Ochoa. 20% freelance written. Eager to work with new/unpublished writers. Monthly tabloid covering art, antiques, and major museum shows. "More than half of our audience are college graduates, over 27% have post-graduate degrees; fifty-nine percent are in $35,000 and over income bracket. Average number of years readers have been collecting art/antiques is 20.5." Circ. 65,100. Pays on publication. Publishes ms an average of 4 months after acceptance. Buys all rights. Submit seasonal/holiday material 2 months in advance. Photocopied submissions OK. Computer printout submissions acceptable; prefers letter-quality to dot-matrix. Reports in 1 month on queries and mss. Sample copy 90¢.
Nonfiction: Discussions of current trends in antiques marketplace; coverage of antiques shows and auctions; profiles of important collectors and dealers; descriptions of decorative arts exhibitions; and book reviews. Recent article example: "The Year for Shaker" (February 1986). No personal material. Buys 6-10 unsolicited mss/year. Length: 1,000-1,500 words. Pays $125 minimum/article. Sometimes pays expenses of writers on assignment.
Photos: State availability of photos. Prefers color transparencies or slides and 5x7 b&w prints. "We rarely pay for photos; usually we pay only for costs incurred by the writer, and this must be on prior agreement." Captions required.
Tips: "Freelancers are important because they offer the ability to cover stories that regular staff and correspondents cannot cover. A story is more likely to interest the editors if there is a timely news peg—if the story is related to a recent or current event or trend in the antiques world. Write in a crisp, newsy style and have a working knowledge of the antiques and decorative arts field."

ANTIQUE REVIEW, Box 538, Worthington OH 43085. Editor: Charles Muller. (614)885-9757. 60% freelance written. Eager to work with new/unpublished writers. For an antique-oriented readership, "generally well-educated, interested in folk art and other early American items." Monthly tabloid. Circ. 8,000 in all 50 states. Pays on publication date assigned at time of purchase. Publishes ms an average of 3 months after acceptance. Buys first North American serial rights, and second (reprint) rights to material originally published elsewhere. Byline given. Phone queries OK. Submit seasonal/holiday material 3 months in advance. Simultaneous, photocopied and previously published submissions OK. Computer printout submissions acceptable; prefers letter-quality to dot-matrix. Reports in 1 month. Free sample copy and writer's guidelines.
Nonfiction: "The articles we desire concern history and production of furniture, pottery, china, and other antiques of the period prior to the 1880s. In some cases, contemporary folk art items are acceptable. We are also interested in reporting on antique shows and auctions with statements on conditions and prices. We do not want

articles on contemporary collectibles." Buys 5-8 mss/issue. Query with clips of published work. Query should show "author's familiarity with antiques and an interest in the historical development of artifacts relating to early America." Length: 200-2,000 words. Pays $80-125. Sometimes pays the expenses of writers on assignment.
Photos: State availability of photos with query. Payment included in ms price. Uses 5x7 or larger glossy b&w prints. Captions required. Articles with photographs receive preference.
Tips: "Give us a call and let us know of specific interests. We are more concerned with the background in antiques than in writing abilities. The writing can be edited, but the knowledge imparted is of primary interest. A frequent mistake is being too general, not becoming deeply involved in the topic and its reserach."

THE ANTIQUE TRADER WEEKLY, Box 1050, Dubuque IA 52001. (319)588-2073. Editor: Kyle D. Husfloen. 25% freelance written. For collectors and dealers in antiques and collectibles. Weekly newspaper; 90-120 pages. Circ. 90,000. Publishes ms an average of 1 year after acceptance. Buys all rights. Buys about 60 mss/year. Payment at beginning of month following publication. Photocopied and simultaneous submissions OK. Computer printout submissions acceptable; no dot-matrix. Submit seasonal/holiday material 4 months in advance. Query or submit complete ms. Sample copy 50¢; free writer's guidelines.
Nonfiction: "We invite authoritative and well-researched articles on all types of antiques and collectors' items and in-depth stories on specific types of antiques and collectibles. No human interest stories. We do not pay for brief information on new shops opening or other material printed as service to the antiques hobby." Pays $5-50 for feature articles; $50-150 for feature cover stories.
Photos: Submit a liberal number of good b&w photos to accompany article. Uses 35mm or larger color transparencies for cover. Offers no additional payment for photos accompanying mss.
Tips: "Send concise, polite letter stating the topic to be covered in the story and the writer's qualifications. No 'cute' letters rambling on about some 'imaginative' story idea. Writers who have a concise yet readable style and know their topic are always appreciated. I am most interested in those who have personal collecting experience or can put together a knowledgable and informative feature after interviewing a serious collector/authority."

THE ARCTOPHILE, Bear-in-Mind, Inc., 20 Beharrell St., Concord MA 01742. (617)369-1167. Editor: Fran Lewis. Managing Editor: Barbara Fivek. 25% freelance written. Works with a small number of new/unpublished writers each year. Quarterly newsletter on Teddy Bears and Teddy Collecting. For adult Teddy Bear collectors who are interested in heartwarming or poignant tales about what Teddys mean to them or how they have helped to share feelings or comfort them in times of need. Circ. 10,000. Pays on publication. Publishes ms an average of 3 months after acceptance. Byline given. Buys first North American serial rights. Submit seasonal/holiday material 6 months in advance. Simultaneous, photocopied and previously published submissions OK. Computer printout submissions acceptable; no dot-matrix. Reports in 2 months. Sample copy for SAE and 1 first class stamp.
Nonfiction: Book excerpts, historical/nostalgic, humor, inspirational, interview/profile, personal experience and photo feature. Buys 12-24 mss/year. Send complete ms. Length: 300-500 words. Pays 4-6¢/word.
Fiction: Fantasy and humorous. Buys 12-24 mss/year. Send complete ms. Length: 300-500 words. Pays 4-6¢/word.
Poetry: Avant-garde, free verse, haiku, light verse and traditional. Buys 4 poems/year. Submit maximum 2 poems. Length: 6-10 lines. Pays $10-15.
Fillers: Jokes, gags, anecdotes, short humor and newsbreaks—all Teddy related. Buys 8-10/year. Length: 15-30 words. Pays $5-10.
Tips: Articles, and fiction and poetry submissions must be Teddy Bear related. Writing should be "direct and crisp."

BANK NOTE REPORTER, Krause Publications, 700 E. State St., Iola WI 54990. (715)445-2214. Editor: Courtney L. Coffing. 30% freelance written. Eager to work with new/unpublished writers. Monthly tabloid for advanced collectors of U.S. and world paper money. Circ. 4,250. Pays on acceptance. Publishes ms an average of 3 months after acceptance. Byline given. Buys first North American serial rights. Photocopied submissions acceptable. Electronic submissions OK with special arrangements. Computer printout submissions acceptable; prefers letter-quality to dot-matrix. Reports in 2 weeks. Free sample copy.
Nonfiction: "We review articles covering any phase of paper money collecting including investing, display, storage, history, art, story behind a particular piece of paper money and the business of paper money." News items not solicited. "Our staff covers the hard news." Buys 4 mss/issue. Send complete ms. Length: 500-3,000 words. Pays 3¢/word to first-time contributors; negotiates fee for later articles. Pays the expenses of writers on assignment.
Photos: Pays $5 minimum for 5x7 b&w glossy prints. Captions and model releases required.
Tips: "The writer has a better chance of breaking in at our publication with short articles and fillers due to the technical nature of the subject matter and sophistication of our readers. Material about bank notes used in a writer's locale would be interesting, useful, encouraged. We like new names."

‡**BASEBALL CARDS**, Krause Publications, 700 E. State St., Iola WI 54990. (715)445-2214. Editor: Bob Lemke. 50% freelance written. A bimonthly magazine covering sports memorabilia collecting. "Geared for the novice collector or general public who might become interested in the hobby." Circ. 100,000. Pays on acceptance. Publishes ms an average of 3 months after acceptance. Byline given. Buys first North American serial rights and second serial (reprint) rights. Submit seasonal/holiday material 6 months in advance. Photocopied submissions OK. Computer printout submissions acceptable; no dot-matrix. Reports in 1 week. Sample copy for 8½x11 SAE with 3 first class-stamps.
Nonfiction: General interest, historical/nostalgic, how-to (enjoy or enhance your collection) and photo feature. No personal reminiscences of collecting baseball cards as a kid or articles that relate to baseball, rather than cards. Buys 18 mss/year. Query. Length: 2,000-4,000 words. Pays up to $250.
Photos: Send photos with submission. Reviews contact sheets and transparencies. Offers no additional payment for photos accepted with ms. Identification of subjects required.
Tips: "The area of our publication most open to freelancers is feature articles."

THE BLADE MAGAZINE, Box 22007, Chattanooga TN 37422. Editor: J. Bruce Voyles. 90% freelance written. For knife enthusiasts who want to know as much as possible about quality knives and edged weapons. Bimonthly magazine. Pays on publication. Buys all rights. Submit seasonal/holiday material 6 months in advance. Previously published submissions OK. Computer printout submissions acceptable; no dot-matrix. Reports in 2 months. Sample copy $2.75.
Nonfiction: Historical (on knives and weapons); how-to; interview (knifemakers); celebrities who own knives; knives featured in movies with shots from the movie; etc., new product; nostalgia; personal experience; photo feature; profile and technical. No poetry. Buys 75 unsolicited mss/year. "We evaluate complete manuscripts and make our decision on that basis." Length: 1,000-2,000 words. Pays 5¢/word minimum, more for better writers.
Photos: Send photos with ms. Pays $5 for 8x10 b&w glossy prints, $25-75 for 35mm color transparencies. Captions required.
Tips: "The ideal article for us concerns a knife maker or a historical article on an old factory—full of well-researched long lost facts with entertaining anecdotes, or a piece bringing out the romance, legend, and love of man's oldest tool—the knife. We also like articles that place knives in people's hands—in life saving situations, adventure modes, etc. (Nothing gory or with the knife as the villain). People and knives are good copy. We are getting more and better written articles from writers who are reading the publication beforehand. That makes for a harder sell for the quickie writer not willing to do his work."

THE COIN ENTHUSIAST'S JOURNAL, Masongate Publishing, Box 1383, Torrance CA 90505. (213)378-4850. Editor: William J. Cook. 50% freelance written. Monthly newsletter covering numismatics (coin collecting) and bullion trading. "Our purpose is to give readers information to help them make sound investment decisions in the areas we cover and to help them get more enjoyment out of their hobby." Circ. 2,000+. Pays on publication. Publishes ms an average of 2 months after acceptance. Byline given. Offers $50 kill fee. Buys all rights. Submit seasonal/holiday material 3 months in advance. Simultaneous queries and simultaneous and photocopied submissions OK. Electronic submissions OK on Apple IIe, but requires hard copy. Computer printout submissions acceptable; prefers letter-quality to dot-matrix. Reports in 2-3 weeks on queries; 3 weeks on mss. Sample copy for SAE and 2 first class stamps; writer's guidelines for SAE and 1 first class stamp.
Nonfiction: How-to (make money from your hobby and be a better trader); opinion (what is the coin market going to do?); personal experience (insiders' "tricks of the trade"); and technical (why are coin prices going up [or down]?). No "crystal ball" predictions, i.e., "I see silver going up to $200 per ounce by mid-1987." Query with published clips. Length: 750-2,500 words. Buys 20 mss/year. Pays $100-250; fees negotiable. Also looking for "staff writers" who will submit material each month or bimonthly.
Photos: State availability of photos with query. Pays $5-25 for b&w prints. Buys one-time rights.
Tips: "We run very few short articles. Be able to show an in-depth knowledge and experience in numismatics and also show the ability to be creative in developing new ideas for the coin industry. Potential topics include gold and silver ratios, futures markets, advantages of buying silver coins instead of silver bars, what influences current prices, how taxes may affect the collector."

COINS, Krause Publications, 700 E. State St., Iola WI 54990. (715)445-2214. Editor: Arlyn G. Sieber. Monthly magazine about U.S. and foreign coins for all levels of collectors, investors and dealers. Circ. 65,000. Average issue includes 8 features.
Nonfiction: "We'd like to see articles on any phase of the coin hobby; collection, investing, displaying, history, art, the story behind the coin, unusual collections, profiles on dealers and the business of coins." No news items. "Our staff covers the hard news." Buys 8 mss/issue. Send complete ms. Computer printout submissions acceptable; prefers letter-quality to dot-matrix. Length: 500-5,000 words. Pays 3¢/word to first-time contributors; fee negotiated for later articles.
Photos: Pays $5 minimum for b&w prints. Pays $25 minimum for 35mm color transparencies used. Captions and model releases required. Buys first rights.

COLLECTOR EDITIONS QUARTERLY, Collector Communications Corp., 170 5th Ave., New York NY 10010. Editor: R. C. Rowe. 25% freelance written. Works with a small number of new/unpublished writers each year. Quarterly magazine for collectors, mostly aged 30-65 in any rural or suburban, affluent area; reasonably well-educated. Quarterly. Circ. 80,000. Rights purchased vary with author and material. Buys first North American serial rights, and sometimes second serial (reprint) rights. Buys 8-10 mss/year. "First assignments are always done on a speculative basis." Pays within 30 days of acceptance. Publishes ms an average of 6 months after acceptance. Photocopied submissions OK. Computer printout submissions acceptable; no dot-matrix. Query with sample photos. Reports in 2 months. Sample copy $2; writer's guidelines for SAE and 1 first class stamp.
Nonfiction: "Short features about collecting, written in tight, newsy style. We specialize in contemporary (postwar) collectibles. Particularly interested in items affected by scarcity; focus on glass and ceramics. Values for pieces being written about should be included." Informational, how-to, interview, profile, exposé, and nostalgia. Length: 500-2,500 words. Pays $100-300.
Columns/Departments: Columns cover stamps and coins, porcelain, glass, auction reports and artist profiles. Length: 750 words. Pays $75. Sometimes pays the expenses of writers on assignment.
Photos: B&w and color photos purchased with accompanying ms with no additional payment. Captions are required. "We want clear, distinct, full-frame images that say something."
Tips: "Unfamiliarity with the field is the most frequent mistake made by writers in completing an article for us."

COLLECTORS NEWS & THE ANTIQUE REPORTER, 506 2nd St., Box 156, Grundy Center IA 50638. (319)824-5456. Editor: Linda Kruger. 20% freelance written. Works with a small number of new/unpublished writers each year. A monthly tabloid covering antiques, collectibles and nostalgic memorabilia. Circ. 22,000. Publishes ms an average of 1 year after acceptance. Buys 100 mss/year. Byline given. Pays on publication. Buys first rights and makes work-for-hire assignments. Submit seasonal material (holidays) 3 months in advance. Computer printout submissions acceptable; no dot-matrix. Reports in 2 weeks on queries; 6 weeks on mss. Sample copy for $1.50 and 9x12 SAE; free writer's guidelines.
Nonfiction: General interest (any subject re: collectibles, antique to modern); historical/nostalgic (relating to collections or collectors); how-to (display your collection, care for, restore, appraise, locate, add to, etc.); interview/profile (covering individual collectors and their hobbies, unique or extensive; celebrity collectors, and limited edition artists); technical (in-depth analysis of a particular antique, collectible or collecting field); and travel (coverage of special interest or regional shows, seminars, conventions—or major antique shows, flea markets; places collectors can visit, tours they can take, museums, etc.). Special issues include January and June show/flea market issues; and usual seasonal emphasis. Buys 100-150 mss/year. Query with sample of writing. Length: 1,200-1,600 words. Pays 75¢/ column inch; $1/column inch for color features.
Photos: Reviews b&w prints and 35mm color slides. Payment for photos included in payment for ms. Captions required. Buys first rights.
Tips: Articles most open to freelancers are on celebrity collectors; collectors with unique and/or extensive collections; transportation collectibles; advertising collectibles; bottles; glass, china & silver; primitives; furniture; toys; political collectibles; and movie memorabilia.

DOLLS, The Collector's Magazine, Collector Communications Corp., 170 5th Ave., New York NY 10010. (212)989-8700. Editor: Krystyna Poray Goddu. 75% freelance written. Works with a small number of new/unpublished writers each year. Bimonthly magazine covering doll collecting "for collectors of antique, contemporary and reproduction dolls. We publish well-researched, professionally written articles that are illustrated with photographs of high quality, color or black-and-white." Circ. 55,000. Pays within 30 days of acceptance. Publishes ms an average of 6 months after acceptance. Byline given. "Almost all first manuscripts are on speculation. We rarely kill assigned stories, but fee would be about 33% of article fee." Buys first serial rights, first North American serial rights ("almost always"), second serial rights if piece has appeared in a non-competing

66 *Our local library was the place I loved best next to home and I wanted to be up there rubbing shoulders on the shelves. I wanted to have written a book. More than twenty years later I realized that if I ever wished to live that ambition I had to write.* **99**

Dorothy Cannell

publication. Submit seasonal/holiday material 6 months in advance. Photocopied submissions considered (not preferred); previously published submissions OK. Computer printout submissions acceptable; no dot-matrix. Reports in 2 months. Sample copy $2; writer's guidelines for SAE and 1 first class stamp.

Nonfiction: Book excerpts; historical (with collecting angle); interview/profile (on collectors with outstanding collections); new product (just photos and captions; "we do not pay for these, but regard them as publicity"); opinion ("A Personal Definition of Dolls"); technical (doll restoration advice by experts only); and travel (museums and collections around the world). "No sentimental, uninformed 'my doll collection' or 'my grandma's doll collection' stories or trade magazine-type stories on shops, etc. Our readers are knowledgeable collectors." Query with clips. Length: 500-2,500 words. Pays $100-350. Sometimes pays expenses of writers on assignment.

Photos: Send photos with accompanying query or ms. Reviews 4x5 color transparencies; 4x5 or 8x10 b&w prints. "We do not buy photographs submitted without manuscripts unless we have assigned them; we pay for the manuscript/photos package in one fee." Captions required. Buys one-time rights.

Columns/Departments: Doll Views—a miscellany of news and views of the doll world includes reports on upcoming or recently held events; possibly reviews of new books. "*Not* the place for new dolls, auction prices or dates; we have regular contributors or staff assigned to those columns." Query with clips if available or send complete ms. Length: 200-500 words. Pays $25-75. Doll Views items are rarely bylined.

Fillers: "We don't really use fillers but would consider it if we got something very good. Hints on restoring, for example, or a nice illustration." Length: 500 words maximum. Pays $25-75.

Tips: "We need experts in the field who are also good writers. The most frequent mistake made by writers in completing an article assignment for us is being unfamiliar with the field; our readers are very knowledgeable. Freelancers who are not experts should know their particular story thoroughly and do background research to get the facts correct. Well-written queries from writers outside NYC area especially welcome. Non-experts should stay away from technical-or-specific-subjects-(restoration; price trends). Short profiles of unusual collectors or a story of a local museum collection, with good photos, might catch our interest. Editors want to know they are getting something from a writer they cannot get from anyone else. Good writing should be a given, a starting point. After that, it's what you know."

EARLY AMERICAN LIFE, Historical Times, Inc., Box 8200, Harrisburg PA 17105. Editor: Frances Carnahan. 70% freelance written. For "people who are interested in capturing the warmth and beauty of the 1600 to 1900 period and using it in their homes and lives today. They are interested in arts, crafts, travel, restoration, and collecting." Bimonthly magazine, 100 pages. Circ. 350,000. Buys all rights. Buys 50 mss/year. Pays on acceptance. Photocopied submissions OK. Free sample copy and writer's guidelines. Reports in 1 month. Query or submit complete ms.

Nonfiction: "Social history (the story of the people, not epic heroes and battles), crafts such as woodworking and needlepoint, travel to historic sites, country inns, antiques and reproductions, refinishing and restoration, architecture and decorating. We try to entertain as we inform and always attempt to give the reader something he can do. While we're always on the lookout for good pieces on any of our subjects, the 'travel to historic sites' theme is most frequently submitted. Would like to see more how-to-do-it (well-illustrated) on how real people did something great to their homes." Length: 750-3,000 words. Pays $50-400.

Photos: Pays $10 for 5x7 (and up) b&w photos used with mss, minimum of $25 for color. Prefers 2¼x2¼ and up, but can work from 35mm.

Tips: "Our readers are eager for ideas on how to bring the warmth and beauty of early America into their lives. Conceive a new approach to satisfying their related interests in arts, crafts, travel to historic sites, and especially in houses decorated in the early American style. Write to entertain and inform at the same time, and be prepared to help us with illustrations, or sources for them."

FIBERARTS, The Magazine of Textiles, 50 College St., Asheville NC 28801. (704)253-0467. Editor: Kate Pulleyn. 75% freelance written. Works with a small number of new/unpublished writers each year. Bimonthly magazine covering textiles as art and craft (weaving, quilting, surface design, stitchery, knitting, fashion, crochet, etc.) for textile artists, craftspeople, hobbyists, teachers, museum and gallery staffs, collectors and enthusiasts. Circ. 26,000. Pays on publication. Publishes ms an average of 4 months after acceptance. Byline given. Rights purchased are negotiable. Submit seasonal/holiday material 8 months in advance. Editorial guidelines and style sheet available. Computer printout submissions acceptable; prefers letter-quality to dot-matrix. Reporting time varies. Sample copy $3; writer's guidelines for SASE with 39¢ postage.

Nonfiction: Book excerpts; historical/nostalgic; how-to; humor; interview/profile; opinion; personal experience; photo feature; technical; travel (for the textile enthusiast, e.g., collecting rugs in Turkey); and education, trends, exhibition reviews and textile news. Buys 25-50 mss/year. Query. "Please be very specific about your proposal. Also an important consideration in accepting an article is the kind of photos—35mm slides and/or b&w glossies—that you can provide as illustration. We like to see photos in advance." Length: 250-1,200 words. Pays $40-250/article. Sometimes (rarely) pays the expenses of writers on assignment.

Tips: "Our writers are very familiar with the textile field, and this is what we look for in a new writer. Familiarity with textile techniques, history, or events determines clarity of an article more than a particular style of writing. The writer should also be familiar with *Fiberarts*, the magazine. We outline our upcoming issues in regular Editorial Agendas far enough in advance for a prospective writer to be aware of our future needs."

FINESCALE MODELER, Kalmbach Publishing Co., 1027 N. 7th St., Milwaukee WI 53233. (414)272-2060. Editor: Bob Hayden. 80% freelance written. Eager to work with new/unpublished writers. Bimonthly magazine "devoted to how-to-do-it modeling information for scale modelbuilders who build non-operating aircraft, tanks, boats, automobiles, figures, dioramas, and science fiction and fantasy models." Circ. 50,000. Pays on acceptance. Publishes ms an average of 1 year after acceptance. Byline given. Buys all rights. Computer printout submissions acceptable; prefers letter-quality to dot-matrix. Reports in 1 month on queries; 2 months on miss. Sample copy for 9x12 SAE and 3 first class stamps; free writer's guidelines.
Nonfiction: How-to (build scale models); and technical (research information for building models). Query or send complete ms. Length: 750-3,000 words. Pays $30/published page minimum.
Photos: Send photos with ms. Pays $7.50 minimum for color transparencies and $5 minimum for 5x7 b&w prints. Captions and identification of subjects required. Buys one-time rights.
Columns/Departments: FSM Showcase (photos plus description of model); and FSM Tips and Techniques (modelbuilding hints and tips). Buys 25-50 Tips and Techniques/year. Query or send complete ms. Length: 100-1,000 words. Pays $5-75.
Tips: "A freelancer can best break in first through hints and tips, then through feature articles. Most people who write for FSM are modelers first, writers second. This is a specialty magazine for a special, quite expert audience. Essentially, 99% of our writers will come from that audience."

GEMS AND MINERALS, 555 Cajon St., B, Redlands CA 92373. (714)798-3585. Editor: Jack R. Cox. Works with a small number of new/unpublished writers each year; eager to work with new/unpublished writers. Monthly for the professional and amateur gem cutter, jewelry maker, mineral collector and rockhound. Buys first North American serial rights. Byline given. Pays on publication. Query. Reports in 1 month. Computer printout submissions acceptable; prefers letter-quality to dot-matrix. Free sample copy and writer's guidelines.
Nonfiction: Material must have how-to slant. No personality stories. Field trips to mineral or gem collecting localities used; must be accurate and give details so they can be found. Instructions on how to cut gems; design and creation of jewelry. 4-8 typed pages plus illustrations preferred, but do not limit if subject is important. Frequently, good articles are serialized if too long for one issue. Buys 75-120 unsolicited mss/year. Pays 50¢/inch for text.
Photos: Pays for b&w prints as part of text. Pays $1/inch for color photos as published.
Tips: "Because we are a specialty magazine, it is difficult for a writer to prepare a suitable story for us unless he is familiar with the subject matter: jewelry making, gem cutting, mineral collecting and display, and fossil collecting. Our readers want accurate instructions on how to do it and where they can collect gemstones and minerals in the field. The majority of our articles are purchased from freelance writers, most of whom are hobbyists (rockhounds) or have technical knowledge of one of the subjects. Infrequently, a freelancer with a knowledge of the subject interviews an expert (gem cutter, jewelry maker, etc.) and gets what this expert tells him down on paper for a good how-to article. However, the problem here is that if the expert neglects to mention all the steps in his process, the writer does not realize it. Then, there is a delay while we check it out. My best advice to a freelance writer is to send for a sample copy of our magazine and author's specification sheet which will tell him what we need. We are interested in helping new writers and try to answer them personally, giving any pointers that we think will be of value to them. Let us emphasize that our readers want how-to and where-to stories. They are not at all interested in personality sketches about one of their fellow hobbyists."

HANDWOVEN, from Interweave Press, 306 N. Washington, Loveland CO 80537. (303)669-7672. Managing Editor: Jane Patrick. 75% freelance written. Bimonthly magazine (except July) covering handweaving, spinning and dyeing. Audience includes "practicing textile craftsmen. Article should show considerable depth of knowledge of subject, although tone should be informal and accessible." Circ. 32,000. Pays on publication. Publishes ms an average of 8 months after acceptance. Byline given. Pays 50% kill fee. Buys first North American serial rights. Simultaneous queries and photocopied submissions OK. Computer printout submissions acceptable; prefers letter-quality to dot-matrix. Sample copy $4.50; writer's guidelines for SASE.
Nonfiction: Historical and how-to (on weaving and other craft techniques; specific items with instructions); and technical (on handweaving, spinning and dyeing technology). "All articles must contain a high level of in-depth information. Our readers are very knowledgeable about these subjects." Query. Length: 500-2,000 words. Pays $35-150.
Photos: State availability of photos. Identification of subjects required.
Tips: "We're particularly interested in articles about new weaving and spinning techniques as well as applying these techniques to finished products."

HOME MECHANIX, (Formerly *Mechanix Illustrated*), 1515 Broadway, New York NY 10036. (212)719-6630. Editor: Joseph R. Provey. Executive Editor: Harry Wicks. Managing Editor: Peter Easton. 50% freelance written. "If it's good, we're interested, whether writer is new or experienced." Monthly magazine for the home and car manager. "Articles on maintenance, repair, and renovation to the home and family car. Information on how to buy, how to select products useful to homeowners/car owners. Emphasis in home-oriented articles is on good design, inventive solutions to styling and space problems, useful home-workshop projects." Circ. 1.6 million. Pays on acceptance. Publishes ms an average of 6 months after acceptance. Byline given. Buys first North American copy rights. Computer printout submissions acceptable; no dot-matrix. Query.

Nonfiction: Feature articles relating to homeowner/car owner, 1,500-2,500 words. "This may include personal home-renovation projects, professional advice on interior design, reports on different or unusual construction methods, energy-related subjects, outdoor/backyard projects, etc. We are no longer interested in high-tech subjects such as aerospace, electronics, photography or military hardware. Most of our automotive features are written by experts in the field, but fillers, tips, how-to repair, or modification articles on the family car are welcome. Workshop articles on furniture, construction, tool use, refinishing techniques, etc., are also sought. Pays $300 minimum for features; fees based on number of printed pages, photos accompanying mss., etc." Sometimes pays expenses of writers on assignment.

Photos: Photos should accompany mss. Pays $600 and up for transparencies for cover. Inside color: $300/1 page, $500/2, $700/3, etc. Home and Shop hints illustrated with 1 photo, $40. Captions and model releases required.

Fillers: Tips and fillers useful to tool users or for general home maintenance. Pays $25 and up for illustrated and captioned fillers.

Tips: "The most frequent mistake made by writers in completing an article assignment for *Home Mechanix* is not taking the time to understand its editorial focus and special needs."

THE HOME SHOP MACHINIST, The Home Shop Machinist, Inc., 2779 Aero Park Dr., Box 1810, Traverse City MI 49685. (616)946-3712. Editor: Joe D. Rice. 95% freelance written. Bimonthly magazine covering machining and metalworking for the hobbyist. Circ. 19,000. Pays on publication. Publishes ms an average of 1 year after acceptance. Byline given. Buys first North American serial rights only. Simultaneous submissions OK. Computer printout submissions acceptable; prefers letter-quality to dot-matrix. Reports in 3 weeks. Free sample copy and writer's guidelines.

Nonfiction: How-to (projects designed to upgrade present shop equipment or hobby model projects that require machining); and technical (should pertain to metalworking, machining, drafting, layout, welding or foundry work for the hobbyist). No fiction. Buys 50 mss/year. Query or send complete ms. Length: open— "whatever it takes to do a thorough job." Pays $40/published page, plus $9/published photo; $70/page for camera-ready art; and $40 for b&w cover photo.

Photos: Send photos with ms. Pays $9-40 for 5x7 b&w prints. Captions and identification of subjects required.

Columns/Departments: Welding; Sheetmetal; Book Reviews; New Product Reviews; Micro-Machining; and Foundry. "Writer should become familiar with our magazine before submitting. Query first." Buys 8 mss/year. Length: 600-1,500 words. Pays $40-70.

Fillers: Machining tips/shortcuts. Buys 12-15/year. Length: 100-300 words. Pays $30-48.

Tips: "The writer should be experienced in the area of metalworking and machining; should be extremely thorough in explanations of methods, processes—always with an eye to safety; and should provide good quality b&w photos and/or clear drawings to aid in description. Visuals are of increasing importance to our readers. Carefully planned photos, drawings and charts will carry a submission to our magazine much farther along the path to publication."

‡THE LEATHER CRAFTSMAN, Target Marketing and Publishing, Box 1386, Fort Worth TX 76101. (817)560-2396. Editor: Stanley Cole. Managing Editor: Nancy Sawyer. 90% freelance written. Eager to work with new/unpublished writers. A bimonthly magazine covering leathercrafting or leather art. "We are dedicated to the preservation of leather craft and leather art. Each issue contains articles on prominent leather crafters, helpful hints and projects that our readers try at home or in their businesses." Circ. 25,000. Pays on publication. Publishes ms an average of 3 months after acceptance. Byline given. Buys all rights. Submit seasonal/holiday material 6 months in advance. Computer printout submissions acceptable; prefers letter-quality to dot-matrix. Reports in 2 weeks on queries; 1 month on mss. Sample copy $2.25; free writer's guidelines.

Nonfiction: How-to on leathercrafting projects. No articles not related to leather in some way. Send complete ms. Pays $50-200.

Photos: Send photos or completed project with submission. Reviews transparencies and prints. Offers no additional payment for photos accepted with ms. Captions required.

Tips: "*The Leather Craftsman* is dedicated to the preservation of leather craft and leather art. All aspects of the craft including carving, stamping, dyeing, sewing, decorating, etc., are presented to our readers through the use of step by step instructions."

LIVE STEAM, Live Steam, Inc., 2779 Aero Park Dr., Box 629, Traverse City MI 49685. (616)941-7160. Editor: Joe D. Rice. 60% freelance written. Eager to work with new/unpublished writers. Monthly magazine covering steam-powered models and full-size engines (i.e., locomotives, traction, cars, boats, stationary, etc.)

"Our readers are hobbyists, many of whom are building their engines from scratch. We are interested in anything that has to do with the world of live steam-powered machinery." Circ. 12,800. Pays on publication. Publishes ms an average of 10 months after acceptance. Byline given. Buys first North American serial rights only. Simultaneous submissions OK. Computer printout submissions acceptable. Reports in 3 weeks. Free sample copy and writer's guidelines.

Nonfiction: Historical/nostalgic; how-to (build projects powered by steam); new product; personal experience; photo feature; and technical (must be within the context of steam-powered machinery or on machining techniques). No fiction. Buys 50 mss/year. Query or send complete ms. Length: 500-3,000 words. Pays $30/published page—$500 maximum. Sometimes pays the expenses of writers on assignment.

Photos: Send photos with ms. Pays $50/page of finished art. Pays $8 for 5x7 b&w prints; $40 for cover (color). Captions and identification of subjects required.

Columns/Departments: Steam traction engines, steamboats, stationary steam, and steam autos. Buys 6-8 mss/year. Query. Length: 1,000-3,000 words. Pays $20-50.

Tips: "At least half of all our material is from the freelancer. Requesting a sample copy and author's guide will be a good place to start. The writer must be well-versed in the nature of live steam equipment and the hobby of scale modeling such equipment. Technical and historical accuracy is an absolute must. Often, good articles are weakened or spoiled by mediocre to poor quality photos. Freelancers must learn to take a *good* photograph."

LOOSE CHANGE, Mead Publishing Corp., 21176 Alameda St., Long Beach CA 90810. (213)549-0730. Publisher: Daniel R. Mead. 20% freelance written. Eager to work with a small number of new/unpublished writers each year. Monthly magazine covering gaming and coin-op machines. Slot machines; trade stimulators; jukeboxes; gumball and peanut vendors; pinballs; scales, etc. "Our audience is predominantly male. Readers are all collectors or enthusiasts of coin-operated machines, particularly slot machines and jukeboxes. Subscribers are, in general, not heavy readers." Circ. 3,000. Pays on acceptance. Publishes ms an average of 2 months after acceptance. Byline given. Prefers to buy all rights, but also buys first and reprint rights. "We may allow author to reprint upon request in noncompetitive publications." Photocopied submissions OK. Previously published submissions must be accompanied by complete list of previous sales, including sale dates. Computer printout acceptable; prefers letter-quality to dot-matrix. Reports in 1 month on queries; 6 weeks on mss. Sample copy $1; free writer's guidelines.

Nonfiction: Historical/nostalgic, how-to, interview/profile, opinion, personal experience, photo feature and technical. "Articles illustrated with clear, black and white photos are always considered much more favorably than articles without photos (we have a picture-oriented audience). The writer must be knowledgable about subject matter because our readers are knowledgeable and will spot inaccuracies." Buys up to 50 mss/year. Length: 900-6,000 words; 3,500-12,000, cover stories. Pays $100 maximum, inside stories; $200 maximum, cover stories.

Photos: "Captions should tell a complete story without reference to the body text." Send photos with ms. Reviews 8x10 b&w glossy prints. Captions required. "Purchase price for articles includes payment for photos."

Fiction: "All fiction must have a gambling/coin-operated-machine angle. Very low emphasis is placed on fiction. Fiction must be exceptional to be acceptable to our readers." Buys maximum 6 mss/year. Send complete ms. Length: 800-2,500 words. Pays $60 maximum.

LOST TREASURE, 15115 S. 76th E. Ave., Bixby OK 74008. Managing Editor: James D. Watts, Jr. 95% freelance written. For treasure hunting hobbyists, relic collectors, amateur prospectors and miners. Monthly magazine; 72 pages. Circ. 55,000. Buys first rights only. Byline given. Buys 100 mss/year. Pays on publication. Will consider photocopied submissions. No simultaneous submissions. Computer printout submissions acceptable. Reports in 2 months. Submit complete ms. Publishes ms an average of 2 months after acceptance. Sample copy and writer's guidelines for 9x12 SASE.

Nonfiction: How-to articles about treasure hunting, coinshooting, personal, profiles, and stories about actual hunts, stories that give an unusual twist to treasure hunting—using detectors in an unorthodox way, odd sidelights on history, unusual finds. *Avoid* writing about the more famous treasures and lost mines. No bottle hunting stories. Length: 1,000-3,000 words. "If an article is well-written and covers its subject well, we'll buy it—regardless of length." Pays 3¢/word.

Photos: Pays $5-10 for b&w glossy prints purchased with mss. Captions required.

Tips: "Read *Lost Treasure* before submitting your stories. We are especially interested in stories that deal with the more unusual aspects of treasure hunting and metal detecting. Try to avoid the obvious—give something different. Also—good photos and graphics are a *must*."

Market conditions are constantly changing! If this is 1988 or later, buy the newest edition of Writer's Market *at your favorite bookstore or order directly from* Writer's Digest Books.

‡McCALL'S NEEDLEWORK & CRAFTS MAGAZINE, 825 7th Ave. (7th fl.), New York NY 10019. Managing Editor: Rosemary Maceiras. Bimonthly. All rights bought for original needlework and handicraft designs.
Nonfiction: Submit preliminary color photos for editorial consideration. Accepted made-up items must be accompanied by directions, diagrams and charts. Payment ranges from a few dollars to a few hundred dollars.

‡THE MAGAZINE ANTIQUES, Brant Publications, 980 Madison Ave., New York NY 10021. (212)734-9797. Editor/Publisher: Wendell Garrett. Managing Editor: Alfred Mayor. "We are backlogged with submissions and prefer not to receive unsolicited submissions at this time."

MINIATURE COLLECTOR, Collector Communications Corp., 170 5th Ave., New York NY 10010. (212)989-8700. Editor: Krystyna Poray Goddu. Managing Editor: Louise Fecher. 25% freelance written. Works with a small number of new/unpublished writers each year. Bimonthly magazine; 64 pages. Circ. 35,000. Byline given. Buys first North American serial rights and occasionally second (reprint) rights to material originally published elsewhere. Pays within 30 days of acceptance. Publishes ms an average of 4 months after acceptance. Submit seasonal/holiday material 4 months in advance. Photocopied and previously published submissions OK. Computer printout submissions acceptable; no dot-matrix. Reports in 2 months. Sample copy $2.
Nonfiction: Louise Fecher, managing editor. How-to (detailed furniture and accessories projects in l/12th scale with accurate patterns and illustrations); interview (with miniaturists, well-established collectors, museum curators; include pictures); new product (very short-caption type pieces—no payment); photo feature (show reports, heavily photographic, with captions stressing pieces and availability of new and unusual pieces); and profile (of collectors, with photos). Buys 1-2 mss/issue. Query. Length: 800-1,200 words. Pays $100-175. "Most short pieces, such as news stories, are staff written. We welcome both short and long (1,000 words) stories from freelancers." First-manuscripts-usually-on-speculation=Sometimes pays-the-expenses of writers on assignment.
Photos: Louise Fecher, managing editor. Send photos with ms; usually buys photo/manuscript package. Buys one-time rights. Captions required.
Tips: "The most frequent mistake made by writers submitting an article to us is that they write with too general a focus; our magazine is for a highly specialized audience, so familiarity with miniatures is a very big plus. Many writers are also unaware of the high quality of the pieces featured in our magazine."

MODEL RAILROADER, 1027 N. 7th St., Milwaukee WI 53233. Editor: Russell G. Larson. For hobbyists interested in scale model railroading. Monthly. Buys exclusive rights. Study publication before submitting material. Reports on submissions within 1 month. Query.
Nonfiction: Wants construction articles on specific model railroad projects (structures, cars, locomotives, scenery, benchwork, etc.). Also photo stories showing model railroads. First-hand knowledge of subject almost always necessary for acceptable slant. Pays base rate of $66/page.
Photos: Buys photos with detailed descriptive captions only. Pays $7.50 and up, depending on size and use. Color: double b&w rate. Full color cover: $210.

‡MOUNTAIN STATES COLLECTOR, Spree Publishing, Box 2525, Evergreen CO 80439. (303)674-1848. Editor: Carol Fertig. Managing Editor: Peg DeStefano. 75% freelance written. A monthly tabloid covering antiques and collectibles. Circ. 8,000. Pays on publication. Publishes ms an average of 2 months after acceptance. Byline given. Not copyrighted. Buys first rights, one-time rights or second serial (reprint) rights to material published elsewhere. Submit seasonal/holiday material at least 3 months in advance. Simultaneous and previously published submissions OK. Computer printout submissions acceptable; prefers letter-quality to dot-matrix. Reports in 3-6 weeks. Sample copy for 9x12 SAE with 4 first class stamps; writer's guidelines for SASE.
Nonfiction: Book excerpts, historical/nostalgic, how-to (collect), interview/profile (of collectors) and photo feature. Buys 75 mss/year. Query with or without published clips, or send complete ms. Length: 500-1,500 words. Pays $5-15. Sometimes pays the expenses of writers on assignment.
Photos: Send photos with submission. Reviews contact sheets, and 5x7 b&w prints. Offers $5/photo used. Captions required. Buys one-time rights.
Tips: "Writers should know their topics well or be prepared to do in-depth interviews with collectors. Prefer down home approach. We need articles on antiques and on collectors and collections; how-to articles on collecting; how a collector can get started; or clubs for collectors."

NATIONAL KNIFE MAGAZINE, Official Journal of the National Knife Collectors Association, Box 21070, Chattanooga TN 37421. (615)899-9456. Editor/Publisher: James V. Allday. 100% freelance written. Prefers to work with published/established writers; works with a small number of new/unpublished writers each year. Monthly magazine covering knife collection, manufacturing, hand crafting, selling, buying, trading; stresses "integrity in all dealings involving knives and bladed tools/weapons." Circ. 16,000+. Pays on publication. Publishes ms an average of 3 months after acceptance. Byline given. Buys all rights. Submit sea-

sonal/holiday material 3 months in advance. Computer printout submissions acceptable; prefers letter-quality to dot-matrix. Sample copy for 9x12 SAE and 6 first class stamps; writer's guidelines for business size SAE and 1 first class stamp.
Nonfiction: Analytical pieces, book reviews, general interest, historical, how-to, humor, interview/profile, new product, personal experience, photo feature, technical, and excerpts. Buys 50+ mss/year. Query with clips of published work. Length: 500-1,500 words. Pays 7¢ or more (negotiable)/word. No kill fee. Sometimes pays the expenses of writers on assignments.
Photos: State availability of photos. Pays $7 for 5x7 prints. Captions and identification of subjects required.
Fillers: Anecdotes. Buys 10/year. Length: open. Pays $25.
Tips: "Get acquainted with the knife world and knife specialists by attending a knife show or the National Knife Museum in Chattanooga. We're a feature magazine aimed at knife collectors/investors."

NEEDLE & THREAD, Bassion Publishing, 4949 Byers, Ft. Worth TX 76107. (817)732-7494. Editor: Margaret Dittman. "We are backlogged with submissions and prefer not to receive unsolicited submissions at this time."

‡NEEDLECRAFT FOR TODAY, Happy Hands Publishing, 4949 Byers, Ft. Worth TX 76107. (817)923-9081. Editor: Charlie Davis. Editorial Director: Joyce Bennett. 90% freelance written. Eager to work with new/unpublished writers. Bimonthly magazine for needlecraft enthusiasts. Circ. 1,200,000. Pays on acceptance "of total project." Publishes ms an average of 4 months after acceptance. Designer credit given. Buys negotiable rights. Submit seasonal/holiday material 1 year in advance. Computer printout submissions acceptable "so long as it's black and clear enough for a typesetter to read"; prefers letter-quality to dot-matrix. Reports in 6 weeks. Sample copy $3; free writer's guidelines with SASE.
Nonfiction: "Crochet, needlepoint, quilting, counted cross-stitch, knitting and dollmaking are used in basically every issue. Any fiber project is of interest to us, including fashions, wall hangings, home decorative items and toys—but of the highest quality and workmanship. How-to must be originally designed project. Provide a finished sample, chart, pattern, list of material and instructions." Buys 240 mss/year. Length: average 1,500 words. Pays "by arrangement, depending on the project."
Photos: "We photograph most finished projects ourselves." Send color photos with query.
Columns/Departments: Forum, guest speaker on any subject of interest to needlecrafters; Needlecraft Principles, explains a craft to a beginner. Send complete ms. Pays $100-200.
Tips: "Writer must be able to write very clear step-by-step instructions for original projects submitted. We seek small bazaar items to advanced projects made from commercially available materials. Be an experienced needlecrafter."

‡NEEDLEPOINT NEWS, EGW International Corp., Box 5967, Concord CA 94524. (415)671-9852. Editor: Jennifer Klein. A bimonthly magazine covering needlepoint. Circ. 15,000. Pays on publication. Publishes ms an average of 6 months after acceptance. Byline given. Buys first North American serial rights. Submit seasonal/holiday material 3 months in advance. Simultaneous queries and submissions, and photocopied submissions OK. Computer printout submissions acceptable. Reports in 6 weeks. Sample copy $2 with 9x12 SAE and 90¢ postage; writer's guidelines for #10 SAE and 1 first class stamp.
Nonfiction: How-to, interview/profile, new product, personal experience, photo feature, and technical. Buys 50 mss/year. Query with or without published clips. Length: 500-1,500 words. Pays $35/published page; pays $70/published page for two-time rights.
Photos: Send photos with accompanying query or ms. Reviews color negatives, 4x5 transparencies, and 5x7 b&w prints. Pays $25 maximum. Captions and identification of subjects required. Buys one-time rights.
Tips: "*Needlepoint News* is devoted exclusively to the art of needlepoint. For the most part we are a forum in which readers can exchange special tips, techniques, and designs with others in the needlepoint arena. We look for articles on any subject related to needlepoint that aids the stitcher. In the past, we have published a wealth of topics, brief and extensive, and some in a series. We also provide information for the serious stitcher on how to sell one's work, open a business or pass the EGA exam."

NOSTALGIA WORLD, for Collectors and Fans, Box 231, North Haven CT 06473. (203)269-8502. Editor: Bonnie Roth. Managing Editor: Stanley N. Lozowski. 50-75% freelance written. Works with a small number of new/unpublished writers each year; eager to work with new/unpublished writers. Bimonthly tabloid covering entertainment collectibles. "Our readership is interested in articles on all eras—everything from early Hollywood, the big bands, country/Western, rock 'n' roll to jazz, pop, and rhythm and blues. Many of our readers belong to fan clubs." Circ. 5,000. Pays on publication. Publishes ms an average of 8 months after acceptance. Byline given. Buys all rights, one-time rights, second serial (reprint) rights, and simultaneous rights. Submit seasonal/holiday material 6 months in advance. Simultaneous queries, and simultaneous, photocopied, and previously published submissions OK. Computer printout submissions acceptable; prefers letter-quality to dot-matrix. Reports in 1 month on queries; 6 weeks on mss. Sample copy $2; writer's guidelines for legal size SAE and 1 first class stamp.

Nonfiction: Historical/nostalgic; how-to (get started in collecting); and interview/profile (of movie, recording, or sport stars). "Articles must be aimed toward the collector and provide insight into a specific area of collecting. *Nostalgiaworld* readers collect records, gum cards, toys, sheet music, movie magazines, posters and memorabilia, personality items, comics, baseball, and sports memorabilia. We do *not* cater to antiques, glass, or other nonentertainment collectibles. Buys 20-30 unsolicited mss/year."

Photos: Send photos with ms. Pays $5-15 for 5x7 b&w prints; reviews b&w contact sheets. Captions and identification of subjects required. Buys all rights.

Columns/Departments: Video Memories (early TV); and 78 RPM-For Collectors Only (advice and tips for the collector of 78 RPM recordings; prices, values, outstanding rarities). Buys varying number of mss/year. Query or send complete ms. Length: 500-1,500 words. Pays $10-25.

Tips: "We have purchased numerous articles from beginning writers who have contacted us through *Writer's Market*. Most of the articles we reject are from writers who *do not read our requirements* and "think" they know what we want. One sample issue will illustrate what we are looking for. We look forward to working with new writers, and find they supply us with some of our best material."

NUTSHELL NEWS, for the complete miniatures hobbyist, Boynton & Associates, Inc., Clifton House, Clifton VA 22024. (703)830-1000. Editor: Bonnie Schroeder. Assistant Editor: Mel Frantz. 90% freelance written. A monthly magazine covering 1" scale dollhouse miniatures. "All articles must be related to the miniatures field. We do not use first-person submissions, and prefer a personal slant of the subject, with quotes. Our readers want to feel they know the subject after reading the article." Circ. 30,000. Pays on publication. Publishes ms an average of 1 year after acceptance. Byline given. Offers $25 kill fee. Buys all rights. Submit seasonal/holiday material 6 months in advance. Computer printout submissions acceptable; prefers letter-quality to dot-matrix. Reports in 2 months on queries; 3 months on mss. Sample copy $3; free writer's guidelines.

Nonfiction: How-to (on making miniatures) and interview/profile. "No articles that do not deal with quality hand-crafted miniatures." Buys 175 mss/year. Query with published clips. Length: 600-2,000 words. Pays 10¢/word.

Photos: Send photos with submission. Reviews 35mm transparencies. Offers 10¢/color photo and $7.50/b&w.

Columns/Departments: Book Reviews (books dealing directly with the miniatures field or reference books that can be used by miniaturists when reproducing full-size items), 100-300 words. Buys 30 mss/year. Send complete ms.

Tips: "Our readership is dedicated to this magazine and their hobby, and want to see articles on fine craftsmanship and outstanding miniatures collections. Even though this is an expensive hobby, our readers already know this, so don't stress 'dollars.' Artisan profiles, articles on collections, miniatures related how-to articles are areas most open to freelancers. How-tos should have step-by-step instructions with photos and diagrams. Articles on miniatures museums and miniatures show coverage are also accepted, as well as articles on decorating styles and periods."

OLD CARS PRICE GUIDE, Krause Publications, 700 E. State St., Iola WI 54990. (715)445-2214. Editor: Dennis Schrimpf. 5% freelance written. Eager to work with new/unpublished writers. Bimonthly magazine of old car prices for old car hobbyists and investors. Circ. 90,000. Pays on acceptance. Publishes ms an average of 2 months after acceptance. Byline given. Buys first North American serial rights. Submit seasonal/holiday material 3 months in advance. Computer printout submissions acceptable; prefers letter-quality to dot-matrix. Reports in 1 week. Sample copy $2.25 and 8x10 SASE.

Nonfiction: How-to (buy and sell collector cars); opinion (on car values market); technical (how to fix a car to increase value); and investment angles. "All articles should be car-value related and include information or actual price lists on recent sales (of more than one car). Articles about brands or types of cars *not* covered in regular price lists are preferred. Plenty of research and knowledge of the old car marketplace is usually essential. Photos required with all articles. No historic or nostalgic pieces." Buys 15-20 mss/year. Send complete ms. Length: 600-1,000 words. Pays $75-150.

Photos: Send photos with ms. Pays $50 minimum for 4x4 color transparencies used on cover; $5 for b&w prints; "undetermined for color." Captions and identification of subjects required. Buys one-time rights.

OLD CARS WEEKLY, Krause Publications, 700 E. State St., Iola WI 54990. (715)445-2214. Editor: John Gunnell. 40% freelance written. Weekly tabloid; 44-48 pages. Circ. 80,000. Pays on publication. Buys all rights. Phone queries OK. Byline given. Reports in 2 weeks. Sample copy $1.

Nonfiction: Short (2-3 pages) timely news reports on old car hobby with 1 photo. Buys 20 mss/issue. Query. Pays 3¢/word.

Photos: Pays $5 for 5x7 b&w glossy prints. Captions required. Buys all rights.

Fillers: Newsbreaks. Buys 50/year. Pays 3¢/word. Pays $10 bonus for usable news tips.

Tips: "We have converted basically to a news package and buy only news. This would include post-event coverage of antique auto shows, summary reports on auctions with list of prices realized, and 'hard' news concerning old cars or people in the hobby."

‡PIPE SMOKER, Journal of Kapnismology, Pipe Collectors International Inc., 6172 Airways Blvd., Box 22085, Chattanooga TN 37422. (615)892-7277. Editor: C. Bruce Spencer. 20% freelance written. A quarterly magazine about collecting smoking pipes and tobacciana. Features articles relative to the past, present and future of smoking pipes, tobacciana and the people and companies involved. Circ. 10,000. Pays on publication. Byline given. Buys all rights; other use with permit. Submit seasonal/holiday material 3 months in advance. Sample copy $2.
Nonfiction: Historical/nostalgic, how-to, interview/profile and new product. No anti-smoking articles. Buys 8-10 mss/year. Send complete ms. Length: 1,500 words maximum. Pays 5¢/word. Sometimes pays the expenses of writers on assignment.
Photos: Send photos with submission. Reviews contact sheets; contract on color. Offers $5 maximum/b&w photo. Captions, model releases and identification of subjects required. Buys one-time rights.
Tips: "Features on related subjects are most open to freelancers, especially if writer is a pipe smoker."

POPULAR WOODWORKING, (formerly *Popular Woodworker*), EGW Publishing Corporation, 1300 Galaxy Way, Concord CA 94520. (415)671-9852. Editor: David M. Camp. Managing Editor: Wien Chod. A bimonthly magazine covering woodworking. "Our readers are the woodworking hobbyist and small woodshop owners. Writers should have a knowledge of woodworking, or be able to communicate information gained from woodworkers." Circ. 20,000. Pays on publication. Publishes ms an average of 10 months after acceptance. Byline given. Buys first North American serial rights and second-time rights ("at our discretion"). Submit seasonal/holiday material 6 months in advance. Simultaneous and photocopied submissions OK. Computer printout submissions acceptable; prefers letter-quality to dot-matrix. Reports in 6 weeks. Sample copy $2.95; writer's guidelines for SAE with 1 first class stamp.
Nonfiction: How-to (on woodworking projects, with plans); humor (woodworking anecdotes); and technical (woodworking techniques). "No stories about bloody accidents from not following safety procedures." Buys 120 mss/year. Query with or without published clips, or send complete ms. Pays $45-75/published page. Sometimes pays the expenses of writers on assignment.
Photos: Send photos with submission. Reviews contact sheets, 4x5 transparencies, 5x7 prints and 35mm color slides. Offers no additional payment for photos accepted for ms; $50 extra for cover photos only. Captions and identification of subjects required. Buys one-time rights.
Columns/Departments: Jig Journal (how to make special fixtures to help a tool do a task), 500-1,500 words. Buys 6 mss/year. Query. Pays $75 maximum/published page.
Fillers: Anecdotes, facts, short humor and shop tips. Buys 15/year. Length: 100-500 words. Pays $45 maximum/published page.
Tips: "Show a technical knowledge of woodworking. Sharp close-up black and white photos of a woodworker demonstrating a technique impress me. We really need project with plans articles. Describe the steps in making a piece of furniture (or other project). Provide a cutting list and a rough diagram (we can redraw). If the writer is not a woodworker, he should have help from a woodworker to make sure the technical information is correct."

THE PROFESSIONAL QUILTER, Oliver Press, Box 4096, St. Paul MN 55104. (612)488-0974. Editor: Jeannie M. Spears. 75% freelance written. Works with a small number of new/unpublished writers each year. Bimonthly magazine on the quilting business. Emphasis on small business, preferably craft or sewing related. Circ. 2,000. Payment negotiated. Publishes ms an average of 6 months after acceptance. Byline given. Buys first North American serial rights, first serial rights, and second serial (reprint) rights. Submit seasonal/holiday material 3 months in advance. Simultaneous queries, and photocopied and previously published submissions OK. Electronic submissions OK on Kaypro CPM, but requires hard copy also. Computer printout submissions acceptable; prefers letter-quality to dot-matrix. Reports in 2 weeks on queries; 1 month on mss. Sample copy $4; writer's guidelines for #10 SAE and 1 first class stamp.
Nonfiction: Darcey M. Spears, articles editor. Historical/nostalgic; how-to (quilting business); humor; interview/profile; new product; opinion; and personal experience (of problems and problem-solving ideas in a quilting business). No quilting or sewing *techniques* or quilt photo spreads. Buys 30 mss/year. Query or send complete ms. Length: 200-2,000 words. Pays $20-100.
Tips: "Please remember that our readers already know that quilting is a time-honored tradition passed down from generation to generation, that quilts reflect the life of the maker, that quilt patterns have revealing names, etc., etc. Ask yourself: If my grandmother had been running a quilting business for the last five years, would she have found this article interesting? Send a letter describing your quilt, craft or business experience with a query or manuscript."

‡QUILT WORLD, House of White Birches, Folly Mill Rd., Box 337, Seabrook NH 03874. (603)474-3587. Editor: Sandra L. Hatch. 75% freelance written. Bimonthly magazine covering quilting. Also publishes the quarterly *Quilt World Omnibook*. "We use patterns of both contemporary and traditional quilts and related articles." Circ. 90,000. Pays on publication. Publishes ms an average of 6 months after acceptance. Byline given. Buys all rights. Submit seasonal/holiday material 6 months in advance. Reports in 1 month. Sample copy $1.75; writer's guidelines for SASE.

Nonfiction: How-to, interview/profile (quilters), new product (quilt products) and photo feature. Buys 12-18 mss/year. Query with or without published clips, or send complete ms. Length: open. Pays $25-150.
Photo: Send photos with submission. Reviews 35mm, 2¼x2¼ or larger transparencies and 3x5 prints. Offers $5-10/photo (except covers). Identification of subjects required. Buys all rights.
Poetry: Free verse and traditional. Buys 10-12 poems/year. Submit maximum of 2 poems. Length: 6-30 lines. Pays $10-25.
Fillers: Gags to be illustrated by cartoonist and short humor. Buys 10-12/year. Length: 50-100 words. Pays $25-40.
Tips: "Send list of previous articles published with resume and a SASE. List ideas which you plan to base your articles around."

QUILTER'S NEWSLETTER MAGAZINE, Box 394, Wheatridge CO 80033. Editor: Bonnie Leman. Monthly. Circ. 150,000. Buys first North American serial rights or second rights. Buys 15 mss/year. Pays on publication, sometimes on acceptance. Free sample copy. Reports in 5 weeks. Submit complete ms.
Nonfiction: "We are interested in articles on the subject of quilts and quiltmakers *only*. We are not interested in anything relating to 'Grandma's Scrap Quilts' but could use material about contemporary quilting." Pays 3¢/word minimum, usually more.
Photos: Additional payment for photos depends on quality.
Fillers: Related to quilts and quiltmakers only.
Tips: "Be specific, brief, and professional in tone. Study our magazine to learn the kind of thing we like. Send us material which fits into our format but which is different enough to be interesting. Realize that we think we're the best quilt magazine on the market and that we're aspiring to be even better, then send us the cream off the top of your quilt material."

RAILROAD MODEL CRAFTSMAN, Box 700, Newton NJ 07860. (201)383-3355. Editor: William C. Schaumburg. 75% freelance written. For model railroad hobbyists, in all scales and gauges. Monthly. Circ. 97,000. Buys all rights. Buys 50-100 mss/year. Pays on publication. Publishes ms an average of 9 months after acceptance. Submit seasonal material 6 months in advance. Computer printout submissions acceptable; prefers letter-quality to dot-matrix. SASE requested for writer's and photographer's information. Sample copy $2; guidelines for SAE and 1 first class postage stamp.
Nonfiction: "How-to and descriptive model railroad features written by persons who did the work are preferred. Almost all our features and articles are written by active model railroaders. It is difficult for non-modelers to know how to approach writing for this field." Minimum payment: $1.75/column inch of copy ($50/page).
Photos: Purchased with or without mss. Buys sharp 8x10 glossy prints and 35mm or larger color transparencies. Minimum payments: $10 for photos or $2/diagonal inch of published b&w photos, $3 for color transparencies and $100 for covers which must tie in with article in that issue. Caption information required.
Tips: The most frequent mistakes made by writers are the photo quality and wordiness in texts.

JOEL SATER'S ANTIQUES & AUCTION NEWS, Box 500, Mount Joy PA 17552. (717)653-9797. Managing Editor: Nancy Malloy. Editor: Kent Ward. Eager to work with new/unpublished writers. For dealers and buyers of antiques, nostalgics and collectibles; and those who follow antique shows, shops and auctions. Biweekly tabloid; 36-40 pages. Circ. 55,000. Pays on publication. Buys all rights. Phone queries OK. Submit seasonal/holiday material 3 months in advance. Simultaneous (if so notified), photocopied and previously published submissions OK. Computer printout submissions acceptable. Reports in 6 weeks. Free sample copy (must identify *Writer's Market*).
Nonfiction: Historical (related to American artifacts or material culture); how-to (restoring and preserving antiques and collectibles); informational (research on antiques or collectibles; "news about activities in our field"); interview; nostalgia; personal experience; photo feature; profile; and travel. Buys 100-150 mss/year. Query or submit complete ms. Length: 500-2,500 words. Pays $5-25.
Photos: Purchased with or without accompanying ms. Captions required. Send prints. Pays $2-10 for b&w photos. Offers no additional payment for photos purchased with mss.

‡SCALE WOODCRAFT, Harbor Press, Inc., Box 510, Georgetown CT 06829. (203)798-2612. Editor: Richard C. West. 80% freelance written. A quarterly magazine covering scale woodworking—ship models, carving, scale structures, etc. "*Scale Woodcraft* is for dedicated scale wood workers and enthusiasts. It is all about ship modeling, carving, miniatures, scale structures—present and past—about techniques, people, periods, materials, tools and events related to scale wood working." Circ. 25,000 +. Pays on publication. Byline given. Offers kill fee. Buys first North American serial rights and right to re-use in book (plans to publish collected articles in appropriate books for readers). Simultaneous, photocopied, and previously published submissions OK. Computer printout submissions acceptable—dot-matrix submissions double dot only; letter-quality submissions preferred. Reports in 3 weeks. Sample copy $3.50; free writer's guidelines.
Nonfiction: Book excerpts; historical; how-to (scale wood working, ship models, carving scale structures); in-

terview/profile; and photo feature. No submissions not scale and wood related. Buys 30-35 mss/year. Query with published clips. Pays $25/column. Sometimes pays the expenses of writers on assignment.
Photos: Send photos with submission. Reviews b&w contact sheets. Captions preferred. Offers $10/photo. Buys one-time rights.
Tips: "Feature articles are most open to freelancers. Know that our readers are serious scale woodworkers. They want well-written, clear how-to information with photos, drawings and other aids. Biographical information about present and past scale woodworkers is also needed. How do/did they work—what wood, tools, methods, techniques, etc.?"

SCOTT STAMP MONTHLY, Box 828, Sidney OH 45365. (513)498-2111. Editor: Richard L. Sine. 30% freelance written. Works with a small number of new/unpublished writers each year. For stamp collectors, from the beginner to the sophisticated philatelist. Monthly magazine; 84 pages. Circ. 24,000. Rights purchased vary with author and material; usually buys first North American serial rights. Byline given. Buys 20 unsolicited mss/year. Pays on publication. Publishes ms an average of 4 months after acceptance. Submit seasonal or holiday material 6 months in advance. Computer printout submissions acceptable. Electronic submissions OK via IBM PC format—300/1200 baud ASCII, but requires hard copy also. Reports in 1 month. Query preferred.
Nonfiction: "We are in the market for articles, written in an engaging fashion, concerning the remote byways and often-overlooked aspects of stamp collecting. Writing should be clear and concise, and subjects should be well-researched and documented. Illustrative material should also accompany articles whenever possible." Query. Pays about $100.
Photos: State availability of photos. Offers no additional payment for b&w photos used with mss.
Tips: "Although most material deals with stamps, new writers are invited to seek assignments. It's rewarding to find a good new writer with good new material. Because our emphasis is on lively, interesting articles about stamps, including historical perspectives and human interest slants, we are open to writers who can produce the same. Of course, if you are an experienced philatelist, so much the better. We do not want stories about the picture on a stamp taken from a history book or an encyclopedia and dressed up to look like research. If an idea is good and not a basic rehash, we are interested."

SEW NEWS, The newspaper for people who sew, PJS Publications, Inc., News Plaza, Box 1790, Peoria IL 61656. (309)682-6626. Editor: Linda Turner Jones. 90% freelance written. Works with a small number of new/unpublished writers each year. Monthly newspaper covering home-sewing. "Our magazine is for the beginning home sewer to the professional dressmaker. It expresses the fun, creativity, and excitement of sewing." Circ. 150,000. Pays on acceptance. Publishes ms an average of 6 months after acceptance. Byline given. Buys all rights. Submit seasonal/holiday material 6 months in advance. Photocopied submissions OK. Computer printout submissions acceptable; no dot-matrix. Reports in 2 months. Sample copy $3; writer's guidelines free.
Nonfiction: Historical/nostalgic (fashion, textiles history); how-to (sewing techniques); interview/profile (interesting personalities in home-sewing field); and new product (written in-house). Buys 200-240 ms/year. Query with published clips. Length: 500-2,000 words. Pays $25-400. Rarely pays expenses of writer on assignment.
Photos: State availability of photos. Prefers b&w contact sheets and negatives. Payment included in ms price. Identification of subjects required. Buys all rights.
Fillers: Anecdotes. Buys 12/year. Length: 50-100 words. Pays $10-25.
Tips: "Query first with writing sample. Areas most open to freelancers are how-to and sewing techniques; give explicit, step-by-step instructions plus rough art."

SHUTTLE SPINDLE & DYEPOT, Handweavers Guild of America, 65 Lasalle Rd., West Hartford CT 06107. (203)233-5124. Managing Editor: Deborah Robson. 95% freelance written. A quarterly magazine covering handweaving, spinning and dyeing. "We take the practical and aesthetic approach to handweaving, handspinning, and related textile arts." Pays on publication. Publishes ms 4-15 months after acceptance. Byline given. Buys first North American serial rights. Submit seasonal/holiday material 1 year in advance. Photocopied submissions OK. Rarely accepts previously published submissions. Electronic submissions OK via Compaq/Multimate disk, sometimes Apple IIc/Appleworks, but requires hard copy also. Computer printout submissions acceptable; prefers letter-quality to dot-matrix. Reports in 2 weeks on queries; 2 months on mss. Sample copy $4.75; free writer's guidelines.
Nonfiction: How-to, interview/profile, personal experience, photo feature and technical. "We want interesting, practical, technical information in our field." Buys 80 mss/year. Query with or without published clips, or send complete ms. Length: 500-2,500 words. Pays $25-100.
Photos: Send photos or state availability of photos with submission. Reviews contact sheets and transparencies. Payment varies. Captions, model releases and identification of subjects required. Buys one-time rights.
Tips: "We are backlogged, but we will still read submissions. However, competition is presently stiff."

SPIN-OFF. Interweave Press, 306 N. Washington, Loveland CO 80537. (303)669-7672. Editors: Lee Raven and Anne Bliss. 10-20% freelance written. Quarterly magazine covering handspinning, dyeing, techniques and projects for using handspun fibers. Audience includes "practicing textile/fiber craftsmen. Article should show considerable depth of knowledge of subject, although the tone should be informal and accessible." Circ. 7,000. Pays on publication. Publishes ms an average of 6 months after acceptance. Byline given. Pays 50% kill fee. Buys first North American serial rights. Simultaneous queries and photocopied submissions OK. Computer printout submissions acceptable; prefers letter-quality to dot-matrix. Sample copy $2.50 and 8½x11 SAE; free writer's guidelines.
Nonfiction: Historical and how-to (on spinning; knitted, crocheted, woven projects from handspun fibers with instructions); interview/profile (of successful and/or interesting fiber craftsmen); and technical (on spinning, dyeing or fiber technology, use, properties). "All articles must contain a high level of in-depth information. Our readers are very knowledgable about these subjects." Query. Length: 2,000 words. Pays $25-125.
Photos: State availability of photos. Identification of subjects required.

SPORTS COLLECTORS DIGEST. Krause Publications, 700 E. State St., Iola WI 54990. (715)445-2214. Editor: Steve Ellingboe. 70% freelance written. Works with a small number of new/unpublished writers each year. Sports memorabilia magazine published 26 times/year. "We serve collectors of sports memorabilia—baseball cards, yearbooks, programs, autographs, jerseys, bats, balls, books, magazines, ticket stubs, etc." Circ. 25,000. Pays after publication. Publishes ms an average of 3 months after acceptance. Byline given. Buys first North American serial rights only. Submit seasonal/holiday material 3 months in advance. Simultaneous queries and photocopied submissions OK. Computer printout submissions acceptable. Reports in 5 weeks on queries; 2 months on mss. Free sample copy and writer's guidelines.
Nonfiction: General interest (new card issues, research on older sets), historical/nostalgic (old stadiums, old collectibles, etc.); how-to (buy cards, sell cards and other collectibles, display collectibles, ways to get autographs, jerseys, and other memorabilia); interview/profile (well-known collectors, ball players—but must focus on collectibles); new product (new card sets) and personal experience ("what I collect and why"-type stories). No sports stories. "We are not competing with *The Sporting News*, *Sports Illustrated* or your daily paper. Sports collectibles only." Buys 40-60 mss/year. Query. Length: 300-3,000 words; prefers 1,000 words. Pays $10-50.
Photos: Unusual collectibles. State availability of photos. Pays $5-15 for b&w prints. Identification of subjects required. Buys all rights.
Columns/Departments: "We have all the columnists we need but welcome ideas for new columns." Buys 100-150 mss/year. Query. Length: 600-3,000 words. Pays $15-60.
Tips: "If you are a collector, you know what collectors are interested in. Write about it. No shallow, puff pieces; our readers are too smart for that. Only well-researched articles about sports memorabilia and collecting. Some sports nostalgia pieces are OK. Write only about the areas you know about."

‡SUNSHINE ARTISTS USA, The Voice Of The Nation's Artists and Craftsman, Sun Country Enterprises, 1700 Sunset Dr., Longwood FL 32750. (305)323-5937. Editor: Joan L. Wahl. Managing Editor: 'Crusty' Sy. A monthly magazine covering art and craft shows in the United States. "We are a top marketing magazine for professional artists, craftspeople and photographers working street and mall shows. We list 10,000 shows/year, critique many of them and publish articles on marketing, selling, and improving arts and crafts." Circ. 16,000+. Pays on publication. Publishes ms an average of 6 months after acceptance. Byline given. Buys first North American serial rights. Reports in 2 weeks on queries; 6 weeks on mss. Sample copy $2.37.
Nonfiction: Interview/profile. No how-to's. Buys 12+ mss/year. Query. Length: 550-2,000 words. Pays $10-50 for assigned articles.
Photos: State availability of photos with submission. Offers no additional payment for photos accepted with ms. Captions, model releases, and identification of subjects required.
Tips: "We are interested in articles that relate to artists and craftsman traveling the circuit. Although we have a permanent staff of 40 writers, we will consider well written, throughly researched articles on successful artists making a living with their work, new ways to market arts and crafts, and rags to riches profiles. Attend some art shows. Talk to the exhibitors. Get ideas from them."

TREASURE. Jess Publishing, 6280 Adobe Rd., 29 Palms CA 92277. (619)367-3531. Editor: Jim Williams. Emphasizes treasure hunting and metal detecting. 90% freelance written. Eager to work with new/unpublished writers. Monthly magazine. Circ. 40,000. Pays on publication. Publishes ms an average of 6 months after acceptance. Buys all rights. Byline given. Phone queries OK. Submit seasonal/holiday material 4 months in advance. Previously published submissions OK. Computer printout submissions acceptable; prefers letter-quality to dot-matrix. Reports in 2 months. Sample copy 40¢; free writer's guidelines for SAE and 1 first class stamp.
Nonfiction: Rhonda Lewis, articles editor. How-to (coinshooting and treasure hunting tips); informational and historical (location of lost treasures with emphasis on the lesser-known); interviews (with treasure hunt-

ers): profiles (successful treasure hunters and metal detector hobbyists); personal experience (treasure hunting); technical (advice on use of metal detectors and metal detector designs). "We would like more coverage of archaeological finds, both professional and amateur, and more reports on recently found caches, whether located purposefully or accidentally—both types should be accompanied by photos of the finds." Buys 6-8 mss/issue. Send complete ms. Length: 300-3,000 words. Pays $30-200. "Our rate of payment varies considerably depending upon the proficiency of the author, the quality of the photographs, the importance of the subject matter, and the amount of useful information given."

Photos: Offers no additional payment for 5x7 or 8x10 b&w glossy prints used with mss. Pays $75 minimum for color transparencies (35mm or 2¼x2¼). Color for cover only. "Clear photos and other illustrations are a must." Model release required.

Tips: "We hope to increase our news coverage of archaeoloical digs and cache finds, opening the doors to writers who would like simply to use their journalistic skills to report a specific event. No great knowledge of treasure hunting will be necessary. The most frequent mistakes made by writers in completing an article for *Treasure* are failure to list sources of information and to supply illustrations or photos with a story. "

TRI-STATE TRADER, Mayhill Publishing, Box 90, Knightstown IN 46148. Editor: Thomas Hoepf. 90% freelance written. Works with a small number of new/unpublished writers each year. Weekly newspaper covering antiques, auctions, collectibles, genealogy, for collectors nationwide. Circ. 38,000. Pays on publication. Publishes ms an average of 2 months after acceptance. Byline given. Buys first rights. Submit seasonal/holiday material 3 months in advance. Simultaneous queries and photocopied submissions OK. Computer printout submissions acceptable; no dot-matrix. Reports in 3 weeks on queries; 1 month on mss. Free sample copy on request; writer's guidelines for SAE and 1 first-class stamp.

Nonfiction: Historical/nostalgic (of interest to collectors) and auction reports that include accurate descriptions of antiques and their selling prices. "We place a premium on well-researched stories about specific antiques and collectibles." Buys 175 mss/year. Query. Length: 300-1,500 words. Pays variable rates.

Tips: "We're interested in general news relating to collectibles and history. Read the *TST* and know this market. We are open to most any writer, but our readers are knowledgeable on our topics and expect the same from writers. We always have a need for stories about 500 words long for the inside news pages."

WESTERN & EASTERN TREASURES, People's Publishing Co., Inc., Box 1095, Arcata CA 95521. Editor: Rosemary Anderson. Emphasizes treasure hunting and metal detecting for all ages, entire range in education, coast-to-coast readership. 90% freelance written. Monthly magazine. Circ. 70,000. Pays on publication. Publishes ms an average of 1 year after acceptance. Buys all rights. Computer printout submissions acceptable; no dot-matrix. Sample copy and writer's guidelines for $2.

Nonfiction: How-to "hands on" use of metal detecting equipment, how to locate coins, jewelry and relics, prospect for gold, where to look for treasures, rocks and gems, etc., "first-person" experiences. "No purely historical manuscripts or manuscripts that require two-part segments or more." Buys 200 unsolicited mss/year. Submit complete ms. Length: maximum 1,500 words. Pays 2¢/word-negotiable.

Photos: Purchased with accompanying ms. Captions required. Submit b&w prints or 35mm Kodachrome color transparencies. Pays $5 maximum for 3x5 and up b&w glossy prints; $35 and up for 35mm Kodachrome cover slides. Model releases required.

Tips: "The writer has a better chance of breaking in at our publication with short articles and fillers as these give the readers a chance to respond to the writer. The publisher relies heavily on reader reaction. Not adhering to word limit is the main mistake made by writers in completing an article for us. Also, not following what the editor has emphasized as needed material to be clearly covered."

‡**WOMEN'S CIRCLE, COUNTED CROSS STITCH.** House of White Birches, Inc., Folly Mill Rd., Box 337, Seabrook NH 03865. (603)474-3587. Editor: Sandra L. Hatch. 100% freelance written. Quarterly magazine covering cross-stitch. Circ. 50,000. Pays on publication. Publishes ms an average of 6 months after acceptance. Byline given. Buys all rights. Submit seasonal/holiday material 6 months in advance. Reports in 1 month. Sample copy $1.75; writer's guidelines for SASE.

Nonfiction: How-to, interview/profile, new product and charted designs. Buys 12-15 mss/year. Query with published clips. Length: open. Pays $25-100.

Photos: Send photos with submission. Reviews 35mm, 2¼x2¼ or larger transparencies or 3x5 or larger prints. Offers $5-10/photo "except covers." Identification of subjects required. Buys all rights.

Fiction: Fantasy, humorous and slice-of-life vignettes (all related to cross-stitch). Buys 4-8 mss/year. Send complete ms. Length: 100-600 words. Pays $25-75.

Poetry: Light verse and traditional (related to cross-stitch). Buys 8-12 poems/year. Submit maximum 2 poems. Length: 6-30 lines. Pays $15-30.

Fillers: Facts and short humor. Buys 4-8/year. Length: 50-150 words. Pays $20-40.

Tips: "All areas open to freelancers."

THE WOODWORKER'S JOURNAL, Madrigal Publishing Co., Inc., 517 Litchfield Rd., Box 1629, New Milford CT 06776. (203)355-2694. Editor: James J. McQuillan. Managing Editor: Thomas G. Begnal. Bi-

monthly magazine covering woodworking for woodworking hobbyists of all levels of skill. Circ. 120,000. Pays on acceptance. Byline given. Buys all rights. Submit seasonal/holiday material 3 months in advance. Reports in 6 weeks. Free sample copy and writer's guidelines.
Nonfiction: "In each issue, we try to offer a variety of plans—some selected with the novice in mind, others for the more experienced cabinetmaker. We also like to offer a variety of furniture styles, i.e., contemporary, colonial, Spanish, etc. We are always in the market for original plans for all types of furniture, wood accessories, jigs, and other shop equipment. We are also interested in seeing carving and marquetry projects." Buys 20-30 mss/year. Send complete ms. Length "varies with project." Pays $80-120/page. "Payment rate is for a complete project submission, consisting of dimensioned sketches, a write-up explaining how the project was built, and at least one high-quality b&w photo."
Photos: Send photos with ms. Reviews 5x7 b&w prints. "Photo payment is included in our basic payment rate of $80-120/page for a complete project submission." Captions required. Buys all rights.

THE WORKBASKET, 4251 Pennsylvania Ave., Kansas City MO 64111. Editor: Roma Jean Rice. Issued monthly except bimonthly June-July and November-December. Buys first rights. Pays on acceptance. Query. Reports in 6 weeks.
Nonfiction: Interested in articles of 400-500 words of step-by-step directions for craft projects and gardening articles of 200-500 words. Pays 7¢/word.
Photos: Pays $7-10 for 8x10 glossies with ms.
Columns/Departments: Readers' Recipes (original recipes from readers); and Making Cents (short how-to section featuring ideas for pin money from readers).

WORKBENCH, 4251 Pennsylvania Ave., Kansas City MO 64111. (816)531-5730. Editor: Jay W. Hedden. 95% freelance written. Prefers to work with published/established writers; works with a small number of new/unpublished writers each year. For woodworkers. Circ. 830,000. Pays on acceptance. Buys all rights then returns all but first rights upon request, after publication. Byline given if requested. Computer printout submissions acceptable. Reports in 2 months. Query. Publishes ms an average of 1 year after acceptance. Free sample copy and writer's guidelines.
Nonfiction: "We have continued emphasis on home improvement, home maintenance, alternate energy projects. Ours is a nuts-and-bolts approach, rather than telling how someone has done it. Because most of our readers own their own homes, we stress 'retrofitting' of energy-saving devices, rather than saying they should rush out and buy or build a solar home. Energy conservation is another subject we cover thoroughly; insulation, weatherstripping, making your own storm windows. We still are very strong in woodworking, cabinetmaking and furniture construction. Projects range from simple toys to complicated reproductions of furniture now in museums. We would like to receive more contemporary furniture items (like those sold in the unfinished furniture stores) that can be easily duplicated by beginning do-it-yourself woodworkers." Pays $125/published page, up or down depending on quality of submission. Additional payment for good color photos.
Columns/Departments: Shop tips bring $30 maximum with drawing and/or photo.
Tips: "If you can consistently provide good material, including photos, your rates will go up and you will get assignments. The field is wide open but only if you produce quality material and clear, sharp b&w photos. If we pay less than the rate, it's because we have to supply photos, information, drawings or details the contributor has overlooked. Contributors should look over the published story to see what they should include next time. Our editors are skilled woodworkers, do-it-yourselfers and photographers. We have a complete woodworking shop at the office, and we use it often to check out construction details of projects submitted to us."

WORLD COIN NEWS, Krause Publications, 700 E. State, Iola WI 54990. (715)445-2214. Editor: Colin Bruce. 30% freelance written. Works with a small number of new/unpublished writers each year. Weekly newsmagazine about non-U.S. coin collecting for novices and advanced collectors of foreign coins, medals, and other numismatic items. Circ. 15,000. Pays on publication. Publishes ms an average of 1 month after acceptance. Byline given. Buys first North American serial rights and reprint rights. Submit seasonal material 1 month in advance. Simultaneous and photocopied submissions OK. Computer printout submissions acceptable; no dot-matrix. Reports in 2 weeks. Free sample copy.
Nonfiction: "Send us timely news stories related to collecting foreign coins and current information on coin values and markets." Send complete ms. Buys 30 mss/year. Length: 500-2,000 words. Pays 3¢/word to first-time contributors; fees negotiated for later articles. Sometimes pays the expenses of writers on assignment.
Photos: Send photos with ms. Pays $5 minimum for b&w prints. Captions and model release required. Buys first rights and first reprint rights.

YESTERYEAR, Yesteryear Publications, Box 2, Princeton WI 54968. (414)787-4808. Editor: Michael Jacobi. 25% freelance written. For antique dealers and collectors, people interested in collecting just about anything, and nostalgia buffs. Monthly tabloid. Circ. 7,000. Pays on publication. Publishes ms an average of 2 months after acceptance. Buys all rights. Byline given. Submit seasonal/holiday material 3 months in advance. Simultaneous, photocopied and previously published submissions OK. Reports in 1 month for queries; 1 month for .mss. Sample copy $1.

Nonfiction: General interest (basically, anything pertaining to antiques, collectible items or nostalgia in general); historical (again, pertaining to the above categories); and how-to (refinishing antiques, how to collect). The more specific and detailed, the better. "We do not want personal experience or opinion articles." Buys 24 mss/year. Send complete ms. Pays $5-25.

Photos: Send photos with ms. Pays $5 for 5x7 b&w glossy or matte prints; $5 for 5x7 color prints. Captions preferred.

Columns/Departments: "We will consider new column concepts as long as they fit into the general areas of antiques and collectibles." Buys 2 mss/issue. Send complete ms. Pays $5-25.

Home and Garden

Most home and garden magazines show readers how other people live and how they can transform their own homes and gardens. Editors look for space- and energy-saving ideas that look and work well. The number of people who are restoring old homes and the interest in "country" designs have added another dimension to home and garden magazines. Some magazines here concentrate on gardens; others on the how-to of interior design. Still others focus upon homes and/or gardens in specific regions.

AUSTIN HOMES & GARDENS, Duena Development Corp., Box 5950, Austin TX 78763. (512)479-8936. Editor: Marsia Hart Reese. 50% freelance written. Prefers to work with published/established writers; works with a small number of new/unpublished writers each year. Monthly magazine emphasizing Austin, Texas homes, people, gardens, and events for current, former, and prospective residents. Circ. 25,000. Average issue includes 16 articles. Pays on publication. Publishes ms an average of 3 months after acceptance. Buys all rights. Byline given. "The material that we buy becomes the sole property of AH&G and cannot be reproduced in any form without written permission." Photocopied submissions OK. Electronic submissions OK via IBM PC (or compatible), PC Write software, but requires hard copy also. Computer printout submissions acceptable; prefers letter-quality to dot-matrix. Reports in 1 month. Sample copy $3.

Nonfiction: General interest (interior design and architecture; trends in home furnishings and landscaping; arts and crafts); historical (local); how-to (on home or garden); and fashion feature. "We are looking for brief, lively, Austin-lifestyle-oriented articles that are aimed at a younger, informed, educated market; we wish to expand our readership as Austin expands and grows." Buys 8 mss/issue. Query with samples of published articles. Length: 700-1,500 words. Pays $100 minimum.

Columns/Departments: Departments include Discoveries (unusual local businesses or services); Travel; and Profile (interesting Austin people). Query. Length: 500-1,000 words. Pays $100 minimum.

Tips: "Always looking for good freelancers, but prefer Austin area writers familiar with city and area."

BETTER HOMES AND GARDENS, 1716 Locust St., Des Moines IA 50336. (515)284-3000. Editor: (Building): Joan McCloskey. Editor (Furnishings): Shirley Van Anate. Editor (Foods): Nancy Byal. Editor (Crafts): Jean LeMon. Editor (Travel): Barbara Humeston. Editor (Garden Outdoor Living): Doug Jimerson. Editor (100s of Ideas, New Products, What's Happening): Steven Coulter. Editor (Health & Education): Paul Krantz. Editor (Money Management, Automotive Features): Margaret Daly. Editor (Home Electronics): Kathy Stechert. 10-15% freelance written. Pays on acceptance. Buys all rights. "We read all freelance articles, but much prefer to see a letter of query rather than a finished manuscript."

Nonfiction: Travel, education, health, cars, money management, and home entertainment. "We do not deal with political subjects or with areas not connected with the home, community, and family." Pays rates "based on estimate of length, quality and importance."

Tips: Direct queries to the department that best suits your story line.

CANADIAN WORKSHOP, The How-to Magazine, Camar Publications (1984) Inc., 130 Spy Ct., Markham, Ontario L3R 5H6 Canada. (416)475-8440. Editor: Bob Pennycook. 90% freelance written. Monthly magazine covering the "do-it-yourself market including projects, renovation and restoration, gardening, maintenance and decoration. Canadian writers only." Circ. 85,000. Pays on publication. Publishes ms an average of 5 months after acceptance. Byline given. Offers 75% kill fee. Buys first serial rights only. Submit seasonal/holiday material 6 months in advance. Simultaneous queries OK. Computer printout submissions acceptable; no dot-matrix. Reports in 3 weeks. Sample copy $2; free writer's guidelines.

Nonfiction: How-to (gardening, home and home machinery maintenance, renovation projects, and woodworking projects). Buys 20-40 mss/year. Query with clips of published work. Length: 1,500-4,000 words. Pays $225-600. Pays expenses of writers on assignment.

Photos: Send photos with ms. Pays $20-150 for 2¼x2¼ color transparencies; covers higher; $10-50 for b&w contact sheets. Captions, model releases, and identification of subjects required.

Tips: "Freelancers must be aware of our magazine format. Product-types used in how-to articles must be readily available across Canada. Deadlines for articles are 5 months in advance of cover date. How-tos should be detailed enough for the amateur but appealing to the experienced. We work with the writer to develop a major feature. That could mean several rewrites, but we've found most writers to be eager. A frequent mistake made by writers is not directing the copy towards our reader. Stories sometimes have a tendency to be too basic."

‡**DISTINGUISHED HOME PLANS**, Matvest Media Corp., Suite 115, 6800 France Ave. S., Minneapolis MN 55435. (612)927-6707. Managing Editor: Anne Welsbacher. Managing Editor: Ed Jackson. 80% freelance written. A quarterly magazine covering new homes and new home building. "*Distinguished Homes* is a compilation of home plans with two to three articles per issue. Readers are middle-upper income, national, people interested in building or dreaming of building homes." Circ. 100,000. Pays 6 weeks after acceptance. Publishes ms an average of 6 months after acceptance. Byline given. Offers 25% kill fee. Buys one-time rights. Submit seasonal/holiday material 9 months in advance. Photocopied submissions OK. Electronic submissions OK via IBM compatible disks, but requires hard copy also. Computer printout submissions acceptable. Reports in 1 month on queries; 3 weeks on mss. Sample copy for 9x11 SAE with 4 first class stamps.

Nonfiction: Historical/nostalgic (on historic homes); how-to (on building and planning homes); and profile (on new homes being built). No unsolicited articles; none too technical. Buys 1-4 mss/year. Query with or without published clips. Length: 1,500-3,000 words. Pays $200-500. Sometimes pays the expenses of writers on assignment.

Photos: State availability of photos or send photos with submissions. Reviews transparencies. Offers $50-175/color photo; pays small add-on fee for b&w with article. Captions, model releases, and identification of subjects required. Buys one-time rights.

Fiction: No unsolicited fiction; no stories not directly focused on homes. Query with published clips. Length: 1,500-3,000 words. Pays $300-500.

Tips: "Query, don't send complete manuscripts. There may be possible stories in the freelancer's location we can use—we can supply leads for possible features in your area. We use very few stories in *Distinguished Homes; Homestyles*, a sister publication, is a better market. For both, we're looking for bright, friendly, informative stories about home planning, decorating and building."

ENERGY SENSE. General Learning Corp., 3500 Western Ave., Highland Park IL 60035. (312)432-2700. Editor: Margaret Mucklo. Senior Associate Editor: Carole Rubenstein (contact). 95% freelance written. Quarterly magazine on energy awareness. "Our purpose is to provide energy information in an easy-to-read style and to promote energy awareness in the home and workplace." Pays 30 days after acceptance. Publishes ms an average of 3 months after acceptance. Offers 25% kill fee. Makes work-for-hire assignments. Simultaneous queries OK. Computer printout submissions acceptable. Reports in 1 month. Sample copy for large SAE and 65¢ postage. Writer's guidelines for #10 SAE and 1 first class stamp.

Nonfiction: General interest. "Our greatest need is for queries in November and December." Buys 40 mss/year. Query with published clips. Length: 1,200-1,600 words. Pays $75-150.

FARMING UNCLE®. Box 91, Liberty NY 12754. Editor: Louis Toro. 25% freelance written. Quarterly magazine on nature, small stock, and gardening. 72 pages (8½"x11").Pays on acceptance. Publishes ms an average of 3 months after acceptance. Byline given. Buys all rights. Reports in 1 week on queries. Sample copy for $3 and $1.50 postage (first class).

Nonfiction: How-to (poultry, small stock, gardening, shelter building, etc.). Buys 12 mss/year. Send complete ms. Length: 500-750 words. Pays $7.50-10.

Photos: Send photos with ms. Pays $3-4 for b&w prints. Captions and identification of subjects not required.

Poetry: "We publish poetry but do not pay for it."

FARMSTEAD MAGAZINE. Box 111, Freedom ME 04941. Business offices: (207)382-6200. Editorial offices: (207)382-6200. Publisher: George Frangoulis. Managing Editor: Heidi Brugger. 50% freelance written. Prefers to work with published/ established writers. Magazine published 6 times/year covering home gardening, shelter/construction, alternative energy, recipes, small-scale livestock (breeds and care), tools, homesteading and country lifestyles. Circ. 150,000. Pays on publication. Publishes ms an average of 6 months after acceptance. Buys first serial rights and second serial (reprint) rights; second serial right may be used in an an-

thology and/or for another issue published by The Farmstead Press. Phone queries OK. Submit seasonal material 1 year in advance. Computer printout submissions acceptable; no dot-matrix. Reports in 3 months. Free sample copy and writer's guidelines with appropriate size SASE.
Nonfiction: General interest (related to rural living and gardening); how-to (gardening, farming, shelter, energy (especially wood heat), construction, conservation, wildlife, livestock, crafts, and rural living); interview (with interesting and/or inspirational people involved with horticulture, or commitment to country living). "We would like to see short subjects related to traditional country skills and knowledge or to new trends and ideas that improve country living today." No sentimentality or nostalgia. Buys 60 mss/year. Submit complete ms. Length: 700-5,000 words. Pays 5¢/word. Sometimes pays the expenses of writers on assignment.
Photos: State availability of photos with ms. Pay starts at $10 for each 5x7 b&w print used; starts at $25 for color; $100 for each color transparency used on cover.
Tips: "Contribute a thorough well-researched or first-hand experience article. B&w photos of good quality, 35mm color transparencies or careful diagrams or sketches are a boon. We look for an unusual but practical how-to article. Send short factual pieces with good photos. Our market is a highly competitive one. As a result we are constantly fine-tuning our focus. For a writer, this will mean a potential shift in acceptable subject matter due to changes in the percentages of topics in the editorial mix. All unsolicited manuscripts must have SASE or we cannot guarantee their return."

FLOWER AND GARDEN MAGAZINE, 4251 Pennsylvania, Kansas City MO 64111. Editor-in-Chief: Rachel Snyder. 50% freelance written. For home gardeners. Bimonthly. Picture magazine. Circ. 600,000. Buys first rights only. Byline given. Pays on acceptance. Publishes ms an average of 1 year after acceptance. Computer printout submissions acceptable; no dot-matrix. Free writer's guidelines. Query. Reports in 6 weeks.
Nonfiction: Interested in illustrated articles on how to do certain types of gardening and descriptive articles about individual plants. Flower arranging, landscape design, house plants, patio gardening are other aspects covered. "The approach we stress is practical (how-to-do-it, what-to-do-it-with). We try to stress plain talk, clarity, and economy of words. An article should be tailored for a national audience." Buys 20-30 mss/year. Length: 500-1,500 words. Pays 7¢/word or more, depending on quality and kind of material.
Photos: Pays up to $12.50/5x7 or 8x10 b&w prints, depending on quality, suitability. Also buys color transparencies, 35mm and larger. "We are using more four-color illustrations." Pays $30-125 for these, depending on size and use.
Tips: "Prospective author needs good grounding in gardening practice and literature. Then offer well-researched and well-written material appropriate to the experience level of our audience. Use botanical names as well as common. Illustrations help sell the story. Describe special qualifications for writing the particular proposed subject."

GARDEN DESIGN, The Fine Art of Residential Landscape Architecture, American Society of Landscape Architects, 1733 Connecticut Ave. NW, Washington DC 20009. (202)466-7730. Editor: Ken Druse. Editor-in-chief: Susan Rademacher Frey. 75% freelance written. Quarterly magazine covering garden making, garden history, garden design emphasizing the *design* aspects of gardening rather than horticulture. "Design elements and considerations are presented in clear, simple language for garden enthusiasts." Circ. 45,000. Pays on publication. Publishes ms an average of 6 months after acceptance. Byline given. Offers negotiable kill fee. Buys one-time rights. Submit seasonal material 1 year in advance. Computer printout submissions acceptable; no dot-matrix. Sample copy $5.
Nonfiction: Historical, interview/profile, opinion, personal experience, photo feature, and travel. Few detailed horticultural or technical articles. Buys 20-30 mss/year. Query with published clips. Length: 500-1,500 words. Pays $50-300.
Photos: Send photos with query or ms. Pays $50-150 for color transparencies. Captions, model releases and identification of subjects required.
Columns/Departments: Almanac (calendar of events); First Garden (how-to); Plant Page (design applications of plants); Focal Point (personal perspectives); Ex Libris (book reviews); and Eclectic (items of interest). Buys 10-15 mss/year. Query with published clips. Length: 100-1,500 words. Pays $50-300.
Tips: "We emphasize the experience of gardening over technique. Our editorial core covers an array of subjects—historical, contemporary, large and small gardens. Departments follow specific subjects—garden news, products, travel, plants, people, etc. Samples of previously published work are welcomed. Outlines or brief article descriptions of specific subjects are helpful. We are willing to work with authors in tailoring specific subjects and style with them."

GARDEN MAGAZINE, The Garden Society, A Division of the New York Botanical Garden, Bronx Park, Bronx NY 10458. Editor: Ann Botshon. 50% freelance written. Works with a small number of new/unpublished writers each year. Emphasizes horticulture, environment and botany for a diverse readership, largely college graduates and professionals united by a common interest in plants and the environment. Most are members of botanical gardens and arboreta. Bimonthly magazine. Circ. 30,000. Publishes ms an average of 1 year after acceptance. Buys first North American serial rights. Submit seasonal/holiday material 6 months in advance.

Photocopied submissions OK. Computer printout submissions acceptable; prefers letter-quality to dot-matrix. Reports in 2 months. Sample copy $3; guidelines for SAE and 1 first class stamp.

Nonfiction: Ann Botshon, editor. "All articles must be of high quality, meticulously researched and botanically accurate." Exposé (environmental subjects); how-to (horticultural techniques, must be unusual and verifiable); general interest (plants in art and history, botanical news, ecology); humor (pertaining to botany and horticulture); and travel (great gardens of the world). Buys 15-20 unsolicited mss/year. Query with clips of published work. Length: 1,000-2,500 words. Pays $100-300. Sometimes pays the expenses of writers on assignment.

Photos: Anne Schwartz, associate editor. Pays $35-50/5x7 b&w glossy print; $40-150/4x5 or 35mm color transparency. Captions preferred. Buys one-time rights.

Tips: "We appreciate some evidence that the freelancer has studied our magazine and understands our special requirements. A writer should write from a position of authority that comes from either personal experience (horticulture); extensive research (environment, ecology, history, art); adequate scientific background; or all three. Style should be appropriate to this approach."

GURNEY'S GARDENING NEWS, A Family Newsmagazine for Gurney Gardeners, Gurney Seed and Nursery Co., 2nd and Capitol, Yankton SD 57079. (605)665-4451. Editor: Pattie Vargas. 85% freelance written. Prefers to work with published/established writers; works with a small number of new/unpublished writers each year. Bimonthly newsmagazine covering gardening, horticulture and related subjects for home gardeners. Circ. 100,000. Pays on acceptance. Publishes ms an average of 9 months after acceptance. Byline given. "We buy first North American serial rights and reprint rights for materials we might reprint or excerpt in our own publications, i.e., customer service bulletins or catalogs. Second rights are assigned to the writer and he is free to resell the material to any publication once we have printed the article." Will also consider second serial (reprint) rights to material originally published elsewhere. Submit seasonal/holiday material 6 months in advance. Computer printout submissions acceptable; no dot-matrix. Reports in 1 month on queries; 2 months on mss. Sample copy for 9x12 SAE; writer's guidelines and themes for each issue for business size SAE.

Nonfiction: "We are interested in well-researched, well-written and illustrated articles on all aspects of home gardening. We prefer articles that stress the practical approach to gardening and are easy to understand. We don't want articles which sound like a rehash of material from a horticultural encyclopedia or how-to-garden guide. We rarely buy articles without accompanying photos or illustrations. We look for a unique slant, a fresh approach, new gardening techniques that work and interesting anecdotes. Especially need short (300-500 words) articles on practical gardening tips, hints, and methods. We are interested in: how-to (raise vegetables, flowers, bulbs, trees); interview/profile (of gardeners); profiles of celebrity gardeners; photo feature (of garden activities); and technical (horticultural-related)." Buys 70 unsolicited mss/year. Query. Length: 700-1,250 words. Pays $50-125. Also buys articles on gardening projects and activities for children. Length: 500-1,000 words. Pays $30-100.

Photos: Purchases photos with ms. Also buys photo features, essays. Pays $10-25 for 5x7 or 8x10 b&w prints or contact sheets. Captions, model releases, and identification of subjects required. Buys one-time rights.

Tips: "Time articles to coincide with the proper season. Read Gurney's Seed and Nursery catalogs and be familiar with Gurney's varieties before you submit an article on vegetables, fruits, flowers, trees, etc. We prefer that it be Gurney's. Our readers know gardening. If you don't, don't write for us."

HERB QUARTERLY, Box 275, Newfane VT 05345. Editor: Sallie Ballantine. 90% freelance written. Quarterly magazine for herb enthusiasts. Circ. 22,000. Pays $25 on publication. Publishes ms an average of 1 year after acceptance. Buys first North American serial rights and second (reprint) rights to manuscripts originally published elsewhere. Electronic submissions OK on IBM PC-WordStar. Computer printout submissions acceptable. Query letters recommended. Reports in 1 month. Sample copy $5; writer's guidelines for SAE and 1 first class stamp.

Nonfiction: Gardening (landscaping, herb garden design, propagation, harvesting); herb businesses; medicinal and cosmetic use of herbs; crafts; cooking; historical (folklore, focused piece on particular period—*not* general survey); interview of a famous person involved with herbs or folksy herbalist; personal experience; and photo essay ("cover quality" 8x10 b&w prints). "We are particularly interested in herb garden design, contemporary or historical." No fiction. Send double-spaced ms. Length: 2,000-10,000 words. Reports in one month.

Tips: "Our best submissions are narrowly focused on herbs with much practical information on cultivation and use for the gardener."

HOME ILLUSTRATED, 1515 Broadway, New York NY 10036. (212)719-6630. Editor: Joseph R. Provey. Executive Editor: Harry Wicks. Home Workshop Editor: Michael Morris. Monthly magazine for the home and car manager. Articles on maintenance, repair, and renovation to the home and family car. Information on how to buy, how to select products useful to home owners/car owners. "Emphasis in home-oriented articles is on good design, inventive solutions to styling and space problems, and useful home-workshop projects." Circ. 1.2 million. Buys first North American serial rights. Byline given. Pays on acceptance. Query.

Nonfiction: Feature articles relating to homeowner/carowner, 1,500-2,500 words. "This may include personal home-renovation projects, professional advice on interior design, reports on different or unusual construction methods, and energy-related subjects; and outdoor/backyard projects, etc. We are no longer interested in high-tech subjects such as aerospace, electronics, photography or military hardware. Most of our automotive features are written by experts in the field, but fillers, tips, how-to repair, or modification articles on the family car are welcome. Workshop articles on furniture, construction, tool use, refinishing techniques, etc., are also sought. Pays $300 minimum for features; fees based on number of printed pages, photos accompanying mss., etc."
Photos: Photos should accompany mss. Pays $600 and up for transparencies for cover. Inside color: Payments vary, starting at $400/doz. Home and Shop Hints illustrated with 1 photo, $35. Captions and model release required.
Fillers: Tips and fillers useful to tool users or for general home maintenance. Pays $35 and up for illustrated and captioned fillers. Pays $75-100 for half-page fillers.
Tips: "If you're planning some kind of home improvement and can write, you might consider doing a piece on it for us. Good how-to articles on home improvement are always difficult to come by."

HOME MAGAZINE, Allied Publications, 1776 Lake Worth Rd., Lake Worth FL 33460. Editor: Mark Adams. 60% freelance written. A general interest bimonthly magazine distributed to patrons of banks, realtors, savings and loans, and insurance companies featuring domestic themes and family values. The magazine serves as a promotion/public relations tool. Circ. 75,000. Pays on acceptance. Byline given. Buys first rights, and second serial (reprint) rights, and may make work-for-hire assignments. Submit seasonal material 6 months in advance. Simultaneous, photocopied and previously published submissions OK. Computer printout submissions acceptable. Reports in 1 month. Sample copy $1 and SAE; writer's guidelines for letter size SASE.
Nonfiction: General interest, humor, motivational, interview/profile (must include subject's picture), personal experience, photo feature, travel lifestyle and fashion. Buys 50-100 mss/year. Send complete ms. Length: 400-1,000 words. Pays 5¢/published word or $25 maximum.
Photos: Send photos with mss. Pays $5 for 8x10 b&w glossy prints or color transparencies. Captions and identification of subjects required. Buys one-time rights.
Fillers: Anecdotes, facts and short humor. Buys 10-20/year. Length: 20-100 words. Pays 5¢/published word or $10 maximum.
Tips: "Type manuscript, double-space and *keep a copy* (we sometimes lose them.) Edit yourself ruthlessly for grammar, spelling, punctuation and style. Is your story unique? Characteristics of stories we accept include brevity, and informal, personal tone, and a sense of humor. No queries—we simply can't answer them. We receive thousands of manuscripts per year, so no SASE, no answer, and no apologies. Follow the rules, be *very* patient and keep trying. We want to publish you."

THE HOMEOWNER, America's How-to Magazine, Family Media Inc., 3 Park Ave., New York NY 10016. Editor: Jim Liston. Managing Editor: Lorraine Ulrich. 30% freelance written. Monthly (combined Jan/Feb; July/Aug) magazine on home improvement, maintenance. Aimed at men and women who want to successfully complete home improvement (even ambitious remodeling) and repair projects. Circ. 650,000. Pays on acceptance. Publishes ms an average of 10 months after acceptance. Byline given. Offers 50% kill fee. Buys first North American serial rights. Submit seasonal/holiday material 8 months in advance. Computer printout submissions acceptable; no dot-matrix. Reports in 1 month. Sample copy $1.95 and 8x10 SAE; writer's guidelines for #10 SAE and 1 first class stamp.
Nonfiction: How-to (remodeling, home maintenance); personal experience (hands-on experience with building a home, remodeling or carpentry project); and technical (sophisticated or engineering how-to, related to home projects). No humor regarding writer's ineptitude as a do-it-yourselfer. Buys 30 mss/year. Length: 1,500 maximum. Pays $35 and up. Sometimes pays the expenses of writers on assignment.

‡HOMESTYLES MAGAZINE, Matvest Media Corp., Suite 115, 6800 France Ave. S., Minneapolis MN 55435. (612)927-6707. Editor: Anne Welsbacher. Managing Editor: Ed Jackson. 80% freelance written. Works with a small number of new/unpublished writers each year. A quarterly magazine covering "the joys of building and living in new homes." Estab. 1986. Circ. 110,000. Pays 6 weeks after acceptance. Publishes ms an average of 6 months after acceptance. Byline given. Offers 25% kill fee. Buys first North American serial rights and second serial (reprint) rights. Submit seasonal/holiday material 6 months in advance. Simultaneous, photocopied and previously published submissions OK. Prefers electronic submissions IBM compatible; 300 or 1200 baud modem; Wordperfect software; but requires hard copy also. "If assigned story is provided on floppy disk with hard copy, 10% bonus will be paid." Computer printout submissions acceptable. Reports in 3 weeks. Free sample copy and writer's guidelines.
Nonfiction: How-to, humor, and informational on interior design, hobbies, energy. "We are looking for lighthearted, fun articles on joys of new home ownership to complement home plans content of the magazine. We would also like general (not overly technical) how-tos on interior design, small and large home projects;

profile of the building process from start to finish of a home using home plans." Special issues: Distinguished Homes, Best Home Designs, and Best Home Plans. No articles that have nothing to do with homes or lifestyle focusing on the home. Buys 12 mss/year. Query. Length: 800-2,000 words. Pays $200-500. Sometimes pays the expenses of writers on assignment.

Photos: Send photos with submission. Reviews transparencies. Offers $50-175/color photo; add-on payment for b&w with article. Model release required. Buys one-time rights.

Fiction: Humorous and slice-of-life vignettes. "Must focus on lifestyle in a new home and revolve around a home as a major focus."

Tips: "Query editor. Our columns are a good place to start to get a feel of *Homestyles*; we want bright, informative, colorful writing giving general information and ideas for home lovers. Writer's need not be experts. There may be suggested assignments in freelancer's backyard of interest to our magazine. That's true especially of newly built homes from home plans we feature in magazine. We have a special interest in photos or home feature stories with photos. We can help with leads. Features about lifestyles of families in regard to their new homes in freelancers vicinity are most open. We will be increasing our editorial space over the next two years and will need more writers. We need stringers in many regions. Inquire."

‡HORTICULTURE, The Magazine of American Gardening, 755 Boylston St., Boston MA 02116. Published by the Horticulture Associates. Editor: Thomas C. Cooper. 90% freelance written. Monthly. Buys first North American serial rights. Byline given. Pays on acceptance. Query. Reports in 6 weeks. Publishes ms an average of 7 months after acceptance.

Nonfiction: Uses articles from 2,000-5,000 words on all aspects of gardening. "We cover indoors and outdoors, edibles and ornamentals, garden design, noteworthy gardens and gardeners." Study publication.

Photos: Color transparencies and top quality b&w prints, 8x10 only; "accurately identified." Buys one-time rights.

HOUSE & GARDEN, The Conde Nast Bldg; 350 Madison Ave., New York NY 10017. Editor-in-Chief: Louis Oliver Gropp. Editors: Denise Otis and Martin Filler. Monthly. Circ. 500,000. Buys first North American rights. Pays on acceptance. Since all its editorial stories are written by staff members or experts, it has no writer's guidelines. It does *not* accept unsolicited manuscripts, photographs, illustrations, or the like.

HOUSE BEAUTIFUL, The Hearst Corp., 1700 Broadway, New York NY 10019. (212)903-5000. Editor: JoAnn Barwick. Executive Editor: Margaret Kennedy. Editorial Director: Mervyn Kaufman. Director of Copy/Features: Carol Cooper Garey. (212)903-5236. 15% freelance written. Prefers to work with published/established writers. Emphasizes design, architecture and building. Monthly magazine; 200 pages. Circ. 840,000. Pays on acceptance. Publishes ms an average of 4 months after acceptance. Byline given. Submit seasonal/holiday material 4 months in advance of issue date. Computer printout submissions acceptable; prefers letter-quality to dot-matrix. Reports in 5 weeks.

Nonfiction: Historical (landmark buildings and restorations); how-to (kitchen, bath remodeling service); interview; new product; and profile. Submit query with detailed outline or complete ms. Length: 300-1,000 words. Pays varying rates.

Photos: State availability of photos with ms.

‡LEAF & LEISURE, Plant, Pool & Patio Magazine, Wordcraft Inc., 902 E. 7th St., Austin TX 78702. (512)482-8199. Editor: Marilyn Good. 100% freelance written. A bimonthly magazine covering horticulture, pools and spas. Circ. 20,000. Pays on publication. Publishes ms an average of 3 months after acceptance. Byline given. Buys first North American serial rights or second serial (reprint) rights. Submit seasonal/holiday material 6 months in advance. Photocopied submissions OK. Computer printout submissions acceptable; prefers letter-quality to dot-matrix. Reports in 1 month. Sample copy $2; free writer's guidelines.

Nonfiction: How-to (horticulture); new product; photo feature (landscape); and technical (horticulture, pool and spa). No information about plant material not specifically of the Southwest. Buys 20 mss/year. Query with or without published clips, or send complete ms. Length: 750-2,000 words. Pays $75-150. Sometimes pays the expenses of writers on assignment.

Photos: State availability of photos with submission. Reviews contact sheets and transparencies. Offers $20-300/photo. Model releases and identification of subjects required. Buys one-time rights.

Columns/Departments: Landscape, Native Plants, Vegetables, Herbs, and Pool and Spa. Buys 15 mss/year. Query. Length: 800-1,000 words. Pays $75.

LOG HOME GUIDE FOR BUILDERS & BUYERS, Muir Publishing Company Ltd., 1 Pacific Ave., Gardenvale, Quebec H9X 1B0 Canada. (514)457-2045. U.S. Editorial Office: Exit 447, I-4D, Hartford TN 37753. (615)487-2256. Editor: Doris Muir. 65% freelance written. Quarterly magazine covering the buying and building of log homes. "We publish for persons who want to buy or build their own log home. The writer should always keep in mind that this is a special type of person—usually a back-to-the-land, back-to-tradition type of individual who is looking for practical information on how to buy or build a log home." Circ. 125,000. Pays on publication. Publishes ms an average of 6 months after acceptance. Byline given. Buys all rights. Submit seasonal/holiday material 4 months in advance. Simultaneous queries, and simultaneous ("writer should explain"), photocopied, and previously published submissions OK. Electronic submissions OK on IBM PC, but requires hard copy. Computer printout submissions acceptable; no dot-matrix. Reports in 2 weeks. Sample copy $3.50 (postage included). Writer's guidelines for SASE.

Nonfiction: General interest; historical/nostalgic (log home historic sites, restoration of old log structures); how-to (anything to do with building log homes); inspirational (sweat equity—encouraging people that they can build their own home for less cost); interview/profile (with persons who have built their own log homes); new product (or new company manufacturing log homes—check with us first); personal experience (author's own experience with building his own log home, with photos is ideal); photo feature (on log home decor, author or anyone else building his own log home); and technical (for "Techno-log" section; specific construction details, i.e., new log buiding details, joining systems). Also, "would like photo/interview/profile stories on famous persons and their log homes—how they did it, where they got their logs, etc." Interested in log commercial structures. "Please no exaggeration—this is a truthful, back-to-basics type of magazine trying to help the person interested in log homes." Buys 25 mss/year. Query with clips of published work or send complete ms. "Prefer queries first with photo of subject house." Length: open. Pays $50-600.

Photos: State availability of photos. Send photos with query "if possible. It would help us to get a real idea of what's involved." Pays $5-25 for b&w, $25-50 for color transparencies. "All payments are arranged with individual author/submitter." Captions and identification of subjects required. Buys all rights unless otherwise arranged.

Columns/Departments: Pro-Log (short news pieces of interest to the log-building world); Techno-Log (technical articles, i.e., solar energy systems; any illustrations welcome); Book-Log (book reviews only, on books related to log building and alternate energy; "check with us first"); Chrono-Log (features on historic log buildings); and Decor (practical information on how to finish and furnish a log house). Buys possible 50-75 mss/year. Query with clips of published work or send complete ms. Length: 100-1,000 words or more. "All payments are arranged with individual author/submitter." Enclose SASE.

Tips: "The writer may have a better chance of breaking in at our publication with short articles and fillers since writing well on log homes requires some prior knowledge of subject. The most frequent mistakes made by writers in completing an article assignment for us are not doing enough research or not having understanding of the subject; not people oriented enough; angled toward wrong audience. They don't study the publication before they submit manuscripts."

NATIONAL GARDENING, Magazine of the National Gardening Association, (formerly *Gardens for All News*), 180 Flynn Ave., Burlington VT 05401. (802)863-1308. Editor: Katharine Anderson. 65% freelance written. Monthly tabloid covering food gardening and food trees. "We publish not only how-to-garden techniques, but also news that affects gardeners, like science advances. Specific, experienced-based articles with carefully worked-out techniques for planting, growing, harvesting, using garden fruits and vegetables sought. Most of our material is for gardeners with several years' experience." Circ. 250,000. Pays on acceptance. Publishes ms an average of 9 months after acceptance. Byline given. Buys first serial rights and occasionally second (reprint) rights to material originally published elsewhere. Submit seasonal/holiday material 4 months in advance. Photocopied and previously published submissions OK. Computer printout submissions acceptable; prefers letter-quality to dot-matrix. SAE. Reports in 2 weeks on queries; 1 month on mss. Sample copy $1; writer's guidelines for SASE and 1 first class stamp.

Nonfiction: How-to, humor, inspirational, interview/profile, new product, personal experience, photo feature and technical. "All articles must be connected with food/gardening." Buys 80-100 mss/year. Query. Length: 300-3,500 words. Pays $30-450/article. Sometimes pays the expenses of writers on assignment.

Photos: Vicki Congdon, photo manager. Send photos with ms. Pays $20-40 for b&w photos; $40 for color photos. Captions, model releases and identification of subjects required.

Tips: "Wordiness is a frequent mistake made by writers. Few writers understand how to write 'tight'. The most irritating easily correctable problem is careless grammar and poor spelling, often even in otherwise well-written pieces."

N.Y. HABITAT MAGAZINE, For Co-op, Condominium and Loft Living, The Carol Group, Ltd., 928 Broadway, New York NY 10010. (212)505-2030. Editor: Carol J. Ott. Managing Editor: Tom Soter. 75% freelance written. Bimonthly magazine covering co-op, condo and loft living in metropolitan New York for "sophisticated, affluent and educated readers interested in maintaining the value of their homes and buying new homes." Circ. 10,000. Pays on publication. Publishes ms an average of 10 weeks after acceptance. Byline given. Offers negotiable kill fee. Buys first North American serial rights. Submit seasonal/holiday material 3 months in advance. Computer printout submissions acceptable. SASE. Reports in 3 weeks. Sample copy for $3, 9x12 SAE and 5 first class stamps; writer's guidelines for business size SAE and 1 first class stamp.

Nonfiction: Only material relating to co-op and condominium living in New York metropolitan area. Buys 20 mss/year. Query with published clips. Length: 750-1,500 words. Pays $25-1,000.

1,001 HOME IDEAS, Family Media, Inc., 3 Park Ave., New York NY 10016. (212)340-9250. Editor: Ellen Frankel. Executive Editor: Kathryn Larson. 40% freelance written. Prefers to work with published/established writers. A monthly magazine covering home furnishings, building, remodeling and home equipment. "We are a family shelter magazine edited for young, mainstream homeowners, providing ideas for decorating, remodeling, outdoor living, and at-home entertaining. Emphasis on ideas that are do-able and affordable." Circ. 1,500,000. Pays on acceptance. Publishes ms an average of 6 months after acceptance. Byline given. Offers 25% kill fee. Buys first North American serial rights, second serial (reprint) rights, or makes work-for-hire assignments. Submit seasonal/holiday material 12 months in advance. Computer printout submissions acceptable. Reports in 1 month. Sample copy $2.50; writer's guidelines for business size SAE with 1 first class stamp.
Nonfiction: Book excerpts (on interior design and crafts only); how-to (on decorating, remodeling and home maintenance); interview/profile (of designers only); new product; photo feature (on homes only); crafts; home equipment; and home furnishings and decor. No travel, religious, technical or exposés. Buys 15 mss/year. Query with or without published clips, or send complete ms. Length: 300-2,000 words. Pays $100-750 for assigned articles; pays $100-500 for unsolicited articles. Sometimes pays the expenses of writers on assignment.
Photos: State availability of photos with submission. Reviews transparencies and prints. Offers $10-100/photo. Captions, model releases, and identification of subjects required. Buys one-time rights.
Columns/Departments: Lunne Cusack, column/department editor. 1,001 Ways to Save $$$ (consumer buymanship, housing, finance, home furnishings, products, etc.) 1,500 words. Buys 12 mss/year. Query. Pays $300-600.
Tips: "The idea is what sells an article to us . . . good ideas for decorating, remodeling and improving the home, and well-researched information on how-to, with any necessary directions and patterns, to help the reader carry out the idea. The department, 1,001 Ways to Save $$$, is the area most open to freelance writers. We also look for features which we can turn into photo features on decorating, remodeling and improving the home."

PHOENIX HOME & GARDEN, Arizona Home Garden, Inc., 3136 N. 3rd Ave., Phoenix AZ 85013. (602)234-0840. Editor: Manya Winsted. Managing Editor: Nora Burba. 50% freelance written. Monthly magazine covering homes, furnishings, entertainment, lifestyle and gardening for Phoenix area residents interested in better living. Circ. 35,000. Pays on publication. Publishes ms an average of 4 months after acceptance. Byline given. Buys all rights. Submit seasonal/holiday material 6 months in advance. Queries *only*. Simultaneous queries OK. Computer printout submissions acceptable; no dot-matrix. Reports in 6 weeks on queries. Sample copy $2, plus $2.10 postage.
Nonfiction: General interest (on interior decorating, architecture, gardening, entertainment, food); historical (on furnishings related to homes); some how-to (on home improvement or decorating); health, beauty, fashion; and travel (of interest to Phoenix residents). Buys 100 or more mss/year. Query with published clips. Length: 1,200 words maximum. Pays $75-300/article.
Tips: "It's not a closed shop. I want the brightest, freshest, most accurate material available. Study the magazine to see our format and style. Major features are assigned to staff and tried-and-true freelancers."

‡PRACTICAL HOME OWNER, (formerly *New Shelter*), Rodale Press, 33 E. Minor St., Emmaus PA 18049. Articles Editor: John Viehman. 75% freelance written. Works with a small number of new/unpublished writers each year. Magazine published 9 times/year about practical homes. Circ. 700,000. Pays on acceptance. Buys all rights. Submit seasonal material at least 6 months in advance. Electronic submissions OK via IBM "XY-Write III", but requires hard copy also. Computer printout submissions acceptable; no dot-matrix. Reports in 6 weeks.
Nonfiction: "We are the magazine of innovative, yet practical, home designs and projects of use to our audience of advanced do-it-yourselfers. We are looking for the work of innovators who are at the cutting edge of affordable housing, alternate energy, water and resource conservation, etc. Our subtitle is, "Practical Ideas for the Homeowner," and that really says it all. We don't want run-of-the-mill, wooden how-to prose. We want lively writing about what real people have done with their homes, telling how and why our readers should do the same." Query with clips of previously published work. Length: 1,000-2,000 words. Rate of payment depends on quality of ms.
Photos: Mitch Mandel, photo editor. State availability of photos. Pays $15-75 for b&w contact sheets with negatives and 8x10 glossy prints with ms. Pays $50 minimum for 2x2 or 35mm color transparencies. Captions and model releases required.
Tips: No hobby/craft or overly general, simplistic articles.

SAN DIEGO HOME/GARDEN, Westward Press, Box 1471, San Diego CA 92101. (714)233-4567. Editor: Peter Jensen. Managing Editor: Dirk Sutro. 50% freelance written. Works with a small number of new/unpublished writers each year. Monthly magazine covering homes, gardens, food, and travel for residents of San Diego city and county. Circ. 36,000. Pays on publication. Publishes ms an average of 3 months after acceptance. Byline given. Buys first North American serial rights only. Submit seasonal material 3 months in advance. Photocopied submissions OK. Computer printout submissions acceptable; prefers letter-quality to dot-matrix. Reports in 1 month. Free writer's guidelines for SASE.

Nonfiction: Residential architecture and interior design (San Diego-area homes only); remodeling (must be well-designed—little do-it-yourself), residential landscape design; furniture; other features oriented towards upscale readers interested in living the cultured good life in San Diego. Articles must have local angle. Buys 5-10 unsolicited mss/year. Query with published clips. Length: 700-2,000 words. Pays $50-200. Pays expenses of writers on assignment.

Tips: "No out-of-town, out-of-state subject material. Most freelance work is accepted from local writers. Gear stories to the unique quality of San Diego. We try to offer only information unique to San Diego—people, places, shops, resources, etc."

SELECT HOMES MAGAZINE, Select Home Designs, 382 W. Broadway, Vancouver, British Columbia V5Y 1R2 Canada. (604)879-4144. Editor: Pam Miller Withers (West). Toronto address: 2000 Ellesmere Rd., Unit 1, Scarborough, Ontario M1H 2W4 Canada. Editor: Jim Adair (East). 40% freelance written. Prefers to work with published/established writers; works with a small number of new/unpublished writers each year for news items. Magazine published 8 times/year covering decorating, energy, finance, and how-to as applied to homes for mostly upper-income single-family homeowners. Circ. 160,000. Pays on acceptance. Publishes ms an average of 5 months after acceptance. Buys 80 or more text/photo packages/year. Byline and photo credits given. Usually buys first Canadian serial rights; simultaneous rights, first rights, or second serial (reprint) rights, if explained. Submit seasonal/holiday material 3-12 months in advance. Simultaneous queries, and simultaneous, photocopied and previously published submissions OK if explained. Computer printout submissions acceptable; no dot-matrix. SASE or SAE, IRCs. Reports in 1 month. Sample copy for $1 and magazine size SAE; writer's guidelines for SAE.

Nonfiction: How-to, humor, and personal experience on decorating, interior design, energy, financial matters and architecture. Special sections include kitchen, spring; bathroom, fall. "We prefer economy of words with lengthier cutlines for photos." No business profiles, lifestyle articles or articles on home finance written by non-Canadians. Buys 80 or more mss/year. Query with published clips. Length: 650-1,500 words. Pays $50 (news and some reprints)-600 (occasionally higher). Sometimes pays expenses of writers on assignment.

Photos: State availability of photos. Reviews contact sheets and 2¼x2¼ transparencies. Pays $50-250, color. "We pay mostly on a negotiable per-day rate, but we like to work from stock lists, too. Send stock lists to the Toronto office." Captions and model release requested. Buys one-time rights.

Columns/Departments: Architecture; The Back Porch (essays, light or humorous, home-related); 1001 Decorating Ideas; Energy; How-To; International Report (new trends in decor or architecture); Maintenance; Money; Outdoor Projects; Renovation. See writer's guidelines for additional details.

Fillers: Newsbreaks. Buys 10/year. Length: 100-500 words. Pays $15-150.

Tips: "Submit clips and outline and tell us what special interests you have (decorating, energy, how-to). Know the magazine well enough to tell us which column your query is aimed at. The editors generate 75% of the magazine's article ideas and assign them to writers whose style or background matches. We actively solicit book excerpts and reprints; please mention if your material is one of these. We retain stringers throughout Canada. See our guidelines to apply."

TEXAS GARDENER, The Magazine for Texas Gardeners, by Texas Gardeners, Suntex Communications, Inc., Box 9005, Waco TX 76714. (817)772-1270. Editor: Chris S. Corby. Managing Editor: Rita Miller. 80% freelance written. Works with a small number of new/unpublished writers each year. Bimonthly magazine covering vegetable and fruit production, ornamentals and home landscape information for home gardeners in Texas. Circ. 37,000. Pays on publication. Publishes ms an average of 4 months after acceptance. Byline given. Buys first North American serial rights and all rights. Submit seasonal/holiday material 6 months in advance. Computer printout submissions acceptable; prefers letter-quality to dot-matrix. Reports in 6 weeks. Sample copy $2.75; writer's guidelines for business size SAE and 1 first class stamp.

Nonfiction: How-to, humor, interview/profile and photo feature. "We use feature articles that relate to Texas gardeners. We also like personality profiles on hobby gardeners and professional horticulturists who are doing something unique." Buys 50-100 mss/year. Query with clips of published work. Length: 800-2,400 words. Pays $50-200.

Photos: "We prefer superb color and b&w photos; 90% of photos used are color." State availability of photos. Pays negotiable rates for 2¼ color transparencies and 8x10 b&w prints and contact sheets. Model release and identification of subjects required.

Tips: "First, be a Texan. Then come up with a good idea of interest to home gardeners in this state. Be specific. Stick to feature topics like "How Alley Gardening Became a Texas Tradition." Leave topics like "How to Control Fire Blight" to the experts. High quality photos could make the difference. We would like to add several writers to our group of regular contributors and would make assignments on a regular basis. Fillers are easy to come up with 'in-house'. We want good writers who can produce accurate and interesting copy. Frequent mistakes made by writers in completing an article assignment for us are that articles are not slanted toward Texas gardening, show inaccurate or too little gardening information or lack good writing style. We will be doing more 'people' features and articles on ornamentals."

YOUR HOME, Meridian Publishing, Inc., Box 10010, Ogden UT 84409. (801)394-9446. Editor: Marjorie H. Rice. 65% freelance written. A monthly inhouse magazine covering home/garden subjects. Circ. 94,000. Pays on acceptance. Publishes ms an average of 8 months after acceptance. Byline given. Buys first rights and second serial (reprint) rights. One year lead time. Submit seasonal/holiday material 10 months in advance. Simultaneous, photocopied and previously published submissions OK. Computer printout submissions acceptable; prefers letter-quality to dot-matrix. Reports in 6 weeks. Sample copy for $1 and 9x12 SAE; writer's guidelines for business size SAE and 22¢ postage. All requests for samples and guidelines should be addressed Attn: Editorial Assistant.

Nonfiction: General interest articles about fresh ideas in home decor, ranging from floor and wall coverings to home furnishings. Subject matter includes the latest in home construction (exteriors, interiors, building materials, design), the outdoors at home (landscaping, pools, patios, gardening), remodeling projects, home management and home buying and selling. Buys 40 mss/year. Length: 1,000-1,400 words. Pays 15¢/word for first rights plus nonexclusive reprint rights. Payment for second serial rights is negotiable.

Photos: State availability of photos or send photos with query. Reviews 35mm or larger transparencies and 5x7 or 8x10 color prints. Pays $35 for inside photo; pays $50 for cover photo. Captions, model releases and identification of subjects required.

Tips: "The key is a well-written query letter that: 1) demonstrates that the subject of the article is practical and useful and has national appeal 2) shows that the article will have a clear, focused theme and will be based on interviews with experts 3) outlines the availability (from the writer or a photographer or a PR source) of top-quality color photos 4) gives evidence that the writer/photographer is a professional."

Humor

Publications listed here *specialize* in gaglines or prose humor. Other publications that use humor can be found in nearly every category in this book. Some have special needs for major humor pieces; some use humor as fillers; many others are interested in material that meets their ordinary fiction or nonfiction requirements but has a humorous slant. Other markets for humorous material can be found in the Cartoon and Comic Books and Gag Writing sections. For a closer look at writing humor, consult *How to Write and Sell (Your Sense of) Humor* by Gene Perret and *The Craft of Comedy Writing* by Sol Saks (Writer's Digest Books).

HUMOR NEWS AND NOVELTIES, People, Books, Records, Movies & Videos, Box 9582, Washington DC 20016. (202)537-1096. Editor: James Roland. 50% freelance written. Eager to work with new/unpublished writers. Bimonthly magazine. "*Humor News and Novelties* is devoted exclusively to humor and to all types of humor products. It reviews books, records, tapes, movies, videos, greeting cards, gifts, gag items, and other humor-type products." Estab. 1985. Circ. 20,000. Pays on acceptance. Publishes ms an average of 2 months after acceptance. Byline given. Buys first serial rights and reprint rights for cartoons; makes work-for-hire assignments. Submit seasonal/holiday material 4 months in advance. Simultaneous queries and photocopied submissions OK. Computer printout submissions acceptable; no dot-matrix. Reports in 1 month. Free writer's guidelines.

Nonfiction: Humor; interview/profile (with humor professionals); personal experience; photo feature; and product reviews (following specific format). Nothing nonhumorous. Query. Length: varies. Payment varies. Sometimes pays the expenses of writers on assignment.

Photos: Reviews contact sheets. Captions, model releases and identification of subjects required. Buys variable rights.

Columns/Departments: Reviews, films, books and records. Query with published clips. Length: varies. Payment varies.

Fiction: Humorous. Query with published clips. Length: varies. Pays $200-300.

Fillers: Jokes, gags, and one-liners. Length: no limit. Payment varies.

Tips: "We would like to see more submissions about agents and producers of comedy. Also, we plan to use more fiction."

LONE STAR HUMOR, Lone Star Publications of Humor, Suite 103, Box 29000, San Antonio TX 78229. Editor: Lauren I. Barnett. 50% (or more) freelance written. A humor book-by-subscription for "the general public and 'comedy connoisseur' as well as the professional humorist." Circ. 1,200. Pays on publication, "but we try to pay before that." Publishes ms an average of 6 months after acceptance. Buys variable rights. Submit seasonal/holiday material 6 months in advance. Photocopied submissions and sometimes previously published work OK. Computer printout submission acceptable; no dot-matrix. Reports in 2 months on queries; 3 months on mss. Inquire for prices and availability of sample copy. Writer's guidelines for business size SAE and 1 first class stamp.

Nonfiction: Humor (on anything topical/timeless); interview/profile (of anyone professionally involved in humor); and opinion (reviews of stand-up comedians, comedy plays, cartoonists, humorous books, *anything* concerned with comedy). "Inquire about possible theme issues." Buys 15 mss/year. Query with clips of published work if available. Length: 500-1,000 words; average is 700-800 words. Pays $5-20 and contributor's copy.

Fiction: Humorous. Buys variable mss/year. Send complete ms. Length: 500-1,000 words. Pays $5-20 and contributor's copy.

Poetry: Free verse, light verse, traditional, clerihews and limericks. "Nothing too 'artsy' to be funny." Buys 10-20/year. Submit maximum 5 poems. Length: 4-16 lines. Inquire for current rates.

Fillers: Clippings, jokes, gags, anecdotes, short humor and newsbreaks—"must be humorous or humor-related." Buys 20-30 mss/year. Length: 450 words maximum. Inquire for current rates.

Tips: "Our needs for freelance material will be somewhat diminished; writers should inquire (with SASE) before submitting material. We will be generating more and more of our humor inhouse, but will most likely require freelance material for books and other special projects. If the words 'wacky, zany, or crazy' describe the writer's finished product, it is *not* likely that his/her piece will suit our needs. The best humor is just slightly removed from reality."

MAD MAGAZINE, E.C. Publications, 485 Madison Ave., New York NY 10022. (212)752-7685. Editors: John Ficarra and Nick Meglin. 100% freelance written. Magazine published 8 times/year on humor, all forms. Circ. 1½ million. Pays on acceptance. Publishes ms an average of 6 months after acceptance. Byline given. Buys all rights. Submit seasonal/holiday material 6 months in advance. Photocopied submissions OK. Computer printout submissions acceptable; prefers letter-quality to dot-matrix. Reports in 1 month. Sample copy $1.50; writer's guidelines for legal size SAE and 1 first class stamp.

Nonfiction: Humor. "We're always on the lookout for new ways to look at hot trends—music, computers, etc." No text pieces. "No formats we're already doing or have done to death like . . . 'You know you're _____ when . . .'." Buys 400 mss/year. Query or send complete ms. Pays $300/*MAD* page. Sometimes pays the expenses of writers on assignment.

Columns/Departments: Don Martin and department ideas. Buys 30 mss/year. Send complete ms. Pays $300/MAD page.

Fiction: Humorous. No text pieces. "We're a visually-oriented magazine." Buys 100 mss/year. Query or send complete ms. Pays $300/MAD page.

Poetry: Free verse, light verse, traditional and parody. Buys 20/year. Pays $300/*MAD* page.

Fillers: Short humor. Buys 100/year. Pays $300/*MAD* page.

Tips: "Freelancers can best break into our magazine with nontopical material (no movie or TV spoofs). If we see even a germ of talent, we will work with that person. We like outrageous but *clean* humor."

‡NATIONAL LAMPOON, National Lampoon Inc., 635 Madison Ave., New York NY 10022. (212)688-4070. Executive Editor: Larry Sloman. 50% freelance written. A monthly magazine of "offbeat, irreverent satire." Circ. 400,000. Pays on acceptance. Publishes ms an average of 2 months after acceptance. Byline given. Offers 20% kill fee. Buys first North American serial rights. Simultaneous submissions OK. Computer printout submissions acceptable; prefers letter-quality to dot-matrix. Reports in 2 months. Sample copy $2 with SAE.

Nonfiction: Humor. Buys 60 mss/year. Query with published clips. Length: approximately 2,000 words. Pays 25-40¢/word. Pays the expenses of writers on assignment.

Columns/Departments: John Bendel, column/department editor. True Facts (weird true-life stories). Special True Facts issue during first quarter of each year. Buys 240/year. Send complete ms. Length: 200 words maximum. Pays $10/item; $20/photo.

Fiction: Humorous. Send complete ms.

Tips: True Facts section is most open to freelancers.

ORBEN'S CURRENT COMEDY, 1200 N. Nash St., #1122, Arlington VA 22209. (703)522-3666. Editor: Robert Orben. For "speakers, toastmasters, businessmen, public relations people, communications professionals." Biweekly. Buys all rights. Pays at the end of the month for material used in issues published that month. "Material should be typed and submitted on standard size paper. Leave three spaces between each item. Computer printout submissions acceptable. Unused material will be returned to the writer within a few days if SASE is enclosed. We do not send rejection slips. If SASE is not enclosed, all material will be destroyed after being considered except for items purchased."

Fillers: "We are looking for funny, performable one-liners, short jokes and stories that are related to happenings in the news, fads, trends and topical subjects. The accent is on laugh-out-loud comedy. Ask yourself, 'Will this line get a laugh if performed in public?' Material should be written in a conversational style, and if the joke permits it, the inclusion of dialogue is a plus. We are particularly interested in material that can be used by speakers and toastmasters: lines for beginning a speech, ending a speech, acknowledging an introduction, specific occasions, anything that would be of use to a person making a speech. We can use lines to be used at roasts, sales meetings, presentations, conventions, seminars and conferences. Short, sharp comment on business trends, fads and events is also desirable. Please do not send us material that's primarily written to be read rather than spoken. We have little use for definitions, epigrams, puns, etc. The submissions must be original. If material is sent to us that we find to be copied or rewritten from some other source, we will no longer consider material from the contributor." Pays $8.

Tips: "Follow the instructions in our guidelines. Although they are quite specific, we have received everything from epic poems to serious novels."

‡TRIFLE MAGAZINE, Imaginary News Reported by Real People, Box 182, Dover NH 03820. (603)749-5114. Editor: Mary Pat Kingsbury. 100% freelance written. A semiannual magazine of humorous fictional "news." "*Trifle Magazine* presents a satirical version of our nation's most venerable news magazines using standard news magazine format." Estab. 1985. Circ. 50,000. Pays on publication. Publishes ms an average of 3 months after acceptance. Byline given. Buys one-time rights. Previously published submissions OK. Computer printout submissions acceptable; no dot-matrix. Reports in 4 months on mss. Sample copy $3; writer's guidelines for letter size SASE.

Photos: Black and white prints, and illustrations should accompany ms.

Columns/Departments: Spouting Off (writers vent frustrations, disillusionment, etc. on social issues, daily life, the human condition—nonfiction with a humorous tone) 150-750 words; and Newsnotes (brief, fictional news items, usually accompanied by black and white prints) 100-200 words. Buys 15 mss/year. Send complete ms. Pays $15-75.

Fiction: Adventure, ethnic, fantasy, historical, humorous, mainstream, mystery, religious, science fiction, slice-of-life vignettes, fictional book, movie, music, concert, theatre, reviews, and fictional articles on politics and world events. All categories should be written in news article format. "No sex, violence or discussion of abortion. Material should be in good taste. We aim to make people laugh out loud." Buys 50 mss/year. Send complete ms. Length: 200-2,000 words. Pays $25-150.

Poetry: Avant-garde, free verse, light verse and traditional. Nothing serious, erotic, violent or melancholy. Poetry is used as filler. Buys 5 poems/year. Length: 20 lines maximum. Pays $10-25.

Fillers: Illustrated gags (illustration must accompany ms) and short humor. Buys 10/year. Length: 25-50 words. Pays $10-25.

Tips: "We are very appproachable, but we do appreciate good organization, neatness, and correct grammar and spelling. Published and unpublished writers should submit material."

In-Flight

Most major in-flight magazines cater to business travelers and vacationers who will be reading, during the flight, about the airline's destinations. Editors of these magazines use general interest material in addition to travel and popular aviation articles. Airline mergers and/or closings can affect these magazines. The "in-flight" magazine writer should watch for airline announcements in the news and in ads. The newest sample copies and writer's guidelines will give you the latest information. In corresponding with in-flight magazines not based in the United States, remember to enclose an International Reply Coupon or an International Postal Money Order for responses. The majority of in-flight magazines pays for articles in cash; there are some, however, that compensate writers with airline coupons, enabling them to travel via the airline that has published their work.

ABOARD, North-South Net, Inc., 777 41st St., Box 40-2763, Miami Beach FL 33140. (305)673-2665 or 673-8577. Editor: Ana C. Mix. 50% freelance written. Eager to work with new/unpublished writers. Bimonthly magazine covering destinations for the Equatorian, Dominican, Panamanian, Paraguayan, Bolivian, Chilean, Salvadoran and Venezuelan national airlines. Entertaining, upbeat stories for the passengers. Circ. 79,000. Pays on publication. Publishes ms an average of 2 months after acceptance. Byline given. Offers $100 kill fee. Buys first Western Hemisphere rights and second serial reprint rights. Simultaneous queries, and simultaneous, photocopied, and previously published submissions OK. Computer printout submissions acceptable; prefers letter-quality to dot-matrix. Reports in 3 weeks on queries; 5 weeks on mss. Sample copy for 11x14 SAE and $1.05 postage; writer's guidelines for #10 SAE and 1 first class stamp.

Nonfiction: General interest, interview/profile, new product, travel, sports, business, science, technology and topical pieces. Nothing "controversial, political, downbeat or in any way offensive to Latin American sensibilities." Buys 60 mss/year. Query. Length: 1,200-1,500 words. Pays $150-250 (with photos).

Photos: State availability of photos with query. Reviews b&w photos and color transparencies. Offers no additional payment for photos accepted with ms. Captions, model release and identification of subjects required.

Tips: "Study *Aboard* and other inflights, write exciting, succinct stories with an upbeat slant and enclose photos with captions. Break in with destination pieces for the individual airline or those shared by all seven. Writers must be accurate. Photos are almost always indispensable. Manuscripts are accepted either in English or Spanish. Translation rights must be granted. All manuscripts are subject to editing and condensation."

‡AIR WISCONSIN, MIDSTATE, JET AMERICA, MIDWAY AIRLINES, FLIGHT CRAFT, GOLDEN PACIFIC, GREAT AMERICAN AIRWAYS, HORIZON AIR, PACIFIC COAST AIRLINES, SAN JUAN AIRWAYS, SCENIC AIRWAYS, WINGS WEST and WEST AIR., Skies America Publishing Co., 9600 SW Oak St., Portland OR 97223. (503)244-2299. Editor: Robert E. Patterson. Managing Editor: Lee A. Sherman. 80% freelance written. Works with a small number of new/unpublished writers each year. Monthly and bimonthly inflight magazines for regional airlines in the western United States. "Our readers are affluent (median income is $40,159; 72% own property in excess of $100,000), well-educated (49% engaged in postgraduate study), businessmen/executives (78% are in professional/technical and managerial/administration fields), with a wide variety of interests and activities." Circ. 1.5 million. Pays on publication. Publishes ms an average of 3 months after acceptance. Byline given. Offers $50 kill fee. Buys first serial rights for articles, one-time rights for photos. Submit seasonal/holiday material 3 months in advance. Simultaneous queries OK. Computer printout submissions acceptable. Reports in 2 weeks. Sample copy for 8½x11 SAE and $1.75 postage; writer's guidelines for business SAE and 1 first class stamp.

Nonfiction: Attractions in the West, Midwest, Florida, and most major air hub cities, business, city features, general interest, health/medicine, historical, investing, humor, corporate profile, interview/profile, new product, photo feature, sports, technical and travel. Buys 60 mss/year. Query. Length: 1,000-1,500 words. Pays $200-400. Sometimes pays the expenses of writers on assignment.

Photos: Prefers that photography accompany articles. State availability of photos. Reviews 35mm transparencies. Pays $25-50 for b&w and color photos. Captions and identification of subjects required.

Tips: We would like to see colorful profiles of entrepreneurs, local celebrities and unusual businesses in Miami, Minneapolis, Cleveland, Boston, New York, Indianapolis, Washington, D.C., Detroit, Kansas City, the U.S. Virgin Islands, New Orleans, Dallas and Chicago.

‡AMERICA WEST AIRLINES MAGAZINES, Skyword Marketing, Inc., Suite 236, 7500 N. Dreamy Draw Dr., Phoenix AZ 85020. (602)997-7200. Editor: Ellen Alperstein. Assistant Editor: Donald Slutes. 85% freelance written. A monthly "general interest magazine with special emphasis in the west and southwest U.S. Some midwestern subject matter is appropriate as well. We look for ideas and people that celebrate opportunity, and those who capitalize on it." Estab. 1986. Pays on acceptance. Publishes ms an average of 4 months after acceptance. Byline given. Offers 33% kill fee. Buys first North American rights. Submit seasonal/holiday material 4 months in advance. Simultaneous submissions OK, "if indicated as such." Reports in 1 month on queries; 5 weeks on mss. Sample copy for 9x12 SAE; writer's guidelines for letter size SAE with 44¢ postage.

Nonfiction: General interest, interview/profile, photo feature and travel. May also consider essays, how-to and humor. No puzzles, reviews or highly controversial features. Buys 72-80 mss/year. Query with published clips. Length: 500-2,200. Pays $200-750. Pays the expenses of writers "as specified in assignment letter."

Photos: State availability of photos. Offers $25-250/photo. Captions, model releases and identification of subjects required. Buys one-time rights.

Columns/Departments: Achievers (mini-profiles of creative entrepreneurs who demonstrate strong connections with the region from which they come); Wild West (natural resources from an area within the route system of America West). Buys 30-40 mss/year. Query with published clips. Length: 500-1,500 words. Pays $200-350.

Fiction: Humor. ("We rarely use humor, but would consider exceptional pieces of a regional orientation.") No horror, inspirational or political. Buys 1 ms/year. Send complete ms. Length: 800-1,800. Pays $200-500.

Tips: "Send a SASE and ask for editorial concept and route map. Telephone queries are not appreciated. Queries should be accompanied by a SASE or we cannot guarantee a reply."

AMERICAN WAY, Mail Drop 2G23, Box 619616, Dallas/Fort Worth Airport TX 75261-9616. (817)355-1583. Editor: Walter A. Damtoft. 98% freelance written. Prefers to work with published/established writers.

Fortnightly inflight magazine for passengers flying with American Airlines. Pays on acceptance. Publishes ms an average of 6 months after acceptance. Buys exclusive world rights; splits reprint fee 50/50 with the author. Simultaneous queries and photocopied submissions OK. Computer printout submissions acceptable; prefers letter-quality to dot-matrix. Free sample copy; writer's guidelines for SASE.

Nonfiction: Business and CEO profiles, the arts and entertainment, sports, personalities, computers, food, science and medicine, and travel. "We are amenable to almost any subject that would be interesting, entertaining or useful to a passenger of American Airlines." Also humor, trivia, trends, and will consider a variety of ideas. "Articles involving current controversies are rarely scheduled; however, we are not Pollyanish. We can and do publish thoughtful articles on serious subjects." Buys 300-350 mss/year. Query with published clips. Length: 1,500-1,750 words. Pays $450 and up; shorter items earn $100 or more. Sometimes pays the expenses of writers on assignment.

Photos: Pays $50 for each published photograph made by a writer while researching an article.

DELTA SKY, Inflight Magazine of Delta Air Lines, Halsey Publishing co., 12955 Biscayne Blvd., N. Miami FL 33181. (305)893-1520. Editor: Lidia de Leon. 90% freelance written. Monthly. "*Delta Sky* is a monthly general-interest magazine with a business/finance orientation whose main purpose is to entertain and inform business travelers aboard Delta Air Lines." Circ. 290,000. Pays on acceptance. Publishes ms an average of 2 months after acceptance. Byline given. Offers 100% kill fee when cancellation through no fault of writer. Buys first North American serial rights. Submit seasonal/holiday material 9 months in advance. Simultaneous and photocopied submissions OK. Computer printout submissions acceptable; prefers letter-quality to dot-matrix. Reports in 1 month. Sample copy for 9x12 SAE; free writer's guidelines.

Nonfiction: General interest. No reprints, religious or first-person/experiential. Buys 160 mss/year. Query with published clips. Length: 1,500-2,500 words. Pays $350-600 for assigned articles; pays $300-500 for unsolicited articles. Pays expenses of writers on assignment.

Photos: State availability of photos with submission. Reviews 5x7 prints. Offers $25-100/photo. Captions, model releases and identification of subjects required. Buys one-time rights.

Columns/Departments: On Management (managerial techniques/methods with current appeal), 1,700 words. Query with published clips. Pays $300-400.

Tips: "Send a comprehensive, well-detailed query tied in to one of the feature categories of the magazine, along with clips of previously published work. Since our lead times call for planning of editorial content 6-9 months in advance, that should also be kept in mind when proposing story ideas. We are always open to good feature-story ideas that have to do with business, and technology. Next in order of priority would be leisure, sports, entertainment, and consumer topics."

‡EAST/WEST NETWORK, INC., 34 E. 51st St., New York NY 10022. Editorial Director: Donald Dewey. "We are backlogged with submissions and prefer not to receive unsolicited submissions at this time."

‡FRONTIER, East/West Network, 5900 Wilshire Blvd., 8th Floor, Los Angeles CA 90036. (213)937-5810. Editor: Joan Jasmine Yee. 90% freelance written. A monthly magazine covering the Rocky Mountain region. Estab. 1986. Circ. 60,000. Pays on acceptance. Publishes ms an average of 2 months after acceptance. Byline given. Offers 25% kill fee. Buys first North American serial rights. Submit seasonal/holiday material 6 months in advance. Can accept most electronic transmissions. Computer printout submissions acceptable; prefers letter-quality to dot-matrix. Reports in 2 weeks. Sample copy $2; writer's guidelines for letter size SAE with 1 first class stamp.

Nonfiction: Essays; general interest; humor; interview/profile; new product (fashion and technology); travel and sports. Buys 85 mss/year. Query. Length: 1,000-3,000 words. Pays $400-700. Pays the expenses of writers on assignment.

❝ *Anyone who sends a manuscript about a generic idea— such as lions—might later see a story about lions in the magazine. In a year, we might get a dozen or more proposals for lion stories. I expect a lot of writers feel their ideas are stolen when, in fact, the 'ideas' are neither original nor specific.* **❞**

Pat Robbins, **National Geographic WORLD**

Photos: State availability of photos with submissions.
Columns/Departments: Pioneers (brief profiles of innovative people/companies), 500 words; and Adventures (extraordinary travel experiences), 1,500 words. Buys 50 mss/year. Query. Pays $150-400.

‡MIDWAY MAGAZINE, Skies America Publishing Co., Suite 310, 9600 S.W. Oak St., Portland OR 97223: (503)244-2299. Editor: Robert Patterson. Managing Editor: Lee Sherman. 75% freelance written. Monthly magazine. Estab. 1986. Circ. approximately 40,000. Pays on publication. Publishes ms an average of 2 months after acceptance. Byline given. Offers $50 kill fee. Buys one-time rights. Submit seasonal/holiday material 6 months in advance. Simultaneous submissions OK. Computer printout submissions acceptable; prefers letter-quality to dot-matrix. Reports in 1 month. Sample copy $3 with SASE; free writer's guidelines.
Nonfiction: Interview/profile, photo feature and travel. "Business features should be timely, well-researched and well-focused. Corporate profiles and personality profiles are encouraged. Travel destination pieces should be original, detailed and lively. No stale pieces that sound like canned promotions." Buys 24 mss/year. Query with published clips. Length: 1,000-2,500 words. Pays $150-400 for assigned articles; pays $150-250 for unsolicited articles. Sometimes pays the expenses of writers on assignment.
Photos: Send photos with submission. Reviews color transparencies and 8x10 b&w prints. Offers no additional payment for photos accepted with ms. Identification of subjects required. Buys one-time rights.
Columns/Departments: Epicure (food department focusing on regional cuisines or individual restaurants that are unusual or outstanding). Buys 10 mss/year. Query with published clips. Length: 1,000-1,500 words. Pays $150-300.
Tips: The cities we focus on are: New York: Boston; Chicago; Indianapolis; Miami; Minneapolis; Dallas; Cleveland: Detroit; New Orleans; Washington, D.C.; Orlando; Virgin Islands; Cincinnati; Kansas City; Philadelphia. Write to us with specific ideas relating to these cities. A fresh, original idea with excellent photo possibilities will receive our close attention. Areas most open to freelancers are corporate profiles; destination travel pieces with an unusual slant; personality profiles on businessmen and women, entrepreneurs."

OZARK MAGAZINE, East/West Network, 8th Floor, 5900 Wilshire Blvd., Los Angeles CA 90036. Editor: Laura Dean Bennet. "We are backlogged with submissions and prefer not to receive unsolicited submissions at this time."

PACE MAGAZINE, Piedmont Airlines Inflight Magazine, Fisher-Harrison Publications Inc., 338 N. Elm St., Greensboro NC 27401. (919)378-6065. Managing Editor: Leslie P. Daisy. 20% freelance written. Monthly magazine covering travel, trends in business for the present and the future and other business-related articles. Circ. 1.7 million. Pays on acceptance. Publishes ms an average of 8 months after acceptance. Byline given. Buys first serial rights. Submit holiday/seasonal material 6 months in advance. Computer printout submissions acceptable: no dot-matrix. Reports in 2 months. Sample copy for $4 and SAE; writer's guidelines for SAE and 1 first class stamp.
Nonfiction: Travel (within the Piedmont flight route), trends in business, business management, employee relations, business psychology and self-improvement as related to business and other business-related articles. No personal, religious, historical, nostalgic, humor, or interview/profile pieces. No cartoons. Buys 40 mss/year. Send query or complete ms. No telephone queries. Length: 1,500-4,000 words. Pays $75-200.
Photos: Send photos with accompanying ms. Captions required.
Tips: "Major features are assigned; I would rarely accept an unsolicited major feature. Writers frequently do not perceive the audience correctly—they must not be familiar with the magazine."

PAN-AM CLIPPER, East/West Network, 34 E. 51st St., New York NY 10022. (212)888-5900. Editor: Richard Kagan. Associate Editor: Paula Rackow. "We are backlogged with submissions and prefer not to receive unsolicited submissions at this time."

PARADISE, Air Niugini, Box 7186, Boroko, Papua New Guinea. 273437/273569. Editor: Geoff McLaughlin, M.B.E. 60% freelance written. Sometimes prefers to work with published/established writers; works with a small number of new/unpublished writers each year; eager to work with new/unpublished writers. Bimonthly magazine covering life and culture in Papua New Guinea. "*Paradise* magazine is a colorful magazine of very high standard that enjoys worldwide distribution. Its popularity stems from the fact that the articles reflect life and culture of present day Papua New Guinea accompanied by photography that is equal to the best in the world." Circ. 40.000 (subscription), 36,000 (give away). Byline given. Not copyrighted. Submit seasonal/holiday material 4 months in advance. Simultaneous and previously published submissions OK. Computer printout submissions acceptable; no dot-matrix. Free sample copy.
Nonfiction: Book excerpts, general interest, historical/nostalgic, interview/profile, new product, personal experience, photo feature and travel. Query. Length: open. Pays K1.00 per column per 10.5 cm. to be paid in the form of a Miscellaneous Charge Order (MCO) for air travel.
Tips: This English language bimonthly concentrates on life and culture in Papua New Guinea. *Paradise* no longer features one destination piece on places along Air Niugini's routes.

‡**PEOPLExpressions**, Halsey Publishing Co., #202, 12955 Biscayne Blvd., Miami FL 33181. (305)893-1520. Editor: Chauncy Mabe. 99% freelance written. A monthly general interest magazine distributed on all flights of People Express Airlines. Estab. 1986. Circ. 200,000. Pays on acceptance. Publishes ms an average of 2 months after acceptance. Byline given. Offers negotiable kill fee. Buys first North American serial rights. Submit seasonal/holiday material 1 year in advance. Simultaneous and photocopied submissions OK. Computer printout submissions acceptable; must be letter-quality, double spaced. Reports in 3 months. Sample copy $3.

Nonfiction: Essays, general interest, historical/nostalgic, humor, interview/profile, new product, opinion, personal experience, photo feature and travel—anything offbeat, well written, in good taste. No political or inspirational. Buys 150 mss/year. Query. Length: 1,000-2,000 words. Pays $300-600 for assigned articles; pays $100-300 for unsolicited articles.

Photos: State availability of photos with submission. Reviews 35mm or larger, color only, no duplicates. Offers $35 minimum/photo. Captions required. Buys one-time rights.

Columns/Departments: Humor, Fitness, Personal Essays, etc. Buys variable number of mss, "but we have contributing editors who provide bulk." Query. Length: 1,000 words. Pays $100-300.

‡**PRESIDENTIAL AIRWAYS MAGAZINE**, Pace Communications, Inc., 338 N. Elm St., Greensboro NC 27401. (919)378-6065. Editor: Dave March. 40% freelance written. Bimonthly in-flight magazine of a Washington DC-based airline covering general information on Washington DC-area business trends and personalities for the business traveler. Also publishes features on destination cities. Estab. 1986. Circ. 5,000. Pays on publication. Byline given. Buys first North American serial rights. Submit seasonal/holiday material 5 months in advance. Reports in 6 weeks.

Nonfiction: Interview/profile (presidents of Washington-area businesses) and features on destination cities. Buys 24 mss/year. Query with published clips. Length: 2,500-3,000 words. Pays $200-300.

Photos: State availability of photos with queries. Reviews color transparencies. Payment is negotiable. Captions required. Buys one-time rights.

Tips: "Send well written query that shows writing style as well as describing slant on the subject. Include information on four-color photo availability or opportunities."

REPUBLIC, East/West Network, Inc., 5900 Wilshire Blvd., Los Angeles CA 90036. (213)937-5810. Editor: Jerry Lazar. 95% freelance written. Prefers to work with published/established writers; works with a small number of new/unpublished writers each year. Monthly in-flight magazine of Republic Airlines covering American popular culture for predominantly business travelers. Circ. 170,000 copies. Pays on acceptance. Publishes ms an average of 2 months after acceptance. Byline given. Pays ⅓ kill fee. Buys first serial rights and second (reprint) rights to material originally published elsewhere (books only). Submit seasonal/holiday material at least 3 months in advance. Computer printout submissions acceptable; no dot-matrix. Reports in 2 weeks on queries; 1 month on mss. Sample copy and writer's guidelines for $2.

Nonfiction: General interest, humor, interview/profile, photo feature, travel, business, media, technology, health, law, Americana, sports and fitness. "Material must be of national interest—topical but noncontroversial. No reviews, but subjects vary widely. We mostly use writers whose work we know." Buys 96 mss/year. Length: 750-2,500 words. Pays $200-600. Query with clips of published work. Sometimes pays the expenses of writers on assignment.

Photos: Ursula Brookbank, art director. State availability of photos. Pays $75 minimum for color transparencies; $25 minimum for 8x10 b&w glossy prints. Captions preferred. Model releases required "where applicable." Buys one-time rights.

Tips: "The writer has a better chance with short articles and fillers because there is more demand, less risk. Freelance writers should be aware of the need for writers to think visually—an awareness of how words will look on the page and what kinds of graphics will accompany them. A frequent mistake is underestimating the sophistication of the audience; failing to perceive that we are targeted for the upscale business traveler."

REVIEW MAGAZINE, Eastern Airline's Inflight Magazine, East/West Network, 34 E. 51st St., New York NY 10022. Editor: John Atwood. Associate Editor: Madeline Johnson. 30% freelance written. Prefers to work with published/established writers. Monthly magazine featuring reprints of articles previously published in leading consumer magazines, plus book excerpts and original articles. Circ. 1 million. Pays on acceptance. Publishes ms an average of 6 months after acceptance. Byline given. Buys one-time rights. Photocopied and previously published submissions should be submitted by original publication, not by individuals. Computer printout submissions acceptable; no dot-matrix. Reports in 2 weeks on queries; 3 weeks on mss. Sample copy $2.

Nonfiction: General interest, historical/nostalgic, humor, interview/profile and photo feature. No how-to or violence-related material. Buys 40 mss/year. Query. Length: 2,000-3,000 words. Pays $500-750 for original articles. Sometimes pays the expenses of writers on assignment.

Photos: Kevin Fisher, art director. State availability of photos. Pays $75-600 for color transparencies; $75-500 for b&w prints. Identification of subjects required.

Tips: "We are always on the lookout for 2,000-word service and essay pieces on New York, Boston, and Washington, especially subjects of interest to passengers on Eastern Air-Shuttle."

SILVER KRIS, Singapore Airlines Inflight Magazine, MPH Magazine (S) Pte Ltd., Pan-I Warehouse Complex #03-01/03, 601 Sims Dr., Singapore 1438. 748-5050. Editor: Steve Thompson. 100% freelance written. Works with a small number of new/unpublished writers each year. Monthly magazine. "We publish mainly travel stories, but also arts and crafts, theater, festivals, sports and humor." Circ. 250,000. Byline given. Pays on publication. Publishes ms an average of 9 months after acceptance. Offers 50% kill fee. Buys one-time rights and first Asian rights. Submit seasonal/holiday material 4 months in advance. Simultaneous queries, and simultaneous, photocopied, and previously published submissions OK. Reports in 1 month. Free sample copy and writer's guidelines.
Nonfiction: Humor (short anecdotes); personal experience; photo feature and travel. No political, religious or moral controversy, no "straight" travel writing with routes, prices and tired cliches. Buys 80 mss/year. Send complete ms. Length: 1,500-3,000 words. Pays $200-800. Sometimes pays the expenses of writers on assignment.
Photos: Send photos with query or ms. Reviews 35mm color transparencies. Pays $50-75. Identification of subjects required. Buys one-time rights.
Fillers: Anecdotes and short humor. Buys 30/year. Length: 1,000-1,500 words. Pays $125-200.
Tips: "Subjects should be offbeat (I'd rather have a photo essay on the rickshaw paintings of Dacca, for instance, than a story on the best hotels or restaurants there), and style should be light and entertaining. An important criterion in *Silver Kris* is the provision of first-rate original color transparencies. Writers will stand a better chance if they can provide these—or at least suggest other sources."

‡SKYLINES, Brighter Square Publishing, Suite 350, 901 Mopac Expwy. S., Austin TX 78746. (512)328-4560. Editor: Elise Nakhnikian. Managing Editor: Ken Lively. 100% freelance written. A monthly general interest, in-flight magazine for New York Air. "We are more of a regional magazine than a typical in-flight, as the greater majority of our readers live in either New York City, Boston, or Washington, D.C." Estab. 1985. Circ. 22,000. Pays on publication. Publishes ms an average of 4 months after acceptance. Byline given. Offers 25% kill fee. Buys first rights or second serial (reprint) rights. Submit seasonal/holiday material 4 months in advance. Sometimes accepts previously published submissions. Computer printout submissions acceptable; no dot-matrix. Reports in 6 weeks on queries; 8 weeks on mss. Sample copy $2; free writer's guidelines.
Nonfiction: Book excerpts, essays, exposé, general interest, humor, interview/profile and photo feature. "We look for stories about people and places in the cities to which New York Air flies. Wit and style are important. No puff pieces; stories about museums, hotels, major tourist attractions, airlines, historical accounts." Buys approximately 130 mss/year. Query with published clips. Length: 1,500-4,000 words. Pays $300-800 for assigned articles; pays $300-600 for unsolicited articles.
Photos: Send photos with submission if available. Reviews transparencies and prints. Offers $50/photo. Captions required. Buys one-time rights.
Columns/Departments: Cuisine (restaurant reviews/restaurant profiles/overviews of a cuisine or type of food); Style (fashion/design); Sports (profiles of teams, players, or coaches/seasonal overviews); and Sidelines (catchall category for any short feature of interest). Buys approximately 60 mss/year. Query with published clips. Length: 1,500-2,000 words. Pays $300-400.
Tips: "Features are most open to freelancers. We are looking for lively writing with an intelligent point of view. It is important—perhaps necessary—to be aware of current trends, issues, and developments in the East Coast corridor."

‡SOUTHWEST SPIRIT, East/West Network, Suite 800, 5900 Wilshire Blvd., Los Angeles CA 90036. (213)937-5810. Editor: Gabrielle Gosgriff. Assistant Editor: Margaret Mittelbach. 90% freelance written. Prefers to work with published/established writers. The monthly magazine of Southwest Airline covering the Southwest, primarily Texas. Pays on acceptance. Publishes ms an average of 2 months after acceptance. Byline given. Offers 25% kill fee. Buys first North American serial rights. Simultaneous and photocopied submissions OK. Computer printout submissions acceptable; prefers letter-quality to dot-matrix. Reports in 1 month. Sample copy $2; writer's guidelines for SASE.
Nonfiction: Essays (issue-oriented); general interest; profile (business); new product (technology, medicine); photo feature (occasionally); travel (very limited); and sports. No historical/nostalgic, personal experience, or unsolicited travel pieces. Buys approximately 120 mss/year. Query with published clips. Length: 250-3,500 words. Pays $150-900. Pays the expenses of writers on assignment.
Photos: State availability of photos with submission. Reviews color transparencies and b&w prints. Identification of subjects required. Buys one-time rights.
Columns/Departments: Cutting Edge (new products, the arts, innovative businesses and ideas—"newsy and energetic"), 250-600 words; Wining & Dining (briefs on Southwest foods, wines, restaurants, chefs, etc.), 500-1,000 words; and Only In . . . (colorful essays on one-of-a-kind places and people in the Southwest), 1,000 words. Buys 60 mss/year. Query with published clips. Pays $150-350.

TWA AMBASSADOR, (for Trans World Airlines), The Paulsen Publishing, Inc. Suite 209, 289 E. 5th St., St. Paul MN 55101. Editor-in-Chief: Bonnie Blodgett. 90% freelance written. "For TWA passengers, top management executives, professional men and women, world travelers; affluent, interested and responsive." Monthly magazine. Circ. 263,000. Pays on acceptance. Buys all rights. Pays 30% kill fee. Byline given. Submit seasonal/holiday material 6 months in advance. Reports in 1 month. Sample copy $2.
Nonfiction: Subjects dealing with substantive issues, the arts, in-depth profiles, business concerns, straight reporting on a variety of subjects and service pieces. Query. Length: 2,500-5,000 words. Pays $600-1,800.
Columns/Departments: Destinations, Science, Business, Personal Finance, The Arts, Media, Books and The Law. Query to Doug Tice, Managing Editor. Length: 1,800-2,000 words. Pays $150-500.

UNITED, East/West Network, 34 East 51st St., New York NY 10022. (212)888-5900. Editor: Jonathan Blake. 90% freelance written. Monthly magazine, a United Airlines inflight publication. Circ. 450,000. Pays on acceptance. Publishes ms an average of 4 months after acceptance. Byline given. Offers 25% kill fee. Buys first North American serial rights. Submit seasonal/holiday material 4-6 months in advance. Computer printout submissions acceptable; no dot-matrix. Reports in 1 month. Sample copy $2; writer's guidelines for SAE.
Nonfiction: Interview/profile (upscale and well-known business owners, restauranteurs, designers, architects, artists, celebrities, etc.); travel (only US and Pacific countries); and trends. No European travel or how-to. Buys 100 mss/year. Query with published clips. Length: 750-2,000 words. Pays $500-1,000. Sometimes pays the expenses of writers on assignment.
Columns/Departments: Lilia Dlaboha, column/department editor. Communique: Short newsy items on new products, events, etc. Buys 25/year. Query with published clips. Length: 200-500 words.

USAIR MAGAZINE, Halsey Publishing Co., 600 3rd Ave, New York NY 10016. Editor: Richard Busch. Senior Editor: Mark Orwoll. 95% freelance written. A monthly general interest magazine published for airline passengers, many of whom are business travelers, male, with high incomes and college educations. Circ. 190,000. Pays on acceptance. Publishes ms an average of 4 months after acceptance. Buys first rights only. Submit seasonal material 6 months in advance. Photocopied submissions OK. Computer printout submissions acceptable; prefers letter-quality to dot-matrix. Reports in 2 weeks. Sample copy $3; free writer's guidelines with SASE.
Nonfiction: Travel, business, sports, health, food, personal finance, nature, the arts, science/technology and photography. "No downbeat stories or controversial articles." Buys 100 mss/year. Query with clips of previously published work. Length: 1,500-3,500 words. Pays $400-1,000. Pays expenses of writers on assignment.
Photos: Send photos with ms. Pays $75-150/b&w print, depending on size; color from $100-250/print or slide. Captions preferred; model release required. Buys one-time rights.
Columns/Departments: Sports, food, money, health, business, living and science. Buys 3-4 mss/issue. Query. Length: 1,200-1,800 words. Pays $300-450.
Tips: "Send irresistible ideas and proof that you can write. It's great to get a clean manuscript from a good writer who has given me exactly what I asked for. Frequent mistakes are not following instructions, not delivering on time, etc."

WINDS, The Inflight Magazine of Japan Air Lines, Japan Air Lines/Emphasis, Inc., Central-Roppongi Bldg., 1-4-27 Roppongi, Minato-ku, Tokyo 106 Japan. (03)585-8857. Editor: Tom Chapman. 85% freelance written. Monthly magazine covering Japan/Asia/Southeast Asia. International inflight magazine devoted to literate and interesting interpretations of Japan and the Japanese, and, now and then, other destinations in Asia of Japan Air Lines. Circ. 280,000. Pays on publication. Publishes ms an average of 8 months after acceptance. Byline given. Kill fee negotiable. Buys first Asian serial rights. Submit seasonal/holiday material 6 months in advance. Simultaneous queries and photocopied submissions OK. Computer printout submissions acceptable; prefers letter-quality to dot-matrix. SAE. IRC. Reports in 3 weeks. Sample copy $10 U.S. via airmail, $4 U.S. via surface mail; "no personal checks, please."
Nonfiction: Book excerpts; interview/profile, personal experience, photo feature and travel. Familiarity with Japan always necessary. Buys 75 mss/year. Query with published clips. Length: 1,000-4,000 words. Pays $300-3,000+. Sometimes pays the expenses of writers on assignment.
Photos: State availability of photos. Reviews 35mm color transparencies. Pays $50-150 and up. Captions, model release, and identification of subjects required. Buys one-time rights.
Tips: "We find it rare to accept unsolicited material from writers who have not spent considerable time in Japan."

ALWAYS submit mss or queries with a stamped, self-addressed envelope (SASE) within your country or International Reply Coupons (IRCs) purchased from the post office for other countries.

Juvenile

Just as children change (and grow), so do juvenile magazines. Children's editors stress that writers must read *recent* issues. This section of *Writer's Market* lists publications for children aged 2-12. Magazines for young people 13-19 appear in the Teen and Young Adult category. Many of the following publications are produced by religious groups, and where possible, the specific denomination is given. Writers should also note in some of the listings that editors will buy "second rights" to stories. This refers to a story which has been previously published in a magazine and to which the writer has already sold "first rights." Payment is usually less for the re-use of a story than for first-time publication. For the writer with a story or article slanted to a specific age group, the following children's index is a quick reference to markets for each age group.

Juvenile publications classified by age

Two- to Five-Year-Olds: *Chickadee, Children's Playmate, The Friend, Happy Times, Highlights for Children, Humpty Dumpty, Nature Friend, Our Little Friend, Owl, Story Friends, Turtle Magazine for Preschool Kids, Wee Wisdom.*

Six- to Eight-Year-Olds: *Bible-in-Life Pix, Boys' Life, Chickadee, Children's Digest, Children's Playmate, Cobblestone, Cricket, Dash, The Dolphin Log, The Electric Company, Faces, The Friend, Happy Times, Highlights for Children, Humpty Dumpty, Jack and Jill, National Geographic World, Nature Friend, Odyssey, Our Little Friend, Owl, Pennywhistle Press, Pockets, Primary Treasure, R-A-D-A-R, Ranger Rick, Stickers and Stuff, Story Friends, 3-2-1 Contact, Touch, Toys 'R Us, Wee Wisdom, Wonder Time, Young American, Young Author, The Young Crusader.*

Nine- to Twelve-Year-Olds: *Action, Bible-in-Life Pix, Boy's Life, Chickadee, Children's Digest, Clubhouse, Cobblestone, Counselor, Cricket, Crusader, Dash, The Dolphin Log, The Electric Company, Enfantaisie, Faces, The Friend, High Adventure, Highlights for Children, National Geographic World, Nature Friend, Odyssey, On the Line, Owl, Pennywhistle Press, Pockets, R-A-D-A-R, Ranger Rick, Stickers and Stuff, Story Friends, 3-2-1 Contact, Touch, Toys 'R Us, Wee Wisdom, Young American, Young Authors, The Young Crusader.*

ACTION, Dept. of Christian Education, Free Methodist Headquarters, 901 College Ave., Winona Lake IN 46590. (219)267-7656. Editor: Vera Bethel. 100% freelance written. Weekly magazine for "57% girls, 43% boys, ages 9-11; 48% city, 23% small towns." Circ. 25,000. Pays on publication. Publishes ms an average of 1 month after acceptance. Rights purchased vary; may buy simultaneous rights, second (reprint) rights or first North American serial rights. Submit seasonal/holiday material 3 months in advance. Simultaneous and previously published submissions OK. Computer printout submissions acceptable; no dot-matrix. SASE must be enclosed. Reports in 1 month. Free sample copy and writer's guidelines for 6x9 SASE.

Nonfiction: How-to (make gifts and craft articles); informational (nature articles with pictures); and personal experience (my favorite vacation, my pet, my hobby, etc.). Buys 50 mss/year. Submit complete ms with photos. Length: 200-500 words. Pays $15.

Fiction: Adventure, humorous, mystery and religious. Buys 50 mss/year. Submit complete ms. Length: 1,000 words. Pays $25. SASE must be enclosed; no return without it.

Poetry: Free verse, haiku, light verse, traditional, devotional and nature. Buys 20/year. Submit maximum 5-6 poems. Length: 4-16 lines. Pays $5.

Tips: "Send interview articles with children about their pets, their hobbies, a recent or special vacation—all with pictures if possible. Kids like to read about other kids. A frequent mistake made by writers is using words too long for a 10-year-old and *too many* long words."

BIBLE-IN-LIFE PIX, David C. Cook Publishing Co., 850 N. Grove Ave., Elgin IL 60120. (312)741-2400. Editor: Charlotte Graeber. 20% freelance written. Weekly magazine covering Christian-oriented material for children ages 8-11. "Nondenominational Sunday school publication for grades 3-6. Features articles with curricular emphasis which help to apply the Christian faith to lives of children." Pays on acceptance. Publishes ms an average of 1 year after acceptance. Byline given. Computer printout submissions acceptable; prefers letter-quality to dot-matrix. Buys all rights; makes work-for-hire assignments. Submit seasonal/holiday material 1-1½ years in advance. Reports in 6 weeks. Sample copy for 8½x11 SAE and 2 first class stamps; free writer's guidelines.
Nonfiction: Historical/nostalgic, how-to, humor, inspirational, interview/profile, personal experience and photo feature; stories about the Christian activities of real children—things Sunday school classes and children's church groups are doing. Query with published clips. Length: 600 words. Pays $70.
Fiction: Adventure, historical, humorous and religious. Query with published clips. Length: 1,000 words. Pays $110.
Tips: "We rarely buy unsolicited manuscripts. Most assignments are made to meet specific curricular needs."

BOYS' LIFE, Boy Scouts of America, Magazine Division, 1325 Walnut Hill Lane, Irving TX 75062. (214)659-2000. Editor: Robert Hood. Monthly magazine covering Boy Scout activities for "ages 8-18—Boy Scouts, Cub Scouts, and others of that age group." Circ. 1.5 million. Length: 1,000-3,000 words. Pays on acceptance. Buys one-time rights. Pays $350 minimum. Reports in 2 weeks.
Nonfiction: "Almost all articles are assigned. We do not encourage unsolicited material."
Columns/Departments: How How's (1-2 paragraphs on hobby tips). Buys 60 mss/year. Send complete ms. Pays $5 minimum.
Fillers: Jokes (Think-and-Grin—1-3 sentences). Pays $1 minimum.

CHICKADEE MAGAZINE, The Magazine for Young Children, The Young Naturalist Foundation, 56 The Espalander, Suite 306, Toronto, Ontario M5E 1A7 Canada. (416)868-6001. Editor: Janis Nostbakken. 25% freelance written. Magazine published 10 times/year (except July and August) for 4-9 year-olds. "We aim to interest (in an entertaining and lively way) children aged nine and under in the world around them." Circ. 84,000. Pays on publication. Byline given. Buys all rights. Submit seasonal/holiday material up to 1 year in advance. Computer printout submissions acceptable. Reports in 2½ months. Sample copy for $1.50 and IRCs; writer's guidelines for IRC.
Nonfiction: How-to (arts and crafts for children); personal experience (real children in real situations); and photo feature (wildlife features). No articles for older children; no religious or moralistic features. Sometimes pays the expenses of writers on assignment.
Photos: Send photos with ms. Reviews 35mm transparencies. Identification of subjects required.
Fiction: Adventure (relating to the 4-9 year old). No science fiction, fantasy, talking animal stories or religious articles. Send complete ms. Pays $100-300.
Tips: "An article—big or small— is either good or it isn't. A frequent mistake made by writers is trying to teach too much—not enough entertainment and fun."

CHILDREN'S DIGEST, Children's Better Health Institute, Box 567, Indianapolis IN 46206. (317)636-8881. Editor: Elizabeth Rinck. 85% freelance written. Works with a small number of new/unpublished writers each year. Magazine published 8 times/year covering children's health for children ages 8-10. Pays on publication. Publishes ms an average of 1 year after acceptance. Byline given. Buys all rights. Submit seasonal/holiday material 8 months in advance. Submit *only* complete manuscripts. "No queries, please." Photocopied submissions acceptable (if clear). Computer printout submissions acceptable; prefers letter-quality to dot-matrix. Reports in 2 months. Sample copy 75¢; writer's guidelines for business size SASE.
Nonfiction: Historical, interview/profile (biographical), craft ideas, health, nutrition, hygiene, exercise and safety. "We're especially interested in factual features that teach readers about the human body or encourage them to develop better health habits. We are *not* interested in material that is simply rewritten from encyclopedias. We try to present our health material in a way that instructs *and* entertains the reader." Buys 15-20 mss/year. Send complete ms. Length: 500-1,200 words. Pays 6¢/word. Sometimes pays the expenses of writers on assignment.
Photos: State availability of photos. Pays $7 for 5x7 b&w glossy prints. Model releases and identification of subjects required. Buys one-time rights.
Fiction: Adventure, humorous, mainstream and mystery. Stories should appeal to both boys and girls. "We need some stories that incorporate a health theme. However, we don't want stories that preach, preferring instead stories with implied morals. We like a light or humorous approach." Buys 15-20 mss/year. Length: 500-1,800 words. Pays 6¢/word.
Poetry: Pays $7 minimum.
Tips: "Many of our readers have working mothers and/or come from single-parent homes. We need more stories that reflect these changing times while communicating good values."

CHILDREN'S PLAYMATE, 1100 Waterway Blvd., Box 567, Indianapolis IN 46206. (317)636-8881. Editor: Elizabeth Rinck. 75% freelance written. Eager to work with new/unpublished writers. "We are looking for articles, stories, and activities with a health, safety, exercise, or nutritionally oriented theme. Primarily we are concerned with preventative medicine. We try to present our material in a positive—not a negative—light, and we try to incorporate humor and a light approach wherever possible without minimizing the seriousness of what we are saying." For children ages 5-7. Magazine published 8 times/year. Buys all rights. Byline given. Pays on publication. Publishes ms an average of 1 year after acceptance. "We do not consider outlines. Reading the whole manuscript is the only way to give fair consideration. The editors cannot criticize, offer suggestions, or review unsolicited material that is not accepted." Submit seasonal material 8 months in advance. Computer printout submissions acceptable; prefers letter-quality to dot-matrix. Reports in 2 months. Sometimes may hold mss for up to 1 year, with author's permission. Write for guidelines. "Material will not be returned unless accompanied by a self-addressed envelope and sufficient postage." Sample copy 75¢; free writer's guidelines with SASE. No query.
Nonfiction: Beginning science, 600 words maximum. A feature may be an interesting presentation on animals, people, events, objects or places, especially about good health, exercise, proper nutrition and safety. Include number of words in articles. Buys 30 mss/year. Pays about 6¢/word.
Fiction: Short stories for beginning readers, not over 700 words. Seasonal stories with holiday themes. Humorous stories, unusual plots. "We are interested in stories about children in different cultures and stories about lesser-known holidays (not just Christmas, Thanksgiving, Halloween, Hanukkah)." Vocabulary suitable for ages 5-7. Pays about 6¢/word. Include number of words in stories.
Fillers: Puzzles, dot-to-dots, color-ins, hidden pictures and mazes. Buys 30 fillers/year. Payment varies.
Tips: Especially interested in stories, poems and articles about special holidays, customs and events.

CLUBHOUSE, Your Story Hour, Box 15, Berrien Springs MI 49103. (616)471-3701. Editor: Elaine Meseraull. 75% freelance written. Works with a small number of new/unpublished writers each year. Magazine published 10 times/year covering many subjects with Christian approach, though not associated with a church. "Stories and features for fun for 9-13 year-olds. Main objective: To provide a psychological 'up' magazine that lets kids know that they are acceptable, 'neat' people." Circ. 15,000. Pays on acceptance. Publishes ms an average of 1 year after acceptance. Byline given. Buys first serial rights or first North American serial rights, one-time rights, simultaneous rights; and second serial (reprint) rights. Simultaneous queries, and simultaneous, photocopied, and previously published submissions OK. Computer printout submissions acceptable; prefers letter-quality to dot-matrix. Reports in 3 weeks. Sample copy for business or larger size SAE and 3 first class stamps; writer's guidelines for business size SAE and 1 first class stamp.
Nonfiction: How-to (crafts), personal experience and recipes (without sugar or artificial flavors and colors). "No stories in which kids start out 'bad' and by peer or adult pressure or circumstances are changed into 'good' people." Send complete ms. Length: 750-800 words ($25); 1,000-1,200 words ($30); feature story 1,200 words ($35).
Photos: Send photos with ms. Pays on publication according to published size. Buys one-time rights.
Columns/Departments: Body Shop (short stories or "ad" type material that is anti-smoking, drugs and alcohol and pro-good nutrition, etc.); and Jr. Detective (secret codes, word search, deduction problems, hidden pictures, etc.). Buys 10/year. Send complete ms. Length: 400 words maximum. Pays $10-30.
Fiction: Adventure, historical, humorous and mainstream. "Stories should depict bravery, kindness, etc., without overt or preachy attitude." No science fiction, romance, confession or mystery. Buys 50 mss/year. Send query or complete ms (prefers ms). Length: 750-800 words ($20); 1,000-1,200 words ($30), lead story ($35).
Poetry: Free verse, light verse and traditional. Buys 8-10/year. Submit maximum 5 poems. Length: 4-24 lines. Pays $5-20.
Fillers: Cartoons. Buys 10-20/year. Pay $10 maximum.
Tips: "All material for any given year is accepted during April-May in the previous year. Think from a kid's point of view and ask, 'Would this story make me glad to be a kid?' Keep the stories moving, exciting, bright and tense. Stay within length guidelines."

COBBLESTONE, Cobblestone Publishing, Inc., 20 Grove St., Peterborough NH 03458. (603)924-7209. Editor-in-Chief: Carolyn P. Yoder. 100% freelance written; (approximately 2 issues/year are by assignment only). Monthly magazine covering American history for children ages 8-14. "Each issue presents a particular theme, approaching it from different angles, making it exciting as well as informative. Half of all subscriptions are for schools." Circ. 44,000. Pays on publication. Publishes ms an average of 4 months after acceptance. Byline given. Buys all rights; makes work-for-hire assignments. All material must relate to monthly theme. Simultaneous and previously published submissions OK. Computer printout submissions acceptable; prefers letter-quality to dot-matrix. Sample copy $2.95; writer's guidelines for SASE.
Nonfiction: Historical/nostalgic, how-to, interview, plays, biography, activities and personal experience. "Request a copy of the writer's guidelines to find out specific issue themes in upcoming months." No Revolutionary War memorabilia, particularly hometown guides to monuments. No material that editorializes rather

than reports. Buys 5-8 mss/issue. Length: 800-1,200 words. Supplemental nonfiction 200-800 words. Query with published clips, outline and bibliography. Pays up to 15¢/word.

Fiction: Adventure, historical, humorous and biographical fiction. "Has to be very strong and accurate." Buys 1-2 mss/issue. Length: 800-1,200 words. Request free editorial guidelines that explain upcoming issue themes and give query deadlines. "Message" must be smoothly integrated with the story. Query with written samples. Pays up to 15¢/word.

Poetry: Free verse, light verse and traditional. Buys 6 mss/year. Submit maximum 2 poems. Length: 5-100 lines. Pays on an individual basis.

Tips: "All material is considered on the basis of merit and appropriateness to theme. Query should state idea for material simply, with rationale for why material is applicable to theme. Request writer's guidelines (includes themes and query deadlines) before submitting a query. Include SASE."

COUNSELOR, A Power Line Paper, Scripture Press Publics, Box 632, Glen Ellyn IL 60138. (312)668-6000. Manager: Joyce Gibson. Editor: Grace Anderson. 60% freelance written. Works with a small number of new/unpublished writers each year. 4-page Sunday School take-home paper issued quarterly for weekly distribution on living today by the power God gives, making the Bible practical. Circ. 160,00. Pays on acceptance. Publishes ms an average of 18 months after acceptance. Byline given. Buys first serial rights and all rights. Computer printout submissions acceptable; prefers letter-quality to dot-matrix. Reports in 2 weeks on queries; 4 weeks on mss. Free sample copy and writer's guidelines.

Nonfiction: Personal experience (first or third person adult or child [9-12], God at work in their lives—true); and photo feature—kids in action, children ages 9-12 involved in helping others. No nature, science, or historical pieces. Buys 12-20 mss/year. Query with or without published clips or send complete ms. Length: 500-1,200. First rights pays 4-7¢/word; all rights pays 5-10¢/word, depending on quality.

Photos: Send photos with query or ms. Photos only with stories. Reviews b&w contact sheets, 35mm or larger color transparencies, and 5x7 b&w and color prints. Pays $15-35 for transparencies; $3-25 for prints. Model release and identification of subjects required. Rights purchased depends on story; usually first serial rights.

Tips: "We would like articles for our World Series. Query about stories on boys and girls, 9 to 12, in other cultures—their way of life, how they came to know Christ and live for Him in their culture. Photos a must. We even will accept photo stories with brief copy."

‡CRICKET, The Magazine for Children, Open Court Publishing Co., 315 5th St., Peru IL 61354. (815)224-6643. Editor: Marianne Carus. Monthly magazine. Circ. 120,000. Pays on publication. Byline given. Buys first North American serial rights. Submit seasonal/holiday material 8 months in advance. Photocopied and previously published submissions OK. Computer printout submissions acceptable; prefers letter-quality to dot-matrix. Reports in 2 months. Sample copy $2; writer's guidelines for SASE.

Nonfiction: Historical/nostalgic, humor, personal experience and travel. Send complete ms. Length: 200-1,200 words. Pays $50-300.

Fiction: Adventure, ethnic, fantasy, historical, humorous, mystery, novel excerpts, science fiction, suspense and western. No didactic, sex, religious, or horror stories. Buys 24-36 mss/year. Send complete ms. Length: 200-1,500 words. Pays $50-375.

Poetry: Buys 8-10 poems/year. Length: 100 lines maximum. Pays $3/line on publication.

CRUSADER MAGAZINE, Box 7244, Grand Rapids MI 49510. Editor: G. Richard Broene. 40% freelance written. Works with a small number of new/unpublished writers each year. Magazine published 7 times/year. "*Crusader Magazine* shows boys (9-14) how God is at work in their lives and in the world around them." Circ. 13,000. Buys 20-25 mss/year. Pays on acceptance. Byline given. Publishes ms an average of 8 months after acceptance. Rights purchased vary with author and material; buys first serial rights, one-time rights, second serial (reprint) rights, and simultaneous rights. Submit seasonal material (Christmas, Easter) at least 5 months in advance. Photocopied and simultaneous submissions OK. Computer printout submissions acceptable; prefers letter-quality to dot-matrix. Reports in 1 month. Free sample copy and writer's guidelines for SAE and 3 first class stamps.

Nonfiction: Articles about young boys' interests: sports, outdoor activities, bike riding, science, crafts, etc., and problems. Emphasis is on a Christian multi-racial perspective, but no simplistic moralisms. Informational, how-to, personal experience, interview, profile, inspirational and humor. Submit complete ms. Length: 500-1,500 words. Pays 2-5¢/word.

Photos: Pays $4-25 for b&w photos purchased with mss.

Fiction: "Considerable fiction is used. Fast-moving stories that appeal to a boy's sense of adventure or sense of humor are welcome. Avoid preachiness. Avoid simplistic answers to complicated problems. Avoid long dialogue and little action." Length: 750-1,500 words. Pays 3¢/word minimum.

Fillers: Uses short humor and any type of puzzles as fillers.

DASH, Box 150, Wheaton IL 60189. Editor: Steve Neideck. For boys ages 8-11. Published bimonthly. Most subscribers are in a Christian Service Brigade program. Circ. 24,000. Rights purchased vary with author and material. Pays on publication. Submit seasonal material 6 months in advance. Sample copy $1.50 plus large SAE and 73¢ postage; writer's guidelines for SAE and 1 first class postage stamp.

Nonfiction: "Our emphasis is on boys and how their belief in Jesus Christ affects their everyday lives." Uses short articles about boys of this age, problems they encounter. Interview and profile. Buys 8-10 mss/year. Query. Length: 1,000-1,500 words. Pays $30-70.

Photos: Pays $25 for 8x10 b&w photos for inside use.

Fiction: Avoid trite, condescending tone. Needs adventure, mystery and action. Christian truth should be worked into the storyline (not tacked on as a "moral of the story"). Length: 1,000-1,500 words. Pays $60-90.

Tips: "Queries must be succinct, well-written and exciting, to draw my interest. Send for sample copies, get a feel for our publication. query with ideas tailored specifically for us."

THE DOLPHIN LOG. The Cousteau Society, 8440 Santa Monica Blvd., Los Angeles CA 90069. (213)656-4422. Editor: Pamela Stacey. 25% freelance written. Prefers to work with published/established writers; works with a small number of new/unpublished writers each year. Quarterly magazine covering marine biology, ecology, environment, natural history, and water-related stories. "The *Dolphin Log* is an educational publication for children ages 7-15 offered by The Cousteau Society. Subject matter encompasses all areas of science, history and the arts which can be related to our global water system. The philosophy of the magazine is to delight, instruct and instill an environmental ethic and understanding of the interconnectedness of living organisms, including people." Circ. 58,000. Pays on publication. Publishes ms an average of 6 months after acceptance. Byline given. "We do not make assignments and therefore have no kill fee." Buys one-time and translation rights. Submit seasonal/holiday material 4 months in advance. Simultaneous queries OK. Computer submissions acceptable. Reports in 4 weeks on queries; 2 months on mss. Sample copy for $2 with SAE and 56¢ postage; writer's guidelines for SASE.

Nonfiction: general interest (per guidelines); how-to (water-related crafts or science); interview/profile (of young person involved with aspect of ocean); personal experience (ocean related); and photo feature (per guidelines). "Of special interest are games involving an ocean/water-related theme which develop math, reading and comprehension skills. Humorous articles and short jokes based on scientific fact are also welcome. Experiments that can be conducted at home and demonstrate a phenomenon or principle of science are wanted as are clever crafts or art projects which also can be tied to any ocean theme. Try to incorporate such activities into any articles submitted." No "talking" animals. Buys 4-12 mss/year. Query or send complete ms. Pays $25-150.

Photos: Send photos with query or ms (duplicates only). Prefers underwater animals, water photos with children, photos which explain text. Pays $25 for b&w; $25-100 for 35mm color transparencies. Captions, model releases and identification of subjects required. Buys one-time and translation rights.

Columns/Departments: Discovery (science experiments or crafts a young person can easily do at home). Buys 4 mss/year. Send complete ms. Length: 200-750. Pays $25-50.

Fiction: Adventure (with ecological message): historical (how early cultures interacted with environment and/or animals): humorous (personal experiences with animals, ocean or environment): and science fiction (new ideas on future relationship with ocean, animals, environment). No anthropomorphism or "talking" animals. Buys "very few fiction manuscripts but would like to find good ones." Length: 500-1,200 words. Pays $25-150.

Poetry: No "talking" animals. Buys 2 poems/year. Pays $25-100.

Fillers: Jokes, anecdotes, short humor and newsbreaks. Buys 8/year. Length: 100 lines maximum. Pays $25-50.

Tips: "A freelancer can best break in at our publication by researching a topic and writing good, scientifically sound articles. We are delighted with articles which offer new insights into a particular species or relationship in nature, or principle of ecology. Feature sections use clear, simple, factual writing style combined with sound, verifiable information."

‡THE ELECTRIC COMPANY MAGAZINE. Children's Television Workshop, 1 Lincoln Plaza, New York NY 10023. (212)595-3456. Editor: Randi Hacker. Associate Editor: Eve Hall. Magazine published 10 times/year. "We are a humor/reading/activity magazine for children 6-10 years old." Circ. 250,000 + . Pays on acceptance. Publishes ms an average of 8 months after acceptance. Byline given. Offers 50% kill fee. Buys all rights. Submit seasonal/holiday material at least 6 months in advance. Simultaneous and photocopied submissions OK. Computer printout submissions acceptable. Reports in 2 weeks. Free sample copy.

Nonfiction: General interest, humor and photo feature. "No articles with heavy moral messages; or those about child abuse, saying 'no,' divorce, single parent households, handicapped children, etc." Buys 2-3 mss/year. Query with or without published clips, or send complete ms. Length: 500 words maximum. Pays $50-200.

Photos: State availability of photos with submission. Reviews transparencies. Offers $75 maximum/photo. Model releases and identification of subjects required.

Fiction: Adventure, fantasy, historical, humorous, mystery and western. "No stories with heavy moral messages; or those about child abuse, saying 'no,' divorce, single parent households, handicapped children, etc."

Buys 2 mss/year. Query or send complete ms. Length: 750-1,000 words. Pays $200 maximum.
Tips: "We are an entertainment magazine for children. Our purpose is to make them laugh and want to read. We are *not* educational per se. We want reading to be tempting and fun. No pedantics, bombastics or pedagogics, please. We publish at least one short story a month. Just think about what you liked to read when you were a kid. Also, any interesting activities or games are welcome."

‡**ENFANTAISIE, La Revue Des Jeunes**, 2603 SE 32nd Ave., Portland OR 97202. (503)235-5304. Editor: Viviane Gould. 5% freelance written. Managing Editor: Michael Gould. Bimonthly educational/classroom children's magazine for learning French. Circ. 2,000. Pays on publication. Publishes ms an average of 5 months after acceptance. Byline given. Buys first rights. Submit seasonal/holiday material 5 months in advance. "We do not publish material relating to religious holidays." Simultaneous, photocopied and previously published submissions OK. Electronic submissions OK via Macintosh disk. Computer printout submissions acceptable; prefers letter-quality to dot-matrix. Reports in 2 weeks on queries; 4 weeks on mss. Sample copy $3 with 9x12 SAE and 4 first class stamps; free writer's guidelines.
Nonfiction: Personal experience, photo feature and French culture pedagogical. No religious, how-to, technical, inspirational, exposé, or book excerpts. Buys 5 mss/year. Query. Length: 250-500 words. Pays $15-25.
Photos: State availability of photos with submission. Offers no additional payment for photos accepted with ms. Buys one-time rights.
Columns/Departments: Teachers' Forum (practical essay on an aspect of teaching French—for example, teaching reading, making visual aids, using games, etc.). Buys 5 mss/year. Send complete ms. Length: 400-500 words. Pays $15-25.
Fiction: Adventure, humorous, family situations, and sibling relations. Buys 5 mss/year. Send complete ms. Length: 250-500 words. Pays $15-25.
Tips: "As we are widely used in the classroom, features submitted in English will be translated into simplified French."

‡**FACES, The Magazine about People**, Cobblestone Publishing, Inc., 20 Grove St., Peterborough NH 03458. (603)924-7209. Editor: Carolyn P. Yoder. 95% freelance written. A magazine published 10 times/year covering world cultures for 8 to 14-year-olds. Articles must relate to the issue's theme. Circ. approximately 9,000. Pays on publication. Byline given. Buys all rights. Simultaneous and photocopied submissions OK. Previously published submissions rarely accepted. Computer printout submissions acceptable. Sample copy $2.95; writer's guidelines for SASE with 1 first class stamp.
Nonfiction: Book excerpts, essays, expose, general interest, historical/nostalgic, how-to (activities), humor, interview/profile, personal experience, photo feature, technical and travel. Articles must relate to the theme. No religious, pornographic, biased or sophisticated submissions. Buys approximately 50 mss/year. Query with published clips. Length: 250-1,000 words. Pays up to 15¢/word.
Photos: State availability of photos with submission. Reviews contact sheets and 8x10 prints. Offers $5-10/photo. Buys one-time and all rights.
Fiction: All fiction must be theme-related. Buys 10 mss/year. Query with published clips. Length: 500-1,000 words. Pays 10-15¢/word.
Poetry: Light verse and traditional. No religious or pornographic poetry or poetry not related to the theme. Buys 10 poems/year. Submit maximum 1 poem. Pays on individual basis.
Tips: "Writers must have an appreciation and understanding of people. All manuscripts for *Faces* are reviewed by the American Museum of Natural History. Writers must not condescend to our readers."

‡**THE FRIEND**, 50 East North Temple, Salt Lake City UT 84150. Managing Editor: Vivian Paulsen. 75% freelance written. Eager to work with new/unpublished writers each year. Appeals to children ages 4-12. Publication of The Church of Jesus Christ of Latter-Day Saints. Special issues: Christmas and Easter. Monthly. Circ. 200,000. Buys all rights. Pays on acceptance. "Submit only complete ms—no queries, please." Submit seasonal material 8 months in advance. Computer printout submissions acceptable. Publishes ms an average of 1 year after acceptance. Free sample copy and guidelines for writers.
Nonfiction: Subjects of current interest, science, nature, pets, sports, foreign countries, and things to make and do. Length: 1,000 words maximum. Pays 8¢/word minimum.
Fiction: Seasonal and holiday stories and stories about other countries and their children. Wholesome and optimistic; high motive, plot, and action. Also, simple but suspense-filled mysteries. Character-building stories preferred. Length: 1,200 words maximum. Stories for younger children should not exceed 700 words. Pays 8¢/word minimum.
Poetry: Serious, humorous and holiday. Any form with child appeal. Pays $15.
Tips: "Do you remember how it feels to be a child? Can you write stories that appeal to children ages 4-12 in today's world? We're interested in stories with an international flavor and those that focus on present-day problems. Send material of high literary quality slanted to our editorial requirements. Let the child solve the problem—not some helpful, all-wise adult. No overt moralizing. Nonfiction should be creatively presented—not an array of facts strung together. Beware of being cutesy."

HAPPY TIMES, The Magazine That Builds Character and Confidence, Eagle Systems International, 5600 N. University Ave., Provo UT 84604. (801)225-9000. Editor: Colleen Hinckley. Circulation Director: Mark Avery. 90% freelance written. Works with a small number of new/unpublished writers each year. Published 10 times/year for children ages 3-6 with emphasis on educational and moral content. "Each concept presented needs to teach or promote a moral value or character trait." Circ. 75,000. Pays on publication. Publishes ms an average of 9 months after acceptance. Byline given. "We usually buy first North American serial rights. In 1987, we will be including a reprinting clause in our contract." Also makes work-for-hire assignments. Submit seasonal/holiday material 10 months in advance. Simultaneous queries, and simultaneous, photocopied, and previously published submissions OK. Computer printout submissions acceptable; prefers letter-quality to dot-matrix. Report in 1 month. Writer's guidelines and theme list for SASE; sample copy for 5 first class stamps.
Nonfiction: General interest, safety, animals, trivia, biographies and unique puzzles that instruct children. "Writers must see our publication *before* submitting, or they'll be out in left field. Most articles are less than 150 words long. The concept is more important than the copy; yet the copy must be super, super tight. Each issue has a theme." Length: 50-300 words. Pays $10-50. Sometimes pays the expenses of writers on assignment.
Photos: State availability of photos. Pays negotiable rates for 35mm transparencies. Captions, model releases, and identification of subjects required. Rights negotiated.
Columns/Departments: Bedtime Story (monthly column that teaches something of value—not just a fun story; prefers nonfiction biographical sketch or story). Buys 10 mss/year. Query with published clips. Length: 500-1,250 words. Pays $50-100.

HIGH ADVENTURE, Assemblies of God, 1445 Boonville, Springfield MO 65802. (417)862-2781, ext. 1497. Editor: Johnnie Barnes. Quarterly magazine "designed to provide boys with worthwhile, enjoyable, leisure reading; to challenge them in narrative form to higher ideals and greater spiritual dedication; and to perpetuate the spirit of the Royal Rangers program through stories, ideas, and illustrations." Circ. 70,000. Pays on acceptance. Byline given. Buys one-time rights. Submit seasonal/holiday material 6-9 months in advance. Simultaneous queries, and simultaneous, photocopied, and previously published submissions OK. Reports in 1 month. Sample copy for 8½x11 SAE; free writer's guidelines.
Nonfiction: Historical/nostalgic, how-to, humor and inspirational. Buys 25-50 mss/year. Query or send complete ms. Length: 1,200 words. Pays 2¢/word.
Photos: Reviews b&w negatives, transparencies and prints. Identification of subjects required. Buys one-time rights.
Fiction: Adventure, historical, humorous, religious and western. Buys 25-50 mss/year. Query or send complete ms. Length: 1,200 words maximum. Pays 2¢/word.
Fillers: Jokes, gags and short humor. Pays $2 for jokes; others vary.

HIGHLIGHTS FOR CHILDREN, 803 Church St., Honesdale PA 18431. Editor: Kent L. Brown Jr. 80% freelance written. Magazine published 11 times/year for children ages 2-12. Circ. 2,000,000. Pays on acceptance. Publishes ms an average of 18 months after acceptance. Buys all rights. Computer printout submissions acceptable; prefers letter-quality to dot-matrix. Reports in about 2 months. Free writer's guidelines with SAE and 1 first class stamp. Sample copy $2.25.
Nonfiction: "We prefer factual features, including history and natural, technical and social science, written by persons with rich background and mastery in their respective fields. Contributions always welcomed from new writers, especially engineers, scientists, historians, teachers, etc., who can make useful, interesting and authentic facts accessible to children. Also writers who have lived abroad and can interpret the ways of life, especially of children, in other countries. Sports material, biographies and general articles of interest to children. Direct, original approach, simple style, interesting content, without word embellishment; not rewritten from encyclopedias. State background and qualifications for writing factual articles submitted. Include references or sources of information." Length: 900 words maximum. Pays $65 minimum. Also buys original party plans for children ages 7-12, clearly described in 400-700 words, including drawings or sample of items to be illustrated. Also, novel but tested ideas in crafts, with clear directions and made-up models. Projects must require only free or inexpensive, easy-to-obtain materials. Especially desirable if easy enough for early primary grades. Also, fingerplays with lots of action, easy for very young children to grasp and parents to dramatize. Avoid wordiness. Pays minimum $30 for party plans; $15 for crafts ideas; $25 for fingerplays.
Fiction: Unusual, wholesome stories appealing to both girls and boys, ages 2-12. Vivid, full of action. "Engaging plot, strong characterization, lively language." Seeks stories that the child ages 8-12 will eagerly read, and the child ages 2-7 will begin to read and/or will like to hear when read aloud. "We print no stories just to be read aloud. We encourage authors not to hold themselves to controlled word lists. Avoid suggestion of material reward for upward striving. The main character should preferably overcome difficulties and frustrations through her or his own efforts. The story should leave a positive moral and emotional impression. We especially need stories in the suspense/adventure/mystery category, and short (200 words and under) stories for the beginning reader, with an interesting plot and a number of picturable situations. Also need rebuses, stories with urban settings, stories for beginning readers (500 words), humorous and horse stories. We also would like to

see more material of 1-page length (300-500 words), both fiction and factual. We need creative-thinking puzzles that can be illustrated, optical illusions, body teasers, and other 'fun' activities. War, crime and violence are taboo. Some fantasy stories published." Length: 400-900 words. Pays $65/minimum.

Tips: "We are pleased that many authors of children's literature report that their first published work was in the pages of *Highlights*. It is not our policy to consider fiction on the strength of the reputation of the author. We judge each submission on its own merits. With factual material, however, we do prefer either authorities in their field or people with first-hand experience. In this manner we can avoid the encyclopedic article that merely restates information readily available elsewhere. We don't make assignments. Query with simple letter to establish whether the nonfiction *subject* is likely to be of interest. A beginning writer should first become familiar with the type of material which *Highlights* publishes. We are most eager for easy stories for very young readers, but realize that this is probably the most difficult kind of writing. Include special qualifications, if any, of author. Write for the child, not the editor."

HUMPTY DUMPTY'S MAGAZINE, Children's Health Publications, 1100 Waterway Blvd., Box 567, Indianapolis IN 46206. Editor: Christine French Clark. Magazine published 8 times/year stressing health, nutrition, hygiene, exercise and safety for children ages 4-6. Combined issues: February/March, April/May, June/July, and August/September. Pays on publication. Buys all rights. Submit seasonal material 8 months in advance. Reports in 10 weeks. Sample copy 75¢; writer's guidelines for SASE.

Nonfiction: "We are open to nonfiction on almost any age-appropriate subject, but we especially need material with a health theme—nutrition, safety, exercise, hygiene. We're looking for articles that encourage readers to develop better health habits without preaching. Very simple factual articles that creatively teach readers about their bodies. Simple crafts, some with holiday themes. We also use several puzzles and activities in each issue—dot-to-dot, hidden pictures, *simple* crosswords, and easy-to-play 'board' games. Keep in mind that most our readers are just *beginning* to learn to read and write, so word puzzles must be very basic." Submit complete ms. "Include number of words in manuscript and Social Security number." Length: 600 words maximum. Pays 6¢/word.

Fiction: "We're primarily interested in stories in rhyme and easy-to-read stories for the beginning reader. Currently we are needing seasonal stories with holiday themes. We use contemporary stories and fantasy, some employing a health theme. We try to present our health material in a positive light, incorporating humor and a light approach wherever possible. Avoid sexual stereotyping. Characters in contemporary stories should be realistic and up-to-date. Remember, many of our readers have working mothers and/or come from single-parent homes. We need more stories that reflect these changing times but at the same time communicate good, wholesome values." Submit complete ms. "Include number of words in manuscript and Social Security number." Length: 600 words maximum. Pays 6¢/word.

Poetry: Short, simple poems. Pays $7 minimum.

JACK AND JILL, 1100 Waterway Blvd., Box 567, Indianapolis IN 46206. (317)636-8881. Editor: Christine French Clark. 85% freelance written. Magazine published 8 times/year for children ages 6-8. Pays on publication. Publishes ms an average of 8 months after acceptance. Buys all rights. Byline given. Submit seasonal material 8 months in advance. Computer printout submissions acceptable. Reports in 10 weeks. May hold material seriously being considered for up to 1 year. "Material will not be returned unless accompanied by self-addressed envelope with sufficient postage." Sample copy 75¢; writer's guidelines for SASE.

Nonfiction: "Because we want to encourage youngsters to read for pleasure and for information, we are interested in material that will challenge a young child's intelligence *and* be enjoyable reading. Our emphasis is on good health, and we are in particular need of articles, stories, and activities with health, safety, exercise and nutrition themes. We are looking for well-written articles that take unusual approaches to teaching better health habits and scientific facts about how the body works. We try to present our health material in a positive light—incorporating humor and a light approach wherever possible without minimizing the seriousness of what we are saying." Straight factual articles are OK if they are short and interestingly written. "We would rather see, however, more creative alternatives to the straight factual article. For instance, we'd be interested in seeing a health message or facts presented in articles featuring positive role models for readers. Many of the personalities children admire—athletes, musicians, and film or TV stars—are fitness or nutrition buffs. Many have kicked drugs, alcohol or smoking habits and are outspoken about the danger of these vices. Color slides, transparencies, or black and white photos accompanying this type of article would greatly enhance salability." Buys 25-30 nonfiction mss/year. Length: 500-1,200 words. Pays approximately 6¢ a word.

Photos: When appropriate, photos should accompany ms. Reviews sharp, contrasting b&w glossy prints. Sometimes uses color slides, transparencies, or good color prints. Pays $10 for b&w. Buys one-time rights.

Fiction: May include, but is not limited to, realistic stories, fantasy adventure—set in past, present or future. All stories need a well-developed plot, action and incident. Humor is highly desirable. "Currently we need stories with holiday themes. Stories that deal with a health theme need not have health as the primary subject. We would like to see more biographical fiction." Length: 500-1,500 words, short stories; 1,500 words/installment, serials of two parts. Pays approximately 6¢ a word. Buys 20-25 mss/year.

Fillers: Puzzles (including various kinds of word and crossword puzzles), poems, games, science projects, and creative craft projects. Instructions for activities should be clearly and simply written and accompanied by models or diagram sketches. "We also have a need for recipes. Ingredients should be healthful; avoid sugar, salt, chocolate, red meat, and fats as much as possible. In all material, avoid references to eating sugary foods, such as candy, cakes, cookies and soft drinks."

Tips: "We are constantly looking for new writers who can tell good stories with interesting slants—stories that are not full of out-dated and time-worn expressions. Our best authors are writers who know what today's children are like. Keep in mind that our readers are becoming 'computer literate', living in an age of rapidly developing technology. They are exploring careers possibilities that may be new and unfamiliar to our generation. They are faced with tough decisions about drug and alcohol use. Many of them are latch-key children because both parents work or they come from single-parent homes. We need more stories and articles that reflect these changing times but that also communicate good, wholesome values. Obtain *current* issues of the magazines and *study* them to determine our present needs and editorial style."

‡JUNIOR TRAILS, Gospel Publishing House, 1445 Boonville Ave., Springfield MO 65802. (417)862-2781. Editor: John Maempa. 100% freelance written. Eager to work with new/unpublished writers. Weekly tabloid covering religious fiction; and biographical, historical, and scientific articles with a spiritual emphasis for boys and girls ages 10-11. Circ. 75,000. Pays on acceptance. Publishes ms an average of 1 year after acceptance. Byline given. Not copyrighted. Buys simultaneous rights, first rights, or second (reprint) rights to material originally published elsewhere. Submit seasonal/holiday material 1 year in advance. Simultaneous and previously published submissions OK. Computer printout submissions acceptable. Reports in 6 weeks on queries; 2 months on mss. Sample copy for 9x12 SAE and 2 first class stamps; writer's guidelines for 9x12 SAE and 2 first class stamps.

Nonfiction: Biographical, historical and scientific (with spiritual lesson or emphasis). Buys 30-40 mss/year. Send complete ms. Length: 500-1,000 words. Pays 2-3¢/word.

Fiction: Adventure (with spiritual lesson or application); and religious. "We're looking for fiction that presents believable characters working out their problems according to Biblical principles. No fictionalized accounts of Bible stories or events." Buys 50-70 mss/year. Send complete ms. Length: 1,000-1,800 words. Pays 2-3¢/word.

Poetry: Free verse and light verse. Buys 6-8 mss/year. Pays 20¢/line.

Fillers: Anecdotes (with spiritual emphasis). Buys 15-20/year. Length: 200 words maximum. Pays 2-3¢/word.

Tips: "Junior-age children need to be alerted to the dangers of drugs, alcohol, smoking, etc. They need positive guidelines and believable examples relating to living a Christian life in an ever-changing world. The most annoying aspect of working with freelance writers is failure to list Social Security number and number of words in mss; threadbare plots that indicate a lack of age-level understanding and creativity/originality."

NATIONAL GEOGRAPHIC WORLD, National Geographic Society, 17th & M Sts. NW, Washington DC 20036. (202)857-7000. Editor: Pat Robbins. Associate Editor: Margaret McKelway. Monthly magazine of factual stories of interest to children ages 8-13 years. "*World* is a strongly visual magazine; all stories must have a visual story line; no unillustrated stories are used." Circ. 3 million. Pays on publication. No byline given. Offers $50 kill fee. Buys all rights. Submit seasonal/holiday material 1 year in advance. Reports in 2 weeks. Free sample copy.

Nonfiction: Subject matter is factual. Subjects include animals, conservation, science and technology, geography, history, sports, outdoor adventure and children's activities. No fiction, poetry, book reviews, TV or current events. Humor, shorts, and game ideas are welcome. Query first. "Writing is always done after pictures are in hand. Freelance assignments are made on a contract basis."

Photos: "Freelance photography is handled in a variety of ways. Photo story submissions are reviewed by the illustrations editor. Photographers who want assignments should send a query letter first. Include a brief description of the proposed story and list the picture possibilities. If the magazine is interested, the illustrations editor will review the photographer's portfolio."

NATURE FRIEND MAGAZINE, Pilgrim Publishers, 22777 State Rd. 119, Goshen IN 46526. (219)534-2245. Editor: Stanley K. Brubaker. 30% freelance written. Prefers to work with published/established writers. Monthly magazine appreciating God's marvelous creation. Audience includes children ages 4-14 and older of Christian families who hold a literal view of Creation. Circ. 5,000. Pays on publication unless delayed more than 2 months. Publishes ms an average of 5 months after acceptance. Byline given. Buys one-time rights. Submit seasonal material 3 or more months in advance. Simultaneous queries, and simultaneous, photocopied, and previously published submissions OK if notified of other submissions or past use. Computer printout submissions acceptable; prefers letter-quality to dot-matrix. Reports in 1 month. Sample copy for 8x10 SAE and 56¢ postage; writer's guidelines $1, 6x9 SAE and 56¢ postage.

Nonfiction: General interest (various length articles on popular and odd creatures); how-to (for children in learning or building, working with nature); inspirational (praise; humbled by God's handiwork); new product (each issue has Nature's Workshop product page); personal experience (especially from child's point of view);

photo feature (about wildlife or other nature fascinating to *children*); and puzzles, projects, etc. "We buy no manuscripts which feature talking or (humanly) thinking creatures." Buys 35-50 mss/year. Send complete ms, clips and photos, if applicable. Length: 200-1,200 words. Pays $6-25.

Photos: Send photos with ms. Reviews 2¼ or 35mm color transparencies and 8x10 b&w prints. Pays $25 maximum for color; $15 maximum for b&w. Captions, model releases, and identification of subjects required. Buys one-time rights.

Fiction: Uses some true-to-life nature study stories with animals or other creature as main character (from animal's perspective). Also families enjoying nature discovery. Buys 30-50 mss/year. Length: 200-1,200 words. Pays $5-25.

Tips: "Subscribe to *Nature Friend Magazine* or study back issues—it has a definite targeted market of fundamental Christians. We want all materials to have a cheerful factual reverential mood. Writers will notice in studying *Nature Friend* that we prefer stories with our particular usage of conversation, questions and concise, fast-flowing description to give accurate and interesting stories for instant reader rapport. We welcome fascinating animal and wildlife biographies, whether stories from human point of view or animal's, but we will *not* use stories where animals think or talk like humans."

ODYSSEY, AstroMedia Corp., 625 E. St. Paul Ave., Milwaukee WI 53202. (414)276-2689. Editor: Nancy Mack. 50% freelance written. Works with a small number of new/unpublished writers each year. Monthly magazine emphasizing astronomy and outer space for children ages 8-12. Circ. 100,000. Pays on publication. Publishes ms an average of 4 months after acceptance. Buys first serial or one-time rights. Submit seasonal/holiday material 4 months in advance. Photocopied and previously published submissions OK. Computer printout submissions acceptable; prefers letter-quality to dot-matrix. Reports in 8 weeks. "Material with little news connection may be held up to one year." Sample copy and writer's guidelines for large SAE and $1.24 postage.

Nonfiction: General interest (astronomy, outer space, spacecraft, planets, stars, etc.); how-to (astronomy projects, experiments, etc.); and photo feature (spacecraft, planets, stars, etc.). "We like short, off-beat articles with some astronomy or space-science tie-in. A recent example: an article about a baseball game that ended with the explosion of a meteorite over the field. Study the styles of the monthly columnists. No general overview articles; for example, a general article on the Space Shuttle, or a general article on stars. We do not want science fiction articles." Buys 12 mss/year. Query with published clips. Length: 750-2,000 words. Pays $100-350 depending on length and type of article. Sometimes pays expenses of writers on assignment.

Photos: State availability of photos. Buys one-time rights. Captions preferred; model releases required. Payment depends upon size and placement.

Tips: "Since I am overstocked and have a stable of regular writers, a query is very important. I often get several manuscripts on the same subject and must reject them. Write a very specific proposal and indicate why it will interest kids. If the subject is very technical, indicate your qualifications to write about it. I will be buying more short articles in 1987 because most major features are being handled by staff or contributing editors. Frequent mistakes writers make are trying to fudge on material they don't understand, using outdated references, and telling me their articles are assignments for the Institute of Children's Literature."

ON THE LINE, Mennonite Publishing House, 616 Walnut Ave., Scottdale PA 15683-1999. (412)887-8500. Editor: Virginia A. Hostetler. 100% freelance written. Works with a small number of new/unpublished writers each year. Weekly magazine for children ages 10-14. Circ. 12,000. Pays on acceptance. Publishes ms an average of 1 year after acceptance. Byline given. Buys one-time rights. Submit seasonal/holiday material 6 months in advance. Simultaneous, photocopied, and previously published submissions OK. Computer printout submissions acceptable; prefers letter-quality to dot-matrix. Reports in 1 month.

Nonfiction: How-to (things to make with easy-to-get materials); and informational (500-word articles on wonders of nature, people who have made outstanding contributions). Buys 95 unsolicited mss/year. Send complete ms. Length: 500-1,200 words. Pays $10-24.

Photos: Photos purchased with or without ms. Pays $10-25 for 8x10 b&w photos. Total purchase price for ms includes payment for photos.

Columns/Departments: Fiction, adventure, humorous and religious. Buys 52 mss/year. Send complete ms. Length: 800-1,200 words. Pays $15-24.

Poetry: Light verse and religious. Length: 3-12 lines. Pays $5-15.

Tips: "Study the publication first. We need short well-written how-to and craft articles. Don't send query; we prefer to see the complete manuscript."

OUR LITTLE FRIEND, PRIMARY TREASURE, Pacific Publishing Association, Box 7000, Boise ID 83707. (208)465-2581. Editor: Lawrence Maxwell. 99% freelance written. Weekly for youngsters of the Seventh-day Adventist church. *Our Little Friend* is for children ages 2-6; *Primary Treasure*, ages 7-9. Buys first serial rights (international); first North American serial rights; one-time rights, second serial (reprint) rights; and simutlaneous rights. Byline given. Publishes ms an average of 1 year or more after acceptance. "The payment we make is for one magazine right. In most cases, it is for the first one. But we make payment for second and third rights also." Simultaneous submissions OK. Computer printout submissions acceptable; prefers letter-quality to dot-matrix. "We do not purchase material during June, July and August."

Nonfiction: All stories must be based on fact, written in story form. True-to-life, character-building stories written from viewpoint of child and giving emphasis to lessons of life needed for Christian living. True-to-life is emphasized more than plot. Nature or science articles, but no fantasy; science must be very simple. All material should be educational or informative and stress moral attitude and religious principle. Buys 300 unsolicited mss/year. Length: 700-1,000 words for *Our Little Friend*, 600-1,200 for *Primary Treasure*. Pays $15-25.

Photos: 8x10 glossy prints for cover. Photo payment: sliding scale according to quality.

Poetry: Juvenile poetry. Up to 12 lines. Pays $1/line.

Tips: "We want true stories presented in narrative form. By truth we mean that the characters actually live or have lived, that they had the problem you say they had, and that they solved it the way you say they solved it."

OWL MAGAZINE, The Discovery Magazine for Children, The Young Naturalist Foundation, 56 The Esplanade, Suite 306, Toronto, Ontario M5E 1A7 Canada. (416)868-6001. Editor: Sylvia S. Funston. 25% freelance written. Magazine published 10 times/year (no July or August issues) covering natural science. Aims to interest children in their environment through accurate, factual information about the world around them presented in an easy, lively style. Circ. 105,000. Pays on publication. Publishes ms an average of 3 months after acceptance. Byline given. Buys all rights; makes work-for-hire assignments. Submit seasonal/holiday material 1 year in advance. Computer printout submissions acceptable; no dot-matrix. Reports in 10 weeks. Sample copy $1.50 and IRC; free writer's guidelines.

Nonfiction: How-to (activities, crafts); personal experience (real life children in real situations); photo feature (natural science, international wildlife, and outdoor features); and science and environmental features. "Write for editorial guidelines first; know your topic. Our magazine never talks down to children." No folk tales, problem stories with drugs, sex or moralistic views, fantasy or talking animal stories. Query with clips of published work.

Photos: State availability of photos. Reviews 35mm transparencies. Identification of subjects required.

Tips: "We accept short, well-written articles about up-to-the-minute science discoveries or developments for our Hoot Club News section."

PENNYWHISTLE PRESS, Gannett Co., Inc., Box 500-P, Washington DC 20044. (703)276-3796. Editor: Anita Sama. 15% freelance written. Works with a small number of new/unpublished writers each year. A weekly tabloid newspaper supplement with stories and features for children ages 6-12. Circ. 2,400,000. Pays on acceptance. Publishes ms an average of 1 year after acceptance. Byline given. Buys all rights. Submit seasonal/holiday material 3-6 months in advance. Reports in 3 months. Sample copy for 75¢, SAE and 2 first class stamps; writer's guidelines for SAE and 1 first class stamp.

Nonfiction: How-to (sports, crafts). Buys 15 mss/year. Length: 500 words maximum. Pays variable rate.

Fiction: For children. Buys 25 mss/year. Send complete ms. Length: 250-850 words. Pays variable rate.

Poetry: Traditional poetry for children. Buys 5-10 poems/year. Submit maximum 1 poem. Pays variable rate.

Tips: Fiction is most open to freelancers.

‡POCKETS, The Upper Room, 1908 Grand Ave., Box 189, Nashville TN 37202. (615)327-2700. Editor: Willie S. Teague. 33% freelance written. A monthly themed magazine (except combined January and February issues) covering children's and families spiritual formation. "We are a Christian, non-denominational publication for children 6 to 12 years of age." Circ. 70,000. Pays on acceptance. Byline given. Offers 4¢/word kill fee. Buys first North American serial rights. Submit seasonal/holiday material 1 year in advance. Photocopied and previously published submissions OK. Computer printout submissons acceptable; prefers letter-quality to dot-matrix. Reports in 6 weeks on manuscripts. Sample copy for 10½x7½ SAE with 4 first class stamps; writer's guidelines and themes for business size SAE with 1 first class stamp.

Nonfiction: Shirley Paris, articles editor. Interview/profile and personal experience. List of themes for special issues available with SASE. No violence or romance. Buys 3 mss/year. Send complete ms. Length: 600-1,500 words. Pays 7¢-10¢/word.

Photos: Send photos with submission. Reviews contact sheets, transparencies and prints. Offers $25-50/photo. Buys one-time rights.

Columns Departments: Refrigerator Door (poetry and prayer related to themes), 25 lines; Pocketsful of Love (family communications activities), and Loaves and Fishes (simplified lifestyle and nutrition) both 300 words. Buys 20 mss/year. Send complete ms. Pays 7¢-10¢/word; recipes $25.

Fiction: Adventure; ethnic; religious (retold scripture stories); and slice-of-life. "Stories should reflect the child's everyday experiences through a Christian approach. This is often more acceptable when stories are not preachy or overtly Christian." Buys 15 mss/year. Send complete ms. Length: 750-1,600 words. Pays 7-10¢/word.

Poetry: Buys 3 poems/year. Length: 4-25 lines. Pays $25-50.

Tips: "Theme stories, role models and retold scripture stories are most open to freelancers. Poetry is also open, but we rarely receive an acceptable poem. It's very helpful if writers send for our themes. These are *not* the same as writer's guidelines."

R-A-D-A-R, 8121 Hamilton Ave., Cincinnati OH 45231. (513)931-4050. Editor: Margaret Williams. 75% freelance written. Prefers to work with published/established writers; works with a small number of new/unpublished writers each year. Weekly for children in grades 3-6 in Christian Sunday schools. Rights purchased vary with author and material; prefers buying first serial rights, but will buy second (reprint) rights. Occasionally overstocked. Pays on acceptance. Publishes ms an average of 1 year after acceptance. Submit seasonal material 1 year in advance. Computer printout submissions acceptable; prefers letter-quality to dot-matrix. Reports in 6 weeks. Free sample copy.
Nonfiction: Articles on hobbies and handicrafts, nature, famous people, seasonal subjects, etc., written from a Christian viewpoint. No articles about historical figures with an absence of religious implication. Length: 500-1,000 words. Pays 3¢/word maximum.
Fiction: Short stories of heroism, adventure, travel, mystery, animals and biography. True or possible plots stressing clean, wholesome, Christian character-building ideas, but not preachy. Make prayer, church attendance and Christian living a natural part of the story. "We correlate our fiction and other features with a definite Bible lesson. Writers who want to meet our needs should send for a theme list." No talking animal stories, science fiction, Halloween stories or first-person stories from an adult's viewpoint. Length: up to 1,000 words. Pays 3¢/word maximum.

RANGER RICK, National Wildlife Federation. 1412 16th St. NW, Washington DC 20036. (703)790-4274. Editorial Director: Trudy D. Farrand. 50% freelance written. Monthly magazine for children from ages 6-12, with the greatest concentration in the 7-10 age bracket. Buys all world rights. Byline given "but occasionally, for very brief pieces, we will identify author by name at the end. Contributions to regular departments usually are not bylined." Pays on acceptance. Publishes ms an average of 18 months after acceptance. Letter quality computer printout submissions acceptable; no dot-matrix. Reports in 2 weeks. "Anything written with a specific month in mind should be in our hands at least 10 months before that issue date."
Nonfiction: "Articles may be written on anything related to nature, conservation, the outdoors, environmental problems or natural science." Buys 20-25 unsolicited mss/year. Query. Pays from $10-350, depending on length and content (maximum length, 900 words).
Fiction: "Same categories as nonfiction plus fantasy and science fiction. The attributing of human qualities to animals is limited to our regular feature, 'The Adventures of Ranger Rick,' so please do not humanize wildlife. The publisher, The National Wildlife Federation, discourages keeping wildlife as pets."
Photos: "Photographs, when used, are paid for separately. It is not necessary that illustrations accompany material."
Tips: "Include in query details of what manuscript will cover; sample lead; evidence that you can write playfully and with great enthusiasm, conviction and excitement (formal, serious, dull queries indicate otherwise). Think of an exciting subject we haven't done recently, sell it effectively with query, and produce a manuscript of highest quality. Read past issues to learn successful styles and unique approaches to subjects. If your submission is commonplace in any way we won't want it."

STICKERS AND STUFF, (formerly *Stickers! Magazine*), For Kids Stuck on Stickers, Ira Friedman, Inc., Suite 1300, 10 Columbus Circle, New York NY 10019. (212)541-7300. 20% freelance written. Prefers to work with published/established writers. Editor: Bob Woods. Quarterly magazine covering all kinds of adhesive-backed stickers, related products, and activities. "Readers are children, generally girls, ages 6-14, who are wild about collecting, trading, and making things with stickers. We also cover other, trendier 'stuff' for kids, such as neon jewelry, jazzy tote bags, and other accessory items. We try to point out humor, education, friendship, sharing, benefits, and other positive aspects of using stickers." Circ. 200,000. Pays on publication. Publishes ms an average of 3 months after acceptance. Byline given. Buys first North American serial rights. Submit seasonal/holiday material 3 months in advance. Photocopied submissions OK. Computer printout submissions acceptable. Reports in 3 weeks on queries; 2 weeks on mss. Sample copy and writer's guidelines for SAE.
Nonfiction: Historical/nostalgic; how-to; humor; interview/profile (with collectors, manufacturers, sticker stores); new product; personal experience; and photo feature. Query with published clips. Length: 250-2,000 words. Pays $50 minimum.
Fillers: Games and puzzles employing stickers.
Tips: "Send a letter that details your idea and lets us know you have more than a casual interest in the subject. We need more than just stories about collectors. Areas most open to freelancers: Stickerama, all sorts of sticker stuff; Best Sticker Ideas, generated by readers; and Sticker People, short profiles."

STORY FRIENDS, Mennonite Publishing House, 616 Walnut Ave., Scottdale PA 15683. (412)887-8500. Editor: Marjorie Waybill. 75% freelance written. Works with a small number of new/unpublished writers each year. Published monthly in weekly parts. For children ages 4-9. Not copyrighted. Buys one-time rights and simultaneous rights. Pays on acceptance. Publishes ms an average of 6 months after acceptance. Byline given. Submit seasonal/holiday material 6 months in advance. Computer printout submissions acceptable. Free sample copy with SAE and 25¢ postage.
Nonfiction: "The over-arching purpose of this publication is to portray Jesus as a friend and helper—a friend

who cares about each happy and sad experience in the child's life. Persons who know Jesus have values which affect every area of their lives." Send complete ms. Sometimes pays the expenses of writers on assignment.
Fiction: "Stories of everyday experiences at home, at church, in school or at play can provide models of these values. Of special importance are relationships, patterns of forgiveness, respect, honesty, trust and caring. We prefer short stories that offer a wide variety of settings, acquaint children with a wide range of friends, and mirror the joys, fears, temptations and successes of the readers. *Story Friends* needs stories that speak to the needs and interests of children of a variety of ethnic backgrounds. Stories should provide patterns of forgiveness, respect, integrity, understanding, caring, sharing; increase the children's sense of self-worth through growing confidence in God's love for them as they are; help answer the children's questions about God, Jesus, the Bible, prayer, death, heaven; develop awe and reverence for God the Creator and for all of His creation; avoid preachiness, but have well-defined spiritual values as an integral part of each story; be plausible in plot; introduce children to followers of Jesus Christ; and develop appreciation for our Mennonite heritage." Send complete ms. Length: 300-800 words. Pays 3-5¢/word.
Poetry: Traditional and free verse. Length: 3-12 lines. Pays $5.

3-2-1 CONTACT, Children's Television Workshop, One Lincoln Plaza, New York NY 10023. (212)595-3456. Editor: Jonathan Rosenbloom. Associate Editor: Richard Chevat. 40% freelance written. Magazine published 10 times/year covering science and technology for children ages 8-14. Circ. 320,000. Pays on acceptance. Publishes ms 6 months after acceptance. Buys all rights "with some exceptions." Submit seasonal material 8 months in advance. Simultaneous, photocopied, and previously published submissions OK if so indicated. Computer printout submissions acceptable; prefers letter-quality to dot-matrix. Reports in 1 month. Sample copy $1.25; free writer's guidelines.
Nonfiction: General interest (space exploration, the human body, animals, computers and the new technology, current science issues); profile (of interesting scientists or children involved in science or with computers); photo feature (centered around a science theme); and role models of women and minority scientists. No articles on travel not related to science. Buys 5 unsolicited mss/year. Query with published clips. Length: 700-1,000 words. Pays $150-400. Sometimes pays expenses of writers on assignment.
Photos: Reviews 8x10 b&w prints and 35mm color transparencies. Model releases required.
Tips: "I prefer a short query, without manuscript, that makes it clear that an article is interesting. When sending an article, include your telephone number. Don't call us, we'll call you. Many submissions we receive are more like college research papers than feature stories. We like articles in which writers have interviewed kids or scientists, or discovered exciting events with a scientific angle. Library research is necessary; but if that's all you're doing, you aren't giving us anything we can't get ourselves. If your story needs a bibliography, chances are, it's not right for us."

TOUCH, Box 7259, Grand Rapids MI 49510. Editor: Joanne Ilbrink. 75% freelance written. Prefers to work with published/established writers. Monthly magazine. Purpose of publication is to show girls ages 8-15 how God is at work in their lives and in the world around them. Circ. 14,000. Pays on acceptance. Publishes ms an average of 6 months after acceptance. Byline given. Buys second serial (reprint) rights and first North American serial rights. Submit seasonal/holiday material 5 months in advance. Simultaneous, photocopied, and previously published submissions OK. Computer printout submissions acceptable; prefers letter-quality to dot-matrix. Reports in 6 weeks. Free sample copy and writer's guidelines for 9x12 SASE and 3 first class stamps.
Nonfiction: How-to (crafts girls can make easily and inexpensively); informational (write for issue themes); humor (needs much more); inspirational (seasonal and holiday); interview; multicultural materials; travel; personal experience (avoid the testimony approach); and photo feature (query first). "Because our magazine is published around a monthly theme, requesting the letter we send out twice a year to our established freelancers would be most helpful. We do not want easy solutions or quick character changes from bad to good. No pietistic characters. Constant mention of God is not necessary if the moral tone of the story is positive. We do not want stories that always have a good ending." Buys 36-45 unsolicited mss/year. Submit complete ms. Length: 100-1,000 words. Pays 2¢/word, depending on the amount of editing.
Photos: Purchased with or without ms. Reviews 5x7 clear b&w (only) glossy prints. Appreciate multi-cultural subjects. Pays $5-25 on publication.
Fiction: Adventure (that girls could experience in their hometowns or places they might realistically visit); humorous; mystery (believable only); romance (stories that deal with awakening awareness of boys are appreciated); suspense (can be serialized) and religious (nothing preachy). Buys 20 mss/year. Submit complete ms. Length: 300-1,500 words. Pays 2¢/word.
Poetry: Free verse, haiku, light verse and traditional. Buys 10/year. Length: 50 lines maximum. Pays $5 minimum.
Fillers: Puzzles, short humor and cartoons. Buys 3/issue. Pays $2.50-7.
Tips: "Prefers not to see anything on the adult level, secular material or violence. Writers frequently over-simplify the articles and often write with a Pollyanna attitude. An author should be able to see his/her writing style as exciting and appealing to girls ages 7-14. The style can be fun, but also teach a truth. The subject should be current and important to *Touch* readers. We would like to receive material that features a multi-cultural slant."

‡TOYS "R" US MAGAZINE, Western Publishing Company, Inc., 5945 Erie St., Racine WI 53402. (414)633-2431. Editor: Barb Mullins. Managing Editor: Don Lesinski. 90% freelance written. A quarterly magazine covering toys, games and fiction of interest to kids aged 6-12. "The focus is on play value combined with strong editorial and graphic content based on the kinds of things kids want to read and see." Estab. 1985. Circ. 300,000. Pays on acceptance. Publishes ms an average of 8 months after acceptance. Byline usually given. Buys first rights. Submit seasonal/holiday material 6 months in advance. Simultaneous, photocopied and previously published submissions OK if queried in advance. Computer printout submissions acceptable; no dot-matrix. Reports in 2 weeks on queries; 5 weeks on mss. Free sample copy if available.

Nonfiction: How-to (geared to young audience), humor (child's), interview/profile (celebrities of interest to kids), new product, personal experience (child's), and photo feature (child's). "No overly lengthy, adult-oriented stuff." Buys 10-15 mss/year. Query. Length: no minimum; 2,000 words maximum. Pays $200-2,000. Sometimes pays the expenses of writers on assignment.

Photos: State availability of photos with submission. Reviews contact sheets, negatives, transparencies and prints. Captions, model releases and identification of subjects required. Buys one-time rights.

Columns/Departments: Discovery (nature topics of interest to children), 1,500-2,000 words; Humor-Jokes, Riddles (lightweight, general subjects), 200-700 words; and Celebrity Interviews (kid stars), 1,500-2,000 words. Buys 10 mss/year. Query. Pays $200-700.

Fiction: Adventure, fantasy, historical, humorous, mystery, science fiction, horror and suspense (light), and western. Buys 10 mss/year. Query. Length: 500-1,000 words. Pays $500-2,000.

Poetry: Free verse, haiku, light verse and traditional for kids. Buys 10 poems/year. Length: 5-30 lines. Pays $200-700.

Fillers: Anecdotes, facts, gags to be illustrated by cartoonist, newsbreaks and short humor. Buys 20/year. Length: 100-500 words. Pays $100-700.

TURTLE MAGAZINE FOR PRESCHOOL KIDS, Children's Better Health Institute, Benjamin Franklin Literary & Medical Society, Inc., 1100 Waterway Blvd., Box 567, Indianapolis IN 46206. (317)636-8881. Editor: Beth Wood Thomas. 95% freelance written. Monthly magazine (bimonthly February/March, April/May, June/July, August/September) for preschoolers emphasizing health, safety, exercise and good nutrition. Pays on publication. Publishes ms an average of 1 year after acceptance. Byline given. Buys all rights. Submit seasonal/holiday material 8 months in advance. Reports in 10 weeks. Sample copy 75¢; writer's guidelines for business size SASE.

Fiction: Fantasy, humorous and health-related stories. "Stories that deal with a health theme need not have health as the primary subject but should include it in some way in the course of events." No controversial material. Buys 40 mss/year. Submit complete ms. Length: 700 words maximum. Pays approximately 6¢/word.

Poetry: "We use many stories in rhyme—vocabulary should be geared to a 3- to 5-year-old. Anthropomorphic animal stories and rhymes are especially effective for this age group to emphasize a moral or lesson without 'lecturing'." Pays variable rates.

Tips: "We are primarily concerned with preventive medicine. We try to present our material in a positive—not a negative—light and to incorporate humor and a light approach wherever possible without minimizing the seriousness of what we are saying. We would like to see more stories, articles, craft ideas and activities with the following holiday themes: New Year's Day, Valentine's Day, President's Day, St. Patrick's Day, Easter, Independence Day, Thanksgiving, Christmas and Hannukah. We like new ideas that will entertain as well as teach preschoolers. Publishing a writer's first work is very gratifying to us. It is a great pleasure to receive new, fresh material."

WEE WISDOM, Unity Village MO 64065. Editor: Ms. Verle Bell. 90% freelance written. "We are happy to work with any freelance writers whose submissions and policies match our needs." Magazine published 10 times/year "for children aged 13 and under, dedicated to the truth that each person has an inner source of wisdom, power, love and health that can be applied in a practical manner to everyday life." Circ. 168,000. Publishes ms an average of at least 8 months after acceptance. Submit seasonal/holiday material 8 months in advance. Pays on acceptance. Byline given. Buys first serial rights only. Computer printout submissions acceptable; no dot-matrix. Free sample copy and editorial policy for SAE and 3 first class stamps.

Nonfiction: Entertaining nature articles or projects/activities to encourage appreciation of all life. Wants only completed mss. Pays 4¢/word minimum.

Fiction: Character-building stories that encourage a positive self-image. Although entertaining enough to hold the interest of the older child, they should be readable by the third grader. "Characters should be appealing; plots should be imaginative but plausible, and all stories should be told without preaching. Life combines fun and humor with its more serious lessons, and our most interesting and helpful stories do the same thing. Language should be universal, avoiding the Sunday school image." Length: 500-800 words. Pay 4¢/word minimum.

Poetry: Very limited. Prefers short, seasonal or humorous poems. Pays $15 minimum, 50¢ per line after 15 lines. Rhymed prose (read aloud) stories are paid at about the same rate as prose stories, depending on excellence.

Fillers: Pays $5-15 for puzzles and games.

WONDER TIME, 6401 The Paseo, Kansas City MO 64131. (816)333-7000. Editor: Evelyn Beals. 75% freelance written. "Willing to read and consider appropriate freelance submissions." Published weekly by Church of the Nazarene for children ages 6-8. Buys first serial rights, second (reprint) rights; simultaneous rights and all rights for curriculum assignments. Pays on acceptance. Publishes ms an average of 2 years after acceptance. Byline given. Computer printout submissions acceptable; prefers letter-quality to dot-matrix. Free sample copy.

Fiction: Buys stories portraying Christian attitudes without being preachy. Uses stories for special days—stories teaching honesty, truthfulness, kindness, helpfulness or other important spiritual truths, and avoiding symbolism. Also, stories about real life problems children face today. "God should be spoken of as our Father who loves and cares for us; Jesus, as our Lord and Savior." Buys 150/mss year. Length: 400-550 words. Pays 3½¢/word on acceptance.

Poetry: Uses verse which has seasonal or Christian emphasis. Length: 4-12 lines. Pays 25¢/line, minimum $2.50.

Tips: "Any stories that allude to church doctrine must be in keeping with Nazarene beliefs. Any type of fantasy must be in good taste and easily recognizable. We are overstocked now with poetry and stories with general themes. A brochure with specific needs available with free sample. *Wonder Time* will change from 2-color to 4-color. We plan to reprint more than before to save art costs, therefore we will be more selective and purchase fewer manuscripts."

YOUNG AMERICAN, America's Newsmagazine for Kids, Young American Publishing Co., Inc., Box 12409, Portland OR 97212. (503)230-1895. Managing Editor: Kristina T. Linden. 20% freelance written. Eager to work with new/unpublished writers. A tabloid-size newsmagazine supplement to suburban newspapers for children and their families. Circ. 125,000. Pays on publication. Publishes ms an average of 6 months after acceptance. Byline given. Buys first North American serial rights and makes work-for-hire assignments. Submit seasonal/holiday material 3 months in advance. Photocopied submissions OK. Computer printout submissions acceptable; prefers letter-quality to dot-matrix. Reports in 4 months on mss. Sample copy $1.50 with 9x12 SAE; writer's guidelines for SAE with 1 first class stamp.

Nonfiction: General interest; historical/nostalgic; how-to (crafts, fitness); humor; interview/profile (of kids, or people particularly of interest to them); and newsworthy kids. No condescending articles or articles relating to religion, sex, violence, drugs or substance abuse. Buys 50 mss/year. No queries; send complete ms. Length: 350 words maximum. Pays $5-75. Sometimes pays the expenses of writers on assignment.

Photos: Send photos with submission. Offers $5 maximum/photo. Identification of subjects required. Buys one-time rights.

Columns/Departments: You and the News (stories about newsworthy kids), science (new developments, things not covered in textbooks), and book reviews (for kids and young teens), maximum 350 words. Buys 20 mss/year. Send complete ms. Pays $5-75.

Fiction: Adventure, ethnic, fantasy, humorous, mystery, science fiction, suspense, western and lore. No condescending stories or stories relating to religion, sex, drugs or substance abuse. Buys 12 mss/year. Send complete ms. Length: 500-1,000 words. Pays $35-75.

Poetry: Light verse and traditional. No "heavy" or depressing poetry. Buys 15 poems/year. Length: 4 lines, 500 words maximum. Pays $5-35.

Fillers: Facts and short humor. Buys 10/year. Length: 30-300 words. Pays $2.10-21.

Tips: "The *Young American* is particularly interested in publishing articles about newsworthy kids and in publishing children's work. These articles should be under 350 words and accompanied by photos—preferably black and white. The *Young American* focus is on children—and they are taken seriously. Articles are intended to inform, entertain, stimulate and enlighten. They give children a sense of being a part of today's important events and a recognition which is often denied them because of age. If applicable, photos, diagrams, or information for illustration helps tremendously as our publication is highly visual. We are currently a monthly but hope to increase our frequency. The fiction we have been receiving is excellent. However, it is more abundant than we can publish. Personal notes are written to those who we sincerely hope will consider us again."

‡YOUNG AUTHOR'S MAGAZINE, Theraplan, Incorporated, 3015 Woodsdale Blvd., Lincoln NE 68502. (402)421-3172. Editor: Susan Steinegger. Managing Editor: Traci Austin. A quarterly literary magazine focusing on creative writing by gifted children. Circ. 6,000. Pays on publication. Publishes ms an average of 4 months after acceptance. Pays on publication. Byline given. Not copyrighted. Buys all rights. Submit seasonal/holiday material 6 months in advance. Photocopied submissions OK. Computer printout submissions acceptable. Reports in 3 months. Sample copy $3; writer's guidelines for SASE.

Nonfiction: General interest, how-to, interview/profile, personal experience and photo feature. "The November/December issue of each year is our 'international' issue which features the creative writing of young authors in other countries, as well as the U.S." Nothing with excessive violence. Buys 40 mss/year. Send complete ms. Length: 1,000-2,500 words. Pays $15 minimum, 3¢/word maximum.

Photos: Reviews 8x10 prints. Pays $20 for b&w; $20-50 for color. Identification of subjects required. Buys one-time rights.

Columns/Departments: Send complete ms. Length of columns and payment varies.
Fiction: Adventure, fantasy, humorous, mystery, science fiction and suspense. Send complete ms. Length and payment varies.
Poetry: Avant-garde, free verse, haiku, light verse and traditional. Buys 100 poems/year. No maximum limit on number of poems submitted. Pays $5.
Tips: "The entire publication is open to young writers. We try not to go over 16 years of age—mostly upper elementary to junior high."

THE YOUNG CRUSADER, 1730 Chicago Ave., Evanston IL 60201. (312)864-1396. Managing Editor: Michael Vitucci. Monthly for children ages 6-12. Not copyrighted. Pays on publication. Submit seasonal material 6 months in advance. Computer printout submissions acceptable. Free sample copy.
Nonfiction: Uses articles on total abstinence, character-building and love of animals. Also science stories. Length: 600 words. Pays ½¢/word.
Fiction: Should emphasize Christian principles and world friendship. Also science stories. Length: 600 words. Pays ½¢/word.
Poetry: Limit submissions to batches of 3. Pays 10¢/line.

YOUNG JUDAEAN, 50 W. 58th St., New York NY 10019. (212)303-8268. Editor: Mordecai Newman. 75% freelance written. A monthly magazine (November through June) for Jewish children ages 8-13, and members of Young Judaea. Publication of Hadassah Zionist Commission. All material must be on some Jewish theme. Circ. 8,000. Byline given. Buys 3-6 mss/year. Sample copy and annual list of themes for 75¢. Buys all rights or first North American serial rights. Will consider photocopied and simultaneous submissions. Computer printout submissions acceptable. Submit seasonal/holiday material 4 months in advance. Reports in 3 months.
Nonfiction: Articles about Jewish—American life, Jewish historical and international interest. Israel and Zionist-oriented material. Try to awaken kids' Jewish consciousness by creative approach to Jewish history and religion, ethics and culture, politics and current events. Style can be didactic but not patronizing." Informational (300-1,000 words), how-to (300-500 words), personal experience, interview, humor, historical, think articles, photo, travel, and reviews (books, theater and novels). Special issues for Jewish/Israeli holidays, or particular Jewish themes which vary from year to year; for example, Hassidim, Holocaust, etc. Submit complete ms. Length 500-1,200 words. Pays $20-40.
Photos: Photos purchased with accompanying mss. Captions required. 5x7 maximum. B&w preferred. Payment included with fee for article. Illustrations also accepted.
Fiction: Experimental, mainstream, mystery, suspense, adventure, science fiction, fantasy, humorous, religious and historical fiction. Submit complete ms. Length: 500-1,000 words. Pays $5-25. Must be of specific Jewish interest.
Poetry: Traditional forms, blank verse, avant-garde forms and light verse. Poetry themes must relate to subject matter of magazine. Submit complete ms. Length: 250-100 lines. Pays $5-15.
Fillers: Newsbreak, jokes and short humor purchased for $5.
Tips: "Think of an aspect of Jewish history, religion or culture which can be handled in a fresh, imaginative way, fictionally or factually. Don't preach; inform and entertain." Prefers not to get material without Jewish relevance or material that deals with Jewish subject matter from a Christian perspective.

Lifestyles

A reader's lifestyle may be conservative or liberal, affluent or back-to-the-land. Lifestyle publications cater to these and other tastes and philosophies. They offer writers a forum for unconventional views or serve as a voice for particular audiences or causes. Here are magazines for single and widowed people, vegetarians, homosexuals, atheists, survivalists, back-to-the-land advocates, and others interested in alternative outlooks and lifestyles. Also included are "free press" publications that offer contributor's copies as payment.

ALBUQUERQUE SINGLES SCENE MAGAZINE, 8421-H Osuna NE, Albuquerque NM 87111. (505)299-4401. Editor: Gail Skinner. 90% freelance written. Eager to work with new/unpublished writers. Monthly tabloid covering singles lifestyles. Pays on publication. Publishes ms an average of 6 months after acceptance. Byline given. Buys first serial rights, second serial (reprint) rights or all rights. Submit seasonal/holiday ma-

terial 3 months in advance. Computer printout submissions acceptable; prefers letter-quality to dot-matrix. Reports in 3 months. Sample copy $1 with SAE and 4 first class stamps. Free writer's guidelines for SAE and 1 first class stamp.
Nonfiction: General interest (to singles); how-to (for singles coping on their own); humor; inspirational; opinion; personal experience. All articles must be singles-oriented. No suggestive or pornographic material. Buys 100 mss/year. Send complete ms. "Keep a copy of the manuscript for your file as we do not return them. If you have photo(s) and/or illustration(s) to accompany the article, do not send them with your story unless you do not want them returned." Also publishes some fiction. Length: 900-2,600 words. Pays $36-150.
Photos: State availability of photos with ms. Captions, model releases, and identification of subjects required.
Columns/Departments: Astrology, finance, real estate, travel, consumer guide, relationships and parenting—all singles-oriented. Buys 75 mss/year. Send complete ms. Length: 800-900 words. Pays $36 minimum.
Tips: "We are looking for articles that deal with every aspect of single living—whether on a local or national level. Our readers are of above-average intelligence, income and education. The majority of our articles are chosen from 'relationships' and 'humor' submissions."

‡AMERICAN ATHEIST, American Atheist Press, Box 2117, Austin TX 78768. (512)458-1244. Editor: R. Murray-O'Hair. Managing Editor: Jon Garth Murray. 40% freelance written. Monthly magazine covering atheism and topics related to it and separation of Church and State. Circ. 50,000. Publishes ms an average of 4 months after acceptance. Byline given. Buys one-time and all rights. Submit seasonal/holiday material 3 months in advance. Simultaneous queries and simultaneous, photocopied and previously published submissions OK. Computer printout submissions acceptable. Reports in 3 weeks on queries; 6 weeks on mss. Publishes ms an average of 4 months after acceptance. Free sample copy and writer's guidelines.
Nonfiction: Book excerpts, expose, general interest, historical, how-to, humor, interview/profile, opinion, personal experience and photo feature, but only as related to State/Church or atheism. "We receive a great many Bible criticism articles—and publish very few. We would advise writers not to send in such works. We are also interested in fiction with an atheistic slant." Buys 40 mss/year. Send complete ms. Length: 400-10,000 words. Pays in free subscription or 15 copies for first-time authors. Repeat authors paid $10 per 1,000 words. Sometimes pays the expenses of writers on assignment.
Photos: Gerald Tholen, photo editor. Send photos with ms. Pays $15 maximum for 2x3 or 4x5 b&w prints; pays $100 for four-color cover photos. Identification of subjects required.
Columns/Departments: Atheism, Church/State separation and humor. Send complete ms. Length: 400-10,000 words.
Poetry: Avant-garde, free verse, haiku, light verse and traditional. Submit unlimited poems. Length: open. Pays $10 per thousand words maximum.
Fillers: Clippings, jokes, short humor and newsbreaks. Length: 300 words maximum, only as related to State/Church separation or atheism.
Tips: "We are starting to have issues which focus on lifestyle topics relevant to atheism. For instance, our June 1986 issue featured atheist weddings. We would like to receive more articles on current events and lifestyle issues. Critiques of *particular* religions would also be likely candidates for acceptance."

AMERICAN SURVIVAL GUIDE, McMullen Publishing, Inc., 2145 W. La Palma Ave., Anaheim CA 92801. (714)635-9040. Managing Editor: Jim Benson. 50% freelance written. Monthly magazine covering "self-reliance, defense, meeting day-to-day and possible future threats—survivalism for survivalists." Circ. 96,000. Pays on publication. Publishes ms up to 2 years after acceptance. Byline given. Not copyrighted. Buys first North American serial rights. Submit seasonal/holiday material 5 months in advance. Computer printout submissions acceptable; prefers letter-quality to dot-matrix. Sample copy $2.50; writer's guidelines for SASE.
Nonfiction: Expose (political); how-to; interview/profile; personal experience (how I survived); photo feature (equipment and techniques related to survival in all possible situations); emergency medical; health and fitness; communications; transportation; food preservation; water purification; self-defense; nutrition; tools; shelter; etc. "No general articles about how to survive. We want specifics and single subjects." Buys 60-100 mss/year. Query or send complete ms. Length: 1,500-2,000 words. Pays $140-350. Sometimes pays the expenses of writers on assignment.
Photos: Send photos with ms. "One of the most frequent mistakes made by writers in completing an article assignment for us is sending photo submissions that are inadequate." Captions, model releases and identification of subjects mandatory. Buys all rights.
Tips: "Prepare material of value to individuals who wish to sustain human life no matter what the circumstance. This magazine is a text and reference."

APPALACHIAN NOTES, Erasmus Press, 225 Culpepper, Lexington KY 40502. Editor: Lawrence S. Thompson. 100% freelance written. Scholarly quarterly magazine on all aspects of history and culture of Appalachia. Circ. 290. Publishes ms an average of 6 months after acceptance. All articles are signed. Computer printout submissions acceptable; prefers letter-quality to dot-matrix. Reports in 1 month on queries; 6 weeks on mss.

Nonfiction: Scholarly. Send complete ms. Length: 300-2,500 words. No payment.
Tips: Historical and documented studies are most open to freelancers.

ASCENSION FROM THE ASHES, The Alternative Magazine, AFTA Press, Suite 2, 153 George St., New Brunswick NJ 08901. (201)828-5467. Editor: Bill-Dale Marcinko. Quarterly magazine covering popular culture (TV, film, books and music), political and sexual issues for young adults (ages 18-30). Circ. 25,000. Pays in copies. Buys first serial rights. Phone queries OK. Submit seasonal material 1 month in advance. Simultaneous, photocopied, and previously published submissions OK. Reports in 2 weeks. Sample copy $3.50.
Nonfiction: Humor (satires on popular books, TV, films, records and social issues); interview (of authors, TV/film writers or directors, rock musicians and political movement leaders); opinion (reviews and reactions); profile; personal experience; and photo feature (on the making of a movie or TV program, coverage of a rock concert or political demonstration). *AFTA* also buys investigative articles on political, consumer and religious fraud. Buys 75 unsolicited mss/year. Query with published clips. Pays in copies.
Photos: State availability of photos. Reviews b&w prints. Pays in copies.
Columns/Departments: Books, Etc. (book reviews, fiction and nonfiction of interest to a young counter-culture audience); Demons in Dustjackets (horror and science fiction book reviews); Medium Banal (TV reviews); Sprockets (film reviews); and Slipped Discs (record reviews). "We use short (3-4 paragraphs) reviews of comic books, underground comics, alternative magazines, recent books, television programs, films and rock albums, especially on gay, lesbian and politically controversial small press magazines and books. Buys 50 mss/year. Query with published clips. Length: 100-1,000 words. Pays in copies.
Fiction: Short stories. Experimental, erotic, humorous, science fiction, suspense and mainstream. Buys 10 mss/year. Query with clips of previously published work. Length: 1,000 words maximum. Pays in copies.
Poetry: Political survival, humorous and erotic subjects. Pays in copies.
Fillers: "We print folk/rock songs on social issues with music. We also have a section in which readers describe their first-time sexual experiences (gay or straight)." Buys 8 mss/year. Pays in copies.
Tips: "Sending for a sample copy is probably the best way to familiarize yourself with the kind of writing in *AFTA*. Write with humor, simplicity, and intensity, first person if possible. Avoid being formal or academic in criticism. Write for a young adult audience. The short stories accepted generally have a style similar to the works of Vonnegut or Tom Robbins, very loose, playful and humorous. *AFTA* doesn't censor language in any submissions and is known for printing material other magazines consider sexually and politically controversial."

‡ATLANTA SINGLES MAGAZINE & DATEBOOK, Sigma Publications, Inc., Suite 115, 6695 Peachtree Industrial Blvd., Box 80158, Atlanta GA 30366. (404)447-8400. Editor: Emily Lane. Managing Editor: J. Bullington. 25% freelance written. Works with a small number of new/unpublished writers each year. A bimonthly magazine for single, widowed or divorced adults, medium to high income level, many business and professionally oriented; single parents, ages 25 to 55. Circ. 6,000. Pays on publication. Publishes ms an average of 6 months after acceptance. Byline given. Buys one-time rights, second serial (reprint) rights and simultaneous rights. Submit seasonal/holiday material 6 months in advance. Simultaneous, photocopied and previously published submissions OK. Computer printout submissions acceptable; prefers letter-quality to dot-matrix. Free sample copy.
Nonfiction: General interest, humor, personal experience, photo feature and travel. No pornography. Buys 12 mss/year. Send complete ms. Length: 600-1,200 words. Pays $15-25 for unsolicited articles; sometimes trades for personal ad.
Photos: Send photos with submission. Reviews prints. Offers no additional payment for photos accepted with ms. Model releases and identification of subjects required. Buys one-time rights.
Columns/Departments: Will consider ideas. Query. Length: 600-800 words. Pays $15-25 per column/department.
Fiction: Confession, fantasy, humorous, mainstream, romance and slice-of-life vignettes. No pornography. Send complete ms. Length: 600-1,200 words. Pays $15-25.
Fillers: Gags to be illustrated by cartoonist and short humor. Length: open. Pays $10-20.
Tips: "We are open to articles on *any* subject that would be of interest to singles, i.e., travel, autos, movies, love stories, fashion, investments, real estate, etc. Although singles are interested in topics like self-awareness, "being single again," and dating, they are also interested in many of the same subjects that married people are, such as those listed."

THE BOSTON PHOENIX, 100 Massachusetts Ave., Boston MA 02115. (617)536-5390. Editor: Richard M. Gaines. 40% freelance written. Weekly alternative newspaper; 140+ pages. For 18-40 age group, educated post-counterculture. Circ. 139,000. Buys first serial rights. Pays on publication. Offers kill fee. Publishes ms an average of 1 month after acceptance. Byline given. Photocopied submissions OK. Computer printout submissions acceptable. Reports in 6 weeks. Sample copy $1.50.
Nonfiction: News (local coverage, national, some international affairs, features, think pieces and profiles); lifestyle (features, service pieces, consumer-oriented tips, medical, food, some humor if topical, etc.); arts (re-

views, essays, interviews); and supplements (coverage of special-interest areas, e.g., stereo, skiing, automotive, computers, pro sound, education, home furnishings with local angle). Query section editor. "Liveliness, accuracy, and great literacy are absolutely required." No fiction or poetry. Query letter preferable to ms. Pays 4¢/word and up. Sometimes pays the expenses of writers on assignment.

‡**BROOMSTICK**, Options for Women over Forty, 3543 18th St., Box 3, San Francisco CA 94110. (415)552-7460. Editors: Mickey Spencer and Polly Taylor. 100% freelance written. *"Broomstick* is a bimonthly feminist, reader-participation magazine by, for, and about women over forty. Circ. approximately 3,000. Byline given. Electronic submissions OK via 8" SD CP/M, or IBM-PC compatible WordStar, but requires hard copy also. Computer printout submissions acceptable; prefers letter-quality to dot-matrix. Sample copy $3.50; writer's guidelines for $2.50.
Nonfiction: Essays, exposé, general interest, humor, interview/profile, opinion and personal experience. No articles not written by, or relevant to, women over 40. Send complete ms. Pays with contributor copies.
Columns/Departments: Watchcraft (examples of ageism); An Apple A Day (health info); and Menopause Update (info on menopause). Send complete ms. Pays with contributor copies.
Fiction: Experimental, fantasy, historical, humorous and slice-of-life vignettes.
Poetry: Will consider all types by and relevant to feminist politics and women over 40. Pays with contributor copies.

CANADIAN KEY,Canada's oldest and largest swingers club, Box 68, Station L, Toronto, Ontario M4P 2G5 Canada. (416)481-2406. Editor: Dawn Evans. 10% freelance written. Magazine published every 2 months. "We are interested in articles and stories directed at the new sexual openness that has come about with swingers and group sex." Circ. 20,000. Pays on acceptance. Publishes ms an average of 2 months after acceptance. Byline given. Offers negotiated kill fee. Buys one-time rights or second serial (reprint) rights. Submit seasonal/holiday material 4 months in advance. Simultaneous queries and simultaneous, photocopied, and previously published submissions OK. Computer printout submissions acceptable. IRCs outside Canada. Reports in 3 weeks. Sample copy for $5 and 9x12 SAE and 96¢ postage; IRCs outside Canada.
Nonfiction: How-to (on anything relating to sex); humor (of a sexual nature); new product (anything relating to sex); personal experience (of a sexual nature); travel (anything for swingers); and swinging. Buys 6 mss/year. Query with published clips or send complete ms. Length: 1,000-3,000 words. Pays $75-200.

THE CELIBATE WOMAN, A Journal for Women Who Are Celibate or Considering This Liberating Way of Relating to Others, 3306 Ross Place NW, Washington DC 20008. (202)966-7783. Editor: Martha Allen. 95% freelance written. Eager to work with new/unpublished writers. Irregularly published (annually thus far) special interest magazine on celibacy and women. Publishes ms an average of 6 months after acceptance. Byline given with biography. Computer printout submissions acceptable. Sample copy $4.
Nonfiction: Reflections on celibacy and sexuality. "The journal is a forum for presenting another view of sexuality—an opening up of alternatives in a sex-oriented society." Articles, artwork, letters, experiences, ideas and theory are welcome. Pays in copies.

‡**CHANGING MEN, Issues in Gender, Sex and Politics**, Feminist Men's Publications, 306 N. Brooks St., Madison WI 53715. Editor: Rick Cote. Managing Editor: Michael Birnbaum. 80% freelance written. Works with a small number of new/unpublished writers each year. A feminist men's journal published two times a year. "We are a forum for anti-sexist men and women to explore issues of masculinity, feminism, sexual orientation, and sex roles." Circ. 4,000. Publishes ms an average of 1 year after acceptance. Byline given. Buys one-time rights. Simultaneous queries, simultaneous, photocopied, and previously published submissions OK. Computer printout submissions acceptable; prefers letter-quality to dot-matrix. Reports in 2 months. Sample copy $4.50; writer's guidelines for business size SAE with 1 first class stamp.
Nonfiction: Book excerpts, humor, interview/profile, opinion, personal experience and photo feature. Plans special issues on male/female intimacy and relationships. No academic articles or theoretical treatises. Query with published clips. Length: 3,500 words maximum. Pays $25 maximum.
Columns/Departments: Men and War (focus on masculinity and how culture shapes male values), Sports (with a feminist slant), and Book Reviews (focus on sexuality and masculinity). Query with published clips. Length: 500-1,500 words. Pays $15 maximum.
Fiction: Franklin Abbott, fiction editor. Erotica, ethnic, experimental, fantasy, humorous and novel excerpts. Buys 1 ms/year. Query with published clips. Length: 3,500 words maximum. Pays $20 maximum.
Poetry: Free verse, haiku and light verse. Submit maximum 3 poems. Length: 50 lines maximum. No payment for poetry.
Fillers: Clippings, jokes and newsbreak. Length: 300 words. No payment for fillers.

‡**COLUMBUS SINGLE SCENE**, Columbus Single Scene, Inc., Suite 202, 55 Caren Ave., Worthington OH 43085. (614)436-2076. Editor: Jeanne Marlowe. 50% freelance written. A monthly magazine covering information of interest to central Ohio singles (of all ages—18 and up)—"positive, upbeat approach to single living,

but we're neither yuppies nor pollyannas." Estab. 1985. Circ. 2,000. Pays on acceptance. Publishes ms an average of 1 month after acceptance. Byline given. Offers 40% kill fee. Buys one-time rights, second serial (reprint) rights or simultaneous rights, or makes work-for-hire assignments. Submit seasonal/holiday material 2 months in advance. Simultaneous, photocopied and previously published submissions OK. Computer printout submissions acceptable; prefers letter-quality to dot-matrix. Reports in 2 weeks on queries; 1 month on mss. Sample copy $1.

Nonfiction: Book excerpts; essays; exposé; general interest; how-to (related to singles, meeting people, relationships); humor; interview/profile; opinion; personal experience; photo feature; and travel. National Singles Week is 3rd week in September; September issue features singles' achievements and community celebrations. "While we will consider negative personal experiences, the overall attitude toward being single should be positive." Buys 50 mss/year. Query with or without published clips, or send complete ms. Length: 500-5,000 words. Pays 10¢/word maximum, $20 maximum/typed page. Sometimes pays in advertising trade. Sometimes pays the expenses of writers on assignment.

Photos: State availability of photos with submission or send photos with submission. Reviews prints (any size). Offers $10 maximum/photo. Model releases and identification of subjects required. Buys one-time rights.

Fiction: Confession, fantasy, humorous, mainstream, mystery, novel excerpts, slice-of-life vignettes. Buys 6 mss/year. Send complete ms. Length: 500-5,000 words. Pays 10¢/word maximum; $20 maximum/page.

Poetry: Jennifer Welch, poetry editor. Avant-garde, free verse, haiku, light verse, and traditional. Submit maximum 12 poems. Length: 1-50 lines. Pays $5 maximum or advertising trade.

Fillers: Anecdotes, facts and short humor. Length: 15-200 words. Pays $5 maximum or advertising trade.

Tips: "We are a low budget, black and white, activities-oriented magazine, best approached as a volunteer. Copy must be concise, well written, and oriented to singles. Writers who prove reliable receive paid-assignments. Freelancers' best approach is to answer our readers' most frequent question: 'How and where do you meet potential dates?'

‡COMMON LIVES/LESBIAN LIVES, A lesbian quarterly, The CL/LL Collective, Box 1553, Iowa City IA 52244. Collective Contacts: Tess Catalano and Tracy Moore. 100% freelance written. Eager to work with new/unpublished writers. A quarterly journal of contemporary lesbian culture. Circ. 2,000. Publishes ms an average of 3 months after acceptance. Byline given. Rights revert to author. Submit seasonal/holiday material 3-6 months in advance. Photocopied submissions OK. Computer printout submissions acceptable; no dot-matrix. Reports in 3 months on queries; 6 months on mss. Sample copy $4; writer's guidelines for SAE and 1 first class stamp.

Nonfiction: Book excerpts, biography, exposé, general interest, historical/nostalgic, humor, inspirational, interview/profile, memoir, opinion, oral history and history, political analysis, personal experience, photo feature, travel and first source material such as journal, diary and correspondence. Buys 25 mss/year. Query or send complete ms. Length: 5,000 words. Pays in copies.

Photos: Send photos with query or ms. Reviews 3x5 b&w prints. Captions and model releases required.

Columns/Departments: Book reviews of lesbian books. Length: 100 words. Query or send complete ms. Pays in copies.

Fiction: Adventure, condensed novels, confession, erotica, ethnic, experimental, fantasy, historical, horror, humorous, mainstream, mystery, novel excerpts, religious, romance, science fiction, suspense, western and political. No serialized novels. Buys 20 mss/year. Send complete ms. Length: 6,000 words maximum. Pays in copies.

Poetry: Free verse, haiku, light verse, traditional and narrative. No esoteric or abstract poetry. Buys 25 poems/year. Length: 400 lines maximum. Pays in copies.

Fillers: Jokes, anecdotes and short humor. Acquires 10/year. Length: 100-300 words. Pays in copies.

Tips: Most lesbians we publish are very new writers or have been published only in a few places. We want original work in lesbians' own voices, especially work from points of view new to our pages. Author's bio, preferably a self-descriptive narrative rather than an academic run-down, *must* accompany ms for consideration."

COSMOPOLITAN CONTACT. Pantheon Press, Box 1566, Fontana CA 92335. Editor-in-Chief: Romulus Rexner. Managing Editor: Nina Norvid. Assistant Editor: Irene Anders. 40% freelance written. Magazine irregularly published 2 or 3 times a year. "It is the publication's object to have as universal appeal as possible to students, graduates and others interested in international affairs, cooperation, contacts, travel, friendships, trade, exchanges, self-improvement and widening of mental horizons through multicultural interaction. This polyglot publication has worldwide distribution and participation, including the Communist countries. Writers participate in its distribution, editing and publishing." Circ. 1,500. Buys first serial rights second serial reprint rights and simultaneous rights. Publishes ms an average of 3 months after acceptance. Pays on publication in copies. Byline given. Simultaneous, photocopied, and previously published submissions OK. Computer printout submissions acceptable; no dot-matrix. Reports in 6 weeks. Sample copy $2.

Nonfiction: Exposé (should concentrate on government, education, etc.); how-to; informational; inspiration-

al; personal experience; personal opinion and travel. "Material designed to promote across all frontiers bonds of spiritual unity, intellectual understanding and sincere friendship among people by means of correspondence, meetings, publishing activities, tapes, records, exchange of hospitality, books, periodicals in various languages, hobbies and other contacts." Submit complete ms. Buys 15-30 mss/year. Maximum 500 words.
Poetry: Traditional. Length: maximum 40 lines.
Tips: "Most of the material is not written by experts to enlighten or to amuse the readers, but it is written by the readers who also are freelance writers. The material is didactic, provocative, pragmatic—not art-for-art's sake—and tries to answer the reader's question, 'What can I do about it?' More short articles and fillers are accepted than major features. The addresses of all contributors are published in order to facilitate global contacts among our contributors, editors and readers/members. Instead of writing, e.g., about Lincoln or history, it is better to be an emancipator and to make history by promoting high ideals of mankind. Consequently, the material submitted to us should not be only descriptive, but it should be analytical, creative, action- and future-oriented. We are not interested in any contribution containing vulgar language, extreme, intolerant, pro-Soviet or anti-American opinions." Recent article example: "On Being a Neighbor" by Eugénie de Rosier Petschel (Vol. XXI, No. 35).

D.I.N. NEWSERVICE, Do It Now Foundation, Box 21126, Phoenix AZ 85036. (602)257-0764. Editor: James D. Parker. Managing Editor: Christina Dye. 20% freelance written. A semiannual magazine on health, behavior, and personal growth. Circ. 2,500. Pays on publication. Byline given. Buys first North American serial rights and one-time rights. Simultaneous, photocopied and previously published submissions OK. Electronic submissions OK via Apple Macintosh. Computer printout submissions acceptable. Reports in 1-3 months. Sample copy $2.50; writer's guidelines for SASE.
Nonfiction: Features, interview/profile, opinion, personal experience short stories. Focus on approaches to health, personal growth and fitness. Special issues include nutrition, sex, consciousness. Buys 10 mss/year. Query. Length: 100-3,000 words. Pays $50-300.
Photos: State availability of photos with query; send photos with submission. Reviews contact sheets. Offers $5-50/photo. Identification of subjects required. Buys one-time rights.
Columns/Departments: Backwords (off-beat, current events, humor, unusual mini-features), 50-250 words; Newsfronts (breaking developments—consciousness, behavior, health, substance abuse, media), 50-400 words; Guestcolumn (opinion, commentary); and Postscripts (personal commentary). Length: 500-800 words. Pays $20-100.
Tips: "Be authoritative but readable. Establish credibility through frequent quotes. Look for original angles. We emphasize issues and groups overlooked by mainstream media, and attempt to convey a healthy skepticism in our reporting. Don't be afraid to be different or provocative."

DAY TONIGHT/NIGHT TODAY, Box 353, Hull MA 02045. Editor: S.R. Jade. 100% freelance written. Eager to work with new/unpublished writers. Magazine published 7 times a year. "We publish women only; nonsexist, nonracist; we try to provide a place for experimental and vivid writing." Circ. 1,250+. Pays in copies. Publishes ms an average of 8 months after acceptance. Byline given. Rights revert to author. Simultaneous queries and simultaneous, photocopied, and previously published submissions OK. Computer printout submissions acceptable; prefers letter-quality to dot-matrix. Reports in 1 month. Sample copy $3.25; writer's guidelines for SAE and 1 first class stamp.
Nonfiction: Book excerpts, historical/nostalgic about specific women's lives or lifestyles; and interview/profile. No travel, religious or fillers. Send complete ms. Length: 3,000 words maximum. Pays in copies.
Fiction: Condensed and serialized novels, ethnic, experimental, fantasy and suspense. Acquires about 15 mss/year. Length: 3,000 words maximum. Pays in copies.
Poetry: Avant-garde, free verse, haiku, light verse and traditional. No "gooey, sentimental, rhyming types of poetry. Acquires about 200/year. Submit maximum 6 poems. Pays in copies.
Tips: Poetry section is most open to freelancers.

EARTH'S DAUGHTERS MAGAZINE, Box 41, Central Park Station, Buffalo NY 14215. Collective editorship. 99% freelance written. Eager to work with new/unpublished writers. Publication schedule varies from 2-4 times a year. For people interested in literature and feminism. Circ. 1,000. Pays in copies. Publishes ms an average of 10 months after acceptance. Byline given. Acquires first North American serial rights; copyright reverts to author after publication. Clear photocopied submissions and clear carbons OK. Computer printout submissions acceptable; prefers letter-quality to dot-matrix. Reports "very slowly; please be patient." Sample copy $4 (includes postage); writer's guidelines and current topics available for SAE and 1 first class stamp to Johnson, Box 143, Lockport NY 14094.
Fiction: Feminist fiction of any and all modes. "Our subject is the experience and creative expression of women. We require a high level of technical skill and artistic intensity, and we are concerned with creative expression rather than propaganda. On occasion we publish feminist work by men." No anti-feminist material; no "hard-line, but shoddy, feminist work." Submit 1 short story/submission. "If it is a part of a larger work, mention this." Length: 1,500 words maximum. Pays in copies only.

Poetry: All modern, contemporary, and avant-garde forms. Submit maximum 6 poems. Length: 40 lines maximum preferred with occasional exceptions.
Tips: "We're doing smaller issues, most of which are topical (see above for information). Shorter fiction and fewer poems will be needed."

EARTHTONE, Publication Development, Inc., Box 23383, Portland OR 97223. (503)620-3917. Editor: Pat Jossy. 90% freelance written. Eager to work with new/unpublished writers. Bimonthly publication for a western U.S. readership interested in developing a self-sufficient lifestyle. "Editorial often deals with a back-to-the-land lifestyle but does not exclude those urban dwellers interested in becoming more independent and self-sufficient in their current residence." Circ. 50,000. Pays on publication. Publishes ms an average of 8 months after acceptance. Byline given. Buys first North American serial rights. Submit seasonal/holiday material 6 months in advance. Simultaneous queries, and simultaneous and photocopied submissions OK. Computer printout submissions acceptable; prefers letter-quality to dot-matrix. Reports in 1 month. Sample copy $2; writer's guidelines for SAE and 1 first class stamp.
Nonfiction: General interest (on country living, food, folk art); historical/nostalgic; how-to (crafts, home projects, small-scale low-cost building); humor; interview/profile (on people living this sort of lifestyle); new product (only if very unusual or revolutionary); personal experience (only if informative on various aspects of homesteading or country living and self-sufficient lifestyle); animal husbandry; health; energy; organic gardening and recreation. How-to articles should be accompanied by photos or illustrations. All articles should have a western U.S. angle. Buys 6-10 mss/issue. Query with published clips if available. Length: 500-3,000 words. Pays $50-300.
Tips: We're open to all kinds of general interest articles, so send us an interesting article and we'll make it work.

EAST WEST, The Journal of Natural Health & Living, Kushi Foundation, Inc., 17 Station St., Box 1200, Brookline Village MA 02147. (617)232-1000. Editor: Mark Mayell. 40% freelance written. Works with a small number of new/unpublished writers each year. Monthly magazine emphasizing natural health for "people of all ages seeking balance in a world of change." Circ. 70,000. Pays on publication. Publishes ms an average of 6 months after acceptance. Buys first serial rights or second (reprint) rights. Byline given. Submit seasonal/holiday material 6 months in advance. Simultaneous, photocopied, and previously published submissions OK. Computer printout submissions acceptable; prefers letter-quality to dot-matrix. Reports in 1 month. Sample copy $1; writer's guidelines for SAE and 1 first class stamp.
Nonfiction: Major focus is on issues of natural health and diet; interviews and features (on the natural foods industry, sustainable farming and gardening, natural healing, human-potential movement, diet and fitness). No negative, politically-oriented, or New Age material. "We're looking for original, first-person articles without jargon or opinions of any particular teachings; articles should reflect an intuitive approach." Buys 15-20 mss/year. Query. Length: 2,000-3,000 words. Pays 8-12¢/word. Sometimes pays expenses of writers on assignment.
Photos: Send photos with ms. Pays $15-40 for b&w prints; $15-175 for 35mm color transparencies (cover only). Captions preferred; model releases required.
Columns/Departments: Body, Whole Foods, Natural Healing, Gardening, and Cooking. Buys 15 mss/year. Submit complete ms. Length: 1,500-2,000 words. Pays 8-12¢/word.
Tips: "Read another issue. Too many freelancers don't take the time to truly understand their market and thus waste their time and ours with innappropriate submissions."

THE EVENER, Freiberg Publications, Box 7, Cedar Falls IA 50613. (319)277-3599. Managing Editor: Susan Salterberg. 45% freelance written. Works with a small number of new/unpublished writers each year. Quarterly magazine on draft horses and other draft animals. *The Evener* is published primarily for draft horse, mule and oxen enthusiasts. Circ. 10,500. Pays on publication. Publishes ms an average of 8 months after acceptance. Byline given. Prefers to buy first North American serial rights, but will make exceptions. Submit seasonal/holiday material 8 months in advance. Photocopied and previously published submissions OK. Computer printout submissions acceptable; prefers letter-quality to dot-matrix. Reports in 4 weeks on queries; 4 months on mss. Sample copy for 9x12 SAE and $1.07 postage; writer's guidelines for business size SAE and 37¢ postage; both $1.41.
Nonfiction: Book excerpts (from horse, mule, oxen or small farm-related books); historical/nostalgic (farming in the past, feature on a heartwarming event or situation related to draft animals, agricultural history of an area); how-to (making or repairing farm equipment, training a draft animal, breeding, shoeing draft horses, show decorations); humor (draft animal or country life related); interview/profile (people using innovative farming/training methods or those who are specialists as breeders, trainers, farmers, judges); old-timers' philosophies and recollections; personal experience (draft horse, mule or oxen related, or a country living or farming angle: experience caring for draft horses on the farm); photo feature (draft horse, mule or oxen or country life related); and technical (horse health and economics of large vs. small farming). No vague how-to articles or

those not relating to subject matter. Buys 15 mss/year. Send complete ms. Length: 300-3,000 words. Pays 3-15¢/word. Sometimes pays expenses of writers on assignment.

Photos: Send photos with ms. Pays $5-40 for b&w prints. Welcomes contact sheets. No negatives. Captions and identification of subjects (if applicable or pertinent) required.

Columns/Departments: Bits 'n Pieces (helpful hints); Lines & Traces (mythical horse remedies, historical facts about draft horses, mules or oxen); and Product Profile (horse products). Buys 5 mss/year. Send complete ms. Length: 30-250 words. Pays 3-15¢/word or free subscription.

Fillers: Anecdotes and newsbreaks. Buys 5/year. Length: 25-750 words. Pays 3-10¢/word or free subscription.

Tips: "Thoroughly peruse the freelance guidelines and the magazine, taking note of our readers' personalities. Submit an objective, concise article with good photos. Possibly attend draft horse and mule shows, horse pulls, sales and other related events. These events give you an excellent opportunity to interact with our audience so you understand our focus and aim. Then send us a 1,500-word manuscript with photos or illustrations. We want articles that teach, evoke emotions, and/or challenge our readers. Clear and easy-to-read writing is a must. Freelancers can best break into our publication with nonfiction, especially how-to, interview/profile, technical and historical/nostalgic. Be creative, search for a unique angle and be credible."

FIRST HAND, Experiences For Loving Men, Firsthand, Ltd., 310 Cedar Lane, Teaneck NJ 07666. (201)836-9177. Editor: Jack Veasey. Managing Editor: Jackie Lewis. 50% freelance written. Monthly magazine of homosexual erotica. Circ. 70,000. Pays 2 months after acceptance. Publishes ms an average of 8 months after acceptance. Byline given. Buys all rights (exceptions made), and second (reprint) rights. Submit seasonal/holiday material 10 months in advance. Photocopied submissions OK. Computer printout submissions acceptable; prefers letter-quality to dot-matrix. Reports in 2 months. Sample copy $3; writer's guidelines for SASE.

Nonfiction: "We seldom use nonfiction except for our 'Survival Kit' section, but will consider full-length profiles, investigative reports, and so on if they are of information/inspirational interest to gay people." Length: 3,000 words maximum. Pays $100-150. "We will consider original submissions only." Query.

Columns/Departments: Survival Kit (short nonfiction articles, up to 1,000 words, featuring practical information on safe sex practices, health, travel, books, video, psychology, law, fashion, and other advice/consumer/lifestyle topics of interest to gay or single men). "These should be written in the second or third person." Query. "For this section, we sometimes also buy reprint rights to appropriate articles previously published in local gay newspapers around the country." Pays $35 to $70, depending on length, if original; if reprint, pays half that rate.

Fiction: Erotic fiction up to 5,000 words in length, average 2,000-3,000 words. "We prefer fiction in the first person which is believable—stories based on the writer's actual experience have the best chance. We're not interested in stories which involve underage characters in sexual situations. Other taboos include bestiality, rape—except in prison stories, as rape is an unavoidable reality in prison—and heavy drug use. Writers with questions about what we can and cannot depict should write for our guidelines, which go into this in more detail. We print mostly self-contained stories; we will look at novel excerpts, but only if they stand on their own."

Poetry: Free verse and light verse. Buys 12/year. Submit maximum 5 poems. Length: 10-30 lines. Pays $25.

Tips: "*First Hand* is a very reader-oriented publication for gay men. Half of each issue is comprised by letters from our readers describing their personal experiences, fantasies and feelings. Our readers are from all walks of life, all races and ethnic backgrounds, all classes, all religious and political affiliations, and so on. They are very diverse, and many live in far-flung rural areas or small towns; for some of them, our magazines are the primary source of contact with gay life, in some cases the only support for their gay identity. Our readers are very loyal and save every issue. We return that loyalty by trying to reflect their interests—for instance, by striving to avoid the exclusively big-city bias so common to national gay publications. So bear in mind the diversity of the audience when you write."

THE FUTURIST, A Journal of Forecasts, Trends, and Ideas about the Future, World Future Society, 4916 St. Elmo Ave., Bethesda MD 20814. (301)656-8274. Editor: Edward S. Cornish. 1% freelance written. Eager to work with new/unpublished writers. Bimonthly magazine on all aspects of the future for general audience. "*The Futurist* focuses on trends and developments that are likely to have a major impact on the way we live in the years ahead. It explores how changes in all areas—science, technology, government, economics, environmental affairs, lifestyles, values, etc.—will affect individuals and society in the next five to fifty years. We cover a very broad spectrum of topics—from assessing how a new technology like computers will affect the way people work to how the institution of marriage may change." Circ. 30,000. Publishes ms an average of 6 months after acceptance. Byline given. Acquires variable rights according to the article. Simultaneous queries, and simultaneous (if so advised), photocopied, and previously published submissions OK. Electronic submissions OK if approved of in advance. Computer printout submissions acceptable; prefers letter-quality to dot-matrix. "SASE must be included or manuscript will not be considered." Writer's guidelines available.

Nonfiction: Timothy Willard, managing editor. Book excerpts, general interest, how-to, interview/profile, new product and opinion. No "vague articles that say, 'Wouldn't it be nice if the future were like this?' or arti-

cles lacking a future orientation.'' Acquires 45-50 mss/year. Query with published clips or send complete ms. Length: 500-5,000 words. Pays in copies.
Tips: ''Feature articles in *The Futurist* come almost entirely from outside authors, usually experts in a particular field. Almost no freelance assignments are given. The Tomorrow in Brief page and the World Trends and Forecasts section are primarily staff written.''

‡GAY CHICAGO MAGAZINE, Ultra Ink, Inc., 1527 N. Wells St., Chicago IL 60606-1305. (312)751-0130. Editor: Dan Di Leo. 50% freelance written. Eager to work with new/unpublished writers. Weekly magazine published for the gay community of metropolitan Chicago. Circ. 19,500. Pays on publication. Publishes ms an average of 2 months after acceptance. Byline given. Buys one-time rights. Submit seasonal/holiday material 2 months in advance. Photocopied submissions OK. Computer printout submissions acceptable. Reports in 1 month. Free sample copy.
Nonfiction: General interest and personal experience. ''Since our magazine is available in many public places, such as restaurants, clothing stores, record stores, etc., the tone of the articles can be erotic but not X-rated pornographic.'' Buys 10-12 mss/year. Send complete ms. Length: 1,200 words maximum. Pays $25-50. Sometimes pays the expenses of writers on assignment.
Photos: Send photos with ms. Pays $5-15 for 5x7 b&w prints. Captions, model releases, and identification of subjects required.
Columns/Departments: Buys 2-3 mss/year. Send complete ms. Length: 500-1,000 words. Pays $10-40.
Fiction: Erotica, fantasy, historical, humorous, mystery and science fiction. ''We seek any type of fiction that would appeal to the male gay reader, though we do accept pieces that would also appeal to the female gay reader.'' Buys 2-3 mss/year. Send complete ms. Length: 1,200 words maximum. Pays $10-50.

‡GAY COMMUNITY NEWS, Bromfield Educational Foundation, Suite 5, 167 Tremont St., Boston MA 02111. (617)426-4469. Managing Editor: Gordon Gottlieb. 50% freelance written. A ''radical newsweekly for gay men and lesbians with an emphasis on national news, gay/lesbian culture and politics.'' Circ. 15,000. We cannot afford to pay freelancers. Byline given. Buys all rights. Submit seasonal/holiday material 2 months in advance. Simultaneous and photocopied submissions OK. Sample copy $1.
Nonfiction: Interview/profile; opinion; personal experience. ''No articles geared primarily towards heterosexuals.'' Query. Length: 500-5,000 words. No payment.
Photos: Send photos with submission. Reviews 4x6 prints. Offers $5/photo. Identification of subjects required. Buys one-time rights.
Columns/Departments: Book Reviews (tie-in to gay/lesbian experience), 500-2,000; Coming Out (personal experience), 500-1,000; Theatrical Review (tie-in to gay/lesbian experience,), 750-1,000. Query with published clips.
Tips: ''Approach subject with a political viewpoint (i.e. incorporate race, class, political, economic issues).''

HANDICAP NEWS, Burns Enterprises, 272 N. 11th Ct., Brighton CO 80601. (303)659-4463. Editor: Phyllis Burns. 20% freelance written. Eager to work with new/unpublished writers. Monthly newsletter on handicaps. *''Handicap News* is written for people with handicaps and those people working with them. Material should be written in an 'upbeat' mode.'' Circ. 500. Pays on publication. Publishes ms an average of 3 months after acceptance. Credit is given for pieces written by handicapped people. In the news section, no credit is given. Not copyrighted. Buys one-time rights. Simultaneous, photocopied, and previously published submissions OK. Reports in 1 month. Sample copy $1 with #10 SAE and 1 first class stamp. Writer's guidelines with sample copy only.
Nonfiction: How-to, humor, inspiration, medical breakthroughs, new product, opinion, personal experience, physical/occupation therapy developments, research findings, technical and travel. ''We request a copy of the study, report or news article which was the source of information. We are sometimes asked for more information by the readers so we must have a file copy.'' No pessimistic articles. Buys 10-20 mss/year. Send complete ms. Length: 75-300 words. Pays in 2 copies of the newsletter in which the article appeared.
Fiction: Fantasy, historical, humorous, mainstream, religious, science fiction and western. ''All fiction must deal directly with the subject (handicapped people and how they respond to certain conditions.) We have not as yet printed any fiction but would be interested in seeing some for the future. This section must be written by handicapped people or their families.'' Query. Length: 500-750 words. Pays in 2 copies of newsletter in which appeared.
Poetry: Will consider any type, length or style as long as it is written by handicapped people or their families. Nothing pessimistic or down beat. Buys 20-30/year. Submit maximum 4 poems. Pays in 2 copies.
Tips: ''In the medical, product, travel, and therapy section, anyone may study the format and submit the material with their documentation. In the poems, experiences, inspirational, and fiction, the material must come from the handicapped person and family. In the latter, we will accept almost any material as long as it falls within the guidelines and is optimistic. We look forward to receiving material from handicapped writers but wish more of them would learn the basic format to sending articles to publications. We do not appreciate paying postage on material we receive from you. If possible, type it. If not, write in a 'readable' manner.''

Close-up

James Lawrence
Editor/Publisher
Harrowsmith

James Lawrence was 29 when he left his reporting job in Kingston, Ontario, to begin publishing and editing *Harrowsmith* in 1976. Lawrence had only 707 prepaid orders for the first issue of *Harrowsmith*, which was named for a small village not far from Kingston. Now its Canadian circulation has grown to something over 154,000; the first U.S. edition was published in January, 1986.

Lawrence found his early newspaper experience valuable—he has a M.S. in magazine journalism from Syracuse University—but he urges aspiring magazine writers/editors to "get out quickly before the ways of newspaper journalism become too ingrained."

Lawrence has lived in a rural setting for 16 years, actively involved with gardening and other rural pursuits covered in *Harrowsmith*. "We are looking for in-depth journalistic pieces in the areas of food, agriculture, health and the environment," Lawrence says. He believes it would be difficult if not impossible to write for the magazine without actual hands-on experience in the lifestyle *Harrowsmith* represents. "Except for our investigative or general-interest pieces, our material tends to come from writers who display real depth of knowledge about our material. One cannot, for example, spend a few afternoons in a reference library and hope to sell us a credible how-to piece."

In addition to depth, Lawrence stresses that an article must be *readable*. "A piece on foraging for wild mushrooms must command the attention of even those readers who would trenchantly refuse to hunt or eat a wild mushroom."

The investigative pieces form the backbone of the magazine. "We like to stir at least one good controversy into each issue," Lawrence maintains, "and we should be considered a prime market for serious journalists." Controversial topics discussed in *Harrowsmith* include the hazards of irradiating food to prevent spoilage and the relationship between failing farms and small-town banks.

Lawrence suggests a writer anxious to submit to *Harrowsmith* begin with a query that "instantly involves the editors in the subject." He appreciates queries that "start with the same intensity as the actual lead of the proposed piece. Writers should define a clear angle to the article and briefly describe how they intend to do the piece," Lawrence says. "Query letters written with less care than we expect to see in finished manuscripts do not get far with us."

Problems Lawrence sometimes faces with freelancers involve "writers who do a first draft and then assume their work is done." *Harrowsmith*'s editors prefer authors who respond well to questions and suggestions during the editing process. Other writers assume *Harrowsmith*'s editors will act as a safety net for their research and/or spelling of technical words. "In fact, our checkers serve this function," says Lawrence, "but when we find a writer whose material consistently shows lapses, red flags go up."

Care in research, writing and self-editing—and a previous knowledge of the subjects likely to fit in with the magazine's themes—can help writers break in. *Harrowsmith* has traditionally been very open to submissions from "undiscovered" talent. Lawrence likes to find "new people who share our interest in good writing, and who are willing to put an uncommon amount of energy into every piece they do for us."

—Laurie Henry

HARROWSMITH MAGAZINE, Camden House Publishing, Ltd., Camden East, Ontario K0K 1J0 Canada. (613)378-6661. Editor/Publisher: James M. Lawrence. 75% freelance written. Published 6 times/year "for those interested in country life, nonchemical gardening, energy, self-sufficiency, folk arts, small-stock husbandry, owner-builder architecture and alternative styles of life." Circ. 154,000. Pays on acceptance. Publishes ms an average of 4 months after acceptance. Byline given. Buys first North American serial rights. Submit seasonal/holiday material 6 months in advance. Computer printout submissions acceptable; prefers letter-quality to dot-matrix. SAE and IRCs. Reports in 6 weeks. Sample copy $5; free writer's guidelines.
Nonfiction: Exposé, how-to, general interest, humor, interview, photo feature and profile. "We are always in need of quality gardening articles geared to northern conditions. No articles whose style feigns 'folksiness.' No how-to articles written by people who are not totally familiar with their subject. We feel that in this field simple research does not compensate for lack of long-time personal experience." Buys 10 mss/issue. Query. Length: 500-4,000 words. Pays $75-750 but will consider higher rates for major stories.
Photos: State availability of photos with query. Pays $50-250 for 8x10 b&w glossy prints and 35mm or larger color transparencies. Captions required. Buys one-time rights. "We regularly run photo essays for which we pay $250-750."
Tips: "We have standards of excellence as high as any publication in the country. However, we are by no means a closed market. Much of our material comes from unknown writers. We welcome and give thorough consideration to all freelance submissions. Our magazine is read by Canadians who live in rural areas or who hope to make the urban to rural transition. They want to know as much about the realities of country life as the dreams. They expect quality writing, not folksy cliches."

I KNOW YOU KNOW, lesbian views & news, Jernan Ltd, Inc., Suite 14, 5335 N. Tacoma, Indianapolis IN 46220. (317)252-5381. Editor: Jeri Edwards. Managing Editor: Mary A. Byrne. 33% freelance written. A monthly "lifestyle magazine for lesbians that includes regular columns, topics, interviews, photography, poetry and short stories. Circ. 15,000. Pays on publication. Publishes ms an average of 5 months after acceptance. Byline given. Buys first North American serial rights. Submit seasonal/holiday material 3 months in advance. Simultaneous submissions OK. Computer printout submissions acceptable; no dot-matrix. Reports in 3 weeks on queries; 2 months on ms. Sample copy $4.75; free writer's guidelines.
Nonfiction: General interest, historical/nostalgic, how-to (home repair), humor, interview/profile, personal experience, spirituality, travel, health and legal. No pornography. Feature articles pertain to the special topics of each issue; contact the managing editor. Query with or without published clips, or send complete ms. Length: 1,000-2,000 words. Payment is in copies.
Photos: State availability of photos with submission. Reviews contact sheets. Offers no additional payment for photos accepted with ms. Model releases required. Buys one-time rights.
Columns/Departments: Health, Legal, Sports/Recreation, Travel, and Spirituality, all of interest to women. Buys 60 mss/year. Query with or without published clips. Length: 500-1,000 words.
Fiction: Adventure, ethnic, fantasy, historical, horror, humorous, mystery, romance, science fiction, suspense, and western. No pornography. Buys 12 mss/year. Send complete ms. Length: 1,000-3,000 words. Pays with copies.
Poetry: Nancy Allbright, poetry editor. Light verse. Buys 12 poems/year. Submit maximum 3 poems. Length: 1-45 lines. Pays with copies.

IN STYLE, For Men, In Touch Inc., 7216 Varna Ave., North Hollywood CA 91605. (818)764-2288. Editor: William Franklin. 85% freelance written. "*In Style For Men* is a bimonthly magazine which circulates throughout the U.S., Great Britain, and Canada. Slant is for sophisticated, upscale, urban men interested in travel, arts, fashion and entertainment comfortable with the gay lifestyle." Circ. 100,000. Pays 30 days after acceptance. Publishes ms an average of 2 months after acceptance. Byline given. Offers 20% kill fee. Buys first North American serial rights. Submit seasonal/holiday material 4 months in advance. Simultaneous, photocopied and previously published submissions OK. Computer printout submissions acceptable; no dot-matrix. Reports in 2 weeks on queries; 3 weeks on mss. Sample copy for 9x12 SAE with 8 first class stamps; free writer's guidelines.
Nonfiction: General interest; historical/nostalgic; how-to (on law, medicine, psychology); humor; interview/profile; new product; photo feature (fashion); and travel (cities in both the U.S. and abroad). "No personal ramblings or diatribes." Buys 50 mss/year. Query with published clips. Length: 1,000-3,000 words. Pays $75-200. Sometimes pays the expenses of writers on assignment.
Photos: State availability of photos with submission. Reviews contact sheets, transparencies, and prints. Offers $35/photo. Captions, model releases and identification of subjects required. Buys one-time rights.
Columns/Departments: Health, grooming, and psychology (for men with a gay orientation), 1,500 words. Buys 30 mss/year. Query with published clips. Pays $75-150.
Tips: "Travel articles are most in demand—we need material on foreign destinations."

IN TOUCH FOR MEN, In Touch Publications International, Inc., 7216 Varna, North Hollywood CA 91605. (818)764-2288. Editor: Bob Stanford. 80% freelance written. Works with a small number of new/unpublished writers each year. A monthly magazine covering the gay male lifestyle, gay male humor and erotica. Circ. 70,000. Pays on acceptance. Byline given. Buys one-time rights. Submit seasonal/holiday material 4 months in advance. Simultaneous and photocopied submissions OK. Computer printout submissions acceptable. Reports in 2 weeks on queries; 6 weeks on mss. Sample copy $3.95; free writer's guidelines.

Nonfiction: Buys 36 mss/year. Send complete ms. Length: 1,000-3,500 words. Pays $25-75.

Photos: State availability of photos with submission. Reviews contact sheets, transparencies, and prints. Offers $35/photo. Captions, model releases and identification of subjects required. Buys one-time rights.

Columns/Departments: Touch and Go (brief comments on various items or pictures that have appeared in the media), 50-500 words. Buys 12 mss/year. Send complete ms. Pays $25.

Fiction: Adventure, confession, erotica, historical, horror, humorous, mainstream, mystery, romance, science fiction, slice-of-life vignettes, suspense, and western; all must be gay male erotica. No "heterosexual, heavy stuff." Buys 36 mss/year. Send complete ms. Length: 2,500-3,500 words. Pays $75 maximum.

Fillers: Short humor. Buys 12/year. Length: 1,500-3,500 words. Pays $50-75.

Tips: "Our publication features male nude photos plus three fiction pieces, several articles, cartoons, humorous comments on items from the media, and photo features. We try to present the positive aspects of the gay lifestyle, with an emphasis on humor. Humorous pieces may be erotic in nature. We are open to all submissions that fit our gay male format; the emphasis, however, is on humor and the upbeat. We receive many fiction manuscripts but not nearly enough articles and humor."

THE INTERNATIONAL AMERICAN, 201 E. 36th St., New York NY 10016. (212)685-4023. Editor: Alison R. Lanier. 33% freelance written. Eager to work with new/unpublished writers. Monthly newsletter of international information for expatriate Americans. "We need practical information pertinent to overseas Americans wherever they may be. Personal experience articles are needed only if they would be really relevant to others." Circ. 5,000. Pays on acceptance. Byline given. Publishes ms an average of 3 months after acceptance. Buys one-time rights. Simultaneous queries and previously published submissions OK. Computer printout submissions acceptable; no dot-matrix. Reports in 3 weeks. Sample copy $1; writer's guidelines for SAE and 1 first class stamp.

Nonfiction: Material should pertain in some way to working, living, attitudes, experiences, short advice, warnings, humor or interests of overseas Americans. Articles should be broadly relevant, not simply personal. Especially needs advice, warnings and helpful information from experienced expatriate Americans, including all aspects of overseas adjustments. No travel tips or personal stories. Buys 6-12 mss/year. Query or send complete ms. Length: 350-400 words maximum. Pays $15-35.

Tips: "We don't need 'beginners' information; we do want financial, cross-cultural, practical in-country material. Stay within the very short word length limits given; material must be pertinent to our audience and carry real practical first-hand experience. Areas most open to freelancers are Just So You Know, Practical Tips (100-150 words); Families Abroad (up to 400 words); and As You Move About the World, short practical travel pointers."

INTERNATIONAL LIVING, Agora Publishing, 824 E. Baltimore St., Baltimore MD 21208. (301)234-0515. Editor: Francine Modderno. 60% freelance written. "We prefer established writers and unpublished writers with original, first-hand experience." Monthly newsletter covering international lifestyles, travel, and investment for Americans. Aimed at affluent and not-so-affluent dreamers to whom the romance of living overseas has a strong appeal, especially when it involves money-saving angles. Circ. 65,000. Pays on acceptance. Publishes ms an average of 6 months after acceptance. Byline given. Buys first North American serial rights and all rights. Submit seasonal/holiday material 2 months in advance. Electronic submissions acceptable via IBM—Multimate and WordStar. Computer printout submissions acceptable; prefers letter-quality to dot-matrix. Reports in 1 month on queries; 6 weeks on mss. Sample copy $2.50; writer's guidelines for business size SAE and 1 first class stamp.

Nonfiction: Book excerpts (overseas, travel, retirement investment, save money overseas, invest overseas); historical/nostalgic (travel, lifestyle abroad); how-to (save money, find a job overseas); interview/profile (famous people and other Americans living abroad); personal experience; travel (unusual, imaginative destinations, give how-to's and costs); and other (humor, cuisine). "We want pithy, fact-packed articles. No vague, long-winded travel articles on well-trodden destinations." Buys 100 mss/year. Query with published clips or send complete ms. Length: 200-2,000 words. Pays $15-200. Sometimes pays the expenses of writers on assignment.

Tips: "We are looking for writers who can combine original valuable information with a style that suggests the romance of life abroad. Break in with highly-specific, well-researched material combining subjective impressions of living in a foreign country or city with information on taxes, cost of living, residency requirements, employment and entertainment possibilities. We do heavy rewrites and usually reorganization because of tight space requirements. We are moving toward more how-to and source lists."

‡**THE LESBIAN INCITER,** Particular Friends, Suite 307, 2215-R Market St., San Francisco CA 94114. (415)333-0454. Editor: Mariel R. Burch. 40% freelance written. A bimonthly newspaper covering all factors/

issues concerning lesbians. "We print only material written by lesbians; we publish with a pseudonym when necessary, but must have name, address and phone number to contact (will be kept confidential)." Circ. 7,000. Pays on publication. Publishes ms an average of 3 months after acceptance. Byline given. Not copyrighted. Buys first North American serial rights. Submit seasonal/holiday material 4 months in advance. Previously published submissions OK. Reports in 6 weeks. Sample copy $2; writer's guidelines for SASE.

Nonfiction: Essay, exposé, general interest, historical/nostalgic, humor, interview/profile, opinion, personal experience and feminist political. Special issue on the impact of aging on the lesbian community. No written work that does not deal with lesbian issues. Buys 12 mss/year. Query with or without published clips, or send complete ms. Length: 600-2,500 words. Pays $15-50 for assigned articles. Pays in copies for most unsolicited articles published. Sometimes pays the expenses of writers on assignment.

Photos: Send photos with submission. Offers no additional payment for photos accepted with ms. Identification of subjects required. Buys one-time rights.

Columns/Departments: Commentary (political/current, relevant, something that is happening currently to affect lesbians), 600-1,800 words. Buys 3-4 mss/year. Send complete ms. Pays $15-35.

Fiction: Ethnic, experimental, humorous, mainstream, romance, serialized novels and slice-of-life vignettes. No erotica. Pays 5 contributor's copies.

Fillers: Anecdotes, facts, gags to be illustrated by cartoonist, newsbreaks and short humor. Pays in copies.

Tips: "Make sure the writing is helpful for lesbians. We want to expand our knowledge and we encourage sharing experience, rather than 'put downs.' Also, submitting new information is welcome. The areas of our publication most open to freelancers are political and personal."

LOBSTER TENDENCIES QUARTERLY, Lobster Tendencies Press, Apt. 8, 141 Ridge St., New York NY 10002. (212)460-8457. Editor: Michael Kaniecki. 50% freelance written. Eager to work with new/unpublished writers. Newsletter published every 3 months about underground lifestyles. "Writing should provide a healthy release of tension/angst for persons/groups who cannot accept mainstream values and wish to resist them. Our politics is American socialist." Circ. 800. Pays on acceptance. Publishes ms an average of 6 months after acceptance. Byine given upon request; otherwise name is listed among others in each issue's co-op. Rights remain with author. Submit seasonal/holiday material 3 months in advance. Simultaneous queries, and simultaneous, photocopied, and previously published submissions OK. Computer printout submissions acceptable; prefers letter-quality to dot-matrix. Reports in 2 weeks on queries; 6 weeks on mss.

Nonfiction: Exposé, humor, inspirational, interview/profile, opinion and personal experience. No academic. Acquires 140 mss/year. Send complete ms. Length: 1,000 words. Pays in copies.

Fiction: Confession, erotica, experimental, fantasy, horror, humorous, religious and romance. "No unemotional—the kind that puts ideas ahead of feelings and is written for over-educated types. We like writing that finds hope and humanity in the most unlikely places and isn't afraid to tackle disturbing emotions. No fluff. Stories should break mundane reality into visionary." Acquires 50 mss/year. Send complete ms. Length: 1,000 words maximum. Pays in copies.

Poetry: Avant-garde, free verse, haiku and light verse. Anything with an attitude. Something combative yet reconciling. No academic, full of references to the classics, etc. Writing should be rooted in the real life or famous life of contemporary life. Acquires 25/year. Length: 1-60 lines. Pays in copies.

Fillers: Jokes, gags, anecdotes and short humor. Acquires 100/year. Length 1-100 words. Pays in copies.

Tips: "We think we have a mission to define unpopular causes because we hate bullies. This magazine circulates largely through an underground mailing network. We are interested in artists wishing to establish in independent magazines and not the corporate writing-academic establishment."

‡LOST GENERATION JOURNAL, Lost Generation Journal Inc., Dept. of Journalism, Temple University, Route 5, Box 134, Salem MO 65560. (314)265-8594. Editors: Dr. Thomas W. Wood Jr. and Deloris Wood. Magazine published 3 times/year covering American expatriates in Paris during the '20s. 85% freelance written. Prefers to work with published/established writers. Pays on publication. Publishes ms an average of 1 year after acceptance. Byline given plus a 200-word biography and 1-column photo of author. Acquires first North American serial rights. Submit seasonal holiday material 6 months in advance. Simultaneous queries, and simultaneous and photocopied submissions OK "if we have first rights to material." Electronic submissions acceptable via Texas Instruments professional computer—TTY, but requires hard copy also. Computer printout submissions acceptable; prefers letter-quality to dot-matrix. Reports in 6 weeks on queries; 2 months on mss. Sample copy $4 (subscription, back issue and sample copy address: *LGJ*, Route 5, Box 134, Salem MO 65560); writer's guidelines for business size envelope and 1 first class stamp.

Nonfiction: Exposé (if research reveals what really happened to some aspect of the expatriate); historical/nostalgic (documentation for the historical presentation of the Paris expatriate—why he went, etc. "A nostalgic article about the life of an expatriate is great."); humor (if it relates to our young Americans in Paris during the '20s); interview/profile ("a well done indepth article on a survivor of the Paris '20s is our priority"); personal issues (if it relates/if the person was in Paris in the '20s); photo feature (old photos of expatriates); travel ("travel articles are welcome if they are about the means of travel used by the American to get to Paris and travel there in the 1920s"). Special issues include poets in Paris during the '20s (Ezra Pound, etc.); The Correspondent in

Paris during the '20s (Ernest Hemingway, William L. Shirer, etc.); The Expatriate Musician; Student and Businesses in Paris during the '20s. We do not want boring pedantic lectures talking down to our readers or articles that assume that the readers have read all the works done, say, by Hemingway. We consider *LGJ* to be a place where a writer can start so prior publication is not necessary, but documentation of material is very important." Accepts 20-30 mss/year. Query or send complete ms. Length: 1,500-3,000 words. Pays in 3 contributor's copies (of issue in which article appears). Sometimes pays the expenses of writers on assignment.

Photos: Send photos with query or ms if possible. Reviews b&w contact sheets, and 3x5, 4x6, 5x7 and 8x10 (cover) b&w prints. Captions, model releases and identification of subjects required. Acquires one-time rights.

Columns/Departments: Between the Book Ends (books about or by Americans who started their careers in Paris between 1919 and 1939 and about places where they worked, like an American newspaper there or the embassy or American hospital). This will resume with Vol. VIII. Send complete ms. Length: 250-500 words. Pays in 2 contributor's copies.

Fiction: "Only fiction written by a survivor of the Paris '20s is used in *LGJ*. The reason *LGJ* was started was to capture and publish the works of the 'Lost Generation.' This section on fiction we hope would be nostalgic with the Paris they knew when they were there." Send complete ms. Length: varies (usually 3-5 double-spaced pages). Pays in 3 contributor's copies.

Poetry: Light verse and traditional. "We do not want to see poetry that does not have a theme of the American in Paris in the '20s." Submit maximum 12 poems. Length: 10-24 lines. Pays in 2 contributor's copies.

Fillers: Clippings. "We usually add drawings, but good fillers would be used if they related to the American in Paris in the '20s." Length: 4-12 lines. Pays in 1 contributor copy.

Tips: "Freelancers can best break in to our publication by telling a story about an American in Paris between 1919-1939 who started his/her career there. Tape record interview and keep a record of your research. Write clearly and make your expatriate come alive without using fiction. Query your idea to the editor and give enough information that he can be assured that you have a good character or topic. Nonfiction is most open to freelancers: features, historical/nostalgic, interview/profile and specials. We are not interested in dull research papers. All research must be footnoted MLA style. Hemingway is always something our readers are interested in reading about if they read it in *LGJ* first."

‡**METRO SINGLES LIFESTYLE**, Metro Publications, Box 28203, Kansas City MO 64118. (816)436-8424. Editor: R.L. Huffstutter. 40% freelance written. Eager to work with new/unpublished writers. A tabloid appearing 9 times/year covering singles lifestyles. Pays on acceptance. Publishes ms an average of 2 months after acceptance. Byline given. Buys one-time rights and second serial (reprint) rights. Submit seasonal/holiday material 3 months in advance. Photocopied submissions OK. Computer printout submissions acceptable. Reports in 1 month. Sample copy $2.

Nonfiction: Essay, general interest, how-to (on meeting the ideal mate, . . . recovering from divorce, etc.), inspirational, interview/profile, personal experience and photo feature. No sexually-oriented material. Buys 2-6 mss/year. Send complete ms. Length: 700-1,200 words. Pays $100 maximum for assigned articles; pays $20-50 for unsolicited articles. Will pay in copies or other if writer prefers.

Photos: Send photos with submission. Reviews 3x5 prints. Offers no additional payment for photos accepted with ms. Captions, model releases, and identification of subjects required. Buys one-time rights.

Columns/Departments: Movie Reviews, Lifestyles, Singles Events, and Book Reviews (about singles), all 400-1,000 words. Buys 3 mss/year. Send complete ms. Pays $20-50.

Fiction: Confession, humorous, romance and slice-of-life vignettes. No political, religion, ethnic or sexually-oriented material. Buys 6 mss/year. Send complete ms. Length: 700-1,200 words. Pays $20-50.

Poetry: Free verse and light verse. Buys 6 poems/year. Submit maximum 3 poems. Length: 21 lines. Pays $5-10.

Tips: "A freelancer can best approach and break in to our publication with positive articles, photo features about singles and positive fiction about singles. Photos and short bios of singles (blue collar, white collar, and professional) at work needed. Photos and a few lines about singles enjoying recreation (swimming, sports, chess, etc.) always welcome. Color photos, close-up, are suitable."

‡**MOM GUESS WHAT NEWSPAPER**, MGW Productions, Inc., Suite 100, 1400 S St., Sacramento CA 95814. (916)441-6397. Editor: Linda Birner. Managing Editor: Karl Ketner. 100% freelance written. A monthly tabloid covering gay rights and gay lifestyles. Circ. 21,000. Pays on publication. Byline given. Buys all rights. Submit seasonal/holiday material 3 months in advance. Photocopied submissions OK. Computer printout submissions acceptable; prefers letter-quality to dot-matrix. Reports in 2 months. Sample copy $1; writer's guidelines for #10 SAE with 3 first class stamps.

Nonfiction: Interview/profile and photo feature. Buys 8 mss/year. Query. Length: 200-1,500 words. Payment depends on article. Pays expenses of writers on assignment.

Photos: State availability of photos with submission. Reviews 5x7 prints. Offers no additional payment for photos accepted with ms. Captions and identification of subjects required. Buys one-time rights.

Columns/Departments: Restaurants, Book Reviews, and Political. Buys 12 mss/year. Query. Payment depends on article.

THE MOTHER EARTH NEWS, Box 70, Hendersonville NC 28791. (704)693-0211. Editor: Bruce Woods. 40% freelance written. Bimonthly magazine. Emphasizes "country living and country skills, for both long-time and would-be ruralites." Circ. 900,000. Pays on acceptance. "We buy all rights. However, after publication of our edited version, the rights to your original material are reassigned to you. Then you may resell the un-edited version as many times as you like." Byline given. Submit seasonal/holiday material 5 months in advance. Computer printout submissions acceptable; prefer letter-quality to dot-matrix. No handwritten mss. Reports within 3 months. Publishes ms an average of 1 year after acceptance. Sample copy $3; writer's guidelines for SASE and 39¢ postage.
Nonfiction: Roselyn Edwards, submissions editor. How-to, home business, alternative energy systems, home building, home retrofit and home maintenance, energy-efficient structures, seasonal cooking, gardening and crafts. Buys 300-350 mss/year. Query or send complete ms. "A short, to-the-point paragraph is often enough. If it's a subject we don't need at all, we can answer immediately. If it tickles our imagination, we'll ask to take a look at the whole piece. No phone queries, please." Length: 300-3,000 words. Pays $100/published page minimum. Sometimes pays the expenses of writers on assignment.
Photos: Purchased with accompanying ms. Send prints or transparencies. Uses 8x10 b&w glossies; any size color transparencies. Include type of film, speed and lighting used. Total purchase price for ms includes payment for photos. Captions and credits required.
Columns/Departments: "Contributions to Mother's Down-Home Country Lore and Barters and Boot-straps are paid by subscription. Profiles pays $25-50."
Fillers: Short how-to's on any subject normally covered by the magazine. Query. Length: 150-300 words. Pays $7.50-25.
Tips: "Probably the best way to break in is to study our magazine, digest our writer's guidelines, and send us a concise article illustrated with color transparencies that we can't resist. When folks query and we give a go-ahead on speculation, we often offer some suggestions. Failure to follow those suggestions can lose the sale for the author. We want articles that tell what real people are doing to take charge of their own lives. Articles should be well-documented and tightly written treatments of topics we haven't already covered. The critical thing is length, and our payment is by space, not word count." No phone queries.

‡THE MOUNTAIN COMMUNIQUE, Stellar-7 Communications, Box 226, Brocton NY 14716-0226. (716)792-9025. Editor: Douglas E. Arters. 70% freelance written. Works with a small number of new/unpublished writers each year. A monthly newsletter covering survival science, financial investments and natural history. "Wholistic survivalism is the principle theme." Estab. 1985. Pays on publication. Publishes ms an average of 4 months after acceptance. Byline given. Offers 50% kill fee. Buys first North American serial rights. Submit seasonal/holiday material 4 months in advance. Photocopied and previously published submissions OK. Computer printout submissions acceptable; prefers letter-quality to dot-matrix. Reports in 2 months. Sample copy for $2 with SAE and 2 first class stamps; writer's guidelines for SAE with 1 first class stamp.
Nonfiction: Historical/nostaglic; how-to (survival science topics; conservation; ecology; financial); inspirational; and information revolution: computers. No erotica. Buys 12+ mss/year. Query with or without published clips, or send complete ms. Length: 100-1,000 words. Pays $1-7, plus copies.
Photos: State availability of photos, or send photos with submission. Reviews prints; prefers small size. Offers $2-4/photo. Captions and identification of subjects required. Buys one-time rights.
Columns/Departments: Financial and Opportunity Notes (financial investments, budgeting, surviving poor economy, saving money, etc.), 50 words minimum. Buys 3 mss/year. Query with or without published clips, or send complete ms. Length: 100-1,000 words. Pays $1-7.
Poetry: Avant-garde, free verse, haiku, light verse and traditional. Pays $1 minimum.
Tips: "Reading the 'Financial and Opportunity Notes' column should give a writer insights into our needs. Additional information is available, and writers should query with ideas."

‡NATURAL FOOD & FARMING, Natural Food Associates, Highway 59, Box 210, Atlanta TX 75551. (214)796-3612. 80% freelance written. Eager to work with new/unpublished writers. Editor: Kathy Hulme. A monthly magazine covering organic gardening and natural foods, preventive medicine, and vitamins and supplements. Circ. 50,000. Pays on acceptance. Publishes ms an average of 3 months after acceptance. Byline given sometimes. Not copyrighted. Buys first rights or second serial (reprint) rights. Submit seasonal/holiday material 2-3 months in advance. Simultaneous, photocopied and previously published submissions OK. Computer printout submissions acceptable. Free sample copy and writer's guidelines.
Nonfiction: Book excerpts; exposé; how-to (gardening, recipes and canning), new product; opinion; personal experience (organic gardening) and photo feature. Buys approximately 150 mss/year. Query with or without published clips, or send complete ms. Length: 1,000-3,000 words. Pays $50-100; sometimes pays in free advertising for company, books or products. Sometimes pays the expenses of writers on assignment.
Photos: State availability or send photos with submission.
Columns/Departments: Bugs, Weeds & Free Advice (organic gardening), 800 words; Food Talk (tips on cooking and recipes), 300-1,500 words; Of Consuming Interest (shorts on new developments in field), 800-

1,500 words; and The Doctor Prescribes (questions and answers on preventive medicine), 800-1,500 words. Buys 96 mss/year. Send complete ms. Pays $50-100 (negotiable).
Fillers: Facts and short humor.
Tips: "Articles on subjects concerning gardening organically or cooking with natural foods are most open to freelancers."

NEW FRONTIER, Magazine of Transformation, New Frontier Education Society, 129 N. 13th St., Philadelphia PA 19107. (215)567-1685. Editor: Sw. Virato. 30% freelance written. Prefers to work with published/ established writers; works with a small number of new/unpublished writers each year. Monthly magazine covering the New Age and holistic health. "The writer must be consciously aware, holistically oriented, familiar with new age subjects." Circ. 35,000. Pays on publcation. Publishes ms an average of 3 months after acceptance. Byline given. Buys first serial rights, one-time rights and second serial (reprint) rights. Submit seasonal/ holiday material 3 months in advance. Simultaneous queries, and simultaneous and photocopied submissions OK. Computer printout submissions acceptable; prefers letter-quality to dot-matrix. Reports in 3 weeks on queries; 2 months on ms. Sample copy $2; writer's guidelines $2.
Nonfiction: General interest, humor, inspirational, opinion, personal experience and photo feature. "We don't want anything aggressive, overtly sexual or negative." Buys 5-10 mss/year. Query with published clips. Length: 750-1,200 words. Pays $35-150. Sometimes pays the expenses of writers on assignment.
Photos: Send photos with query. Pays $10-50 for 5x7 b&w prints. Captions, model releases, and identification of subjects required.
Tips: "Write a piece to stimulate awareness or expand consciousness. We relish short works that have high impact."

‡NORTH DAKOTA REC, North Dakota Association of Rural Electric Cooperatives, Box 727, Mandan ND 58554. (701)663-6501. Editor: Leland Ulmer. Managing Editor: Dennis Hill. Monthly magazine. "We cover the rural electric program, primarily funded through the Rural Electrification Administration, and the changes the REA program brought to rural North Dakota. Our focus is on the member/owners of North Dakota's 21 rural electric cooperatives, and we try to report each subject through the eyes of our members." Circ. 75,000. Pays on acceptance. Byline given. Offers one-third of agreed price as kill fee. Buys first North American serial rights. Submit seasonal/holiday material 3-5 months in advance. Simultaneous queries and photocopied submissions OK. Computer printout submissions acceptable; prefers letter-quality to dot-matrix. Reports in 2 weeks on queries; 2 months on mss. Sample copy for 9x12 SAE and $1.39 postage; free writer's guidelines.
Nonfiction: General interest (changes in ND agriculture); historical/nostalgic (on changes REA brought to country); how-to (on efficient use of electricity); and interview/profile (on notable North Dakota rural leaders). No articles that do not show impact, benefit applicability to rural North Dakotans. Buys 12-15 mss/year. Query. Length: 400-2,000 words. Pays $35-200.
Photos: State availability of photos with query letter or ms. Pays $2.50-5 for b&w contact sheet; $25 maximum for 35mm color transparencies. Captions required. Buys one-time rights.
Fiction: Historical. Buys 2-3 mss/year. Query. Length: 400-1,200 words. Pays $35-150.
Poetry: JoAnn Wimstorfer, family editor. Buys 2-4 poems/year. Submit maximum 8 poems. Pays $5-50.
Tips: "Write about a North Dakotan—one of our members who has done something notable in the ag/energy/ rural electric/rural lifestyle areas. Also needs energy efficiency articles on North Dakotans who make wise use of rural electric power."

PHILADELPHIA GAY NEWS, Masco Communications, 254 S. 11th St., Philadelphia PA 19107. (215)625-8501. Managing Editor: Stan Ward. Publisher: Mark Segal. "We are backlogged with submissions and prefer not to receive unsolicited submissions at this time."

‡A POSITIVE APPROACH, A National Magazine for the Physically Challenged, PMJ Publications, Inc., Box 2179, South Vineland NJ 08360. (609)455-0725. Editor: Patricia M. Johnson. 80% freelance written. A bimonthly magazine for the physically disabled/handicapped. "We're a positive profile on living and for the creation of a barrier-free lifestyle. Each profile is aimed at encouraging others with that same handicap to better their situations and environments. Covers all disabilities." Estab. 1986. Circ. 300,000. Pays on publication. Publishes ms an average of 2 months after acceptance. Byline given. Buys one-time rights and second serial (reprint) rights. Submit seasonal/holiday material 2-3 months in advance. Simultaneous, photocopied and previously published submissions OK. Computer printout submissions acceptable; no dot-matrix. Reports in 2 weeks on queries; 3 weeks on mss. Sample copy $2; free writer's guidelines.
Nonfiction: Nancy Melendez, articles editor. Book excerpts, general interest, how-to (make life more accessible), humor, inspirational, interview/profile, personal experience, photo feature and travel (for the disabled). No religious, depressing, poorly researched, death and dying articles. Buys 60-70 mss/year. Query with or without published clips, or send complete ms. Length: 500-800 words. Pays 20¢/word for assigned articles; pays 10-20¢/word for unsolicited articles. Sometimes pays the expenses of writers on assignment.

Photos: State availability of photos with submission. Reviews 3x5 or larger prints. Offers $10-20/photo. Identification of subjects required. Buys one-time rights.

Columns/Departments: Pat Swart, column/department editor. Hair Styling (easy hair-do for the disabled), 500 words; Wardrobe (fashionable clothing/easy dressing), 500 words; Travel (accessible travel throughout U.S. and Europe), 500-700 words; Workshops (employment, self-improvement), 500 words and Profiles (positive approach on life with goals), 500 words. Buys 30 mss/year. Query with published clips or send complete ms. Pays 10-20¢/word.

Tips: "Research newspapers. Learn what problems exist for the physically challenged. Know that they want to better their lifestyles and get on with their lives to the best of their abilities. Learn their assets and write on what they can do and not on what can't be done! The area of our publication most open to freelancers is profiles."

PSYCHIC GUIDE, Island Publishing Co. Inc., Box 701, Providence RI 02901. (401)351-4320. Editor: Paul Zuromski. Managing Editor: John Kramer. 50% freelance written. Works with a small number of new/unpublished writers each year. Quarterly magazine covering New Age, natural living, and metaphysical topics. "Our editorial is slanted toward assisting people in their self-transformation process to improve body, mind and spirit. We take a holistic approach to the subjects we present. They include spirituality, health, healing, nutrition, new ideas, interviews with new age people, travel, books, music, even a psychic weather report. We avoid sensationalizing and present material with the idea that an individual should decide what he should or shouldn't accept or believe." Circ. 125,000. Pays on publication. Publishes ms an average of 6-12 months after acceptance. Byline given. Offers negotiable kill fee. Buys first North American serial rights. Submit seasonal/holiday material 8 months in advance. Simultaneous queries OK. Computer printout submissions acceptable. Reports in 2 months on queries; 4 months on mss. Sample copy $3.95 with SAE and $1 postage; writer's guidelines for SAE and 1 first class stamp.

Nonfiction: Book excerpts, historical/nostalgic (research on the roots of the New Age movement and related topics); how-to (develop psychic abilities, health, healing, proper nutrition, etc., based on holistic approach); inspirational; interview/profile (of New Age people); new product (or services offered in this field—must be unique and interesting); opinion (on any New Age, natural living or metaphysical topic); and travel (example: to Egypt based on past life research). Don't send "My life as a psychic" or "How I became psychic" articles. Buys 10 mss/year. Query with published clips. Length: 3,000 maximum. Pays $100-300. Sometimes pays the expenses of writers on assignment.

Photos: State availability of photos with query. Pays $10-20 for b&w contact sheets. Captions, model release and identification of subjects required. Buys one-time rights.

Fillers: Clippings, anecdotes or newsbreaks on any interesting or unusual New Age, natural living, or metaphysical topic. Buys 15-20 fillers/year. Length: 500 words maximum. Pays $5-10.

Tips: "Examine our unique approach to the subject matter. We avoid sensationalism and overly strange or unbelievable stories. Reading an issue should give you a good idea of our approach to the subject. We are increasing the number of health-related features."

R F D, A Country Journal for Gay Men Everywhere, Rt. 1, Box 127-E, Bakersville NC 28705. (704)688-2447. Managing Editor: Ron Lambe. 90% freelance written. Eager to work with new/unpublished writers. Quarterly magazine of rural gay male concerns. "We look for nonsexist, nonexploitative, positive, open-minded explorations of who we are as gay rural men." Circ. 2,000. Pays on publication. Publishes ms an average of 4 months after acceptance. Byline given. Not copyrighted. Buys one-time rights. Submit seasonal/holiday material 3 months in advance. Simultaneous queries, and simultaneous, photocopied, and previously published submissions OK. Computer printout submissions acceptable; prefers letter-quality to dot-matrix. Reports in 3 months on queries. Sample copy $4.25 postpaid.

Nonfiction: Richard Chumley, articles editor. Exposé, how-to, humor, inspirational, interview/profile, opinion, personal experience and travel. No common or trendy pieces. Acquires 8-10 mss/year. Send complete ms. Length: 500-5,000 words. Pays in 2 copies of journal.

Photos: Prefers b&w prints, (color of high contrast); of rural, nature, or male themes. Pays in 2 copies of journal. Model releases and identification of subjects required. Buys one-time rights. Pays in 2 copies of journal.

Fiction: Adventure, erotica, fantasy and romance. No sexist or insensitive exploitative. Acquires 8 mss/year. Send complete ms. Length: 1,000-5,000 words. Pays in 2 copies of journal.

Poetry: Franklin Abbott, poetry editor. Avant-garde, free verse, haiku, light verse and traditional. Acquires 40 poems/year. Submit maximum 5 poems. Length: 3-100 lines. Pays in 2 copies of journal.

Tips: "Offer original and thematic work. We prefer simplicity and clarity in style."

RADICAL AMERICA, Alternative Education Project, Inc., #14, 38 Union Square, Somerville MA 02143. (617)628-6585. Editor: John P. Demeter. Managing Editor: Ann Holder. 35% freelance written. Bimonthly political journal of radical history, socialism, feminism, and community and workplace organizing; cultural analysis and commentary. "*RA* is a popularly written, nonacademic journal aimed at feminists, political activists and left academics written from socialist (independent) and feminist perspectives." Circ. 5,000. Pays in copies. Publishes ms an average of 6 months after acceptance. Byline given. Buys all rights. Submit seasonal/holiday material 3 months in advance. Simultaneous queries, and simultaneous, photocopied, and previously published submissions OK. Computer printout submissions acceptable; no dot-matrix. Reports in 2 weeks on queries; 1 month on mss. Sample copy $2; free writer's guidelines.

Nonfiction: James Stark, articles editor. Political opinion and history. No strictly journalistic accounts without analysis or commentary. Query with published clips. Length: 2,000-7,000 words. Pays in copies.

Photos: Phyllis Ewen, photo editor. State availability of photos. Pays $5-10 for b&w contact sheet. Captions and identification of subjects required. Buys one-time rights.

Poetry: J.S. Smutt, poetry editor. Avant-garde and free verse. No poetry without political or social theme. Length: 10-50 lines.

THE ROBB REPORT, 1 Acton Place, Acton MA 01720. (617)263-7749. Managing Editor: M.H. Frakes. 70% freelance written. Monthly magazine covering leisure interests of the wealthy. Circ. 50,000. Pays on publication. Publishes ms an average of 5 months after acceptance. Byline given. Rights negotiable. Submit seasonal/holiday material 6 months in advance. Simultaneous queries and previously published submissions OK. Computer printout submissions acceptable; prefers letter-quality to dot-matrix. SASE. Reports in 1 month. Sample copy $8.50; writer's guidelines for business size SAE.

Nonfiction: Book excerpts, expose, interview/profile, trend pieces, how-to and travel. "Articles are usually focused in the following areas: automobiles, home and office design, collectibles, travel, investments, fashion, wine and liquors, food and dining, and boating. These articles must be useful and informative to the reader, enabling him to make intelligent choices with his high level of disposable income." Buys 84 mss/year. Query. Length: 1,500-2,500 words. Pays $500-750.

Tips: "Writing should be lively enough to hold the reader's attention through a long piece. The most frequent mistakes made by writers in completing an article for us are poorly researched and organized material; mundane writing; relying too much on information from books or other articles rather than going to the source; and lacking quotes because they haven't talked to anyone. Unless written by an expert in the field, manuscript should contain quotes from the sources. We're looking for the newest and most interesting subjects, not the same humdrum treatment of the same predictable topics. First-person reminiscences discouraged."

ROOM OF ONE'S OWN, A Feminist Journal of Literature & Criticism, Growing Room Collective, Box 46160, Station G, Vancouver, British Columbia V6R 4G5 Canada. Editors: Gayla Reid, Robin Bellamy, Mary Schendlinger, Eleanor Wachtel, Jeannie Wexler and Jean Wilson. 100% freelance written. Quarterly magazine of original fiction, poetry, literary criticism, and reviews of feminist concern. Circ 1,200. Pays on publication. Publishes ms an average of 6 weeks after acceptance. Byline given. Buys first serial rights. Photocopied submissions OK. Computer printout submissions acceptable "if readable and not in all caps"; prefers letter-quality to dot-matrix. Reports in 2 months. Sample copy $2.75.

Nonfiction: Interview/profile (of authors) and literary criticism. Buys 8 mss/year. Send complete ms. Length: 1,500-6,000 words. Pays $50.

Fiction: Quality short stories by women with a feminist outlook. Not interested in fiction written by men. Buys 12 mss/year. Send complete ms. Length: 1,500-6,000 words. Pays $50.

Poetry: Avant-garde, eclectic free verse and haiku. Not interested in poetry from men. Buys 32 poems/year. Submit maximum 10 poems. Length: open. Pays $10-25.

RSVP, The Magazine of Good Living, Davick Publications, 828 Fort St. Mall, Honolulu HI 96816. (808)523-9871. Editor: Rita Ariyoshi. Managing Editor: Cheryl Tsutsumi. 30% freelance written. Monthly magazine covering all topics for people who live and desire good life. "*RSVP* is a publication for the upper demographic market of Hawaii. Our readers are affluent, educated, usually professional or entrepreneurial types who have made it big and enjoy the fruits of their labors. It appeals to society types and aspirants. Any articles should be from the perspective of the insider. It is someone with class and money writing for those with class and money. While the tone is irreverent at times, it is never derogatory of the values of the wealthy." Circ. 7,000. Pays on publication. Publishes ms an average of 10 months after acceptance. Byline given. Offers negotiable kill fee. Buys all rights. Submit seasonal/holiday material 1 year in advance. Photocopied submissions OK. Computer printout submissions acceptable; no dot-matrix. Reports in 2 months.

Nonfiction: General interest, humor, art and collectibles. No articles poking fun at the wealthy or from perspective of the "man in the street". Buys 20 mss/year. Query. Length: 1,000-2,500 words. Pays 10¢/word. Sometimes pays the expenses of writers on assignment.

Photos: State availability of photos with query. Pays $50 for color transparencies. Model releases and identification of subjects required. Buys one-time rights.

‡SAN FRANCISCO BAY GUARDIAN, 2700 19th St., San Francisco CA 94110. (415)824-7660. Editor/Publisher: Bruce Brugmann. Department Editors: Kim Gale (photos); Alan Kay (articles). 50% freelance written. Works with a small number of new/unpublished writers each year. An alternative newsweekly specializing in investigative, consumer and lifestyle reporting for a sophisticated, urban audience. Circ. 75,000; Bay Guardian After Dark (arts & entertainment section), 100,000. Pays 1 month after publication. Publishes ms an average of 2 months after acceptance. Byline given. Buys 200 mss/year. Buys first rights. Photocopied submissions OK; no simultaneous or multiple submissions. Electronic submissions OK via 5¼" disk (other than Apple); Kaypro CP/M and WordStar preferred. Computer printout submissions acceptable.

Nonfiction: Publishes "incisive local news stories, investigative reports, features, analysis and interpretation, how-to, consumer and entertainment reviews. All stories must have a Bay Area angle." Freelance material should have a "public interest advocacy journalism approach." Sometimes pays the expenses of writers on assignment.

Photos: Purchased with or without mss.

Tips: "Work with our volunteer and intern projects in investigative, political and consumer reporting. We teach the techniques and send interns out to do investigative research. We like to talk to writers in our office before they begin doing a story."

SIMPLY LIVING, Otter Publications Pty/Ltd., 53 Sydney Road, Manly, N.S.W. 2095, Australia. (02)977-8566. Editor: Mr. Pip Wilson. Managing Editor: Verna Simpson. 99% freelance written. Eager to work with new/unpublished writers. Quarterly magazine covering the environment and anti-nuclear, spiritual and natural health topics. Circ. 32,000. Pays on publication. Publishes ms an average of 3 months after acceptance. Byline given. Buys first serial rights, one time rights, and second serial (reprint) rights. Submit seasonal/holiday material 4 months in advance. Simultaneous queries and previously published submissions OK. Computer printout submissions acceptable. Sample for $6 (Australian) and 8½x11½ SAE; writer's guidelines $1 and SAE. Do not send U.S. stamps. IRC.

Nonfiction: Animal conservation; exposé (environmental); how-to (environmental, spiritual); humor; bioregion; alternatives; interview/profile; new product (energy conservation) and photo feature. "We are very keen on celebrity interviews on our topics. Allow for sub-editing of American idiom." Buys 24 mss/year. Query with or without published clips. Length: 1,000-5,000 words. Pays $100/1,000 words (Oz currency). Sometimes pays the expenses of writers on assignment.

Photos: Stephen Costello, photo editor. Send photos with query. Pays $85/page for color transparencies. Captions, model releases, and identification of subjects required. Buys one-time rights.

Fiction: Adventure, fantasy, humorous, religious/spiritual, on environment, animal and anti-nuclear issues. Buys 4 mss/year. Length: 1,500-2,000 words. Pays $100/1,000 words.

Tips: "We are looking for a global unity perspective. A freelancer can break in to our publication with a soft approach, new angle and commitment to philosophy. We are like a New Age Journal with National Geo production."

SINGLELIFE MAGAZINE, SingleLife Enterprises, Inc., 606 W. Wisconsin Ave., Milwaukee WI 53203. (414)271-9700. Editor: Gail Rose. 30% freelance written. Prefers to work with published/established writers; works with a small number of new/unpublished writers each year. Bimonthly magazine covering singles lifestyles. Circ. 24,000. Pays on publication. Publishes ms an average of 6 months after acceptance. Byline given. Buys one-time rights, second serial (reprint) rights and simultaneous rights. Submit seasonal material 4 months in advance. Simultaneous submissions, photocopies, computer printouts and previously published submissions OK. Electronic submissions OK on Apple IIe and Screenwriter. Reports in 1-6 weeks. Sample copy $3.50.

Nonfiction: Leifa Butrick, articles editor. Up-beat and in-depth articles on significant areas of interest to single people such as male/female relationships, travel, health, sports, food, finances, places to go and things to do. Prefers third person point of view and ms to query letter. No articles on the bar scene or what men are like. Our readers are between 25 and 50. Length: 1,000-3,000 words. Pays $50-150.

Photos: Send photos with query or ms. Pays $10-100 for b&w contact sheet, 2¼" transparencies and 8x10 prints; pays $20-200 for 2¼" color transparencies and 8x10 prints. Captions, model releases and identification of subjects required.

Fiction and Poetry: Leifa Butrick, editor. Buys 3-4 stories or poems which are well-written and cast a new light on what being single means. No simple boy meets girl at the laundromat. Length: not over 2,500 words. Submit any number of poems that pertain to being single. Pays $25-50.

Tips: "The easiest way to get in is to write something light, unusual, but also well-developed."

STALLION MAGAZINE, The Magazine of the Alternate Lifestyle, Charlton Publications, 351 W. 54th St., New York NY 10019. (212)586-4432. Editor: Jerry Douglas. 75% freelance written. Works with a small number of new/unpublished writers each year. Monthly magazine for gay community. Text includes articles and fiction for gay males; pictorially, male nudes. Circ. 80,000. Pays on publication. Publishes ms an average of 4 months after acceptance. Byline given. Buys first North American serial rights. Submit seasonal/holiday material 6 months in advance. Simultaneous queries, and simultaneous and photocopied submissions OK; rarely accepts previously published submissions. Computer printout submissions acceptable; no dot-matrix. Reports in 4 months on mss. Free writer's guidelines.

Nonfiction and Fiction: Book excerpts, expose, general interest, historical/nostalgic, inspirational, interview/profile, opinion, personal experience and photo feature. "We publish one piece of fiction in each issue, and

while we certainly do not avoid erotic content in the stories, the work must have some other quality besides sexual heat. In other words, we are not looking for 'stroke pose' per se. We have accepted a wide range of fiction pieces, the only common denominator being that the work deal with some aspect of the gay experience." Buys 12 fiction/36 nonfiction mss/year. Send complete ms. Length: 2,000-3,000 words. Pays $200.
Tips: "Although the visual content of the magazine is strictly erotic, the textual content is not, and we seek articles and fiction of interest to the gay community, beyond the strictly erotic. We are more interested in articles than fiction."

TAT JOURNAL, Box 236, Bellaire OH 43906. Editor: Louis Khourey. 75% freelance written. Eager to work with new/unpublished writers each year. Annual magazine for all interested in depth philosophy, parapsychology, poetry, astrology, esoteric psychology and holistic health. Circ. 3,000. Pays in copies. Publishes ms an average of 9 months after acceptance. Returns copyright to author after publication. Simultaneous, photocopied, and previously published submissions OK. Computer printout submissions acceptable; prefers letter-quality to dot-matrix. Reports in 6 weeks. Sample copy $3; free writer's guidelines with SASE.
Nonfiction: Exposé (occult rip-offs, cults and spiritual gimmicks); how-to (psychological self-change techniques); opinion; personal experience (new insights into the unsolved mysteries of the universe); and forum (short philosophic pieces from a personal viewpoint). "No articles that proselytize a fanatical belief." Accepts 15 mss/issue. Send complete ms. Length: 300-10,000 words. Pays in copies.
Tips: "We want material that stimulates the reader's curiosity, allowing him to come to his own conclusions; a more psychological bent as opposed to New Age or occult."

THE UNSPEAKABLE VISIONS OF THE INDIVIDUAL INC., Box 439, California PA 15419. Editors-in-Chief: Arthur Winfield Knight, Kit Knight. 50% freelance written. Annual magazine/book for an adult audience, generally college-educated (or substantial self-education) with an interest in Beat (generation) writing. Circ. 2,000. Payment (if made) on acceptance. Publishes ms an average of 2 months after acceptance. Buys first North American serial rights. Computer printout submissions acceptable; no dot-matrix. Reports in 2 months. Sample copy $3.50.
Nonfiction: Interviews (with Beat writers), personal experience and photo feature. "Know who the Beat writers are—Jack Kerouac, Allen Ginsberg, William S. Burroughs, etc." Uses 20 mss/year. Query or submit complete ms. Length: 300-15,000 words. Pays 2 copies, "sometimes a small cash payment, i.e., $10."
Photos: Used with or without ms or on assignment. Send prints. Pays 2 copies to $10 for 8x10 b&w glossies. Uses 40-50/year. Captions required.
Fiction: Uses 10 mss/year. Submit complete ms. Pays 2 copies to $10.
Poetry: Avant-garde, free verse and traditional. Uses 10 poems/year. Submit maximum 10 poems. Length: 100 lines maximum. Pays 2 copies to $10.

VEGETARIAN TIMES, Box 570, Oak Park IL 60303. (312)848-8100. Editor: Sally Hayhow. 50% freelance written. Monthly magazine. Circ. 100,000. Rights purchased vary with author and material. Buys first serial rights or all rights ("always includes right to use article in our books or 'Best of' series"). Byline given unless extensive revisions are required or material is incorporated into a larger article. Pays 30 days after acceptance. Publishes ms an average of 6 months after acceptance. Photocopied and simultaneous submissions OK. Computer printout submissions acceptable. Submit seasonal material 6 months in advance. Reports in 1 month. Query. Sample copy $2.
Nonfiction: Features concise articles related to vegetarian cooking, health foods and articles about vegetarians. "All material should be well documented and researched. It would probably be best to see a sample copy." Informational, how-to, experience, interview, profile, historical, successful health food business operations and restaurant reviews. Length: average 1,500 words. Pays 5-20¢/word. Will also use 500- to 1,000-word items for regular columns.
Photos: Prefers b&w ferrotype. Pays $15 for b&w; $50 for color.
Tips: "The worst thing about freelance writers is that everybody who can type thinks they are writers. And the less experience a writer has the more he/she hates to be edited. Some novices scream bloody murder when you delete their paragraphs or add words to make the copy flow better. They also think we editors have nothing to do all day but critique their article. Nevertheless, many writers have broken into print in our magazine." Write query with brevity and clarity.

VINTAGE '45, A Uniquely Supportive Quarterly Journal for Women, Vintage '45 Press, Box 266, Orinda CA 94563. (415)254-7266. Editor: Susan L. Aglietti. 100% freelance written. Eager to work with new/unpublished writers. Quarterly magazine for women. "*Vintage '45* is designed for the active, introspective woman who is interested in personal growth and self-development and who has wearied of traditional women's publications. All material is nonjudgmental and supportive of each woman's right to self-development." Pays in one-year subscriptions only. Publishes ms an average of 6 months after acceptance. Byline given. Buys first serial rights. Photocopied and previously published submissions OK; previously published work must be identified as such. Reports in 3 weeks on queries; 2 months on mss. Computer printout submissions acceptable;

prefers letter-quality to dot-matrix. Sample copy $2.50; writer's guidelines for legal size SAE and 1 first class stamp.

Nonfiction: Nonfiction articles are generally written by women professionals in various fields (e.g., law, health, mental health) who address specific topic in depth. "I don't want to see anything unless it relates clearly and specifically to the needs, interests and concerns of mid-life women and is written by a woman." How-to and personal experience (coping or success account of how a woman has dealt with a particular situation). Uses 10-15 mss/year. Query. Length: 1,000-1,500 words. Pays in one-year subscriptions.

Poetry: Traditional. "No jingles and cliché-filled doggerel; or verse too abstruse to be understandable without several readings. All poems must relate *clearly* and *specifically* to mid-life women." Uses 10 poems/year. Submit maximum 5 poems. Pays in 1-year subscription.

Tips: "*Vintage '45* is a good outlet for talented women who want to get publishing credit. Include a cover letter telling a little about your background and interests. Give professional qualifications if you want to contribute nonfiction. Familiarize yourself with this publication—especially article length."

THE WASHINGTON BLADE, Washington Blade, Inc., Suite 315, 930 F St. NW, Washington DC 20004. (202)347-2038. Managing Editor: Lisa M. Keen. 20% freelance written. Works with a small number of new/unpublished writers each year. Weekly news tabloid covering the gay/lesbian community. Articles (subjects) should be written from or directed to a gay perspective. Circ. 20,000. Pays in 30 days. Publishes ms an average of 1 month after acceptance. Byline given. Offers $15 kill fee. Buys first North American serial rights. Submit seasonal/holiday material 1 month in advance. Photocopied submissions OK. Computer printout submissions acceptable; prefers letter-quality to dot-matrix. Free sample copy and writer's guidelines.

Nonfiction: Exposé (of government, private agency, church, etc., handling of gay-related issues); historical/nostalgic; interview/profile (of gay community/political leaders; persons, gay or nongay, in positions to affect gay issues; outstanding achievers who happen to be gay; those who incorporate the gay lifestyle into their professions); photo feature (on a nationally or internationally historic gay event); and travel (on locales that welcome or cater to the gay traveler). *The Washington Blade* basically covers two areas: news and lifestyle. News coverage of D.C. metropolitan area gay community, local and federal government actions relating to gays, some national news of interest to gays. Section also includes features on current events. Special issues include: Annual gay pride issue (early June). No sexually explicit material. Buys 30 mss/year, average. Query with published clips and resume. Length: 500-1,500 words. Pays 5-10¢/word. Sometimes pays the expenses of writers on assignment.

Photos: "A photo or graphic with feature/lifestyle articles is particularly important. Photos with news stories are appreciated." State availability of photos. Reviews b&w contact sheets and 5x7 glossy prints. Pays $25 minimum. Captions preferred; model releases required. On assignment, photographer paid mutually agreed upon fee, with expenses reimbursed. Publication retains all rights.

Tips: "Send good examples of your writing and know the paper before you submit a manuscript for publication. We get a lot of submissions which are entirely inappropriate." Greatest opportunity for freelancers resides in current events, features, interviews and book reviews.

‡THE WEEKLY NEWS, The Weekly News Inc., 901 NE 79th St., Miami FL 33138. (305)757-6333. Editor: Joseph McQuay. Managing Editor: Bill Watson. 40% freelance written. Weekly gay tabloid. Circ. 32,000. Pays on publication. Byline given. Buys one-time rights. Submit seasonal/holiday material 2 months in advance. Simultaneous, photocopied and previously published submissions OK. Sample copy for 9½x12½ SAE with $1.50 postage.

Nonfiction: Exposé, humor and interview/profile. Buys 8 mss/year. Send complete ms. Length: 1,000-5,000 words. Pays $25-125. Sometimes pays the expenses of writers on assignment.

Photos: State availability of photos with submission. Reviews 3x5 prints. Offers $5-20/photo. Buys first and future use.

Columns/Departments: Send complete ms. Length: 900 words maximum. Pays $15-30.

Fillers: Anecdotes, gags to be illustrated by cartoonist and short humor. Pays $15-30.

‡WHAT'S NEW MAGAZINE, The Good Times Magazine, Multicom 7 Inc., 11 Allen Rd., Boston MA 02135. (617)787-3636. Editor: Bob Leja. 80% freelance written. A monthly magazine covering music, entertainment, sports and lifestyles for the "baby-boom" generation. Circ. 125,000. Pays on publication. Publishes ms an average of 2 months after acceptance. Byline given. Offers 25% kill fee. Buys one-time rights. Submit seasonal/holiday material 4 months in advance. Photocopied submissions OK. Electronic submissions OK; call system operator. Computer printout submissions acceptable; prefers letter-quality to dot-matrix. Reports in 2 months. Sample copy $3 with 9x11 SAE and $1.40 postage.

Nonfiction: Book excerpts, general interest, humor, new product, photo feature and travel. Special issues include motorcycle buyer's guide, consumer elect buyer's guide, and automotive buyer's guide. Buys 120 mss/year. Query with published clips. Length: 150-3,000 words. Pays $25-250 for assigned articles. Sometimes pays the expenses of writers on assignment.

Photos: State availability of photos with submission. Reviews contact sheets. Offers $15 for first photo, $5 for each additional photo published in 1 issue. Captions, model releases and identification of subjects required. Buys one-time rights.

Columns/Departments: Great Escapes (undiscovered or under-explored vacation possibilities); Food Department (new and unusual developments in food and drink); and Fads, Follies and Trends (weird things that everyone is doing—from buying breakdancing accessories to brushing with pump toothpaste). Buys 150 mss/year. Query with published clips. Length: 150-3,000 words. Pays $25-250.

Tips: *"What's New* will remain a unique magazine by continuing to combine informative coverage of established, mainstream artists with reports on the newest bands, movies, fads or trends and by writing about them in the same snappy, witty and irreverent style that has singled it out in the past. It covers these artists even though, in many cases, it does not have the clout to get the 'exclusive interview.' And it avoids doing the story that everyone else will be doing on these superstars. The magazine will remain creative enough to find the angle that others fail to see. This calls for some extraordinary talent, and the magazine is fortunate to have such a resource in its national network of freelance writers."

WOMEN'S RIGHTS LAW REPORTER, 15 Washington St., Newark NJ 07102. (201)648-5320. Quarterly legal journal emphasizing law and feminism for lawyers, students and feminists. Circ. 1,300. No payment. Buys all rights. Sample copy $6 individuals; $12 institutions.
Nonfiction: Historical and legal articles. Query or submit complete ms with published clips and education data. Length: 20-100 pages plus footnotes.

_____ *Literary and "Little"*

Literary and "little" magazines contain fiction, poetry, book reviews, essays and articles of literary criticism. Some include humor; others have a particular regional or scholarly focus. Many are published by colleges and universities.

Literary magazines launch many writers into print for the first time. Serious "literary" writers will find great opportunities here; some agents read these magazines to find promising potential clients.

Writers who want to get a story into print in a few months might have to wait a few years. Literary magazines, especially semiannuals, will buy good material and save it for a 1989 edition, for example. Submitting work to a "literary," the writer may encounter frequent address changes or unbusinesslike responses. On the other hand, many editors read submissions several times and send personal notes to writers.

Literary and "little" magazine writers will notice that again this year *Writer's Market* does not contain a Poetry section. Writer's Digest Books now publishes *Poet's Market*, edited by Judson Jerome, with detailed information just for the poet. For more information about fiction techniques and markets, see *Fiction Writer's Market*, also published by Writer's Digest Books.

ACM, Another Chicago Magazine, Thunder's Mouth Press, Box 11223, Chicago IL 60611. (312)524-1289. Editors: Lee Webster and Barry Silesky. 98% freelance written. Eager to work with new/unpublished writers. Literary journal published biannually and funded by the National Endowment for the Arts. Circ. 1,100. Pays on acceptance. Publishes ms an average of 6 months after acceptance. Byline given. Buys first serial rights. Simultaneous queries, and simultaneous and photocopied submissions OK. Electronic submissions OK via disk with DOS ASCII file, but requires hard copy also. Computer printout submissions acceptable; prefers letter-quality to dot-matrix. Reports in 6 weeks. Sample copy $5; writer's guidelines for #10 SAE and 1 first class stamp.
Nonfiction: Interview (contemporary poets and fiction writers) and reviews of small press publications. Buys 1-2 mss/year. Query. Length: 1,000-20,000 words. Pays $5-25.
Fiction: Sharon Solwitz, fiction editor. Erotica, ethnic, experimental, novel excerpts and serious fiction. Buys 10-20 mss/year. Send complete ms. Length: 50-20,000 words. Pays $5-25.

Poetry: Serious poetry. No light verse or inspirational. Buys 100 poems/year. Length: 1-1,000 lines. Pays $5-25.

‡**ALASKA QUARTERLY REVIEW**, College of Arts & Sciences, University of Alaska Anchorage, Dept. of English, 3221 Providence Dr., Anchorage AK 99508. (907)786-1731. Editor: Ronald Spatz. 100% freelance written. Prefers to work with published/established writers; eager to work with new/unpublished writers. A semiannual magazine publishing fiction and poetry, both traditional and experimental styles, and literary criticism and reviews, with an emphasis on contemporary literature. Circ. 1,000. Pays honorariums on publication when funding permits. Publishes ms an average of 6 months after acceptance. Byline given. Buys first North American serial rights. Upon request, rights will be transferred back to author after publication. Photocopied submissions OK. Computer printout submissions acceptable; prefers letter-quality to dot-matrix. Reports in 4 months. Sample copy $2.50; writer's guidelines for legal-size SAE.
Nonfiction: James Jakob Liszka, articles editor. Literary criticism, reviews and philosophy of literature. No essays. Buys 1-5 mss/year. Query. Length: 1,000-20,000 words. Pays $50-100 subject to funding; pays in copies when funding is limited.
Fiction: Experimental and traditional literary forms. No romance, children's, or inspirational/religious. Buys 10-20 mss/year. Send complete ms. Length: 500-20,000 words. Pays $50-150 subject to funding; sometimes pays in contributor's copies only.
Poetry: Thomas Sexton, poetry editor. Avant-garde, free verse, haiku, and traditional. No light verse. Buys 10-30 poems/year. Submit maximum 10 poems. Length: 2 lines minimum. Pays $10-50 subject to availability funds.
Tips: "All sections are open to freelancers. We rely exclusively on unsolicited manuscripts. *AQR* is a nonprofit literary magazine and does not always have funds to pay authors."

AMELIA MAGAZINE, Amelia Press, 329 E St., Bakerfield CA 93304. (805)323-4064. Editor: Frederick A. Raborg Jr. 100% freelance written. "*Amelia* is a quarterly international magazine publishing the finest poetry and fiction available, along with expert criticism and reviews intended for all interested in contemporary literature. *Amelia* also publishes three supplements each year: *Cicada*, which publishes only high quality traditional or experimental haiku and senryu; *SPSM&H*, which publishes the highest quality traditional and experimental sonnets available; and the annual winner of the Charles William Duke long poem contest." Circ. 1,000. Pays on acceptance. Publishes ms an average of 3 months after acceptance. Byline given. Offers 50% kill fee. Buys first North American serial rights. Submit seasonal/holiday material 2 months in advance. Computer printout submissions acceptable; prefers letter-quality to dot-matrix. Reports in 2 months on mss. Sample copy $4.75 (includes postage); writer's guidelines for business size SAE and 1 first class stamp. Sample copy of any supplement $2.
Nonfiction: Historical/nostalgic (in the form of belles lettres); humor (in fiction or belles lettres); interview/profile (poets and fiction writers); opinion (on poetry and fiction only); personal experience (as it pertains to poetry or fiction in the form of belles lettres); travel (in the form of belles lettres only); and criticism and book reviews of poetry and small press fiction titles. "Nothing overtly slick in approach. Criticism pieces must have depth; belles lettres must offer important insights into the human scene." Buys 8 mss/year. Send complete ms. Length: 1,000-2,000 words. Pays $25 or by arrangement. "Ordinarily payment for all prose is a flat rate of $25/piece, more for exceptional work." Sometimes pays the expenses of writers on assignment.
Fiction: Adventure; book excerpts (original novel excerpts only); erotica (of a quality seen in Anais Nin or Henry Miller only); ethnic; experimental; fantasy; historical; horror; humorous; mainstream; mystery; novel excerpts; science fiction; suspense; and western. "We would consider slick fiction of the quality seen in *Redbook* and more excellent submissions in the genres—science fiction, wit, Gothic horror, traditional romance, stories with complex *raisons d'etre*; avant-garde ought to be truly avant-garde and not merely exercises in vulgarity (read a few old issues of *Evergreen Review* or *Avant-Garde*)." No pornography ("good erotica is not the same thing"). Buys 12-16 mss/year. Send complete ms. Length: 1,000-5,000 words. Pays $35 or by arrangement for exceptional work.
Poetry: Avant-garde, free verse, haiku, light verse and traditional. "No patently religious or stereotypical newspaper poetry." Buys 80-120 poems/year depending on lengths. Prefers submission of at least 3 poems. Length: 3-100 lines. Pays $2-25; additional payment for exceptional work, usually by established professionals. *Cicada* pays $10 each to three "best of issue" poets; *SPSM&H* pays $14 to two "best of issue" sonnets; winner of the long poem contest receives $100 plus copies and publication.
Tips: "*Have something to say* and say it well. If you insist on waving flags or pushing your religion, then do it with subtlety and class. We enjoy a good cry from time to time, too, but sentimentality does not mean we want to see mush. Read our fiction carefully for depth of plot and characterization, then try very hard to improve on it. In poetry, we also often look for a good 'storyline' so to speak. Above all we want to feel a sense of honesty and value in every piece. As in the first issue of *Amelia*, 'name' writers are used, but newcomers who have done their homework suffer no disadvantage here. So often the problem seems to be that writers feel small press publications allow such a sloughing of responsibility. It is not so."

‡**THE AMERICAN VOICE,** The Kentucky Foundation for Women, Inc., Suite 1215, Heyburn Building, at 4th Ave., Louisville KY 40202. (502)562-0045. Editor: Frederick Smock. A quarterly literary magazine "for readers of varying backgrounds and educational levels, though usually college-educated. We aim to be an eclectic reader—to define the American voice in all its diversity, including writers from Canada, the U.S., and South America." Estab. 1985. Circ. 1,500. Pays on publication. Publishes ms an average of 3 months after acceptance. Byline given. Offers 50% kill fee. Buys first North American rights. Photocopied submissions OK. Computer printout submissions acceptable; prefers letter-quality to dot-matrix. Reports in 1 month on queries; 2 months on mss. Sample copy $3.50; writer's guidelines for SASE.
Nonfiction: Essays, opinion, photo feature, and criticism. Buys 10 mss/year. Send complete ms. Length: 10,000 words maximum. Pays $400/essay; $150 to translator. Sometimes pays the expenses of writers on assignment.
Fiction: Buys 30 mss/year. Send complete mss. Pays $400/story; $150 to translator.
Poetry: Avant-garde and free verse. Buys 40 poems/year. Submit maximum 10 poems. Pays $150/poem; $75 to translator.
Tips: "We are looking only for vigorously original fiction, poetry, and essays, from new and established writers, and will consider nothing that is in any way sexist, racist or homophobic."

ANTAEUS, The Ecco Press, 18 W. 30th St., New York NY 10001. (212)685-8240. Editor: Daniel Halpern. Managing Editor: Katherine L. Bourne. 100% freelance written. "We try to maintain a mix of new and established writers." Semiannual magazine with fiction and poetry. Circ. 5,000. Pays on publication. Publishes ms an average of 1 year after acceptance. Byline given. Buys first North American serial rights. Photocopied submissions OK. Computer printout submissions acceptable; prefers letter-quality to dot-matrix. Reports in 3 weeks on queries; 6 weeks on mss. Sample copy $5; free writer's guidelines.
Nonfiction: General essays and essays for issues devoted to a particular subject.
Fiction: Stories and novel excerpts. Buys 10-15 mss/year. Send complete ms. Length: no minimum or maximum. Pays $10/printed page.
Poetry: Avant-garde, free verse, light verse and traditional. Buys 30-35 poems/year. Submit maximum 8 poems. Pays $10.

ANTIOCH REVIEW, Box 148, Yellow Springs OH 45387. Editor: Robert S. Fogarty. 80% freelance written. Quarterly magazine for general, literary and academic audience. Buys all rights. Byline given. Pays on publication. Publishes ms an average of 10 months after acceptance. Computer printout submissions acceptable; prefers letter-quality to dot-matrix. Reports in 6 weeks.
Nonfiction: "Contemporary articles in the humanities and social sciences, politics, economics, literature and all areas of broad intellectual concern. Somewhat scholarly, but never pedantic in style, eschewing all professional jargon. Lively, distinctive prose insisted upon." Length: 2,000-8,000 words. Pays $10/published page.
Fiction: Quality fiction only, distinctive in style with fresh insights into the human condition. No science fiction, fantasy or confessions. Pays $10/published page.
Poetry: Concrete visual imagery. No light or inspirational verse. Contributors should be familiar with the magazine before submitting.

THE ASYMPTOTICAL WORLD, 341 Lincoln Ave., Box 1372, Williamsport PA 17703. (717)322-7841. Editor: Michael H. Gerardi. 75% freelance written. Annual magazine covering psychodramas, science fiction, fantasy and experimental. "*The Asymptotical World* is a collection of short tales which attempts to elucidate the moods, sensations and thoughts of a curious world created in the mind of man. The tales touch upon themes of darkness, desolation and death. From each tale, the reader may relive a personal experience or sensation, and he may find relevance or discomfort. The tales were not written to be satanic or sacriligious statements. The stories were penned simply to be dark fantasies which would provide bizarre playgrounds for inquisitive minds." Circ. 1,300. Pays on acceptance. Publishes ms an average of 1 year after acceptance. Byline given. Buys first North American serial rights. Simultaneous queries and photocopied submissions OK. Computer printout submissions acceptable; prefers letter-quality to dot-matrix. Reports in 2 months on queries; 4 months on mss. Sample copy $6.95 with 9x12 SAE and 8 first class stamps; writer's guidelines for 4x9½ SAE and 1 first class stamp.
Fiction: Experimental, fantasy, science fiction and psychodrama. Buys 10-15 mss/year. Query with published clips or send complete ms. Length: 1,000-2,500 words. Pays $20-50.
Poetry: Buys 4-6 poems/year. Submit maximum 4 poems. Length: 5-100 lines. Pays $5-50. Would like to see more black and white illustrations.

The double dagger before a listing indicates that the listing is new in this edition. New markets are often the most receptive to freelance contributions.

Tips: "*The Asymptotical World* is definitely unique. It is strongly suggested that a writer review a copy of the magazine to study the format of a psychodrama and the manner in which the plot is left 'open-ended.' The writer will need to study the atmosphere, mood, and plot of published psychodramas before preparing a feature work. The magazine is very young and is willing to explore many fields."

‡BLACK WARRIOR REVIEW, University of Alabama, Box 2936, University AL 35486. (205)348-4518. Editor: Lynn Domina. Managing Editor: Alan Holmes. 100% freelance written. A semiannual magazine of fiction and poetry. Circ. 1,500. Pays on publication. Publishes ms an average of 6 months after acceptance. Byline given. Buys first rights. Photocopied submissions OK. Reports in 2 weeks on queries; 3 months on mss. Sample copy $3.50; writer's guidelines for #10 SAE with 1 first class stamp.
Nonfiction: Interview/profile and book reviews. Buys 5 mss/year. Query or send complete ms. No limit on length. Payment varies.
Photos: State availability of photos with submission. Offers no additional payment for photos accepted with ms. Identification of subjects required. Buys one-time rights.
Fiction: Tom Chiarella, fiction editor. Experimental, mainstream, novel excerpts, and literary fiction. No romance or religious fiction. Buys 10 mss/year. Send complete ms. No limit on length. Payment varies.
Poetry: Janet McAdams, poetry editor. Avant-garde, free verse and traditional. No haiku or light verse. Buys 50 poems/year. Submit maximum 6 poems. No limit on length. Payment varies.
Tips: "The areas of our publication most open to freelancers are poetry, fiction, book reviews and interviews."

BOOK FORUM, Hudson River Press, Box 126, Rhinecliff NY 12574. Editor: Marshall Hayes. Editorial Director: Marilyn Wood. "Serious writers not yet recognized are welcome to query." Quarterly magazine; averages 32 pages (8½x11). Emphasizes contemporary literature, the arts, and foreign affairs for "intellectually sophisticated and knowledgable professionals: university-level academics, writers, people in government, and the professions." 95% freelance written. Circ. 5,200. Pays on publication. Publishes ms an average of 6 months after acceptance. Buys first serial rights. Pays 33⅓% kill fee. Byline given. Photocopied submissions OK. Reports in 1 month. Sample copy $3.
Nonfiction: "We seek highly literate essays that would appeal to the same readership as, say, the *London Times Literary Supplement* or *Encounter*. Our readers are interested in professionally written, highly literate and informative essays, profiles and reviews in literature, the arts, behavior, and foreign and public affairs. We cannot use material designed for a mass readership. Think of us as an Eastern establishment, somewhat snobbish literary and public affairs journal and you will have it right." General interest, interview (with select contemporary writers, scientists, educators, artists, film makers), profiles, and essays about contemporary innovators. Buys 20-40 unsolicited mss/year. Query. Length: 800-2,000 words. Pays $25-100.
Tips: "To break in, send with the query letter a sample of writing in an area relevant to our interests. If the writer wants to contribute book reviews, send a book review sample, published or not, of the kind of title we are likely to review—literary, social, biographical, art."

THE BOSTON REVIEW, 33 Harrison Ave., Boston MA 02111. (617)350-5353. Editor: Mark Silk. 95% freelance written. Works with a small number of new/unpublished writers each year. Bimonthly magazine of the arts, politics and culture. Circ. 10,000. Pays on acceptance. Publishes ms an average of 4 months after acceptance. Buys first serial rights. Byline given. Photocopied and simultaneous submissions OK. Computer printout submissions acceptable. Reports in 2 months. Sample copy $3.
Nonfiction: Critical essays and reviews, natural and social sciences, literature, music, painting, film, photography, dance and theatre. Buys 20 unsolicited mss/year. Length: 1,000-3,000 words. Sometimes pays the expenses of writers on assignment.
Fiction: Length: 2,000-4,000 words. Pays according to length and author, ranging from $50-200.
Poetry: Pays according to length and author.
Tips: "Short (500 words) color pieces are particularly difficult to find, and so we are always on the look-out for them. We look for in-depth knowledge of an area, an original view of the material, and a presentation which makes these accessible to a sophisticated reader who may or may not be informed on that topic. We will be looking for more and better articles which anticipate ideas and trends on the intellectual and cultural frontier."

C.S.P. WORLD NEWS, Editions Stencil, Box 2608, Station D, Ottawa, Ontario K1P 5W7 Canada. Editor-in-Chief: Guy F. Claude Hamel. 100% freelance written. Monthly literary journal emphasizing book reviews. Publishes ms an average of 2 months after acceptance. Buys first serial rights and first North American serial rights. Photocopied submissions OK. Computer printout submissions acceptable; no dot-matrix. SAE, IRCs. Reports in 2 months. Sample copy $2.50.
Nonfiction: Sociology and criminology. Buys 12 mss/year. Send complete ms. Length: 2,600 words. Typewritten, double-spaced.
Columns/Departments: Writer's Workshop material. Buys unlimited items/year. Send complete ms. Length: 20-50 words.

Poetry: Publishes avant-garde forms. Submit complete unlimited ms. Length: 6-12 lines.
Fillers: Jokes, gags and anecdotes. Payment negotiated.
Tips: The writer has a better chance of breaking in with short articles and fillers. "We wish to know our writers and give them a chance to know us. A frequent mistake made by writers is their refusal to subscribe—we need their complete support in helping them to publish their work, especially for the first time."

CANADIAN FICTION MAGAZINE, Box 946, Station F, Toronto, Ontario M4Y 2N9 Canada. Editor: Geoffrey Hancock. Quarterly magazine; 148 pages. Emphasizes Canadian fiction, short stories and novel excerpts. Circ. 1,800. Pays on publication. Buys first North American serial rights. Byline given. SASE (Canadian stamps). Reports in 6 weeks. Back issue $6 (in Canadian funds). Current issue $7.50 (in Canadian funds).
Nonfiction: Interview (must have a definite purpose, both as biography and as a critical tool focusing on problems and techniques) and book reviews (Canadian fiction only). Buys 35 mss/year. Query. Length: 1,000-3,000 words. Pays $10/printed page plus 1-year subscription.
Photos: Purchased on assignment. Send prints. Pays $10 for 5x7 b&w glossy prints; $50 for cover. Model releases required.
Fiction: "No restrictions on subject matter or theme. We are open to experimental and speculative fiction as well as traditional forms. Style, content and form are the author's prerogative. We also publish self-contained sections of novel-in-progress and French-Canadian fiction in translation, as well as an annual special issue on a single author such as Mavis Gallant, Leon Rooke, Robert Harlow or Jane Rule. Please note that *CFM* is an anthology devoted exclusively to Canadian fiction. We publish only the works of writers and artists residing in Canada and Canadians living abroad." Pays $10/printed page.
Tips: "Prospective contributors must study several recent issues carefully. *CFM* is a serious professional literary magazine whose contributors include the finest writers in Canada."

CAROLINA QUARTERLY, University of North Carolina, Greenlaw Hall 066A, Chapel Hill NC 27514. (919)933-0244. Editor: Emily Stockard. Managing Editor: Elizabeth Sheppard. 100% freelance written. Eager to work with new/unpublished writers. Literary journal published 3 times/year. Circ. 1,000. Pays on publication. Publishes ms an average of 4 months after acceptance. Byline given. Buys first North American serial rights. Photocopied submissions OK. Computer printout submissions acceptable; prefers letter-quality to dot-matrix. Reports in 4 months. Sample copy $4 (includes postage); writer's guidelines for SAE and 1 first class stamp.
Nonfiction: Book reviews and photo feature. Publishes 6 reviews/year, 12 photographs/year.
Fiction: "We are interested in maturity: control over language; command of structure and technique; understanding of the possibilities and demands of prose narrative, with respect to stylistics, characterization, and point of view. We publish a good many unsolicited stories; *CQ* is a market for newcomer and professional alike." No pornography. Buys 12-18 mss/year. Send complete ms. Length: 7,000 words maximum. Pays $3/printed page.
Poetry: "*CQ* places no specific restrictions on the length, form or substance of poems considered for publication." Submit 2-6 poems. Buys 60 mss/year. Pays $5/printed poem.
Tips: "Send *one* fiction manuscript at a time; no cover letter is necessary. Address to appropriate editor, not to general editor. Look at the magazine, a recent number if possible."

CHAPMAN, 35 E. Claremont St., Edinburgh EH7 4HT Scotland. (031)556-5863. Editor: Joy M. Hendry. 50% freelance written. "Priority is given to Scottish writers, but some outside work is used." Triannual magazine of Scottish literature and culture. Circ. 2,000. Pays on publication. Publishes ms an average of 1 year after acceptance. No byline given. Buys first serial rights. Computer printout submissions acceptable; prefers letter-quality to dot-matrix. Reports in 2 weeks on queries; 1 month on mss. Sample copy $3 and 2 IRCs.
Nonfiction: Literary criticism and linguistic material (Scottish or Gaelic). "Few American writers would be in a position to write about Scottish literature." Buys 15 mss/year. Length: 1,000-4,000 words. Pays $10-50.
Fiction: Buys 15 mss/year. Send complete ms. Length: 1,500-4,000 words. Pays $10-50.
Poetry: Buys 250 poems/year. Pays $5-50.

THE CHARITON REVIEW, Northeast Missouri State University, Kirksville MO 63501. (816)785-4499. Editor: Jim Barnes. 100% freelance written. Semiannual (fall and spring) magazine covering contemporary fiction, poetry, translation and book reviews. Circ. 600. Pays on publication. Byline given. Buys first North American serial rights. Computer printout submissions acceptable; no dot-matrix. Reports in 1 week on queries; 2 weeks on mss. Sample copy for $2 and 7x10 SAE and 63¢ postage.
Nonfiction: Book reviews. Buys 2-5 mss/year. Query or send complete ms. Length: 1,000-5,000. Pays $15.
Fiction: Ethnic, experimental, mainstream, novel excerpts and traditional. "We are not interested in slick material." Buys 6-8 mss/year. Send complete ms. Length: 1,000-6,000 words. Pays $5/page.
Poetry: Avant-garde, free verse and traditional. Buys 50-55 poems/year. Submit maximum 10 poems. Length: open. Pays $5/page.
Tips: "Read *Chariton* and similar magazines. Know the difference between good literature and bad. Know

' what magazine might be interested in your work. We are not a trendy magazine. We publish only the best. All sections are open to freelancers. Know your market or you are wasting your time—and mine.''

CONFRONTATION, C.W. Post College of Long Island University, Greenvale NY 11548. (576)299-2391. Editor: Martin Tucker. 90% freelance written. Works with a small number of new/unpublished writers each year. Semiannual magazine; 190 pages. Emphasizes creative writing for a "literate, educated, college-graduate audience." Circ. 2,000. Pays on publication. Pays 50% kill fee. Publishes ms an average of 9 months after acceptance. Byline given. Buys first serial rights. Phone queries, simultaneous and photocopied submissions OK. Computer printout submissions acceptable; no dot-matrix. SASE. Reports in 2 months. Sample copy $2.
Nonfiction: "Articles are, basically, commissioned essays on a specific subject." Memoirs wanted. Buys 6 mss/year. Query. Length: 1,000-3,000 words. Pays $10-100. Sometimes pays the expenses of writers on assignment.
Fiction: William Fahey, fiction editor. Experimental, humorous and mainstream. Buys 25-30 mss/year. Submit complete ms. Length: open. Pays $15-100.
Poetry: W. Palmer, poetry editor. Avant-garde, free verse, haiku, light verse and traditional. Buys 60 poems/year. Submit maximum 8 poems. No length requirement. Pays $5-50.
Tips: "At this time we discourage fantasy and light verse. We do, however, read all manuscripts. It's rewarding discovering a good manuscript that comes in unsolicited."

‡DECEMBER ROSE, December Rose Association, 255 S. Hill St., Los Angeles CA 90012. (213)617-7002. Editor: Donald R. Jarman. Publisher: Verna Harshfield. 20% freelance written. Works with a small number of new/unpublished writers each year. A quarterly magazine covering creative arts among older adults. "Our magazine is dedicated to discovering, developing and honoring the creative talents of America's seniors. We tell the story of older writers, photographers, musicians, dancers, craftspeople—many of whom have just begun to bloom." Circ. 80,000. Publishes ms an average of 3 months after acceptance. Byline given. Buys first North American serial rights. Submit seasonal/holiday material 6 months in advance. Photocopied submissions OK. Reports in 6 weeks on queries; 2 months on mss. Sample copy $3; writer's guidelines for SASE.
Nonfiction: Essay; how-to (art and literature); humor; interview/profile; personal experience; and photo feature. Special Christmas issue. No political, advocacy or how-to-grow-old-gracefully articles. Buys 5 mss/year on assignment. Query or send complete ms. Length: 1,500 words maximum. Pays $100-400 for assigned articles; pays in copies for unsolicited articles of note. Sometimes pays the expenses of writers on assignment.
Photos: Send photos with submission. Reviews 5x7 prints. Offers no additional payment for photos accepted with ms. Identification of subjects required. Buys one-time rights.
Tips: "Freelancers can best break in by being a member of a December Rose Association Chapter; through writers' workshops and being over 62 and a 'blooming' writer. We seek out professionals to do some special features. Nonfiction articles about persons who have achieved in the arts in their later years, and persons who have turned their avocations into creative vocations are of special interest."

THE DENVER QUARTERLY, University of Denver, Denver CO 80208. (303)753-2869. Editor: David Milofsky. Quarterly magazine for generally sophisticated readership. Circ. 700. Pays on publication. Buys first North American serial rights. Phone queries OK. Photocopied submissions OK. Computer printout submissions acceptable; no dot-matrix. Reports in 3 months. Sample copy $4.
Nonfiction: "Most reviews are solicited; we do publish a few literary essays in each number." Send complete ms. Pays $5/printed page.
Fiction: Buys 10-15 mss/year. Send complete ms. Pays $5/printed page.
Poetry: Buys 50 poems/year. Send poems. Pays $10/printed page.
Tips: "We decide on the basis of quality only. Prior publication is irrelevant. Promising material, even though rejected, may receive some personal comment from the editor; some material can be revised to meet our standards through such criticism. I receive more good stuff than *DQ* can accept, so there is some subjectivity and a good deal of luck involved in any final acceptance."

‡ELDRITCH TALES, Magazine in the Weird Tales Tradition, Yith Press, 1051 Wellington Rd., Lawrence KS 66044. (913)843-4341. Editor: Crispin Burnham. 90% freelance written. A semiannual magazine of supernatural horror. Circ. 500. Pays on publication. Byline given. Buys first North American rights. Photocopied and previously published submissions OK. Computer printout submissions acceptable; prefers letter-quality to dot-matrix. Reports in 1 week on queries; 5 months on mss. Sample copy $6; free writer's guidelines.
Nonfiction: Essays and interview/profile. Buys 1-2 mss/year. Send complete ms. Length: 10-500 words. Pays ¼-1¢/word; pays in copies if author prefers.
Photos: State availability of photos with submission.
Columns/Departments: Eldritch Eye (film review columns) and Book Reviews. Buys 1-2 mss/year. Query. Length: 200 words. Pays ¼-1¢/word.
Fiction: Horror, novel excerpts, serialized novels and suspense. No "mad slashers, sword and sorcery, or hard science fiction." Buys 10-12 mss/year. Send complete ms. Length: 500-10,000 words. Pays ¼-1¢/word.

Poetry: Free verse. Buys 5-10 poems/year. Submit maximum 3 poems. Length: 5-20 lines. Pays 10-25¢/line.
Fillers: Facts and newsbreaks. Buys 10/year. Length: 5-25 words. Pays 10-25¢/line.

ENCOUNTER, Encounter, Ltd., 43/44 Gt. Windmill St., London W1V 7PA England. Editors: Melvin J. Lasky and Richard Mayne. Monthly magazine (except August and September) covering current affairs and the arts. Circ. 17,000. Pays on publication. Buys one-time rights. SAE, IRC. Reports in 2 weeks on queries; 6 weeks on mss. Sample copy $4.50 including surface mail cost.
Nonfiction: Mainly articles on current affairs. Length: 1,500-5,000 words. Pays variable fee, but "averages £20/1,000 words."
Fiction: "Submit just good up-market stories." Length: 1,500-5,000 words. Pays variable fee, averages £20/1,000 words.
Poetry: "Submit just good up-market poetry." Submit maximum 6 poems. Length: 12-100 lines. Pays variable fee.
Tips: "Study the magazine first. A straight submission will be carefully considered." Stories and poems most open to freelancers.

EPOCH, Cornell University, 251 Goldwin Smith, Ithaca NY 14853. (607)256-3385. Editor: C.S. Griscombe. 50-98% freelance written. Works with a small number of new/unpublished writers each year. Literary magazine of original fiction and poetry published 3 times/year. Circ. 1,000. Pays on publication. Publishes ms 2 months-1 year after acceptance. Byline given. Buys first North American serial rights. Sample copy $3.50. Send SASE for listing of nearest library carrying *Epoch*.
Fiction: "Potential contributors should *read* a copy or two. There is *no other way* for them to ascertain what we need or like." Buys 15-20 mss/year. Send complete ms. Pays $10/page.
Poetry: "Potential contributors should read magazine to see what type of poetry is used." Buys 20-30 poems/year. Pays $1/line.

EROTIC FICTION QUARTERLY, EFQ Publications, Box 4958, San Francisco CA 94101. Editor: Richard Hiller. 100% freelance written. Small literary magazine for thoughtful people interested in a variety of highly original and creative short fiction with sexual themes. Pays on acceptance. Byline given. Buys all rights. Photocopied submissions OK. Computer printout submissions acceptable; prefers letter-quality to dot-matrix. Writer's guidelines for SASE.
Fiction: Heartful, intelligent erotica, any style. Also, stories—not necessarily erotic—about some aspect of authentic sexual experience. No standard pornography or men's magazine-type stories; no contrived or formula plots or gimmicks; no broad satire or parody; no poetry. Send complete ms. Length: 500-5,000 words, average 1,500 words. Pays $35 minimum.
Tips: "I specifically encourage beginners who have something to say regarding sexual attitudes, emotions, roles, etc. Story ideas should come from real life, not media; characters should be real people. There are essentially no restrictions on content, style, explicitness, etc.; *originality*, *clarity*, and *integrity* are most important."

EVENT, % Douglas College, Box 2503, New Westminster, British Columbia V3L 5B2 Canada. Managing Editor: Vye Flindall. 100% freelance written. Works with a small number of new/unpublished writers each year; eager to work with new/unpublished writers. Biannual magazine for "those interested in literature and writing." Circ. 1,000. Uses 80-100 mss/year. Small payment and contributor's copy only. Publishes ms an average of 4 months after acceptance. Buys first serial rights. Byline given. Photocopied submissions OK. Computer printout submissions acceptable; prefers letter-quality to dot-matrix. Reports in 4 months. Submit complete ms. SAE, IRCs.
Nonfiction: "High quality work." Reviews of Canadian books and essays.
Fiction: Short stories and drama.
Poetry: Submit complete ms. "We are looking for high quality modern poetry."

FICTION NETWORK MAGAZINE, Fiction Network, Box 5651, San Francisco CA 94101. (415)391-6610. Editor: Jay Schaefer. 100% freelance written. Eager to work with new/unpublished writers. Magazine of short stories. Fiction Network distributes short stories to newspapers, regional magazines, and other periodicals and also publishes *Fiction Network Magazine* (for agents, editors and writers). Circ. 6,000. Pays on publication. Publishes ms an average of 6 months after acceptance. Byline given. Buys first serial rights. Each story accepted may appear in several newspapers and magazines through our syndicate. Photocopied submissions OK. Computer printout submissions acceptable; no dot-matrix. Reports in 3 months. Does not return foreign submissions—notification only with SASE. Sample copy $4 USA and Canada; $6.50 elsewhere. Writer's guidelines for business size SAE, and 1 first class stamp.
Fiction: All types of stories and subjects are acceptable; novel excerpts will be considered only if they stand alone as stories. No poetry, essays, reviews or interviews. No children's or young adult material. Buys 100 mss/year. Send complete ms. "Do not submit a second manuscript until you receive a response to the first man-

uscript." Length: 5,000 words maximum (2,000 words preferred). Pays $25 minimum for magazine and 50% of syndicate sales.

Tips: "We offer both known and unknown writers excellent exposure while we open up new markets for stories. Our greatest need is for short-short stories." Contributors include Alice Adams, Max Apple, Ann Beattie, Andre Dubus, Lynne Sharon Schwartz, Marian Thurm, Ken Chowder and Bobbie Ann Mason.

THE FIDDLEHEAD, University of New Brunswick, Old Arts Bldg., Box 4400, Fredericton, New Brunswick E3B 5A3 Canada. (506)454-3591. Editor: Michael Taylor. 90% freelance written. Eager to work with new/unpublished writers. Quarterly magazine covering poetry, short fiction, photographs and book reviews. Circ. 1,100. Pays on publication. Publishes ms an average of 1 year after acceptance. Not copyrighted. Buys first North American serial rights. Submit seasonal/holiday material 6 months in advance. Simultaneous queries and photocopied submissions (if legible) OK. Computer printout submissions acceptable; no dot-matrix. SAE, IRCs. Reports in 3 weeks on queries; 2 months on mss. Sample copy $4.25, Canada; $4.50, U.S.

Fiction: Kent Thompson. "Stories may be on any subject—acceptance is based on quality alone. Because the journal is heavily subsidized by the Canadian government, strong preference is given to Canadian writers." Buys 20 mss/year. Pays $12/page.

Poetry: Robert Gibbs. "Poetry may be on any subject—acceptance is based on quality alone. Because the journal is heavily subsidized by the Canadian government, strong preference is given to Canadian writers." Buys average of 60 poems/year. Submit maximum 10 poems. Pays $12/page; $100 maximum.

Tips: "Quality alone is the criterion for publication. Return postage (Canadian, or IRCs) should accompany all manuscripts."

FM FIVE, a Quarterly of Short Fiction, (formerly *Fiction Monthly*), Box 882108, San Francisco CA 94188. Publisher/Editor: Dwight Gabbard. 70% freelance written. Works with a small number of new/unpublished writers each year; eager to work with new/unpublished writers. Literary tabloid magazine published 4 times/year. "*FM Five* offers a forum for issues of concern to short story writers, offering interviews, reviews and essays. *FM Five* also publishes short fiction." Circ. 1,600. Pays on acceptance. Not copyrighted. Buys first North American serial rights and second serial (reprint) rights. Photocopied and simultaneous submissions OK. Reports in 3 weeks on queries; 3 months on mss. Sample copy $3; writer's guidelines for SAE with 1 first class stamp.

Nonfiction: Interviews with prominent short story writers. Publishes 4-6 mss/year. Query. Length: 1,500-2,000 words. Pays $20/page, $180 maximum.

Columns/Departments: Page One (thoughts on the short story), 1,500-2,000 words. Pays $100.

Fiction: Stephen Woodhams, fiction editor. Literary. No science fiction, fantasy or erotica. Send complete ms. Length: 500-4,000 words. Pays in copies and a one year subscription.

Tips: "We welcome all kinds of stories as long as they are well-crafted, convincing and, in some way, needing to be told. Though we keep an open mind, we tend to prefer stories with a strong narrative line and focus. We are not much given to stories based on a clever idea, a trick ending, or elaborate plotting if the other elements of short story writing are neglected."

‡**THE GENEVA REVIEW,** 19 rue Centrale, 1580 Avenches, Switzerland. Editor-in-Chief: Jed Curtis. Executive Editor: Collin Gonze. "We are backlogged with submissions and prefer not to receive unsolicited submissions at this time."

‡**GOLDEN ISIS,** Box 9116, Downers Grove IL 60515. Editor: Gerina Dunwich. 99% freelance written. A quarterly digest-size magazine of poetry and fiction "reflecting New Age awareness, fantasy, mystical surrealism and paganism as an art form." Circ. 400. Pays on publication. Publishes ms an average of 3 months after acceptance. Byline given. Buys first North American serial rights or second serial (reprint) rights. Submit seasonal/holiday material 2 months in advance. Simultaneous, photocopied, and previously published submissions OK. Computer printout submissions acceptable; prefers letter-quality to dot-matrix. Reports in 3 weeks. Sample copy $1.95 ($3.70 overseas); writer's guidelines for 4x9½ SASE.

Nonfiction: Historical/nostalgic (ancient Egypt, Salem witch trials, 60's nostalgia); and personal experience (encounters with the supernatural); astrology; e.s.p.; and psychic phenomena and prediction. "We do not want religious or pornographic material. Articles should be interesting and off-beat." Buys 2 mss/year. Send complete ms. Length: 1,500 words maximum. Pays $5 for personal experience articles only.

Fiction: Experimental, fantasy, historical, horror, bizarre humor, mystery, romance, science fiction and suspense. "No religious fiction or pornography. We do *not* want any Satanic cult themes, political or sexual (unless it is abstract erotica.) Do not send us anything that is in obvious bad taste." Buys 5 mss/year. Send complete ms. Length: 250-1,000 words. Pays 1 contributor's copy.

Poetry: Avant-garde, free verse, haiku, traditional and blank verse. "We are not interested in poetry that is cute, unimaginative, or obscene." Buys 250 poems/year. Submit maximum 5 poems. Length: 50 lines maximum; "short poems under 20 lines have a better chance of being accepted since the journal is limited by space." No payment at this time.

Tips: "Send us poetry and fiction that is mystical, surrealistic, abstract, Egyptian/mythological, cosmic, or occult-oriented. We are always open to new ideas and we welcome the work of poets who are rejected by other magazines because they dare to be different." Poetry and fiction are most open to freelancers.

GRAIN, Saskatchewan Writers' Guild, Box 1154, Regina, Saskatchewan S4P 3B4 Canada. (306)522-0811 (daytime). Editor: Brenda Riches. 100% freelance written. "Eager to work with *any* writer who's good." A literary quarterly magazine that "seeks to extend the boundaries of convention and challenge readers and writers." Circ. 850. Pays on acceptance. Publishes ms an average of 3 months after acceptance. No byline given. Not copyrighted. Buys one-time rights. Photocopied submissions OK. Computer printout submissions acceptable; no dot-matrix. SAE, IRC. Reports in 1 month on queries; 3 months on mss. Sample copy $3, 5x8 SAE and 65¢ postage.
Nonfiction: Literary essays. Buys up to 4 mss/year. Query. Pays $30-100.
Fiction: Brenda Riches and Bonnie Burnard, fiction editors. "Literary art only. No fiction of a popular nature." Buys 12-15 mss/year. Send complete ms. Length: 300-8,000 words. Pays 30-100.
Poetry: Brenda Riches and Garry Radison, poetry editors. "Only poetry that has substance." Buys 30-60/ year. Submit maximum 8 poems. Length: 3-200 lines. Pays $20.
Tips: "Only work of the highest literary quality is accepted. Read several back issues. Get advice from a practicing writer to make sure the work is ready to send. Then send it."

GRANTA, A Paperback Magazine of New Writing, Granta Publications, Ltd., 44a Hobson St., Cambridge CB1 1NL England. (0223)315290. Editor: William Buford. Assistant Editor: Graham Coster. U.S. Office: 13 White St., New York NY 10013. U.S. Editor: Jon Levi. In U.K., *Granta* published in association with Penguin Books Ltd.; in the U.S., in association with Viking Penguin, Inc. 90% freelance written. Works with a small number of new/unpublished writers each year. Literary and political publication, published bi-monthly covering literate, contemporary culture and politics. Circ. 45,000. Pays on publication. Publishes ms an average of 4 months after acceptance. Byline given. Offers kill fee if accepted and not published or if commissioned and not published. Buys first serial world rights (English language). Simultaneous and photocopied submissions OK. Computer printout submissions acceptable; prefers letter-quality to dot-matrix. Reports in 1 week on queries; 6 weeks on mss. Sample copy $6.95.
Nonfiction: Book excerpts (6-9 months lead time); humor (comic/literary writing); interview (literary); opinion (political, cultural); personal experience (autobiography); photo feature (photo essays, photo and text); and travel. Buys 40 mss/year. Query with or without published clips. Length: 300-40,000 words. Pays $100-5,000. Sometimes pays the expenses of writers on assignment.
Fiction: Novel excerpts (6-9 months lead time); serialized novels, and serious literary fiction. Buys 40 mss/ year. Send complete ms. Length: 300-40,000 words. Pays $100-5,000.
Tips: The magazine has included material by Saul Bellow, Paul Theroux and Gabriel Garcia Marquez.

HIBISCUS MAGAZINE, Short Stories, Poetry, Art, Hibiscus Press, Box 22248, Sacramento CA 95822. Editor: Margaret Wensrich. 100% freelance written. Works with a small number of new/unpublished writers each year. Magazine "for people who like to read." Estab. 1985. Circ. 2,000. Pays on publication. Publishes ms 6-18 months after acceptance. Byline given. Buys first North American serial rights. Photocopied submissions OK. Reports in 3-4 months on queries. Sample copy $3; writer's guidelines for SAE with 2 first class stamps.
Fiction: Adventure, fantasy, humorous, mainstream, mystery, romance, science fiction, slice-of-life vignettes, suspense and western. Buys 9-12 mss/year. Send complete ms. Length: 1,500-3,000 words. Pays $15-25.
Poetry: Joyce Odam, poetry editor. Free verse, haiku, light verse and traditional. No subject or line limit. Buys 20-25 poems/year. Submit maximum 4 poems. Pays $5-25.
Fillers: Short humor. Buys 4-6/year. Length: 25-100 words. Pays $2-5.
Tips: "We receive hundreds of submissions each month. We are slow to read and return mss, but we do serve each writer and poet as fast as we can. We are a limited market. We regret we must return work that ought to be published because we do not have enough space."

THE HUDSON REVIEW, 684 Park Ave., New York NY 10021. Managing Editor: Ronald Koury. Quarterly. Pays on publication. Buys first world serial rights in English. Reports in 6-8 weeks.
Nonfiction: Articles, translations and reviews. Length: 8,000 words maximum.
Fiction: Uses "quality fiction". Length: 10,000 words maximum. Pays 2½¢/word.
Poetry: 50¢/line for poetry.
Tips: Unsolicited mss will be read according to the following schedule: *Nonfiction:* Jan. 1 through March 31, and Oct. 1 through Dec. 31; *Poetry:* April 1 through Sept. 30; *Fiction:* June 1 through Nov. 30.

IMAGE MAGAZINE, A Magazine of the Arts, Cornerstone Press, Box 28048, St. Louis MO 63119. (314)752-3704. Managing Editor: Anthony J. Summers. General Editor: James J. Finnegan. 100% freelance

written. Triannual literary journal "for the educated, open-minded, thinking person." Circ. 600. Pays on publication. Publishes ms an average of 3 months after acceptance. Byline given. Offers negotiable kill fee. Buys one-time rights. Simultaneous queries OK. Computer printout submissions acceptable. Reports in 3 weeks on queries; 7 weeks on mss. Sample copy $3 and 50¢ postage; free writer's guidelines.
Fiction: Erotica, ethnic, experimental, fantasy, horror, humorous, novel excerpts and science fiction. No "cutesy, self-congratulating material." Buys variable number mss/year. Query or send complete ms. Length: open. Pays $1-100.
Poetry: Avant-garde, free verse, haiku, light verse and traditional. No "overly religious, Elvis poetry, 'the world is neat and happy' type, etc." Buys 20-100/year. Submit maximum 10 poems. Length: open. Pays $1-100.
Tips: "We receive very few reviews, interviews, interesting articles on the literary world, as well as plays and experimental material. Try these for a better shot."

INKBLOT, Inkblot Publications, 1506 Bonita, Berkeley CA 94709. (415)848-7510. Editor: Theo Green. 25% freelance written. Works with a small number of new/unpublished writers each year. Quarterly magazine on experimental/avante garde literature and visuals. "Our readership is throughout the U.S. and Europe." Circ. 1,500. Pays on publication. Publishes ms an average of 6 months after acceptance. Byline given. Buys first North American serial rights and one-time rights. Submit seasonal/holiday material 1 year in advance. Simultaneous queries, and simultaneous, photocopied, and previously published submissions OK. Computer printout submissions acceptable; prefers letter-quality to dot-matrix. Reports in 2 weeks on queries; 3 months on mss. Sample copy $3.
Nonfiction: Book excerpts, exposé, inspirational, interview/profile, opinion, personal experience. No humor or anything nonliterary. Buys 2 mss/year. Query. Length: 1,000-2,000 words. Pays $25 maximum.
Fiction: Erotica, ethnic, experimental and novel excerpts. No science fiction or mainstream. Buys 10 mss/year. Query. Length: 1,000-2,000 words. Pays $25 maximum.
Poetry: Avant-garde and free verse. No traditional poetry. Buys 10 poems/year. Submit maximum 6 poems. Length: 2-100 lines. Pays $25 maximum.
Tips: "Write something off the wall, different. Visual writing is preferred. Fiction is most open to freelancers."

THE IOWA REVIEW, 369 EPB, The University of Iowa, Iowa City IA 52242. (319)353-6048. Editor: David Hamilton, with the help of colleagues, graduate assistants, and occasional guest editors. Magazine published 3 times/year. Buys first serial rights. Photocopied submissions OK. Reports in 3 months.
Nonfiction, Fiction and Poetry: "We publish essays, stories and poems and would like for our essays not always to be works of academic criticism." Buys 65-85 unsolicited mss/year. Submit complete ms. Pays $1/line for verse; $10/page for prose.

IRON, From the North-East, IRON Press, 5 Marden Terrace, Cullercoats, North Shields, Tyne & Wear NE304PD United Kingdom. (091)2531901. Editor: Peter Mortimer. 80% freelance written. Literary magazine published three times/year including literature (poetry, fiction), and graphics. "We publish new, original writing (poetry prose). No special slant." Circ. 750. Pays on publication. Publishes ms an average of 10 months after acceptance. Byline given. Buys first United Kingdom serial rights. Computer printout submissions acceptable; no dot-matrix. SAE, IRC. Reports in 2 weeks on queries. Sample copy $4.
Fiction: Experimental, fantasy, humorous, mainstream and science fiction. Buys 20 mss/year. Send complete ms. Length: 200-7,000 words. Pays $15-70.
Poetry: Avant-garde, free verse, haiku, light verse and traditional. Nothing in the "greetings card" verse area. Buys 80/year. Submit maximum 5 poems. Length: 1-200 lines. Pays $5-50.
Artwork: Clare Brannen, art editor. "We also pay small amounts to artists for illustrations. These are commissioned, and artists should contact us first with samples of their work."

JAM TO-DAY, Box 249, Northfield VT 05663. Editors: Judith Stanford and Don Stanford. 90% freelance written. Annual literary magazine featuring high quality poetry, fiction and reviews. Especially interested in unknown or little-known authors. Circ. 300. Pays on publication. Publishes ms an average of 6 months after acceptance. Byline given. Buys first rights and nonexclusive anthology rights. Photocopied submissions OK. Computer printout submissions acceptable; prefers letter-quality to dot-matrix. Reports in 6 weeks. Sample copy $3.50 (includes postage).
Fiction: "We will consider quality fiction of almost any style or genre. However, we prefer not to receive material that is highly allegorical, abstruse, or heavily dependent on word play for its effect." Buys 1-2 mss/year. Send complete ms. Length: 1,500-7,500 words. Pays $5/page.
Poetry: Avant-garde, free verse, haiku and traditional. No light verse. Buys 30-50/year. Submit 5 poems maximum. Length: open. Pays $5/poem; higher payment for poems more than 3 pages in length.

JAPANOPHILE, Box 223, Okemos MI 48864. Editor: Earl Snodgrass. 80% freelance written. Works with a small number of new/unpublished writers each year. Quarterly magazine for literate people who are interested in Japanese culture anywhere in the world. Pays on publication. Publishes ms an average of 5 months after acceptance. Buys first North American serial rights. Previously published submissions OK. Computer printout submissions acceptable; no dot-matrix. Reports in 4 weeks. Sample copy $3, postpaid. Writer's guidelines with SASE.

Nonfiction: "We want material on Japanese culture in *North America or anywhere in the world*, even Japan. We want articles, preferably with pictures, about persons engaged in arts of Japanese origin: a Michigan naturalist who is a haiku poet, a potter who learned raku in Japan, a vivid 'I was there' account of a Go tournament in California. We use some travel articles if exceptionally well-written, but we are *not* a regional magazine about Japan. We are a little magazine, a literary magazine. Our particular slant is a certain kind of culture wherever it is in the world: Canada, the U.S., Europe, Japan. The culture includes flower arranging, haiku, religion, art, photography and fiction. It is important to study the magazine." Buys 8 mss/issue. Query preferred but not required. Length: 1,200 words maximum. Pays $8-15.

Photos: State availability of photos. Pays $10-20 for 8x10 b&w glossy prints.

Fiction: Experimental, mainstream, mystery, adventure, science fiction, humorous, romance and historical. Themes should relate to Japan or Japanese culture. Length: 1,000-10,000 words. Pays $20. Contest each year pays $100 to best short story.

Columns/Departments: Regular columns and features are Tokyo Scene and Profile of Artists. "We also need columns of Japanese culture in other cities." Query. Length: 1,000 words. Pays $20 maximum.

Poetry: Traditional, avant-garde and light verse related to Japanese culture or in a Japanese form such as haiku. Length: 3-50 lines. Pays $1-100.

Fillers: Newsbreaks, puzzles, clippings and short humor of up to 200 words. Pays $1-50.

Tips: "We prefer to see more articles about Japanese culture in the U.S., Canada and Europe." Lack of convincing fact and detail is a frequent mistake.

KALEIDOSCOPE, International Magazine of Literature, Fine Arts, and Disability, Kaleidoscope Press, 326 Locust St., Akron OH 44302. (216)762-9755, ext. 474. Editor: Darshan C. Perusek. 75% freelance written. Works with a small number of new/unpublished writers each year; eager to work with new/unpublished writers. Semiannual magazine with international collection of literature and art by disabled/nondisabled people for writers, artists, and anyone interested in fine art and literature and disability. Circ. 1,500. Pays on acceptance. Byline given. Buys first North American serial rights. Simultaneous queries, and photocopied and previously published submissions OK. Computer printout submissions acceptable; no dot-matrix. Reports in 6 months. Publishes ms an average of 6 months after acceptance. Free sample copy; writer's guidelines for SAE and 1 first class stamp.

Nonfiction: Book excerpts, reviews, historical/nostalgic, humor, articles spotlighting arts/disability, interview/profile (on prominent disabled people in the arts), opinion, the craft of fiction, personal experience, photo feature and travel. Publishes 14 mss/year. Query with clips if available or send complete ms. Length: 5,000 words maximum. Payment of up to $25. All contributors receive 3 complimentary copies.

Photos: Pays up to $25/photo. Reviews 3x5, 5x7 8x10 b&w and color prints. Captions and identification of subjects required.

Fiction: Experimental, fantasy, historical, horror, humorous, mainstream, mystery, romance, science fiction, suspense. Short stories, plays, novel excerpts. Publishes 16 mss/year; purchases 4/year. Query with clips if available or send complete ms. Length: 5,000 words maximum.

Poetry: Avant-garde, free verse, haiku, light verse and traditional. Publishes 30 poems/year. Submit maximum 6 poems. Pays up to $50 for a body of work.

Fillers: Anecdotes and short humor. Length: open.

Tips: "Study the magazine and know the editorial requirements. Avoid triteness and stereotypes in all writing. Articles about arts programs for disabled people are sought. Fiction and poetry are most open to freelancers. For fiction, have strong, believable characterizations. Poetry should be vivid and free of cliches. Non-disabled writers who write disability-related literature are considered."

LITERARY SKETCHES, Box 711, Williamsburg VA 23187. (804)229-2901. Editor: Mary Lewis Chapman. Monthly newsletter for readers with literary interests; all ages. Circ. 500. Not copyrighted. Byline given. Pays on publication. Photocopied and simultaneous submissions OK. Reports in 1 month. Sample copy for SASE.

Nonfiction: "We use only interviews of well-known writers and biographical material on past writers. Very informal style; concise. Centennial or bicentennial pieces relating to a writer's birth, death or famous works are usually interesting. Look up births of literary figures and start from there." Buys 12 mss/year. Submit complete ms. Length: 1,000 words maximum. Pays ½¢/word.

LOS ANGELES TIMES BOOK REVIEW, Times Mirror, Times Mirror Sq., Los Angeles CA 90053. (213)972-7777. Editor: Jack Miles. 70% freelance written. Weekly tabloid reviewing current books. Circ. 1.3 million. Pays on publication. Publishes ms an average of 3 weeks after acceptance. Byline given. Offers variable kill fee. Buys first North American serial rights. Computer printout submissions acceptable; prefers letter-quality to dot-matrix. Accepts no unsolicited book reviews or requests for specific titles to review. "Query with published samples—book reviews or literary features." Buys 500 mss/year. Length: 200-1,500 words. Pays $75-500.

THE MALAHAT REVIEW, The University of Victoria, Box 1700, Victoria, British Columbia V8W 2Y2 Canada. Contact: Editor. 100% freelance written. Eager to work with new/unpublished writers. Magazine published 4 times/year covering poetry, fiction, drama and criticism. Circ. 850. Pays on acceptance. Publishes ms up to 18 months after acceptance. Byline given. Offers 100% kill fee. Buys first serial rights. Photocopied submissions OK. Computer printout submissions acceptable; prefers letter-quality to dot-matrix. SASE (Canadian postage or IRC). Reports in 2 weeks on queries; 3 months on mss. Sample copy $6.
Nonfiction: Interview/profile (literary/artistic). Buys 2 mss/year. Send complete ms. Length: 1,000-5,000 words. Pays $35-175.
Photos: Pays $10-50 for b&w prints. Captions required.
Fiction: Buys 20 mss/year. Send complete ms. Length: 1,000-8,000 words. Pays $35-280.
Poetry: Avant-garde, free verse and traditional. Buys 100/year. Pays $15.

THE MASSACHUSETTS REVIEW, Memorial Hall, University of Massachusetts, Amherst MA 01003. (413)545-0111. Editors: John Hicks and Mary Heath. "As pleased to consider new writers as established ones." Quarterly. Pays on publication. Publishes ms 6-18 months after acceptance. Buys first North American serial rights. Computer printout submissions acceptable; no dot-matrix. Reports in 3 months. Mss will not be returned unless accompanied by SASE. Sample copy for $4 plus 50¢ postage.
Nonfiction: Articles on literary criticism, women, public affairs, art, philosophy, music and dance. Length: 6,500 words average. Pays $50.
Fiction: Short stories or chapters from novels when suitable for independent publication. Length: 15-22 typed pages. Pays $50.
Poetry: 35¢/line or $10 minimum.

MICHIGAN QUARTERLY REVIEW, 3032 Rackham Bldg., University of Michigan, Ann Arbor MI 48109. Editor: Laurence Goldstein. 75% freelance written. Prefers to work with published/established writers; works with a small number of new/unpublished writers each year. Quarterly. Circ. 2,000. Publishes ms an average of 1 year after acceptance. Pays on publication. Buys first serial rights. Computer printout submissions acceptable; no dot-matrix. Reports in 4 weeks for mss submitted in September-May; in summer, 8 weeks. Sample copy $2 with 2 first class stamps.
Nonfiction: "*MQR* is open to general articles directed at an intellectual audience. Essays ought to have a personal voice and engage a significant subject. Scholarship must be present as a foundation, but we are not interested in specialized essays directed only at professionals in the field. We prefer ruminative essays, written in a fresh style and which reach interesting conclusions. We also like memoirs and interviews with significant historical or cultural resonance. " Length: 2,000-5,000 words. Pays $80-150, sometimes more.
Fiction and Poetry: No restrictions on subject matter or language. "We publish about 10 stories a year and are very selective. We like stories which are unusual in tone and structure, and innovative in language." Send complete ms. Pays $8-10/published page.
Tips: "Read the journal and assess the range of contents and the level of writing. We have no guidelines to offer or set expectations; every manuscript is judged on its unique qualities. On essays—query with a very thorough description of the argument and a copy of the first page. Watch for announcements of special issues, which are usually expanded issues and draw upon a lot of freelance writing. Be aware that this is a university quarterly that publishes a limited amount of fiction and poetry; that it is directed at an educated audience, one that has done a great deal of reading in all types of literature."

MID-AMERICAN REVIEW, Dept. of English, Bowling Green State University, Bowling Green OH 43403. (419)372-2725. Editor: Robert Early. 100% freelance written. Semiannual literary magazine of "the highest quality fiction and poetry." Also publishes critical articles and book reviews of contemporary literature. Pays on publication. Publishes ms an average of 3 months after acceptance. Byline given. Buys one-time rights. Do not query. Photocopied submissions OK. Reports in 2 months or less. Sample copy $4.50.
Fiction: Character-oriented, literary. Buys 12 mss/year. Send complete ms. Pays $5/page up to $75.
Poetry: Strong imagery, strong sense of vision. Buys 60 poems/year. Pays $5/page. Annual prize for best fiction, best poem.
Tips: "We want quality fiction and poetry—nothing more or less."

‡MIDWEST POETRY REVIEW, Box 776, Rock Island IL 61201. Editor: Hugh Ferguson. Managing Editor: Tom Tilford. 100% freelance written. A quarterly magazine of poetry. Pays on acceptance. Byline given. Buys first North American serial rights. Submit seasonal/holiday material 6 months in advance. Computer printout submissions acceptable; no dot-matrix. Reports in 2 weeks. Sample copy $3 with 9½x6½ SAE and 3 first class stamps; writer's guidelines for SAE and 1 first class stamp.

Nonfiction: Poetry reviews and technical (on poetry). Buys 4 mss/year. Query. Length: 800-1,500 words. Pays $10 minimum.

Columns/Departments: Comment (poetry enhancement, improvement) 800-1,500 words. Buys 4 mss/year. Query. Pays $10 minimum.

Poetry: Avant-garde, free verse, haiku, light verse, and traditional. No jingles. Buys 400 poems/year. Submit maximum 5 poems; must be subscriber to submit. Pays $5 minimum.

‡**MILKWEED CHRONICLE/MILKWEED EDITIONS,** Milkweed Chronicle/Milkweed Editions, Box 24303, Minneapolis MN 55424. (612)332-3192. Editors: Emilie Buchwald, R.W. Scholes. Managing Editor: Deborah Keenan. 80% freelance written. Interested in seeing work from new/unpublished writers. A literary magazine published three times a year featuring poetry, essays, fiction, photographs and graphic arts. "We look for the highest quality writing and art work we can find. Each issue of the journal is based on a different theme, for example; Healing, Magic, The Uses of Power, etc." Circ. 2,000. Pays on publication. Publishes ms an average of 6 months after acceptance. Byline given. Buys first and one-time rights. Photocopied submissions OK. Computer printout submissions acceptable; no dot-matrix. Reports in 2 weeks on queries; 6 months on mss. Sample copy $4 with 11½x14½ SAE; free writer's guidelines.

Nonfiction: Book excerpts and essays (upon editor's request) and photo feature (b&w). "No diatribes and political parties, no religious pieces, gratuitously violent pieces, or pornography, etc." Buys 6-9 mss/year. Do not submit material on themes that are not yet chosen—query. Length: 1,200-6,000 words. Pays $50-300; plus a free copy when work appears.

Photos: Send photos with submission. Offers $15-30/photo. Buys one-time rights.

Fiction: Mainstream and novel excerpts (when requested). "Only really well-written fiction." Buys 1-6 mss/year. Query or send complete ms. Length: 1,200-6,000 words. Pays $50-300.

Poetry: Avant-garde, free verse and haiku. "No bad, rhyming poetry, no light verse, violent poetry, pornographic poetry, or song lyrics." Buys 90-150 poems/year. Submit maximum 3-5 poems. Pays $20-100.

Tips: "We are interested in collaborative manuscripts: collaboration between two writers, or a writer and an artist."

MISSOURI REVIEW, University of Missouri, 231 Arts & Science, Columbia MO 65211. (314)882-6066. Editor: Speer Morgan. Managing Editor: Greg Michalson. Triannual magazine. Circ. 2,000. Pays on publication. Byline given. Offers negotiable kill fee. Buys first North American serial rights. Simultaneous queries and photocopied submissions OK. Reports in 1 month on queries; 10 weeks on mss. Sample copy $4.

Nonfiction: "Informed/informal essays of wide-ranging literary interest." Buys 10-12 mss/year. Query with published clips or send complete ms. Pays $10/page minimum to $500 (for a lead essay) maximum.

Fiction: Bill Peden, fiction editor. "We want fiction with a distinctly contemporary orientation." No young adult material. Buys 20-30 mss/year. Send complete ms. Pays $10/page minimum to $300 maximum.

Poetry: Sherod Santos or Garrett Hongo, poetry editors. Buys 100 poems/year. Submit maximum 6 poems. Pays $10 minimum.

Tips: Address submissions to correct department editors and don't make simultaneous submissions. Don't mix genres in a single submission.

NEW OREGON REVIEW, Transition Publications, 537 NE Lincoln St., Hillsboro OR 97124. (503)640-1375. Is backlogged with submissions, and prefers not to receive unsolicited mss at this time.

the new renaissance, An International Magazine of Ideas and Opinions, Emphasizing Literature and the Arts, 9 Heath Road, Arlington MA 02174. Editor: Louise T. Reynolds. 92% + freelance written. "We are beginning to get backlogged and writers in 1987 might want to query with SASE or IRC, before submitting." International biannual literary magazine covering literature, visual arts, ideas, opinions for general literate, sophisticated public. Circ. 1,500. Pays after publication. Publishes ms 12-15 months after acceptance. Buys all rights. Simultaneous and photocopied submissions OK if so notified. Computer printout submissions acceptable; prefers letter-quality to dot-matrix. Does not read any ms without SASE or IRCs. Answers no queries without SASE, IRCs or stamped postcards. Does not read mss from July 1 through December 31 of any year. Reports in 1 month on queries; 7 months on mss. Sample copy $5.10 for back issues; $4.30 recent issue; $5.60 current issue.

Nonfiction: Interview/profile (literary/performing artists); opinion; and literary/artistic essays. "We prefer expert opinion in a style suitable for a literary magazine (i.e., *not* journalistic). Send in complete manuscript or essays. Because we are biannual, we prefer to have writers query us, with outlines, etc., on political/sociological articles and give a sample of their writing." Buys 3-6 mss/year. Query with published clips. Length: 11-35 pages. Pays $24-95.

Photos: State availability of photos or send photos with query. Pays $5-7 for 5x7 b&w prints. Captions, model releases, and identification of subjects required, if applicable. Buys one-time rights.

Fiction: No fiction before January 1, 1987. Quality fiction, well-crafted, serious; occasionally, experimental. No "formula or plotted stories; no pulp or woman's magazine fiction; no academic writing. We are looking for writing with a personal voice and for writing which has something to say." Buys 5-12 mss/year. Send complete ms. Length: 2-35 pages. On ms 4 pp. or less, send 3 stories *only*; 10 pp. or less, 2 stories only; over 11 pp., send only 1 story. Pays $20-60.

Poetry: James E. S. Woodbury, poetry editor. No poetry before January 1, 1987. Avant-garde, free verse, light verse, traditional, and translations (with originals). No heavily academic poetry; we publish only occasional light verse and do not want to see 'Hallmark Card' writing. Submit maximum 6 average length poems; 8 short; 2-3 long poems. Reports in 4 months. Buys 20-49 poems/year. Pays $10-30.

Tips: "Know your markets. We still receive manuscripts that, had the writer any understanding of our publication, would have been directed elsewhere. Don't submit to independent small magazines unless you've bought or studied an issue. *tnr* is a unique litmag and should be *carefully* perused. Close reading of one or two issues will reveal that we have a classicist philosophy and want manuscripts that hold up to re-readings. Fiction and poetry are very open to freelancers. Writers most likely to break in to *tnr* are serious writers, poets, those who feel 'compelled' to write. We don't want to see 'pop' writing, trendy or formula writing. Nor do we want writing where the 'statement' is imposed on the story, or writing where the author shows off his superior knowledge or sensibility. Respect the reader and do not 'explain' the story to him/her. If we've rejected your work and our comments make some sense to you, keep on submitting to us. But always send us your best work. New writers frequently don't know how to structure or organize for greatest impact, and don't feel deeply enough about the subject to revise or re-write. Do not submit anything from July 1 through December 31. Submissions during those months will be returned unread. We now have a backlog of material but are still reading manuscripts."

THE NEW SOUTHERN LITERARY MESSENGER, The Airplane Press, 400 S. Laurel St., Richmond VA 23220. (804)780-1244. Editor: Charles Lohmann. 100% freelance written. Works with a small number of new/unpublished writers each year. Quarterly literary tabloid featuring short stories and political satire. Circ. 500. Pays on publication. Publishes ms an average of 9 months after acceptance. Byline given. Buys first serial rights and second (reprint) rights. Queries and previously published submissions OK. Computer printout submissions acceptable; no dot-matrix. Reports in 1 week on queries; 6 weeks on mss. Sample copy for $1 and SAE with 3 first class stamps; writer's guidelines for 4x9 SASE.

Fiction: Short prose and political satire. Avoid fantasy and science fiction. No formula short stories. Buys 16-20 mss/year. Query. Length: 500-2,500 words. Pays $5.

Tips: "Reading computer printout manuscripts, an editor is often troubled by the thought that perhaps the author spent less time writing than the editor does reading."

THE NORTH AMERICAN REVIEW, University of Northern Iowa, Cedar Falls IA 50614. (319)273-2681. Editor: Robley Wilson Jr. 50% freelance written. Quarterly. Circ. 4,000. Buys all rights for nonfiction and North American serial rights for fiction and poetry. Pays on acceptance. Publishes ms an average of 1 year after acceptance. Computer printout submissions acceptable; prefers letter-quality to dot-matrix. Familiarity with magazine helpful. Reports in 10 weeks. Sample copy $2.50.

Nonfiction: No restrictions, but most nonfiction is commissioned by magazine. Query. Rate of payment arranged.

Fiction: No restrictions; highest quality only. Length: open. Pays minimum $10/page. Fiction department closed (no mss read) from April 1 to December 31.

Poetry: Peter Cooley, department editor. No restrictions; highest quality only. Length: open. Pays 50¢/line minimum.

THE OHIO REVIEW, Ellis Hall, Ohio University, Athens OH 45701-2979. (614)593-1900. Editor: Wayne Dodd. 40% freelance written. Published 3 times/year. "A balanced, informed engagement of contemporary American letters, with special emphasis on poetics." Circ. 2,000. Publishes ms an average of 8 months after acceptance. Rights acquired vary with author and material; usually buys first serial rights or first North American serial rights. Submit complete ms. Unsolicited material will be read only September-May. Computer printout submissions acceptable; prefers letter-quality to dot-matrix. Reports in 10 weeks.

Nonfiction, Fiction and Poetry: Buys essays of general intellectual and special literary appeal. Not interested in narrowly focused scholarly articles. Seeks writing that is marked by clarity, liveliness, and perspective. Interested in the best fiction and poetry. Buys 75 unsolicited mss/year. Pays minimum $5/page, plus copies.

Tips: "Make your query very brief, not gabby—one that describes some publishing history, but no extensive bibliographies. We publish mostly poetry—short fiction, some book reviews. Generally short length material."

ORBIS, An International Quarterly of Poetry and Prose, 199 The Long Shoot, Nuneaton, Warwickshire CV11 6JQ England. Tel. (0203)327440. Editor: Mike Shields. 75% freelance written. Quarterly magazine covering literature in English and other languages. Circ. 500 (in 30 countries). Pays on publication. Publishes ms an average of 6 months after acceptance. Extra prizes totalling 50 pounds in each issue. Byline given. Buys first serial rights. Photocopied submissions OK. Computer printout submissions acceptable; prefers letter-quality to dot-matrix. SAE, IRCs. Reports in 6 weeks. Sample copy $2; writer's guidelines for 3 IRCs (*not* U.S. postage stamps).

Nonfiction: Literary criticism, how to write poetry, and how to develop a literary work. "No excessively literary or academically pretentious work; keep it practical. Wild avant-garde or ultra-traditional work unlikely to be used." Buys few mss/year. "We reject more than 98% of work received for simple lack of space, so don't be disappointed." Send complete ms. Length: 1,200 words maximum. Pays £2.

Columns/Departments: Letters (not paid for); Past Master (not paid for), "poem from the past accompanied by about 100 words on 'why' "; and Poem in Progress (description of how a favorite poem was developed). Pays £2.

Fiction: "We are looking for short (1,200 words) pieces of original and interesting work; prose poems, mood pieces, short stories, etc. No 'magazine' or 'formula' fiction." Buys few mss/year. Send complete ms. Length: 1,200 words maximum. Pays £2.

Poetry: Free verse, light verse and traditional. "We do not specifically exclude any type of poetry, but we feel that there are far too many undistinguished haiku around, and we will not publish the meaningless gobbledegook which has featured in many magazines recently. No unoriginal rhymed poetry. We are looking for original poems which communicate modern thought and expression and show an excellence of language. Length is not a major factor, but we cannot handle *very* long poems. We also use American poetry, long poems, English dialect poems and translated poetry." Buys 250/year. Submit maximum 6 poems. Length: "over 100 lines may be difficult." Pays £2. U.S. stamps cannot be used to return material from the U.K.; IRCs should be enclosed. Acts as sponsor for three major international poetry competitions per year; prizes already paid thousands of pounds total. Also features evaluative index of other magazines, regularly updated.

THE PARIS REVIEW, 45-39 171st Place, Flushing NY 11358. Submit to 541 E. 72nd St., New York NY 10021. Editor: George A. Plimpton. Quarterly. Buys all rights. Pays on publication. Address submissions to proper department and address. Computer printout submissions acceptable; no dot-matrix.
Fiction: Study publication. No length limit. Pays up to $250. Makes award of $500 in annual fiction contest.
Poetry: Study publication. Pays $35/1-24 lines; $50/25-59 lines; $75/60-99 lines; and $150-175/100 lines and over. Poetry mss must be submitted to Jonathan Galassi at 541 E. 72nd St., New York NY 10021. Sample copy $6.

PARTISAN REVIEW, 141 Bay State Rd., Boston MA 02215. (617)353-4260. Editor: William Phillips. Executive Editor: Edith Kurzweil. 90% freelance written. Works with a small number of new/unpublished writers each year. Quarterly literary journal covering world literature, politics and contemporary culture for an intelligent public with emphasis on the arts and political/social commentary. Circ. 8,200. Pays on publication. Publishes ms an average of 1 year after acceptance. Buys first serial rights. Byline given. Photocopied submissions OK. Computer printout submissions acceptable; prefers letter-quality to dot-matrix. Reports in 3-4 months. Sample copy $4.50; free writer's guidelines.
Nonfiction: Essays; interviews and book reviews. Buys 30-40 mss/year. Send complete ms. Pays $50-150.
Fiction: High quality, serious and contemporary fiction. No science fiction, mystery, confession, romantic or religious material. Buys 8-10 mss/year. Send complete ms. Pays $50-150.
Poetry: Buys 20 poems/year. Submit maximum 6 poems. Pays $25.
Tips: "If, after reading *PR* a writer or poet feels that he or she writes with comparable originality and quality, then of course he or she may well be accepted. Standards of self-watchfulness, originality and hard work apply and reap benefits."

‡PASSAGES NORTH, William Bonifas Fine Arts Center, Escanaba MI 49829. (906)786-3833. Editor: Elinor Benedict. Managing Editor: Carol R. Hackenbruch. 100% freelance written. A semiannual tabloid of poetry, fiction and graphic arts. Circ. 2,000. Pays on publication. Publishes ms an average of 3 months after acceptance. Byline given. Buys first rights. Computer printout submissions acceptable; no dot-matrix. Reports in 1 month on queries; 3 months on manuscripts. Sample copy $1.50; writer's guidelines for #10 SAE with 1 first class stamp.
Fiction: "High quality" fiction. Buys 6-8 mss/year. Send complete ms. Length: 4,000 words maximum. Pays 3 copies minimum, $50 maximum.
Poetry: No "greeting card" or sentimental poetry and no song lyrics. Buys 80 poems/year. Submit maximum 4 poems. Length: prefers 40 lines maximum. Pays 3 copies minimum, $15 maximum.
Tips: "We want poems and stories of high quality that make the reader see, imagine and experience."

‡THE PENNSYLVANIA REVIEW, University of Pittsburgh, English Dept./526 CL, Pittsburgh PA 15260. (412)624-0026. Managing Editor: Ellen Darion. 95% freelance written. A semiannual magazine publishing contemporary fiction, poetry and nonfiction. Estab. 1985. Circ. approximately 1,000. Pays on publication. Publishes ms an average of 6 months after acceptance. Byline given. Buys first rights. Photocopied submissions OK. Reports in 10 weeks. Sample copy $5; writer's guidelines for legal size SAE.

Nonfiction: Essays, criticism reviews, and interviews. Buys 5-10 mss/year. Send complete ms. Length: 5,000 words maximum. Pays $5/page.
Fiction: Barbara Mellix, fiction editor. Novel excerpts and drama. "No formula fiction; nothing cute; genre fiction (science fiction, romance, mystery) discouraged." Buys 10-20 mss/year. Send complete ms. Length: 5,000 words maximum. Pays $5/page.
Poetry: James Gyure, poetry editor. Free verse and traditional. No light verse. Buys 50-75 poems/year. Submit maximum 6 poems. Length: open. Pays $3/page.

PIG IRON MAGAZINE, Pig Iron Press, Box 237, Youngstown OH 44501. (216)783-1269. Editors-in-Chief: Jim Villani and Rose Sayre. 90% freelance written. Annual magazine emphasizing literature/art for writers, artists and intelligent lay audience interested in popular culture. Circ. 1,500. Buys one-time rights. Pays on publication. Publishes ms an average of 18 months after acceptance. Byline given. Photocopied and previously published submissions OK. Computer printout submissions acceptable. Reports in 4 months. Sample copy $2.50; writer's guidelines with SASE.
Nonfiction: General interest, personal opinion, criticism, new journalism and lifestyle. Buys 3 mss/year. Query. Length: 8,000 words maximum. Pays $2/page minimum.
Photos: Submit photo material with query. Pays $2 minimum for 5x7 or 8x10 b&w glossy prints. Buys one-time rights.
Fiction: Fantasy, avant-garde, experimental, psychological fiction and metafiction, humor, western and frontier. Buys 4-12 mss/issue. Submit complete ms. Length: 8,000 words maximum. Pays $2 minimum.
Poetry: Terry Murcko and George Peffer, poetry editors. Avant-garde and free verse. Buys 25-50/issue. Submit in batches of 5 or less. Length: open. Pays $2 minimum.
Tips: "Send one story at a time. Show us your ability to remake the conventions of story telling."

PLOUGHSHARES, Box 529, Dept. M, Cambridge MA 02139. Editor: DeWitt Henry. Quarterly magazine for "readers of serious contemporary literature: students, educators, adult public." Circ. 4,100. Pays on publication. Rights purchased vary with author and material; usually buys all rights or may buy first North American serial rights. Photocopied submissions OK. Reports in 6 months. Sample copy $5.
Nonfiction: Interview and literary essays. Buys 25-50 unsolicited mss/year. Length: 5,000 words maximum. Pays $50. Reviews (assigned). Length: 500 words maximum. Pays $15.
Fiction: Experimental and mainstream. Length: 300-6,000 words. Pays $5-50.
Poetry: Buys traditional forms, blank verse, free verse and avant-garde. Length: open. Pays $10/poem.

‡POETRY AUSTRALIA, South Head Press, The Market Place, Berrima, New South Wales. 2577 Australia (048)911407. Editor: Grace Perry. Managing Editor; John Millett. 100% freelance written. A quarterly literary magazine of poetry and criticism. Circ. 2,000. Pays on publication. Byline sometimes given. Buys first and second serial (reprint) rights. Submit seasonal/holiday material 1 month in advance. Photocopied submissions OK. Computer printout submissions acceptable; prefers letter-quality to dot-matrix. Reports in 1 month. Sample copy $5.
Nonfiction: Essays, inspirational and opinion. "We would like articles on present day Canadian/U.S. poetry of up to about 10 printed pages." No articles unrelated to poetry. Buys 2-3 mss/year. Send complete ms. Length: 250-6,000 words. "Our funding body's guidelines (the Australian Council), make it necessary to pay by giving a one year's subscription to overseas contributors."
Poetry: Avant-garde, free verse, haiku, light verse and traditional. "No badly-written, sentimental, or moralistic poetry." Buys approximately 30 poems/year. Submit maximum 4 poems. Pays overseas contributors with year's subscription; pays $10 minimum to Australian contributors.

PRAIRIE SCHOONER, Andrews Hall, University of Nebraska, Lincoln NE 68588. Editor: Hugh Luke. Poetry Editor: Hilda Raz. 95% freelance written. Quarterly. Pays in copies of offprints and prizes. Publishes ms an average of 9 months after acceptance. Acquires all rights, but rights will be reverted to author upon request after publication. Computer printout submissions acceptable; prefers letter-quality to dot-matrix. Reports in 3 months.
Nonfiction: Uses 1-2 articles/issue. Subjects of literary or general interest. No academic articles. Length: 5,000 words maximum.
Fiction: Uses several stories/issue.
Poetry: Uses 20-30 poems in each issue of the magazine. These may be on any subject, in any style. Occasional long poems are used, but preference is for shorter length. High quality necessary.

PRISM INTERNATIONAL, Department of Creative Writing, University of British Columbia, Vancouver, British Columbia V6T 1W5 Canada. Editor-in-Chief: Wayne Hughes. Managing Editor: Dianne Maguire. 100% freelance written. Eager to work with new/unpublished writers. Quarterly magazine emphasizing contemporary literature, including translations. For university and public libraries, and private subscribers. Circ. 900. Pays on publication. Publishes ms an average of 3 months after acceptance. Buys first North American serial rights. Photocopied submissions OK. Computer printout submissions acceptable; prefers letter-quality to dot-matrix. SAE, IRCs. Reports in 6 weeks. Sample copy $4.

Fiction: Experimental and traditional. Buys 3 mss/issue. Send complete ms. Length: 5,000 words maximum. Pays $25/printed page and 1-year subscription.

Poetry: Avant-garde and traditional. Buys 30 poems/issue. Submit maximum 6 poems. Pays $25/printed page and 1-year subscription.

Drama: One-acts preferred. Pays $25/printed page and 1-year subscription.

Tips: "As well as poetry and fiction, we are especially open to translations of all kinds, very short fiction pieces and drama which works well on the page."

‡PULPSMITH magazine, The Smith, 5 Beekman St., New York NY 10038. (212)732-4822. Editor: Harry Smith. Managing Editor: Tom Tolnay. 90% freelance written. A quarterly literary magazine "for a literate audience that seeks entertainment thrills from fiction, essays, articles, poetry of high quality." Circ. 6,000. Pays on acceptance. Byline given. Buys first North American serial rights. Simultaneous, photocopied and previously published submissions OK. Computer printout submissions acceptable; prefers letter-quality to dot-matrix. Reports in 1 month on queries; 2 months on mss. Sample copy $2 and 69¢ fourth class postage; writer's guidelines for SASE.

Nonfiction: Essays. Buys 20 mss/year. Query. Length: 5,000 words maximum. Pays $25-100.

Fiction: Nancy Hallinan, fiction editor. Adventure, fantasy, horror, humorous, mainstream, mystery, science fiction, suspense and western. Buys 75 mss/year. Send complete ms. Length: 500-5,000 words. Pays $25-100.

Poetry: Joseph Lazarus, poetry editor. Avant-garde, free verse, haiku and traditional. Buys 100 poems/year. Submit maximum 4 poems. Pays $10-75.

QUARRY, Quarry Press, Box 1061, Kingston, Ontario K7L 4Y5 Canada. (613)376-3584. Editor: Bob Hilderley. 99% freelance written. Quarterly magazine covering poetry, prose, reviews. "We seek high quality new writers who are aware of their genre and who are committed to their art." Circ. 1,000. Pays on publication. Publishes ms an average of 6 months after acceptance. Byline given. Buys first North American serial rights. Simultaneous queries and photocopied submissions OK. Computer printout submission acceptable; prefers letter-quality to dot-matrix. Reports in 3 weeks on queries; 3 months on mss. Sample copy $4; writer's guidelines for business size SAE and 65¢ in IRCs.

Nonfiction: Short stories, poetry and book reviews. "We need book reviews of Canadian work. We are not interested in reviews of American or United Kingdom books. No literary criticism." Buys 100 mss/year. Send complete ms. Length: open. Pays $5-$10/page plus 1 year subscription.

Fiction: Any short fiction of high quality. "No nonliterary fiction." Send complete ms. Length: 10-15 pages maximum. Pays $5-10/page.

Poetry: Avant-garde, free verse, haiku, light verse and traditional. "No amateur, derivative poetry." Buys 200 poems/year. Submit maximum 10 poems. Length: open. Pays $5-10/page.

Tips: "Please send IRCs with SAE, not U.S. postage. Try to read a copy of the magazine before submitting. Ask at your library or request a sample copy."

QUEEN'S QUARTERLY, A Canadian Review, Queen's University, Kingston, Ontario K7L 3N6 Canada. (613)547-6968. Editors: Dr. Grant Amyot and Mrs. Marcia Stayer. Quarterly magazine covering a wide variety of subjects, including: science, humanities, arts and letters, politics, and history for the educated reader. 15% freelance written. Circ. 1,900. Pays on publication. Publishes ms an average of 1 year after acceptance. Byline given. Buys first North American serial rights. Photocopied submissions OK. Computer printout submissions acceptable; prefers letter-quality to dot-matrix. Reports in 2 weeks on queries; 3 months on mss. Sample copy $4.50; free writer's guidelines.

Fiction: Fantasy, historical, humorous, mainstream and science fiction. Buys 4-6 mss/year. Send complete ms. Length: 5,000 words maximum. Pays $25-100.

Poetry: Avant-garde, free verse, haiku, light verse and traditional. No "sentimental, religious, or first efforts by unpublished writers". Buys 25/year. Submit maximum six poems. Length: open. Pays $10-25.

Tips: "Poetry and fiction are most open to freelancers. Include curriculum vita and brief description of what's unique about the submission. Don't send less than the best. No multiple submissions. No more than 6 poems or one story per submission. We buy just a few freelance submissions."

‡SCRIVENER, Creative Journal, Scrivener, 853 Sherbrooke St. W., Montreal, Quebec H3A 2T6 Canada. (514)392-4483. Editor: Andrew Burgess. A semiannual magazine for literary and visual arts. "We publish the best of new material from North American poets, prose writers, graphic artists, photographers and scholars, both established and soon to be established." Circ. 1,250. Pays on publication. Publishes ms an average of 6 months after acceptance. Byline sometimes given. Not copyrighted. Buys first North American serial rights and simultaneous rights. Simultaneous and photocopied submissions OK. Computer printout submissions acceptable; prefers letter-quality to dot-matrix. Reports in 1 month on queries; 6 months on mss. Sample copy $2; writer's guidelines for letter-sizeSAE with 1 Canadian stamp or IRC.

Nonfiction: Martha Klironomos and Laila Abdalla, articles editors. Essays, interview/profile, photo feature and scholarly/literary articles on contemporary North American literature. No racist, sexist or homophobic submissions. Buys 10-20 mss/year. Send complete ms. Length: 2,000 words maximum. Pays $3-10; pays copies in addition to cash.

Photos: Send photos with submission. Reviews prints. Offers no additional payment for photos accepted with ms. Buys one-time rights.

Columns/Departments: Reviews (scholarly reviews of currently important books, anthologies, etc.), maximum 2,000 words. Buys 5-10 mss/year. Send complete ms. Pays $3-10.

Fiction: Will consider all kinds of fiction, "so long as it is good." Buys 5-10 mss/year. Send complete ms. Length: 4,000 words maximum. Pays $3-10.

Poetry: Tara Spevack, poetry editor. Avant-garde, free verse, haiku, light verse and traditional. Buys 50 poems/year. Submit maximum 20-25 poems. Maximum length 5 pages. Pays $3-10.

Tips: "Include some biographical data, and some statements about your approach to literature. Be patient with our staff—bitchy letters saying, 'where's my stuff?' will get you nowhere. The areas most open to freelancers are poetry and fiction. *Scrivener* receives a large volume of work, and so is able to pick and choose. We like innovation, craftsmanship, and insight."

SEWANEE REVIEW, University of the South, Sewanee TN 37375. (615)598-1246. Editor: George Core. "Freelance writing rarely accepted." Works with a small number of new/unpublished writers each year. Quarterly magazine for audience of "variable ages and locations, mostly college-educated and with interest in literature." Circ. 3,400. Buys first serial rights and second serial (reprint) rights for anthologies. Pays on publication. Publishes ms an average of 9 months after acceptance. Computer printout submissions acceptable; prefers letter-quality to dot-matrix. Reports in 1 month. Sample copy $4.75, writers guidelines for SAE with 1 first class stamp.

Nonfiction and Fiction: Short fiction (but not drama); essays of critical nature on literary subjects (especially modern British and American literature); and essay-reviews and reviews (books and reviewers selected by the editor). Length: 5,000-7,500 words. Payment varies: averages $12/printed page.

Poetry: Selections of 4 to 6 poems preferred. In general, light verse and translations not acceptable. Maximum payment is 70¢ per line.

SING HEAVENLY MUSE!, Women's Poetry and Prose, Sing Heavenly Muse! Inc., Box 13299, Minneapolis MN 55414. (612)822-8713. 100% freelance written. Prefers to work with published/established writers; eager to work with new/unpublished writers. A semi-annual journal of women's literature. Circ. 1,500. Pays on publication. Publishes ms an average of 6 months after acceptance. Byline given. Buys first North American serial rights. Photocopied submissions OK. Computer printout submissions acceptable; prefers letter-quality to dot-matrix. Reports in 3 months on queries. Sample copy $3.50; writer's guidelines for #10 SAE with 1 first class stamp.

Fiction: Women's literature, journal pieces, memoir. Buys 10-12 mss/year. Send complete ms. Length: 5,000 words maximum. Pays $15-25; contributors receive 2 free copies.

Poetry: Avant-garde, free verse, haiku, light verse and traditional. Buys 50-75 poems/year. Submit maximum 10 poems. No limit on length. Pays $15-25.

Tips: "To meet our needs, writing must be feminist and women-centered. We read manuscripts generally in April and September. Issues are related to a specific theme. Writer should query for guidelines and upcoming themes."

THE SOUTHERN CALIFORNIA ANTHOLOGY, The Master of Professional Writing Program, D.C.C. 201, University of Southern California, Los Angeles CA 90089. (213)743-8255. Editor: Carol Fuchs. Managing Editor: Laraine Crampton. 50% freelance written. Works with a small number of new/unpublished writers each year. Annual literary magazine about contemporary literature. "We want honest, consistent, well-crafted writing, regardless of style." Circ. 1,500. Pays on publication. Publishes ms an average of 4 months after acceptance. Rights revert to author. Submit all material between September and early January. All final decisions are made by mid-February. No submissions accepted during summer. Legible photocopied submissions OK. Computer printout submissions acceptable; no dot-matrix. Reports in 1 month on queries; 4 months on mss. Sample copy $8.95, which includes first-class postage. Writer's guidelines for SASE.

Fiction: Adrienne Subotnik/Jeff Clark, fiction editors. Erotica, ethnic, experimental, humorous and novel excerpts. No religious, confession, romance or science fiction. Buys 10-12 mss/year. Send complete mss. Length: 2-22 pages, 25 page maximum. Pays $25.

Poetry: Natalie Costanza/Charles Freericks, poetry editors. Avant-garde, free-verse and experimental. No confessional or romance. Poetry should be contemporary—old forms are acceptable as long as the syntax is modern. Buys 10-20 poems/year. Pays $10. Submit 3-5 poems, 8 maximum.

Tips: The only nonfiction area open to freelancers is interviews.

THE SOUTHERN REVIEW, 43 Allen Hall, Louisiana State University, Baton Rouge LA 70803. (504)388-5108. Editors: James Olney and Lewis Simpson. 90% freelance written. Works with a small number of new/

unpublished writers each year. Quarterly magazine for academic, professional, literary, intellectual audience. Circ. 3,500. Buys first serial rights only. Byline given. Pays on publication. Publishes ms an average of 18 months after acceptance. Sample copy $5. No queries. Computer printout submissions acceptable; prefers letter-quality to dot-matrix. Reports in 2 to 3 months.

Nonfiction: Essays with careful attention to craftsmanship and technique and to seriousness of subject matter. "Willing to publish experimental writing if it has a valid artistic purpose. Avoid extremism and sensationalism. Essays exhibit thoughtful and sometimes severe awareness of the necessity of literary standards in our time." Emphasis on contemporary literature, especially Southern culture and history. Minimum number of footnotes. Buys 80-100 mss/year. Length: 4,000-10,000 words. Pays $12/page for prose.

Fiction and Poetry: Short stories of lasting literary merit, with emphasis on style and technique. Length: 4,000-8,000 words. Pays $12/page for prose; $20/page for poetry.

SOUTHWEST REVIEW, Box 4374, Southern Methodist University, Dallas TX 75275. (214)373-7440. Editor: Willard Spiegelman. 100% freelance written. Works with a small number of new/unpublished writers each year. Quarterly magazine for "adults and college graduates with literary interests and some interest in the Southwest, but subscribers are from all over America and some foreign countries." Circ. 1,400. Pays on publication. Publishes ms an average of 1 year after acceptance. Buys first North American serial rights. Computer printout submissions acceptable; prefers letter-quality to dot-matrix. Byline given. Buys 65 mss/year. Reports in 3 months. Sample copy $3.

Nonfiction: "Literary criticism, social and political problems, history (especially Southwestern), folklore (especially Southwestern), the arts, etc. Articles should be appropriate for literary quarterly; no feature stories. Critical articles should consider writer's whole body of work, not just one book. History should use new primary sources or new perspective, not syntheses of old material." Interviews with writers, historical articles. Query. Length: 3,500-7,000 words.

Fiction: No limitations on subject matter for fiction; high literary quality is only criterion. Prefers stories of experimental and mainstream. Submit complete ms. Length: 1,500-7,000 words. The John H. McGinnis Memorial Award of $1,000 made in alternate years for fiction and nonfiction pieces that appeared in *SWR* during preceding two years.

Poetry: No limitations on subject matter. Not particularly interested in broadly humorous, religious, or sentimental poetry. Free verse, some avant-garde forms; open to all serious forms of poetry. "There are no arbitrary limits on length, but we find shorter poems are easier to fit into our format." The Elizabeth Matchett Stover Memorial Award of $100 made annually for a poem published in *SWR*.

Tips: "The most frequent mistakes we find in work that is submitted for consideration are lack of attention to grammar and syntax and little knowledge of the kind of thing we're looking for. Writers should look at a couple of issues before submitting."

‡STAR*LINE, Newsletter of the Science Fiction Poetry Association, Science Fiction Poetry Association, Box 1764, Cambridge MA 02238. (617)935-8315. Editor: Elissa Malcohn. Managing Editor: Robert Frazier. A bimonthly newsletter covering science fiction, fantasy, horror poetry for association members. Circ. 200. Pays on acceptance. Byline given. Buys one-time rights. Submit seasonal/holiday material 3 months in advance. Simultaneous and photocopied submissions OK. Computer printout submissions acceptable; prefers letter-quality to dot-matrix. Reports in 3 weeks. Sample copy $1.50; writer's guidelines for #10 SAE with 1 first class stamp.

Nonfiction: Articles must display familiarity with the genre. How to (write a poem); interview/profile (of science fiction, fantasy and horror poets); opinion (science fiction and poetics); and essays. Buys 4-6 mss/year. Send complete ms. Length: 500-2,000 words. Pays $1-5 plus complimentary copy.

Columns/Department: Reviews (books, chapbooks, magazines, collections of science fiction, fantasy or horror poetry) 50-500 words; and Markets (current markets for science fiction, fantasy or horror poetry) 20-100 words. Buys 40-60 mss/year. Send complete ms. Pays 50¢-$2.

Poetry: Avant-garde, free verse, haiku, light verse and traditional. "Poetry must be related to speculative fiction subjects." Buys 60-80 poems/year. Submit maximum 3 poems. Length: 1-100 lines. Pays $1-10 plus complimentary copy.

Fillers: Speculative-oriented quotations—prose or poetic. Length: 10-50 words. Pays $1.

‡STONE COUNTRY, A Magazine of Poetry, Reviews & Graphics, The Nathan Mayhew Seminars of Martha's Vineyard, Box 132, Menemsha MA 02552. (617)693-5832 or (617)645-2829. Editor: Judith Neeld. 98% freelance written. A semiannual literary magazine. "We look on poetry as disquisition, not exposition. This is not a journal for beginners. Our purpose is to be an outlet for achieving poets whose work deserves serious and growing attention." Circ. 800. Pays on publication. Byline given. Buys one-time rights. Photocopied submissions OK; simultaneous submissions OK if notified. Computer printout submissions acceptable; no dot-matrix. Reports in 1 week on queries 2 months on manuscripts. Sample copy $4; writer's guidelines for SAE and 1 first class stamp.

Nonfiction: Robert Blake Truscott, reviews editor. Judith Neeld, editor (for essays and interview/profiles).

Essays (on elements of poetry, currently and historically, only); interview/profile (of current notable poets only); and reviews of poetry books. Buys 2-4 mss/year. Send complete ms. Length: 1,500-2,500 words. Pays $15-25. Poetry contributors receive 1 complimentary copy.

Columns/Departments: Commentary (essays on contemporary poetry and/or poetry from an historical perspective as it relates to contemporary poetry. "Not a column as such, but the section is published in each issue.") Buys 2 mss/year. Send complete ms. Length: 1,500-2,500 words. Pays $15-25.

Poetry: Avant-garde, free verse and traditional. "No light verse or poetry on a soap box." Buys 100-150 poems/year. Submit maximum 5 poems. Length: 5-40 lines. Pays 1 contributor copy.

Tips: "We are most open to poets and their poetry, but welcome reviews and essays of mature quality. Please read a sample copy before submitting."

STORIES, 14 Beacon St., Boston MA 02108. Editor: Amy R. Kaufman. 80% freelance written. Works with a small number of new/unpublished writers each year. Bimonthly magazine publishing short fiction. "It is designed to encourage the writing of stories that evoke an emotional response—for which, the editor believes, there is a demand." Circ. 2,000. Pays on publication. Publishes ms an average of 2 months after acceptance. Byline given. Buys first North American serial rights. Photocopied and simultaneous submissions OK (if so marked). Computer printout submissions acceptable; no dot-matrix. No queries. Reports in 10 weeks on mss. Sample copy $3 (postpaid); writer's guidelines for business size SAE and 1 first class stamp.

Fiction: Contemporary, ethnic, historical (general), humor/satire, literary, serialized/excerpted novel and translations. "Ordinarily, romance, mystery, fantasy, political pieces and science fiction do not suit our purposes, but we will not exclude any story on the basis of genre; we wish only that the piece be the best of its genre." Buys 30-36 mss/year. Send complete ms. Length: 750-15,000 words; 4,000-7,000 words average. Pays $150 minimum.

Tips: "We look for characters identifiable not by name, age, profession, or appearance, but by symbolic qualities; timeless themes and styles that are sophisticated but not affected, straightforward but not artless, descriptive but not nearsighted."

‡THE SUN, A Magazine Of Ideas, The Sun Publishing Company, Inc., 412 W. Rosemary St., Chapel Hill NC 27514. (919)942-5282. Editor: Sy Safransky. 75% freelance written. Monthly magazine. Circ. 5,000. Pays on publication. Publishes ms an average of 2 months after acceptance. Byline given. Buys first-rights. Photocopied and previously published submissions OK. Reports in 1 month. Sample copy $2.75; writer's guidelines for 4x6 SASE.

Nonfiction: General interest. Buys 40 mss/year. Send complete ms. Length: 10,000 words maximum. Pays $10 plus copies and a subscription.

Photos: Send photos with submissions. Offers no additional payment for photos accepted with ms. Model releases required. Buys one-time rights.

Fiction: General. Buys 15 mss/year. Send complete ms. Length: 10,000 words maximum. Pays $10.

Poetry: General. Buys 25 poems/year. Submit maximum 6 poems. Length: open. Pays $5.

Tips: "We're interested in any writing that makes sense and enriches our common space."

‡THRESHOLD OF FANTASY, Fandom Unlimited Enterprises, Box 70868, Sunnyvale CA 94086. (415)960-1151. Editor: Randall D. Larson. 90% freelance written. A magazine published irregularly (1-2 issues/year) covering horror, fantasy, and science fiction in literature and interviews with new and notable writers/artists. Circ. 1,000. Pays 50% on acceptance; 50% on publication. Publishes ms an average of 1 year after acceptance. Byline given. Offers 50% kill fee. Buys first North American serial rights. Photocopied submissions OK. Electronic submissions via ASCII file OK (prefers disk copy only after acceptance), but requires hard copy also. Computer printout submissions acceptable. Reports in 3 weeks on queries; 6 weeks on mss. Sample copy $3.50; writer's guidelines for legal size SASE.

Nonfiction: Interview/profile and reviews. Buys 4 mss/year. Query. Length: 1,500-5,000 words for articles; 1,000 words for reviews. Pays $20 for articles; pays in copies for reviews.

Photos: Send photos with submission; required with interview. Offers no additional payment for photos accepted with ms. Identification of subjects required.

Fiction: Fantasy, horror, humorous, mystery and science fiction. "No pastiches of other writers; abstract or 'new wave' writing; stories which *tell* a plot but never *show* the events through effective narrative structure and style; or overly wordy narrations." Buys 30 mss/year. Send complete ms. Length: 500-8,000 words. Pays 1/s¢/word.

Tips: Short stories are most open to freelancers.

TRIQUARTERLY, 1735 Benson Ave., Northwestern University, Evanston IL 60201. (312)491-3490. Editor: Reginald Gibbons. Published 3 times/year. Publishes fiction, poetry, and essays, as well as artwork. Pays on publication. Buys first serial rights and nonexclusive reprint rights. Computer printout submissions acceptable; no dot-matrix. Reports in 10 weeks. Study magazine before submitting. Sample copy $4.

Nonfiction: Query before sending essays (no scholarly or critical essays except in special issues).

Fiction and Poetry: No prejudice against style or length of work; only seriousness and excellence are required. Buys 20-50 unsolicited mss/year. Pays $12/page.

‡2PLUS2, Mylabris Press Ltd., case postale 35, 100 Lausanne 25 Switzerland 1018. (021)33-50-94. Editor: James Gill. Managing Editor: Ms. Jamie Lehrer. 80% freelance written. Published annually in the fall, a collection of international writing includes fiction, poetry, essays and drama. Writers from many countries are represented, often in parallel translation. Uses only previously unpublished material, or work translated into English for the first time. Circ. 5,000. Pays on publication. Byline given. Buys first North American serial rights; revert to authors on request. Photocopied submissions OK. Computer printout submissions acceptable; no dot-matrix. Reports in 2 weeks on queries; 5 weeks on mss. SAE and IRCs required. Sample copy $8.50.
Nonfiction: Book excerpts, essays, historical/nostalgic and interview/profile. No travel, inspirational, product or erotic. Buys 15 mss/year. Query with published clips. Length: 1,500-5,000 words. Pays $150-750 for assigned articles; pays $100-600 for unsolicited articles.
Photos: State availability of photos with submission. No additional payment for photos accepted with ms. Identification of subjects required. Buys one-time rights.
Fiction: Mainstream, novel excerpts, experimental, historical, slice-of-life vignettes. Buys 30 mss/year. Send complete mss. Length 1,500-10,000 words. Pays $150-1,000.
Poetry: Traditional, free verse and avant-garde. No religious, topical, erotic, light verse or political. Buys 100 poems/year. Submit maximum 4 poems. Length: 4-250 lines. Pays negotiable rates, $25 minimum.

‡UNIVERSITY OF TORONTO QUARTERLY, University of Toronto Press, 63 A St. George Street, Toronto, Ontario M5S 1A6 Canada. Editor-in-Chief: T.H. Adamowski. 66% freelance written. Quarterly magazine emphasizing literature and the humanities for the university community. Pays on publication. Publishes ms an average of 1 year after acceptance. Acquires all rights. Byline given. Photocopied submissions OK. Computer printout submissions acceptable; prefers letter-quality to dot-matrix. SAE and IRC's. Sample copy $8.95.
Nonfiction: Scholarly articles on the humanities; literary criticism and intellectual discussion. Buys 12 unsolicited mss/year. Pays $50 maximum.

UNIVERSITY OF WINDSOR REVIEW, Windsor, Ontario N9B 3P4 Canada. (519)253-4232. Editor: Eugene McNamara. Biannual for "the literate layman, the old common reader." Circ. 300 + . Buys first North American serial rights. Reports in 4-6 weeks. Sample copy $5 plus postage. Enclose SAE, IRCs.
Nonfiction: "We publish some articles on literature. I think we reflect competently the Canadian intellectual scene and are equally receptive to contributions from outside the country; I think we are good and are trying to get better." Follow *MLA Style Sheet*. Buys 50 mss/year. Length: about 6,000 words. Pays $25.
Photos: Contact Evelyn McLean.
Fiction: Alistair MacLeod, department editor. Publishes mainstream prose with open attitude toward themes. Length: 2,000-6,000 words. Pays $25.
Poetry: John Ditsky, department editor. Accepts traditional forms, blank verse, free verse and avant-garde. No epics. Pays $10.

THE VIRGINIA QUARTERLY REVIEW, 1 W. Range, Charlottesville VA 22903. (804)924-3124. Editor: Staige Blackford. 50% freelance written. Quarterly. Pays on publication. Publishes ms an average of 2 years after acceptance. Byline given. Buys first serial rights. Reports in 4 weeks. Sample copy $3.
Nonfiction: Articles on current problems, economic, historical; and literary essays. Length: 3,000-6,000 words. Pays $10/345-word page.
Fiction: Good short stories, conventional or experimental. Length: 2,000-7,000 words. Pays $10/350-word page. Prizes offered for best short stories and poems published in a calendar year.
Poetry: Generally publishes 15 pages of poetry in each issue. No length or subject restrictions. Pays $1/line.
Tips: Prefers not to see pornography, science fiction or fantasy.

‡WEBSTER REVIEW, Webster Review, Inc., Webster University, 470 E. Lockwood, Webster Groves MO 63119. (314)432-2657. Editor: Nancy Schapiro. 100% freelance written. A semiannual magazine. "*Webster Review* is an international literary magazine publishing fiction, poetry, essays and translations of writing in those categories. Our subscribers are primarily university and public libraries, and writers and readers of quality fiction and poetry." Circ. 1,000. Pays on publication. Publishes ms an average of 6-8 months after acceptance. Byline given. Buys first North American serial rights. Simultaneous and photocopied submissions OK. Reports in 6 weeks on manuscripts. Sample copy for 9½x6½ SAE with 50¢ postage.
Nonfiction: Essays. Send complete ms.
Fiction: Will consider all types of literature. Buys 6 mss/year. Send complete ms. Pays $25-50, (if funds are available).
Poetry: Pamela White Hadas, poetry editor. Buys 100 poems/year. Pays $10-50 (if funds are available).

WESTERN HUMANITIES REVIEW, University of Utah, Salt Lake City UT 84112. (801)581-7438. Managing Editor: Scott Cairns. 60% freelance written. Works with a small number of new/unpublished writers each

year. Quarterly magazine for educated readers. Circ. 1,000. Pays on acceptance. Publishes ms an average of 3 months after acceptance. Buys all rights. Phone queries OK. Simultaneous and photocopied submissions OK. Computer printout submissions acceptable; prefers letter-quality to dot-matrix. Reports in 1 month.
Nonfiction: Barry Weller, editor-in-chief. Authoritative, readable articles on literature, art, philosophy, current events, history, religion and anything in the humanities. Interdisciplinary articles encouraged. Departments on film and books. "We commission book reviews." Buys 40 unsolicited mss/year. Pays $50-150. Pays expenses of writers on assignment.
Fiction: Larry Levis, poetry and fiction editor. Any type or theme. Buys 2 mss/issue. Send complete ms. Pays $25-150.
Poetry: Larry Levis, poetry editor. Avant-garde, free verse and traditional. "We seek freshness and significance. Do not send poetry without having a look at the magazine first." Buys 5-10 poems/issue. Pays $50.
Tips: "The change in editorial staff will probably mean a slight shift in emphasis. We will probably be soliciting more submissions and relying less on uninvited materials. More poetry and scholarly articles (and perhaps less fiction) may be included in the future."

‡WIDE OPEN MAGAZINE, Wide Open Press, 326 I St., Eureka CA 95501. (707)445-3847. Editor: Clif Simms. A quarterly magazine covering solutions to current problems. "Our audience consists of students, teachers, writers, counselors, and other thinking, feeling and doing people. We believe that problems can be solved once narrow, shallow attitudes are dispelled." Circ. 500. Pays on publication. Publishes ms an average of 3 months after acceptance. Byline given. Buys one-time rights; may make work-for-hire assignments. Photocopied and previously published submissions OK. Computer submissions acceptable. Reports in 1 month. Sample copy $5; writer's guidelines for #10 SAE with 1 first class stamp.
Nonfiction: Clif Simms or Lynn L. Simms, articles editors. Essays, how-to (solve problems); humor; interview/profile (of people who have solved problems); opinion (will consider); and personal experience (of solving problems). "No illogical or unsupported arguments; no arguments from authority, only." Buys up to 8 mss/year. Query or send complete ms. "No clips or biographies." Length: 500-2,500 words. Pays $5-25.
Fiction: Clif Simms or Lynn L. Simms, fiction editors. Adventure, ethnic, experimental, fantasy, historical, humorous, mainstream, mystery, science fiction, suspense and western. "All fiction must have a strong plot and show the characters solving their own problems. No *Deus ex Machina* plots." Buys 4-8 mss/year. Send complete ms. Length: 2,500 words maximum. Pays $5-25.
Poetry: Clif Simms or Lynn L. Simms, poetry editors. Avant-garde, free verse, haiku, light verse and traditional. Buys 800 poems/year. Submit maximum 5 poems. Length: 16 lines maximum. No payment.
Tips: "Be logical and find the root causes of problems. Write for a general audience with common sense. And show or tell the process for reaching solutions, too. All areas are open to freelancers."

‡YELLOW SILK, Journal of Erotic Arts, verygraphics, Box 6374, Albany CA 94706. (415)841-6500. Editor: Lily Pond. 90% freelance written. A quarterly magazine of erotic literature and visual arts. "Editorial policy: All persuasions; no brutality. Our publication is artistic and literary, not pornographic or pandering. Humans are involved: heads, hearts and bodies—not just bodies alone; and the excellence of art is as important as the erotic content." Circ. 10,000. Pays on publication. Publishes ms an average of 6 months after acceptance. Byline given. Buys all publication rights for one year, at which time they revert to author, reprint and anthology rights for duration of copyright. Photocopied submissions OK. Computer printout submissions acceptable; prefers letter-quality to dot-matrix. Reports in 3 months on manuscripts. Sample copy $4.
Nonfiction: Book excerpts, essays, humor and reviews. "We often have theme issues, but non-regularly and usually not announced in advance." No pornography, romance-novel type writing, sex fantasies. No first-person accounts or blow-by-blow descriptions. No articles. No novels." Buys 5 mss/year. Send complete ms. No specified length requirements. Pays $10 and 3 contributor copies (plus possible $200 prize.)
Photos: Photos may be submitted independently, not as illustration for submission. Reviews photocopies, contact sheets, transparencies and prints. Offers $50/issue for series of 9-12 used, plus copies. Buys one-time rights and reprint rights.
Columns/Departments: Reviews (book, movie, art, dance, food, anything). "Erotic content and how it's handled is focus of importance. Old or new does not matter. Want to bring readers information of what's out there". Buys 8 mss/year. Send complete ms or query. Pays $10 plus copies.
Fiction: Erotica, including ethnic, experimental, fantasy, humorous, mainstream, novel excerpts and science fiction. No pornography, romance novel type writing, sex fantasies. No first-person accounts or blow-by-blow descriptions. Buys 12 mss/year. Send complete ms. Pays $10 plus copies and possibility of $200 prize.
Poetry: Avant-garde, free verse, haiku, light verse and traditional. "No greeting-card poetry. Buys 55 poems/year. No limit on number of poems submitted, "but don't send book-length manuscripts." Pays $5 plus copies and possibility of $200 prize.
Tips: "The best way to get into *YELLOW SILK* is to be an excellent, well-crafted writer who can approach erotica with freshness and strength of voice, beauty of language, and insight into character."

ZYZZYVA, The Last Word: West Coast Writers and Artists, Zyzzyva, Inc., Suite 400, 55 Sutter St., San Francisco CA 94104. (415)387-8389. Editor: Howard Junker. 100% freelance written. Works with a small number of new/unpublished writers each year. Quarterly magazine. "We feature work by West Coast writers only. We are essentially a literary magazine, but of wide-ranging interests and a strong commitment to nonfiction." Estab. 1985. Circ. 2,500. Pays on acceptance. Publishes ms an average of 3 months after acceptance. Byline given. Buys first North American serial rights and one-time anthology rights. Photocopied submissions OK. Computer printout submissions acceptable; prefers letter-quality to dot-matrix. Reports in 1 week on queries; 2 weeks on mss. Sample copy $6.

Nonfiction: Book excerpts, general interest, historical/nostalgic, humor and personal experience. Buys 25 mss/year. Query. Length: open. Pays $25-100.

Fiction: Ethnic, experimental, humorous, mainstream and mystery. Buys 30 mss/year. Send complete ms. Length: open. Pays $25-100.

Poetry: Buys 40 poems/year. Submit maximum 5 poems. Length: 3-200 lines. Pays $25-50.

Men's

Men's magazines run the gamut from pictorials to service features. Editors will sometimes shift the focus of their publications to meet or rebuff the competition. Men's magazines are becoming more specialized, not general in theme as *Playboy* and *Penthouse*. Magazines that also use material slanted toward men can be found in Business and Finance, Lifestyles, Military and Sports sections.

ADAM, Publishers Service, Inc., 8060 Melrose Ave., Los Angeles CA 90046. Monthly for the adult male. General subject: Human sexuality in contemporary society. Circ. 500,000. Buys first North American serial rights. Occasionally overstocked. Pays on publication. Reports in 6 weeks, but occasionally may take longer.

Nonfiction: "On articles, query first. We like hard sex articles, but research must be thorough." Length: 2,500 words. Pays $100-250.

Photos: All submissions must contain model release including parent's signature if under 21; fact sheet giving information about the model, place or activity being photographed, including all information of help in writing a photo story, and SASE. Photo payment varies, depending upon amount of space used by photo set.

BUF PICTORIAL, The Only Newsstand Magazine Devoted to Heavy Women, G&S Publications, 1472 Broadway, New York NY 10036. (212)840-7224. Editor: Will Martin. Managing Editor: R.B. Kendennis. 70% freelance written. Bimonthly. "Stories and articles written for *Buf* should be flattering to attractive heavy women. Short factual features about chubbies and plumpers, contemporary or historical, are especially welcome, as well as fiction and humor." Circ. 100,000. Pays on assignment to a specific issue. Publishes ms an average of 6 months after acceptance. Byline given. Buys all rights. Submit seasonal/holiday material 6 months in advance. Computer printout submissions acceptable; no dot-matrix. Reports in 1 month on queries; 3 months on mss. Sample copy $3.95; free writer's guidelines.

Columns/Departments: Buys 12-24 mss/year. Query or send complete ms. Length: 300-600 words. Pays $40-60.

Fiction: "We use sex-related but nonpornographic copy ranging from short-shorts of several hundred words to a maximum of 2,500 or so." Violence is out. No pornography. We do not use explicit, graphic descriptions of sex acts. Buys 12-20 mss/year. Length: 1,000-2,500 words. Pays $60-100.

Tips: "The writer should know his market and submit material that fits our format."

CAVALIER, Suite 204, 2355 Salzedo St., Coral Gables FL 33134. (305)443-2370. Editor: Douglas Allen. 80% freelance written. Works with published/established and new/unpublished writers each year. Monthly magazine for "young males, ages 18-29, 80% college graduates, affluent, intelligent, interested in current events, sex, sports, adventure, travel and good fiction." Circ. 250,000. Pays on publication. Publishes ms an average of 3 months after acceptance. Byline given. Buys first serial and second serial (reprint) rights. Buys 44 or more mss/year. See past issues for general approach to take. Submit seasonal material at least 3 months in advance. Computer printout submissions acceptable; prefers letter-quality to dot-matrix. Reports in 3-5 weeks.

Nonfiction: Personal experience, interview, humor, think pieces, exposé and new product. "Be frank—we are open to dealing with controversial issues." No timely material (have 4 months lead time) and prefer the

'unusual' subject matter as well as sex-oriented (but serious) articles." Query. Length: 2,800-3,500 words. Pays maximum $500 with photos. Sometimes pays the expenses of writers on assignment.
Photos: Photos purchased with or without captions. No cheesecake.
Fiction: Nye Willden, department editor. Mystery, science fiction, humorous, adventure, and contemporary problems "with at least one explicit sex scene per story." Send complete ms. Length: 2,500-3,500 words. Pays $250 maximum, higher for special.
Tips: "Our greatest interest is in originality—new ideas, new approaches; no tired, overdone stories—both feature and fiction. We do not deal in 'hack' sensationalism but in high quality pieces. Keep in mind the intelligent 18 to 29 year-old male reader. We will be putting more emphasis in articles and fiction on sexual themes. We prefer serious articles. Pornography—fiction can be very imaginative and sensational."

‡CHERI MAGAZINE, All-True Sex News, 801 Second Ave., 19th Floor, New York NY 10017. (212)661-7878. Editor: Brian Riley. Managing Editor: Robin D. Beard. 5% freelance written. Works with a small number of new/unpublished writers each year. Monthly erotic men's magazine for predominantly blue-collar audience ages 18-40. Circ. 750,000. Pays on publication. Byline given. Offers variable kill fee. Buys first North American serial rights and second serial (reprint) rights; makes some work-for-hire assignments. Submit seasonal/holiday material 6 months in advance. Simultaneous queries, and simultaneous, photocopied and previously published submissions OK. Computer printout submissions acceptable; no dot-matrix. Reports in 2 months on queries; 3 months on mss. Publishes ms an average of 4 months after acceptance. Writer's guidelines for business size SASE.
Nonfiction and Fiction: Robin D. Beard, managing editor. "We can't use any political exposé-type stories. We are interested in heavily sexual features especially if hot photos accompany, with model releases. About the only thing we really buy freelance is fiction pieces, preferably written first person, very hot and exciting, no s&m, incest, brutality, etc. We call these 'sizzlers' and generally publish 1 per issue. Query for nonfiction. Send complete ms for fiction. Pays $75 for Sizzlers. Typed only." Length: 1,000-2,000 words.
Photos: "We buy 'homebodies,' girl-next-door-type photos—no Polaroids—for Homebody Contestants section. $100 if used. Must have model release obtainable in magazine. We prefer *real* women, not professional models."

CHIC MAGAZINE, Larry Flynt Publications, Suite 3800, 2029 Century Park E., Los Angeles CA 90067. Executive Editor: Tim Conaway. 10% freelance written. Prefers to work with published/established writers. Monthly magazine for men, ages 20-35 years, college-educated and interested in current affairs, entertainment and sports. Circ. 250,000. Pays 1 month after acceptance. Publishes ms an average of 3 months after acceptance. Buys exclusive English and English translation world-wide magazine rights. Pays 20% kill fee. Computer printout submissions acceptable; prefers letter-quality to dot-matrix. Byline given unless writer requests otherwise. Reports in 2 months.
Nonfiction: Sex-related topics of current national interest; interview (personalities in news and entertainment); and celebrity profiles. Buys 12-18 mss/year. Query. Length: 4,500 words. Pays $750. Sometimes pays the expenses of writers on assignment.
Columns/Departments: Dope, and Sex Life, 2,000 words. Pays $350. Odds and Ends (front of the book shorts; study the publication first) 100-300 words. Pays $50. Close Up (short Q&As) columns, 1,000 words. Pays $350.
Fiction: "At present we are buying stories with emphasis on erotic themes. These may be adventure, action, mystery or horror stories, but the tone and theme must involve sex and eroticism. The erotic nature of the story should not be subordinate to the charactizations and plot; the sex must grow logically from the people and the plot, not be contrived or forced."
Tips: "We do not buy poetry or science fiction. Refrain from stories with drug themes, sex with minors, incest and bestiality."

ESQUIRE, 2 Park Ave., New York NY 10016. (212)561-8100. Editorial Director: Betsy Carter. Editor: Lee Eisenberg. 99% freelance written. Monthly. Pays on acceptance. Publishes ms an average of 6 months after acceptance. Usually buys first serial rights. Computer printout submissions acceptable; prefers letter-quality to dot-matrix. Reports in 3 weeks. "We depend chiefly on solicited contributions and material from literary agencies. We are unable to accept responsibility for unsolicited material." Query.
Nonfiction: Articles vary in length, but features usually average 3,000-7,000 words. Articles should be slanted for sophisticated, intelligent readers; however, not highbrow in the restrictive sense. Wide range of subject matter. Rates run roughly between $300 and $3,000, depending on length, quality, etc. Sometimes pays expenses of writers on assignments.
Photos: Ellen Madere, photo editor. Payment depends on how photo is used, but rates are roughly $300 for b&w; $500-750 for color. Guarantee on acceptance. Buys first periodical publication rights.
Fiction: L. Rust Hills, fiction editor. "Literary excellence is our only criterion." Length: about 1,000-6,000 words. Payment: $1,500-5,000.

Tips: The writer sometimes has a better chance of breaking in at *Esquire* with short, lesser-paying articles and fillers (rather than with major features) "because we need more short pieces."

FLING, Relim Publishing Co., Inc., 550 Miller Ave., Mill Valley CA 94941. (415)383-5464. Editor: Arv Miller. Managing Editor: Ted Albert. 30% freelance written. Prefers to work with published/established writers; works with a small number of new/unpublished writers each year. Bimonthly magazine of men's sophisticate field. Young male audience of adults ages 18-34. Sexual-oriented field. Circ. 100,000. Pays on acceptance. Publishes ms an average of 3 months after acceptance. Buys first North American serial rights and second serial (reprint) rights; makes work-for-hire assignments. Submit seasonal/holiday material 8 months in advance. Computer printout submissions acceptable; prefers letter-quality to dot-matrix. Does not consider multiple submissions. Reports in 1 week on queries; 2 weeks on mss. Sample copy $4; writer's guidelines for SAE and 1 first class stamp.
Nonfiction: Exposé, how-to (better relationships with women, better lovers); interview/profile; personal experience; photo feature; and taboo sex articles. Buys 15 mss/year. Query. Length: 1,500-3,000 words. Pays $150-250. Sometimes pays expenses of writers on assignment.
Photos: Send photos with query. Reviews b&w contact sheets and 8x10 prints; 35mm color transparencies. Pays $10-25 for b&w; $20-35 for color. Model releases required. Buys one-time rights.
Columns/Departments: Buys 12 mss/year. Query or send complete ms. Length: 100-200 words. Pays $15-125.
Fiction: Confession, erotica and sexual. No science fiction, western, plotless, private-eye, "dated," or adventure. Buys 20 mss/year. Send complete ms. Length: 2,000-3,000 words. Pays $135-200.
Fillers: Clippings. Buys 50/year. Length: 100-500 words. Pays $5-15.
Tips: "Nonfiction and fiction are wide open areas to freelancers. Always query with one-page letter to the editor before proceeding with any writing. Also send a sample photocopy of published material, similar to suggestion."

‡FORUM, The International Journal of Human Relations, Penthouse International, 1965 Broadway, New York NY 10023. (212)496-6100. Executive Editor: John Heideury. 50% freelance written. A monthly magazine. "*Forum* is the only serious publication in the U.S. to cover human sexuality in all its aspects for the layman—not only the erotic, but the medical, political, legal, etc." Circ. 400,000. Pays on acceptance. Byline given. "Pseudonym mandatory for first-person sex stories." Offers 25% kill fee. Buys all rights. Submit seasonal/holiday material 6 months in advance. Photocopied submissions OK. Reports in 1 month on queries. Free sample copy.
Nonfiction: Book excerpts and personal experience. "Most of our freelance submissions are true first-person sexual tales." No submissions of a specialized nature, medical, fiction or poetry. Buys 40-60 mss/year. Query or send complete ms. Length: 2,000-5,000 words. Pays $800-2,500 for assigned articles; pays $800-1,200 for unsolicited articles. Pays expenses of writers on assignment.
Photos: State availability of photos with submission. Reviews transparencies and 8x11 prints. Offers $40 minimum per photo. Captions, model releases and identification of subjects required.
Tips: "We are interested in true first-person sexual adventures. Pornographic embellishment—that is, mere titillation for the reader—is both discouraged and edited out, though explicit sexual description (there is a difference) is acceptable."

GALLERY MAGAZINE, Montcalm Publishing Corp., 800 2nd Ave., New York NY 10017. (212)986-9600. Editor-in-Chief: March Lichter. Managing Editor: Barry Janoff. Design Director: Michael Monte. 30% freelance written. Monthly magazine "focusing on features of interest to the young American man." Circ. 500,000. Pays 50% on acceptance, 50% on publication. Publishes ms an average of 4 months after acceptance. Byline given. Pays 25% kill fee. Buys first North American serial rights; makes work-for-hire assignments. Submit seasonal/holiday material 6 months in advance. Photocopied submissions OK. Reports in 1 month on queries; 2 months on mss. Sample copy $3.50 plus $1.75 postage and handling. Free writer's guidelines.
Nonfiction: Investigative pieces, general interest, how-to, humor, interview, new products and profile. "We *do not* want to see articles on pornography." Buys 7-9 mss/issue. Query or send complete mss. Length: 1,000-3,000 words. Pays $200-1,500. "Special prices negotiated."
Photos: Send photos with accompanying mss. Pay varies for b&w or color contact sheets and negatives. Buys one-time rights. Captions preferred; model release required.
Fiction: Adventure, erotica, experimental, humorous, mainstream, mystery and suspense. Buys 1 mss/issue. Send complete ms. Length: 500-3,000 words. Pays $250-1,000.

GEM, G&S Publications, 1472 Broadway, New York NY 10036. (212)840-7224. Editor: Will Martin. Managing Editor: R.B. Kendennis. 70% freelance written. Bimonthly magazine. Pays when ms is assigned to a specific issue. Sample copy $3.95.
Nonfiction: Sex-related but nonpornographic articles. Length: "several hundred"-2,500 words. Also,

sports, fitness, movies, cars, travel, food, etc. Length: 700-800 words. Pays $50-100.
Fiction: Sex-related but nonpornographic. Pays $50-100.
Tips: "We do not use explicit, graphic descriptions of sex acts or manuscripts with violence. Humor, satire and spoofs of sexual subjects that other magazines treat seriously are welcome."

‡GENESIS MAGAZINE, 770 Lexington Ave., New York NY 10021. Editor: Joseph J. Kelleher. 85% freelance written. Prefers to work with published/established writers. Monthly magazine. Circ. 600,000. Publishes ms an average of 4 months after acceptance. Computer printout submissions acceptable; prefers letter-quality to dot-matrix. Reports in 2 months.
Nonfiction: Articles about serious contemporary issues, how-to-live-better service features, humor, celebrity interviews, features about young successful men on the rise, and comment on contemporary relationships. Query. Sometimes pays the expenses of writers on assignment.
Photos: Photo essays of beautiful women.

GENT, Suite 204, 2355 Salzedo St., Coral Gables FL 33134. (305)443-2378. Editor: John C. Fox. 75% freelance written. Monthly magazine for men from every strata of society who enjoy big breasted, full-figured females. Circ. 200,000. Buys first North American serial rights. Byline given. Pays on publication. Publishes ms an average of 2 months after acceptance. Computer printout submissions acceptable; prefers letter-quality to dot-matrix. Reports in 6 weeks. Writer's guidelines for legal size SASE.
Nonfiction: Looking for traditional men's subjects (cars, racing, outdoor adventure, science, gambling, etc.) as well as sex-related topics. Query first. Length: 1,500-3,500 words. Buys 70 mss/year. Pays $100-200.
Photos: B&w and color photos purchased with mss. Captions (preferred).
Fiction: Erotic. "Stories should contain a huge-breasted female character, as this type of model is *Gent*'s main focus. And this character's endowments should be described in detail in the course of the story. Some of our stories also emphasize sexy, chubby women, pregnant women and their male admirers." Submit complete ms. No fiction queries. Length: 2,000-3,500 words. Pays $100-200.
Tips: "Study sample copies of the magazine before trying to write for it. We like custom-tailored stories and articles."

GENTLEMEN'S QUARTERLY, Condé Nast, 350 Madison Ave., New York NY 10017. Editor-in-Chief: Arthur Cooper. Managing Editor: Eliot Kaplan. 60% freelance written. Circ. 607,000. Monthly magazine emphasizing fashion, general interest and service features for men ages 25-45 with a large discretionary income. Pays on acceptance. Byline given. Pays 25% kill fee. Submit seasonal/holiday material 6 months in advance. Computer printout submissions acceptable; prefers letter-quality to dot-matrix. Reports in 1 month.
Nonfiction: Politics, personality profiles, lifestyles, trends, grooming, nutrition, health and fitness, sports, travel, money, investment and business matters. Buys 4-6 mss/issue. Query with published clips. Length: 1,500-4,000 words. Pays $750-3,000.
Columns/Departments: Eliot Kaplan, managing editor. Body & Soul (fitness, nutrition and grooming); Money (investments); Going in Style (travel); Health; Music; Tech (consumer electronics); Dining In (food); Wine & Spirits; Hur; Fiction; Games (sports); Books; The Male Animal (essays by men on life); and All About Adam (nonfiction by women about men). Buys 5-8/issue. Query with published clips or submit complete ms. Length: 1,000-2,500 words. Pays $750-2,000.
Tips: "Major features are usually assigned to well-established, known writers. Pieces are almost always solicited. The best way to break in is through the columns, especially Male Animal, All About Adam, Games, Health or Humor."

NUGGET, Suite 204, 2355 Salzedo St., Coral Gables FL 33134. (305)443-2378. Editor: John Fox. 75% freelance written. Magazine "primarily devoted to fetishism." Pays on publication. Publishes ms an average of 2 months after acceptance. Byline given. Buys first North American serial rights. Computer printout submissions acceptable; prefers letter-quality to dot-matrix. Reports in 6 weeks.
Nonfiction: Articles on fetishism—every aspect. Buys 20-30 mss/year. Submit complete ms. Length: 2,000-3,000 words. Pays $100-200.
Photos: Erotic pictorials of women and couples—essay types in fetish clothing (leather, rubber, underwear, etc.) or women wrestling or boxing other women or men, preferably semi- or nude. Captions or short accompanying ms desirable. Reviews color or b&w photos.
Fiction: Erotic and fetishistic. Should be oriented to *Nugget*'s subject matter. Length: 2,000-3,000 words. Pays $100-200.
Tips: "We require queries on articles only, and the letter should be a brief synopsis of what the article is about. Originality in handling of subject is very helpful. It is almost a necessity for a freelancer to study our magazine first, be knowledgeable about the subject matter we deal with and able to write explicit and erotic fetish material."

PLAYBOY, 919 N. Michigan, Chicago IL 60611. 50% freelance written. Prefers to work with published/established writers; works with a small number of new/unpublished writers each year. Monthly. Pays on accept-

ance. Publishes ms an average of 6 months after acceptance. Offers 20% kill fee. Buys first serial rights and others. Computer printout submissions acceptable; prefers letter-quality to dot-matrix. Reports in 1 month.
Nonfiction: John Rezek, articles editor. "We're looking for timely, topical pieces. Articles should be carefully researched and written with wit and insight. Little true adventure or how-to material. Check magazine for subject matter. Pieces on outstanding contemporary men, sports, politics, sociology, business and finance, music, science and technology, games, all areas of interest to the contemporary urban male." Query. Length: 3,000-5,000 words. Pays $3,000 minimum. *Playboy* interviews run between 10,000 and 15,000 words. After getting an assignment; the freelancer outlines the questions, conducts and edits the interview, and writes the introduction. Pays $4,000 minimum. For interviews contact G. Barry Golson, Executive Editor, 747 3rd Ave., New York NY 10017. Pays expenses of writers on assignment.
Photos: Gary Cole, photography director, suggests that all photographers interested in contributing make a thorough study of the photography currently appearing in the magazine. Generally all photography is done on assignment. While much of this is assigned to *Playboy*'s staff photographers, approximately 50% of the photography is done by freelancers, and *Playboy* is in constant search of creative new talent. Qualified freelancers are encouraged to submit samples of their work and ideas. All assignments made on an all rights basis with payments scaled from $600/color page for miscellaneous features such as fashion, food and drink, etc.; $300/b&w page; $1,000/color page for girl features; cover, $1,500. Playmate photography for entire project: $10,000-13,000. Assignments and submissions handled by senior editor: Jeff Cohen and associate editors: Janice Moses, James Larson and Michael Ann Sullivan, Chicago; Marilyn Grabowski and Linda Kenney, Los Angeles. Assignments made on a minimum guarantee basis. Film, processing, and other expenses necessitated by assignment honored.
Fiction: Alice Turner, fiction editor. Both light and serious fiction. "Entertainment pieces are clever, smoothly written stories. Serious fiction must come up to the best contemporary standards in substance, idea and style. Both, however, should be designed to appeal to the educated, well-informed male reader." General types include comedy, mystery, fantasy, horror, science fiction, adventure, social-realism, "problem" and psychological stories. Fiction lengths are 3,000-6,000 words; short-shorts of 1,000 to 1,500 words are used. Pays $2,000; $1,000 short-short. Rates rise for additional acceptances.
Fillers: Party Jokes are always welcome. Pays $50 each. Also interesting items for Playboy After Hours, section (check it carefully before submission). The After Hours front section pays anywhere from $75 for humorous or unusual news items (submissions not returned) to $500 for original reportage. Subject matter should be new trends, fads, personalities and cultural developments. Has regular movie, book and record reviewers. Ideas for Playboy Potpourri pay $75. Query to David Stevens, Chicago. Games, puzzles and travel articles should be addressed to New York office.

PLAYERS MAGAZINE, Players International Publications, 8060 Melrose Ave., Los Angeles CA 90046. (213)653-8060. Editor: H.L. Sorrel. Associate Editor: Leslie Spencer. Monthly magazine for the black male but "we have a high female readership—perhaps as high as 40%." Circ. 240,000. Pays on publication. Buys all rights. Submit seasonal/holiday material 6 months in advance. Photocopied submissions OK. Reports in 3 weeks minimum.
Nonfiction: "*Players* is *Playboy* in basic black." Expose, historical, humor, inspirational, sports, travel, reviews of movies, books, records, profile/interview on assignment. Length: 1,000-5,000 words. Pays 10¢/word.
Photos: Photos purchased on assignment. Pays $25 minimum for b&w; $250 maximum/layout. Model release required.
Fiction: Adventure, erotica, fantasy, historical (black), humorous, science fiction and experimental. Length: 1,000-4,000 words. Pays 6¢/word.
Tips: "Follow current style with novel theme in query or article. We are looking for: city night life of cities other than New York, Chicago, Los Angeles; interviews with black political leaders; black writers and trend setters; and black history."

SAGA, Lexington Library, Inc., 355 Lexington Ave., New York NY 10017. (212)391-1400. Editors: Stephen Ciacciarelli, Thomas Walsh. 95% freelance written. Annual general interest men's magazine. "We offer an alternative to the many 'skin' magazines across the country in that we give an exciting, contemporary look at America today without the porn. A man's magazine that can be read by the entire family." Circ. 300,000. Pays on acceptance. Publishes ms an average of 2 months after acceptance. Byline given. Buys first North American serial rights. Computer printout submissions acceptable; prefers letter-quality to dot-matrix. Reports in 1 month. Sample copy $2.
Nonfiction: Exposé (government), how-to (save money), humor (topical), interview, new product, profile and travel. Buys 12-15 mss/year. Query. Length: 1,500-3,500 words. Pays $250-600.
Photos: Photos purchased with accompanying ms or on assignment. Pays $35 minimum for b&w photos; $75 minimum for 35mm color photos. Query for photos. Captions and model releases required.
Tips: "A reduced publication schedule will lessen our need for material."

SCREW, Box 432, Old Chelsea Station, New York NY 10011. Managing Editor: Manny Neuhaus. 95% freelance written. Eager to work with new/unpublished writers. Weekly tabloid newspaper for a predominantly male, college-educated audience; ages 21 through mid-40s. Circ. 125,000. Pays on publication. Publishes ms an average of 3 months after acceptance. Byline given. Buys all rights. Computer printout submissions acceptable; prefers letter-quality to dot-matrix. Reports in 3 months. Free sample copy and writer's guidelines.
Nonfiction: "Sexually related news, humor, how-to articles, first person and true confessions. Frank and explicit treatment of all areas of sex; outrageous and irreverent attitudes combined with hard information, news and consumer reports. Our style is unique. Writers should check several recent issues." Buys 150-200 mss/year. Submit complete ms for first person, true confession. Length: 1,000-3,000 words. Pays $100-200. Will also consider material for Letter From . . . , a consumer-oriented wrap-up of commercial sex scene in cities around the country; and My Scene, a sexual true confession. Length: 1,000-2,500 words. Pays about $40. Sometimes pays the expenses of writers on assignment.
Photos: Reviews b&w glossy prints (8x10 or 11x14) purchased with or without manuscripts or on assignment. Pays $10-50.
Tips: "All mss get careful attention. Those written in *Screw* style on sexual topics have the best chance. I anticipate a need for more aggressive, insightful political humor."

SWANK, GCR Publishing Corp., 888 7th Ave., New York NY 10106. (212)541-7100. Editor: Eve Ziegler. 15% freelance written. Monthly magazine on "sex and sensationalism, lurid. High quality adult erotic entertainment." Audience of men ages 18-38, high school and some college education, low to medium income, skilled blue-collar professionals, union men. Circ. 350,000. Pays on publication. Publishes ms an average of 3 months after acceptance. Byline given; pseudonym, if wanted. Pays 10% kill fee. Buys first North American serial rights. Submit seasonal/holiday material 4 months in advance. Computer printout submissions acceptable. Reports in 3 weeks on queries; 2 months on mss. Sample copy $3.50; writer's guidelines for SAE and 1 first class stamp.
Nonfiction: Exposé (researched); personal experience (confession if it's something fascinating and lurid); and photo feature. Be innovative. Buys 8 mss/year. Query with or without published clips. Pays $350-500. Sometimes pays the expenses of writers on assignment.
Photos: Bruce Perez, photo editor. State availability of photos. Model releases required.
Fiction: Erotica and suspense. "We want Elmore Leonard-type material." Buys 12 mss/year. Send complete ms. Length: 2,500-3,000 words. Pays $150-350.
Tips: "Pornography should not be hacked out. Skill and expertise in writing is a must."

Military

Technical and semitechnical publications for military commanders, personnel and planners, as well as those for military families and civilians interested in Armed Forces activities are listed here. These publications emphasize military or paramilitary subjects or aspects of military life.

ARMED FORCES JOURNAL INTERNATIONAL, Suite 104, 1414 22nd St. NW, Washington DC 20037. Editor: Benjamin F. Schemmer. 30% freelance written. Monthly magazine for "senior career officers of the U.S. military, defense industry, Congressmen and government officials interested in defense matters, international military and defense industry." Circ. 42,000. Pays on publication. Publishes ms an average of 2 months after acceptance. Buys all rights. Photocopied submissions OK. Computer printout submissions acceptable; no dot-matrix. Reports in 1 month. Sample copy $2.75.
Nonfiction: Publishes "national and international defense issues: weapons programs, research, personnel programs and international relations (with emphasis on defense issues). We do not want broad overviews of a general subject; we are more interested in detailed analysis which lays out *both* sides of a specific program or international defense issue. Our readers are decision-makers in defense matters—hence, subject should not be treated too simplistically. Be provocative. We are not afraid to take issue with our own constituency when an independent voice needs to be heard." Buys informational, profile and think pieces. No poetry, biographies, or non defense topics. Buys 40-45 mss/year. Send complete ms. Length: 1,000-3,000 words. Pays $100-200/page. Sometimes pays the expenses of writers on assignment.

Tips: "The most frequent mistakes made by writers are: 1) one-dimensional and one-sided articles; 2) broad-brush generalities versus specificity; and 3) poorly-written gobbledygook."

ARMY MAGAZINE, 2425 Wilson Blvd., Arlington VA 22201. (703)841-4300. Editor-in-Chief: L. James Binder. Managing Editor: Mary Blake French. 80% freelance written. Monthly magazine emphasizing military interests. Circ. 171,000. Pays on publication. Publishes ms an average of 6 months after acceptance. Buys all rights. Byline given except for back-up research. Submit seasonal/holiday material 3 months in advance. Photocopied submissions OK. Computer printout submissions acceptable; prefers letter-quality to dot-matrix. Free sample copy and writer's guidelines.
Nonfiction: Historical (military and original); humor (military feature-length articles and anecdotes); interview; new product; nostalgia; personal experience; photo feature; profile; and technical. No rehashed history. "We would like to see more pieces about interesting military personalities. We especially want material lending itself to heavy, contributor-supplied photographic treatment. The first thing a contributor should recognize is that our readership is very savvy militarily. 'Gee-whiz' personal reminiscences get short shrift, unless they hold their own in a company in which long military service, heroism and unusual experiences are commonplace. At the same time, Army readers like a well-written story with a fresh slant, whether it is about an experience in a foxhole or the fortunes of a corps in battle." Buys 12 mss/issue. Submit complete ms. Length: 4,500 words. Pays 12-17¢/word.
Photos: Submit photo material with accompanying ms. Pays $15-50 for 8x10 b&w glossy prints; $35-150 for 8x10 color glossy prints or 2¼x2¼ color transparencies, but will accept 35mm. Captions preferred. Buys all rights.
Columns/Departments: Military news, books, comment (*New Yorker*-type "Talk of the Town" items). Buys 8/issue. Submit complete ms. Length: 1,000 words. Pays $40-150.

ASIA-PACIFIC DEFENSE FORUM, Commander-in-Chief, U.S. Pacific Command, Box 13, Camp H.M. Smith HI 96861. (808)477-5027/6924. Editor-in-Chief: Lt. Col. Paul R. Stankiewicz. Editor: Major Robert Teasdale. 12% (maximum) freelance written. Quarterly magazine for foreign military officers in 51 Asian-Pacific, Indian Ocean and other countries; all services—Army, Navy, Air Force and Marines. Secondary audience—government officials, media and academicians concerned with defense issues. "We seek to keep readers abreast of current status of U.S. forces and of U.S. national security policies, and to enhance international professional dialogue on military subjects." Circ. 30,000. Pays on acceptance. Publishes ms an average of 4 months after acceptance. Byline given. Buys simultaneous rights, second serial (reprint) rights or one-time rights. Phone queries OK. Simultaneous, photocopied, and previously published submissions OK. Computer printout submissions OK; prefers letter-quality to dot-matrix. Requires only a self-addressed label. Reports in 3 weeks on queries; 10 weeks on mss. Free sample copy and writer's guidelines (send self-addressed label).
Nonfiction: General interest (strategy and tactics, current type forces and weapons systems, strategic balance and security issues and Asian-Pacific armed forces); historical (occasionally used, if relation to present-day defense issues is clearly apparent); how-to (training, leadership, force employment procedures, organization); interview and personal experience (rarely used, and only in terms of developing professional military skills). "We do not want overly technical weapons/equipment descriptions, overly scholarly articles, controversial policy, and budget matters; nor do we seek discussion of in-house problem areas. We do not deal with military social life, base activities or PR-type personalities/job descriptions." Buys 2-4 mss/year. Query or send complete ms. Length: 1,000-3,000 words. Pays $100-300.
Photos: State availability of photos with query or ms. "We provide nearly all photos; however, we will consider good quality photos with manuscripts." Reviews 5x7 and 8x10 b&w glossy prints or 35mm color transparencies. Offers no additional payment for photos accompanying mss. Photo credits given. Captions required. Buys one-time rights.
Tips: "The most frequent mistake made by writers is writing in a flashy, Sunday supplement style. Our audience is relatively staid, and fact-oriented articles requiring a newspaper/journalistic approach is used more than a normal magazine style. Develop a 'feel' for our foreign audience orientation. Provide material that is truly audience-oriented and easily illustrated with photos."

EAGLE, For the American Fighting Man, Command Publications, 1115 Broadway, New York NY 10010. (212)807-7100. Editor: Harry Kane. 100% freelance written. Bimonthly magazine on military adventure. "We are a fact magazine dedicated to a bellicose audience. We publish stories on weapons, military equipment and adventure stories of contemporary combat." Circ. 150,000. Pays on acceptance. Publishes ms an average of 2 months after acceptance. Byline given. Buys all rights or negotiable rights. Simultaneous queries and simultaneous, photocopied and previously published submissions OK. Computer printout submissions acceptable; prefers letter-quality to dot-matrix. Reports in 1 week. Sample copy for 9x12 SAE and 4 first class stamps.
Nonfiction: Book excerpts, how-to, interview/profile, new product, personal experience and technical. No fiction or historical earlier than Vietnam. Buys 60 mss/year. Send complete ms. Length: 1,000-2,000 words. Pays $150-500.

Photos: Send photos with ms. Reviews 35mm color transparencies and 5x7 b&w prints. Payment normally included in fee for article. Captions and model release required. Buys all rights or negotiable rights.

FAMILY MAGAZINE, The Magazine for Military Wives, Box 4993, Walnut Creek CA 94596. (415)284-9093. Editor: Mary Jane Ryan. 100% freelance written. "We are backlogged but will be accepting a few manuscripts." A monthly magazine for military wives who are young, high school educated and move often. Circ. 545,000. Pays on publication. Publishes ms an average of 15 months after acceptance. Byline given. Buys first North American serial rights. Submit seasonal/holiday material 6 months in advance. Simultaneous and photocopied submissions OK. Computer printout submissions acceptable; prefers letter-qualtiy to dot-matrix. Reports in 1 month. Sample copy $1.25; writer's guidelines for SAE with 1 first class stamp.
Nonfiction: Humor, personal experience, photo feature and travel of interest to military wives. No romance, anything to do with getting a man or aging. Buys 10 mss/year. Send complete ms. Length: 2,000 words maximum. Pays $75-200. .
Photos: Send photos with submissions. Reviews contact sheets, transparencies and prints. Offers $25-50/photo. Identification of subjects required. Buys one-time rights.
Fiction: Humorous, mainstream and slice-of-life vignettes. No romance or novel excerpts. Buys 5 mss/year. Length: 2,000 words. Pays $75-150.

FOR YOUR EYES ONLY, Military Intelligence Summary, Tiger Publications, Box 8759, Amarillo TX 79114. (806)655-2009. Editor: Stephen V. Cole. 5% freelance written. Eager to work with new/unpublished writers. A biweekly newsletter covering military intelligence (post 1980). Circ. 1,200. Pays on publication. Publishes ms an average of 3 months after acceptance. Byline given. Offers variable kill fee. Buys all rights. Simultaneous queries, and simultaneous, photocopied, and previously published submissions OK. Electronic submissions OK on Modem 300 or 1200 Baud ASCII; and Apple 3.3 disk. Computer printout submissions acceptable. Reports in 2 weeks on queries; 1 month on mss. Sample copy $2; writer's guidelines for SAE and 1 first class stamp.
Nonfiction: Exposé, interview/profile, personal experience, technical, how-to, arms sales, tests, current research, wars, battles and military data. "We're looking for technical material presented for nontechnical people, but our readership is highly intelligent and sophisticated, so do not talk down to them. Our emphasis is on how and why things work (and don't work)." No superficial or humorous material; nothing before 1981. Buys 20 mss/year. Query. Length: 50-2,000 words. Pays 3¢/word.
Photos: State availability of photos or send photos with ms. Pays $5-35 for b&w prints. Captions required. Buys one-time rights or negotiable rights.
Fillers: Newsbreaks. Buys 50-100/year. Length: 30-150 words. Pays $1-5.
Tips: "Read publication and author's guide; be aware of how much we generate internally. Briefings (100-300 words) and Newsnotes (30-150 words) are most open to freelancers."

INFANTRY, Box 2005, Fort Benning GA 31905-0605. (404)545-2350. Editor: Albert N. Garland. 80% freelance written. Eager to work with new/unpublished writers. Bimonthly magazine published primarily for combat arms officers and noncommissioned officers. Circ. 20,000. Not copyrighted. Buys first serial rights. Pays on publication. Payment cannot be made to U.S. government employees. Publishes ms an average of 1 year after acceptance. Computer printout submissions acceptable; prefers letter-quality to dot-matrix. Reports in 1 month. Free sample copy and writer's guidelines.
Nonfiction: Interested in current information on U.S. military organization, weapons, equipment, tactics and techniques; foreign armies and their equipment; lessons learned from combat experience, both past and present; and solutions to problems encountered in the Active Army and the Reserve Components. Departments include Letters, Features and Forum, Training Notes, and Book Reviews. Uses 70 unsolicited mss/year. Recent article example: "The Ambush" (January-February 1986). Length of articles: 1,500-3,500 words. Length for Book Reviews: 500-1,000 words. Query with writing sample. Accepts 75 mss/year.
Photos: Used with mss.
Tips: Start with letters to editor, book reviews to break in.

LEATHERNECK, Box 1775, Quantico VA 22134. (703)640-3171. Editor: William V.H. White. Managing Editor: Tom Bartlett. Emphasizes all phases of Marine Corps activities. Monthly magazine. Circ. 90,000. Pays on acceptance. Buys first rights. Phone queries OK. Submit seasonal/holiday material 3 months in advance. Reports in 2 weeks. Free sample copy and writer's guidelines.
Nonfiction: "All material submitted to *Leatherneck* must pertain to the U.S. Marine Corps and its members." General interest, how-to, humor, historical, interview, nostalgia, personal experience, profile, and travel. "No articles on politics, subjects not pertaining to the Marine Corps, and subjects that are not in good taste." Buys 24 mss/year. Query. Length: 1,500-3,000 words. Pays $50 and up/magazine page.
Photos: "We like to receive a complete package when we consider a manuscript for publication." State availability of photos with query. No additional payment for 4x5 or 8x10 b&w glossy prints. Captions required. Model release required. Buys first rights.

Fiction: Adventure, historical and humorous. All material must pertain to the U.S. Marine Corps and its members. Buys 3 mss/year. Query. Length: 1,000-3,000 words. Pays $50 and up/magazine page.
Poetry: Light verse and traditional. No poetry that does not pertain to the U.S. Marine Corps. Buys 40 mss/ year. Length: 16-20 lines. Pays $10-20.

LIFE IN THE TIMES, (formerly *The Times Magazine*), Times Journal Co., Springfield VA 22159-0200. (703)750-8672. Editor: Barry Robinson. Managing Editor: Donna Peterson. Eager to work with new/unpublished writers. 30% freelance written. Weekly lifestyle section of Army, Navy and Air Force Times covering current lifestyles and problems of career military families around the world. Circ. 380,000. Pays on acceptance. Publishes ms an average of 2 months after acceptance. Byline given. Offers negotiable kill fee. Buys all rights. Submit seasonal/holiday material 6 months in advance. Electronic submissions OK; call office for requirements. Double- or triple-spaced computer printout submissions acceptable; no dot-matrix. Reports in about 2 months. Writer's guidelines for SASE.
Nonfiction: Expose (current military); how-to (military wives); interview/profile (military); opinion (military topic); personal experience (military only); and travel (of military interest). "We accept food articles and short items about unusual things military people and their families are doing." No poetry, cartoons or historical articles. Buys 200 mss/year. Query with published clips. Length: 750-2,000 words. Pays $75-350. Sometimes pays the expenses of writers on assignment.
Photos: State availability of photos or send photos with ms. Reviews 35mm color contact sheets and prints. Captions, model releases, and identification of subjects required. Buys all rights.
Tips: "In query write a detailed description of story and how it will be told. A tentative lead is nice. Just one good story 'breaks in' a freelancer. Follow the outline you propose in query letter and humanize articles with quotes and examples. We would like to build up a network of good freelance writers who can contribute on a regular basis."

THE MILITARY ENGINEER, 607 Prince St., Box 21289, Alexandria VA 22320-2289. (703)549-3800. Editor: John J. Kern. 90% freelance written. Prefers to work with published/established writers, but willing to work with new authors as well. Bimonthly magazine. Circ. 29,000. Pays on publication. Publishes ms an average of 9 months after acceptance. Byline given. Buys all rights. Phone queries OK. Computer printout submissions acceptable. Reports in 1 month. Sample copy and writer's guidelines $4.
Nonfiction: Well-written and illustrated semitechnical articles by experts and practitioners of civil and military engineering, constructors, equipment manufacturers, defense contract suppliers and architect/engineers on these subjects and on subjects of military biography and history. "Subject matter should represent a contribution to the fund of knowledge, concern a new project or method, be on R&D in these fields; investigate planning and management techniques or problems in these fields, or be of militarily strategic nature." Buys 50-70 unsolicited mss/year. Length: 1,000-2,000 words. Query.
Photos: Mss must be accompanied by 6-10 well-captioned photos, maps or illustrations; b&w glossy, generally. Pays approximately $25/page.

MILITARY LIVING, Box 4010, Arlington VA 22204. (703)237-0203. Editor: Ann Crawford. For military personnel and their families. Monthly. Circ. 30,000. Buys first serial rights. "Very few freelance features were used last year; most were staff-written." Pays on publication. Sample copy $1 in coin or stamps. "Slow to report due to small staff and workload." Submit complete ms.
Nonfiction: "Articles on military life in greater Washington D.C. area. We would especially like recreational features in the Washington D.C. area. We specialize in passing along morale-boosting information about the military installations in the area, with emphasis on the military family—travel pieces about surrounding area, recreation information, etc. We do not want to see depressing pieces, pieces without the military family in mind, personal petty complaints or general information pieces. Prefer 700 words or less, but will consider more for an exceptional feature. We also prefer a finished article rather than a query." Payment is on an honorarium basis, 1-1½¢/word.
Photos: Photos purchased with mss. 5x7 or larger b&w glossy prints only. Pay $5 for original photos by author.

MILITARY LIVING R&R REPORT, Box 4010, Arlington VA 22204. (703)237-0203. Publisher: Ann Crawford. Bimonthly newsletter for "military consumers worldwide. Please state when sending submission that it is for the *R&R Report Newsletter* so as not to confuse it with our monthly magazine which has different requirements." Pays on publication. Buys first serial rights but will consider other rights. Sample copy $1.
Nonfiction: "We use information on little-known military facilities and privileges, discounts around the world and travel information. Items must be short and concise. Stringers are wanted around the world. Payment is on an honorarium basis, 1-1½¢/word."

MILITARY REVIEW, U.S. Army Command and General Staff College, Fort Leavenworth KS 66027-6910. (913)684-5642. Editor-in-Chief: Col. Frederick Timmerman Jr. Managing Editor: Major Thomas Conrad. Associate Editor: Lt. Col. Lynn Havach. Business Manager: Major Linda Ewing. 65% freelance written. Eager to work with new/published writers. Monthly journal emphasizing the military for military officers, students and scholars. Circ. 27,000. Pays on publication. Publishes ms an average of 8 months after acceptance. Byline given. Buys first serial rights and reserves right to reprint for training purpose. Phone queries and photocopied submissions OK. Computer printout submissions acceptable; prefers letter-quality to dot-matrix. Reports in 1 month. Free writer's guidelines.

Nonfiction: Operational level of war, military history, international affairs, tactics, new military equipment, strategy and book reviews. Prefers not to get poetry or cartoons. Buys 100-120 mss/year. Query. Length: 2,000-3,000 words. Pays $50-200.

Tips: "We need more articles from military personnel experienced in particular specialties. Examples: Tactics from a tactician, military engineering from an engineer, etc. By reading our publication, writers will quickly recognize our magazine as a forum for any topic of general interest to the U.S. Army. They will also discover the style we prefer: concise and direct, in the active voice, with precision and clarity, and moving from the specific to the general."

‡NATIONAL DEFENSE, American Defense Preparedness Association, Suite 905, 1700 N. Moore St., Arlington VA 22209. (703)522-1820. Editor: Col. D. Ballou. 80% freelance written. Association journal published 10 times annually. "We concentrate on defense technology and focus on defense management executives, engineers and scientists in defense industry, the Department of Defense, and the military services. Each issue contains departments on small arms, tanks and automotive, space, missiles and aeronautics, sea services, foreign military developments and new developments." Pays on publication. Publishes ms an average of 2 months after acceptance. Byline given. Offers negotiable kill fee. Buys first rights. Submit seasonal/holiday material 3 months in advance. Simultaneous (if advised) and photocopied submissions OK. Computer printout submissions acceptable; prefers letter-quality to dot-matrix. Reports in 2 weeks on queries; 2 months on mss. Free sample copy and writer's guidelines.

Nonfiction: General interest (defense); how-to (defense/management); interview/profile (defense); new product (defense); photo feature (defense); and technical. "Each of our issues focuses on a specific theme for that month. They include: NATO Lifelines, Naval Warfare, Global Warfare, Space and Space Defense, Land Warfare, Air Warfare, and Research and High technology." Buys 50 mssyear. Query. Length: 1,800-2,500 words. Pays $500-1,000. Pays the expenses of writers on assignment.

Photos: State availability of photos with submission. Reviews contact sheets, negatives, 35mm and larger transparencies and 3x5 and larger prints. Offers $50 maximum/photo or by agreement if used. Captions required. Buys one-time rights; if desired, will return photos.

Fillers: Facts and newsbreaks. Length: 50-200 words. Pays $25.

Tips: "Features are most open to freelancers. Study our Theme Calendar."

NEW BREED, The Magazine for Bold Adventurers, New Breed Publications, Inc., 30 Amarillo Dr., Nanuet NY 10954. (914)623-8426. Editor: Harry Belil. Managing Editor: Richard Schwartzberg. 85% freelance written. Eager to work with new/unpublished writers. Bimonthly magazine covering military adventures, new weapons, survival. For persons interested in "where the action is—hot spots on the globe where the voice of adventure calls." Circ. 60,000. Pays on publication. Publishes ms an average of 7 months after acceptance. Byline given. Buys first serial rights. Photocopied and previously published submissions OK, if so indicated. Computer printout submissions acceptable; prefers letter-quality to dot-matrix. Would rather have typed copy. Reports in 2 weeks on queries; 3 weeks on mss. Sample copy for $2, 9x12 SAE, and first class postage; writer's guidelines for SASE.

Nonfiction: "Give us the best possible information on state-of-the-art field weaponry, combat practice and survival techniques for the professional soldier. Material should be slightly right-wing, pro-weapons (including handguns), somewhat hawkish in diplomacy, pro-freedom, pro-constitution, thus, libertarian and capitalist (in the real sense of the term) and consequently anti-totalitarian. Submit mss on all units of the armed forces, as well as soldiers of fortune, police officers and individuals who can be classified as 'New Breed.' " Special annual "combat guns" issue. Buys 80 mss/year. Send complete ms. Length: 3,000-4,000 words. Pays $150-250 for articles with b&w and color photos. Sometimes pays the expenses of writers on assignment.

Tips: "The most frequent mistake made by writers in completing an article for us is not studying our publication for format, style and type of material desired. It would help sell the story if some visual material was included."

OFF DUTY, U.S.: Suite C-2, 3303 Harbor Blvd., Costa Mesa CA 92626. Editor: Bruce Thorstad. Europe: Eschersheimer Landstrasse 69, Frankfurt/M, West Germany. Editor: J.C. Hixenbaugh. Pacific: 14/F Park Commercial Centre, 8 Shelter St., Causeway Bay, Hong Kong. Editor: Jim Shaw. 50% freelance written. "We are backlogged with submissions and prefer only to receive queries from writers who know our audience and our magazine." Monthly magazine for U.S. military personnel and their families stationed around the world. Most readers ages 18-35. Combined circ. 708,000. Buys first serial rights or second serial (reprint) rights. Pays on acceptance. Publishes ms an average of 6 months after acceptance. Computer printout submissions acceptable. Writer's guidelines and sample copy $1.

Nonfiction: Three editions—American, Pacific and European. "Emphasis is on off-duty travel, leisure, military shopping, wining and dining, sports, hobbies, music, and getting the most out of military life. Overseas editions lean toward foreign travel and living in foreign cultures. They also emphasize what's going on back home. In travel articles we like anecdotes, lots of description, color and dialogue. American edition uses more American trends and how-to/service material. Material with special U.S., Pacific or European slant should be sent to appropriate address above; material useful in all editions may be sent to U.S. address and will be forwarded as necessary." Buys 30-50 mss/year for each of three editions. Query. Length: 1,500 words average. Also needs 200-word shorties. Pays 13¢/word for use in one edition; 16¢/word for use in 2 or more. Sometimes pays expenses of writers on assignment.

Photos: Bought with or without accompanying ms. Pays $25 for b&w glossy prints; $50 for color transparencies; $100 for full page color; $200 for covers. "Covers must be vertical format 35mm; larger format transparencies preferred."

Tips: "All material should take into account to some extent our special audience—the U.S. military and their dependents. Our publication is subtitled 'The Military Leisure Time Magazine,' and the stories we like best are about how to get more out of the military experience. That 'more' could range from more fun to more satisfaction to more material benefits such as military privileges. We've got a fairly strict idea by this time of how our main travel feature or our main cooking feature should read, so when we're handing out assignments, we go with a writer we know. Other features are more loosely structured. Generally, by the time I get an article that I've assigned, the writer and I have talked about it enough so that there are really no major surprises. Query writers very often mistake the basic nature of our magazine. If we do an article on running, we'll get a raft of queries for running articles. That's wrong. We're a general interest magazine; if we've just done running, it's going to be quite a while before we do it again. We've got *dozens* of other subjects to cover."

OVERSEAS!, The Leisure Time Magazine for the Military Man in Europe, Military Consumer Today, Inc., Kolpingstr 1, 6906 Leimen, West Germany 06221-25431/32/33. Editorial Director: Charles L. Kaufman. Managing Editor: Greg Ballinger. 95% freelance written. Eager to work with new/unpublished writers; "we don't get enough submissions." Monthly magazine. "Overseas! is aimed at the U.S. military in Europe. It is the leading men's lifestyle magazine slanted towards life in Europe, specifically directed to males ages 18-35." Circ. 83,000. Pays on acceptance. Publishes ms an average of 3 months after acceptance. Byline given. Offers kill fee depending on circumstances and writer. Buys one-time rights. Submit seasonal/holiday material at least 4 months in advance. Simultaneous queries, and simultaneous, photocopied, and previously published submissions OK. Computer printout submissions acceptable; prefers letter-quality to dot-matrix. SASE, IRCs. Reports in 2 weeks on queries; 1 month on mss. Sample copy for SAE and 4 IRCs; writer's guidelines for SAE and 1 IRC.

Nonfiction: General interest (lifestyle for men and other topics); how-to (use camera, buy various types of video, audio, photo and computer equipment); humor (no military humor; "we want travel/tourist humor like old *National Lampoon* style. Must be humorous."); interview/profile (music, personality interviews; current music stars for young audience); personal experience (relating to travel in Europe); technical (video, audio, photo, computer; how to purchase and use equipment); travel (European, first person adventure; write toward male audience); men's cooking; and men's fashion/lifestyle. Special issues include Video, Audio, Photo, and Military Shopper's Guide. Needs 250-750 word articles on video, audio, photo and computer products. Published in September every year. No articles that are drug- or sex-related. No cathedrals or museums of Europe stories. Buys 30-50 mss/year "but would buy more if we got better quality and subjects." Query with or without pulished clips or send complete ms. Length: 750-2,000 words. Pays 10¢/word. Usually pays expenses of writers on assignment; negotiable.

Photos: Send photos with accompanying query or ms. Pays $20 minimum, b&w; $35 color transparencies, 35mm or larger. Photos must accompany travel articles—"color slides. Also, we are always looking for photographs of pretty, unposed, dressed, nonfashion, active *women* for our covers." Pays $250 minimum. Identification of subjects required. Buys one-time rights. Buys 12 covers/year.

Columns/Departments: Back Talk—potpourri page of humor, cartoons and other materials relating to life in Europe for Americans. Buys 12-20 mss/year. Query with published clips. Length: 1-150 words. Pays $25-150/piece used. "Would buy more if received more."

Fiction: Adventure (relating to travel in Europe); experimental ("Query or send manuscript. We're always looking for something new."); humorous (travel in Europe—what it's like being a tourist); and travel ("Mix fact with fiction to make adventure travel story read better. Please label as fiction."). No pornography or life in military. Buys 5 mss/year; "would buy more if we received good manuscripts on subjects we require—i.e, travel in Europe."

Tips: "We would especially like to get submissions on men's cooking—short 25-150 word cooking, food-related tips; needs 4-5 each month. Travel writing humor, men's fashion and articles on video, audio, photo and computer equipment and use are most open to freelancers. Writing should be lively, interesting, with lots of good information. We anticipate a change in the length of articles. Articles will be shorter with more sidebars, because readers don't have time to read longer articles. *Overseas!* magazine is the *Travel & Leisure/GQ/Play-boy/Esquire* of this market; any articles that would be suitable for these magazines would probably work in *Overseas!*"

PARAMETERS: JOURNAL OF THE U.S. ARMY WAR COLLEGE, U.S. Army War College, Carlisle Barracks PA 17013. (717)245-4943. Editor: Col. William R. Calhoun Jr., U.S. Army. Quarterly. Readership consists of senior leadership of U.S. defense establishment, both uniformed and civilian, plus members of the media, government, industry and academia interested in scholarly articles devoted to national and international security affairs, military strategy, military leadership and management, art and science of warfare, and military history (provided it has contemporary relevance). Most readers possess a graduate degree. Circ. 9,000. Not copyrighted; unless copyrighted by author, articles may be reprinted with appropriate credits. Buys first serial rights. Byline given. Pays on publication. Publishes ms an average of 6 months after acceptance. Computer printout submissions acceptable; prefers letter-quality to dot-matrix. Reports in 1 month.
Nonfiction: Articles preferred that deal with current security issues, employ critical analysis, and provide solutions or recommendations. Liveliness and verve, consistent with scholarly integrity, appreciated. Theses, studies and academic course papers should be adapted to article form prior to submission. Documentation in endnotes. Submit complete ms. Length: 5,000 words, preferably less. Pays $100 minimum; $150 average (including visuals).
Tips: "Research should be thorough; documentation should be complete."

PERIODICAL, Council on America's Military Past, 4970 N. Camino Antonio, Tucson AZ 85718. Editor-in-Chief: Dan L. Thrapp. 90% freelance written. Works with a small number of new/unpublished writers each year. Quarterly magazine emphasizing old and abandoned forts, posts and military installations; military subjects for a professional, knowledgeable readership interested in one-time defense sites or other military installations. Circ. 1,500. Pays on publication. Publishes ms an average of 3 months after acceptance. Buys one-time rights. Simultaneous, photocopied, and previously published (if published a long time ago) submissions OK. Reports in 3 weeks.
Nonfiction: Historical, personal experience, photo feature and technical (relating to posts, their construction/operation and military matters). Buys 4-6 mss/issue. Query or send complete ms. Length: 300-4,000 words. Pays $2/page minimum .
Photos: Purchased with or without ms. Query. Reviews glossy, single-weight 8x10 b&w prints. Offers no additional payment for photos accepted with accompanying ms. Captions required.

THE RETIRED OFFICER MAGAZINE, 201 N. Washington St., Alexandria VA 22314. (703)549-2311. Editor: Colonel Minter L. Wilson Jr., USA-Ret. 60% freelance written. Works with a small number of new/unpublished writers each month. Monthly for officers of the 7 uniformed services and their families. Circ. 345,000. Pays on acceptance. Publishes ms an average of 6 months after acceptance. Byline given. Buys all rights or first serial rights. Submit seasonal material (holiday stories with a military theme) at least 6 months in advance. Electronic submissions OK on Digital word processor, but requires hard copy also. Computer printout submissions acceptable; prefers letter-quality to dot-matrix. Reports on material accepted for publication within 6 weeks. Free sample copy and writer's guidelines.
Nonfiction: Recent military history, humor, hobbies, travel, second-career job opportunities and current affairs. Also, upbeat articles on aging, human interest and features pertinent to a retired military officer's milieu. True military experiences are also useful. "We tend to use articles less technical than a single-service publication. We do not publish poetry or fillers." Buys 48 unsolicited mss/year. Submit complete ms. Length: 1,000-2,500 words. Pays $100-400.
Photos: Reviews 8x10 b&w photos (normal halftone). Pays $15. Original slides or transparencies for magazine cover must be suitable for color separation. Pays up to $150.
Tips: "We're looking for more upbeat articles on Vietnam."

RUSI JOURNAL, Royal United Services Institute for Defence Studies, Whitehall, London SW1A 2ET England. Editor: Dr. Brian Holden Reid. Quarterly magazine emphasizing defense and military history. For the defense community: service officers, civil servants, politicians, journalists, academics, industrialists, etc. Circ. 6,500. Pays on publication. Buys all rights. Photocopied submissions OK. SAE, IRC. Sample copy $10 or £5.
Nonfiction: Learned articles on all aspects of defense; historical military articles with particular reference to current defense problems; weapon technology; international relations and civil/military relations. Buys 40 unsolicited mss/year. Query. Length: 2,500-6,000 words. Pays £12.5/printed page.
Photos: No additional payment is made for photos, but they should accompany articles whenever possible.

SEA POWER, 2300 Wilson Blvd., Arlington VA 22201-3308. Editor: James D. Hessman. Issued monthly by the Navy League of the U.S. for naval personnel and civilians interested in naval maritime and defense matters. 10% freelance written. "We prefer queries from experts/specialists in maritime industry." Computer printout

submissions acceptable; prefers letter-quality to dot-matrix. Pays on publication. Publishes ms an average of 3 months after acceptance. Buys all rights. Reports in 6 weeks. Free sample copy.
Nonfiction: Factual articles on sea power in general, U.S. industrial base, mineral resources, and the U.S. Navy, the U.S. Marine Corps, U.S. Coast Guard, U.S. Merchant Marine and naval services and other navies of the world in particular. Should illustrate and expound the importance of the seas and sea power to the U.S. and its allies. Wants timely, clear, nonpedantic writing for audience that is intelligent and well-educated but not necessarily fluent in military/hi-tech terminology. No personal analysis. Material should be presented in the third person, well documented and complete attribution. No historical articles, commentaries, critiques, abstract theories, poetry or editorials. Query first. Length: 500-2,500 words. Pays $100-500 depending upon length and research involved.
Photos: Purchased with ms.
Tips: "The writer should be invisible. Copy should be understandable without reference to charts, graphs or footnotes."

SOLDIER OF FORTUNE, The Journal of Professional Adventurers, Omega Group, Ltd., Box 693, Boulder CO 80306. (303)449-3750. Editor/Publisher: Robert K. Brown. Executive Editor: Bill Guthrie. 80% freelance written. Monthly magazine covering the military, police and the outdoors. "We take a strong stand on political issues such as maintenance of a strong national defense, the dangers of communism, and the right to keep and bear arms." Circ. 225,000. Pays on publication. Publishes ms an average of 4 months after acceptance. Byline given. Offers 25% kill fee "for proven freelancers." Buys first world rights: makes work-for-hire assignments. Submit seasonal/holiday material 6 months in advance. Computer printout submissions acceptable on North Star Horizon CPM. Computer printout submissions acceptable; prefers letter-quality to dot-matrix. Reports in 1 month. Sample copy $4; writer's guidelines for SAE.
Nonfiction: Expose (in-depth reporting from the world's hot spots—Afghanistan, Angola, etc.); general interest (critical focus on national issues—gun control, national defense); historical (soldiers of fortune, adventurers of past, history of elite units, Vietnam); how-to (outdoor equipment, weaponry, self-defense); humor (military, police); interview/profile (leaders or representatives of issues); new product (usually staff-assigned; outdoor equipment, weapons); personal experience ("I was there" focus); photo feature; and technical (weapons, weapons systems, military tactics). Buys 75-100 mss/year. Query. Length: 1,000-3,500 words. Pays $175-1,000.
Photos: Photos with ms are integral to package. Separate submissions negotiable. Captions and identification of weapons and military equipment required. Buys first world rights.
Columns/Departments: I Was There/It Happened to Me (adventure and combat stories). Buys 12 mss/year. Send complete ms. Length: 500 words maximum. Pays $50.
Tips: "All authors should have a professional background in the military or police work."

‡WORLD WAR II, Empire Press, 105 Loudoun Street SW, Leesburg VA 22075. (703)771-9400. Editor: Brian Kelly. Editorial Director: Carl Gnam. 95% freelance written. A bimonthly magazine covering "military operations in World War II—events, personalities, strategy, national policy, etc." Estab. 1986. Circ. 110,000. Pays on publication. Publishes ms an average of 6-12 months after acceptance. Byline given. Buys first North American serial rights. Submit seasonal/holiday material 6-12 months in advance. Reports in 1 month on queries; 3 months on mss. Sample copy $3.95; free writer's guidelines.
Nonfiction: Book excerpts (if in advance of book publication), profile, personal experience, technical, and World War II military history. No fiction. Buys 24 mss/year. Query. Length: 4,000 words. Pays $200.
Photos: State availability of photos with submission. (For photos and other art, send photocopies and cite sources. "We'll order.") Offers no additional payment for photos accepted with ms. Captions and identification of subjects required.
Columns/Department: Undercover (espionage, resistance, sabotage, intelligence gathering, behind the lines, etc.); personalities (WW II personalities of interest); and Armaments (weapons, their use and development); all 2,000 words. Book reviews, 300-375 words. Buys 18 mss/year (plus book reviews). Query. Pays $100.
Tips: "List your sources and suggest further readings, in standard format at the end of your piece—as a bibliography for our files in case of factual challenge or dispute. All submissions are on speculation. When the story's right, but the writing isn't, we'll pay a small research fee for use of the information in our own style and language."

ALWAYS submit MSS or queries with a stamped, self-addressed envelope (SASE) within your country or International Reply Coupons (IRCs) purchased from the post office for other countries.

Music

Music fans follow the latest music industry news in these publications. Musicians and different types of music (such as jazz, opera, rock and bluegrass) are the sole focus of some magazines. Publications geared to music industry professionals can be found in the music section
of Trade Journals. Additional music- and dance-related markets are included in the Theatre,
Movie, TV, and Entertainment section.

THE ABSOLUTE SOUND, The High End Journal, Harry Pearson Jr., Box 115, Sea Cliff NY 11579.
(516)676-2830. Editor: Harry Pearson Jr. Managing Editor: Sallie Reynolds. 25% freelance written. Prefers to
work with published/established writers. Quarterly magazine covering the music reproduction business, audio
equipment and records for "up-scale, high tech men and women between 20 and 40, toy freaks." Pays on publication. Publishes ms an average of 4 months after acceptance. Byline given. Buys all rights. Electronic submissions acceptable via IBM compatible (ASC II), but requires hard copy also. Computer printout submissions
acceptable; no dot-matrix. Sample copy $7.
Nonfiction: Exposé (of bad-commercial audio practices); interview/profile (famous engineers, famous conductors); new product (audio); opinion (audio and record reviews); and technical (how to improve your stereo
system). Special Recordings Issue (Autumn). No puff pieces about industry. Query with published clips.
Length: 250-5,000 words. Pays $125-1,000. Sometimes pays the expenses of writers on assignment.
Columns/Departments: Audio Musings (satires), and Reports from Overseas (audio fairs, celebrities, re-
cord companies). Buys 12 mss/year. Query with published clips. Length: 250-750 words. Pays $125-200.
Fillers: Clippings, newsbreaks; "They Say" approach like *The New Yorker,* but audio or recording related.
Buys 30/year. Length: 50-200 words. Pays $10-40.
Tips: "Writers should know about audio recordings and the engineering of same—as well as live music. The
approach is *literate* witty, investigative—good journalism."

BAM, Rock and Video/The California Music Magazine, BAM Publications, 5951 Canning St., Oakland
CA 94609. (415)652-3810. Senior Editor: Dave Zimmer. Associate Editor: Bill Forman. 60% freelance written. Biweekly tabloid. Circ. 110,000. Pays on publication. Publishes ms an average of 3 months after acceptance. Byline given. Offers negotiable kill fee. Buys first North American serial rights. Submit seasonal/holi-
day material 3 months in advance. Computer printout submissions acceptable; no dot-matrix. Reports in 3
weeks. Sample copy $2.
Nonfiction: Book excerpts, interview/profile and new product. Special issue, Annual Video. No personal experience without an interview subject. Buys 100 mss/year. Query with published clips. Length: 1,500-8,000
words. Pays $40-300. Sometimes pays expenses of writers on assignment.
Tips: "*BAM*'s focus is on both the personality and the craft of musicians. Writers should concentrate on bringing out their subject's special traits and avoid bland, cliched descriptions and quotes. Clear, crisp writing is essential. Many potential *BAM* writers try to be too clever and end up sounding stupid. Also, it helps to have a
clear focus. Many writers tend to ramble and simply string quotes together."

BAM, The California Music Magazine, BAM Publications, 5951 Canning St., Oakland CA 94609.
(415)652-3810. Senior Editor: Dave Zimmer. Assistant editor: Bill Forman. A biweekly contemporary music
tabloid. Circ. 110,000. Pays on publication. Publishes ms an average of 2-6 months after acceptance. Byline
given. Offers negotiable kill fee. Submit seasonal/holiday material at least 6 weeks in advance. Computer
printout submissions acceptable; no dot-matrix.
Nonfiction: Book excerpts, interview/profile, new product, photo feature, and live reviews and record reviews of musicians. "Most of *BAM*'s articles deal with rock and roll, slanted towards the 18-35 years of age
market with frequent pro musician features and some coverage of pop, jazz, country and blues." No self-indul-
gent, personal experience material. Buys 100-150 mss/year. Query with published clips. Pays $35-200. Some-
times pays the expenses of writers on assignment.
Photos: Richard McCaffrey, photo editor. State availability of photos. Reviews b&w contact sheets. Pays
$15-30 for 5x7 or 8x10 b&w prints; $50-150 for 5x7 or 8x10 color prints. Identification of subjects required.
Buys one-time rights.
Columns/Departments: Industry News, Radio and Media News, Video, and Film. Buys 20 mss/year. Query with published clips. Length: 1,000-3,000 words. Pays variable rates.

Tips: "A good selection of clips and a crisply written cover letter always gets a response. Most of our major profiles are freelance. They are *assigned* however; so query first. Avoid first-person journalism when writing about another individual or group. At the same time, inject plenty of spirit and personality into features. Our main need at this time is in the area of video."

BLUEGRASS UNLIMITED, Bluegrass Unlimited, Inc., Box 111, Broad Run VA 22014. (703)361-8992. Editor: Peter V. Kuykendall. 80% freelance written. Monthly magazine on bluegrass and old-time country music. Circ. 19,500. Pays on publication. Publishes ms an average of 4 months after acceptance. Byline given. Kill fee negotiated. Buys first North American serial rights, one-time rights, all rights, and second serial (reprint) rights. Submit seasonal/holiday material 4 months in advance. Photocopied submissions OK. Computer printout submissions acceptable. Reports in 2 weeks on queries; 2 months on mss. Free sample copy and writer's guidelines.
Nonfiction: General interest, historical/nostalgic, how-to, interview/profile, personal experience, photo feature and travel. No "fan" style articles. Buys 75-80 mss/year. Query with or without published clips. No set word length. Pays 4-5¢/word.
Photos: State availability of photos or send photos with query. Reviews 35mm color transparencies and 3x5, 5x7, and 8x10 b&w and color prints. Pays $20-30 for b&w transparencies; $40-125 for color transparencies; $20-50 for b&w prints; and $40-125 for color prints. Identification of subjects required. Buys one-time rights and all rights.
Fiction: Ethnic and humorous. Buys 3-5 mss/year. Query. No set word length. Pays 4-5¢/word.
Tips: "We would prefer that articles be informational, based on personal experience or an interview with lots of quotes from subject, profile, humor, etc."

CINEMASCORE, The Film Music Journal, Fandom Unlimited Entrps., Box 70868, Sunnyvale CA 94086. (415)960-1151. Editor: Randall D. Larson. Magazine published twice annually covering music for motion pictures and television, history and criticism. "We are devoted to the review and appreciation on the art and technique of music for motion pictures, emphasizing interviews with industry professionals." Circ. 1,500. Pays 50% on acceptance; 50% on publication. Publishes ms an average of 1 year after acceptance. Byline given. Offers 50% kill fee. Buys first North American serial rights. Photocopied and previously published submissions (rarely) OK. Electronic submissions OK via ASCII File (prefer disk copy only after acceptance), but requires hard copy also. Computer printout submissions acceptable. Reports in 3 weeks on queries; 6 weeks on mss. Sample copy $2; writer's guidelines for SAE and 1 first class stamp.
Nonfiction: Interview/profile, technical, critique, musicological analysis and reviews. No general-type reviews. "We want *specific*, in-depth reviews and criticism, and perceptive, though not necessarily technical, analysis." Buys 5-10 mss/year. Query with published clips or send complete ms. Word length open. Pays $15-100 for major research articles; pays in subscriptions for shorter pieces and reviews.
Photos: State availability of photos. Prefers b&w prints. Payment considered part of ms. Identification of subjects required. Buys one-time rights.
Tips: "Have an interest in and knowledge of the use, history, and technique of movie music, and be able to contact industry professionals or insightfully examine their music in an analytical article/profile. Writers should be familiar with the publication before trying to break in. Be willing to buy a copy to ensure writer and publication are compatible."

CREEM, Suite 209, 210 S. Woodward Ave., Birmingham MI 48011. (313)642-8833. Editor: Dave DiMartino. 80% freelance written. Works with a small number of new/unpublished writers each year. Pays on publication. Publishes ms an average of 2 months after acceptance. Buys all rights. Computer printout submissions acceptable; no dot-matrix. Reports in 6 weeks.
Nonfiction: Short articles, mostly music-oriented. "Feature length stories are mostly staff written, but we're open for newcomers to break in with short pieces. Freelancers are used a lot in the Newbeats section. Please send queries and sample articles to Bill Holdship, submissions editor. We bill ourselves as 'America's Only Rock 'n' Roll Magazine'." Query. Pays $50 minimum for reviews, $300 minimum for full-length features. Sometimes pays the expenses of writers on assignment.
Photos: Freelance photos.
Tips: "You can't study the magazine too much—our stable of writers have all come from the ranks of our readers. The writer can save his time and ours by studying what we do print and producing similar copy that we can use immediately. Send short stuff—no epics on the first try. We really aren't a good market for the professional writer looking for another outlet—a writer has to be pretty obsessed with music and/or pop culture in order to be published in our book. We get people writing in for assignments who obviously have never even read the magazine, and that's totally useless to us."

‡EAR, Magazine of New Music, New Wilderness Foundation, Inc., Room 208, 325 Spring St., New York NY 10013. (212)807-7944. Editor: Carol E. Tuynman. 100% freelance written. A tabloid published 5 times per year for artists interested in the avant garde. Circ. 6,000. Publishes ms an average of 6 months after acceptance. Byline given. Writer holds rights. Submit seasonal/holiday material 6 months in advance. Computer printout submissions acceptable; prefers letter-quality to dot-matrix. Reports in 1 month on queries; 3 months on mss. Sample copy $2.

Nonfiction: Essay; how-to; humor (music related); interview/profile; new product; opinion; personal experience (musicians and composers only); photo feature; and technical. Special issues include Regionalism in New Music, Radio/Audio Art, and Special Edition Instruments. No general opinions or fiction. Buys 5 mss/year. Query. Length: 250-1,000 words. Pays $0-50 for assigned articles; pays $0-25 for unsolicited articles. "Usually we don't pay, or at most, a $25 honorarium is given." All published contributors receive 1 year subscription plus 3 copies of issue they are in.

Photos: Send photos with submission. Reviews 5x7 prints. Offers no additional payment for photos accepted with ms. Captions required. Buys one-time rights.

Columns/Departments: Radio (critical look at radio whether public or commercial, new music U.S. and international), 750 words; Healing Arts (how sound/music and related technologies are interfacing in the healing arts), 750 words; Artists of International Repute (profiles/interviews on music makers—composers or performers who are exerting influence on other musics either outside their style or outside their country), 1,000 words. Buys 5 mss/year. Pays $0-100 for radio only.

Fillers: Newsbreaks and short humor. Length: 25-100 words. Pays $0-10.

Tips: "Be knowledgable about contemporary music, be a clear writer, don't send poorly edited, messy material. We're not interested in the classical European music tradition."

FRETS MAGAZINE, GPI Publications, 20085 Stevens Creek Blvd., Cupertino CA 95014. (408)446-1105. Editor: Phil Hood. 60% freelance written. Monthly magazine for amateur and professional acoustic string music enthusiasts; for players, makers, listeners and fans. Country, jazz, classical, blues, pop and bluegrass. For instrumentalists interested in banjo, mandolin, guitar, violin, upright bass, dobro, dulcimer and others. Circ. open. Pays on acceptance. Publishes ms an average of 6 months after acceptance. Buys first serial rights. Submit seasonal/holiday material 6 months in advance. Computer printout submissions on 8½x11 sheets with legible type acceptable if not a photocopy or multiple submission. "All-caps printout unacceptable." Reports in 6 weeks. Free sample copy and writer's guidelines.

Nonfiction: General interest (artist-oriented); historical (instrument making or manufacture); how-to (instrument craft and repair); interview (with artists or historically important individuals); profile (music performer); and technical (instrument making, acoustics, instrument repair). Prefers not to see humor; poetry; general-interest articles that really belong in a less-specialized publication; articles (about performers) that only touch on biographical or human interest angles, without getting into the 'how-to' nuts and bolts of musicianship. Buys 24 mss/year. Query with published clips or sample lead paragraph. Length: 1,000-2,500 words. Pays $125-300. Experimental (instrument design, acoustics). Pays $100-175. Sometimes pays expenses of writers on assignment.

Photos: State availability of photos. Pays $25 minimum for b&w prints (reviews contact sheets); $100 and up for cover shot color transparencies. Captions and credits required. Buys one-time rights.

Columns/Departments: Repair Shop (instrument craft and repair); and *Frets* Visits (on-location visit to manufacturer or major music festival). Buys 10 mss/year. Query. Length: 1,200-1,700 words. Pays $75-175, including photos.

Fillers: Newsbreaks, upcoming events and music-related news.

Tips: "Our focus also includes ancillary areas of string music—such as sound reinforcement for acoustic musicians, using personal computers in booking and management, recording techniques for acoustic music, and so on. We enjoy giving exposure (and encouragement) to talented new writers. We do not like to receive submissions or queries from writers who have only a vague notion of our scope and interest. We do not cover electric guitarists."

GUITAR PLAYER MAGAZINE, GPI Publications, 20085 Stevens Creek, Cupertino CA 95014. (408)446-1105. Editor: Tom Wheeler. 70% freelance written. Monthly magazine for persons "interested in guitars, guitarists, manufacturers, guitar builders, bass players, equipment, careers, etc." Circ. 170,000. Buys first serial and limited reprint rights. Pays on acceptance. Publishes ms an average of 5 months after acceptance. Byline given. Computer printout submissions acceptable; prefers letter-quality to dot-matrix. Reports in 6 weeks. Free sample copy.

Nonfiction: Publishes "wide variety of articles pertaining to guitars and guitarists: interviews, guitar craftsmen profiles, how-to features—anything amateur and professional guitarists would find fascinating and/or helpful. On interviews with 'name' performers, be as technical as possible regarding strings, guitars, techniques, etc. We're not a pop culture magazine, but a magazine for musicians." Also buys features on such subjects as a guitar museum, role of the guitar in elementary education, personal reminiscences of past greats, technical gadgets and how to work them, analysis of flamenco, etc." Buys 30-40 mss/year. Query. Length: open. Pays $100-300. Sometimes pays expenses of writers on assignment.

Photos: Photos purchased. Reviews b&w glossy prints. Pays $35-75. Buys 35mm color transparencies. Pays $250 (for cover only). Buys one time rights.

‡**HIT PARADER**, Charlton Publishing, Suite 808, 441 Lexington Ave., New York NY 10017. (212)370-0986. Editor: Andy Secher. Managing Editor: Anne Leighton. 65% freelance written. A monthly magazine covering music—heavy metal and hard rock. "We're geared to the kids who love heavy metal music. Sometimes we like a little controversy in our articles, where one performer knocks another performer. There can't be any fact inaccuracy in any articles, because the kids know when there's a wrong fact." Circ. 500,000. Pays on publication. Byline given. Buys all rights. Submit seasonal material 3 months in advance—"seasonal material defined by who has a record or tour happening. We have a 3 month lead time." Photocopied submissions OK. Reports in 6 weeks on queries. Sample copy for 8½x11 SAE with 6 first class stamps; "writer's guidelines are given when the assignment is given."
Nonfiction: Interview/profile. No articles that are not on hard rock or heavy metal. Also, no more articles against the PMRC or 'God vs the devil—is rock evil?' " Buys 80 mss/year. Query with published clips. Length: 250-1,000 words. Pays $70-120.
Photos: "We get photos from separate sources—photographers, publicists." Reviews slides. Offers $30-70/photo.
Columns/Departments: "Our four columns are Instrumentally Speaking, Rate a Record, Artists Top Ten and Shooting Stars. If someone comes out with a new angle we wouldn't ignore it and might be interested." Query with published clips. Payment negotiable.
Tips: "Be aware of the music. We tell all young writers to interview every band that comes to their town and write-write-write for every music tabloid they can find. Once you get the first piece of feedback from Andy Secher, stay in touch with him with heavy metal/hard rock interviews you've done. Sometimes he'll give you an assignment. Love the music. Be hungry to learn more."

ILLINOIS ENTERTAINER, Box 356, Mount Prospect IL 60056. (312)298-9333. Editor: Guy C. Arnston. 95% freelance written. Prefers to work with published/established writers. Monthly tabloid covering music and entertainment for consumers within 100-mile radius of Chicago interested in music. Circ. 80,000. Pays on publication. Publishes ms an average of 2 months after acceptance. Byline given. Offers 100% kill fee. Buys one-time rights. Submit seasonal/holiday material 2 months in advance. Simultaneous queries OK. Computer printout submissions acceptable "if letters are clear"; no dot-matrix. Reports in 1 week on queries; 1 month on mss. Sample copy $2; free writer's guidelines.
Nonfiction: Interview/profile (of entertainment figures). No Q&A interviews. Buys 200 mss/year. Query with published clips. Length: 500-2,000 words. Pays $15-100. Sometimes pays expenses of writers on assignment.
Photos: State availability of photos. Pays $10-20 for 5x7 or 8x10 b&w prints; $100 for color cover photo, both on publication only. Captions and identification of subjects required.
Columns/Departments: Software (record reviews stress record over band or genre); film reviews; and book reviews. Buys 500 mss/year. Query with published clips. Length: 150-250 words. Pays $6-20.
Tips: "Send samples in mail (published or unpublished) with phone number, and be patient. Articles and fillers offer freelancers the best chance of breaking in, as full staff has seniority. If you know the ins and outs of the entertainment biz, and can balance that knowledge with a broad sense of humor, then you'll do."

INTERNATIONAL MUSICIAN, American Federation of Musicians, Suite 600, Paramount Building, 1501 Broadway, New York NY 10036. (212)869-1330. Editor: Kelly L. Castleberry II. Monthly for professional musicians. Pays on acceptance. Byline given. Reports in 2 months.
Nonfiction: Articles on prominent instrumental musicians (classical, jazz, rock or country). Send complete ms. Length: 1,500-2,000 words.

‡**JAM, The Music Magazine**, Gwenny Lenny Corporation, Box 110322, Arlington TX 76007. (817)540-2113. Editor: David C. Huff, Jr. Managing Editor: Bev Owens. 20% freelance written. Eager to work with new/unpublished writers. A monthly music magazine covering rock, jazz, country and new music. "Write your story so a 12 year old could understand it, but you don't offend the intelligence of a 25 year old." Circ. 20,000. Pays on acceptance. Publishes ms an average of 2 months after acceptance. Byline given. Buys second serial (reprint) rights or makes work-for-hire assignments. Submit seasonal/holiday material 2 months in advance. Previously published submissions OK. Computer printout submissions acceptable; prefers letter-quality to dot-matrix. Reports in 2 weeks on queries. Free sample copy.
Columns/Departments: *Jam* Movie Review (an in-depth look at current releases), and *Jam* Album Review (an in-depth album review of current releases, "intelligently written"). Buys 15 mss/year. Query with published clips. Length: 250-1,500 words. Pays $25.
Tips: "Absolutely no *Circus* or *Creem* types of article submissions taken. Well written, humorous or even funny stories acceptable. No mindless who, what, where stories. Feature and album reviews are most open to freelancer."

KEYBOARD MAGAZINE, GPI Publications, 20085 Stevens Creek Blvd., Cupertino CA 95014. (408)446-1105. Editor: Dominic Milano. 10% freelance written. Prefers to work with published/established writers.

Monthly magazine for those who play synthesizer, piano, organ, harpsichord, or any other keyboard instrument. All styles of music; all levels of ability. Circ. 70,000. Pays on acceptance. Publishes ms 1-6 months after acceptance. Byline given. Buys first serial rights and second serial (reprint) rights. Phone queries OK. Electronic submissions OK but "contact our offices for requirements, prefer not to receive unsolicited submissions via modem." Computer printout submissions acceptable; prefers letter-quality to dot-matrix. Reports in 2 weeks. Free sample copy and writer's guidelines.

Nonfiction: "We publish articles on a wide variety of topics pertaining to keyboard players and their instruments. In addition to interviews with keyboard artists in all styles of music, we are interested in historical and analytical pieces, how-to articles dealing either with music or with equipment (including MIDI and computers), profiles on well-known instrument makers and their products. In general, anything that amateur and professional keyboardists would find interesting and/or useful." Buys 20 unsolicited mss/year. Query: letter should mention topic and length of article and describe basic approach. "It's nice (but not necessary) to have a sample first paragraph." Length: approximately 2,000-5,000 words. Pays $100-350. Sometimes pays the expenses of writers on assignment.

Tips: "Query first (just a few ideas at a time, rather than twenty). A musical background helps, and a knowledge of keyboard instruments is valuable."

MODERN DRUMMER, 870 Pompton Ave., Cedar Grove NJ 07009. (201)239-4140. Editor-in-Chief: Ronald Spagnardi. Features Editor: Rick Mattingly. Managing Editor: Rick Van Horn. Monthly for "student, semi-pro and professional drummers at all ages and levels of playing ability, with varied specialized interests within the field." 60% freelance written. Circ. 50,000. Pays on publication. Publishes ms an average of 3 months after acceptance. Buys all rights. Photocopied and previously published submissions OK. Computer printout submissions acceptable; prefers letter-quality to dot-matrix. Reports in 1 month. Sample copy $2.75; free writer's guidelines.

Nonfiction: How-to, informational, interview, new product, personal experience and technical. "All submissions must appeal to the specialized interests of drummers." Buys 20-30 mss/year. Query or submit complete ms. Length: 5,000-8,000 words. Pays $200-500. Pays expenses of writers on assignment.

Photos: Purchased with accompanying ms. Reviews 8x10 b&w prints and color transparencies.

Columns/Departments: Jazz Drummers Workshop, Rock Perspectives, In The Studio, Show Drummers Seminar, Teachers Forum, Drum Soloist, The Jobbing Drummer, Strictly Technique, Book Reviews, and Shop Talk. "Technical knowledge of area required for most columns." Buys 40-50 mss/year. Query or submit complete ms. Length: 500-2,500 words. Pays $25-150.

MODERN PERCUSSIONIST, A Contemporary Magazine for the Serious Drummer/Percussionist, Modern Drummer Publications, Inc., 870 Pompton Ave., Cedar Grove NJ 07009. (201)239-4140. Editor: Rick Mattingly. Managing Editor: Susan Hannum. 50% freelance written. Works with a small number of new/unpublished writers each year. Quarterly magazine on percussion and percussionists. "Our audience includes percussionists at all levels from student to pro. Writers must have a good general knowledge of the field." Circ. 15,000. Pays on publication. Publishes ms an average of 6 months after acceptance. Byline given. Offers variable kill fee. Buys all rights. Simultaneous queries, and photocopied and previously published submissions OK. Computer printout submissions acceptable; no dot-matrix. Reports in 2 weeks on queries; 1 month on mss. Sample copy $2; writer's guidelines for legal size SAE and 1 first class stamp.

Nonfiction: Historical/nostalgic (performers and instruments from the past); how-to (building or repairing percussion instruments); interview/profile (professional players and teachers); new product (new percussion equipment); and technical (percussion techniques). No "fan-magazine" type articles. Buys 20 mss/year. Query with published clips. Length: 4,000-5,000 words. Pays $150-350. Sometimes pays expenses of writers on assignment.

Photos: David Creamer, photo editor. State availability of photos. Reviews b&w contact sheets and 8x10 prints; color transparencies. Pays $10-45 for b&w; $50-100 for color. Captions, model releases, and identification of subjects required.

Columns/Departments: Percussion Today (contemporary and avant-garde); Around The World (instruments and techniques from other countries); and Workshop (care and repair). Buys 12-15 mss/year. Query. Length: 750-1,500 words. Pays $25-100.

Tips: "Feature interviews with prominent performers is the area most open to freelancers."

MUSIC CITY NEWS, Suite 601, 50 Music Square W., Nashville TN 37203. (615)329-2200. Editor: Neil Pond. 5% freelance written. Monthly tabloid emphasizing country music. Circ. 100,000. Publishes ms an average of 2 months after acceptance. Buys all rights. Phone queries OK. Submit seasonal or holiday material 2 months in advance. Photocopied submissions OK. Computer printout submissions acceptable; prefers letter-quality to dot-matrix. Reports in 10 weeks. Free sample copy.

Nonfiction: "We publish interview articles with country music personalities, narrative/quote, focusing on new and fresh angles about the entertainer rather than biographical histories." Buys 5-10 unsolicited mss/year. Query. Length: 500-1,250 words. Pays $100-125/feature, $75/junior feature, and $50/vignettes.

Photos: Purchased on acceptance by assignment. Query. Pays $10 maximum for 8x10 b&w glossy prints.
Tips: "Stories need to be of interest to country music *fans* as well as *industry*."

MUSIC MAGAZINE, Barrett & Colgrass Inc., Suite 202, 56 The Esplanade, Toronto, Ontario M5E 1A7 Canada. (416)364-5938. Editor: Ulla Colgrass. 90% freelance written. Prefers to work with published/established writers; works with a small number of new/unpublished writers each year. Bimonthly magazine emphasizing classical music. Circ. 11,000. Pays on publication. Publishes ms an average of 4 months after acceptance. Byline given. Buys first North American rights, one-time rights, and second serial (reprint) rights. Phone queries OK. Submit seasonal/holiday material 4 months in advance. Photocopied and previously published submissions (book excerpts) OK. Computer printout submissions (double-spaced) acceptable; no dot-matrix. SAE, IRCs (no American stamps). Reports in 2 months. Sample copy and writer's guidelines $2.
Nonfiction: Interview, historical articles, photo feature and profile. "All articles should pertain to classical music and people in that world. We do not want any academic analysis or short pieces of family experiences in classical music." Query with published clips. Unsolicited articles will not be returned. Length: 1,500-3,500 words. Pays $100-500.
Photos: State availability of photos. Pays $15-25 for 8x10 b&w glossy prints or contact sheets; $100 for color transparencies. No posed promotion photos. "Candid lively material only." Buys one-time rights. Captions required.
Tips: "Send a sample of your writing with suggested subjects. Off-beat subjects are welcome but must be thoroughly interesting to be considered. A famous person or major subject in music are your best bets."

‡NIGHTLIFE, Concert News, Nightlife Enterprises, Inc., Box 6372, Moore OK 73153. (405)685-3675. Editor: Vernon L Gowdy III. 25% freelance written. Eager to work with new/unpublished writers. A monthly tabloid. "We cater to the 14-35 age group with special interest in rock and roll. We publish stories on current groups on tour; especially interviews." Circ. 10,000. Pays on publication. Publishes ms an average of 2 months after acceptance. Byline given. Offers $15 kill fee. Buys one-time rights. Submit seasonal/holiday material 3 months in advance. Simultaneous, photocopied, and previously published submissions OK. Computer printout submissions acceptable; no dot-matrix. Reports in 1 month. Free sample copy with SAE only.
Nonfiction: Interview/profile, and album reviews on occasion. Buys 8 mss/year. Send complete ms. Length 400-1,200 words. Pays $15-35.
Photos: State availability of photos with submissions. Reviews contact sheets. Offers $15-35/photo. Captions, model releases, and identification of subjects required.
Tips: "Only entertainment stories on rock and roll groups are used. Use good quotes and avoid 'Cheesecake, Star-Studded' stories."

OPERA CANADA, Suite 433, 366 Adelaide St. E., Toronto, Ontario M5A 3X9 Canada. (416)363-0395. Editor: Ruby Mercer. 80% freelance written. Prefers to work with published/established writers. Quarterly magazine for readers who are interested in serious music; specifically, opera. Circ. 7,000. Pays on publication. Publishes ms an average of 1 year after acceptance. Byline given. Not copyrighted. Buys first serial rights. Photocopied and simultaneous submissions OK. Computer printout submissions acceptable; no dot-matrix. Reports on material accepted for publication within 1 year. Returns rejected material in 1 month. SAE, IRCs. Sample copy $3.50.
Nonfiction: "Because we are Canada's only opera magazine, we like to keep 75% of our content Canadian, i.e., by Canadians or about Canadian personalities and events. We prefer informative and/or humorous articles about any aspect of music theater, with an emphasis on opera. The relationship of the actual subject matter to opera can be direct or indirect. We accept record reviews (*only* operatic recordings); book reviews (books covering any aspect of music theater); and interviews with major operatic personalities. Please, no reviews of performances; we have staff reviewers." Buys 10 mss/year. Query or submit complete ms. Length (for all articles except reviews of books and records): 1,000-3,000 words. Pays $50-200. Length for reviews: 100-500 words. Pays $15.
Photos: No additional payment for photos used with mss. Captions required.

OVATION, 320 W. 57th St., New York NY 10019. Editor: Frederick Selch. 75% freelance written. Monthly magazine for classical music listeners covering classical music and the equipment on which to hear it. Average issue includes 4 features plus departments. Pays on publication. Publishes ms an average of 6 months after acceptance. Byline given. Buys all rights. Submit seasonal material 4 months in advance. Computer printout submissions acceptable; no dot-matrix. Reports in 1 month. Sample copy $2.79.
Nonfiction: "We are primarily interested in interviews with and articles about the foremost classical music artists. Historical pieces will also be considered." Buys 5 unsolicited mss/year. Query with published clips. Length: 800-4,500 words. Pays $5/inch.
Photos: State availability of photos. May offer additional payment for photos accepted with ms. Captions required. Buys one-time rights.

PULSE!, Tower Records, 2500 Del Monte, Building C W. Sacramento CA 95691. (916)321-2450. Editor: Mike Farrace. Contact: Laurie MacIntosh or Jackson Brian Griffith. 80% freelance written. Monthly tabloid covering recorded music. Circ. 100,000. Pays on publication. Publishes ms an average of 2 months after acceptance. Byline given. Buys first serial rights. Simultaneous and photocopied submissions OK. Computer printout submissions acceptable; prefers letter-quality to dot-matrix. Reports in 5 weeks. Free sample copy; writer's guidelines for SAE.

Nonfiction: Feature stories and interview/profile (angled toward artist's taste in music, such as ten favorite albums, first record ever bought, anecdotes about early record buying experiences). Always looking for good hardware reviews, concise news items and commentary about nonpopular musical genres. Buys 200-250 mss/ year. Query or send complete ms. Length: 200-2,500 words. Pays $20-500. Sometimes pays expenses of writers on asignment.

Photos: State availability of photos. Color transparencies preferred, but will also review b&w prints. Caption and identification of subjects required. Buys one-time rights.

Fillers: Newsbreaks.

Tips: "Break in with 200-500 word news-oriented featurettes on recording artists or on fast breaking, record-related news, personnel changes, unusual match-ups, reissues of great material. Any kind of music. The more obscure genres are the hardest for us to cover, so they stand a good chance of being used. Writers have a better chance writing articles and fillers. Less copy means easier rewrites, and less guilt when we don't like it, thereby making the relationship with the writer easier, more honest and ultimately more productive. We are not only a magazine about records, but one that is owned by a record retailer."

RELIX MAGAZINE, Music for the Mind, Relix Magazine, Inc., Box 94, Brooklyn NY 11229. (212)645-0818. Editor: Toni A. Brown. 90% freelance written. Bimonthly magazine covering rock 'n' roll music and specializing in Grateful Dead, and other San Francisco and 60's related groups for readers ages 15-45. Circ. 20,000. Pays on publication. Publishes ms an average of 6 months after acceptance. Byline given. Buys all rights. Photocopied submissions OK. Computer printout submissions acceptable; prefers letter-quality to dot-matrix. Sample copy $2.

Nonfiction: Historical/nostalgic, interview/profile, new product, personal experience, photo feature and technical. Special issues include November photo special. Query with published clips if available or send complete ms. Length open. Pays variable rates.

Columns/Departments: Query with published clips, if available or send complete ms. Length: open. Pays variable rates.

Fiction: Query with clips of published work, if available, or send complete ms. Length: open. Pays variable rates. "We are seeking science fiction, rock and roll stories for a potential book."

Tips: "The most rewarding aspects of working with freelance writers are fresh writing and new outlooks."

‡ROCK & SOUL, Charlton Publications, Suite 808, 441 Lexington Ave., New York NY 10017. (212)370-0986. Editor: Charley Crespo. Managing Editor: Ann Leighton. 80% freelance written. A monthly magazine covering black music and black entertainment. Circ. 100,000. Pays on publication. Publishes ms an average of 3 months after acceptance. Byline given. 50% kill fee. Buys one-time rights and second serial (reprint) rights. Submit seasonal/holiday material 4 months in advance. Simultaneous, photocopied and previously published submissions OK. Computer printout submissions acceptable; prefers letter-quality to dot-matrix. Reports in 1 month. Free sample copy.

Nonfiction: Book excerpts (music topics), interview/profile (80% of the magazine) and photo feature. No record reviews, articles on unknown recording artists, movie reviews, TV reviews or fiction. Buys 150 mss/year. Query with published clips. Length: 750-2,000 words. Pays $70-225.

Photos: State availability of photos with submission. Reviews transparencies and prints. Offers $30-200 when photos are used. Unused photos are returned. "We do not pay for publicity freebie shots sent by the writer."

Columns/Departments: Newsmakers (stays on a current events topic; not a profile), 750-1,500 words. Buys 25 mss/year. Query with published clips. Pays $70-125.

Tips: "We never use articles that simply flatter a recording artist. Use objectivity when writing about an entertainer. Almost the entire publication is written by freelancers, but most are regular freelancers, contributing every month or almost every month, and many have been with us for years. A writer new to us must submit clips of published work and a strong pitch for a particular idea. We look forward to hearing from writers."

ROCKBILL, Rave Communications, Suite 1201, 850 7th Ave., New York NY 10019. (212)977-7745. Editor: Robert Edelstein. Art Director/Editor: Cliff Sloan. 30% freelance written. Monthly magazine focusing on rock music and related topics for distribution at rock music clubs. Circ. 530,000. Pays on publication. Publishes ms an average of 2 months after acceptance. Byline given. Buys one-time rights. Simultaneous queries OK. Computer printout submissions acceptable; no dot-matrix. No guarantee on return of submissions. Free sample.

Nonfiction: Interview/profile, lifestyle and new music articles. "We're primarily interested in new artists on the verge. We try to cover interesting topics related to music on a grand scope before anyone else has written

about it." Buys 50 mss/year. Length: 500-1,000 words. Pays $25-75.
Photos: Uses color transparencies only. Identification of subjects required. No guarantee of returns.
Columns/Departments: Fashion, electronics, movies, jazz, country music, classical music, international music, classic album reviews, essays on cities, science and technology, new age-related topics, video, radio, essays on youth, brief interviews with notables, satire, travel, etc. Length: 500-800 words. Innervisions ("essays dealing with the way music affects your daily life or the way music has changed you"), 400-1,200 words.
Tips: "We try to publish at least one new writer per issue. Our best advice is to write with as much feeling as possible; think in terms of the big as well as the small, the apparent as well as the hidden, the molecular as well as the universal. The best way into our hearts is to write with integrity about something important to you and to everyone. And, remember, we're a small magazine in page size only. Our mottos are 'More with Less' and 'Dare to be Naive'."

ROLLING STONE, 745 5th Ave., New York NY 10151. Managing Editor: Robert Wallace. 25-50% freelance written. Biweekly tabloid/magazine on contemporary music and lifestyle. "We seldom accept freelance material. All our work is assigned or done by our staff." Byline given. Offers 25% kill fee. Buys first rights only.
Nonfiction: Seeks new general interest topics. Queries must be concise, no longer than 2 pages. Send queries about musicians and music industry to music editor. Writers knowledgeable about computers, VCRs, or sound equipment can submit an idea for the technology column that ranges from 50-word picture captions to 750-word pieces. Does not provide writer's guidelines; recommends reading *Rolling Stone* before submitting query.

THE $ENSIBLE SOUND, 403 Darwin Dr., Snyder NY 14226. Editor/Publisher: John A. Horan. 20% freelance written. Quarterly magazine. "All readers are high fidelity enthusiasts, and many have a high fidelity industry-related job." Circ. 5,200. Pays on acceptance. Publishes ms an average of 3 months after acceptance. Byline given. Buys all rights. Simultaneous, photocopied, and previously published submissions OK. Computer printout submissions OK *if triple spaced*; prefers letter-quality to dot-matrix. Reports in 2 weeks. Sample copy $2.
Nonfiction: Expose; how-to; general interest; humor; historical; interview (people in hi-fi business, manufacturers or retail); new product (all types of new audio equipment); nostalgia (articles and opinion on older equipment); personal experience (with various types of audio equipment); photo feature (on installation, or how-to tips); profile (of hi-fi equipment); and technical (pertaining to audio). "Subjective evaluations of hi-fi equipment make up 70% of our publication. We will accept 10/issue." Buys 2 mss/issue. Submit outline. Pays $25 maximum. Sometimes pays expenses of writers on assignment.
Columns/Departments: Bits & Pieces (short items of interest to hi-fi hobbyists); Ramblings (do-it-yourself tips on bettering existing systems); and Record Reviews (of records which would be of interest to audiophiles). Query. Length: 25-400 words. Pays $10/page.

‡SONG HITS, Charlton Publications, Charlton Bldg., Division St., Derby CT 06418. (203)735-3381. Editor: Mary Jane Canetti. Associate Editor: Jo Ann Sardo. 75% freelance written. A monthly magazine covering recording artists—rock, pop, soul and country. "*Song Hits* readers are between the ages of 10 and 21. Our philosophy in writing is to gear our material toward what is currently popular with our audience." Circ. 175,000. Pays on publication. Publishes ms an average of 3 months after acceptance. Byline given. Offers 25% kill fee. Buys all rights. Simultaneous and photocopied submissions OK. Computer printout submissions acceptable; prefers letter-quality to dot-matrix. Reports in 2 weeks. Free sample copy and writer's guidelines.
Nonfiction: Interview/profile. "We are not interested in articles about pop and rock people that are too adult for our young audience." Buys 60 mss/year. Query with published clips. Length: 1,250-3,000 words. Pays $150. Sometimes pays the expenses of writers on assignment.
Photos: State availability of photos with submission. Reviews contact sheets, 2x2 transparencies and 8x10 prints. Offers $15-30/photo. Identification of subjects required. Buys one-time rights.
Columns/Departments: Concert Review (current reviews of popular touring groups), and Pick of the Litter (album reviews of current and/or up and coming talent; 8-10 per issue). Buys 15 mss/year. Query with published clips. Length: 500-1,000 words. Pays $75.

‡STEREO REVIEW, CBS Magazines, 1 Park Ave., New York NY 10016. (212)503-5050. Editor: William Livingstone. Managing Editor: Louise Boundas. A monthly magazine. Circ. 550,000. Pays on publication. Publishes ms an average of 5 months after acceptance. Byline given. Buys first North American serial rights, first rights, or all rights. Computer printout submissions acceptable. Sample copy available.
Nonfiction: Technical and music interview/profile. Buys approximately 25 mss/year. Query with published clips. Length: 1,500-3,000 words. Pays $350-750 for assigned articles.

TRADITION, Prairie Press, 106 Navajo, Council Bluffs IA 51501. (712)366-1136. Editor: Robert Everhart. 20% freelance written. Quarterly magazine emphasizing traditional country music and other aspects of pioneer living. Circ. 2,500. Pays on publication. Not copyrighted. Byline given. Buys one-time rights. Submit seasonal/holiday material 6 months in advance. Simultaneous queries, and simultaneous, photocopied, and previously published submissions OK. Computer printout submissions acceptable. Reports in 1 month. Free sample copy.

Nonfiction: Historical (relating to country music); how-to (play, write, or perform country music); inspirational (on country gospel); interview (with country performers, both traditional and contemporary); nostalgia (pioneer living); personal experience (country music); and travel (in connection with country music contests or festivals). Query. Length: 800-1,200 words. Pays $25-50.

Photos: State availability of photos with query. Payment included in ms price. 5x7 b&w prints. Captions and model releases required. Buys one-time rights.

Poetry: Free verse and traditional. Buys 4 poems/year. Length: 5-20 lines. Submit maximum 2 poems. Pays $2-5.

Fillers: Clippings, jokes and anecdotes. Buys 5/year. Length: 15-50 words. Pays $5-10.

Tips: "Material must be concerned with what we term 'real' country music as opposed to today's 'pop' country music. Freelancer must be knowledgeable of the subject; many writers don't even know who the father of country music is, let alone write about him."

Mystery

These magazines buy fictional accounts of crime, detective work and mystery. Additional mystery markets can be found in the Literary and "Little" category of this book. Several magazines in the Detective and Crime category (nonfictional accounts) also buy mystery fiction. Skim through other sections to identify markets for fiction; some will buy mysteries too.

ALFRED HITCHCOCK'S MYSTERY MAGAZINE, Davis Publications, Inc., 380 Lexington Ave., New York NY 10017. Editor: Cathleen Jordan. Magazine published 13 times a year emphasizing mystery fiction. Circ. 200,000. Pays on acceptance. Byline given. Buys first serial rights, second serial (reprint) rights and foreign rights. Submit seasonal/holiday material 7 months in advance. Photocopied submissions OK. Reports in 2 months or less. Writer's guidelines for SASE.

Fiction: Original and well-written mystery and crime fiction. Length: 1,000-14,000 words.

ELLERY QUEEN'S MYSTERY MAGAZINE, Davis Publications, Inc., 380 Lexington Ave., New York NY 10017. Editor: Eleanor Sullivan. 100% freelance written. Magazine published 13 times/year. Circ. 375,000. Pays on acceptance. Publishes ms an average of 6 months after acceptance. Byline given. Buys first serial rights or second serial (reprint) rights. Submit seasonal/holiday material 7 months in advance. Simultaneous, photocopied, and previously published submissions OK. Computer printout submissions acceptable; prefers letter-quality to dot-matrix. Reports in 1 month. Writer's guidelines for SASE.

Fiction: Special consideration will be given to "anything timely and original. We publish every type of mystery: the suspense story, the psychological study, the deductive puzzle—the gamut of crime and detection from the realistic (including stories of police procedure) to the more imaginative (including 'locked rooms' and impossible crimes). We always need detective stories but do not want sex, sadism or sensationalism-for-the-sake-of-sensationalism." No gore or horror; seldom publishes parodies or pastiches. Buys 13 mss/issue. Length: 6,000 words maximum; occasionally higher but not often. Pays 3-8¢/word.

Tips: "We have a department of First Stories to encourage writers whose fiction has never before been in print. We publish an average of 13 first stories a year."

‡THE NEW BLACK MASK QUARTERLY, Harcourt Brace Jovanovich/Harvest Imprint, 2006 Sumter St., Columbia SC 29201. (803)771-4642. Co-Editors: Matthew J. Bruccoli and Richard Layman. 100% freelance written. A quarterly "bookazine," a revival of old *Black Mask*; slanted to hard-boiled mystery and detective fiction. Estab. 1985. Pays on publication. Publishes ms an average of 4 months after acceptance. Byline given. Buys first serial worldwide rights. Simultaneous and photocopied submissions OK. Computer printout submissions acceptable; prefers letter-quality to dot-matrix. Reports in 3 weeks on queries; 6 weeks on mss. Writer's guidelines for SASE.

Fiction: Adventure, mystery, novel excerpts and suspense. Buys 25 mss/year. Query with published clips. Length: 2,000-10,000 words. Pays negotiable rates.

Close-up

Richard Layman
Co-editor and Publisher
New Black Mask

In the twenties and thirties, when gangsters were a constant topic in the news and prohibition encouraged many average citizens to disobey the law, H. L. Mencken's pulp magazine, *Black Mask*, flourished. The magazine offered readers hard-boiled detective fiction and gave talented new writers a place to display their skills. Although some frowned on mystery/detective fiction as mere escapism, *Black Mask* had a loyal following until it folded in 1951. Issues of the pulp magazine are now considered literary treasures.

In 1984, William Jovanovich approached publishers Richard Layman and Matthew Bruccoli with the proposal that the two revive *Black Mask*. *New Black Mask* would be receptive to new talent and would publish quality mystery fiction, as the old *Black Mask* had. In doing so, the *New Black Mask* would also meet with the same criticism of its subject matter. "The idea of mystery fiction as simply a literature of escape is being shown to be a foolish misconception," says Richard Layman.

The emphasis at *New Black Mask* is on quality. Layman finds that the most serious difficulty is with the writer's perception of the mystery/detective genre. "I think many writers who approach a genre think of their material in terms of the cliches of the genre. Writers end up placing restrictions on themselves that are needless, in our case at least, and are also damaging to the material. Our position is that we publish stories about crime. We're uncomfortable with the term genre fiction. It implies there are certain rules and, by extension, that there are certain restrictions on the material . . . and on good imaginative, daring fiction. *New Black Mask* stories are characterized by their subject matter; they deal with the most compelling subjects of our lives—crime, death, and mutations of normal behavior, if you will."

Though Layman looks for fiction that is not limited by genre restrictions, he doesn't think writers can risk being careless with plot and characterization. "The plot should be plausible; it will probably be unusual, but it *must* be believable," says Layman. "We do not like stories about the supernatural or about super cops and master criminals. We expect a certain amount of detail in the plot and characterization. If a story and characters are interesting enough to attract a reader's attention, he normally wants to know details—where a story is located; what the weather is; how the characters speak, dress, move, and think."

For beginning mystery writers, Layman has four kinds of advice. "First, read widely. You can certainly read the masters of American crime fiction—Hammett, Chandler, and Ross Macdonald. But don't restrict your reading to that. Read Fitzgerald, Hemingway, John Dos Passos, and contemporary fiction as well. The more you read, the better you write.

"Second, once you've read all this material, don't try to imitate it. Try to find an original and imaginative voice. We like to see originality, not imitation of the masters.

"Third, simply try to tell good stories. The skills and qualities necessary for good mystery fiction are the same as for any other fiction—knowledge of the material, the ability to observe keenly, a facility with language, and intelligence.

"And, finally, the best way to learn how to write is to practice."

—Sheila Freeman

———— *Nature, Conservation and Ecology*

These publications promote reader awareness of the natural environment, wildlife, nature preserves and ecosystems. They do not publish recreation or travel articles except as they relate to conservation or nature. Other markets for this kind of material can be found in the Regional, Sports, and Travel, Camping, and Trailer categories, although the magazines listed there require that nature or conservation articles be slanted to their specialized subject matter and audience. Some juvenile and teen publications such as *National Geographic World* buy nature-related material for young audiences. Energy conservation topics for professionals are covered in the Trade Energy category.

AMERICAN FORESTS, American Forestry Association, 1319 18th St. NW, Washington DC 20036. (202)467-5810. Editor: Bill Rooney. 70% freelance-written. Monthly magazine. "The magazine of trees and forests, published by a citizens' organization for the advancement of intelligent management and use of our forests, soil, water, wildlife, and all other natural resources necessary for an environment of high quality." Circ. 40,000. Pays on acceptance. Publishes ms an average of 8 months after acceptance. Byline given. Buys one-time rights. Phone queries OK but written queries preferred. Submit seasonal/holiday material 5 months in advance. Computer printout submissions acceptable; no dot-matrix. Reports in 6-8 weeks. Sample copy $1; writer's guidelines for SAE and 1 first class stamp.
Nonfiction: General interest, historical, how-to, humor and inspirational. All articles should emphasize trees, forests, forestry and related issues. Buys 5 mss/issue. Query. Length: 2,000 words. Pays $200-400.
Photos: State availability of photos. Offers no additional payment for photos accompanying ms. Uses 8x10 b&w glossy prints; 35mm or larger color transparencies, originals only. Captions required. Buys one-time rights.
Tips: "Query should have honesty and information on photo support."

THE ATLANTIC SALMON JOURNAL, The Atlantic Salmon Federation, Suite 1030, 1435 St. Alexandre, Montreal, Quebec H3A 2G4 Canada. (514)842-8059. Editor: Joanne Eidinger. 75% freelance written. Works with a small number of new/unpublished writers each year. A quarterly magazine covering conservation efforts for the Atlantic salmon for an "affluent and responsive audience—the dedicated angler and conservationist of the Atlantic salmon." Circ. 20,000. Pays on publication. Publishes ms an average of 6 months after acceptance. Byline given. Buys first serial rights to articles and one-time rights to photos. Submit seasonal/holiday material 3 months in advance. Simultaneous queries, and simultaneous and photocopied submissions OK. Electronic submissions OK on Micom floppy disk, but requires hard copy also. Computer printout submissions acceptable; prefers letter-quality to dot matrix. Reports in 6-8 weeks. Sample copy for SAE and 64¢ (Canadian), or SAE with IRC; free writer's guidelines.
Nonfiction: Expose, historical/nostalgic, how-to, humor, interview/profile, new product, opinion, personal experience, photo feature, technical, travel, conservation, cuisine, science and management. "We are seeking articles that are pertinent to the focus and purpose of our magazine, which is to inform and entertain our membership on all aspects of the Atlantic salmon and its environment, preservation and conservation." Buys 15-20 mss/year. Query with published clips and state availability of photos. Length: 1,500-3,000 words. Pays $100-325. Sometimes pays the expenses of writers on assignment.
Photos: State availability of photos with query. Pays $35-50 for 3x5 or 5x7 b&w prints; $35-150 for 2¼x3¼ or 16mm color slides. Captions and identification of subjects required.
Columns/Departments: Adventure Eating (cuisine); First Person (nonfiction, anecdotal, from first person viewpoint, can be humorous). Buys about 6 mss/year. Length: 1,000-1,500 words. Pays $175.
Fiction: Adventure, fantasy, historical, humorous and mainstream. "We don't want to see anything that does not deal with Atlantic salmon directly or indirectly. Wilderness adventures are acceptable as long as they deal with Atlantic salmon." Buys 3 ms/year. Query with published clips. Length: 3,000 words maximum. Pays $150-325.
Fillers: Clippings, jokes, anecdotes and short humor. Length: 100-300 words average. Does not pay. Cartoons, single or multi-panel, $35-75.

Tips: "Articles must reflect informed and up-to-date knowledge of Atlantic salmon. Writers need not be authorities, but research must be impeccable. Clear, concise writing is a plus, and submissions must be typed. Anecdote, River Log and photo essays are most open to freelancers. The odds are that a writer without a background in outdoors writing and wildlife reporting will not have the 'informed' angle I'm looking for. Our readership is well-read and critical of simplification and generalization. I will be purchasing more freelance material due to an expanded editorial budget."

BIRD WATCHER'S DIGEST, Pardson Corp., Box 110, Marietta OH 45750. Editor: Mary Beacom Bowers. 60% freelance written. Works with a small number of new/unpublished writers each year. Bimonthly magazine covering natural history—birds and bird watching. "*BWD* is a nontechnical magazine interpreting ornithological material for amateur observers, including the knowledgable birder, the serious novice and the backyard bird watcher; we strive to provide good reading and good ornithology." Circ. 45,000. Pays on publication. Publishes ms up to 2 years after acceptance. Byline given. Buys one-time rights, first serial rights and second serial (reprint) rights. Submit seasonal/holiday material 6 months in advance. Previously published submissions OK. Computer printout submissions acceptable; no dot-matrix. Reports in 6 weeks. Sample copy $2; writer's guidelines for #10 SAE and 1 first class stamp.
Nonfiction: Book excerpts, how-to (relating to birds, feeding and attracting, etc.), humor, personal experience and travel (limited—we get many). "We are especially interested in fresh, lively accounts of closely observed bird behavior and displays and of bird watching experiences and expeditions. We often need material of less common species or on unusual or previously unreported behavior of common species." No articles on pet or caged birds; none on raising a baby bird. Buys 75-90 mss/year. Send complete ms. Length: 600-3,500 words. Pays $25-50.
Photos: Send photos with ms. Pays $10 minimum for b&w prints; $25 minimum for color transparencies. Buys one-time rights.
Poetry: Avant-garde, free verse, light verse and traditional. No haiku. Buys 12-18 poems/year. Submit maximum 3 poems. Length 8-20 lines. Pays $10.
Tips: "We are aimed at an audience ranging from the backyard bird watcher to the very knowledgable birder; we include in each issue material that will appeal at various levels. We always strive for a good geographical spread, with material from every section of the country. We leave very technical matters to others, but we want facts and accuracy, depth and quality, directed at the veteran bird watcher and at the enthusiastic novice. We stress the joys and pleasures of bird watching, its environmental contribution, and its value for the individual and society."

‡ENVIRONMENT, 4000 Albemarle St. NW., Washington DC 20016. Managing Editor: Jane Scully. 2% freelance written. For citizens, scientists, business and government executives, teachers, high school and college students interested in environment or effects of technology and science in public affairs. Magazine published 10 times/year. Circ. 17,000. Buys all rights. Byline given. Pays on publication to professional writers. Publishes ms an average of 5 months after acceptance. Photocopied submissions OK. Computer printout submissions acceptable; no dot-matrix. Reports in 6-8 weeks. Query or submit 3 double-spaced copies of complete ms. Sample copy $3.50.
Nonfiction: Scientific and environmental material, and effects of technology on society. Preferred length: 2,500-4,500 words for full-length article. Pays $100-300, depending on material. Also accepts shorter articles (1,100-1,700 words) for "Overview" section. Pays $75. "All full-length articles must be annotated (referenced), and all conclusions must follow logically from the facts and arguments presented." Prefers articles centering around policy-oriented, public decision-making, scientific and technological issues.

FORESTS & PEOPLE, Official Publication of the Louisiana Forestry Association, Louisiana Forestry Association, Drawer 5067, Alexandria LA 71301. (318)443-2558. Editor: Kathryn T. Johnston. 50% freelance written. Quarterly magazine covering forests, forest industry, wood-related stories, wildlife for general readers, both in and out of the forest industry. Circ. 8,500. Pays on acceptance. Publishes ms an average of 6 months after acceptance. Byline given. Not copyrighted. Submit seasonal/holiday material 2 months in advance. Simultaneous queries, and simultaneous, photocopied, and previously published submissions OK. Reports in 2 weeks on queries; 3 weeks on mss. Sample copy $1.75; free ms guidelines.
Nonfiction: "General interest (recreation, wildlife, crafts with wood, festivals); historical/nostalgic (logging towns, historical wooden buildings, forestry legends); interview/profile (of forest industry execs, foresters, loggers, wildlife managers, tree farmers); photo feature (of scenic forest, wetlands, logging operations); and technical (innovative equipment, chemicals, operations, forestland studies, or industry profiles). No research papers. Articles may cover a technical subject but must be understandable to the general public." Buys 12 mss/year. Query with published clips. Length: open. Pays $100.
Photos: State availability of photos. Reviews b&w and color slides. Identification of subjects required.

HIGH COUNTRY NEWS, High Country Foundation, Box 1090, Paonia CO 81428. (303)527-4898. Editor: Betsy Marston. 80% freelance written. Works with a small number of new/unpublished writers each year.

Biweekly tabloid covering environment and natural resource issues in the Rocky Mountain states for environmentalists, politicians, companies, college classes, government agencies, etc. Circ. 4,500. Pays on publication. Publishes ms an average of 2 months after acceptance. Byline given. Buys one-time rights and second serial (reprint) rights. Submit seasonal/holiday material 6 weeks in advance. Computer printout submissions acceptable if "double spaced (at least) and legible"; prefers letter-quality to dot-matrix. Reports in 1 month. Free sample copy and writer's guidelines.

Nonfiction: Reporting (local issues with regional importance); expose (government, corporate); interview/profile; opinion; personal experience; and centerspread photo feature. Special issues include those on states in the region. Buys 100 mss/year. Query. Length: 3,000 word maximum. Pays 5-10¢/word. Sometimes pays the expenses of writers on assignment.

Photos: Send photos with ms. Reviews b&w contact sheets and prints. Captions and identification of subjects required.

Poetry: Chip Rawlins, poetry editor, Box 51, Boulder WY 82923. Avant-garde, free verse, haiku, light verse and traditional. Pays in contributor copies.

Tips: "We use a lot of freelance material, though very little from outside the Rockies. Start by writing short, 500-word news items of timely, regional interest."

INTERNATIONAL WILDLIFE, National Wildlife Federation, 1412 16th St. NW, Washington DC 20036. Managing Editor: Jonathan Fisher. 85% freelance written. Prefers to work with published/established writers. Bimonthly for persons interested in natural history, outdoor adventure and the environment. Circ. 400,000. Publishes ms an average of 4 months after acceptance. Usually buys all rights to text; usually one-time rights to photos and art. Pays on acceptance. "We are now assigning most articles but will consider detailed proposals for quality feature material of interest to a broad audience." Computer printout submissions acceptable; dislikes poor-quality dot-matrix. Reports in 6 weeks.

Nonfiction: Focuses on world wildlife, environmental problems and man's relationship to the natural world as reflected in such issues as population control, pollution, resource utilization, food production, etc. Especially interested in articles on animal behavior and other natural history, first-person experiences by scientists in the field, well-reported coverage of wildlife-status case studies which also raise broader themes about international conservation, and timely issues. Query. Length: 2,000-2,500 words. Also in the market for short, 750-word "one pagers." Examine past issue for style and subject matter. Pays $750 minimum. Sometimes pays expenses of writers on assignment.

Photos: Purchases top-quality color photos; prefers packages of related photos and text, but single shots of exceptional interest and sequences also considered. Prefers Kodachrome transparencies.

Tips: "Send us a detailed query that will speak for itself; if we respond favorably, the writer's plugged in."

‡MICHIGAN NATURAL RESOURCES MAGAZINE, State of Michigan Department of Natural Resources, Box 30034, Lansing MI 48909. (517)373-9267. Editor: N.R. McDowell. Managing Editor: Richard Morscheck. 60% freelance written. Works with a small number of new/unpublished writers each year. Bimonthly magazine covering natural resources in the Great Lakes area. Circ. 125,000. Pays on acceptance. Publishes ms an average of 6 months after acceptance. Byline given. Offers 100% kill fee. Buys first rights only. Submit seasonal/holiday material 1 year in advance. Computer printout submissions acceptable; no dot-matrix. Reports in 1 month. Sample copy for $2.50 and 9x12 SAE; writer's guidelines for business size SAE and 1 first class stamp.

Nonfiction: "All material must pertain to this region's natural resources: lakes, rivers, wildlife, flora and special features. No personal experience, domestic animal stories or animal rehabilitation." Buys 24 mss/year. Query with clips of published work or send complete ms. Length: 1,000-4,000 words. Pays $150-400. Sometimes pays the expenses of writers on assignment.

Photos: Gijsbert (Nick) vanFrankenhuyzen, photo editor. "Photos submitted with an article can help sell it, but they must be razor sharp in focus." Send photos with ms. Pays $50-200 for 35mm color transparencies. Model releases and identification of subjects required. Buys one-time rights.

NATIONAL PARKS, 1701 18th St. NW, Washington DC 20009. (202)265-2717. Senior Editor: Michele Strutin. 75% freelance written. Prefers to work with published/established writers. Bimonthly magazine for a highly educated audience interested in preservation of National Park System Units, natural areas and protection of wildlife habitat. Circ. 40,000. Pays on acceptance. Publishes ms an average of 6 months after acceptance. Buys first North American serial rights and second serial (reprint) rights. Submit seasonal/holiday material 5 months in advance. Electronic submissions acceptable via IBM XYWrite, but prefers hard copy also. Computer printout submissions acceptable if legible; prefers letter-quality to dot-matrix. Reports in 10 weeks. Sample copy $3; writer's guidelines for SASE.

Nonfiction: Expose (on threats, wildlife problems to national parks); descriptive articles about new or proposed national parks and wilderness parks; brief natural history pieces describing park geology, wildlife, or plants; "adventures" in national parks (crosscountry skiing, bouldering, mountain climbing, kayaking, canoeing, backpacking); and travel tips to national parks. All material must relate to national parks. No poetry or philosophical essays. Buys 6-10 unsolicited mss/year. Query or send complete ms. Length: 1,000-1,500 words. Pays $75-200.

Photos: State availability of photos or send photos with ms. Pays $25-50 for 8x10 b&w glossy prints; $35-100 for color transparencies; offers no additional payment for photos accompanying ms. Captions required. Buys first North American serial rights.

NATIONAL WILDLIFE, National Wildlife Federation, 8925 Leesburg Pike, Vienna VA 22184. (703)790-4510. Editor: John Strohm. Managing Editor: Mark Wexler. 75% freelance written. Works with a small number of new/unpublished writers each year. Bimonthly magazine on wildlife, natural history and environment. "Our purpose is to promote wise use of the nation's natural resources and to conserve and protect wildlife and its habitat. We reach a broad audience that is largely interested in wildlife conservation and nature photography. We avoid too much scientific detail and prefer anecdotal, natural history material." Circ. 850,000. Pays on acceptance. Publishes ms an average of 6 months after acceptance. Offers 25% kill fee. Buys all rights. Submit seasonal/holiday material 8 months in advance. Photocopied submissions OK. Computer printout submissions acceptable; prefers letter-quality to dot-matrix. Reports in 6 weeks. Sample copy for magazine size SAE and 4 first class stamps; writer's guidelines for letter size SAE and 1 first class stamp.

Nonfiction: Book excerpts (nature related); general interest (2,500-word features on wildlife, new discoveries, behavior, or the environment); how-to (an outdoor or nature related activity); personal experience (outdoor adventure); photo feature (wildlife); and short 700-word features on an unusual individual or new scientific discovery relating to nature. Buys 50 mss/year. Query with or without published clips. Length: 750-2,500 words. Pays $500-1,750. Sometimes pays expenses of writers on assignment.

Photos: John Nuhn, photo editor. State availability of photos or send photos with query. Reviews 35mm color transparencies. Pays $250-750. Buys one-time rights.

Tips: "Writers can break in with us more readily by proposing subjects (initially) that will take only one or two pages in the magazine (short features)."

OCEANS, Ocean Magazine Associates, Inc., 2001 W. Main St., Stamford CT 06902. Editor: Michael Robbins. 100% freelance written. Prefers to work with published/established writers. Bimonthly magazine; 72 pages. For people who love the sea. Circ. 40,000. Pays on acceptance. Publishes ms an average of 3 months after acceptance. Byline given. Buys first serial rights; some second serial (reprint) rights. Submit seasonal/holiday material 4 months in advance. Simultaneous and photocopied submissions OK, if identified as such. Electronic submissions acceptable via IBM compatible; requires hard copy also. Computer printout submissions acceptable if legible; prefers letter-quality to dot-matrix. Reports in 2 months. Sample copy $3; writer's guidelines for SASE.

Nonfiction: "We want articles on the world-wide realm of salt water; marine life (biology and ecology), oceanography, maritime history, marine painting and other arts, geography, undersea exploration, voyages, ships, coastal areas including environmental problems, seaports and shipping, islands, aquaculture, peoples of the sea, including anthropological materials. Writing should be direct, factual, very readable; not cute, flippant or tongue-in-cheek. We want articles on rarely visited islands, ports or shores that have intrinsic interest, but not treated in purely travelogue style. We can use more on environmental concerns." Buys 60 mss/year. Query with SASE. Length: 1,000-6,000 words. Pays $750-1,000. Sometimes pays expenses of writers on assignment.

OCEANUS, The International Magazine of Marine Science and Policy, Woods Hole Oceanographic Institution, Woods Hole MA 02543. (617)548-1400, ext. 2386. Editor: Paul R. Ryan. Assistant Editor: James Hain. 10% freelance written. "*Oceanus* is an international quarterly magazine that monitors significant trends in ocean research, technology and marine policy. Its basic purpose is to encourage wise, environmentally responsible use of the oceans. In addition, two of the magazine's main tasks are to explain the significance of present marine research to readers and to expose them to the substance of vital public policy questions." Circ. 15,000. Pays on publication. Publishes ms an average of 3 months after acceptance. Byline given. Buys all rights. Simultaneous queries OK. Computer printout submissions acceptable; no dot-matrix. Reports in 2 months.

Nonfiction: Interview/profile and technical. *Oceanus* publishes 4 thematic issues/year. Most articles are commissioned. Length: 2,700-3,500 words. Pays $300 minimum. Sometimes pays expenses of writers on assignment.

Photos: State availability of photos. Reviews b&w and color contact sheets and 8x10 prints. Pays variable rates depending on size; $125 full-page b&w print. Captions required. Buys one-time rights.

Tips: The writer has a better chance of breaking in at this publication with short articles and fillers. "Most of our writers are top scientists in their fields."

OUTDOOR AMERICA, Suite 1100, 1701 N. Ft. Myer Dr., Arlington VA 22209. (703)528-1818. Editor: Carol Dana. 50-75% freelance written. Prefers to work with published/established writers. Quarterly magazine about natural resource conservation and outdoor recreation for sportsmen and local conservationists who are members of the Izaak Walton League. Circ. 50,000. Pays on publication. Publishes ms an average of 4 months after acceptance. Byline given. Buys all rights or first serial rights, depending on arrangements with author. "Considers previously published material if there's not a lot of audience overlap." Query first. Submit seasonal material 6 months in advance. Simultaneous and photocopied submissions OK, if so indicated. Computer printout submissions acceptable; no dot-matrix. Reports in 2 months. Sample copy $1.50; writer's guidelines with SASE.

Nonfiction: "We are interested in thoroughly researched, well-written pieces on current natural resource issues of national importance (threats to water, fisheries, wildlife habitat, air, public lands, soil, etc.); articles on wildlife management controversies, and first-person or how-to articles on outdoor recreation (fishing, hunting, camping, woodcraft, photography, ethical outdoor behavior, etc.)." Length: 1,500-2,500 words. Payment: minimum 15¢/word. Sometimes pays the expenses of writers on assignment.

Columns/Departments: Interested in shorter articles for the following departments: "Hands-On Conservation" (how-to articles on conservation projects that can be undertaken by individuals or local groups); "From the Naturalist's Notebook" (pieces that give insight into the habits and behavior of animals, fish, birds). Length: 500-600 words. Payment: minimum 10¢/word.

Photos: Reviews 5x7 b&w glossy prints and 35mm and larger color transparencies. Additional payment for photos with ms negotiated. Pays $200 for covers. Captions and model releases required. Buys one-time rights.

Tips: "Writers should obtain guidelines and sample issue *before* querying us. They will understand our needs and editorial focus much better if they've done this. Queries submitted without the writer having read the guidelines are *almost always* off base and almost always rejected."

‡**PACIFIC DISCOVERY**, California Academy of Sciences, Golden Gate Park, San Francisco CA 94118. (415)221-5100. Editor: Sheridan Warrick. 100% freelance written. "A journal of nature and culture around the world read by scientists, naturalists, teachers, students, and others having a keen interest in knowing the natural world more thoroughly." Published quarterly by the California Academy of Sciences. Circ. 25,000. Buys first North American serial rights on articles; one-time rights on photos. Pays on publication. Query with 100-word summary of projected article for review before preparing finished ms. Computer printout submissions acceptable; prefers letter-quality to dot-matrix. Usually reports within 3 months. Publishes ms an average of 1 year after acceptance.

Nonfiction: "Subjects of articles include behavior and natural history of animals and plants, ecology, evolution, anthropology, geology, paleontology, biogeography, taxonomy, and related topics in the natural sciences. Occasional articles are published on the history of natural science, exploration, astronomy and archeology. Emphasis is on current research findings. Authors need not be scientists; however, all articles must be based, at least in part, on firsthand fieldwork." Length: 1,000-3,000 words. Pays 24¢/word.

Photos: Send photos with submission "even if an author judges that his own photos should not be reproduced. Referrals to professional photographers with coverage of the subject will be greatly appreciated." Reviews 35mm, 4x5 or other color transparencies or 8x10 b&w glossy prints. Offers $70-100 and $175 for the cover. Buys one-time rights.

SEA FRONTIERS, 3979 Rickenbacker Causeway, Virginia Key, Miami FL 33149. (305)361-5786. Editor: Jean Bradfisch. 95% freelance written. Works with a small number of new/unpublished writers each year. Bimonthly. "For anyone interested in the sea, its conservation, and the life it contains. Our audience is professional people for the most part; people in executive positions and students." Circ. 30,000. Pays on publication. Publishes ms an average of 1 year after acceptance. Byline given. Buys first serial rights. Will consider photocopied submissions "if very clear." Computer printout submissions acceptable; no dot-matrix. Reports on material within 2 months. Sample copy $3; writer's guidelines for SASE.

Nonfiction: "Articles (with illustrations) covering interesting and little known facts about the sea, marine life, chemistry, geology, physics, fisheries, mining, engineering, navigation, influences on weather and climate, ecology, conservation, explorations, discoveries or advances in our knowledge of the marine sciences, or describing the activities of oceanographic laboratories or expeditions to any part of the world. Emphasis should be on research and discoveries rather than personalities involved." Buys 40-50 mss/year. Query. Length: 500-3,000 words. Pays $50-300.

Photos: Reviews 8x10 b&w glossy prints and 35mm (or larger) color transparencies. Pays $50 for color used on front and $35 for the back cover. Pays $25 for color used on inside covers.

Tips: "Query to include a paragraph or two that tells the subject, the angle or approach to be taken, and the writer's qualifications for covering this subject or the authorities with whom the facts will be checked."

SIERRA, 730 Polk St., San Francisco CA 94109. (415)923-5656. Editor-in-Chief: James Keough. Associate Editors: Joan Hamilton, Jonathan F. King, Annie Stine. 80% freelance written. Works with a small number of new/unpublished writers each year. Magazine published 6 times/year; 96-120 pages. Emphasizes conservation and environmental politics for people who are well educated, activist, outdoor-oriented, and politically well informed with a dedication to conservation. Circ. 290,000. Pays on acceptance. Publishes ms an average of 6 months after acceptance. Byline given. Buys first North American serial rights. Photocopied submissions OK.

Electronic submissions OK on ASC II files (or XyWrite), but requires hard copy also. Computer printout submissions acceptable; prefers letter-quality to dot-matrix. Reports in 6 weeks. Writer's guidelines for SAE and 3 first class stamps.

Nonfiction: Expose (well-documented on environmental issues of national importance such as energy, wilderness, forests, etc.); general interest (well-researched pieces on areas of particular environmental concern); historical (relevant to environmental concerns); how-to and equipment pieces (on camping, climbing, outdoor photography, etc.); interview (with very prominent figures in the field); photo feature (photo essays on threatened areas); and technical (on energy sources, wildlife management, land use, solid waste management, etc.). No "My trip to . . ." or "why we must save wildlife nature" articles; no poetry or general superficial essays on environmentalism and local environmental issues. Buys 5-6 mss/issue. Query with published clips. Length: 800-2,500 words. Pays $200-500. Sometimes pays expenses of writers on assignment (up to $50).

Photos: Linda Smith, art and production manager. State availability of photos. Pays $200 maximum for color transparencies; $200 for cover photos. Buys one-time rights.

Columns/Departments: Book reviews. Buys 20-25 mss/year. Length: 750-1,000 words. Pays $100. Query. For Younger Readers, natural history and conservation topics presented for children ages 8 to 13. Pays $200-400. Submit queries to Jonathan King, associate editor.

Tips: "Queries should include an outline of how the topic would be covered and a mention of the political appropriateness and timeliness of the article. Familiarity with Sierra Club positions and policies is recommended. Statements of the writer's qualifications should be included. We don't have articles and fillers in our format. Our redesign involves new departments that use shorter pieces than we've been able to use previously."

SNOWY EGRET, 205 S. 9th St., Williamsburg KY 40769. (606)549-0850. Editor: Humphrey A. Olsen. 75% freelance written. Semiannual for "persons of at least high school age interested in literary, artistic, philosophical and historical natural history." Circ. less than 500. Pays on publication. Publishes ms an average of 6 weeks after acceptance. Byline given. Buys first North American serial rights. Usually reports in 2 months. Sample copy $2; writer's guidelines for SAE and 1 first class stamp.

Nonfiction: Subject matter limited to material related to natural history (preferably living organisms), especially literary, artistic, philosophical and historical aspects. Criticism, book reviews, essays and biographies. No columns. Buys 40-50 mss/year. Pays $2/printed page. Send nonfiction prose mss and books for review to Humphrey A. Olsen.

Photos: No photos, but drawings acceptable.

Fiction: "We are interested in considering stories or self-contained portions of novels. All fiction must be natural history or man and nature. The scope is broad enough to include such stories as Hemingway's 'Big Two-Hearted River' and Warren's 'Blackberry Winter.' " Length: maximum 10,000 words. Pays $2/printed page. Send mss for consideration and poetry and fiction books for review to Alan Seaburg, poetry and fiction editor, 17 Century St., West Medford MA 02155. "It is preferable to query first."

Poetry: No length limits. Pays $4/printed page, minimum $2.

Personal Computing

Personal computing magazines continue to be among the most changeable publications in the marketplace. Many add or eliminate computer models that they report on; the newer publications are still learning about their readers and how they can serve them. Many computer magazines have folded. Make sure you see the most recent issue of a magazine before submitting material to it.

Owners of personal computers rely on these magazines to learn more about their PCs. Business applications for home computers are covered in the Consumer Business and Finance section. Magazines on computer games and recreational computing are in the Games and Puzzles category. Publications for data processing personnel are listed in the Data Processing section of Trade Journals. Uses of computers in specific professions are covered in the appropriate Trade Journals sections.

‡A+, **THE INDEPENDENT GUIDE TO APPLE COMPUTING**, Ziff-Davis, Suite 206, 11 Davis Dr., Belmont CA 94002. (415)594-2290. Editor-in-Chief: Maggie Canon. Managing Editor: Leslie Steere. Executive Editor: Fred Davis. 95% freelance written. Monthly magazine covering the Apple Computer product line

and related products. "*A +* aims to educate the Apple II, IIe, IIc, and Macintosh owner on professional uses of the various products." Circ. 200,000. Pays 6 weeks after acceptance. Byline given. Offers $50-100 kill fee. Buys first world-wide rights. Submit (all) seasonal/holiday material 4 months in advance. Computer printout submissions acceptable. Publishes ms an average of 6 months after acceptance.

Nonfiction: How-to, new product and technical. Buys 200 mss/year. Query with published clips. Length: 1,000-2,500 words. pays negotiable rates.

Tips: "If you know about Apple computers and their uses and have some writing experience, we will consider you for a freelance assignment."

AHOY!, Ion International Inc., Suite 407, 45 W. 34th St., New York NY 10001. (212)239-0855. Editor: David Allikas. Managing Editor: Michael R. Davila. 80% freelance written. Eager to work with new/unpublished writers. A monthly magazine for users of Commodore-64, VIC 20, Plus/4, C-128, and Amiga home computers. Pays on acceptance. Publishes ms a average of 2 months after acceptance. Byline given. Offers variable kill fee. Buys first serial rights. Submit seasonal/holiday material 3 months in advance. Simultaneous queries and simultaneous, photocopied and previously published submissions OK. Electronic submissions OK on disk or cassette for Commodore-64, VIC 20, Plus/4, C-128 and Amiga. Computer printout submissions acceptable. Sample copy $2.75; writer's guidelines for SASE.

Nonfiction: Book excerpts (Commodore-related books); general interest (modern technology); how-to (programming, maintaining, repairing, and customizing Commodore computers); interview/profile (computer industry leaders); new product (new Commodore-64, Vic-20, Plus-4, and Amiga software and peripherals); and technical (how-to programming articles, mechanics of computers and peripherals). Buys 40 mss/year and 80 programs. Query with published clips. Length: 250-5,000 words. Pays $500 maximum. Pays expenses of writers on assignment.

Fillers: Gags for cartoons. Pays $15/cartoon gag; $50/full cartoon.

Tips: "Our major need is programs—much more so than feature articles. We buy 8-10 programs per month from freelancers, only 1 or 2 feature articles. Only Commodore computer users with a good deal of expertise should consider writing for *Ahoy!* We'll be buying far less material for the Vic 20 and Plus/4, and concentrate on the C-64 and C-128, with some treatment of the Amiga as well."

ANTIC MAGAZINE, The Atari Resource, Antic Publishing Co., 524 2nd St., San Francisco CA 94107. (415)957-0886. Editor: Nat Friedland. 25% freelance written. Monthly magazine for Atari 400/800, 1200XL, 600XL, 800XL, and 1450LXD computer users and owners of Atari game machines, compatible equipment and software. Circ. 100,000. Pays on publication. Publishes ms an average of 3 months after acceptance. Byline given. Offers $60 kill fee. Buys all rights. Submit seasonal/holiday material 3 months in advance. Simultaneous queries and photocopied submissions OK. Electronic submissions OK on Atari DOS compatible, but requires hard copy also. Computer printout submissions acceptable; prefers letter-quality to dot-matrix. Reports in 2 weeks on queries; 1 month on mss. Sample copy $3; free writer's guidelines. Request text files on disks and printout.

Nonfiction: How-to, interview/profile, new product, photo feature and technical. Especially wants article plus programs—games, utilities, productivity, etc. Special issues include Education (October) and Buyer's Guide (December). No generalized, nontechnical articles. Buys 250 mss/year. Send complete ms. Length: 500-2,500 words. Pays $20-180.

Photos: State availability of photos or send photos with ms. Reviews color transparencies and b&w prints; b&w should accompany article. Identification of subjects required.

Columns/Departments: Starting Line (beginner's column); Assembly Language (for advanced programmers); Profiles (personalities in the business); and Product Reviews (software/hardware products). Buys 36 mss/year. Send complete ms. Length: 1,500-2,500 words. Pays $120-180.

Tips: "Write for the Product Reviews section. We need 400 to 600-word articles on a new software or hardware product for the Atari 400/800 computers. Give a clear description; personal experience with product; comparison with other available product; or product survey with charts. The most frequent mistakes made by writers in completing an article are failure to be clear and specific, and writing overly-long submissions."

BYTE MAGAZINE, 70 Main St., Peterborough NH 03458. (603)924-9281. Editor: Philip Lemmone. Monthly magazine covering personal computers for college-educated, professional users of computers. Circ. 399,000. Pays on publication. Buys all rights. Double-spaced computer disk submissions OK. Computer printout submissions acceptable; prefers letter-quality to dot-matrix. Reports on rejections in 3 months; 6 months if accepted. Sample copy $2.95; writer's guidelines for SASE.

Nonfiction: How-to (technical information about computers) and technical. Buys 160 mss/year. Query. Length: 3,000-5,000 words. Pay is competitive.

Tips: "Many *Byte* authors are regular readers of the magazine, and most readers use a computer either at home or at work. Back issues of the magazine give prospective authors an idea of the type of article published in *Byte*. Articles can take one of several forms: tutorial articles on a given subject, how-to articles detailing a specific implementation of a hardware or software project done on a small computer, survey articles on the future of microcomputers, and sometimes theoretical articles describing work in computer science (if written in an informal, 'friendly' style). Authors with less technical orientation should consider writing for our other publication, *Popular Computing Magazine*. Author's guides are available for both publications."

CLOSING THE GAP, INC., Box 68, Henderson MN 56044. (612)248-3294. Editor: Budd Hagen. Managing Editor: Michael Gergen. 40% freelance written. Eager to work with new/unpublished writers. Bimonthly tabloid covering microcomputers for handicapped readers, special education and rehabilitation professionals. "We focus on currently available products and procedures written for the layperson that incorporate microcomputers to enhance the educational opportunities and quality of life for pesons with disabilities." Circ. 10,000. Pays on publication. Publishes ms an average of 2 months after acceptance. Byline given. Buys first serial rights. Simultaneous queries, and simultaneous, photocopied, and previously published submissions OK. Electronic submissions OK via Apple IIe, 64K or Macintosh S12K. Computer printout submissions acceptable (dot-matrix with descenders). Reports in 2 weeks. Free sample copy and writer's guidelines.
Nonfiction: How-to (simple modifications to computers or programs to aid handicapped persons); interview/profile (users or developers of computers to aid handicapped persons); new product (computer products to aid handicapped persons); personal experience (use of microcomputer to aid, or by, a handicapped person); articles on current research on projects on microcomputers to aid persons with disabilities; and articles that examine current legislation, social trends and new projects that deal with computer technology for persons with handicaps. No highly technical "computer hobbyist" pieces. Buys 25 mss/year. Query. Length: 500-2,000 words. Pays $25 and up (negotiable). "Many authors' material runs without financial compensation."
Tips: "Knowledge of the subject is vital, but freelancers do not need to be computer geniuses. Clarity is essential; articles must be able to be understood by a layperson. All departments are open to freelancers. We are looking for new ideas. If you saw it in some other computer publication, don't bother submitting. *CTG*'s emphasis is on increasing computer user skills in our area of interest, not developing hobbyist or technical skills. The most frequent mistakes made by writers in completing an article for us is that their submissions are too technical—they associate 'computer' with hobbyist, often their own perspective—and don't realize our readers are not hobbyists or hackers."

COMMODORE MAGAZINE, (formerly *Commodore Microcomputers* and *Commodore Power/Play*), Commodore Business Machines, 1200 Wilson Dr., West Chester PA 19380. (215)431-9100. Editor: Diane LeBold. 90% freelance written. Monthly magazine for owners of Commodore computers, using them for business, programming, education, communications, art, recreation, etc. Circ. 200,000. Pays on publication. Publishes ms an average of 3 months after acceptance. Byline given. Buys all rights; makes occasional work-for-hire assignments. Submit seasonal/holiday material 5 months in advance. Simultaneous queries and previously published submissions OK. All programs should be submitted on disk with accompanying hardcopy list. Reports in 1 month on queries; 2 months on mss. Free sample copy; writer's guidelines for legal size SAE and 1 first class stamp.
Nonfiction: Book reviews; how-to (write programs, use software); new product (reviews); personal experience; photo feature; and technical. "Write for guidelines." Buys 360 mss/year. Query or send complete ms. Length: 750-2,500 words. Pays $60-100/published page.
Photos: Send photos with ms. Reviews 5x7 b&w and color prints. Captions required. Buys all rights.
Tips: "Write or phone the editor. Talk about several specific ideas. Use Commodore computers. We're open to programming techniques and product reviews."

COMPUTE! The Leading Magazine of Home, Educational, and Recreational Computing, Compute! Publications, 324 W. Wendover Ave., Greensboro NC 27408. (919)275-9809. Senior Editor: Richard Mansfield. Managing Editor: Kathleen Martinek. 50% freelance written. Monthly magazine covering consumer and personal computing. Circ. 350,000. Pays on acceptance. Publishes ms an average of 4 months after acceptance. Byline given. Buys all rights. Submit seasonal/holiday material 6 months in advance. Simultaneous queries OK. Electronic submissions OK. Computer printout submissions acceptable. Reports in 2 weeks on queries; 6 weeks on mss. Sample copy $2.95; free writer's guidelines.
Nonfiction: How-to (compute) and technical (programs, games, utility programs for computers). No reviews. Send complete ms. Length: 500 words minimum. Pays $75-600.
Photos: Reviews 5x7 b&w glossy prints.
Tips: "We stress clarity and a tutorial approach and publish computer programs for many popular computers. Write for guidelines."

‡COMPUTER SHOPPER, Patch Publishing, 407 S. Washington Ave., Box F, Titusville FL 32796. (305)269-3211. Editor: Stanley Veit. 50% freelance written. A monthly tabloid covering personal computing. "Our readers are experienced computer users. They are interested in using and comparing machines and software, and in saving money." Circ. 160,000. Pays on publication. Publishes ms an average of 1 month after acceptance. Byline given. Offers $25 kill fee. Buys first North American serial rights and 1 reprint right. Submit seasonal/holiday material 4 months in advance. Electronic submissions OK via IBM PC, Wordstar, but requires hard copy also. Computer printout submissions acceptable; prefers letter-quality to dot-matrix. Reports in 1 week on queries; 2 weeks on mss. Sample copy $2.25.

Nonfiction: How-to (computer boards), new product reviews, and technical. "No rank beginner articles." Buys 250 mss/year. Query. Length: 1,500-2,500 words. Pays 6-10¢/word.

Photos: State availability of photos with submission. Reviews b&w prints or line drawings. Offers no additional payment for photos or drawings accepted with ms.

COMPUTERITER, Microcomputer News and Views for the Writer/Editor, Creative Business Communications, Box 476, Columbia MD 21045. (301)596-5591. Editor: Linda J. Elengold. 25-50% freelance written. Eager to work with new/unpublished writers. Bimonthly newsletter on computers/word processing. "We like to hear about writers' experiences with specific computers, peripherals and software." Circ. 1,000. Pays on acceptance. Publishes ms an average of 3 months after acceptance. Byline given. Offers 50% kill fee. Buys one-time rights and second serial (reprint) rights (occasionally). Submit seasonal/holiday material 6 months in advance. Simultaneous queries, photocopied and previously published submissions OK. Electronic submissions acceptable via IBM PC disk in WordStar or Word Perfect. Computer printout submissions acceptable; prefers letter-quality to dot-matrix. Reports in 2 weeks on queries; 1 month on mss. Sample copy $4; writer's guidelines for SAE and 1 first class stamp.

Nonfiction: Book excerpts, how-to (computer use), interview/profile, new product, personal experience and technical. No "Why I chose to use a computer"—wants very specific how-to's and reviews. Buys 24 mss/year. Query with published clips or send complete ms. Length: 100-500 words. Negotiates payment on individual basis; usually makes outright purchase (for one-time rights).

Tips: "Analyze your personal experiences with computers and software and develop some tips or hints other writers could share. We need interviews of prominent or successful writers on their use of computers, personal experience, reviews and how-to articles. Reviews are assigned. Approximately 50% of the newsletter is staff-written. We are accepting more manuscripts from freelancers. We insist upon queries."

COMPUTE!'s GAZETTE, ABC Publishing, Suite 200, 324 W. Wendover Ave., Greensboro NC 27408. (919)275-9809. Editor-in-Chief: Robert Lock. Managing Editor: Kathleen Martinek. 50% freelance edited. Monthly magazine of personal and consumer computing for owners/users of VIC and Commodore 64 computer systems. "Our audience is mostly beginning and novice computer users." Circ. 275,000. Pays on acceptance. Publishes ms an average of 3 months after acceptance. Byline given. Buys all rights. Submit seasonal/holiday material 6 months in advance. Simultaneous queries OK. Electronic submissions OK, but requires hard copy also. Computer printout submissions acceptable. Reports in 2 weeks on queries; 6 weeks on mss. Sample copy $2.50; free writer's guidelines.

Nonfiction: How-to (compute); personal experience (with programming/computers); and technical (programs, games, utility programs for computers). No reviews. "We stress clarity and a tutorial approach, and publish quality computer programs for Commodore computers. Follow the suggestions in our author's guide. Send complete ms." Length: 500 words minimum. Pays $75 minimum.

‡COMPUTING NOW!, Canada's Personal Computing Magazine, Moorshead Publications, 1300 Don Mill Rd., Toronto, Ontario, M3B 3M8 Canada. (416)445-5600. Editor: Steve Rimmer. 15-20% freelance written. Eager to work with new/unpublished writers. A monthly magazine covering micro computing, the use of micro computers in small businesses, computer hacking (intermediate to advanced). Circ. 20,000. Pays on publication. Publishes ms an average of 6 months after acceptance. Byline given. Buys first rights. Electronic submissions acceptable; whether hard copy is required depends on the article. Computer printout submissions acceptable; prefers letter-quality to dot-matrix. Free writer's guidelines.

Nonfiction: How-to (on computer hacking); new product (occasional hardware or software review); and technical. No humor, inspirational or general/historical articles. Query. Length: 2,000-3,000 words. Pays 10¢/word. Sometimes pays the expenses of writers on assignment.

Photos: State availability of photos with submission. Reviews prints. Captions, model releases, and identification of subjects required.

‡COMPUTIST, The Magazine for Serious Users of Apple II Computers, Softkey Publishing, 5233 S. Washington, Box 110846, Tacoma WA 98411. (206)474-5750. Editor: Robert Knowles. Managing Editor: Ray Darrah. 98% freelance written. A monthly technical journal covering Apple II software deprotection. "*Computist* is read by honest users who wish to backup their valuable software." Circ. 10,000. Pays on publication. Publishes ms an average of 2 months after acceptance. Byline given. Buys all rights. Submit seasonal/holiday material 3 months in advance. Simultaneous, photocopied and previously published submissions OK. Electronic submissions OK via Apple II DOS 3.3 text file; prefers hard copy also. Computer printout submissions acceptable. Reports in 3 months. Sample copy $4.75. Free writer's guidelines.

Nonfiction: Contact: Manuscript Editor. How-to (deprotect Apple software); new product (reviews); highly technical; computer programs. All submissions must be directly related to Apple computers. Buys 170 mss/year. Send complete ms; do not query. Length: 50-5,000 words. Pays $10-500.

Photos: Send photos with submission. Reviews prints. Photos accepted with ms increase article payment.
Tips: "Send original disk for verification with ms. Be sure to include step-by-step instructions on how to de-protect the program in question. Learn the ins and outs of copy protection schemes."

‡DATA BASED ADVISOR, Featuring Database Management System, Data Based Solutions, Inc., Suite 105, 1975 5th Ave., San Diego CA 92101. (619) 236-1182. David M. Kalman. Technical Editor: David J. Irwin. 50% freelance written. Works with a small number of new/unpublished writers each year. A monthly magazine covering microcomputer software. Circ. 30,000. Pays on publication. Publishes ms an average of 3 months after acceptance. Byline given. Buys all rights. Electronic submissions OK via IBM PC/and most CPM formats, but requires hard copy also. Computer printout submissions acceptable. Reports in 2 weeks on queries; 1 month on manuscripts. Free sample copy and writer's guidelines.
Nonfiction: How-to (on optimizing database programs, etc.); new product (reviews); technical (academic discussion of software/database issues); and actual computer programs that can be used by readers. No human interest or corporate submissions. Buys 50 mss/year. Query with published clips. Length: 1,500 words. Pays $350 maximum for assigned articles; pays $150 maximum for unsolicited articles. Will consider barter upon request of author. Pays the expenses of writers on assignment.
Photos: State availability of photos with submission. Offers no additional payment for photos accepted with ms. Captions required. Buys all rights.
Columns/Departments: dBase Program Tips (tutorial or productivity oriented with working programs), 1,500-2,500 words; and Software Reviews (personal experience rather than laboratory testing) 1,500-3,500 words. Buys 25 mss/year. Query with published clips. Pays $150 maximum.
Tips: "Detail your programming experience. We are interested in 'real world' tips based on the experience of database users at all levels."

DIGITAL REVIEW, The Magazine for DEC Computing, Ziff-Davis Publishing, 160 State St., Boston MA 02109. (617)367-7190. Editor: Jonathan Cohler. Managing Editor: Debra Highberger. Monthly magazine covering Digital Equipment Corporation computers and related hardware, software, services, supplies and applications. Circ. 70,000. Pays on acceptance. Byline given. Offers 15% kill fee. Buys first North American serial rights, one-time rights, and all rights; makes work-for-hire assignments. Simultaneous queries OK. Electronic submissions OK on 300/1200 baud async ASCII modem transmissions, DEC Rainbow or IBM PC single-sided diskettes. Computer printout submissions acceptable. Reports in 2 weeks. Free sample copy and writer's guidelines.
Nonfiction: Book excerpts, expose, how-to, interview/profile, new product, personal experience and technical. Buys 100 mss/year. Query with published clips. Length: 2,000-4,000 words. Pays $500-2,500.

80 MICRO, 80 Pine St., Peterborough NH 03458. (603)924-9471. Publisher: C.W. Communications/Peterborough. Editor: Eric Maloney. 50% freelance written. Monthly magazine about microcomputing for owners and users of Tandy microcomputers. Circ. 100,000. Pays on acceptance. Publishes ms an average of 6 months after acceptance. Buys all rights. Written queries preferred. Photocopied submissions OK. Requires hard copy of articles and disk or tape of programs. Computer printout submissions acceptable. Reports in 2 months. Sample copy $4; writer's guidelines for SASE.
Nonfiction: Applications programs for business, education, science, home and hobby; utilities; programming techniques; and tutorials. "We're looking for articles that will help the beginning, intermediate, and advanced Tandy microcomputer user become a better programmer. We also publish hardware construction projects. We buy about five manuscripts per issue. Query first; we are glutted." Length: 1,000 words average. Pays $60/printed page.
Reviews: Writers interested in reviewing current available software are asked to query the review editor, stating areas of interest and equipment owned. Buys 5-8 reviews/issue.
Photos: Offers no additional payment for photos accepted with ms. Buys all rights.

LINK-UP, Learned Information, Inc., 143 Old Marlton Pike, Medford NJ 08055. (609)654-6266. Editor: Loraine Page. 80% freelance written. Monthly tabloid on small-computer communications. *"Link-Up* is a guide to the 'nuts and bolts' of using your computer and modem to go online with the numerous informational and communications-oriented database services. Our publication speaks to the business-person, the educator, and the computer-user at home who want to be kept abreast of what services are useful for them to 'link-up' to.'' Pays on publication. Publishes ms an average of 1 month after acceptance. Byline given. Buys first serial rights. Submit seasonal/holiday material 4 months in advance. Simultaneous queries, and simultaneous and photocopied submissions OK. Electronic mail submissions OK "by modem to our ID numbers on the following services: CompuServe 72105,1753; MCI Mail 276-3464; The Source STU329; Dialmail (Dialog) 11440." Computer printout submissions acceptable. Reports in 2 weeks on queries; 6 weeks on mss. Sample copy for $2, 10x12 SAE and $1.25 postage; writer's guidelines for business size SAE and 1 first class stamp.
Nonfiction: How-to (computer/communications) and features on various topics dealing with going online. Buys 40-50 mss/year. Query with published clips or send complete ms. Length: 1,000-2,000 words. Pays $80-200.

Photos: Send photos with query or ms. Reviews 35mm and larger color transparencies and (minimum) 5x7 prints. Pays variable/negotiable rates. Captions, model release, and identification of subjects required. Buys one-time rights.

Fillers: Anecdotes, short humor and newsbreaks. Buys few fillers. Length: 50-200 words. Pays $25-35.

Tips: "Study an issue or two-that's very important. We're dealing with technical material, but the publication is meant to be easily understandable. Feature articles on computer communications for home and business—databases, information networks, person-to-person-via-computer and how people are using the online technology—are the areas most open to freelancers."

MACWORLD, The Macintosh Magazine, PC World Communications, Inc., 555 DeHaro St., San Francisco CA 94107. (415)861-3861. Editor: Jerry Borrell. 70% freelance written. Works with a small number·of new/unpublished writers each year. Monthly magazine covering use of Apple's Macintosh computer. Circ. 200,000. Pays on acceptance. Publishes ms an average of 6 months after acceptance. Byline given. Offers negotiable kill fee. Buys first serial rights. Submit seasonal/holiday material 6 months in advance. Electronic submissions on Macintosh disk with MacWrite or Microsoft Word text files, IBM PC disk with WordStar, Async comm. via modem, but requires hard copy also. Computer printout submissions acceptable. Reports in 8 weeks. Sample copy $5. Free writer's guidelines.

Nonfiction: How-to, hands-on and practical experiences, interview/profile, new product, opinion, personal experience, photo feature, technical, community, general interest. Buys 120 mss/year. Query with published clips. Length: 500-3,500 words. Pays $50-750. Sometimes pays expenses of writers on assignment.

Photos: State availability of photos or send photos with query. Pays $25-50 for color slides and 5x7 or 8x10 b&w prints. Captions, model releases, and identification of subjects required. Buys one-time rights.

Tips: "We seek clearly written, useful articles. Send in article proposal first. Short reviews and new items are the best areas to start with. It is important that the writer knows the Macintosh and the subject area, e.g., business, graphics, finance."

‡MICROAGE QUARTERLY, MicroAge Computer Stores, Inc., Box 1920, Tempe AZ 85281. (602)968-3168. Managing Editor: Bruce Guptill. 65% freelance written. A quarterly magazine for "new, potential and first-time computer users." Estab. 1985. Circ. 150,000. Pays on publication. Publishes ms an average of 2 months after acceptance. Byline given. Offers 20% kill fee. Buys first North American serial rights, one-time rights and second serial (reprint) rights. Previously published submissions OK. Electronic submissions OK via IBM PC, AT&T 6300, MS/PC DOS; also televideo C/PM; requires hard copy also. Computer printout submissions acceptable; no dot-matrix. Reports in 1 week on queries. Free sample copy and writer's guidelines.

Nonfiction: Book excerpts, general interest, interview/profile, and new product. Buys 18-25 mss/year. Query with published clips. Length: 800-3,000 words. Pays $280-1,200. Sometimes pays the expenses of writers on assignment.

Columns/Departments: Changing Market (changes in marketing of business-oriented computer equipment—what affects the market, and how it changes); Changing Technology (changes/improvements in computer technology which affect the computer market); and Changing Industry (adaptations in computer retail and manufacturing which affect the market and users); all 1,000-3,000 words. Market Focus (specific "verticals"—construction, accounting, etc.—and how computers are used in these markets), 2,000-2,500 words. Buys 16-20 mss/year. Query with published clips. Length: 1,000-3,000 words. Pays $300-1,200.

Tips: "We're looking for problem-solving articles on office automation, and new different computer applications oriented toward small and medium size businesses (especially in vertical markets, such as accounting, banking, real estate, medicine, law, construction, retail, etc.) We're willing to discuss ideas with experienced business or computer-literate writers."

‡MICROpendium, Covering the TI99/4A and Compatible, Burns-Koloen Communications Inc., Box 1343, Round Rock TX 78664. (512)255-1512. Editor: Laura Burns. 30% freelance written. Eager to work with new/unpublished writers. A monthly tabloid magazine for users of the "orphaned" TI99/4A. "We are interested in helping users get the most out of their home computers." Circ. 6,000. Pays on publication. Publishes manuscript ms an average of 4 months after acceptance. Byline given. Buys second serial rights. Photocopied and previously published submissions OK. Electronic submissions OK via D/V 80 files. Computer printout submissions acceptable. Reports in 2 weeks on queries; 2 months on manuscripts. Free sample copy and writer's guidelines.

Nonfiction: Book excerpts; how-to (computer applications); interview/profile (of computer "personalities," e.g. a software developer concentrating more on "how-to" than personality); and opinion (product reviews, hardware and software). Interested in reviews of tax software for April issue; query by January. Buys 30 mss/year. Query with or without published clips, or send complete ms. "We can do some articles as a series if they are lengthy, yet worthwhile." Pays $10, depending on length; may pay with contributor copies or other premiums if writer requests. No pay for product announcements. Sometimes pays the expenses of writers on assignment.

Photos: Send photos with submission. Reviews contact sheets, negatives, transparencies, and prints (b&w preferred). Buys negotiable rights.
Columns/Departments: User Notes (tips and brief routines for the computer) 100 words and up. Buys 35-40 mss/year. Send complete ms. Pays $10.
Tips: "We have more regularly scheduled columnists, which may reduce the amount we accept from others. The area most open to freelancers is product reviews on hardware and software. The writer should be a sophisticated TI99/4A computer user. We are more interested in advising our readers of the availability of good products than in 'panning' poor ones."

NIBBLE, The Reference for Apple Computing, Micro-SPARC Inc., 45 Winthrop St., Concord MA 01742. (617)371-1660. Editor: David Szetela. Managing Editor: David Krathwohl. 90% freelance written. A monthly magazine for Apple II computer reference. Authors should submit programs that run on Apple computers. Pays on acceptance. Byline given. Buys all rights. Submit seasonal/holiday material 4 months in advance. Photocopied submissions OK. Computer printout submissions acceptable. Reports in 1 week on queries; 1 month on manuscripts. Free sample copy and writer's guidelines.
Nonfiction: New product, and technical. No product reviews or fiction. Buys 175 mss/year. Query. Length: 500-3,000 words. Pays $50-500.
Photos: State availability of photos with submission. Offers no additional payment for photos accepted with ms. Buys all rights.
Tips: "Authors should submit original Apple programs along with descriptive articles."

‡ONLINE TODAY, The Computer Communications Magazine, CompuServe Inc., 5000 Arlington Centre Blvd., Columbus OH 43220. (614)457-8600. Editor: Douglas G. Branstetter. "We are backlogged with submissions and prefer not to receive unsolicited submissions at this time."

‡PC, The Independent Guide to IBM Personal Computers, Ziff-Davis Publishing Co., 1 Park Ave., New York NY 10016. (212)503-5255. Editor: Bill Machrone. Executive Editor/Features: Barry Owen. Senior Editor/News: Bill Howard. Fortnightly magazine for users/owners of IBM Personal Computers and compatible systems. Pays on acceptance. Byline given. Buys all rights. Submit seasonal/holiday material 5 months in advance to executive editor. Photocopied submissions OK. Reports in 4 weeks. Sample copy $5.
Nonfiction: How-to (software and hardware); technical; product evaluations; and programs. Buys 800 mss/year. Send complete ms. Length: 1,000-8,000 words.

PC WORLD, The Comprehensive Guide to IBM Personal Computers and Compatibles, PC World Communications, Inc., 555 De Haro St., San Francisco CA 94107. (415)861-3861. Editor: Harry Miller. 80% freelance written. Monthly magazine covering IBM Personal Computers and compatibles. Circ. 250,000. Pays on acceptance. Byline given. Offers negotiable kill fee. Buys all rights. Submit material at least 6 months in advance. Electronic submissions OK on ASCII files and WordStar, but requires hard copy also. Computer printout submissions acceptable. Reports in 6 weeks. Free writer's guidelines.
Nonfiction: Book excerpts, general interest, historic/nostalgic, humor, opinion, personal experience, photo feature, how-to, interview/profile, new product and technical. "*PC World* is composed of five sections: State of the Art, Getting Started, Review, Hands On, and Community. In State of the Art, articles cover developing technologies in the computer industry. The Getting Started section is specifically aimed at the growing number of new computer users. In Review, new hardware and software are critically and objectively analyzed by experienced users. Hands On offers 'how-to' articles, giving readers instructions on setting up 1-2-3 worksheets, inserting memory boards, developing programming skills and other related topics. Community covers a wide range of subjects, focusing on how society is being shaped by the influx of microcomputers in work places, schools and homes." No articles not related to the IBM PC or compatibles. Query with or without published clips or send complete ms. Buys 50 mss/year. Length: 1,500-2,500 words. Pays $35-1,200.
Photos: State availability of photos and send with query or ms. Reviews color transparencies and 8x10 b&w prints. Pays $25-50. Captions, model releases, and identification of subjects required. Buys one-time rights.
Columns/Departments: REMark (personal opinions about microcomputer-related issues); PC World View (industry news and human interest); Password: Communicate (developments in telecommunications). Buys 150 mss/year. Query with or without published clips or send complete ms.
Tips: "Familiarity with the IBM PC or technical knowledge about its operations often determines whether we accept a query. Send all queries to the attention of Proposals—Editorial Department. The Hands On section is especially open to freelancers with practical applications to offer."

PCM, The Personal Computing Magazine for Tandy Computer Users, Falsoft, Inc., Falsoft Bldg., 9529 U.S. Highway 42, Box 385, Prospect KY 40059. (502)228-4492. Editor: Lawrence C. Falk. Managing Editor: Dan Humphress. 75% freelance written. A monthly (brand specific) magazine for owners of the Tandy Model 100, 200 and 600 portable computer and the Tandy 1000, 1200, 2000 and 3000. Circ. 25,000. Pays on publication. Publishes ms an average of 3 months after acceptance. Byline given. Buys full rights, and rights for disk service reprint. Submit seasonal/holiday material 4 months in advance. Photocopied submissions OK. Electronic submissions OK, but requires hard copy also. Computer printout submissions acceptable. Reports in 2 months. Sample copy for SASE; free writer's guidelines.

Nonfiction: Jutta Kapfhammer, submissions editor. How-to. "We prefer articles with programs." No general interest material. Buys 80 mss/year. Send complete ms. "Do not query." Length: 300 words minimum. Pays $40-50/page.

Photos: State availability of photos. Rarely uses photos.

Tips: "At this time we are only interested in submissions for the Tandy MS-DOS and portable computers. Strong preference is given to submissions accompanied by brief program listings. All listings must be submitted on tape or disk as well as in hardcopy form."

PERSONAL COMPUTING MAGAZINE, Hayden Publishing Company, Inc., 10 Mulholland Dr., Hasbrouck Heights NJ 07604. (201)393-6104. Editor: Chuck Martin. Managing Editor: Fred Abatemarco. 25% freelance written. Monthly magazine on personal computers. "A special-interest magazine that meets the needs of growing users. Editorial content designed to serve business people whose curiosity about the benefits of personal computer use is developing into serious interest and active involvement. Articles and features serve that level of interest without demanding years of experience or advanced knowledge of the technology." Circ. 525,000. Pays on acceptance. Publishes ms an average of 3 months after acceptance. Byline given. Buys first North American serial rights. Submit seasonal/holiday material 2 months in advance. Simultaneous queries, and simultaneous and photocopied submissions OK. Electronic submissions OK via IBM/MS-DOS/ASCII, but requires hard copy also. Computer printout submissions acceptable. Reports in 3 weeks. Free writer's guidelines.

Nonfiction: Technical and feature articles on people in computing. No product reviews. Query with or without published clips. Pay varies. Sometimes pays the expenses of writers on assignment.

Tips: "If the writer's reporting and writing style and expertise meets the test of providing information and help to business people who use personal computers, chances are we can work together. We ar interested in working with business-savvy journalists who are aware and interested in service, how-to articles about sophisticated personal computer use."

‡PORTABLE 100/200/600, Tandy Briefcase Computing, Camden Communications, Inc. Highland Mill, Box 250, Camden ME 04843. (207)236-4365. Editor: J.D. Hildebrand. Senior Editor: Park M. Morrison. 80% freelance written. Eager to work with new/unpublished writers. A monthly magazine for users and prospective users of Kyrocera-designed laptop computers marketed in U.S. by Tandy Corp., NEC, and Docutel/Olivetti. "We provide reviews of new product, programming (BASIC) articles and application stories. Informed, conversational style." Circ. 25,000. Pays on publication. Publishes an average of 3 months after acceptance. Byline given. Offers 10% kill fee. Buys first North American serial rights. Submit seasonal/holiday material 6 months in advance. Previously published submisions OK. Electronic submissions OK, via IBM-compatible diskettes, cassete or via modem, but requires hard copy also. Computer printout submissions acceptable; prefers letter-quality to dot-matrix. Reports in 2 months. Free writer's guidelines.

Nonfiction: How-to, new product and personal experience. No " 'I'm a happy portable computer user' type stories." Buys 79 mss/year. Query with published clips. Length: 1,000-2,500 words. Pays $100-400 for assigned articles; pays $25-250 for unsolicited articles.

Photos: Send photos with submissions. Offers no additional payment for photos accepted with ms. Captions and identification of subjects required. Buys one-time rights.

Fillers: Short utility programs. Buys 10-15/year. Length: 250 words plus listing. Pays $25 maximum.

Tips: "We get pre-release versions of products so there is no use sending us reviews—we will have assigned them already. We're always looking for qualified reviewers though. If you've written a program in BASIC that enhances the functionality of your computer, we want to know about it. It could be a hobby, or for your job, or for fun. The article should tell why the program was developed, and explain the code and give directives on how it works."

PROFILES, The Magazine for Kaypro Users, Kaypro Corporation, 533 Stevens Ave., Solana Beach CA 92075. (619)259-4431. Co-Editors: Diane Ingalls and Terian Tyre. 90% freelance written. "We are trying to build a 'stable' of reliable, competent writers, whether they're 'established' or not." A monthly machine-specific computer magazine covering Kaypro Computers (MS-DOS & CP/M). Articles must speak to owners and users of Kaypro computers. Interested in how-to articles concerning software used on these machines. Technical level of readership ranges from total novice to very advanced. Circ. 100,000. Pays on acceptance. Publishes ms an average of 4 months after acceptance. Byline given. Offers 30% kill fee. Buys first serial rights. Submit seasonal/holiday material 5 months in advance. Electronic submission OK, via MS-DOS or CP/M 2.2, but requires hard copy also. Computer printout submissions acceptable. Reports in 6 weeks. Free sample copy and writer's guidelines.

Nonfiction: How-to (on using specific software/hardware); new product (reviews or evaluations of new hardware or software); and technical (modifications or explanations of specific hardware). No "how I learned to love/hate my computer." Buys 75 mss/year. Query with or without published clips, or send complete ms. Length: 750-2,500 words. Pays $150-400 for assigned articles. Pays $50-350 for unsolicited articles. Sometimes pays the expenses of writers on assignment.

Photos: State availability of photos with submission. Reviews negatives. Negotiable payment policy on photos. Model releases and identification of subjects required. Buys one-time rights.

Columns/Department: Beginner's Luck (explanation in the most simple terms possible of computer concepts, commands, etc.), 1,500-2,000 words. Buys 12 mss/year. Query with published clips. Pays $250 maximum.

Tips: "We particularly need feature material for beginners and for advanced computer users. Most of the material we now receive is for intermediate/general audiences. Hand-holding instructional material for beginners is appropriate. Advanced users are also seeking how-to material at their level. A lively (but *not* cute) style is welcome, but accuracy, clarity and brevity are more important. No 'think' pieces. We also seek material written by and for those who use computers for business/office applications, as well as programming tutorials with listings (Pascal, assembly language, etc.). Articles should be for both CP/M and MS-DOS users when possible. As Kaypro shifts its focus to MS-DOS computers, we will need more material about that operating environment, but we will continue to support CP/M users. Queries must be complete and specific. Don't make us guess what your article is about."

RAINBOW MAGAZINE, Falsoft, Inc., The Falsoft Bldg., 9529 U.S. Highway 42, Box 385, Prospect KY 40059. (502)228-4492. Editor: Lawrence C. Falk. Managing Editor: James E. Reed. 60% freelance written. Monthly magazine covering the Tandy Color Computer. Circ. 75,000. Pays on publication. Publishes ms an average of 4 months after acceptance. Byline given. Buys full rights and rights for "tape" service reprint. Submit seasonal/holiday material 6 months in advance. Electronic submissions on disk or magnetic tape OK, but requires hard copy also. Computer printout submissions acceptable. Reports in 3 months. Sample copy $3.95; free writer's guidelines.

Nonfiction: Jutta Kapfhammer, submissions editor. Technical (computer programs and articles for Tandy Color Computer. No general "overview" articles. "We want articles *with* programs or tutorials." Buys 300+ mss/year. Send complete ms. Pays $25-50/page.

Fillers: Cartoons (must be Color Computer-related).

SOFT SECTOR, Falsoft, Inc., The Falsoft Bldg., 9529 U.S. Highway 42, Box 385, Prospect KY 40059. (502)228-4492. Editor: Lawrence C. Falk. Managing Editor: Ed Ellers. "A monthly bound specific magazine for the Sanyo MS-DOS-based, IBM PC data compatible computer." Pays on publication. Byline given. Buys full rights and rights for disk service reprint. Submit seasonal/holiday material 4 months in advance. Photocopied submissions OK. Electronic submissions OK if ASCII file. Reports in 2 months. Free sample copy; writer's guidelines for SAE.

Nonfiction: Interested only in articles and programs specifically for the Sanyo MS-DOS computers. No general interest or computer commentary. Buys 120 mss/year. Send complete ms. Length: 200 words minimum. Pays $50 maximum/printed magazine page.

Tips: "Know specific computer or don't submit."

‡TI PROFESSIONAL COMPUTING, The Magazine for Texas Instruments Computer Users, Publications and Communications, Inc., 12416 Hymeadow Dr., Austin TX 78750. (512)250-9023. Editor: Dean J. Whitehair. Managing Editor: Harold Sims. 20% freelance written. A monthly magazine of technical articles relating to Texas Instruments Pro, Business Pro, and 990 series. Circ. 15,000. Pays on publication. Publishes ms an average of 3 months after acceptance. Byline given. Buys first North American serial rights and reprints from other PCI magazines. Submit seasonal/holiday material 5 months in advance. Simultaneous submissions and photocopied submissions OK. Electronic submissions OK via MS-DOS ASCII Files. Computer printout submissions acceptable. Free sample copy.

Nonfiction: How-to, interview/profile, new product, opinion and technical. No humor or non-TI-oriented articles. Buys 50 mss/year. Query with or without published clips, or send complete ms. Length 500-4,000 words. Pays 7¢/word maximum for assigned articles; occasionally pays with subscription or other premiums. Will negotiate. Sometimes pays the expenses of writers on assignment.

Photos: State availability of photos with submissions. Reviews contact sheets, transparencies, and prints. Offers $20 maximum/photo. Captions, model releases and identification of subjects required. Buys one-time rights.

‡II COMPUTING, For Apple II Users, 524 2nd St., San Francisco CA 94107. (415)957-0886. Executive Editor: DeWitt Robbeloth. Editor: Anita Malnig. 60% freelance written. Eager to work with new/unpublished writers. "*IIComputing* serves people who use Apple II computers in their homes for programming, home productivity, children's education, entertainment or home business." Estab. 1985. Circ. 60,000. Pays on acceptance. Publishes ms an average of 4 months after acceptance. Byline given. Offers 33% kill fee. Buys all rights; pays extra for reprinting. Submit seasonal/holiday material 4 months in advance. Simultaneous submissions

OK. Electronic submissions OK via Apple II or AppleWorks word processing. Computer printout submissions acceptable; prefers letter-quality to dot-matrix. Reports in 1 month. Sample copy $2 with 8½x11 SAE and $1.40 postage; free writer's guidelines.

Nonfiction: Book excerpts, how-to, interview/profile, new product, and technical. All articles must relate to using, or obtaining information about, Apple II computers. Nothing about computers other than the Apple II family. Query with published clips or send complete ms. Length: 1,500-5,000 words. Pays $100/published page. "We go up from there depending on experience and expertise." May trade for advertising as payment. Sometimes pays the expenses of writers on assignment.

Photos: State availability of photos with submission. Reviews transparencies. May include photo fee in overall payment. Model releases and identification of subjects required.

Columns/Departments: Reviews (product/hardware), 500-750 words; Profile (personalities in the Apple world), Assembly Language (articles that explore assembly language), and Power Programming (advanced programming, usually in BASIC), 1,500-5,000 words. Query with published clips, send complete ms. Pays $100/published page.

Tips: "Become as familiar and creative as possible with Apple II (IIe, IIc, IIt) computers and software. Features, reviews, and all programming features are most open to freelancers. Do some digging. Address some important issues in the computer/high-tech area."

Photography

If you want to develop a photographer's eye or to write articles about photography, these publications will help you. Readers of these magazines use their cameras for enjoyment and for weekend assignments. Magazines geared to the professional photographer can be found in Trade Journals.

‡**DARKROOM & CREATIVE CAMERA TECHNIQUES**, Preston Publications, Inc., Box 48312, 7800 Merrimac Ave., Niles IL 60648. (312)965-0566. Publisher: Seaton Preston. Editor: David Alan Jay. 75% freelance written. Prefers to work with published/established writers; works with a small number of new/unpublished writers each year. Bimonthly magazine focusing mainly on darkroom techniques, photochemistry, and photographic experimentation and innovation—particularly in the areas of photographic processing, printing and reproduction—plus general user-oriented photography articles aimed at advanced workers and hobbyists. Circ. 45,000. Pays on publication within 1 week. Publishes ms an average of 6 months after acceptance. Byline given. Buys one-time rights. Submit seasonal/holiday material 6 months in advance. Photocopied submissions OK. Electronic submissions acceptable; "check with us first on communication protocol and disk format." Computer printout submissions acceptable (but discouraged); prefers letter-quality to dot-matrix. Sample copy $3; free writer's guidelines with SASE.

Nonfiction: General interest articles within above topics; how-to, technical product reviews and photo features. Query or send complete ms. Length open, but most features run approximately 2,500 words or 4-5 magazine pages. Pays $100/published page for well-researched technical articles. Sometimes pays expenses of writers on assignment.

Photos: Send photos with ms. Ms payment includes photo payment. Prefers color transparencies and 8x10 b&w prints. Captions, model releases (where appropriate), and identification of subjects required. Buys one-time rights.

Tips: "Successful writers for our magazine are doing what they write about. They have tried the photo technique and write detailed how-to articles—new twists for use with existing materials, etc."

DARKROOM PHOTOGRAPHY MAGAZINE, TL Enterprises, 1 Hallidie Plaza, San Francisco CA 94102. (415)989-4360. Editor: Richard Senti. Managing Editor: Kim Torgerson. A photography magazine with darkroom emphasis, published 8 times/year for both professional and amateur photographers "interested in what goes on *after* the picture's been taken: processing, printing, manipulating, etc." Circ. 80,000. Pays on publication; pays regular writers on acceptance. Byline given. Offers 50% kill fee. Buys one-time rights. Photocopied submissions OK. Computer printout submissions acceptable. Reports in 6 weeks. Sample copy and writer's guidelines for SASE.

Nonfiction: Historical/nostalgic (some photo-history pieces); how-to (darkroom equipment build-its); interview/profile (famous photographers); and technical (articles on darkroom techniques, tools, and tricks). No stories on shooting techniques, strobes, lighting, or in-camera image manipulation. Query or send complete ms. Length: varies. Pays $50-500, depending on project.
Photos: State availability or send photos with query or ms. Reviews transparencies and prints. "Supporting photographs are considered part of the manuscript package."
Columns/Departments: Darkroom Basics, Tools & Tricks, Special Effects, Making Money, and Larger Formats. Query or send complete ms. Length: 800-1,200 words. "Published darkroom-related 'tips' receive free one-year subscriptions." Length: 100-150 words.

‡**OUTDOOR PHOTOGRAPHER**, Werner & Werner Corp., 16200 Ventura Blvd., Encino CA 91436. (818)986-8400. Editor: Steve Werner. Managing Editor: Lynne Werner. 80% freelance written. A magazine published 9 times a year covering sports, nature and travel photography. Estab. 1985. Circ. 60,000. Pays on publication. Byline given. Submit seasonal/holiday material 6 months in advance. Simultaneous, photocopied and previously published submissions OK. Reports in 1 month. Sample copy for 8½x11 SAE with $2.50 postage.
Nonfiction: How-to, interview/profile, new product, personal experience, photo feature, technical and travel. Buys 50 mss/year. Query with or without published clips, or send complete ms. Length: 1,000-3,000 words. Pays $200-500. Sometimes pays expenses of writers on assignment.
Photos: Send photos with submission. Reviews transparencies and prints. Offers $75-200/photo. Captions and identification of subjects required. Buys one-time rights.
Tips: "*Outdoor Photographer* takes a fresh look at our modern photographic world by encouraging photography as part of a lifestyle associated with outdoor recreation. Editorial is intended to de-mystify the use of modern equipment by emphasizing the practical use of the camera in the field, high-lighting the technique rather than the technical."

PETERSEN'S PHOTOGRAPHIC MAGAZINE, Petersen Publishing Co., 8490 Sunset Blvd., Los Angeles CA 90069. (213)657-5100. Group Publisher: Paul Tzimoulis. Editor: Bill Hurter. 40% freelance written. Prefers to work with published/established writers; eager to work with new/unpublished writers. Monthly magazine; 100 pages. Emphasizes how-to photography. Circ. 300,000. Pays on publication. Publishes ms an average of 9 months after acceptance. Buys all rights. Submit seasonal/holiday material 5 months in advance. Photocopied submissions OK. Computer printout submissions acceptable. Reports in 2 months. Sample copy $2.50.
Nonfiction: How-to (equipment reports, darkroom, lighting, special effects, and studio photography). "We don't cover personalities." Buys 12-30 unsolicited mss/year. Send story, photos and captions. Pays $60/printed page. Sometimes pays the expenses of writers on assignment.
Photos: With coupon to Photo Contest Editor. Photos purchased with or without accompanying ms. Pays $25-35 for b&w and color photos. Model releases and technical details required.
Tips: "Freelancers should study the easy conversational style of our articles. We are a how-to-do-it magazine which requires clearly detailed text and step-by-step illustration. Write for our writer's and photographer's guide for details of our requirements."

PHOTO LIFE, 100 Steelcase Rd. E, Markham, Ontario L3R 1E8 Canada. (416)475-8440. Editor: Norm Rosen. 60% freelance written. Works with a small number of new/unpublished writers each year; eager to work with new/unpublished writers. Monthly magazine. "Canada's leading magazine for the amateur photographer, providing information, entertainment and technical tips which help readers develop their interest in photography." Reader participation emphasized through gallery sections, contests and portfolio features. All articles and photography assigned specifically, but most assignments given to readers who contact *Photo Life* with ideas or sample photography. Canadian photos and articles given priority, although features of interest to Canadian photographers but not written or photographed by Canadians will also be considered. Circ. 85,000. Pays on publication. Publishes ms an average of 3 months after acceptance. Byline given. Buys first North American serial rights. Most content assigned 6 months prior to publication. Computer printout submissions acceptable. Sample copy and writer's guidelines for $2 and SASE; photo guidelines with SAE and 37¢ Canadian postage.
Nonfiction: Interested in all subjects of interest to amateur photographers. Uses 8x10 glossy b&w prints. Pays $25 (Canadian) minimum/photo. Uses 35mm or larger color transparencies or 8x10 color prints, glossy preferred. Unless assigned, covers are derived from content of each issue. Uses vertical format 35mm slides or larger form slides only. Pays $200/cover. Canadian content only. Article ideas are welcome but *no* unsolicited mss. Payment for articles ranges from $100 Canadian minimum.
Tips: "Contact us prior to sending unsolicited material. We operate by assignment exclusively. Topics suggested by freelancers will be given a target length when assigned."

‡**STRATEGIES, The Self-Promotion Newsletter for Photographers**, The Simon Gallery, Box 838, Montclair NJ 07042. (201)783-5480. Editor: Harold Simon. 10-15% freelance written. Works with a small

number of new/unpublished writers each year. Bimonthly newsletter on marketing for fine art photographers. *Strategies* shows fine art photographers how to develop their careers. "We provide first hand information from publishers, photographers, museum curators and gallery directors. Information about every aspect of the fine art photography world—grants, exhibits, portfolios, etc.—is presented." Pays on publication. Byline given. Makes work-for-hire assignments. Simultaneous submissions, photocopied submissions, and previously published submissions OK. Electronic submissions OK via Apple Macintosh disks only. Computer printout submissions acceptable. Reports in 1 month. Sample copy $3.

Nonfiction: How-to (about getting exhibits, grants, or being published, putting together portfolios, invitations, or unique promotional experiences); interview/profile; and personal experience. No technical articles about photo equipment, or book/exhibition reviews. Buys 6 mss/year. Query with or without published clips, or send complete ms. Length: 250-1,500 words. Pays $25 plus copies.

‡**WILDLIFE PHOTOGRAPHY**, The Wildlife Photography Association, Box 691, Greenville PA 16125. (412)588-3492. Editor: Charles Burchfield, 327 S. Highland St., DuBois PA 15801. (814)371-6818. 80% freelance written. Bimonthly newsletter. "We are dedicated to the pursuit and capture of wildlife on film. Emphasis on how-to and where-to." Estab. 1985. Circ. 2,000. Pays on acceptance. Publishes ms an average of 6 months after acceptance. Byline given. Buys first rights, one-time rights or second serial (reprint) rights. Submit seasonal/holiday material 3 months in advance. Simultaneous, photocopied and previously published submissions OK. Computer printout submissions acceptable; prefers letter-quality to dot-matrix. Reports in 2 weeks on queries; 6 weeks on mss. Sample copy $2; free writer's guidelines.

Nonfiction: Book excerpts; how-to (work with animals to take a good photo); interview/profile (of professionals); new product (of particular interest to wildlife photography); personal experience (with cameras in the field) and travel (where to find superb photo opportunities of plants and animals). No fiction or photography of pets, sports and scenery. Buys 30 mss/year. Query or send complete ms. Length: 200-3,000 words. Pays $10-50.

Photos: Send photos with submission. Reviews contact sheets, negatives, transparencies and 5x7 prints as part of ms package. Photos not accepted separate from ms. Offers no additional payment for photos accepted with ms. Captions and identification of subjects required. Buys one-time rights.

Fillers: Anecdotes and facts. Buys 12/year. Length: 50-200 words. Pays $5-15.

Tips: "Give solid how-to info on how to photograph a specific species of wild animal. Send photos, not only of the subject, but of the photographer and his gear in action. The area of our publication most open to freelancers is feature articles."

Politics and World Affairs

These publications cover politics for the reader interested in current events. Nuclear issues, terrorist attacks, and hostage confrontations have prompted more readers than ever to follow world news. Other publications that will consider articles about politics and world affairs are listed under Business and Finance, Regional and General Interest. For listings of publications geared toward the professional, see Trade Journals/Government and Public Service and Trade Journals/International Affairs.

AFRICA REPORT, 833 United Nations Plaza, New York NY 10017. (212)949-5731. Editor: Margaret A. Novicki. 60% freelance written. Bimonthly. For U.S. citizens, residents with a special interest in African affairs for professional, business, academic or personal reasons. Not tourist-related. Circ. 10,500. Pays on publication. Publishes ms an average of 2 months after acceptance. Rights purchased vary with author and material; usually buys all rights, very occasionally first serial rights. Offers negotiable kill fee. Byline given unless otherwise requested. Sample copy for $4; free writer's guidelines.

Nonfiction: Interested in "African political, economic and cultural affairs, especially in relation to U.S. foreign policy and business objectives. Style should be journalistic but not academic or light. Articles should not be polemical or long on rhetoric but may be committed to a strong viewpoint. I do not want tourism articles." Would like to see in-depth topical analyses of lesser known African countries, based on residence or several months' stay in the country. Buys 15 unsolicited mss/year. Pays $150-250.

Photos: Photos purchased with or without accompanying mss with extra payment. Reviews b&w only. Pays $25. Submit 12x8 "half-plate."
Tips: "Read *Africa Report* and other international journals regularly. Become an expert on an African or Africa-related topic. Make sure your submissions fit the style, length, and level of *Africa Report*."

‡C.L.A.S.S. MAGAZINE, C.L.A.S.S. Promotions, Inc., 27 Union Square West, New York NY 10003. Editor: D. Alex Harris. 70% freelance written. Works with a small number of new/unpublished writers each year. Monthly magazine covering Caribbean/American Third World news and views. Circ. 200,000. Pays on acceptance. Publishes ms an average of 1 month after acceptance. Byline given. Buys first rights and second (reprint) rights to material originally published elsewhere. Submit seasonal/holiday material 4 months in advance. Simultaneous queries and previously published submissions OK. Computer printout submissions acceptable; prefers letter-quality to dot-matrix. Reports in 1 month on queries; 6 weeks on mss. Free sample copy and writer's guidelines.
Nonfiction: Features, book excerpts, general interest, historical/nostalgic, inspirational, interview/profile, travel and international news, views and lifestyles in Third World countries. Query or send complete ms. Length: 150-2,500 words. Articles over 700 words must be of international flavor in content. Sometimes pays expenses of writers on assignment.
Poetry: Avant-garde, free verse, haiku, light verse and traditional. Buys 10-20 poems/year. Submit maximum 10 poems. Length: 22-30 lines. Pays $10 minimum.
Tips: "Submit written queries; stick to Afro American/Third World interests and relate to an international audience."

CALIFORNIA JOURNAL, The California Center, 1714 Capitol Ave., Sacramento CA 95814. (916)444-2840. Editor: Richard Zeiger. Managing Editor: A.G. Block. 50% freelance written. Prefers to work with published/established writers. Monthly magazine; 60 pages. Emphasizes analysis of California politics and government. Circ. 18,000. Pays on publication. Publishes ms an average of 2 months after acceptance. Byline given. Buys all rights. Electronic submissions OK via 1200 Baud, IBM PC. Computer printout submissions acceptable; prefers letter-quality to dot-matrix.
Nonfiction: Profiles of state and local government and political analysis. No outright advocacy pieces. Buys 25 unsolicited mss/year. Query. Length: 900-3,000 words. Pays $150-500. Sometimes pays the expenses of writers on assignment.

CRITIQUE: A JOURNAL OF CONSPIRACIES & METAPHYSICS, Box 11451, Santa Rosa CA 95406. (707)525-9401. Editor: Bob Banner. Managing Editor: M. Banovitch. 60% freelance written. Eager to work with new/unpublished writers. Semiannual journal "that explores conspiracy scenarios, behind-the-scenes news, expose, and unusual news that frequently creates debacles within the ordinary mind set. *Critique* also explores assumptions, beliefs and hypotheses that we use to understand ourselves, our 'world' and the metaphysical crisis of our time." Circ. 5,000. Pays on publication. Publishes ms an average of 1 month after acceptance. Byline given. Submit seasonal material 4 months in advance. Simultaneous queries, and simultaneous, photocopied, and previously published submissions OK. Electronic submissions OK if compatible with Text Files operable in DOS for Apple IIe, but requires hard copy also. Computer printout submissions acceptable. Reports in 4 months. Sample copy $5; free writer's guidelines.
Nonfiction: Book excerpts; book reviews; expose (political, metaphysical, cultural); interview/profile (those in the specified area); and personal experience (as it relates to cultural ideology). Not interested in "anything that gets published in ordinary, established media." Buys 8-25 mss/year. Send complete ms with bio/resume. Length: 200-3,000 words. Pays $30 maximum. "We also publish books. Send us your book proposal."
Tips: "We have published articles, reviews and essays that are difficult to categorize in the simplistic, dualistic Left or Right ideological camps. The material's purpose has been, and will be, to provoke critical thinking; to discriminate between valuable and manipulative information; to incite an awareness of events, trends, phases and our roles/lives within the global psyche that no ordinary consumer of ordinary media could even begin to conceive, let alone use such an awareness to affect his/her life. Writers have a better chance of breaking in at our publication with short articles and fillers as it gives us the chance to get acquainted, to feel their styles. The most frequent mistakes made by writers in completing an article are tedious writing and poor organizational structure. Send for a sample and request writer's guidelines."

EUROPE, 2100 M St. NW, 707, Washington DC 20037. Editor: Webster Martin. 20% freelance written. Magazine published 10 times a year for anyone with a professional or personal interest in Western Europe and European/U.S. relations. Circ. 50,000. Pays on acceptance. Publishes ms an average of 2 months after acceptance. Buys first serial rights and all rights. Submit seasonal material 3 months in advance. Computer printout submissions acceptable; prefers letter-quality to dot-matrix. Reports in 1 month.
Nonfiction: Interested in current affairs (with emphasis on economics and politics), the Common Market and Europe's relations with the rest of the world. Publishes occasional cultural pieces, with European angle. "High quality writing a must. We publish anything that might be useful to people with a professional interest in Eu-

rope." Buys 100 mss/year. Query or submit complete ms. Include resume of author's background and qualifications. Length: 500-2,000 words. Pays $100-325.

Photos: Photos purchased with or without accompanying mss. Buys b&w and color. Pays $25-35 for b&w print, any size; $50 for inside use of color transparencies; $200-300 for color used on cover.

THE FREEMAN, 30 S. Broadway, Irvington-on-Hudson NY 10533. (914)591-7230. Editor: Brian Summers. 60% freelance written. Eager to work with new/unpublished writers. Monthly for "fairly advanced students of liberty and the layman." Buys all rights, including reprint rights. Byline given. Pays on publication. Publishes ms an average of 2 months after acceptance. Computer printout submissions acceptable; prefers letter-quality to dot-maxtrix.

Nonfiction: "We want nonfiction clearly analyzing and explaining various aspects of the free market, private enterprise, limited government philosophy, especially as pertains to conditions in the United States. Though a necessary part of the literature of freedom is the exposure of collectivistic cliches and fallacies, our aim is to emphasize and explain the positive case for individual responsibility and choice in a free economy. Especially important, we believe, is the methodology of freedom—self-improvement, offered to others who are interested. We try to avoid name-calling and personality clashes and find satire of little use as an educational device. Ours is a scholarly analysis of the principles underlying a free market economy. No political strategy or tactics." Buys 44 mss/year. Length: 3,500 words maximum. Pays 5¢/word.

Tips: "It's most rewarding to find freelancers with new insights, fresh points of view. Facts, figures, and quotations cited should be fully documented, to their original source, if possible."

GUARDIAN, Independent Radical Newsweekly, Institute for Independent Social Journalism, 33 W. 17th St., New York NY 10011. (212)691-0404. Editor: William A. Ryan. Weekly newspaper covering U.S. and international news and politics for a broad left and progressive audience. Circ. 25,000. Pays on publication. Byline given. Simultaneous queries, and simultaneous and photocopied submissions OK if indicated. Reports in 3 weeks on queries; 1 month on mss. Sample copy for $1, 9x12 SAE and 5 first class stamps; writer's guidelines for business-size SAE and 1 first class stamp.

Nonfiction: Jill Benderly, articles editor. Expose (of government, corporations, etc.). "About 90% of our publication is hard news and features on current events." Buys 200 mss/year. Query with published clips. Length: 200-1,800 words. Pays $10-90.

Photos: Jeff Jones, photo editor. State availability of photos. Pays $15 for b&w prints. Captions required.

Columns/Departments: Women, Labor, The Left, and Blacks. Buys 30 mss/year. Query with published clips. Length: 200-700 words. Pays $10-30.

IN THESE TIMES, Institute for Public Affairs, 1300 W. Belmont Ave., Chicago IL 60657. Editor: James Weinstein. Managing Editor: Sheryl Larson. 50% freelance written. Prefers to work with published/established writers; works with a small number of new/unpublished writers each year. Weekly tabloid covering national and international news. Circ. 30,000. Pays on publication. Publishes ms an average of 1 month after acceptance. Byline given. Buys variable rights. Submit seasonal/holiday material 2 months in advance. Simultaneous queries, and simultaneous, photocopied, and previously published submissions OK. Computer printout submissions acceptable; prefers letter-quality to dot-matrix. Reports in 6 weeks. Sample copy for SAE and 4 first class stamps.

Nonfiction: Salim Muwakkil, articles editor. Book excerpts, expose, historical, interview/profile and personal experience. "The labor movement, community groups, feminist and minority issues, and anti-corporate movements in general receive special emphasis." Buys 100 mss/year. Query. Length: 400-1,600 words. Pays $150 maximum. Sometimes pays the expenses of writers on assignment.

Photos: State availability of photos. Pays $25 maximum for 8x10 b&w prints. Identification of subjects required. Buys one-time rights.

Columns/Departments: Reviews (books, film, etc.). Buys 45 mss/year. Query. Length: 400-1,600. Pays $25.

THE INTELLECTUAL ACTIVIST, In Defense of Individual Rights, The Intellectual Activist, Inc., Suite 101, 131 5th Ave., New York NY 10003. (212)982-8357. Editor: Peter Schwartz. 33% freelance written. Works with a small number of new/unpublished writers each year. Monthly published newsletter of political and economic analysis. "Our fundamental theme is the defense of individual rights, within the framework of the philosophy of objectivism. We are especially interested in the exploration of issues in their formative stages, when readers can still influence the outcome by expressing their views in appropriate forums." Pays on publication. Publishes ms an average of 2 months after acceptance. Byline given. Offers 20% kill fee. Buys all rights. Computer printout submissions acceptable; no dot-matrix. Sample copy $2.50. Writer's guidelines for #10 SAE and 1 first class stamp.

Nonfiction: Political/economic analysis. Buys 10 mss/year. Query with or without published clips. Length: 2,000-4,000 words. Pays $250-600. Sometimes pays the expenses of writers on assignment.

Tips: "Read several issues, ask for author's guide, then submit well-thought-out query. Articles require a firm pro-individual rights orientation."

‡THE JOURNAL/The Institute for Socioeconomic Studies, The Institute for Socioeconomic Studies, Airport Rd., White Plains NY 10604. (914)428-7400. Editor: B.A. Rittersporn, Jr. 99% freelance written. A semiannual magazine covering socioeconomic issues. "A national, nonpartisan forum for all serious points of view on a broad range of socioeconomic issues such as economic development, social motivation, poverty, urban regeneration, the elderly, etc." Circ. 17,500. Pays on publication. Publishes ms an average of 2 months after acceptance. Byline given. Buys all rights and makes work-for-hire assignments. Photocopied submissions OK. Computer printout submissions acceptable; no dot-matrix. Reports in 4 weeks. Sample copy $3.
Nonfiction: Essays and opinion. "We do not want to see anything but brief queries in our specific field of interest. Usually, we seek the experts to write the articles." Buys 28-32 mss/year. Query. Length: 2,500 words. Pays $1,000-1,500.
Photos: State availability of photos with submission. Offers no additional payment for photos accepted with ms. Captions and identification of subjects required. Buys one-time rights.
Columns/Departments: Book reviews (only appropirate titles—query first), 600-700 words. Buys 20 mss/year. Query. Pays $150.

‡THE LIBERTARIAN DIGEST, The Gutenberg Press, 1920 Cedar St., Berkeley CA 94709. (415)548-3776. Editor: Fred Foldvary. 75% freelance written. Eager to work with new/unpublished writers. A bimonthly newsletter which summarizes periodicals of libertarian interest. No original material included. Circ. 200. Pays on acceptance. Publishes ms an average of 2 months after acceptance. Byline given at option of writer. Not copyrighted. Buys all rights. Makes work-for-hire assignment. Simultaneous submissions, photocopied submissions, and previously published submissions OK. Electronic submissions OK via 300 Baud, ASCII. Computer printout submissions acceptable "if high quality." Reports in 1 week. Sample copy $2; writer's guidelines and free sample page for SAE with 1 first class stamp.
Nonfiction: Summaries and book reviews. Query. No unsolicited submissions; no original works. Pays 25¢ per column inch, no maximum amount. Pays writer with contributor copies or other premiums "if writer desires." Pays expenses of writers on assignment.
Photos: State availability of photos with submissions. Reviews prints. Offers 25¢/column inch. Buys one-time rights.
Fillers: Anecdotes, facts, newsbreaks, and short humor. Variable number of fillers. Pays 25¢/column inch.
Tips: "All copy must be camera-ready. We supply magazines to summarize. Anyone who can submit well-written, camera-ready copy can break in."

THE NATION, 72 5th Ave., New York NY 10011. Editor: Victor Navasky. Weekly. Buys first serial rights. Computer printout submissions acceptable; prefers letter-quality to dot-matrix.
Nonfiction: "We welcome all articles dealing with the social scene, particularly if they examine it with a new point of view or expose conditions the rest of the media overlooks." Queries encouraged. Buys 100 mss/year. Length 2,500 words maximum. Payment negotiable. Modest rates.
Tips: "We are firmly committed to reporting on the issues of labor, national politics, business, consumer affairs, environmental politics, civil liberties and foreign affairs. Those issues can never be over-reported."

NATIONAL JOURNAL, 1730 M St. NW, Washington DC 20036. (202)857-1400. Editor: Richard Frank. "No freelance material accepted because fulltime staff produces virtually all of our material."

NEWSWEEK, 444 Madison Ave., New York NY 10022. (212)350-4547. My Turn Editor: Phyllis Malamud. Although staff written it does accept unsolicited mss for My Turn, a column of opinion. The 1,000- to 1,100-word essays for the column must be original and contain verifiable facts. Payment is $1,000, on publication, for all rights. Computer printout submissions acceptable; no dot-matrix. Reports in 1 month.

THE PROGRESSIVE, 409 E. Main St., Madison WI 53703. (608)257-4626. Editor: Erwin Knoll. 75% freelance written. Monthly. Pays on publication. Publishes ms an average of 6 weeks after acceptance. Byline given. Buys all rights. Computer printout submissions acceptable "if legible and double-spaced"; prefers letter-quality to dot-matrix. Reports in 2 weeks. Query.
Nonfiction: Primarily interested in articles which interpret, from a progressive point of view, domestic and world affairs. Occasional lighter features. "*The Progressive* is a *political* publication. General-interest material is inappropriate." Length: 3,000 words maximum. Pays $75-250.
Tips: "Display some familiarity with our magazine, its interests and concerns, its format and style. We want query letters that fully describe the proposed article without attempting to sell it—and that give an indication of the writer's competence to deal with the subject."

REASON MAGAZINE, Box 40105, Santa Barbara CA 93140. (805)963-5993. Editor: Mary Zupan. 50% freelance written. Monthly. For a readership interested in individual liberty, economic freedom, private enterprise alternatives to government services, individualist cultural and social perspectives. Circ. 40,000. Pays after acceptance. Publishes ms an average of 2 months after acceptance. Rights purchased vary with author and material; may buy all rights, first North American serial rights, or first serial rights. Byline given. Offers kill fee sometimes. Photocopied submissions OK. Double- or triple-spaced, typed mss only. Reports in 2 months. Sample copy $2.

Nonfiction: "*Reason* deals with social, economic and political issues, supporting both individual liberty and economic freedom. The following kinds of articles are desired: investigative articles exposing government wrongdoing and bungling; investigative articles revealing examples of private (individual, business, or group) ways of meeting needs; individualist analysis of policy issues (e.g., education, victimless crimes, regulation); think pieces exploring implications of individual freedom in economic, political, cultural, and social areas." Query. Buys 50-70 mss/year. Length: 1,000-5,000 words.

‡ROLL CALL, The Newspaper of the US Congress, 236 Massachusetts Ave. NE, Washington DC 20002. (202)546-3080. Editor: Sidney Yudain. Weekly tabloid covering national politics for Congress, congressional aides, the White House, political writers, newspeople, etc. Circ. 7,500. Pays on publication. Byline given. Buys first rights only. Submit seasonal/holiday material 1 month in advance. Simultaneous queries OK. Computer printout submissions acceptable; prefers letter-quality to dot-matrix. Reports in 2 weeks on queries; 1 month on mss. Sample copy for 9x12 SAE and 3 first class stamps.

Nonfiction: Historical/nostalgic, humor, interview/profile, personal experience and photo feature. Special issues include Anniversary Issue (June); and Welcome Congress Issue (January). "No material *not* pertaining to Congress except topical satire on a national political event such as Watergate, the election, major cabinet reshuffle, etc." Buys 6 mss/year. "We will be more liberal in use of submitted material if guidelines are followed." Send complete ms. Length: 1,800 words maximum. Pays $5-25.

Photos: Send photos with ms. Pays $5 maximum for 8x10 b&w prints. Identification of subjects required.

Poetry: Light verse. No heavy, serious verse about nonpolitical or non-Congressional subjects. Buys 12/year. Length: open. Pays $2-10.

Fillers: Jokes, gags, anecdotes and short humor. Pays $2 maximum.

Tips: "Submit well-researched original Congressional articles (oddities, statistical compilations, historical retrospectives), topical verse or topical satirical pieces and one-liners. No serious material far removed from the Congressional political world—material on national or international issues—we have all the 'experts' at our doorstep."

‡UTNE READER, The Best of the Alternative Press, LENS Publishing, 2732 W. 43rd St., Minneapolis MN 55410. (612)929-2670. Editors: Helen Cordes, Eric Utne and Jay Walljasper. 5% freelance written; 90% reprints of previously published articles. A bimonthly magazine. "We reprint articles that have already been published, generally in alternative magazines." Circ. 30,000. Pays on publication. Publishes ms an average of 2 months after acceptance. Byline given. Buys second serial (reprint) rights. Submit seasonal/holiday material 4 months in advance. Simultaneous, photocopied and previously published submissions OK. Computer printout submissions acceptable; prefers letter-quality to dot-matrix. Reports in 2 months on queries; 3 months on mss. Sample copy $4.

Nonfiction: Book excerpts, essays, humor, interview/profile and opinion. "We don't want to see articles on topics that have been thoroughly hashed through in the mainstream press." Buys 12 mss/year. Send complete ms. Pays $20 minimum; pays premiums rather than a cash payment only if agreed on in advance.

Photos: Send photos with submission. Buys one-time rights.

Tips: "We generally publish only articles that have been published in alternative magazines. Get your article published, and *then* send us a clipping. Be sure to send a copy of the publication in which it appeared."

WASHINGTON MONTHLY, 1711 Connecticut Ave., Washington DC 20009. (202)462-0128. Editor-in-Chief: Charles Peters. 35% freelance written. For "well-educated, well-read people interested in politics, the press and government." Monthly. Circ. 35,000. Rights purchased depend on author and material; buys all rights, first rights, or second serial (reprint) rights. Buys 20-30 mss/year. Pays on publication. Sometimes does special topical issues. Query or submit complete ms. Computer printout submissions acceptable. Tries to report in 4-6 weeks. Publishes ms an average of 6 weeks after acceptance. Sample copy $3.

Nonfiction: Responsible investigative or evaluative reporting about the U.S. government, business, society, the press and politics. "No editorial comment/essays." Also no poetry, fiction or humor. Length: "average 2,000-6,000 words." Pays 5-10¢/word.

Photos: Buys b&w glossy prints.

Tips: "Best route is to send 1-2 page proposal describing article and angle. The most rewarding aspect of working with freelance writers is getting a solid piece of reporting with fresh ideas that challenge the conventional wisdom."

WORLD POLICY JOURNAL, World Policy Institute, 777 UN Plaza, New York NY 10017. (212)490-0010. Editor: Sherle Schwenninger. 80% freelance written. "We are eager to work with new or unpublished writers as well as more established writers." A quarterly magazine covering international politics, economics and security issues. "We hope to bring a new sense of imagination, principle and proportion, as well as a restored sense of reality and direction to America's discussion of its role in the world." Circ. 10,000. Pays on acceptance. Publishes ms an average of 3 months after acceptance. Byline given. Offers variable kill fee. Buys all rights. Photocopied submissions OK. Computer printout submissions acceptable; prefers letter-quality to dot-matrix. Reports in 2 months. Sample copy for $4.95 and SAE; free writer's guidelines.

Nonfiction: Articles that "define policies that reflect the shared needs and interests of all nations of the world." Query. Length: 30-40 pages (8,500 words maximum). Pays variable commission rate. Sometimes pays the expenses of writers on assignment.

Tips: "By providing a forum for many younger or previously unheard voices, including those from Europe, Asia, Africa, and Latin America, we hope to replace lingering illusions and fears with new priorities and aspirations. Articles submitted on speculation very rarely suit our particular needs—the writers clearly haven't taken time to study the kind of article we publish."

Regional

Some regional publications rely on staff-written material; others depend on freelance writers who live in or know the region. The best regional publication is the one in your hometown; you probably know this market best. It can be a city or state magazine or a Sunday magazine in a newspaper. Listed below are general interest magazines slanted toward residents of and visitors to a particular region. Next, regional publications are categorized alphabetically by state (including the District of Columbia), followed by categories for Puerto Rico, Canada and foreign countries. Many regional publications buy manuscripts on conservation and the natural wonders of their area; additional markets for such material can be found under the Nature, Conservation, and Ecology, and Sports headings. Publications that report on the business climate of a region are grouped in the regional division of the Business and Finance category. Recreation and travel publications specific to a geographical area are listed in the Consumer Travel section.

General

INLAND, The Magazine of the Middle West, Inland Steel Co., 30 W. Monroe St., Chicago IL 60603. (312)346-0300. Managing Editor: Sheldon A. Mix. 30-40% freelance written. Prefers to work with published/established writers. Biannual magazine; 24 pages. Emphasizes steel products, services and company personnel. Circ. 8,000. Pays on acceptance. Publishes ms an average of 1 year after acceptance. Buys first serial rights and first North American serial rights. Kill fee: "We have always paid the full fee on articles that have been killed." Byline given. Submit seasonal/holiday material at least 1 year in advance. Simultaneous submissions OK. Computer printout submissions acceptable; no dot-matrix. Reports in 3 months. Free sample copy.

Nonfiction: Essays, humorous commentaries, personal experience, profile, historical, think articles, personal opinion and photo essays. "We encourage individuality. At least half of each issue deals with staff-written steel subjects; half with widely ranging nonsteel matter. Articles and essays related somehow to the Midwest (Illinois, Wisconsin, Minnesota, Michigan, Missouri, Iowa, Nebraska, Kansas, North Dakota, South Dakota, Indiana and Ohio) in such subject areas as business, entertainment, history, folklore, sports, humor, current scene generally. But subject is less important than treatment. We like perceptive, thoughtful writing, and fresh ideas and approaches. Please don't send slight, rehashed historical pieces or any articles of purely local interest." Personal experience, profile, humor, historical, think articles, personal opinion and photo essays. Buys 5-10 unsolicited mss/year. Length: 1,200-5,000 words. Payment depends on individual assignment or unsolicited submission (usual range: $300-750). Sometimes pays expenses of writers on assignment.

Photos: Purchased with or without mss. Captions required. "Payment for pictorial essay same as for text feature."

Tips: "Our publication particularly needs humor that is neither threadbare nor in questionable taste, and shorter pieces (800-1,500 words) in which word-choice and wit are especially important. The most frequent mistake made by writers in completing an article for us is untidiness in the manuscript (inattentiveness to good form, resulting in errors in spelling and facts, and in gaping holes in information). A writer who knows our needs and believes in himself or herself should keep trying." Recently published material: "Chicago Introduces Lincoln," "Lake Woebegone's Favorite Son," "Train to Galena."

ISLANDS, An International Magazine, Islands Publishing Company, 3886 State St., Santa Barbara CA 93105. Editor: Nancy Zimmerman. 95% freelance written. Prefers to work with published/established writers. Bimonthly magazine covering islands throughout the world. "We invite articles from many different perspectives: scientific, historical, exploratory, cultural, etc. We ask our authors to avoid the typical travel magazine style and concentrate on stimulating and informative pieces that tell the reader something he or she might not know about a particular island." Circ. 110,000. Pays 50% on acceptance and 50% within 30 days after publication. Publishes ms an average of 8 months after acceptance. Byline given. Buys all rights. Computer printout submissions acceptable; prefers letter-quality to dot-matrix. Reports in 1 month on queries; 6 weeks on ms. Sample copy for $4.65; writer's guidelines with SASE.

Nonfiction: General interest, historical/nostalgic, interview/profile, personal experience, photo feature, technical, and any island-related material. "Each issue contains a major centerpiece of up to 5,000 words, 5 or 6 feature articles of roughly 3,000 words, and 4 or 5 topical articles for departments, each of which runs approximately 500-1,500 words. Any authors who wish to be commissioned should send a detailed proposal for an article, an estimate of costs (if applicable), and samples of previously published work." No "I went here and did this/I went there and ate that" travel articles. Buys 100 mss/year. "The majority of our manuscripts are commissioned." Query with published clips or send complete ms. Length: 500-4,000 words. Pays $100-3,000. Pays expenses of writers on assignment.

Photos: State availability or send photos with query or ms. Pays $50-300 for 35mm color transparencies. "Fine color photography is a special attraction of *Islands*, and we look for superb composition, image quality and editorial applicability." Label slides with name and address, include captions, and submit in protective plastic sleeves. Identification of subjects required. Buys one-time rights.

Columns/Departments: "Columns and departments are generally assigned, but we have accepted short features for our Island Hopping department. These should be highly focused on some travel-oriented aspect of islands." Buys 10-20 mss/year. Query with published clips. Length: 500-2,000 words. Pays $100-750.

Tips: "A freelancer can best break in to our publication with short (1,000-2,000 word) features that are highly focused on some aspect of island life, history, people, etc. Stay away from general, sweeping articles. We are always looking for topics for our Islanders and Island Pantry columns. These are a good place to break in. We will be using more big name writers for major features; will continue to use newcomers and regulars for columns and departments."

MID-ATLANTIC COUNTRY MAGAZINE, A Guide-From the Appalachians to the Atlantic, (formerly *Country Magazine*), Country Sun, Inc., Box-246, Alexandria VA 22313. (703)548-6177. Editor: Jim Scott. Managing Editor: Kathy Davis. 90% freelance written. Prefers to work with published/established writers. Monthly magazine of living in the mid-Atlantic region. "Our coverage aims at promoting an appreciation of the region, especially through writing about travel, history, leisure pursuits, outdoor sports, food, nature, the environment, interior decor, gardening, the arts, and people in these states: Virginia, Maryland, Delaware, D.C., West Virginia, North Carolina, Pennsylvania and New Jersey." Circ. 100,000. Pays on publication. Publishes ms an average of 6 months after acceptance. Byline given. Buys one-time rights. Submit seasonal/holiday material 6 months in advance. Photocopied submissions OK. Computer printout submissions (double-spaced) acceptable. Reports in 1 month. Sample copy for $1 with 9x12 SAE and $1.22 postage; writer's guidelines for business size SAE and 1 first class stamp.

Nonfiction: Book excerpts (of regional interest); historical (mid-Atlantic history with current news peg); how-to (deal with country living: how to buy country property, how to tap a sugar maple, etc.); interview/profile (of mid-Atlantic residents); photo feature (regional); and travel (mid-Atlantic—off the beaten path). Buys 120 mss/year. Query with published clips if available. Length: 250-1,500 words. Pays $3.50/column inch, more for regular writers. Sometimes pays the expenses of writers on assignment.

Photos: State availability of photos. Pays $35-50 for 35mm color transparencies and 5x7 b&w prints. Captions, model releases, and identification of subjects required.

Columns/Departments: People, Places and Pleasures, 250-750 words. Pays $3.50/column inch.

Fiction: Historical, mainstream and novel excerpts directly related to region. No nonregional fiction; "we seldom run fiction." Buys 1 ms/year. Query with published clips if available. Length: 1,200-1,500 words. Pays $3.50/column inch, more for name writers.

Poetry: "We seldom publish poetry."

Tips: "We are especially open to how-to, gardening and people stories pegged to the mid-Atlantic region." Follow the editor's requirements.

NORTHWEST MAGAZINE, the magazine of *The Oregonian*, 1320 SW Broadway, Portland OR 97201. Editor: Jack Hart. 90% freelance written. Prefers to work with published/established writers. Weekly newspaper Sunday supplement magazine; 24-40 pages. For an upscale, 25-49 year-old audience distributed throughout the Pacific Northwest. Circ. 420,000. Buys first serial rights for Oregon and Washington state. Pays mid-month in the month following acceptance. Publishes ms an average of 4 months after acceptance. All mss on speculation. Simultaneous submissions considered. Computer printout submissions acceptable; prefers letter-quality to dot-matrix. Electronic submissions OK via modem; call (503)221-8228. Reports in 2 weeks. Free writer's guidelines.
Nonfiction: "Contemporary, regional articles with a strong hook to concerns of the Pacific Northwest. Cover stories usually deal with regional issues and feature 'professional-level' reporting and writing. Personality profiles focus on young, Pacific Northwest movers and shakers. Short humor, personal essays, regional destination travel, entertainment, the arts and lifestyle stories also are appropriate. No history without a contemporary angle, boilerplate features of the type that are mailed out en masse with no specific hook to our local audience, poorly documented and highly opinionated issue stories that lack solid journalistic underpinnings, routine holiday features, or gushy essays that rhapsodize about daisies and rainbows. We expect top-quality writing and thorough, careful reporting. A contemporary writing style that features involving literary techniques like scenic construction stands the best chance." Buys 400 mss/year. Query much preferred, but complete ms considered. Length: 800-3,000 words. Pays $75-500/mss. Sometimes pays the expenses of writers on assignment.
Photos: Photographs should be professional quality b&w prints, contact sheets with negatives or Kodachrome slides. Pays $25-50.
Poetry: Paul Pintarich, book review editor. "*Northwest Magazine* seeks poetry with solid imagery, skilled use of language and having appeal to a broad and intelligent audience. We do not accept cutesy rhymes, jingles, doggeral or verse written for a specific season, i.e., Christmas, Valentine's Day, etc. We currently are only accepting poems from poets in the Pacific Northwest region (Oregon, Washington, Idaho, Montana, Northern California, British Columbia and Alaska). Poems from Nevada and Hawaii receive consideration. We are looking for a few fine and distinctive poems each week. Poems on dot-matrix printers accepted if near letter-quality only. No handwritten submissions or threats." Send at least 3 poems for consideration. Length: 23 lines maximum. Pays $5 on acceptance.
Tips: "Pay rates and editing standards are up, and this market will become far more competitive. However, new writers with talent and good basic language skills still are encouraged to try us. Printing quality and flexibility should improve, increasing the magazine's potential for good color photographers and illustrators."

THE ORIGINAL NEW ENGLAND GUIDE, Historical Times, Inc., 2245 Kohn Rd., Box 8200, Harrisburg PA 17105. (717)657-9555. Editor: Kathie Kull. Consulting Editor: Mimi E.B. Steadman. 70% freelance written. Works with a small number of new/unpublished writers each year. Annual magazine covering New England travel and vacations. *The Guide* is a complete travel planner and on-the-road guide to the six New England states. It has a strong family focus and spring-summer-fall coverage of growing or unusual destinations, events and attractions." Circ. 160,000. Pays 2 months after acceptance. Publishes ms up to 6 months after acceptance. Buys all rights. November 15 deadline for following April publication date. Computer printout submissions acceptable. Reports in 2 weeks. Sample copy for 9x12 SAE and $2.40 postage; writer's guidelines for # 10 SAE and 1 first class stamp.
Nonfiction: Photo feature and travel—New England only. No historical or business. Buys 8 mss/year. Query with published clips. Length: 500-1,500 words. Pays $100-400. Sometimes pays mail and telephone expenses.
Photos: State availability of photos. Reviews 35mm color transparencies and 8x10 prints. Pays $25-75 for b&w; $50-400 for color. Identification of subjects required. Buys one-time rights.
Fillers: Rarely used.
Tips: "Choose New England-related places or activities that appeal to a wide range of readers—active and sedentary, young and old, single and families. Areas most open to freelancers are region-wide features and state-specific sidebars. Copy must 'sell' the area or activity to the traveler as worth a special stop or trip. We do not promote commercial establishments in features. We are service-oriented and provide factual information that helps the reader plan a trip, not just descriptions of places and things."

RURALITE, Box 557, Forest Grove OR 97116. (503)357-2105. Editor: Ken Dollinger. 50% freelance written. Works with a small number of new/unpublished writers each year. Monthly magazine primarily slanted toward small town and rural families, served by consumer-owned electric utilities in Washington, Oregon, Idaho, Nevada and Alaska. "Ours is an old-fashioned down-home publication, with something for all members of the family." Circ. 223,000. Pays on acceptance. Publishes ms 1 month-1 year after acceptance. Buys first serial rights and occasionally second (reprint) rights. Byline given. Submit seasonal material at least 3 months in advance. Computer printout submissions acceptable; prefers letter-quality to dot-matrix. Sample copy and writer's guidelines for $1.

Nonfiction: Walter J. Wentz, nonfiction editor. Primarily human-interest stories about rural or small-town folk, preferably living in areas (Northwest states and Alaska) served by Rural Electric Cooperatives. Articles emphasize self-reliance, overcoming of obstacles, cooperative effort, hard or interesting work, unusual or interesting avocations, odd or unusual hobbies or histories, public spirit or service and humor. Also considers how-to, advice for rural folk, little-known and interesting Northwest history, people or events. "We are looking specifically for energy (sources, use, conservation) slant and items relating to rural electric cooperatives." No "sentimental nostalgia or subjects outside the Pacific Northwest; nothing racy." Buys 15-20 mss/year. Query. Length: 500-1,200 words. Pays $30-100, depending upon length, quality, appropriateness and interest, number and quality of photos.
Photos: Reviews b&w negatives with contact sheets. Offers no additional payment for photos accepted with ms.
Tips: "Freelance submissions are evaluated and decided upon immediately upon arrival. Due to a loss of feature pages, we will be judging freelance submissions much more critically."

YANKEE, Dublin NH 03444. (603)563-8111. Editor-in-Chief: Judson D. Hale. Managing Editor: John Pierce. 50% freelance written. Works with a small number of new/unpublished writers each year. Monthly magazine emphasizing the New England region. Circ. 1,000,000. Pays on acceptance. Publishes ms an average of 10 months after acceptance. Byline given. Buys all rights, first North American serial rights or one-time rights. Submit seasonal/holiday material at least 4 months in advance. Electronic submissions OK via IBM and XYRite, but requires hard copy also. Computer printout submissions acceptable; no dot-matrix. Reports in 6 weeks. Free sample copy and writer's guidelines.
Nonfiction: Historical (New England history, especially with present-day tie-in); how-to (especially for Forgotten Arts series of New England arts, crafts, etc.); humor; interview (especially with New Englanders who have not received a great deal of coverage); nostalgia (personal reminiscence of New England life); photo feature (prefers color, captions essential); profile; travel (to the Northeast only, with specifics on places, prices, etc.); current issues; antiques; and food. Buys 50 mss/year. Query with brief description of how article will be structured (its focus, etc.); articles must include a New England "hook." Length: 1,500-3,000 words. Pays $150-850. Pays expenses of writers on assignment.
Photos: Purchased with ms or on assignment; (without accompanying ms for This New England feature only; color only). Captions required. Reviews prints or transparencies. Pays $25 minimum for 8x10 b&w glossy prints. $150/page for 2¼x2¼ or 35mm transparencies; 4x5 for cover or centerspread. Total purchase price for ms usually includes payment for photos.
Columns/Departments: Traveler's Journal (with specifics on places, prices, etc.); Antiques to Look For (how to find, prices, other specifics); and At Home in New England (recipes, gardening, crafts). Buys 10-12 mss/year. Query. Length: 1,000-2,500 words. Pays $150-400.
Fiction: Deborah Navas, fiction editor. Emphasis is on character development. Buys 12 mss/year. Send complete ms. Length: 2,000-4,000 words. Pays $1,000.
Poetry: Jean Burden, poetry editor. Free verse or traditional. Buys 3-4 poems/issue. Send poems. Length: 32 lines maximum. Pays $35 for all rights, $25 for first magazine rights. Annual poetry contest with awards of $150, $100 and $50 for three best poems during the preceding year.

Alabama

BIRMINGHAM, Birmingham Area Chamber of Commerce, 2027 First Ave. N., Birmingham AL 35203. (205)323-5461. Managing Editor: Ray Martin. 95% freelance written. Prefers to work with published/established writers. A monthly magazine primarily for residents of the Birmingham area, including area Chamber of Commerce members. Circ. 10,000. Pays on publication. Publishes ms an average of 3 months after acceptance. Byline given. Buys first North American serial rights. Submit seasonal/holiday material 4 months in advance. Photocopied submissions OK. Computer printout submissions acceptable; no dot-matrix. Reports in 1 month. Sample copy $1.25.
Nonfiction: General interest (subject and its relationship to Birmingham, including local individuals who are involved with a particular hobby, business, sport, organization or occupation); historical/nostalgic (focus on the Birmingham of the past, often comparing an area's past history and appearance with its current characteristics); interview/profile (individual's personality in addition to mentioning the person's accomplishments and how the accomplishments were attained; individuals with interesting or unusual occupations are often the subjects of profiles); and personal experience (usually relating the unique experiences of Birmingham residents, often humorous; another type is one which presents the writer's reflections on a specific event or experience). No stories that have no direct connection with Birmingham. Buys 144 mss/year. Query with published clips. Length: 4-15 double-spaced typed pages. Pays $50-175.
Tips: "We present Birmingham and its people in an informative, entertaining and positive manner. Rather than

reshaping current events and competing with other media on stories having current news value, *Birmingham* prefers to take a deeper look at local individuals who are exceptional in some way. The emphasis of *Birmingham* is always on people rather than things. These people might have an unusual career, hobby or business, but their story always has a tangible connection to our area. *Birmingham* strives for a 50-50 mix of quotes and narrative material. Writers are encouraged to present the atmosphere surrounding their subject as well as descriptions of the individual's physical characteristics."

Alaska

‡ALASKA, The Magazine of Life on the Last Frontier, Box 99050, Anchorage AK 99509. (907)563-5100. Editor: Tom Gresham. Managing Editor: Ron Dalby. 60% freelance written. A monthly magazine covering topics "uniquely Alaskan." Circ. 150,000. Pays on acceptance. Publishes ms 6 months to 2 years after acceptance. Byline given. Buys first North American serial rights. Submit seasonal/holiday material 1 year in advance. Electronic submissons OK via IBM floppies; but requires hard copy also. Computer printout submissions acceptable. Reports in 1 month on queries; 2 months on manuscripts. Sample copy $2; writer's guidelines for #10 SAE with 1 first class stamp.
Nonfiction: Historical/nostalgic; how-to (on anything Alaskan); humor; interview/profile; personal experience and photo feature. Buys 80 mss/year. Send complete ms. Length: 100-3,500 words. Pays $25 minimum, up to $400 for feature with photos. Sometimes pays the expenses of writers on assignment.
Photos: Send photos with submission. Reviews 35mm transparencies. Captions and identification of subjects required. Pays $25 minimum, $200 for covers; $150 for 2-page spread, $100 for full-page and $50 for half-page.

NEW ALASKAN, Rt. 1, Box 677, Ketchikan AK 99901. Publisher: R.W. Pickrell. 20% freelance written. Works with a small number of new/unpublished writers each year. Monthly tabloid magazine, 28 pages, for residents of Southeast Alaska. Circ. 5,500. Pays on publication. Publishes ms an average of 6 months after acceptance. Byline given. Rights purchased vary with author and material; buys all rights, first serial rights, one-time rights, simultaneous rights, or second serial (reprint) rights. Photocopied submissions OK. Computer printout submissions acceptable. Sample copy $1.50.
Nonfiction: Bob Pickrell, articles editor. Feature material about Southeast Alaska. Emphasis is on full photo or art coverage of subject. Informational, how-to, personal experience, interview, profile, inspirational, humor, historical, nostalgia, personal opinion, travel, successful business operations and new product. Buys 30 mss/year. Submit complete ms. Length: 1,000 words minimum. Pays 1½¢/word. Sometimes pays the expenses of writers on assignment.
Photos: B&w photos purchased with or without mss. Minimum size: 5x7. Pays $5 per glossy used; pays $2.50 per negative. Negatives are returned. Captions required.
Fiction: Bob Pickrell, articles editor. Historical fiction related to Southeast Alaska. Length: open. Pays 1½¢/word.

WE ALASKANS MAGAZINE, Anchorage Daily News, Box 6616, Anchorage AK 99502. (907)786-4318. Editor: Kathleen McCoy. Managing Editor: Howard C. Weaver. 20% freelance written. Sunday tabloid magazine for daily newspaper. Circ. 60,000. Pays on publication. Publishes ms an average of 2 months after acceptance. Byline given. Buys first North American serial rights. Submit seasonal/holiday material 6 months in advance. Simultaneous queries, and photocopied and previously published submissions OK. Computer printout submissions acceptable. Reports in 2 weeks on queries; 1 month on mss. Sample copy for SAE and 60¢ postage; writer's guidelines for SAE and 22¢ postage.
Nonfiction: Book excerpts, historical/nostalgic and personal experience. No general interest articles; only material that relates specifically to Alaska. "We prefer warm, human stories." Buys 12 mss/year. Query with published clips. Length: 1,000-2,000 words. Pays $100-300.
Photos: Richard Murphy, photo editor. State availability or send photos with query. Reviews b&w negatives and 35mm color transparencies. Captions, model releases, and identification of subjects required. Buys one-time rights.
Tips: "Writers have a better chance of breaking in with articles of approximately 1,000 words. Some articles are too general, too clichéd, or don't move the reader."

Arizona

ARIZONA HIGHWAYS, 2039 W. Lewis Ave., Phoenix AZ 85009. (602)258-6641. Editor: Merrill Windsor. 90% freelance written. State-owned magazine designed to help attract tourists into and through the state. Pays on acceptance. Publishes ms an average of 6 months after acceptance. Computer printout submissions acceptable; no dot-matrix. Sample copy for 98¢ postage; writer's guidelines for SAE and 1 first class stamp.

Nonfiction: Contact: managing editor. "Quality writing is what we're looking for so long as it suits our 1,500-2,000 word length." Subjects include narratives and exposition dealing with contemporary events, popular geography, history, anthropology, nature, special things to see and do, outstanding arts and crafts, travel, profiles, etc.; all must be oriented toward Arizona and the Southwest. Buys 6 mss/issue. Buys first serial rights. Query with "a lead paragraph and brief outline of story. We deal with professionals only, so include list of current credits." Length: 1,500-2,000 words. Pays 35-50¢/word. Sometimes pays expenses of writers on assignment.

Photos: "We will use 2¼,, 4x5 or larger, and 35 mm when it displays exceptional quality or content. We prefer Kodachrome in 35mm. Each transparency *must* be accompanied by information attached to each photograph: where, when, what. No photography will be reviewed by the editors unless the photographer's name appears on *each* and *every* transparency." Pays $80-350 for "selected" color transparencies. Buys one-time rights.

Tips: "Writing must be of professional quality, warm, sincere, in-depth, well-peopled and accurate. Avoid themes that describe first trips to Arizona, Grand Canyon, the desert, etc. Emphasis to be on Arizona adventure and romance and themes that can be photographed. Double check for general accuracy."

METRO PHOENIX MAGAZINE, (formerly *Phoenix Magazine*), 4707 N. 12th St., Phoenix AZ 85014. (602)248-8900. Editorial Director: Fern Stewart Welch. Editor: Bob Early. 50% freelance written. "We are mainly interested in finding good reporters with mature judgment." Monthly magazine for professional, general audience. Circ. 40,000. Pays within 2 weeks of publication. Publishes ms an average of 2 months after acceptance. Byline given in most cases. Occasionally offers kill fee. Usually buys all rights. Submit special issue material 3 months in advance. Computer printout submissions acceptable; prefers letter-quality to dot-matrix. Reports in 1 month. Sample copy $1.95 plus $1.25 for postage; writer's guidelines with SASE.

Nonfiction: Predominantly features subjects unique to Phoenix life: urban affairs, arts, lifestyle, etc. Subject should be locally oriented. Informational, how-to, thought-provoking, profile and historical. Each issue also embraces 1 or 2 in-depth reports on crucial, frequently controversial issues that confront the community. January issue: SuperGuide to what to see and do in area; February issue: Gardening Guide; March issue: Arizona Lifestyle; June issue: Summer SuperGuide; July issue: The Phoenix Book of Lists; August issue: Valley Progress Report; November issue: Home Decorating. Buys 120 mss/year. Query or submit complete ms. Length: 1,000-3,000 words. Payment is negotiable; payment for features averages $100-400. Sometimes pays the expenses of writers on assignment.

Photos: Photos are purchased with ms with no additional payment, or on assignment.

Tips: "Our main interest is complete, accurate reporting; writing style is secondary. Best way to sell a story is to call the editor and discuss story idea."

PHOENIX LIVING, 4621 N. 16th St., Phoenix AZ 85016. (602)279-2394. Editor: Patt Dodd. 30% freelance written. Bimonthly magazine covering housing for newcomers and prospective home buyers. Circ. 70,000. Pays on acceptance. Publishes ms an average of 2 months after acceptance. Byline given. Buys all rights. Submit seasonal/holiday material 4 months in advance. Simultaneous queries, and photocopied and previously published submissions OK. Computer printout submissions acceptable; prefers letter-quality to dot-matrix. Reports in 1 month. Free sample copy. Writer's guidelines for business size SAE and 1 first class stamp.

Nonfiction: General housing information, real estate, Arizona business, employment overviews, custom buildings and apartment living—all locally oriented. Buys 20 mss/year. Query with published clips. Length: 700-1,000 words; longer features are assigned locally. Pays 10-20¢/word. Sometimes pays expenses of writers on assignment.

Photos: State availability of photos. Pays negotiable fee for 8x10 b&w glossy prints. Captions and model releases required. Buys all rights.

Tips: "The writer may have a better chance of breaking in at our publication with short articles and fillers. Because we specialize entirely in upbeat articles to stimulate the housing market, we must know that our writers are very familiar with what we do. Frequent mistakes made by writers include failing to focus on the particular facts (with an occasional, well-placed adjective) that will stimulate the housing market and failure to capture the 'character' of a home or related topic in its most positive light."

‡TUCSON LIFESTYLE, Old Pueblo Press, Suite 13, 7000 E. Tangue Verde Rd., Tucson AZ 85715. (602)721-2929. Editor: Sue Giles. 90% freelance written. Prefers to work with published/established writers. A monthly magazine covering city-related events and topics. Circ. 29,000. Pays on acceptance. Publishes ms an average of 6 months after acceptance. Byline given. Buys first rights and second serial (reprint) rights. Submit seasonal/holiday material 1 year in advance. Previously published submissions OK. Computer printout submissions acceptable; prefers letter-quality to dot-matrix. Reports in 6 weeks on queries; 2 months on mss. Sample copy and writer's guidelines available.

Nonfiction: Historical/nostalgic, humor, interview/profile, personal experience, travel and local stories. Special Christmas issue (December). "We do not accept *anything* that does not pertain to Tucson or Arizona." Buys 100 mss/year. Query. Length: open. Pays $50-300. Sometimes pays expenses of writers on assignment.

Photos: Reviews contact sheets, 2¼x3¼ transparencies, and 5x7 prints. Offers $25-100/photo. Identification of subjects required. Buys one-time rights.
Columns/Departments: HQ Tucson (Local business, headquarted in Tucson, with national clout); Desert Living (environmental living in Tucson: homes, offices); and Biblioteca (Southwest books and authors). Buys 36 mss/year. Query. Length: open. Pays $100-200.
Tips: Features are most open to freelancers. " 'Style' is not of paramount importance; good, clean copy with interesting leads are 'musts.' "

Arkansas

ARKANSAS TIMES, Arkansas Writers' Project, Inc., Box 34010, Little Rock AR 72203. (501)375-2985. Editor: Mel White. 25% freelance written. Monthly magazine. "We are an Arkansas magazine. We seek to appreciate, enliven and, where necessary, improve the quality of life in the state." Circ. 30,000. Pays on acceptance. Publishes ms an average of 3 months after acceptance. Byline given. Not copyrighted. Buys first serial rights. Submit seasonal/holiday material 5 months in advance. Simultaneous, photocopied, and previously published submissions OK. Computer printout submissions acceptable. Reports in 2 weeks on queries; 1 month on mss. Sample copy $3.25; writer's guidelines with SASE.
Nonfiction: Book excerpts; expose (in investigative reporting vein); general interest; historical/nostalgic; humor; interview/profile; opinion; recreation; and entertainment, all relating to Arkansas. "The Arkansas angle is all-important." Buys 24 mss/year. Query. Length: 250-6,000 words. Pays $100-400. Sometimes pays the expenses of writers on assignment.
Photos: Mary Jo Meade, photo editor. State availability of photos. Pays $25-75 for 8x10 b&w or color prints. Identification of subjects required. Buys one-time rights.
Columns/Departments: Mike Trimble, column editor. I Speak Arkansaw (articles on people, places and things in Arkansas or with special interest to Arkansans). "This is the department that is most open to freelancers." Buys 25 mss/year. Query. Length: 250-100 words. Pays $100.
Fiction: Adventure, historical, humorous, mainstream and romance. "All fiction must have an Arkansas angle." Buys 4 mss/year. Send complete ms. Length: 1,250-5,000 words. Pays $200-300.
Tips: "The most annoying aspect of freelance submissions is that so many of the writers have obviously never seen our magazine. Only writers who know something about Arkansas should send us mss."

California

BAKERSFIELD LIFESTYLE, 123 Truxtun Ave., Bakersfield CA 93301. (805)325-7124. Editor and Publisher: Steve Walsh. Monthly magazine covering local lifestyles for college educated males/females ages 25-49 in a balanced community of industrial, agricultural and residential areas. Circ. 10,000. Byline and brief bio given. Buys all rights. Simultaneous queries, and simultaneous and photocopied submissions OK. Computer printout submissions acceptable. Reports in 6 months. Sample copy $2.50.
Nonfiction: General interest (topical issues); travel (up to 1,500 words); and articles on former residents who are now successful freelance. No investigative reporting, politics or negative editorial. Buys 12-15 mss/year. Length: 2,500 words maximum. Pays $10.
Photos: Send photos with ms. Pays $1/photo used.
Fiction: "Anything in good taste." Buys 20 mss/year. Length: 3,000 words maximum. Pays $10 maximum.

CALIFORNIA MAGAZINE, 11601 Wilshire Blvd., Los Angeles CA 90025. (213)479-6511. Editor: Harold Hayes. Managing Editor: Louise Damberg. 90% freelance written. Prefers to work with published/established writers. Monthly magazine about California. Articles should be based on California—lifestyle, the arts, politics, business, crime, education, technology, etc. Circ. 330,000. Pays on acceptance. Publishes ms an average of 3 months after acceptance. Byline given. Offers variable kill fee. Buys first North American serial rights. Submit seasonal/holiday material 3 months in advance. Photocopied submissions OK. Computer printout submissions acceptable; prefers letter-quality to dot-matrix. Reports in 6 weeks on queries. Sample copy $2.
Nonfiction: Robin Green, features editor. Book excerpts, expose (environment, government, education, business), general interest, historical/nostalgic, humor, interview/profile, new product, photo feature and travel; *all* must pertain to California. No stories *not* related to California; no inspirational. Buys 40 mss/year. Query with published clips. Length: 800-4,000 words. Pays $100-2,000. Pays expenses of writers on assignment.
Photos: Michael Rey, photo editor. "We assign almost all photos. We will review portfolios." Captions, model releases, and identification of subjects required. Buys one-time rights.
Columns/Departments: Open to freelance: Books, Eloges (intimate profiles), Roots (history), Local Color,

and New West Notes (familiar essay). Buys 30 mss/year. Query with published clips. Length: 750-2,000 words. Pays $450-750.

Tips: "Query first with clips. *Don't* send complete manuscript. Read the magazine—it has changed a lot recently—to get a feel for it."

GENTRY MAGAZINE, The Magazine of Orange County People, Orange County GENTRY, Inc., Suite 15, 333 E. 17th, Costa Mesa CA 92627. (714)650-1950. Editor: Nora Lehman. "We are backlogged with submissions and prefer not to receive unsolicited submissions at this time."

LOS ANGELES MAGAZINE, ABC/Capital Cities, 1888 Century Park East, Los Angeles CA 90067. (213)557-7569. Editor: Geoff Miller. 98% freelance written. Monthly magazine about southern California. "The primary editorial role of the magazine is to aid a literate, upscale audience in getting the most out of life in the Los Angeles area." Circ. 165,000. Pays on acceptance. Publishes ms an average of 4 months after acceptance. Byline given. Offers 30% kill fee. Buys first North American serial rights. Submit seasonal/holiday material 3-6 months in advance. Computer printout submissions acceptable; prefers letter-quality to dot-matrix. Reports in 6 weeks. Sample copy $4; writer's guidelines for SAE and 1 first class stamp.

Nonfiction: Rodger Claire, articles editor. Book excerpts (about L.A. or by famous L.A. author); expose (any local issue); general interest; historical/nostalgic (about L.A. or Hollywood); and interview/profile (about L.A. person). Buys 400 mss/year. Query with published clips. Length: 250-3,500 words. Pays $50-1,200. Sometimes pays expenses of writers on assignment.

Photos: Rodger Claire, photo editor. State availability of photos.

Columns/Departments: Rodger Claire, column/department editor. Buys 170 mss/year. Query with published clips. Length: 250-1,200 words. Pays $50-500.

LOS ANGELES READER, 8471 Melrose Ave., Second Floor, Los Angeles CA 90069. (213)655-8810. Editor: Dan Barton. Entertainment Editor: Kyle Counts. Assistant Editor: Tara Strohmeier. 85% freelance written. Only serious, polished work by experienced writers should be submitted. Weekly tabloid of features and reviews for "affluent young Los Angelenos interested in the arts and popular culture." Circ. 82,000. Pays on publication. Publishes ms an average of 3 months after acceptance. Byline given. Buys one-time rights. Submit seasonal/holiday material 2 months in advance. Simultaneous queries and photocopied submissions OK. Computer printout submissions acceptable; prefers letter-quality to dot-matrix. Reports in 2 months. Sample copy $1; free writer's guidelines.

Nonfiction: Expose, general interest, journalism, historical/nostalgic, interview/profile, personal experience and photo features—all with strong local slant; moodpieces, possible reprints from other alternative newsweeklies, media analysis—no dull self-analysis. Buys "dozens" of mss/year. Send complete ms. Length: 200-4,000 words. Pays $10-300.

Fiction: Interested in serious fiction. Buys 45 mss/year. Send complete ms. Length: 1,000-4,000 words. Pays $50-200.

Tips: "Break in with submission for our Cityside page: short news items on Los Angeles happenings/semi-hard news. We are nearly entirely a local publication and want only writing about local themes, topics, people by local writers. Anything exciting."

LOS ANGELES TIMES MAGAZINE, Los Angeles Times, Times Mirror Sq., Los Angeles CA 90053. Editorial Director: Wallace Guenther. Editor: Michael Parrish. 50% freelance written. "We welcome all queries." Weekly magazine of regional general interest. Estab. 1985. Circ. 1,300,000 + . Payment schedule varies. Publishes ms an average of 2 months after acceptance. Byline given. Buys first North American serial rights. Submit seasonal/holiday material 3 months in advance. Simultaneous queries and submissions OK. Computer printout submissions acceptable; no dot-matrix. Reports in 1 month. Sample copy for 9x12 SAE and 6 first class stamps. Writer's guidelines for SAE and 2 first class stamps.

Nonfiction: General interest (regional); historical/nostalgic (regional); interview/profile; personal experience and photo feature. Must have Southern California tie-in, but no need to be set in Southern California. Query with published clips. Length: 400-1,800 words. Pays $400-2,000. Sometimes pays the expenses of writers on assignment.

Photos: Query first. Reviews color transparencies and b&w prints. Payment varies. Captions, model releases, and identification of subjects required. Buys one-time rights.

Tips: "The writer should know the subject well or have researched it adequately. As for style, the best style is when the writer goes to the trouble of employing proper English and self-edits an article prior to submission."

MONTEREY LIFE, The Magazine of California's Spectacular Central Coast, Box 2107, Monterey CA 93942. (408)372-9200. Editor: William Morem. 70% freelance written. Prefers to work with published/established writers. Monthly magazine covering art, photography, regional affairs, music, sports, environment and lifestyles for "a sophisticated readership in the central California coast area." Circ. 20,000.

Pays on publication. Publishes ms an average of 3 months after acceptance. Byline given. Offers variable kill fee. Buys first North American serial rights. Submit seasonal/holiday material 4 months in advance. Simultaneous queries, and simultaneous and photocopied submissions OK. Electronic submissions acceptable via Macintosh II, but requires hard copy also. Computer printout submissions acceptable; no dot-matrix. Reports in 3 weeks on queries; 6 weeks on mss. Sample copy for $3.50 and SAE.

Nonfiction: Historical/nostalgic, humor, interview/profile, photo feature and travel. No poetry. "All articles must pertain to issues and lifestyles within the counties of Monterey, Santa Cruz and San Benito except Getaway which covers travel within one day's drive." Buys 75 mss/year. Query with published clips if available. Length: 175-3,000 words. Pays 5-10¢/word. Sometimes pays expenses of writers on assignment.

Photos: State availability of photos. Pays $20-100 for color transparencies; $15-25 for 5x7 and 8x10 b&w prints. Captions, model releases, and identification of subjects required. Buys one-time rights.

Columns/Departments: Community Focus. Query with published clips. Length: 250-1,000 words. Pays $25-40.

Tips: "Since we have a core of very capable freelance writers for longer articles, it is easier to break in with short articles and fillers. Ask probing questions."

NORTHCOAST VIEW, Blarney Publishing, Box 1374, Eureka CA 95502. (707)443-4887. Publishers/Editors: Scott K. Ryan and Damon Maguire. 100% freelance written. A monthly magazine covering entertainment, recreation, the arts, consumer news, in-depth news, fiction and poetry for Humboldt County audience, mostly 18-50 year olds. Circ. 20,000. Pays on publication. Publishes ms an average of 1-6 months after acceptance. Byline given. Generally buys all rights, but will reassign. Submit seasonal/holiday material 6 months in advance. Simultaneous queries, and simultaneous (so long as not in our area), photocopied, and previously published (so long as rights available) submissions OK. Electronic submissions OK via Compugraphic 7500, 8" disk, hard-sectered. Computer printout submissions acceptable; prefers letter-quality to dot-matrix. Reports in 6 weeks on queries; 4 months on mss. Sample copy $1; writer's guidelines for SASE.

Nonfiction: Book excerpts (locally written); expose (consumer, government); historical/nostalgic (local); humor; interview/profile (entertainment, recreation, arts or political people planning to visit county); new product (for arts); photo feature (local for art section); and travel (weekend and short retreats accessible from Humboldt County). "Most features need a Humboldt County slant." Special issues include Kinetic Sculpture Race (May), Christmas (December), and St. Patrick's Day (March). Buys 30-40 mss/year. Query with published clips or send complete ms. Length: 1,250-2,500 words. Pays $25-75.

Photos: State availability of photos with query letter or ms and send proof sheet, if available. Pays $5-15 for 5x7 b&w prints; $25-100 for 35mm Ecktachrome slides. Captions, model releases, and identification of subjects required. Buys all rights but will reassign.

Columns/Departments: A La Carte (restaurant reviews of county restaurants); Ex Libris (books); Reel Views (film); Vinyl Views (albums); Cornucopia (calendar); Poetry; Rearview (art). Buys 80-100 mss/year. Send complete ms. Length: 500-750 words. Pays $10-25.

Fiction: Adventure, condensed novels, erotica (light), experimental, fantasy, horror, humorous, mystery, novel excerpts (local), science fiction and suspense. "We are open to most ideas and like to publish new writers. Topic and length are all very flexible—quality reading the only criteria." No cliche, contrived or predictable fiction—"we like a twist to stories." Buys 10-15 mss/year. Send complete ms. Length: 600-4,500 words; "longer good piece may run 2-3 months consecutively, if it breaks well."

Poetry: Stephen Miller and Mary Johnson, poetry editors. Avant-garde, free verse, haiku, light verse and traditional. Open to all types. No "sappy, overdone or symbolic poetry." Buys work of 12-20 poets (3-4 poems each)/year. Submit maximum 5 poems. Length: 12-48 lines. Pays $25.

Tips: "Our greatest need always seems to be for reviews—book, album and film. Films need to be fairly current, but remember that some films take a while to get up to Humboldt County. Book and album—we're always looking for somewhat current but lesser known works that are exceptional. The most frequent mistakes made by writers are using too few quotes and too much paraphrasing."

PREVIEWS MAGAZINE, A Community Magazine, Santa Monica Bay Printing & Publishing Co., # 245, 919 Santa Monica Blvd., Santa Monica CA 90401. (213)458-3376. Editor: Jan Loomis. 66% freelance written. Works with a small number of new/unpublished writers each year. Monthly magazine of the community of West Los Angeles. "We are a sophisticated magazine with local events and people as our focus, sent free to the entire community." Circ. 40,000. Pays on publication. Publishes ms an average of 3 months after acceptance. Byline given. Buys first North American serial rights and all rights; makes work-for-hire assignments. Submit seasonal/holiday material 6 months in advance. Photocopied submissions OK. Electronic submissions OK on IBM PC/Hayes modem, but requires hard copy also. Computer printout submissions acceptable; prefers letter-quality to dot-matrix. Reports in 1 month on queries. Free sample copy and writer's guidelines.

Nonfiction: Historical/nostalgic, interview/profile, opinion, photo feature and travel. No extreme positions, titillation, pornography, etc. Buys 20 mss/year. Query with published clips. Length: 200-2,500 words. Pays $25-500.

Photos: State availability of photos. Reviews color and b&w contact sheets, 4x4 transparencies and 8x10 glossy prints. Pays $35-50 for b&w; $35-75 for color.

Fiction: Fantasy, humorous and mainstream. No pornography. Buys 2-4 mss/year. Query with published clips. Length: 1,500-2,500 words. Pays $150-500.

Poetry: Light verse and traditional. No long poems. Buys 2-3 poems/year. Submit maximum 6 poems. Length: 35-60 lines. Pays $25-100.

Tips: "We're looking for fiction and interviews. Query with clips of a good idea that would appeal to upscale readers (average income $60,000; average age 39)."

RANCH & COAST, American Ranch & Coast Publishing, Inc., Box 806, Solana Beach CA 92075. (619)481-7659. Editor: Mary Shepardson. 30% freelance written. Monthly magazine targeted at a sophisticated, upper-income readership, primarily in Southern California. Circ. 25,000. Pays on publication. Publishes ms an average of 3 months after acceptance. Byline given. Offers 20% kill fee. Buys various rights. Submit seasonal/holiday material 4 months in advance. Simultaneous queries, photocopied and previously published submissions OK. Computer printout submissions acceptable; prefers letter-quality to dot-matrix. Reports in 1 month. Sample copy $3; free writer's guidelines.

Nonfiction: Book excerpts, general interest, historical/nostaglic, humor (if specifically appropriate), interview/profile, photo feature, travel, and lifestyle (social and charitable events). No articles aimed at unsophisticated audience, budget or how-to pieces. Buys 25-40 mss/year. Query with published clips. Length: 350-2,000 words. Pays 10¢/word minimum.

Photos: State availability of photos with query. "High-quality photographs and other illustrations are very important to *Ranch & Coast*. Many submissions have inadequate 'snapshot' quality illustrations." Pays $15 and more for 5x7 and 8x10 b&w; $25 and more for color transparencies. Captions, model releases, and identification of subjects required. Buys one-time rights.

Columns/Departments: Most columns/departments are written on regular contract basis. Areas include the arts and investments. Buys 8 mss/year. Query with published clips. Length: 500-1,000 words. Pays 10¢/word minimum.

Fiction: *Ranch & Coast* no longer accepts unsolicited fiction manuscripts.

Tips: "Submissions should be appropriate in style and content. Writers should be familiar with current format of magazine which has changed markedly in recent years. We need profiles of prominent and interesting people from freelancers. These should have something new to say and should be well-illustrated."

SACRAMENTO MAGAZINE, Box 2424, Sacramento CA 95811. Editor: Cheryl Romo. 60% freelance written. Monthly magazine emphasizing a strong local angle on politics, local issues, human interest and consumer items for readers in the middle to high income brackets. Pays on acceptance within a 30-day billing period. Publishes ms an average of 3 months after acceptance. Rights vary; generally buys first North American serial rights, rarely second serial (reprint) rights. Original mss only (no previously published submissions). Computer printout submissions acceptable; prefers letter-quality to dot-matrix. No phone calls; query by letter. Reports in 6 weeks. Sample copy $3.50; writer's guidelines for SASE.

Nonfiction: Local issues vital to Sacramento quality of life. Buys 15 unsolicited feature mss/year. Query first. Length: 2,000-3,000 words, depending on author, subject matter and treatment.

Photos: State availability of photos. Payment varies depending on photographer, subject matter and treatment. Captions (including IDs, location and date) required. Buys one-time rights.

Columns/Departments: Media, parenting, first person essays, local travel, gourmet, profile, sports and city arts (850-1,250 words); City Lights (250 words).

SAN DIEGO MAGAZINE, Box 85409, San Diego CA 92138. (619)225-8953. Managing Editor: Winke Self. Editor-in-Chief: Edwin F. Self. 30% freelance written. Prefers to work with published/established writers; works with a small number of new/unpublished writers each year. Emphasizes San Diego. Monthly magazine; 310 pages. Circ. 60,000. Pays on publication. Publishes ms an average of 3 months after acceptance. Buys all rights, but will negotiate. Byline given. Submit seasonal/holiday material 6 months in advance of issue date. Simultaneous and photocopied submissions OK. Computer printout submissions acceptable; prefers letter-quality to dot-matrix. Reports in 2 months. Sample copy $3.

Nonfiction: Expose (serious, documented); general interest (to San Diego region); historical (San Diego region); interview (with notable San Diegans); nostalgia; photo essays; profile; service guides; and travel. Buys variable number of mss/issue. Prefers query with clips of published work. Send photocopies. Length: 2,000-5,000 words. Pays $600 maximum. Pays the expenses of writers on assignment.

Photos: State availability of photos with query. Pays $25-100 b&w; $50-100 color; $250 minimum for cover. Captions required. Buys all rights. Model release required.

Columns/Departments: Topics include Up and Coming (fine and popular arts); Books; Music and Dance; Films; and Urban Eye (San Diego related short items). Length: 500-100 words. Pays $50-75.

Tips: "Write better lead paragraphs; write shorter, with greater clarity; wit and style appreciated; stick to basic magazine journalism principles."

THE SAN DIEGO UNION, Box 191, San Diego CA 92112. (618)291-3131. Associate Editor: Ed Nichols. 40% freelance written. "The bulk of the material we buy is for our Sunday section, Opinion. Optimum pieces are analytical essays on international, geo-political developments or commentary on domestic social, economic, scientific and political trends. We're looking for in-depth research, some original material in the article, and cogency of thought." Byline given. Pays $150 on publication. Length: 1,200 words. Op-ed page: interested in material on a broad range of topics related to current events and in-depth pieces on world events. Uses the whole spectrum of original writing—but piece must have a purpose (such as humor) or throw new light on an issue. Length: 750 words. Electronic submissions OK, but query first. Computer printout submissions acceptable.

SAN FRANCISCO FOCUS, The Monthly Magazine for the San Francisco Bay Area, KQED Inc., 500 8th St., San Francisco CA 94103. (415)553-2119. Editor: Mark K. Powelson. Managing Editor: Warren Sharpe. 80% freelance written. Prefers to work with published/established writers; works with a small number of new/unpublished writers each year. A monthly city/regional magazine. Circ. 160,000. Pays on publication. Publishes ms an average of 2 months after acceptance. Byline given. Offers 33% kill fee. Buys one-time rights. Submit seasonal/holiday material 5 months in advance. Simultaneous queries and previously published submissions OK. Electronic submissions OK, but requires hard copy also. Computer printout submissions acceptable; prefers letter-quality to dot-matrix. Reports in 6 weeks. Sample copy $1.95; free writer's guidelines.
Nonfiction: Expose, humor, interview/profile and travel. All stories should relate in some way to the San Francisco Bay Area (travel excepted). Query with published clips or send complete ms. Length: 750-3,000 words. Pays $75-750. Sometimes pays the expenses of writers on assignment.

SAN FRANCISCO MAGAZINE, #210, 450 Sonsome St., San Francisco CA 94110. (415)777-5555. Editor: Judith Gorn. 40% freelance written. Eager to work with new/unpublished writers. Monthly magazine covering general interest topics for San Francisco and northern California residents. Circ. 50,000. Pays within 30 days of the issue's appearance on the newsstand. Publishes ms an average of 3 months after acceptance. Byline and brief bio given. No kill fee. Buys first North American serial rights. Photocopied submissions OK. Computer printout submissions acceptable. Reports in 3 weeks.
Nonfiction: General interest (lifestyles, fashion); humor; interview/profile (of person with a Northern California connection); personal experience (first person pieces); photo feature; consumer; and science. "Topics may be of national scope. We want well-researched, well-written articles with a northern California fix." Buys fewer than 10 unsolicited mss/year. Query with clips of published work or send complete ms. Length: 2,000-5,000 words. Pays $500 average.
Photos: State availability of photos. Reviews 35mm color transparencies and 8x10 b&w glossy prints. Negotiates pay separately for package of photos or ms/photo package.

THE SAN GABRIEL VALLEY MAGAZINE, Miller Books, 2908 W. Valley Blvd., Alhambra CA 91803. (213)284-7607. Editor-in-Chief: Joseph Miller. 75% freelance written. Bimonthly magazine; 52 pages. For middle- to upper-income people who dine out often at better restaurants in Los Angeles County. Circ. 3,400. Pays on publication. Publishes ms an average of 45 days after acceptance. Buys simultaneous rights, second serial (reprint) rights and one-time rights. Phone queries OK. Submit seasonal/holiday material 1 month in advance. Simultaneous, photocopied, and previously published submissions OK. Computer printout submissions acceptable. Reports in 2 weeks. Sample copy $1.
Nonfiction: Expose (political); informational (restaurants in the Valley); inspirational (success stories and positive thinking); interview (successful people and how they made it); profile (political leaders in the San Gabriel Valley); and travel (places in the Valley). Interested in 500-word humor articles. Buys 18 unsolicited mss/year. Length: 500-10,000 words. Pays 5¢/word.
Columns/Departments: Restaurants, Education, and Valley News and Valley Personality. Buys 2 mss/issue. Send complete ms. Length: 500-1,500 words. Pays 5¢/word.
Fiction: Historical (successful people) and western (articles about Los Angeles County). Buys 2 mss/issue. Send complete ms. Length: 500-10,000 words. Pays 5¢/word.
Tips: "Send us a good personal success story about a Valley or a California personality. We are also interested in articles on positive thinking."

SIERRA LIFE MAGAZINE, The Magazine of the High Sierra, Pramann Publishing, 699 W. Line St., Bishop CA 93514. (619)873-3320. Publisher: Sandie Pramann. Editor: Marty Forstenzer. 50% freelance written. Works with a small number of new/unpublished writers each year. Bimonthly magazine on the Sierra region. "Our magazine is about the history, current events, people, and recreational opportunities of the Sierra Nevada region." Pays on publication. Publishes ms an average of 6 months after acceptance. Byline given. Buys second serial (reprint) rights. Submit seasonal/holiday material 6 months in advance. Simultaneous queries, and simultaneous, photocopied, and previously published submissions OK. Computer printout submissions acceptable; prefers letter-quality to dot-matrix. Reports in 3 months. Sample copy $3, 9x11 SAE and $1 postage; writer's guidelines for #10 SAE and 1 first class stamp.

Nonfiction: Book excerpts; general interest; historical/nostalgic (history of Sierra Nevada region); how-to (about appropriate subjects); interview/profile (about people related to Sierra); personal experience; photo feature; technical; travel; arts; outdoor; and wildlife. All articles must be related to Sierra Nevada region. Also publishes *Sierra Life* hunting guide/fishing guide/hiking guide/four-wheel drive guide. No fiction or fantasy. Buys 18 mss/year. Length: 500-10,000 words. Pays $20-400. Sometimes pays expenses of writers on assignment.

Photos: Janice Kabala, photo editor. State availability of photos or send photos with query or ms. Reviews 5x7 b&w prints. "We sometimes request color transparencies." Pays $5 for b&w; $10-50 for color. Identification of subjects required. Buys two-time rights.

Poetry: Traditional (on the Sierra). Buys 12/year. Submit maximum 3 poems. Pays $5-25.

Tips: "We buy a number of historical and outdoor sports articles (skiing, backpacking, fishing) each year. Our reading audience is educated and sophisticated. Articles should reflect that."

VALLEY MAGAZINE, World of Communications, Inc., Suite 275, 16800 Devonshire St., Granada Hills CA 91344. (818)368-3353. Editor: Anne Framroze. 95% freelance written. Prefers to work with published/established writers, but eager to work with new/unpublished writers. Monthly magazine. *Valley Magazine* is a general interest, lifestyle magazine catering to the residents of the San Fernando Valley. Circ. 30,000. Pays 6-8 weeks after acceptance. Publishes ms an average of 3 months after acceptance. Byline given. Offers 20% kill fee. Buys first serial rights. Submit seasonal/holiday material 4 months in advance. Simultaneous queries, and simultaneous and photocopied submissions OK. Computer printout submissions acceptable; no dot-matrix. Free sample copy; writer's guidelines for 8x11 SAE and 1 first class stamp.

Nonfiction: Expose (good investigative reporting); general interest (all types); interview/profile (prominent Valley citizens); travel. Special issues include health, fitness, and travel (weekend getaways). No fiction, first person humorous personal accounts or opinion pieces. Buys 150 mss/year. Query with published clips. Length: 1,000-3,000 words. Pays $200-400. Sometimes pays expenses of writers on assignment.

Photos: Emily Borden, art director. State availability of photos or send with query or ms. Captions, model releases, and identification of subjects required.

Columns/Departments: Books, theatre, food, music, travel, business (finance). Buys 60 mss/year. Query with published clips. Length: 750-1,500 words. Payment depends on piece.

Tips: "Send a strong query letter with clips of previous work. Manuscripts must have a Valley angle, but can include a general interest slant which is of major significance—for instance, the changing field of health care."

VENTURA COUNTY & COAST REPORTER, The Reporter, VCR Inc., Suite 213, 1583 Spinnaker Dr., Ventura CA 93001. (805)658-2244; (805)656-0707. Editor: Nancy Cloutier. 12% freelance written. Weekly tabloid covering local news. Circ. 25,000. Pays on publication. Publishes ms an average of 2 weeks after acceptance. Byline given. Buys first North American serial rights. Computer printout submissions acceptable. Reports in 3 weeks.

Nonfiction: General interest, humor, interview/profile and travel (local—within 500 miles). Local (Ventura County) slant predominates. Length: 2-5 double-spaced typewritten pages. Pays $10-25.

Photos: State availability of photos with ms. Reviews b&w contact sheet.

Columns/Departments: Boating Experience (Southern California). Send complete ms. Pays $10-25.

Tips: "As long as topics are up-beat with local slant, we'll consider it."

VICTOR VALLEY MAGAZINE, Desert Alive Publishing Company, Box 618, Victorville CA 92392. Editor: Grace Hauser. 20% freelance written. Prefers to work with published/established writers. Magazine published monthly except January/February and July/August combined. Circ. 5,000. Pays within 1 month of publication. Publishes ms an average of 3 months after acceptance. Byline given. Buys first North American serial rights. Submit seasonal/holiday material 3 months in advance. Simultaneous queries, and simultaneous, photocopied, and previously published submissions OK. Computer printout submissions acceptable "if upper and lower case; prefers letter-quality to dot-matrix." Reports in 3 months. Free sample copy; writer's guidelines for SAE and 2 first class stamps.

Nonfiction: General interest, historical/nostalgic, how-to, interview/profile, photo feature and travel. Book reviews, film reviews, controversy and political articles acceptable; also articles on sex and singles. Buys 50 mss/year. Send complete ms. Length: 600-1,000 words. Pays $20-75.

Photos: Send photos with ms. Pays $25-50 for color transparencies; $5-25 for 4x5 b&w prints. Captions, model releases, and identification of subjects required. Buys one-time rights.

Columns/Departments: Desert Alive (stories about the animal and plant life in and around the high desert area: what nature enthusiasts can look for, how desert-dwellers can better live with the local wildlife, etc.); History and Lore (stories about the western development of the high desert area); Family Living Today (dealing with family and social relationships, children, self-improvement, popular culture, etc.); and Desert Personalities (interesting locals, not necessarily of prominence.

Tips: "Our readers have expressed a strong interest in local history (Mojave Desert), interesting personalities, and living better. Start with wildlife and desert-related activities (rock hounding, prospecting, 4-wheeling, etc.) I'll buy more syndicated material because it's on time, professionally written, and costs less."

WEST, 750 Ridder Park Dr., San Jose CA 95190. (408)920-5602. Editor: Jeffrey Klein. For a general audience. 50% freelance written. Prefers to work with published/established writers. Weekly rotogravure newspaper/magazine, published with the *San Jose Mercury News.* Circ. 300,000. Pays on acceptance. Publishes ms an average of 3 months after acceptance. Byline given. Buys first serial rights, and occasionally second serial (reprint) rights. Submit seasonal material (skiing, wine, outdoor living) 3 months in advance. Will consider photocopied and simultaneous submissions if the simultaneous submission is out of their area. Computer printout submissions acceptable; prefers letter-quality to dot-matrix. Reports in 1 month. Free sample copy.
Nonfiction: A general newspaper-magazine requiring that most subjects be related to California (especially the Bay Area) and the interests of California. Will consider subjects outside California if subject is of broad or national appeal. Length: 1,000-4,000 words. Query with published clips. Pays $250-600. Sometimes (but infrequently) pays expenses of writers on assignment.
Photos: Payment varies for b&w and color photos purchased with or without mss. Captions required. Queries should be submitted to the attention of Carol Doup Muller.

WESTWAYS, Automobile Club of Southern California, 2601 S. Figueroa St., Los Angeles CA 90007. (213)741-4760. Editor: Mary Ann Fisher. 90% freelance written. Prefers to work with published/established writers. Monthly magazine. *"Westways* is a regional publication on travel in the West and world travel. Emphasis is on pleasing and interesting subjects—art, historical and cultural. Our audience is southern California upper-income readers who enjoy leisure and culture." Circ. 475,000. Pays 30 days prior to publication. Publishes ms an average of 6 months after acceptance. Byline given. Offers $75 kill fee. Buys first North American serial rights. Submit seasonal/holiday material 6 months in advance. Photocopied submissions OK. Computer printout submissions acceptable; prefers letter-quality to dot-matrix. Reports in 2 weeks. Sample copy $1; free writer's guidelines.
Nonfiction: General interest, historical, humor, interview/profile, photo feature and travel. "We are always interested in Christmas/holiday suggestions but need them by May/June prior to season. We do not accept political, controversial or first person articles. Buys 120-130 mss/year. Query with or without published clips or send complete ms. Length: 1,500 words maximum. Pays $150-350. Sometimes pays expenses of writers on assignment.
Photos: Send photos with query or ms. Reviews 35mm color transparencies. Pays $25-50 per photo published. Captions, model releases, and identification of subjects required. Buys one-time rights.
Columns/Departments: "We have regular monthly columnists for sections/columns except Wit & Wisdom." Buys 24-28 mss/year. Send complete ms. Length: 750-900 words. Pays $100-150.

Colorado

SPRINGS MAGAZINE, Sunrise Publishing, 716 N. Tejon, Box 9166, Colorado Springs CO 80932. (303)636-2001. Managing Editor: Peggy Zimmerman. 60% freelance written. Monthly tabloid that covers the Pikes Peak region and Colorado. "We are a regional city magazine; our audience is above average in education and income. We want literate, well-conceived and well-executed writing." Circ. 22,500. Pays 15 days after publication. Byline given. Offers 50% kill fee if on assignment basis. Buys one-time rights, first serial rights, and second serial (reprint) rights; makes work-for-hire assignments. Submit seasonal/holiday material 6 months in advance. Simultaneous queries, and simultaneous, photocopied, and previously published submissions OK. Computer printout submissions acceptable, but requires hard copy also. Reports in 6 weeks. Sample copy for 10x13 SAE and 5 first class stamps; free writer's guidelines.
Nonfiction: Expose, general interest, historical/nostalgic, humor, interview/profile, personal experience, photo feature and travel. Special issues include Western and Outdoor Adventure, in summer. Otherwise Lifestyle sections: Finance, Real Estate, Health Care, Education, Quality of Life, and Skiing. "We rarely use topics/subjects outside Colorado, unless it has a strong regional tie." Buys 150 mss/year. Query with or without published clips, or send complete ms. Length: 1,000-4,000 words. Pays 3-6¢/word—approximately $30-300. Sometimes pays expenses of writers on assignment.
Photos: Send photos with query or ms. Prefers strong b&w photos suitable for reproduction. Reviews 35mm color transparencies and 5x7 or 8x10 b&w prints. Pays $15-50 for b&w, $50-150 for color. Captions, model release, and identification of subjects. Buys one-time rights.
Columns/Departments: All columns written by contract writers. Columns include Arts, Performing Arts, Culinary Arts, Travel and Wine. Some short reviews in calendar section. Buys 55 mss/year. Query with or without published clips. Needs to review publication for style and content. Length: 1,000-1,500 words. Pays up to 6¢/word.
Fiction: "We run fiction occasionally. It has to have strong writing and regional ties to Colorado. No western fiction please." Buys 2-3 mss/year. Send complete ms. Length: 1,000-3,000 words. Pays up to 6¢/word.
Tips: "We need good original ideas that relate to Colorado and the Pikes Peak region. We are starting to run more 'mini-features' that are ideal for new writers. We need confidence in your ability to put together a larger story. We like loyal contributers and appreciate their input. New ideas are always needed."

‡**SUNDAY MAGAZINE**, (formerly *NOW*), *Rocky Mountain News*, 400 W. Colfax Ave., Denver CO 80204. (303)892-5000. Feature/Lifestyle Editor: Carole McKelvey. Sunday supplement of daily newspaper covering general interest topics; newspaper circulates throughout Colorado and southern part of Wyoming. Circ. 380,000. Pays on publication. Buys one-time rights. Submit seasonal/holiday material 2 months in advance. Simultaneous and previously published submissions OK ("if outside circulation area—Colorado and Southern Wyoming"). Reports in 1 month.
Nonfiction: Investigative; general interest; historical; photo feature; articles with Western angle on an out-of-the-way place; travel articles. Also looking for commentary pieces for Sunday newspapers; query Jean Otto. Buys 20 mss/year. Send complete ms. Length: 1,500-2,000 words. Pays $30-100.
Photos: State availability of photos or send photos with ms ("if article covers an event we can't cover ourselves"). Reviews color transparencies and 8x10 b&w glossy prints. Pay varies. Captions required. Buys one-time rights.

Connecticut

‡**CONNECTICUT MAGAZINE**, Communications International, 789 Reservoir Ave., Bridgeport CT 06606. (203)576-1205. Editor: Sara Cuneo. Managing Editor: Dale Salm. 80% freelance written. A monthly magazine covering the state of Connecticut. "For an affluent, sophisticated, suburban audience. We want only articles that pertain to living in Connecticut." Circ. 68,000. Pays on publication. Publishes ms an average of 4 months after acceptance. Byline given. Offers 20% kill fee. Buys first North American serial rights. Submit seasonal/holiday material 4 months in advance. Photocopied submissions OK. Computer printout submissions acceptable; prefers letter-quality to dot-matrix. Reports in 6 weeks on queries. Writer's guidelines for #10 SAE with 1 first class stamp.
Nonfiction: Book excerpts, expose, general interest, interview/profile and other topics of service to Connecticut readers. No personal essays. Buys 50 mss/year. Query with published clips. Length: 2,500-3,500 words. Pays $500-1,000. Sometimes pays the expenses of writers on assignment.
Photos: State availability of photos with submission. Reviews contact sheets and transparencies. Offers $50 minimum/photo. Model releases and identification of subjects required. Buys one-time rights.
Columns/Departments: Business, Health, Politics, Connecticut Guide, Lively Arts, Gardening, Environment, Education, People, Sports, Law and Courts, Media and From the Past. Buys 50 mss/year. Query with published clips. Length: 1,000-2,000 words. Pays $300-500.
Fillers: Around and About editor—Julie Rosson, assistant editor. Anecdotes and facts. Buys 50/year. Length: 150-400 words. Pays $50 maximum.
Tips: "Submit queries that are relevant to our state and style. Make certain that your idea is not something that has been covered to death by the local press and can withstand a time lag of a few months. Freelancers can best break in with Around and About: find a Connecticut story that is offbeat and write it up in a fun, light-hearted, interesting manner. Again, we don't want something that has already gotten a lot of press."

CONNECTICUT TRAVELER, Official Publication of the Connecticut Motor Club/AAA, Connecticut Motor Club/AAA, 2276 Whitney Ave., Hamden CT 06518. (203)281-7505. Editor: Elke Martin. 25% freelance written. Monthly tabloid covering anything of interest to the Connecticut motorist for Connecticut Motor Club members. Circ. 155,000. Pays on publication. Publishes ms an average of 6 months after acceptance. Byline given. Buys first North American serial rights, first serial rights, and second serial (reprint) rights. Submit seasonal/holiday material 4 months in advance. Photocopied and previously published submissions OK. Computer printout submissions acceptable; prefers letter-quality to dot-matrix. Reports in 2 weeks on queries; 1 month on mss. Sample copy for 8½x11 SASE; writer's guidelines for legal size SASE.
Nonfiction: How-to (variety, how to make traveling with children fun, etc.); and travel (regional economy or low-budget with specifics, i.e., what accommodations, restaurants, sights, recreation are available). "We are a regional publication and focus on events, traveling and other topics within the New England area. International destination features are written in-house. We do not want to see mechanical or highly complicated automotive how-tos." Buys 20 mss/year. Query. Length: 500-1,500 words. Pays $25-150.
Photos: Send b&w photos with ms. Does not accept color. Buys 8x10 glossies as part of ms package. Captions, model releases, and identification of subjects required. Buys one-time rights.
Tips: "If you can get us a story on a travel destination that's unusual and hasn't been beaten to death and cover the specifics in an interesting and fun-to-read manner, we'll definitely consider the story for publication. We stress a regional slant, suitability (will senior citizen, children, etc., enjoy this trip?), and what makes the particular destination special."

NORTHEAST MAGAZINE, *The Hartford Courant*, 285 Broad St., Hartford CT 06115. (203)241-3700. Editor: Lary Bloom. 50% freelance written. Eager to work with new/unpublished writers. Weekly magazine for a Connecticut audience. Circ. 300,000. Pays on acceptance. Publishes ms an average of 1 month after acceptance. Byline given. Buys one-time rights. Previously published submissions OK. Unsolicited ms or

queries accepted; reports in 3 weeks. Computer printout submissions acceptable; prefers letter-quality to dot-matrix.
Nonfiction: General interest; in-depth investigation of stories behind news; historical/nostalgic; interview/profile (of famous or important people with Connecticut ties); and personal essays (humorous or anecdotal). No poetry. Buys 100-150 mss/year. Length: 750-4,500 words. Pays $200-1,000.
Photos: Most assigned; state availability of photos. "Do not send originals."
Fiction: Well-written, original short stories. Length: 750-4,500 words.

District of Columbia

THE WASHINGTON POST, 1150 15th St. NW, Washington DC 20071. (202)334-6000. Travel Editor: Morris D. Rosenberg. Weekly travel section (Sunday). Pays on publication. Byline given. "We are now emphasizing staff-written articles as well as quality writing from other sources. Stories are rarely assigned to freelance writers; all material comes in on speculation; there is no fixed kill fee." Buys first serial rights. Computer printout submissions acceptable if legible; no dot-matrix. Usually reports in 3 weeks.
Nonfiction: Emphasis is on travel writing with a strong sense of place, color, anecdote and history. Query with published clips. Length: 1,500-2,000 words.
Photos: State availability of photos with ms (b&w only).

THE WASHINGTON POST MAGAZINE, *The Washington Post*, 1150 15th St., NW, Washington D.C. 20071. Managing Editor: Stephen Petranek. 50% freelance written. Weekly magazine featuring regional and national interest articles for people of all ages and all interests. Circ. 1.1 million (Sunday). Average issue includes 4-6 feature articles and 7-10 columns. Pays on acceptance. Publishes ms an average of 2 months after acceptance. Byline given. Buys all rights or first North American serial rights, depending on fee. Submit seasonal material 4 months in advance. Photocopied submissions OK. Computer printout submissions acceptable; no dot-matrix. Reports in 1 month on queries; 3 weeks on mss. Free sample copy.
Nonfiction: Controversial and consequential articles. Subject areas include children, science, politics, law and crime, media, money, arts, behavior, sports, society, and photo feature. Buys 2 ms/issue. Query with published clips. Length: 1,500-6,500 words. Pays $200-up.
Photos: Reviews 4x5 or larger b&w glossy prints and 35 mm or larger color transparencies. Offers no additional payment for photos accepted with ms. Model releases required.
Fiction: Fantasy, humorous, mystery, historical and mainstream. Buys 6 mss/year. Send complete ms. Length: 3,000 words maximum. Pays $200-$750.

‡**THE WASHINGTONIAN MAGAZINE**, 1828 L St. NW, Washington DC 20036. Editor: John A. Limpert. 33% freelance written. Prefers to work with published/established writers who live in the Washington area. For active, affluent and well-educated audience. Monthly magazine; 310 pages. Circ. 144,000. Buys first rights only. Buys 75 mss/year. Pays on publication. Publishes ms an average of 2 months after acceptance. Simultaneous and photocopied submissions OK. Computer printout submissions acceptable; prefers letter-quality to dot-matrix. Reports in 4-6 weeks. Query or submit complete ms.
Nonfiction: "*The Washingtonian* is written for Washingtonians. The subject matter is anything we feel might interest people interested in the mind and manners of the city. The style, as Wolcott Gibbs said, should be the author's—if he is an author, and if he has a style. The only thing we ask is thoughtfulness and that no subject be treated too reverently. Audience is literate. We assume considerable sophistication about the city, and a sense of humor." Buys how-to, personal experience, interview/profile, humor, coverage of successful business operations, think pieces and exposes. Length: 1,000-7,000 words; average feature 4,000 words. Pays 30¢/word. Sometimes pays the expenses of writers on assignment.
Photos: Photos rarely purchased with mss.
Fiction and Poetry: Margaret Cheney, department editor. Must be Washington-oriented. No limitations on length. Pays 20¢/word for fiction. Payment is negotiable for poetry.

Florida

‡**BOCA RATON**, J E S Publishing, 114 NE 2nd St., Boca Raton FL 33432. (305)392-3406. Editor: Shirley Bartley. 70% freelance written. A bimonthly magazine covering "sophisticated material on Palm Beach County residents." Circ. 13,000. Pays on publication. Byline given. Offers $25 kill fee. Buys first North American serial rights. Submit seasonal/holiday material 6 months in advance. Electronic submissions OK on Wordstar, but requires hard copy also. Computer printout submissions acceptable; prefers letter-quality to dot-matrix. Reports in 3 weeks on queries. Sample copy $3; free writer's guidelines.
Nonfiction: Expose, general interest, and interview/profile. No first-person narrative. Buys 50 mss/year. Query with published clips. Length: 1,000-4,000 words. Pays $125-500.

Photos: State availability of photos with submission. Reviews contact sheets, negatives, transparencies and prints. Captions, model releases and identification of subjects required. Buys one-time rights.
Tips: "Articles should feature Palm Beach County residents. The area of our publication most open to freelancers is features. Be provocative. We use lots of interviews."

CENTRAL FLORIDA MAGAZINE, Central Scene Publications, Inc., 341 N. Maitland Ave., Maitland FL 32751. (305)628-8850. Editor: Mimi Martin. Monthly magazine covering the lifestyles of central Florida. "Our readers are affluent, recreation and business-oriented area residents who enjoy the good life. Content is positive, upbeat." Circ. 25,000. Pays on publication. Byline given. Offers $25 kill fee. Buys one-time rights; makes work-for-hire assignments. Submit seasonal/holiday material 4 months in advance. Simultaneous queries, and simultaneous, photocopied, and previously published submissions OK. Reports in 1 month. Sample copy for $1.50, 9x12 SAE and $1.57 postage; writer's guidelines for business size SAE and 1 first class stamp.
Nonfiction: General interest (with local slant); historical/nostalgic (local); interview/profile (local); photo feature (local); and travel. Special issues include interior design, boating and shopping (expensive retail). Buys 20-30 mss/year. Query with published clips if available. Length: 750-2,500 words. Pays $35-750.
Photos: Send photos with query or ms. Pays $25-100 for 35mm color transparencies; $10 for 5x7 and larger b&w prints. Model releases and identification of subjects required. Buys negotiable rights.
Fiction: Humorous and mainstream—"only if it has a local tie-in." Buys 1-2 mss/year. Send complete ms. Length: 1,000-3,500 words. Pays $50-300.
Fillers: Clippings, anecdotes, short humor and newsbreaks—"with a local slant."
Tips: "Focus pieces on the activities of people in central Florida. Query with list of five to ten article ideas."

FLORIDA GULF COAST LIVING MAGAZINE, Baker Publications Inc., Suite 109, 1311 N. Westshore Blvd., Tampa FL 33607. Publications Director: Tina Stacy. Executive Editor: Milana McLead Petty. Magazine published 7 times/year covering real estate and related subjects for "newcomers and local residents looking for new housing in the area we cover." Circ. 490,000 annually. Pays on acceptance. Buys all rights. Submit seasonal/holiday material 3 months in advance. Photocopied submissions OK. Reports in 2 months. Sample copy $2; free writer's guidelines.
Nonfiction: General interest (on housing-related subjects, interior decorating, retirement living, apartment living, moving tips). No personal views. Buys 5-10 mss/year. Query with published clips or send complete ms. Length: 500-1,200 words. Pays $15-125.
Photos: Buys one-time rights or all rights, depending on the subject.
Tips: "Housing features, retirement living, interiors, home marketplace, products and services, and other ideas, are the departments most open to freelancers. Be sure the subject is pertinent to our magazine. Know our magazine's style and write for it."

FLORIDA KEYS MAGAZINE, Crain Communication, Inc., Box 818, 6161 O/S Hwy., Marathon FL 33050. (305)743-3721. Editor: David Ethridge. 90% freelance written. Bimonthly general interest magazine covering the Florida Keys for residents and tourists. Circ. 10,000. Pays on publication. Publishes ms an average of 3 months after acceptance. Byline given. Buys first serial rights. Submit seasonal/holiday material 3 months in advance. Simultaneous queries and simultaneous-and-photocopied submissions OK. Computer printout submissions acceptable; prefers letter-quality to dot-matrix. Reports in 1 month. Sample copy $2.
Nonfiction: General interest; historical/nostalgic; how-to (must be Florida Keys related: how to clean a conch; how to catch a lobster); interview/profile; new product; personal experience; photo feature and local travel. Query with published clips. Length: 400-2,000 words. Pays $3.50/inch.
Photos: State availability of photos. Reviews 35mm transparencies. Pays $5-20 for 5x7 b&w prints; $15-100 for 5x7 color prints. Identification of subjects required.

‡FUTURE FLORIDA, Bonjour International Publications, Inc., Box 11796, Ft. Lauderdale FL 33339. (305)786-0722. Editor: Jean Emond. Managing Editor: James G. Azar. 20% freelance written. A bimonthly official hotel magazine for selected South Florida hotels covering business/leisure/travel. "Our magazine reaches the young urban professional in the South Florida community and the business traveler within the state of Florida. Our articles include up-to-date information on business, travel, fashion, dining, future scenario, profile. Circ. 40,000 +. Pays on acceptance. Publishes ms an average of 6 months after acceptance. Byline given. Buys first North American serial rights, second serial (reprint) rights, or simultaneous rights. Submit seasonal/holiday material 6 months in advance. Simultaneous, photocopied and previously published submissions OK. Computer printout submissions acceptable. Reports in 6 weeks. Sample copy for 8½x11 SAE with 2 first class stamps.
Nonfiction: Essays, general interest, historical/nostalgic, humor, interview/profile, new product, technical and travel. "No heavy controversy, politics, religion or golly-gee-whiz stuff." Buys 8-20 mss/year. Query with published clips. Length: 750-3,000 words. Pays $50-200 for assigned articles; pays $25-100 for unsolicited articles; sometimes pays in copies if requested. Sometimes pays the expenses of writers on assignment.

Photos: Send photos with submission. Reviews transparencies, all sizes. Offers $10-25/photo. Captions, model releases and identification of subjects required. Buys all rights.
Fiction: Adventure, humorous, mainstream, mystery, science fiction and suspense. "Nothing bawdy, racy, trite or nonsensical." Buys 3 mss/year. Send complete ms. Length: 1,250-3,000 words. Pays $100-350.
Poetry: Avant-garde and free verse. No doggerel, political, inspirational, trite or confessional. Buys 3 poems/year. Submit maximum 3 poems. Length: 5-35 lines. Pays $10-25.
Tips: "Highly creative articles describing future scenarios or our changing American lifestyle are always welcome. Keep the Yuppie in mind—remember that these are conservative capitalists with fresh approaches to business. Business articles are most open to freelancers. Recent titles have been: 'Eight Guidelines for Effective Brainstorming,' 'The Inefficiency of Waste,' 'Moneymaking Metals,' and 'Predictions for 1986: Business Onward.' "

GULFSHORE LIFE, Gulfshore Publishing Co., Inc., 3620 Tamiami Trail N., Naples FL 33940. (813)262-6425. Editor: Anita Atherton. 25% freelance written. Monthly magazine "for an upper-income audience of varied business and academic backgrounds; actively employed and retired; interested in travel, leisure, business, and sports, as well as local environmental issues." Circ. 18,000. Pays on publication. Publishes ms an average of 5 months after acceptance. Byline given. Buys first serial rights and requests permission for subsequent reprint rights in other publications published by the firm. Submit seasonal material 6 months in advance. Photocopied and simultaneous submissions OK. Computer printout submissions acceptable.
Nonfiction: Local personalities, sports, travel, nature, environment, business, boating and fishing and historical pieces. Everything must be localized to the southwest coast of Florida. No political or controversial articles. Query. Length: 1,500-2,500 words. Pays $75-300.
Tips: "Familiarize yourself with the magazine and the location: Naples, Marco Island, Ft. Myers, Ft. Myers Beach, Sanibel-Captiva, Whiskey Creek, Punta Gorda Isles and Port Charlotte. Submissions accepted at any time."

ISLAND LIFE, The Enchanting Barrier Islands of Florida's Southwest Gulf Coast, Island Life Publications, Box X, Sanibel FL 33957. (813)472-4344. Editor: Joan Hooper. Editorial Associate: Susan Shores. 40% freelance written. Prefers to work with published/established writers, but works with a small number of new/unpublished writers each year. Quarterly magazine of the Barrier Islands from Longboat Key to Marco Island, for upper-income residents and vacationers of Florida's Gulf Coast area. Circ. 20,000. Pays on publication. Publishes ms an average of 1 year after acceptance. Byline given. Buys first serial rights and second serial (reprint) rights. Simultaneous queries, and simultaneous and photocopied submissions OK. Computer printout submissions acceptable; no dot-matrix. Reports in 1 month on queries; 3 months on mss. Sample copy for $3; writer's guidelines for business size SASE.
Nonfiction: General interest, historical. "Travel and interview/profile done by staff. Our past use of freelance work has been heavily on Florida wildlife, Florida cuisine, and Florida parks and conservancies. We are a regional magazine. No fiction or first person experiences. Our editorial emphasis is on the history, culture, wildlife, art, scenic, sports, social and leisure activities of the area." Buys 10-20 mss/year. Query with ms and photos. Length: 500-1,500 words. Pays 5¢/word.
Photos: Send photos with query. No additional payment. Captions, model releases, and identification of subjects required.
Tips: "Submissions are rejected if not enough research has gone into the article. Also, we *never* buy first person slant."

JACKSONVILLE MAGAZINE, Box 329, Jacksonville FL 32201. (904)353-0313. 80% freelance written. Works with a small number of new/unpublished writers each year. Bimonthly. Circ. 15,000. Pays on acceptance. Publishes ms an average of 6 months after acceptance. Buys all rights. Query. Submit seasonal material 3-6 months in advance. Electronic submissions OK via IBM or Apple compatible floppy disks, but requires hard copy also. Computer printout submissions acceptable. Reports in 3 weeks.
Nonfiction: Historical, business and other feature articles mostly pertaining specifically to Jacksonville or Northeast Florida. Buys 40-45 mss/year. Length: usually 1,500-2,500 words. Pays $100-300.
Photos: Reviews b&w glossy prints with good contrast and color transparencies. Pays $30 minimum for b&w; color terms to be arranged. Sometimes pays the expenses of writers on assignment.
Tips: "Stories with a business/economic angle are preferred."

‡JACKSONVILLE TODAY, White Publishing Co., 1032 Hendricks Ave., Box 5610, Jacksonville FL 32207. (904)396-8666. Editor: Marie B. Speed. Managing Editor: Carole Caldwell. 90% freelance written. A monthly city lifestyle magazine "which explores all facets of the North Florida experience—from politics and people to recreation and leisure." Circ. 25,000. Pays on publication. Publishes ms an average of 3 months after acceptance. Byline given. Buys all rights. Submit seasonal/holiday material 3 months in advance. Photocopied submissions OK. Computer printout submissions acceptable; prefers letter-quality to dot-matrix. Reports in 3 weeks on queries; 6 weeks on manuscripts. Sample copy and writer's guidelines for SASE.

Nonfiction: Exposé, general interest, historical, how-to (general), interview, photo feature and travel. Special issue features gulf-oriented material (March material due Jan. 9). No fiction, essays, opinion, religious, non-localized features, humor, or book and film reviews. Buys 60 mss/year. Query with or without published clips, or send complete ms. Length: 600-1,500 words. Pays $150-400. Sometimes pays the expenses of writers on assignment.

Photos: State availability of photos with submission. Reviews contact sheets. Offers $25 minimum per photo. Model releases and identification of subjects required.

Columns/Departments: Living Well (leisure, recreation, home and garden, furnishings, etc.) Ways & Means (personal finance and investment), and Outside (sports and recreation). Buys 72 mss/year. Query with published clips. Length: 800-1,500 words. Pays $150-300.

Tips: "The areas of our publication most open to freelancers are the Escape (travel) and At Home (leisure, possessions, new trends in consumer purchases) departments. All articles must be localized to the Jacksonville/North Florida area."

THE LOCAL NEWS, The Local News, Inc., Box 466, Windermere FL 32786-0466. (305)298-2401. Associate Editor: Darrell R. Julian. 20% freelance written. A biweekly newsmagazine serving Central Florida. "Our readers tend to fall into two distinct groups: the 25-40 years age group, college educated, upper middle-class from all over the country and the world; and 55 years old or older age group; (perhaps 40% of our readership) most of whom are middle-class retirees from across the nation." Circ. 5,000. Pays on acceptance. Publishes ms an average of 2 months after acceptance. Byline given. Buys one-time rights, first serial rights, and second serial (reprint) rights. Submit seasonal/holiday material 2 months in advance. Photocopied and previously published submissions OK; prefers previously unpublished material. Computer printout submissions acceptable. Reports in 2 months minimum.

Nonfiction: General interest, humor, interview/profile, opinion and travel. "Although we serve Central Florida, we are not interested in regional material since we develop this work from our staff. All articles must be in good taste; no erotic or tasteless material would be suitable." Buys 30 mss/year. Send complete ms. Length: 750-3,000 words. Pays $10.

Photos: Send photos with accompanying ms. Buys one-time rights.

Columns/Departments: "We would like to develop a regular column with wit and humor, and a political column with a conservative orientation." Send complete ms. Pays $10.

Fillers: Jokes, anecdotes and short humor. Buys 10/year. Pays $10.

Tips: "The *Local News* plans to become a weekly publication. Articles suited to the Sunday magazine section of a daily newspaper would be desirable. We will consider most material submitted during this transition. Do not send originals. Send photocopied materials and no SASE, as any materials submitted cannot be returned."

MIAMI MENSUAL (MIAMI MONTHLY), The International Magazine of South Florida, Quintus Communications Group, 265 Sevilla, Coral Gables FL 33134. (305)444-5678. Editor: Frank Soler. "We are backlogged with submissions and prefer not to receive unsolicited submissions at this time."

MIAMI/SOUTH FLORIDA MAGAZINE, Box 340008, Coral Gables FL 33134. (305)856-5011. Editor: Erica Rauzin. Managing Editor: Rick Eyerdan. 30-35% freelance written. Works with a small number of new/unpublished writers each year. Monthly magazine for involved, generally well-educated citizens of South Florida. Circ. 30,000+. Pays on publication. Publishes ms an average of 3 months after acceptance. Rights purchased vary with author and material; usually buys first serial rights; rarely buys second serial (reprint) rights. Electronic submissions on Apple IIe or III compatible disk OK; prefer hard copy also. Computer printout submissions acceptable. Reports in 2-3 months. Sample copy $1.95 and 55¢ postage; free writer's guidelines.

Nonfiction: Investigative pieces on the area; thorough, general features; exciting, in-depth writing. Informational, how-to, interview, profile, local-hook celebrity stories, business stories and repertorial expose. Strong local angle and fresh, opinionated and humorous approach. "No travel stories from freelancers—that's mostly staff generated. We do not like to get freelance manuscripts that are thinly disguised press releases. Writers should read the magazine first—then they'll know what to send and what not to send." Buys about 30 unsolicited mss/year. Query preferred or submit complete ms. Length: 3,000 words maximum. Pays $100-600. Sometimes pays expenses of writers on assignment (with pre-set limit).

Columns/Departments: Humor, business, books, art (all kinds), profiles and home design. Length: 1,500 words maximum. Pays $100-250.

Tips: "We are regional in our outlook, not just Miami, but also Key West and Ft. Lauderdale. The writer should know, based on an analytical reading, whether his/her work fits our book. We're like most city/regionals: very local, a little brash, a little trendy, and very focused on good writing. We anticipate increased budget consciousness and ever shorter stories. It's time for freelancers and editors to become more businesslike."

NEW VISTAS, General Development Corp., Corp. Communications Dept., 1111 S. Bayshore Dr., Miami FL 33131. (305)350-1256. Editor: Robert C. Ross. Managing Editor: Otis Wragg. 50% freelance written. Prefers to work with published/established writers. Magazine published 3 times/year on Florida—growth, travel, lifestyle. Reaches residents of General Development's planned communities in Florida (Port Charlotte, Port St. Lucie, Port Malabar, Port LaBelle, Silver Springs Shores, North Port) plus those who own home sites there. Majority of circulation is in Northeast and Midwest U.S. Interested in people activities, and growth of these communities. Circ. 250,000+. Pays on publication. Publishes ms an average of 6 months after acceptance. Byline given. Buys first serial rights. Submit seasonal/holiday material 3 months in advance. Computer print-out submissions acceptable; prefers letter-quality to dot-matrix. Reports in 2 weeks. Free sample copy.
Nonfiction: General interest, historical/nostalgic, how-to, photo feature, and travel, all Florida-related. Buys 8 mss/year. Query. Length: 500-2,000 words. Pays $100-600. Sometimes pays expenses of writers on assignment.
Photos: State availability of photos or send photos with query. Reviews 35mm color transparencies. Captions required. Buys one-time rights.
Tips: "*New Vista* defines and articulates the dream of living in Florida for a largely out-of-state readership. Stories about Florida living and economics—keyed to General Development's planned communities—are always sought. Familiarity with Florida, and General Development's planned communities is a plus. We usually buy one Florida travel article per issue. Destinations close to General Development communities are best."

ORLANDO-LAND MAGAZINE, Box 2207, Orlando FL 32802. (305)644-3355. Editor-in-Chief: E.L. Prizer. Managing Editor: Carole De Pinto. 10% freelance written. Works with a small number of new/unpublished writers each year; happy to work with new/unpublished writers. Monthly magazine; 208 pages. Emphasizes central Florida information for "a readership made up primarily of people new to Florida—those here as visitors, traveling businessmen, new residents." Circ. 26,000. Pays on acceptance. Publishes ms an average of 6 months after acceptance. Byline given. Buys all rights or first North American serial rights. Phone queries OK. Submit seasonal/holiday material 4 months in advance. Photocopied and previously published submissions OK. Computer printout submissions acceptable. Reports in 6 weeks. Sample copy $3.
Nonfiction: Historical, how-to and informational. "Things involved in living in Florida." Pays $50-150.
Photos: Reviews b&w glossy prints. Pays $5.
Tips: "We are always in need of *useful* advice-type material presented as first person experience that relates to the central Florida area. Also, travel (excursion) pieces to places open to the general public within one day's (there and back) journey of Orlando or experience pieces (hobbies, sports, etc.) that would not be practical for staff writers—sky diving, delta kites, etc. Must be available in central Florida. Specialized topical columns are being added in health, environment, architecture and travel."

‡SENIOR VOICE NEWSPAPER, Florida's Leading Senior Citizens Newspaper, T.J.L. Publications Inc., Suite 6002, 6541 44th St., Pinellas Park FL 33565. (813)521-4026. Editor: Thomas J. Lubina. Managing Editor: David K. Hollenbeck. 30-40% freelance written. Prefers to work with published/established writers; works with a small number of new/unpublished writers each year. A monthly newspaper for mature adults fifty years of age and over. Circ. 40,000. Pays on publication. Publishes ms an average of 2 months after acceptance. Byline given. Buys one-time rights. Submit seasonal/holiday material 2 months in advance. Simultaneous and previously published submissions OK. Computer printout submissions acceptable; no dot-matrix. Reports in 1 month. Sample copy $1 with 10x13 SAE and 4 first class stamps.
Nonfiction: Exposé, general interest, historical/nostalgic, how-to, humor, inspirational, interview/profile, opinion, photo feature, travel, health and finance, all slanted to a senior audience. No religious or youth oriented submissions. Buys 40 mss/year. Query or send complete ms. Length: 300-600 words. Pays $15 minimum or 3¢/word maximum.
Photos: Send photos with submission. Reviews 5x2 prints. Offers $3/photo. Identification of subjects required.
Columns/Departments: Washington Letter (senior citizen legislative interests); Travel (senior slant); V.I.P. Profiles (mature adults). Buys 20 mss/year. Send complete ms. Length: 300-600 words. Pays $15 minimum or 3¢/word maximum.
Fillers: Anecdotes, facts, political cartoons, gags to be illustrated by cartoonist, and short humor. Buys 10/year. Length: 150-250 words. Pays $15.
Tips: "Travel, political issues, celebrity profiles, and general interest are the areas of our publication most open to freelancers. Keep in mind that *Senior Voice* readers are 50 years of age and older. A working knowledge of issues and problems facing seniors today and a clean precise style will suffice."

SOUTH FLORIDA HOME & GARDEN, Meyer Publications, 75 SW 15 Rd., Miami FL 33129. (305)374-5011. Editor: Erica Rauzin. Managing Editor: Rosemary Barrett. 40% freelance written. Works with a small number of new/unpublished writers each year. Monthly magazine of South Florida homes, interior design, architecture, gardening, landscaping, cuisine and home entertainment. "We want beautiful, clever, interesting, practical specific coverage of subjects listed as they relate to South Florida." Circ. 17,000. Pays 15 days before publication. Publishes ms an average of 5 months after acceptance. Byline given. Offers $25 kill fee by pre-agreement only. Buys first North American serial rights, plus unlimited reuse in our magazine (not resale). Submit seasonal/holiday material 6 months in advance. Electronic submissions OK on Apple IIE or III disk, but requires hard copy also. Computer printout submissions acceptable. Sample copy $2.50; writer's guidelines for #10 SAE and 1 first class stamp.

Nonfiction: General interest (in our subjects); how-to (interior design, cuisine [yes, recipes, but with a South Florida twist] and gardening for southern Florida climate); new product (short); technical (popularized, well-written); and travel (home architecture or garden destinations only). Buys 36 mss/year. Query with or without published clips. Length: 200-1,000 words. Pays $50-300; (rarely more). Pays expenses of writers on assignment.

Photos: Debra Yates, photo editor. State availability of photos or send photos with query. Reviews 35mm, 4x5 or 2" color transparencies or 2" b&w prints. Captions and identification of subjects required. Buys one-time rights plus unlimited re-use of separations.

Columns/Departments: Homecare—specific home how-to; Garden Care; Ideas; Cuisine; Home Business; Parties; Architecture; and Florida Artists. Buys 36 mss/year. Query with or without published clips. Length: 200-1,000 words. Pays $75-300.

Tips: "This is a very specifically focused magazine with an almost parochial local emphasis. The writer must know his/her subject well enough to mesh it with our unique geography, lifestyle and climate. We are running shorter stories with more specific angles, more detailed. We are increasingly mindful of getting the most for our budget."

SUNSHINE: THE MAGAZINE OF SOUTH FLORIDA, The News & Sun-Sentinel Co., Box 14430, Fort Lauderdale FL 33302. (305)761-4017. Editor: John Parkyn. A general interest Sunday magazine for the News/Sun-Sentinel's 750,000 readers in South Florida. Circ. 300,000. Pays within 1 month of acceptance. Byline given. Offers 25% kill fee. Buys first serial rights or one-time rights in the state of Florida. Submit seasonal/holiday material 2 months in advance. Simultaneous queries, and simultaneous, photocopied, and previously published submissions OK. Reports in 2 weeks on queries; 1 month on mss. Free sample copy and writer's guidelines.

Nonfiction: General interest, how-to, interview/profile and travel. "Articles must be relevant to the interests of adults living in South Florida." Buys about 100 mss/year. Query with published clips. Length: 1,000-3,000 words; preferred length 2,000-3,000 words. Pays 20-25¢/word to $750 maximum (occasionally higher).

Photos: State availability of photos. Pays negotiable rate for 35mm color slides and 8x10 b&w prints. Captions, model releases, and identification of subjects required. Buys one-time rights for the state of Florida.

Tips: "Do not phone—we don't have the staff to handle calls of this type—but do include your phone number on query letter. Keep your writing tight and concise—readers don't have the time to wade through masses of 'pretty' prose. Be as sophisticated and stylish as you can—Sunday magazines have come a long way from the Sunday 'supps' of yesteryear."

TALLAHASSEE MAGAZINE, Marketplace Communications, Inc., Box 12848, Tallahassee FL 32317. (904)385-3310. Editor: William L. Needham. Managing Editor: W.R. Lundquist. 80% freelance written. Quarterly magazine covering people, events and history in and around Florida's capital city. Circ. 16,000. Pays on publication. Publishes ms an average of 3 months after acceptance. Buys first serial rights. Submit seasonal/holiday material 6 months in advance. Simultaneous queries, and photocopied and previously published submissions OK. Computer printout submissions acceptable; prefers letter-quality to dot-matrix. Reports in 1 month. Sample copy for 9x12 SAE.

Nonfiction: General interest (relating to Florida or Southeast); historical/nostalgic (for Tallahassee, North Florida, South Georgia); and interview/profile (related to North Florida, South Georgia). No fiction, poetry or topics unrelated to area. Buys 20 mss/year. Query. Length: 500-1,400 words. Pays 10¢/word.

Photos: State availability of photos with query. Pays $35 minimum for 35mm color transparencies; $20 minimum for b&w prints. Model releases and identification of subjects required. Buys one-time rights.

Tips: "We seek to show positive aspects of life in and around Tallahassee. Know the area. A brief author biographic note should accompany manuscripts."

‡WATERFRONT NEWS, Ziegler Publishing Co., Inc., 320 S.W. 2nd St., Ft. Lauderdale FL 33312. (305)524-9450. Editor: John Ziegler. 75% freelance written. Eager to work with new/unpublished writers and those who are published and established. A monthly tabloid covering marine and boating topics for the Ft. Lauderdale waterfront community. Circ. 25,000. Pays on publication. Publishes ms an average of 2 months after acceptance. Byline given. Buys first serial rights; second serial (reprint) rights or simultaneous rights. Submit seasonal/holiday material 3 months in advance. Photocopied and previously published submissions OK. Computer printout submissions acceptable; prefers letter-quality to dot-matrix. Reports in 2 weeks on queries. Sample copy $1 with 9x12 SAE and 73¢ postage; free writer's guidelines.

Nonfiction: Historical/nostalgic (nautical or Southern Florida); new marine product; opinion (on marine topics); technical (on marine topics); and marine travel. Buys 50 mss/year. Query with or without published clips, or send complete ms. Length: 500-2,000 words. Pays $50-200 for assigned articles; pays $ 25-200 for unsolicited articles. Sometimes pays the expenses of writers on assignment.

Photos: State availability of photos or send photos with submission. Reviews contact sheets and 3x5 or larger prints. Offers $5/photo. Buys one-time rights.

Columns/Departments: Query with published clips. Length 500-2,000 words. Pays $25-100.

Fiction: Adventure, humorous, and novel excerpts, all with a nautical or South Florida hook. Buys 3 mss/year. Query. Length: 500-2,000 words. Pays $25-200.

Poetry: Avant-garde, free verse, light verse and traditional. Buys 10 poems/year. Submit maximum 5 poems. Length: 3 lines minimum. Pays $10-200.

Fillers: Anecdotes, facts, nautical one-liners to be illustrated by cartoonist, newsbriefs and short humor. Buys 12/year. Length 100-500 words. Pays $10-200.

Tips: "The writer should be well versed in nautical topics and/or be familiar with the boating scene in Southeastern Florida. If my publication continues to grow as it has, I anticipate buying more and longer articles with more pictures and/or graphics."

Georgia

GEORGIA JOURNAL, Agee Publishers, Inc., Box 526, Athens GA 30603. (404)548-5269. Editor: Jane Agee. 85% freelance written. Works with a small number of new/unpublished writers each year. Bimonthly magazine covering the state of Georgia. Circ. 5,000. Pays on acceptance. Publishes ms an average of 3 months after acceptance. Byline given. Buys first serial rights. Submit seasonal/holiday material 4-6 months in advance. Photocopied submissions OK. Computer printout submissions acceptable; no dot-matrix. Reports in 1 month. Sample copy $3; writer's guidelines for SAE and 1 first class stamp.

Nonfiction: "We are interested in almost everything going on within the state. Although we specialize in an area, we maintain a general interest format. We do prefer to get pieces that are current that have a human interest slant. We are also very interested in natural science pieces. We do our special focus issues and suggest that writers send for special focus schedule. We are always swamped with historical articles, and we are not interested in sentimental reminiscences, anything risque, specifically political or religious pieces. Buys 30-40 mss/year. Query. Length: 1,200-2,000 words. Pays $25-40. Sometimes pays expenses of writers on assignment.

Photos: State availability of photos or send photos with query or ms. Reviews sharp 8x10 b&w glossies. Captions, model releases, and identification of subjects required.

Columns/Departments: "We have a new short section called Seeing Georgia—a travel column featuring places to go in Georgia."

Fiction: Hugh Agee, fiction editor. "Because we are in almost all school systems in the state, fiction must be suitable for all ages." Buys 3-4 mss/year. Send complete ms. Length: 1,200-2,000 words. Pays $25.

Poetry: Janice Moore, poetry editor. Free verse, haiku, light verse and traditional. No poetry specifically dealing with another part of the country (out of the South) or anything not suitable for school children. "Most of our school-age readers are middle school and older." Uses 20 poems/year. Submit maximum 4 poems. Length: 5 lines. Pays in copies.

Tips: "We have a section of short pieces (3-8 paragraphs) called Under the Chinaberry Tree where we always need good general interest submissions. These pieces are usually on topics not meriting feature article length. See a sample copy for Chinaberry Tree pieces that have been used."

Hawaii

ALOHA, THE MAGAZINE OF HAWAII AND THE PACIFIC, Davick Publishing Co., 828 Fort Street Mall, Honolulu HI 96813. Editor: Rita Ariyoshi. 50% freelance written. *Aloha* is a bimonthly regional magazine of international interest. "Most of our audience does not live in Hawaii, although most readers have been to the islands at least once. Even given this fact, the magazine is directed primarily to residents of Hawaii in the belief that presenting material to an immediate critical audience will result in a true and accurate presentation that can be appreciated by everyone. *Aloha* is not a tourist or travel publication and is not geared to such a readership, although travelers will find it to be of great value." Circ. 80,000. Pays on publication. Publishes ms an average of 8 months after acceptance; unsolicited ms can take a year or more. Byline given. Offers variable kill fee. Buys all rights. Submit seasonal/holiday material 1 year in advance. Photocopied submissions OK. Computer printout submissions acceptable; no dot-matrix. Reports in 2 months. Sample copy $2.50; writer's guidelines for SAE with 1 first class stamp.

Nonfiction: Book excerpts; historical/nostalgic (historical articles must be researched with bibliography); interview/profile; and photo feature. Subjects include the arts, business, people, sports, special places, food, interiors, history and Hawaiian. "We don't want stories of a tourist's experiences in Waikiki or odes to beautiful scenery. We don't want an outsider's impressions of Hawaii, written for outsiders." Buys 24 mss/year. Query with published clips. Length: 1,000-4,000 words. Pays 10¢/word. Sometimes pays expenses of writers on assignment.

Photos: State availability of photos with query. Pays $25 for b&w prints; prefers negatives and contact sheets. Pays $50 for 35mm (minimum size) color transparencies used inside; $150 for color transparencies used as cover art. "*Aloha* features two photo essays in each issue. Beautiful Hawaii, a collection of photographs illustrating that theme, appears in every issue. A second photo essay by a sole photographer on a theme of his/her own choosing is also a regular feature. Queries are essential for the sole photographer essay." Model releases and identification of subjects required. Buys one-time rights.

Fiction: Ethnic and historical. "Fiction depicting a tourist's adventures in Waikiki is not what we're looking for. As a general statement, we welcome material reflecting the true Hawaiian experience." Buys 2 mss/year. Send complete ms. Length: 1,000-2,500 words. Pays 10¢/word.

Poetry: Haiku, light verse and traditional. No seasonal poetry or poetry related to other areas of the world. Buys 6 poems/year. Submit maximum 6 poems. Prefers "shorter poetry." Pays $25.

Tips: "Read *Aloha*. Be meticulous in research and have good illustrative material available, i.e., photos in most cases."

HONOLULU, Honolulu Publishing Co., Ltd., 36 Merchant St., Honolulu HI 96813. (808)524-7400. Editor: Brian Nicol. 20% freelance written. Prefers to work with published/established writers. Monthly magazine covering general interest topics relating to Hawaii. Circ. 35,000. Pays on acceptance. Publishes ms an average of 4 months after acceptance. Byline given. Offers $50 kill fee. Buys first serial rights. Submit seasonal/holiday material 5 months in advance. Simultaneous queries, and simultaneous and photocopied submissions OK. Computer printout submissions acceptable; prefers letter-quality to dot-matrix. Sample copy $2 with 9x11 SAE and $2.30 postage.

Nonfiction: Expose, general-interest, historical/nostalgic, and photo feature—all Hawaii-related. "We run regular features on food, fashion, interior design, travel, etc., plus other timely, provocative articles. No personal experience articles." Buys 10 mss/year. Query with published clips if available. Length: 2,500-5,000 words. Pays $250-400. Sometimes pays expenses of writers on assignment.

Photos: Teresa Black, photo editor. State availability of photos. Pays $15 maximum for b&w contact sheet; $25 maximum for 35mm color transparencies. Captions and identification of subjects required. Buys one-time rights.

Columns/Departments: Calabash (light, "newsy," timely, humorous column on any Hawaii-related subject). Buys 15 mss/year. Query with published clips or send complete ms. Length: 250-1,000 words. Pays $25-35.

Illinois

CHICAGO MAGAZINE, 3 Illinois Center, Chicago IL 60601. Editor-in-Chief: Don Gold. Editor: John Fink. 40% freelance written. Prefers to work with published/established writers; works with a small number of new/unpublished writers each year. Monthly magazine for an audience which is "95% from Chicago area; 90% college-trained; upper income; overriding interests in the arts, dining, good-life in the city and suburbs. Most are in 25-50 age bracket, well-read and articulate. Generally liberal inclination." Circ. 217,000. Buys first serial rights. Pays on acceptance. Publishes ms an average of 6 months after acceptance. Submit seasonal material 4 months in advance. Computer printout submissions acceptable "if legible"; no dot-matrix. Reports in 2 weeks. Query; indicate "specifics, knowledge of city and market, and demonstrable access to sources." For sample copy, send $3 to Circulation Dept.; writer's guidelines for SASE.

Nonfiction: "On themes relating to the quality of life in Chicago: past, present, and future." Writers should have "a general awareness that the readers will be concerned, influential longtime Chicagoans reading what the writer has to say about their city. We generally publish material too comprehensive for daily newspapers or of too specialized interest for them." Personal experience and think pieces, interviews, profiles, humor, spot news, historical articles, travel and exposes. Buys about 50 mss/year. Length: 1,000-6,000 words. Pays $100-$2,500. Pays expenses of writers on assignment.

Photos: Reviews b&w glossy prints, 35mm color transparencies or color prints. Usually assigned separately, not acquired from writers.

Tips: "Submit plainly, be business-like and avoid cliche ideas."

CHICAGO READER, Box 11101, Chicago IL 60611. (312)828-0350. Editor: Robert A. Roth. 80% freelance written. Eager to work with new/unpublished writers. "The *Reader* is distributed free in Chicago's lakefront neighborhoods. Generally speaking, these are Chicago's best educated, most affluent neighborhoods—and they have an unusually high concentration of young adults." Weekly tabloid; 128 pages. Circ. 120,000. Pays "by 15th of month following publication." Publishes ms up to 1 year after acceptance. Buys all rights. Byline given. Phone queries OK. Photocopied submissions OK. Computer printout submissions acceptable; prefers letter-quality to dot-matrix. Reports "very slow," up to 1 year or more.

Nonfiction: "We want magazine features on Chicago topics. Will also consider reviews." Buys 500 mss/year. Submit complete ms. Length: "Whatever's appropriate to the story." Pays $60-800.
Photos: By assignment only.
Columns/Departments: By assignment only.

‡**ILLINOIS MAGAZINE, The Magazine of the Prairie State,** Sunshine Park, Box 40, Litchfield IL 62056. (217)324-3425. Editor: Peggy Kuethe. 85% freelance written. Works with a small number of new/unpublished writers each year. A bimonthly magazine devoted to the heritage of the state. Emphasizes history, current interest, and travel in Illinois for historians, genealogists, students and others who are interested in the state. Circ. 16,000. Pays on publication. Publishes ms an average of 6 months after acceptance. Byline given. Buys first North American serial rigths or one-time rights. Submit seasonal/holiday material 6 months in advance. Photocopied submissions OK. Computer printout submissions acceptable; prefers letter-quality to dot-matrix. Reports in 1 month on queries; 2 months on mss. Sample copy $1; writer's guidelines for #10 SASE.
Nonfiction: Essays, general interest, historical/nostalgic, interview/ profile, photo feature and travel. Also, festivals (annual events, county fairs), biography, points of interest, botany, animals, scenic areas that would be of interest to travelers. "We do not want to see family history/family tree/genealogy articles." Buys 75-85 mss/year. Send complete ms. Length: 100-2,000 words. Pays $10-200.
Photos: Send photos with submission. Reviews contact sheets, 35mm or 4x5 transparencies and 3x5, 5x7 and 8x10 prints. Offers $5-50 photo. Captions, model releases, and identification of subjects required. Buys one-time rights.
Fillers: Anecdotes, facts and short humor. Buys 3-5/year. Length: 50-200 words. Pays $10-25.
Tips: "Be sure to include a phone number where you can be reached during the day. Also, try if at all possible to obtain photographs for the article if it requires them. And don't forget to include sources or references for factual material used in the article."

ILLINOIS TIMES, Downstate Illinois' Weekly Newspaper, Illinois Times, Inc., Box 3524, Springfield IL 62708. (217)753-2226. Editor: Fletcher Farrar Jr. 50% freelance written. Weekly tabloid covering that part of the state outside of Chicago and its suburbs for a discerning, well-educated readership. Circ. 23,000. Pays on publication. Publishes ms an average of 2 months after acceptance. Byline given. Buys first serial rights and second serial (reprint) rights. Submit seasonal/holiday material 1 month in advance. Simultaneous queries, and simultaneous, photocopied, and previously published submissions OK. Computer printout submissions acceptable. Reports in 3 weeks on queries; 8 weeks on mss. Sample copy 50¢.
Nonfiction: Book excerpts, expose, general interest, historical, how-to, interview/profile, opinion, personal experience, photo feature, travel ("in our area"), book reviews, politics, environment, energy, etc. "We are not likely to use a story that has no Illinois tie-in." Annual special issues: Lincoln (February); Health & Fitness (March); Gardening (April); Summer (June); Fall Home (September); and Christmas (books). No articles filled with "bureaucratese or generalities; no articles naively glorifying public figures or celebrity stories for celebrity's sake." Buys 50 mss/year. Query or send complete ms. Length: From 1,500 to 2,500 words maximum. Pays 4¢/word; $100 maximum.
Photos: State availability of photos. Pays $15 for 8x10 prints. Identification of subjects required. Buys one-time rights.
Columns/Departments: Guestwork (opinion column, any subject of personal experience with an Illinois angle). Buys 25 mss/year. Send complete ms. Length: 1,500 words maximum. Pays 4¢/word; $60 maximum.
Tips: "The ideal *IT* story is one the reader hates to put down. Good writing, in our view, is not necessarily fancy writing. It is (in the words of a colleague) 'whatever will engage the disinterested reader.' In other words, nothing dull, please. But remember that any subject—even the investment policies of public pension funds—can be made 'engaging.' It's just that some subjects require more work than others. Good illustrations are a plus. As an alternative newspaper we prefer to treat subjects in depth or not at all. Please, no general articles that lack an Illinois angle."

‡**STYLE,** Chicago Tribune, Room 400, 435 N. Michigan Ave., Chicago IL 60011. (312)222-4176. Managing Editor: John Lux. 15% freelance written. A weekly (Wednesday) lifestyle/fashion tabloid section of the *Chicago Tribune.* Estab. 1985. Circ. 760,000. Pays on publication. Publishes an average of 1 month after acceptance. Offers variable kill fee. Buys first North American serial rights or second serial (reprint) rights. Submit seasonal/holiday material 3 months in advance. Simultaneous, photocopied and previously published submissions OK. Computer printout submissions acceptable; prefers letter-quality to dot-matrix. Reports in 2 weeks on queries; 3 weeks on mss.
Nonfiction: Essays about some kind of relationship for alternating "He" and "She" column; humor, interview/profile (of some "name" person); new product (from an agent's view); personal experience. No fashion or grooming articles. Buys 50 mss/year. Query with published clips; send complete ms for "He" and "She" only. Length 100-2,000 words; 800-1,000 words for "He" and "She." Pays $25-250 for assigned articles; pays $25-150 for unsolicited articles.

Photos: Rarely buys photos.
Columns/Departments: Kid stuff (Parenting, kids' products); High tech (expert writing on new consumer-oriented high-tech merchandise). Buys 8 mss/year. Query. Length: 1,000 words. Pays $50-125.

Indiana

INDIANAPOLIS, 32 E. Washington St., Indianapolis IN 46204. (317)639-6600. Editor: Nancy Comiskey. 90% freelance written. Prefers to work with published/established writers. Monthly magazine emphasizing Indianapolis-related problems/features or regional related topics. Circ. 25,000. Pays on publication. Publishes ms an average of 4 months after acceptance. Byline given. Buys one-time rights. Queries only. Submit seasonal/holiday material 4 months in advance. Simultaneous, photocopied, and previously published submissions OK. Electronic submissions OK via Asynchronous, 300 or 1200 baud rate. Computer printout submissions acceptable; prefers letter-quality to dot-matrix. Reports in 1 month. Sample copy $2; writer's guidelines for SASE.
Nonfiction: Issues ("We're interested in any Indianapolis-related topic including government and education."); historical (Indianapolis-related only); how-to (buying tips); interview (Indianapolis-related person, native sons and daughters); nostalgia; profile; and travel (within a day's drive of Indianapolis). "We *only* want articles with Indianapolis or central Indiana ties, no subjects outside of our region. No essays or opinions—unless they are qualified by professional credits for an opinion/essay. We aren't very interested in broad-based, national topics without a local angle. National issues can be broken into 'how does it affect Indianapolis?' or 'what does it mean for Indianapolis?' (We're big on sidebars.)" Query. Length: 500-3,500 words. Pays $40-300.
Photos: State availability of photos. Pays $30 for b&w; $50 for color transparencies. Captions required. Buys one-time rights.
Columns/Departments: Business, life style, issues, sports, marketplace, leisure, money, politics, health and people.
Tips: "We are interested in trends and issues facing Indianapolis now. Manuscripts have a *strong* local angle."

‡**INDIANAPOLIS MONTHLY**, Mayhill Publications, Suite 225, 8425 Keystone Crossing, Indianapolis IN 46260. (317)259-8222. Editor: Deborah Paul. Associate Editor: Steve Bell. 50% freelance written. A monthly magazine of "upbeat material reflecting current trends. Heavy on lifestyle, homes and fashion. Material must be regional in appeal." Circ. 40,000. Pays on publication. Byline given. Offers 50% kill fee. Buys first North American serial rights and makes work-for-hire assignments. Submit seasonal/holiday material 3 months in advance. Computer printout submissions acceptable; prefers letter-quality to dot-matrix. Reports in 1 month. Sample copy $1.75; free writer's guidelines.
Nonfiction: General interest, historical/nostalgic, interview/profile and photo feature. Special issue is the 500 Mile Race issue (May). No poetry, domestic humor or stories without a regional angle. Buys 18 mss/year. Query with or without published clips, or send complete ms. Length: 200-5,000 words. Pays $35-400. Sometimes pays the expenses of writers on assignment.
Photos: Send photos with submission. Reviews 35mm or 2¼ transparencies. Offers $25 minimum/photo. Identification of subjects required. Buys one-time rights.
Columns/Departments: Business (local made-goods), Sport (heroes, trendy sports), Health (new specialties, technology), and Retrospect (regional history), all 1,000 words. Buys 6-9 mss/year. Query with published clips or send complete mss. Pays $100-300.
Tips: "Monthly departments are open to freelancers. We also run monthly special sections—write for editorial special section lineups."

MICHIANA, Sunday Magazine of *The South Bend Tribune*, Colfax at Lafayette, South Bend IN 46626. (219)233-6161. Editor: Bill Sonneborn. 80% freelance written. Works with a small number of new/unpublished writers each year. Weekly for "average daily newspaper readers; perhaps a little above average since we have more than a dozen colleges and universities in our area." Circ. 125,000. Pays on publication. Publishes ms an average of 3 months after acceptance. Byline given. Buys first North American serial rights or simultaneous rights providing material offered will be used outside of Indiana and Michigan. Will consider photocopied submissions if clearly legible. Computer printout submissions acceptable; prefers letter-quality to dot-matrix. Reports in 3 weeks.
Nonfiction: "Articles of general and unusual interest written in good, clear, simple sentences with logical approach to subject. We use almost no material except that which is oriented to the Midwest, especially Indiana, Michigan, Ohio and Illinois. We avoid all freelance material that supports movements of a political nature. We seldom use first person humor. We use no poetry." Submit complete ms. Buys 100 unsolicited mss/year. Length: 800-3,000 words. Payment is $50-60 minimum, with increases as deemed suitable. Sometimes pays the expenses of writers on assignment.
Photos: "We prefer articles that are accompanied by illustrations, b&w photos or 35mm or larger color transparencies."

RIGHT HERE, The Hometown Magazine, Right Here Publications, Box 1014, Huntington IN 46750. Editor: Emily Jean Carroll. 90% freelance written. Works with a small number of new/unpublished writers each year. Bimonthly magazine of general family interest reaching a northern Indiana audience. Circ. 2,000. Pays 2 weeks after date of issue. Publishes ms an average of 4 months after acceptance. Byline given. Buys first serial rights, one-time rights, simultaneous rights, and second serial (reprint) rights. Submit, seasonal/holiday material 5 months in advance. Simultaneous, photocopied, and previously published submissions OK. Computer printout submissions acceptable; prefers letter-quality to dot-matrix. Reports in 4 weeks on queries; 2 months on mss. Sample copy $1.25; writer's guidelines for SAE and 1 first class stamp.
Nonfiction: General interest, historical/nostalgic, how-to, humor, inspirational, interview/profile, opinion, and travel. "We are looking for short pieces on all aspects of Hoosier living." Profiles, nostalgia, history, recreation, travel, music and various subjects of interest to area readers. Buys 18 mss/year. Send complete ms. Length: 900-2,000 words. Pays $5-20.
Photos: Send photos with ms. Reviews b&w prints. Pays $2-5. Model releases and identification of subjects required. Buys one-time rights.
Columns/Departments: Listen To This (opinion pieces of about 1,000 words); Here and There (travel pieces in or near Indiana); Remember? (nostalgia, up to 2,000 words); Keeping Up (mental, spiritual, self-help, up-lifting, etc., to 2,000 words); Here's How (short how-tos, hints, special recipes, instructional); My Space (writers 19 years old and under, to 1,000 words); and Kid Stuff (puzzles, poems, stories to 1,000 words). Buys 30-40 mss/year. Query or send complete ms. Length: 800-2,000 words. Pays $5-20.
Fiction: Humorous, mainstream, mystery and romance. Needs short stories of about 2,000 words. Buys 6-8 mss/year. Send complete ms. Length: 900-3,000 words. Pays $5-20.
Poetry: Free verse, light verse and traditional. Buys 30-40/year. Submit maximum 6 poems. Length: 4-48 lines. Pays $1-4 for poetry featured separately; pays one copy for poetry used as filler or on poetry page.
Fillers: Anecdotes and short humor. Buys 6-8/year. Length: 300 words maximum. Pays $3 maximum. Pays one copy for material under 300 words.
Tips: "All departments are open. Keep it light—keep it tight. Send short cover letter."

Iowa

THE IOWAN MAGAZINE, Mid-America Publishing Corp., 214 9th St., Des Moines IA 50309. (515)282-8220. Editor: Charles W. Roberts. 85% freelance written. Quarterly magazine covering history, people, places and points of interest in Iowa. Circ. 24,000. Pays on publication. Publishes ms an average of 1 year after acceptance. Byline given. Buys first serial rights. Submit seasonal/holiday material 5 months in advance. Photocopied and previously published submissions OK. Computer printout submissions acceptable. Reports in 3 months. Sample copy for $3.75, 9x12 SAE and $2 postage; free writer's guidelines.
Nonfiction: General interest; historical (history as in American heritage, not personal reminiscence); interview/profile; and travel. No "articles from nonIowans who come for a visit and wish to give their impression of the state." Buys 32 mss/year. Query with published clips. Length: 750-3,000 words. Pays $75-400. Sometimes pays expenses of writers on assignment.
Photos: Send photos with ms. Pays $20 for b&w; $50 for color transparency. Captions and identification of subjects required.
Tips: "If you are writing about Iowa, write on a specific topic. Don't be *too* general. Write a query letter with maybe two or three ideas."

Kansas

KANSAS!, Kansas Department of Economic Development, 503 Kansas Ave., 6th Floor, Topeka KS 66603. (913)296-3479. Editor: Andrea Glenn. 90% freelance written. Quarterly magazine; 40 pages. Emphasizes Kansas "faces and places for all ages, occupations and interests." Circ. 48,000. Pays on acceptance. Publishes ms an average of 1 year after acceptance. Byline given. Buys one-time rights. Submit seasonal/holiday material 8 months in advance. Computer printout submissions acceptable; no dot-matrix. Reports in 2 months. Free sample copy and writer's guidelines.
Nonfiction: "Material must be Kansas-oriented and have good potential for color photographs. We feature stories about Kansas people, places and events that can be enjoyed by the general public. In other words, events must be open to the public, places also. People featured must have interesting crafts, etc." General interest, interview, photo feature, profile and travel. Query. "Query letter should clearly outline story in mind. I'm especially interested in Kansas freelancers who can supply their own photos." Length: 5-7 pages double-spaced, typewritten copy. Pays $75-175. Sometimes pays expenses of writers on assignment.
Photos: "We are a full-color photo/manuscript publication." State availability of photos with query. Pays $25-50 (generally included in ms rate) for 35mm color transparencies. Captions required.

Tips: "History and nostalgia stories do not fit into our format because they can't be illustrated well with color photography."

KANSAS CITY MAGAZINE, 3401 Main St., Kansas City MO 64111. (816)561-0444. Editor: William R. Wehrman. 75% freelance written. Prefers to work with published/established writers. Monthly; 80-96 pages. Circ. 16,000. Freelance material is considered if it is about Kansas City issues, events or people. Publishes ms an average of 3 months after acceptance. Buys all rights. Written queries only; queries and mss should be accompanied by SASE. Electronic submissions OK on WordStar or TypeEdit for IBM PC, but requires hard copy also. Computer printout submissions acceptable; prefers letter-quality to dot-matrix. Reports in 1 month. Sample copy $3.

Nonfiction: Editorial content is issue- or personality-oriented, arts, investigative reporting, profiles, or lengthy news features. Short items of 250-350 words considered for City Window column; pays $25. Longer stories of 2,000-8,000 words pay negotiable depending on story, plus expenses. Columns, which include inside business, travel, lifestyle, dining out, art, theater, sports, music, health and a Postscript essay, are from 1,600-3,000 words and pay $100-200. All material must have a demonstrable connection to Kansas City. Bylines are always given. Sometimes pays expenses of writers on assignment.

Tips: Freelancers should show some previous reporting or writing experience of a professional nature. "The writer has a better chance of breaking in at our publication with short articles. We like to see their work on easier-to-verify stories, such as Lifestyle before committing to longer, tougher reporting."

Kentucky

KENTUCKY HAPPY HUNTING GROUND, Kentucky Dept. of Fish and Wildlife Resources, 1 Game Farm Rd., Frankfort KY 40601. (502)564-4336. Editor: John Wilson. Less than 10% freelance written. Works with a small number of new/unpublished writers each year. A bimonthly state conservation magazine covering hunting, fishing, general outdoor recreation, conservation of wildlife and other natural resources. Circ. 35,000. Pays on publication. Publishes ms an average of 6 months after acceptance. Byline given. Buys one-time rights. Submit seasonal/holiday material 3 months in advance. Previously published submissions OK. Computer printout submissions acceptable. Reports in 3 weeks on queries; 2 months on mss. Free sample copy.

Nonfiction: General interest, historical/nostalgic, how-to, humor, interview/profile, personal experience and photo feature. All articles should deal with some aspect of the natural world, with outdoor recreation or with natural resources conservation or management, and should relate to Kentucky. "No 'Me and Joe' stories (i.e., accounts of specific trips); nothing off-color or otherwise unsuitable for a state publication." Buys 3-6 mss/year. Query or send complete ms. Length: 500-2,000 words. Pays $50-150 (with photos).

Photos: State availability of photos with query; send photos with accompanying ms. Reviews color transparencies (2¼ preferred, 35mm acceptable) and b&w prints (5x7 minimum). No separate payment for photos, but amount paid for article will be determined by number of photos used.

Tips: "We would be much more kindly disposed toward articles accompanied by several good photographs (or other graphic material) than to those without. We will probably be mostly staff-written in 1987 due to budget restraints."

RURAL KENTUCKIAN, Box 32170, Louisville KY 40232. (502)451-2430. Editor: Gary W. Luhr. 75% freelance written. Monthly feature magazine primarily for Kentucky residents. Circulation: 295,000. Pays on acceptance. Publishes ms an average of 8 months after acceptance. Byline given. Not copyrighted. Buys first serial rights for Kentucky. Submit seasonal/holiday material at least 4 months in advance. Will consider photocopied, previously published and simultaneous submissions if previously published and simultaneous submissions if outside Kentucky. Computer printout submissions acceptable; prefers letter-quality to dot-matrix. Reports in 2 weeks. Free sample copy.

Nonfiction: Prefers Kentucky-related profiles (people, places or events), history, biography, recreation, travel, leisure or lifestyle articles or book excerpts; articles on contemporary subjects of general public interest and general consumer-related features including service pieces. Publishes some humorous and first person articles of exceptional quality and opinion pieces from qualified authorities. No general nostalgia. Buys 24-36 mss/year. Query or send complete ms. Length: 800-2000 words. Pays $50-$250. Sometimes pays the expenses of writers on assignment.

Photos: State availability of photos. Reviews color slide transparencies and b&w prints. Identification of subjects required. Payment included in payment for ms. Pays extra if photo used on cover.

Tips: "The quality of writing and reporting (factual, objective, thorough) is considered in setting payment price. We prefer well-documented pieces filled with quotes and anecdotes. Avoid boosterism. Writers need not confine themselves to subjects suited only to a rural audience but should avoid subjects of a strictly metropolitian nature. Well-researched, well-written feature articles, particularly on subjects of a serious nature, are given preference over light-weight material. Despite its name, *Rural Kentuckian* is not a farm publication."

Louisiana

‡**NEW ORLEANS MAGAZINE**, Box 26815, New Orleans LA 70186. (504)246-2700. Editor: Sandy Shilstone. 50% freelance written. Monthly magazine; 125 pages. Circ. 37,000. Pays on publication. Buys first-time rights. Byline given. Submit seasonal/holiday material 4 months in advance. Computer printout submissions acceptable; prefers letter-quality to dot-matrix. Reports in 2 months. Publishes ms an average of 4 months after acceptance.
Nonfiction: General interest, interview and profile. Buys 3 mss/issue. Submit complete ms. Length: 1,200-3,000 words. Pays $100-500.
Photos: David Maher, art director. State availability of photos with ms. Captions required. Buys one-time rights. Model releases required.

‡**SHREVEPORT**, Shreveport Chamber of Commerce, Box 20074, Shreveport LA 71120-9982. (318)226-8521. Editor: Peter H. Main. 90% freelance written. "Submissions are judged on an individual basis, without regard to the writer's publishing history." A monthly magazine focusing on business and economic development with reporting, analysis and features on topics of interest to the Shreveport area business community in general and membership of the Shreveport Chamber of Commerce in particular. "The magazine strives to offer its readership solid reporting on issues affecting business in the Shreveport area. It is written for well-educated, upper and middle income readers in the Shreveport-Bossier City area." Circ. 5,200. Pays on acceptance. Publishes ms an average of 3 months after acceptance. Byline given. Buys first North American serial rights. Submit seasonal/holiday 3 months in advance. "Computer printout submissions, as long as they are legible, are fine"; prefers letter-quality to dot-matrix. Reports in 6 weeks on queries; 2 months on mss. Sample copy $1.75 and $1.50 postage.
Nonfiction: General interest (business oriented), success profiles and At Large (an eye on Shreveport—especially the offbeat and amusing.) Buys 30-45 mss/year. Query with clips or send mss for review. Length: 1,000-4,000 words. Pays $50-175. Sometimes pays the expenses of writers on assignment.
Photos: Send photos with ms. Pays $50-100 for color transparencies; $25-75 for 8x10 color prints. Captions, model releases and identification of subjects required. Buys one-time rights.
Columns/Departments: Monthly departments include Observer (news briefs) and Commercial Notes (promotions, opening, etc.), Managing Your Business and Personal Money Management. Buys 20-35 mss/year. Query with clips or send mss for review. Length: 500-2,000 words. Pays $50-150.
Tips: "We look for tight, in-depth reporting."

SUNDAY ADVOCATE MAGAZINE, Box 588, Baton Rouge LA 70821. (504)383-1111, ext. 319. Editor: Larry Catalanello. 5% freelance written. Prefers to work with published/established writers; works with a small number of new/unpublished writers each year. Byline given. Pays on publication. Publishes ms an average of 1 month after acceptance. Computer printout submissions acceptable; prefers letter-quality to dot-matrix.
Nonfiction and Photos: Well-illustrated, short articles; must have local, area or Louisiana angle, in that order of preference. Photos purchased with mss. Rates vary. Sometimes pays the expenses of writers on assignment.
Tips: "Styles may vary. Subject matter may vary. Local interest is most important. No more than 4-5 typed, double-spaced pages."

Maine

DOWN EAST MAGAZINE, Camden ME 04843. (207)594-9544. Editor: Davis Thomas. 50% freelance written. Works with a small number of new/unpublished writers each year. Emphasizes Maine people, places, events and heritage. Monthly magazine. Circ. 70,000. Pays on acceptance for text; on publication for photos. Publishes ms an average of 6 months after acceptance. Byline given. Offers 15% kill fee. Buys first North American serial rights. Phone queries OK. Submit seasonal/holiday material 6 months in advance. Computer printout submissions acceptable; prefers letter-quality to dot-matrix. Reports in 1 month. Sample copy $2.50; free writer's guidelines with SASE.
Nonfiction: Submit to Manuscript Editor. All material must be directly related to Maine: profiles, biographies, nature, gardening, nautical, travel, recreation, historical, humorous, nostalgic pieces, and photo essays and stories. Recent article example: "Winds of Change Buffet the Isles of Maine" (January 1986). Buys 40 unsolicited mss/year. Length: 600-2,500 words. Pays up to $300, depending on subject and quality. Sometimes pays the expenses of writers on assignment.
Photos: Purchases on assignment or with accompanying ms. Accepts 35mm color transparencies and 8x10 b&w. Also purchases single b&w and color scenics for calendars. Each photo or transparency must bear photographer's name. Captions and model releases required. Pays page rate of $50.

Columns/Departments: Short Travel (600-1,500 words, tightly written travelogs focusing on small geographic areas of scenic, historical or local interest); I Remember (short personal accounts of some incident in Maine, less than 1,000 words); and It Happened Down East (1-2 paragraphs, humorous Maine anecdotes). Pay depends on subject and quality.

Tips: "We depend on freelance writers for the bulk of our material—mostly on assignment and mostly from those known to us; but unsolicited submissions are valued."

GREATER PORTLAND MAGAZINE, Chamber of Commerce of the Greater Portland Region, 142 Free St., Portland ME 04101. (207)772-2811. Editor: Daniel W. Weeks. 75% freelance written. "We enjoy offering talented and enthusiastic new writers the kind of editorial guidance they need to become professional freelancers." A quarterly magazine covering metropolitan and island lifestyles of Greater Portland. "We cover the arts, night life, islands, people, and progressive business in and around Greater Portland." Circ. 10,000. Pays on acceptance. Publishes ms an average of 2 months after acceptance. Byline given. Buys first serial rights or second serial reprint rights. Submit seasonal/holiday material 6 months in advance. Computer printout submissions acceptable; prefers letter-quality to dot-matrix. Reports in 1 week on queries; 2 weeks on mss. Free sample copy with $1 postage.

Nonfiction: General interest, humor, interview/profile and personal experience. "*Greater Portland* is largely freelance written. We have an in-town lifestyle slant and are looking for well-researched essayistic features, not just verbal scenery. For example, if you write a story about our luxury ferry, The Scotia Prince, stay overnight and take the readers aboard. We prefer well-focused essays to comprehensive—but—shallow surveys. First person essays are welcome." Buys 30 mss/year. Query with published clips or send complete ms. Length: 500-2,000 words. Pays $150 maximum. Sometimes pays expenses of writers on assignment.

Photos: Buys b&w and color slides with or without ms. Captions required.

Fiction: Short, mainstream fiction that deals with some aspect of life in Greater Portland; humor, suspense, mystery, and historical fiction welcome. Length: 1,000 words maximum.

Tips: "Send some clips with several story ideas. We're looking for informal, essayistic features structured around a well-defined point or theme. A lively, carefully-crafted presentation is as important as a good subject. We enjoy working closely with talented non-fiction and fiction writers of varying experience to produce a literate (as opposed to slick or newsey) magazine."

MAINE LIFE, 8 St. Pierre St., Lewiston ME 04240. Associate Publisher: Bradbury Blake. 80% freelance written. Monthly for readers of all ages in urban and rural settings. 50% of readers live in Maine; balance are readers in other states who have an interest in Maine. Circ. 30,000. Pays on publication. Publishes ms an average of 3 months after acceptance. Buys first serial rights and second serial (reprint) rights. Submit seasonal/holiday material 3 months in advance. Computer printout submissions acceptable; prefers letter-quality to dot-matrix. Reports in 3 months. Free sample copy.

Nonfiction: Contemporary Maine issues, Maine travel, home and lifestyles, wildlife and recreation, arts and culture; Maine people, business, and environment. Query. Length: 500-3,000 words. Pays 5¢/word. Sometimes pays the expenses of writers on assignment.

Photos: B&w and color slides purchased with or without accompanying ms. Captions required.

Tips: "The writer will notice we accept a variety of styles and also have available short article space under the heading 'Omnibus'. *Maine Life* wants to increase the number of feature articles which deal with contemporary Maine issues."

MAINE MOTORIST, Maine Automobile Assn., Box 3544, Portland ME 04104. (207)774-6377. Editor: Eric Baxter. 25% freelance written. Bimonthly tabloid on travel, car care, AAA news. "Our readers enjoy learning about travel opportunities in the New England region and elsewhere. In addition, they enjoy topics of interest to automobile owners." Circ. 100,000. Pays on publication. Publishes ms an average of 3 months after acceptance. Byline given. Not copyrighted. Buys simultaneous rights; makes work-for-hire assignments. Submits seasonal/holiday material 3 months in advance. Simultaneous and photocopied submissions OK. Computer printout submissions acceptable; prefers letter-quality to dot-matrix. Free sample copy and writer's guidelines.

Nonfiction: Historical/nostalgic (travel); how-to (car care, travel); humor (travel); and travel (New England, U.S. and foreign). No exotic travel destinations that cost a great deal. Send complete ms. Length: 500-1,250 words. Pays $50-150.

Photos: State availability of photos. Reviews 5x7 color and b&w transparencies. Pays $10-25 for b&w; $25-100 for color. Captions required. Buys one-time rights.

Tips: "Travel (particularly New England regional) material is most needed. Interesting travel options are appreciated. Humorous flair sometimes helps."

Maryland

BALTIMORE MAGAZINE, 26 S. Calvert St., Baltimore MD 21202. (301)752-7375. Editor: Stan Heuisler. 50% freelance written. Monthly magazine; 150 pages. Circ. 52,047. Pays on publication. Publishes ms an average of 3 months after acceptance. Byline given. Buys first serial rights. Submit seasonal/holiday material 3 months in advance. Electronic submission information supplied on request. Computer printout submissions acceptable; prefers letter-quality to dot-matrix. Reports in 6 weeks. Sample copy $2.34; writer's guidelines with SASE.
Nonfiction: Consumer, profile, lifestyle, issues, narratives and advocacy. Must have local angle. "We do not want to see any soft, nonlocal features." Buys 4 mss/issue. Length: 1,000-5,000 words. Pays $100-500. Sometimes pays expenses of writers on assignment.
Photos: State availability of photos. Reviews color and b&w glossy prints. Captions preferred.
Columns/Departments: Frontlines (local news tips), Tips (local unusual retail opportunities), Class Cars and Tech Talk (high-tech product advice). Query.

CHESAPEAKE BAY MAGAZINE, Suite 200, 1819 Bay Ridge Ave., Annapolis MD 21403. (301)263-2662. Editor: Betty D. Rigoli. 40% freelance written. Works with a small number of new/unpublished writers each year. Monthly magazine; 80 pages. "*Chesapeake Bay Magazine* is a regional publication for those who enjoy reading about the Bay and its tributaries. Our readers are yachtsmen, boating families, fishermen, ecologists—anyone who is part of Chesapeake Bay life." Circ. 18,000. Pays either on acceptance or publication, depending on "type of article, timeliness and need." Publishes ms an average of 14 months after acceptance. Buys first North American serial rights and all rights. Submit seasonal/holiday material 4 months in advance. Simultaneous (if not to magazines with overlapping circulations) and photocopied submissions OK. Computer printout submissions acceptable; no dot-matrix. Reports in 1 month. Sample copy $2; writer's guidelines for SASE.
Nonfiction: "All material must be about the Chesapeake Bay area—land or water." How-to (fishing and sports pertinent to Chesapeake Bay); general interest; humor (welcomed, but don't send any "dumb boater" stories where common safety is ignored); historical; interviews (with interesting people who have contributed in some way to Chesapeake Bay life: authors, historians, sailors, oystermen, etc.); and nostalgia (accurate, informative and well-paced—no maudlin ramblings about "the good old days"); personal experience (drawn from experiences in boating situations, adventures, events in our geographical area); photo feature (with accompanying ms); profile (on natives of Chesapeake Bay); technical (relating to boating, fishing); and Chesapeake Bay folklore. "We do not want material written by those unfamiliar with the Bay area, or general sea stories. No personal opinions on environmental issues or new column (monthly) material and no rehashing of familiar ports-of-call (e.g., Oxford, St. Michaels)." Recent article example: "The Best Way to Sail" (Feb. 86). Buys 25-40 unsolicited mss/year. Query or submit complete ms. Length: 1,000-2,500 words. Pays $75-85.
Photos: Virginia Leonard, art director. Submit photo material with ms. Reviews 8x10 b&w glossy prints and color transparencies. Pays $100 for 35mm, 2¼x2¼ or 4x5 color transparencies used for cover photos; $15/color photo used inside. Captions and model releases required. Buys one-time rights with reprint permission.
Fiction: "All fiction must deal with the Chesapeake Bay and be written by persons familiar with some facet of bay life." Adventure, fantasy, historical, humorous, mystery and suspense. "No general stories with Chesapeake Bay superimposed in an attempt to make a sale." Buys 8 mss/year. Query or submit complete ms. Length: 1,000-2,500 words. Pays $75-90.
Poetry: Attention: Poetry Editor. Free verse and traditional. Must be about Chesapeake Bay. "We want well crafted, serious poetry. Do not send in short, 'inspired' seasick poetry or 'sea-widow' poems." Buys 2 poems/year. Submit maximum 4 poems. Length: 5-30 lines. Pays $25-35. Poetry used on space available basis only.
Tips: "We are a regional publication entirely about the Chesapeake Bay and its tributaries. Our readers are true 'Bay' lovers, and look for stories written by others who obviously share this love. We are particularly interested in material from the Lower Bay (Virginia) area and the Upper Bay (Maryland/Delaware) area. We will be looking for more personal experience Chesapeake boating articles/stories."

‡CITY PAPER, City Paper Inc., 2612 N. Charles St., Baltimore MD 21218. (301)889-6600. Editor: Russ Smith. 20% freelance written. A weekly tabloid of general interest for the Baltimore metropolitan area. Circ. 70,000. Pays 1 month after publication. Byline given. Buys first rights. Submit seasonal/holiday material 2 months in advance. Simultaneous submissions OK. Sample copy $1 with 9x12 SAE and 6 first class stamps.
Nonfiction: Book excerpts, essays, historical/nostalgic, humor, interview/profile and personal experience. Query with or without published clips, or send complete ms. Length: 500 words. Pays $25-400. Sometimes pays the expenses of writers on assignment.
Photos: State availability of photos with submissions.

Fiction: Richard Rabicoff, fiction editor. Confession, ethnic, experimental, historical, humorous, mainstream, slice-of-life vignettes and suspense. Buys 25 mss/year. Query with published clips. Length: 500 words. Pays $25-100.

MARYLAND MAGAZINE, Department of Economic and Community Development, 45 Calvert St., Annapolis MD 21401. (301)269-3507. Editor: Bonnie Joe Ayers. Managing Publisher: D. Patrick Hornberger. 95% freelance written. Prefers to work with published/established writers. Quarterly magazine promoting the state of Maryland. Circ. 45,000. Pays on acceptance. Publishes ms 6 months-1 year after acceptance. Byline given. Offers 25% kill fee. Buys all rights. Submit seasonal/holiday material 1 year in advance. Photocopied submissions OK. Computer printout submissions acceptable; no dot-matrix. Reports in 8 weeks. Sample copy $2.25; writer's guidelines for business size SAE and 1 first class stamp.
Nonfiction: General interest, historical/nostalgic, humor, interview/profile, photo feature and travel. Articles on any facet of Maryland life except conservation/ecology. No poetry, fiction or controversial material or any topic *not* dealing with the state of Maryland; no trendy topics, or one that has received much publicity elsewhere. Buys 32 mss/year. Query with published clips or send complete ms. Length: 900-2,200 words. Pays $115-300. Pays expenses of writers on assignment.
Tips: "All sections are open to freelancers; however, our tendency is to purchase more historically-oriented articles from freelancers. Thoroughly research your topic and give sources (when applicable)."

Massachusetts

BOSTON GLOBE MAGAZINE, *Boston Globe,* Boston MA 02107. Editor-in-Chief: Ms. Ande Zellman. 25% freelance written. Weekly magazine; 64 pages. Circ. 792,750. Pays on publication. Publishes ms an average of 2 months after acceptance. No reprints of any kind. Buys first serial rights. Submit seasonal/holiday material 3 months in advance. Computer printout submissions acceptable; no dot-matrix. SASE must be included with ms or queries for return. Reports in 4 weeks.
Nonfiction: Expose (variety of issues including political, economic, scientific, medicine and the arts); interview (not Q&A); profile; and book excerpts (first serial rights only). No travelogs or personal experience pieces. Buys 65 mss/year. Query. Length: 3,000-5,000 words. Pays $600-900.
Photos: Purchased with accompanying ms or on assignment. Reviews contact sheets. Pays standard rates according to size used. Captions required.

‡CAPE COD COMPASS, Quarterdeck Communications, Inc., 935 Main St., Box 375, Chatham MA 02633. (617)945-3542. Editor: Andrew Scherding. Managing Editor: Donald Davidson. 80% freelance written. A semiannual magazine about Cape Cod, Martha's Vineyard and Nantucket (Mass.) region. Circ. 34,000. Pays on acceptance. Publishes ms an average of 4 months after acceptance. Byline given. Offers variable kill fee. Buys first North American serial rights or one-time rights. Photocopied submissions OK. Computer printout submissions acceptable. Reports in 2 weeks on queries; 1 month on mss. Sample copy $4; free writer's guidelines.
Nonfiction: Essays, general interest, historical/nostalgic, interview/profile and photo feature. "Articles must have a theme connected with this region of New England. We rarely publish first-person articles." Buys 30 mss/year. Query with published clips, or send complete ms. Length: 1,500-7,000 words. Pays $300-700 for assigned articles; pays $200-400 for unsolicited articles. Sometimes pays the expenses of writers on assignment.
Photos: Send photos with submission, if any. Reviews transparencies. Offers $60/photo. Model releases and identification of subjects required. Buys one-time rights.
Fiction: Condensed novels, historical, humorous, mainstream, novel excerpts, and slice-of-life vignettes. "No fiction that is not connected with this region." Buys 2 mss/year. Query with published clips or send complete ms. Length: 1,500-3,000 words. Pays $200-400.
Poetry: Buys 4-6 poems/year. Submit maximum 4 poems. Length: open. Pays $35-60.
Tips: "We are quite willing to correspond at length with potential contributors about ideas and potential manuscripts. Telephone calls initiated by the contributor are discouraged. Our magazine is largely nonfiction. We would suggest that the writer become thoroughly knowledgeable about a subject before he or she writes about it with the intention of submitting it to our magazine."

‡LYNN, THE NORTH SHORE MAGAZINE, Hastings Group, 45 Forest Ave., Swampscott MA 01907. (617)592-0160. Editor: Robert Hastings. Associate Editor: Susan Sutherland. 90% freelance written. A bimonthly magazine covering topics of interest to readers residing on the North shore of Boston. "*Lynn* is a controlled circulation magazine distributed to households with an income over $35,000. All of our articles have a local flavor. We publish articles on money, fashion, sports, medicine, culture, business and humor." Circ. 75,000. Pays on acceptance. Publishes ms an average of 2 months after acceptance. Byline given. Buys first rights. Submit seasonal/holiday material 4 months in advance. Photocopied submissions OK. Computer printout submissions acceptable; prefers letter-quality to dot-matrix. Reports in 1 month on queries; 3 weeks on mss. Sample copy $2.50; free writer's guidelines.

Nonfiction: Essays, how-to, humor, interview/profile, opinion, personal experience, money, fashion, business, sports, culture and the ocean. Special issues include holidays (December/January) and home guide (April/May). Buys 40 mss/year. Query with published clips. Length: 1,000-2,500 words. Pays $100-250. Pays expenses of writers on assignment.

Photos: State availability of photos with submission. Reviews contact sheets and negatives. Offers $50-200/photo. Model releases and identification of subjects required. Buys one-time rights.

Tips: "We are constantly looking for humor pieces of general interest to upscale readers. This does not need to have the local flavor we are seeking in other articles."

NEW BEDFORD, 488 Pleasant St., New Bedford MA 02740. Editor: Dee Giles Forsythe. 90% freelance written. Works with a small number of new/unpublished writers each year; eager to work with new/unpublished writers. Bimonthly magazine primarily focusing on southeastern Massachusetts. Pays within period of publication. Publishes ms an average of 1 year after acceptance. Buys first serial rights and second serial (reprint) rights. Submit seasonal material 6 months in advance. Computer printout submissions acceptable; prefers letter-quality to dot-matrix. Reports in 1 month. Sample copy $1.50; writer's guidelines with SASE.

Nonfiction: Social, political and natural history; biography and people profiles; environmental and other pertinent public policy issues; boating, commercial fishing, and other maritime-related businesses; the arts; education; and lifestyles. Query. Length: 1,500-2,500 words. Pays approximately $100.

Photos: Prefers b&w glossy prints; will consider 35mm color transparencies. Pays on publication; negotiable fee. Captions and credit lines required.

Fiction: "This magazine occasionally runs short fiction up to 3,000 words. Such manuscripts should have some connection to the sea, the coast, or to southern New England's history or character. There are no restrictions on style; the main criterion is quality." Query or send complete ms.

Tips: "We look for the unusual story or angle, the fresh approach, pieces about events, issues or people in the southeastern Massachusetts and Rhode Island area with whom readers can identify. Our philosophy is one of personal communication between the writer and reader; informal writing, but of high quality and accuracy, will always find a home at *New Bedford*. Because we are a small journal, we enjoy giving new writers a chance, and work personally with them. We do not offer 'a course in journalism' however, and accept only well written material."

‡**SUNDAY MORNING MAGAZINE**, *Worcester Sunday Telegram*, 20 Franklin St., Worcester MA 01613. (617)793-9100. Sunday Editor: Robert Z. Nemeth. 25% freelance written. Sunday supplement serving a broad cross-section of Central Massachusetts residents; 20 pages. Circ. 110,000. Pays on publication. Buys first North American serial rights. Byline given. Phone queries OK. Submit seasonal/holiday material 2 months in advance. Free sample copy.

Nonfiction: Expose (related to circulation area); humor; informational (should have broad application); personal experience (something unusual); photo feature; profile and travel. Buys 2 mss/issue. Query. Length: 600-2,400 words. Pays $50-100. "All pieces must have a local angle."

Photos: Photos purchased with or without accompanying ms or on assignment. Captions required. Pays $5 for 5x7 b&w glossy prints.

Columns/Departments: Open to suggestions for new columns and departments.

Michigan

‡**ABOVE THE BRIDGE MAGAZINE**, 1321 W. M-35, Gwinn MI 49841. (906)346-6060. Editor: Patrice Olivier Cross. 100% freelance written. A monthly magazine. "Most material, including fiction, has an Upper Peninsula of Michigan slant. Our readership is past and present Upper Peninsula residents." Estab. 1985. Circ. 1,500. Pays on publication. Publishes ms an average of 2 months after acceptance. Byline given; requests several lines of biographical information. Offers 50% kill fee. Buys one-time rights or second serial (reprint) rights. Submit seasonal/holiday material 2 months in advance. Photocopied and previously published submissions OK. Electronic submissions OK via Epson QX10 compatibility but requires hard copy also. Computer printout submissions acceptable; prefers letter-quality to dot-matrix. Reports in 2 weeks. Sample copy for 9x12 SAE with 5 first class stamps; writer's guidelines for business size SAE with 1 first class stamp.

Nonfiction: Book excerpts (from books by an Upper Peninsula writer); essays; general interest; historical/nostalgic (on the Upper Pensinsula); how-to (with an Upper Peninsula link); humor; interview/profile (of an Upper Peninsula personality); personal experience; photo feature (on the Upper Peninsula); travel (in the Upper Peninsula area). "This is a family magazine; children are encouraged to read it, therefore no material in poor taste." Accepts submissions from children—fiction, nonfiction and poetry. Buys 50 mss/year. Send complete ms. Length: 1,500 words maximum. Pays 2¢/word.

Photos: Send photos with submission. Reviews 5x7 prints (or larger). Offers no additional payment for photos accepted with ms. Model releases and identification of subjects required. Buys one-time rights.
Columns/Departments: Book review (of a recent book [written the past three years] by an Upper Peninsula writer). Buys "as many as are available." Send complete ms. Length: 1,500 words maximum. Pays 2¢/word.
Fiction: Ethnic (Upper Peninsula heritage); humorous (especially needed); mainstream; mystery; science fiction; slice-of-life vignettes; suspense and children's stories (1,000 word maximum). "All material must be suitable for family reading; profanity will be deleted, even common usage words such as damn. No religious, horror, or erotica will be considered. If the piece is set in an Upper Peninsula setting, it will have much more of a chance to see publication." Buys 50 mss/year. Send complete ms. Length: 2,500 words maximum. Pays 2¢/word.
Poetry: Free verse, haiku, light verse and traditional. "No abstractions such as Life, Love, etc. Be specific, preferably specific about the Upper Pennisula of Michigan—humor is our first choice." Buys 75 poems/year. Submit maximum 10 poems. Length is open, but the shorter ones are preferred. Pays $5-10.
Fillers: Anecdotes and short humor. Buys 25/year. Pays $5 or 2¢/word maximum.
Tips: "Need mysteries, fiction of general interest, science fiction, humor, and children's stories. Be familiar with the Upper Peninsula of Michigan in order to break into the non-fiction areas. General interest articles must relate specifically to areas of interest to the resident of Upper Michigan."

ANN ARBOR OBSERVER, Ann Arbor Observer Company, 206 S. Main, Ann Arbor MI 48104. Editor: Don Hunt. 50% freelance written. Monthly magazine featuring stories about people and events in Ann Arbor. Circ. 46,500. Pays on publication. Publishes ms an average of 2 months after acceptance. Byline given. Buys one-time rights. Electronic submissions OK via WordStar. Computer printout submissions acceptable. Reports in 3 weeks on queries; 4 weeks on mss. Sample copy $1.
Nonfiction: Expose, historical/nostalgic, brief vignettes and photo feature. Must pertain to Ann Arbor. Buys 75 mss/year. Length: 100-7,000 words. Pays up to $1,200/article. Sometimes pays expenses of writers on assignment.
Tips: "If you have an idea for a story, write up a 100-200 word description telling us why the story is interesting. We are most open to intelligent, insightful features of up to 5,000 words about interesting aspects of life in Ann Arbor."

‡DETROIT MAGAZINE, *The Detroit Free Press*, 321 W. Lafayette Blvd., Detroit MI 48231. (313)222-6446. Associate Editor: James G. Cobb. 20% freelance written. Prefers to work with published/established writers; works with a small number of new/unpublished writers each year. For a general newspaper readership; urban and suburban. Weekly magazine. Circ. 800,000. Pays within 6 weeks of publication. Buys first or second serial rights. Kill fee of ⅓ the agreed-upon price. Byline given. Computer printout submissions acceptable; prefers letter-quality to dot-matrix. Reports in 3-4 weeks. Publishes ms an average of 6 months after acceptance.
Nonfiction: "Seeking quality magazine journalism on subjects of interest to Detroit and Michigan readers: lifestyles and better living, trends, behavior, health and body, business and political intrigue, crime and cops, money, success and failure, sports, fascinating people, arts and entertainment. *Detroit Magazine* is bright and cosmopolitan in tone. Most desired writing style is literate but casual—the kind you'd like to read—and reporting must be unimpeachable." Buys 40-50 mss/year. Query or submit complete ms. "If possible, the letter should be held to one page. It should present topic, organizational technique and writing angle. It should demonstrate writing style and give some indication as to why the story would be of interest to us. It should not, however, be an extended sales pitch." Length: 2,000 words maximum. Pays $125-500. Sometimes pays the expenses of writers on assignment.
Photos: Purchased with or without accompanying ms. Pays $25 for b&w glossy prints or color transparencies used inside; $100 for color used as cover.
Tips: "We will be accepting fewer nostalgia, history and first-person stories than in the past. We are aiming to be more polished, sophisticated and 'slicker' and have recently redesigned our magazine to reflect this. Try to generate fresh ideas, or fresh approaches to older ideas. Always begin with a query letter and not a telephone call. If sending a complete ms, be very brief in your cover letter; we really are not interested in previous publication credits. If the story is good for us, we'll know, and if the most widely published writer sends us something lousy, we aren't going to take it."

‡DETROIT MONTHLY, Crain Communications, 1400 Woodbridge, Detroit MI 48207. (313)446-0316. Editor: Martin Fischhoff. 35% freelance written. A monthly magazine covering "the people, places and issues of interest to a well-educated, sophisticated Michigan audience." Pays on acceptance. Byline given. Buys first rights or all rights—negotiable. Submit seasonal/holiday material at least 3 months in advance. Contact editor for electronic submission requirements.
Nonfiction: Book excerpts; historical/nostalgic (on Detroit and Michigan); humor; new product; some travel; well-researched, well-written journalism. Buys 100 mss/year. Query with published clips. Length: 1,000-4,000 words. Pays $100-1,000.

Photos: State availability of photos with submission. Payment negotiable. Captions, model releases and identification of subjects required. Usually buys one-time rights.
Columns/Department: Wine and Spirits (local angle), Food (local angle), Discoveries (new products), Health. Buys 75 mss/year. Query with published clips. Length: 1,100-1,500 words. Pays $100-500.

GRAND RAPIDS MAGAZINE, Suite 1040, Trust Bldg., 40 Pearl St., NW, Grand Rapids MI 49503. (616)459-4545. Publisher: John H. Zwarensteyn. Editor: Ronald E. Koehler. Managing Editor: William Holm. 45% freelance written. Eager to work with new/unpublished writers. Monthly general feature magazine serving western Michigan. Circ. 13,500. Pays on 15th of month of publication. Publishes ms an average of 4 months after acceptance. Buys first serial rights. Phone queries OK. Submit seasonal material 3 months in advance. Photocopied and previously published submissions OK. Electronic submissions OK via IBM 5¼" floppy (MS DOS) or NBI 8" disk (MS DOS), but requires hard copy also. Computer printout submissions acceptable; prefers letter-quality to dot-matrix. Reports in 2 months.
Nonfiction: Western Michigan writers preferred. Western Michigan subjects only: government, labor, education, general interest, historical, interview/profile and nostalgia. Inspirational and personal experience pieces discouraged. No breezy, self-centered "human" pieces or "pieces not only light on style but light on hard information." Humor appreciated but must be specific to region. Buys 5-8 unsolicited mss/year. "If you live here, see Bill Holm before you write. If you don't, send a query letter with published clips, or phone." Length: 500-4,000 words. Pays $15-150. Sometimes pays the expenses of writers on assignment.
Photos: State availability of photos. Pays $15 + /5x7 glossy print and $22 + /35 or 120mm color transparency. Captions and model releases required.
Tips: "Television has forced city/regional magazines to be less provincial and more broad-based in their approach. People's interests seem to be evening out from region to region. The subject matters should remain largely local, but national trends must be recognized in style and content. And we must *entertain* as well as inform."

MICHIGAN: The Magazine of the Detroit News, 615 W. Lafayette, Detroit MI 48231. (313)222-2620. Articles Editor: Lisa Velders. 50% freelance written. Prefers to work with published/established writers; eager to work with new/unpublished writers. Weekly rotogravure featuring the state of Michigan for general interest newspaper readers. Circ. 860,000. Average issue includes 2 feature articles, departments and staff-written columns. Pays on publication. Publishes ms an average of 2 months after acceptance. Byline given. Offers variable kill fee. Buys first serial rights or second serial (reprint) rights. Phone queries OK. Submit seasonal material 2 months in advance. Simultaneous, photocopied and previously published submissions OK, if other publication involved is outside of Michigan. Computer printout submissions acceptable; prefers letter-quality to dot-matrix. Reports in 3 weeks. Sample copy for 11½x14½ SAE; free writer's guidelines.
Nonfiction: Profiles, places, and topics with Michigan connections. Buys 100 mss/year. Send complete ms. Length: 1,000-5,000 words. Pays $150-650.
Photos: State availability of photos with submission. Pays $100-150 per page; $350 per cover. Captions and identification of subjects required.
Columns/Departments: Private Lives (essay—first or third person—on relationships). Buys 52 mss/year. Send complete ms. Length: 1,000 words. Pays $200 maximum.
Fiction: Adventure, ethnic, fantasy, historical, horror, humorous, mainstream, mystery, slice-of-life, vignettes and suspense. Buys 10 mss/year. Send complete ms. Lenght: 1,500-3,000 words. Pays $250-450.
Tips: "Magazines are looking for more people-oriented stories now than ever before, in roto magazines, specifically. There's a great effort to run articles more in the vein of a city-oriented magazine and less of the old-style 'roto' (a la *Parade*) type pieces."

WEST MICHIGAN MAGAZINE, West Michigan Telecommunications Foundation, 7 Ionia SW, Grand Rapids MI 49503. (616) 774-0204. Editor: Dotti Clune. 80% freelance written. Monthly magazine covering geographical region of West Michigan. Circ. 20,000. Pays on publication. Publishes ms an average of 3 months after acceptance. Byline given. Buys first serial rights. Submit seasonal/holiday material 3 months in advance. Simultaneous queries, and photocopied, and previously published submissions OK. Computer printout submissions acceptable; prefers letter-quality to dot-matrix. Reports in 2 weeks on queries; 1 month on mss. Send SAE and $1.15 for sample copy and writer's guidelines.
Nonfiction: Arts, business, dining, entertainment, recreation, travel, expose (government/politics), interview/profile and photo feature. Buys 50 mss/year. Query with published clips if available. Length: 500-2,500 words. Pays $25-250.
Photos: State availability of photos.
Tips: "We look for thought-provoking articles ranging from serious examinations of important issues to humorous glimpses at the lighter side of life in West Michigan. We like articles offering taste, style, and compelling reading; articles capturing the personality of West Michigan—the quality of life in the region and the spirit of its people; and articles appealing to a discriminating audience. We look for colorful, specific, lively material. Many writers aren't imaginative enough. Leads and conclusions are often weak."

Minnesota

LAKE SUPERIOR PORT CITIES, Lake Superior Port Cities, Inc., 325 Lake Ave. S., Duluth MN 55802. (218)722-5002. Editor: Paul L. Hayden. 80% freelance written. Works with a small number of new/unpublished writers each year. A bimonthly regional magazine covering contemporary and historical people, places and current events around Lake Superior. Circ. 14,000. Pays on publication. Publishes ms an average of 6 months after acceptance. Byline given. Offers $25 kill fee. Buys first North American serial rights and second serial (reprint) rights. Submit seasonal/holiday material 8 months in advance. Photocopied submissions OK. Electronic submissions OK via Apple based (DOS or SOS), but requires hard copy also. Computer printout submissions acceptable; prefers letter-quality to dot-matrix. Reports in 3 months on manuscripts. Sample copy $3.50 and $1.92 postage; writer's guidelines for SAE and 1 first class stamp.
Nonfiction: Book excerpts, general interest, historical/nostalgic, humor, interview/profile (local), personal experience, photo feature (local), travel (local), regional business. Buys 45 mss/year. Query with published clips. Length 300-5,000 words. Pays $80-200 maximum.
Photos: State availability of photos with submission. Reviews contact sheets, 2x2 transparencies and 4x5 prints. Offers $10 for b&w and $15 for color transparencies. Captions, model releases, and identification of subjects required.
Columns/Departments: Current events and things to do (for Events Calendar section) short, under 300 words; Shore Lines (letters and short pieces on events and highlights of the Lake Superior Region), up to 150 words; and Book Reviews (Regional targeted or published books), up to 450 words. Direct book reviews to Barbara Landfield, book review editor. Buys 20 mss/year. Query with published clips. Pays $10-35.
Fiction: Ethnic, historical, humorous, mainstream and slice-of-life vignettes. Must be regionally targeted in nature. Buys 5 mss/year. Query with published clips. Length: 300-2,500 words. Pays $1-200.
Tips: "Well-researched queries are attended to. We actively seek queries from writers in Lake Superior communities. Provide enough information on why the subject is important to the region and our readers, or why and how something is unique. We want details. The writer must have a thorough knowledge of the subject and how it relates to our region. We prefer a fresh, unused approach to the subject which provides the reader with an emotional involvement."

MPLS. ST. PAUL MAGAZINE, Suite 1030, 12 S. 6th St., Minneapolis MN 55402. (612)339-7571. Editor: Brian Anderson. Managing Editor: Sylvia Paine. 90% freelance written. Monthly general interest magazine covering the metropolitan area of Minneapolis/St. Paul and aimed at college-educated professionals who enjoy living in the area and taking advantage of the cultural, entertainment and dining out opportunities. Circ. 48,000. Pays on acceptance. Publishes ms an average of 3 months after acceptance. Byline given. Offers 33% kill fee. Buys first North American serial rights. Submit seasonal/holiday material 5 months in advance. Computer printout submissions acceptable; prefers letter-quality to dot-matrix. Reports in 1 month. Sample copy $3.50; free writer's guidelines.
Nonfiction: Book excerpts; expose (local); general interest; historical/nostalgic; interview/profile (local); new product; photo feature (local); and travel (local). Buys 250 mss/year. Query with published clips. Length: 1,000-4,000 words. Pays $100-600. Sometimes pays expenses of writers on assignment.
Photos: Tara Christopherson, photo editor.
Columns/Departments: Nostalgic—Minnesota historical; Arts—local; Home—interior design, local; Last Page—essay with local relevance. Query with published clips. Length: 750-2,000 words. Pays $100-200.
Tips: People profiles (400 words) and Nostalgia are areas most open to freelancers.

TWIN CITIES READER, News, Opinion & Entertainment Weekly, MCP, Inc., 600 1st Ave. N, Minneapolis MN 55403. (612)338-2900. Editor: Deborah L. Hopp. 10% freelance written. Prefers to work with published/established writers. "We are a general interest weekly tabloid serving the needs of the community via investigative features, local news and profiles, politics, consumer information, lifestyle trends, general arts and entertainment (with special emphasis on film, music and theatre) and food and dining features. We try to address the special needs and interests of our reader, leaving the daily press to cover topics or angles best suited to the general population of Minneapolis/St. Paul. Our readers are 25-44 years old and enjoy largely managerial/professional positions. They are well educated and active; they also participate enthusiastically in the arts and entertainment opportunities of our community and are considered to be both well-read and well-informed." Circ. 140,000. Pays on publication. Publishes ms an average of 1 month after acceptance. Byline given. Buys one-time rights. Submit seasonal/holiday material 1 month in advance. Simultaneous queries, and simultaneous and photocopied submissions OK. Computer printout submissions acceptable; no dot-matrix. Reports in 3 weeks. Sample copy for 10x13 SAE and $1.22 postage.
Nonfiction: Travel, fitness and health. Special issues include fitness/health, general real estate, and home interiors. Buys 100 mss/year. Send complete ms. Length: 750-1,500 words. Pays $25-100.
Photos: Greg Helgeson, photo editor. Send photos with accompanying ms. Reviews b&w contact sheets.

Pays $10-100 for 5x7 or 8½x11 b&w prints; $50-300 for 5x7 color transparencies. Model releases and identification of subjects required.
Columns/Departments: Books. Buys 20 mss/year. Send complete ms. Length: 500-1,250 words. Pays $30-100.
Tips: "Our readers are young, well-educated, savvy. Do not write for 'general' readers or the unsophisticated. Books, travel, and health and fitness are most open to freelancers. We like a short, light style with a sense of humor. We have a larger staff so expect to use less freelance."

Mississippi

DELTA SCENE, Box B-3, Delta State University, Cleveland MS 38733. (601)846-1976. Editor-in-Chief: Dr. Curt Lamar. Business Manager: Ms. Sherry Van Liew. 50% freelance written. Quarterly magazine; 32 pages. For an art-oriented or history-minded audience wanting more information (other than current events) on the Mississippi Delta region. Circ. 2,000. Pays on publication. Publishes ms an average of 2 years after acceptance. Buys first serial rights. Byline given. Submit seasonal/holiday material 4 months in advance. Simultaneous, photocopied, and previously published submissions OK. Computer printout submissions acceptable; no dot-matrix. Reports in 1 month. Sample copy $2.
Nonfiction: Historical and informational articles, interviews, profiles, travel and technical articles (particularly in reference to agriculture). "We have a list of articles available free to anyone requesting a copy." Buys 2-3 mss/issue. Query. Length: 1,000-2,000 words. Pays $5-20.
Photos: Purchased with or without ms, or on assignment. Pays $5-15 for 5x7 b&w glossy prints or any size color transparency.
Fiction: Humorous and mainstream. Buys 1/issue. Submit complete ms. Length: 1,000-2,000 words. Pays $10-20.
Poetry: Traditional forms, free verse and haiku. Buys 1/issue. Submit unlimited number of poems. Pays $5-10.
Tips: "The freelancer should follow our magazine's purpose. We generally only accept articles about the Delta area of Mississippi, the state of Mississippi, and the South in general. We are sponsored by a state university so no articles, poetry, etc., containing profanity or other questionable material. Nonfiction has a better chance of making it into our magazine than short stories or poetry."

Missouri

SPRINGFIELD! MAGAZINE, Springfield Communications Inc., Box 4749, Springfield MO 65808. (417)882-4917. Editor: Robert C. Glazier. 85% freelance written. Works with a small number of new/unpublished writers each year; eager to work with new/unpublished writers. Monthly magazine. "This is an extremely local and provincial magazine. No *general* interest articles." Circ. 10,000. Pays on publication. Publishes ms an average of 6 months after acceptance. Byline given. Buys first serial rights. Submit seasonal/holiday material 6-12 months in advance. Simultaneous queries OK. Computer printout submissions acceptable; prefers letter-quality to dot-matrix. Reports in 3 months on queries; 6 months on mss. Sample copy $1.50 and SAE.
Nonfiction: Book excerpts (by Springfield authors only); expose (local topics only); historical/nostalgic (top priority but must be local history); how-to (local interest only); humor (if local angle); interview/profile (needs more on females than on males); personal experience (local angle); photo feature (local photos); and travel (1 page per month). No stock stuff which could appeal to any magazine anywhere. Buys 150+ mss/year. Query with published clips or send complete ms. Length: 500-5,000 words. Pays $25-250. Sometimes pays expenses of writers on assignment.
Photos: State availability of photos or send photos with query or ms. Reviews b&w and color contact sheets; 4x5 color transparencies; and 5x7 b&w prints. Pays $5-35 for b&w; $10-50 for color. Captions, model releases, and identification of subjects required. Buys one-time rights.
Columns/Departments: Buys 250 mss/year. Query or send complete ms. Length varies widely but usually 500-2,500 words. Pays scale.
Tips: "We prefer that a writer read eight or ten copies of our magazine prior to submitting any material for our consideration. The magazine's greatest need is for features which comment on these times in Springfield. We are overstocked with nostalgic pieces right now. We also are much in need of profiles about young women and men of distinction."

Market conditions are constantly changing! If this is 1988 or later, buy the newest edition of Writer's Market at your favorite bookstore or order directly from Writer's Digest Books.

Nevada

NEVADA MAGAZINE, Carson City NV 89710. (702)885-5416. Managing Editor: David Moore. 50% freelance written. Works with a small number of new/unpublished writers each year. Bimonthly magazine published by the state of Nevada to promote tourism in the state. Circ. 75,000. Pays on publication. Publishes ms an average of 4 months after acceptance. Byline given. Buys first North American serial rights. Phone queries OK. Submit seasonal/holiday material 6 months in advance. Computer printout submissions acceptable; no dot-matrix. Reports in 2 months. Sample copy $1; free writer's guidelines.
Nonfiction: Nevada topics only. Historical, nostalgia, photo feature, people profile, recreational and travel. "We welcome stories and photos on speculation." Buys 40 unsolicited mss/year. Submit complete ms or queries to features editor Jim Crandall. Length: 500-2,000 words. Pays $75-300.
Photos: Send photo material with accompanying ms. Pays $10-50 for 8x10 glossy prints; $15-75 for color transparencies. Name, address and caption should appear on each photo or slide. Buys one-time rights.
Tips: "Keep in mind that the magazine's purpose is to promote tourism in Nevada. Keys to higher payments are quality and editing effort (more than length). Send cover letter, no photocopies. We look for a light, enthusiastic tone of voice without being too cute; articles bolstered by amazing facts and thorough research; and unique angles on Nevada subjects."

THE NEVADAN, *The Las Vegas Review Journal*, Box 70, Las Vegas NV 89101. (702)385-4241. Editor-in-Chief: A.D. Hopkins. 15% freelance written. Works with a small number of new/unpublished writers each year. Weekly tabloid; 16 pages. For Las Vegas and surrounding small town residents of all ages "who take our Sunday paper—affluent, outdoor-oriented." Circ. 100,000. Pays on publication. Publishes ms an average of 4 months after acceptance. Byline given. Buys one-time rights and simultaneous rights. Phone queries OK. Submit seasonal/holiday material 2 months in advance. Photocopied and previously published submissions OK. Computer printout submissions acceptable; no dot-matrix. Reports in 3 weeks. Free sample copy and writer's guidelines; mention *Writer's Market* in request.
Nonfiction: Historical (more of these than anything else, always linked to Nevada, southern Utah, northern Arizona and Death Valley); personal experience (any with strong pioneer Nevada angle, pioneer can be 1948 in some parts of Nevada). "We also buy a few contemporary pieces of about 2,400-3,000 words with good photos. An advance query is absolutely essential for these. No articles on history that are based on doubtful sources; no current show business material; and no commercial plugs." Buys 52 mss/year. Query. Length: Average 2,500 words (contemporary pieces are longer). Usually pays $75-100.
Photos: State availability of photos. Pays $10 for 5x7 or 8x10 b&w glossy prints; $15 for 35 or 120mm color transparencies. Captions required. Buys one-time rights on both photos and text.
Tips: "Offer us articles on little-known interesting incidents in Nevada history and good historic photos. In queries come to the point. Tell me what sort of photos are available, whether historic or contemporary, black-and-white or color transparency. Be specific in talking about what you want to write. We may buy a few more freelance personality pieces and art pieces, but these pieces must have strong angles for our area."

New Hampshire

NEW HAMPSHIRE PROFILES, Goals Communications, Inc., Box 4638, Portsmouth NH 03801. (603)433-1551. Editor: Lynn Harnett. 75% freelance written. Monthly magazine; approximately 96 pages. Articles concentrate on audience ages 25 and up, consumer-oriented readers who want to know more about the quality of life in New Hampshire. Pays on publication. Buys first serial rights. Electronic submissions OK via Digital Decmate. Computer printout submissions acceptable. Reports in 2 months. Sample copy $2; writer's guidelines with SASE.
Nonfiction: Interview, profile, photo feature and interesting activities for and about the state of New Hampshire and people who live in it. Buys 4-6 mss/issue. Query with published clips or send complete ms. Length varies from 1,000-3,000 words, depending on subject matter. Pays $75-350.
Photos: State availability of photos. Pays $15-25 for 5x7 or 8x10 b&w glossy prints; $25-75 for 2¼x2¼ or 35mm color transparencies used as color photos in magazine.
Tips: "Query before submitting manuscript, and don't send us your only copy of the manuscript—photocopy it."

New Jersey

‡NEW JERSEY LIVING, LJM Associates, 830 Raymond Road, R.D. 4, Princeton NJ 08540. (201)329-2100. Editor: John J. Turi. Managing Editor: Marie C. Turi. 75% freelance written. A monthly magazine. Circ. 25,000. Pays on publication. Publishes ms an average of 4 months after acceptance. Byline given. Buys first rights and second serial (reprint) rights. Submit seasonal/holiday material 4 months in advance. Simultaneous, photocopied and previously published submissions OK. Computer printout submissions acceptable; prefers letter-quality to dot-matrix. Reports in 3 weeks on queries. Sample copy $2 with SASE; writer's guidelines for SASE.

Nonfiction: Books excerpts, general interest, historical/nostalgic, humor, inspirational, interview/profile, personal experience, photo feature and travel. Buys 24 mss/year. Query with published clips. Length: 1,500-3,000 words. Pays $50.

Photos: Reviews contact sheets, negatives, 4x5 transparencies and 4x5 prints. Offers no additional payment for photos accepted with ms. Captions, model releases, and identification of subjects required.

Poetry: Light verse and traditional. Submit maximum 5 poems. Length: 5-50 lines. No cash payment.

Fillers: Anecdotes, facts, gags to be illustrated by cartoonist and short humor. Length: 5-100 words. No cash payment.

Tips: Features are most open to freelancers.

THE SANDPAPER, Newsmagazine of the Jersey Shore, The SandPaper, Inc., 1816 Long Beach Blvd., Surf City NJ 08008. (609)494-2034. Editor: Curt Travers. Managing Editor: Gail Travers. 20% freelance written. Weekly tabloid covering subjects of interest to Jersey shore residents and visitors. *"The Sandpaper* publishes three editions covering many of the Jersey Shore's finest resort communities. Each issue includes a mix of hard news, human interest features, opinion columns and entertainment/calendar listings." Circ. 85,000. Pays on publication. Publishes ms an average of 1 month after acceptance. Byline given. Offers 100% kill fee. Buys first rights or all rights. Submit seasonal/holiday material 3 months in advance. Simultaneous, photocopied, and previously published submissions OK. Computer printout submissions acceptable; prefers letter-quality to dot-matrix. Reports in 1 month. Free sample copy.

Nonfiction: Essays, general interest, historical/nostalgic, humor, opinion and environmental submissions relating to the ocean, wetlands and pinelands. Must pertain to New Jersey shore locale. Also, arts and entertainment news and reviews if they have a Jersey shore angle. Buys 25 mss/year. Send complete ms. Length: 200-2,000 words. Pays $15-100. Sometimes pays the expenses of writers on assignment.

Photo: State availability of photos with submission. Offers $6-25/photo. Buys one-time rights or all rights.

Columns/Departments: Speak Easy (opinion and slice-of-life; often humorous); Food for Thought (cooking); and Commentary (forum for social science perspectives); all 500-1,500 words. Buys 50 mss/year. Send complete ms. Pays $15-35.

Fiction: Humorous and slice-of-life vignettes. Buys 25 mss/year. Send complete ms. Length: 500-1,500 words. Pays $15-35.

Tips: "Anything of interest to sun worshippers, beach walkers, nature watchers, water sports lovers is of potential interest to us. The opinion page and columns are most open to freelancers. We are steadily increasing the amount of entertainment-related material in our publication."

‡THE WAVE, The WAVE Press, Catalyst Communications Enterprises, 300 First Ave., Spring Lake NJ 07762. (201)382-8450. Editor: Michael E. Napoliello Jr. Publisher: Jason Mark Moskowitz. 75% freelance written. Eager to work with new/unpublished writers. A weekly tabloid covering art/entertainment/science/social politics of local interest to people in New Jersey. Circ. 50,000. Pays on acceptance. Publishes ms an average of 1 month after acceptance. Byline given. Offers 33% kill fee plus expenses. Buys simultaneous rights. Submit seasonal/holiday material 2 weeks in advance. Simultaneous queries and photocopied submissions OK. Electronic submissions OK via IBM PC; send disk, or transmit. Computer printout submissions acceptable; prefers letter-quality to dot-matrix. Reports in 2 weeks on queries; 1 week on mss. Sample copy for $1 and large envelope with 3 first class stamps; writer's guidelines for SAE and 1 first class stamp.

Nonfiction: J.T.M. Templi, articles editor. Expose, general interest, humor, inspirational, interview/profile, opinion, art reviews, social commentary and satire. "We seek articles dealing with personal growth, like a New Age publication might. We appreciate comment and insight into popular as well as sub-culture entertainment, like the *Rolling Stone* or *Vanity Fair*. We want stories of local interest to people in the state of New Jersey—articles that take the uncommon, the deep, the revealing, the people's, etc., point of view. Stories that present the personal, or the little known side of national issues, philosophies, science, and general interest matter are also candidates for publication. All of this could be summed up simply—we want articles that reflect the essence of a conversation amongst good and concerned friends." Buys 80 mss/year. Send complete ms. Length: 100-5,000 words. No mss longer than 5 typed pages unless it can be printed in subsequent issues. Pays $10-150 plus expenses if applicable; must be certified by editor.

Photos: Marc Stuarts, photo editor. Send photos with accompanying query or ms. Prefers expressionistic, experimental, additive to story, etc. Reviews 4x5 b&w prints. Pays additional 10% of ms rate.

Columns/Departments: Michael Napoleillo, column/department editor. Send for writer's guidelines. Query with published clips.

Fiction: Jean Valjean, fiction editor. Adventure, experimental, fantasy, horror, humorous, science fiction and philosophy. Buys 54 mss/year. Send complete ms. Length: 100-5,000 words. Pays $15-150.

Poetry: Michael Arroyo, poetry editor. Avant-garde, free verse, haiku, light verse, traditional. "All types are welcome." Buys 200 poems/year. Length: open. Most poems are submitted contributions. Pay can be discussed with poetry editor.

Tips: "As far as an overall or general policy, we look for articles that have the characteristics of a popular song: catchy, bright, moving, to the point. Articles that have their source in New Jersey, or that appeal to general humanistic concerns (art, science, society, etc.) are considered first. Writing that is factual or imaginative in content, and unique in style is encouraged. Literally all sections of the paper are open to freelancers. Short articles (600-1,200 words) dealing with art, entertainment, or New Jersey issues and social growth, are priority."

New Mexico

NEW MEXICO MAGAZINE, Joseph Montoya State Bldg., 1100 St. Francis Drive, Santa Fe NM 87503. Editor: Emily Drabanski. Managing Editor: Scottie King. 85% freelance written. Monthly magazine; 64-96 pages. Emphasizes New Mexico for a college educated readership, above average income, interested in the Southwest. Circ. 100,000. Pays on acceptance. Publishes ms an average of 6 months after acceptance. Buys first North American serial rights. Submit seasonal/holiday material 8 months in advance. Computer printout submissions acceptable; no dot-matrix. Reports in 10 days to 6 weeks. Sample copy $1.75.

Nonfiction: New Mexico subjects of interest to travelers. Historical, cultural, humorous, nostalgic and informational articles. "We are looking for more short, light and bright stories for the 'Asi Es Nuevo Mexico' section." No columns or cartoons, no nonNew Mexico subjects. Buys 5-7 mss/issue. Query with 3 published writing samples. Length: 500-2,000 words. Pays $60-300. Sometimes pays expenses of writers on assignment.

Photos: Purchased with accompanying ms or on assignment. Query or send contact sheet or transparencies. Pays $30-50 for 8x10 b&w glossy prints; $30-75 for 35mm—prefers Kodachrome. Submit in plastic-pocketed viewing sheets. Captions and model releases required. Buys one-time rights.

Tips: "Send a superb short (300 words) manuscript on a little-known event, aspect of history or place to see in New Mexico. Faulty research will immediately ruin a writer's chances for the future. Good style, good grammar. No generalized odes to the state or the Southwest. No sentimentalized, paternalistic views of Indians or Hispanics. No glib, gimmicky 'travel brochure' writing."

New York

ADIRONDACK LIFE, Route 86, Box 97, Jay NY 12941. Editor: Jeffery G. Kelly. 50% freelance written. Prefers to work with published/established writers; works with a small number of new/unpublished writers each year. Emphasizes the Adirondack region and the North Country of New York State for readers ages 30-60, whose interests include outdoor activities, history, and natural history directly related to the Adirondacks. Bimonthly magazine; 80 pages. Circ. 40,000. Pays on publication. Publishes ms an average of 1 year after acceptance. Buys one-time rights. Byline given. Submit seasonal/holiday material 4 months in advance. Previously published book excerpts OK. Computer printout submissions acceptable; no dot-matrix. Reports in 6 weeks. Sample copy $4; free writer's guidelines.

Nonfiction: Outdoor recreation (Adirondack relevance only); natural history, how-to, where-to (should relate to activities and lifestyles of the region); photo feature (all photos must have been taken in the Adirondacks); profile (Adirondack personality); and historical. "We are seeking articles on flourishing Adirondack businesses, especially small businesses." Buys 24-28 unsolicited mss/year. Query. Length: For features, 3,000 words maximum; for departments, 500-1,000 words. Pays $100-400. Sometimes pays the expenses of writers on assignment.

Photos: Purchased with or without ms or on assignment. All photos must be identified as to subject or locale and must bear photographer's name. Submit color slides or b&w prints. Pays $25 for b&w transparencies; $50 for color transparencies; $300 for cover (color only, vertical in format). Credit line given.

Tips: "We are looking for clear, concise, well-organized manuscripts, written with flair. We are continually trying to upgrade the editorial quality of our publication."

‡**CITY LIMITS, News for the Other New York**, City Limits Community Information Service, Inc., 424 W. 33rd St., New York NY 10001. (212)239-8440. Editor: Annette Fuentes. Associate Editor: Doug Turetsky. 50% freelance written. Works with a small number of new/unpublished writers each year. A monthly magazine covering housing and related urban issues. "We cover news and issues in New York City as they relate to the city's poor, moderate and middle-income residents. We are advocacy journalists with a progressive or 'left' slant." Circ. 5,400. Pays on publication. Publishes ms an average of 1-2 months after acceptance. Byline given. Buys first North American serial rights, one-time rights, or second serial (reprint) rights. Electronic submissions OK via CP/M-Kaypro, but requires hard copy also. Computer printout submissions acceptable; prefers letter-quality to dot-matrix. Reports in 3 weeks. Sample copy $2.

Nonfiction: Exposé, interview/profile, opinion hard news and community profile. "No fluff, no propaganda." Length: 600-2,500 words. Pays $50-150. Sometimes pays expenses of writers on assignment.
Photos: Reviews contact sheets and 5x7 prints. Offers $10-40/photo, cover only. Identification of subjects required. Buys one-time rights.
Columns/Departments: Short Term Notes (brief descriptions of programs, policies, events, etc.), 250-400 words; Book Reviews (housing, urban development, planning, etc.), 250-600 words; Pipeline (covers community organizations, new programs, government policies, etc.), 600-800 words; People (who are active in organizations, community groups, etc.), 600-800 words; and Organize (groups involved in housing, job programs, health care, etc.), 600-800 words. Buys 50-75 mss/year. Query with published clips or send complete ms. Pays $25-35.
Tips: "We are open to a wide range of story ideas that fit our subtitle: 'News for the other New York.' If you don't have particular expertise in housing, urban planning etc., start with a community profile or pertinent book or film review. Short Term Notes is also good for anyone with reporting skills. We're looking for writing that is serious and informed but not academic nor heavy handed."

HUDSON VALLEY MAGAZINE, Box 425, Woodstock NY 12498. (914)679-5100. Editor: Joanne Michaels. 100% freelance written. Prefers to work with published/established writers. Monthly. Circ. 26,000. Pays on publication. Publishes ms an average of 6 months after acceptance. Byline given. Buys first North American serial rights, one-time rights, and second serial (reprint) rights. Submit seasonal/holiday material 3 months in advance. Simultaneous submissions OK. Computer printout submissions acceptable; no dot-matrix. Reports in 1 month on queries.
Nonfiction: Book excerpts; general interest; historical (Hudson Valley); how-to (home improvement); interview/profile (of area personalities); photo feature. No fiction or personal stories. Length: 1,500-2,000 words. Query. Pays $20-50.
Photos: State availability of photos. Reviews 5x7 b&w prints. Captions required.
Tips: "The writer must live in the region and be familiar with it."

NEW YORK ALIVE, The Magazine of Life and Work in the Empire State, The Business Council of New York State, Inc., 152 Washington Ave., Albany NY 12210. (518)465-7511. Editor: Mary Grates Stoll. 85% freelance written. Works with a small number of new/unpublished writers each year. Bimonthly magazine about New York state—people, places, events, history. "Devoted to promoting the culture, heritage and lifestyle of New York state. Aimed at people who enjoy living and reading about the New York state experience. All stories must be positive in tone and slanted toward promoting the state." Circ. 35,000. Pays within 30 days of acceptance. Publishes ms an average of 8 months after acceptance. Byline given. Offers 25% of agreed-upon purchase price kill fee. Buys one-time rights. Submit seasonal/holiday material 4 months in advance. Simultaneous queries and previously published submissions OK. Electronic submissions OK via IBM PC Wordstar, but requires hard copy also. Computer printout submissions acceptable. Reports in 3 months on queries; 1 month on mss. Sample copy $2.45; writer's guidelines for legal size SAE and 1 first class stamp.
Nonfiction: Historical/nostalgic, humor, interview/profile, personal experience, photo feature and travel. In all cases subject must be a New York state person, place, event or experience. No stories of general nature (e.g. nationwide trends); political; religious; nonNew York state subjects. Query with published clips. Buys 30-40 mss/year. Length: 1,500-3,000 words. Pays $200-350. Pays expenses of writers on assignment.
Photos: State availability of photos. Reviews b&w contact sheets, 35mm color transparencies, and b&w prints. Pays $15-30 for b&w and $30-250 for color. Model releases and identification of subjects required.
Columns/Departments: Buys 80-100 mss/year. Query with published clips. Length: 500-1,000 words. Pays $50-150.
Tips: "We buy more short articles. The writer should enjoy and feel comfortable with writing straightforward, promotional type of material."

NEW YORK DAILY NEWS, Travel Section, 220 E. 42 St., New York NY 10017. (212)210-1699. Travel Editor: Harry Ryan. 40% freelance written. Weekly tabloid. Circ. 2 million. "We are the largest circulating newspaper travel section in the country and take all types of articles ranging from experiences to service oriented pieces that tell readers how to make a certain trip." Pays on publication. Byline given. Makes work-for-hire assignments. Submit seasonal/holiday material 4 months in advance. Contact first before submitting electronic submissions; requires hard copy also. Computer printout submissions acceptable "if crisp"; prefers letter-qualtiy to dot-matrix. Reports "as soon as possible." Writer's guidelines for SAE and 1 first class stamp.
Nonfiction: General interest, historical/nostalgic, humor, inspirational, personal experience and travel. "Most of our articles involve practical trips that the average family can afford—even if it's one you can't afford every year. We put heavy emphasis on budget saving tips for all trips. We also run stories now and then for the Armchair Traveler, an exotic and usually expensive trip. We are looking for professional quality work from professional writers who know what they are doing. The pieces have to give information and be entertaining at

the same time." No How I Spent My Summer Vacation type articles. No PR hype. Buys 60 mss/year. Query with SASE. Length: 1,500 words maximum. Pays $75-125.
Photos: "Good pictures always help sell good stories." State availability of photos with ms. Reviews contact sheets and negatives. Captions and identification of subjects required. Buys all rights.
Columns/Departments: Short Hops is based on trips to places within a 300 mile radius of New York City. Length: 800-1,000 words. Travel Watch gives practical travel advice.
Tips: "A writer might have some luck gearing a specific destination to a news event or date: In Search of Irish Crafts in March, for example, but do it well in advance."

NEW YORK MAGAZINE, News America Publishing, Inc. 755 2nd Ave., New York 10017. (212)880-0700. Editor: Edward Kosner. Managing Editor: Laurie Jones. Weekly magazine emphasizing the New York metropolitan area. 30% freelance written. Pays on acceptance. Publishes ms an average of 1 month after acceptance. Buys first North American serial rights. Submit seasonal/holiday material 2 months in advance. Photocopied submissions OK. Computer printout submissions acceptable; prefers letter-quality to dot-matrix. Reports in 1 month.
Nonfiction: Expose, general interest, interview, profile, behavior/lifestyle, health/medicine, local politics and entertainment. Query. Pays $850-2,000.
Tips: "The writer has a better chance of breaking in with shorter articles. The magazine very rarely assigns a major feature to a new writer."

THE NEW YORK TIMES, 229 W. 43rd St., New York NY 10036. (212)556-1234. SASE.
Nonfiction: *The New York Times Magazine* appears in *The New York Times* on Sunday. "Views should be fresh, lively and provocative on national and international news developments, science, education, family life, social trends and problems, arts and entertainment, personalities, sports and the changing American scene. Freelance contributions are invited. Articles must be timely. They must be based on specific news items, forthcoming events or significant anniversaries, or they must reflect trends. Our full-length articles run approximately 4,000 words, and for these we pay from $1,500 to $2,500 on acceptance. Our shorter pieces run from 1,000-2,500 words, and for these we pay from $750 to $1,500 on acceptance." Unsolicited articles and proposals should be addressed to Articles Editor. *Arts and Leisure* section of *The New York Times* appears on Sunday. Wants "to encourage imaginativeness in terms of form and approach—stressing ideas, issues, trends, investigations, symbolic reporting and stories delving deeply into the creative achievements and processes of artists and entertainers—and seeks to break away from old-fashioned gushy, fan magazine stuff." Length: 4,000 words. Pays $100-250, depending on length. *Arts and Leisure* Editor: William H. Honan.
Photos: Send to Photo Editor. Pays $75 minimum for b&w photos.
Tips: "The Op Ed page is always looking for new material and publishes many people who have never been published before. We want material of universal relevance which people can talk about in a personal way. When writing for the Op Ed page, there is no formula, but the writing itself should have some polish. Don't make the mistake of pontificating on the news. We're not looking for more political columnists. Op Ed length runs about 750 words, and pays about $150."

NEW YORK'S NIGHTLIFE AND LONG ISLAND'S NIGHTLIFE, MJC Publications Inc., 1770 Deer Park Ave., Deer Park NY 11729. (516)242-7722. Publisher: Michael Cutino. Managing Editor: Bill Ervolino. A monthly entertainment magazine. Circ. 50,000. Pays on publication. Byline given. Offers $15 kill fee. Buys first North American serial rights and all rights. Submit seasonal/holiday material 10 weeks in advance. Simultaneous queries and photocopied submissions OK. Reports in 10 weeks. Free sample copy and writer's guidelines.
Nonfiction: General interest, humor, inspirational, interview/profile, new product, photo feature, travel and entertainment. Length: 500-1,500 words. Pays $25-75.
Photos: Send photos with ms. Reviews b&w and color contact sheets. Pays $10 for color transparencies and b&w prints. Captions and model releases required. Buys all rights.
Columns/Departments: Films, Movies, Albums, Sports, Fashion, Entertainment, and Groups. Buys 150 mss/year. Send complete ms. Length: 400-600 words. Pays $25.
Fillers: Clippings, jokes, gags, anecdotes, short humor and newsbreaks. Buys 10/year. Length: 25-100 words. Pays $10.

NEWSDAY, Long Island NY 11747. Viewpoints Editor: Ilene Barth. 75% freelance written. Opinion section of daily newspaper. Byline given. Computer printout submissions acceptable.
Nonfiction: Seeks "opinion on current events, trends, issues—whether national or local government or lifestyle. Must be timely, pertinent, articulate and opinionated. Strong preference for authors within the circulation area. It's best to consult before you start writing." Length: 600-2,000 words. Pays $75-300.
Tips: "The writer has a better chance of breaking in at our publication with short articles since the longer essays are commissioned from experts and well-known writers."

‡UPSTATE MAGAZINE, *Democrat and Chronicle*, 55 Exchange St., Rochester NY 14614. (716)232-7100. Editor: Melinda Meers. 90% freelance written. Works with a small number of new/unpublished writers each year. A Sunday magazine appearing weekly in the *Democrat and Chronicle*. A regional magazine covering topics of local interest written for the most part by area writers. Circ. 260,000. Pays on publication. Byline given. Buys first North American serial rights and second (reprint) rights to material originally published elsewhere. Submit seasonal/holiday material 3 months in advance. Computer printout submissions acceptable. Reports in 6-8 weeks. Publishes ms an average of 4 months after acceptance.
Nonfiction: General interest (places and events of local interest); historical/nostalgic; humor; interview/profile (of outstanding people in local area); personal experience; photo feature (with local angle). Buys 100 mss/year. Query. Length: 750-1,500 words; shorter is better. Pays $60-250. Do not send fiction or fillers. Sometimes pays the expenses of writers on assignment.
Tips: "Is the writer's style and the subject matter compelling to a *very* well-educated, affluent readership? If advertising revenue improves, the books will get larger, and *Upstate* will buy more and longer articles."

North Carolina

CHARLOTTE MAGAZINE, Box 36639, Charlotte NC 28236. (704)375-8034. Editor: Diane Clemens. 95% freelance written. Monthly magazine emphasizing probing, researched and upbeat articles on local people, places and events. Circ. 20,000. Pays on publication. Publishes ms an average of 2 months after acceptance. Buys first serial rights. Computer printout submissions acceptable; prefers letter-quality to dot-matrix. SASE. Reports in 3 weeks. Sample copy $2.50.
Nonfiction: Departments: lifestyles (alternative and typical); business (spotlight successful, interesting business and people); town talk (short, local articles of interest); theater, arts, book reviews and sports. No PR promos. "We are seeking articles indicating depth and research in original treatments of subjects. Our eagerness increases with articles that give our well-educated audience significant information through stylish, entertaining prose and uniqueness of perspective. Remember our local/regional emphasis." Query or send complete ms. Length: 1,000-2,000 words. Pays 10¢/word for feature articles. Sometimes pays expenses of writers on assignment.
Photos: State availability of photos. Buys b&w and color prints; pay negotiable. Captions preferred; model release required.
Columns/Departments: "Will consider all types of articles." Buys 6 columns/issue. Query. Length: 1,000-1,500 words. Pays 10¢/word.

SOUTHERN EXPOSURE, Box 531, Durham NC 27702. (919)688-8167. Contact: Editor. Bimonthly magazine, 64-128 pages for Southerners interested in "left-liberal" political perspective and the South; all ages; well-educated. Circ. 7,500. Pays on publication. Buys all rights. Offers kill fee. Byline given. Will consider photocopied and simultaneous submissions. Submit seasonal material 6 months in advance. SASE. Reports in 2-3 months. "Query is appreciated, but not required."
Nonfiction: "Ours is probably the only publication about the South *not* aimed at business or upper-class people; it appeals to all segments of the population. *And*, it is used as a resource—sold as a magazine and then as a book—so it rarely becomes dated." Needs investigative articles about the following subjects as related to the South: politics, energy, institutional power from prisons to universities, women, labor, Black people and the economy. Informational interview, profile, historical, think articles, expose, opinion and book reviews. Length: 6000 words maximum. Pays $50-200. Smaller fee for short items.
Photos: "Very rarely purchase photos, as we have a large number of photographers working for us." 8x10 b&w preferred; no color. Payment negotiable.
Fiction: "Fiction should concern the South, e.g., Black fiction, growing up Southern, etc." Buys 6 short stories or plays/year. Length: 6,000 words maximum. Pays $50-200.
Poetry: All forms of poetry accepted if they relate to the South, its problems, potential, etc. Length: open. Pays $15-100. Buys 6-10 poems/year.

THE STATE, *Down Home in North Carolina*, Box 2169, Raleigh NC 27602. Editor: W.B. Wright. 70% freelance written. Publishes material from published and unpublished writers from time to time. Monthly. Buys first serial rights. Pays on acceptance. Deadlines 1 month in advance. Computer printout submissions acceptable; prefers letter-quality to dot-matrix. Sample copy $1.
Nonfiction: General articles about places, people, events, history, nostalgia and general interest in North Carolina. Emphasis on travel in North Carolina, (devotes features regularly to resorts, travel goals, dining and stopping places). Will use humor if related to region. Length: 1,000-1,200 words average. Pays $15-50, including illustrations.
Photos: B&w photos. Pays $3-20, "depending on use."

Ohio

BEACON MAGAZINE, Akron Beacon Journal, 44 E. Exchange St., Akron OH 44328. (216)375-8268. Editor: Sanford Levenson. 25% freelance written. Eager to work with new/unpublished writers. Sunday newspaper magazine of general interest articles with a focus on Ohio and Ohioans. Circ. 225,000. Pays on publication. Publishes ms an average of 2 months after acceptance. Byline given. Offers 50% kill fee. Buys one-time rights, simultaneous rights, and second serial (reprint) rights. Submit seasonal/holiday material 2 months in advance. Simultaneous queries, and simultaneous and previously published submissions OK. Electronic submissions OK via 300 Baud. Computer printout submissions acceptable; prefers letter-quality to dot-matrix. Reports in 1 month. Free sample copy.
Nonfiction: General interest, historical/nostalgic, short humor and interview/profile. Buys 50 mss/year. Query with or without published clips. Length: 500-3,000 words. Pays $100-500. Sometimes pays expenses of writers on assignment.
Photos: State availability of photos. Pays $25-50 for 35mm color transparencies and 8x10 b&w prints. Captions and identification of subjects required. Buys one-time rights.
Tips: "Include Social Security number with story submission."

BEND OF THE RIVER® MAGAZINE, 143 W. Third St., Box 239, Perrysburg OH 43551. (419)874-7534. Publishers: Christine Raizk Alexander and R. Lee Raizk. 75% freelance written. "We buy material that we like whether by an experienced writer or not." Monthly magazine for readers interested in Ohio history, antiques, etc. Circ. 3,000. Pays on publication. Publishes ms an average of 6 months after acceptance. Byline given. Buys one-time rights. Submit seasonal material 2 months in advance; deadline for holiday issue is October 15. Computer printout submissions acceptable; prefers letter-quality to dot-matrix. Reports in 6 weeks. Sample copy $1.
Nonfiction: "We deal heavily in Ohio history. We are looking for well-researched articles about local history and modern day pioneers doing the unusual. We'd like to see interviews with historical (Ohio) authorities; travel sketches of little-known but interesting places in Ohio; articles about grass roots farmers, famous people from Ohio like Doris Day, Gloria Steinem, etc. and preservation. Our main interest is to give our readers happy thoughts and good reading. We strive for material that says 'yes' to life, past and present." No personal reflection or nostalgia unless you are over 65. Buys 75 unsolicited mss/year. Submit complete ms. Length: 1,500 words. Pays $10-25.
Photos: Purchases b&w photos with accompanying mss. Pays $1 minimum. Captions required.
Tips: "Any Toledo area, well-researched history will be put on top of the heap. Send us any unusual piece that is either cleverly humorous, divinely inspired or thought provoking. We like articles about historical topics treated in down-to-earth conversational tones. We pay a small amount (however, we're now paying more) but usually use our writers often and through the years. We're loyal."

‡CAPITOL MAGAZINE, The Columbus Dispatch, 34 S. 3rd St., Columbus OH 43216. (614)461-5251. Editor: T.R. Fitchko. Managing Editor: Dick Otte. 30% freelance written. Prefers to work with published/established writers. "*Capitol* is the Sunday-magazine-of-*The Columbus-Dispatch*. Cover stories generally have a Columbus or central Ohio angle. Inside stories include humor and fiction." Circ. Approximately 350,000. Pays on publication. Publishes ms an average of 3 months after acceptance. Byline given. Buys first rights and one-time rights. Submit seasonal/holiday material 4 months in advance. Simultaneous, photocopied, and previously published submissions OK. Computer printout submissions acceptable. Reports in 1 month. Sample copy for 10x13 SAE; free writer's guidelines.
Nonfiction: Essays, humor and photo feature. Buys 10 mss/year. Query with published clips. Length: 3,000 words maximum. Pays $50-400.
Photos: State availability of photos with submission. Reviews negatives. Offers no additional payment for photos accepted with ms. Captions, model releases, and identification of subjects required. Buys one-time rights.
Fiction: Buys 3-5 mss/year. Send complete ms. Length: 1,000-3,500 words. Pays $50-400.
Tips: "Humor and personal essays are the area of our publication most open to freelancers. Well-written, well-researched articles sell themselves."

CINCINNATI MAGAZINE, Suite 300, 35 E. 7th St., Cincinnati OH 45202. (513)421-4300. Editor: Laura Pulfer. Monthly magazine emphasizing Cincinnati living. Circ. 32,000. Pays on acceptance. Byline given. Offers 33% kill fee. Buys all rights. Submit seasonal/holiday material 3 months in advance. Simultaneous, photocopied, and previously published submissions OK. Reports in 5 weeks.
Nonfiction: How-to, informational, interview, photo feature, profile and travel. No humor. Buys 4-5 mss/issue. Query. Length: 2,000-4,000 words. Pays $150-400.
Photos: Thomas Hawley, art director. Photos purchased on assignment only. Model release required.

Columns/Departments: Travel, how-to, sports and consumer tips. Buys 5 mss/issue. Query. Length: 750-1,500 words. Pays $75-150.

Tips: "It helps to mention something you found particularly well done in our magazine. It shows you've done your homework and sets you apart from the person who clearly is not tailoring his idea to our publication. Send article ideas that probe the whys and wherefores of major issues confronting the community, making candid and in-depth appraisals of the problems and honest attempts to seek solutions. Have a clear and well defined subject about the city (the arts, politics, business, sports, government, entertainment); include a rough outline with proposed length; a brief background of writing experience and sample writing if available. We are looking for critical pieces, smoothly written, that ask and answer questions that concern our readers. We do not run features that are 'about' places or businesses simply because they exist. There should be a thesis that guides the writer and the reader. We want balanced articles about the city—the arts, politics, business, etc."

‡CLEVELAND MAGAZINE, City Magazines, Inc., 1621 Euclid Ave., Cleveland OH 44120. (216)771-2833. Editor: Michael D. Roberts. Managing Editor: Frank Bentayou. 40% freelance written. Monthly magazine covering the Greater Cleveland area. Editorial material "ranges from soft lifestyle features (on food, travel, decor, the arts) to hard investigative articles about the city and its institutions. *Cleveland Magazine* tends toward the hard-hitting." Circ. 55,000. Pays on publication. Byline given. Submit seasonal/holiday material 3 months in advance. Simultaneous queries OK. Computer printout submissions acceptable. Reports in 6 weeks. Publishes ms an average of 3 months after acceptance.

Nonfiction: "*Cleveland Magazine* looks for depth and good reporting from its writers. We maintain a close relationship between writer and editor so that articles proceed in the direction that will best meet the needs of our upscale and literate readers." Buys 60 mss/year. Query with published clips. Length: 1,500-4,000 words. Pays $200-500.

Photos: Gary Sluzewski, art director. State availability of photos. Reviews contact sheets and transparencies. Model releases and identification of subjects required. Buys one-time rights.

Columns/Departments: Media; Personality (shorter in-depth profiles); Et Cetera (a back-page essay of 700-2,000 words); Personal Finance; and Epicure. Buys 30 mss/year. Query with published clips. Length: 1,000-2,000 words. Pays $150-250.

Fiction: "We run fiction only once a year (December) when we publish the winner of a fall fiction contest.

Tips: "The best bet for a freelancer is to aim for our Inside Cleveland section of short, upfront items (300-700 words). We look for bright, witty pieces for this section or for little 'zingers' about government or other institutions. Good reporting is very important in these shorts."

COLUMBUS HOMES & LIFESTYLES, Columbus Lifestyles, Inc., Box 21208, Columbus OH 43221. (614)486-2483. Editor: Eugenia Snyder Morgan. 80% freelance written. Works with a small number of new/unpublished writers each year. A bimonthly magazine covering homes and lifestyles in Columbus and central Ohio. Circ. 15,000. Pays on publication. Publishes ms an average of 4 months after acceptance. Byline given. Offers $25 kill fee. Buys first North American serial rights or second serial (reprint) rights. Submit seasonal/holiday material 6 months in advance. Photocopied and previously published submissions OK. Computer printout submissions acceptable; prefers letter-quality to dot-matrix. Reports in 6 weeks. Sample copy $3.50.

Nonfiction: Lifestyles (interesting people, community leaders, and personalities in Columbus), home decorating and design, food and entertaining, and historical perspectives. Special themes include Thanksgiving/Christmas, apartment living, condominium living, office trends, spring fashion and fall fashion. No personal essays, or articles that have nothing to do with Central Ohio or Columbus. Buys 4-6 mss/issue. Query with published clips, or send complete ms. Length: 500-3,000 words. Pays $50-300.

Photos: State availability of photos with submission. Reviews contact sheets, 35mm slides and any standard size print. Payment varies. Captions, model releases, and identification of subjects required. Buys one-time rights.

Columns/Departments: People & Events (includes personality profiles, news stories on local events) 300-1,500 words. Buys 1-2 mss/issue. Query with published clips. Pays $50-100.

Tips: "All sections of the magazine are open to freelance writers; however, articles must have a regional slant. Be specific in your query. To determine whether an article would work for our publication, we need to know what slant would be taken, what sources would be used, and what expertise the writer has on the proposed article subject."

COLUMBUS MONTHLY, 171 E. Livingston Ave., Columbus OH 43215. (614)464-4567. Editorial Director: Lenore E. Brown. 20-40% freelance written. Prefers to work with published/established writers; works with a small number of new/unpublished writers each year. Monthly magazine emphasizing subjects specifically related to Columbus and central Ohio. Pays on publication. Publishes ms an average of 2 months after acceptance. Buys all rights. Byline given. Computer printout submissions acceptable; prefers letter-quality to dot-matrix. Reports in 1 month. Sample copy $3.20.

Nonfiction: No humor, essays or first person material. "I like query letters which are well-written, indicate

the author has some familiarity with *Columbus Monthly*, give me enough detail to make a decision, and include at least a basic biography of the writer." Buys 4-5 unsolicited mss/year. Query. Length: 100-4,500 words. Pays $15-400. Sometimes pays the expenses of writers on assignment.
Photos: State availability of photos. Pay varies for b&w or color prints. Model release required.
Columns/Departments: Art, business, food and drink, movies, politics, sports and theatre. Buys 2-3 columns/issue. Query. Length: 1,000-2,000 words. Pays $100-175.
Tips: "It makes sense to start small—something for our Around Columbus section, perhaps. Stories for that section run between 400-1,000 words."

DAYTON MAGAZINE, Dayton Area Chamber of Commerce, 1980 Kettering Tower, Dayton OH 45423. (513)226-1444. Editor: Linda Lombard. 90% freelance written. Bimonthly magazine covering the Dayton area and its people; "promotes Dayton-area business, people, places and events through informative, timely features and departments." Circ. 10,000. Pays on publication. Publishes ms an average of 2 months after acceptance. Byline given. Buys first serial rights. Submit seasonal/holiday material 4 months in advance. Computer printout submissions acceptable; no dot-matrix. Reports in 2 months. Sample copy for SAE and $1.50 postage.
Nonfiction: General interest, historical/nostalgic, how-to, interview/profile, opinion and photo feature. Must relate to Dayton area. No articles lacking local appeal or slant. Buys approximately 36 mss/year. Query with published clips. Length: 1,400-3,000 words.
Photos: Send photos with ms. Reviews b&w and color contact sheets and color transparencies. Payment "depends on feature." Captions, model releases, and identification of subjects required. Buys one-time rights.
Columns/Departments: Buys 60/year. Query with published clips. Length: 1,000-1,200 words.

OHIO MAGAZINE, Ohio Magazine, Inc., Subsidiary of Dispatch Printing Co., 40 S. 3rd St., Columbus OH 43215. Editor-in-Chief: Robert B. Smith. Managing Editor: Ellen Stein. 65% freelance written. Works with a small number of new/unpublished writers each year. Monthly magazine; 96-156 pages. Emphasizes news and feature material of Ohio for an educated, urban and urbane readership. Circ. 100,943. Pays on publication. Publishes ms an average of 5 months after acceptance. Buys all rights, second serial (reprint) rights, one-time rights, first North American serial rights, or first serial rights. Byline given except on short articles appearing in sections. Submit seasonal/holiday material 5 months in advance. Simultaneous, photocopied, and previously published submissions OK. Computer printout submissions acceptable; no dot-matrix. Reports in 2 months. Sample copy $2.50; writer's guidelines for SASE.
Nonfiction: Features: 2,000-8,000 words. Pays $250-700. Cover pieces $600-850; Ohioana and Ohioans (should be offbeat with solid news interest; 50-250 words, pays $15-50); Ohioguide (pieces on upcoming Ohio events, must be offbeat and worth traveling for; 100-300 words, pays $10-15); Diner's Digest ("We are still looking for writers with extensive restaurant reviewing experience to do 5-10 short reviews each month in specific sections of the state on a specific topic. Fee is on a retainer basis and negotiable"); Money (covering business related news items, profiles of prominent people in business community, personal finance—all Ohio angle; 300-1,000 words, pays $50-250); and Living (embodies dining in, home furnishings, gardening and architecture; 300-1,000 words, pays $50-250). "Send submissions for features to Robert B. Smith, editor-in-chief, or Ellen Stein, managing editor; Ohioguide and Diner's Digest to services editor; and Money to Ellen Stein, managing editor. No political columns or articles of limited geographical interest (must be of interest to all of Ohio). Buys 40 unsolicited mss/year. Sometimes pays expenses of writers on assignment.
Columns/Departments: Contact Ellen Stein. Sports, Last Word, travel, fashion and wine. Open to suggestions for new columns/departments.
Photos: Ellen Stein, managing editor. Rate negotiable.
Tips: "Freelancers should send a brief prospectus prior to submission of the complete article. All articles should have a definite Ohio application."

TOLEDO MAGAZINE, The Blade, 541 Superior St., Toledo OH 43660. (419)245-6121. Editor: Sue Stankey. Managing Editor: Edson Whipple. 75% freelance written. Weekly general interest magazine that appears in the Sunday newspaper. Circ. 225,000. Pays on publication. Publishes ms an average of 1 month after acceptance. Byline given. Buys one-time rights. Submit seasonal/holiday material 4-6 months in advance. Simultaneous queries and submissions OK. Computer printout submissions acceptable; no dot-matrix. Reports in 2 weeks on queries; 1 month on mss. Sample copy for SAE.
Nonfiction: General interest, historical/nostalgic, humor, interview/profile and personal experience. Buys 100-200 mss/year. Query with or without published clips. Length: 500-6,000 words. Pays $75-500. Sometimes pays expenses of writers on assignment.
Photos: Dave Cron, photo editor. State availability of photos. Reviews b&w and color contact sheets. Payment negotiable. Captions, model release, and identification of subjects required. Buys one-time rights.
Tips: "Submit a well-organized story proposal and include copies of previously published stories."

TRI-STATE MAGAZINE, (formerly *The Enquirer* Magazine), The Cincinnati Enquirer (Gannett), 617 Vine St., Cincinnati OH 45201. (513)369-1938. Editor: Bill Thompson. 35% freelance written. Sunday newspaper magazine covering a wide range of local topics. Circ. 300,000. Pays on publication. Publishes ms an average of 4 months after acceptance. Byline given. Pays 20% kill fee. Buys first serial rights. Submit seasonal/holiday material 3 months in advance. Simultaneous queries, and simultaneous, photocopied, and previously published submissions OK. Computer printout submissions acceptable; prefers letter-quality to dot-matrix. Reports in 2 weeks on queries. Writer's guidelines for SASE.

Nonfiction: Book excerpts, general interest, historical/nostalgic, humor, interview/profile and travel (rarely), pertaining to the Cincinnati tri-state area only. No editorials, how-to, new products, inspirational or technical material. Buys 25-40 mss/year. Send complete ms. Length: 1,000-2,400 words. Pays $100-350.

Photos: State availability of photos. Pays $25 per photo. Identification of subjects required. Buys one-time rights.

Oklahoma

OKLAHOMA LIVING MAGAZINE, Criss-Cross Numerical Directory, Inc., Blythe Publications, Box 76179, Oklahoma City OK 73147. (405)943-4289. Managing Editor: Lu Hollander. 5% freelance written. A bimonthly magazine for home buyers and of general interest in central Oklahoma. "We have three magazines within the cover of *Oklahoma Living*: City Living, Home Living, and Apartment Living. Many articles are centered around the building industry." Pays 75 days after acceptance. Publishes ms an average of 2 months after acceptance. Buys first serial rights and second serial (reprint) rights. Computer printout submissions acceptable; no dot-matrix.

Nonfiction: "Each magazine has its own cover story. We want and require localized stories and may want a story of national interest and add a side-bar on a local slant of our own." Buys 8-10 mss/year. Query with published clips. Pays $75/published page (4 double-spaced typed pages).

Photos: State availability of photos. Pays $15-20 for 5x7 b&w prints. Captions, model releases, and identification of subjects required.

Columns/Departments: "We have our own local columns but would consider columns on related subjects." Query with published clips.

OKLAHOMA TODAY, Oklahoma Department of Tourism and Recreation, Box 53384, Oklahoma City OK 73152. Editor-in-Chief: Sue Carter. Managing Editor: Kate Jones. 90% freelance written. Works with a small number of new/unpublished writers each year. Bimonthly magazine covering travel and recreation in the state of Oklahoma. "We are interested in showing off the best Oklahoma has to offer; we're pretty serious about our travel slant but will also consider history and personality profiles." Circ. 35,000. Pays on acceptance. Publishes ms an average of 9 months after acceptance. Byline given. Buys first serial rights. Submit seasonal/holiday material 1 year in advance "depending on photographic requirements." Simultaneous queries and photocopied submissions OK. "We don't mind letter-quality computer printout submissions at all, provided they are presented in manuscript format, i.e., double spaced and on 8½x11 sheets, or a size close to that. No scrolls, no dot-matrix." Reports in 2 months. Sample copy $2; writer's guidelines with SASE.

Nonfiction: Book excerpts (pre-publication only, on Oklahoma topics); photo feature and travel (in Oklahoma). "We are a specialized market; no first person reminiscences or fashion, memoirs, though just about any topic can be used if given a travel slant." Buys 35-40 mss/year. Query with published clips; no phone queries. Length: 1,000-1,500 words. Pays $150-250. Sometimes pays expenses of writers on assignment.

Photos: High-quality color transparencies, b&w prints. "We are especially interested in developing contacts with photographers who either live in Oklahoma or have shot here. Send samples and price range." Free photo guidelines with SASE. Send photos with ms. Pays $50-100 for b&w and $50-250 for color; reviews 2¼ and 35mm color transparencies. Model releases, identification of subjects, and other information for captions required. Buys one-time rights plus right to use photos for promotional purposes.

Tips: "The best way to become a regular contributor to *Oklahoma Today* is to query us with one or more story ideas, each developed to give us an idea of your proposed slant. We're looking for *lively* writing, writing that doesn't need to be heavily edited and is newspaper style. We have a two-person editorial staff, and freelancers who can write and have done their homework get called again and again. Since we're a magazine interested only in Oklahoma topics, the two big questions are 1)Do I have an Oklahoma query, and 2) Can I write with authority on that topic?"

Oregon

CASCADES EAST, 716 NE 4th St., Box 5784, Bend OR 97708. (503)382-0127. Editor: Geoff Hill. 100% freelance written. Eager to work with new/unpublished writers. Quarterly magazine; 48 pages. For "all ages as long as they are interested in outdoor recreation in central Oregon: fishing, hunting, sight-seeing, hiking, bicycling, mountain climbing, backpacking, rockhounding, skiing, snowmobiling, etc." Circ. 10,000 (distributed throughout area resorts and motels and to subscribers). Pays on publication. Publishes ms an average of 6 months after acceptance. Buys all rights. Byline given. Submit seasonal/holiday material 6 months in advance. Computer printout submissions acceptable; no dot-matrix. Reports in 6 weeks. Sample copy $2.

Nonfiction: General interest (first person experiences in outdoor central Oregon—with photos, can be dramatic, humorous or factual); historical (for feature, "Little Known Tales from Oregon History," with b&w photos); and personal experience (needed on outdoor subjects: dramatic, humorous or factual). "No articles that are too general, sight-seeing articles that come from a travel folder, or outdoor articles without the first person approach." Buys 20-30 unsolicited mss/year. Query. Length: 1,000-3,000 words. Pays 3-10¢/word.

Photos: "Old photos will greatly enhance chances of selling a historical feature. First person articles need black and white photos, also." Pays $8-15 for b&w; $15-50 for color transparencies. Captions preferred. Buys one-time rights.

Tips: "We are expanding editorial area south to Klamath Falls, north to the Dalles and Hood River areas. Submit stories a year or so in advance of publication. We are seasonal and must plan editorials for summer '87 in the spring of '86, etc., in case seasonal photos are needed."

Pennsylvania

ERIE & CHAUTAUQUA MAGAZINE, Charles H. Strong Bldg., 1250 Tower Ln., Erie PA 16505. (814)452-6070. Editor: Mary J. Brownlie. 80% freelance written. Biannual magazine covering the region of Erie (city), Erie County, Crawford County, Warren County, Pennsylvania and Chautauqua County, New York; for upscale readers with above average education and income. Circ. 30,000. Pays 30 days after publication. Buys all rights. Will reassign rights to author upon written request after publication. Computer printout submissions acceptable; prefers letter-quality to dot-matrix. Reports in 1 month. Sample copy $2.50; writer's guidelines for SASE.

Nonfiction: Feature articles (usually five per issue) on "key issues affecting our coverage area, lifestyle topics, major projects or events which are of importance to our readership, area history with relevance to life today, preservation and restoration, arts and cultural subjects." Query first. Length: 3,000 words maximum for articles. Pays $35/published page. "All material *must* have relevance to our coverage area." Sometimes pays expenses of writers on assignment.

Photos: Color photos for covers by assignment only to local photographer. Will consider 8x10 b&w glossies with stories. Pays $15 per b&w for all rights 30 days after publication. Model releases and captions required.

Columns/Departments: Business, education, social life, arts and culture, travel (within 100-200 miles of Erie), food/wine/fashions and medical items written by contributing editors. Will consider new departments on basis of resume showing expertise and two sample columns. Length: 750 words maximum.

Tips: "It's rewarding to see a variety of ideas and styles in freelancers. We enjoy being able to give new writers a start and finding the person with special expertise for a special story. But we regret reviewing inappropriate material and notice a lack of discipline in meeting deadlines and inadequate research—stories without 'meat'."

PENNSYLVANIA, Pennsylvania Magazine Co., Box 576, Camp Hill PA 17011. (717)761-6620. Editor: Albert E. Holliday. Managing Editor: Joan Holliday. 90% freelance written. Quarterly magazine. Circ. 22,500. Pays on acceptance for assigned articles. Publishes ms an average of 6 months after acceptance. Byline given. Offers 33% kill fee. Buys first North American serial rights. Computer printout submissions acceptable; prefers letter-quality to dot-matrix. Reports in 2 weeks on queries; 3 weeks on mss. Sample copy $2.50; writer's guidelines for #10 SAE and 1 first class stamp.

Nonfiction: General interest, historical/nostalgic, inspirational, personal experience, photo feature, and travel. Nothing on Amish topics, hunting or skiing. Buys 50-75 mss/year. Query. Length: 250-2,500 words. Pays $25-250. Sometimes pays the expenses of writers on assignment.

Photos: State availability of photos. Reviews 35mm and color transparencies and 5x7 b&w prints. Pays $5-50 for b&w; $10-100 for color. Captions and identification of subjects required. Buys one-time rights.

Columns/Departments: Panorama—short items about people, unusual events.

PENNSYLVANIA HERITAGE, Pennsylvania Historical and Museum Commission, Box 1026, Harrisburg PA 17108-1026. (717)787-1396. Editor: Michael J. O'Malley III. 85% freelance written. Prefers to work with published/established writers. Quarterly magazine covering Pennsylvania history and culture. "*Pennsylvania Heritage* introduces readers to Pennsylvania's rich culture and historic legacy, educates and sensitizes them to the value of preserving that heritage and entertains and involves them in such as way as to ensure that Pennsylvania's past has a future. The magazine is intended for intelligent lay readers." Circ. 9,000. Pays on acceptance. Publishes ms an average of 9 months after acceptance. Byline given. Buys all rights. Simultaneous queries, and simultaneous and photocopied submissions OK. Computer printout submissions acceptable; prefers letter-quality to dot-matrix. Reports in 3 weeks on queries; 6 weeks on mss. Sample copy for $2.50; free writer's guidelines.

Nonfiction: Art, science, biographies, industry, business, politics, transportation, military, historic preservation, archaeology, photography, etc. No articles which in no way relate to Pennsylvania history or culture. "Our format requires feature-length articles. Manuscripts with illustrations are especially sought for publication." Buys 20-24 mss/year. Query. Length: 2,000-3,500 words. Pays $0-100.

Photos: State availability or send photos with query or ms. Pays $25-100 for color transparencies; $5-10 for b&w photos. Captions and identification of subjects required. Buys one-time rights.

Tips: "We are looking for well-written, interesting material that pertains to any aspect of Pennsylvania history or culture. Potential contributors should realize that, although our articles are popularly styled, they are not light, puffy or breezy; in fact they demand strident documentation and substantiation (sans footnotes). The most frequent mistake made by writers in completing articles for us is making them either too scholarly or too nostalgic. We want material which educates, but also entertains. Authors should make history readable and entertaining."

PHILADELPHIA MAGAZINE, 1500 Walnut St., Philadelphia PA 19102. Editor: Ron Javers. 50% freelance written. Works with a small number of new/unpublished writers each year. Monthly magazine for sophisticated middle- and upper-income people in the Greater Philadelphia/South Jersey area. Circ. 152,272. Pays on acceptance. Publishes ms an average of 2 months after acceptance. Buys first serial rights. Pays 20% kill fee. Byline given. Computer printout submissions acceptable; prefers letter-quality to dot-matrix. Reports in 1 month. Free writer's guidelines for SASE. Queries and mss should be sent to Bill Tonelli, articles editor.

Nonfiction: "Articles should have a strong Philadelphia focus but should avoid Philadelphia stereotypes—we've seen them all. Lifestyles, city survival, profiles of interesting people, business stories, music, the arts, sports and local politics, stressing the topical or unusual. Intelligent, entertaining essays on subjects of specific local interest. No puff pieces. We offer lots of latitude for style." Buys 50 mss/year. Length: 1,000-7,000 words. Pays $100-1,000. Sometimes pays expenses of writers on assignment.

PITTSBURGH MAGAZINE, Metropolitan Pittsburgh Public Broadcasting, Inc., 4802 5th Ave., Pittsburgh PA 15213. (412)622-1360. Editor-in-Chief: Bruce VanWyngarden. 60% freelance written. Prefers to work with published/established writers; works with a small number of new/unpublished writers each year. "The magazine is purchased on newsstands and by subscription and is given to those who contribute $25 or more a year to public TV in western Pennsylvania." Monthly magazine; 132 pages. Circ. 56,700. Pays on publication. Publishes ms an average of 2 months after acceptance. Buys first North American serial rights and second serial (reprint) rights. Pays kill fee. Byline given. Submit seasonal/holiday material 6 months in advance. Electronic submissions OK via IBM PC. Computer printout submissions acceptable; prefers letter-quality to dot-matrix. Reports in 2 months. Publishes ms an average of 2 months after acceptance. Sample copy $2; free writer's guidelines.

Nonfiction: Expose, lifestyle, sports, informational, service, interview, nostalgia and profile. Query or send complete ms. Length: 2,500 words. Pays $50-500. Query for photos. Model releases required. Sometimes pays the expenses of writers on assignment.

Columns/Departments: Art, books, films, dining, health, sports and theatre. "All must relate to Pittsburgh or western Pennsylvania."

Tennessee

MEMPHIS, MM Corporation, Box 370, Memphis TN 38101. (901)521-9000. Editor: Kenneth Neill. 60% freelance written. Eager to work with new/unpublished writers. Circ. 30,000. Pays on publication. Publishes ms an average of 3 months after acceptance. Byline given. Buys first North American serial rights. Pays $35 kill fee. Simultaneous, photocopied, and previously published submissions OK. Computer printout submissions acceptable; prefers letter-quality to dot-matrix. Reports in 6 weeks. Sample copy $2.

Nonfiction: Expose, general interest, historical, how-to, humor, interview and profiles. "Virtually all our material has strong Southern connections." Buys 25 freelance mss/year. Query or submit complete ms or published clips. Length: 1,500-5,000 words. Pays $100-1,000. Sometimes pays expenses of writers on assignment.

Tips: "The kinds of manuscripts we most need have a sense of story (i.e., plot, suspense, character), an abundance of evocative images to bring that story alive, and a sensitivity to issues at work in Memphis. The most frequent mistakes made by writers in completing an article for us are lack of focus, lack of organization, factual gaps and failure to capture the magazine's style. Tough investigative pieces would be especially welcomed."

MID-SOUTH MAGAZINE, *Commercial Appeal*, Box 334, Memphis TN 38101. (901)529-2794. Editor: Scott Hill. 10% freelance written. Sunday newspaper supplement. Circ. 300,000. Pays after publication. Publishes ms an average of 3 months after acceptance. Byline given. Buys one-time rights. Simultaneous queries, and photocopied and previously published submissions (if so indicated) OK. Computer printout submissions acceptable. Reports in 3 weeks.

Nonfiction: General interest (with regional tie-in). Buys 12 mss/year. Query with published clips. Length: 1,500-2,000 words. Pays $100 maximum.
Photos: State availability of photos. Reviews color transparencies and 5x7 b&w glossy prints. Photos are paid for with payment for ms. Buys one-time rights.

Texas

DALLAS LIFE MAGAZINE, Sunday Magazine of *The Dallas Morning News*, Belo Corporation, Communications Center, Dallas TX 75265. (214)745-8432. Editor: Melissa East. Weekly magazine. "We are a lively, topical, sometimes controversial city magazine devoted to informing, enlightening and entertaining our urban sunbelt readers with material which is specifically relevant to Dallas lifestyles and interests." Pays on acceptance. Byline given. Buys first North American serial rights or simultaneous rights. Simultaneous queries and submissions OK ("if not competitive in our area"). Computer printout submissions acceptable; prefers letter-quality to dot-matrix. Reports in 1 month on queries; 6 weeks on mss. Sample copy $1.
Nonfiction: General interest; humor (short); interview/profile. 'All material must, repeat *must*, have a Dallas metropolitan area frame of reference." Special issues include: Spring and Fall home furnishings theme. Buys 15-25 unsolicited mss/year. Query with published clips or send complete ms. Length: 750-3,000 words. Pays $200-650.
Photos: State availability of photos. Pays $15-25 for b&w contact sheets; $25-150 for 35mm or larger color transparencies. Captions, model releases, and identification of subjects required. Buys one-time rights.

EL PASO MAGAZINE, El Paso Chamber of Commerce, 10 Civic Center Plaza, El Paso TX 79901. (915)544-7880. Editor: Russell S. Autry. 100% freelance written. Works with a small number of new/unpublished writers each year. Monthly magazine that "takes a positive look at El Paso people and businesses. Readers are owners and managers of El Paso businesses." Circ. 5,000. Pays on publication. Publishes ms an average of 2 months after acceptance. Byline given. Buys first North American serial rights. Submit seasonal/holiday material 3 months in advance. Simultaneous queries, and simultaneous and photocopied submissions OK. Computer printout submissions acceptable; prefers letter-quality to dot-matrix. Reports in 2 months. Free sample copy and writer's guidelines.
Nonfiction: General interest, business, historical/nostalgic, interview/profile and photo feature. Buys 75 mss/year. Query with published clips. Length: 1,000-2,500 words. Pays 7¢/word.
Photos: Send photos with ms. Pays $10/photo; $300 for cover photo. Captions, model releases and identification of subjects required. Buys one-time rights.
Tips: "An article for *El Paso Magazine* must talk about an area business and its successes."

FORT WORTH Magazine, Fort Worth Chamber, 700 Throckmorton St., Fort Worth TX 76102. (817)336-2491. Executive Editor: Barbara Winkle. Editor: Gail Young. 75% freelance written. Works with a small number of new/unpublished writers each year. A monthly community magazine about people, places and happenings within Tarrant County for an "affluent, well-educated readership including civic leaders, the chief executive officers of local corporations, and out-of-state FORTUNE 500 companies interested in a reflection of the Fort Worth lifestyle." Circ. 10,000. Pays on acceptance. Publishes ms an average of 6 months after acceptance. Byline given. Buys all rights and first North American serial rights. Computer printout submissions acceptable; no dot-matrix. Reports in 2 months. Sample copy $2.33; free writer's guidelines.
Nonfiction: Cultural (Fort Worth); business (local angle); photo feature (Fort Worth link); and Fort Worth and Tarrant County events. No personal experience. Buys 60 mss/year. Query with published clips. Length: 2,000 words. Pays $100. Sometimes pays the expenses of writers on assignment.
Photos: Susan Abbenante, art director. Send photos with accompanying query or ms. Reviews photos of Fort Worth, cover quality. Pays $75 for 35mm slides or transparencies; $15 for 8x10 b&w prints. Captions, model releases and identification of subjects required. Buys one-time rights.
Tips: Feature articles are most open to freelancers. "Because of the Fort Worth Chamber's strong involvement in business, the quality of life and tourism, all of these issues are addressed in some way in the planning of the magazine."

HOUSTON CITY MAGAZINE, Suite 1450, 1800 W. Loop S., Houston TX 77027. (713)850-7600. Publisher: Lute Harmon. Editor: Fred Rhodes. "We are backlogged with submissions and prefer not to receive unsolicited submissions at this time."

NIGHTBEAT MAGAZINE, "Houston's Only Complete Entertainment Magazine", Nightbeat Magazine, Inc., Box 55573. Houston TX 77255. (713)954-1393. Editor-in-Chief: Menda Stewart. 40% freelance written. Eager to work with new/unpublished writers. Monthly magazine covering entertainment in Houston including entertainer's biographies and interviews and restaurant and club listings. Circ. 100,000. Pays on acceptance. Publishes ms an average of 3 months after acceptance. Byline given. Offers $50 kill fee. Makes work-for-hire assignments. Submit seasonal/holiday material 3 months in advance. Simultaneous queries and photocopied submissions OK. Electronic submissions OK via floppy disk compatible with Compugraphic. Computer printout submissions acceptable; no dot-matrix. Reports in 2 weeks on queries; 6 weeks on mss. Sample copy and writer's guidelines for 11x17 SAE.

Nonfiction: General interest (entertainers); humor (entertainment); photo feature (entertainers); and travel. Buys 50 mss/year. Query. Length: 500-1,500 words. Pays $50-150. Sometimes pays expenses of writers on assignment.

Photos: State availability of photos or send photos with query or ms. Reviews contact sheets and transparencies. Pays $20 for 35mm color slides; $18-50 for b&w contact sheets; $25-50 for 5x7 color prints; $25-50 for color contact sheets. Captions, model release and identification of subjects required. Buys rights by individual arrangement.

Columns/Departments: Film, entertainers, records and events. "All items cover *fun* events." Buys 24 mss/year. Query. Length: 400-1,000 words. Pays $50-100.

Fillers: Jokes, short humor, and newsbreaks (entertainers). Buys 250/year. Length: 100-750 words. Pays $50.

Tips: "Our direction is entertainment. We feature young unknown artists as well as national stars. We need qualified writers to cover concerts, dramas and special events."

SAN ANGELO MAGAZINE, San Angelo Standard Inc., 34 W. Harris, San Angelo TX 76903. (915)653-1221. Editor: Soren W. Nielsen. Executive Editor: Kandis Gatewood. 10% freelance written. Works with a small number of new/unpublished writers each year. Monthly magazine about San Angelo, Texas and immediate area. "San Angelo magazine is a city magazine with an upscale audience, offering a wide variety of features and profiles." Circ. 7,000. Pays on publication. Publishes ms an average of 3 months after acceptance. Byline given. Buys first serial rights. Submit seasonal/holiday material 4 months in advance. Computer printout submissions acceptable; prefers letter-quality to dot-matrix. Reports in 1 month. Sample copy for 9x12 SAE and 4 first class stamps; writer's guidelines for SAE and 1 first class stamp.

Nonfiction: General interest, historical/nostalgic, interview/profile and travel. General interest and historical articles of San Angelo area. No articles not applicable to San Angelo area. Buys 10 mss/year. Query with published clips. Pays $25-100. Rarely pays expenses of writers on assignment.

Tips: "Writer should note that first-person articles are not used."

SAN ANTONIO HOMES & GARDENS, Duena Development Corp., Box 5950, Austin TX 78763. (512)441-1980. Publisher: Hazel W. Gully. Monthly magazine emphasizing San Antonio homes, people, events and gardens for current, former and propsective residents. Anticipated circulation 10,000. See *Austin Homes & Gardens* for format, departments, rates and requirements.

Tips: Looking for steady freelancers in the San Antonio, Texas, area.

‡SAN ANTONIO MONTHLY, Harte-Hanks Magazines, Inc., Box 17554, San Antonio TX 78217. (512)377-3226. Editor: Rick Casey. Managing Editor: Niki McDaniel. 80% freelance written. A monthly magazine covering all aspects of life in the city of San Antonio. Circ. 18,000. Pays on acceptance. Publishes ms an average of 3 months after acceptance. Byline given. Will negotiate kill fee. Buys first North American serial rights. Simultaneous, photocopied, and previously published submissions OK. Electronic submissions OK via 300 baud. Computer printout submissions acceptable; prefers letter-quality to dot-matrix. Reports in 2 weeks on queries; 1 month on manuscripts. Sample copy for 9x12 SAE with $1.92 postage.

Nonfiction: Book excerpts, essays, exposé, general interest, profile, photo feature and travel. Buys 30 mss/year. Query with published clips. Length: 1,000-4,000 words. Pays $75-500. Sometimes pays expenses of writers on assignment.

Photos: State availability of photos with submission. Identification of subjects required. Buys one-time rights.

Fiction: Occasionally publishes fiction by local writers or with a local theme.

THIRD COAST MAGAZINE, The Magazine of Austin, Third Coast Media Inc., Box 592, Austin TX 78767. (512)472-2016. Editor: John Taliaferro. Managing Editor: Kate Berger. 75% freelance written. A monthly magazine covering the city of Austin, Texas. Circ. 20,000. Pays on publication. Publishes ms an average of 3 months after acceptance. Byline given. Offers 25% kill fee. Buys first rights. Submit seasonal/holiday material 3 months in advance. Simultaneous, photocopied, and previously published submissions OK. Computer printout submissions acceptable; prefers letter-quality to dot-matrix.

Nonfiction: Book excerpts, essays, general interest, historical/nostalgic, humor, interview/profile, photo feature and travel. Query with or without published clips. Length: 500-7,000 words. Pays $100-800. Sometimes pays the expenses of writers on assignment.

Photos: Send photos with submissions. Reviews contact sheets and prints. Offers $50-200/photo. Captions, model releases, and identification of subjects required. Buys one-time rights.

Columns/Departments: David Stansbury, column/department editor. Art, books, music, performances, profiles, politics, urban affairs, and humor related to Austin, Texas. Buys 30 mss/year. Query with or without published clips or send complete ms. Length: 800-1,500 words. Pays $150-200.

Vermont

VERMONT LIFE MAGAZINE, 61 Elm St., Montpelier VT 05602. (802)828-3241. Editor-in-Chief: Thomas K. Slayton. 90% freelance written. Prefers to work with published/established writers. Quarterly magazine. Circ. 120,000. Publishes ms an average of 9 months after acceptance. Byline given. Offers kill fee. Buys first serial rights. Submit seasonal/holiday material 1 year in advance. Simultaneous queries, and simultaneous, photocopied, and previously published submissions OK. Computer printout submissions acceptable; prefers letter-quality to dot-matrix. Reports in 1 month. Writer's guidelines on request.
Nonfiction: Wants articles on today's Vermont, those which portray a typical or, if possible, unique aspect of the state or its people. Style should be literate, clear and concise. Subtle humor favored. No Vermont dialect attempts as in "Ayup", outsider's view on visiting Vermont, or "Vermont cliches"—maple syrup, town meetings or stereotyped natives. Buys 60 mss/year. Query by letter essential. Length: 1,500 words average. Pays 20¢/word. Seldom pays expenses of writers on assignment.
Photos: Buys photographs with mss and with captions and seasonal photographs alone. Prefers b&w contact sheets to look at first on assigned material. Color submissions must be 4x5 or 35mm transparencies. Rates on acceptance: $75 inside, color; $200 for cover. Gives assignments but only with experienced photographers. Query in writing. Captions, model releases, and identification of subjects required. Buys one-time rights, but often negotiates for re-use rights.
Tips: "Writers who read our magazine are given more consideration because they understand that we want Vermontish articles about Vermont. If a writer has a genuine working knowledge of Vermont, his or her work usually shows it. Writers who have only visited the state tend to write in predictable ways on stereotyped subjects."

VERMONT VANGUARD PRESS, Statewide Weekly, Vanguard Publishing, 87 College St., Burlington VT 05401. (802)864-0506. Editor: Joshua Mamis. Managing Editor: Gail E. Hudson. 70% freelance written. Works with a small number of new/unpublished writers each year. A weekly alternative newspaper, locally oriented, covering Vermont politics, environment, arts, development, etc. Circ. 20,000. Pays on publication. Publishes ms an average of 1½ months after acceptance. Byline given. Offers 50% kill fee only after written acceptance. Buys first serial rights. Submit seasonal/holiday material 1 month in advance. Simultaneous queries, and simultaneous, photocopied, and previously published submissions OK. Electronic submissions OK via IBM PC or 1200 baud modem. Computer printout submissions acceptable; no dot-matrix. Reports in 1 month.
Nonfiction: Expose and humor. Articles should have a Vermont angle. Buys about 12 mss/year. Query with published clips. Length: 500-2,500 words. Pays $20-100. Sometimes pays expenses of writers on assignment.
Photos: Glenn Russell, photo editor. State availability of photos. Pays $10-20 for b&w contact sheets and negatives. Captions, model releases, and identification of subjects required. Buys one-time rights.
Tips: "Short news stories are most open to freelancers. Knowledge of Vermont politics is essential."

Virginia

THE ROANOKER, Leisure Publishing Co., 3424 Brambleton Ave., Box 12567, Roanoke VA 24026. (703)989-6138. Editor: Kurt Rheinheimer. 75% freelance written. Monthly magazine covering people and events of Western Virginia. "*The Roanoker* is a general interest city magazine edited for the people of Roanoke, Virginia, and the surrounding area. Our readers are primarily upper-income, well-educated professionals between the ages of 35 and 60. Coverage ranges from hard news and consumer information to restaurant reviews and local history." Circ. 10,000. Pays on publication. Publishes ms an average of 6 months after acceptance. Byline given. Buys all rights; makes work-for-hire assignments. Submit seasonal/holiday material 4 months in advance. Simultaneous queries OK. Computer printout submissions acceptable; prefers letter-quality to dot-matrix. Reports in 2 months. Sample copy $2.
Nonfiction: Expose; historical/nostalgic; how-to (live better in western Virginia); interview/profile (of well-known area personalities); photo feature; and travel (Virginia and surrounding states). "We are attempting to broaden our base and provide more and more coverage of western Virginia, i.e., that part of the state west of Roanoke. We place special emphasis on consumer-related issues and how-to articles." Periodic special sections on fashion, real estate, media, banking, investing. Buys 100 mss/year. Query with published clips or send complete ms. Length: 3,000 words maximum. Pays $35-200. Sometimes pays expenses of writers on assignment.
Photos: Send photos with ms. Reviews color transparencies. Pays $5-10 for 5x7 or 8x10 b&w prints; $10 maximum for 5x7 or 8x10 color prints. Captions and model releases required. Rights purchased vary.
Tips: "It helps if freelancer lives in the area. The most frequent mistake made by writers in completing an article for us is not having enough Roanoke area focus: use of area experts, sources, slants, etc."

THE VIRGINIAN, Shenandoah Valley Magazine Corp., Box 8, New Hope VA 24469. (703)885-0388. Editor: Hunter S. Pierce, IV. Bimonthly magazine. Circ. 20,000. Pays on publication. Byline given. Offers negotiable kill fee. Buys negotiable rights. Submit seasonal/holiday material 4 months in advance. Simultaneous queries, and simultaneous, photocopied, and previously published submissions OK. Reports in 1 month. Sample copy $3.50.
Nonfiction: Book excerpts, general interest, historical/nostalgic, food, how-to, humor, inspirational, interview/profile, personal experience, photo feature and travel. Buys 20 mss/year. Query with or without published clips, or send complete ms. Length: 1,000-1,500 words. Pays negotiable rate.
Photos: State availability of photos. Buys one-time rights.
Tips: "Be familiar enough with the magazine to know the tone and character of the feature articles."

Washington

THE SEATTLE WEEKLY, Sasquatch Publishing, 1931 2nd Ave., Seattle WA 98101. (206)441-5555. Editor: David Brewster. 30% freelance written. Eager to work with new/unpublished writers. Weekly tabloid covering arts, politics, food, business, sports and books with local and regional emphasis. Circ. 30,000. Pays 3 weeks after publication. Publishes ms an average of 1 month after acceptance. Byline given. Offers variable kill fee. Buys first North American serial rights. Submit seasonal/holiday material 2 months in advance. Simultaneous queries OK. Computer printout submissions acceptable; prefers letter-quality to dot-matrix. Reports in 1 month. Sample copy 75¢; free writer's guidelines.
Nonfiction: Book excerpts; expose; general interest; historical/nostalgic (Northwest); how-to (related to food and health); humor; interview/profile; opinion; travel; and arts-related essays. Buys 25 cover stories/year. Query with resume and published clips. Length: 700-4,000 words. Pays $75-800. Pays expenses of writers on assignment.
Tips: "The *Weekly* publishes stories on Northwest politics and art, usually written by regional and local writers, for a mostly upscale, urban audience; writing is high quality magazine style. We may decide to publish a new regional magazine, either quarterly or bi-monthly, for a slightly different audience."

WASHINGTON, The Evergreen State Magazine, Evergreen Publishing Co., 1500 Eastlake Ave. E., Seattle WA 98102. Editor/Publisher: Kenneth A. Gouldthorpe. Executive Editor: Knute O. Berger. Managing Editor: David W. Fuller. 70% freelance written. A bimonthly magazine covering all facets of life in Washington for an in-state audience. Circ. 70,000. Pays on acceptance for assigned stories; on publication for "on spec" material. Publishes ms an average of 6 months after acceptance. Byline given. Offers 20% kill fee on accepted stories. Submit seasonal/holiday material 6 months in advance. Electronic submissions OK; call for details. Computer printout submissions acceptable, but leave margins and double-space; prefers letter-quality to dot-matrix. Reports in 1 month on queries; 6 weeks on mss. Sample copy for $2.95; free writer's guidelines.
Nonfiction: Book excerpts (unpublished Washington-related); general interest; historical/nostalgic; humor; interview/profile; personal experience; photo feature; and travel. "Evergreen Publishing Company undertakes book and one-shot publication projects. Washington state ideas encouraged. No political, expose, reviews, or anything not pertaining to Washington or Washingtonians." Query with published clips. Length: features, 1,500-2,500 words; sidebars, 200-600 words. Pays $150-700. Sometimes pays expenses of writers on assignment.
Photos: Carrie Seglin, photo editor. Large format. State availability of photos with query or send photos with query. Pays $50-250 for b&w; $125-325 for 35mm color slides. Captions, model releases, and identification of subjects required. Buys one-time rights.
Columns/Departments: As Others See Us (how Washington is viewed by outsiders); Interiors (homes, architecture, decorating, interiors); State of Mind (thoughts and perspectives on the Evergreen State); Washington Post (our letters column); The Attic (Our back page potpourri of ads, pictures, curios etc.); Our Town (where we live, from backwoods to small towns and places you've never seen before); Journeys End (inns, lodges, bed and breakfast hideaways); Players (sports and athletes, games and gamesmen); Statewatch (a round-up from all corners: people, quotes and anecdotes from the lighter side of life); Enterprise (business and commerce); Wildside (wildlife, nature); Open air (outdoors and outdoor activities, from backpacking to picnics, from hang gliding to kite flying); Wordsmith (books, writers and wordsmithing); Repasts (great dining, from grand souffles to small cafes); and Almanac (a compendium of history, weather, wit and wisdom). Buys 75 mss/year. Query with published clips. Length: 600-1,200 words. Pays $150-250.
Fillers: Clippings, jokes, gags, anecdotes, short humor and newsbreaks. Length: 50-250 words. Pays $25-100. Must be Washington related.
Tips: "All areas are open, but the writer has a better chance of breaking in at our publication with short articles and fillers since we buy more departmental material. Our articles emphasize people—sometimes writers get sidetracked. We're also looking for original thinking, not tired approaches."

Wisconsin

FOX RIVER PATRIOT, Weir Publishing, Box 31, Princeton WI 54968. (414)295-6252. Publisher: Barbara J. Weir. For country folks of all ages. Monthly tabloid. Circ. 6,000. Pays on publication. Buys first North American serial rights and one-time rights. Byline given. Submit seasonal/holiday material 2 months in advance. Simultaneous, photocopied and previously published submissions OK. Reports in 1 month. Sample copy $1.
Nonfiction: Expose, general interest, historical, how-to, humor, interview, nostalgia, personal experience, photo feature, profile, and travel. "In general, we are a country-oriented publication—we stress environment, alternative energy technology, alternative building trends, farming and gardening, etc.—submissions should be in this general area." Buys 4 mss/issue. Send complete ms. Pays $5-25.
Photos: Send photos with ms. Pays $5 for 5x7 b&w prints; $5 for 5x7 color prints. Captions preferred.

MADISON MAGAZINE, Box 1604, Madison WI 53701. Editor: James Selk. 50% freelance written. Prefers to work with published/established writers. Monthly magazine; 100-150 pages. General city magazine aimed at upscale audience. Circ. 24,000. Pays on publication. Publishes ms an average of 2 months after acceptance. Buys all rights. Reports on material accepted for publication 10 days after acceptance. Returns rejected material immediately. Query. Computer printout submissions acceptable; prefers letter-quality to dot-matrix. Sample copy $3.
Nonfiction: General human interest articles with strong local angles. Buys 100 mss/year. Length: 1,000-5,000 words. Pays $25-500. Pays the expenses of writers on assignment.
Photos: Offers no additional payment for b&w photos used with mss. Captions required.

WISCONSIN, *The Milwaukee Journal Magazine*, Box 661, Milwaukee WI 53201. (414)224-2341. Editor: Beth Slocum. 50% freelance written. Weekly general interest magazine appealing to readers living in Wisconsin. Circ. 530,000. Pays on publication. Publishes ms an average of 4 months after acceptance. Byline given. Buys first serial rights. Submit seasonal/holiday material 4 months in advance. Simultaneous queries OK. Computer printout submissions acceptable; prefers letter-quality to dot-matrix. Reports in 1 month on queries; 6 months on mss. Sample copy and writer's guidelines for SASE.
Nonfiction: Book excerpts, expose, general interest, humor, interview/profile, opinion, personal experience and photo feature. Special issues planned on fitness, finance. No nostalgic reminiscences. Buys 100 mss/year. Query. Length: 150-2,000 words. Pays $75-500. Sometimes pays expenses of writers on assignment.
Photos: State availability of photos.
Columns/Departments: Opinion, Decorating and Essays. Buys 100 mss/year. Query. Length: 150-300 words. Pays $75-150.

WISCONSIN TRAILS, Box 5650, Madison WI 53705. (608)241-5603. Managing Editor: Susan Pigorsch. 70% freelance written. Prefers to work with published/established writers; works with a small number of new/unpublished writers each year. Bimonthly magazine for readers interested in Wisconsin; its contemporary issues, personalities, recreation, history, natural beauty; and the arts. Circ. 35,000. Buys first serial rights, and one-time rights sometimes. Pays on publication. Submit seasonal material at least 1 year in advance. Publishes ms an average of 6 months after acceptance. Byline given. Photocopied submissions OK. Computer printout submissions acceptable; prefers letter-quality to dot-matrix. Reports in 1 month. Writer's guidelines available.
Nonfiction: "Our articles focus on some aspect of Wisconsin life; an interesting town or event, a person or industry, history or the arts and especially outdoor recreation. We do not use first person essays or biographies about people who were born in Wisconsin but made their fortunes elsewhere. No poetry. No articles that are too local for our regional audience, or articles about obvious places to visit in Wisconsin. We need more articles about the new and little-known." Buys 3 unsolicited mss/year. Query or send outline. Length: 1,000-3,000 words. Pays $100-300, depending on assignment length and quality. Sometimes pays expenses of writers on assignment.
Photos: Purchased with or without mss or on assignment. Prefers 2¼" or larger transparencies, 35mm OK. Color photos usually illustrate an activity, event, region or striking scenery. Prefer photos with people in scenery. B&w photos usually illustrate a given article. Pays $10-20 each for b&w on publication. Pays $50 for inside color; $100 for covers. Captions preferred.
Tips: "We're looking for active articles about people, places, events, and outdoor adventures in Wisconsin. We want to publish one in-depth article of state-wide interest or concern per issue, and several short (1,000-word) articles about short trips, recreational opportunities, restaurants, inns, and cultural activities. We will be looking for more articles about out-of-the-way places in Wisconsin that are exceptional in some way."

‡WOMEN & CO., The Magazine for Women in the La Crosse/Winona Area, MCP Inc., Suite 131, 505 King St., La Crosse WI 54601. (608)782-2130. Editor: Vickie Lyons. A monthly tabloid about working women. "We write for the woman of the '80s who is trying to balance tradition with progress." Estab. 1985.

Circ. 13,500. Pays on publication. Publishes ms an average of 1 month after acceptance. Byline given. Buys first North American serial rights. Submit seasonal/holiday material 3 months in advance. Simultaneous and photocopied submissions OK. Computer printout submissions acceptable. Reports in 4 weeks. Sample copy for 8x11 SAE.

Nonfiction: General interest, humor, inspirational and personal experience. No Hollywood profiles or international corporate success stories. Buys 36 mss/year. Query. Length: 750-1,500 words. Pays $20-50. Sometimes pays the expenses of writers on assignment.

Photos: Send photos with submission. Reviews contact sheets. Offers $10-30/photo. Model releases required. Buys one-time rights.

Tips: "To get published in *Women & Co.*, I look for a writer with Midwestern focus. My writers typically live in small cities or towns, have had some writing experience and are pitching a dynamite self-improvement story. Nonfiction articles represent 95% of writing I purchase. Write to me with your story. Why are you interested in archaeology? How did you relate to your midwife? Who do you know who has changed her life? And include past clips."

Puerto Rico

WALKING TOURS OF SAN JUAN, Magazine/Guide, Caribbean World Communications, Inc., First Federal Building, Office 301, Santurce PR 00909. (809)722-1767. Editor: Al Dinhofer. Managing Editor: Carmen Merino. 5% freelance written. Prefers to work with published/established writers. Magazine published 2 times/year (January and July). Circ. 22,000. Pays on publication. Publishes ms an average of 3 months after acceptance. Byline given. Buys one-time rights. Computer printout submissions acceptable. Reports in 1 month. Sample copy $3 with 9x12 SAE and $2 postage.

Nonfiction: Historical/nostalgic. "We are seeking historically based articles on San Juan: any aspect of Spanish colonial culture, art, architecture, etc. We must have sources—in fact, we will publish source material at the end of each article for reader reference." Buys 4 mss/year. Query. Length: 2,000-3,000 words. Pays $150. Sometimes pays the expenses of writers on assignment.

Canada

CANADIAN GEOGRAPHIC, 488 Wilbrod St., Ottawa, Ontario K1N 6M8 Canada. Publisher: J. Keith Fraser. Editor: Ross Smith. Managing Editor: Ian Darragh. 90% freelance written. Circ. 150,000. Bimonthly magazine. Pays on acceptance. Publishes ms an average of 3 months after acceptance. Buys first Canadian rights; interested only in first time publication. Computer printout submissions acceptable; prefers letter-quality to dot-matrix. Writer's guidelines on request.

Nonfiction: Buys authoritative geograpical articles, in the broad geographical sense, written for the average person, not for a scientific audience. Predominantly Canadian subjects by Canadian authors. Buys 30-45 mss/year. Length: 1,500-3,000 words. Pays 25¢/word minimum. Usual payment for articles $500-1,500 and up. Higher fees reserved for commissioned articles on which copyright remains with publisher unless otherwise agreed.

Photos: Reviews 35mm slides, 2¼ transparencies or 8x10 glossies. Pays $60-200 for color photos, depending on published size.

OTTAWA MAGAZINE, Ottawa Magazine Inc., 192 Bank St., Ottawa, Ontario K2P 1W8 Canada. (613)234-7751. Editor: Louis Valenzuela. 50% freelance written. Prefers to work with published/established writers. Monthly magazine covering life in Ottawa and environs. "*Ottawa Magazine* reflects the interest and lifestyles of its readers who tend to be female ages 35-55, upwardly mobile and suburban." Circ. 42,500. Pays on acceptance. Publishes ms an average of 6 months after acceptance. Byline given. "Kill fee depends on agreed-upon fee; very seldom used." Buys first North American serial rights and second serial (reprint) rights. Simultaneous queries, and photocopied and previously published submissions OK. Computer printout submissions acceptable. Reports in 2 months. Sample copy $1.

Nonfiction: Book excerpts (by local authors or about regional issues); expose (federal or regional government, education); general interest; interview/profile (on Ottawans who have established national or international reputations); photo feature (for recurring section called Freezeframe); and travel (recent examples are Brazil, Trinidad & Tobago, Copenhagen). "No articles better suited to a national or special interest publication." Buys 100 mss/year. Query with published clips. Length: 2,000-3,500 words. Pays $400-750 Canadian.

Columns/Departments: Trevor Cole, column/department editor. Lifelines (short editorial style glimpses at the city, including the best (Bull's-Eye) and worst (Bull) aspects of Ottawa. Buys 50 mss/year. Send complete ms. Length: 50-250 words. Pays $25-100 Canadian.

Tips: "A phone call to our associate editor is the best way to assure that queries receive prompt attention. Once a query interests me the writer is assigned a detailed 'treatment' of the proposed piece which is used to determine viability of story. We will be concentrating on more issue-type stories with good, solid fact-researched base, also doing more fluffy pieces—60 great reasons Ottawa is a great city—that sort of stuff. Harder for out-of-town writers to furnish. The writer should strive to inject a personal style and avoid newspaper style reportage. *Ottawa Magazine* also doesn't stoop to boosterism and points out the bad along with the good."

WINDSOR THIS MONTH MAGAZINE, Box 1029, Station A, Windsor, Ontario N9A 6P4 Canada. (519)966-7411. Editor: Laura Rosenthal. 75% freelance written. *"Windsor This Month* is mailed out in a system of controlled distribution to 19,000 households in the area. The average reader is a university graduate, of middle income, and active in leisure areas." Circ. 22,000. Pays on publication. Buys first North American serial rights. Submit seasonal/holiday material 4 months in advance. "We will accept computer printout submissions or industry compatible magnetic media." SAE, IRCs. Reports in 1 month.
Nonfiction: Windsor-oriented editorial: issues, answers, interviews, lifestyles, profiles, photo essays and opinion. How-to accepted if applicable to readership. Special inserts: design and decor, gourmet and travel featured periodically through the year. Buys 5 mss/issue. Query (phone queries OK). Buys 15 unsolicited mss/year. Length: 500-5,000 words. Pays $20-200.
Photos: State availability of photos with query. Pays $10 for first published and $5 thereafter for b&w prints. Captions preferred. Buys all rights.
Tips: "If experienced, arm yourself with published work and a list of ten topics that demonstrate knowledge of the Windsor market, and query the editor.

Foreign

GLIMPSES OF GUAM & MICRONESIA, (formerly *Glimpses of Micronesia*), Box 8066, Tamuning, Guam 96911. Editor: Pedro C. Sanchez. 100% freelance written. Works with a small number of new/unpublished writers each year. Quarterly magazine; 68-100 pages. "A regional publication for Micronesia lovers, travel buffs and readers interested in the United States' last frontier. Our audience covers all age levels and is best described as well educated and fascinated by our part of the world." Circ. 10,000. Pays on publication. Publishes ms an average of 9 months after acceptance. Byline given. Pays 10% kill fee on assignments. Buys all rights. Submit seasonal/holiday material 8 months in advance. Reports in 2 months. Sample copy $3.
Nonfiction: "Range of subjects is broad, from political analysis of Micronesia's newly emerging governments to examination of traditional culture; historical (anything related to Micronesia that is lively and factual); personal experience (first person adventure); interviews/personality profiles of outstanding Micronesian or western Pacific individuals; scientific/natural history (in lay terms); photo features (we're very photo-oriented—query us on island or Pacific themes); and travel (we use one per issue about destinations in Asia and the Pacific). No articles from fly-by-night (overnight) visitors to Micronesia." Buys 30 mss/year. Query. Length: up to 1,200 words preferred; but longer pieces will be considered. All materials subject to editing to meet publication requirements. Pays 5-10¢/word. Sometimes pays expenses of writers on assignment.
Photos: Purchased with or without accompanying ms. Pays minimum $5 for 8x10 b&w prints or $10-15 for 4x5 color transparencies or 35mm slides. Pay $100-200 for photo essays; $75-100 for covers. Captions required. Photo credit given.
Columns/Departments: Short think pieces on contemporary Micronesia are accepted for the Island Views section. Opinions are welcomed but must be well founded and must reflect the writer's familiarity with the subject. Length: 500-1,200 words. Pays $30.
Poetry: "We use very little but are willing to look at Pacific related themes to be used with photos." Only traditional forms. Pays minimum $10.
Tips: "Writers living in or having first hand experience with Micronesia and the western Pacific are scarce. If you have that experience, have made yourself familiar with *Glimpses*, have a good story idea that is relevant to our region, then we're willing to work with you in developing a good article."

‡LIVING, M.P.H. Magazines (S) Pte. Limited, #03-01/03, 601 Sims Dr., Pan 1 Warehouse Complex, Singapore 1438. (Singapore)748-5050. Editor: Jessica Sully. 65% freelance written. A monthly magazine covering interior design. Circ. 58,000. Pays on publication. Publishes ms an average of 3 months after acceptance. Byline given. Buys all rights or first rights. Submit seasonal/holiday material 4 months in advance. Simultaneous queries, photocopied and previously published submissions OK. Computer printout submissions acceptable; no dot-matrix. Reports in 6 weeks on queries; 1 month on mss. Free sample and writer's guidelines.
Nonfiction: General interest; how-to (furnishing, decorations, etc.); interview/profile; photo feature (relevant to magazine content); technical; travel and interior design; decor; gardening, etc. Annual produced every January, book on beautiful homes each autumn. No articles obviously inappropriate to a Southeast Asian

interior design magazine, e.g., clothes shopping in New York. Buys 300 mss/year. Query with published clips or send complete ms. Length: 3,000 words. Pays 15-20 Singapore cents/word.
Photos: Reviews 35mm (at minimum) transparencies. Pays $50-65 (Signapore dollars). Identification of subjects required. Buys one-time rights or all rights.
Columns/Departments: Buys 150 mss/year. Query with published clips or send complete ms. Length: 100-1,000 words. Pays 15-20¢/word (Singapore).
Fillers: Small items of integrity relevant to home design and decor. Length: 100-500 words. Pays 15-20¢/word (Singapore).
Tips: "The areas of our publication most open to freelancers are illustrated, knowledgeable features and articles on house and apartment interiors, decorating, furnishings, etc. Research each feature individually before writing it. Magazine publishing here (Singapore) is improving rapidly. The market is opening up for talented freelancers to work for increasingly prestigious publications."

‡PASSION, The Magazine of Paris, Passion Communications Limited, 18 rue du Pont-Neuf, Paris 75001 France. 42-33-00-24. Editor: Robert Sarner. Managing Editor: Maia Wechsler. 90% freelance written. A tabloid published 7 times/year. "*Passion* is the only magazine published in English in Paris devoted to reflecting life in the French capital for both residents and visitors." Circ. 50,000. Pays 3 months after publication. Publishes ms an average of 4 months after acceptance. Byline given. No kill fee. Buys first and one-time rights for Europe. Submit seasonal/holiday material 4 months in advance. Simultaneous and photocopied submissions OK. Reports in 1 month on queries; 2 weeks on mss. Sample copy $3; free writer's guidelines.
Nonfiction: Exposé, general interest, historical/nostalgic, humor, interview/profile, opinion and photo feature—all related to Paris or France. Special fashion issues (March and October) and 1 special cinema issue (May). No articles without a relationship to life in Paris (or France). Buys 100 mss/year. Query with published clips. Length: 500-3,500 words. Pays $50-300.
Photos: State availability of photos with submission. Reviews contact sheets. Offers $20-100/photo. Identification of subjects required. Buys one-time rights.
Columns/Departments: Books, Theatre, Film and Music columns (on what's happening in France). Buys 50-75 mss/year. Query with published clips. Length: 800-1,600 words. Pays $50-100.
Fiction: Adventure, erotica, ethnic, experimental, humorous, mainstream, mystery, novel excerpts, slice-of-life vignettes, suspense and fiction relating to Paris. Buys 8 mss/year. Send complete ms. Length: 850-1,500 words. Pays $50-100.
Tips: "Be familiar with life in Paris—beyond the superficial."

Religious

Each religious magazine relishes certain subjects, styles and beliefs. Such diversity makes reading each magazine essential for the writer hoping to break in. Educational and inspirational material of interest to church members, workers, and leaders within a denomination or religion is needed by the publications in this category. Publications intended to assist lay and professional religious workers in teaching and managing church affairs are classified in Church Administration and Ministry in the Trade Journals section. Religious magazines for children and teenagers can be found in the Juvenile, and Teen and Young Adult classifications. Other religious magazines can be found in the Ethnic/Minority section.

AGLOW, Today's Publication for Christian Women, Aglow Publications, Box I, Lynnwood WA 98046-1557. (206)775-7282. Editor: Gwen Weising. 80% freelance written. Works with a small number of new/unpublished writers each year. Bimonthly nondenominational Christian charismatic magazine for women. Pays on acceptance. Publishes ms an average of 9 months after acceptance. Byline given. Buys North American serial rights, and reprint rights for use in *Aglow* magazine in other countries. Submit seasonal/holiday material 6 months in advance. Simultaneous queries and photocopied submissions acceptable. Computer printout submissions OK; prefers letter-quality to dot-matrix. Reports in 2 months. Writer's guidelines for business size SAE and 1 first class stamp.

Nonfiction: Christian women's spiritual experience articles (first person) and some humor. "Each article should be either a testimony of or teaching about Jesus as Savior, as Baptizer in the Holy Spirit, or as Guide and Strength in everyday circumstances." Queries only. "We would like to see material about 'Women of Vision' who have made and are making an impact on their world for God." Length: 1,000-2,000 words. Pays up to 10¢/word.

‡AIM, A Magazine for Young Adults, Young Adult Ministries, Box 7259, 1333 Alger SE, Grand Rapids MI 49510. (616)241-5616. Editor: Steven Geurink. 100% freelance written. A bimonthly religious publication covering Christian young adult ministry with articles of general interest on topics of particular interest to young adults, 18-30+. Circ. 5,000. Pays on publication. Byline given. Buys one-time or second serial (reprint) rights. Submit seasonal/holiday material 6 months in advance. Photocopied submissions OK. Computer print-out submissions acceptable; prefers letter-quality to dot-matrix. Reports in 1 month. Sample copy $1 with SAE and 2 first class stamps; writer's guidelines for SAE and 1 first class stamp.

Nonfiction: Essays, general interest, historical/nostalgic, humor, inspirational, interview/profile, opinion, personal experience and religious. Upcoming themes: Counseling/Friendship (January/February 1987, copy due Nov. 7); Substance Abuse (March/April 1987, copy due Jan. 2). No reprints. Buys 12 mss/year. Query with published clips. Length: 700-1,600 words. Pays $30-50 for assigned articles; pays $15-40 for unsolicited articles.

Photos: Offers $15-25/photo. Model releases and identification of subjects required. Buys one-time rights.

Columns/Departments: Single File (addresses the concerns of singles in the church); People in Pairs (addresses relational issues—marriage, dating, sex); On Campus (addresses concerns of students); Professions (explores the living of Christian faith in the work place); Models (examples of existing young adult groups). Buys 6-8 mss/year. Query with published clips or send complete ms. Length: 700-800 words. Pays $15-30.

Fiction: Adventure, confession, ethnic, fantasy, historical, humorous, mainstream, mystery, religious, romance, science fiction, slice-of-vignettes, suspense and western (all with religious slant). Buys 3 mss/year. Query with published clips or send complete ms. Length: 700-1,400 words. Pays $15-40.

Poetry: Avant-garde, free verse, haiku, light verse and traditional. Buys 3 poems/year. Submit maximum 3 poems. Pays $15-25.

Fillers: Anecdotes, facts and short humor. Buys 2/year. Length: 300-500 words. Pays $15-25.

THE ANNALS OF SAINT ANNE DE BEAUPRE, Redemptorist Fathers, 9597 St. Anne Blvd., St. Anne De Beaupre, Quebec G0A 3C0 Canada. (418)824-4538. Editor: Bernard Mercier. Managing Editor: Roch Achard. 60% freelance written. "Anyone can submit manuscripts. We judge." Monthly magazine on religion. "Our aim is to promote devotion to St. Anne and Christian family values." Circ. 54,000. Pays on acceptance. Publishes ms an average of 1 year after acceptance. Byline given. Buys first North American serial rights. Submit seasonal/holiday material 2½ months in advance. Simultaneous queries and photocopied submissions OK. Reports in 2 weeks. Free sample copy and writer's guidelines.

Nonfiction: Expose, general interest, inspirational and personal experience. No articles without spiritual thrust. Buys 30 mss/year. Send complete ms. Length: 500-1,200 words. Pays 2-4¢/word.

Fiction: Religious. Buys 15 mss/year. Send complete ms. Length: 500-1,200 words. Pays 2-4¢/word.

Poetry: Traditional. Buys 12/year. Submit maximum 2-3 poems. Length: 12-20 lines. Pays $5-8.

Tips: "Write something educational, inspirational, objective and uplifting. Reporting rather than analysis is simply not remarkable."

‡THE ASSOCIATE REFORMED PRESBYTERIAN, Associate Reformed Presbyterian General Synod, 1 Cleveland St., Greenville SC 29601. (803)232-8297. Editor: Ben Johnston. 5-10% freelance written. Works with a small number of new/unpublished writers each year. A Christian publication serving a conservative, evangelical and Reformed denomination, most of whose members are in the Southeast U.S. Circ. 6,300. Pays on acceptance. Publishes ms an average of 4 months after acceptance. Byline given. Not copyrighted. Buys first rights, one-time rights, or second serial (reprint) rights. Submit seasonal/holiday material 4 months in advance. Simultaneous submissions and previously published submissions OK. Computer printout submissions acceptable; prefers letter-quality to dot-matrix. Reports in 1 month. Sample copy $1. Writer's guidelines are now available.

Nonfiction: Book excerpts, essays, inspirational, opinion, personal experience, and religious. Buys 10-15 mss/year. Query. Length: 400-2,000 words. $50 maximum.

Photos: State availability of photos with submission. Reviews 5x7 reprints. Offers $25 maximum per photo. Captions and identification of subjects required. Buys one-time rights.

Fiction: Religious and children's. Buys 5-8 mss/year. Query. Length: 400-1,500 words. Pays $50 maximum.

Tips: "Feature articles are the area of our publication most open to freelancers. Focus on a contemporary problem and offer Bible-based solutions to it. Provide information that would help a Christian struggling in his daily walk. Writers should understand that we are denominational, conservative, evangelical, Reformed, and Presbyterian. A writer who appreciates these nuances would stand a much better chance of being published here than one who does not.''

AXIOS, 800 S. Euclid St., Fullerton CA 92632. (714)526-2131. Editor: David Gorham. 20% freelance written. Eager to work with new/unpublished writers. Monthly journal seeking spiritual articles mostly on Orthodox Christian background, either Russian, Greek, Serbian, Syrian or American. Circ. 4,789. Pays on publication. Publishes ms an average of 3 months after acceptance. Byline given. Offers 50% kill fee. Buys all rights. Submit seasonal/holiday material 4 months in advance. Simultaneous queries, and simultaneous, photocopied, and previously published submissions OK. Electronic submissions OK on MS-DOS. Computer printout submissions acceptable; prefers letter-quality to dot-matrix. Reports in 1 month. Sample copy $2 and 44¢ postage.
Nonfiction: Book excerpts; expose (of religious figures); general interest; historical/nostalgic; interview/profile; opinion; personal experience; photo feature; and travel (shrines, pilgrimages). Special issues include The Persecution of Christians in Iran, Russia, behind Iron Curtain or in Arab lands; Roman Catholic interest in the Orthodox Church. Nothing about the Pope or general "all-is-well-with-Christ" items. Buys 14 mss/year. Send complete ms. Length: 1,000-3,000 words. Pays 4¢/word minimum. Sometimes pays expenses of writers on assignment.
Columns/Departments: Reviews religious books and films. Buys 80 mss/year. Query.
Tips: "We need some hard hitting articles on the 'political' church—the why, how and where of it and why it lacks the timelessness of the spiritual. Here in *Axios* you can discuss your feelings, your findings, your needs, your growth; give us your outpouring. Don't mistake us for either Protestant or Roman Catholic; we are the voice of Catholics united with the Eastern Orthodox Church, also referred to as the Greek Orthodox Church.''

BAPTIST LEADER, Valley Forge PA 19482-0851. (215)768-2153. Editor: Linda Isham. For pastors, teachers, and leaders in church schools. 25% freelance written. Monthly; 64 pages. Buys first serial rights. Pays on acceptance. Publishes ms an average of 8 months after acceptance. Deadlines are 8 months prior to date of issue. Computer printout submissions acceptable; prefers letter-quality to dot-matrix. Writer's guidelines for SASE.
Nonfiction: Educational topics. How-to articles for local church school teachers and leaders. Length: 1,500-2,000 words. Pays $25-75.

BIBLICAL ILLUSTRATOR, The Sunday School Board, 127 9th Ave. N., Nashville TN 37234. Editor: Michael J. Mitchell. "We are backlogged with submissions and prefer not to receive unsolicited submissions at this time.''

‡CATHOLIC DIGEST, Box 64090, St. Paul MN 55164. Editor: Henry Lexau. Managing Editor: Richard Reece. 50% freelance written. Eager to work with new/unpublished writers. Monthly magazine covering the daily living of Roman Catholics for an audience that is 60% female, 40% male; 37% is college educated. Circ. 600,000. Publishes ms an average of 5 months after acceptance. Byline given. Buys first North American serial rights or one-time reprint rights. Submit seasonal material 6 months in advance. Previously published submissions OK, if so indicated. Computer printout submissions acceptable; prefers letter-quality to dot-matrix. Reports in 3 weeks.
Nonfiction: General interest (daily living and family relationships); interview (of outstanding Catholics, celebrities and locals); nostalgia (the good old days of family living); profile; religion; travel (shrines); humor; inspirational (overcoming illness, role model people); and personal experience (adventures and daily living). Buys 25 articles/year. No queries. Send complete ms. Length: 500-3,000 words, 2,000 average. Pays on acceptance—$200-400 for originals, $100 for reprints.
Columns/Departments: "Check a copy of the magazine in the library for a description of column needs. Payment varies and is made on publication. We buy about 5/issue.''
Fillers: Jokes, anecdotes and short humor. Buys 10-15 mss/issue. Length: 10-300 words. Pays $3-50 on publication.

CATHOLIC LIFE, 35750 Moravian Dr., Fraser MI 48026. Editor-in-Chief: Robert C. Bayer. 40% freelance written. Monthly (except July or August) magazine; 32 pages. Emphasizes foreign missionary activities of the Catholic Church in Burma, India, Bangladesh, the Philippines, Hong Kong, Africa, etc., for middle-aged and older audience with either middle incomes or pensions. High school educated (on the average), conservative in both religion and politics. Circ. 17,300. Pays on publication. Publishes ms an average of 3 months after acceptance. Buys all rights. Byline given. Submit seasonal/holiday material 4 months in advance. Simultaneous submissions OK. Computer printout submissions acceptable. Reports in 2 weeks.
Nonfiction: Informational and inspirational foreign missionary activities of the Catholic Church. Buys 20-25 unsolicited mss/year. Query or send complete ms. Length: 1,000-1,500 words. Pays 4¢/word.
Tips: "Query with short, graphic details of what the material will cover or the personality involved in the biographical sketch. Also, we appreciate being advised on the availability of good black-and-white photos to illustrate the material.''

CATHOLIC NEAR EAST MAGAZINE, Catholic Near East Welfare Association, 1011 1st Ave., New York NY 10022. (212)826-1480. Editor: Michael Healy. 90% freelance written. Quarterly magazine; 24 pages. For a general audience with interest in the Near East, particularly its religious and cultural aspects. Circ. 130,000. Pays on publication. Publishes ms an average of 4 months after acceptance. Byline given. Buys all rights. Submit seasonal material (Christmas and Easter in different Near Eastern lands or rites) 6 months in advance. Photocopied submissions OK if legible. Computer printout submissions acceptable; no dot-matrix. Reports in 1 month. Free sample copy and writer's guidelines.
Nonfiction: "Cultural, territorial, devotional material on the Near East, its history, peoples and religions (especially the Eastern Rites of the Catholic Church). Style should be simple, factual, concise. Articles must stem from personal acquaintance with subject matter, or thorough up-to-date research. No preaching or speculations." Length: 1,200-1,800 words. Pays 10¢/word.
Photos: "Photographs to accompany manuscript are always welcome; they should illustrate the people, places, ceremonies, etc. which are described in the article. We prefer color but occasionally use black and white. Pay varies depending on the quality of the photos."
Tips: "Writers please heed: stick to the Near East. Send factual articles; concise, descriptive style preferred, not too flowery. Pictures are a big plus; if you have photos to accompany your article, please send them at the same time."

CATHOLIC TWIN CIRCLE, Twin Circle Publishing, Suite 900, 6404 Wilshire Blvd., Los Angeles CA 90048. (213)653-2200. Executive Editor: Mary Louise Frawley. 30% freelance written. Weekly tabloid covering Catholic personalities and Catholic interest topics for a mostly Catholic family readership. Circ. 60,000. Pays on publication. Publishes ms an average of 2 months after acceptance. Byline given. Buys all rights. Submit seasonal material 2 months in advance. Simultaneous and photocopied submissions OK if so indicated. Computer printout submissions acceptable; prefers letter-quality to dot-matrix. Reports in 2 months on queries; 1 month on mss. Writer's guidelines for SASE. Not responsible for unsolicited mss.
Nonfiction: "We are looking for articles about prominent Catholic personalities in sports, entertainment, politics and business; ethnic stories about Catholics from other countries and topical issues of concern to Catholics. We are interested in writers who are experienced and write on an ongoing basis." No theological issues. Average issue includes 6-7 feature articles. Buys 3-4 mss/issue. Length: 250-2,000 words. Pays 10¢/word. Pays expenses of writers if assigned.
Photos: State availability of photos. Reviews 5x7 or 8x10 b&w glossy prints. Price negotiated. Captions required. Rights vary.
Tips: Writer has a better chance of breaking in with shorter pieces, as "they give a truer example of a writer's style, strengths and weaknesses. Research thoroughly and use quotes from acceptable sources."

CHARISMA, The Magazine About Spirit-Led Living, Strang Communications Co. Inc., 190 N. Westmonte Dr., Altamonte Springs FL 32714. (305)869-5005. Editor/Publisher: Stephen Strang. 60% freelance written. Prefers to work with published/established writers. Monthly magazine covering Christianity, especially Charismatic, Pentecostal and Protestant movements. Circ. 150,000. Pays on publication. Publishes ms an average of 3 months after acceptance. Byline given. Buys all rights. Submit seasonal material 6 months in advance. Electronic submissions OK via 8086/8088 WordStar, but requires hard copy also. Computer submissions acceptable; prefers letter-quality to dot-matrix. Reports in 1 month. Sample copy $1.95; writer's guidelines for 9x12 SAE and 2 first class stamps.
Nonfiction: Contact Howard Earl. Narrative faith stories (verifiable healings, rescues, testimony, everyday faith experiences, etc.), call to action (issues oriented, morality, Christian standards, etc.), Christian family, historical personalities and movements, and seasonal (Mother's Day, Easter, Christmas, Thanksgiving, Valentine's Day). "Articles on Christian personalities, music, colleges, Israel and the Questions and Answers interviews are assigned only to established writers with whom we have a working relationship." Special issues include: Bible in January, Israel in June, family in August, college in October and March, Christian music in February and July, missions in December. Buys 18 mss/year. Submit completed ms. Length: 1,500-2,000 words. Pays $100-$150 for first time authors; more for established authors. Also articles on Charismatic, Pentecostal and Protestant issues and events. Query first. Pays $50-100 on publication. Pays the expenses of writers on assignment.
Tips: "News, testimony and family articles are the best place for new writers to break in. Read the magazine before submitting anything. We will be buying less freelance material 'over the transom' because we plan carefully and solicit articles from our pool of authors."

CHICAGO STUDIES, Box 665, Mundelein IL 60060. (312)566-1462. Editor: Rev. George J. Dyer. 50% freelance written. Magazine published 3 times/year; 112 pages. For Roman Catholic priests and religious educators. Circ. 10,000. Pays on acceptance. Buys all rights. Photocopied submissions OK. Computer printout submissions acceptable. Reports in 2 months. Sample copy $5.
Nonfiction: Nontechnical discussion of theological, Biblical and ethical topics. Articles aimed at a nontech-

nical presentation of the contemporary scholarship in those fields. Submit complete ms. Buys 30 mss/year. Length: 3,000-5,000 words. Pays $35-100.

THE CHRISTIAN CENTURY, 407 S. Dearborn St., Chicago IL 60605. (312)427-5380. Editor: James M. Wall. Senior Editors: Martin E. Marty and Dean Peerman. Managing Editor: Linda-Marie Delloff. 70% freelance written. Eager to work with new/unpublished writers. Weekly magazine; 24-32 pages. For ecumenically-minded, progressive church people, both clergy and lay. Circ. 37,000. Pays on publication. Publishes ms an average of 2 months after acceptance. Usually buys all rights. Computer printout submissions acceptable; prefers letter-quality to dot-matrix. Reports in 1 month. Free sample copy.
Nonfiction: "We use articles dealing with social problems, ethical dilemmas, political issues, international affairs, and the arts, as well as with theological and ecclesiastical matters. We focus on concerns that arise at the juncture between church and society, or church and culture." Query appreciated, but not essential. Length: 2,500 words maximum. Payment varies, but averages $30/page.

CHRISTIAN HOME & SCHOOL, Christian Schools International, 3350 East Paris Ave. SE, Box 8709, Grand Rapids MI 49508. (616)957-1070. Editor: Gordon L. Bordewyk. Assistant Editor: Judy Zylstra. 30% freelance written. Works with a small number of new/unpublished writers each year. Magazine published 8 times/year covering family life and Christian education. "The magazine is designed for parents who support Christian education. We feature material on a wide range of topics of interest to parents." Pays on publication. Publishes ms an average of 4 months after acceptance. Byline given. Buys first North American serial rights. Submit seasonal/holiday material 4 months in advance. Simultaneous queries and photocopied submissions OK. Computer printout submissions acceptable; prefers letter-quality to dot-matrix. Reports in 3 weeks on queries; 1 month on mss. Sample copy for 9x12 SAE·and 4 first class stamps.
Nonfiction: Book excerpts, interview/profile, opinion, personal experience, and articles on parenting and school life. "We publish features on issues which affect the home and school and profiles on interesting individuals, providing that the profile appeals to our readers and is not a tribute or eulogy of that person." Buys 40 mss/year. Send complete ms. Length: 500-2,000 words. Pays $25-85. Sometimes pays the expenses of writers on assignment.
Photos: "If you have any black-and-white photos appropriate for your article, send them along."
Tips: "Features are the area most open to freelancers. We are publishing articles that deal with contemporary issues which affect parents; keep that in mind. Use an informal easy-to-read style rather than a philosophical, academic tone. Try to incorporate vivid imagery and concrete, practical examples from real life."

CHRISTIAN LIFE MAGAZINE, 190 N. Westmonte Dr., Altamonte Springs FL 32714. (305)869-5005. Editorial Director: Bert Ghezzi. 50% freelance written. Monthly Christian magazine for evangelicals. Circ. 100,000. Pays on publication. Buys all rights. Submit seasonal/holiday material 8-12 months in advance. Reports in 1 month. Sample copy $1; free writer's guidelines.
Nonfiction: Adventure articles (usually in the first person, told in narrative style); devotional (include many anecdotes, preferably from the author's own experience); general features (wide variety of subjects, with special programs of unique benefit to the community); inspirational (showing the success of persons, ideas, events and organizations); personality profiles (bright, tightly written articles on what Christians are thinking); news (with human interest quality dealing with trends); news feature (providing interpretative analysis of person, trend, events and ideas); and trend (should be based on solid research). Pays $200 maximum.

CHRISTIAN SINGLE, Family Ministry Dept., Baptist Sunday School Board, 127 9th Ave. N., Nashville TN 37234. (615)251-2228. Editor: Cliff Allbritton. 50-70% freelance written. Prefers to work with published/established writers; works with a small number of new/unpublished writers each year. Monthly magazine covering items of special interest to Christian single adults. "*Christian Single* is a contemporary Christian magazine that seeks to give substantive information to singles for living the abundant life. It seeks to be constructive and creative in approach." Circ. 102,000. Pays on acceptance "for immediate needs"; on publication "for unsolicited manuscripts." Publishes ms 1-3 years after acceptance. Byline given. Buys all rights; makes work-for-hire assignments. Submit seasonal/holiday material 1 year in advance. Computer printout submissions acceptable; prefers letter-quality to dot-matrix. Reports in 6 weeks. Sample copy and writer's guidelines for large SASE.
Nonfiction: Humor (good, clean humor that applies to Christian singles); how-to (specific subjects which apply to singles; query needed); inspirational (of the personal experience type); high adventure personal experience (of single adults); photo feature (on outstanding Christian singles; query needed); and travel (appropriate for Christian singles; query needed). No "shallow, uninformative mouthing off. This magazine says something, and people read it cover to cover." Buys 120-150 unsolicited mss/year. Query with published clips. Length: 300-1,200 words. Pays 5¢/word. Pays expenses of writers on assignment.
Tips: "We look for freshness and creativity, not duplication of what we have already done. We seek variety targeted to singles' needs. We give preference to Christian single adult writers but publish articles by *sensitive* and *informed* married writers also. Remember that you are talking to educated people who attend church."

CHRISTIANITY & CRISIS, 537 W. 121st St., New York NY 10027. (212)662-5907. Editor: Leon Howell. Managing Editor: Gail Hovey. 10% freelance written. Works with a small number of new/unpublished writers each year. Biweekly Protestant journal of opinion. "We are interested in special issues, foreign affairs, liberation theology and other theological developments with social or ethical implications. As an independent religious journal it is part of *C&C's* function to discuss church policies from a detached and sometimes critical perspective. We carry no 'devotional' material but welcome solid contemplative reflections. Most subscribers are highly educated, well-informed." Circ. 13,000. Pays on publication. Publishes ms an average of 2 months after acceptance. Byline given. Offers variable kill fee. Submit seasonal/holiday material 2 months in advance. Simultaneous queries and photocopied submissions OK. Computer printout submissions acceptable if double-spaced. Reports in 1 month. Sample copy $1.35; free writer's guidelines.
Nonfiction: Buys 150 mss/year. Query with or without published clips. Length: 1,000-4,000 words. Pays 3¢/word. Rarely pays expenses of writers on assignment.
Tips: "We have been publishing more international stories and need to build up reporting on U.S. issues."

CHRISTIANITY TODAY, 465 Gundersen Dr., Carol Stream IL 60188. 20% freelance written. Works with a small number of new/unpublished writers each year. Emphasizes orthodox, evangelical religion. Semimonthly magazine; 55 pages. Circ. 180,000. Pays on acceptance. Publishes ms an average of 6 months after acceptance. Usually buys first serial rights. Submit seasonal/holiday material at least 8 months in advance. Computer printout submissions acceptable; prefers letter-quality to dot-matrix. Reports in 2 months. Free sample copy and writer's guidelines.
Nonfiction: Theological, ethical, historical and informational (not merely inspirational). Buys 4 mss/issue. Query only. Unsolicited mss not accepted and not returned. Length: 1,000-4,000 words. Pays negotiable rates. Sometimes pays the expenses of writers on assignment.
Columns/Departments: Ministries (practical and specific, not elementary); and Refiner's Fire (Christian review of the arts). Buys 12 mss/year. Send complete ms. Length: 800-900 words. Pays negotiable rates.
Tips: "We are developing more of our own manuscripts and requiring a much more professional quality of others."

CHRYSALIS, Box 24111, St. Louis MO 63103. Editor: J. Anthony Daniel Jr. 95% freelance written. Eager to work with new/unpublished writers. A quarterly religious literary magazine. "We are dedicated to the proposition that all art is a creative gift of God. We exist to help the Christian lead a more creative life." Circ. 500. Pays on acceptance. Publishes ms an average of 4 months after acceptance. Byline given. Buys one-time rights. Simultaneous and photocopied submissions OK. Computer printout submissions acceptable; prefers letter-quality to dot-matrix. Reports in 1 month. Sample copy for $1 with 6x9 SAE and 1 first class stamp; writer's guidelines for SAE and 1 first class stamp.
Nonfiction: Historical/nostalgic, humor, inspirational, interview/profile, book reviews, and personal experience. "Writers should not limit themselves to religious topics, but should remember that our readership is mostly Christian in one form or another. We like unusual slants in our articles. Please, do not send your testimony. We also frown on pop psychology." Buys 4-5 mss/year. Send complete ms. Length: 10,000 words. Pays $5-10. "We pay poorly—but we do pay. Rates vary according to the editorial judgment of the worth of a piece and the length."
Fiction: Adventure, experimental, fantasy, historical, humorous, mainstream, mystery, religious and science fiction. "We like to see craftsmanship in a story. We see too many obvious first drafts. Lovingly choose your words and we will lovingly publish them." Buys 6-8 mss/year. Send complete ms. Length: 15,000 words maximum. Pays according to length and author.
Poetry: Avant-garde, free verse and traditional. "Please don't send us free verse if you haven't tried traditional. Be specific and restrained with your sentiments. Keep your conversion experience between you and God." Buys 10-15 poems/year. Length: open. Pays $5-10.
Tips: "Send us anything you have written that comes close to art. That is really all we ask. A writer must have a distinct voice—we look not only at content, but at style. Read us and submit; if you don't ever submit, you are not leading the abundant, creative life Christ has promised you."

CHURCH & STATE, Americans United for Separation of Church and State, 8120 Fenton St., Silver Spring MD 20910. (301)589-3707. Managing Editor: Joseph Conn. 15% freelance written. Monthly magazine; 24 pages. Emphasizes religious liberty and church/state relations matters. Readership "includes the whole spectrum, but is predominantly Protestant and well-educated." Circ. 50,000. Pays on acceptance. Publishes ms an average of 2 months after acceptance. Buys all rights. Simultaneous, photocopied, and previously published submissions OK. Reports in 1 month. Free sample copy and writer's guidelines.
Nonfiction: Expose, general interest, historical and interview. Buys 11 mss/year. Query. Length: 3,000 words maximum. Pays negotiable fee.
Photos: State availability of photos with query. Pays negotiable fee for b&w prints. Captions preferred. Buys one-time rights.

COLUMBIA, Drawer 1670, New Haven CT 06507. Editor: Elmer Von Feldt. Monthly magazine for Catholic families; caters particularly to members of the Knights of Columbus. Circ. 1,390,429. Pays on acceptance. Buys all rights. Submit seasonal material 6 months in advance. Reports in 1 month. Free sample copy and writer's guidelines.
Nonfiction: Fact articles directed to the Catholic layman and his family dealing with current events, social problems, Catholic apostolic activities, education, ecumenism, rearing a family, literature, science, humor, satire, arts, sports and leisure. Color glossy prints, transparencies or contact prints with negatives are required for illustration. Articles without ample illustrative material are not given consideration. Pays $600 minimum, including photos. Photo stories are also wanted. Buys 30 mss/year. Query or submit complete ms. Length: 2,500-3,500 words. Humor or satire should be directed to current religious, social or cultural conditions. Length: 1,000 words. Pays $200.
Photos: Pays $50 per photo used. Pays 10¢/word.

‡COMMENTS, From the Friends, Comments from the Friends, Box 840, Stoughton MA 02072. Editor: David A. Reed. 20% freelance written. "A quarterly Christian newsletter written especially for Jehovah's Witnesses, ex-Jehovah's Witnesses and persons concerned about Jehovah's Witnesses, relatives, friends, and neighbors." Circ. 1,200. Pays on publication. Publishes ms an average of 3 months after acceptance. Byline sometimes given. Buys second serial (reprint) and simultaneous rights. Submit seasonal/holiday material 4 months in advance. Simultaneous, photocopied and previously published submissions OK. Electronic submissions OK via Macintosh MacWrite. Computer printout submissions acceptable; prefers letter-quality to dot-matrix. Reports in 1 month on mss. Sample copy $1 with #10 SAE and 2 first class stamps; writer's guidelines for #10 SAE and 2 first class stamps.
Nonfiction: Book excerpts, essays, exposé, how-to (witnessing tips), humor, inspirational, interview/profile, personal experience, religious and book reviews of books on cults only. Special issue topic will be The Next Watchtower President (replacing Fred Franz). "No general religious material not written specifically for our unique readership." Buys 8 mss/year. Send complete ms. Length: 200-1,000 words. Pays $2-20. May pay with contributor copies rather than a cash payment "when a writer contributes an article as a gift to this ministry."
Columns/Departments: Witnessing Tips (brief, powerful and effective approaches), 250-300 words; and News Briefs (current events involving Jehovah's Witnesses and ex-Jehovah's Witnesses), 60-240 words. Buys 4 mss/year. Send complete ms. Length: 60-300 words. Pays $2-10.
Fillers: Facts, newsbreaks and quotes. Buys 4/year. Length: 10-50 words. Pays $1-5.
Tips: "Acquaint us with your background that qualifies you to write in this field. Write well-documented, germane articles in layman's language."

COMMONWEAL, 232 Madison Ave., New York NY 10016. (212)683-2042. Editor: Peter Steinfels. Biweekly magazine edited by Roman Catholic laymen. For college-educated audience. Special book and education issues. Circ. 20,000. Pays on acceptance. Submit seasonal material 2 months in advance. "A number of our articles come in over-the-transom. I suggest a newcomer provide sufficient material to establish his or her expertise and let us know something about him/herself (credentials, tearsheets, education or past experience)." Reports in 3 weeks. Free sample copy.
Nonfiction: "Articles on timely subjects: politics, literature and religion. Original, brightly written mss on value-oriented themes; think pieces." Buys 50 mss/year. Length: 1,000-3,000 words. Pays 2¢/word.
Poetry: Department editors: Rosemary Deen and Marie Ponsot. Contemporary and avant-garde. Length: maximum 150 lines ("long poems very rarely used"). Pays $7.50-25.

THE COMPANION OF ST. FRANCIS AND ST. ANTHONY, Conventual Franciscan Friars, Box 535, Postal Station F, Toronto, Ontario M4Y 2L8 Canada. (416)924-6349. Editor-in-Chief: Friar Philip Kelly, OFM Conv. 60% freelance written. Monthly magazine. Emphasizing religious and human values and stressing Franciscan virtues—peace, simplicity, joy. Circ. 10,000. Pays on acceptance. Publishes ms an average of 6 months after acceptance. Buys first North American serial rights. Phone queries OK. Submit seasonal/holiday material 6 months in advance. Computer printout submissions acceptable; prefers letter-quality to dot-matrix. SAE with IRCs. Reports in 3 weeks. Writer's guidelines for SAE, IRCs.
Nonfiction: Historical; how-to (medical and psychological coping); informational; inspirational; interview; nostalgia; profile; and family. No old time religion, antiCatholic or pro-abortion material. No poetry. Buys 6 mss/issue. Send complete ms. Length: 800-1,000 words. Pays 6¢/word, Canadian funds.
Photos: Photos purchased with accompanying ms. Pays $8 for 5x7 (but all sizes accepted) b&w glossy prints. Send prints. Total purchase price for ms includes payment for photos. Captions required.
Fiction: Adventure, humorous, mainstream and religious. Canadian settings preferred. Buys 6 mss/year. Send complete ms. Length: 800-1,000 words. Pays 6¢/word, Canadian funds.
Tips: "Manuscripts on human interest with photos are given immediate preference. In the year ahead we will be featuring shorter articles, more Canadian and Franciscan themes, and better photos. Use a good typewriter, good grammar and good sense."

CONSCIENCE, A Newsjournal of Prochoice Catholic Opinion, Catholics for a Free Choice, 2008 17th St. NW, Washington DC 20009. (202)638-1706. Editor: Susan J. Boyd. Production Editor: Kathleen Regie. 80% freelance written. Eager to work with new/unpublished writers. Bimonthly newsjournal covering reproductive rights, specifically abortion rights. "A feminist, pro-choice perspective is a must, and knowledge of Christianity and specifically Catholicism is helpful." Circ. 10,000. Pays on publication. Publishes ms an average of 4 months after acceptance. Byline given. Buys first North American serial rights; makes work-for-hire assignments. Submit seasonal/holiday material 4 months in advance. Simultaneous queries, and simultaneous, photocopied, and previously published submissions OK. Electronic submissions OK via IBM-XT, Multimate. Computer printout submissions acceptable; prefers letter-quality to dot-matrix. Reports in 2 months; free sample copy for #10 SASE with 1 first class stamp; free writer's guidelines for #10 SAE with 1 first class stamp.
Nonfiction: Book excerpts, interview/profile, opinion and personal experience. Especially needs "expose/refutation of antichoice misinformation and specific research into the implications of new reproductive technology and fetal personhood bills/court decisions. Buys 8-12 mss/year. Query with published clips or send complete ms. Length: 1,000-3,500 words. Pays $100-150. "Writers should be aware that we are a nonprofit organization." A substantial number of articles is contributed without payment by writers. Sometimes pays the expenses of writers on assignment.
Photos: State availability of photos with query or ms. Prefers 3x5 b&w prints. Identification of subjects required. Buys all rights.
Columns/Departments: Book reviews. Buys 6-10 mss/year. Send complete ms. Length: 1,000-2,000 words. Pays $50 maximum.
Fillers: Clippings and newsbreaks. Uses 6/year. Length: 25-100 words. No payment.
Tips: "Say something new on the abortion issue. Thoughtful, well-researched and well-argued articles needed. Try a book review first. The most frequent mistakes made by writers in completing an article for us are untimeliness and wordiness. When you have shown you can write thoughtfully, we may hire you for other types of articles."

CORNERSTONE, Jesus People USA, 4707 N. Malden, Chicago IL 60640. Editor: Dawn Herrin. Works with a small number of new/unpublished writers each year; eager to work with new/unpublished writers. A bimonthly magazine covering contemporary issues in the light of Evangelical Christianity. Circ. 90,000. Pays on publication. Byline given. Buys first serial rights. Submit seasonal/holiday material 6 months in advance. Simultaneous, photocopied and previously published submissions OK. Computer printout submissions acceptable; no dot-matrix. Reports in 1 month. Sample copy for 8½x11 SAE and 73¢ postage; writer's guidelines for business size SAE and 1 first class stamp.
Nonfiction: Essays, personal experience, religious. Buys 1-2 mss/year. Query. Length: 2,700 words maximum. Pays negotiable rate.
Photos: Send photos with accompanying ms. Reviews 8x10 b&w and color prints and 35mm slides. Identification of subjects required. Buys negotiable rights.
Columns/Departments: Music (interview with artists, mainly rock, focusing on artist's world view and value system as expressed in his/her music); Current Events; Personalities; Film and Book Reviews (focuses on meaning as compared and contrasted to Biblical values). Buys 2-6 mss/year. Query. Length: 100-2,500 words (negotiable). Pays negotiable rate.
Fiction: "Articles may express Christian world-view but should not be unrealistic or 'syrupy.' Other than smut, the sky's the limit. We want fiction as creative as the Creator." Buys 1-4 mss/year. Send complete ms. Length: 250-2,500 words (negotiable). Pays negotiable rate.
Poetry: Avant-garde, free verse, haiku, light verse and traditional. No limits *except* for epic poetry ("We've not the room!"). Buys 10-50 poems/year. Submit maximum 10 poems. Payment negotiated.
Fillers: Anecdotes, facts, short humor and newsbreaks. Buys 5-15 year. Length: 20-200 words (negotiable). Payment negotiable.
Tips: "A display of creativity which expresses a biblical world view without cliches or cheap shots at non-Christians is the ideal. We are known as the most avant-garde magazine in the Christian market, yet attempt to express orthodox beliefs in language of the '80s. *Any* writer who does this may well be published by *Cornerstone*. Creative fiction is begging for more Christian participation. We anticipate such contributions gladly. Interviews where well-known personalities respond to the gospel are also strong publication possibilities. Much of our poetry and small feature content is published without payment to the writer. This does not mean we do not pay ever, but rather that many of our readers enjoy being published as payment in and of itself. Inform us of a desire for payment and we will contact you before any decision to publish."

THE COVENANT COMPANION, 5101 N. Francisco Ave., Chicago IL 60625. (312)784-3000. Editor-in-Chief: James R. Hawkinson. 25% freelance written. Monthly magazine; 48 pages. Emphasizes Christian life and faith. Circ. 27,500. Pays following publication. Publishes ms an average of 4 months after acceptance. Submit seasonal/holiday material 3 months in advance. Simultaneous, photocopied, and previously published submissions OK. Computer printout submissions acceptable; prefers letter-quality to dot-matrix. Reports in 3 months. Sample copy $1.50 and $1 postage.

Nonfiction: Humor; informational; inspirational (especially evangelical Christian); interviews (Christian leaders and personalities); and personal experience. "No articles promoting organizations or people not in the church we serve (Evangelical Covenant Church)." Buys 20-30 mss/year. Length: 100-110 lines of typewritten material at 70 characters/line (double-spaced). Pays $15-35.

DAILY MEDITATION, Box 2710, San Antonio TX 78299. Editor: Ruth S. Paterson. Quarterly. Byline given. Rights purchased vary. Payment on acceptance. Submit seasonal material 6 months in advance. Sample copy 50¢.
Nonfiction: "Inspirational, self-improvement and nonsectarian religious articles, 750-1,600 words, showing the path to greater spiritual growth."
Fillers: Length: 400 words maximum. Pays 1-1½¢/word for prose.
Poetry: Inspirational. Length: 16 lines maximum. Pays 14¢/line.
Tips: "All our material is freelance submission for consideration except our meditations which are staff written. We buy approximately 250 manuscripts a year. We must see finished manuscripts; no queries, please. Checking copy is sent upon publication."

DAUGHTERS OF SARAH, 2716 W. Cortland, Chicago IL 60647. (312)252-3344. Editorial Coordinator: Reta Finger. Managing Editor: Annette Huizenga. 25-33% freelance written. Works with a small number of new/unpublished writers each year. Bimonthly magazine covering Christian feminism. Circ. 3,900. Pays upon acceptance. Publishes ms an average of 10 months after acceptance. Byline given. Offers 33-50% kill fee. Buys first serial rights and first North American serial rights. Submit seasonal/holiday material 4 months in advance. Computer printout submissions acceptable; prefers letter-quality to dot-matrix. Reports in 2 weeks on queries; 2 months on mss. Sample copy $2; writer's guidelines for SAE with 1 first class stamp.
Nonfiction: Book excerpts (book reviews on Christian feminist books); historical (on Christian women); humor (feminist); inspirational (biblical articles about women or feminist issues); personal experience (women's—or men's—experiences from Christian feminist point of view); and issues of social justice relating to women. Special issues include women and the health care system, inclusive language, patriarchy in the Hebrew scriptures, feminist theology, and women and healing. "No general, elementary aspects of Christian feminism; we've gone beyond that. We particularly do not want pieces about women or women's issues that are not written from a feminist and Christian point of view." Buys 10-15 mss/year. Query with or without published clips. Length: 500-2,000 words. (Book reviews on Christian feminist books, 100-500 words). Pays $15-60.
Fiction: Christian feminist. Buys 2-4 mss/year. Query with published clips. Length: 500-2,000 words. Pays $15-60.
Tips: "The writer has a better chance of breaking in at our publication with short articles and fillers. Usually we solicit our feature articles on a particular topic that most freelance writers may not be familiar with. The most frequent mistakes made by writers in completing an article for us are writing too-long articles (we have a small magazine); writing on an unrelated topic; or writing about women but not particularly from a feminist point of view."

THE DISCIPLE, Box 179, St. Louis MO 63166. Editor: James L. Merrell. 10% freelance written. Monthly published by Christian Board of Publication of the Christian Church (Disciples of Christ). For ministers and church members, both young and older adults. Circ. 58,000. Pays month after publication. Publishes ms an average of 9 months after acceptance. Buys first serial rights. Photocopied and simultaneous submissions OK. Computer printout submissions acceptable; no dot-matrix. Submit seasonal material at least 6 months in advance. Reports in 1 month. Sample copy $1.25; free writer's guidelines for SAE and 1 first class stamp.
Nonfiction: Articles and meditations on religious themes, short pieces, and some humorous. No fiction. Buys 100 unsolicited mss/year. Length: 500-800 words. Pays $10-50.
Photos: Reviews 8x10 b&w glossy prints. Occasional b&w glossy prints, any size, used to illustrate articles. Occasional color. "We are looking for b&w photos of church activities—worship, prayer, dinners, etc." Pays $10-25; $35-100/cover. Pays for photos at end of month after acceptance.
Poetry: Uses 3-5 poems/issue. Traditional forms, blank verse, free verse and light verse. Length: 16 lines limit. Themes may be seasonal, historical, religious and occasionally humorous. Pays $3-20.
Tips: "We're looking for personality features about lay disciples, churches. Give a good summary of story idea in query. Queries on Christian values in television, radio, film and music desired. We use articles primarily from disciples, ministers and lay persons since our magazine is written to attract the denomination. We are barraged with features that mainly deal with subjects that don't interest our readers; fillers are more general, thus more easily placed. We work with more secular poets than writers and the poets write in religious themes for us."

DISCIPLESHIP JOURNAL, NavPress, a division of The Navigators, Box 6000, Colorado Srings CO 80934. (303)598-1212. Editor: Susan Maycinik. Managing Editor: Don Simpson. 85% freelance written. Works with a small number of new/unpublished writers each year. Bimonthly magazine of Christian discipleship. "The

mission of *Discipleship Journal* is to help people examine, understand, and practice the truths of the Bible, so that they may know Jesus Christ, become like Him, and labor for His Kingdom by gathering other men and women into the fellowship of His committed disciples." Circ. 80,000. Pays on publication. Publishes ms an average of 2 months after acceptance. Byline given. Offers kill fee. Buys first North American serial rights and second serial (reprint) rights. Submit seasonal/holiday material 6 months in advance. Simultaneous queries, and simultaneous and previously published submissions OK. Electronic submissions OK via IBM PC-compatible, but requires hard copy also. Computer printout submissions acceptable; no dot-matrix. Reports in 4 weeks on queries; 3 months on mss. Sample copy and writer's guidelines for 9x12 SAE and $1.24 postage.
Nonfiction: Book excerpts (rarely); how-to (grow in Christian faith and disciplines; help others grow as Christians; serve people in need; understand and apply the Bible); inspirational; interview/profile (of Christian leaders, focusing on discipleship); personal experience; and interpretation/application of the Bible. No personal testimony; humor; anything not directly related to Christian life and faith; politically partisan articles. Buys 85 mss/year. Query with published clips or send complete ms if under 1,000 words. Length: 750-3,000 words. Pays 2¢/word reprint; 7¢/word first rights. Pays the expenses of writers on assignment.
Tips: "Our articles are meaty, not fluffy (we turn down roughly 98% of unsolicited submissions, despite our using few solicited articles) and try to use similar approaches. Don't waste words. Polish before submitting."

ENGAGE/SOCIAL ACTION, 100 Maryland Ave. NE, Washington DC 20002. (202)488-5632. Editor: Lee Ranck. 2% freelance written. Monthly for "United Methodist clergy and lay people interested in in-depth analysis of social issues, with emphasis on the church's role or involvement in these issues." Circ. 5,500. May buy all rights. Pays on publication. Rights purchased vary with author and material. Photocopied submissions OK, but prefers original. Computer printout submissions acceptable; prefers letter-quality to dot-matrix. Returns rejected material in 4-5 weeks. Reports on material accepted for publication in several weeks. "Query to show that writer has expertise on a particular social issue, give credentials, and reflect a readable writing style." Free sample copy and writer's guidelines.
Nonfiction: "This is the social action publication of the United Methodist Church published by the denomination's General Board of Church and Society. Our publication tries to relate social issues to the church—what the church can do, is doing; why the church should be involved. We only accept articles relating to social issues, e.g., war, draft, peace, race relations, welfare, police/community relations, labor, population problems, drug and alcohol problems." No devotional, 'religious,' superficial material, highly technical articles, personal experiences or poetry. Buys 25-30 mss/year. Query or submit complete ms. Length: 2,000 words maximum. Pays $75-100. Sometimes pays the expenses of writers on assignment.
Tips: "Write on social issues, but not superficially; we're more interested in finding an expert who can write (e.g., on human rights, alcohol problems, peace issues) than a writer who attempts to research a complex issue."

EPIPHANY JOURNAL, Epiphany Press, Box 14727, San Francisco CA 94114. Editor: Philip Tolbert. 10% freelance written. Works with a small number of new/unpublished writers each year. Quarterly magazine covering religious topics for the contemplative Christian. Circ. 3,000. Pays on publication. Publishes ms an average of 6 months after acceptance. Byline given. Buys first serial rights and one-time rights. Submit seasonal/holiday material 6 months in advance. Simultaneous queries, and simultaneous and previously published submissions OK. Computer printout submissions OK; prefers letter-quality to dot-matrix. Reports in 1 month on queries; 2 months on mss. "Sample copy and writer's guidelines available for $5, which will be refunded with payment for your first article." Guidelines only for SAE and 1 first class stamp.
Nonfiction: Essays (applications of traditional patristic spirituality for the practicing Christian in the post-modern world and explorations of the embodiment of traditional Christian culture expressed through literature, craft, art and folklore); interviews with current Christian figures ("Interviews should be topical or issues oriented, not biographical."); and stories from the lives of the Saints and teachers of the Christian tradition. Buys 4-8 mss/year. Query or send complete ms. Length: 2,000-6,000 words. Pays 2¢/word ($100 maximum). Also book excerpts (from forthcoming or recently published spiritual or religious works). No poetry.
Columns/Departments: Book reviews (any current literature of interest to the Christian thinker). Buys 10-15 mss/year. Query or send complete ms. Length: 1,000-2,500 words. Pays 2¢/word ($30 maximum).
Tips: "Get to know our magazine, then send us a query letter or ask for an assignment suggestion. We prefer not to see first person/anecdotal accounts. The writer must have a clear grasp of Christian principles and not merely base their views on sentiment; they must be able to contrast these principles with the modern world view in a way that provides a radical critique of contemporary culture while maintaining a pastoral concern for souls. This perspective must be developed in a writer. The most frequent mistakes made by writers in completing an article for us are unclear thought due to poor grasp of principles, lack of penetration into the subject, lack of relevance to daily spiritual life and contemporary problems, and lack of grounding in the living tradition of orthodox Christianity."

THE EPISCOPALIAN, 1930 Chestnut St., Philadelphia PA 19103. (215)564-2010. Publisher: Richard Crawford. Managing Editor: Judy Mathe Foley. 60% freelance written. Works with a small number of new/unpublished writers each year. Monthly tabloid about the Episcopal Church for Episcopalians. Circ. 250,000. Pays on publication. Publishes ms an average of 2 months after acceptance. Byline given. Submit seasonal/holiday material 2 months in advance. Previously published submissions OK. Computer printout submissions acceptable; prefers letter-quality to dot-matrix. Reports in 1 month. Sample copy for 3 first class stamps.

Nonfiction: Inspirational, and interview/profile (of Episcopalians participating in church or community activities). "I like action stories about people doing things and solving problems." No personal experience articles. Buys 24 mss/year. Send complete ms. Length: 1,000-1,500 words. Pays $25-200. Sometimes pays expenses of writers on assignment.

Photos: Pays $10 for b&w glossy prints. Identification of subjects required. Buys one-time rights.

Tips: Likes quotes, photos, and active voice.

ETERNITY MAGAZINE, The Evangelical Monthly, Evangelical Ministries, Inc. 1716 Spruce St., Philadelphia PA 19103. (215)546-3696. Assistant Editor: Anita Palmer. A monthly magazine intended "to help readers apply God's Word to all areas of life today." Circ. 40,000. Pays on the 15th of the month previous to issue publication. Byline given. Offers $25-50 kill fee. Buys first North American serial rights. Submit seasonal/holiday material 6 months in advance. Computer printout submissions acceptable; prefers letter-quality to dot-matrix. Reports in 6 weeks. Sample copy $2; writer's guidelines for SAE and 1 first class stamp.

Nonfiction: General interest (the Christian in the culture); how-to (apply Scripture to problems); and interview/profile (well-known evangelicals). No fiction; no short, devotional fillers. Buys 20 mss/year. Query. Length: 500-1,500 words. Pays $35-150.

Poetry: Lois Sibley, poetry editor. Buys 10-12 poems/year. Submit maximum 3 poems. Length: 10-15 lines. Pays $20-40.

Tips: "For general articles, begin with an illustration, apply Scriptural principles to current problems/topics and include an application that will help readers. In poetry, we are looking for a good use of imagery, effectively controlled emotion, and words that elicit a sensory response—a memorable poem. And, the poem must be a good expression of biblical theology."

EVANGEL, Dept. of Christian Education, Free Methodist Headquarters, 901 College Ave., Winona Lake IN 46590. (219)267-7161. Editor: Vera Bethel. 100% freelance written. Weekly magazine; 8 pages. Audience is 65% female, 35% male; married, 25-31 years old, mostly city dwellers, high school graduates, mostly nonprofessional. Circ. 35,000. Pays on publication. Publishes ms an average of 1 year after acceptance. Buys simultaneous rights, second serial (reprint) rights or one-time rights. Submit seasonal/holiday material 3 months in advance. Computer printout submissions acceptable; no dot-matrix. Reports in 4 weeks. Sample copy and writer's guidelines for 6x9 SAE.

Nonfiction: Interview (with ordinary person who is doing something extraordinary in his community, in service to others); profile (of missionary or one from similar service profession who is contributing significantly to society); and personal experience (finding a solution to a problem common to young adults; coping with handicapped child, for instance, or with a neighborhood problem. Story of how God-given strength or insight saved a situation). Buys 100 mss/year. Submit complete ms. Length: 300-1,000 words. Pays $10-25.

Photos: Purchased with accompanying ms. Captions required. Send prints. Pays $5-10 for 8x10 b&w glossy prints; $2 for snapshots.

Fiction: Religious themes dealing with contemporary issues dealt with from a Christian frame of reference. Story must "go somewhere". Buys 50 mss/year. Submit complete ms. Length: 1,200-1,500 words. Pays $35-40.

Poetry: Free verse, haiku, light verse, traditional and religious. Buys 50 poems/year. Submit maximum 6 poems. Length: 4-24 lines. Pays $5.

Tips: "Seasonal material will get a second look (won't be rejected so easily) because we get so little. Write an attention grabbing lead followed by a body of article that says something worthwhile. Relate the lead to some of the universal needs of the reader—promise in that lead to help the reader in some way. Remember that everybody is interested most in himself. Lack of SASE brands author as a nonprofessional; I seldom even bother to read the script. If the writer doesn't want the script back, it probably has no value for me, either."

THE EVANGELICAL BEACON, 1515 E. 66th St., Minneapolis MN 55423. (612)866-3343. Editor: George Keck. 30% freelance written. Works with a small number of new/unpublished writers each year. Denominational magazine of the Evangelical Free Church of America—evangelical Protestant readership; published 17 titles/year (every third Monday, except for a 4 week interval, June-August). Pays on publication. Publishes ms an average of 6 months after acceptance. Rights purchased vary with author and material. Buys first rights or all rights, and some reprints. Computer printout submissions acceptable; prefers letter-quality to dot-matrix. Reports in 8-10 weeks. Sample copy and writer's guidelines for 75¢.

Nonfiction: Articles on the church, Christ-centered human interest and personal testimony articles, well researched on current issues of religious interest. Desires crisp, imaginative, original writing—not sermons on paper. Length: 250-2,000 words. Pays 3¢/word with extra payment on some articles, at discretion of editor.

Photos: Prefers 8x10 b&w photos. Pays $10 minimum.

Fiction: Not much fiction used, but will consider. Length: 100-1,500 words.

Poetry: Very little poetry used. Pays variable rate, $3.50 minimum.

Tips: "Articles need to be helpful to the average Christian—encouraging, challenging, instructive. Also needs material presenting reality of the Christian faith to nonChristians. Some tie-in with the Evangelical Free Church of America is helpful but not required."

EVANGELIZING TODAY'S CHILD, Child Evangelism Fellowship Inc., Warrenton MO 63383. (314)456-4321. Editor: Mrs. Elsie Lippy. 75% freelance written. Prefers to work with published/established writers. Bimonthly magazine; 72 pages. "Our purpose is to equip Christians to win the world's children to Christ and disciple them. Our readership is Sunday school teachers, Christian education leaders and children's workers in every phase of Christian ministry to children up to 12 years old." Circ. 28,000. Pays within 90 days of acceptance. Publishes ms an average of 6 months after acceptance. Byline given. Offers 30% kill fee if assigned. Buys first serial rights. Submit seasonal/holiday material 6 months in advance. Simultaneous queries and photocopied submissions OK. Computer printout submissions acceptable; no dot-matrix. Reports in 3 weeks on queries; 2 months on mss. Free sample copy; writer's guidelines with SASE.

Nonfiction: Unsolicited articles welcomed from writers with Christian education training or current experience in working with children. Buys 35 mss/year. Query. Length: 1,800-2,000. Pays 6-8¢/word.

Photos: Submissions of photos on speculation accepted. Needs photos of children or related subjects. Pays $20-25 for 8x10 b&w glossy prints; $75-100 for color transparencies.

FESTIVALS, (formerly *Family Festivals*), Resource Publications, Inc., Suite 290, 160 E. Virginia St., San Jose CA 95112. (408)286-8505. Editor: Kenneth Guentert. 60% freelance written. Works with a small number of new/unpublished writers each year. Bimonthly devoted to discovery-of-the sacred in ordinary life. Christian slant with openess to other religious and eultural traditions. Circ. 15,000. Pays 3 months after publication. Publishes ms an average of 9 months after acceptance. Byline given. Buys all rights. Submit seasonal/holiday material 9 months in advance. Electronic submissions OK via 8in CPM, but requires hard copy also. Simultaneous queries and simultaneous, photocopied and previously published submissions OK. Computer printout submissions acceptable. Reports in 6 weeks on queries; 2 months on mss. Sample copy for $3 with SAE and 2 first class stamps; writer's guidelines for #10 SAE with 1 first class stamp.

Nonfiction: Historical/nostalgic (memories of family customs), how-to articles on ritual or celebration, recipes and interview/profile (experts in ritual and celebration. Query. Length: 300 words. Pays $10.

Fiction: Religious (fables, parables and legends).

FUNDAMENTALIST JOURNAL, Old-Time Gospel Hour, Langhorne Plaza, Lynchburg VA 24514. (804)528-4112. Executive Editor: Jerry Falwell. Editor: Deborah Wade Huff. 40% freelance written. A Christian magazine (nonprofit organization) published monthly (July/August combined) covering "matters of interest to all Fundamentalists, providing discussion of divergent opinions on relevant issues; also human interest stories and news reports." Audience is 65% Baptist; 35% other denominations; 30% pastors; 70% other. Circ. 70,000. Pays on publication. Publishes ms an average of 8 months after acceptance. Byline given. Offers negotiable kill fee. Buys all rights; makes work-for-hire assignments. Submit seasonal/holiday material 6 months in advance. Previously published submissions OK. Computer printout submissions acceptable; prefers letter-quality to dot-matrix. Reports in 3 months. Free sample copy; writer's guidelines for SAE and 1 first class stamp.

Nonfiction: Earlene R. Goodwin, articles editor. Book excerpts; expose (government, communism, education); general interest; historical/nostalgic (regarding the Bible, Christianity, great Christians of old); inspirational, interview/profile; opinion, and personal experience. "Writing must be consistent with Fundamentalist doctrine. We do not want articles that are critical in naming leaders of churches or Christian organizations." Buys 77 mss/year. Query. Length: 800-2,500 words. Pays 10¢/printed word. Sometimes pays the expenses of writers on assignment.

Columns/Departments: Length: 300-2,000 words. Pays 10¢/printed word; $25-50 for book reviews.

Tips: "We are looking for more articles to encourage and support the Christian family. We will be asking writers to submit query first. News is usually by assignment; various articles of general interest to Fundamentalist Christian readers, perspective, profiles, missions articles, successful teaching ideas are most open to freelancers."

THE GEM, Churches of God, General Conference, Box 926, Findlay OH 45839. (419)424-1961. Editor: Marilyn Rayle Kern. 98% freelance written. Works with a small number of new/unpublished writers each year. "We are backlogged with submissions but still hope to find new submissions of high quality." Weekly magazine; adult and youth church school take-home paper. "Our readers expect to find true-to-life help for daily living as growing Christians." Circ. 7,500. Pays on publication. Byline given. Not copyrighted. Buys simultaneous rights, first serial rights or second serial (reprint) rights. Submit seasonal/holiday material 3 months in advance. Simultaneous, photocopied and previously published submissions OK. Electronic submissions acceptable via Kaypro 2, Perfect Writer or New Word. Computer printout submissions acceptable; prefers letter-quality to dot-matrix. Reports in 6 months. Sample copy and writer's guidelines for 4x9 SAE and 1 first class stamp (unless more than 1 copy).

Nonfiction: General interest, historical/nostalgic, humor, inspirational and personal experience. No preachy, judgmental articles, or use of quotes from other sources. Buys 50 mss/year. Send complete ms. Length: 600-1,600 words. Pays $10-15.

Fiction: Adventure, historical, humorous and religious. No mss which are preachy or inauthentic. Buys 50 mss/year. Send complete ms. Length: 1,000-1,600 words. Pays $10-15.

Fillers: Anecdotes and short humor. Buys 40/year. Length: 100-500 words. Pays $5-7.50.

Tips: "Humor, which does not put down people and leads the reader to understand a valuable lesson, is always in short supply."

GOOD NEWS, The Bimonthly Magazine For United Methodists, Box 165, Wilmore KY 40390. (606)858-4661. Editor: James V. Heidinger II. Executive Editor: James S. Robb. 20% freelance written. Works with a small number of new/unpublished writers each year. Bimonthly magazine for United Methodist lay people and pastors, primarily middle income; conservative and Biblical religious beliefs; broad range of political, social and cultural values. "We are the only evangelical magazine with the purpose of working within the United Methodist Church for Biblical reform and evangelical renewal." Circ. 19,000. Pays on acceptance. Publishes ms an average of 8 months after acceptance. Byline given. Buys first serial rights, simultaneous rights, and second serial (reprint) rights. Phone queries OK. Submit seasonal/holiday material 6 months in advance. Simultaneous submissions with noncompeting publications OK. Prefers original mss and not photocopies of reprinted material. Computer printout submissions acceptable. Reports in 3 months. Sample copy $1.50; free writer's guidelines.

Nonfiction: Historical (prominent people or churches from the Methodist/Evangelical United Brethren tradition); how-to (build faith, work in local church); humor (good taste); inspirational (related to Christian faith); personal experience (case histories of God at work in individual lives); and any contemporary issues as they relate to the Christian faith and/or the United Methodist Church. No sermons or secular material. Buys 25 mss/year. Query with a "brief description of the article, perhaps a skeleton outline. Show some enthusiasm about the article and writing (and research). Tell us something about yourself including whether you or the article has United Methodist tie-in. Send ms in care of associate editor." Length: 1,500-2,500 words. Pays 5-7¢/word, more on occasion for special assignments. Sometimes pays the expenses of writers on assignment.

Photos: Extra payment for photos with accompanying ms. Uses fine screen b&w prints. Total purchase price for ms includes payment for photos. Payment negotiable. Captions required.

Tips: "Writers must be either United Methodists themselves or intimately familiar with the mindset of our church members. Evangelical slant is a must for all articles, yet we are not fundamentalist or sentimental. We are now moving away from predictable testimony pieces (though there is still room for the fresh testimony which ties in with burning issues, especially when written by Methodists). What we are looking for now are 1,200 word, newspaper style sketches of vibrant, evangelically-oriented United Methodist churches. Photos are a must. We'll hire a pro if we need to. We also need personality profiles of dynamic, unusual United Methodists with accompanying professional quality photo (evidence of vital faith in subject is required)."

GOOD NEWS BROADCASTER, Box 82808, Lincoln NE 68501. (402)474-4567. Editor: Warren Wiersbe. 40% freelance written. Monthly interdenominational magazine for adults from 17 years of age and up. Circ. 150,000. Pays on acceptance. Buys first serial rights or first North American serial rights, or occasionally second serial (reprint) rights. Submit seasonal material at least 1 year in advance. Computer printout submissions acceptable if double spaced; no dot-matrix. Reports in 5 weeks. Sample copy $1; writer's guidelines with SASE.

Nonfiction: Managing Editor, Norman A. Olson. Articles which will help the reader learn and apply Christian Biblical principles to his life from the writer's or the subject's own experience. Writers are required "to affirm agreement with our doctrinal statement. We are especially looking for true, personal experience 'salvation,' church, children's ages 4-10, missions, 'youth' (17 years and over), 'parents', 'how to live the Christian life' articles, reports and interviews regarding major and interesting happenings and people in fundamental, evangelical Christian circles." Nothing rambling or sugary sweet, or without Biblical basis. Details or statistics should be authentic and verifiable. Style should be conservative but concise. Prefers that Scripture references be from the *New American Standard Bible* or the *Authorized Version* or the *New Scofield Reference Bible.* Buys approximately 100 mss/year. Length: 1,500 words maximum. Pays 4-10¢/word. "When you can get us to assign an article to you, we pay nearer the maximum. More manuscripts are now rejected if unaccompanied by photos." Sometimes pays expenses of writers on assignment.

Photos: Pays $25 maximum for b&w glossies; $75 maximum for color transparencies. Photos paid on publication.

Tips: "The basic purpose of the magazine is to explain the Bible and how it is relevant to life because we believe this will accomplish one of two things—to present Christ as Saviour to the lost or to promote the spiritual growth of believers, so don't ignore our primary purposes when writing for us. Nonfiction should be Biblical and timely; at the least Biblical in principle. Use illustrations of your own experiences or of someone else's when God solved a problem similar to the reader's. Be so specific that the meanings and significance will be crystal clear to all readers."

GOSPEL CARRIER, Messenger Publishing House, Box 850, Joplin MO 64802. (417)624-7050. Editor-in-Chief: Roy M. Chappell, D.D. 75% freelance written. Prefers to work with published/established writers; works with a small number of new/unpublished writers each year. Quarterly publication in weekly parts; 104 pages. Denominational Sunday school take-home paper for adults, ages 20 through retirement. Circ. 3,500. Pays quarterly. Publishes ms an average of 1 year after acceptance. Byline given. Buys simultaneous rights, second serial (reprint) rights and one-time rights. Submit seasonal/holiday material 1 year in advance. Simultaneous, photocopied, and previously published submissions OK. Reports in 3 months. Sample copy and writer's guidelines for 50¢ and SAE with 1 first class stamp.
Nonfiction: Historical (related to great events in the history of the church); informational (may explain the meaning of a Bible passage or a Christian concept); inspirational (must make Christian point); nostalgia (religious significance); and personal experience (Christian concept). No puzzles, poems and filler material.
Fiction: Adventure, historical, romance and religious. Must have Christian significance. Buys 13-20 mss/issue. Submit complete ms. Length: 1,500-1,800 words. Pays 1¢/word.
Tips: "The most frequent mistake made by writers in completing an article for us is that they forget we are a Christian publication and will not publish articles that have mentioned subjects we do not accept in our guidelines."

GUIDEPOSTS MAGAZINE, 747 3rd Ave., New York NY 10017. Editor: Van Varner. 30% freelance written. "Works with a small number of new/unpublished writers each year, because we still read all unsolicited manuscripts. *Guideposts* is an inspirational monthly magazine for all faiths in which men and women from all walks of life tell how they overcame obstacles, rose above failures, met sorrow, learned to master themselves, and became more effective people through the direct application of the religious principles by which they live." Publishes ms an average of "indefinite" number of months after acceptance. Pays 25% kill fee for assigned articles. Byline given. "Most of our stories are first person ghosted articles, so the author would not get a byline unless it was his/her story." Buys all rights and second serial (reprint) rights. Computer printout submissions acceptable; prefers letter-quality to dot-matrix.
Nonfiction and Fillers: Articles and features should be written in simple, anecdotal style with an emphasis on human interest. Short mss of approximately 250-750 words (pays $25-100) would be considered for such features as Quiet People and general one-page stories. Full-length mss, 750-1,500 words pays $200-300. All mss should be typed, double-spaced and accompanied by a stamped, self-addressed envelope. Annually awards scholarships to high school juniors and seniors in writing contest. Buys 40-60 unsolicited mss/year. Pays expenses of writers on assignment.
Tips: "Study the magazine before you try to write for it. The freelancer would have the best chance of breaking in by aiming for a one-page or maybe two-page article. That would be very short, say two and a half pages of typescript, but in a small magazine such things are very welcome. A sensitively written anecdote that could provide us with an additional title is extremely useful. And they are much easier to just sit down and write than to have to go through the process of preparing a query. They should be warm, well-written, intelligent and upbeat. We like personal narratives that are true and have some universal relevance, but the religious element does not have to be hammered home with a sledge hammer. A writer succeeds with us if he or she can write a true article in short-story form with scenes, drama, tension and a resolution of the problem presented." Address short items to Edward Pitoniak.

HICALL, Gospel Publishing House, 1445 Boonville Ave., Springfield MO 65802. (417)862-2781, ext. 5484. Editor: Jennifer J. Eller. 100% freelance written. Assemblies of God (denominational) weekly magazine of Christian fiction and articles for church-oriented teenagers, 12-17. Circ. 120,000. Pays on acceptance. Publishes ms an average of 6 months after acceptance. Byline given. Buys first North American serial rights, one-time rights, simultaneous rights, and second serial (reprint) rights. Submit seasonal/holiday material 1 year in advance. Simultaneous queries, and simultaneous, photocopied, and previously published submissions OK. Computer printout submissions acceptable; prefers letter-quality to dot-matrix. Reports in 6 weeks. Sample copy for 5x7 SAE and 1 first class stamp; writer's guidelines for SAE.
Nonfiction: Book excerpts; historical; general interest; how-to (deal with various life problems); humor; inspirational; and personal experience. Buys 80-100 mss/year. Send complete ms. Length: 500-2,000 words. Pays 2-3¢/word.
Photos: Photos purchased with or without accompanying ms. Pays $25/8x10 b&w glossy print; $30/35mm.
Fiction: Adventure, humorous, mystery, romance, suspense, western and religious. Buys 80-100 mss/year. Send complete ms. Length: 500-2,000 words. Pays 2-3¢/word.
Poetry: Free verse, light verse and traditional. Buys 30 poems/year. Length: 10-30 lines. Pays 3¢/word; 25¢/line.
Fillers: Clippings, jokes, gags, anecdotes, short humor and newsbreaks. Buys 30/year. Pays 2-3¢/word.

INDIAN LIFE, Intertribal Christian Communications, Box 3765, Station B, Winnipeg, Manitoba R2W 3R6 Canada. (204)661-9333. Editor: George McPeek. 70% freelance written. Bimonthly magazine of Christian experience from a native American (Indian) point of view for readers in 30 different denominations and missions. Circ. 12,000. Pays on publication. Publishes ms an average of 4 months after acceptance. Byline given. Buys first serial rights and second serial (reprint) rights. Submit seasonal/holiday material 4 months in advance. Photocopied and previously published submissions OK. Computer printout submissions acceptable; no dot-matrix. IRCs outside Canada. Reports in 3 weeks on queries; 6 weeks on mss. Sample copy for 9x12 SAE and $1 Canadian postage; writer's guidelines for $1 with business size SAE and 39¢ Canadian postage.
Nonfiction: Historical/nostalgic (with a positive approach); inspirational; interview/profile (of Indian Christian personalities); personal experience; photo feature; general news (showing Indian achievements); and human interest (wholesome, but not necessarily religious). No political, sexually suggestive, or negative articles on personalities, groups or points of view. "Keep your writing style simple, but not childish. Watch those multi-syllable words and lengthy sentences. Paragraphs should be short." Buys 12 mss/year. Query with published clips. Length: 500-1,500 words. Pays $20-45; less for news items.
Photos: State availability of photos. Pays $3-5 for b&w contact sheets; $10-20 for 35mm slides or other color transparencies; $5-10 for 5x7 b&w prints. Captions, model releases, and identification of subjects required. Buys one-time rights.
Fiction: Adventure, confession, historical, religious and legends with Christian applications. No explicit sex or negative themes. Buys 4-6 mss/year. Query with published clips. Length: 500-1,200 words. Pays $20-40.
Fillers: Clippings, jokes, anecdotes, short humor and newsbreaks. Buys 25-30/year. Length: 50-200 words. Pays $3-10.
Tips: "First person stories must be verifiable with references (including one from pastor or minister) attached. Most material is written by Indian people, but some articles by nonIndians are accepted. Maintain an Indian point of view. We seek to build a positive self-image, provide culturally relevant material and serve as a voice for the Indian church."

INTERLIT, David C. Cook Foundation, Cook Square, Elgin IL 60120. (312)741-2400, ext. 322. Editor-in-Chief: Gladys J. Peterson. 90% freelance written on assignment. Works with a small number of new/unpublished writers each year. Quarterly journal; 24 pages. Emphasizes sharpening skills in Christian communications and journalism. Especially for editors, publishers, and writers in the Third World (developing countries). Also goes to missionaries, broadcasters and educational personnel in the U.S. Circ. 9,000. Pays on acceptance. Publishes ms an average of 6 months after acceptance. Buys all rights. Photocopied submissions OK. Computer printout submissions acceptable; prefers letter-quality to dot-matrix. Reports in 2 weeks. Free sample copy.
Nonfiction: Technical and how-to articles about communications, media and literacy. "Please study publication and query before submitting manuscripts." Also photo features. Buys 7 mss/issue, mostly on assignment. Length: 500-1,500 words. Pays 6¢/word.
Photos: Purchased with accompanying ms only. Uses b&w. Query or send prints. Captions required.

INTERNATIONAL CHRISTIAN NEWS, ICN, International Christian News, Box 489, Rush Springs OK 73082. (405)476-2383. Editor: Joan Hash Cox. Managing Editor: Joanna Watts. 60% freelance written. "We try to treat unpublished and published writers equally." Monthly Christian tabloid providing informative and entertaining Christian news. "We have a good variety of entertaining and informational material that appeals to the whole family. We desire our newspaper to be a positive, people-pleasing newspaper that will give the whole family that uplifting feeling a Christian should have in life." Circ. 2,500. Pays on publication. Publishes ms an average of 6 months after acceptance. Byline given. Buys first serial rights. Submit seasonal/holiday material 4 months in advance. Photocopied and previously published submissions OK; simultaneous submissions OK "only if we are informed." Computer printout submissions acceptable; no dot-matrix. Reports in 6 weeks. Sample copy $1.50; writer's guidelines for SASE.
Nonfiction: Book excerpts (religion); expose (anything considered in opposition to Christian principles); historical/nostalgic ("we thrive on spiritual heritage and nostalgia"); how-to (a few); humor (none offensive to any person); inspirational; interview/profile (if the person has influence on the Christian believers); opinion (some will be considered); personal experience ("we thrive on good Christian experience"); photo essays (picturesque churches from around the world with a paragraph description); travel; Bible notes found in old Bibles or books, helpful hints, crosswords that teach the Bible and recipes. "We will have an annual God & Country special patriotic issue every July 4th. Our Easter and Christmas issues will always be special." No fiction, except children's stories that are used to reach a truth about the Bible or life. Buys 100 mss/year. Send complete ms. Length: 500-2,000 words. Pays $10-100; front page articles with photo $100.
Photos: Tammy Sherylanne Cox, photo editor. State availability of photos with ms. Pays $10-25 for 3x5 or 5x7 b&w prints. Captions, model releases, and identification of subjects required. Buys one-time rights.
Columns/Departments: All material must touch on Christian principles except Recipes and Travel, although we prefer it to be somewhere that would interest a Christian. How-To; Letters to the Editor; Teen Scene and Care Kids stories, poems, puzzles, letters, dot to dot; Flaming Thought; Opinion; Sunday Dinner Stories;

and Spiritual Heritage. Personal experiences and inspirational are the backbone articles of this publication. Query with published clips. Buys 80 mss/year. Length: 500-1,500 words. Pays $10-100.

Fiction: Religious (for children only). Buys 10 mss/year. Send complete ms. Length: 500-750 words. Pays $10-25.

Poetry: Free verse and traditional. No nonsense or erotic poetry. Buys 120-144 poems/year. Submit maximum 5 poems. Length: 4-30 lines. Pays 10¢/word.

Fillers: Anecdotes, short humor and newsbreaks (all pertaining to religion). Buys 50/year. Length: 250-500 words. Pays $5-15.

Editor's note: As we go to press, we have just learned that *International Christian News* has ceased publication.

KEEPING POSTED, Union of American Hebrew Congregations, 838 5th Ave., New York NY 10021. (212)249-0100. Editor: Aron Hurt-Manheimer. Managing Editor: Joy Weinberg. 50% freelance written. Magazine published 6 times/year on Jewish issues. "*Keeping Posted* is published by the UAHC, a nonprofit Jewish organization, and is distributed to teachers and children in reform Jewish religious schools, adult education, and other interested readers." Pays on publication. Publishes ms an average of 3 months after acceptance. Byline given. Offers negotiable kill fee. Buys first North American serial rights. Photocopied submissions OK. Computer printout submissions acceptable; prefers letter-quality to dot-matrix. Reports in 2 weeks on queries; 3 weeks on mss. Sample copy $1.

Nonfiction: Book excerpts, expose, general interest, historical/nostalgic, inspirational, interview/profile, opinion, personal experience. Buys 24 mss/year. Send complete ms. Length: 750-2,000 words. Pays $100-300. Sometimes pays expenses of writers on assignment.

Photos: Send photo with ms. Pays $25-75. Identification of subjects required. Buys one-time rights.

Fiction: Ethnic, humorous, mainstream and religious. Buys 6 mss/year. Send complete ms. Length: 750-2,000 words. Pays $100-200.

Poetry: Free verse. Buys 2 poems/year.

LIGHT AND LIFE, Free Methodist Church of North America, 901 College Ave., Winona Lake IN 46590. Managing Editor: Lyn Cryderman. 35% freelance written. Works with a small number of new/unpublished writers each year. Monthly magazine; 36 pages. Emphasizes evangelical Christianity with Wesleyan slant for a cross section of adults. Circ. 45,000. Pays on publication. Publishes ms an average of 6 months after acceptance. Byline given. Prefers first serial rights; sometimes buys second serial (reprint) rights. Submit seasonal/holiday material 6 months in advance. Previously published submissions OK. Computer printout submissions acceptable; no dot-matrix. Reports in 6 weeks. Sample copy $1.50; writer's guidelines for SASE.

Nonfiction: "Each issue includes a mini-theme (two or three articles addressing contemporary topics such as entertainment media, personal relationships, Christians as citizens), so freelancers should request our schedule of mini-theme topics. We also need fresh, upbeat articles showing the average layperson how to be Christ-like at home, work and play. Never submit anything longer than 2,500 words." Submit complete ms. Buys 70-80 unsolicited ms/year. Pays 4¢/word. Sometimes pays expenses of writers on assignment.

Photos: Purchased without accompanying ms. Send prints. Pays $5-35 for b&w photos. Offers additional payment for photos accepted with accompanying ms.

LIGUORIAN, Liguori MO 63057. Editor: Rev. Norman Muckerman. 50% freelance written. Prefers to work with published/established writers; works with a small number of new/unpublished writers each year. Monthly. For families with Catholic religious convictions. Circ. 525,000. Pays on acceptance. Publishes ms an average of 3 months after acceptance. Byline given "except on short fillers and jokes." Buys all rights but will reassign rights to author *after* publication upon written request. Submit seasonal material 6 months in advance. Electronic submissions OK on disk compatible with TRS 80 Model III, "but we ask contributors to send printout first, disk upon acceptance." Computer printout submissions acceptable; no dot-matrix. Reports in 8 weeks.

Nonfiction: "Pastoral, practical and personal approach to the problems and challenges of people today. No travelogue approach or unresearched ventures into controversial areas. Also, no material found in secular publications—fad subjects that already get enough press, pop psychology, negative or put-down articles." Recent article example: "The Silent Scream Is Being Heard" (January 1986). Buys 60 unsolicited mss/year. Length: 400-2,000 words. Pays 7-10¢/word. Sometimes pays expenses of writers on assignment.

Photos: Photos purchased with mss. Reviews b&w glossy prints.

LIVE, 1445 Boonville Ave., Springfield MO 65802. (417)862-2781. Editor: Kenneth D. Barney. 100% freelance written. Weekly. For adults in Assemblies of God Sunday schools. Circ. 200,000. Pays on acceptance. Publishes ms an average of 1 year after acceptance. Not copyrighted. Submit seasonal material 4 months in advance; do not mention Santa Claus, Halloween or Easter bunnies. Computer printout submissions acceptable; prefers letter-quality to dot-matrix. Reports on material within 6 weeks. Free sample copy and writer's guidelines for SASE. Letters without SASE will not be answered.

Nonfiction: Articles with reader appeal emphasizing some phase of Christian living presented in a down-to-earth manner. Biography or missionary material using fiction techniques. Historical, scientific or nature material with spiritual lesson. "Be accurate in detail and factual material. Writing for Christian publications is a ministry. The spiritual emphasis must be an integral part of your material." Prefers not to see material on highly controversial subjects. Buys about 120 mss/year. Length: 1,000-1,600 words. Pays 3¢/word for first serial rights; 2¢/word for second serial (reprint) rights, according to the value of the material and the amount of editorial work necessary. "Please do not send large numbers of articles at one time."

Photos: Color photos or transparencies purchased with mss, or on assignment. Pay open.

Fiction: "Present believable characters working out their problems according to Bible principles; in other words, present Christianity in action without being preachy. We use very few serials, but we will consider three to four-part stories if each part conforms to average word length for short stories. Each part must contain a spiritual emphasis and have enough suspense to carry the reader's interest from one week to the next. Stories should be true to life but not what we would feel is bad to set before the reader as a pattern for living. Stories should not put parents, teachers, ministers or other Christian workers in a bad light. Setting, plot and action should be realistic, with strong motivation. Characterize so that the people will live in your story. Construct your plot carefully so that each incident moves naturally and sensibly toward crisis and conclusion. An element of conflict is necessary in fiction. Short stories should be written from one viewpoint only. We do not accept fiction based on incidents in the Bible." Length: 1,200-1,600 words. Pays 3¢/word for first serial rights; 2¢/word for second serial (reprint) rights. "Please do not send large numbers of articles at one time."

Poetry: Traditional, free and blank verse. Length: 12-20 lines. "Please do not send large numbers of poems at one time." Pays 20¢/line.

Fillers: Brief and purposeful, usually containing an anecdote, and always with a strong evangelical emphasis. Length: 200-600 words.

‡LIVING WITH TEENAGERS, Baptist Sunday School Board, 127 9th Ave. N, Nashville TN 37234. (615)251-2273. Editor: Jimmy Hester. 50% freelance written. Works with a small number of new/unpublished writers each year. Quarterly magazine about teenagers for Baptist parents of teenagers. Circ. 40,000. Pays within 2 months of acceptance. Publishes ms an average of 15 months after acceptance. Buys all rights. Submit seasonal material 1 year in advance. Computer printout submissions acceptable. Reports in 2 months. Publishes ms an average of 15 months after acceptance. Send 75¢ postage for a sample copy.

Nonfiction: "We are looking for a unique Christian element. We want a genuine insight into the teen/parent relationships." General interest (on communication, emotional problems, growing up, drugs and alcohol, leisure, sex education, spiritual growth, working teens and parents, money, family relationships, and church relationships); inspirational; and personal experience. Buys 60 unsolicited mss/year. Query with clips of previously published work. Length: 600-2,000 words. Pays 5¢/published word.

Fiction: Humorous and religious, but must relate to parent/teen relationship. "No stories from the teen's point of view." Buys 2 mss/issue. Query with clips of previously published work. Length: 600-2,000 words. Pays 5¢/published word.

Poetry: Free verse, light verse, traditional and devotional inspirational; all must relate to parent/teen relationship. Buys 3 mss/issue. Submit 5 poems maximum. Length: 33 characters maximum. Pays $2.10 plus $1.25/line for 1-7 lines; $5.40 plus 75¢/line for 8 lines minimum.

Tips: "A writer can meet our needs if they have something to say to parents of teenagers, concerning an issue the parents are confronting with the teenager."

THE LOOKOUT, 8121 Hamilton Ave., Cincinnati OH 45231. (513)931-4050. Editor: Mark A. Taylor. 50-60% freelance written. Eager to work with new/unpublished writers. Weekly for the adult and young adult of Sunday morning Bible school. Pays on acceptance. Publishes ms an average of 4 months after acceptance. Byline given. Buys first serial rights, one-time rights, second serial (reprint) rights, or simultaneous rights. Simultaneous submissions OK. Computer printout submissions acceptable; prefers letter-quality to dot-matrix. Reports in 2 months. Sample copy and writer's guidelines 50¢.

Nonfiction: "Seeks stories about real people or Sunday school classes; items that shed Biblical light on matters of contemporary controversy; and items that motivate, that lead the reader to ask, 'Why shouldn't I try that?' or 'Why couldn't our Sunday school class accomplish this?' Articles should tell how real people are involved for Christ. In choosing topics, *The Lookout* considers timeliness, the church and national calendar, and the ability of the material to fit the above guidelines. Tell us about ideas that are working in your Sunday school and in the lives of its members. Remember to aim at laymen." Submit complete ms. Length: 1,200-1,800 words. Pays 4-6¢/word. We also use inspirational short pieces. "About 600-800 words is a good length for these. Relate an incident that illustrates a point without preaching." Pays 4-5¢/word.

Fiction: "A short story is printed in most issues; it is usually between 1,200-1,800 words long and should be as true to life as possible while remaining inspirational and helpful. Use familiar settings and situations. Most often we use stories with a Christian slant."

Photos: Reviews b&w prints, 4x6 or larger. Pays $5-25. Pays $50-150 for color transparencies for covers and inside use. Needs photos of people, especially adults in a variety of settings.

THE LUTHERAN, 2900 Queen Lane, Philadelphia PA 19129. (215)438-6580. Editor: Edgar R. Trexler. 25% freelance written. Prefers to work with published/established writers. General interest magazine of the Lutheran Church in America published twice monthly, except single issues in July, August and December. Pays on acceptance. Publishes ms an average of 6 months after acceptance. "We need informative, detailed query letters. We also accept manuscripts on speculation only, and we prefer not to encourage an abundance of query letters." Buys one-time rights or first North American serial rights. Electronic submissions OK via IBM PC, but requires hard copy also. Computer printout submissions acceptable; prefers letter-quality to dot-matrix. Free sample copy and writer's guidelines.
Nonfiction: Popularly written material about human concerns with reference to the Christian faith. "We are especially interested in articles in four main fields: Christian ideology; personal religious life, social responsibilities; Church at work; and human interest stories about Lutheran people in whom considerable numbers of other people are likely to be interested. Write primarily to convey information rather than opinions. Every article should be based on a reasonable amount of research or should explore some source of information not readily available. Most readers are grateful for simplicity of style. Sentences should be straightforward with a minimum of dependent clauses and prepositional phrases." Length: 500-2,000 words. Pays $100-300.
Photos: Buys photos submitted with ms. Reviews good 8x10 glossy prints. Pays $15-25. Also color for cover use. Pays up to $300.
Tips: "A great need exists for personal experience writing that is creative, relevant to these times and written for a wide audience."

LUTHERAN FORUM, 308 W. 46th St., New York NY 10036-3894. (212)757-1292. Editor: Glenn C. Stone. 25% freelance written. Works with a small number of new/unpublished writers each year. Quarterly magazine; 40 pages. For church leadership, clerical and lay. Circ. 4,500. Pays on publication. Publishes ms an average of 3 months after acceptance. Byline given. Rights purchased vary with author and material; buys all rights, first North American serial rights, second serial (reprint) rights, and simultaneous rights. Will consider photocopied and simultaneous submissions. Computer printout submissions acceptable; prefers letter-quality to dot-matrix. Reports in 9 weeks. Sample copy $1.50.
Nonfiction: Articles about important issues and developments in the church's institutional life and in its cultural/social setting. Special interest in articles on the Christian's life in secular vocations. No purely devotional/inspirational material. Buys 8-10 mss/year. Query or submit complete ms. Length: 1,000-3,000 words. Payment varies; $30 minimum. Informational, how-to, interview, profile, think articles and expose. Length: 500-3,000 words. Pays $25-75.
Photos: Purchased with ms and only with captions. Prefers 4x5 prints. Pays $15 minimum.

THE LUTHERAN JOURNAL, 7317 Cahill Rd., Edina MN 55435. Editor: Rev. Armin U. Deye. Quarterly magazine; 32 pages. Family magazine for Lutheran Church members, middle age and older. Circ. 136,000. Pays on publication. Byline given. Will consider photocopied and simultaneous submissions. Reports in 2 months. Free sample copy.
Nonfiction: Inspirational, religious, human interest and historical articles. Interesting or unusual church projects. Informational, how-to, personal experience, interview, humor and think articles. Buys 12-15 mss/year. Submit complete ms. Length: 1,500 words maximum; occasionally 2,000 words. Pays 1-3¢/word.
Photos: B&w and color photos purchased with accompanying ms. Captions required. Payment varies.
Fiction: Mainstream, religious and historical fiction. Must be suitable for church distribution. Length: 2,000 words maximum. Pays 1-1½¢/word.
Poetry: Traditional poetry, blank verse and free verse, related to subject matter.

THE LUTHERAN STANDARD, 426 S. 5th St., Box 1209, Minneapolis MN 55440. (612)330-3300. Editor: Rev. Lowell G. Almen. 30% freelance written. "We look for manuscripts that meet the needs of our readers and do not really draw practical distinctions between new and established writers." Semimonthly. For families in congregations of the American Lutheran Church. Circ. 565,000. Pays on acceptance. Publishes ms an average of 9 months after acceptance. Byline given. Usually buys one-time rights. Computer printout submissions acceptable; prefers letter-quality to dot-matrix. Reports in 3 weeks. Free sample copy.
Nonfiction: Inspirational articles, especially about members of the American Lutheran Church who are practicing their faith in noteworthy ways, or congregations with unusual programs. Articles "should be written in language clearly understandable to persons with a mid-high school reading ability." Also publishes articles that discuss current social issues and problems (crime, family life, divorce, etc.) in terms of Christian involvement and solutions. No poetry. Buys 30-50 mss/year. Query. Length: limit 1,200 words. Pays 10¢/word. Sometimes pays the expenses of writers on assignment.
Tips: "We are interested in personal experience pieces with a strong first person approach. The manuscript may be on a religious and social issue, but with evident human interest using personal anecdotes and illustrations. How has an individual faced a serious problem and overcome it? How has faith made a difference in a person's life? We prefer letters that clearly describe the proposed project. Excerpts from the project or other samples of the author's work are helpful in determining whether we are interested in dealing with an author. We

would appreciate it if more freelance writers seemed to have a sense of who our readers are and an awareness of the kinds of manuscripts we in fact publish.''

LUTHERAN WOMEN, 2900 Queen Ln., Philadelphia PA 19129. Editor: Terry Schutz. 20% freelance written. Published 10 times/year. Circ. 35,000. Publishes ms 4-12 months after acceptance. Buys first North American serial rights and second serial (reprint) rights, and simultaneous rights. Prefers to see mss 6 months ahead of issue, at beginning of planning stage; can consider up to 3 months before publication. Computer printout submissions acceptable; no dot-matrix. Reports in 2 months. Sample copy 75¢.
Nonfiction: Anything of interest to mothers—young or old—professional or other working women related to the contemporary expression of Christian faith in daily life, community action and international concerns. Family publication standards. No recipes or housekeeping hints. Length: 1,500-2,000 words. Some shorter pieces accepted. Pays up to $50 for full length ms with photos.
Photos: Purchased mostly with mss. Should be clear, sharp b&w.
Fiction: Should show deepening of insight; story expressing new understanding in faith; story of human courage, self-giving and building up of community. Length: 2,000 words. Pays $30-40.
Poetry: Very little is used. ''The biggest taboo for us is sentimentality. We are limited to family magazine type contributions regarding range of vocabulary, but we don't want almanac type poetry.'' No limit on number of lines. Pays $20-35/poem.

LUTHERANS IN STEP, Division of Service to Military Personnel/LCUSA, Suite 300, 122 C St. NW, Washington DC 20001. (202)738-7501. Editor: Bertram C. Gilbert. 15% freelance written. Works with a small number of new/unpublished writers each year. Informational/inspirational paper for Lutheran military people, published 5 times/year. ''Our slant is church news and commentary for pastors to send to their members in the service.'' Circ. 40,000. Publishes ms an average of 6 months after acceptance. Byline given. Buys first serial rights. Submit seasonal/holiday material 9 months in advance. Photocopied submissions OK. Computer printout submissions acceptable; no dot-matrix. Reports in 3 weeks. Free sample copy and writer's guidelines.
Nonfiction: How-to, humor, inspirational, interview/profile, personal experience and travel. ''We need articles on subjects of interest to or about young soldiers, sailors and air personnel which relate to the Christian faith or to our particular denomination. Humor and breeziness are desirable. Willingness to express simple faith concepts in a new or double-take-causing way makes us happy.'' No items that are negative about the military experience or not tied to religion in some way. Buys 10 mss/year. Query. Length: 500-1,000 words. Pays $30-50.
Photos: State availability of photos with query. Pays $25 for 6x9 b&w prints. Captions, model releases, and identification of subjects required. Buys one-time rights.
Tips: ''Authors should not send manuscripts but should send concepts. We are looking for budding writers who know the military scene well enough to make reference to that in up-to-date terms. We are not interested in the fame of the authors so consider ourselves a good place for a novice to get started. In fact, several of ours have become quite successful.''

MARRIAGE & FAMILY LIVING, St. Meinrad IN 47577. (812)357-8011. Managing Editor: Kass Dotterweich. 50% freelance written. Monthly magazine. Circ. 40,000. Pays on acceptance. Byline given. Buys first international serial rights, first book reprint option, and control of other reprint rights. Query. Computer printout submissions acceptable; prefers letter-quality to dot-matrix. Reports in 6 weeks. Sample copy $1.
Nonfiction: Articles which support Christian couples and parents and deepens and awakens a conviction of God's presence in their lives: personal essays relating amusing, heartwarming or insightful incidents which reflect the rich human side of marriage and family life. Length: 2,500 words maximum. Pays 7¢/word. Pays expenses of writers on assignment.
Photos: Attention, art director. Reviews 8x10 b&w glossy prints and color transparencies or 35mm slides (vertical preferred). Pays $250/4-color cover or center spread photo. Uses approximately 6-8 photos (b&w/color) and illustrations inside. Pays variable rate on publication. Photos of couples, families and individuals especially desirable. Model releases required.
Poetry: Any style and length. Pays $15 on publication.
Tips: Query with a brief outline of article and opening paragraphs.

MARYKNOLL MAGAZINE, Maryknoll Fathers, Maryknoll NY 10545. (914)941-7590. Editor: Moises Sandoval. Managing Editor: Frank Maurovich. ''We are backlogged with submissions and prefer not to receive unsolicited submissions at this time.''

‡MENNONITE BRETHREN HERALD, 3-169 Riverton Ave., Winnipeg, Manitoba R2L 2E5 Canada. Contact: Editor. 25% freelance written. Prefers to work with published/established writers. Family publication ''read mainly by people of the Mennonite faith, reaching a wide cross-section of professional and occupational groups, but also including many homemakers. Readership includes people from both urban and rural communities.'' Biweekly. Circ. 12,500. Pays on publication. Publishes ms an average of 4 months after accept-

ance. Not copyrighted. Byline given. Electronic submissions OK via IBM, but requires hard copy also. Sample copy 75¢. Reports in 2 months. SAE and IRCs.
Nonfiction: Articles with a Christian family orientation; youth directed, Christian faith and life, and current issues. Wants articles critiquing the values of a secular society, attempting to relate Christian living to the practical situations of daily living; showing how people have related their faith to their vocations. 1,500 words. Pays $25-40. Pays the expenses of writers on assignment.
Photos: Photos purchased with mss; pays $5.

‡THE MESSENGER OF THE SACRED HEART, 661 Greenwood Ave., Toronto, Ontario M4J 4B3 Canada. Editor: Rev. F.J. Power, S.J. For "adult Catholics in Canada and the U.S. who are members of the Apostleship of Prayer." 20% freelance written. Monthly. Circ. 16,000. Buys first rights only. Byline given. Pays on acceptance. Submit seasonal material 3 months in advance. Computer printout submissions acceptable; prefers letter-quality to dot-matrix. Reports in 1 month. SAE and IRCs. Sample copy $1.
Nonfiction: Mary Pujolas, department editor. "Articles on the Apostleship of Prayer and on all aspects of Christian living." Current events and social problems that have a bearing on Catholic life, family life, Catholic relations with nonCatholics, personal problems, the liturgy, prayer and devotion to the Sacred Heart. Material should be written in a popular, nonpious style. "We are not interested in column material." Buys 12 mss/year. Unsolicited manuscripts, unaccompanied by return postage, will not be returned. Length: 1,800-2,000 words. Pays 2¢ word.
Fiction: Mary Pujolas, department editor. Wants fiction which reflects the lives, problems and preoccupations of reading audience. "Short stories that make their point through plot and characters." Length: 1,800-2,000 words. Pays 2¢/word.

MESSENGER OF ST. ANTHONY, Prov. Pad. F.M.C. Editore, Basilica del Santo, 35123 Padova, Italy. (049)664-322. Editor: G. Panteghini. 20% freelance written. Monthly magazine covering family, social and religious issues with a Christian outlook. Circ. 20,000. Pays on publication. Publishes ms an average of 1 year after acceptance. Byline given. Offers 30% kill fee. Buys first serial rights and second serial (reprint) rights. Submit seasonal/holiday material 4 months in advance. Simultaneous queries, and simultaneous and photocopied submissions OK. Electronic submissions acceptable via IBM 6250 BPI and 1800 BPI, 2 density memo, records-tapes unlocked, but requires hard copy also. Computer printout submissions acceptable; prefers letter-quality to dot-matrix. Reports in 1 month on queries; 6 weeks on mss. Free sample copy and writer's guidelines.
Nonfiction: Historical/nostalgic, humor, inspirational, personal experience, photo feature and travel. No sexist articles. Buys 60 mss/year. Query. Length: 1,000-1,200 words. Pays $60-130.
Photos: Prefers 10x14 or 13x18 cm photos. Send photos with ms. Pays $10-15 for color prints; $5-10 for b&w prints. Identification of subjects required. Buys one-time rights.
Columns/Departments: Religion, health, living together (social and family issues), religion and art, and science (human dimensions). Buys 40 mss/year. Query with or without published clips. Length: 1,000-1,200 words. Pays $60-130.
Fiction: Confession (religious witness), ethnic, historical, humorous, and religious. "Only fiction with human, social or religious value." Buys 12-15 mss/year. Query. Length: 1,000-1,200 words. Pays $60-130.
Tips: "Submissions should have a clear, fresh and original approach with a spiritual content."

THE MIRACULOUS MEDAL, 475 E. Chelten Ave., Philadelphia PA 19144. Editorial Director: Rev. Robert P. Cawley, C.M. 40% freelance written. Pays on acceptance. Publishes ms an average of 2 months after acceptance. Buys first North American serial rights. Buys articles only on special assignment. Computer printout submissions acceptable; no dot-matrix. Free sample copy.
Fiction: Should not be pious or sermon-like. Wants good general fiction—not necessarily religious, but if religion is basic to the story, the writer should be sure of his facts. Only restriction is that subject matter and treatment must not conflict with Catholic teaching and practice. Can use seasonal material; Christmas stories. Length: 2,000 words maximum. Occasionally uses short-shorts from 750-1,250 words. Pays 2¢/word minimum.
Poetry: Maximum of 20 lines, preferably about the Virgin Mary or at least with religious slant. Pays 50¢/line minimum.

MODERN LITURGY, Suite 290, 160 E. Virginia St., San Jose CA 95112. Editor: Kenneth Guentert. 80% freelance written. Magazine; 40-48 pages published 9 times/year for artists, musicians and creative individuals who plan group worship, services; teachers of religion. Circ. 15,000. Buys first serial rights. Pays 3 months after publication. Publishes ms an average of 6 months after acceptance. Byline given. Electronic submissions OK via CPM, but requires hard copy. Computer printout submissions acceptable; prefers letter-quality to dot-matrix. Reports in 6 weeks. Sample copy $4; free writer's guidelines for SAE and 1 first class stamp.
Nonfiction and Fiction: Articles (historical, theological and practical) which address special interest topics in the field of liturgy; example services; and liturgical art forms (music, poetry, stories, dances, dramatiza-

tions, etc.). Practical, creative ideas; and art forms for use in worship and/or religious education classrooms. "No material out of our field." Buys 10 mss/year. Query. Length: 750-2,000 words. Pays $5-30.
Tips: "Don't be preachy; use too much jargon; or make articles too long."

NATIONAL CHRISTIAN REPORTER, Box 222198, Dallas TX 75222. (214)630-6495. Editor/General Manager: Spurgeon M. Dunnam III. Managing Editor: John A. Lovelace. 5% freelance written. Prefers to work with published/established writers. Weekly newspaper for an interdenominational national readership. Circ. 475,000. Pays on acceptance. Publishes ms an average of 1 month after acceptance. Byline given. Not copyrighted. Computer printout submissions acceptable; prefers letter-quality to dot-matrix. Free sample copy and writer's guidelines.
Nonfiction: "We welcome short features, approximately 500 words. Articles need not be limited to a United Methodist angle but need to have an explicit 'mainstream' Protestant angle. Write about a distinctly Christian response to human need or how a person's faith relates to a given situation. Preferably including evidence of participation in a local Protestant congregation." Send complete ms. Pays 4¢/word. Sometimes pays the expenses of writers on assignment.
Photos: Purchased with accompanying ms. "We encourage the submission of good action photos (5x7 or 8x10 b&w glossy prints) of the persons or situations in the article." Pays $10.
Poetry: "Good poetry welcome on a religious theme; blank verse or rhyme." Length: 4-20 lines. Pays $2.
Tips: "Read our publications before submitting. First person stories seldom fit our needs, but opinion pieces of no more than 500 words will be considered without pay for My Witness and Here I Stand."

THE NEW ERA, 50 E. North Temple, Salt Lake City UT 84150. (801)531-2951. Managing Editor: Brian K. Kelly. 60% freelance written. "We work with both established writers and newcomers." Monthly magazine; 51 pages. For young people of the Church of Jesus Christ of Latter-Day Saints (Mormon); their church leaders and teachers. Circ. 180,000. Pays on acceptance. Publishes ms an average of 1 year after acceptance. Byline given. Buys all rights. Submit seasonal material 1 year in advance. Electronic submissions OK via Wang. "Contact us to make arrangements—would prefer hard copy." Computer printout submissions acceptable; prefers letter-quality to dot-matrix. Reports in 1 month. Query preferred. Sample copy 90¢; writer's guidelines for SAE and 1 first class stamp.
Nonfiction: Material that shows how the Church of Jesus Christ of Latter-Day Saints is relevant in the lives of young people today. Must capture the excitement of being a young Latter-Day Saint. Special interest in the experiences of young Mormons in other countries. No general library research or formula pieces without the *New Era* slant and feel. Uses informational, how-to, personal experience, interview, profile, inspirational, humor, historical, think pieces, travel and spot news. Length: 150-3,000 words. Pays 3-12¢/word. *For Your Information* (news of young Mormons around the world). Pays expenses of writers on assignment.
Photos: Uses b&w photos and color transparencies with mss. Payment depends on use in magazine, but begins at $10.
Fiction: Experimental, adventure, science fiction and humorous. Must relate to young Mormon audience. Pays minimum 3¢/word.
Poetry: Traditional forms, blank verse, free verse, avant-garde forms, light verse and all other forms. Must relate to editorial viewpoint. Pays minimum 25¢/line.
Tips: "The writer must be able to write from a Mormon point of view. We have increased our staff size and anticipate using more staff-produced material. This means freelance quality will have to improve."

NEW WORLD OUTLOOK, Room 1351, 475 Riverside Dr., New York NY 10115. (212)870-3758. Editor: Arthur J. Moore. Executive Editor: George M. Daniels. Associate Editor: Gladys N. Koppole. 70% freelance written. Monthly magazine (combined issues July/August and November/December); 48 pages. For United Methodist lay people; not clergy generally. Circ. 40,000. Pays on publication. Publishes ms an average of 3 months after acceptance. Buys first serial rights. Electronic submissions OK via Wang or IBM PC 5¼ floppy disk, but requires hard copy also. Computer printout submissions acceptable; no dot-matrix. Free sample copy and writer's guidelines.
Nonfiction: Articles about the involvement of the church around the world, including the U.S. in outreach and social concerns and Christian witness. "Write with good magazine style. Facts and actualities are important. Use quotes. Relate what Christians are doing to meet problems. Use specifics. We have too much on New York and other large urban areas. We need more good journalistic efforts from smaller places in U.S. Articles by freelancers in out-of-the-way places in the U.S." Buys 50-60 mss/year. Query or submit complete ms. Length: 1,000-2,000 words. Usually pays $50-150 but more on occasion. "Writers are encouraged to illustrate their articles photographically if possible." Pays expenses of writers on assignment "if it originates with us or if article is one in which we have a special interest."
Photos: Generally use b&w but covers (4-color) will be considered. "Photos are purchased separately at standard rates."
Tips: "A freelancer should have some understanding of the United Methodist Church, or else know very well a local situation of human need or social problem which the churches and Christians have tried to face. Too much

freelance material we get tries to paint with broad strokes about world or national issues. The local story of meaning to people elsewhere is still the best material. Avoid pontificating on the big issues. Write cleanly and interestingly on the 'small' ones. We're interested in major articles and photos (including photo features from freelancers)."

NORTH AMERICAN VOICE OF FATIMA, Fatima Shrine, Youngstown NY 14174. Editor: Anthony M. Bianco C.R.S.P. 40% freelance written. Works with a small number of new/unpublished writers each year. For Roman Catholic readership. Circ. 3,000. Pays on acceptance. Not copyrighted. Buys first North American serial rights. Reports in 6 weeks. Computer printout submissions acceptable; prefers letter-quality to dot-matrix. Free sample copy.
Nonfiction and Fiction: Inspirational, personal experience, historical and think articles. Religious and historical fiction. Length: 700 words. All material must have a religious slant. Pays 2¢/word.
Photos: B&w photos purchased with ms.

OBLATES MAGAZINE, Missionary Association of Mary Immaculate, 15 S. 59th St., Belleville IL 62222. (618)233-2238. Contact: Managing Editor. 15-50% freelance written. Prefers to work with published/established writers; works with a small number of new/unpublished writers each year. Bimonthly religious magazine for Christian families. Circ. 500,000. Pays on acceptance. Publishes ms an average of 4 months after acceptance. Byline given. Buys first North American serial rights. Submit seasonal/holiday material 6 months in advance. Computer printout submissions acceptable; prefers letter-quality to dot-matrix. Reports in 1 month. Free sample copy and writer's guidelines.
Nonfiction: Inspirational, personal experience and articles on Oblates around the world. Stories should be inspirational, give insight, and present Gospel values. "Don't be preachy or pious." Send complete ms. Length: 500 words. Pays $75. Sometimes pays the expenses of writers on assignment.
Poetry: Light verse—reverent, perceptive, traditional. "Nothing that takes too much effort to decipher. Emphasis should be on inspiration, insight and relationship with God." Submit maximum 3 poems. Length: 8-16 lines. Pays $25.
Tips: "Our readership is made up mostly of mature Americans who are looking for comfort, encouragement and applicable Christian direction. They don't want to spend a lot of time wading through theology laden or personal spiritual journey pieces. But if you can take an incident from Christ's life, for example, and in a creative and clever way parallel that with everyday living or personal experience, all in about 500 words, we're holding a couple of pages for you. This formula will also work for any Gospel theme, e.g., forgiveness, self-lessness, hope. In other words, make the Gospel message work in today's world."

THE OTHER SIDE, Jubilee, Inc., Box 3948, Fredericksburg VA 22402. Editor: Mark Olson. Managing Editor: Kathleen Hayes. Assistant Editors: John Linscheid and William O'Brien. 67% freelance written. Prefers to work with published/established writers; works with a small number of new/unpublished writers each year. Magazine published 10 times/year focusing on "peace, justice and economic liberation from a radical Christian perspective." Circ. 15,000. Pays on acceptance. Publishes ms an average of 5 months after acceptance. Byline given. Buys all serial rights (book rights retained by author). Query about electronic submissions. Computer printout submissions acceptable. Reports in 6 weeks. Sample copy $3; free writer's guidelines.
Nonfiction: Eunice A. Smith, articles editor. Current social, political and economic issues in the U.S. and around the world: personality profiles, interpretive essays, interviews, how-to's, personal experiences and investigative reporting. "Articles must be lively, vivid and down-to-earth, with a radical Christian perspective." Length: 500-6,000 words. Pays $25-300. Sometimes pays expenses of writers on assignment.
Photos: Cathleen Boint, art director. Photos or photo essays illustrating current social, political, or economic reality in the U.S. and Third World. Pays $15-75 for b&w and $50-300 for color.
Fiction: Joseph Comanda, fiction editor. "Short stories, humor and satire conveying insights and situations that will be helpful to Christians with a radical commitment to peace and justice." Length: 300-6,000 words. Pays $25-250.
Poetry: Rosemary Camilleri, poetry editor. "Short, creative poetry that will be thought-provoking and appealing to radical Christians who have a strong commitment to peace and justice." Length: 3-50 lines. Pays $15-20.
Tips: "We're looking for tightly written pieces (500-1,000 words) on interesting and unusual Christians (or Christian groups) who are putting their commitment to peace and social justice into action in creative and useful ways. We're also looking for practical, down-to-earth articles (500-6,000 words) for Christian parents who seek to instill in their children their values of personal faith, peace, justice, and a concern for the poor."

OUR FAMILY, Oblate Fathers of St. Mary's Province, Box 249, Battleford, Saskatchewan S0M 0E0 Canada. (306)937-2131, 937-7344. Editor-in-Chief: Albert Lalonde, O.M.I. 60% freelance written. Prefers to work with published/established writers; works with a small number of new/unpublished writers each year. Monthly magazine for average family men and women with high school and early college education. Circ. 14,265. Pays on acceptance. Publishes ms an average of 6 months after acceptance. Byline given. Offers 100% kill fee. Generally purchases first North American serial rights; also buys all rights, simultaneous rights, second serial (reprint) rights or one-time rights. Submit seasonal/holiday material 4 months in advance. Simultaneous, photocopied, and previously published submissions OK. Electronic submissions OK via disks. Computer printout submissions acceptable; no dot-matrix. "Writer should inquire with our office before sending letter-quality computer printout or disk submissions." Reports in 1 month. Sample copy $1.50 and SAE, IRC; writer's guidelines for 35¢ (Canadian fund). (U.S. postage cannot be used in Canada).

Nonfiction: Humor (related to family life or husband/wife relations); inspirational (anything that depicts people responding to adverse conditions with courage, hope and love); personal experience (with religious dimensions); and photo feature (particularly in search of photo essays on human/religious themes and on persons whose lives are an inspiration to others). Phone queries OK. Buys 72-88 unsolicited mss/year. Pays expenses of writers on assignment.

Photos: Photos purchased with or without accompanying ms. Pays $25 for 5x7 or larger b&w glossy prints and color photos (which are converted into b&w). Offers additional payment for photos accepted with ms (payment for these photos varies according to their quality). Free photo spec sheet with SASE.

Fiction: Humorous and religious. "Anything true to human nature. No romance, he-man adventure material, science fiction, moralizing or sentimentality." Buys 1-2 ms/issue. Send complete ms. Length: 700-3,000 words. Pays 7-10¢/word minimum for original material. Free fiction requirement guide with SASE.

Poetry: Avant-garde, free verse, haiku, light verse and traditional. Buys 4-10 poems/issue. Length: 3-30 lines. Pays 75¢-$1/line.

Fillers: Jokes, gags, anecdotes and short humor. Buys 2-10/issue.

Tips: "Writers should ask themselves whether this is the kind of an article, poem, etc. that a busy housewife would pick up and read when she has a few moments of leisure. We are particularly looking for articles on the spirituality of marriage. We will be concentrating more on recent movements and developments in the church to help make people aware of the new church of which they are a part."

PARISH FAMILY DIGEST, Our Sunday Visitor, Inc., 200 Noll Plaza, Huntington IN 46750. (219)356-8400. Editor: Louis F. Jacquet. 100% freelance written. Bimonthly magazine; 48 pages. "*Parish Family Digest* is geared to the Catholic family and to that family as a unit of the parish." Circ. 150,000. Pays on acceptance. Publishes ms an average of 6 months after acceptance. Byline given. Buys all rights on a work-for-hire basis. Submit seasonal/holiday material 5 months in advance. Photocopied and previously published submissions OK; all mss are retyped as edited. Computer printout submissions acceptable; prefers letter-quality to dot-matrix. Reports in 2 weeks on queries; 3 weeks on mss. Sample copy and writer's guidelines for 2 first class stamps.

Nonfiction: General interest, historical, inspirational, interview, nostalgia (if related to overall Parish involvement), and profile. No personal essays or preachy first person "thou shalt's or shalt not's." Send complete ms. Buys 82 unsolicited mss/year. Length: 1,000 words maximum. Pays $5-50.

Photos: State availability of photos with ms. Pays $10 for 3x5 b&w prints. Buys one-time rights. Captions preferred; model releases required.

Fillers: Anecdotes and short humor. Buys 6/issue. Length: 100 words maximum.

Tips: "If an article does not deal with some angle of Catholic family life, the writer is wasting time in sending it to us. We rarely use reprints; we prefer fresh material that will hold up over time, not tied to an event in the news. We will be more oriented to young families with kids and the problems they face in the Church. Articles on how to overcome these problems will be welcomed."

PENTECOSTAL EVANGEL, The General Council of the Assemblies of God, 1445 Boonville, Springfield MO 65802. (417)862-2781. Editor: Richard G. Champion. 33% freelance written. Works with a small number of new/unpublished writers each year. Weekly magazine; 32 pages. Emphasizes news of the Assemblies of God for members of the Assemblies and other Pentecostal and charismatic Christians. Circ. 290,000. Usually pays on acceptance. Byline given. Buys first serial rights, simultaneous rights, second serial (reprint) rights or one-time rights. Submit seasonal/holiday material 6 months in advance. Simultaneous, photocopied, and previously published submissions OK. Computer printout submissions acceptable; prefers letter-quality to dot-matrix. Reports in 3 months. Free sample copy and writer's guidelines.

Nonfiction: Informational (articles on homelife that convey Christian teachings); inspirational; and personal experience. Buys 5 mss/issue. Send complete ms. Length: 500-2,000 words. Pays 4¢/word maximum. Sometimes pays the expenses of writers on assignment.

Photos: Photos purchased without accompanying ms. Pays $7.50-15 for 8x10 b&w glossy prints; $10-35 for 35mm or larger color transparencies. Total purchase price for ms includes payment for photos.

Poetry: Religious and inspirational. Buys 1 poem/issue. Submit maximum 6 poems. Pays 20-40¢/line.

Tips: "Break in by writing up a personal experience. We publish first person articles concerning spiritual experiences; that is, answers to prayer for help in a particular situation, of unusual conversions or healings through faith in Christ. All articles submitted to us should be related to religious life. We are Protestant, evangelical, Pentecostal, and any doctrines or practices portrayed should be in harmony with the official position of our denomination (Assemblies of God)."

‡PLUS, The Magazine of Positive Thinking, Foundation for Christian Living, Box FCL, Route 22, Pawling NY 12564. (914)855-5000. Editor: Eric J. Fellman. 40% freelance written. Prefers to work with published/established writers; works with a small number of new/unpublished writers each year. Magazine published 10 times/year. "Our audience looks for inspiration and practical ways to apply their faith every day." Circ. 900,000. Pays on publication. Publishes ms an average of 5 months after acceptance. Byline given. Buys first North American serial rights, or second serial (reprint) rights. Submit seasonal/holiday material 6 months in advance. Photocopied and previously published submissions OK. Computer printout submissions acceptable; prefers letter-quality to dot-matrix. Reports in 1 month on queries; 6 weeks on mss. Sample copy for SAE with 2 first class stamps; writer's guidelines for SAE with 1 first class stamp.
Nonfiction: Rosemarie Dunn Stokes, articles editor. Book excerpts, inspirational, personal experience and religious. "We look for articles that emphasize a how-to focus—how to take the principles of faith and positive thinking and apply them to daily living. We like well-written, succinct, visual anecdotes in the articles we use. We are not interested in preachy, long-winded articles, nor are we interested in anything resembling a theological treatise. Articles that deal with popular controversial issues are also not our style." Pays "good rates".

PRAIRIE MESSENGER, Catholic Weekly, Benedictine Monks of St. Peter's Abbey, Box 190, Muenster, Saskatchewan S0K 2Y0 Canada. (306)682-5215. Editor: Andrew Britz. "We are backlogged with submissions and prefer not to receive unsolicited submissions at this time."

PRESBYTERIAN RECORD, 50 Wynford Dr., Don Mills, Ontario M3C 1J7 Canada. (416)444-1111. Editor: Rev. James Dickey. 60% freelance written. Eager to work with new/unpublished writers. Monthly magazine for a church-oriented, family audience. Circ. 75,000. Buys 35 mss/year. Pays on publication. Publishes ms an average of 4 months after acceptance. Buys first serial rights, one-time rights, simultaneous rights. Submit seasonal material 3 months in advance. Computer printout submissions acceptable; prefers letter-quality to dot-matrix. Reports on ms accepted for publication in 2 months. Returns rejected material in 3 months. Query. SAE and Canadian stamps or IRC. Free sample copy.
Nonfiction: Material on religious themes. Check a copy of the magazine for style. Also, personal experience, interview, and inspirational material. No material solely American in context. Buys 15-20 unsolicited mss/year. Length: 1,000-2,000 words. Pays $45-55. (U.S. funds)
Photos: Pays $15-20 for b&w glossy photos. Uses positive color transparencies for cover. Pays $50. Captions required.
Tips: "There is a trend away from maudlin, first person pieces redolent with tragedy and dripping with simplistic pietistic conclusions."

PRESBYTERIAN SURVEY, Presbyterian Publishing House, Inc., 341 Ponce de Leon Ave. NE, Atlanta GA 30365. (404)873-1549. Editor: Vic Jameson. Managing Editor: Catherine Cottingham. 65% freelance written. Prefers to work with published/established writers; works with a small number of new/unpublished writers each year; eager to work with new/unpublished writers. Denominational magazine published 10 times/year covering religion, denominational activities and public issues for members of the Presbyterian Church (U.S.A.). Pays on acceptance. Publishes ms an average of 9 months after acceptance. Byline given. Offers variable kill fee. Buys first North American serial rights. Submit seasonal/holiday material 6 months in advance. Simultaneous submissions OK. Computer printout submissions acceptable; prefers letter-quality to dot-matrix. Reports in 2 weeks on queries; 1 month on mss. Free sample copy and writer's guidelines.
Nonfiction: Inspirational and Presbyterian programs, issues, people; any subject from a Christian viewpoint. No secular subjects. Buys 65 mss/year. Send complete ms. Length: 800-2,500 words. Pays $50-150. Sometimes pays expenses of writers on assignment.
Photos: Linda Colgrove Crittenden, photo editor. State availability of photos. Reviews color transparencies and 8x10 b&w prints. Pays $15-25 for b&w; $25-50 for color. Identification of subjects required. Buys one-time rights.
Columns/Departments: "The only column not by a regular columnist is an op-ed page for readers of the magazine (As I See It)." Buys 10 mss/year. Send complete ms. Length: 600-750 words. No payment.

PURPOSE, 616 Walnut Ave., Scottdale PA 15683. (412)887-8500. Editor: James E. Horsch. 95% freelance written. Weekly magazine "for adults, young and old, general audience with interests as varied as there are persons. My particular readership is interested in seeing Christianity work in tough situations." Circ. 18,800. Pays on acceptance. Publishes ms an average of 8 months after acceptance. Byline given, including city, state/province. Buys one-time rights. Submit seasonal material 6 months in advance. Photocopied and simultaneous submissions OK. Computer printout submissions acceptable if legible; prefers letter-quality to dot-matrix. Submit complete ms. Reports in 6 weeks. Sample copy and writer's guidelines for 6x9 SASE.
Nonfiction: Inspirational articles from a Christian perspective. "I want material that goes to the core of human problems in business, politics, religion, sex and any other area—and shows how the Christian faith resolves them. I want material that's upbeat. *Purpose* is a story paper which conveys truth either through quality fiction or through articles that use the best fiction techniques. Our magazine accents Christian discipleship.

Christianity affects all of life, and we expect our material to demonstrate this. I would like to see story-type articles on how individuals, groups and organizations are intelligently and effectively working at some of the great human problems such as overpopulation, hunger, poverty, international understanding, peace, justice, etc., motivated by their faith." Buys 175-200 mss/year. Submit complete ms. Length: 1,200 words maximum. Pays 5¢/word maximum.

Photos: Photos purchased with ms. Pays $5-25 for b&w, depending on quality. Must be sharp enough for reproduction; prefers prints in all cases. Can use color prints. Captions desired.

Fiction: Humorous, religious and historical fiction related to theme of magazine. "Produce the story with specificity so that it appears to take place somewhere and with real people. It should not be moralistic."

Poetry: Traditional poetry, blank verse, free verse and light verse. Length: 12 lines maximum. Pays 50¢-$1/line.

Fillers: Jokes, short humor, and items up to 600 words. Pays 4¢/word maximum.

Tips: "We are looking for articles which show that Christianity is working at issues where people hurt, but stories need to be told and presented professionally. Good photographs help place material with us."

REFORM JUDAISM, Union of American Hebrew Congregations, 838 5th Ave., New York NY 10021. (212)249-0100. Editor: Aron Hert-Manheimer. Managing Editor: Joy Weinberg. 50% freelance written. Quarterly magazine of reform Jewish issues. "*Reform Judaism* is published by the UAHC, a nonprofit Jewish organization, and is distributed to members of reform Jewish congregations and other interested readers." Payment on publication. Publishes ms an average of 3 months after acceptance. Byline given. Offers negotiable kill fee. Buys first North American serial rights. Submit seasonal/holiday material 3 months in advance. Photocopied and previously published submissions OK. Computer printout submissions acceptable; prefers letter-quality to dot-matrix. Reports in 2 weeks on queries; 3 weeks on mss. Sample copy $1.

Nonfiction: Book excerpt (reviews), expose, general interest, historical/nostalgic, inspirational, interview/profile, opinion, personal experience, photo feature and travel. Buys 60 mss/year. Send complete ms. Submit complete ms. Length: 750-2,000 words. Pays $100-200. Sometimes pays expenses of writers on assignment.

Photos: Send photos with ms. Prefers 8x10 b&w prints. Pays $25-75. Identification of subjects requied. Buys one-time rights.

Fiction: Ethnic, humorous, mainstream and religious. Buys 4 mss/year. Send complete ms. Length: 750-2,000 words. Pays $100-200.

Poetry: Free verse. Buys 2 poems/year. Submit maximum 3 poems. Length: 20 lines maximum. Pays $25-50.

REVIEW FOR RELIGIOUS, 3601 Lindell Blvd., Room 428, St. Louis MO 63108. (314)535-3048. Editor: Daniel F.X. Meenan, S.J. 100% freelance written. "Each ms is judged on its own merits, without reference to author's publishing history." Bimonthly. For Roman Catholic priests, brothers and sisters. Pays on publication. Publishes ms an average of 9 months after acceptance. Byline given. Buys first North American serial rights and rarely second serial (reprint) rights. Computer printout submissions acceptable; no dot-matrix. Reports in 8 weeks.

Nonfiction: Articles on ascetical, liturgical and canonical matters only; not for general audience. Length: 2,000-8,000 words. Pays $6/page.

Tips: "The writer must know about religious life in the Catholic Church and be familiar with prayer, vows and problems related to them."

ST. ANTHONY MESSENGER, 1615 Republic St., Cincinnati OH 45210. Editor-in-Chief: Norman Perry. 55% freelance written. "Eager to work with new/unpublished writers if their writing is of a professional caliber." Monthly magazine, 59 pages for a national readership of Catholic families, most of which have children in grade school, high school or college. Circ. 430,000. Pays on acceptance. Publishes ms an average of 9 months after acceptance. Byline given. Buys first North American serial rights. Submit seasonal/holiday material 6 months in advance. Electronic submissions OK if compatible with CPT word processor, but requires hard copy also. Computer printout submissions acceptable; no dot-matrix. Free sample copy and writer's guidelines.

Nonfiction: How-to (on psychological and spiritual growth, problems of parenting/better parenting, marriage problems/marriage enrichment); humor; informational; inspirational; interview; personal experience (if pertinent to our purpose); personal opinion (limited use; writer must have special qualifications for topic); and profile. Buys 35-50 mss/year. Length: 1,500-3,500 words. Pays 12¢/word. Sometimes pays the expenses of writers on assignment.

Fiction: Mainstream and religious. Buys 12 mss/year. Submit complete ms. Length: 2,000-3,500 words. Pays 12¢/word.

Tips: "The freelancer should ask why his or her proposed article would be appropriate for us, rather than for *Redbook* or *Saturday Review*. We treat human problems of all kinds, but from a religious perspective. Get authoritative information (not merely library research); we want interviews with experts. Write in popular style. We will be enlarging our type so word length will be an important consideration."

ST. JOSEPH'S MESSENGER & ADVOCATE OF THE BLIND, Sisters of St. Joseph of Peace, St. Joseph's Home, Box 288, Jersey City NJ 07303. Editor-in-Chief: Sister Ursula Maphet. 25% freelance written. Quarterly magazine; 30 pages. Circ. 35,000. Pays on acceptance. Publishes ms an average of 6 months after acceptance. Buys first serial rights and second serial (reprint) rights, but will reassign rights back to author after publication asking only that credit line be included in next publication. Submit seasonal/holiday material 3 months in advance (no Christmas issue). Simultaneous and previously published submissions OK. Reports in 3 weeks. Free sample copy and writer's guidelines.
Nonfiction: Humor, inspirational, nostalgia, personal opinion and personal experience. Buys 24 mss/year. Submit complete ms. Length: 300-1,500 words. Pays $3-15.
Fiction: "Fiction is our most needed area." Romance, suspense, mainstream and religious. Buys 30 mss/year. Submit complete ms. Length: 600-1,600 words. Pays $6-25.
Poetry: Light verse and traditional. Buys 25 poems/year. Submit maximum 10 poems. Length: 50-300 words. Pays $5-20.
Tips: "It's rewarding to know that someone is waiting to see freelancers' efforts rewarded by 'print'. It's annoying, however, to receive poor copy, shallow material or inane submissions."

SCOPE, 426 S. 5th St., Box 1209, Minneapolis MN 55440. (612)330-3413. Editor: Constance Lovaas. 40% freelance written. Prefers to work with published/established writers. Monthly, for women of the American Lutheran Church. Circ. 250,000. Pays on acceptance. Publishes ms an average of 6 months after acceptance. Byline given. Buys first North American serial rights. Submit seasonal material 5 months in advance. Computer printout submissions acceptable; no dot-matrix. Reports in 4 weeks. Sample copy for SAE and 2 first class stamps.
Nonfiction: "The magazine transmits Bible-study material for group meetings and provides articles for inspiration and growth as well as information about the mission and concerns of the church. "We also want articles that tell how the Christian faith relates to current social concerns, especially the lives of women of all ages in their work, leisure and relationships. Writers need not be Lutheran." Buys 200-300 mss/year. Submit complete ms. Length: 500-1,000 words. Pays $30-80.
Photos: Buys 3x5 or 8x10 b&w photos with ms or with captions only. Pays $10-30.
Poetry: Very little poetry used. Pays $15-25.
Fillers: "We can use interesting, brief, pithy, significant or clever filler items. We do not buy cute sayings of children." Pays $10-20.
Tips: "Writers should be aware of the need for inclusive language to avoid discrimination among races, sexes or persons who are disabled or elderly; recognition of women active in all aspects of the marketplace."

‡SCP NEWSLETTER, Spiritual Counterfeits Project, Box 4308, Berkeley CA 94704. (415)540-0300. Editor: Robert J. L. Burrows. 40% freelance written. "The *SCP Newsletter* is a quarterly newsletter that analyzes new religious movements and spiritual trends from a Christian perspective. Its targeted audience is the educated lay person." Circ. 16,500. Pays on publication. Publishes ms an average of 3 months after acceptance. Byline given. Makes work-for-hire assignments. Simultaneous and previously published submissions OK. Computer printout submissions acceptable. Free sample copy and writer's guidelines.
Nonfiction: Book excerpts, essays, exposé, historical/nostalgic, inspirational, interview/profile, opinion, personal experience and religious. Buys 10 mss/year. Query with published clips. Length: 2,500-3,500 words. Pays $25-200.
Photos: State availability of photos with submission. Reviews contact sheets and prints. Offers no additional payment for photos accepted with ms. Captions, model releases and identification of subjects required. Buys one-time rights.
Tips: "The area of our publication most open to freelancers are reviews of books relevant to subjects covered by *SCP*. These should be brief and not exceed 3 type written, double-spaced pages, 750 words. Send samples of work that are relevant to the *SCP Newsletter*'s area of interest."

‡SEABURY JOURNAL, Foundation for Anglican Tradition, Inc., Box 1106 S.M.S, Fairfield CT 06430. (203)576-0303. Editor: R.B. Baxter. 75% freelance written. A monthly magazine of articles and commentary of interest to Traditionalist Episcopalian/Anglicans. Circ. 5,000. Pays on acceptance. Publishes an average of 2 months after acceptance. Byline given. Buys all rights. Submit seasonal/holiday material 3 months in advance. Simultaneous, photocopied, and previously published submissions OK. Computer printout submissions acceptable; prefers letter-quality to dot-matrix. Reports in 5 weeks. Free sample copy.
Nonfiction: Essays, exposé, historical/nostalgic, humor, inspirational, interview/profile, opinion and religious. Buys 35 mss/year. Send complete ms.

SEEK, Standard Publishing, 8121 Hamilton Ave., Cincinnati OH 45231. (513)931-4050, ext. 365. Editor: Eileen H. Wilmoth. 98% freelance written. Prefers to work with published/established writers; works with a small number of new/unpublished writers each year. Sunday school paper; 8 pages. Quarterly, in weekly issues for young and middle-aged adults who attend church and Bible classes. Circ. 45,000. Pays on acceptance.

Publishes ms an average of 1 year after acceptance. Byline given. Buys first serial rights and second serial (reprint) rights. Buys 100-150 mss/year. Submit seasonal material 1 year in advance. Computer printout submissions acceptable; prefers letter-quality to dot-matrix. Reports in 10-20 days. Sample copy and writer's guidelines for SASE.

Nonfiction: "We look for articles that are warm, inspirational, devotional, of personal or human interest; that deal with controversial matters, timely issues of religious, ethical or moral nature, or first person testimonies, true-to-life happenings, vignettes, emotional situations or problems; communication problems and examples of answered prayers. Article must deliver its point in a convincing manner but not be patronizing or preachy. They must appeal to either men or women, must be alive, vibrant, sparkling and have a title that demands the article be read. We always need stories of families, marriages, problems on campus and life testimonies." No poetry. Buys 100-150 mss/year. Submit complete ms. Length: 400-1,200 words. Pays 3¢/word.

Photos: B&w photos purchased with or without mss. Pays $10 minimum for good 8x10 glossy prints.

Fiction: Religious fiction and religiously slanted historical and humorous fiction. Length: 400-1,200 words. Pays 2½¢/word.

Tips: Submit mss which tell of faith in action or victorious Christian living as central theme. "We select manuscripts as far as one year in advance of publication. Complimentary copies are sent to our published writers immediately following printing."

SHARING THE VICTORY, Fellowship of Christian Athletes, 8701 Leeds Rd., Kansas City MO 64129. (816)921-0909. Editor: Skip Stogsdill. Managing Editor: Jack Roberts. 20% freelance written. Prefers to work with published/established writers; works with a small number of new/unpublished writers each year. A bimonthly magazine. "We seek to encourage and enable athletes and coaches at all levels to take their faith seriously on and off the 'field.' " Circ. 47,000. Pays on publication. Publishes ms an average of 4 months after acceptance. Byline given. Buys first rights. Submit seasonal/holiday material 4 months in advance. Computer printout submissions acceptable; no dot-matrix. Reports in 1 week on queries; 2 weeks on manuscripts. Sample copy $1 with 8½x11 SAE and 3 first class stamps; free writer's guidelines.

Nonfiction: Humor, inspirational, interview/profile, personal experience, and photo feature. No "sappy articles on 'I became a Christian and now I'm a winner.' " Buys 6 mss/year. Query. Length: 500-1,000 words. Pays $25-75 for unsolicited articles.

Photos: State availability of photos with submission. Reviews contact sheets. Pay depends on quality of photo. Model releases required. Buys one-time rights.

Columns/Departments: Sports Conscience (deals with a problem issue in athletics today and some possible solutions or alternatives). Buys 4 mss/year. Query. Length 700-1,500 words. Pays $30-75.

Poetry: Free verse. Buys 3 poems/year. Pays $15-30.

Tips: "The area most open to freelancers is profiles on or interviews with well-known athletes or coaches (male, female, minorities) or of offbeat sports."

SIGNS OF THE TIMES, Pacific Press Publishing Association, Box 7000, Boise ID 83707. (208)465-2500. Editor: Kenneth J. Holland. Managing Editor: B. Russell Holt. 40% freelance written. Works with a small number of new/unpublished writers each year. Monthly magazine on religion. "We are a Christian publication encouraging the general public to put into practice the principles of the Bible." Circ. 400,000. Pays on acceptance. Publishes ms an average of 5 months after acceptance. Byline given. Offers $100 kill fee. Buys first North American serial rights and simultaneous rights. Submit seasonal/holiday material 8 months in advance. Simultaneous queries and submissions, and photocopied and previously published submissions OK. Computer printout submissions acceptable; prefers letter-quality to dot-matrix. Reports in 2 weeks on queries; 1 month on mss. Free sample copy and writer's guidelines.

Nonfiction: General interest (home, marriage, health—interpret current events from a Biblical perceptive); how-to (overcome depression, find one's identity, answer loneliness and guilt, face death triumphantly); humor; inspirational (human interest pieces that highlight a Biblical principle); interview/profile; personal experience (overcome problems with God's help); and photo feature. "We want writers with a desire to share the good news of reconciliation with God. Articles should be people-oriented, well-researched and should have a sharp focus and include anecdotes." Buys 150 mss/year. Query with or without published clips, or send complete ms. Length: 500-3,000 words. Pays $100-400. Sometimes pays the expenses of writers on assignment.

Photos: Ed Guthero, photo editor. Send photos with query or ms. Reviews b&w contact sheets; 35mm color transparencies; 5x7 or 8x10 b&w prints. Pays $35-300 for transparencies; $20-50 for prints. Model releases and identification of subjects required (captions helpful). Buys one-time rights.

Tips: "One of the most frequent mistakes made by writers in completing an article assignment for us is trying to cover too much ground. Articles need focus, research, and anecdotes. We don't want essays."

SISTERS TODAY, The Liturgical Press, St. John's Abbey, Collegeville MN 56321. Editor-in-Chief: Sister Mary Anthony Wagner, O.S.B. Associate Editor: Sister Nancy Bauer, O.S.B. 80% freelance written. Prefers to work with published/established writers; works with a small number of new/unpublished writers each year. Magazine, published 10 times/year, for religious women of the Roman Catholic Church, primarily. Circ.

9,000. Pays on publication. Publishes ms 1-2 years after acceptance. Byline given. Buys first rights. Submit seasonal/holiday material 4 months in advance. Computer printout submissions acceptable; no dot-matrix. Reports in 3 months. Sample copy $1.50.

Nonfiction: How-to (pray, live in a religious community, exercise faith, hope, charity etc.), informational; and inspirational. Also articles concerning religious renewal, community life, worship, and the role of Sisters in the world today. Buys 50-60 unsolicited mss/year. Query. Length: 500-2,500 words. Pays $5/printed page.

Poetry: Free verse, haiku, light verse and traditional. Buys 3 poems/issue. Submit maximum 4 poems. Pays $10.

Tips: "Some of the freelance material evidences the lack of familiarity with *Sisters Today*. We would prefer submitted articles not to exceed eight or nine pages."

SOCIAL JUSTICE REVIEW, 3835 Westminister Place, St. Louis MO 63108. (314)371-1653. Contact: editor. 25% freelance written. Works with a small number of new/unpublished writers each year. Bimonthly. Publishes ms an average of 3 months after acceptance. Not copyrighted; "however special articles within the magazine may be copyrighted, or an occasional special issue has been copyrighted due to author's request." Buys first serial rights. Computer printout submissions acceptable; prefers letter-quality to dot-matrix.

Nonfiction: Wants scholarly articles on society's economic, religious, social, intellectual and political problems with the aim of bringing Catholic social thinking to bear upon these problems. Query. Length: 2,500-3,500 words. Pays about $7/column.

‡SOLOING, Sonlight Christian Newspapers, Dennis Lombard (dba), 4623 Forest Hill (109-1), West Palm Beach FL 33415. (305)967-7739. Editor: Dennis Lombard. 65% freelance written. A monthly tabloid distributed free to singles in churches and the public, geared to all denominations. Estab. 1985. Circ. 10,000. Pays on publication. Byline given. Offers 100% kill fee. Not copyrighted. Buys first North American serial rights, one-time rights, second serial (reprint) rights, or simultaneous rights, and makes work-for-hire assignments (locally). Submit seasonal/holiday material 2 months in advance. Simultaneous, photocopied, or previously published submissions OK. Computer printout submissions acceptable; prefers letter-quality to dot-matrix. Reports in 1 week. Sample copy $1 with 9x12 SAE and 2 first class stamps; writer's guidelines for #10 SAE with 1 first class stamp.

Nonfiction: Books excerpts and reviews; essays; general interest (Christian subjects); how-to (adjust to singleness); humor; inspirational; interview/profile; personal experience; photo feature; and religious. "All require inter-denominational, non-doctrinal viewpoint." No critical attitudes. Buys 30 mss/year. Send complete ms. Length: 500-1,500 words. Pays $10-50 for assigned articles; pays $5-25 for unsolicited articles. Sometimes pays expenses of writers on assignment.

Photos: Send photos with submission. Reviews contact sheets and 4x5 b&w glossy prints. Offers $3-10/photo. Captions, model releases, and identification of subjects required. Buys one-time rights.

Columns/Departments: Looking for regular singles column—light/humorous. Query.

Poetry: Free verse, light verse and traditional. Buys 5-10 poems/year. Submit maximum 3 poems. Length: 2-50 lines. Pays $3-10. Nothing too abstract or overly sentimental.

Fillers: Anecdotes and short humor. Length: 50-200 words. Pays $1-5.

Tips: "New writers are welcome. How-to and personal experience articles are most open to freelancers. Testimonial articles should include an informal b&w photo of subject and subject's signed release. We're looking for the light and inspirational side."

SPIRIT! MAGAZINE, (formerly *Choice Magazine*), Box 1231, Sisters OR 97759. Editor: Jerry Jones. 95% freelance written. Works with a small number of new/unpublished writers each year. Bimonthly magazine. "The Christian magazine about career, lifestyle and relationships." Aimed for evangelicals in their 20's and 30's who are career oriented, college educated. Circ. 40,000. Pays on publication. Publishes ms an average of 10 months after acceptance. Submit seasonal material 8 months in advance. Accepts queries only. No unsolicited mss. Computer printout submissions acceptable; no dot-matrix. Reports in 3 months on queries. Sample copy and writer's guidelines $2.50 with large magazine size SASE.

Nonfiction: Topics featured are career, contemporary issues, relationships, finances, humor, daily living, human interest and networking. "No articles that are not in harmony with Christian principles and Christ's teachings." Buys 20-30 mss/year. Length: 200-2,000 words. Pays 5-10¢/word. Sometimes pays the expenses of writers on assignment.

Tips: "Get a copy of our magazine to know our market *before* submitting query. Ask friends in their 20's and 30's what kinds of things they would most want to see in a magazine specifically for them, and write about it. Wherever their greatest needs and interests are, there are our stories."

SPIRITUAL LIFE, 2131 Lincoln Rd. NE, Washington DC 20002. (202)832-6622. Co-Editors: Rev. Christopher Latimer, O.C.D. and Rev. Stephen Payne, O.C.D. 80% freelance written. Quarterly. "Largely Catholic, well-educated, serious readers. A few are nonCatholic or nonChristian." Circ. 17,000. Pays on acceptance. Publishes ms an average of 1 year after acceptance. Buys first North American serial rights. "Brief auto-

biographical information (present occupation, past occupations, books and articles published, etc.) should accompany article." Reports in 2 weeks. Free sample copy and writer's guidelines.
Nonfiction: Serious articles of contemporary spirituality. High quality articles about our encounter with God in the present day world. Language of articles should be college level. Technical terminology, if used, should be clearly explained. Material should be presented in a positive manner. Sentimental articles or those dealing with specific devotional practices not accepted. Buys inspirational and think pieces. No fiction or poetry. Buys 20 mss/year. Length: 3,000-5,000 words. Pays $50 minimum. "Five contributor's copies are sent to author on publication of article." Book reviews should be sent to Rev. Steven Payne, O.C.D.

SPIRITUALITY TODAY, Aquinas Institute, 3642 Lindell Blvd., St. Louis MO 63108. Editor: Rev. Richard Woods, O.P. 25% freelance written. Works with a small number of new/unpublished writers each year. Magazine "for those interested in a more integral and fuller Christian life in the contemporary world." Pays on publication. Publishes ms an average of 14 months after acceptance. Byline given. Buys all rights but reassigned on request without fee. Computer printout submissions acceptable. Sample copy $1; free writer's guidelines.
Nonfiction: Articles that seriously examine important issues concerning the spiritual life, or Christian life, in the context of today's world. Scriptural, biographical, doctrinal, liturgical and ecumenical articles are acceptable. No poetry. Generally Catholic readership, but ecumenically open. Buys 15 unsolicited mss/year. Submit complete ms. Length: 4,000 words. Pays 1¢/word.
Tips: "Examine the journal. It is not a typical devotional or inspirational magazine. Given its characteristics, the style of writing required is deeper and richer than regular freelance writers usually employ."

STANDARD, Nazarene International Headquarters, 6401 The Paseo, Kansas City MO 64131. (816)333-7000, ext. 460. Editor: Sheila Boggess. 95% freelance written. Works with a small number of new/unpublished writers each year. Weekly inspirational "story paper" with Christian leisure reading for adults. Circ. 177,000. Pays on acceptance. Publishes ms an average of 15 months after acceptance. Byline given. Buys one-time rights and second serial (reprint) rights. Submit seasonal/holiday material 9 months in advance. Computer printout submissions acceptable; prefers letter-quality to dot-matrix. Reports in 2 weeks on queries; 4 weeks on mss. Free sample copy; writer's guidelines for SAE with 1 first class stamp.
Nonfiction: How-to (grow spiritually); inspirational; and personal experience (with an emphasis on spiritual growth). Buys 100 mss/year. Send complete ms. Length: 300-1,500 words. Pays 3½¢/word for first rights; 2¢/word for reprint rights. Sometimes pays expenses of writers on assignment.
Photos: Send photos with ms. Pays $15-45 for 8x10 b&w prints. Buys one-time rights.
Fiction: Adventure, religious, romance and suspense—all with a spiritual emphasis. Buys 100 mss/year. Send complete ms. Length: 500-1,500 words. Pays 3½¢/word for first rights; 2¢/word for reprint rights.
Poetry: Free verse, haiku, light verse and traditional. No "lengthy" poetry. Buys 50 poems/year. Submit maximum 5 poems. Length: 50 lines maximum. Pays 25¢/line.
Fillers: Jokes, anecdotes and short humor. Buys 52/year. Length: 300 words maximum. Pays same as nonfiction and fiction.
Tips: "Articles should express Biblical principles without being preachy. Setting, plot and characterization must be realistic."

SUNDAY DIGEST, 850 N. Grove Ave., Elgin IL 60120. Editor: Judith Couchman. 75% freelance written. Prefers to work with published/established writers; works with a small number of new/unpublished writers each year. Issued weekly for Christian adults, mainly Protestants. "*Sunday Digest* provides a combination of original articles and reprints, selected to help adult readers better understand the Christian faith, to keep them informed of issues within the Christian community, and to challenge them to a deeper personal commitment to Christ." Pays on acceptance. Publishes ms an average of 9 months after acceptance. Buys first serial rights. Computer printout submissions acceptable; no dot-matrix. Reports in 6-8 weeks. Sample copy and writer's guidelines for 6½x9½ SAE and 2 first-class stamps.
Nonfiction: Needs articles applying the Christian faith to personal and social problems, articles of family interest and on church subjects, inspirational self-help, personal experience and anecdotes. Submit complete ms. Length: 500-1,800 words. Pays 10¢/word.
Fiction: Uses true-to-life fiction that is hard-hitting, fast-moving, with a real woven-in, not "tacked on", Christian message. Also publishes allegory, fantasy, satire, and other fiction types. Length: 1,000-1,500 words. Pays 10¢/word.
Poetry: Would like uplifting free verse poetry with a Christian message.

Market conditions are constantly changing! If this is 1988 or later, buy the newest edition of Writer's Market at your favorite bookstore or order directly from Writer's Digest Books.

Tips: "It is crucial that the writer is committed to high quality Christian communication. The writer should express an evangelical outlook in a crisp, clear writing style. We will be printing few Biblical retellings."

SUNDAY SCHOOL COUNSELOR, General Council of the Assemblies of God, 1445 Boonville, Springfield MO 65802. (417)862-2781. Editor: Sylvia Lee. 60% freelance written. Monthly magazine on religious education in the local church—the official Sunday school voice of the Assemblies of God channeling programs and help to local, primarily lay, leadership. Circ. 37,000. Pays on acceptance. Publishes ms an average of 9 months after acceptance. Byline given. Offers variable kill fee. Buys first North American serial rights, one-time rights, all rights, simultaneous rights, first serial rights, or second serial (reprint) rights; makes work-for-hire assignments. Submit seasonal/holiday material 7 months in advance. Simultaneous and previously published submissions OK. Computer printout submissions acceptable; prefers letter-quality to dot-matrix. Reports in 2 weeks on queries; 1 month on mss. Sample copy $1; free writer's guidelines.
Nonfiction: How-to, inspirational, interview/profile, personal experience and photo feature. All related to religious education in the local church. Buys 100 mss/year. Send complete ms. Length: 300-1,800 words. Pays $25-90.
Photos: Send photos with ms. Reviews b&w and color prints. Model releases and identification of subjects required. Buys one-time rights.

‡THIS PEOPLE MAGAZINE, Reflecting the LDS Lifestyle, This People Publishing, a division of StratAmerica, Suite 500, 5 Triad Center, Salt Lake City UT 84180. (801)575-6900. Editor: Sheri Dew. 75% freelance written. A lifestyle magazine published 8 times annually, geared to members of The Church of Jesus Christ of Latter-Day Saints (Mormons). "*This People* is a human-interest, consumer publication that profiles the LDS lifestyle and its people. Its tone would be described as upbeat and conservative." Circ. 35,000. Pays on publication. Byline given. Buys first North American serial rights. Submit seasonal/holiday material 6 months in advance. Photocopied submissions OK. Electronic submissions OK. Computer printout submissions acceptable; prefers letter-quality to dot-matrix. Reports in 3 months on queries; 2 months on manuscripts. Sample copy for 9x12 SAE with $1.09 postage; free writer's guidelines.
Nonfiction: Book excerpts, essays, historical/nostalgic, inspirational, interview/profile, personal experience, photo feature and religious. No poetry, fiction or travel. Buys 95 mss/year. Query with published clips. Length: 750-3,500 words. Pays $175-650 for assigned articles; pays $150-300 for unsolicited articles. Sometimes pays the expenses of writers on assignment.
Photos: State availability of photos with submission. Reviews contact sheets, transparencies and prints. Captions and identification of subjects required. Buys all rights.
Fillers: Anecdotes, facts and short humor. Length 100-350 words. Pays $50-100.
Tips: "Because our magazine is profile-oriented, freelancers will find the most success by becoming familiar with *This People*'s content, then making profile suggestions to the editor. It is imperative that the writer be very familiar with the material *This People* has published in the past."

TODAY'S CHRISTIAN PARENT, 8121 Hamilton Ave., Cincinnati OH 45231. (513)931-4050. Editor: Mrs. Mildred Mast. 70% freelance written. Quarterly. Pays on acceptance. Publishes ms an average of 1 year after acceptance. Buys first North American serial rights and occasionally second (reprint) rights. Computer printout submissions acceptable; prefers letter-quality to dot-matrix. Free sample copy and writer's guidelines for 7x9 or larger SASE.
Nonfiction: Devotional, inspirational and informational articles for the family. Also articles concerning the problems and pleasures of parents, grandparents and the entire family; Christian childrearing. Timely articles on moral issues, ethical and social situations, in-depth as much as possible in limited space. Enclose SASE with query for return of manuscript. Query not required on articles less than 900 words. Length: 600-1,200 words. Can use short items on Christian family living; and serious or humorous fillers. Very little poetry. Study magazine before submitting. Pays up to 2½¢/word.
Tips: "Write about familiar family situations in a refreshingly different way, so that help and inspiration shine through the problems and pleasures of parenthood. Manuscript should be crisp, tightly-written. Avoid wordiness and trite situations or formats. Slant: from a Christian perspective."

THE UNITED BRETHREN, United Brethren in Christ Church, 302 Lake St., Huntington IN 46750. (219)356-2312. Editor: Steve Dennie. 20% freelance written. A monthly magazine for the United Brethren denomination, having a conservative evangelical slant. Circ. 5,000. Pays on acceptance. Publishes ms an average of 5 months after acceptance. Byline given. Not copyrighted. Buys one-time rights or second serial (reprint) rights. Submit seasonal/holiday material 5 months in advance. Photocopied, and previously published submissions OK. Computer printout submissions acceptable; prefers letter-quality to dot-matrix. Reports in 6 weeks. Sample copy $2; writer's guidelines for #10 SAE with 1 first class stamp.
Nonfiction: Humor, inspirational, personal experience and religious. Buys 25 mss/year. Send complete ms. Length: 400-2,200 words. Pays $10-45.

Photos: State availability of photos with submissions. Offers $10-15/photo. Identification of subjects required. Buys one-time rights.
Fiction: Humorous and religious. Buys 5 mss/year. Length: 500-2,000 words. Pays $10-45.
Tips: "We like lively, humorous articles which keep the reader interested, yet make a strong spiritual point. It's helpful if you include a brief note with a few sentences about yourself, especially if it's a first-time submission. Short articles in the 500-1,200 word range have the best chance. Also, we need well-researched articles on Christian subjects."

THE UNITED CHURCH OBSERVER, 85 St. Clair Ave. E., Toronto, Ontario M4T 1M8 Canada. (416)960-8500. Publisher and Editor: Hugh McCullum. Managing Editor: Muriel Duncan. 40% freelance written. Prefers to work with published/established writers. A 60-page monthly newsmagazine for people associated with The United Church of Canada. Deals primarily with events, trends and policies having religious significance. Most coverage is Canadian, but reports on international or world concerns will be considered. Pays on publication. Publishes ms an average of 4 months after acceptance. Byline usually given. Buys first serial rights and occasionally all rights. Computer printout submissions acceptable; no dot-matrix.
Nonfiction: Occasional opinion features only. Extended coverage of major issues usually assigned to known writers. No opinion pieces, poetry. Submissions should be written as news, no more than 1,200 words length, accurate and well-researched. Queries preferred. Rates depend on subject, author and work involved. Pays expenses of writers on assignment "as negotiated."
Photos: Buys photographs with mss. B&w should be 5x7 minimum; color 35mm or larger format. Payment varies.
Tips: "The writer has a better chance of breaking in at our publication with short articles; it also allows us to try more freelancers. Include samples of previous *news* writing with query. Indicate ability and willingness to do research, and to evaluate that research. The most frequent mistakes made by writers in completing an article for us are organizational problems, lack of polished style, short on research, and a lack of inclusive language."

UNITED EVANGELICAL ACTION, Box 28, Wheaton IL 60189. (312)665-0500. Editor: Donald R. Brown. Managing Editor: Kevin Piecuch. 75% freelance written. Bimonthly magazine; alternating 16-20 pages. Offers "an objective evangelical viewpoint and interpretive analysis of specific issues of consequence and concern to the American Church and updates readers on ways evangelicals are confronting those issues at the grass-roots level." Circ. 10,500. Pays on publication. Publishes ms an average of 2 months after acceptance. Buys first serial rights. Phone queries OK. Computer printout submissions acceptable. Reports in 1 month. Sample copy and writer's guidelines with SASE.
Nonfiction: Issues and trends in the Church and society that affect the ongoing witness and outreach of evangelical Christians. Content should be well thought through, and should provide practical suggestions for dealing with these issues and trends. Buys 8-10 mss/year. Query. Length: 900-1,000 words. Pays $50-175.
Tips: Editors would really like to see news (action) items that relate to the National Association of Evangelicals. "Keep writing terse, to the point, and stress practical over theoretical."

UNITED METHODIST REPORTER, Box 660275, Dallas TX 75266-0275. (214)630-6495. Editor/General Manager: Spurgeon M. Dunnam, III. Managing Editor: John A. Lovelace. Weekly newspaper for a United Methodist national readership. Circ. 475,000. Pays on acceptance. Byline given. Not copyrighted. Free sample copy and writer's guidelines.
Nonfiction: "We accept occasional short features, approximately 500 words. Articles need not be limited to a United Methodist angle but need to have an explicit Protestant angle, preferably with evidence of participation in a local congregation. Write about a distinctly Christian response to human need or how a person's faith relates to a given situation." Send complete ms. Pays 4¢/word.
Photos: Purchased with accompanying ms. "We encourage the submission of good action photos (5x7 or 8x10 b&w glossy prints) of the persons or situations in the article." Pays $10.
Tips: "Read our publications before submitting. First person stories seldom fit our needs, but opinion pieces of no more than 500 words will be considered without pay for My Witness and Here I Stand."

UNITY MAGAZINE, Unity School of Christianity, Unity Village MO 64065. Editor: Pamela Yearsley. 90% freelance written. A monthly magazine covering metaphysics, spirituality and Christian literature. Circ. 500,000. Pays on acceptance. Publishes ms an average of 7 months after acceptance. Byline given. Buys first North American serial rights. Submit seasonal material 6 months in advance. Photocopied submissions OK. Computer printout submissions acceptable; prefers letter-quality to dot-matrix. Reports in 3 weeks on queries; 2 months on manuscripts. Free sample copy and writer's guidelines.
Nonfiction: Inspirational and metaphysical. Buys 200 mss/year. Submit complete ms. Length: 2,000 maximum words. Pays $10.
Photo: State availability of photos with submission. Reviews 4x5 transparencies. Model releases and identification of subjects required. Buys one-time rights.

Poetry: Any type as long as subject fits the magazine. Buys 120 poems/ year. Submit maximum 10 poems. Length: 30 lines maximum. Pays 50¢/line.
Fillers: Buys 12/year.

THE UPPER ROOM, DAILY DEVOTIONAL GUIDE, The Upper Room, 1908 Grand Ave., Nashville TN 37202. (615)327-2700. World Editor: Janice T. Grana. Managing Editor: Mary Lou Redding. 95% freelance written. Eager to work with new/unpublished writers. Bimonthly magazine "offering a daily inspirational message which includes a Bible reading, text, prayer, 'Thought for the Day,' and suggestion for prayer. Each day's meditation is written by a different person and is usually a personal witness about discovering meaning and power for Christian living through some experience from daily life." Circ. 2,225,000 (U.S.); 385,000 outside U.S. Pays on publication. Publishes ms an average of 1 year after acceptance. Byline given. Buys first North American serial rights and translation rights. Submit seasonal/holiday material 14 months in advance. Computer printout submissions acceptable; prefers letter-quality to dot-matrix. Reports in 6 weeks on mss. Sample copy and writer's guidelines for SAE and 2 first class stamps.
Nonfiction: Inspirational and personal experience. No poetry, lengthy "spiritual journey" stories. Buys 360 unsolicited mss/year. Send complete ms. Length: 250 words maximum. Pays $10.
Tips: "The best way to break into our magazine is to send a well-written manuscript that looks at the Christian faith in a fresh way. Standard stories and sermon illustrations are immediately rejected. We very much want to find new writers and welcome good material. We are particularly interested in meditations based on Old Testament characters and stories. Good repeat meditations can lead to work on longer assignments for our other publications, which pay more. A writer who can deal concretely with everyday situations, relate them to spiritual truths, and write clear, direct prose should be able to write for *The Upper Room*. We want material that provides for more interaction on the part of the reader—meditation suggestions, journaling suggestions, space to reflect and link personal experience with the meditation for the day."

VIRTUE, Box 850, Sisters OR 97759. (503)549-8261. Editor: Becky Durost. 70% freelance written. Monthly Christian magazine for women. Circ. 125,000. Average issue includes 15 feature articles. Pays on publication. Publishes ms an average of 4 months after acceptance. Byline given. Buys first North American rights. Submit seasonal material 6 months in advance. Simultaneous and previously published submissions OK, if so indicated. Computer printout submissions acceptable; prefers letter-quality to dot-matrix. Reports in 1 month on queries. Sample copy $2.50; free writer's guidelines.
Nonfiction: Interviews with Christian women; current issues; how-to (upkeep and organizational tips for home); inspirational (spiritual enrichment); personal experience; and family information for husbands, wives and children. "No mystical or preachy articles." Buys 20 mss/issue. Query. Length: 1,000-1,500 words. Pays 10¢/word.
Photos: Reviews 3x5 b&w glossy prints. Offers additional payment for photos accepted with ms. Captions required. Buys all rights or first serial rights.
Columns/Departments: Opinion piece (reader editorial); foods (recipes and entertaining); and crafts, decorating, gardening, fitness, health, and creative projects. Buys 4-8 mss/issue. Query. Length: 1,000-1,500 words. Pays 10¢/word.
Fiction: Christian adventure, humor and romance. Buys 1 ms/issue. Send complete ms. Length: 1,500-1,800 words. Pays 10¢/word.
Fillers: Anecdotes, short humor, newsbreaks and thought-provoking family stories. Buys 2/issue. Pays 10¢/word.
Tips: "We may be increasing our standard magazine size and will be needing more well-researched articles on current issues."

VISTA, Wesleyan Publishing House, Box 2000, Marion IN 46952. Address submissions to Editor of *Vista.* 25% freelance written. Works with a small number of new/unpublished writers each year. Weekly publication of The Wesleyan Church for adults. Circ. 60,000. Pays on publication. Publishes ms an average of 8 months after acceptance. Byline given. Not copyrighted. "Along with manuscripts for first use, we also accept simultaneous submissions, second rights, and reprint rights. It is the writer's obligation to secure clearance from the original publisher for any reprint rights." Submit material 9 months in advance. Computer printout submissions acceptable; prefers letter-quality to dot-matrix. "SASE for sample copy and with all manuscripts." Not responsible for unsolicited mss. Reports in 2 months.
Nonfiction: Devotional, biographical, and informational articles with inspirational, religious, moral or educational values. Favorable toward emphasis on: New Testament standard of living as applied to our day; soul-winning (evangelism); proper Sunday observance; Christian youth in action; Christian education in the home, the church and the college; good will to others; worldwide missions; clean living, high ideals, and temperance; wholesome social relationships. Disapproves of liquor, tobacco, theaters, dancing. Mss are judged on basis of human interest, ability to hold reader's attention, vivid characterizations, thoughtful analysis of problems, vital character message, expressive English, correct punctuation, proper diction. "Know where you are going

and get there." Length: 500-1,500 words. Pays 2½-3¢/word for quality material, 2¢/word for second rights and reprints.
Photos: Pays $15-40 for 5x7 or 8x10 b&w glossy print portraying people in action, seasonal emphasis, or scenic value. Various reader age groups should be considered.
Fiction: Stories should have definite Christian emphasis and character-building values, without being preachy. Setting, plot and action should be realistic. Length: 1,500 words; also short-shorts and vignettes. Pays 2½-3¢/word for quality material, 2¢/word for second rights and reprints.
Tips: "We often need a 400-600 word filler to complete an issue; and since we don't receive too many of this type of article, those we do get have a greater chance of being published. Our publication is meant to be leisurely Sunday afternoon reading, so we need light-reading inspirational articles that will keep the reader's attention."

VITAL CHRISTIANITY, Warner Press, Inc., 1200 E. 5th St., Anderson IN 46018. (317)644-7721. Editor-in-Chief: Arlo F. Newell. Managing Editor: Richard L. Willowby. 25% freelance written. "Always glad to work with talented people—previously published or not." Magazine covering Christian living for people attending local Church of God congregations; published 20 times/year. Circ. 30,000. Pays on acceptance. Byline given. Offers 100% kill fee. Buys one-time rights. Submit seasonal/holiday material 6 months in advance. Computer printout and disk submissions OK but not preferable. Reports in 6 weeks. Sample copy and writer's guidelines with SASE and $1.
Nonfiction: Humor (with religious point); inspirational (religious—not preachy); interview/profile (of church-related personalities); opinion (religious/theological); and personal experience (related to putting one's faith into practice). Buys 125 mss/year. Query. Length: 1,200 words maximum. Pays $10-100; more for some assigned articles. Sometimes pays the expenses of writers on assignment.
Photos: State availability of photos. Pays $50-300 for 5x7 color transparencies; $20-40 for 8x10 b&w prints. Identification of subjects (when related directly to articles) required. Buys one-time rights. Reserves the right to reprint material it has used for advertising and editorial purposes (pays second rights for editorial re-use).
Tips: "Fillers, personal experience, personality interviews, profiles and good holiday articles are areas of our magazine open to freelancers. All submissions are reviewed. Writers should request our guidelines and list of upcoming topics of interest to determine if they have interest or expertise in writing for us."

WAR CRY, The Official Organ of the Salvation Army, 799 Bloomfield Ave., Verona NJ 07044. Editor: Henry Gariepy. Biweekly magazine for "persons with evangelical Christian background; members and friends of the Salvation Army; the 'man in the street.' " Circ. 300,000. Pays on acceptance. Buys first serial rights and second serial (reprint) rights. Reports in 2 months. Free sample copy.
Nonfiction: Inspirational and informational articles with a strong evangelical Christian slant, but not preachy. In addition to general articles, needs articles slanted toward most of the holidays including Easter, Christmas, Mother's Day, Father's Day, etc. Buys 50 mss/year. Length: approximately 1,000-1,400 words. Pays 5¢/word.
Photos: Occasionally buys photos submitted with ms, but seldom with captions only. Pays $25-35 for b&w glossy prints; $150 for color prints.
Fiction: Prefers complete-in-one-issue stories, with a strong Christian slant. Can have modern or Biblical setting, but must not run contrary to Scriptural account. Length: 1,100-1,400 words. Pays 4¢/word.
Poetry: Religious or nature poems. Length: 4-24 lines. Pays $10-25.

THE WESLEYAN ADVOCATE, The Wesleyan Church Corp., Box 2000, Marion IN 46952. (317)674-3301. Editor: Dr. Wayne E. Caldwell. "We are backlogged with submissions and prefer not to receive unsolicited submissions at this time."

THE WITTENBERG DOOR, 1224 Greenfield Dr., El Cajon CA 92021. (619)440-2333. Contact: Mike Yaconelli. 40% freelance written. Works with a small number of new/unpublished writers each year. Bimonthly magazine for men and women connected with the church. Circ. 19,000. Pays on publication. Publishes ms an average of 1 year after acceptance. Buys all rights. Computer printout submissions acceptable. Reports in 3 months.
Nonfiction: Satirical articles on church renewal, Christianity, and organized religion. Few book reviews. Buys about 30 mss/year. Submit complete ms. Length: 1,000 words maximum, 500-750 preferred. Pays $25-100. Sometimes pays expenses of writers on assignments.
Tips: "We look for someone who is clever, on our wave length, and has some savvy about the evangelical church. We are very picky and highly selective. The writer has a better chance of breaking in at our publication with short articles and fillers since we are a bimonthly publication with numerous regular features and the magazine is only 32 pages. The most frequent mistake made by writers is that they do not understand satire. They see we are a humor magazine and consequently come off funny/cute (like *Reader's Digest*) rather than funny/satirical (like *National Lampoon*)."

Retirement

Most retirement magazine readers don't sit on front porches sipping fruit drinks all day. That's the kind of stereotype that editors want to avoid in retirement magazines. Some people are retiring in their fifties; others are starting a second business—the one they've always dreamed of. Many retirement-age readers prefer to travel or pursue hobbies. These publications give readers specialized information. Some want service articles; others want material to make free time more enjoyable.

GOLDEN YEARS MAGAZINE, Golden Years Senior News, Inc., 233 E. New Haven Ave., Melbourne FL 32902-0537. (305)725-4888. Editor: Carol Brenner-Hittner. 50% freelance written. Monthly magazine covering the "50+" generation. "We serve the needs and interests of Florida's fastest growing generation. Editorial presented in a positive, uplifting, straight-forward manner." Circ. 500,000. Pays on publication. Byline given. Buys first serial rights and first North American serial rights. Submit seasonal/holiday material 6 months in advance. Simultaneous queries, and simultaneous, and photocopied submissions OK. Computer printout submissions acceptable; prefers letter-quality to dot-matrix. Sample copy $1; writer's guidelines for SAE with 1 first class stamp.
Nonfiction: Profile (Florida senior celebrities), travel, health, exercise and nutrition articles (with recipes). Buys 150 mss/year. Query with published clips or send complete ms. Length: 500 words maximum. Pays 10¢/word.
Photos: "We like to include a lot of photos." Send photos with query or ms. Pays $25 for color transparencies. Captions, model releases, and identification of subjects required. Buys one-time rights.
Tips: "We're looking for profiles on Florida people. Our magazine is a small one; all our articles are short and special—that's why we are successful."

‡**GRANDPARENTING!**, Grandparenting!, 801 Cumberland Hills Dr., Hendersonville TN 37075. (615)822-8586. Editor: Betty Adler. 100% freelance written. A bimonthly tabloid for grandparents covering positive, unique personality of grandparents, and interesting activities. Circ. 5,000. Pays on publication. Byline given. Submit seasonal/holiday material 3 months in advance. Simultaneous submissions OK. Reports in 6 weeks on queries. Sample copy for 50¢ postage and handling.
Nonfiction: Humor, interview/profile, personal experience, and travel for grandparents. No articles about senior citizens, retirees, nursing homes, etc. Query. Length: 500-2,500 words. Pays $75.
Photos: Send photos with submission. Reviews 3x5 prints. Offers no additional payment for photos accepted with ms. Captions and identification of subjects required. Buys all rights.
Columns/Departments: Length: 500 words maximum. Pays $50.

MATURE LIVING, A Christian Magazine for Senior Adults, Sunday School Board of the Southern Baptist Convention, 127 9th Ave. N., Nashville TN 37209. (615)251-2191. Editor: Jack Gulledge. Assistant Editor: Zada Malugen. 70% freelance written. A monthly leisure reading magazine for senior adults 60 and older. Circ. 360,000. Pays on acceptance. Byline given. Buys all rights and rarely one-time rights. Submit seasonal/holiday material 18 months in advance. Photocopied submissions OK. Computer printout submissions acceptable; prefers letter-quality to dot-matrix. Reports in 6 weeks. Sample copy for 9x12 SAE with 69¢ postage affixed; writer's guidelines for SAE with 1 first class stamp.
Nonfiction: General interest, historical/nostalgic, how-to, humor, inspirational, interview/profile, personal experience, photo feature and travel. No pornography, profanity, occult; liquor, dancing, drugs, gambling; no book reviews. Buys 100 mss/year. Send complete ms. Length: 1,475 words maximum. Pays 5¢/word accepted.
Photos: State availability of photos with submission. Offers $10-15/photo. Buys one-time rights.
Fiction: Humorous, mainstream and slice-of-life vignettes. No reference to liquor, dancing, drugs, gambling; no pornography, profanity or occult. Buys 12 mss/year. Send complete ms. Length: 900-1,475 words. Pays 5¢/word.
Poetry: Light verse and traditional. Buys 50 poems/year. Submit maximum 5 poems. Length: open. Pays $5-24.
Fillers: Anecdotes, facts and short humor. Buys 15/year. Length: 50 words maximum. Pays $5.

MATURE YEARS, 201 8th Ave., S., Nashville TN 37202. Editor: Daisy D. Warren. 30% freelance written. Prefers to work with published/established writers; works with a small number of new/unpublished writers each year. Quarterly magazine for retired persons and those facing retirement; persons seeking help on how to handle problems and privileges of retirement. Pays on acceptance. Publishes ms an average of 14 months after acceptance. Rights purchased vary with author and material; usually buys first North American serial rights. Submit seasonal material 14 months in advance. Reports in 6 weeks. Free writer's guidelines.
Nonfiction: *"Mature Years* is different from the secular press in that we like material with a Christian and church orientation. Usually we prefer materials that have a happy, healthy outlook regarding aging. Advocacy (for older adults) articles are at times used; some are freelance submissions. We need articles dealing with many aspects of pre-retirement and retirement living, and short stories and leisure-time hobbies related to specific seasons. Give examples of how older persons, organizations, and institutions are helping others. Writing should be of interest to older adults, with Christian emphasis, though not preachy and moralizing. No poking fun or mushy, sentimental articles. We treat retirement from the religious viewpoint. How-to, humor and travel are also considered." Buys 24 unsolicited mss/year. Submit complete ms. Length: 1,200-1,500 words.
Photos: 8x10 b&w glossy prints, color prints or color transparencies purchased with ms or on assignment.
Fiction: "We buy fiction for adults. Humor is preferred. No children's stories and no stories about depressed situations of older adults." Length: 1,000-1,500 words. Payment varies, usually 4¢/word.
Tips: "We like writing to be meaty, timely, clear, and concrete."

MODERN MATURITY, American Association of Retired Persons, 3200 E. Carson, Lakewood CA 90712. Editor-in-Chief: Ian Ledgerwood. 75% freelance written. Bimonthly magazine for readership of persons over 50 years of age. Circ. 14 million. Pays on acceptance. Publishes ms an average of 4 months after acceptance. Byline given. Buys first North American serial rights. Submit seasonal/holiday material 6 months in advance. Computer printout submissions acceptable; prefers letter-quality to dot-matrix. Reports in 1 month. Free sample copy and writer's guidelines.
Nonfiction: Careers, workplace, practical information in living, investments, financial and legal matters, personal relationships, and consumerism. Query preferred. Length: up to 2,000 words. Pays up to $2,500.
Photos: Photos purchased with or without accompanying ms. Pays $250 and up for color and $150 and up for b&w.
Fiction: Write for guidelines.
Poetry: All types. Length: 40 lines maximum. Pays $75.
Fillers: Clippings, jokes, gags, anecdotes, newsbreaks, puzzles (find-the-word, not crossword) and short humor. Pays $50 minimum.
Tips: "The most frequent mistake made by writers in completing an article for us is poor follow-through with basic research. The outline is often more interesting than the finished piece."

‡NEW ENGLAND SENIOR CITIZEN/SENIOR AMERICAN NEWS, Prime National Publishing Corp., 470 Boston Post Rd., Weston MA 02193. Editor-in-Chief: Ira Alterman. 80% freelance written. For men and women aged 60 and over who are interested in travel, finances, retirement lifestyles, special legislation, nostalgia, etc. Monthly newspaper; 24-32 pages. Circ. 60,000. Pays on publication. Publishes ms an average of 9 months after acceptance. Buys all rights. Byline given. Submit seasonal/holiday material 3 months in advance. Previously published material OK. Computer printout submissions acceptable. Reports in 4 months. Sample copy 50¢.
Nonfiction: General interest; how-to (anything dealing with retirement years); inspirational; historical; humor; interview; nostalgia; profile; travel; personal experience; photo features; and articles about medicine relating to gerontology. Buys 10-15 mss/issue. Submit complete ms. Length: 500-1,500 words. Pays $25-50.
Photos: Purchased with ms. Captions required. Pays $5-15/5x7 or 8x10 b&w glossy print. Captions and model releases required.
Fiction: Adventure, historical, humorous, mystery, romance, suspense and religious. Buys 1 ms/issue. Submit complete ms. Length: 500-1,500 words. Pays $25-50.
Tips: "Submit clean, typed, top-quality copy aimed at older tastes, interests, lifestyles and memories."

PRIME TIMES, Grote Deutsch & Co., Suite 120, 2802 International Ln., Madison WI 53704. Managing Editor: Russell H. Grote. Associate Managing Editor: Joan Donovan. 75% freelance written. Prefers to work with published/established writers, but "we will work at times with unpublished writers." Quarterly magazine for people who "are at the height of their careers and planning a dynamic retirement lifestyle, or interested in redefining middle age." The audience is primarily people aged 40-64 who were or are credit union members and want to plan and manage their retirement. Circ. 75,000. Pays on publication. Buys first North American serial rights and second serial (reprint) rights. Publishes ms an average of 6 months after acceptance. Submit seasonal material 6 months in advance. Previously published submissions OK as long as they were not in another national maturity-market magazine. Computer printout submissions acceptable; no dot-matrix. Reports in 2 months. Sample copy only with 9x12 SAE and 5 first class stamps; writer's guidelines for SASE.
Nonfiction: Expose; how-to, new research and updates (related to financial planning methods, consumer

activism, preventive health and fitness, travel, and working/dynamic lifestyle after retirement); interviews of prime-life adults engaged in active or important retirements or otherwise redefining mid-life living; opinion; profile; travel; popular arts; self-image; personal experience; humor; and photo feature. "No rocking chair reminiscing." Articles on health and medical issues and research *must* be founded in sound scientific method and must include current, up-to-date data. "Health related articles are an easy sale, but you must do your homework and be able to document your research. Don't waste your time or ours on tired generalizations about how to take care of the human anatomy. If you've heard it before, so have we. We want to know why and how. We want to know who is doing new research, what the current findings may be, and what scientists on the cutting edge of new research say the future holds, preferably in the next one to five years. Is anyone doing basic research into the physiology of the aging process? If so, who? And what have they found? What triggers the aging process? Why do some people age faster than others? What are the common denominators? Does genetic coding and recombinant DNA research hold the answers to slowing or halting the aging process? Get the picture? Give us the facts, only the facts, and all of the facts. Allow the scientists and our audience to draw their own conclusions." Buys 30-40 mss/year, about half from new talent. Query with published clips. Length: 1,000-3,000 words. Pays $50-1,000. "Be sure to keep a photocopy—just in case gremlins pinch the original." Sometimes pays the expenses of writers on assignment.

Photos: Pays $25-50 for 8x10 glossy high-contrast prints; $25-50 for 35mm color transparency, or according to ASMP guidelines or negotiation; $7.50 for cutline. Will not reproduce color prints. Captions and model releases required. Buys one-time rights. "Do not send irreplaceable *anything*."

Fiction: Length: 1,500-3,500 words. Pays $150-750.

Tips: Query should state qualifications (such as expertise or society memberships). Special issues requiring freelance work include publications on adult friendship; prime-life "passages" (development changes); health and medical research and updates; second careers; money management; continuing education; consequences of the ongoing longevity revolution; and the "creation of new lifestyles for prime-life adults (ages 40-60 primarily) who are well-educated, affluent, and above all, *active*. "Whether urban or rural, male or female, if an attempt at humor, lightness or tongue-in-cheek seems off-target to you, it will to us, too. And we don't gloss over important matters. If you identify a problem, try to identify a solution. Many *Prime Times* readers are not retired but may be interested in planning a dynamic retirement lifestyle; many are well-educated, affluent career professionals or homemakers. About 55% of our readers are women. All are active and redefining the middle years with creative energy and imagination. Age irrelevant writing very desirable. If your work does not promote such dynamic images of people over 40, it will not be on target with us."

‡SENIOR WORLD OF CALIFORNIA, (formerly *Senior World of San Diego/Senior World of Santa Barbara*), Californian Publishing Co., Box 1565, El Cajon CA 92022. (619)442-4404. Executive Editor: Laura Impastato. Travel Editor: Jerry Goodrum. 10% freelance written. Prefers to work with published/established writers. Monthly tabloid newspaper for active older adults living in San Diego, Orange, Santa Barbara, Ventura and San Luis Obispo counties. Circ. 250,000. Pays on publication. Publishes ms an average of 6 months after acceptance. Buys first serial rights. Simultaneous and photocopied submissions OK. Reports in 2 months. Sample copy $2; free writer's guidelines.

Nonfiction: "We are looking for stories on health stressing wellness and prevention; travel—international, domestic and how-to; profiles of senior celebrities and remarkable seniors; finance and investment tips for seniors; interesting hobbies; some food and cooking material geared to older persons." Send query or complete ms. Length: 200-1,000 words. Pays $25-75.

Photos: State availability of photos. Need b&w with model release. Will pay extra for photos. Buys all rights to photos selected to run with a story.

Columns/Departments: Most of our columns are local or staff-written. We will consider a query on a column idea accompanied by a sample column.

Tips: "No 'pity the poor seniors' material. Remember that we are primarily a news publication and that our content and style reflect that. Our readers are active, vital adults 55 years of age and older. No nostalgia about how grandma used to do things." No telephone queries.

ALWAYS submit mss or queries with a stamped, self-addressed envelope (SASE) within your country or International Reply Coupons (IRCs) purchased from the post office for other countries.

Romance and Confession

Whether a story's romantic intrigue has blossomed in real life or in the writer's mind, readers still enjoy *the escape*. Listed here are publications that need these stories, as well as publications that help writers write better romances. To help you write better romances, consider Writer's Digest Books' *Writing Romance Fiction—For Love and Money*, by Helene Schellenberg Barnhart.

AFFAIRE DE COEUR, Leading Publication for Romance Readers and Writers, Affaire de Coeur, Inc., 5660 Roosevelt Pl., Fremont CA ·94538. (415)656-4804. Editors/Publishers: Beth Rowe and Barbara N. Keenan. "We are backlogged with submissions and prefer not to receive unsolicited submissions at this time."

‡BLACK ROMANCE, INTIMACY MAGAZINE, Lexington Library Inc., 13th Floor, 355 Lexington Ave., New York NY 10017. (212)391-1400. Editor: Judy Andrews. Assistant Editor: Lisa Cochran. 95% freelance written. A monthly confessions magazine. "Our magazine is geared to black women between the ages of 13 and 25." Circ. 60,000. Pays on acceptance. Byline given sometimes. Offers 10% kill fee. Buys all rights and makes work-for-hire assignments. Submit seasonal/holiday material 3 months in advance. Simultaneous submissions OK. Reports in 1 month. Free sample copy and writer's guidelines.
Nonfiction: How-to, opinion and personal experience. No soft porn confessions or stereotypical subjects about black men and women. Buys 120 mss/year. Send complete ms. Length: 3,000-5,000 words. Pays $100-150 for assigned articles; pays $75-100 for unsolicited articles.
Photos: State availability of photos with submission. Reviews contact sheets and 8x10 prints. Offers $25-250 maximum/photo. Model releases required. Buys one-time rights.
Columns/Departments: Horoscope; Fashion; Beauty; Advice; Starcast; Trends (current); and The Loveline. Length: 500-1,500 words. Pays $100-150.
Fiction: Adventure, confession, ethnic, historical, horror, mystery, romance, slice-of-life vignettes and suspense. No erotica, fantasy, or experimental. "Stories for our readers must be pertinent to social issues and very current topics, e.g.; abortion, rape, career women, etc."
Tips: "If you have true-to-life confessions from a black male or female perspective, send the manuscript. We cater specifically to beginning writers. We understand how hard it is for writers to get published; therefore, 95% of our material is written by beginners. All sections are open to freelancers. The only thing that we are usually displeased with is when writers who are not black try to write about black lifestyles under a pen name. Usually the language and circumstance are stereotyped. We strongly discourage this. But we do welcome all writers."

MODERN ROMANCES, Macfadden Women's Group, Inc., 215 Lexington Ave., New York NY 10016. Editor: Jean Sharbel. 100% freelance written. Monthly magazine; 80 pages for blue-collar, family-oriented women, ages 18-35 years old. Circ. 200,000. Pays the last week of the month of issue. Buys all rights. Submit seasonal/holiday material 6 months in advance. Reports in 2 months.
Nonfiction: General interest, baby and child care, how-to (homemaking subjects), humor, inspirational, and personal experience. Submit complete ms. Length: 200-1,500 words. Pay depends on merit. "Confession stories with reader identification and a strong emotional tone. No third person material." Buys 14 mss/issue. Submit complete ms. Length: 1,500-8,500 words. Pays 5¢/word.
Poetry: Light, romantic poetry. Length: 24 lines maximum. Pay depends on merit.

SECRETS, Macfadden Women's Group, 215 Lexington Ave., New York NY 10016. (212)340-7500. Vice President and Editorial Director: Florence J. Moriarty. Editor: Jean Press Silberg. 100% freelance written. Prefers to work with published/established writers; works with a small number of new/unpublished writers each year. Monthly magazine for blue-collar family women, ages 18-35. Pays on publication. Publishes ms an average of 4 months after acceptance. Buys all rights. Submit seasonal material 5 months in advance. Reports in 3 months.
Nonfiction and Fiction: Wants true stories of special interest to women: family, marriage and romance themes, "woman-angle articles," or self-help or inspirational fillers. "No pornographic material; no sadistic or abnormal angles. Stories must be written in the first person." Buys 150 mss/year. Submit complete ms. Length: 300-1,000 words for features; 2,500-7,500 words for full-length story. Occasional 10,000-worders. Greatest need: 4,500-6,000 words. Pays 3¢/word for story mss.

Tips: "Know our market. We are keenly aware of all contemporary life styles and activities that involve women and family—i.e., current emphasis on child abuse, or renewed interest in the image of marriage, etc."

‡TORCH ROMANCES, Quest Communications Corp., Box 3307, McLean VA 22103. (703)356-7777. Editor: Elizabeth Brandon-Brown. 80% freelance written. Bimonthly. *"Torch* is a bimonthly romantic lifestyle magazine that publishes a book-length romance, articles and features and a serialized romantic suspense story." Circ. 65,000. Pays on publication. Publishes ms an average of 3 months after acceptance. Byline given. Buys second serial (reprint) rights or all rights. Submit seasonal/holiday material 5 months in advance. Photocopied submissions OK. Computer printout submissions acceptable; no dot-matrix. Reports in 6 weeks on queries. Sample copy $1.75 with SAE and 65¢ postage; writer's guidelines for SASE.
Nonfiction: Kathie Porta, articles editor. Beauty, fashion, how-to, travel and relationships. Buys 24 mss/year. Query with or without published clips, or send complete ms. Length: 600-1,500 words. Pays $50-150. Sometimes pays the expenses of writers on assignment.
Photos: State availability of photos with submission. Offers $10/photo. Model releases and identification of subjects required. Buys one-time rights.
Fiction: Mystery (romantic suspense); romance; and slice-of-life (slanted towards romance). No fiction that does not have a romance theme. Buys 12 or more mss/year. Query or send complete ms. Length: novella, 6,000-8,000 words; book-length novel, 52,000-54,000 words; suspense short story, 6,000-8,000 words; short, short love stories, 500-1,500 words. Pays $75-1,500.
Fillers: Kathie Porta, fillers editor. Buys 12/year. Length: 250-500 words. Pays $50-75.
Tips: "Best way to break in to our publication is through the short story department or romantic suspense stories. Writers should send SASE for free tip sheets."

TRUE CONFESSIONS, Macfadden Women's Group, 215 Lexington Ave., New York NY 10016. Editor: Barbara J. Brett. 90% freelance written. Eager to work with new/unpublished writers. For high-school-educated, blue-collar women, teens through maturity. Monthly magazine. Circ. 250,000. Buys all rights. Byline given on poetry and some articles. Pays during the last week of month of issue. Publishes ms an average of 6 months after acceptance. Submit seasonal material 6 months in advance. Reports in 4 months. Submit complete ms. Computer printout submissions acceptable; prefers letter-quality to dot-matrix. No simultaneous submissions.
Stories, Articles, and Fillers: Timely, exciting, emotional first-person stories on the problems that face today's young women. The narrators should be sympathetic, and the situations they find themselves in should be intriguing, yet realistic. Every story should have a strong romantic interest and a high moral tone, and every plot should reach an exciting climax. Careful study of a current issue is suggested. Length: 2,000-6,000 words; 5,000 word stories preferred; also book lengths of 8,000-10,000 words. Pays 5¢/word. Also, articles and short fillers.
Poetry: Romantic poetry, free verse and traditional, of interest to women. Submit maximum 4 poems. Length: 16 lines maximum. Pays $10 minimum.

TRUE EXPERIENCE, Macfadden Women's Group, 215 Lexington Ave., New York NY 10016. Editor: Paula Misiewicz. Monthly magazine; 80 pages. For young marrieds, blue-collar, high school education. Interests: children, home, arts, crafts, family and self-fulfillment. Circ. 225,000. Pays 30 days after publication. Byline given. Buys all rights. No photocopied or simultaneous submissions. Submit seasonal material 5 months in advance. Reports in 3 months.
Nonfiction: Stories on life situations, e.g., love, divorce, any real-life problems. Romance and confession, first-person narratives with strong identification for readers. Articles on health, self-help or child care. "Remember that we are contemporary. We deal with women's self-awareness and consciousness of their roles in society." Buys 100 mss/year. Submit complete ms. Length: 250-1,500 words for nonfiction; 1,000-7,500 words for personal narrative. Pays 3¢/word.
Poetry: Only traditional forms. Length: 4-20 lines. Payment varies.
Tips: "Study the magazine for style and editorial content."

TRUE LOVE, Macfadden Women's Group, 215 Lexington Ave., New York NY 10016. (212)340-7500. Editor: Colleen Brennan. Monthly magazine; 80 pages. For young, blue-collar women. Circ. 225,000. Pays after publication. Byline given. Buys all rights. Submit seasonal material 6 months in advance. Reports in 2 months.
Nonfiction: Confessions, true love stories (especially young romance); problems and solutions; health problems; marital and child-rearing difficulties. Avoid graphic sex. Stories dealing with reality, current problems, everyday events, with emphasis on emotional impact. Buys 150 mss/year. Submit complete ms. Length: 1,500-8,000 words. Pays 3¢/word. Informational and how-to articles. Length: 250-800 words. Pays 5¢/word minimum.
Tips: "The story must appeal to the average blue-collar woman. It must deal with her problems and interests. Characters—especially the narrator—must be sympathetic."

TRUE ROMANCE, Macfadden Women's Group, 215 Lexington Ave., New York NY 10016. (212)340-7500. Editor: Susan Weiner. Monthly magazine. "Our readership ranges from teenagers to senior citizens. The majority are high school educated, married, have young children and also work outside the home. They are concerned with contemporary social issues, yet they are deeply committed to their husbands and children. They have high moral values and place great emphasis on love and romance." Circ. 225,000. Pays 1 month after publication. Buys all rights. Submit seasonal/holiday material at least 5 months in advance. Reports in 3 months.

Nonfiction: How-to and informational. Submit complete ms. Length: 300-1,000 words. Pays 3¢/word, special rates for short features and articles. Confession. "We want *only* true contemporary stories about relationships." Buys 13 stories/issue. Submit complete ms. Length: 2,000-7,500 words. Pays 3¢/word; slightly higher flat rate for short-shorts.

Poetry: Light verse and traditional. Buys 15/year. Length: 4-20 lines. Pays $10 minimum.

Tips: "The freelance writer is needed and welcomed. A timely, well-written story that is told by a sympathetic narrator who sees the central problem through to a satisfying resolution is all that is needed to break into *True Romance*. We are always looking for good love stories."

‡TRUE STORY, Macfadden Women's Group, 215 Lexington Ave., New York NY 10016. Editor: Helen Vincent. 80% freelance written. For young married, blue-collar women, 20-35; high school education; increasingly broad interests; home-oriented, but looking beyond the home for personal fulfillment. Monthly magazine. Circ. 1,700,000. Buys all rights. Byline given "on articles only." Pays on publication. Submit seasonal material 4 months in advance; make notation on envelope that it is seasonal material. Reports in 4 months.

Nonfiction: Pays a flat rate for columns or departments, as announced in the magazine. Query for fact articles.

Photos: Gus Gazzola, art director. Query about all possible photo submissions.

Fiction: "First-person stories covering all aspects of women's interests: love, marriage, family life, careers, social problems, etc. The best direction a new writer can be given is to carefully study several issues of the magazine; then submit a fresh, exciting, well-written true story. We have no taboos. It's the handling and believability that make the difference between a rejection and an acceptance." Buys about 125 full-length mss/year. Submit only complete mss for stories. Length: 1,500-10,000 words. Pays 5¢/word; $150 minimum.

Science

These publications are edited for laymen interested in technical and scientific developments and discoveries, applied science, and technical or scientific hobbies. Some magazines in the Science Fiction category also buy factual science articles. Publications of interest to the personal computer owner/user are listed in the Personal Computing category. Journals for scientists, engineers, repairmen, etc., are listed in Trade Journals in various categories.

ALTERNATIVE SOURCES OF ENERGY MAGAZINE, 107 S. Central Ave., Milaca MN 56353. Executive Editor: Donald Marier. 15% freelance written. Monthly magazine emphasizing certain alternative energy sources including windpower, hydropower, photovoltaics, cogeneration, waste-to-energy, district-heating. Audience is predominantly male, age 36, college educated and concerned about energy and environmental limitations. Circ. 23,000. Pays on publication. Publishes ms an average of 4 months after acceptance. Buys first North American serial rights returning full rights after publication. Phone queries OK. Simultaneous, photocopied, and previously published submissions OK, "if specified at time of submission." Computer printout submissions acceptable; prefers letter-quality to dot-matrix. Reports in 6 weeks. Sample copy $4.25.

Nonfiction: "Freelance articles published cover a broad range, but we especially look for pieces which deal with technical innovations in the fields mentioned, company profiles, new approaches to financing renewable energy projects, international news, interviews with innovators in the field, progress reports on unique projects, legislative updates, etc. We insist on full addresses for all companies mentioned (unless irrelevant), solid documentation, and a business style. We also advise tight leads, subheaded body copy and short, relevant con-

clusions." Length: "Articles accepted are generally between 500 and 2,000 words. We are always interested in short pieces on very specific topics. This would typically be a 500 word piece on a new wind, hydro,or pv installation with one quality picture. Unless a SASE is included, your article will not be returned. We strongly urge that you forward a short outline prior to beginning a longer article. We'll let you know our level of interest promptly. Pays 7¢/word and two free author copies. If we like the piece, but feel it must be shortened, payment will be based on the printed version.
Photos: $15 per photo or camera ready graphic and two free author copies.
Tips: "*Alternative Sources of Energy Magazine (ASE)* is 'the magazine of the Independent Power Production industry.' Specifically, we cover those industries involved in the production of electricity from renewable energy, including windpower, hydropower, photovoltaics, biomass and cogeneration projects. Writers have a better chance of breaking in at our publication with short articles and fillers because they're tough to get and assure limited 'fluff.' "

ELECTRONICS TODAY, 1300 Don Mills Rd., Don Mills, Toronto, Ontario M3B 3M8 Canada. (416)445-5600. Editor: Bill Markwick. 40-50% freelance written. Eager to work with new/unpublished writers each year. Monthly magazine; 88 pages. Emphasizes audio, electronics and personal computing for a wide-ranging readership, both professionals and hobbyists. Circ. 20,000. Pays on publication. Publishes ms an average of 2 months after acceptance. Byline given. Buys all rights. Phone queries OK. Submit seasonal/holiday material 4 months in advance. Photocopied submissions OK. Electronic submissions OK; prefer IBM or Apple format disks with ASCII files. Computer printout submissions acceptable. SAE, IRC. Reports in 4 weeks. Sample copy $3; free writer's guidelines.
Nonfiction: How-to (technical articles in electronics field); humor (if relevant to electronics); new product (if using new electronic techniques); and technical (on new developments, research, etc.). Buys 10 unsolicited mss/year. Query. Length: 600-3,500 words. Pays $75-100/1,000 words.
Photos: "Ideally we like to publish two photos or diagrams per 1,000 words of copy." State availability of photo material with query. Additional payment for photos accepted with accompanying manuscript. Captions required. Buys all rights.
Tips: "Less computer coverage will result in a shift to general science and hi-tech."

EQUILIBRIUM, The Science of All Sciences, Eagle Publishing Co., Box 162, Golden CO 80402. Editor: Gary A. Eagle. "Equilibrium is a new scientific theory or a new dimension in science being proven by published articles. Opposites are equal with relative value. The dissemination of the balancing of the universe is from many aspects or perspectives. Nearly the full contents is known or understood by a general audience. However, these articles are all linked to one concept. One important theme is held throughout the entire contents." Magazine published for "the average intelligent individual." 30% freelance written. Pays on acceptance or publication. Publishes ms an average of 12 months after acceptance. Byline given. Offers 50% kill fee; varies for ghosts. Buys all rights. Computer printout submissions acceptable; no dot-matrix. Simultaneous queries, and simultaneous, photocopied, and previously published submissions OK. Reports in 3 months on queries; 6 months on mss. Sample copy for $3 with 9x12 SAE and 4 first class stamps; writer's guidelines for business size SAE and 1 first class stamp.
Nonfiction: Historical/nostalgic (history repeats itself); how-to (physics, psychology, political science, medical, evolution, economics, philosophical, religion, actual UFO occurrences with photo); photo feature (any photo to show balance of something, with article or without); and technical. All should have an equilibrium slant—anything to prove our point. Think of opposites and equal values. Inquire about special issues. Modern events are accepted. No profanity, direct defamation or anything not of the common interest. "Much of our literature is controversial." Buys 20 mss/year. Query. Length: 50-1,000 words; more than 1,000 words if article series. Pays $50-500.
Photos: State availability or send photos with query or ms. Pays $20-40 for 1" b&w and color slides, and b&w and color prints. Captions required.
Columns/Departments: Especially wants editorials; must speak favorably for equilibrium theory. Length: 250 words. Pays $50-100.
Poetry: Light verse, traditional. "None will be accepted if not dealing with the balance of the universe." Submit maximum 10 poems. Length: 5-20 lines. Pays $10-50.
Fillers: Clippings, jokes, gags, short humor, cartoons. Buys 20/year. Length: 5-20 words. Pays $10-50.
Tips: "Article should be written simply even if you are a professional. State what the balancing aspect of the universe is in query." Tell what the "opposite and equal" reaction is plainly. Encourages new writers. "We read everything that comes in. Though our program has been geared toward the philosophical, we are receptive to a variety of subjects . . . our needs are flexible. We're looking for anything to prove this theory of equilibrium—large or small." First-, second- *and* third-person approach OK; controversial material acceptable. "The most frequent mistakes made by writers in completing an article for us are that they fail to illustrate *or* demonstrate the opposites and equals. They also fail to use the common household dictionary."

‡**FUSION, Science-Technology-Economics-Politics**, Fusion Energy Foundation, Box 17149, Washington DC 20041-0149. (703)689-2490. Editor: Carol White. Managing Editor: Marjorie Hecht. 30% freelance written. A bimonthly magazine covering "space, science history, biophysics, nuclear fusion, defense (SDI), advanced technology and astronomy for a scientific and lay audience. Fusion is progrowth, pronuclear and covers the frontier areas of science." Circ. 80,000. Pays on publication. Publishes ms an average of 6 months after acceptance. Byline given. Buys first North American serial rights, one-time rights or makes work-for-hire assignments. Simultaneous, photocopied and previously published submissions OK. Computer printout submissions acceptable; prefers letter-quality to dot-matrix. Reports in 2 weeks on queries. Sample copy $3.
Nonfiction: Expose (science issues), historical (science), how-to (children's science project), interview/profile (science), new product (high technology), opinion (science issues), technical and international energy and development issues. Buys 3-4 mss/year; would like to buy more. Query. Length: 500 minimum. Pays $100-400.
Photos: State availability of photos with submission. Reviews prints. Offers no additional payment for photos accepted with ms. Captions, model releases and identification of subjects required.
Columns/Departments: The Young Scientist (covers space news, astronomy, history, energy, experiments—slant is challenging), 450-1,500 words; Books (reviews of books in the areas magazine covers), 250-700 words; Viewpoint (opinion on issues of controversy), 450-1,000 words. Query. Pays up to $100.
Tips: "The areas of our publication most open to freelancers are the Young Scientist, books and news articles, particularly international coverage."

HANDS-ON ELECTRONICS, (formerly *Special Projects*), Gernsback Publishing Co., 500-B Bi County Blvd., Farmingdale NY 11735. (516)293-3000. Editor: Julian S. Martin. 95% freelance written. Eager to work with new/unpublished writers each year. Bimonthly magazine for electronics hobbyists in the areas of shortwave listening, amateur radio, project designing and building, antique radio, personal computers, theory buffs, home appliance repair, etc. Circ. 110,000. Pays on acceptance. Publishes ms an average of 3 months after acceptance. Byline given. Makes work-for-hire assignments. Submit seasonal/holiday material 6 months in advance. Simultaneous queries, and simultaneous, photocopied, and previously published submissions OK. Electronic submissions OK via IBM PC, but requires hard copy also. Computer printout submissions acceptable. Reports on queries within 2 weeks; 3 weeks on mss. Free sample copy.
Nonfiction: Book excerpts, how-to, new product, photo feature and technical. No business, industry or trade articles. Buys 125 mss/year. Query or send complete ms. Length: 50-3,000 words. Pays $100-300. Sometimes pays the expenses of writers on assignment.
Photos: Send photos with query or ms. Reviews 5x7 or 8x10 b&w prints. Photos purchased with ms, not individually. Captions, model releases, and identification of subjects required. Buys all rights.
Columns/Departments: Editorial, Bookshelf, New Products, and Test Bench Tips. Departments/columns assigned to professional writers and are not purchased "over the transom." Buys 50 mss/year. Query. Length: determined prior to assignment. Pays $25.
Fillers: Cartoons. Buys 25/year. Length: 50-1,000 words. Pays $25.
Tips: "Be a reader of the magazine and know the subject matter as a hobbyist. Writers should be specialized in a minimum of subject areas. We are going monthly with the November 1986 issue."

MODERN ELECTRONICS, For electronics and computer enthusiasts, Modern Electronics Publishing, Inc., 76 N. Broadway, Hicksville NY 11801. (516)681-2922. 90% freelance written. Monthly magazine covering consumer electronics, personal computers, electronic circuitry, construction projects, and technology for readers with a technical affinity. Circ. 75,000. Pays on acceptance. Publishes ms an average of 3 months after acceptance. Byline given. Offers 25% kill fee. Buys first North American serial rights. Submit seasonal/holiday material minimum 4 months in advance. Computer printout submissions acceptable; prefers letter-quality to dot-matrix. Reports in 1 week on queries; 3 weeks on mss. Sample copy $1; writer's guidelines for business size SAE and 1 first class stamp.
Nonfiction: General interest (new technology, product buying guides); how-to (construction projects, applications); new product (reviews); opinion (experiences with electronic and computer products); technical (features and tutorials: circuits, applications); includes stereo, video, communications and computer equipment. "Articles must be technically accurate. Writing should be 'loose,' not textbookish." No long computer pro-

 The double dagger before a listing indicates that the listing is new in this edition. New markets are often the most receptive to freelance contributions.

grams. Buys 100 mss/year. Query. Length: 500-4,000 words. Pays $80-150/published page. Sometimes pays expenses of writers on assignment.

Photos: Send photos with query or ms. Reviews color transparencies and 5x7 b&w prints. Captions, model releases, and identification of subjects required. Buys variable rights depending on mss.

Tips: "The writer must have technical or applications acumen and well-researched material. Articles should reflect the latest products and technology. Sharp, interesting photos are helpful, as are rough, clean illustrations for re-drawing. Cover 'hot' subjects (avoid old technology). Areas most open to freelancers include feature articles, technical tutorials, and projects to build. Some writers exhibit problems with longer pieces due to limited technical knowledge and/or poor organization. We can accept more short pieces."

OMNI, 1965 Broadway, New York NY 10023-5965. Executive Editor: Gurney Williams, III. 90% freelance written. Prefers to work with published/established writers; works with a small number of new/unpublished writers each year. Monthly magazine of the future covering science fact, fiction, and fantasy for readers of all ages, backgrounds and interests. Circ. 850,000. Average issue includes 2-3 nonfiction feature articles and 1-2 fiction articles; also numerous columns and 2 pictorials. Pays on acceptance. Publishes ms an average of 5 months after acceptance. Offers 25% kill fee. Buys exclusive worldwide and exclusive first English rights and rights for *Omni* Anthologies. Submit seasonal material 4-6 months in advance. Photocopied submissions OK. Computer printout submissions acceptable; prefers letter-quality to dot-matrix. Reports in 6 weeks. Free writer's guidelines with SASE (request fiction or nonfiction).

Nonfiction: "Articles with a futuristic angle, offering readers alternatives in housing, energy, transportation, medicine and communications. Scientists can affect the public's perception of science and scientists by opening their minds to the new possibilities of science journalism. People want to know, want to understand what scientists are doing and how scientific research is affecting their lives and their future. *Omni* publishes articles about science in language that people can understand. We seek very knowledgable science writers who are ready to work with scientists to produce articles that can inform and interest the general reader." Send query/proposal. Length: 2,500-3,500 words. Pays $1,750-2,000.

Photos: Frank DeVino, graphic director. State availability of photos. Reviews 35mm slides and 4x5 transparencies. Pays the expenses of writers on assignment.

Columns/Departments: Explorations (unusual travel or locations on Earth); Breakthroughs (new products); Mind (by and about psychiatrists and psychologists); Earth (environment); Life (biomedicine); Space (technology); Arts (theatre, music, film, technology); Interview (of prominent person); Continuum (newsbreaks); Antimatter and UFO Update (unusual newsbreaks, paranormal); Stars (astronomy); First/Last Word (editorial/humor); Artificial Intelligence (computers); The Body (medical). Query with clips of previously published work. Length: 1,500 words maximum. Pays $750-850; $150 for Continuum and Antimatter items.

Fiction: Contact Ellen Datlow. Fantasy and science fiction. Buys 2 mss/issue. Send complete ms. Length: 10,000 words maximum. Pays $1,250-2,000.

Tips: "Consider science fact and science fiction pictorials with a futuristic leaning. We're interested in thematic composites of excellent photos or art with exciting copy."

POPULAR COMMUNICATIONS, Popular Communications, Inc., 76 N. Broadway, Hicksville NY 11801. (516)681-2922. Editor: Tom Kneitel. 25% freelance written. Works with a small number of new/unpublished writers each year. Monthly magazine on shortwave radio monitoring and other communications topics. Circ. 86,000. Pays on publication. Publishes ms an average of 1 year after acceptance. Byline given. Buys first North American serial rights. Submit seasonal/holiday material 5 months in advance. Simultaneous queries and photocopied submissions OK. Computer printout submissions acceptable; prefers letter-quality to dot-matrix. Reports in 1 month on queries; 2 months on mss. Free sample copy and writer's guidelines.

Nonfiction: Book excerpts (from author of book; on any communications topic); historical/nostalgic (old-time radio station or radio people stories); how-to (build projects for antennas and communications equipment); new product (reviews of communications products—tested); what scanner listeners are monitoring; and new radio stations around the world. No personal experience; interviews with TV/radio personalities; personal opinion; or technical. Buys 30-40 mss/year. Query or send complete ms. Pays $35/published page.

Tips: "We prefer third person features on objective radio communication subjects. We are only interested in writers who have an easy, natural style, no technical or 'my adventure' style."

‡POPULAR MECHANICS, 224 W. 57th St., New York NY 10019. (212)262-4815. Editor: Joe Oldham. Managing Editor: Bill Hartford. 50% freelance written. Monthly magazine; 200 pages. Circ. 1,625,000. Computer printout submissions acceptable; must be letter-quality. Buys all rights. Byline given. Pays "promptly." Publishes ms an average of 6 months after acceptance.

Nonfiction: Principal subjects are cars, woodworking, metalworking, home improvement, home maintenance, new technology, sports, electronics, boats, science, photography, audio and video. Also looking for adventure articles with a technology emphasis. No fiction. Looking for reporting on a new and unusual developments. The writer should be specific about what makes it new, different, better, cheaper, etc. Query. Length: 300-2,000 words. Pays $300-1,500.

Photos: Dramatic photos are most important, and they should show people and things in action. Topnotch photos are a must for Home and Shop Section articles. Can also use remodeling of homes, rooms and outdoor structures.

POPULAR SCIENCE, 380 Madison Ave., New York NY 10017. Editor-in-Chief: C.P. Gilmore. 40% freelance written. Prefers to work with published/established writers. Monthly magazine; 150-200 pages. For the well-educated adult, interested in science, technology, new products. Circ. 1,800,000. Pays on acceptance. Publishes ms an average of 4 months after acceptance. Byline given. Buys all rights. Pays negotiable kill fee. Free guidelines for writers. Any electronic submissions OK. Computer printout submissions acceptable; prefers letter-quality to dot-matrix. Submit seasonal/holiday material 4 months after acceptance. Reports in 3 weeks. Query. Writer's guidelines for SAE and 1 first class stamp.
Nonfiction: "*Popular Science* is devoted to exploring (and explaining) to a nontechnical but knowledgable readership the technical world around us. We cover the physical sciences, engineering and technology, and above all, products. We are largely a 'thing'-oriented publication: things that fly or travel down a turnpike, or go on or under the sea, or cut wood, or reproduce music, or build buildings, or make pictures, or mow lawns. We are especially focused on the new, the ingenious and the useful. We are consumer-oriented and are interested in any product that adds to the enjoyment of the home, yard, car, boat, workshop, outdoor recreation. Some of our 'articles' are only a picture and caption long. Some are a page long. Some occupy 4 or more pages. Contributors should be as alert to the possibility of selling us pictures and short features as they are to major articles. Freelancers should study the magazine to see what we want and avoid irrelevant submissions. No biology or life sciences." Buys several hundred mss/year. Pays $200/published page minimum. Uses both color and b&w photos. Pays expenses of writers on assignment.
Tips: "Probably the easiest way to break in here is by covering a news story in science and technology that we haven't heard about yet. We need people to be acting as scouts for us out there and we are willing to give the most leeway on these performances. We are interested in good, sharply focused ideas in all areas we cover. We prefer a vivid, journalistic style of writing, with the writer taking the reader along with him, showing the reader what he saw, through words. Please query first."

RADIO-ELECTRONICS, 500-B Bi-County Blvd., Farmingdale NY 11735. (516)293-3000. Editorial Director: Art Kleiman. For electronics professionals and hobbyists. Monthly magazine, 128 pages. Circ. 211,000. Buys all rights. Byline given. Pays on acceptance. Submit seasonal/holiday material 8 months in advance. Reports in 3 weeks. Send for "Guide to Writing."
Nonfiction: Interesting technical stories on all aspects of electronics, including video, radio, computers, communications, and stereo written from viewpoint of the electronics professional, serious experimenter, or layman with technical interests. Construction (how-to-build-it) articles used heavily. Unique projects bring top dollars. Cost of project limited only by what item will do. Emphasis on "how it works, and why." Much of material illustrated with schematic diagrams and pictures provided by author. Also high interest in how-to articles. Length: 1,000-5,000 words. Pays about $50-500.
Photos: State availability of photos. Offers no additional payment for b&w prints or 35mm color transparencies. Model releases required.
Columns/Departments: Pays $50-200/column.
Fillers: Pays $15-35.
Tips: "The simplest way to come in would be with a short article on some specific construction project. Queries aren't necessary; just send the article, 5 or 6 typewritten pages."

66 *Many of our writers expect a personal response to each manuscript we evaluate. This is simply prohibitive. We send checklists so the author has an idea of what problems we discovered.* **99**

Patrick Lucien Price, AMAZING Stories

73 FOR RADIO AMATEURS, Peterborough NH 03458. (603)924-9261. Publisher: Wayne Green. Editor: Stu Norwood. For amateur radio operators and experimenters. Monthly. Buys all rights. Pays on acceptance. Reports on submissions within a few weeks. Query.
Nonfiction: Articles on anything of interest to radio amateurs, experimenters and computer hobbyists—construction projects. Pays $40-50/page.
Photos: Photos purchased with ms.
Tips: Query letter "should be as specific as possible. Don't hold back details that would help us make a decision. We are not interested in theoretical discussions, but in practical ideas and projects which our readers can use."

TECHNOLOGY REVIEW, Alumni Association of the Massachusetts Institute of Technology, Room 10-140, Massachusetts Institute of Technology, Cambridge MA 02139. Editor-in-Chief: John I. Mattill. 20% freelance written. Emphasizes technology and its implications for scientists, engineers, managers and social scientists. Magazine published 8 times/year. Circ. 75,000. Pays on publication. Publishes ms an average of 3 months after acceptance. Buys first rights. Phone queries OK. Submit seasonal/holiday material 6 months in advance of issue date. Simultaneous and photocopied submissions OK. Computer printout submissions acceptable. Reports in 6 weeks. Sample copy $2.50.
Nonfiction: General interest, interview, photo feature and technical. Buys 5-10 mss/year. Query. Length: 1,000-6,000 words. Pays $50-750. Sometimes pays the expenses of writers on assignment.
Columns/Departments: Book Reviews; Trend of Affairs; Technology and Economics; and "Prospects" (guest column). Also special reports on other appropriate subjects. Query. Length: 750-4,000 words. Pays $50-750.

Science Fiction

These magazines specialize in science fiction and fantasy; some also buy factual science articles. Additional science fiction markets are in the Literary and "Little" category.

AMAZING® Stories, TSR, Inc., Box 110, Lake Geneva WI 53147-0110. Managing Editor: Patrick L. Price. 90% freelance written. Eager to work with new/unpublished writers. Bimonthly magazine of science fiction and fantasy short stories. "Audience does not need to be scientifically literate, but the authors must be, where required. *AMAZING* is devoted to the best science fiction and fantasy by new and established writers. There is no formula. We require the writers using scientific concepts be scientifically convincing, and that every story contain believable and interesting characters and some overall point." Circ. 13,000. Pays on acceptance. Publishes ms an average of 18 months after acceptance. Byline given. Buys first North American serial rights; "single, non-exclusive re-use option (with additional pay)." Photocopied submissions OK. Computer printout submissions acceptable; no dot-matrix. Reports in 4-6 weeks. Sample copy for $2.50; writer's guidelines $2, postpaid.
Nonfiction: Historical (about science fiction history and figures); interview/profile and science articles of interest to science fiction audiences; reviews and essays about major science fiction movies written by big names. No "pop pseudo-science trends: The Unified Field Theory Discovered; How I Spoke to the Flying Saucer People; Interpretations of Past Visits by Sentient Beings, as Read in Glacial Scratches on Granite, etc." Buys 4-8 mss/year. Query with or without published clips. Length: 300-10,000 words. Pays 6¢/word up to 7,500 words; 5¢/word for 12,000 or more words. Sometimes pays the expenses of writers on assignment.
Fiction: Heroic fantasy; novel excerpts (rarely—query); science fiction. "We are looking for hard or speculative science fiction, space fantasy/opera, and heroic fantasy. We don't want horror fiction or fairy tales. No 'true' experiences, media-derived fiction featuring *Star Wars* (etc.) characters, stories based on UFO reports or standard occultism." Buys 50-60 mss/year. Send complete ms. Length: 500-25,000 words. "Anything longer, ask." Pays 6¢/word to 7,500 words; 5¢/word for 12,000 or more words.
Poetry: All types are OK. No prose arranged in columns. Buys 5 poems/year. Submit maximum 3 poems.

Length: 45 lines maximum; ideal length, 30 lines or less. Pays 50¢-$1/line.

Tips: "Short fiction is the best way for freelancers to break in to our publication. We basically want good stories. We look for larger pieces by established writers, because their names help sell our product. Don't try to especially tailor one for our 'slant.' We want original concepts, good writing, and well-developed characters. Avoid certain obvious clichés: UFO landings in rural areas, video games which become real (or vice-versa), stories based on contemporary newspaper headlines. '*Hard*' science fiction, that is, science fiction. which is based on a plausible extrapolation from real science, is increasingly rare and very much in demand. The standard pseudo-medieval fantasy is very easy to get, but dull because of its standardness. Exceptional originality is required in that area."

ANALOG SCIENCE FICTION/SCIENCE FACT, 380 Lexington Ave., New York NY 10017. Editor: Dr. Stanley Schmidt. 100% freelance written. Eager to work with new/unpublished writers. For general future-minded audience. Monthly. Buys first North American serial rights and nonexclusive foreign serial rights. Publishes ms an average of 10 months after acceptance. Byline given. Computer printout submissions (with dark ink) acceptable; prefers letter-quality to dot-matrix. Good dot-matrix submissions are acceptable. Reports in 1 month. Sample copy $2.50 (no SASE needed); free writer's guidelines for SAE and 1 first class stamp.

Nonfiction: Illustrated technical articles dealing with subjects of not only current but future interest, i.e., with topics at the present frontiers of research whose likely future developments have implications of wide interest. Buys about 12 mss/year. Query. Length: 5,000 words. Pays 5.75¢/word.

Fiction: "Basically, we publish science fiction stories. That is, stories in which some aspect of future science or technology is so integral to the plot that, if that aspect were removed, the story would collapse. The science can be physical, sociological or psychological. The technology can be anything from electronic engineering to biogenetic engineering. But the stories must be strong and realistic, with believable people doing believable things—no matter how fantastic the background might be." Buys 60-100 unsolicited mss/year. Send complete ms on short fiction; query about serials. Length: 2,000-60,000 words. Pays 4.0-4.6¢/word for novelettes and novels; 6.0-7.0¢/word for shorts under 7,500 words. $430-525 for intermediate lengths; on acceptance for first North American serial rights.

Tips: "In query give clear indication of central ideas and themes and general nature of story line—and what is distinctive or unusual about it. We have no hard-and-fast editorial guidelines, because science fiction is such a broad field that I don't want to inhibit a new writer's thinking by imposing 'Thou Shalt Not's.' Besides, a really good story can make an editor swallow his preconceived taboos. I want the best work I can get, regardless of who wrote it—and I need new writers. So I work closely with new writers who show definite promise, but of course it's impossible to do this with *every* new writer. No occult or fantasy."

‡BEYOND . . ., Science Fiction and Fantasy, Other World Books, Box 1124, Fair Lawn NJ 07410-1124. (201)791-6721. Editor: Shirley Winston. Managing Editor: Robera Rogow. 80% freelance written. Works with a small number of new/unpublished writers each year. A science fiction and fantasy magazine published 3 times a year. "Our audience is mostly science fiction fans." Estab. 1985. Circ. 300. Pays on publication. Publishes ms an average of 6 months after acceptance. Byline given. Buys first North American serial rights. Submit seasonal/holiday material 6 months in advance. Photocopied submissions OK. Electronic submissions OK via Kaypro II, Wordstar, but requires hard copy also. Computer printout submissions acceptable; no dot-matrix. Reports in 3 weeks. Sample copy $4; writer's guidelines for SASE.

Nonfiction: Essays and humor. Buys 3 mss/year. Send complete ms. Length: 500-1,500 words. Pays $1.25-3.75 and 1 copy.

Columns/Departments: Reviews (of books and periodicals in science fiction and fantasy area), 500-1,500 words. Buys 3 mss/year. Send complete ms. Length: 500-1,500 words. Pays $1.25-3.75.

Fiction: Fantasy and science fiction only. "We enjoy using stories with a humorous aspect. No horror stories, excessive violence or explicit sex; nothing degrading to women or showing prejudice based on race, religion, or planet of origin. No predictions of universal destruction; we prefer an outlook on the future in which the human race survives and progresses." Buys 20 mss/year. Send complete ms. Length: 500-8,000 words; prefers 4,000-5,000 words. Pays $1.25-20 and 1 copy.

Poetry: Free verse, haiku, light verse and traditional. "Poetry should be comprehensible by an educated reader literate in English, take its subject matter from science fiction or fantasy, need not rhyme but should fall musically on the ear." No poetry unrelated to science fiction or fantasy. Buys 18 poems/year. Submit maximum 3 poems. Length: 4-65 words. Pays 2¢/line and 1 copy.

Tips: Fiction and poetry are most open to freelancers.

FANTASY BOOK, Box 60126, Pasadena CA 91106. Executive Editor: Dennis Mallonee. Editor: Nick Smith. 100% freelance written. Quarterly magazine of illustrated fantasy fiction for all ages; "bulk of the readership is in the 17-35 range." Circ. 5,000. Pays on "approval of galleys." Publishes ms an average of 6 months after acceptance. Byline given. Buys first North American serial rights. Submit seasonal/holiday material 6 months in advance. Photocopied submissions OK. Computer printout submissions acceptable. Reports in 6 weeks on mss. Sample copy $4; writer's guidelines for legal size SAE and 1 first class stamp.

Fiction: "We will consider any story related to fantasy fiction. We look for stories with strong characterization and carefully developed plot." Buys 50 mss/year. Send complete ms. Length: 2,000-10,000 words. Pays 3-5¢/word.

Poetry: Light verse, traditional. Buys 8/year. Submit maximum 4 poems. Length: open. Pays $5-20.

FANTASY REVIEW, Florida Atlantic University, 500 NW 20th St., Boca Raton FL 33431. (305)393-3839. Editor: Robert A. Collins. Managing Editor: Catherine Fischer. 50% freelance written. A monthly genre literary magazine of fantasy/horror/science fiction for authors, fans, scholars, editors, publishers, dealers, book store owners and students. Circ. 3,500. Pays on publication. Publishes ms an average of 2 months after acceptance. Byline given. Buys first North American serial rights. Submit seasonal/holiday material 4 months in advance. Simultaneous queries, and simultaneous and photocopied submissions OK. Electronic submissions 8" single side, single density CP/M system (sysgen) for disks; 300 baud, CP/M MODEM 9 handholding program for modems, but requires hard copy also. Computer printout submissions acceptable; prefers letter-quality to dot-matrix. Reports in 3 weeks on queries; 6 weeks on mss. Sample copy $2; free writer's guidelines.

Nonfiction: General interest (essays directed to fans); historical/nostalgic (about authors, publishers, artist in field); humor (concerning genre literature); interview/profile (of articles and authors in field); new product (new books, films, magazines, art in field); opinion (reviews of books, films, art); personal experience (by authors on getting published); photo feature (fantasy and science fiction events); and surveys of foreign fiction, foreign fandom. "We don't want breezy fluff. We need solid research and reasoning, knowledge of field, plus easy style. No 'little green men invade our city' stuff. Writers must know the field." Buys 36 mss/year. Query or send complete ms. Length: 1,000-5,000 words. Pays 2-3¢/word.

Photos: State availability of photos with query letter, send photos with ms. Pays $5-25 for 5x7 or 8x10 b&w prints. Captions, model release, and identification of subjects required. Buys one-time rights.

Columns/Departments: Commentary Department: reviews of *forthcoming* books, films, magazines, art shows; Opinion: topics of fan interest. Other columns are assigned. Buys 50 mss/year. Length: 500-1,000 words. Pays $10-20.

Poetry: Free verse, haiku, light verse, traditional. "Poems must have a fantasy, horror, or science fiction twist. We don't want conventional topics." Buys 12 poems/year. Submit maximum 5 poems. Length: 3-30 lines. Pays $5-25.

Fillers: Clippings, jokes, gags, newsbreaks. Fillers must have genre interest. Length: 50-150 words. Pays $5.

Tips: "We especially need good articles (*solid thinking,* entertaining style) on odd or representative authors, trends, topics within the field; also interviews with up-and-coming authors and artists *with* pictures."

‡**HAUNTS,** Nightshade Publications, Box 3342, Providence RI 02906. (401)781-9438. Editor: Joseph K. Cherkes. 98% freelance written. Eager to work with new/unpublished writers. "We are a literary quarterly geared to those fans of the 'pulp' magazines of the 30's, 40's and 50's, with tales of horror, the supernatural, and the bizzare. We are trying to reach those in the 18-35 age group." Circ. 1,000. Pays on publication. Publishes ms an average of 7 months after acceptance. Byline given. Buys first North American serial rights. Photocopied submissions OK. Computer printout submissions acceptable; prefers letter-quality to dot-matrix. Reports in 3 weeks on queries; 2 months on mss. Sample copy $2.50; writer's guidelines free.

Fiction: Fantasy, horror and suspense. "No fiction involving blow-by-blow dismemberment, explicit sexual scenes, or pure adventure." Buys 36 fiction mss/year. Query. Length: 1,500-10,000 words. Pays $5-33.

Poetry: Free verse, light verse and traditional. Buys 4 poems/year. Submit maximum 3 poems. Offers contributor's copies.

Tips: "How the writer handles revisions often is a key to acceptance."

THE HORROR SHOW, Phantasm Press, 14848 Misty Springs Ln., Oak Run CA 96069-9801. (916)472-3540. Editor: David B. Silva. 95% freelance written. Eager to work with new/unpublished writers. Quarterly horror magazine. Circ. 2,500. Publishes ms an average of 3 months after acceptance. Buys first serial rights. Computer printout submissions acceptable. Reports in 3 weeks. Sample copy for $4 and $1 postage; writer's guidelines for SAE and 1 first class stamp.

Columns/Departments: Curses (letters to the editor); Nightmares (news about the horror field).

Fiction: Contemporary horror. "Articles should *not* splash over into science fiction or fantasy (sword and sorcery). We are specifically looking for material with well-developed characters. Do not over-indulge in sex or violence." Send complete ms. Length: 4,000 words maximum. Pays ½¢/word plus contributor's copy.

Tips: "We enjoy the honor of publishing first stories and new writers, but we always expect a writer's best effort. Read the magazine. Come up with a unique premise, polish every word, then send it our way. A frequent mistake made by writers in completing an article for us is that the article is not directed at the reader. We look for informative articles directly related to the horror genre. In 1987, we will be slanting each issue toward a specific author or artist in the field of horror."

‡INFINITUM, Science Fiction-Fantasy, William H. Doyle, 5737 Louetta Rd., Spring TX 77379. (713)376-9693. Editor: William H. Doyle. 100% freelance written. Works with a small number of new/unpublished writers each year. A seminannual magazine of science fiction, fantasy and horror. Estab. 1985. Circ. 400. Pays on publication. Publishes ms an average of 6 months after acceptance. Byline given. Offers 50% kill fee. Buys first North American serial rights or second serial (reprint) rights. Photocopied and previously published submissions OK. Computer printout submissions acceptable; prefers letter-quality to dot-matrix. Reports in 6 weeks. Sample copy $3; writer's guidelines for SASE.
Fiction: Science fiction, fantasy, or horror; can be adventure, experimental or humor-oriented. No "clichéd 'after the bomb' science fiction. Buys 20 mss/year. Send complete ms. Length: 300-6,000 words. Pays ¼¢/word.
Poetry: Light verse and traditional. No avant-garde. Buys 5 poems/year. Submit maximum 4 poems. Length: 40 lines maximum. Pays in contributor's copy.
Fillers: Short humor. Buys 4/year. Pays in contributor's copy.
Tips: "If a writer's style and expertise measure up to our standards, and he has something to say in a creative manner, he should certainly give us a try."

INTERZONE, 21 The Village St., Leeds LS4 2PR England. Editors: Simon Ounsley and David Pringle. 100% freelance written. Eager to work with new/unpublished writers. A quarterly magazine of science fiction, fantasy and related imaginative fiction. Circ. 2,500. Pays on publication. Publishes ms an average of 4 months after acceptance. Byline given. Buys first English language serial rights. Photocopied submissions OK. SAE and IRCs. Computer printout submissions acceptable. Simultaneous submissions are *not* acceptable. Sample copy $3 from U.S. agent, 124 Osborne Rd., Brighton, BN1 GLU, England.
Fiction: Fantasy (not sword and sorcery); mainstream (but must have some fantasy/surreal content); and science fiction. Buys 20 mss/year. Send complete ms—"1 story at a time." Length: 1,000-8,000 words. Pays £30-35/1,000 words.
Tips: "Read *Interzone* before you submit. Optimum length is 5,000 words. Best to submit disposable double-spaced photocopies with IRCs for our letter of reply. *Two* IRCs for an airmail letter. Please do not send U.S. stamps. They are of no use to us. We like to publish fiction which is topical; it should be innovative yet entertaining; science fiction stories should be aware of recent technological advances, not regurgitations of science fiction clichés from past decades."

ISAAC ASIMOV'S SCIENCE FICTION MAGAZINE, Davis Publications, Inc., 380 Lexington Ave., New York NY 10017. (212)557-9100. Editor-in-Chief: Gardner Dozois. 98% freelance written. Works with a small number of new/unpublished writers each year. Emphasizes science fiction. 13 times a year magazine; 192 pages. Circ. 125,000. Pays on acceptance. Publishes ms an average of 6 months after acceptance. Buys first North American serial rights, nonexclusive foreign serial rights and occasionally reprint rights. "Clear and dark" photocopied submissions OK but no simultaneous submissions. Computer printout submissions acceptable; prefers letter-quality to dot-matrix. Reports in 6 weeks. Publishes ms an average of 6 months after acceptance. Writer's guidelines for SASE.
Nonfiction: Science. Query first.
Fiction: Science fiction primarily. Some fantasy and poetry. "It's best to read a great deal of material in the genre to avoid the use of some *very* old ideas." Buys 10 mss/issue. Submit complete ms. Length: 100-20,000 words. Pays 4-7¢/word.
Tips: Query letters not wanted, except for nonfiction. "Response time will be somewhat slower than in years past, and I'll be using a higher proportion of 'form' rejection slips."

NIGHT CRY, Montcalm Publishing Corp., 800 2nd Ave., New York NY 10017-4798. Editor: Alan Rodgers. 100% freelance written. Works with a small number of new/unpublished writers each year. Quarterly magazine of horror and dark fantasy. "We publish fiction almost exclusively; our audience is the audience for Stephen King, Peter Straub, James Herbert, and the other writers who've done so well in the genre in the last ten years." Circ. 30,000. Pays half on acceptance, half on publication. Publishes ms an average of 6 months after acceptance. Byline given. Offers 50% kill fee. Buys first North American serial rights. Submit seasonal/holiday material 8 months in advance. Simultaneous, photocopied, and previously published submissions OK. Computer printout submissions acceptable; no dot-matrix. Reports in 3 months on mss. Sample copy $2.95; writer's guidelines for #10 SAE and 1 first class stamp.
Fiction: Fantasy, horror and science fiction. Buys 60 mss/year. Send complete ms. Pays 5-10¢/word.
Poetry: Avant-garde, free verse, haiku and traditional. "We don't particularly want to see cutesy poetry. However, if you think it's appropriate to an audience that enjoys stylishly written horror and fantasy, send it in." Submit maximum of 6 poems. Pays $20-150.

PANDORA, Role-Expanding Science Fiction and Fantasy, Empire Books, Box 625, Murray KY 42071. Editors: Jean Lorrah and Lois Wickstrom. 95% freelance written. Works with a small number of new/unpublished writers each year; eager to work with new/unpublished writers. Magazine published 2 times/year covering science fiction and fantasy. Circ. 600. Pays on acceptance. Publishes ms an average of 6 months after acceptance. Byline given. Offers $10 kill fee. Buys first North American serial rights and second serial (reprint) rights; one-time rights on some poems. Photocopied submissions OK. Readable computer printout submissions on white 8½x11 paper acceptable. Reports in 6 weeks. Sample copy $3.50; writer's guidelines for SAE with 1 first class stamp.

Columns/Departments: Books Briefly. "We buy 200-word reviews of science fiction and fantasy books that a reader truly loves and feels are being ignored by the regular reviewers. Small press titles as well as major press titles are welcome." Buys 3-4 mss/year. Query or send complete ms. Length: 200-250 words. Pays 1¢/word.

Fiction: Experimental, fantasy, science fiction. "No pun stories. Nothing x-rated. No inaccurate science." Buys 15 mss/year. Send complete ms. Length: 1,000-5,000 words "except for controversial stories which may go to 10,000 words." Pays 1¢/word.

Poetry: Ruth Berman, 5620 Edgewater Blvd., Minneapolis MN 55417. Buys 9 poems/year. Length: open.

Tips: "Send us a complete short story. If we like it, we'll send you a critique with suggestions, if we don't want it just the way it is, but would want it with some more work. You don't have to do exactly what we've suggested, but you should fix weak spots in your story. Inexperienced writers often break in with a book or game review. We use very few articles, basically science articles or articles about writing science fiction. People sometimes submit totally unacceptable things they'd know we'd never touch if they'd been reading the magazine. For example, one writer sent a long gossipy scandal article appropriate to a newsstand scandal sheet, naming names and claiming claims. Definitely not for any magazine of our kind, as he'd have known if he had read previous issues."

SPACE AND TIME, 138 W. 70th St., New York NY 10023. Editor: Gordon Linzner. Biannual magazine covering fantasy fiction, with a broad definition of fantasy that encompasses science fiction, horror, swords and sorcery, etc. Circ. 500. 99% freelance written. Eager to work with new/unpublished writers. Pays on acceptance. Publishes ms an average of 2 years after acceptance. Byline given. Buys first North American serial rights. Photocopied submissions OK. Computer printout submissions acceptable; prefers letter-quality to dot-matrix. Reports in 2 months. Sample copy $4.

Fiction: Fantasy, horror and science fiction. "Submit skillful writing and original ideas. We lean toward strong plot and character. No fiction based on TV shows or movies (*Star Trek, Star Wars*, etc.) or popular established literary characters (e.g., Conan) except as satire or other special case. No UFO, gods from space, or material of that ilk, unless you've got a drastically new slant." Buys 24 unsolicited mss/year. Length: 15,000 words maximum. Pays ¼¢/word plus contributor's copies.

Poetry: Buys 12 poems/year. Submit maximum 5 poems. Length: open. Pays in contributor's copies. "Currently overstocked through 1987 and only interested in narrative poems."

Tips: "All areas are open to freelancers, but we would particularly like to see more hard science fiction, and fantasies set in 'real' historical times. No nonfiction or no fiction that cannot be considered science fiction or fantasy. We particularly enjoy uncovering new talent and offbeat stories for which there are few (if any) markets otherwise; seeing *S&T* authors go on to better paying, wider circulating markets. We regret that we can't publish more material more often. A lot of good, interesting stories have to be passed over, and there are few other markets for genre fiction."

STARLOG MAGAZINE, The Science Fiction Universe, Starlog Group, 8th Floor, 475 Park Ave. South, New York NY 10016. (212)689-2830. Editor: David McDonnell. Managing Editor: Carr D'Angelo. 95% freelance written. Works with a small number of new/unpublished writers each year. Monthly magazine covering "the science fiction-fantasy-adventure genre: its films, TV, books, art and personalities. We explore the fields of science fiction and fantasy with occasional forays into adventure (i.e., the James Bond and Indiana Jones films). We concentrate on the personalities and behind-the-scenes angles of science fiction/fantasy films with comprehensive interviews with actors, directors, screenwriters, producers, special effects technicians and others." Pays on publication *or* after 3 months from deadline date if article held and budget allows. Publishes ms an average of 4 months after acceptance. Byline given. All contributors are also credited in masthead. Offers kill fee "only to mss *written* or interviews *done*." Buys first North American serial rights to material with option to reprint (for an additional fee) certain articles in annual *Best of Starlog*. Buys second serial (reprint) rights to certain other material. Submit seasonal/holiday material 6 months in advance. Simultaneous queries and photocopied submissions OK. Computer printout submissions acceptable; prefers letter-quality to dot-matrix. Reports in 4 weeks on queries; 6 weeks on mss. "We provide an assignment sheet to *all* writers with deadline and other info, thus authorizing a queried piece." Sample copy $3. Send SASE for writer's guidelines. "Be aware: 'sci fi' is mostly considered a derogatory term by our readers and by *us*."

Nonfiction: Interview/profile (actors, directors, screenwriters who have made past or current contributions to science fiction films, and science fiction novelists); photo features; special effects how-tos (on filmmaking only); retrospectives of famous SF films and TV series; occasional pieces on science fiction fandom, conventions, etc., and aspects of that area of fans' lives. "We also cover animation (especially Disney and WB)." No personal opinion or views of *Star Wars, Star Trek* or memories of when the writer first saw some film. *No* first person. "We prefer article format as opposed to question-and-answer." No reviews. Buys 150 or more mss/year. Query first with published clips. Length: 500-3,000 words. Pays $25-225. Avoid articles on horror films/creators—see listing for sister magazine *Fangoria* in movie magazine section.

Photos: State availability of photos. Pays $10-25 for color slide transparencies and 8x10 b&w prints depending on quality. "No separate payment for photos provided by film studios." Captions, model releases, identification of subjects, and credit line on photos required. Buys all rights.

Columns/Departments: Future Life (science articles for the layman from 500-1,000 words, *very* much needed, think *Omni Junior*); Fan Network (articles on science fiction fandom and its aspects—basically staff-written); Booklog (genre book news and mini-interviews with new and veteran authors); Medialog (news of upcoming science fiction films and TV projects and mini-interviews with those involved); and Videolog (video-cassette and disk releases of genre interest). "We also require science fiction news items of note, Comics Scene items (profiles of upcoming genre-oriented comic books/strips), items on fantasy, merchandising items of interest, toys, games and old science fiction film/TV reunion photos/feature material." Buys 24-30 mss/year. Query with published clips. Length: 300-750 words. No kill fee on logs. Payment for department items $25-35 on publication only.

Fiction: "We do *not* publish any fiction. *Stop* sending it to us."

Tips: "The most frequent mistakes made by writers are unprofessionally prepared manuscripts (especially word-processed mss), ignorance of—and no questions or quotes about—one (or more) of interviewee's film credits or history, misspellings of film crew members' names (and others whose names are hard to research anywhere), missed deadlines due to inadequacies of (and overreliance on) overnight mail services, failure to ask obvious questions and shoddy research (and inadequate reference material). A writer can best break in with author mini-interviews or other such department items which show initiative. Another way: get an unusual interview or article that we can't get through normal channels (for example, an interview with Dino De Laurentis or Stanley Kubrick). We are always looking for *new* angles on *Star Wars, Star Trek, Doctor Who* and seek a small number of features investigating aspects (i.e., cast & crew) of series which remain very popular with many readers: *Lost in Space, Space 1999, Battlestar Galactica, The Twilight Zone.* Know science fiction media before you try us. Most full-length major assignments go to freelancers with whom we're already dealing. A writer can more easily prove himself with a short item. Discovering new freelancers and helping them to break into print is a special joy. We love it. We're fans of this material—and a prospective writer must be, too—but we were *also* freelancers. And if your love for science fiction shows through, we would love to *help* you break in."

STARWIND, The Starwind Press, Box 98, Ripley OH 45167. (513)392-4549. Editor: David F. Powell. Managing Editor: Susannah C. West. 75% freelance written. Eager to work with new/unpublished writers. A quarterly magazine "for the young adult (18-25 or thereabouts) who has an interest in science and technology, and who also enjoys reading well-crafted science fiction and fantasy." Circ. 2,500. Pays on publication. Publishes ms an average of 6 months after acceptance. Byline given. Rights vary with author and material; negotiated with author. Usually first serial rights and second serial reprint rights (nonfiction). Photocopied submissions OK. Electronic submissions OK on IBM PC or PC compatible and Apple Macintosh. Computer printout submissions acceptable. Photocopied and dot-matrix submissions OK. "In fact, we encourage disposable submissions; easier for us and easier for the author. Just enclose SASE for our response. We prefer non-simultaneous submissions." Reports in 3 months. Sample copy for $2.50; writer's guidelines for business size SAE and 1 first class stamp.

Nonfiction: How-to (technological interest, e.g., how to build a robot eye, building your own radio receiver, etc.); interview/profile (of leaders in science and technology fields); and technical ("did you know" articles dealing with development of current technology). "No speculative articles, dealing with topics such as the Abominable Snowman, Bermuda Triangle, etc. At present, nonfiction is staff-written or reprinted from other sources. We hope to use more freelance written work in the future." Query. Length: 1,000-5,000 words. Pays 1-4¢/word.

Photos: Send photos with accompanying query or ms. Reviews b&w contact sheets and prints. Model releases and identification of subjects required. "If photos are available, we prefer to purchase them as part of the written piece." Buys negotiable rights.

Fiction: Fantasy and science fiction. "No stories whose characters were created by others (e.g., *Lovecraft, Star Trek, Star Wars* characters, etc.)." Buys 15-20 mss/year. Send complete ms. Length: 2,000-10,000 words. Pays 1-4¢/word. "We prefer previously unpublished fiction."

Tips: "Our need for nonfiction is greater than for fiction at present. Almost all our fiction and nonfiction is unsolicited. We rarely ask for rewrites, because we've found that rewrites are often disappointing; although the writer may have rewritten it to fix problems, he/she frequently changes parts we liked, too."

THRUST—SCIENCE FICTION AND FANTASY REVIEW, Thrust Publications, 8217 Langport Terrace, Gaithersburg MD 20877. (301)948-2514. Editor: D. Douglas Fratz. 30% freelance written. Prefers to work with published/established writers. A semiannual literary review magazine covering science fiction and fantasy literature. "*Thrust—Science Fiction and Fantasy Review* is the highly acclaimed, Hugo-Award-nominated magazine about science fiction and fantasy. Since 1972, *Thrust* has been featuring in-depth interviews with science fiction's best known authors and artists, articles and columns by the field's most outspoken writers, and reviews of current science fiction books. *Thrust* has built its reputation on never failing to take a close look at the most sensitive and controversial issues concerning science fiction, and continues to receive the highest praise and most heated comments from professionals and fans in the science fiction field." Circ. 1,500. Pays on publication. Publishes ms an average of 6 months after acceptance. Byline given. Buys first North American serial rights, one-time rights and second serial (reprint) rights. Submit seasonal/holiday material 3-6 months in advance. Simultaneous queries, and simultaneous, photocopied and previously published submissions OK. Electronic submissions OK on IBM compatible-MS-DOS or PC-DOS with WordStar. Computer printout submissions acceptable; prefers letter-quality to dot-matrix. Reports in 2 weeks on queries; 2 months on mss. Sample copy for $2.50; writer's guidelines for SAE and 1 first class stamp.

Nonfiction: Humor, interview/profile, opinion, personal experience and book reviews. Buys 5-10 mss/year. Query or send complete ms. Length: 2,000-5,000 words. Pays ½-2¢/word.

Photos: "We publish only photos of writers being interviewed." State availability of photos. Pays $1-10 for smaller than 8x10 b&w prints. Buys one-time rights.

Columns/Departments: Uses science fiction and fantasy book reviews and film reviews. Buys 25-30 mss/year. Send complete ms. Length: 100-1,000 words. Pays ½-1¢/word. (Reviews usually paid in subscriptions, not cash.)

Tips: "Reviews are best way to break into *Thrust*. Must be on current science fiction and fantasy books. The most frequent mistake made by writers in completing articles for us is writing to a novice audience; *Thrust*'s readers are science fiction and fantasy experts."

TWILIGHT ZONE, Montcalm Publishing Co., 800 2nd Ave., New York NY 10017. (212)986-9600. Editor: Michael Blaine. Managing Editor: Robin Bromley. 60% freelance written. Bimonthly magazine of fantasy fiction with stories by authors as diverse as Stephen King, Bruce Jay Friedman, Julia Cortezar and Isaac Singer. Circ. 110,000. Pays half on acceptance, half on publication. Publishes ms an average of 3 months after acceptance. Byline given. Offers 25% kill fee. Buys first North American serial rights, first serial rights and second serial (reprint) rights. Submit seasonal/holiday material 8 months in advance. Simultaneous and photocopied submissions OK. Computer printout submissions acceptable; prefers letter-quality to dot-matrix. Reports in 3 months. Sample copy $3.

Fiction: Fantasy, understated horror and some surrealism. No sword and sorcery; hardware-oriented science fiction; vampire, werewolf or deals-with-the-devil stories. Buys 35 mss/year. Send complete ms. Length: 5,000 words maximum. Pays 5-9¢/word; $150 minimum.

Social Science and Self-Improvement

These publications focus on how and why readers can improve their own outlooks—and how to understand people in general. Each magazine covers a wide range of topics but is slanted to a particular audience.

‡JOURNAL OF GRAPHOANALYSIS, 111 N. Canal St., Chicago IL 60606. Editor: V. Peter Ferrara. For audience interested in self-improvement. Monthly. Buys all rights. Pays negotiable kill fee. Byline given. Pays on acceptance. Reports on submissions in 1 month.

Nonfiction: Self-improvement material helpful for ambitious, alert, mature people. Applied psychology and personality studies, techniques of effective living, etc.; all written from intellectual approach by qualified writers in psychology, counseling and teaching, preferably with degrees. Length: 2,000 words. Pays about 5¢/word.

‡PRACTICAL KNOWLEDGE, 111 N. Canal St., Chicago IL 60606. Editor: Lee Arnold. Monthly. A self-advancement magazine for active and involved men and women. Buys all rights, "but we are happy to cooperate with our authors." Pays on acceptance. Reports in 2-3 weeks.

Nonfiction and Photos: Uses success stories of famous people, past or present, applied psychology, articles on mental hygiene and personality by qualified writers with proper degrees to make subject matter authoritative. Also human interest stories with an optimistic tone. Up to 5,000 words. Photographs and drawings are used when helpful. Pays 5¢/word minimum; $20 each for illustrations.

‡PSYCHOLOGY TODAY, American Psychological Association, 1200 17th St. NW, Washington DC 20036. (202)955-7800. Editor: Patrice Horn. Managing Editor: Wray Herbert. 85% freelance written. A monthly magazine covering psychology and the social and behavioral sciences. Circ. 850,000. Pays on acceptance. Publishes ms an average of 5 months after acceptance. Byline given. Offers 20% kill fee. Buys first North American serial rights, one-time rights, second serial (reprint) rights or all rights. Submit seasonal/holiday material 6 months in advance. Photocopied submissions OK. Computer printout submissions acceptable; prefers letter-quality to dot-matrix. Reports in 6 weeks. Sample copy for 8½x11 SAE with 4 first class stamps. Writer's guidelines for letter size SAE with 1 first class stamp.
Nonfiction: Book excerpts, essays, exposé, general interest, interview/profile, opinion, and technical. No inspirational/personal experience. Buys 75 mss/year. Query with published clips. Length: 1,000-3,500 words. Pays $500-2,500. Pays expenses of writers on assignment.
Photos: State availability of photos with submission.
Columns/Departments: Crosstalk (research summaries—contact Richard Camer), and Books (reviews—contact Wray Herbert). Buys 240 mss/year. Query. Length: 300-1,000 words. Pays $150-500.

ROSICRUCIAN DIGEST, Rosicrucian Order, AMORC, Rosicrucian Park, San Jose CA 95191. (408)287-9171, ext. 320. Editor-in-Chief: Robin M. Thompson. 50% freelance written. Monthly magazine emphasizing mysticism, science and the arts. For "men and women of all ages, seeking answers to life's questions." Circ. 70,000. Pays on acceptance. Publishes ms an average of 6 months after acceptance. Buys first serial rights and rights to reprint. Byline given. Submit seasonal or holiday material 5 months in advance. Photocopied and previously published submissions OK. Computer printout submissions acceptable; no dot-matrix. Reports in 2 months. Free sample copy and writer's guidelines.
Nonfiction: How to deal with life's problems and opportunities in a positive and constructive way. Informational articles—new ideas and developments in science, the arts, philosophy and thought. Historical sketches, biographies, human interest, psychology, philosophical and inspirational articles. No religious, astrological or political material or articles promoting a particular group or system of thought. Buys 20-30 mss/year. Query. Length: 1,000-1,500 words. Pays 6¢/word.
Photos: Purchased with accompanying ms. Send prints. Pays $10/8x10 b&w glossy print.
Fillers: Short inspirational or uplifting (not religious) anecdotes or experiences. Buys 6/year. Query. Length: 25-250 words. Pays 2¢/word.
Tips: "Be specific about what you want to write about—the subject you want to explore—and be willing to work with editor. Articles should appeal to worldwide circulation. The most rewarding aspect of working with freelance writers is to see an article 'grow' from the original 'seed' into something that will touch the lives of our readers."

Sports

The publications in this category buy articles for sports fans and activists on how to practice and enjoy both team and individual sports, material on conservation of streams and forests, and articles reporting on and analyzing professional sports. For the convenience of writers who specialize in one or two areas of sport and outdoor writing, the publications are subcategorized by the sport or subject matter they emphasize. Publications in related categories (for example, Hunting and Fishing; Archery and Bowhunting) often buy similar material. Writers should read through this entire Sports category to become familiar with the subcategories. Publications on horse breeding, hunting dogs or the use of animals in sports are classified in the Animal category, while horse racing is listed here. Publications dealing with automobile or motorcycle racing can be found in the Automotive and Motorcycle category. Markets interested in articles on exercise and fitness are listed in the Health and Fitness section. Outdoor publications that promote the preservation of nature, placing only secondary emphasis on nature as a setting for sport, are in the Nature, Conservation, and Ecology category. Regional magazines are frequently interested in conservation or sports material with a local angle. Camping publications are classified in the Travel, Camping, and Trailer category.

Archery and Bowhunting

BOW AND ARROW HUNTING, Box HH/34249 Camino Capistrano, Capistrano Beach CA 92624. Editorial Director: Roger Combs. 80% freelance written. Eager to work with new/unpublished writers. Bimonthly magazine. For bowhunters. Pays on acceptance. Publishes ms an average of 6 months after acceptance. Buys first serial rights. Byline given. Computer printout submissions acceptable; prefers letter-quality to dot-matrix. Reports on submissions in 2 months. Author must have some knowledge of archery terms.
Nonfiction: Articles: bowhunting, techniques used by champs, how to make your own tackle, and off-trail hunting tales. Likes a touch of humor in articles. "No dead animals or 'my first hunt.' " Also uses one technical and how-to article per issue. Submit complete ms. Length: 1,500-2,500 words. Pays $150-300. Sometimes pays the expenses of writers on assignment.
Photos: Purchased as package with mss; 5x7 minimum. Pays $75-100 for cover chromes, 35mm or larger.
Tips: "Subject matter is more important than style—that's why we have editors and copy pencils. Good b&w photos are of primary importance. Don't submit color prints. We staff-write our shorter pieces."

BOWHUNTER MAGAZINE, 3150 Mallard Cove Lane, Fort Wayne IN 46804. (219)432-5772. Editor: M. R. James. Managing Editor: Wayne von Zwoll. 90% freelance written. Eager to work with new/unpublished writers. Bimonthly magazine; 112 pages. For "readers of all ages, backgrounds and experience who share two common passions—hunting with the bow and arrow and a love of the great outdoors." Circ. 180,000. Buys first publication rights. Pays on acceptance. Publishes ms an average of 8 months after acceptance. "We include our Bowhunting Annual as part of the subscription package. This means we have seven issues each year including the Annual (on sale in July) which has been designated a Special Deer Hunting Issue." Submit seasonal material 8 months in advance. Reports in 6 weeks. Computer printout submissions acceptable; prefers letter-quality to dot-matrix. Sample copy $2; writer's guidelines for SAE with 1 first class postage stamp.
Nonfiction: "We want articles that inform as well as entertain readers. Writers should anticipate every question a reader may ask and answer questions in the article or accompanying sidebar. Most features deal with big or small game bowhunting (how-to, where-to-go, etc.) The 'Me and Joe' article is still considered here, but we do not cover all aspects of archery—only bowhunting. Unusual experiences are welcome and freshness is demanded, especially when covering common ground. Readers demand accuracy, and writers hoping to sell to us must have a thorough knowledge of bowhunting. No writer should attempt to sell material to us without first studying one or more issues of the magazine. We especially like articles that promote responsible bowhunting and combat anti-hunting attacks. Humor, personal experiences, interviews and personality profiles, nostaglia, personal opinions, and historical articles are good bets. No 'See what animal I bagged—ain't I great' articles." Buys approximately 100 mss/year. Query or submit complete ms. Length: 200-3,500 words. Pays $25-250; sometimes more. Sometimes pays the expenses of writers on assignment.
Photos: Photos purchased with or without accompanying ms. Pays $20-35 for 5x7 or 8x10 b&w prints; $50 minimum for 35mm or 2¼x2¼ color. Captions optional.
Tips: "Keep the reader foremost in mind. Write for him, not yourself. Know the sport and share your knowledge. Weave helpful information into the storyline (e.g., costs involved, services of guide or outfitter, hunting season dates, equipment preferred and why, tips on items to bring, where to write for information, etc.). We have no set formula per se, but most features are first person narratives and most published material will contain elements mentioned above. We enjoy working with promising newcomers who understand our magazine and our needs. Most writers submit material 'on spec.' We reserve most assignments for staffers. We're upgrading the quality of our photos/illustrations and are editing more tightly. We still encourage submissions from non-professionals, but all should have useful information, hard facts, a slant to the average bowhunter."

Bicycling

‡BICYCLE GUIDE, Raben Publishing Co., 711 Boylston St., Boston MA 02116. (617)236-1885. Editor: Theodore Costantino. 30% freelance written. "We're equally happy working with established writers and new writers." Magazine published 9 times/year covering "the world of high-performance cycling. We cover racing, touring, and mountain biking from an enthusiast's point of view." Circ. 150,000. Pays on publication. Publishes ms an average of 3 months after acceptance. Byline given. Offers $150 kill fee. Buys first North

American serial rights. Submit seasonal/holiday material 6 months in advance. Simultaneous submissions OK. Computer printout submissions acceptable; prefers letter-quality to dot-matrix. Reports in 3 weeks on queries; 1 month on mss. Sample copy for 8½x11 SAE with 2 first class stamps; writer's guidelines for SAE with 1 first class stamp.

Nonfiction: Humor; interview/profile, new product, opinion; photo feature; technical; and travel (short rides in North America only). Buyers' annual published in April. "We need 'how-to-buy' material by preceding November." No entry-level how-to repairs or projects; long overseas tours; puff pieces on sports medicine; or 'my first ride' articles. Buys 18 mss/year. Query. Length: 900-3,500 words. Pays $200-600. Sometimes pays expenses of writers on assignment.

Photos: Send photos with submissions. Reviews transparencies and 5x8 b&w prints. Offers $25-125/photo. Captions, model releases, and identification of subjects required. Buys one-time rights.

Columns/Departments: What's Hot (new product reviews, personalities, events), 100-200 words; En Route (helpful hints for high performance cycling; on-the-road advice) 100 words; and Guest Column (thoughtful essay of interest to our readers) 900-1,200 words. Buys 30 mss/year. Query. Pays $25-450.

Tips: "Freelancers should be cyclists with a thorough knowledge of the sport. Area most open to freelancers are Training Methods (cover specific routines) and Technical Pages (cover leading edge, technical innovations, new materials)."

‡**BICYCLE RIDER**, TL Enterprises Inc., 29901 Agoura Rd., Agoura CA 91301. (818)991-4980. Editor: Bob Mendel. Managing Editor: Stephanie Robinson. 50% freelance written. Pubished 9 times a year. "A special interest magazine for the enthusiast who enjoys the sport of cycling for recreation, fitness, travel. Emphasis on reader participation rather than competition." Pays on publication. Byline given. Buys first North American serial rights. Submit seasonal/holiday material 5-6 months in advance. Sample copy $2; writer's guidelines for SASE.

Nonfiction: Book excerpts, essays, nostalgic, humor, inspirational, interview/profile, opinion, personal experience, photo feature, technical and travel. Buys 55 mss/year. Query with published clips. Length: 500-3,000 words. Pays $100-400 for assigned articles; pays $75-350 for unsolicited articles.

Photos: Send photos with submission. Reviews color transparencies. Offers no additional payment for photos accepted with ms.

Columns/Departments: How To (technical and technique tips); Maintenance (bicycle repair); For Beginners Only (basic, introductory cycling information). Query with published clips. Length: 500-750 words. Pays $200.

CYCLING USA, The Official Publication of the U.S. Cycling Federation, 1750 E. Boulder St., Colorado Springs CO 80909. (303)578-4581. Editor: Diane Fritschner. 50% freelance written. Monthly magazine covering reportage and commentary on American bicycle racing, personalities, and sports physiology for USCF licensed cyclists. Circ. 19,000. Pays on publication. Publishes ms an average of 4 months after acceptance. Byline given. Offers 30% kill fee. Buys first serial rights and second serial (reprint) rights. Submit seasonal/holiday material 1 month in advance. Simultaneous queries, and photocopied and previously published submissions OK. Computer printout submissions acceptable; no dot-matrix. Reports in 2 weeks. Sample copy for 10x12 SAE and 60¢ postage.

Nonfiction: How-to (train, prepare for a bike race); interview/profile; opinion; personal experience; photo feature; technical; and race commentary on major cycling events. No comparative product evaluations. Buys 15 mss/year. Query with published clips. Length: 500-2,000 words. Pays 10¢/word.

Photos: State availability of photos. Pays $10-25 for 5x7 b&w prints; $175 for color transparencies used as cover. Captions required. Buys one-time rights.

Columns/Departments: Athlete's Kitchen, Nuts & Bolts, Coaches Column.

Tips: "A background in bicycle racing is important because the sport is somewhat insular, technical and complex. Most major articles are generated inhouse. Race reports are most open to freelancers. Be concise, informative and anecdotal. The most frequent mistake made by writers in completing an article for us is that it is too lengthy; our format is more compatible with shorter (500-800 word) articles than longer features."

VELO-NEWS, A Journal of Bicycle Racing, Box 1257, Brattleboro VT 05301. (802)254-2305. Associate Editor: Geoff Drake. 20% freelance written. Works with a small number of new/unpublished writers each year. Monthly tabloid October-March, biweekly April-September covering bicycle racing. Circ. 14,000. Pays on publication. Publishes ms an average of 1 month after acceptance. Byline given. Buys all rights. Simultaneous queries, and simultaneous, photocopied, and previously published submissions OK. Electronic submissions OK; call first. Computer printout submissions acceptable; prefers letter-quality to dot-matrix. Reports in 2 weeks. Sample copy for 9x12 SAE.

Nonfiction: How-to (on bicycle racing); interview/profile (of people important in bicycle racing); opinion; photo feature; and technical. Buys 50 mss/year. Query. Length: 300-3,000 words. Pays $3/column inch.

Photos: State availability of photos. Pays $15-30 for 8x10 b&w prints. Captions and identification of subjects required. Buys one-time rights.

Boating

BAY & DELTA YACHTSMAN, Recreation Publications, 2019 Clement Ave., Alameda CA 94501. (415)865-7500. Editor: Dave Preston. 25% freelance written. Works with a small number of new/unpublished writers each year. Emphasizes recreational boating for small boat owners and recreational yachtsmen in northern California. Monthly tabloid newspaper; 90-166 pages. Circ. 22,000. Pays on publication. Publishes ms an average of 6 months after acceptance. Byline given. Buys first serial rights. Phone queries OK. Submit seasonal/holiday material 3 months in advance. Photocopied submissions OK. Electronic submissions OK via IBM Wordstar compatible, but requires hard copy also. Computer printout submissions OK. Reports in 1 month. Free writer's guidelines.
Nonfiction: Historical (nautical history of northern California); how-to (modifications, equipment, supplies, rigging, etc., aboard both power and sailboats); humor (no disaster or boating ineptitude pieces); informational (government legislation as it relates to recreational boating); interview; nostalgia; personal experience ("How I learned about boating from this" type of approach); photo feature (to accompany copy); profile; and travel. Buys 5-10 unsolicited mss/issue. Query. Length: 1,200-2,000 words. Pays $1/column inch.
Photos: Photos purchased with accompanying ms. Pays $5 for b&w glossy or matte finish photos. Total purchase price for ms includes payment for photos. Captions required.
Fiction: Adventure (sea stories, cruises, races pertaining to West Coast and points South/South West.); fantasy; historical; humorous; and mystery. Buys 4 mss/year. Query. Length: 500-1,750 words. Pays $1/column inch.
Tips: "Think of our market area: the waterways of northern California and how, why, when and where the boatman would use those waters. Writers should be able to comprehend the boating and Bay Area references in our magazine. Think about unusual onboard application of ideas (power and sail), special cruising tips, etc. We're very interested in local boating interviews—both the famous and unknown. Write for a knowledgeable boating public."

BOAT PENNSYLVANIA, Pennsylvania Fish Commission, Box 1673, Harrisburg PA 17105. (717)657-4520. Editor: Art Michaels. 75% freelance written. Bimonthly magazine covering motorboating, sailing, canoeing, water skiing, kayaking and rafting in Pennsylvania. Pays 6-8 weeks after acceptance. Publishes ms an average of 8 months after acceptance. Byline given. Buys all rights, but will reassign rights on written request after publication. Submit seasonal/holiday material 8 months in advance. Computer printout submissions acceptable; prefers letter-quality to dot-matrix. Reports in 1-3 weeks on queries; 2 months on manuscript. Writer's guidelines for #10 SAE with 1 first class stamp.
Nonfiction: How-to, photo feature, technical, and historical/nostalgic, all related to water sports in Pennsylvania. No saltwater material. Buys 40+ mss/year. Query. Length: 250-2,000 words. Pays $25-300.
Photos: Send photos with submission. Reviews 35mm and larger color transparencies and 8x10 b&w prints. Captions, model releases, and identification of subjects required. Buys all rights, but rights can be reassigned on written request after publication.
Columns/Departments: Safety (any safety-related subject that directly relates to non-angling boating in Pennsylvania). Buys 8 mss/year. Query. Length: 250-500 words. Pays $25-75.

CANADIAN YACHTING MAGAZINE, Maclean Hunter Bldg., 7th Floor, 777 Bay St., Toronto, Ontario M5W 1A7 Canada. Editor: John Morris. 80% freelance written. Monthly magazine aimed at owners of power and sail pleasure boats, both cruising and racing. Canadian writers usually favored. Circ. 30,000. Pays on acceptance. Publishes ms an average of 6 months after acceptance. Buys first North American serial rights. Previously published submissions OK, but remember "our obligation not to duplicate material published in larger American magazines available in our reader area." Computer printout submissions acceptable.
Nonfiction: "Much of our 'entertainment' coverage of important racing events must be handled by U.S. freelancers. Cruise and humorous stories are welcome from anyone." Also uses technical pieces, especially on motor maintenance. No general interest. Buys 40 unsolicited mss/year. Send complete ms. Length: 1,000-2,500 words. Pays $180-500.
Photos: Pays $15-40 for 8x10 b&w prints; $2-200 for 35mm color transparencies.
Tips: "Query should contain writer's experience and reassurance of photo quality (usually sample). In writing for us, stick to the outline, keep it Canadian and keep it relevant to our readers."

CANOE MAGAZINE, Canoe Associates, Box 3146, Kirkland, WA 98083. (206) 827-6363. George Thomas. 90% freelance written. A bimonthly magazine on canoeing, whitewater kayaking, and kayaking. Circ. 55,000. Pays on publication. Byline given. Offers 25% kill fee (rarely needed). Buys all rights. Submit seasonal/holiday material 4 months in advance. Electronic submissions OK via MS-DOS formatted 5¼" disc or ASCII data file transmitted at 300 or 1,200 Baud, but requires hard copy also. Computer printout submissions acceptable; prefers letter-quality to dot-matrix. Reports in 1 month. Free sample copy and writer's guidelines.

Nonfiction: Steve Simpson, articles editor. Essays, general interest, historical/nostalgic, how-to, humor, interview/profile, new product, opinion, personal experience, photo feature, technical and travel. Plans a special entry-level guide to canoeing and kayaking. No "trip diaries." Buys 60 mss/year. Query with or without published clips, or send complete ms. Length: 500-2,500 words. Pays $5-5.75/column inch. Pays the expenses of writers on assignment.
Photos: State availability of photos with submission or send photos with submission. Reviews contact sheets, negatives, transparencies and prints. "Some activities we cover are canoeing, kayaking, canoe sailing or poling, canoe fishing, camping, backpacking (when compatible with the main activity,) and occasionally inflatable boats. We are not interested in groups of people in rafts, photos showing disregard for the environment, gasoline-powered, multi-horsepower engines unless appropriate to the discussion, or unskilled persons taking extraordinary risks." Offers $50-150/photo. Model releases and identification of subjects required. Buys one-time rights.
Columns/Departments: Steve Simpson, column/department editor. Competition (racing); Continuum (essay); Counter Currents (environmental); Put-In (short interesting articles)—all 1,500 words. Buys 60 mss/year. Pays $5-5.75/column inch.
Fiction: Uses very little fiction. Buys 5 mss/year.
Fillers: Anecdotes, facts, gags to be illustrated by cartoonist, and newsbreaks. Buys 20/year. Length: 500-1,000 words. Pays $5-5.75/column inch.
Tips: "Start with Put-In articles (short featurettes), of approximately 500 words, book reviews, or short, unique equipment reviews. Or give us the best, most exciting article we've ever seen—with great photos. Short Strokes is also a good entry forum focusing on short trips on good waterways accessible to lots of people. Query for specifics."

CRUISING WORLD, 524 Thames St., Newport RI 02840. (401)847-1588. Editor: George Day. 75% freelance written. For all those who cruise under sail. Monthly magazine; 220 pages. Circ. 120,000. Pays on acceptance. Publishes ms an average of 8 months after acceptance. Rights purchased vary with author and material. Buys first North American serial rights or first world serial rights. Reports in about 2 months. Electronic submissions OK via IBM-PC, Wordstar, but requires hard copy also. Computer printout submissions acceptable; prefers letter-quality to dot-matrix.
Nonfiction: "We are interested in seeing informative articles on the technical and enjoyable aspects of cruising under sail. Also subjects of general interest to seafarers." Buys 135-140 unsolicited mss/year. Submit complete ms. Length: 500-3,500 words. Pays $50-500. Sometimes pays expenses of writers on assignment.
Photos: 5x7 b&w prints and color transparencies purchased with accompanying ms.
Tips: "The most frequent mistakes made by writers in completing an article assignment for us are missing our audience; missing our style; missing the point of the whole exercise; typing single-space; supplying unusable photos; writing too much but saying too little."

‡CURRENTS, Voice of the National Organization for River Sports, 314 N. 20th St., Colorado Springs CO 80904. (303)473-2466. Editor: Eric Leaper. Managing Editor: Mary McCurdy. 25% freelance written. Bimonthly magazine covering river running (kayaking, rafting, river canoeing). Circ. 10,000. Pays on publication. Publishes ms an average of 6 months after acceptance. Byline given. Offers 25% kill fee. Buys first North American serial rights, first rights and one-time rights. Submit seasonal/holiday material 2 months in advance. Simultaneous queries, and simultaneous, photocopied, and previously published submissions OK. Computer printout submissions acceptable. Reports in 2 weeks on queries; in 1 month on mss. Sample copy $1; writer's guidelines for #10 SAE and 1 first class stamp.
Nonfiction: How-to (run rivers and fix equipment); in-depth reporting on river conservation and access issues and problems; humor (related to rivers); interview/profile (any interesting river runner); new product; opinion; personal experience; technical; travel (rivers in other countries). "We tell river runners about river conservation, river access, river equipment, how to do it, when, where, etc." No trip accounts without originality; no stories about "my first river trip." Buys 20 mss/year. Query with or without clips of published work. Length: 500-2,500 words. Pays $12-75.
Photos: State availability of photos. Pays $10-35. Reviews b&w or color prints or slides; b&w preferred. Captions and identification of subjects (if racing) required. Buys one-time rights.
Columns/Departments: Book and film reviews (river-related). Buys 5 mss/year. Query with or without clips of published work or send complete ms. Length: 100-500 words. Pays $5-50.
Fiction: Adventure (river). Buys 2 mss/year. Query. Length: 1,000-2,500 words. Pays $25-75.
Fillers: Clippings, jokes, gags, anecdotes, short humor, newsbreaks. Buys 5/year. Length: 25-100 words. Pays $5-10.
Tips: "Go to a famous river and investigate it; find out something we don't know—especially about rivers that are *not* in Colorado or adjacent states—we already know about the ones near us."

LAKELAND BOATING, 106 W. Perry St., Port Clinton OH 43452. (419)734-5774. Editor: David G. Brown. 70% freelance written. Eager to work with new/unpublished writers, if they know boating. Monthly magazine emphasizing pleasure boating on freshwater lakes; both sail and power, but more emphasis on power. Circ. 46,000. Pays on publication. Publishes ms an average of 6 months after acceptance. Buys first serial rights. Electronic submissions OK via MS-DOS, but requires hard copy also. Computer printout submissions acceptable if legible. Reports in 1 month. Sample copy $2 with SAE and 39¢ postage.

Nonfiction: 2-3 "Cruise" stories/issue. May be personal experiences, but reader must get enough details on ports, marinas, dangers, etc. to perform a similar cruise. Include sketches, maps, lists of marinas, access ramps, harbors of refuge. "We need 'people' stories about individuals living a water lifestyle on the Great Lakes or major inland rivers. We also need stories about waterfront developments such as new harbors, condominiums with dockage and tourist-type attractions which can be visited by boat." Query first. Length: 1,500-2,500 words. Pays 10-20¢/word. Sometimes pays the expenses of writers on assignment.

Photos: Send photos with ms. 5x7 or 8x10 b&w can also be submitted separately. Send negatives if you cannot have professional quality prints made. Original 35mm or larger transparencies for color stories. Captions required or identification of all pictures, prints or transparencies. "Please stamp every transparency with name and address." Original photo materials are returned.

Tips: "We are a regional publication, so all stories must have a Great Lakes or Midwestern freshwater slant. Cruise stories must give details. We don't want a 'Me 'n Joe' narrative of every breakfast and fuel stop. The waters being cruised and ports being visited are always more important than the people doing the cruising. The writer has a better chance of breaking in at our publication with short articles and fillers as there is greater need for them. Also, much of our editorial material is planned 6 to 12 months in advance. Biggest reason for stories being rejected is failure to meet our regional needs (failure to read our magazine to learn our slant and style). We would rather spend time developing a story right from the beginning than reject an otherwise well-written manuscript."

MOTORBOATING AND SAILING, 224 W. 57th St., New York NY 10019. (212)262-8768. Editor: Peter A. Janssen. Monthly magazine covering powerboats and sailboats for people who own their own boats and are active in a yachting lifestyle. Circ. 140,000. Pays on acceptance. Byline given. Buys one-time rights. Reports in 3 months.

Nonfiction: General interest (navigation, adventure, cruising), and how-to (maintenance). Buys 5-6 mss/issue. Average issue includes 8-10 feature articles. Query. Length: 2,000 words.

Photos: Reviews 5x7 b&w glossy prints and 35mm or larger color transparencies. Offers no additional payment for photos accepted with ms. Captions and model releases required.

OFFSHORE, New England's Boating Magazine, Offshore Publications, Inc., Box 148, Waban MA 02168. (617)244-7520. Editor: Herbert Gliick. 80% freelance written. Monthly magazine (oversize) covering boating and the New England coast for New England boat owners. Circ. 21,000. Pays within 1 month of acceptance. Publishes ms an average of 2 months after acceptance. Byline given. Offers negotiable kill fee. Buys first North American serial rights. Submit seasonal/holiday material 2 months in advance. Simultaneous queries, and simultaneous, photocopied, and previously published submissions OK. Electronic submissions OK via Kaypro PC disk, ASCI via phone, but requires hard copy also. Computer printout submissions acceptable. Reports in 1 week. Sample copy for 11x14 SAE and 88¢ postage.

Nonfiction: Articles on boats, boating and New England coastal places and people. Thumbnail and/or outline of topic will elicit immediate response. Buys 125 mss/year. Query with published clips or send complete ms. Length: 1,000-3,500 words. Pays 6-10¢/word.

Photos: Reviews photocopies of 5x7 prints. Identification of subjects required. Buys one-time rights.

Tips: "Demonstrate familiarity with boats or New England coast and ability to recognize subjects of interest to regional boat owners. Those subjects need not be boats. *Offshore* does not take itself as seriously as most national boating magazines. The most frequent mistake made by writers in completing an article for us is failing to build on a theme (what is the point of the story?)."

PACIFIC YACHTING, Power and Sail in British Columbia, S.I.P. Division, Maclean Hunter, Ltd., 1132 Hamilton St., Vancouver, British Columbia V6B 2S2 Canada. (604)687-1581. Editor: Paul Burkhart. Monthly magazine of yachting and recreational boating. Circ. 20,000. 50% freelance written. Pays mostly on publication. Byline given. Buys first and second serial (reprint) rights and makes work-for-hire assignments. Submit seasonal/holiday material 4 months in advance. Simultaneous queries, and simultaneous, photocopied, and previously published submissions OK. Computer printout submissions acceptable; prefers letter-quality to dot-matrix. SAE and IRCs. Reports in 2 months on queries; 6 months on mss. Publishes ms an average of 6 months after acceptance. Sample copy $2.

Nonfiction: Book excerpts, how-to, humor, interview/profile, new product, opinion, personal experience, photo feature, technical, travel. "Freelancers can break in with first-person articles about yachting adventures on the west coast of Canada accompanied by good 35mm photos. We're open to 'how-to' pieces by writers with strong technical backgrounds in the marine recreation field." No "poetry, religious, or first sailing experiences." Buys 150 mss/year. Will buy fewer stories in the year ahead. Query. Length: 100-2,000 words. Pays 10¢/word.

Photos: Send photos with ms. Reviews b&w contact sheets, b&w and color negatives, 35mm color transparencies (preferred) and prints. Captions and identification of subjects required. Buys various rights.
Columns/Departments: Scuttlebutt (news and light items, new gear, book reviews) and Boat Care (how-to). Buys 80 mss/year. Send complete ms. Length: 100-400 words. Pays $10-40.
Fillers: Clippings, newsbreaks. Length: 100-200 words. Pays $10-25.
Tips: "In working with freelancers we enjoy discovering fresh new perspectives in our own backyard. We regret, however, their failure to inquire or check out our magazine style."

POWERBOAT MAGAZINE, 15917 Strathern St., Van Nuys CA 91406. Editor: Mark Spencer. 60% freelance written. Works with a small number of new/unpublished writers each year; eager to work with new/unpublished writers. For performance-conscious boating enthusiasts. January, West Coast Runabout Performance Trials; February, East Coast Runabout Performance Trials; March, Offshore Performance Trials; April, Water Ski Issue; May, Awards for Product Excellence; June through November/December, Race reporting and various other features on recreational boating. Circ. 75,000. Pays on publication. Publishes ms an average of 3 months after acceptance. Buys all rights or one-time North American serial rights. Reports in 2 weeks. Free sample copy.
Nonfiction: Uses articles about power boats and water skiing that offer special interest to performance-minded boaters, how-to-do-it pieces with good b&w pictures, developments in boating, profiles on well-known boating and skiing individuals, competition coverage of national and major events. Query required. Length: 1,500-2,000 words. Pays $150-250/article.
Photos: Photos purchased with mss. Prefers 35mm Kodachrome slides. Pays $100 for one-time cover use only.
Tips: "We are interested in publishing more technical articles, i.e., how to get better performance out of a boat, engine or tow vehicle. When submitting an article, it should be in the area of *high performance* boating only. We *do not* cover sailing, large yachts, fishing boats, etc."

‡RIVER RUNNER MAGAZINE, Rancher Publications, Box 2047, Vista CA 92083. (619)744-7170/727-0120. Editor-in-Chief: Mark C. Larson. 80% freelance written. Bimonthly magazine covering rafting, canoeing, and kayaking. "Audience is predominately male, college educated, and approximately 20-45 years old. The editorial slant favors white-water action. Stories reflect the natural beauty and excitement of running rivers." Circ. 20,000. Pays on publication. Publishes ms an average of 2 months after acceptance. Byline given. Buys first North American serial rights. Submit seasonal/holiday material 6 months in advance. Computer printout submissions acceptable; no dot-matrix. Reports in 1 month on queries; 2 months on mss. Sample copy $2.50; writer's guidelines for 4x9 SAE and 1 first class stamp.
Nonfiction: Book excerpts (soon-to-be-published books relevant to river running); historical/nostalgic (articles on human history of a river are welcome, as are articles on river running pioneers, and interesting periods in paddling history); how-to (authoritative, well-researched technical pieces offering sound advice to canoers, kayakers, and rafters); interview/profile (personality profiles of prominent river runners or others of interest to our outdoor-oriented readership); new products (detailed, critical evaluations of boats and gear of interest to river runners); opinion (responsible opinions of interest to river runners); technical (expert commentary on equipment and techniques of interest to river runners); and a regular feature on sea kayaking. "Solid, well-researched conservation pieces and equipment reviews are also welcome. We publish one story per issue aimed toward novice boaters. Submit stories that reflect an intimacy with the sport." Buys 42 mss/year. Query with or without published clips or send complete ms. Length: 1,500-2,500 words. Pays $50-100.
Photos: State availability of photos with query letter or ms. Pays $10-25 for color transparencies; $10-15 for b&w contact sheets and prints. "We need good, sharp photographs that prominently portray strong human emotion or natural beauty. Transparencies must have high technical quality." Captions and identification of subjects required. Buys all rights.
Columns/Departments: "Damwatch (focus on immediate, specific threats to rivers); Upfront (short, bright, lively commentary of not more than 500 words)." Relevant book reviews are also welcome; pays $10 on publication. Forum is a nonpaid column provided for recognized river spokespersons to voice opinions of interest to the paddling community." Buys 25 mss/year. Send complete ms. Length: 500-850 words.
Fillers: Clippings, anecdotes, short humor and newsbreaks. "We can use any river-related clippings, or outdoor items of interest to an outdoor readership." Buys 20 mss/year. Length: 50-500 words. Pays $5-25.
Tips: "Submit fresh, original story ideas with strong supporting photographs. Be persistent, and constantly on the lookout for new and unused story ideas. The prime need is for original, well-written river feature stories. We have often published at least one hair-boating, first descent story per issue. (If you don't understand what this means, you probably can't write for this publication.) Stories should be written for the intermediate-level paddler. Freelance writers and photographers are a vital part of *River Runner.* We encourage and appreciate your continued submissions."

SAIL, Charlestown Navy Yard, 100 First Ave., Charleston MA 02129-2097. (617)241-9500. Editor: Keith Taylor. 50% freelance written. Works with a small number of new/unpublished writers each year. Monthly magazine for audience that is "strictly sailors, average age 42, above average education." Pays on publication. Publishes ms an average of 6 months after acceptance. Buys first North American serial rights. Submit seasonal or special material at least 3 months in advance. Reports in 8 weeks. Computer printout submissions acceptable; no dot-matrix. Free sample copy.

Nonfiction: Patience Wales, managing editor. Wants "articles on sailing: technical, techniques and feature stories." Interested in how-to, personal experience, profiles, historical and new products. "Generally emphasize the excitement of sail and the human, personal aspect. No logs." Special issues: "Cruising issues, chartering issues, fitting-out issues, special race issues (e.g., America's Cup), boat show issues." Buys 200 mss/year (freelance and commissioned). Length: 1,500-3,000 words. Pays $100-800. Sometimes pays the expenses of writers on assignment.

Photos: Offers additional payment for photos. Uses b&w glossy prints or Kodachrome 64 color transparencies. Pays $600 if photo is used on the cover.

Tips: Request an articles specification sheet.

SAILING MAGAZINE, 125 E. Main St., Port Washington WI 53074. (414)284-3494. Editor and Publisher: William F. Schanen, III. Monthly magazine; 82 pages. For readers ages 25-44, majority professionals. About 75% of them own their own sailboat. Circ. 35,000. Pays on publication. Photocopied and simultaneous submissions OK. Reports in 6 weeks. Free writer's guidelines.

Nonfiction: Micca Leffingwell Hutchins, editor. "Experiences of sailing, whether cruising, racing or learning. We require no special style. We're devoted exclusively to sailing and sailboat enthusiasts, and particularly interested in articles about the trend toward cruising in the sailing world." Informational, personal experience, profile, historical, travel and book reviews. Buys 24 mss/year. Query or submit complete ms. Length: open. Payment negotiable. Must be accompanied by photos.

Photos: B&w and color photos purchased with or without accompanying ms. Captions required. Pays flat fee for article.

SAILORS' GAZETTE, Main Line Publications, Suite 110, 337 22nd Ave. N., St. Petersburg FL 33704. (813)823-9172. Editor: Alice N. Eachus. Associate Editor: Dianne Marcou. 70% freelance written. Monthly magazine covering sailing in the southeastern states for sailboat owners. Circ. 16,000. Pays on publication. Publishes ms an average of 2 months after acceptance. Byline given. Offers 50% kill fee. Buys first serial rights and second serial reprint rights. Submit seasonal/holiday material 3 months in advance. Computer printout submissions acceptable. Reports in 1 month on queries; 6 weeks on mss. Sample copy $2; free writer's guidelines and editorial emphasis list.

Nonfiction: Historical/nostalgic (sailboats with direct ties to Southeastern states); interview/profile (with sailboat owners); personal experience (sailboat cruising in Southeast); photo feature (b&w on sailing or waterfront scenes in Southeastern states); and technical (sailboat maintenance, not general boat maintenance). No articles about sailboats without a connection to Southeastern states or articles about first-time sailors. Buys 150 mss/year. Query with published clips. Length: 500-1,800 words. Pays 6¢/word minimum.

Photos: State availability of photos. Pays $10-25 for high contrast 8x10 b&w prints. Captions, model releases, and identification of subjects required. Buys one-time rights.

Tips: "The manuscripts that we turn down are usually too general and far removed from the Southeastern themes. We're open to where-to and how-to, as it pertains to the Southeast; also interviews with cruising and racing sailors and racing personalities of the Southeast."

‡SEA KAYAKER, Sea Kayaker, Inc., 1670 Duranleau St., Vancouver, British Columbia, V6H 3S4, Canada. (604)689-7859. Editor: John Dowd. Managing Editor: Beatrice Dowd. 50% freelance written. A quarterly magazine on the sport of sea kayaking. Circ. 10,000. Pays on publication. Byline sometimes given. Offers 20% kill fee. Buys first North American serial rights or second serial (reprint) rights. Submit seasonal/holiday material 6 months in advance. Previously published submissions OK. Computer printout submissions acceptable; prefers letter-quality to dot-matrix. Reports in 2 months. Sample copy $3.45; free writer's guidelines.

Nonfiction: Essays, historical/nostalgic, how-to (on making equipment), humor, inspirational, interview/profile, opinion, personal experience, photofeature, technical and travel. Buys 15 mss/year. Query with or without published clips, or send complete ms. Length: 750-4,000 words. Pays $75-400 for assigned articles; pays $50-200 for unsolicited articles. May negotiate payment with contributor copies or premiums rather than cash if requested by writer. Sometimes pays the expenses of writers on assignment.

Photos: State availability of photos with submission. Reviews contact sheets. Offers $15-35/photo. Captions, model releases, and identification of subjects required. Buys one-time rights.

Columns/Department: History, Safety, Environment, and Humor. Buys 6 mss/year. Length: 750-4,000 words. Pays $50-400.

Fiction: Adventure, experimental, fantasy, historical, horror, humorous, mainstream, mystery, romance, science fiction, slice-of-life vignettes and suspense. Buys 6 mss/year. Send complete ms. Length: 750-4,000 words. Pays $50-400.

Tips: "We do not accept telephone queries. We consider unsolicited mss that include a SASE, but we give greater priority to brief (several paragraphs) descriptions of proposed articles accompanied by at least two samples—published or unpublished—of your writing. Enclose a statement as to why you're qualified to write the piece and indicate whether photographs or illustrations are available to accompany the piece."

‡SOUNDINGS, The Nation's Boating Newspaper, Pratt St., Essex CT 06426. (203)767-0906. Editorial Director: Christine Born. Eager to work with new/unpublished writers. National monthly boating newspaper with nine regional editions. Features "news—hard and soft—for the recreational boating public." Circ. 80,000. Pays on "the 10th of the month of publication." Publishes ms an average of 3 months after acceptance. Byline given. Buys one-time rights. Deadline 5th of month before issue. Simultaneous queries and simultaneous and photocopied submissions OK. Electronic submissions OK via 1,200 baud. Computer printout submissions acceptable. Reports in 2 months on queries; 5 weeks on mss. Sample copy for 8½x11 SAE and 7 first class stamps; free writer's guidelines.
Nonfiction: General interest, historical/nostalgic, interview/profile, opinion and photo feature. Race coverage is also used; supply full names, home towns and the full scores for the top 10 winners in each division. No personal experiences. Send complete ms. Length: 250-1,000 words. Pays $10-150.
Photos: Send photos with ms. Pays $15 minimum for 8x10 b&w prints. Identification of subjects required. Buys one-time rights.
Fillers: Short humor, newsbreaks. Length: 50-100 words. Pays $10-20.

TRAILER BOATS MAGAZINE, Poole Publications, Inc., Box 2307, Gardena CA 90248. (213)323-9040. Editor: Jim Youngs. Managing Editor: Bob Kovacik. 30-40% freelance written. Works with a small number of new/unpublished writers each year. Monthly magazine (November/December issue combined); 100 pages. Emphasizes legally trailerable boats and related activities. Circ. 80,000. Pays on publication. Publishes ms an average of 2 months after acceptance. Byline given. Buys all rights. Submit seasonal/holiday material 3 months in advance. Computer printout submissions acceptable; prefers letter-quality to dot-matrix. Reports in 1 month. Sample copy $1.25; writer's guidelines for SASE.
Nonfiction: General interest (trailer boating activities); historical (places, events, boats); how-to (repair boats, installation, etc.); humor (almost any boating-related subject); nostalgia (same as historical); personal experience; photo feature; profile; technical; and travel (boating travel on water or highways). No "How I Spent My Summer Vacation" stories, or stories not even remotely connected to trailerable boats and related activities. Buys 18-30 unsolicited mss/year. Query or send complete ms. Length: 500-3,000 words. Pays $50 minimum. Pays expenses of writers on assignment.
Photos: Send photos with ms. Pays $7.50-50 for 5x7 or 8x10 b&w glossy print; $15-100 for 35mm color transparency. Captions required.
Columns/Departments: Boaters Bookshelf (boating book reviews); Over the Transom (funny or strange boating photos); and Patent Pending (an invention with drawings). Buys 2/issue. Query. Length: 100-500 words. Pays 7¢-10¢/word. Mini-Cruise (short enthusiastic approach to a favorite boating spot). Need map and photographs. Length: 500-750 words. Pays $50. Open to suggestions for new columns/departments.
Fiction: Adventure, experimental, historical, humorous and suspense. "We do not use too many fiction stories but we will consider them if they fit the general editorial guidelines." Query or send complete ms. Length: 500-1,500 words. Pays $50 minimum.
Tips: "Query should contain short general outline of the intended material; what kind of photos; how the photos illustrate the piece. Write with authority covering the subject like an expert. Frequent mistakes are not knowing the subject matter or the audience. Use basic information rather than prose, particularly in travel stories. The writer may have a better chance of breaking in at our publication with short articles and fillers if they are typically hard to find articles. We do most major features inhouse."

‡WATERFRONT MAGAZINE, Southern California's Boating News Magazine, Duncan McIntosh Co. Inc., Suite C-2, 1760 Monrovia Ave. Costa Mesa CA 92627; Box 1337, Newport Beach CA 92663. (714)646-3963. Editor: Duncan McIntosh Jr. Managing Editor: Linda L. Yuskaitis. 60% freelance written. Prefers to work with published/established writers; works with a small number of new/unpublished writers each year. A monthly magazine covering recreational sail and power boating, offshore sportfishing and coastal issues in Southern California. "*Waterfront* readers are well-educated, boat owners, and have knowledge of sail and power boating beyond the fundamentals." Circ. 32,640. Pays on publication. Publishes ms an average of 2 months after acceptance. Byline given. Offers negotiable kill fee. Buys first North American serial rights, or second serial (reprint) rights. Submit seasonal/holiday material 4 months in advance. Photocopied submissions OK, but prefers original; previously published submissions OK in some cases. Electronic submissions OK via WordStar wordprocessing format only, but requires hard copy also. Computer printout submissions acceptable; prefers letter-quality to dot-matrix. Reports in 2 months on queries; 1 month on mss. Free sample copy and writer's guidelines.
Nonfiction: General interest (boating/coastal topics; historical/nostalgic (maritime lore; histories of ports, old ships) how-to (tips on caring for a boat); humor (boating related); interview/profile (of prominent Southern California boating personality); new product (marine-related new products); and opinion (re: state of boating,

race rules, coastal issues, etc.). Special news and feature articles covering the match races (January 1987) in Fremantle, Australia. No first-person cruising accounts; features on places a great distance from Southern California; extremely technical maintenance articles; or reviews on the performance of new boats. Buys 75 mss/ year. Query with or without published clips, or send complete ms. Length: 250 (news)-2,200 (features). Pays $75-275 for assigned articles; pays $50-225 for unsolicited articles. Pays the expenses of writers on assignment.

Photos: Send photos with submission. Reviews contact sheets, 2x2 transparencies and 5x7 prints. Offers $15-20/photo. Identification of subjects required. Buys one-time rights.

Columns/Departments: Channel Islands (coastal news and race results from Santa Barbara/Ventura/Oxnard area); Newport (coastal news and race results from Newport Beach/Oceanside/Dana Pt.); Marina del Rey to Long Beach (coastal news and race results from Marina del Rey/Los Angeles/Long Beach areas); San Diego (coastal News and race results from Oceanside/San Diego/Coronado areas); Fishing (record catches and regulation changes affecting Southern California anglers); Industry (news of promotions and business relocations of marine industry in Southern California); and Waterfront Forum (opinion pieces on issues affecting Southern California boatmen and their environment). Buys 70 mss/year. Send complete ms. All columns 250-750 words, except Waterfront Forum, 500-1,200 words. Pays $1.50/column inch-$50.00 maximum.

Fillers: Facts, newsbreaks and short humor. Buys 5-10/year. Length: 250-1,000 words. Pays $25-50.

Tips: "First-time contributors should include resume or some information that identifies their writing qualifications and knowledge about the story subject. All subregional news departments (Channel Islands, Marina del Rey to Long Beach, Newport, San Diego) are very receptive to freelance contributions. Because of news slant here, material must be timely according to our deadlines, which are about six weeks prior to month of issue. Free deadline schedule available to writers."

WATERWAY GUIDE, 850 3rd Ave., New York NY 10022. (212)715-2629. Managing Editors: Nancy Brokaw and Queene Hooper. 10% freelance written. Works with a small number of new/unpublished writers each year. Annual magazine. "A pleasure-boater's cruising guide to the Intracoastal Waterway, East Coast waters and the Great Lakes." Four regional editions. Computer printout submissions acceptable; prefers letter-quality to dot-matrix.

Nonfiction: "We occasionally have a need for a special, short article on some particular aspect of pleasure cruising—such as living aboard, sailing versus powerboating, having children or pets on board—or a particular stretch of coast—a port off the beaten track, conditions peculiar to a certain area, a pleasant weekend cruise, anchorages and so on." Query with ms.

Photos: State availability of photos. "We have a need for good photographs, taken from the water, of ports, inlets and points of interest." Reviews b&w prints. Payment varies. Guidelines on request with SASE."

Tips: "Keep the query simple and friendly. Include a short bio and boating experience. We prefer to see manuscript sample attached. No personal experiences, i.e., we need information, not reminiscences. We publish very few feature articles."

WOODENBOAT MAGAZINE, The Magazine for Wooden Boat Owners, Builders, and Designers, WoodenBoat Publications, Inc., Box 78, Brooklin ME 04616. (207)359-4651. Editor: Jon Wilson. Executive Editor: Billy R. Sims. Senior Editor: Peter H. Spectre. Managing Editor: Jennifer Buckley. 60% freelance written. Bimonthly magazine for wooden boat owners, builders, and designers. "We are devoted exclusively to the design, building, care, preservation, and use of wooden boats, both commercial and pleasure, old and new, sail and power. We work to convey quality, integrity, and involvement in the creation and care of these craft, to entertain, to inform, to inspire, and to provide our varied readers with access to individuals who are deeply experienced in the world of wooden boats." Circ. 100,000. Pays on publication. Publishes ms an average of 1 year after acceptance. Byline given. Offers variable kill fee. Buys first North American serial rights. Submit seasonal/holiday material 3 months in advance. Simultaneous queries and submissions (with notification) and photocopied and previously published submissions OK. Computer printout submissions acceptable. Reports in 3 weeks on queries; 4 weeks on mss. Sample copy $3.50; free writer's guidelines, SASE appreciated.

Nonfiction: Technical (repair, restoration, maintenance, use, design and building wooden boats). No poetry, fiction. Buys 100 mss/year. Query with published clips. Length: 1,500-5,000 words. Pays $6/column inch. Sometimes pays expenses of writers on assignment

Photos: Send photos with query. Negatives must be available. Pays $15-75 for b&w; $25-250 for color. Identification of subjects required. Buys one-time rights.

Columns/Departments: On the Waterfront pays for *information* on wooden boat-related events, projects, boatshop activities, etc. Buys 25/year. "We use the same columnists for each issue." Send complete information. Length: 250-1,000 words. Pays $5-50 for information.

Tips: "We appreciate a detailed, articulate query letter, accompanied by photos, that will give us a clear idea of what the author is proposing. We appreciate samples of previously published work. It is important for a prospective author to become familiar with our magazine first. It is extremely rare for us to make an assignment with a writer with whom we have not worked before. Most work is submitted on speculation. The most common failure is not exploring the subject material in enough depth."

‡**THE YACHT**, Bayview Corp., Box 280, Oxford MD 21654. (301)820-8252. Senior Editor: Kip Requardt. Editor: Roger Vaughan. Managing Editor: Dan Segal. 65% freelance written. A bimonthly magazine covering pleasure sail and powerboats. Pays on acceptance. Byline given. Buys first rights. Electronic submissions OK via 1200 baud, ASCII. Computer printout submissions acceptable; prefers letter-quality to dot-matrix. Sample copy for 9x12 SAE with $2.40 postage; writer's guidelines for SAE with 1 first class stamp.

Nonfiction: Humor, interview/profile, personal experience and photo feature. No how-to, nuts-and-bolts, or product descriptions. Buys 50-60 mss/year. Query with published clips. Length: 250-2,500 words. Pays $250-1,000. Pays the expenses of writers on assignment.

Photos: Reviews contact sheets and transparencies. Model releases and identification of subjects required. Buys one-time rights.

Columns/Departments: In The Wind (short, personal, anecdotal), 250-750 words; Statesman (profile of person who has had an effect on sport), 1,200 words; and Guest on Board (excerpt or opinion), 1,000 words. Buys 40 mss/year. Query with published clips. Length: 200-1,200 words. Pays $250-500.

Tips: "Ideas for the 'In the Wind' section most appreciated."

YACHT RACING & CRUISING MAGAZINE, North American Publishing Co., 111 East Ave., Norwalk CT 06851. Editor: John Burnham. 50% freelance written. Magazine published 12 times/year; 120 pages. Circ. 50,000. Pays on publication. Publishes ms an average of 4 months after acceptance. Buys first North American serial rights. Byline given. Electronic submissions OK via Macintosh—MacWrite disk, but requires hard copy also. Computer printout submissions acceptable; prefers letter-quality to dot-matrix. Reports in 2 months. Sample copy $2.50.

Nonfiction: How-to for performance racing/cruising sailors, personal experience, photo feature, profile, regatta reports, and travel. No travelogs. Buys 5-10 unsolicited mss/year. Query. Length: 750-2,000 words. Pays $150 per equivalent of one magazine page.

Tips: "Send query with outline and include your experience. The writer may have a better chance of breaking in at our publication with short articles and fillers such as regatta news reports from his or her own area."

Bowling

BOWLERS JOURNAL, 875 N. Michigan, Chicago IL 60611. (312)266-7171. Editor-in-Chief: Mort Luby. Managing Editor: Jim Dressel. 30% freelance written. Prefers to work with published/established writers; works with a small number of new/unpublished writers each year. Emphasizes bowling. Monthly magazine; 100 pages. Circ. 19,000. Pays on acceptance. Publishes ms an average of 2 months after acceptance. Buys all rights. Submit seasonal/holiday material 3 months in advance of issue date. Photocopied submissions OK. Computer printout submissions acceptable; prefers letter-quality to dot-matrix. Reports in 6 weeks. Sample copy $2.

Nonfiction: General interest (stories on top pros); historical (stories of old-time bowlers or bowling alleys); interview (top pros, men and women); and profile (top pros). "We publish some controversial matter, seek outspoken personalities. We reject material that is too general; that is, not written for high average bowlers and bowling proprietors who already know basics of playing the game and basics of operating a bowling alley." Buys 5-6 unsolicited mss/year. Query, phone queries OK. Length: 1,200-3,500 words. Pays $75-200.

Photos: State availability of photos with query. Pays $5-15 for 8x10 b&w prints; and $15-25 for 35mm or 2¼x2¼ color transparencies. Buys one-time rights.

THE WOMAN BOWLER, 5301 S. 76th St., Greendale WI 53129. (414)421-9000. Editor: Paula McMartin. Monthly (except for combined July/August) magazine; 64 pages. Circ. 155,000. Emphasizes bowling for women bowlers, ages 8-90. Buys all rights. Pays on acceptance. Byline given "except on occasion, when freelance article is used as part of a regular magazine department. When this occurs, it is discussed first with the author." Submit seasonal/holiday material 2 months in advance. Photocopied and previously published submissions OK. Reports in 1 month. Free sample copy and writer's guidelines.

Nonfiction: Interview; profile; and spot news. Buys 25 mss/year. Query. Length: 1,500 words maximum (unless by special assignment). Pays $25-100.

Photos: Purchased with accompanying ms. Query. Pays $25 for b&w glossy prints. Model releases and identification of subjects required.

YABA WORLD, 5301 S. 76th St., Greendale WI 53129. (414)421-4700. Official publication of Young American Bowling Alliance. Editor: Paul Bertling. For boys and girls ages 21 and under. 10% freelance written. Monthly, November through April. Circ. 80,000. Pays on publication. Publishes ms an average of 2 months after acceptance. Buys all rights. Byline given "except if necessary to do extensive rewriting." Reports in 3 weeks. Query. No computer printout or disk submissions.

Nonfiction and Photos: Subject matter of articles must be based on tenpin bowling and activities connected with Young American Bowling Alliance only. Audience includes youngsters down to 6 years of age, but material should feature the teenage group. "The magazine is designed for and about youth bowlers. We found they are more interested in fillers rather than full-length features." Buys 3-5 unsolicited mss/year. Length: 500-800 words. Accompanying photos or art preferred. Pays $30-100/article. Photos should be 8x10 b&w glossy prints related to subject matter. Pays $5 minimum.

Tips: "We are primarily looking for feature stories on a specific person or activity. The most frequent mistake made by writers is that stories are about bowling in general. We prefer stories about youth bowlers, specifically our members (Young American Bowling Alliance). Stories about a specific person generally should center around the outstanding bowling achievements of that person in an YABA sanctioned league or tournament. Articles on special leagues for high average bowlers, physically or mentally handicapped bowlers, etc. should focus on the unique quality of the league. *YABA World* also carries articles on YABA sanctioned tournaments, but these should be more than just a list of the winners and their scores. Again, the unique feature of the tournament should be emphasized."

Football

FOOTBALL FORECAST, Baltimore Bulletin, 2601 Sisson St., Baltimore MD 21211. (301)243-1700. Editor: Rick Snider. 75% freelance written. Weekly seasonal sports tabloid covering professional and college football. Circ. 30,000 (seasonal). Pays on publication. Publishes ms an average of 1 month after acceptance. Byline given. Not copyrighted. Buys first, and second serial (reprint) rights; makes work-for-hire assignments. Submit seasonal/holiday material 1 month in advance. Photocopied and previously published submissions OK. Computer printout submissions acceptable; no dot-matrix. Reports in 1 month. Free sample copy and writer's guidelines.

Nonfiction: Interview/profile (on coaches, players). "Our audience likes articles on the backstage life of football." Buys 10 mss/year. Query. Length: 500-2,000 words. Pays $25-100.

Photos: State availability of photos. Needs "action, backstage, artsy" photos. Pays $10-50 for 5x7 b&w prints. Captions and identification of subjects required. Buys reprint rights.

Columns/Departments: Opinion. Buys 5 mss/year. Query. Length: 1,000-2,000 words. Pays $50-100.

Fiction: Sports. Buys 5 mss/year. Query. Length: 750-1,500 words. Pays $50-100.

Poetry: Must pertain to person, event of big-time sports. Buys 5 poems/year. Submit maximum 5 poems. Length: 20-40 lines. Pays $20-40.

Tips: "We only publish from September until the Super Bowl and do not accept submissions during the off months. If you can write something that teaches our readers something about a player or team that they didn't know before, you're on the right track."

Gambling

‡**GAMBLING TIMES MAGAZINE**, 1018 N. Cole Ave., Hollywood CA 90038. (213)463-4833. Editor: Len Miller. Address mss to Ms. Athene Mikhalis, Associate Editor. 50% freelance written. Monthly magazine; 100 pages. 50% freelance written. Circ. 70,000. Pays on publication. Buys first North American serial rights. Byline given. Submit seasonal/holiday material 5-6 months in advance of issue date. Computer printout submissions acceptable; prefers letter-quality to dot-matrix. Write for instructions on specific ms preparation for electronic typesetting equipment after query acceptance. Double-space all submissions, maximum 10 pp. Reports in 4-6 weeks. Publishes ms an average of 5 months after acceptance. Free writer's guidelines; mention *Writer's Market* in request.

Nonfiction: How-to (related to gambling systems, betting methods, etc.); humor; photo feature (racetracks, jai alai, casinos); and travel (gambling spas and resort areas). "Also interested in investigative reports focusing on the political, economical and legal issues surrounding gambling in the U.S. and the world and new gambling developments. No cutesy stuff. Keep your style clean, hard-edged and sardonic (if appropriate). Writers may query on any subject which is germane to our format." Buys 100 mss/year; prefers pictures with mss. Query. Pays $50-150.

Fiction: "We only use heavily gambling-related material and prefer fast-paced, humorous stories. Please, no more 'man scores big and dies' stuff." Buys 12 mss/year. Submit complete ms double spaced, maximum 9 pp. Pays $50-100.

Tips: "Know gambling thoroughly. *Pictures with mss will add $50 to the payment.* Action shots—always people shots. Photographs must show something unique to the subject in article. We enjoy the feeling of accomplishment when we've helped an amateur or beginner to make it into print. But we dislike a writer to begin a series of phone inquiries the day after he or she has mailed a submission."

POKER PLAYER, Gambling Times, Inc., 1018 N. Cole Ave., Hollywood CA 90038. (213)466-5261. Managing Editor: Gary Thompson. 70% freelance written. Biweekly tabloid covering poker games. "This is

the only poker publication in the U.S." Circ. 27,000. Pays on acceptance. Publishes ms an average of 1 month after acceptance. Byline given. Buys all rights. Electronic submissions OK on DOS PLUS - TRS 80 Bell 103 or 212 Protocol for modem, but requires hard copy also. Computer printout submissions acceptable; no dot-matrix (except as samples). Reports in 1 month. Sample copy $1; free writer's guidelines.
Nonfiction: Book excerpts; how-to; humor; interview/profile; personal experience; photo feature; and technical (poker strategy). Also, needs articles on tournaments, local club news and regional legislative news. Anecdotes also considered. All articles must be poker related. Query. Length: 150-2,000 words. Pays $50 maximum.
Photos: State availability of photos. Reviews b&w prints.
Tips: "A solid, informative and well-written piece will be accepted regardless of length. Writers tend to think they are writing for a bunch of yahoos. Our readers know poker and want solid information. Vernacular is fine, but it can't be used to hide a lack of substance."

General Interest

‡CHAMPION, Canada's High Performance Amateur Sport Magazine, Athlete Information Bureau, 333 River Rd., Tower C, 10th Floor, Ottawa, Ontario K1L 8H9 Canada. (613)748-5601. Editor: David J. Stubbs. 75% freelance written. Works with a small number of new/unpublished writers each year. Quarterly, bilingual (French-English) amateur sports magazine featuring Canadian Olympic- and international-calibre athletes and sports programs exclusively. Read by Canadian athletes, coaches, and sport medicine professionals and the Canadian media. Circ. 23,000. Pays on acceptance. Publishes ms an average of 3 months after acceptance. Byline given. Offers negotiable kill fee. Buys first North American serial rights. Submit seasonal/holiday material 3 months in advance. Simultaneous queries and photocopied submissions OK. Electronic submissions OK via AES (Lanier) word processor disks only (5¼"—disks returned on request); prefers hard copy also. Computer printout submissions acceptable; no dot-matrix. Reports in 2 weeks on queries; 1 month on ms. Sample copy $2.
Nonfiction: Book reviews, humor, interview/profile, and personal experience, such as overcoming a disability or fear to achieve personal success in sports. "All articles must focus on or be related to topics of concern to Canadian Olympic- and international-calibre athletes, coaches, administrators, and sport medicine professionals." Special issue will be Pan-American Games preview (summer '87). Buys 20 mss/year. Query with published clips. Length: 200-2,000 words. Pays $150-1,000 (Canadian). Sometimes pays expenses of writers on assignment.
Photos: Prefers action and/or candid personality stills. Reviews 35mm transparencies and 8x10 prints. Requires captions and identification of subjects. Buys one-time rights.
Tips: "Freelancers should realize that as a quarterly, we do not stress 'News' stories, but rather backgrounders and analyses of trends that affect amateur sports today and in the future, and profiles of people in the news. Personality profiles and analysis of national and international programs are most open. Be thorough, clear, and colorful in your writing."

CITY SPORTS MAGAZINE, 118 King St, Box 3693, San Francisco CA 94119. Editors: Dan Tobin (in northern California, at 1120 Princeton Dr., Marina del Rey CA 90291) and Will Balliet. 80% freelance written. Monthly controlled circulation tabloid covering participant sports for active sports participants. Circ. in California 203,000. Two editions published monthly—for Northern and Southern California. "For the most part, we use separate writers for each edition." Pays on publication. Publishes ms an average of 2 months after acceptance. Byline given. Pays negotiable kill fee. Buys one-time rights. Simultaneous queries OK; previously published submissions ("from outside readership area") OK. Computer printout submissions acceptable. Reports in 1 month on queries. Sample copy $3.
Nonfiction: Interview/profile (of athletes); travel; and instructional and service pieces on sports. Special issues include: April, Tennis; May, Running; June, Outdoors and Biking; July, Water Sports; November, Skiing; December, Cross Country Skiing and Indoor Sports. Buys 60 mss/year. Query with clips of published work. Length: 1,800-2,800 words. Pays $150-400.
Photos: Pays $50-300 for 35mm color; $25-35 for b&w 8x10 glossy prints. Model releases and identification of subjects required.

‡COLORADO SPORTSTYLES MAGAZINE, (formerly *Colorado Sports Monthly*), Columbine Communications and Publications, Inc., Box 3519, Evergreen CO 80439. (303)670-3700. Editor: Robert Erdmann. 100% freelance written. A monthly tabloid covering participatory sports indigenous to Colorado. Circ. 35,000. Pays 30 days after publication. Byline given. Buys first North American serial rights. Submit seasonal/holiday material 1 year in advance. Simultaneous submissions OK. Computer printout submissions acceptable; prefers letter-quality to dot-matrix. Reports in 1 month. Sample copy and writer's guidelines for 9x12 SAE.

Nonfiction: Book excerpts, general interest, how-to, humor, interview/profile, personal experience, photo feature and travel—all with a Colorado hook. Buys 100 mss/year. Query with or without published clips, or send complete ms. Length: 2,000 words. Pays $50. May pay writers with contributor copies or other premiums rather than a cash payment.

Photos: Send photos with submission. Reviews b&w contact sheets and transparencies. Model releases and identification of subjects required. Buys one-time rights.

Columns/Departments: Send complete ms. Pays $50.

‡**MASSACHUSETTS/NEW HAMPSHIRE OUT-OF-DOORS**, MOOD, 510 King St., Box 248, Littleton MA 01460. (617)486-4785. Editor: Bryan "Red" Chaplin. 20% freelance written. A monthly tabloid covering hunting, fishing, snowmobiling, camping, shooting: "useful news and information on how to, where to, in New England area, adjoining states and Northeastern Canadian provinces; occasional philosophical pieces." Circ. 19,302. Pays on publication. Publishes an average of 3 months after acceptance. Byline given. Buys one-time rights. Submit seasonal/holiday material 3 months in advance. Computer printout submissions acceptable. Reports in 2 weeks. Sample copy for 9x12 SAE.

Nonfiction: How-to (hunt, fish, camp, snowmobile, shoot, aimed at mature sportsmen who don't need beginner basics); inspirational (*why* we hunt/fish philosophical "mood" pieces); personal experience; and travel (where to). "We do not accept product/service pieces about non-advertisers obviously written to pay off free product or trip writer received." Buys 40-50 mss/year. Length: 800-1,800 words (flexible). Pays $1/typeset column inch.

Photos: Send photos with submissions; 1-5 maximum. Reviews b&w prints only. Offers $5 inside; $20 cover. Captions required. Buys one-time rights.

Tips: "Front-or-book feature articles are most open to freelancers. Don't expect to write about New England hunting/fishing if you live somewhere else . . . it won't go. We abhor the writer who thinks he can localize every story by just changing place names. Know your subject first of all . . . writing is secondary."

OUTDOOR CANADA MAGAZINE, Suite 301, 801 York Mills Rd., Don Mills, Ontario M3B 1X7 Canada. (416)443-8888. Editor-in-Chief: Teddi Brown. 50% freelance written. Emphasizes noncompetitive outdoor recreation in Canada *only*. Magazine published 8 times/year; 72-120 pages. Circ 141,000. Pays on publication. Pubishes ms an average of 3 months after acceptance. Buys first rights. Submit seasonal/holiday material 5-6 months in advance of issue date. Byline given. Originals only. Computer printout submissions acceptable; no dot-matrix. *SAE with IRCs or material not returned.* Reports in 1 month. Sample copy $1.50; writer's guidelines 50¢; mention *Writer's Market* in request.

Nonfiction: Expose (only as it pertains to the outdoors, e.g. wildlife management); and how-to (in-depth, thorough pieces on how to select equipment for various subjects, or improve techniques only as they relate to outdoor subjects covered). Buys 35-40 mss/year. Submit complete ms. Length: 1,000-5,000 words. Pays $100-500.

Photos: Submit photo material with accompanying ms. Pays $10-45 for 8x10 b&w glossy prints and $20-175 for 35mm color transparencies; $250/cover. Captions preferred. Buys all rights. Model releases required.

Fillers: Outdoor tips. Buys 20/year. Length: 350-500 words. Pays $25-75.

‡**OUTSIDE**, Mariah Publication Corp., 1165 N. Clark St., Chicago IL 60610. (312)951-0990. Editor: John Rasmus. 90% freelance written. Works with a small number of new/unpublished writers each year. A monthly magazine emphasizing outdoor subjects. Circ. 240,000. Pays on publication (on acceptance for features). Publishes ms an average of 6 months after acceptance. Byline given. Offers 25% kill fee. Buys first North American serial rights. Submit seasonal/holiday material 4 months in advance. Computer printout submissions acceptable; no dot-matrix. Reports in 1 month on queries; 2 months on mss. Sample copy $3; free writer's guidelines.

Nonfiction: Investigative (environmental/political and consumer outdoor equipment); general interest (as pertains to the outdoors); expedition and adventure stories; historical (profiles of early pioneers and expeditions); how-to (photography, equipment, techniques used in outdoor sports); profiles (leaders and major figures associated with sports, politics, ecology of the outdoors); new product (hardware/software, reviews of performance of products used in camping, backpacking, outdoor sports, etc.); personal experience (major and minor expeditions and adventures); photo feature (outdoor photography); technical (of outdoor equipment); and travel (to exotic regions and cultures rarely visited). Buys 150 mss/year. Query with published clips. Length: 1,000-4,000 words. Pays $350-1,200.

Photos: Send photos with ms. Pays $50-200 for 35mm color transparencies. Buys one-time rights. Captions required.

Columns/Departments: Dispatches (news items); Equipage (articles on broad categories of outdoor equipment); Hardware/Software (short equipment reviews, slant to new innovative products, must include evaluation); Destinations (travel); Law of the Land (legal and political issues that affect the outdoors). Buys 3-4/issue. Query with published clips. Length: 200-1,500 words. Pays $150-400.

REFEREE, Referee Enterprises, Inc., Box 161, Franksville WI 53126. (414)632-8855. Editor: Tom Hammill. For well-educated, mostly 26- to 50-year-old male sports officials. 20-40% freelance written. Eager to work with new/unpublished writers. Monthly magazine. Circ. 42,000. Pays on acceptance of completed manuscript. Publishes ms an average of 6 months after acceptance. Rights purchased varies. Submit seasonal/holiday material 6 months in advance. Photocopied and previously published submissions OK. Computer printout submissions acceptable. Reports in 2 weeks. Free sample copy.
Nonfiction: How-to, informational, humor, interview, profile, personal experience, photo feature and technical. Buys 54 mss/year. Query. Length: 700-2,500 words. Pays 4-10¢/word. "No general sports articles." Recent article example: "Story about a 22-year-old amateur league umpire whose goal was to become a major umpire. He worked for a year in the minor leagues, but was released after the 1983 season. In July 1984 he committed suicide by hanging himself." (May 1986). Sometimes pays the expenses of writers on assignment.
Photos: Purchased with or without accompanying ms or on assignment. Captions preferred. Send contact sheet, prints, negatives or transparencies. Pays $15-25 for each b&w used; $25-40 for each color used; $75-100 for color cover. Sometimes pays the expenses of writers on assignment.
Columns/Departments: Arena (bios); Law (legal aspects); Take Care (fitness, medical). Buys 24 mss/year. Query. Length: 200-800 words. Pays 4¢/word up to $100 maximum for Law and Take Care. Arena pays about $15 each, regardless of length.
Fillers: Jokes, gags, anecdotes, puzzles and referee shorts. Query. Length: 50-200 words. Pays 4¢/word in some cases; others offer only author credit lines.
Tips: "Queries with a specific idea appeal most to readers. Generally, we are looking more for feature writers, as we usually do our own shorter/filler-type material. It is helpful to obtain suitable photos to augment a story. Don't send fluff—we need hard-hitting, incisive material tailored just for our audience. Anything smacking of public relations is a no sale. Don't gloss over the material too lightly or fail to go in-depth looking for a quick sale (taking the avenue of least resistance)."

SPORT, Sport Magazine Association, 119 W. 40th St., New York NY 10018. (212)869-4700. Managing Editor: Peter Griffin. Editor: Neil Cohen. 70% freelance written. Monthly magazine covering primarily college and pro sports—baseball, football, basketball, hockey, boxing, tennis, others—for sports fans. Circ. 1.25 million. Pays on acceptance. Publishes ms an average of 2 months after acceptance. Byline given. Offers 25% kill fee. Buys first North American serial rights. Submit seasonal/holiday material 3 months in advance. Reports in 2 weeks.
Nonfiction: General interest, interview (sport interview in Q&A format), and investigative reports on the world of sports. Buys 75 mss/year. Query with published clips. No telephone queries. Length: 2,500-3,000 words. Pays $1,000 minimum.
Columns/Departments: Barry Shapiro, associate editor. Sport Talk (briefs on news or offbeat aspects of sport). Buys 48 mss/year. Length: 250-500 words. Pays $100-150, depending on length and type of piece.
Tips: "Writers should read the magazine to keep up with the broadening subjects we're dealing with."

SPORTING NEWS, 1212 N. Lindbergh Blvd., St. Louis MO 63132. "We do not actively solicit freelance material."

‡SPORTSCAN™, Brannigan-Demarco Communications, Inc., 141 5th Ave., New York NY 10010. (212)505-7600. Editor-in-Chief: Vincent Parry. Assistant Editor: Susanne J. Hollander. 75% freelance written. A bimonthly magazine covering sports nostalgia. "*Sportscan* is sponsored by a pharmaceutical company and sent free to doctors and pharmacists." Estab. 1985. Circ. 75,000. Pays on acceptance. Publishes an average of 4 months after acceptance. Offers 15% kill fee. Buys all rights. Submit seasonal/holiday material 4 months in advance. Photocopied and previously published submissions OK. Computer printout submissions acceptable; prefers letter-quality to dot-matrix. Reports in 2 weeks on queries; 1 month on mss. Free sample copy and writer's guidelines.
Nonfiction: Historical/nostalgic (sports related); humor (sports "shorts"); interview/profile (sports figures, especially nostalgic slant); and analysis of trends in sports. No sports medicine. Buys 40 mss/year. Query with published clips, or send complete ms. Length: 1,000-1,500 words. Pays $500-1,000 for assigned articles; pays $300-1,000 for unsolicited articles.
Photos: State availability of photos with submission. Reviews contact sheets. Offers $50-100/photo. Captions required. Buys one-time rights.
Columns/Departments: Fast Break (sports shorts, trivia, humorous news items, etc.), 200-250 words; Book Scan (book reviews of sports-related topics), 200-250 words; and Where Have You Gone (interviews with sports legends no longer in the public eye), 1,000-1,500 words. Buys 10 mss/year. Query with published clips or send complete ms. Pays $100-500.
Fillers: Anecdotes, facts, gags to be illustrated by cartoonist, newsbreaks and short humor. Length: 200-250 words. Pays $50-100.
Tips: "Send written query outlining the proposed article and any writing sample that might demonstrate the tone or angle. Sports nostalgia features and Fast Break items are most open to freelancers."

SPORTS PARADE, Meridian Publishing Co., Inc., Box 10010, Odgen UT 84409. (801)394-9446. Editor: Robyn Walker. 65% freelance written. Works with a small number of new/unpublished writers each year. A monthly general interest sports magazine distributed by business and professional firms to employees, customers, clients, etc. Readers are predominantly upscale, mainstream, family oriented. Circ. 23,000. Pays on acceptance. Publishes ms an average of 8 months after acceptance. Byline given. Buys first rights, second serial (reprint) rights or nonexclusive reprint rights. Submit seasonal/holiday material 6 months in advance. Simultaneous, photocopied and previously published submissions OK. Computer printout submissions acceptable; prefers letter-quality to dot-matrix. Reports in 6 weeks. Sample copy $1 with 9x12 SAE; writer's guidelines for business size SAE and 1 first class stamp.
Nonfiction: General interest, historical/nostalgic and interview/profile. "General interest articles covering the entire sports spectrum, from the National Football league to horseshoes. Personality profiles on top flight professional and amateur sports figures are used as cover stories. Stories about heroes of the past are also welcome if color photos and/or artwork are available." Buys 20 mss/year. Query. Length: 1,100-1,200 words. Pays 15¢/word.
Photos: Send with query or ms. Pays $35 for color transparencies; $50 for cover. Captions and model releases required.
Tips: "I will be purchasing more articles based on personalities—today's stars as well as yesterday's heroes."

WISCONSIN SILENT SPORTS, Waupaca Publishing Co., Box 152, Waupaca WI 54981. (715)258-7731. Editor: Greg Marr. 75% freelance written. Eager to work with new/unpublished writers. Monthly magazine on running, cycling, cross-country skiing, canoeing, camping, backpacking, hiking. A regional publication aimed at people who run, cycle, cross-country ski, canoe, camp and hike in Wisconsin. Not a "coffee-table" magazine. "Our readers are participants from rank amateur weekend athletes to highly competitive racers." Circ. 10,000. Pays on publication. Publishes ms an average of 3 months after acceptance. Byline given. Offers 20% kill fee. Buys one-time rights. Submit seasonal/holiday material 2 months in advance. Simultaneous queries, and photocopied and previously published submissions OK. Computer printout submissions acceptable; prefers letter-quality to dot-matrix. Reports in 1 month. Sample copy and writer's guidelines for large SAE and 5 first class stamps.
Nonfiction: General interest, how-to, interview/profile, new product, opinion, technical and travel. No first person unless it is of Edward Abbey/Norman Mailer quality. Buys 25 mss/year. Query. Length: 2,500 words maximum. Pays $15-100. Sometimes pays expenses of writers on assignment.
Tips: "Where-to-go, how-to, and personality profiles are areas most open to freelancers. Writers should keep in mind that this is a regional Wisconsin-based publication. We do drift over into border areas occasionally but center on Wisconsin."

WOMEN'S SPORTS AND FITNESS MAGAZINE, Women's Sports Publications, Inc., 310 Town & Country Village, Palo Alto CA 94301. Editor: Martha Nelson. 80% freelance written. Works with a small number of new/unpublished writers each year. Monthly magazine; 72 pages. Emphasizes women's sports, fitness and health. Circ. 125,000. Pays on publication. Publishes ms an average of 3 months after acceptance. Generally buys all rights. Submit seasonal/holiday material 3 months in advance. Computer printout submissions acceptable; no dot-matrix. Reports in 1 month on queries; 6 weeks on mss. Sample copy $2; writer's guidelines for SASE.
Nonfiction: Profile, service piece, interview, how-to, historical, personal experience, personal opinion, travel, new product and reviews. "All articles should pertain to women's sports and fitness or health. All must be of national interest." Buys 5 mss/issue. Length: 2,500-3,000 words. Pays $300-800 for features. Sometimes pays the expenses of writers on assignment.
Photos: State availability of photos. Pays about $25-50 for b&w prints; $100-250 for 35mm color transparencies. Buys one-time rights.
Columns/Departments: Buys 6-8/issue. Query with published clips. Length: 500-1,500 words. Pays $100 minimum.
Fillers: Health and fitness information. Length: 100-250 words.
Tips: "We prefer queries to manuscripts. The best query letters often start with a first paragraph that could be the first paragraph of the article the writer wants to do. Queries should indicate that the writer has done the preliminary research for the article and has an 'angle' or something to give the article personality. Published clips help too. Freelancers can best break into *Women's Sports and Fitness* by submitting short items for the Sports Pages and Sportif sections or opinion pieces for End Zone. We are looking for profiles of athletes that demonstrate a real understanding of the athlete; we are looking for items of concern to active women—and we interpret that broadly—from the water she drinks to women to watch or remember, from adventure/travel to event coverage to home exercise equipment."

Golf

GOLF DIGEST, 5520 Park Ave., Trumbull CT 06611. (203)373-7000. Executive Editor: Jerry Tarde. 30% freelance written. Emphasizes golfing. Monthly magazine. Circ. 1.2 million. Pays on acceptance. Publishes ms an average of 6 weeks after acceptance. Buys all rights. Byline given. Submit seasonal/holiday material 4 months in advance. Photocopied submissions OK. Computer printout submissions acceptable; prefers letter-quality to dot-matrix. Reports in 6 weeks.
Nonfiction: Expose, how-to, informational, historical, humor, inspirational, interview, nostalgia, opinion, profile, travel, new product, personal experience, photo feature and technical; "all on playing and otherwise enjoying the game of golf." Query. Length: 1,000-2,500 words. Pays 20¢/edited word minimum.
Photos: Nick DiDio, art director. Purchased without accompanying ms. Pays $10-150 for 5x7 or 8x10 b&w prints; $25-300/35mm color transparency. Model release required.
Poetry: Lois Hains, assistant editor. Light verse. Buys 1-2/issue. Length: 4-8 lines. Pays $25.
Fillers: Lois Hains, assistant editor. Jokes, gags, anecdotes, and cutlines for cartoons. Buys 1-2/issue. Length: 2-6 lines. Pays $10-25.

‡GOLF ILLUSTRATED, Family Media, Inc., 3 Park Ave., New York NY 10016. (212)340-9200. Editor: Al Barkow. Managing Editor: Lee R. Schreiber. 60% freelance written. Eager to work with new/unpublished writers. A monthly magazine covering personalities and developments in the sport of golf. Estab. 1985. Circ. 100,000. Pays on acceptance. Publishes ms an average of 2 months after acceptance. Offers 10% kill fee. Buys all rights. Submit seasonal/holiday material 6 months in advance. Computer printout submissions acceptable; no dot-matrix. Reports in 3 weeks on queries; 6 weeks on manuscripts.
Nonfiction: Essays, historical/nostalgic, how-to, humor, interview/profile, opinion, personal experience, photo feature, and travel. Buys 70 mss/year. Query with published clips. Length: 750-2,000 words. Pays $500-1,500 for assigned articles; pays $250-1,000 for unsolicited articles. Sometimes pays the expenses of writers on assignment.
Photos: State availability of photos with submission. Reviews contact sheets and transparencies. Offers $50-400/photo. Captions and identification of subjects required. Buys one-time right.
Columns/Departments: Health and Fitness, Food, and Opinion (all related to golf), approximately 750 words. Query with published clips. Pays $500-1,000.
Fillers: Anecdotes, facts, gags to be illustrated by cartoonist and short humor. Buys 30/year. Length: 100-500 words. Pays $25-300.
Tips: "A freelancer can best break in to our publication by following the personalities—the PGA, LPGA and PGA Senior tour pros."

GOLF MAGAZINE, Times Mirror Magazines, Inc., 380 Madison Ave., New York NY 10017. (212)687-3000. Editor: George Peper. 25% freelance written. Works with a small number of new/unpublished writers each year. Monthly magazine; 150 pages. Golf audience, 95% male, ages 15-80, college-educated, professionals. Circ. 825,000. Pays on acceptance. Publishes ms an average of 6 months after acceptance. Byline given. Buys all rights. Submit seasonal/holiday material 4 months in advance. Photocopied submissions OK. Dot-matrix submissions acceptable if double-spaced. Reports in 4 weeks. Send mss to specific section editors—feature, instruction, Golf Reports, etc. General mss direct to James A. Frank, Executive Editor. Sample copy $2.
Nonfiction: How-to (improve game, instructional tips); informational (news in golf); humor; profile (people in golf); travel (golf courses, resorts); new product (golf equipment, apparel, teaching aids); and photo feature (great moments in golf—must be special; most photography on assignment only). Buys 4-6 unsolicited mss/year. Query. Length: 1,200-2,500 words. Pays $600-1,000. Sometimes pays expenses of writers on assignment.
Photos: Purchased with accompanying ms or on assignment. Captions required. Query. Pays $50 for 8½x11 glossy prints (with contact sheet and negatives); $75 minimum for 3x5 color prints. Total purchase price for ms includes payment for photos. Captions and model releases required.
Columns/Departments: Golf Reports (interesting golf events, feats, etc.); What's Going On (news of golf tours). Buys 5-10 mss/year. Query. Length: 250 words maximum. Pays $75. Open to suggestions for new columns/departments.
Fiction: Humorous or mystery. Must be golf-related. Buys 1-2 mss/year. Looking to do more in future. Query. Length: 1,200-2,000 words. Pays $500-750.
Tips: "Best chance is to aim for a light piece which is not too long and is focused on a personality. Anything very technical that would require a consummate knowledge of golf, we would rather assign ourselves. But if you are successful with something light and not too long, we might use you for something heavier later. We are looking for detailed knowledge of golf. Shorter items are a good test of knowledge. Probably the best way to break in would be by our Golf Reports section in which we run short items on interesting golf feats, events and so forth. If you send us something like that, about an important event in your area, it is an easy way for us to get acquainted."

GULF COAST GOLFER, Gulf Coast Golfer, Inc., 9182 Old Katy Rd., Houston TX 77055. (713)464-0308. Editor: Bob Gray. 60% freelance written. Monthly magazine covering results of major area competition, data on upcoming tournaments, reports of new and improved golf courses, and how-to tips for active, competitive golfers in Texas Gulf Coast area. Circ. 33,000. Pays on publication. Publishes ms an average of 2 weeks after acceptance. Byline given. Buys one-time rights. Submit seasonal/holiday material 3 months in advance. Computer printout submissions acceptable; prefers letter-quality to dot-matrix. Reports in 3 weeks. Sample copy for 9x12 SAE; free writer's guidelines.

Nonfiction: How-to and personal experience golf articles. No routine coverage. Query. Length: by arrangement. Pays negotiable rates.

Tips: Especially wants articles on how-to subjects about golf in Gulf Coast area.

THE LINKS LETTER, The Newsletter for Golfers Who Travel, The Bartlett Group, Inc., 1483 Fairview Road NE, Atlanta GA 30306. Editor: James Y. Bartlett. 5% freelance written. Monthly newsletter covering golf travel, golf resorts and international travel with news of interest to traveling golfers: where to stay, where to play, what else to do and how much. Circ. 3,000. Pays on publication. Publishes ms an average of 2 months after acceptance. Byline given. Buys first North American serial rights. Submit seasonal/holiday material 3-4 months in advance. Computer printout submissions acceptable. Reports in 3 weeks on queries. Sample copy for $7.50, 5x7 SAE and 1 first class stamp.

Nonfiction: Travel (not just puffs). Annual issues include Florida, Scotland, Fall Foliage and Spring Azalea resorts. "We don't run any flowery travel pieces. Our readers want down and dirty, hard information, recommendations, places to visit and places to avoid." Buys 3-5 mss/year. Query. Length: 500 words maximum. Pays $25 maximum.

Tips: "Read the newsletter for style and content, then query with an idea for someplace we haven't been (and we've been almost everywhere)."

‡NORTH TEXAS GOLFER, GULF COAST GOLFER, Texas, Louisiana Golf Group, Golfer Magazines, Inc., 9182 Old Katy Rd., Houston TX 77055. (713)464-0308. Editor: Bob Gray. 30% freelance written. A monthly tabloid covering golf in Texas and Louisiana. Emphasizes "grass roots coverage of regional golf course activities" and detailed, localized information on tournaments and competition in Texas and Louisiana. Circ. 60,000 (combined). Pays on publication. Byline given. Buys one-time rights. Submit seasonal/holiday material 3 months in advance. Computer printout submissions acceptable; no dot-matrix. Reports in 2 weeks. Free sample copy.

Nonfiction: How-to, humor, interview/profile, personal experience and travel. Nothing outside of Texas or Louisiana. Buys 20 mss/year. Query. Length: 500-1,500 words. Pays $50-250 for assigned articles. Sometimes pays expenses of writers on assignment.

Photos: Send photos with submission. Offers no additional payment for photos accepted with ms. Identification of subjects required.

Tips: "We publish mostly how-to, where-to articles. They're about people and events in Texas and Louisiana. We could use profiles of successful amateur and professional golfers in our two states—but only on a specific assignment basis. Most of the Tour players already have been assigned to the staff or to freelancers. Do *not* approach people, schedule interviews, then tell us about it."

SCORE, Canada's Golf Magazine, Canadian Controlled Media Communications, 287 MacPherson Ave., Toronto, Ontario M4V 1A4 Canada. (416)961-5141. Managing Editor: Lisa A. Leighton. 85% freelance written. Magazine published 7 times/year covering golf. "*Score* magazine provides seasonal coverage of the Canadian golf scene, professional, amateur, senior and junior golf for men and women golfers in Canada, the U.S. and Europe through profiles, history, travel, editorial comment and instruction. Circ. over 170,000. Pays on publication. Publishes ms an average of 3 months after acceptance. Byline given. Offers negotiable kill fee. Buys all rights and second serial (reprint) rights. Submit seasonal/holiday material 8 months in advance. Computer printout submissions acceptable; no dot-matrix. SAE with IRCs. Reports within 1 month. Sample copy for $2 (Canadian), 9x12 SAE and IRCs; writer's guidelines for business size SAE and IRC.

Nonfiction: Book excerpts (golf); historical/nostalgic (golf and golf characters); humor (golf); interview/profile (prominent golf professionals); photo feature (golf); and travel (golf destinations only). The yearly April/May issue, includes tournament results from Canada, the U.S., Europe, Asia, Australia, etc., history, profile, and regular features. "No personal experience, technical, opinion or general-interest material. Most articles are by assignment only." Buys 25-30 mss/year. Query with published clips or send complete ms. Length: 700-3,500 words. Pays $140-800.

Photos: Send photos with query or ms. Pays $50-100 for 35mm color transparencies (positives) or $30 for 8x10 or 5x7 b&w prints. Captions, model release (if necessary), and identification of subjects required. Buys all rights.

Columns/Departments: Profile (historical or current golf personalities or characters); Great Moments ("Great Moments in Canadian Golf"—description of great single moments, usually game triumphs); New Equipment (Canadian availability only); Travel (golf destinations, including "hard" information such as greens fees, hotel accommodations, etc.); Instruction (by special assignment only; usually from teaching golf professionals); The Mental Game (psychology of the game, by special assignment only); humor (golf humor); and History (golf equipment collections and collectors, development of the game, legendary figures and events). Buys 17-20 mss/year. Query with published clips or send complete ms. Length: 700-1,700 words. Pays $140-400.

Fiction: Historical (golf only) and humorous (golf only). No science fiction or adventure. Buys 1-3 mss/year. Query with published clips or send complete ms. Length: 700-1,700 words. Pays $140-400.

Fillers: Clippings, jokes, anecdotes, short humor and newsbreaks. Buys 5/year. Length: 50-100 words. Pays $10-25.

Tips: "Only writers with an extensive knowledge of golf and familiarity with the Canadian and/or U.S. golf scene(s) should query or submit in-depth work to *Score*. Golf-oriented humor is the only exception to this rule. Many of our features are written by professional people who play the game for a living or work in the industry. All areas mentioned under Columns/Departments are open to freelancers. Most of our *major* features are done on assignment only. These are given to regular contributors on the basis of past performances and expertise, etc. Writers wishing to break into the magazine best 'prove' their capabilities with shorter work to begin with. On queries and unsolicited material, frequent mistakes made by writers are faulty or poor presentation, showing a lack of definite direction, poor spelling, grammar and sloppy typing. On assignments, providing the writer is willing to listen to what we need and to discipline him/herself to write accurately and tightly, there shouldn't be major problems. Background research is sometimes not as thorough as we would like."

Guns

‡AMERICAN HANDGUNNER, Publishers' Development Corp., Suite 200, 591 Camino de la Reina, San Diego CA 92108. (619)297-5352. Editor: Cameron Hopkins. 90% freelance written. A bimonthly magazine covering handguns, handgun sports, and handgun accessories. "Semi-technical publication for handgun enthusiasts of above-average knowledge/understanding of handguns. Writers must have ability to write about technical designs of handguns as well as ability to write intelligently about the legitimate sporting value of handguns." Circ. 180,000. Pays on publication. Publishes ms an average of 5 months after acceptance. Byline given. Offers $50 kill fee. Buys first North American serial rights. Submit seasonal/holiday material 7 months in advance. Previously published submissions OK. Computer printout submissions acceptable; prefers letter-quality to dot-matrix. Reports in 1 week. Free sample copy and writer's guidelines.

Nonfiction: How-to, interview/profile, new product, photo feature, technical and iconoclastic think pieces." Special issue is the *American Handgunner Annual*. No handgun competition coverage. Buys 60-70 mss/year. Query. Length: 500-3,000 words. Pays $175-600 for assigned articles; pays $100-400 for unsolicited articles. Sometimes pays the expenses of writers on assignment.

Photos: Send photos with submission. Reviews contact sheets, 35mm and 4x5 transparencies and 5x7 b&w prints. Offers no additional payment for b&w photos accepted with ms; offers $50-250/color photo. Captions and identification of subjects required. Buys all rights.

Columns/Departments: Combat Shooting (techniques, equipment, accessories for sport of combat shooting—no blood and guts"), 600-800 words. Buys 40-60 mss/year. Query. Pays $175-200.

Tips: "We are always interested in 'round-up' pieces covering a particular product line or mixed bag of different products lines of the same theme. If vacation/travel takes you to on exotic place, we're interested in, say, 'The Guns of Upper Volta.' "

THE AMERICAN MARKSMAN, National Rifle Association, Publications Division, 1600 Rhode Island Ave. NW, Washington DC 20036. (202)828-6395. Editor: John Zent. 10% freelance written. A monthly association journal covering competition shooting. Circ. 8,000. Pays on acceptance. Publishes ms an average of 3 months after acceptance. Byline given. Buys first North American serial rights. Simultaneous queries OK. Computer printout submissions acceptable; no dot-matrix. Reports in 1 month. Sample copy and writer's guidelines free.

Nonfiction: General interest (on national/international competition); how-to (coaching, equipment modification); humor (experiences in practice, competition); interview/profile (of champion shooters, coaches); new product; and technical (equipment evaluation—request detailed requirements). Special issues include Olympics and World Shooting Championships. No political articles. Buys 15 mss/year. Send complete ms. Length: 1,500-3,000 words. Pays $50-250.

Photos: Send photos with ms. Reviews 8x12 prints. Identification of subjects required. Buys one-time rights.

‡FIREPOWER, The Magazine of Exotic Weaponry, Turbo Publishing, Inc., Box 397, Cornville AZ 86325. (602)634-6127. Editor: Everett Moore, Jr., 50% freelance written. A bimonthly magazine. Pays on publication. Byline given. Buys all rights. Previously published submissions usually OK; some exceptions apply. Computer printout submissions acceptable; prefers letter-quality to dot-matrix. Free sample copy and writer's guidelines.

Nonfiction: General interest, historical/nostalgic, how-to, interview/profile, new product, opinion, personal experience and technical. Buys 50 mss/year. Query with published clips. Length: 500-2,000 words. Pays $50-300.

Photos: Send photos with submission. Reviews transparencies and 3x5 and 5x7 prints. Offers no additional payment for photos accepted with ms. Captions, model releases and identification of subjects requried.

Columns/Departments: The Firing Line (new products) and Intelligence Briefs (book review). Buys 10-12 mss/year. Query with published clips. Length: 500-800 words. Pays $50-150.

GUN DIGEST, HANDLOADER'S DIGEST, DBI Books, Inc., 4092 Commercial Ave., Northfield IL 60062. (312)441-7010. Editor-in-Chief: Ken Warner. 40-80% freelance written. Prefers to work with published/established writers; works with a small number of new/unpublished writers each year; eager to work with new/unpublished writers. Annual journal covering guns and shooting. Pays on acceptance. Publishes ms an average of 20 months after acceptance. Byline given. Buys all rights. Computer printout submissions acceptable if legible. Reports in 1 month.

Nonfiction: Buys 50 mss/issue. Query. Length: 500-5,000 words. Pays $100-600; includes photos or illustration package from author.

Photos: State availability of photos with query letter. Reviews 8x10 b&w prints. Payment for photos included in payment for ms. Captions required.

Tips: Award of $1,000 to author of best article (juried) in each issue.

GUN WORLD, 34249 Camino Capistrano, Box HH, Capistrano Beach CA 92624. Editorial Director: Jack Lewis. 50% freelance written. For ages that "range from mid-20s to mid-60s; many professional types who are interested in relaxation of hunting and shooting." Monthly. Circ. 136,000. Buys 80-100 unsolicited mss/year. Pays on acceptance. Publishes ms an average of 6 months after acceptance. Buys first rights. Byline given. Submit seasonal material 4 months in advance. Reports in 6 weeks, perhaps longer. Computer printout submissions acceptable; prefers letter-quality to dot-matrix. Copy of editorial requirements for SASE.

Nonfiction and Photos: General subject matter consists of "well-rounded articles—not by amateurs—on shooting techniques, with anecdotes; hunting stories with tips and knowledge integrated. No poems or fiction. We like broad humor in our articles, so long as it does not reflect upon firearms safety. Most arms magazines are pretty deadly and we feel shooting can be fun. Too much material aimed at pro-gun people. Most of this is staff-written and most shooters don't have to be told of their rights under the Constitution. We want articles on new developments; off-track inventions, novel military uses of arms; police armament and training techniques; do-it-yourself projects in this field." Buys informational, how-to, personal experience and nostalgia articles. Pays up to $300, sometimes more. Purchases photos with mss and captions required. Wants 5x7 b&w. Sometimes pays the expenses of writers on assignment.

Tips: "The most frequent mistake made by writers in completing an article for us is surface writing with no real knowledge of the subject. To break in, offer an anecdote having to do with proposed copy."

GUNS MAGAZINE, 591 Camino de la Reina, San Diego CA 92108. (619)297-5352. Editor: J. Rakusan. 60% freelance written. Eager to work with new/unpublished writers. Monthly magazine for firearms enthusiasts. Circ. 135,000. Pays on publication. Publishes ms an average of 4 months after acceptance. Buys all rights. Computer printout submissions acceptable; no dot-matrix. Reports in 3 weeks. Free sample copy.

Nonfiction: Test reports on new firearms; how-to on gunsmithing, reloading; round-up articles on firearms types. Historical pieces. Does not want to see anything about "John and I went hunting" or rewrites of a general nature, or controversy for the sake of controversy, without new illumination. "More short, punchy articles will be used in the next year. Payments will not be as large as for full-length features, but the quantity used will give more writers a chance to get published." Buys 100-150 mss/year. Length: 1,000-2,500 words. Pays $100-350. Sometimes pays the expenses of writers on assignment.

Photos: Major emphasis is on good photos. No additional payment for b&w glossy prints purchased with mss. Pays $50-100 for color; 2¼x2¼ minimum.

SHOTGUN SPORTS, Shotgun Sport, Inc., Box 340, Lake Havasu City AZ 86403. (602)855-0100. Editor: Frank Kodl. Managing Editor: Fredi Kodl. 90% freelance written. Monthly magazine covering the sport of shotgunning. Circ. 110,000. Pays on publication. Publishes ms an average of 8 months after acceptance. Byline given. Buys one-time rights. Submit seasonal/holiday material 3 months in advance. Computer printout submissions acceptable. Reports in 1 month. Free sample copy and writer's guidelines.

Nonfiction: Book excerpts, expose, general interest, historical/nostalgic, how-to, humor, inspirational, interview/profile, new product, opinion, personal experience, photo feature, technical and travel; "all articles must be related directly to shotgunning to include trap, skeet or hunting." Buys 50-70 mss/year. Query or send complete mss. Length: open. Pays $50-200.

Photos: State availability of photos or send photos with ms. Reviews 5x7 b&w prints. "Photos included in payment for ms." Captions required.

‡S.W.A.T.: SPECIAL WEAPONS AND TACTICS, "For the Prepared American", Turbo Publishing, Inc., Box 397, Cornville AZ 86325. (602)634-6127. Editor: Rolland Huff. 50% freelance written. A bimonthly magazine. Pays on publication. Byline given. Buys all rights. Most previously published sumbissions OK. Computer printout submissions acceptable; prefers letter-quality to dot-matrix. Free sample copy and writer's guidelines.
Nonfiction: General interest, historical/nostalgic, how-to, interview/profile, law enforcement, new product, opinion, personal experiences and technical. No fiction. Buys 50 mss/year. Query with published clips. Length: 500-2,000 words. Pays $50-300.
Photos: Send photos with submission. Reviews transpariences and 3x5 and 5x7 prints. Offers no additional payment for photos accepted with ms. Captions, model releases, and identification of subjects required. Buys all rights.
Columns/Departments: FYI (For Your Information—general information), S.W.A.T. Emporium (new products); S.W.A.T. Library (book review). Buys 10-12 mss/year. Query with published clips. Length: 500-800 words. Pays $50-150.
Tips: "The biggest disappointment we often encounter is having to reject good articles because of poor or insufficient photography."

Horseracing

THE BACKSTRETCH, 19363 James Couzens Hwy., Detroit MI 48235. (313)342-6144. Editor: Ann Moss. Managing Editor: Ruth LeGrove. 25% freelance written. Works with a small number of new/unpublished writers each year. Quarterly magazine; 100 pages. For Thoroughbred horse trainers, owners, breeders, farm managers, track personnel, jockeys, grooms and racing fans who span the age range from very young to very old. Publication of United Thoroughbred Trainers of America, Inc. Circ. 25,000. Publishes ms an average of 3 months after acceptance. Sample copy $2.
Nonfiction: "*Backstretch* contains mostly general information. Articles deal with biographical material on trainers, owners, jockeys, horses and their careers on and off the track, historical track articles, etc. Unless writer's material is related to Thoroughbreds and Thoroughbred racing, it should not be submitted. Articles accepted on speculation basis—payment made after material is used. If not suitable, articles are returned immediately. Articles that do not require printing by a specified date are preferred. There is no special length requirement and amount paid depends on material. It is advisable to include photos, if possible. Articles should be original copies and should state whether presented to any other magazine, or whether previously printed in any other magazine. Submit complete ms. We do not buy crossword puzzles, cartoons, newspaper clippings, fiction or poetry."

THE FLORIDA HORSE, The Florida Horse, Inc., Box 2106, Ocala FL 32678. (904)629-8082. Editor: F.J. Audette. 25% freelance written. Monthly magazine covering the Florida thoroughbred horse industry. "We seek contemporary coverage and feature material on the Florida breeding, racing and sales scene." Circ. 12,000. Pays on publication. Publishes ms an average of 2 months after acceptance. Byline given. Buys first North American serial rights. Computer printout submissions acceptable; prefers letter-quality to dot-matrix. Reports in 2 weeks. Free sample copy.
Nonfiction: Bill Giauque, associate editor. Articles covering horses and people of the Florida thoroughbred industry. Buys 18-24 mss/year. Length: 1,500-3,000 words. Pays $125-200. Sometimes pays expenses of writers on assignment.
Photos: Send photos with ms. Pays $15-25 for sharp, well-composed 8x10 b&w prints. Captions and identification of subjects required. Buys one-time rights.
Columns/Departments: Medically Speaking (veterinarian analysis of equine problems); Legally Speaking (legal analysis of equine legal considerations); and Track Talk (news and features from racetracks—Florida angle only). Buys 24-36 mss/year. Send complete ms. Length: 800-960 words. Pays $35-50.
Tips: "We recommend that writers be at the scene of the action—racetracks, nurseries, provide clean, focused writing from the Florida angle and submit lively, interesting material full of detail and background."

HOOF BEATS, United States Trotting Association, 750 Michigan Ave., Columbus OH 43215. (614)224-2291. Editor: Dean A. Hoffman. 35% freelance written. Works with a small number of new/unpublished writers each year. Monthly magazine covering harness racing for the participants of the sport of harness racing. "We cover all aspects of the sport—racing, breeding, selling, etc." Circ. 26,000. Pays on publication. Publishes ms an average of 3 months after acceptance. Byline given. Buys negotiable rights. Submit seasonal/holiday material 3 months in advance. Computer printout submissions acceptable. Reports in 3 weeks. Free sample copy, postpaid.
Nonfiction: General interest, historical/nostalgic, humor, inspirational, interview/profile, new product, personal experience, photo feature. Buys 15-20 mss/year. Query. Length: open. Pays $100-400. Pays the expenses of writers on assignment "with approval."

Photos: State availability of photos. Pays variable rates for 35mm transparencies and prints. Identification of subjects required. Buys one-time rights.
Fiction: Historical, humorous, interesting fiction with a harness racing theme. Buys 2-3 mss/year. Query. Length: open. Pays $100-400.

HUB RAIL, Hub Rail, Inc., Box 1831, Harrisburg PA 17105. (717)234-5099. Publisher: David M. Dolezal. Editor: Charlotte Maurer, 5 E. Hyde Rd., Yellow Springs OH 45387. (513)767-7184. Eager to work with new/unpublished writers. Bimonthly magazine; 100 pages. Emphasizes harness horse racing or breeding. Circ. 7,500. Pays on publication. Publishes ms an average of 4 months after acceptance. Buys all rights. Submit seasonal/holiday material 3 months in advance. Photocopied submissions OK. Computer printout submissions acceptable if double-spaced; prefers letter-quality to dot-matrix. Reports in 1 month.
Nonfiction: General interest, historical, humor and nostalgia. Articles must pertain to harness racing. Phone or mail queries to Charlotte Maurer. Length: 1,000-5,000 words. Pays $50-200. Seldom pays expenses of writers on assignment.
Fiction: "We use short stories pertaining to harness racing." Length: 2,500-7,000 words. Pays $50-200.
Tips: "We are specialized and a writer who doesn't understand the harness racing business shows it clearly. Know who our readers are."

SPEEDHORSE MAGAZINE, Speedhorse, Inc., Box 1000, Norman OK 73070. (405)288-2391. Editor: Margaret S. Jaffe. 30% freelance written. Prefers to work with published/established writers. A monthly journal "devoted to those involved with breeding or racing quarter horses. It is *not* a general circulation horse publication." Circ. 9,000. Pays on publication. Publishes ms an average of 2 months after acceptance. Byline given. Offers negotiable kill fee. Buys negotiable rights. Simultaneous queries OK. Computer printout submissions acceptable; prefers letter-quality to dot-matrix. Reports in 1 month. Sample copy $3; free writer's guidelines.
Nonfiction: How-to (directed specifically at racing); interview/profile (of prominent horsemen); and photo feature (of racing). "Our articles address those topics which interest an experienced horseman. Articles dealing with ranch operations, racing bloodlines and race coverage are of special interest." No general interest stories. Special issues include Stallion articles (November, March); Stakes Winner Issue (April); Service Issue, articles on various services offered horsemen, i.e., transportation, trainers, travel, etc. (May); Broodmare Issue (June); Horse sales and auctions (July, August); Racing Wrap-up (September); and Thoroughbred Issue (October). Buys 3 mss/year. Query. Length: 1,000 words minimum. Pays $25-300. Sometimes pays the expenses of writers on assignment.
Photos: Andrew Golden, photo editor. State availability of photos with query or ms. Reviews b&w and color contact sheets. Pays $5-25 for b&w and color. Identification of subjects required. Buys one-time rights.
Columns/Departments: Book Review and Vet Medicine, by assignment only. Buys 1-2 mss/year. Query. Length: 1,000 words. Pays $50-75.
Fiction: Adventure (race related); historical; humorous; and western. "All fiction must appeal to racing industry." Buys 3 mss/year. Query. Length: 1,000 words minimum. Pays $25-200.
Tips: "If the writer has a good working knowledge of the horse industry and access to people involved with the quarter horse racing industry, the writer should call the editor to discuss possible stories. Very few blind articles are accepted. Most stories are assigned with much editorial direction. Most feature stories are assigned to freelance writers who have been regular contributors to *Speedhorse*. They are located in areas of the country with active quarter horse racing. Many are track publicity directors or newspaper sports writers. The most frequent mistake made by writers in completing an article for us is that they do not write for the market. They send general interest articles rather than technical articles."

SPUR, Box 85, Middleburg VA 22117. (703)687-6314. Managing Director: Kerry Phelps. 80% freelance written. Prefers to work with published/established writers; works with a small number of new/unpublished writers each year. Bimonthly magazine covering Thoroughbred horses and the people who are involved in the business and sport of the Thoroughbred industry. Circ. 10,000. Pays on publication. Publishes ms an average of 3 months after acceptance. Byline given. Buys all rights. Computer printout submissions acceptable; prefers letter-quality to dot-matrix. Reports in 1 month on mss and queries. Sample copy $3.50; writer's guidelines for business size SAE and 1 first class stamp.
Nonfiction: Historical/nostalgic, Thoroughbred care, personality profile, farm, special feature, regional, photo essay, steeplechasing and polo. Buys 30 mss/year. Query with clips of published work, "or we will consider complete manuscripts." Length: 300-4,000 words. Payment negotiable. Sometimes pays the expenses of writers on assignment.
Photos: State availability of photos. Reviews color and b&w contact sheets. Captions, model releases and identification of subjects required. Buys all rights "unless otherwise negotiated."
Columns/Departments: Query or send complete ms to Editorial Dept. Length: 100-500 words. Pays $50 and up.
Fillers: Anecdotes, short humor. Length: 50-100 words. Pays $25 and up.

Tips: "Writers must have a knowledge of horses, horse owners, breeding, training, racing, and riding—or the ability to obtain this knowledge from a subject."

TROT, 233 Evans Ave., Toronto, Ontario M8Z 1J6 Canada. Advertising and Managing Director: Larry Simpson. Editor: Rolly Ethier. 60% freelance written. Official publication of the Canadian Trotting Association. "Quite a number of our readers derive all their income from harness racing." Circ. 20,000. Pays on acceptance. Publishes ms an average of 3 months after acceptance. Buys first North American serial rights. Computer printout submissions acceptable; prefers letter-quality to dot-matrix. SAE and International Reply Coupons.
Nonfiction: General material dealing with any aspect of harness racing or prominent figures in the sport. Seeking more humorous pieces with a harness racing connection. U.S. contributors should note that preference is given to material with a Canadian angle. Proposed story outlines invited. Length: 1,000-1,800 words. Pays $150-250. Sometimes pays the expenses of writers on assignment.
Tips: "Many U.S. submissions do not adhere to the Canadian angle. Most of the material used is generally assigned by the editor—roughly 80 percent."

Hunting and Fishing

ALABAMA GAME & FISH, Game & Fish Publications, Inc., Box 741, Marietta GA 30061. (404)953-9222. Editor: Rick Lavender. Monthly how-to, where-to, when-to hunting and fishing magazine covering Alabama. Pays on acceptance. Byline given. Buys one-time rights. Submit seasonal material 8 months in advance. Simultaneous queries, and simultaneous and photocopied submissions OK. Computer printout submissions acceptable; no dot-matrix. Reports in 2 months. Sample copy for $2.50 and 10x12 SAE; writer's guidelines for SASE.
Nonfiction: How-to (hunting and fishing *only*); humor (on limited basis); interview/profile (of successful hunter/angler); personal experience (hunting or fishing adventure). No hiking, backpacking or camping. No fiction or poems. No "my first deer" articles. Buys 60 mss/year. Query with or without published clips. Length: 1,800-2,200 words. Pays $150.
Photos: State availability of photos. Pays $75 for full-page, color leads; $225 for covers; $25 for b&w photos not submitted as part of story package. Captions and identification of subjects required. Buys one-time rights.

ALASKA OUTDOORS, Swensen's Publishing, Box 8-3550, Fairbanks AK 99708. (907)276-2672. Editor: Christopher Batin. 50% freelance written. Bimonthly magazine covering hunting and fishing in Alaska. Circ. 73,000. Pays on acceptance. Publishes ms an average of 4 months after acceptance. Byline given. Buys first serial rights. Submit seasonal/holiday material 6 months in advance. Computer printout submissions acceptable; prefers letter-quality to dot-matrix. Reports in 2 weeks. Sample copy $2; writer's guidelines for 4x9½ SAE and 1 first class stamp.
Nonfiction: How-to, investigative reports on outdoor issues in Alaska, and articles on where to go to fish and hunt in Alaska. "Articles should include a sidebar that will aid the reader in duplicating your adventure. No survival-type articles or personal brushes with death." Buys 75 unsolicited mss/year. Query. Length: 800-1,800 words. Pays $50-300; "$200 minimum for article with photographic support."
Photos: Send photos with ms to the attention of photo editor. Pays $10-25 for b&w contact sheets; $50-200 for 2¼x2¼ or 35mm color transparencies. Captions required. Buys one-time rights.
Tips: "Include more information and more descriptive writing, and less storytelling and Me 'n Joe type articles. No first-person accounts. Most of our writers have visited or live in Alaska. We are more than just a regional publication; we're distributed nationally."

ARKANSAS SPORTSMAN, Game & Fish Publications, Inc., Box 741, Marietta GA 30061. (404)953-9222. Editor: Keith Brooks. Monthly how-to, where-to and when-to hunting and fishing magazine covering Arkansas. Pays on acceptance. Byline given. Buys one-time rights. Submit seasonal material 8 months in advance. Simultaneous queries, and simultaneous and photocopied submissions OK. Computer printout submissions acceptable; no dot-matrix. Reports in 2 months. Sample copy for $2.50 and 10x12 SAE; writer's guidelines for SASE.
Nonfiction: How-to (hunting and fishing *only*); humor (on limited basis); interview/profile (of successful hunter/angler); personal experience (hunting or fishing adventure). No hiking, backpacking or camping. No "my first deer" articles. Buys 60 mss/year. Query with or without published clips. Length: 1,800-2,200. Pays $150.
Photos: State availability of photos. Pays $75 for full-page, color leads; $225 for covers; $25 for b&w photos not submitted as part of story package. Captions and identification of subjects required. Buys one-time rights.

BADGER SPORTSMAN, Vercauteren Publishing, Inc., 19 E. Main, Chilton WI 53014. (414)849-4651. Editor: Mark Ibach. Managing Editor: Gary Vercauteren. 80% freelance written. Monthly tabloid covering Wisconsin outdoors. Circ. 22,560. Pays on publication. Publishes ms an average of 1 month after acceptance. Byline given. Buys one-time rights. Submit seasonal/holiday material 2 months in advance. Previously published submissions OK. Computer printout submissions acceptable; prefers letter-quality to dot-matrix. Sample copy for 9x13 SAE with 56¢ postage; free writer's guidelines.
Nonfiction: General interest; how-to (fishing, hunting, etc., in the Midwest outdoors); humor; interview/profile; personal experience; technical. Buys 400-500 mss/year. Query. Length: open. Pays 35¢/column inch ($15-40).
Photos: Send photos with accompanying query or ms. Reviews 3x5 or larger b&w and color prints. Pays by column inch. Identification of subjects required.
Tips: "We publish stories about *Wisconsin* fishing, hunting, camping; outdoor cooking; and general animal stories."

BASSIN', The Official Magazine for the Weekend Angler, National Reporter Publications, Inc., 15115 S. 76th E. Ave., Bixby OK 74008. (918)366-4441. Managing Editor: André Hinds. 90% freelance written. Works with a small number of new/unpublished writers each year. Magazine published 8 times/year covering freshwater fishing with emphasis on black bass. Publishes ms an average of 6 months after acceptance. Circ. 250,000. Pays on acceptance. Byline given. Buys first serial rights. Submit seasonal material 6 months in advance. Prefers queries but will examine mss accompanied by SASE. Electronic submissions OK via 300/1200 baud modem (ASCII text) or Macintosh disk. Computer printout submissions acceptable. Reports in 4-6 weeks. Sample copy and writer's guidelines available on request.
Nonfiction: How-to and where-to stories on bass fishing. Prefers queries. Length: 1,200-2,500 words. Pays $200-350 on acceptance.
Photos: Send photos with ms. Pays $25-100 for inside color photos. Pays $300 for color cover. Send b&w prints or color transparencies. Buys one-time rights. Photo payment on publication.
Columns/Departments: Send complete ms. Fishing tips, regional lake reports, product reviews. Length: 100-700 words. Pays $30-50 on publication.
Tips: "Reduce the common fishing slang terminology when writing for *Bassin'* (and other outdoor magazines). This slang is usually regional and confuses anglers in other areas of the country. Good strong features will win me over much more quickly than short articles or fillers."

BASSMASTER MAGAZINE, B.A.S.S. Publications, Box 17900, Montgomery AL 36141. (205)272-9530. Editor: Dave Precht. 80% freelance written. Prefers to work with published/established writers. Bimonthly magazine (monthly January-April) about largemouth, smallmouth, spotted bass and striped bass for dedicated beginning and advanced bass fishermen. Circ. 400,000. Pays on acceptance. Publication date of ms after acceptance "varies—seasonal material could take years"; average time is 8 months. Byline given. Buys all rights. Submit seasonal material 6 months in advance. Simultaneous and photocopied submissions OK, if so indicated. Letter-quality computer printout submissions acceptable, "but we still prefer typewritten material." Reports in 1 week. Sample copy $2; writer's guidelines for SAE and 1 first class stamp..
Nonfiction: Historical; interview (of knowledgable people in the sport); profile (outstanding fishermen); travel (where to go to fish for bass); how-to (catch bass and enjoy the outdoors); new product (reels, rods and bass boats); and conservation related to bass fishing. "No 'Me and Joe Go Fishing' type articles." Query. Length: 400-2,100 words. Pays $100-300.
Columns/Departments: Short Cast/News & Views (upfront regular feature covering news-related events such as new state bass records, unusual bass fishing happenings, conservation, new products and editorial viewpoints); 250-400 words.
Photos: "We want a mixture of black and white and color photos." Pays $15 minimum for b&w prints. Pays $100-150 for color cover transparencies. Captions required; model releases preferred. Buys all rights.
Fillers: Anecdotes, short humor and newsbreaks. Buys 4-5 mss/issue. Length: 250-500 words. Pays $50-100.
Tips: "Editorial direction continues in the short, more direct how-to article. Compact, easy-to-read information is our objective. Shorter articles with good graphics, such as how-to diagrams, step-by-step instruction, etc., will enhance a writer's articles submitted to *Bassmaster Magazine*. The most frequent mistakes made by writers in completing an article for us are poor grammar, poor writing, poor organization and superficial research."

BC OUTDOORS, SIP Division, Maclean Hunter Ltd., 202-1132 Hamilton St., Vancouver British Columbia V6B 2S2 Canada (604)687-1581. Editor: Henry L. Frew. 80% freelance written. Outdoor recreation magazine published 10 times/year. *BC Outdoors* covers fishing, camping, hunting, and the environment of outdoor recreation. Circ. 37,000. Pays on acceptance. Publishes ms an average of 6 months after acceptance. Byline given. Offers negotiable kill fee. Buys first North American serial rights. Submit seasonal/holiday material 6 months in advance. Computer printout submissions acceptable; no dot-matrix. Reports in 1 month on queries; 2 months on mss. Free sample copy and writer's guidelines.

Nonfiction: How-to (new or innovative articles on outdoor subjects); personal experience (outdoor adventure); and outdoor topics specific to British Columbia. Buys 80-90 mss/year. Query. Length: 1,200-1,600 words. Pays $125-300. Sometimes pays the expenses of writers on assignment.
Photos: State availability of photos with query. Pays $10-30 on publication for 5x7 b&w prints; $15-50 for color contact sheets and 35mm transparencies. Captions and identification of subjects required. Buys one-time rights.
Tips: "Subject must be specific to British Columbia. We receive many manuscripts written by people who obviously do not know the magazine or market. The writer has a better chance of breaking in at our publication with short lesser-paying articles and fillers, because we have a stable of regular writers in constant touch who produce most main features."

CAROLINA GAME & FISH, Game & Fish Publications, Inc., Box 741, Marietta GA 30061. (404)953-9222. Editor: Aaron Pass. 80% freelance written. Works with a small number of new/unpublished writers each year. Monthly how-to, where-to, when-to hunting and fishing magazine covering North and South Carolina. Pays on "scheduling" of articles into a given edition—3 months prior to publication. Byline given. Buys one-time rights. Submit seasonal material 10 months in advance. Simultaneous queries OK but no simultaneous photocopied mss. Computer printout submissions acceptable; no dot-matrix. Sample copy for $2 and 10x12 envelope; writer's guidelines for SAE with 39¢ postage.
Nonfiction: Very state-specific approach; how-to (hunting and fishing *only*); humor/nostalgia (on limited basis); interview/profile (of successful hunter/angler); personal experience (hunting or fishing adventure). No hiking, backpacking or camping. No "my first deer" articles. Buys 75-80 mss/year. Query with or without published clips. Length: 2,000-2,500 words. Pays $150-175.
Photos: State availability of photos. Pays $75 for full-page, color leads; $225 for covers; $25 for b&w photos. Captions and identification of subjects required. Buys one-time rights.
Tips: "We don't use short, lesser-paying articles and fillers. Most unsolicited writers haven't really understood our market/slant. Assigned articles are seldom a problem—we *make sure* the writer knows what we want. Read our books and find out what we publish."

DEER AND DEER HUNTING, The Stump Sitters, Inc., Box 1117, Appleton WI 54912. (414)734-0009. Editors: Al Hofacker and Dr. Rob Wegner. 75% freelance written. Prefers to work with published/established writers. Bimonthly magazine covering deer hunting for individuals who hunt with bow, gun, or camera. Circ. 90,000. Pays on publication. Publishes ms an average of 6 months after acceptance. Byline given. Offers $50 kill fee. Buys first North American serial rights and second serial (reprint) rights. Submit seasonal/holiday material 4 months in advance. Computer printout submissions acceptable; prefers letter-quality to dot-matrix. Reports in 1 week on queries; 2 weeks on mss. Free sample copy and writer's guidelines.
Nonfiction: Historical/nostalgic; how-to (hunting techniques); opinion; personal experience; photo feature; technical; book review. "Our readers desire factual articles of a technical nature, that relate deer behavior and habits to hunting methodology. We focus on deer biology, management principles and practices, habitat requirements, natural history of deer, hunting techniques, and hunting ethics." No hunting "Hot Spot" or "local" articles. Buys 40 mss/year. Query with clips of published work. Length: 1,000-4,000 words. Pays $40-250. Sometimes pays the expenses of writers on assignment.
Photos: State availability of photos. Pays $100 for 35mm color transparencies; $350 for front cover; $30 for 8x10 b&w prints. Captions and identification of subjects required. Buys one-time rights.
Columns/Departments: Review Stand (reviews of books of interest to deer hunters); Deer Browse (unusual observations of deer behavior). Buys 20 mss/year. Query. Length: 200-800 words. Pays $10-50.
Fillers: Clippings, anecdotes, newsbreaks. Buys 20/year. Length: 200-800 words. Pays $10-40.
Tips: "Break in by providing material of a technical nature, backed by scientific research, and written in a style understandable to the average deer hunter. We focus primarily on white-tailed deer."

‡THE FISHERMAN, LIF Publishing Corp., Bridge St., Sag Harbor NY 11963. (516)725-4200. Editor: Fred Golofaro. Senior Editor: Pete Barrett. 4 regional editions: *Long Island*, *Metropolitan New York*, Fred Golofrano, editor; *New England*, Tim Coleman, editor; *New Jersey*, Russ Wilson, editor; and *Delaware-Maryland-Virginia*, Eric Burnley, editor. 75% freelance written. A weekly magazine covering fishing and boating. Combined circ. 82,000. Pays on publication. Byline given. Offers variable kill fee. Buys all rights. Articles may be run in one or more regional editions by choice of the editors. Submit seasonal/holiday material 2 months in advance. Computer printout submissions acceptable; prefers letter-quality to dot-matrix. Reports in 3 weeks. Free sample copy and writer's guidelines.
Nonfiction: Send submission to editor of regional edition. General interest, historical/nostalgic, how-to, interview/profile, personal experience, photo feature, technical and travel. Special issues include Trout Fishing (April), Offshore Fishing (July), Bass Fishing (August), Surf Fishing (September), Tackle (October) and Electronics (November). "No 'me and Joe' tales. We stress how, where, when, why." Buys approx. 500 mss/year; each edition. Length: 1,200-2,400 words. Pays $50-100 for unsolicited articles.

Photos: Send photos with submission; also buys single photos for cover use. Offers no additional payment for photos accepted with ms. Identification of subjects required.
Tips: "Freelance feature stories are most open to freelancers."

FISHING AND HUNTING NEWS, Outdoor Empire Publishing Co., Inc., 511 Eastlake Ave. E., Box C-19000, Seattle WA 98109. (206)624-3845. Managing Editor: Vence Malernee. Assistant Managing Editor: Roland Stephan. Emphasizes fishing and hunting. Weekly tabloid. Circ. 140,000. Pays on acceptance. Buys all rights. Submit seasonal/holiday material 3 months in advance. Photocopied submissions OK. Computer printout submissions OK.
Nonfiction: How-to (fish and hunt successfully, things that make outdoor jaunts more enjoyable/productive); photo feature (successful fishing/hunting in the western U.S.); informational. No first-person personal accounts of the 'me and Joe' variety or dated materials, as we are a weekly news publication." Buys 65 or more mss/year. Query. Length: 100-1,000 words. Pays $25 minimum.
Photos: Purchased with or without accompanying ms. Captions required. Submit prints or transparencies. Pays $5 minimum for b&w glossy prints; $25 minimum for 35mm or 2¼x2¼color transparencies.
Tips: "Competition in the outdoor publishing industry is very keen, and we are meeting it with increasingly timely and prognosticative articles. Writers should look for the new, the different, and the off-the-beaten track in hunting, fishing and outdoor activities."

FISHING WORLD, 51 Atlantic Ave., Floral Park NY 11001. Editor: Keith Gardner. 100% freelance written. Bimonthly. Circ. 335,000. Pays on acceptance. Buys first North American serial rights. Pays on acceptance. Publishes ms an average of 6 months after acceptance. Photocopied submissions OK. Computer printout submissions acceptable. Reports in 2 weeks. Free sample copy.
Nonfiction: "Feature articles range from 1,000-2,000 words with the shorter preferred. A good selection of color transparencies should accompany each submission. Subject matter can range from a hot fishing site to tackle and techniques, from tips on taking individual species to a story on one lake or an entire region, either freshwater or salt. However, how-to is definitely preferred over where-to, and a strong biological/scientific slant is best of all. Where-to articles, especially if they describe foreign fishing, should be accompanied by sidebars covering how to make reservations and arrange transportation, how to get there, where to stay. Angling methods should be developed in clear detail, with accurate and useful information about tackle and boats. Depending on article length, suitability of photographs and other factors, payment is up to $300 for feature articles accompanied by suitable photography. Color transparencies selected for cover use pay an additional $300. B&w or unillustrated featurettes are also considered. These can be on anything remotely connected with fishing. Query. Length: 1,000 words. Pays $25-100 depending on length and photos. Detailed queries accompanied by photos are preferred.
Photos: "Cover shots are purchased separately, rather than selected from those accompanying mss. The editor favors drama rather than serenity in selecting cover shots. Underwater horizontal portraits of fish are purchased (one-time rights) for centerfold use at the rate of $300 per transparency."

‡FLORIDA SPORTSMAN, Wickstrom Publishers Inc., 5901 S.W. 74 St., Miami FL 33143. (305)661-4222. Editor: Vic Dunaway. Managing Editor: Biff Lampton. 80% freelance written. Eager to work with new/unpublished writers. A monthly magazine covering fishing, boating and related sports—Florida and Caribbean only. Circ. 90,000. Pays on publication. Publishes ms an average of 6 months after acceptance. Byline given. Offers 50% kill fee. Buys first North American serial rights. Submit seasonal/holiday material 6 months in advance. Computer printout submissions acceptable; prefers letter-quality to dot-matrix. Reports in 1 week on queries; 1 month on mss. Free sample copy and writer's guidelines.
Nonfiction: Essays (environment or nature); how-to (fishing, hunting, boating); humor (outdoors angle); personal experience (in fishing, etc.); and technical (boats, tackle,etc., as particularly suitable for Florida specialties). "We use reader service pieces almost entirely—how-to, where-to, etc. One or two environmental pieces per issue as well. Writers *must* be Florida based, or have lengthy experience in Florida outdoors. All articles must have strong Florida emphasis. We do not want to see general how-to-fish-or-boat pieces which might well appear in a national or wide-regional magazine." Buys 120 mss/year. Query with or without published clips, or send complete ms. Length: 1,500-2,500 words. Pays $250-350 for assigned articles; pays $150-300 for unsolicited articles.
Photos: Send photos with submission. Reviews 35mm transparencies and 4x5 and larger prints. Offers no additional payment for photos accepted with ms. Buys one-time rights.
Columns/Departments: Sportsman Scene (news-feature items on outdoors subjects), 100-500 words; Angler's Clinic (short, detailed fishing how-to), 250-750 words; and Sportsman Recipe (recipes for Florida fish and game), 250-1,000 words. Buys 50 mss/year. Send complete ms. Pays $15-100.
Tips: "Feature articles are most open to freelancers; however there is little chance of acceptance unless contributor is an accomplished and avid outdoorsman *and* a competent writer-photographer with considerable experience in Florida."

FLORIDA WILDLIFE. Florida Game & Fresh Water Fish Commission, 620 South Meridian St., Tallahassee FL 32301. (904)488-5563. Editor: John M. Waters, Jr. About 75% freelance written. Bimonthly state magazine covering hunting, fishing and wildlife conservation. "In outdoors sporting articles we seek themes of wholesome recreation. In nature articles we seek accuracy and conservation purpose." Circ. 29,000. Pays on publication. Publishes ms 6 months to 1 year after acceptance. Byline given. Buys first North American serial rights and occasionally second serial (reprint) rights. Submit seasonal/holiday material 6 months in advance. Simultaneous queries, and simultaneous, photocopied, and previously published submissions OK. "Inform us if it is previously published work." Computer printout submissions acceptable if double-spaced. Reports in 6 weeks on queries; variable on mss. Sample copy $1.25; free writer's guidelines.
Nonfiction: General interest (bird watching, hiking, camping, boating); how-to (hunting and fishing); humor (wildlife related; no anthropomorphism); inspirational (conservation oriented); personal experience (wildlife, hunting, fishing, outdoors); photo feature (Florida species: game, nongame, botany); and technical (rarely purchased, but open to experts). "In a nutshell, we buy general interest hunting, fishing and nature stories. No 'me and Joe' stories, stories that humanize animals, or opinionated stories not based on confirmable facts." Buys 50-60 mss/year. Query. Length: 500-2,500 words. Pays $35-250, depending on availability and use of photos.
Photos: John Roberge, photo editor. State availability of photos with query. Prefers 35mm color slides of hunting, fishing, and natural science series of Florida wildlife species. Pays $10-50 for inside photos; $100 for front cover photos, $50 for back cover. "We like short, specific captions." Buys one-time rights.
Fiction: "We rarely buy fiction, and then only if it is true to life and directly related to good sportsmanship and conservation. No fairy tales, erotica, profanity, or bathroom humor." Buys 2-3 mss/year. Send complete mss and label "fiction." Length: 500-2,500 words. Pays $50-150.
Tips: "Read and study recent issues for subject matter, style and examples of our viewpoint, philosophy and treatment. The area of hunting is one requiring sensitivity. Blood and guts are out. We look for wholesome recreation, ethics, safety, and good outdoor experience more than bagging the game in our stories. Of special need at this time are well-written hunting and fishing in Florida articles. Unsolicited articles sent to us generally fail to be well written, and accurate, and lack reader interest."

FLY FISHERMAN, Historical Times, Inc., 2245 Kohn Rd., Box 8200, Harrisburg PA 17105. (717)657-9555. Editor: John Randolph. Associate Editor: Jack Russell. 90% freelance written. Magazine published 6 times/year on fly fishing. Circ. 137,000. Pays on acceptance. Publishes ms an average of 8 months after acceptance. Byline given. Buys first North American serial rights and (selectively) all rights. Submit seasonal/holiday material 1 year in advance. Electronic submissions OK on Wang, but requires hard copy also. Computer printout submissions acceptable; prefers letter-quality to dot-matrix. Reports in 3 weeks on queries; 6 weeks on mss. Sample copy for 11x14 SAE and 4 first class stamps. Free writer's guidelines.
Nonfiction: Book excerpts, how-to, humor, interview/profile, technical and essays on fly fishing, fly tying, shorts and fishing technique shorts and features. Where-to. No other types of fishing, including spin or bait. Buys 75 mss/year. Query or send complete ms. Length: 50-3,000 words. Pays $35-500.
Photos: State availability of photos or send photos with query or ms. Reviews b&w contact sheets and 35mm transparencies. Pays $35-100 for contact sheets; $25-200 for transparencies; $400 for cover photos. Captions, model release and identification of subjects required. Buys one-time rights.
Columns/Departments: Fly Fisherman's Bookshelf—500 to 1,000-word book reviews ($75 each); reviews of fly fishing video tapes $75, same length. Buys 8 mss/year. Query. Length: 500-1,000 words. Pays $75.
Fiction: Essays on fly fishing, humorous and serious. No long articles, anything over 3,000 words. Buys 4 mss/year. Query with published clips. Length: 1,200-3,000 words. Pays $125-500.
Fillers: Short humor and newsbreaks. Buys 30/year. Length: 25-1,000 words. Pays $25-250.
Tips: "Our magazine is a tightly focused, technique-intensive special interest magazine. Articles require fly fishing expertise and writing must be tight and in many instances well researched. The novice fly fisher has little hope of a sale with us, although perhaps 30 percent of our features are entry-level or intermediate-level in nature. Fly fishing technique pieces that are broadly focused have great appeal. Both features and departments—short features—have the best chance of purchase. Accompany submissions with excellent color slides (35mm), black and white 8x10 prints or line drawing illustrations."

THE FLYFISHER, 1387 Cambridge, Idaho Falls ID 83401. (208)523-7300. Editor: Dennis G. Bitton. 60% freelance written. "We are backlogged but any good submission gets worked in." Quarterly magazine; 64-72 pages. *"The Flyfisher* is the official publication of the Federation of Fly Fishers, a nonprofit organization of member clubs and individuals in the U.S., Canada, United Kingdom, France, New Zealand, Chile, Argentina, Japan and other nations. It serves an audience of conservation-minded fly fishermen." Circ. 10,000. Pays after publication. Publishes ms an average of 3 months after acceptance. Byline given. Buys first North American serial rights. Submit seasonal/holiday material 60 days in advance. Computer printout submissions acceptable; no dot-matrix. Reports in 2 weeks. Sample copy $3, available from FFF, Box 1088, West Yellowstone MT 59758. Writer's guidelines for SASE; write to 1387 Cambridge, Idaho Falls ID 83401.
Nonfiction: How-to (fly fishing techniques, fly tying, tackle, etc.); general interest (any type including where to go, conservation); historical (places, people, events that have significance to fly fishing); inspiration-

al (looking for articles dealing with Federation clubs on conservation projects); interview (articles of famous fly fishermen, fly tiers, teachers, etc.); nostalgia (articles of reminiscences on flies, fishing personalities, equipment and places); and technical (about techniques of fly fishing in salt and fresh waters). Buys 6-8 mss/issue. Query. Length: 500-2,500 words. Pays $50-200.

Photos: Pays $15-50 for 8x10 b&w glossy prints; $20-80 for 35mm or larger color transparencies for inside use and $100-150 for covers. Captions required. Buys one-time rights. Prefers a selection of transparencies and glossies when illustrating a manuscript, which are purchased as a package.

Fiction: (Must be related to fly fishing). Adventure, conservation, fantasy, historical, humorous, and suspense. Buys 2 mss/issue. Query. Length, 500-2,000 words. Pays $75-200.

Tips: "We make every effort to assist a writer with visuals if the idea is strong enough to develop. We will deal with freelancers breaking into the field. Our only concern is that the material be in keeping with the quality established. We prefer articles submitted by members of FFF, but do not limit our selection of good articles."

FUR-FISH-GAME, 2878 E. Main, Columbus OH 43209. Editor: Ken Dunwoody. 65% freelance written. Works with a small number of new/unpublished writers each year. Monthly magazine; 64-88 pages. For outdoorsmen of all ages who are interested in hunting, fishing, trapping, dogs, camping, conservation and related topics. Circ. 180,000. Pays on acceptance. Publishes ms an average of 7 months after acceptance. Byline given. Buys first serial rights or all rights. Prefers nonsimultaneous submissions. Computer printout submissions acceptable; prefers letter-quality to dot-matrix. Reports in 6 weeks. Submit complete ms with photos and SASE. Writer's guidelines for SASE; sample copy $1.

Nonfiction: "We are looking for informative, down-to-earth stories about hunting, fishing, trapping, dogs, camping, boating, conservation and related subjects. Nostalgic articles are also used. Many of our stories are 'how-to' and should appeal to small-town and rural readers who are true outdoorsmen. Some recent articles have told how to train a gun dog, catch big-water catfish, outfit a bowhunter and trap late-season muskrat. We also use personal experience stories and an occasional profile, such as an article about an old-time trapper. 'Where-to' stories are used occasionally if they have broad appeal. Length: 1,500-3,000 words. Pays $75-150 depending upon quality, photo support, and importance to magazine. Short filler stories pay $35-80."

Photos: Send photos with ms. Photos are part of ms package and receive no additional payment. Prefer b&w but color prints or transparencies OK. Prints can be 5x7 or 8x10. Caption information required. Photos are also purchased without accompanying ms and usually pay $10-15.

Tips: "We are always looking for quality articles that tell how to hunt or fish for game animals or birds that are popular with everyday outdoorsmen but often overlooked in other publications, such as catfish, bluegill, crappie, squirrel, rabbit, crows, etc. We also use articles on standard seasonal subjects such as deer and pheasant, but like to see a fresh approach or new technique. Trapping articles, especially instructional ones based on personal experience, are useful all year. Articles on gun dogs, ginseng and do-it-yourself projects are also popular with our readers. An assortment of photos and/or sketches greatly enhances any ms, and sidebars, where applicable, can also help."

‡GALLANT/CHARGER'S FISHING & BOATING ILLUSTRATED, Gallant/Charger Publications, Inc., Box HH, Capistrano Beach CA 92624. (714)493-2101. Editor: Jack Lewis. Managing Editor: Mark Thiffault. 50% freelance written. An annual magazine covering fishing and boating. *"Fishing & Boating Illustrated* is aimed at recreational fishermen and boaters who enjoy both. Geographic coverage is national, with how-to stories on many fish species." Circ. 100,000. Pays on acceptance. Byline given. Buys one-time rights and makes work-for-hire assignments. Need queries by late spring for the coming March edition. Computer printout submissions acceptable. Reports in 1 month. Sample copy $3.

Nonfiction: How-to (catching specific species of fish, maintaining boats) and technical (on boating projects). Buys 20 mss/year. Query. Length: 250-3,000 words. Pays $25-350.

Photos: Send photos with accompanying query or manuscript. Reviews 35mm transparencies and 8x10 prints. Pays $5-10 for prints, $25-100 for transparencies. Captions, model releases and identification of subjects required.

Tips: "We need queries by late spring for editorial planning. If a manufacturer's product tie-in is possible, so state. Photography must be excellent."

GEORGIA SPORTSMAN, Game & Fish Publications, Box 741, Marietta GA 30061. (404)953-9222. Editor: Rick Lavender. Monthly how-to, where-to, when-to hunting and fishing magazine covering Georgia. Pays on acceptance. Byline given. Buys one-time rights. Submit seasonal material 10 months in advance. Simultaneous queries OK; no simultaneous or photocopied submissions. Computer printout submissions acceptable. Sample copy for $2 and 10x12 SAE; writer's guidelines for SASE.

Nonfiction: Very state-specific approach; how-to (hunting and fishing *only*); humor/nostalgia (on limited basis); interview/profile (of successful hunter/angler); personal experience (hunting or fishing adventure). No hiking, backpacking or camping. No "my first deer" articles. Buys 75-80 mss/year. Query with or without published clips. Length: 1,800-2,200 words. Pays $150-175.

Photos: State availability of photos. Pays $75 for color leads; $225 for covers; $25 for b&w photos. Captions and identification of subjects required. Buys one-time rights.

GREAT LAKES FISHERMAN, Great Lakes Fisherman Publishing Co., 1570 Fishinger Rd., Columbus OH 43221. (614)451-9307. Publisher/Executive Editor: Woody Earnheart. Editor: Ottie M. Snyder, Jr. 95% freelance written. Eager to work with new/unpublished writers. Monthly magazine covering how, when and where to fish in the Great Lakes region. Circ. 68,000. Pays on acceptance. Publishes ms an average of 4 months after acceptance. Byline given. Offers $40 kill fee. Buys first North American serial rights. Submit seasonal/holiday material 4-6 months in advance. Computer printout submissions acceptable; prefers letter-quality to dot-matrix. Reports in 5 weeks. Free sample copy and writer's guidelines.
Nonfiction: How-to (where to and when to freshwater fish). "No humor, me and Joe or subject matter outside the Great Lakes region." Buys 84 mss/year. Query with clips of published work. "Letters should be tightly written, but descriptive enough to present no surprises when the ms is received. Prefer b&w photos to be used to illustrate ms with query." Length: 1,500-2,500 words. Pays $125-200. Sometimes pays the expenses of writers on assignment.
Photos: Send photos with ms. "Black and white photos are considered part of manuscript package and as such receive no additional payment. We consider b&w photos to be a vital part of a ms package and return more packages because of poor quality photos than any other reason. We look for four types of illustration with each article: scene (a backed off shot of fisherman); result (not the typical meat shot of angler grinning at camera with big stringer but in most cases just a single nice fish with the angler admiring the fish); method (a lure shot or illustration of special rigs mentioned in the text); and action (angler landing a fish, fighting a fish, etc.). Illustrations (line drawings) need not be finished art but should be good enough for our artist to get the idea of what the author is trying to depict." Prefers cover shots to be verticals with fish and fisherman action shots. Pays $100 minimum for 35mm color transparencies; reviews 8x10 b&w prints. Captions, model releases and identification of subjects required. Buys one-time rights.
Tips: "Our feature articles are 99.9 percent freelance material. The magazine is circulated in the eight states bordering the Great Lakes, an area where one-third of the nation's licensed anglers reside. All of our feature content is how, when or where, or a combination of all three covering the species common to the region. Fishing is an age-old sport with countless words printed on the subject each year. A fresh new slant that indicates a desire to share with the reader the author's knowledge is a sale. We expect the freelancer to answer any anticipated questions the reader might have (on accommodations, launch sites, equipment needed, etc.) within the ms. We publish an equal mix each month of both warm- and cold-water articles."

GULF COAST FISHERMAN, Harold Wells Gulf Coast Fisherman, Inc., 205 Bowie, P.O. Drawer P, Port Lavaca TX 77979. (512)552-8864. Editor: Gary M. Ralston. 95% freelance written. A quarterly magazine covering Gulf Coast saltwater fishing. "All editorial material is designed to expand the knowledge of the Gulf Coast angler and promote saltwater fishing in general. Our audience is composed principally of persons from managerial/professional occupations." Circ 8,500. Pays on publication. Publishes ms an average of 2 months after acceptance. Byline given. Offers $90-150 kill fee. Buys first North American serial rights. Submit seasonal/holiday material 2 months in advance. Computer printout submissions acceptable; prefers letter-quality to dot-matrix. Free sample and writer's guidelines.
Nonfiction: How-to (any aspect relating to saltwater fishing that provides the writer specifics on use of tackle, boats, finding fish, etc.); interview/profile; new product; personal experience; and technical. Buys 25 mss/year. Query with or without published clips, or send complete ms. Length: 900-1,800 words. Pays $90-150. Sometimes pays the expenses of writers on assignment.
Photos: State availability of photos with submission. Offers no additional payment for photos accepted with ms. Captions and identification of subjects required. Buys one-time rights.
Tips: "Features are the area of our publication most open to freelancers. Subject matter should concern some aspect or be in relation to saltwater fishing in coastal bays or offshore."

LOUISIANA GAME & FISH, Game & Fish Publications, Inc., Box 741, Marietta GA 30061. (404)953-9222. Editor: Keith Brooks. 80% freelance written. Monthly how-to, where-to, when-to hunting and fishing magazine covering Louisiana. Pays on acceptance. Byline given. Buys one-time rights. Submit seasonal material 10 months in advance. Computer printout submissions are acceptable "only if double-spaced." Reports in 2 months. Sample copy for $2 and 10x12 SAE; writer's guidelines for SAE and 1 first class stamp.
Nonfiction: Where-to (hunting and fishing *only*); humor (on limited basis); interview/profile (of successful hunter/angler); personal experience (hunting or fishing adventure). No hiking, backpacking or camping. No "my first deer" articles. Buys 60 mss/year. Query with or without published clips. Length: 1,800-2,200 words. Pays $150.
Photos: State availability of photos. Pays $75 for full-page, color leads; $225 for covers; $25 for b&w photos. Captions and identification of subjects required. Buys one-time rights.
Tips: "We don't run shorts or fillers. The most frequent mistakes made by writers in completing an article for us are not enough specific *where-to* info in hunting and fishing articles; too much *how-to*."

THE MAINE SPORTSMAN, Box 365, Augusta ME 04330. Editor: Harry Vanderweide. 100% freelance written. "Eager to work with new/unpublished writers, but because we run over 30 regular columns, it's hard to get into the Maine Sportsman as a beginner." Monthly tabloid. Circ. 23,000. Pays "during month of publication." Buys first rights. Publishes ms an average of 3 months after acceptance. Byline given. Computer printout submissions acceptable; prefers letter-quality to dot-matrix. Reports in 2-4 weeks.

Nonfiction: "We publish only articles about Maine hunting and fishing activities. Any well-written, researched, knowledgable article about that subject area is likely to be accepted by us." Expose, how-to, general interest, interview, nostalgia, personal experience, opinion, profile, and technical. Buys 25-40 mss/issue. Submit complete ms. Length: 200-2,000 words. Pays $20-80. Sometimes pays the expense of writers on assignment.

Photos: "We can have illustrations drawn, but prefer 1-3 b&w photos." Submit photos with accompanying ms. Pays $5-50 for b&w print.

Tips: "It's rewarding finding a writer who has a fresh way of looking at ordinary events. Specific where-to-go about Maine is needed."

MICHIGAN OUT-OF-DOORS, Box 30235, Lansing MI 48909. (517)371-1041. Editor: Kenneth S. Lowe. 50% freelance written. Works with a small number of new/unpublished writers each year. Emphasizes outdoor recreation, especially hunting and fishing, conservation and environmental affairs. Monthly magazine; 116 pages. Circ. 110,000. Pays on acceptance. Publishes ms an average of 6 months after acceptance. Byline given. Buys first North American serial rights. Phone queries OK. Submit seasonal/holiday material 6 months in advance. Computer printout submissions acceptable; prefers letter-quality to dot-matrix. Reports in 1 month. Sample copy $1.50; free writer's guidelines.

Nonfiction: Expose, historical, how-to, informational, interview, nostalgia, personal experience, personal opinion, photo feature and profile. No humor. "Stories *must* have a Michigan slant unless they treat a subject of universal interest to our readers." Buys 8 mss/issue. Send complete ms. Length: 1,000-3,000 words. Pays $75 minimum for feature stories. Pays expenses of writers on assignment.

Photos: Purchased with or without accompanying ms. Pays $15 minimum for any size b&w glossy prints; $60 maximum for color (for cover). Offers no additional payment for photos accepted with accompanying ms. Buys one-time rights. Captions preferred.

Tips: "Top priority is placed on true accounts of personal adventures in the out-of-doors—well-written tales of very unusual incidents encountered while hunting, fishing, camping, hiking, etc. The most rewarding aspect of working with freelancers is realizing we had a part in their development. But it's annoying to respond to queries that never produce a manuscript."

‡MICHIGAN SPORTSMAN, Great Lakes Sportsman Group, Box 2266, Oshkosh WI 54903. (414)233-1327. Editor: Thomas C. Petrie. Managing Editor: Charles Petrie. 85% freelance written. A magazine covering hunting, fishing and the outdoors. Published 7 times a year. Pays on acceptance. Publishes ms an average of 4 months after acceptance. Byline given. Buys first rights or makes work-for-hire assignments. Submit seasonal/holiday material 6 months in advance. Photocopied and previously published submissions OK. Computer printout submissions acceptable. Reports in 3 weeks on queries; 5 weeks on mss. Sample copy $1 with 8½x11 SAE and 95¢ postage. Writer's guidelines for SASE.

Nonfiction: Michigan editor. Book excerpts, exposé, historical/nostalgic, how-to, humor, interview/profile and opinion. General articles are stories of interest to readers in two to four-states. Can be how-to's, broad-based fiction, conservation issue of broad appeal, natural history piece. State articles are same as for general articles but with focus on a specific state in the Great Lakes group area. Special emphasis on where-to's and stories of interest about state history, personalities, some fiction. Prefer sidebar material which can give the reader more information about topics, locations, etc. Buys 60 mss/year. Query with published clips. Length: 1,200-2,000 words (general); 1,200-1,600 words (state). General articles pay from $150-600; state articles pay $100-300.

Photos: Send photos with submission. Reviews transparencies for general articles and 5x7 prints for state articles. Payment varies. Captions required. Buys one-time rights.

Tips: "Our publications strive for high quality graphics. Therefore, chances of acceptance are enhanced when manuscripts are accompanied by good photographs. Our state articles require a strong where-to slant in many instances and requires contributors to really be acquainted with the state/region. We publish very few squirrel or rabbit hunting articles."

MID WEST OUTDOORS, Mid West Outdoors, Ltd., 111 Shore Drive, Hinsdale (Burr Ridge) IL 60521. (312)887-7722. Editor: Gene Laulunen. Emphasizes fishing, hunting, camping and boating. Monthly tabloid. 100% freelance written. Circ. 57,000. Pays on publication. Buys simultaneous rights. Byline given. Submit seasonal material 2 months in advance. Simultaneous, photocopied and previously published submissions OK. Reports in 3 weeks. Publishes ms an average of 3 months after acceptance. Sample copy $1; free writer's guidelines.

Nonfiction: How-to (fishing, hunting, camping in the Midwest) and where-to-go (fishing, hunting, camping within 500 miles of Chicago). "We do not want to see any articles on 'my first fishing, hunting or camping experiences,' 'Cleaning My Tackle Box,' 'Tackle Tune-up,' or 'Catch and Release.' " Buys 840 unsolicited mss/year. Send complete ms. Length: 1,000-1,500 words. Pays $15-25.

Photos: Offers no additional payment for photos accompanying ms; uses b&w prints. Buys all rights. Captions required.

Columns/Departments: Fishing, Hunting. Open to suggestions for columns/departments. Send complete ms. Pays $20.

Tips: "Break in with a great unknown fishing hole within 500 miles of Chicago. Where, how, when and why. Know the type of publication you are sending material to."

‡**MINNESOTA SPORTSMAN**, Great Lakes Sportsman Group, Box 2266, Oshkosh 54093. (414)233-1327. Editorial Director: Thomas C. Petrie. Editor: Charles Petrie. 85% freelance written. A magazine covering hunting, fishing and outdoors, published 7 times a year. Pays on acceptance. Publishes ms an average of 4 months after acceptance. Byline given. Buys first rights or makes work-for-hire assignments. Submit seasonal/holiday material 6 months in advance. Photocopied and previously published submissions OK. Computer printout submissions acceptable. Reports in 3 weeks on queries; 5 weeks on mss. Sample copy $1 with 8½x11 SAE and 95¢ postage; writer's guidelines for SASE.

Nonfiction: Book excerpts, exposé, historical/nostalgic, how-to, humor, interview/profile and opinion. General articles are stories of interest to readers in two to four states. Can be how-to, broad-based fiction, conservation issue of broad appeal, natural history piece. State articles focus on a specific state in the Great Lakes area. Special emphasis on where-to's and stories of interest about state history, personalities, some fiction. Prefer sidebar material which can give the reader more information about topics, locations, etc. Hunting/fishing emphasis. Buys 60 mss/year. Query with published clips. Length: 1,200-2,000 words (general); 1,200-1,600 words (state). General articles pay from $150-600; state articles pay $100-300. Reviews transparencies for general articles and 5x7 prints for state articles. Payment varies. Captions required. Buys one-time rights.

Tips: "Our publications strive for high quality graphics. Therefore, chances of acceptance are enhanced when manuscripts are accompanied by good photographs. Our state articles require a strong where-to slant in many instances and requires contributors to really be acquainted with the state/region. We publish very few squirrel or rabbit hunting articles."

MISSISSIPPI GAME & FISH, Game & Fish Publications, Box 741, Marietta GA 30061. (404)953-9222. Editor: Bill Hartlage. Monthly how-to, where-to, when-to hunting and fishing magazine covering Mississippi. Pays on acceptance. Byline given. Buys one-time rights. Submit seasonal material 8 months in advance. Simultaneous queries, and simultaneous and photocopied submissions OK. Reports in 2 months. Sample copy for $2.50 and 10x12 SAE; writer's guidelines for SASE.

Nonfiction: How-to (hunting and fishing *only*); humor (on limited basis); interview/profile (of successful hunter/angler); personal experience (hunting or fishing adventure). No hiking, backpacking, camping. No fiction or poems. No "my first deer" articles. Buys 60 mss/year. Query with or without published clips. Length: 1,800-2,200 words. Pays $150.

Photos: State availability of photos. Pays $75 for full-page, color leads; $225 for covers; $25 for b&w photos not submitted as part of story package. Captions and identification of subjects required. Buys one-time rights.

‡**NEW YORK AFIELD**, Great Lakes Sportmans Group, Box 2266 Oshkosh WI 54903. (414)233-1327. Editor: Thomas C. Petrie. Managing Editor: Charles Petrie. 85% freelance written. A magazine covering hunting, fishing and the outdoors, published 7 times a year. Pays on acceptance. Publishes ms an average of 4 months after acceptance. Byline given. Buys first rights or makes work-for-hire assignments. Submit seasonal/holiday material 6 months in advance. Photocopied and previously published submissions OK. Computer printout submissions acceptable. Reports in 3 weeks on queries; 5 weeks on manuscripts. Sample copy $1 with 8½x11 SAE and 95¢ postage; writer's guidelines for SASE.

Nonfiction: Book excerpts, exposé, historical/nostalgic, how-to, humor, interview/profile and opinion. "General articles are stories of interest to readers in 2 to 4 states. Can be how-to; broad based fiction, conservation issue of broad appeal, natural history piece. State articles focus on a specific state in the Great Lakes Group area. Special emphasis on where-to's and stories of interest about state history; personalities, some fiction." Prefer sidebar material which can give the reader more information about topics, locations, etc. Buys 60 mss/year. Query with published clips. Length: 1,200-2,000 words (general); 1,200-1,600 words (state). General articles pay from $150-600; state articles pay $100-300.

Photos: Send photos with submission. Reviews transparencies for general articles and 5x7 prints for state articles. Payment varies. Captions required. Buys one-time rights.

Tips: "Our publications strive for high quality graphics. Therefore, chances of acceptance are enhanced when manuscripts are accompanied by good photographs. Our state articles require a strong where-to slant in many instances and require contributors to really be acquainted with the state/region. We publish very few squirrel or rabbit hunting articles."

‡**NORTH AMERICAN HUNTER, Official Publication of the North American Hunting Club**, North American Hunting Club, Box 35557, Minneapolis MN 55435. (612)941-7654. Editor: Mark LaBarbera. As-

sociate Editor: Bill Miller. 50% freelance written. A bimonthly magazine for members of the North American Hunting Club covering strictly North American hunting. "The purpose of the NAHC is to enhance the hunting skill and enjoyment of its 100,000 members." Circ. 100,000. Pays on acceptance. Publishes ms an average of 10 months after acceptance. Byline given. Buys first North American serial rights, first rights, one-time rights, second serial (reprint) rights, or all rights. Submit seasonal/holiday material 1 year in advance. Electronic submissions OK via IBM PC compatible, but requires hard copy also. Computer printout submissions acceptable; prefers letter-quality to dot-matrix. Reports in 3 weeks. Sample copy $3; writer's guidelines for 4x9 SAE with 1 first class stamp.

Nonfiction: Exposé (on hunting issues); how-to (on hunting); humor; interview/profile; new product; opinion; personal experience; photo feature and where-to-hunt. No fiction or "Me and Joe". Buys 18-24 mss/year. Query. Length 1,000-2,500 words. Pays $200-325 for assigned articles; pay $25-325 for unsolicited articles.

Photos: Send photos with submissions. Reviews transparencies and 5x7 or 8x10 prints. Offers no additional payment for photos accepted with ms. Captions and identification of subjects required. Buys one-time rights.

Tips: "Write stories as if they are from one hunting friend to another."

NORTH AMERICAN WHITETAIL, "The Magazine devoted to the serious trophy deer hunter", Game & Fish Publications, Inc., Suite 136, 2121 Newmarket Pkwy., Marietta GA 30067. (404)953-9222. Editor: Gordon Whittington. 90% freelance written. Monthly magazine on hunting and fishing. "*North American Whitetail* is an in-depth magazine covering all aspects of whitetail deer hunting, with special emphasis on trophy bucks. Game & Fish Publications also publishes 9 separate magazines—Georgia, Tennessee, Arkansas and Texas Sportsman and Oklahoma, Louisiana, Mississippi, Alabama and Carolina Game and Fish. The state editions cover the where, when, how and who of hunting and fishing in their respectives states." Circ. combined 325,000. Pays 15th day of month 3 months prior to issue month. Publishes ms an average of 3 months after acceptance. Byline given. Buys first North American serial rights. Submit seasonal/holiday material 8 months in advance. Simultaneous queries and submissions OK. Reports in 2 months. Sample copy $2.50; free writer's guidelines.

Nonfiction: Aaron Pass and Keith Brooks, articles editors. Book excerpts, how-to, humor, interview/profile, personal experience, technical and where-to. Buys 840 mss/year. Query with published clips. Length: 2,000-3,000 words. Pays $150-350.

Photos: State availability of photos. Reviews 35mm color transparencies and 5x7 or 8½x11 b&w prints. Pays $25 for b&w, $75 for color. Captions and identification of subjects required. Buys one-time rights.

Tips: "Our editorial needs are very specific. I suggest studying our publications. We *do* welcome multiple query submissions. They will be held on file and reviewed each time we prepare an editorial outline. Our greatest need is for feature manuscripts."

OHIO FISHERMAN, Ohio Fisherman Publishing Co., 1570 Fishinger Rd., Columbus OH 43221. (614)451-5769. Publisher/Executive Editor: Woody Earnheart. Editor: Ottie M. Snyder, Jr. 99% freelance written. Works with a small number of new/unpublished writers each year. Monthly magazine covering the how, when and where of Ohio fishing. Circ. 45,000. Pays on publication. Publishes ms an average of 6 months after acceptance. Byline given. Offers $40 kill fee. Buys first rights. Submit seasonal/holiday material 4-6 months in advance. Computer printout submissions acceptable; prefers letter-quality to dot-matrix. Reports in 5 weeks. Free sample copy and writer's guidelines.

Nonfiction: How-to (also where to and when to fresh water fish). "Our feature articles are 99% freelance material, and all have the same basic theme—sharing fishing knowledge. No humorous or 'me and Joe' articles." Buys 84 mss/year. Query with clips of published work. Letters should be "tightly written, but descriptive enough to present no surprises when the ms is received. Prefer b&w photos to be used to illustrate ms with query." Length: 1,500-2,500 words. Pays $100-150. Sometimes pays the expenses of writers on assignment.

Photos: "Need cover photos constantly. Study cover format carefully. 99% of covers purchased are verticals involving fishermen and fish—action preferred." Send photos with query. "We consider b&w photos to be a vital part of a ms package and return more mss because of poor quality photos than any other reason. We look for four types of illustration with each article: scene (a backed off shot of fisherman); result (not the typical meat shot of angler grinning at camera with big stringer, but in most cases just a single nice fish with the angler admiring the fish); method (a lure or illustration of special rigs mentioned in the text); and action (angler landing a fish, fighting a fish, etc.). Illustrations (line drawings) need not be finished art but should be good enough for our artist to get the idea of what the author is trying to depict." Pays $100 minimum for 35mm color transparencies (cover use); also buys 8x10 b&w prints as part of ms package—"no additional payments." Captions and identification of subjects required. Buys one-time rights.

Tips: "The specialist and regional markets are here to stay. They both offer the freelancer the opportunity for steady income. Fishing is an age-old sport with countless words printed on the subject each year. A fresh new slant that indicates a desire to share with the reader the author's knowledge is a sale. We expect the freelancer to answer any anticipated questions the reader might have (on accommodations, launch sites, equipment needed, etc.) within the ms. The most frequent mistakes made by writers in completing an article for us are bad photos—sending in color instead of b&w prints to accompany stories; massive re-writing needed; or material is too seasonal and past time for our needs."

OKLAHOMA GAME & FISH, Game & Fish Publications, Box 741, Marietta GA 30061. (404)953-9222. Editor: Keith Brooks. A monthly how-to, where-to, when-to hunting and fishing magazine covering Oklahoma. Pays on acceptance. Byline given. Buys one-time rights. Submit seasonal material 8 months in advance. Simultaneous queries, and simultaneous and photocopied submissions OK. Reports in 2 months. Sample copy for $2.50 and 10x12 SAE; writer's guidelines for SASE.
Nonfiction: How-to (hunting and fishing *only*); humor (on limited basis); interview/profile (of successful hunter/angler); personal experience (hunting or fishing adventure). No hiking, backpacking or camping. No "my first deer" articles. Buys 60 mss/year. Query with or without published clips. Length: 1,800-2,200 words. Pays $150.
Photos: State availability of photos. Pays $75 for full-page, color leads; $225 for covers; $25 for b&w photos not submitted as part of story package. Captions and identification of subjects required. Buys one-time rights.

ONTARIO OUT OF DOORS, 7th Floor, 777 Bay St., Toronto, Ontario M5W 1A7 Canada. (416)368-3011. Editor-in-Chief: Burton J. Myers. 80% freelance written. "We prefer a blend of both experienced and new writers." Emphasizes hunting, fishing, camping, and conservation. Monthly magazine; 80 pages. Circ. 55,000. Pays on acceptance. Publishes ms an average of 6 months after acceptance. Buys first North American serial rights. Phone queries OK. Computer printout submissions acceptable; no dot-matrix. Submit seasonal/holiday material 5 months in advance of issue date. Reports in 6 weeks. Free sample copy and writer's guidelines; mention *Writer's Market* in request.
Nonfiction: Expose of conservation practices; how-to (improve your fishing and hunting skills); humor; photo feature (on wildlife); travel (where to find good fishing and hunting); and any news on Ontario. "Avoid 'Me and Joe' articles or funny family camping anecdotes." Buys 20-30 unsolicited mss/year. Query. Length: 150-3,500 words. Pays $35-350. Sometimes pays the expenses of writers on assignment.
Photos: Submit photo material with accompanying query. No additional payment for b&w contact sheets and 35mm color transparencies. "Should a photo be used on the cover, an additional payment of $350-500 is made."
Fillers: Outdoor tips. Buys 24 mss/year. Length: 20-50 words. Pays $20.
Tips: "It's rewarding for us to find a freelancer who reads and understands a set of writer's guidelines, but it is annoying when writers fail to submit supporting photography."

‡OUTDOOR LIFE, Times Mirror Magazines, Inc., 380 Madison Ave., New York NY 10017. (212)687-3000. Editor: Mr. Clare Conley. Executive Editor: Vin T. Sparano. 95% freelance written. A monthly magazine covering hunting and fishing. Circ. 1.5 million. Pays on acceptance. Publishes ms an average of 6 months after acceptance. Byline given. Buys first North American serial rights. Submit seasonal/holiday material 6 months in advance. Previously published submissions OK on occasion. Computer printout submissions acceptable; prefers letter-quality to dot-matrix. Reports in 3 weeks on queries; 1 month on mss. Writer's guidelines for SASE.
Nonfiction: Book excerpts; essays; how-to (must cover hunting, fishing, or related outdoor activities); humor; interview/profile; new product; personal experience; photo feature; technical; and travel. Special issues include Bass and Freshwater Fishing Annual (March), Deer and Big Game Annual (Aug.), and Hunting Guns Annual (Sept.). No articles that are too general in scope—need to write specifically. Buys 400 mss/year. Query or send ms—"either way, photos are *very important.*" Length: 800-3,000 words. Pays $300-1,200.
Photos: Send photos with submission. Reviews 35mm transparencies and 8x10 prints. Offers variable payment. Captions and identification of subjects required. Buys one-time rights. "May offer to buy photos after first use if considered good and have potential to be used with other articles in the future (file photos)."
Columns/Departments: This Happened to Me (true-to-life, personal outdoor adventure, harrowing experience), approximately 300 words. Buys 12 mss/year. Pays $50.
Fillers: Newsbreaks and do-it-yourself for hunters and fishermen. Buys unlimited number/year. Length: 1,000 words maximum. Payment varies.
Tips: "It is best for freelancers to break in by writing features for one of the regional sections—East, Midwest, South, West. These are where-to-go oriented and run from 800-1,500 words. Writers must send one-page query with photos."

PENNSYLVANIA ANGLER, Pennsylvania Fish Commission, Box 1673, Harrisburg PA 17105-1673. (717)657-4520. Editor: Art Michaels. 75% freelance written. Monthly magazine covering fishing and related conservation topics in Pennsylvania. Circ. 60,000. Pays 2 months after publication. Byline given. Buys all rights, but will reassign rights on written request after publication. Submit seasonal/holiday material 8 months in advance. Computer printout submissions acceptable; prefers letter-quality to dot-matrix. Reports in 3 weeks on queries; 2 months on mss. Sample copy for 9x12 SAE with 4 first class stamps; writer's guidelines for #10 SAE with 1 first class stamp.
Nonfiction: Historical/nostalgic, how-to, photo feature, and technical. No saltwater or hunting material. Buys 60+ mss/year. Query. Length: 250-2,500 words. Pays $25-300.
Photos: Send photos with submission. Reviews 35mm and larger color transparencies and 8x10 prints. Offers no additional payment for photos accepted with ms. Captions, model releases and identification of subjects required.

PENNSYLVANIA GAME NEWS, Pennsylvania Game Commission, 8000 Derry St., Harrisburg PA 17105-1567. (717)787-4250. Editor: Bob Bell. 60% freelance written. Works with a small number of new/unpublished writers each year. A monthly magazine covering hunting and outdoors in Pennsylvania. Emphasizes sportsmanlike actions of hunters. Circ. 175,000. Pays on acceptance. Publishes ms an average of 8 months after acceptance. Byline given. Buys all rights; "we return unused rights after publication." Submit seasonal/holiday material 2 months in advance. Simultaneous and photocopied submissions OK. Computer printout submissions acceptable; no dot-matrix. Reports in 3 weeks on queries; 6 weeks on mss. Free sample copy and writer's guidelines.
Nonfiction: General interest and personal hunting experiences. "We consider material on any outdoor subject that can be done in Pennsylvania *except* fishing and boating." Buys 60 mss/year. Query. Length: 2,500 words maximum. Pays $250 maximum.
Photos: Send photos with submission. Offers $5-20/photo. Captions required. Buys all rights.
Fiction: Must deal with hunting or outdoors; no fishing. Buys a few mss/year. Send complete ms.
Tips: "True hunting experiences—'me and Joe' stuff—are best chances for freelancers. Must take place in Pennsylvania."

‡PENNSYLVANIA OUTDOORS, Great Lakes Sportsman Group, Box 2266, Oshkosh WI 54903. (414)233-1327. Editor: Thomas C. Petrie. Managing Editor: Charles Petrie. 85% freelance written. A magazine covering hunting, fishing and the outdoors. Published 7 times a year. Pays on acceptance. Publishes ms an average of 4 months after acceptance. Byline given. Buys first rights or makes work-for-hire assignments. Submit seasonal/holiday material 6 months in advance. Photocopied and previously published submissions OK. Computer printout submissions acceptable. Reports in 3 weeks on queries; 5 weeks on mss. Sample copy $1 with 8½x11 SAE and 95¢ postage. Writer's guidelines for SASE.
Nonfiction: Pennsylvania editor. Book excerpts, exposé, historical/nostalgic, how-to, humor, interview/profile and opinion. General articles are stories of interest to readers in two to four states. Can be how-to, broadbased fiction, conservation issue of broad appeal, natural history piece. State articles are same as for general articles but with focus on a specific state in the Great Lakes group area. Special emphasis on where-to's and stories of interest about state history, personalities, some fiction. Prefer sidebar material which can give the reader more information about topics, locations, etc. Buys 60 mss/year. Query with published clips. Length: 1,200-2,000 words (general); 1,200-1,600 words (state). General articles pay from $150-600; state articles pay $100-300.
Photos: Send photos with submission. Reviews transparencies for general articles and 5x7 prints for state articles. Payment varies. Captions required. Buys one-time rights.
Tips: "Our publications strive for high quality graphics. Therefore, chances of acceptance are enhanced when manuscripts are accompanied by good photographs. Our state articles require a strong where-to slant in many instances and requires contributors to really be acquainted with the state/region. We publish very few squirrel or rabbit hunting articles."

PENNSYLVANIA SPORTSMAN, Box 5196, Harrisburg PA 17110. Editor: Lou Hoffman. 40% freelance written. Covering hunting, fishing, camping, boating and conservation in Pennsylvania. Pays on publication. Publishes ms an average of 6 months after acceptance. Byline given. Buys one-time rights. Simultaneous and previously published submissions OK. Computer printout submissions acceptable "10pt ds." Reports in 6 weeks. Sample copy and writer's guidelines for SASE.
Nonfiction: How-to and where-to articles on hunting, fishing, camping and boating. No material *not* related to field sports. Buys 30-40 unsolicited mss/year. Submit complete ms or query with photos. Length: 800-1,200 words. Pays $40-100. Sometimes pays the expenses of writers on assignment.
Photos: Pays $10/5x7 b&w print; $75/color cover; $20/color inside. Prefers 35mm slides. Captions and model releases are required.
Fillers: "Fillers welcome. Subjects should be different, e.g., 'How to Make a Fishy Pegboard,' 'A Camp Toaster.' We are also looking for helpful hints." Length: 300-400 words. Pays $25 each; $10 additional for b&w used with article.

PETERSEN'S HUNTING, Petersen's Publishing Co., 8490 Sunset Blvd., Los Angeles CA 90069. (213)854-2184. Editor: Craig Boddington. Managing Editor: Jeanne Frissell. 30% freelance written. Works with a small number of new/unpublished writers each year. A monthly magazine covering sport hunting. "We are a 'how to' magazine devoted to all facets of sport hunting, with the intent to make our readers more knowledgeable, more successful and safer hunters." Circ. 275,000. Pays on acceptance. Publishes ms an average of 9 months after acceptance. Byline given. Offers $50 kill fee. Buys all rights. Submit seasonal/holiday material 1 year in advance. Computer printout submissions acceptable; prefers letter-quality to dot-matrix. Reports in 2 weeks. Free sample copy and writer's guidelines.
Nonfiction: General interest; historical/nostalgic; how-to (on hunting techniques); humor; and travel. Special issues include Hunting Annual (August) and the Deer Hunting Annual (September). "No 'me and Joe went

hunting.' Articles must include how-to and where-to material along with anecdotal material.'' Buys 30 mss/ year. Query. Length: 2,000-3,000 words. Pays $300 minimum.
Photos: Send photos with submission. Reviews 35mm transparencies and 8x10 b&w prints. Offers no additional payment for b&w photos accepted with ms; offers $50-250/color photo. Captions, model releases and identification of subjects required. Buys one-time rights.

‡POPULAR LURES, National Reporter Publications, Inc., 15115 S. 76 E. Ave., Bixby OK 74008. (918)366-4441. Managing Editor: Andre Hinds. 95% freelance written. Eager to work with new/unpublished writers. Magazine published 6 times/year February, March, April, May, Summer, Fall and covering freshwater abd saltwater fishing, dealing primarily with the proper lures to use. Estab. 1986. Circ. 50,000. Pays on acceptance. Publishes ms an average of 6 months after acceptance. Byline given. Offers 30% kill fee. Not copyrighted. Buys first North American serial rights or second serial (reprint) rights. Submit seasonal/holiday material 6 months in advance. Photocopied and previously published submissions OK. Electronic submissions OK via 300/1200 baud modem: ASCII text; via disk: Macintosh. Computer printout submissions acceptable. Reports in 6 weeks on queries; 1 month on mss. Free sample copy and writer's guidelines.
Nonfiction: Book excerpts; how-to (fishing, & tackle techniques); interview/profile; new product; opinion; personal experience; and photo feature. Buys 85 mss/year. Query with or without published clips, or send complete ms. Length: 1,200-3,000 words. Pays $200-225 for assigned articles; pays $175-200 for unsolicited articles.
Photos: Send photos with submission. Reviews 35mm transparencies and 5x8 prints. Offers no additional payment for b&w photos accepted with ms. Offers $35-100/color photo. Captions required. Buys one-time rights.
Columns/Departments: How To Make It (step-by-step guide to making lures). Buys 6 mss/year. Length: 1,200-1,800 words. Pays $175-225.
Fillers: Newsbreaks. Buys 40/year. Length: 100-1,000 words. Pays $25-50.
Tips: ''The writer should have more than just a working knowledge of the subject, he or she must have a fresh, new angle. All areas are open to freelancers. We are particularly looking for beginners and freelance writers who have never written for outdoor magazines before. This, we hope, will give our magazine a fresher look than other outdoor magazines.''

SAFARI MAGAZINE, The Journal of Big Game Hunting, Safari Club International, Suite 1680, 5151 E. Broadway, Tucson AZ 85711. (602)747-0260. Editor: William R. Quimby. 90% freelance written. Bimonthly club journal covering international big game hunting and wildlife conservation. Circ. 11,000. Pays on publication. Publishes ms an average of 1 year after acceptance. Byline given. Offers $100 kill fee. Buys all rights. Submit seasonal/holiday material 1 year in advance. Previously published submissions OK under certain circumstances. Computer printout submissions acceptable; prefers letter-quality to dot-matrix. Reports in 2 weeks on queries; 1 month on mss. Sample copy $3.50; writer's guidelines for SAE.
Nonfiction: Doug Fulton; articles editor. Historical/nostalgic (big game hunting); photo feature (wildlife); and technical (firearms, hunting techniques, etc.). Special issues will include hunting and wildlife photos, and stories covering Alaska and Canada. ''Contributors should avoid sending simple hunting narratives that do not contain certain new approaches.'' Buys 36 mss/year. Query or send complete ms. Length: 1,500-2,500 words. Pays $200.
Photos: State availability of photos with query or ms, or send photos with query or ms. Pays $35 for 5x7 or larger b&w prints; $50-150 for 5x9 or larger color prints. Captions, model releases, and identification of subjects required. Buys one-time rights.
Tips: ''Study the magazine. Send manuscripts and photo packages with query. Make it appeal to affluent, knowledgable, world-travelled big game hunters. Features on conservation contributions from big game hunters around the world are most open to freelancers. We have enough stories on first-time African safaris, ordinary deer hunts, Alaska dall sheep hunts. We need South American and eastern Canada hunting stories plus stories dealing with hunting and conservation.''

SALT WATER SPORTSMAN, 186 Lincoln St., Boston MA 02111. (617)426-4074. Editor-in-Chief: Barry Gibson. Emphasizes saltwater fishing. 85% freelance written. Works with a small number of new/unpublished writers each year. Monthly magazine; 120 pages. Circ. 116,000. Pays on acceptance. Publishes ms an average of 5 months after acceptance. Byline given. Buys first North American serial rights. Offers 100% kill fee. Submit seasonal material 8 months in advance. Computer printout submissions acceptable; no dot-matrix. Reports in 1 month. Sample copy and writer's guidelines for $1.41 postage.
Nonfiction: How-to, personal experience, technical and travel (to fishing areas). ''Readers want solid how-to, where-to information written in an enjoyable, easy-to-read style. Personal anecdotes help the reader identify with the writer.'' Prefers new slants and specific information. Query. ''It is helpful if the writer states experience in salt water fishing and any previous related articles. We want one, possibly two well-explained ideas per query letter—not merely a listing.'' Buys 100 unsolicited mss/year. Length: 1,500-2,000 words. Pays $200 and up. Sometimes pays the expenses of writers on assignment.

Photos: Purchased with or without accompanying ms. Captions required. Uses 5x7 or 8x10 b&w prints and color slides. Pays $300 minimum for 35mm, 2¼x2¼ or 8x10 color transparencies for cover. Offers additional payment for photos accepted with accompanying ms.
Columns: Sportsman's Workbench (how to make fishing, or fishing-related boating equipment), 100-300 words.
Tips: "There are a lot of knowledgable fishermen/budding writers out there who could be valuable to us with a little coaching. Many don't think they can write a story for us, but they'd be surprised. We work with writers. Shorter articles that get to the point which are accompanied by good, sharp photos are hard for us to turn down. Having to delete unnecessary wordage—conversation, cliches, etc.—that writers feel is mandatory is annoying. Often they don't devote enough attention to specific fishing information."

SOUTH CAROLINA WILDLIFE, Box 167, Rembert Dennis Bldg., Columbia SC 29202. (803)758-0001. Editor: John Davis. Managing Editor: Tom Poland. For South Carolinians interested in wildlife and outdoor activities. 60% freelance written. Bimonthly magazine; 64 pages. Circ. 64,000. Byline given. Pays on acceptance. Publishes ms an average of 2 months after acceptance. Buys first rights. Free sample copy. Reports in 6 weeks. Computer printout submissions acceptable "if double-spaced."
Nonfiction and Photos: Articles on outdoor South Carolina with an emphasis on preserving and protecting our natural resources. "Realize that the topic must be of interest to South Carolinians and that we must be able to justify using it in a publication published by the state wildlife department—so if it isn't directly about hunting, fishing, a certain plant or animal, it must be somehow related to the environment and conservation. Readers prefer a broad mix of outdoor related topics (articles that illustrate the beauty of South Carolina's outdoors and those that help the reader get more for his/her time, effort, and money spent in outdoor recreation). These two general areas are the ones we most need. Subjects vary a great deal in topic, area and style, but must all have a common ground in the outdoor resources and heritage of South Carolina. Review back issues and query with a one-page outline citing sources, giving ideas for graphic design, explaining justification and giving an example of the first two paragraphs." Does not need any column material. Manuscripts or photographs submitted to *South Carolina Wildlife* should be addressed to: The Editor, Box 167, Columbia SC 29202, accompanied by SASE. The publisher assumes no responsibility for unsolicited material. Buys 25-30 mss/year. Length: 1,000-3,000 words. Pays an average of $200-400 per article depending upon length and subject matter. Sometimes pays the expenses of writers on assignment.
Tips: "We need more writers in the outdoor field who take pride in the craft of writing and put a real effort toward originality and preciseness in their work. Query on a topic we haven't recently done. The most frequent mistake made by writers in completing an article is failure to check details and go in-depth on a subject."

SOUTHERN OUTDOORS MAGAZINE, B.A.S.S. Publications, Number 1 Bell Rd., Montgomery AL 36141. Editor: Larry Teague. Emphasizes Southern outdoor activities, including hunting, fishing, boating, shooting, camping. 90% freelance written. Prefers to work with published/established writers. Published 9 times/year. Circ. 240,000. Pays on acceptance. Publishes ms an average of 6 months after acceptance. Buys all rights. Computer printout submissions acceptable; no dot-matrix. Reports in 1 month. Sample copy $1.50.
Nonfiction: Articles should be service-oriented, helping the reader excel in outdoor sports. Emphasis is on techniques and trends. Some "where-to" stories purchased on Southern destinations with strong fishing-or-hunting theme. Buys 120 mss/year. Length: 2,000 words maximum. Pays 15¢/word. Sometimes pays the expenses of writers on assignment.
Photos: Usually purchased with manuscripts. Pays $50-75 for 35mm color transparencies without ms, and $250-400 for covers.
Fillers: Needs short articles (50-500 words) with newsy slant for Southern Shorts. Emphasis on irony and humor. Also needs humorous or thought-provoking pieces (750-1,200 words) for S.O. Essay feature.
Tips: "It's easiest to break in with short features of 500-1,000 words on 'how-to' fishing and hunting topics. We buy very little first person. Query first, and send sample of your writing if we haven't done business before. Stories most likely to sell: bass fishing, deer hunting, other freshwater fishing, inshore saltwater fishing, bird and small-game hunting, shooting, camping and boating. The most frequent mistakes made by writers in completing an article for us are first-person usage; clarity of articles; applicability of topic to the South; lack of quotes from qualified sources."

‡SPORT FISHING, The Magazine of Offshore Fishing, World Publications, Suite H, 809 S. Orlando Ave., Box 2456, Winter Park FL 32790. (305)628-4802. Editor: Pierce Hoover. 60% freelance written. A bimonthly magazine covering offshore fishing for both big game and light-tackle enthusiasts—from the occasional to active fisherman. Readers are sophisticated, well-traveled, with median income of $80,000. Estab. 1986. Circ. 90,000. Pays on acceptance or on publication. Byline given. Offers kill fee. Buys first North American serial rights. Submit seasonal/holiday material 6 months in advance. Computer printout submissions acceptable. Reports in 1 month. Free sample copy and writer's guidelines.
Nonfiction: Historical/nostalgic; how-to (need to be well-versed on off-shore fishing); humor; interview/profile; new product (area of expertise needed); photo feature; technical; and travel (seasonal, locations, fishing,

facilities); and general—worldwide with emphasis on states). "No strictly regional techniques with no interest or application to a national readership." Buys 20 mss/year. Query with published clips or query by phone. Length: 400-3,000 words. Pays $200-500 for assigned articles; pays $100-500 for unsolicited articles. Sometimes pays the expenses of writers on assignment.

Photos: State availability of photos with submission, or send photos with submission. Reviews 35mm slides and b&w glossy prints. Offers $35-200/photo. Captions, model releases and identification of subjects required. Buys one-time rights.

Columns/Departments: Rotating Columns; Power Plants and Maintenance, Seamanship, Light Tackle Fishing, Rigging, and Fishing Techniques. Length: 1,000-2,000 words. Pays $150-200.

Fiction: Adventure (as pertains to offshore fishing); and historical. Buys 3 mss/year. Query. Length: 2,000-5,000 words. Pays $200-300.

Fillers: Anecdotes, facts, gags to be illustrated by cartoonist, newsbreaks and short humor. Buys 30/year. Length: 300-900 words. Pays $50-200.

Tips: "Contributors must be very knowledgeable of boats and offshore fishing."

‡SPORTING CLASSICS, Indigo Press, Inc., Highway 521 S., Box 1017, Camden SC 29020. (803)425-1003. Editor John Culler. Executive Editor: Charles A. Wechsler. 50% freelance written. A bimonthly magazine covering hunting and fishing for well-educated and above-average-income sportsmen. Circ. 42,000. Pays within 60 days after publication. Publishes ms an average of 6 months after acceptance. Byline given. Offers $300 kill fee. Buys first North American serial rights. Submit seasonal/holiday material 6 months in advance. Computer printout submissions acceptable; no dot-matrix. Reports in 2 weeks. Free sample copy and writer's guidelines.

Nonfiction: Book excerpts, historical/nostalgic, humor, personal experience, photo feature, travel. Buys 35 mss/year. Query. Length: 2,500-4,500 words. Pays $300-750 for assigned articles; pays $300-500 for unsolicited articles. Sometimes pays expenses of writers on assignment.

Photos: Send photos with submissions and state availability of other photos. Reviews 35mm and larger transparencies and prints. Offers no additional payment for photos accepted with ms. Captions and model releases required. Buys one-time rights.

Columns/Departments: My View (places, people, events, etc. in the great outdoors). Buys 6 mss/year. Query. Length: 1,000-1,500 words. Pays $300 minimum.

Fillers: Anecdotes, facts, newsbreaks and short humor. Buys 12/year. Length: 25-1,000 words. Pays $50-150.

Tips: "We're always looking for features—about hunting and fishing, exotic or unusual places to hunt and fish; about great sportsmen; conservation issues that affect game species: sporting dogs; wildlife painters, carvers and sculptors; firearms and decoys."

SPORTS AFIELD, 250 W. 55th St., New York NY 10019. Editor: Tom Paugh. Managing Editor: Fred Kesting. 33% freelance written. Eager to work with new/unpublished writers. For people of all ages whose interests are centered around the out-of-doors (hunting and fishing) and related subjects. Monthly magazine. Circ. 518,010. Buys first North American serial rights for features, and all rights for *SA Almanac*. Pays on acceptance. Publishes ms an average of 6 months after acceptance. Byline given. "Our magazine is seasonal and material submitted should be in accordance. Fishing in spring and summer; hunting in the fall; camping in summer and fall." Submit seasonal material 6 months in advance. Computer printout submissions acceptable; prefers letter-quality to dot-matrix. Reports in 1 month. Query or submit complete ms.

Nonfiction and Photos: "Informative where-to articles and personal experiences with good photos on hunting, fishing, camping, boating and subjects such as conservation and travel related to hunting and fishing. We want first-class writing and reporting." Buys 15-17 unsolicited mss/year. Recent article example: "Dude Fishing" (April 1985). Length: 500-2,500 words. Pays $750 minimum, depending on length and quality. Photos purchased with or without ms. Pays $50 minimum for 8x10 b&w glossy prints. Pays $50 minimum for 35mm or larger transparencies. Sometimes pays the expenses of writers on assignment.

Fiction: Adventure, humor (if related to hunting and fishing).

Fillers: Send to *Almanac* editor. *Almanac* pays $25 and up depending on length, for newsworthy, unusual, how-to and nature items. Payment on publication. Buys all rights.

Tips: "We seldom give assignments to other than staff. Top-quality 35mm slides to illustrate articles a must. Read a recent copy of *Sports Afield* so you know the market you're writing for. Family-oriented features will probably become more important because more and more groups/families are sharing the outdoor experience."

THE SPORTSMEN MAGAZINE, The National Sportsmen's Show Magazine (Canada), W.T. Sports Publishing, Division of CRV Publications Canada, Ltd., 2077 Dundas St. E, Mississauga, Ontario L4X 1M2 Canada. (416)624-8218. Editor: Reg Fife. Annual magazine featuring the outdoor activities of Canadian sportsmen. (Published February. Deadline: Dec. 15.) Distributed at eight sportsmen's shows across Canada. "Designed to awaken the interest of persons attending the shows to topics, such as fishing, hunting, conservation, cottaging, boating, canoeing, nature, etc." Circ. 335,000. Pays on publication. Byline given. Buys first rights. Submit seasonal/holiday material 5 months in advance. Simultaneous queries OK. Reports in 1 month on queries; 2 months on mss. Free sample copy and writer's guidelines.

602 Writer's Market '87

Nonfiction: Photo feature (outdoor sports, nature); wildlife; adventure. "Material should have Canadian slant and appeal." Buys 10 mss/year. Query with or without clips of published work. Length: 1,200-2,000 words. Pays $200-500.

Photos: Send photos with ms. Photos are "usually bought with ms." Reviews b&w contact sheets, and 5x7 prints, and color transparencies. Captions required. Buys one-time rights.

Fiction: Nature fiction. Buys 1-2 mss/year. Query. Length: 1,200-2,000 words. Pays negotiable fee.

TENNESSEE SPORTSMAN, Game & Fish Publications, Box 741, Marietta GA 30061. (404)953-9222. Editor: Bill Hartlage. Monthly how-to, where-to, when-to hunting and fishing magazine covering Tennessee. Pays on acceptance. Byline given. Buys one-time rights. Submit seasonal material 10 months in advance. Simultaneous queries OK, no simultaneous or photocopied manuscripts. Computer printout submissions acceptable. Reports in 2 months. Sample copy for $2 and 10x12 SAE; writer's guidelines for SASE.

Nonfiction: Very state-specific approach; how-to (hunting and fishing *only*); humor/nostalgia (on limited basis); interview/profile (of successful hunter/angler); personal experience (hunting or fishing adventure). No hiking, backpacking or camping. No "my first deer" articles. Buys 60 mss/year. Query with or without published clips. Length: 1,800-2,200 words. Pays $150-175.

Photos: State availability of photos. Pays $75 for color leads; $225 for covers; $25 for b&w photos. Captions and identification of subjects required. Buys one-time rights.

THE TEXAS FISHERMAN, A Complete Guide to the Texas Outdoors, Scripps-Howard Magazines, 5314 Bingle Rd., Houston TX 77092. Editor/Manager: Larry Bozka. 80% freelance written. Prefers to work with published/established writers; works with a small number of new/unpublished writers each year. A tabloid published 9 times a year for freshwater and saltwater fishermen in Texas. Circ. 61,152. Rights purchased vary with author and material. Byline given. Usually buys second serial (reprint) rights. Buys 5-8 mss/month. Pays on acceptance. Publishes ms an average of 3 months after acceptance. Electronic submissions OK, but requires hard copy also; contact production manager Terry Kelly at (713)688-8811. Computer printout submissions acceptable; no dot-matrix. Reports in 1 month. Query. Free sample copy and writer's guidelines.

Nonfiction and Photos: General how-to, where-to, features on all phases of fishing in Texas. Strong slant on informative pieces. Strong writing. Good saltwater stories (Texas only). Length: 1,200-1,500 words. Pays $75-250, depending on length and quality of writing and photos. Mss must include 4-7 good action b&w photos or illustrations. Color slides will be considered for cover or inside use.

Tips: "Query should be a short, but complete description of the story that emphasizes a specific angle. When possible, send black and white photos with queries. Good art will sell us a story that is mediocre, but even a great story can't replace bad photographs, and better than half submit poor quality photos. How-to, location, or personality profile stories are preferred."

TEXAS SPORTSMAN, Game & Fish Publications, Box 741, Marietta GA 30061. (404)953-9222. Editor: Gordon Whittington. 80% freelance written. Works with a small number of new/unpublished writers each year. Monthly how-to, where-to, when-to hunting and fishing magazine covering Texas. Pays 75 days prior to publication. Publishes ms an average of 7 months after acceptance. Byline given. Buys one-time rights. Submit seasonal material 10 months in advance. Computer printout submissions acceptable "only if double-spaced." Reports in 2 months. Sample copy for $2 and 10x12 SASE; writer's guidelines for SAE and 1 first class stamp.

Nonfiction: Where-to (hunting and fishing *only*); humor (on very limited basis); interview/profile (of successful hunter/angler); personal experience (hunting or fishing how-to). No hiking, backpacking or camping. No "my first deer" articles. Buys 60 mss/year. Query with or without published clips. Length: 2,200 words. Pays $150-175.

Photos: State availability of photos. Pays $75 for full-page, color leads; $225 for covers; $25 for b&w photos. Captions and identification of subjects required. Buys one-time rights.

Tips: "We don't run shorts or fillers. The most frequent mistakes made by writers in completing articles for us are not enough specific *where-to* info in hunting and fishing articles; too much *how-to* not specific to an exact place."

THE TRAPPER, Spearman Publishing & Printing, Inc., 213 N. Saunders, Box 550, Sutton NE 68979. (402)773-4343. Editor: Rich Faler, Box 691, Greenville PA 161225 (412)588-3492. 75% freelance written. Eager to work with new/unpublished writers. A monthly tabloid covering trapping, outdoor occupations, fur farming, medicinal roots and herbs, calling predators and fur markets for both novice and pro audience, male and female, all ages. Circ. 51,000. Pays on publication. Publishes ms an average of 18 months after acceptance. Byline given. Buys first North American serial rights, one-time rights, and all rights. Submit seasonal/holiday material 4 months in advance. Computer printout submissions acceptable; prefers letter-quality to dot-matrix. Reports in 6 weeks on mss. Sample copy for $2; writer's guidelines for SAE and 1 first class stamp.

Nonfiction: How-to (trapping, raising fur, etc.); and personal experience (trapping, outdoor-related experiences). "We do not want to see anything that refers to or condones overharvesting, bragging, etc." Buys 120 mss/year. Query. Length: 500-3,000 words. Pays $20-200.

Photos: Send photos with accompanying query or ms. Pays $5-40 for 8x10 b&w and color prints. Captions required. Buys one-time rights and all rights.

Tips: "A good feature with excellent photos is really needed all the time. We stress good outdoor ethics, conservation and public relations. How-to articles are always needed; look for fresh ideas or different slant. The most frequent mistakes made by writers in completing an article for us is that the articles are too thin or basic; the market is missed (audience not targeted). Being a professional writer isn't as important as knowing your subject inside out. We need articles delivering very specific, in-depth information."

TURKEY, 3941 N. Paradise Rd., Flagstaff AZ 86001. (602)774-6913. Editor: Gerry Blair. 60% freelance written. Works with a small number of new/unpublished writers each year. A monthly magazine covering turkey hunting, biology and conservation of the wild turkey, gear for turkey hunters, where to go, etc. for both novice and experienced wild turkey enthusiasts. "We stress wildlife conservation, ethics, and management of the resource." Circ. 30,000. Pays on publication. Publishes ms an average of 1 year after acceptance. Byline given. Computer printout submissions acceptable; prefers letter-quality to dot-matrix.

Nonfiction: Book excerpts (turkey related); how-to (turkey-related); and personal experience (turkey hunting). Buys 75-100 mss/year. "The most frequent mistake made by writers in completing an article for us is inadequate photo support." Query. Length: 500-3,000 words. Pays $20-150.

Photos: Send photos with accompanying query or ms. Pays $5-20 for 8x10 b&w and color prints; $50 for color slides for cover.

Columns/Departments: "Nearly all columns are done inhouse."

Fillers: Clippings and newsbreaks that relate to or could affect turkey hunting or management. Length: 50-200 words. Pays $10-25.

Tips: "How-to articles, using fresh ideas, are most open to freelancers. We also need more short articles on turkey management programs in all states."

TURKEY CALL, Wild Turkey Bldg., Box 530, Edgefield SC 29824. (803)637-3106. Editor: Gene Smith. 50% freelance written. "Will expect to mix the work of published and new writers and photographers." An educational publication for members of the National Wild Turkey Federation. Bimonthly magazine. Circ. 28,000. Buys one-time rights. Byline given. Publishes ms an average of 6 months after acceptance. Pays on acceptance. Reports in 4 weeks. No queries necessary. Submit complete package. Wants original ms only (no carbons or other copies). No multiple submissions. Computer printout submissions acceptable; prefers letter-quality to dot-matrix. "Double strike dot-matrix OK." Sample copy $2.

Nonfiction and Photos: Feature articles dealing with the hunting and management of the American wild turkey. Must be accurate information and must appeal to national readership of turkey hunters and wildlife management experts. No poetry or first-person accounts of unremarkable hunting trips. May use some fiction that educates or entertains in a special way. Length: 1,500-2,000 words. Pays $25 for items, $50 for short fillers of 400-500 words, $200-300 for illustrated features. "We want quality photos submitted with features." Art illustrations also acceptable. "We are using more and more inside color illustrations." Prefers b&w 8x10 glossies. Color transparencies of any size are acceptable. Wants no typical hunter-holding-dead-turkey photos or setups using mounted birds or domestic turkeys. Photos with how-to stories must make the techniques clear (example: how to make a turkey call; how to sculpt or carve a bird in wood). Pays $10 minimum for one-time rights on b&w photos and simple art illustrations; up to $75 for inside color, reproduced any size. Covers: Most are donated. Any purchased are negotiated.

Tips: The writer "should simply keep in mind that the audience is 'expert' on wild turkey management, hunting, life history and restoration/conservation history. He/she *must know the subject*. We will be buying more third person, more fiction—in an attempt to avoid the 'predictability trap' of a single subject magazine."

VIRGINIA WILDLIFE, Box 11104, Richmond VA 23230. (804)257-1000. Editor: Harry L. Gillam. Send manuscripts to Editor, V. Shepherd. 80% freelance written. Works with a small number of new/unpublished writers each year. For sportsmen and outdoor enthusiasts. Pays on acceptance. Publishes ms an average of 1 year after acceptance. Buys first North American serial rights and reprint rights. Byline given. Computer printout submissions acceptable; prefers letter-quality to dot-matrix. Free sample copy and writer's guidelines for 8½x11 SASE.

Nonfiction: Uses factual outdoor stories, set in Virginia. "Currently need boating subjects, wildlife and nature in urban areas. Always need good fishing and hunting stories—not of the 'me and Joe' genre, however. Slant should be to enjoy the outdoors and what you can do to improve it. Material must be applicable to Virginia, sound from a scientific basis, accurate and easily readable. No subjects which are too controversial for a state agency magazine to address; poetry and cartoons; sentimental or humorous pieces (not because they're inherently bad, but because so few writers are good at either); 'how I nursed an abandoned _____ back to health' or stories about wildlife the author has become 'pals' with." Submit photos with ms. Length: prefers approximately 1,200 words. Pays 10¢/word.

Photos: Buys photos with mss; "and occasionally buys unaccompanied good photos." Prefers color transparencies, Kodachrome 64. Captions required. Pays $10/b&w photo; $10-15 for color.

Tips: "We are currently receiving too many anecdotes and too few articles with an educational bent—we want instructional, 'how-to' articles on hunting, fishing and outdoor sports, and also want semi-technical articles on wildlife. We are not receiving enough articles with high-quality photographs accompanying them; also, photos are inadequately labeled and protected. Catering to these needs will greatly enhance chances for acceptance of manuscripts. We have more 'backyard bird' articles than we could ever hope to use, and not enough good submissions on trapping or trout fishing. We are cutting back substantially on number of freelance, over-the-transom submissions we purchase, in favor of making assignments to writers with whom we have established relationships and articles written by our own staff. The trend in our magazine is to pay more for fewer, longer, more in-depth, higher-quality stories. As always, a fresh angle sells, especially since we are basically publishing the same topics year after year. We need more ecosystem approach articles which aim to educate the public on the interrelatedness of the environment."

WATERFOWLER'S WORLD, Waterfowl Publications, Ltd., Box 38306, Germantown TN 38183. (901)767-7978. Editor: Cindy Dixon. 75% freelance written. Bimonthly magazine covering duck and goose hunting for the serious hunter and experienced waterfowler, with an emphasis on improvement of skills. Circ. 35,000. Pays on publication. Publishes ms an average of 1 year after acceptance. Buys first North American serial rights. Reports in 2 months. Computer printout submissions acceptable; no dot-matrix. Sample copy $2.50; writer's guidelines for $1.
Nonfiction: General interest (where to hunt); how-to written for the serious duck hunter. Query. Length: 1,500 words. Pays $75-200.
Photos: Reviews 8x10 b&w prints and 35mm color transparencies. Pays $50/cover.
Columns/Departments: Fowlweather Gear (outdoor clothes and supplies).
Tips: "The most frequent mistakes made by writers in completing articles for us are not sending SASE for return of manuscript, and not realizing our audience already knows the basics of duck hunting."

WESTERN OUTDOORS, 3197-E Airport Loop, Costa Mesa CA 92626. (714)546-4370. Editor-in-Chief: Burt Twilegar. 75% freelance written. Emphasizes hunting, fishing, camping, boating for 11 Western states only, Baja California, Canada, Hawaii and Alaska. Monthly magazine; 88 pages. Circ. 150,000. Pays on acceptance. Publishes ms an average of 6 months after acceptance. Buys first North American serial rights. Query (in writing). Submit seasonal material 4-6 months in advance. Photocopied submissions OK. Computer printout submissions are acceptable if double-spaced; prefers letter-quality to dot-matrix. Reports in 4-6 weeks. Sample copy $1.50; writer's guidelines for SASE.
Nonfiction: Where-to (catch more fish, bag more game, improve equipment, etc.); informational; photo feature. "We do not accept fiction, poetry, cartoons." Buys 70 assigned mss/year. Query or send complete ms. Length: 1,000-1,800 words maximum. Pays $300-500.
Photos: Purchased with accompanying ms. Captions required. Uses 8x10 b&w glossy prints; prefers Kodachrome II 35mm slides. Offers no additional payment for photos accepted with accompanying ms. Pays $150-200 for covers.
Tips: "Provide a complete package of photos, map, trip facts and manuscript written according to our news feature format. Stick with where-to type articles. Both b&w and color photo selections make a sale more likely. The most frequent mistake made by writers in completing an article for us is that they don't follow our style. Our guidelines are quite clear."

WESTERN SPORTSMAN, Box 737, Regina, Saskatchewan, S4P 3A8 Canada. (306)352-8384. Editor: Rick Bates. 90% freelance written. For fishermen, hunters, campers and others interested in outdoor recreation. "Note that all our coverage area is Alberta and Saskatchewan." Bimonthly magazine; 64-112 pages. Circ. 28,000. Rights purchased vary with author and material. May buy first North American serial rights or second serial (reprint) rights. Byline given. Pays on publication. Sample copy $3.50; free writer's guidelines. "We try to include as much information as possible on all subjects in each edition. Therefore, we usually publish fishing articles in our winter issues along with a variety of winter stories. If material is dated, we would like to receive articles 2 months in advance of our publication date." Reports in 4 weeks. SAE and IRCs.
Nonfiction: "It is necessary that all articles can identify with our coverage area of Alberta and Saskatchewan. We are interested in mss from writers who have experienced an interesting fishing, hunting, camping or other outdoor experience. We also publish how-to and other informational pieces as long as they can relate to our coverage area. We are more interested in articles which tell about the average guy living on beans, guiding his own boat, stalking his game and generally doing his own thing in our part of Western Canada than a story describing a well-to-do outdoorsman traveling by motorhome, staying at an expensive lodge with guides doing everything for him except catching the fish, or shooting the big game animal. The articles that are submitted to us need to be prepared in a knowledgable way and include more information than the actual fish catch or animal or bird kill. Discuss the terrain, the people involved on the trip, the water or weather conditions, the costs, the planning that went into the trip, the equipment and other data closely associated with the particular event in a factual manner. We're always looking for new writers." Buys 120 mss/year. Submit complete ms. Length: 1,500-2,000 words. Pays $100-325.

Photos: Photos purchased with ms with no additional payment. Also purchased without ms. Pays $20-25/5x7 or 8x10 b&w print; $175-250/35mm or larger transparency for front cover.

WISCONSIN SPORTSMAN, Great Lakes Sportsman Group, Box 2266, Oshkosh WI 54903. (414)233-1327. Editor: Thomas C. Petrie. Managing Editor: Charles Petrie. 85% freelance written. A magazine covering hunting, fishing and the outdoors. Published 7 times a year. Pays on acceptance. Publishes ms an average of 4 months after acceptance. Byline given. Buys first rights or makes work-for-hire assignments. Submit seasonal/ holiday material 6 months in advance. Photocopied and previously published submissions OK. Computer printout submissions acceptable. Reports in 3 weeks on queries; 5 weeks on mss. Sample copy $1 with 8½x11 SAE and 95¢ postage. Writer's guidelines for SASE.
Nonfiction: Wisconsin editor. Book excerpts, exposé, historical/nostaligc, how-to, humor, interview/profile and opinion. General articles are stories of interest to readers in two to four states. Can be how-to, broad-based fiction, conservation issue of broad appeal, natural history piece. State articles are the same as for general articles but with focus on a specific state in the Great Lakes group area. Special emphasis on where-to's and stories of interest about state history, personalities, some fiction. Prefer sidebar material which can give the reader more information about topics, locations, etc. Buys 60 mss/year. Query with published clips. Length: 1,200-2,000 words (general); 1,200-1,600 words (state). General articles pay from $150-600; state articles pay $100-300.
Photos: Send photos with submission. Reviews transparencies for general articles and 5x7 prints for state articles. Payment varies. Captions required. Buys one-time rights.
Tips: "Our publications strive for high quality graphics. Therefore, chances of acceptance are enhanced when manuscripts are accompanied by good photographs. Our state articles require a strong where-to slant in many instances and requires contributors to really be acquainted with the state/region. We publish very few squirrel or rabbit hunting articles."

Martial Arts

‡**AMERICAN KARATE**, Condor Books, Inc., 351 W. 54th St., New York NY 10019. (212)586-4432. Editor: Alan Paul. Managing Editor: David Weiss. 80% freelance written. A bimonthly magazine covering martial arts in America and Canada. "*AK* is directed at American and Canadian martial artists and the ways in which they have adapted and changed the oriental fighting arts to better suit our way of life." Estab. 1986. Circ. 100,000. Pays on publication. Byline given. Offers $50-75 kill fee. Buys first North American serial rights. Submit seasonal/holiday material 3 months in advance. Photocopied submissions OK. Computer printout submissions acceptable; prefers letter-quality to dot-matrix. Reports in 2 weeks on queries; 1 month on mss. Sample copy for 9x12 SAE with 5 first class stamps.
Nonfiction: Book excerpts, general interest, historical/nostalgic, how-to, inspirational, interview/profile, new product, personal experience and technical. No articles of an overly general nature on martial arts. Buys 50 mss/year. Query with or without published clips, or send complete ms. Length: 2,000-3,000 words. Pays $100-200. Sometimes pays the expenses of writers on assignment.
Photos: Send photos with submission. Reviews contact sheets, 35mm transparencies and 5x7 or 8x10 prints. Offers no additional payment for b&w photos accepted with ms; offers $35-100/color photo. Captions and identification of subjects required. Buys one-time rights.
Columns/Departments: AK-TV (martial arts videos), 1,500 words; AK Profile (inspirational pieces about martial artists), 1,500 words; State of the Martial Arts (review of martial arts in American states), 2,000-2,500 words; and Fit to Fight (exercise and weight training for martial artists), 1,500-2,000 words. Buys 25 mss/year. Send complete ms. Pays $75-200.
Tips: "Freelancer can break into our publication by concentrating on the *American* approach our magazine has taken. We are not interested in pieces on Oriental practitioners or systems. We also are interested in good quality color and b&w photos. Every area is open. We are very interested in expanding our stable of contributors."

ATA MAGAZINE, Martial Arts and Fitness, ATA Magazine Co., Inc., Box 240835, Memphis TN 38124-0835. (901)761-2821. Editor: Milo Dailey. Managing Editor: Carla Dailey. 20% freelance written. Works with a small number of new/unpublished writers each year. *ATA Magazine* is the official publication of the American Taekwondo Association and ATA Fitness Centers, Inc. covering general health and fitness with emphasis on martial arts (Taekwondo), aerobics, and strength training equipment. Circ. 15,000. Pays on publication. Publishes ms an average of 3 months after acceptance. "Most of publication copyrighted." Buys first North American serial rights unless otherwise arranged. Submit seasonal/holiday material at least 6 months in advance. Sometimes accepts previously published submissions. Computer printout submissions acceptable; dot-matrix submissions OK "if on non-heat-sensitive paper." Reports in 3 weeks. Sample copy $2.25; writer's guidelines for SAE.
Nonfiction: Interview/profile (on persons notable in other fields who train under *ATA* programs). "Special slant is that martial arts are primarily for fitness and personal development. Defense and sports aspects are to reinforce primary aims. Freelancers who are not ATA members should concentrate on non-martial arts aspects

of fitness or on ATA martial artists' personalities. *We're not interested in fads, non-ATA martial arts or overt 'sex' orientation.*" Currently articles are staff-written, assigned to ATA experts or ATA member freelancers; would possibly buy 4-6 outside freelance mss. Query. Length: depends on material. Pays $25-150.
Photos: Payment for photos included in payment for ms. Prefers b&w prints of size appropriate to quality reproduction. Model releases and identification of subjects "with enough information for a caption" required.
Fiction: "We would take a look at fiction—but because of the overall magazine subject matter, would be very, very, very leery. It would almost take a writer who is an ATA martial arts member to get the right outlook."
Tips: "So far *ATA Magazine* has served as a developmental organ for ATA members who are or wish to be writers. We're willing to work with writers on nontechnical coverage of subjects of interest to our readership—which is mostly 'adult' in its approach to martial arts and fitness in general. Most ATA centers have a good story. Most martial arts and strength-training articles are staff-written or assigned to association experts. This leaves nutrition and special personality pieces most open to freelancers, along possibly with fiction. But to get the right slant, proximity to ATA sources (which are currently in about 200 communities coast to coast) is almost mandatory. It seems a major problem in writing for most magazines today is to have expert knowledge with ability to communicate at the non-expert level. A middle ground is the 'special interest' magazine such as ours which allows presumption of both interest and a basic knowledge of the subject. Still, it's easy to become too technical and forget that emotion retains readers—not just facts. The most blatant mistake is not reading the entry in *Writer's Market*. *We do not use karate movie stars or non-ATA martial artists.* Other publications answer this interest segment. We're a small staff with a lot of hats to wear. Unsolicited manuscripts may get dumped by default. Handwritten ones certainly are. *If writers actually read all of our listing, it would save all a lot of time.* One well-known martial arts writer queried, determined we're not 'her thing', and we're both happier . . .'"

BLACK BELT, Rainbow Publications, Inc., 1813 Victory Place, Burbank CA 91504. (818)843-4444. Executive Editor: Jim Coleman. 80-90% freelance written. Works with a small number of new/unpublished writers each year. Emphasizes martial arts for both practitioner and layman. Monthly magazine; 132 pages. Circ. 110,000. Pays on publication. Publishes ms an average of 3 months after acceptance. Buys first North American serial rights, retains right to republish. Submit seasonal/holiday material 6 months in advance. Photocopied submissions OK. Computer printout submissions acceptable; prefers letter-quality to dot-matrix. Reports in 1 month.
Nonfiction: Expose, how-to, informational, interview, new product, personal experience, profile, technical and travel. Also survival, military-related, soldier of fortune type manuscripts, and how they relate to the martial arts. No biography, material on teachers or on new or Americanized styles. Buys 8-9 mss/issue. Query or send complete ms. Length: 1,200 words minimum. Pays $10-20/page of manuscript.
Photos: Very seldom buys photos without accompanying mss. Captions required. Total purchase price for ms includes payment for photos. Model releases required.
Fiction: Historical. Buys 2-3 mss/year. Query. Pays $100-175.

FIGHTING STARS NINJA, Rainbow Publications, 1813 Victory Pl., Box 7728, Burbank CA 91510-7728. (818)843-4444. Executive Editor: William Groak. 75% freelance written. Works with a small number of new/unpublished writers each year. Bimonthly magazine about the history, tradition and training of the ninja warrior. Circ. 60,000. Pays on publication. Publishes ms an average of 2 months after acceptance. Buys first North American serial rights. Submit seasonal material 4 months in advance, but best to send query letter first. Simultaneous and photocopied submissions OK. Computer print-out submissions acceptable; prefers letter-quality to dot-matrix. Reports in 6 weeks. Writer's guidelines for SASE.
Nonfiction: General interest, history or training articles (with well-known martial artists) on the art of ninjutsu; profiles (on art's top teachers); how-to (on the art of survival). Buys 30-40 unsolicited mss/year. Send query or complete ms. Length: 1,000-2,000 words. Pays $50-200.
Photos: State availability of photos. Most ms should be accompanied by photos. Reviews 5x7 and 8x10 b&w and color glossy prints. Can reproduce prints from negatives. Will use illustrations. Offers no additional payment for photos accepted with ms. Model releases required. Buys all rights.
Fiction: Must be related to ninja or art of ninjutsu.
Tips: "The art of ninjutsu is the fastest growing martial art in the world. As such, we welcome an array of articles dealing with its history, weapons, training and personalities. The writer, however, must use care in selecting the subject for his piece. "Fighting Stars" will feature only those instructors who have received training from Masaaki Hatsumi or students whose teachers have studied with him. *Fighting Stars Ninja* might become a monthly soon, hence, more freelance material will be needed."

FIGHTING WOMAN NEWS, Martial Arts, Self-Defense, Combative Sports Quarterly, Box 1459, Grand Central Station, New York NY 10163. (212)228-0900. Editor: Valerie Eads. Nearly 100% freelance written. Prefers to work with published/established writers. Quarterly magazine. "*FWN* combines sweat and philosophy, the deadly reality of street violence and the other worldliness of such eastern disciplines as Zen. Our audience is composed of adult women actually practicing martial arts with an average experience of 4 +

years. Since our audience is also 80 + % college grads and 40% holders of advanced degrees we are an action magazine with footnotes. Our material is quite different from what is found in newsstand martial arts publications." Circ. 6,734. Pays on publication. Publishes ms an average of 2 years after acceptance. Byline given. Buys one-time rights. Submit seasonal/holiday material 6 months in advance. Simultaneous queries, and simultaneous, photocopied, and previously published submissions OK. "For simultaneous and previously published we *must* be told about it." Electronic submissions acceptable via CPM, but requires hard copy also. Computer printout submissions acceptable; prefers letter-quality to dot-matrix. If computer printout submissions "are unreadable we throw them out." Reports as soon as possible. Sample copy $3.50; writer's guidelines for business size SAE and 37¢ postage.

Nonfiction: Book excerpts, expose (discrimination against women in martial arts governing bodies); historical/nostalgic; how-to (martial arts, self-defense techniques); humor; inspirational (e.g., self-defense success stories); interview/profile ("we have assignments waiting for writers in this field"); new product; opinion; personal experience; photo feature; technical; travel. "All materials *must* be related to our subject matter. No tabloid sensationalism, no 'sweat is sexy too' items, no fantasy presented as fact, no puff pieces for an instructor or school with a woman champion inhouse." Buys 12 mss/year. Query. Length: 1,000-5,000 words. Pays in copies or $10 maximum. Sometimes pays the expenses of writers on assignment; expenses negotiated in some cases.

Photos: Muskat Buckby, photo editor. State availability of photos with query or ms. Reviews "technically competent" b&w contact sheets and 8x10 b&w prints. "We negotiate photos and articles as a package. Sometimes expenses are negotiated. Captions and identification of subjects required. The need for releases depends on the situation."

Columns/Departments: Notes & News (short items relevant to our subject matter); Letters (substantive comment regarding previous issues); Sports Reports; and Reviews (of relevant materials in any medium). Query or send complete ms. Length: 100-1,000 words. Pays in copies or negotiate payment.

Fiction: Muskat Buckby, fiction editor. Adventure, fantasy, historical and science fiction. "Any fiction must feature a woman skilled in martial arts." Buys 0-1 mss/year. Query. Length: 1,000-5,000 words. "We will consider serializing longer stories." Pays in copies or negotiates payment.

Poetry: Muskat Buckby, poetry editor. "We'll look at all types. Must appeal to an audience of martial artists. Buys 3-4 poems/year. Length: open. Pays in copy or negotiated payment.

Tips: "Our greatest need is for solid martial arts material. Non-martial-artist writers can be given interview assignments. The writer may have a better chance of breaking in at our publication with short articles and fillers since it's easier to find a spot for a borderline filler. We are tight on article space."

INSIDE KARATE, The Magazine for Today's Total Martial Artist, Unique Publications, 4201 Vanowen Pl., Burbank CA 91505. (818)845-2656. Editor: Dave Cater. 90% freelance written. Works with a small number of new/unpublished writers each year. Monthly magazine covering the martial arts. Circ. 120,000. Publishes ms an average of 3 months after acceptance. Byline given. Buys first North American serial rights. Submit seasonal/holiday material 4 months in advance. Simultaneous queries, and simultaneous and photocopied submissions OK. Computer printout submissions acceptable; prefers letter-quality to dot-matrix. Reports in 3 weeks on queries; in 6 weeks on mss. Sample copy $2.50, 9x12 SAE and 5 first class stamps; free writer's guidelines.

Nonfiction: Book excerpts; expose (of martial arts); historical/nostalgic; humor; interview/profile (with approval only); opinion; personal experience; photo feature; and technical (with approval only). *Inside Karate* seeks a balance of the following in each issue: tradition, history, glamour, profiles and/or interviews (both by assignment only), technical, philosophical and think pieces. To date, most "how to" pieces have been done inhouse. Buys 70 mss/year. Query. Length: 1,000-2,500 words; prefers 10-12 page mss. Pays $25-125.

Photos: Send photos with ms. Reviews b&w contact sheets, negatives and 8x10 prints. Captions and identification of subjects required. Buys one-time rights.

Tips: "In our publication, writing style and/or expertise is not the determining factor. Beginning writers with martial arts expertise may submit. Trends in magazine publishing that freelance writers should be aware of include the use of less body copy, better (and interesting) photos to be run large with 'story' caps. If the photos are poor and the reader can't grasp the whole story by looking at photos and copy, forget it."

INSIDE KUNG-FU, The Ultimate In Martial Arts Coverage!, Unique Publications, 4201 Vanowen Pl., Burbank CA 91505. (818)845-2656. Editor: Dave Cater. 75% freelance written. Monthly magazine covering martial arts for those with "traditional, modern, athletic and intellectual tastes. The magazine slants toward little-known martial arts, and little-known aspects of established martial arts." Circ. 100,000. Pays on publication. Publishes ms an average of 6 months after acceptance. Byline given. Buys first North American serial rights. Submit seasonal/holiday material 4 months in advance. Simultaneous queries, and simultaneous and photocopied submissions OK. Computer printout submissions acceptable; no dot-matrix. SASE. Reports in 3 weeks on queries; 4 weeks on mss. Sample copy $2.50 with 9x12 SAE and 5 first class stamps; free writer's guidelines.

Nonfiction: Expose (topics relating to the martial arts); historical/nostalgic; how-to (primarily technical materials); cultural/philosophical; interview/profile; personal experience; photo feature; and technical. "Articles must be technically or historically accurate." No "sports coverage, first-person articles, or articles which constitute personal aggrandizement." Buys 100 mss/year. Query or send complete ms. Length: 10-15 pages, typewritten and double-spaced.

Photos: Send photos with accompanying ms. Reviews b&w contact sheets, b&w negatives and 8x10 b&w prints. "Photos are paid for with payment for ms." Captions and model release required.

Fiction: Adventure, historical, humorous, mystery and suspense. "Fiction must be short (1,000-2,000 words) and relate to the martial arts. We buy very few fiction pieces." Buys 2-3 mss/year.

Tips: "The writer may have a better chance of breaking in at our publication with short articles and fillers since smaller pieces allow us to gauge individual ability, but we're flexible—quality writers get published period. The most frequent mistakes made by writers in completing an article for us are ignoring photo requirements and model releases (always number one—and who knows why? All requirements are spelled out in writer's guidelines)."

KARATE/KUNG-FU ILLUSTRATED, (formerly *Karate Illustrated*), Rainbow Publications, Inc., 1813 Victory Place, Burbank CA 91504. (818)843-4444. Publisher: Michael James. 80% freelance written. Eager to work with new/unpublished writers. Emphasizes karate and kung fu from the traditional standpoint and training techniques. Monthly magazine. Circ. 80,000. Pays on publication. Buys all rights. Photocopied submissions OK. Reports in 1-2 weeks. Sample copy for 8½x11 SASE.

Nonfiction: Expose, historical, how-to, informational, interview, new product, opinion, photo feature, technical and travel. Need historical and contemporary Kung Fu pieces, including styles, how-tos, Chinese philosophy. Buys 6 mss/issue. Query or submit complete ms. Pays $100-200.

Photos: Purchased with or without accompanying ms. Submit 5x7 or 8x10 b&w or color transparencies. Total purchase price for ms includes payment for photos.

Fillers: Query.

Tips: "Style must be concise, authoritative and in third person."

‡OFFICIAL KARATE, 351 W. 54th St., New York NY 10019. Editor: Al Weiss. Managing Editor: Alan Paul. 80% freelance written. Eager to work with new/unpublished writers. A bimonthly magazine for karatemen or those interested in the martial arts. Circ. 100,000. Pays on publication. Publishes ms an average of 3 months after acceptance. Rights purchased vary with author and material; generally, first publication rights. Pays 50% kill fee. Byline given. Will consider photocopied submissions. Reports in 1 month.

Nonfiction: "Biographical material on leading and upcoming karateka, tournament coverage, controversial subjects on the art ('Does Karate Teach Hate?', 'Should the Government Control Karate?', etc.). We cover the 'little man' in the arts rather than devote all space to established leaders or champions; people and happenings in out-of-the-way areas along with our regular material." Informational, how-to, interview, profile, spot news. Buys 60-70 mss/year. Query or submit complete ms. Length: 1,000-3,000 words. Pays $50-200.

Photos: Reviews b&w contact sheets or prints. Pays $10-15.

Tips: "We need articles on fighting and self-defense techniques; interviews with leading martial artists; exercise/weight training; nutrition; and training pieces for the karate fighter."

Miscellaneous

BALLS AND STRIKES, Amateur Softball Association, 2801 NE 50th St., Oklahoma City OK 73111. (405)424-5266. Editor: Bill Plummer III. 30% freelance written. Works with a small number of new/unpublished writers each year. "Only national monthly tabloid covering amateur softball." Circ. 254,000. Pays on publication. Publishes ms an average of 2 months after acceptance. Buys first rights. Byline given. Computer printout submissions acceptable; no dot-matrix. Reports in 3 weeks. Free sample copy.

Nonfiction: General interest, historical/nostalgic, interview/profile and technical. Query. Length: 2-3 pages. Pays $50-65.

Tips: "We generally like shorter features because we try to get many different features in each issue. There is a possibility we will be using more freelance material in the future."

BASKETBALL WEEKLY, 17820 E. Warren, Detroit MI 48224. (313)881-9554. Publisher: Roger Stanton. Editor: Matt Marsom. 20 issues during season, September-May. Circ. 45,000. Buys all rights. Pays on publication. Sample copy for SASE and $1. Reports in 2 weeks.

Nonfiction, Photos and Fillers: Current stories on teams and personalities in high school, college and pro basketball. Length: 800-1,200 words. Pays $55. 8x10 b&w glossy photos purchased with mss. Also uses newsbreaks. Do not send general basketball information.

Tips: "Include information about your background that qualifies you to do a particular story."

FLORIDA RACQUET JOURNAL, Racquetball-Sports, Florida Racquet Journal, Inc., Box 11657, Jacksonville FL 32239. (904)721-3660. Editor: Norm Blum. Managing Editor: Kathy Blum. Monthly tabloid covering racquetball in the Southeast. 50% freelance written. Circ. 20,000. Pays on acceptance. Byline given. Makes work-for-hire assignments and buys second (reprint) rights to material originally published elsewhere. Offers $25 kill fee. Submit seasonal/holiday material 3 months in advance. Simultaneous queries, and simultaneous, photocopied and previously published submissions OK. Computer printout submissions acceptable. Reports in 2 weeks. Sample copy for $1, SAE, and 2 first class stamps.
Nonfiction: Book excerpts (from racquetball books); expose (of racquetball clubs); historical/nostalgic; humor; new product; personal experience. "No how-to or instructional articles." Buys 12-15 mss/year. Query. Length: 400-900 words. Pays $10-40.
Columns/Departments: Horoscope, crossword puzzle, and health items—all for racquetball players. Buys 36 mss/year. Query. Length: 400-800 words. Pays $10-30.
Fiction: Humorous. Buys variable number mss/year. Query. Length: 500-1,500 words. Pays $10-30.
Poetry: Free verse. Buys variable number/year. Length: 30-60 lines. Pays $5-10.
Fillers: Clippings, jokes, gags, anecdotes, short humor, newsbreaks. Length: 30-50 words. Pays $1-5.
Tips: "We don't want your opinion—let the subject tell the story. If we like your first article we'll keep using you."

INDIANA RACQUET SPORTS, 207 S. Main, Box 216, Frankfort IN 46041. (317)654-6721. Editor: Michael Curts. 10-20% freelance written. Eager to work with new/unpublished writers. Monthly tabloid newspaper. Circ. 8,000. Pays on publication. Publishes ms an average of 1 month after acceptance. Byline given. Buys first and second rights to the same material. Submit seasonal/holiday material 2 months in advance. Simultaneous, photocopied and previously published submissions OK. Computer printout submissions acceptable. Reports in 2 weeks. Sample copy for 9x12 SAE and 2 first class stamps; writer's guidelines for business size SAE and 1 first class stamp.
Nonfiction: Health/nutrition; any racquet sport with Indiana connection—tennis, platform tennis, squash, table tennis, badminton, racquetball. Length: open. Pays $20 minimum. Sometimes pays the expenses of writers on assignment.
Photos: Send photos with ms. Pays $5-10 minimum for 5x7 b&w prints. Buys one-time rights.
Columns/Departments: Buys 12 mss/year. Query. Length: open. Pays $20 minimum.
Fillers: Buys 50/year. Length: 75 words maximum.

‡INSIDE RUNNING & FITNESS, "The Tabloid Magazine That Runs Texas", Inside Running, 9514 Bristlebrook Dr., Houston TX 77083. (713)498-3208. Editor: Joanne Schmidt. 50% freelance written. A monthly tabloid covering running and fitness. "Our audience is Texas runners and triathletes who may also be into cross training with biking and swimming." Circ. 10,000. Pays on acceptance. Publishes ms an average of 3 months after acceptance. Byline given. Buys first rights, one-time rights, second serial (reprint) rights and all rights. Submit seasonal/holiday material 2 months in advance. Previously published submissions OK. Reports in 1 month on queries; 6 weeks on mss. Sample copy $1.25; writer's guidelines for #10 SAE with 1 first class stamp.
Nonfiction: Book excerpts, essays, exposé, general interest, historical/nostalgic, humor, inspirational, interview/profile, opinion, photo feature, technical and travel. No personal experience such as "Why I Love to Run," "How I Ran My First Marathon." Buys 18 mss/year. Query with published clips, or send complete ms. Length: 500-2,500 words. Pays $100 maximum for assigned articles; $50 maximum for unsolicited articles.
Photos: Send photos with submission. Reviews contact sheets and 5x7 prints. Offers $25 maximum/photo. Captions required. Buys one-time rights.
Columns/Departments: Send complete ms. Length: 500-600 words. Pays $35 maximum.
Fiction: Adventure, fantasy, historical, horror, humorous, mainstream, mystery, science fiction, slice-of-life vignettes and suspense. No stories on how a character started running (or what made him take up running) and how it solved all his problems. Buys 6 mss/year. Send complete ms. Length: 500-2,000 words. Pays $10-50.
Fillers: Buys 3/year. Length: 100-200 words. Pays $15 maximum; may pay in copies.
Tips: "Writers should be familiar with the sport and understand race strategies, etc. The basic who, what, where, when and how also applies. The best way to break into our publication is to submit brief (3 or 4 paragraphs) writeups on road races to be used in the Results section."

INTERNATIONAL OLYMPIC LIFTER, IOL Publications, 3916 Eagle Rock, Box 65855, Los Angeles CA 90065. (213)257-8762. Editor: Bob Hise. Managing Editor: Herb Glossbrenner. 20% freelance written. Eager to work with new/unpublished writers. Bimonthly magazine covering the Olympic sport of weight lifting. Circ. 10,000. Pays on publication. Publishes ms an average of 3 months after acceptance. Byline given. Offers $25 kill fee. Buys one-time rights or negotiable rights. Submit seasonal/holiday material 5 months in advance. Photocopied submissions OK. Reports in 6 weeks. Sample copy $2.50; writer's guidelines for SAE and 4 first class stamps.
Nonfiction: Training articles, contest reports, diet—all related to Olympic weight lifting. Buys 6 mss/year.

Query. Length: 250-2,000 words. Pays $25-100. Pays expenses of writers on assignment.

Photos: Action (competition and training). State availability of photos. Pays $1-5 for 5x7 b&w prints. Identification of subjects required.

Poetry: Dale Rhoades, poetry editor. Light verse, traditional—related to Olympic lifting. Buys 6-10 poems/year. Submit maximum 3 poems. Length: 12-24 lines. Pays $10-20.

Tips: "First—a writer must be acquainted with Olympic-style weightlifting. Since we are an international publication we do not tolerate ethnic, cultural, religious or political inclusions. Since 1987 will be lead-up year to Olympics in Seoul, Korea, Olympic-slanted articles are good. A new American weightlifting association has been formed. Articles relating to AWA are readily accepted."

‡**MOUNTAIN NEWS**, Outdoor Access Publications, 1612 W. 3rd Ave., Vancouver, British Columbia V6J 1K2 Canada. (604)732-1351. Editor: David Milligan. 85% freelance written. A quarterly magazine covering outdoor adventure sports for outdoor enthusiasts interested in self-propelled experiences: hiking, kayaking, mountain biking, backpacking, ski touring, telemarking, etc. Circ. 42,000. Pays on publication. Publishes ms an average of 2 months after acceptance. Byline given. Buys first rights, second serial (reprint) rights or other rights. Submit seasonal/holiday material 4 months in advance. Photocopied and previously published submissions OK. Computer printout submissions acceptable. Reports in 1 month. Free sample copy and writer's guidelines.

Nonfiction: General interest; historical/nostalgic; how-to (related to backpacking, hiking, ski touring); interview/profile (famous people of hiking/climbing); and travel (unique destinations for outdoor enthusiasts). No trip reports. Buys 20 mss/year. Query with published clips. Length: 500-2,000 words. Pays 5-7¢/word; sometimes trades for backpacking equipment.

Photos: State availability of photos with submissions, or send photos with submission if possible. Offers no additional payment for inside photos accepted with ms. Pays $150 for cover photo. Identification of subjects required.

Columns/Departments: Destinations (unique outdoor adventure destinations), 1,500 words; In Retrospect (anecdotal and reminiscent look at people of the past), 500-800 words; and Safety (common safety hints on outdoor pursuits), 800-1,000 words. Buys 16 mss/year. Query with published clips. Length: 500-1,500 words. Pays 5-7¢/word.

Fillers: Anecdotes and short humor. Buys 5/year. Length: 50-500 words. Pays 5-7¢/word.

NATIONAL RACQUETBALL, Publication Management, Inc., P.O. Drawer 6126, Clearwater FL 33518. Publisher: Joe Massarelli. Editorial Director: Chuck Leve. For racquetball players of all ages. Monthly magazine. 40% freelance written. Eager to work with new/unpublished writers. Circ. 39,000. Pays on publication. Publishes ms an average of 3 months after acceptance. Buys all rights. Byline given. Submit seasonal/holiday material 2-3 months in advance. Computer printout submissions acceptable. Publishes ms an average of 3 months after acceptance; no dot-matrix. Sample copy $2.

Nonfiction: How-to (play better racquetball or train for racquetball); interview (with players or others connected with racquetball business); opinion (usually used in letters but sometimes fullblown opinion features on issues confronting the game); photo feature (on any subject mentioned); profile (short pieces with photos on women or men players interesting in other ways or on older players); health (as it relates to racquetball players—food, rest, eye protection, etc.); and fashion. No material on tournament results. Buys 4 mss/issue. Query with clips of published work. Length: 500-2,500 words. Pays $50/published page. Sometimes pays the expenses of writers on assignment.

Photos: State availability of photos or send photos with ms. Offers no additional payment for photos accompanying ms. Uses b&w prints or color transparencies. Buys one-time rights. Captions and model releases required. Pays $5/b&w photo and $10/color.

Fiction: Adventure, humorous, mystery, romance, science fiction and suspense. "Whatever an inventive mind can do with racquetball." Buys 3 mss/year. Send complete ms. Pays $50/published page.

Tips: "Break into *National Racquetball* by writing for monthly features—short pieces about racquetball players you know. We need more contributions from all over the country. Our object is national and international coverage of the sport of racquetball."

‡**NEW YORK RUNNING NEWS**, New York Road Runners Club, 9 E. 89th St., New York NY 10128. (212)860-2280. Editor: Ken Glass. Managing Editor: Raleigh Mayer. 75% freelance written. A bimonthly regional sports magazine covering running, racewalking, nutrition and fitness. Material should be of interest to members of the New York Road Runners Club. Circ. 45,000. Pays on publication. Time to publication varies. Byline given. Offers ⅓ kill fee. Buys first North American serial rights. Submit seasonal/holiday material 4 months in advance. Simultaneous submissions and previously published submissions OK. Computer printout submissions acceptable; no dot-matrix. Reports in 1 month. Sample copy for 9x12 SAE with $1.75 postage.

Nonfiction: Running and marathon articles. Special issues include N.Y.C Marathon (submissions in by August 1). No non-running stories. Buys 25 mss/year. Query. Length: 750-1,750 words. Pays $50-250. Pays documented expenses of writers on assignment.

Fiction: Running stories. Buys 25 mss/year. Query. Length: 750-1,750 words. Pays $50-250.
Poetry: Nancy Quinn, poetry editor. Avant-garde, free verse, haiku, light verse, and traditional. Submit maximum 2 poems. Length: 3-50 lines. No cash payment for poetry.
Fillers: Anecdotes. Length: 250-500 words. No payment for fillers.
Tips: "Be knowlegeable about the sport of running. Write like a runner."

PRIME TIME SPORTS & FITNESS, GND Prime Time Publishing, Box 6091, Evanston IL 60204. (312)864-8113/276-2143. Editor: Dennis A. Dorner. Managing Editor: Nicholas J. Schmitz. 75-80% freelance written. Eager to work with new/unpublished writers. A monthly magazine covering racquet and health club sports and fitness. Circ. 35,000. Pays on publication. Publishes ms an average of 5 months after acceptance. Byline given. Buys all rights; will assign back to author in 85% of cases. Submit seasonal/holiday material 3 months in advance. Photocopied and previously published submissions OK. No simultaneous submissions. Computer printout submissions acceptable; no dot-matrix. Reports in 2 weeks. Sample copy for SAE and 3 first class stamps; writer's guidelines for business size SAE and 1 first class stamp.
Nonfiction: Book excerpts (fitness and health); expose (in tennis, fitness, racquetball, health clubs, diets); adult (slightly risque and racy fitness); historical/nostalgic (history of exercise and fitness movements); how-to (expert instructional pieces on any area of coverage); humor (large market for funny pieces on health clubs and fitness); inspirational (on how diet and exercise combine to bring you a better body, self); interview/profile; new product; opinion (only from recognized sources that know what they are talking about); personal experience (definitely—humor); photo feature (on related subjects); technical (on exercise and sport); travel (related to fitness, tennis camps, etc.); news reports (on racquetball, handball, tennis, running events). Special issues: Swimsuit and Resort Issue (March); Baseball Preview (April); Summer Fashion (July); Fall Fashion (October); Ski Issue (November); Christmas Gifts and related articles (December). " We love short articles that get to the point. No articles on local only tennis and racquetball tournaments without national appeal except when from Chicago/Milwaukee area." Buys 50 mss/year. Length: 2,000 + words maximum. Pays $20-150. Sometimes pays the expenses of writers on assignment.
Photos: Eric Matye, photo editor. Send photos with ms. Pays $5-75 for b&w prints. Captions, model releases and identification of subjects required. Buys all rights, "but returns 75% of photos to submitter."
Columns/Departments: Linda Jefferson, column/department editor. New Products; Fitness Newsletter; Handball Newsletter; Racquetball Newsletter; Tennis Newsletter; News & Capsule Summaries; Fashion Spot (photos of new fitness and bathing suits); related subjects. Buys 100 mss/year. Send complete ms. Length: 50-250 words ("more if author has good handle to cover complete columns"). Pays $5-25.
Fiction: Joy Kiefer, fiction editor. Erotica (if related to fitness club); fantasy (related to subjects); humorous (definite market); religious ("no God-is-my shepherd, but Body-is-God's-temple OK"); romance (related subjects). "No raunchy or talking down exercise stories, upbeat is what we want." Buys 10 mss/year. Send complete ms. Length: 500-2,500 words maximum. Pays $20-150.
Poetry: Free verse, haiku, light verse, traditional on related subjects. Length: up to 150 words. Pays $10-25.
Fillers: Linda Jefferson, fillers editor. Clippings, jokes, gags, anecdotes, short humor, newsbreaks. Buys 400/year. Length: 25-200 words. Pays $5-15.
Tips: "Send us articles dealing with court club sports, exercise and nutrition that exemplify an upbeat 'you can do it' attitude. Good short fiction or humorous articles can break in. Expert knowledge of any related subject can bring assignments; any area is open. A humorous/knowledgable columnist in weight lifting, aerobics, running and nutrition is presently needed. We review the author's work on a nonpartial basis. We consider everything as a potential article, but are turned off by credits, past work and degrees. We have a constant demand for well-written articles on instruction, health and trends in both. Other articles needed are professional sports training techniques, fad diets, tennis and fitness resorts, photo features with aerobic routines. A frequent mistake made by writers is length—articles are too long. When we assign an article, we want it newsy if it's news and opinion if opinion. Too many writers are incapable of this task."

RACING PIGEON PICTORIAL, The Racing Pigeon Publishing Co. Ltd., 19 Doughty St., London WCIN 2PT, England. Editor-in-Chief: Colin Osman. 50-60% freelance written. Eager to work with new/unpublished writers. Emphasizes racing pigeons for "all ages, occupations and backgrounds, both sexes. Stress on international aspects, reports on non-UK subjects welcome." Monthly magazine. Circ. 13,000. Pays on publication.

ALWAYS submit mss or queries with a stamped, self-addressed envelope (SASE) within your country or International Reply Coupons (IRCs) purchased from the post office for other countries.

Publishes ms an average of 3 months after acceptance. Buys first rights, first and second rights to the same material, and second (reprint) rights to material originally published elsewhere. Submit seasonal/holiday material 3 months in advance. Photocopied and previously published submissions OK. Computer printout submissions acceptable; prefers letter-quality to dot-matrix. SAE and IRCs. Reports in 5 weeks. Sample copy $2.

Nonfiction: Michael Shepherd, articles editor. How-to (methods of famous fanciers, treatment of diseases, building lofts, etc.); historical (histories of pigeon breeds); informational (practical information for pigeon fanciers); interview (with winning fanciers); and technical (where applicable to pigeons). "Don't bother, if you're not a specialist." Buys 4 mss/issue. Submit complete ms. Length: 6,000 words minimum. Pays $50/page minimum. Sometimes pays the expenses of writers on assignment.

Photos: Rick Osman, photo editor. Purchased with or without accompanying ms or on assignment. Captions required. Send 8x10 b&w glossy prints or 2¼x2¼ or 35mm color transparencies.

Tips: "Principal need is for information, if necessary our staff completely rewrites so that we can use the article. If in doubt send everything connected with the article. More color material will be used, so more color originals will be required."

THE RUNNER, 1 Park Ave., New York NY 10016. Editor-in-Chief: Marc Bloom. Emphasizes the world of running in the broadest scope with its main thrust in jogging, roadrunning and marathoning/fitness and health. 75% freelance written. Prefers to work with published/established writers; works with a small number of new/unpublished writers each year. Monthly magazine. Circ. 275,000. Pays on acceptance. Publishes ms an average of 6 months after acceptance. Buys most first North American serial rights. Pays 20% kill fee. Byline given. Submit seasonal/holiday material 6 months in advance. Electronic submissions OK "but not on unsolicited manuscripts, only on assignment." Computer printout submissions acceptable; prefers letter-quality to dot-matrix. Reports in 2-3 weeks. Free sample copy.

Nonfiction: Profiles, body science, event coverage, training, lifestyle, sports medicine, nutrition and humor. Buys 5-6 mss/issue. Query with clips of published work. Length: 2,000-3,000 words. Pays usually $500-1,000. Pays the expenses of writers on assignment.

Photos: State availability of photos. Pay is negotiable for b&w contact sheets and 35mm color transparencies. Buys one-time rights. Captions required.

Columns/Departments: Training, statistical listings, humor, food, medicine, and physiology. Regular columnists used. Buys 3-4/issue. Length: 900-1,200 words. Pays $200 and up.

Warmups: Short news items, whimsical items, and advice on improving running. Length: 100-500 words. Pays $75.

Tips: "The writer may have a better chance of breaking in at our publication with short articles and fillers because we find it risky to commit to larger pieces with people new to us. The writer must be informed about running and its lifestyle and be able to communicate the piece with authority. Our readers (and we) can spot fakers. More attention will be given to older runners (35 and up), nutrition, and matters of special concern to women runners."

RUNNER'S WORLD, Rodale Press, 33 E. Minor St., Emmaus PA 18049. (215)967-5171. Editorial Director: James C. McCullagh. Managing Editor: David Bumke. 25% freelance written. Prefers to work with published/established writers. Monthly magazine covering the world of recreational and competitive running. Circ. 300,000. Pays on publication. Publishes ms an average of 3 months after acceptance. Byline given. Offers 25% kill fee. Buys first serial rights and second serial (reprint) rights. Submit seasonal/holiday material 4 months in advance (query only). Electronic submissions OK via Unison. Computer printout submissions acceptable. Reports in 1 month. Sample copy for SAE; writer's guidelines for SAE.

Nonfiction: How-to (training pieces); profile; photo feature (outstanding races or unusual personalities); technical (running mechanics, new developments in shoes); and medical and diet. No inspirational ("our readers already know about the joys and frustrations of running"), fiction or poetry. Buys 36 mss/year. Query with or without published clips. Length: 1,000-3,000 words. Pays $300-1,500. Sometimes pays the expenses of writers on assignment.

Departments: Dan Ferrara, assistant managing editor. Research-oriented news with direct impact on runners. Length: 100-1,000 words. Pays $75-500.

SIGNPOST MAGAZINE, 16812 36th Ave. W., Lynnwood WA 98037. Publisher: Washington Trails Association. Editor: Ann L. Marshall. About hiking, backpacking and similar trail-related activities, mostly from a Pacific Northwest viewpoint. 10% freelance written. Monthly. Will consider any rights offered by author. Buys 12 mss/year. Pays on publication. Publishes ms an average of 6 months after acceptance. Free sample copy. Will consider photocopied submissions. Reports in 3 weeks. Query or submit complete ms. Computer printout submissions acceptable; prefers letter-quality to dot-matrix.

Nonfiction and Photos: "Most material is donated by subscribers or is staff-written. Payment for purchased material is low, but a good way to break into print or spread a particular point of view."

Tips: "We cover only *self-propelled* outdoor sports; won't consider mss about trail bikes, snowmobiles, power boats. Since we are so specialized, we look for quality and appropriateness rather than length of item."

SKYDIVING, Box 1520, Deland FL 32721. (904)736-9779. Editor: Michael Truffer. 10% freelance written. Monthly tabloid featuring skydiving for sport parachutists, worldwide dealers and equipment manufacturers. Circ. 7,200. Average issue includes 3 feature articles and 3 columns of technical information. Pays on publication. Publishes ms an average of 2 months after acceptance. Byline given. Buys one-time rights. Simultaneous, photocopied and previously published submissions OK, if so indicated. Electronic submissions OK via IBM PC. Computer printout submissions acceptable. Reports in 1 month. Sample copy $2; writer's guidelines with SASE and 73¢ postage.
Nonfiction: "Send us news and information on equipment, techniques, events and outstanding personalities who skydive. We want articles written by people who have a solid knowledge of parachuting." No personal experience or human-interest articles. Query. Length: 500-1,000 words. Pays $25-100.
Photos: State availability of photos. Reviews 5x7 and larger b&w glossy prints. Offers no additional payment for photos accepted with ms. Captions required.
Fillers: Newsbreaks. Length: 100-200 words. Pays $25 minimum.
Tips: "The most frequent mistake made by writers in completing articles for us is that the writer isn't knowledgable about the sport of parachuting."

Skiing and Snow Sports

AMERICAN SKATING WORLD, Independent Publication of the American Ice Skating Community, Business Communications Inc., 2545-47 Brownsville Rd., Pittsburgh PA 15210. (412)885-7600. Editor: Robert A. Mock. Assistant Editor: Doug Graham. 70% freelance written. Monthly tabloid on ice skating. Circ. 15,000. Pays on publication on the tenth day of the following month. Publishes ms an average of 2-3 months after acceptance. Byline given. Buys first North American serial rights and occasional second serial rights. Submit seasonal/holiday material 3 months in advance. Computer printout submissions acceptable; prefers letter-quality to dot-matrix. Reports in 6 weeks. Sample copy and writer's guidelines $1.
Nonfiction: Expose; general interest; historical/nostalgic; how-to (technique in figure skating); humor; inspirational; interview/profile; new product; opinion; personal experience; photo feature; technical and travel. Special issues include recreational (July), classic skaters (August), annual fashion issue (September), adult issue (December). No fiction. Buys 200 mss/year. Send complete ms. "Include phone number; response time longer without it." Length: 600-1,000 words. Pays $25-100. Usually does not pay the expenses of writers on assignment.
Photos: Bill Simmons, photo editor. Send photos with query or ms. Reviews color transparencies and b&w prints. Pays $5 for b&w; $15 for color. Identification of subjects required. Buys all rights for b&w; one-time rights for color.
Columns/Departments: Bill Simmons, column/department editor. Buys 60 mss/year. Send complete ms. Length: 500-750 words. Pays $25-75.
Fillers: Clippings and anecdotes. No payment for fillers.
Tips: Event coverage is most open to freelancers, confirm with assistant editor to ensure event has not been assigned. "AP Style Guidelines are the primary style source. Short, snappy paragraphs desired. Questions are welcome, call assistant editor 10 a.m. to 5 p.m. EST."

SKI, 380 Madison Ave., New York NY 10017. (212)687-3000. Editor: Dick Needham. "We are backlogged with submissions and prefer not to receive unsolicited submissions at this time."

SKI RACING MAGAZINE, International Journal of Skiing, Ski Racing International, 2 Bentley Ave., Poultney VT 05764. (802)287-9090. Editor: Don A. Metivier. Tabloid covering major ski competition events worldwide for the serious skier and ski industry person. 50% freelance written. Works with a small number of new/unpublished writers each year. Published 20 times during the ski season (September-April). Circ. 40,000. Pays on publication. Publishes ms an average of 3 days after acceptance. Byline given. Buys one-time rights. Reports "at once, because of the time frame of events we cover." Electronic submissions OK on IBM PC, TRS 100 and Hewlett Packard, but requires hard copy also. Computer printout submissions acceptable; no dot-matrix. Free sample copy.
Nonfiction: "We cover only news and interviews with those making it. Prefer not to get opinion from writers." Buys 200 mss/year. Query with clips of published work. Length: "depends on the story; from minimum of a paragraph and list of top 5 finishers to maximum of 500-750 words." Pays $25-50 for news stories; $50-100 for longer assignments; negotiates fees prior to assignment on interviews. Sometimes pays the expenses of writers on assignment.
Photos: Pays $10-25 for photos; $50 for covers, action photos, and candids for picture pages and interviews. $50 and up for photos (b&w only) used by advertisers.
Tips: "It's frustrating working with freelance writers who miss deadlines. We publish 3 times a month—old news isn't news. The writer has a better chance of breaking in at our publication with short articles and fillers

since we have a large group of regular writers anxious to write ski stories. The most frequent mistake made by writers in completing an article is lack of detail. Most writers are not good reporters; they will look up a word, but not recheck facts."

SKIING, CBS Magazines, 1 Park Ave., New York NY 10016. (212)503-3920. Editor: Bill Grout. 40% freelance written. A magazine published 7 times a year. *"Skiing* is a service magazine for skiing enthusiasts." Circ. 440,000. Pays on publication. Publishes ms an average of 4 months after acceptance. Byline given. Offers ½ kill fee. Buys first North American serial rights. Submit seasonal/holiday material 8 months in advance. Computer printout submissions acceptable; prefers letter-quality to dot-matrix. Reports in 6 weeks on queries; 2 months on mss.
Nonfiction: Essays, how-to, humor, interview/profile, personal experience and travel. No fiction, ski equipment evaluations or 'How I Learned to Ski' stories. Buys 35 mss/year. Query with published clips. Length: 500-2,000 words. Pays $50-1,000 for assigned articles; pays $50-750 for unsolicited articles. Pays the expenses of writers on assignment.
Photos: State availability of photos with submission. Reviews contact sheets and negatives. Offers $50-300/photo. Captions, model releases and identification of subjects required. Buys one-time rights.

SNOWMOBILE CANADA, Suite 202, 2077 Dundas St. E., Mississauga, Ontario L4X 1M2 Canada. (416)624-8218. Editor: Reg Fife. Snowmobiling magazine published in September, October and November "to satisfy the needs of Canada's snowmobilers from coast to coast." Circ. 60,000. Pays on publication. Byline given. Buys first rights. Submit seasonal/holiday material "by July for fall publication." Simultaneous queries acceptable. Computer printout submissions acceptable. Reports in 1 month on queries; 2 months on mss. Free sample copy.
Nonfiction: Personal experience (on snowmobiling in Canada); photo feature (nature in winter); technical (new snowmobile developments); travel (snowmobile type). "We look for articles on nature as it relates to snowmobile use; trail systems in Canada; wilderness tips; the racing scene; ice fishing using snowmobiles, maintenance tips and new model designs." Buys 12 mss/year. Query or send complete ms. Length: 800-2,000 words. Pays $75-150.
Photos: Captions required. Buys one-time rights.

SNOWMOBILE WEST, 520 Park Ave., Box 981, Idaho Falls ID 83402. Editor: Steve Janes. For recreational snowmobile riders and owners of all ages. Magazine; 48 pages. 5% freelance written. Publishes 4 issues each winter. Circ. 200,000. Buys first North American serial rights. Pays kill fee if previously negotiated at time of assignment. Byline given on substantive articles of two pages or more. Buys 5 mss/year. Pays on publication. Publishes ms an average of 3 months after acceptance. Free sample copy and writer's guidelines. Reports in 2 months. Articles for one season are generally photographed and written the previous season. Query. Computer printout submissions acceptable.
Nonfiction and Photos: Articles about snowtrail riding in the Western U.S.; issues affecting snowmobilers; and maps of trail areas with good color photos and b&w. Pays 3¢/word; $5/b&w; $10/color. B&w should be 5x7 or 8x10 glossy print; color should be 35mm transparencies or larger, furnished with mss. With a story of 1,000 words, typically a selection of 5 b&w and 5 color photos should accompany. Longer stories in proportion. Length: 500-2,000 words.
Tips: "It's rewarding finding a freelance writer who understands the nature and personality of our publication. It's annoying when writers say they have the story that we *really need* to use."

Soccer

‡SOCCER AMERICA, Box 23704, Oakland CA 94623. (415)549-1414. Editor-in-Chief: Lynn Berling-Manuel. For a wide range of soccer enthusiasts. Weekly tabloid. 10% freelance written. Circ. 12,000. Pays on publication. Buys all rights. Byline given. Submit seasonal/holiday material 30 days in advance. Reports in 2 months. Publishes ms an average of 2 months after acceptance. Sample copy and writer's guidelines $1.
Nonfiction: Expose (why a pro franchise isn't working right, etc.); historical; how-to; informational (news features); inspirational; interview; photo feature; profile; and technical. "No 'Why I Like Soccer' articles in 1000 words or less. It's been done." Buys 1-2 mss/issue. Query. Length: 200-1,500 words. Pays 50¢/inch minimum.
Photos: Photos purchased with or without accompanying ms or on assignment. Captions required. Pays $12 for 5x7 or larger b&w glossy prints. Query.
Tips: "Freelancers mean the addition of editorial vitality. New approaches and new minds can make a world of difference. But if they haven't familiarized themselves with the publication . . . total waste of my time and theirs."

Tennis

‡RACQUET, Heather and Pine International, Room 204, 32 W. 39th St. New York NY 10018. (212)221-6990. Editor: H.K. Pickens. 65% freelance written. Eager to work with new/unpublished writers. A quarterly magazine covering tennis and the tennis lifestyle. "*Racquet* is a fancy tennis/lifestyle magazine targeted at the private club and resort markets." Circ. 102,000. Pays on publication. Publishes ms an average of 5 months after acceptance. Byline given. Offers variable kill fee. Buys first serial rights. Submit seasonal/holiday material 3 months in advance. Simultaneous, photocopied and previously published submissions OK. Computer printout submissions acceptable; prefers letter-quality to dot-matrix. Reports in 3 weeks. Sample copy $3.
Nonfiction: Hank Kimmel, articles editor. Book excerpts, essays, general interest, historical/nostalgic, humor, interview/profile, personal experience, photo feature and travel. No how-to articles. Length: 800-5,000 words. Pays $100-1,000; sometimes pays in copies or premiums by mutual arrangement. Sometimes pays the expenses of writers on assignment.
Photos: Reviews contact sheets. Buys one-time rights.
Fiction: Constance Drayton, fiction editor. Experimental, historical and humorous. Must be tennis or country club related. Buys 6 mss/year. Query with published clips, or send complete ms. Length: 800-5,000 words. Pays $100-1,000.
Poetry: Kate Hodgin, poetry editor. Avant-garde and traditional—tennis or country club related. Buys 2-3 poems/year. Payment varies.
Fillers: Kate Hodgin, fillers editor. Anecdotes, facts, gags to be illustrated by cartoonist, newsbreaks and short humor. Buys 8/year. Length 100-1,500 words. Pays $25-200.
Tips: "We're open to many ideas. Manuscripts or queries are fine. Our readers expect well-written, in-depth features similar to the *New Yorker*. We use travel, fashion, tennis and 'Good Life' (spirits) features, so our needs vary."

‡TENNIS, 5520 Park Ave., Trumbull CT 06611. Publisher: Mark Adorney. Editor: Shepherd Campbell. 25% freelance written. Works with a small number of new/unpublished writers each year. For persons who play tennis and want to play it better. Monthly magazine. Circ. 500,000. Buys all rights. Byline given. Pays on publication. Publishes ms an average of 6 months after acceptance.
Nonfiction and Photos: Emphasis on instructional and reader service articles, but also seeks lively, well-researched features on personalities and other aspects of the game, as well as humor. Query. Length varies. Pays $200 minimum/article, considerably more for major features. Pays $50-150/8x10 b&w glossies; $75-350/color transparencies.
Tips: "When reading our publication the writer should note the depth of the tennis-expertise in the stories and should note the conversational, informal writing styles that are used."

Water Sports

‡DIVER, Seagraphic Publications, Ltd., 8051 River Rd., Richmond, British Columbia V6X 1X8 Canada. (604)273-4333. Publisher: Peter Vassilopoulos. Editor: Neil McDaniel. 75% freelance written. Emphasizes scuba diving, ocean science and technology (commercial and military diving) for a well-educated, outdoor-oriented readership. Published 9 times/year. Magazine; 48-56 pages. Circ. 25,000. Payment "follows publication." Buys first North American serial rights. Byline given. Query (by mail only). Submit seasonal/holiday material 3 months in advance of issue date. Computer printout submissions acceptable; prefers letter-quality to dot-matrix. SAE and IRCs. Reports in 6 weeks. Publishes ms an average of 2 months after acceptance.
Nonfiction: How-to (underwater activities such as photography, etc.); general interest (underwater oriented); humor; historical (shipwrecks, treasure artifacts, archeological); interview (underwater personalities in all spheres—military, sports, scientific or commercial); personal experience (related to diving); photo feature (marine life); technical (related to oceanography, commercial/military diving, etc.); and travel (dive resorts). No subjective product reports. Buys 40 mss/year. Submit complete ms. Length: 800-2,000 words. Pays $2.50/column inch.
Photos: "Features are mostly those describing dive sites, experiences, etc. Photo features are reserved more as specials, while almost all articles must be well illustrated with b&w prints supplemented by color transparencies." Submit photo material with accompanying ms. Pays $7 minimum for 5x7 or 8x10 glossy b&w prints; $15 minimum for 35mm color transparencies. Captions and model releases required. Buys one-time rights.
Columns/Departments: Book reviews. Submit complete ms. Length: 200 words maximum. Pays $2.50/column inch.
Fillers: Anecdotes, newsbreaks and short humor. Buys 8-10/year. Length: 50-150 words. Pays $2.50/column inch.

Tips: "It's rewarding finding a talented writer who can make ordinary topics come alive. But dealing with unsolicited manuscripts that don't even come close to being suitable for *Diver* is the most frustrating aspect of working with freelancers."

SCUBA TIMES, The Active Diver's Magazine, Poseidon Publishing Corp., Box 6268, Pensacola FL 32503. (904)478-5288. Managing Editor: Jean Jerigan. Publisher: M. Wallace Poole. 80% freelance written. Prefers to work with published/established writers. Bimonthly magazine covering scuba diving. "Our reader is the young, reasonably affluent scuba diver looking for a more exciting approach to diving than he could find in the other diving magazines." Circ. 60,000. Pays 2 months after publication. Publishes ms an average of 4 months after acceptance. Byline given. Buys first world serial rights. Computer printout submissions acceptable; no dot-matrix. Reports in 2 months. Sample copy $3. Writer's guidelines for business size SAE and 1 first class stamp.
Nonfiction: General interest; how-to; interview/profile ("of 'name' people in the sport, especially if they're currently doing something interesting"); new products (how to more effectively use them); personal experience (good underwater photography pieces); and travel (pertaining to diving). Especially want illustrated articles on avant garde diving and diving travel, such as nude diving, singles only dive clubs, deep diving, new advances in diving technology, etc. No articles without a specific theme. Buys 40 mss/year. Query with clips of published work. Length: 1,200-2,000 words. Pay varies with author. Base rate is $80/published page (30 column inches). Sometimes pays the expenses of writers on assignment.
Photos: Art Dept. "Underwater photography must be of the *highest* quality in order to catch our interest. We can't be responsible for unsolicited photo submissions." Pays $25-250 for 35mm color transparencies; reviews 8x10 b&w prints. Captions, model releases, and identification of subjects required. Buys first world rights. Enclose 9x12 SASE and postage if you want material returned.
Tips: "Our current contributors are among the top writers in the diving field. A newcomer must have a style that captures the inherent adventure of scuba diving, leaves the reader satisfied at the end of it, and makes him want to see something else by this same author soon. Writing for diving magazines has become a fairly sophisticated venture. Writers must be able to compete with the best in order to get published. We only use contributors grounded in underwater photojournalism."

SKIN DIVER, Petersen Publishing Co., 8490 Sunset Blvd., Los Angeles CA 90069. (213)657-5100. Executive Editor: Bonnie J. Cardone. Managing Editor: Connie Johnson. 85% freelance written. Eager to work with new/unpublished writers. Monthly magazine on scuba diving. "*Skin Diver* offers broad coverage of all significant aspects of underwater activity in the areas of recreation, ocean exploration, scientific research, commercial diving and technological developments." Circ. 209,676. Pays on publication. Publishes ms an average of 9 months after acceptance. Byline given. Buys one-time rights. Submit seasonal/holiday material 6 months in advance. No simultaneous submissions. Computer printout submissions acceptable. Reports in 3 weeks on queries; 3 months on mss. Sample copy $2.50; free writer's guidelines.
Nonfiction: How-to (catch game, modify equipment, etc.); interview/profile; personal experience; travel; local diving; adventure and wreck diving. No Caribbean travel; "how I learned to dive." Buys 200 mss/year. Send complete ms. Length: 300-2,000 words; 1,200 preferred. Pays $50/published page.
Photos: Send photos with query or ms. Reviews 35mm transparencies and 8x10 prints. Pays $50/published page. Captions and identification of subjects required. Buys one-time rights.
Fillers: Newsbreaks and cartoons. Length: 300 words. Pays $15 for cartoons; $50/published page.
Tips: "Forget tropical travel articles and write about local diving sites, hobbies, game diving, local and wreck diving."

‡SURFER, Surfer Publications, 33046 Calle Aviador, San Juan Capistrano CA 92675. (714)496-5922. Editor: Paul Holmes. 20% freelance written. A monthly magazine "aimed at experts and beginners with strong emphasis on action surf photography." Circ. 92,000. Pays on publication. Byline given. Buys all rights. Submit seasonal/holiday material 6 months in advance. Simultaneous and photocopied submissions OK. Electronic submissions OK via WordStar, Microsoft Word (IBM compatible), but requires hard copy also. Computer printout submissions acceptable; prefers letter-quality to dot-matrix. Reports in 1 month on queries; 10 weeks on mss. Sample copy for 8½x11" SAE with $3.50; free writer's guidelines.
Nonfiction: How-to (technique in surfing); humor, inspiratonal, interview/profile, opinion, and personal experience (all surf-related); photo feature (action surf and surf travel); technical (surfboard design); and travel (surf exploration and discovery—photos required). Buys 30-50 mss/year. Query with or without published clips, or send complete ms. Length: 500-2,500 words. Pays 10-15¢/word. Sometimes pays the expenses of writers on assignment.
Photos: Send photos with submission. Reviews 35mm negatives and transparencies. Offers $10-250/photo. Identification of subjects required. Buys one-time and reprint rights.
Columns/Departments: Our Mother Ocean (environmental concerns to surfers), 1,000-1,500 words; Surf Stories (personal experiences of surfing), 1,000-1,500 words; Reviews (surf-related movies, books),

500-1,000 words; and Sections (humorous surf-related items with b&w photos), 100-500 words. Buys 25-50 mss/year. Send complete ms. Pays 10-15¢/word.
Fiction: Surf-related adventure, fantasy, horror, humorous, and science fiction. Buys 10 mss/year. Send complete ms. Length: 750-2,000 words. Pays 10-15¢/word.
Tips: "All sections are open to freelancers but interview/profile are usually assigned. Stories must be authoritative and oriented to the hard-core surfer."

SURFING MAGAZINE, Western Empire, 2720 Camino Capistrano, San Clemente CA 92672. (714)492-7873. Editor: David Gilovich. 5% freelance written. Works with a small number of new/unpublished writers each year. Monthly magazine covering all aspects of the sport of surfing. "*Surfing Magazine* is a contemporary, beach lifestyle/surfing publication. We reach the entire spectrum of surfing enthusiasts." Circ. 85,000. Pays on publication. Publishes ms an average of 3 months after acceptance. Byline given. Buys all rights. Submit seasonal/holiday material 4 months in advance. Photocopied submissions OK. Electronic submissions OK via MS-DOS. " 'Basic' language needed." Computer printout submissions acceptable; prefers letter-quality to dot-matrix. Reports in 2 weeks. Sample copy and writer's guidelines for SAE.
Nonfiction: Book excerpts (on surfing, beach lifestyle, ocean-related); how-to (surfing-related); interview/profile (of top surfing personality); new product; photo feature (of ocean, beach lifestyle, surfing); travel (to surfing locations only). Buys 50 mss/year. Query with clips of published work or send complete ms. Length: 3,000 words maximum. Pays 10-15¢/word. Sometimes pays the expenses of writers on assignment.
Photos: Larry Moore, photo editor. State availability of photos or send photos with ms. Pays $35-500 for 35mm color transparencies; $20-75 for b&w contact sheets and negatives. Identification of subjects required. Buys one-time rights.
Columns/Departments: Bill Sharp, column/department editor. Currents—mini-features of current topical interest about surfing, beach & ocean environment. This department includes reviews of books, films, etc. Buys 36 mss/year. Query with clips of published work, if available, or send complete ms. Length: 100-500 words. Pays $75-100.
Fiction: Adventure, humorous. No fantasy fiction. Buys 3 mss/year. Send complete ms. Length: 1,000-4,000 words. Pays 10-15¢/word.
Tips: "Begin by contributing small, mini-news features for our Currents department."

SWIM MAGAZINE, R. Magnus Enterprises, Inc., Box 2168, Simi Valley CA 93062. (805)527-2708. Editor: Robert M. Hansen. 75% freelance written. Prefers to work with published/established writers. Bimonthly magazine. "*Swim Magazine* is for adults interested in swimming for fun, fitness and competition. Readers are fitness-oriented adults from varied social and professional backgrounds who share swimming as part of their lifestyle. Reader ages are evenly distributed from 20 to 90, so articles must appeal to a broad age group." Circ. 7,500. Pays approximately 4 weeks after publication. Publishes ms an average of 4 months after acceptance. Byline given. Buys first serial rights. Submit seasonal/holiday material 4 months in advance. Simultaneous queries and photocopied submissions OK. Reports in 1 month on queries; 3 months on ms. Sample copy for $2.25 and a 9x12 SAE with 7 first class stamps; free writer's guidelines.
Nonfiction: How-to (training plans and techniques); humor (sophisticated adult-oriented humor); interview/profile (people associated with fitness and competitive swimming); new product (articles describing new products for fitness and competitive training); personal experience (related to how swimming has become an integral part of one's lifestyle); travel (articles on vacation spots where swimming pools, lakes or warm ocean are available for training); diet and health (articles on diet, health and self-help that relate to, or include swimming). "Articles need to be informative as well as interesting. In addition to fitness and health articles, we are interested in exploring interesting topics dealing with swimming that have not been covered by past publications. We want to burst the myth that swimming is a boring sport or way to stay in shape." Buys 30-40 mss/year. Send complete ms. Query first on photo features and travel articles. Length: 1,000-5,000 words. Pays $3/published column inch. "No payment for articles about personal experiences."
Photos: Send photos with ms. Offers no additional payment for photos accepted with ms. Captions, model releases, and identification of subjects required. Buys one-time rights.
Tips: "Our 'how-to' articles and physiology articles best typify *Swim Magazine*'s projected style for fitness and competitive swimmers. *Swim Magazine* will accept medical guideline and diet articles only by M.D.'s and Ph.D's."

‡UNDERCURRENT, Box 1658, Sausalito CA 94965. Managing Editor: Ben Davison. 20-50% freelance written. Works with a small number of new/unpublished writers each year. Monthly consumer-oriented *scuba diving newsletter*; 12 pages. Circ. 13,000. Pays on publication. Publishes ms an average of 2 months after acceptance. Buys first rights. Pays $50 kill fee. Byline given. Simultaneous (if to other than diving publisher), photocopied and previously published submissions OK. Electronic submissions OK via IMB/Wang. Computer printout submissions acceptable. Reports in 4-6 weeks. Free sample copy and writer's guidelines; mention *Writer's Market* in request.
Nonfiction: Equipment evaluation, how-to, general interest, new product, and travel review. Buys 2

mss/issue. Query with brief outline of story idea and credentials. Will commission. Length: 2,000 words maximum. Pays 10¢/word. Sometimes pays the expenses of writers on assignment.
Fillers: Buys clippings and newsbreaks. Buys 20/year. Length: 25-500 words. Pays $5-50.

WATER SKI MAGAZINE, (formerly *World Waterskiing Magazine*), World Publications, Box 2456, Winter Park FL 32790. (305)628-4802. Publisher: Terry L. Snow. Editor: Theresa T. Temple. Magazine published 8 times/year. Covers various levels of water skiing. Circ. 80,000. Pays on publication. Byline given. Buys variable rights. Submit seasonal/holiday material 6 months in advance. Simultaneous queries, and simultaneous, photocopied, and previously published submissions OK. Reports in 3 weeks.
Nonfiction: Historical/nostalgic (anything dealing with water skiing); how-to (tips on equipment and repair of skis, bindings, etc.); humor ("always looking for a good laugh about water skiing"); inspirational (someone who beat the odds—handicapped skier, for example); interview/profile (only on assignment); photo feature (action or special effects); technical (on assignment only); travel (picturesque water skiing sites); sports medicine. No first-person accounts or fiction. Buys 10-30 mss/year. Query with or without clips of published work. Pays $150-200/feature story; $75/medical, sports medicine; $40/tips.
Photos: Tom King, senior photographer. "We need lots of sharp photos for our annual issue in October. Send photos with ms. Prefers b&w prints or contact sheet, 35mm or 2 ¼ color slides/transparencies. Model releases and identification of subjects required. Buys negotiable rights.
Columns/Departments: Buys 5-15 mss/year. Query with clips of published work. Length: 250-300 words. Pays $40-75.
Fillers: Buys 5/year. Length: 100-150 words. Pays $5-15.
Tips: "We would love to hear from good sportswriters with a lively interest in water skiing. We're especially open to features and sports medicine articles. Medical writing would require background in specialized area and proof with resume, etc."

THE WATER SKIER, Box 191, Winter Haven FL 33882. (813)324-4341. Editor: Duke Cullimore. Official publication of the American Water Ski Association. 50% freelance written. Published 7 times/year. Circ. 18,000. Buys North American serial rights only. Byline given. Buys limited amount of freelance material. Query. Pays on acceptance. Publishes ms an average of 3 months after acceptance. Reports on submissions within 10 days. Computer printout submissions acceptable "if double-spaced and standard ms requirements are followed"; prefers letter-quality to dot-matrix.
Nonfiction and Photos: Occasionally buys exceptionally offbeat, unusual text/photo features on the sport of water skiing. Emphasis on technique, methods, etc.
Tips: "Freelance writers should be aware of specializations of subject matter in magazine publishing; need for more expertise in topic; more professional writing ability."

Teen and Young Adult

Teen magazines address problems that teens in every era have faced—growing up, coping with school, friends and family, and dating. They are becoming more issue-oriented and continue to reflect the latest trends. The publications in this category are for young people aged 13-18. Publications for college students are listed in Career, College, and Alumni.

ALIVE FOR YOUNG TEENS, Christian Board of Publication, Box 179, St. Louis MO 63166. Editor: Mike Dixon. 90% freelance written. Eager to work with new/unpublished writers. Ecumenical, mainline publication with a Protestant slant; aimed at young teens. "We especially appreciate submissions of useable quality from 12- to 15-year-olds. Those in this age range should include their age with the submission. We appreciate use of humor that early adolescents would appreciate. Please keep the age group in mind." Publishes ms an average of 14 months after acceptance. Buys first rights. Computer printout submissions acceptable; prefers letter-quality to dot-matrix. Sample copy $1.
Nonfiction: "Articles should concern interesting youth, church youth groups, projects and activities. There is little chance of our taking an article not accompanied by at least 3-4 captioned b&w photos." Length: 800-1,000 words. Pays 3¢/word; photos $3-5.

Fiction: "Give us fiction concerning characters in the *Alive for Young Teens* readers' age group (12-15), dealing with problems and situations peculiar to that group." Length: 100-1,200 words. Pays 3¢/word. Uses 6-10 photo features/issue. Pays $5/photo maximum.
Photos: Send photos with ms. Submit in batches. Pays $10-20 for b&w prints.
Poetry: Length: 20 lines maximum. Pays 25¢/line.
Fillers: Puzzles, riddles and daffy definitions. Pays $10 maximum.
Tips: "A most frequent mistake made by writers in completing articles for us is missing the age-range interests."

AMERICAN NEWSPAPER CARRIER, American Newspaper Boy Press, Box 15300, Winston-Salem NC 27103. Editor: Marilyn H. Rollins. 50% freelance written. Works with a small number of new/unpublished writers each year. Usually buys all rights but may be released upon request. Pays on acceptance. Publishes ms an average of 3 months after acceptance. Queries not required. Computer printout submissions acceptable. Reports in 30 days.
Fiction: Uses a limited amount of short fiction written for teen-age newspaper carriers, male and female. It is preferable that stories be written around newspaper carrier characters. Humor, mystery and adventure plots are commonly used. No drugs, sex, fantasy, supernatural, crime or controversial themes. Length: 1,200 words. Pays $25.
Tips: "Fillers are staff-written, usually."

BOYS' LIFE, Boy Scouts of America, Magazine Division, 1325 Walnut Hill Lane, Irving TX 75062. (214)659-2000. Editor: Robert Hood. 85% freelance written. Monthly magazine covering Boy Scout activities for "ages 8-18—Boy Scouts, Cub Scouts, and others of that age group." Circ. 1.5 million. Pays on acceptance. Publishes ms an average of 6 months after acceptance. Byline given. Computer printout submissions acceptable.
Nonfiction: "Almost all articles are assigned. We do not encourage unsolicited material."
Columns/Departments: Hobby How's (1-2 paragraphs on hobby tips). Buys 60 mss/year. Send complete ms. Pays $5 minimum. Pays expenses of writers on assignment.
Fillers: Jokes (Think and Grin—1-3 sentences). Pays $1 minimum.
Tips: "The most frequent mistake made by writers is failure to read *Boys' Life*."

BREAD, Nazarene Publishing House, 6401 The Paseo, Kansas City MO 64131. (816)333-7000. Editor: Gary Sivewright. 40% freelance written. A monthly magazine for Nazarene teens. Circ. 26,000. Pays on acceptance. Publishes ms an average of 8 months after acceptance. Byline given. Buys one-time rights. Submit seasonal/holiday material 10 months in advance. Simultaneous, photocopied, and previously published submissions OK. Computer printout submissions acceptable; prefers letter-quality to dot-matrix. Reports in 6 weeks on queries; 2 months on mss. Sample copy and writer's guidelines for 9x12 SAE with 2 first class stamps.
Nonfiction: How-to and personal experience, both involving teens and teen problems and how to deal with them. Buys 70 mss/year. Send complete ms. Length: 1,200-1,500 words. Pays 3-3½¢/word.
Columns/Departments: Pays $10-40.
Fiction: Adventure, humorous and romance, all demonstrating teens living out Christian commitment in real life.

CAMPUS LIFE MAGAZINE, Christianity Today, Inc., 465 Gundersen Dr., Carol Stream IL 60188. Executive Editor: Scott Bolinder. Senior Editors: Gregg Lewis and Jim Long. Associate Editor: Chris Lutes. Assistant Editor: Diane Eble. 30% freelance written. Prefers to work with published/established writers. For a readership of young adults, high school and college age. "Though our readership is largely Christian, *Campus Life* reflects the interests of all young people—music, bicycling, photography, media and sports." Largely staff-written. "*Campus Life* is a Christian magazine that is *not* overtly religious. The indirect style is intended to create a safety zone with our readers and to reflect our philosophy that God is interested in all of life. Therefore, we publish message stories side by side with general interest, humor, etc." Monthly magazine. Circ. 180,000. Pays on acceptance. Publishes ms an average of 6 months after acceptance. Buys first serial and one-time rights. Byline given. Submit seasonal/holiday material 6 months in advance. Simultaneous, photocopied and previously published submissions OK. Computer printout submissions acceptable. Reports in 2 months. Sample copy $2; writer's guidelines for SASE.
Nonfiction: Personal experiences, photo features, unusual sports, humor, short items—how-to, college or career and travel, etc. Query or submit complete manuscript. Length: 500-3,000 words. Pays $100-300. Sometimes pays the expenses of writers on assignment.
Photos: Pays $50 minimum/8x10 b&w glossy print; $90 minimum/color transparency; $250/cover photo. Buys one-time rights.
Fiction: Stories about problems and experiences kids face. Trite, simplistic religious stories are not acceptable.
Tips: "The best ms for a freelancer to try to sell us would be a well-written first-person story (fiction or nonfic-

tion) focusing on a common struggle young people face in any area of life—intellectual, emotional, social, physical or spiritual. Most manuscripts that miss us fail in quality or style. We are always looking for good humor pieces for high school readers. These could be cartoon spreads, or other creative humorous pieces that would make kids laugh."

‡CAREERS, The Magazine for Today's Teens, E.M. Guild, Inc., 1001 Avenue of the Americas, New York NY 10018. (212)354-8877. Editor: Elizabeth Bibb. 100% freelance written. A magazine published 3 times a year covering career choices and educational opportunities for high school juniors and seniors. "*Careers* is designed to offer a taste of the working world, new career opportunities, and stories covering the best ways to reach those opportunities—through education, etc." Circ. 600,000. Pays 30 days after acceptance. Publishes ms an average of 2-3 months after acceptance. Byline given. Offers 25% kill fee. Buys first North American serial rights. Sumbit seasona/holiday material 6 months in advance. Sometimes accepts previously published submissions. Computer printout submissions acceptable; prefers letter quality to dot-matrix. Reports in 2 months on queries; 3 weeks on mss. Sample copy $2; writer's guidelines for letter size SAE with 1 first class stamp.

Nonfiction: Book excerpts, how-to, interview/profile, photo feature, travel. No humor manuscripts. Buys 25 mss/year. Query with published clips. Length: 500-1,200 words. Pays $300-800. Sometimes pays the expenses of writers on assignment.

Photos: State availability of photos with submission. Reviews contact sheets and transparencies. Offers $100 minimum/photo. Captions, model releases, and identification of subjects required. Buys one-time rights.

Columns/Departments: Globerunner (travel for teens, interesting opportunities) and Shape Up. Buys 15 mss/year. Length: 500 words. Pays $300-400.

Tips: Needs features taking "novel approaches to standard stories—resume writing, financing college, preparing for the SAT, etc."

CHRISTIAN ADVENTURER, Messenger Publishing House, Box 850, Joplin MO 64802. (417)624-7050. Editor-in-Chief: Roy M. Chappell, D.D. Managing Editor: Rosmarie Foreman. 75% freelance written. Prefers to work with published/established writers; works with a small number of new/unpublished writers each year. A denominational Sunday School take-home paper for teens, 13-19. Quarterly; 104 pages. Circ. 3,500. Pays quarterly. Publishes ms an average of 1 year after acceptance. Buys simultaneous, second serial (reprint) or one-time rights. Byline given. Submit seasonal/holiday material 1 year in advance. Photocopied and previously published submissions OK. Reports in 6 weeks. Sample copy and writer's guidelines 50¢ and 1 first class stamp.

Nonfiction: Historical (related to great events in the history of the church); informational (explaining the meaning of a Bible passage or a Christian concept); inspirational; nostalgia; and personal experience. Send complete ms. Length: 1,500-1,800 words. Pays 1¢/word.

Fiction: Adventure, historical, religious and romance. Length: 1,500-1,800 words. Pays 1¢/word.

Tips: "The most frequent mistake made by writers in completing an article for us is that they forget we are a Christian publication. They also do not follow the guidelines."

CHRISTIAN LIVING FOR SENIOR HIGHS, David C. Cook Publishing Co., 850 N. Grove, Elgin IL 60120. (312)741-2400. Editor: Anne E. Dinnan. "A take-home paper used in senior high Sunday School classes. We encourage Christian teens to write to us." 75% freelance written. Quarterly magazine; 4 pages. Pays on acceptance. Publishes ms an average of 15 months after acceptance. Buys all rights. Byline given. Computer printout submissions acceptable; prefers letter-quality to dot-matrix. Reports in 3-5 weeks. Free sample copy and writer's guidelines for SAE and 1 first class postage stamp.

Nonfiction: How-to (Sunday School youth projects); historical (with religious base); humor (from Christian perspective); inspirational and personality (nonpreachy); personal teen experience (Christian); poetry written by teens and photo feature (Christian subject). "Nothing not compatible with a Christian lifestyle. Since this is difficult to define, author must query doubtful topics." Submit complete ms. Length: 900-1,200 words. Pays $80-100; $40 for short pieces.

Fiction: Adventure (with religious theme); historical (with Christian perspective); humorous; mystery; and religious. Buys 2 mss/issue. Submit complete ms. Length: 900-1,200 words. Pays $80-100. "No preachy experiences."

Photos: Cindy Carter, photo editor. Photos purchased with or without accompanying ms or on assignment. Send contact sheet, prints or transparencies. Pays $25-40 for 8½x11 b&w photos; $50 minimum for color transparencies. "Photo guidelines available."

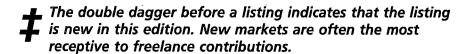

✚ **The double dagger before a listing indicates that the listing is new in this edition. New markets are often the most receptive to freelance contributions.**

Tips: "Our demand for manuscripts should increase, but most of these will probably be assigned rather than bought over-the-transom. Authors should query us, sending samples of their work. That way we can keep them on file for specific writing assignments. Our features are always short. Frequent mistake made by writers in completing articles for us is misunderstanding our market. Writing is often not Christian at all, or it's too 'Christian,' i.e. pedantic, condescending and moralistic."

CIRCLE K MAGAZINE, 3636 Woodview Trace, Indianapolis IN 46268. Executive Editor: Karen J. Pyle. 60% freelance written. "Our readership consists almost entirely of above-average college students interested in voluntary community service. They are politically and socially aware and have a wide range of interests." Published 5 times/year. Magazine; 16 pages. Circ. 12,000. Pays on acceptance. Publishes ms an average of 3 months after acceptance. Normally buys first North American serial rights. Byline given. Submit seasonal/holiday material 6 months in advance. Computer printout submissions acceptable; no dot-matrix. Reports in 1 month. Sample copy and writer's guidelines for large SASE.
Nonfiction: Articles published in *Circle K* are of two types—serious and light nonfiction. "We are interested in general-interest articles on topics concerning college students and their lifestyles, as well as articles dealing with community concerns." No "first-person confessions, family histories, or travel pieces." Recent article example: "I Hate to Critize, *But*. . ." (March 1986). Queries are preferred. Length: 2,000-2,500 words. Pays $175-250.
Photos: Purchased with accompanying ms. Captions required. Query. Total purchase price for ms includes payment for photos.
Tips: "Query should indicate author's familiarity with the field and sources. Subject treatment must be objective and in-depth, and articles should include illustrative examples and quotes from persons involved in the subject or qualified to speak on it. Humorous examples and a lighter writing style are valued when appropriate."

‡CONNECTIONS, The National Publication for High School Students, 505 Market St., Knoxville TN 37902. (615)521-0600. Editor: Bill Gubbins. Senior Editor: Peter Moore. 80% freelance written. A biweekly "magazine" covering educational subjects of interest to high school students. "*Connections* is four large posters located in high school hallways. Each issue covers a single topic (i.e., Careers, Studying, etc.)." Estab. 1986. Circ. 1.8 million readers. Pays on acceptance. Publishes ms an average of 10 weeks after acceptance. Byline sometimes given. Offers $500 kill fee. Buys first North American serial rights. Electronic submissions OK; query for compatibility. Computer printout submissions acceptable; prefers letter-quality to dot-matrix. Reports in months.
Nonfiction: General interest for high school students. Buys 18 mss/year. Query with published clips. Length: 1,500-3,500 words. Pays $1,000-2,000. Pays expenses of writers on assignment.
Tips: "Send ideas for single-topic issues."

CURRENT CONSUMER & LIFESTUDIES, The Practical Guide to Real Life Issues, General Learning Corp., 3500 Western Ave., Highland Park IL 60035. (312)432-2700. Editor: Margaret Mucklo. Senior Associate Editor: Carole Rubenstein. 90% freelance written. Monthly (during the school year) magazine on consumer and psychology issues with emphasis on life skills. "*CC&L* is an educational periodical for high school students in consumer, psychology, business, social studies, and home economic curricula nationwide." Circ. 80,000. Pays on publication. Byline given. Publishes ms an average of 3 months after acceptance. Offers 25% kill fee. Makes work-for-hire assignments. Simultaneous queries OK. Only queries will be read; direct queries to senior associate editor. Computer printout submissions acceptable. Reports in 1 month. Sample copy for large SAE and 65¢ postage. Writer's guidelines for #10 SAE and 1 first class stamp.
Nonfiction: General interest and how-to (e.g., deal with disappointments, organize important papers). Queries in July and August. Buys 72 mss/year. Query with published clips. Length: 1,200-1,600 words. Pays $100-125.

DOLLY MAGAZINE, Magazine Promotions, 57 Regent St., Chippendale, New South Wales 2008 Australia. (02)699-3622. Editor: Deborah Bibby. 25% freelance written. Works with a small number of new/unpublished writers each year; eager to work with new/unpublished writers. Monthly magazine. Informed entertainment for girls 14-20. Fashion, beauty, personalities, general interest. Circ. 237,000. Pays on acceptance. Publishes ms an average of 4 months after acceptance. Byline given. Offers 50% kill fee. Buys first, all, or second serial reprint rights (depends on story). Submit seasonal/holiday material 4 months in advance. Simultaneous and previously published submissions OK. Computer printout submissions acceptable; prefers letter-quality to dot-matrix. SAE and IRC. Reports in 2 weeks on queries; 1 month on mss. Sample copy for 37x27 cms SAE and $2 postage.
Nonfiction: General interest (aimed at teenage girls); interview/profile (of pop stars, actors, etc.); photo feature (cover, beauty shots). No heavy sex mss. Buys 50 mss/year. Query with clips of published work or send complete ms. Length: 1,000-2,500 words. Pay "decided on sight."
Photos: Send photos with ms. Pay "depends on sighting" for 2¼x2¼ color transparencies. Captions, model

releases and identification of subjects required. Buys one-time rights.

Columns/Departments: Decor—ideas for teenage rooms, flats, etc. Buys 150 mss/year. Query with clips of published work. Length: 100-1,000 words. Pay "depends on sighting."

Fiction: Deborah Bibby, fiction editor. Adventure (with a touch of romance); very condensed novels; confession; fantasy (not kinky); historical (romance); humor/satire; juvenile; romance (contemporary); suspense/mystery; women's; young adult. "Characters to be between 17 and 20 and unmarried. We like element of romance." Buys 2 mss/issue. Query with clips of published work and IRCs. Length: 1,000-25,000 words; 2,500 words average. Payment "depends on story and content."

EXPLORING MAGAZINE, The Journal for Explorers, Boy Scouts of America, 1325 Walnut Hill Ln., Irving TX 75038-3096. (214)659-2365. Executive Editor: Scott Daniels. 85% freelance written. Prefers to work with published/established writers; works with a small number of new/unpublished writers each year. Magazine published 4 times/year—January, March, May, September. Covers the educational teen-age Exploring program of the BSA. Circ. 400,000. Pays on acceptance. Publishes ms an average of 6 months after acceptance. Byline given. Buys one-time and first rights. Submit seasonal/holiday material 6 months in advance. Simultaneous queries OK. Computer printout submissions acceptable; prefers letter-quality to dot-matrix. Reports in 2 weeks. Sample copy for 8½x10 SAE and $1 postage; writer's guidelines for business size SAE and 1 first class stamp.

Nonfiction: General interest, how-to (achieve outdoor skills, organize trips, meetings, etc.); interview/profile (of outstanding Explorer); travel (backpacking or canoeing with Explorers). Buys 15-20 mss/year. Query with clips. Length: 800-2,000 words. Pays $300-450. Pays expenses of writers on assignment.

Photos: Gene Daniels, photo editor. State availability of photos with query letter or ms. Reviews b&w contact sheets. Captions required. Buys one-time rights.

Tips: "Contact the local Exploring Director in your area (listed in phone book white pages under Boy Scouts of America). Find out if there are some outstanding post activities going on and then query magazine editor in Irving, TX. Strive for shorter texts, faster starts and stories that lend themselves to dramatic photographs." Write for guidelines and "What is Exploring?" fact sheet.

FREEWAY, Box 632, Glen Ellyn IL 60138. Editor: Cindy Atoji. For "young Christian adults of high school and college age." 80% freelance written. Works with a small number of new/unpublished writers each year; eager to work with new/unpublished writers. Weekly. Circ. 70,000. Prefers first serial rights but buys some reprints. Purchases 100 mss/year. Byline given. Reports on material accepted for publication in 5-6 weeks. Publishes ms an average of 1 year after acceptance. Returns rejected material in 4-5 weeks. Computer printout submissions acceptable; prefers letter-quality to dot-matrix.

Nonfiction: *"FreeWay's* greatest need is for personal experience stories showing how God has worked in teens' lives. Stories are best written in first person, 'as told to' author. Incorporate specific details, anecdotes, and dialogue. Show, don't tell, how the subject thought and felt. Weave spiritual conflicts and prayers into entire manuscript; avoid tacked-on sermons and morals. Stories should show how God has helped the person resolve a problem or how God helped save a person from trying circumstances (1,000 words or less). Avoid stories about accident and illness; focus on events and emotions of everyday life. (Examples: How I overcame shyness; confessions of a food addict.) Short-short stories are also needed as fillers. We also need self-help or how-to articles with practical Christian advice on daily living; and trend articles addressing secular fads from a Christian perspective. We do not use devotional material, poetry, or fictionalized Bible stories. " Pays 4-7¢/word. Sometimes pays the expenses of writers on assignment.

Photos: Whenever possible, provide clear 8x10 or 5x7 b&w photos to accompany mss (or any other available photos). Payment is $5-30.

Fiction: "We use little fiction, unless it is allegory, parables, or humor."

Tips: "Write to us for our 'Tips to Writers' pamphlet and free sample copy. Study them, then query or send complete mss. In your cover letter include information about who you are, writing qualifications, and experience working with teens. Include SASE."

GROUP, Thom Schultz Publications, Box 481, Loveland CO 80539. (303)669-3836. Editor: Gary Richardson. 60% freelance written. For leaders of high-school-age Christian youth groups. Magazine published 8 times/year. Circ. 70,000. Pays on acceptance. Publishes ms an average of 2 months after acceptance. Buys all rights. Byline given. Phone queries OK. Submit seasonal/holiday material 5 months in advance. Special Easter, Thanksgiving and Christmas issues. Computer printout submissions acceptable; prefers letter-quality to dot-matrix. Reports in 1 month. Sample copy $1; writer's guidelines for SASE.

Nonfiction: How-to (fundraising, membership-building, worship, games, discussions, activities, crowd breakers, simulation games); informational; (drama, worship, youth group projects, service projects); inspirational (ministry encouragement). Buys 7 mss/issue. Query. Length: 1,200-1,700 words. Pays up to $150. Sometimes pays the expenses of writers on assignment.

Columns/Departments: Try This One (short ideas for games, crowd breakers, discussions, worship, fund raisers, service projects, etc.). Buys 5 mss/issue. Send complete ms. Length: 300 words maximum. Pays $15.

News, Trends and Tips (leadership tips). Buys 1 mss/issue. Send complete ms. Length: 500 words maximum. Pays $25.
Tips: "A writer with youth ministry experience and a practical, conversational writing style will be more likely to be published in *Group*."

GUIDE, 55 W. Oak Ridge Dr., Hagerstown MD 21740. Editor: Jeannette Johnson. 90% freelance written. A Seventh-Day Adventist journal for junior youth and early teens. "Its content reflects Seventh-Day Adventist beliefs and standards. Another characteristic which probably distinguishes it from many other magazines is the fact that all its stories are nonfiction." Weekly magazine; 32 pages. Circ. 52,000. Buys first serial rights, simultaneous rights, and second (reprint) rights to material originally published elsewhere. Buys about 300 mss/year. Pays on acceptance. Publishes ms an average of 9 months after acceptance. Byline given. Submit seasonal/holiday material 6 months in advance. Electronic submissions OK via modem—file upload and file download capabilities; but requires hard copy also. Computer printout submissions acceptable; no dot-matrix. Reports in 6 weeks. Sample copy 40¢.
Nonfiction: Wants nonfiction stories of character-building and spiritual value. All stories must be true and include dialogue. Should emphasize the positive aspects of living, obedience to parents, perseverance, kindness, etc. "We use a limited number of stories dealing with problems common to today's Christian youth, such as peer pressure, parents' divorce, chemical dependency, etc. Also stories about boys, ethnic groups (from their own perspective). We can always use 'drama in real life' stories that show God's protection. We can always use seasonal stories—Christmas, Thanksgiving, special holidays. We do not use stories of hunting, fishing, trapping or spiritualism." Send complete ms (include word count). Length: 1,500-2,000 words. Pays 3-4¢/word. Also buys serialized true stories. Length: 10 chapters.
Poetry: Buys traditional forms of poetry; also some free verse. Length: 4-16 lines. Pays 50¢-$1/line.
Tips: "We often buy short 'fillers,' and an author who does not fully understand our needs is more likely to sell with a short-short. Frequently writers do not understand our unique needs. Our target age is 10-15. Our most successful writers are those who present stories from the viewpoint of a young teen-ager. Stories that sound like an adult's sentiments passing through a young person's lips are *not* what we're looking for. Use believable dialogue."

IN TOUCH, Wesley Press, Box 2000, Marion IN 46952. (317)674-3301. Editor: James Watkins. 50% freelance written. Eager to work with new/unpublished writers. A weekly Christian teen magazine. Circ. 26,000. Pays on acceptance. Publishes ms an average of 10 months after acceptance. Byline given. Offers 30% kill fee. Not copyrighted. Buys first rights or second serial (reprint) rights. Submit seasonal/holiday material 10 months in advance. Simultaneous, photocopied, and previously published submissions OK. Computer printout submissions acceptable; prefers letter-quality to dot-matrix. Reports in 6 weeks on manuscripts. Writer's guidelines for business size SAE with 1 first class stamp.
Nonfiction: Book excerpts, essays, how-to, humor, interview/profile, opinion, personal experience, photo feature from Christian perspective. "Our articles are teaching oriented and contain lots of humor." Buys 100 mss/year Send complete ms. Length: 500-1,200 words. Pays $15-45. Sometimes pays the expenses of writers on assignment.
Photos: Send photos with submissions. Reviews contact sheets and 8x10 prints. Pays $15-25/photo. Buys one-time rights.
Tips: "1. Take the editor to lunch. 2. Read writer's guidelines before submitting manuscripts."

INSIGHT, The Young Calvinist Federation, Box 7244, Grand Rapids MI 49510. (616)241-5616. Editor: John Knight. Assistant Editor: Martha Kalk. 25% freelance written. Eager to work with new/unpublished writers. For young people ages 16-21, a Christian youth magazine. Monthly (except June and August) magazine; 28 pages. Circ. 18,500. Pays on publication. Publishes ms an average of 4 months after acceptance. Byline given. Buys simultaneous, second serial (reprint) and first North American serial rights. Submit seasonal/holiday material 6 months in advance. Simultaneous, photocopied and previously published submissions OK. Computer printout submissions acceptable; prefers letter-quality to dot-matrix. Sample copy and writer's guidelines for 9x12 SASE.
Photos: Photos purchased without accompanying ms. Pays $15-35/8x10 b&w glossy print; $50-200 for 35mm or larger color transparencies. Total purchase price for ms includes payment for photos.
Fiction & Nonfiction: Humorous, mainstream and religious. "Looks for short stories and nonfiction that lead readers to a better understanding of how the Christian faith is relevant to daily life, social issues and the arts. They must do more than entertain—must make the reader see things in a new light. We would like to see submissions dealing with current youth trends, media, merchandising, values, fads, fears, expressions." No sentimental, moralistic guidance articles. Buys 1-2 mss/issue. Send complete ms. Length: 1,000-3,000 words. Pays $45-125.
Poetry: Free verse. Buys 10 poems/year. Length: 4-25 lines. Pays $20-25.
Fillers: Youth oriented cartoons, puzzles and short humor. Length: 50-300 words. Pays $10-35.
Tips: "Test your writing on a 17- or 18-year-old, somewhat typical high school student. If it grabs him/her,

chances are we'll take a good look at your submission. We are looking for shorter contributions and short, short stories.''

‡KEYNOTER, Key Club International, 3636 Woodview Trace, Indianapolis IN 46268. (317)875-8755, ext. 432. Executive Editor: Jack Brockley. 65% freelance written. Eager to work with new/unpublished writers. A youth magazine published monthly Oct.-May (Dec./Jan. combined issue), distributed to members of Key Club International, a high school service organization for young men and women. Circ. 100,000. Pays on acceptance. Publishes ms an average of 5 months after acceptance. Byline given. Buys first North American serial rights. Submit seasonal/holiday material 7 months in advance. Simultaneous queries and submissions(if advised), photocopied and previously published submissions OK. Computer printout submissions acceptable; prefers letter-quality to dot-matrix. Reports in 1 month. Sample copy for 9x12 SAE and 3 first class stamps; writer's guidelines for 9½x4 SAE and 1 first class stamp.
Nonfiction: Book excerpts (may be included in articles but are not accepted alone); general interest (must be geared for intelligent teen audience); historical/nostalgic (generally not accepted); how-to (if it offers advice on how teens can enhance the quality of lives or communities); humor (accepted very infrequently; if adds to story, OK); interview/profile (rarely purchased, "would have to be on/with an irresistible subject"); new product (only if affects teens); photo feature (if subject is right, might consider); technical (if understandable and interesting to teen audience); travel (sometimes OK, but must apply to club travel schedule); subjects that entertain and inform teens on topics that relate directly to their lives. "Please, no first-person confessions, no articles that are written down to our teen readers." Buys 5-10 mss/year. Query. Length: 1,500-2,500 words. Pays $125-250. Sometimes pays the expenses of writers on assignment.
Photos: State availability of photos. Reviews b&w contact sheets and negatives. Identification of subjects required. Buys one-time rights. Payment for photos included in payment for ms.
Tips: "We want to see articles written with attention to style and detail that will enrich the world of teens. Articles must be thoroughly researched and should draw on nationally and internationally respected sources. Our readers are 13-15, mature and dedicated to community service. We are very committed to working with good writers, and if we see something we like in a well written query, we'll try to work it through to publication."

‡LIGHTED PATHWAY, Church of God, 922 Montgomery Ave., Cleveland TN 37311. (615)476-4512. Editor: Marcus V. Hand. 25% freelance written. A monthly magazine emphasizing Christian living for youth and young marrieds ages 13-25. Circ. 22,000. Pays on acceptance. Publishes ms an average of 3 months after acceptance. Byline given. Buys first North American serial rights and one-time rights. Submit seasonal/holiday material 4 months in advance. Simultaneous queries, and simultaneous, photocopied, and previously published submissions OK. Computer printout submissions acceptable. Reports in 2 weeks on queries; 1 month on mss. Free sample copy and writer's guidelines.
Nonfiction: Inspirational, interview/profile, personal experience, photo feature and travel. "Our primary objective is inspiration, to portray happy, victorious living through faith in God." Buys 40 mss/year. Query or send complete ms. Length: 1,000-2,000 words. Pay 2-4¢/word.
Photos: State availability of photos or send photos with query or ms. Pays $10-20 for 8x10 b&w prints. Buys one-time rights and all rights.
Fiction: Adventure, historical and religious. No westerns, gothics, mysteries, animal. Buys 24 mss/year. Query or send complete ms. Length: 1,000-2,000 words. Pays 2-4¢/word.
Tips: "Write to evangelical, conservative audience, about current subjects involving young people today." Fiction and human interest stories are most open to freelancers.

NEW DRIVER, The Continuing Guide to Driver Education and Energy Conservation, General Learning Corp., Inc., 3500 Western Ave., Highland Park IL 60035. (312)432-2700. Editor: Margaret Mucklo. Senior Associate Editor: Carole Rubenstein. 90% freelance written. Quarterly magazine on driver education. "*ND* is an educational periodical for high school students in driver education classes." Circ. 40,000. Pays 2 months after acceptance. Publishes ms an average of 3 months after acceptance. No byline given. Offers 25% kill fee. Makes work-for-hire assignments. Simultaneous queries OK. Only queries will be read; direct queries to senior associate editor. Computer printout submissions acceptable. Reports in 1 month. Sample copy for large SAE and 65¢ postage; writer's guidelines for #10 SAE and 1 first class stamp.
Nonfiction: General interest and how-to (maintain a car, drive a car safely). Queries most needed in July and August. Buys 40 mss/year. Query with published clips. Length: 1,200-1,600 words. Pays $100-150.

PURPLE COW, The Newspaper for Teens, Purple Cow, Inc., Suite 107, 1447 Peachtree St., Atlanta GA 30309. (404)872-1927. Editor: Meg Thornton. 8% freelance written. A monthly tabloid appealing to 12 to 18-year-olds. Circ. 36,000. Pays on publication. Publishes ms 1 month after acceptance. Byline given. Buys first rights, second serial (reprint) rights and sydnication rights. Submit seasonal/holiday material 2 months in advance. Simultaneous queries and submissions and photocopied and previously published submissions OK. Computer printout submissions acceptable. Reports in 2 weeks on queries; 2 months on mss. Sample copy for $1 and 8½x11 SAE. Writer's guidelines $1 and SAE with 1 first class stamp.

Nonfiction: General interest, how-to, humor, interview/profile (musicians and film stars), photo feature and anything of interest to teenagers. No opinion or anything which talk down to teens. Buys 25 mss/year. Query or send complete ms. Length: 2,000 words maximum. Pays $5-10.

Photos: Photo Editor: Della Niekirk. State availabiity of photos or send submission. Reviews 8½x11 b&w prints. Pays $2-5. Requires model releases and identification of subjects. Buys one-time rights and syndication rights.

Columns/Departments: Danise Nabarro, editor. Help, Music. Buys 20 mss/year. Query with published clips or send complete ms. Length: 2,000 words maximum. Pays $5-10.

Fillers: Tim Murphy, editor. Jokes. Buys 10/year. Pays $5-10.

Tips: "A freelancer can best break in to our publication with articles which help teens. How-to and interviews are areas most open to freelancers."

‡SCHOLASTIC SCOPE, Scholastic Magazines, Inc., 730 Broadway, New York NY 10003. Editor: Fran Claro. Circ. 800,000. Buys all rights. Byline given. Issued weekly. 4-6th grade reading level; 15-18 age level. Computer printout submissons acceptable; no dot-matrix. Reports in 4-6 weeks.

Nonfiction and Photos: Articles with photos about teenagers who have accomplished something against great odds, overcome obstacles, performed heroically, or simply done something out of the ordinary. Prefers articles about people outside New York area. Length: 400-1,200 words. Pays $125 and up.

Fiction and Drama: Problems of contemporary teenagers (drugs, prejudice, runaways, failure in school, family problems, etc.); relationships between people (interracial, adult-teenage, employer-employee, etc.) in family, job, and school situations. Strive for directness, realism, and action, perhaps carried through dialogue rather than exposition. Try for depth of characterization in at least one character. Avoid too many coincidences and random happenings. Although action stories are wanted, it's not a market for crime fiction. Occasionally uses mysteries and science fiction. Length: 400-1,200 words. Uses plays up to 15,000 words. Pays $150 minimum.

SCHOLASTIC UPDATE, Scholastic, Inc., 730 Broadway, New York NY 10003-9538. (212)505-3000. Editor: Eric Oatman. Classroom periodical published 18 times/year (biweekly during the school year). "A public affairs magazine for social studies students in grades 8-12. Each issue covers a specific problem, country, or institution." Circ. 340,000. Pays on publication. Byline given. Offers 50% kill fee. Buys all rights. Submit seasonal/holiday material 4 months in advance. No simultaneous queries, or simultaneous, photocopied or previously published submissions. Computer printout submissions acceptable. Reports in 2 months. Sample copy $5 and SAE.

Nonfiction: Interview/profile. Buys 20 mss/year. Query with clips of published work. Length: 750-1,500 words. Pays $150/printed page.

SEVENTEEN, 850 3rd Ave., New York NY 10022. Editor-in-Chief: Midge Turk Richardson. Senior Editor: Sarah Crichton. 80% freelance written. Works with a small number of new/unpublished writers each year. Monthly. Circ. 1,700,000. Buys one-time rights for nonfiction and fiction by adult writers; buys full rights for work by teenagers. Pays 25% kill fee. Pays on acceptance. Publishes ms an average of 6 months after acceptance. Byline given. Computer printout submissions acceptable; prefers letter-quality to dot-matrix. Reports in 3 weeks.

Nonfiction: Katherine Russell Rich, articles editor. Articles and features of general interest to young women who are concerned with the development of their own lives and the problems of the world around them; strong emphasis on topicality, and helpfulness. Send brief outline and query, including a typical lead paragraph, summing up basic idea of article. Also like to receive articles and features on speculation. Length: 1,200-2,000 words. Pays $50-150 for articles written by teenagers but more to established adult freelancers. Articles are commissioned after outlines are submitted and approved. Fees for commissioned articles generally range from $650-1,500. Sometimes pays the expenses of writers on assignment.

Photos: Melissa Warner, art director. Photos usually by assignment only.

Fiction: Bonni Price, fiction editor. Thoughtful, well-written stories on subjects of interest to young women between the ages of 12 and 20. Avoid formula stories—"My sainted Granny," "My crush on Brad," etc.— heavy moralizing, condescension of any sort. Humorous stories and mysteries are welcome. Best lengths are 1,500-3,000 words. Pays $700-1,000. "Publishes a novelette every June (not to exceed 25 doubled-spaced manuscript pages). Submissions due January 1. " Conducts an annual short story contest for teenage writers.

Poetry: Teen features editor. By teenagers only. Pays $15. Submissions are nonreturnable unless accompanied by SASE.

Tips: "Writers have to ask themselves whether or not they feel they can find the right tone for a *Seventeen* article—a tone which is empathetic yet never patronizing; lively yet not superficial. Not all writers feel comfortable with, understand or like teenagers. If you don't like them, *Seventeen*'s the wrong market for you. The best way for beginning teenage writers to crack the *Seventeen* lineup is for them to contribute suggestions and short pieces to the You Said It! column, a literary format which lends itself to just about every kind of writing: profiles, puzzles, essays, exposes, reportage, and book reviews."

STRAIGHT, Standard Publishing Co., 8121 Hamilton Ave., Cincinnati OH 45231. (513)931-4050. Editor: Dawn B. Korth. 90% freelance written. "Teens, age 13-19, from Christian backgrounds generally receive this publication in their Sunday School classes or through subscriptions." Weekly (published quarterly) magazine; 12 pages. Pays on acceptance. Publishes ms an average of 1 year after acceptance. Buys first rights, second serial (reprint) rights or simultaneous rights. Byline given. Submit seasonal/holiday material 1 year in advance. Reports in 3-6 weeks. Free sample copy; writer's guidelines with SASE. Computer printout submissions acceptable. Include Social Security number on ms.
Nonfiction: Religious-oriented topics, teen interest (school, church, family, dating, sports, part-time jobs), humor, inspirational, personal experience. "We want articles that promote Christian values and ideals." No puzzles. Query or submit complete ms. "We're buying more short pieces these days; 12 pages fill up much too quickly." Length: 800-1,500 words.
Fiction: Adventure, historical, humorous, religious and suspense. "All fiction should have some message for the modern Christian teen." Fiction should deal with all subjects in a forthright manner, without being preachy and without talking down to teens. No tasteless manuscripts that promote anything adverse to Bible's teachings. Submit complete ms. Length: 1,000-1,500 words. Pays 2-3½¢/word; less for reprints.
Photos: May submit photos with ms. Pays $20-25 for 8x10 b&w glossy prints. Model releases should be available. Buys one-time rights.
Tips: "Don't be trite. Use unusual settings or problems. Use a lot of illustrations, a good balance of conversation, narration, and action. Style must be clear, fresh—no sermonettes or sickly-sweet fiction. Take a realistic approach to problems. Be willing to submit to editorial policies on doctrine; knowledge of the *Bible* a must. Also, be aware of teens today, and what they do. Language, clothing, and activities included in mss should be contemporary. We are becoming more and more selective about freelance material and the competition seems to be stiffer all the time."

TEEN MAGAZINE, 8490 Sunset Blvd., Hollywood CA 90069. Editor: Roxanne Camron. 10-20% freelance written. Prefers to work with published/established writers. For teenage girls. Predominantly staff-written. Freelance purchases are limited. Monthly magazine; 100 pages. Circ. 1,000,000. Publishes ms an average of 6 months after acceptance. Buys all rights. Reports in 4 months. Computer printout submissions acceptable; no dot-matrix.
Fiction: Dealing specifically with teenagers and contemporary teen issues. More fiction on emerging alternatives for young women. Suspense, humorous and romance. "Young love is all right, but teens want to read about it in more relevant settings." Length: 2,500-4,000 words. Pays $100. Sometimes pays the expenses of writers on assignment.
Tips: "No nonfiction; no fiction with explicit language, casual references to drugs, alcohol, sex, or smoking; no fiction with too depressing outcome."

TEENAGE MAGAZINE, The Magazine for Young Adults, Highwire Assoc., 175 Middlesex Turnpike, Bedford MA 01730. (617)271-0330. Editor: Andrew Calkins. Managing Editor: John Kittridge. 40% freelance written. Monthly magazine for for college-minded young women written and edited largely by teenagers. Circ. 200,000. Pays on publication. Publishes ms an average of 4 months after acceptance. Byline given. Offers 25% kill fee. Buys first North American serial rights. Submit seasonal/holiday material 6 months in advance. Simultaneous queries, and simultaneous, photocopied and previously published submissions OK. Computer printout submissions acceptable; prefers letter-quality to dot-matrix. Reports in 1 month. Sample copy $2.50 and 9x12 SAE and 65¢ postage. Writer's guidelines for SAE.
Nonfiction: Articles editor. Book excerpts; general interest (to teenagers); how-to (on college, careers, health); humor (shorts); interview/profile (especially of entertainers); opinion (from teenagers only—300 words); and personal experience. No overly general surveys or how-to's. We need specific information. Buys 25 mss/year. Query with or without published clips. Length: 300-2,500 words. Pays $50-1,000. Sometimes pays the expenses of writers on assignment.
Columns/Departments: Nancy Rourke, column/department editor. Mind & Body, Career's, College, and Wheels (cars). Buys 6 mss/year. Query with published clips. Length: 800-1,200 words. Pays $100-350.
Fiction: Fiction editor. Adventure, humorous, mystery, novel excerpts, suspense, and youth-related issues, plots, and characters. Buys 3 mss/year. Send complete ms. Length: 1,000-2,500 words. Pays $350 maximum.
Tips: Areas most open to freelancers include Frontlines (opinions by teenagers), how-to-, health and beauty and entertainer profiles.

TEENS TODAY, Church of the Nazarene, 6401 The Paseo, Kansas City MO 64131. (816)333-7000. Editor: Gary Sivewright. 25% freelance written. For junior and senior high teens, to age 18, attending Church of the Nazarene Sunday School. Weekly magazine; 8 pages. Circ. 70,000. Publishes ms an average of 8 months after acceptance. Pays on acceptance. Byline given. Buys first rights and second rights. Submit seasonal/holiday material 10 months in advance. Simultaneous, photocopied and previously published submissions OK. Computer printout submissions acceptable. Reports in 6-8 weeks. Free sample copy and writer's guidelines for SASE.

Photos: Photos purchased with or without accompanying ms or on assignment. Pays $10-30 for 8x10 b&w glossy prints. Additional payment for photos accepted with accompanying ms. Model releases required.
Fiction: Adventure (if Christian principles are apparent); humorous; religious; and romance (keep it clean). Buys 1 ms/issue. Send complete ms. Length: 1,200-1,500 words. Pays 3½¢/word, first rights; 3¢/word, second rights.
Poetry: Free verse; haiku; light verse; and traditional. Buys 15 poems/year. Pays 25¢/line.
Tips: "We're looking for quality nonfiction dealing with teen issues: peers, self, parents, vocation, Christian truths related to life, etc."

TIGER BEAT MAGAZINE, D.S. Magazines, Inc., 1086 Teaneck Road, Teaneck NJ 07666. (201)833-1800. Editor: Diane Umansky. 25% freelance written. For teenage girls ages 14 to 18. Monthly magazine; 80 pages. Circ. 400,000. Pays on publication. Publishes ms an average of 3 months after acceptance. Buys all rights. Buys 50+ manuscripts per year. Electronic submissions OK on single-sided CP/M or MS/DOS disks, but requires hard copy also. Computer printout submissions acceptable; no dot-matrix.
Nonfiction: Stories about young entertainers; their lives, what they do, their interests. Also service-type, self-help articles. Quality writing expected, but must be written with the 14-18 age group in mind. "Skill, style, ideas, and exclusivity are important to *Tiger Beat*. If a writer has a fresh, fun idea, or access to something staffers don't have, he or she has a good chance." Length: 100-750 words depending on the topic. Pays $50-100. Send query. Sometimes pays the expenses of writers on assignment. Also seeks good teenage fiction, with an emphasis on entertainment and romance.
Photos: Pays $25 for b&w photos used with mss; captions optional. Pays $50-75 for color used inside; $75 for cover. 35mm transparencies preferred.
Tips: "A freelancer's best bet is to come up with something original and exclusive that the staff couldn't do or get. Writing should be aimed at a 17- or 18-year-old intelligence level. Trends in magazine publishing that freelance writers should be aware of include shorter articles, segmenting of markets, and much less 'I' journalism. The most frequent mistake made by writers in completing an article for us is a patronizing attitude toward teens or an emphasis on historical aspects of subject matter. Don't talk down to young readers; they sense it readily."

TIGER BEAT STAR, D.S. Magazines, Inc., 105 Union Ave., Cresskill NJ 07626. (201)569-5055. Editor: Lisa Arcella. Associate Editor: Jeanine Walker. 50% freelance written. Monthly teenage fan magazine for young adults interested in movie, TV and recording stars. "It differs from other teenage fan magazines in that we feature many soap opera stars as well as the regular teenage TV, movie and music stars." Circ. 400,000. Average issue includes 20 feature interviews, and 2 or 3 gossip columns. "We have to take each article and examine its worth individually—who's popular this month, how it is written, etc. But we prefer shorter articles most of the time." Pays upon publication. Publishes ms an average of 1 month after acceptance. Byline given. Buys all rights. Submit seasonal material 10 weeks in advance. Previously published submissions discouraged. Electronic submissions OK on disk for Victor 9000 system, but requires hard copy also. Computer printout submissions acceptable; no dot-matrix. Reports in 2 weeks.
Nonfiction: Interview (of movie, TV and recording stars). Buys 1-2 mss/issue. Query with clips of previously published work. "Write a good query indicating your contact with the star. Investigative pieces are preferred." Length: 200-400 words. Pays $50-125.
Photos: State availability of photos. Pays $25 minimum for 5x7 and 8x10 b&w glossy prints. Pays $75 minimum for 35mm and 2¼ color transparencies. Captions and model releases required. Buys all rights.
Tips: "Be aware of our readership (teenage girls, generally ages 9-17); be looking for articles that are clearly and intelligently written, factual and fun. Don't talk down to the reader, simply because they are teenaged. We want to give the readers information they can't find elsewhere. Keep in mind that readers are young and try to include subheads and copybreakers."

TRIUMPH, Randall House Publications, Box 17307, Nashville TN 37217. (615)361-1221. Editor-in-Chief: H.D. Harrison. 5% freelance written. Works with a small number of new/unpublished writers each year. Quarterly teen training manual for church training curriculum. Audience is 10th-12th graders in Free Will Baptist churches; conservative theological. Circ. 2,000. Pays on publication. Publishes ms an average of 9 months after acceptance. Byline given. Buys one-time rights. Submit seasonal/holiday material 9 months in advance. Simultaneous and previously published submissions OK. Electronic submissions OK via MS-DOS 2.1 (IBM-PC compatible, WordStar files preferred). Computer printout submissions acceptable; prefers letter-quality to dot-matrix. Reports in 1 month. Free sample copy.
Nonfiction: Mrs. Odell Walton, articles editor. Inspirational. Buys 5-10 mss/year. Send complete ms. Length: 500-1,500 words. Pays $20 maximum.
Photos: Send photos with ms. Buys one-time rights.
Fiction: Mrs. Odell Walton, fiction editor. Religious. Prefers fiction teaching morals. Buys 20-30 mss/year. Send complete ms. Length: 500-1,500 words. Pays $20 maximum.

YM, (formerly *Young Miss*), 685 3rd Ave., New York NY 10017. Editor-in-Chief: Phyllis Schneider. 85% freelance written. Prefers to work with published/established writers. Published 10 times/year for teen girls, aged 12-19. Pays on acceptance. Publishes ms an average of 18 months after acceptance. Byline given. Buys first rights. Reports on submissions in 2 months. Sample copy $2 and 10x13 SASE; writer's guidelines for SASE.

Nonfiction: Deborah Purcell, articles/fiction editor. Psychological concerns and personal growth; contemporary issues and problems involving teenagers; all aspects of relationships; compelling, life-and-death style profiles; celebrity profiles; first-person humor; quizzes. Buys 10-20 unsolicited mss/year. Query. Length: 1,500-2,500 words. Pays $75 and up for fillers (850 words maximum); $250 and up for articles. No illustrations.

Fiction: Deborah Purcell, articles/fiction editor. "All fiction should be aimed at young adults, not children; when in doubt, develop older rather than younger characters. Stories about relationships and unique resolutions of personal dilemmas are particularly welcomed. The protagonist may be either male or female." Length: 2,500-3,500 words. Pays $350 and up.

Tips: "Queries for nonfiction should express original thought; desire and ability to do thorough research where applicable; clear understanding of the interests and needs of young women; fresh angles. We are not interested in lightweight nonfiction material or style except where applicable (e.g., humor). Fitness and health, fashion and beauty, food and lifestyles articles are all done inhouse."

YOUNG AMBASSADOR, The Good News Broadcasting Association, Inc., Box 82808, Lincoln NE 68501. (402)474-4567. Editor-in-Chief: Warren Wiersbe. Managing Editor: Nancy Bayne. 50% freelance written. Works with a small number of new/unpublished writers each year. Monthly magazine emphasizing Christian living for Protestant church-oriented teens, ages 12-17. Circ. 80,000. Buys first serial rights or second serial (reprint) rights. Publishes ms an average of 10 months after acceptance. Byline given. Phone queries OK. Submit seasonal/holiday material 1 year in advance. Previously published submissions OK. Computer printout submissions acceptable; prefers letter-quality to dot-matrix. Reports in 8 weeks. Free sample copy and writer's guidelines.

Nonfiction: Interviews with Christian sports personalities; well-researched articles on science and technology that relate to teens; features on teens making unusual achievements or involved in unique pursuits—spiritual emphasis a must. Buys 1-3 mss/issue. Query or send complete ms. Length: 500-1,800 words. Pays 4-7¢/word for unsolicited mss; 7-10¢ for assigned articles. Sometimes pays expenses of writers on assignment.

Fiction: Needs stories involving problems common to teens (dating, family, alcohol and drugs, peer pressure, school, sex, talking about one's faith to non-believers, standing up for convictions, etc.) in which the resolution (or lack of it) is true to our readers' experiences. "In other words, no happy-ever-after endings, last-page spiritual conversions, or pat answers to complex problems. We are interested in the everyday (though still profound) experiences of teen life. If the story was written just to make a point, or grind the author's favorite axe, we don't want it. Most of our stories feature a protagonist 14-17 years old. The key is the spiritual element—how the protagonist deals with or makes sense of his/her situation in light of Christian spiritual priciples and ideals, without being preached to or preaching to another character or to the reader." Buys 35 mss/year. Query or send complete ms. Length: 800-1,800 words. Pays 4-7¢/word for unsolicited mss; 7-10¢/word for assigned fiction.

Fillers: Puzzles on Biblical themes. Send complete mss. Pays $3-10.

Tips: "Articles for YA need to be written in an upbeat style attractive to teens. No preaching. Writers must be familiar with the characteristics of today's teenagers in order to write for them."

YOUNG AND ALIVE, Christian Record Braille Foundation, Inc., Editorial Dept., 4444 S. 52nd St., Lincoln NE 68506. Editor: Richard Kaiser. "We are backlogged with submissions and prefer not to receive unsolicited submissions at this time."

YOUNG SALVATIONIST, A Christian Living Magazine, The Salvation Army, 799 Bloomfield Ave., Verona NJ 07044. (201)239-0606. Editor: Capt. Dorothy Hitzka. Editor-in-Chief: Major Henry Gariepy. 75% freelance written. Works with a small number of new/unpublished writers each year. Monthly magazine for high school teens. "Only material with a definite Christian message will be considered." Circ. 43,000. Pays on acceptance. Publishes ms an average of 10 months after acceptance. Byline given. Submit seasonal/holiday material 6 months in advance. Computer printout submissions acceptable; prefers letter-quality to dot-matrix. Reports in 1 month on mss. Sample copy for 8½x11 SAE with 3 first class stamps; writer's guidelines for business size SAE and 1 first class stamp.

Nonfiction: Inspirational. "Lead articles should carry Christian truth but not in a 'preachy' manner; should deal with 'real life' issues facing teens today; must be factual; and any references to The Salvation Army must be authentic. Articles must have a logical progression of thoughts with a definite conclusion or solution but no tacked-on morals. The lesson or point should be inherent in the article itself." Buys 36 mss/year. Send complete ms. "State whether your submission is for the Young Salvationist or the Young Soldier section." Length: 800-1,200 words. Pays 3-5¢/word.

Columns/Departments: Magazine includes a Young Soldier "pull-out" section for children ages 6-12 with

600-800 word stories (fiction) relating to children rather than teens. "Two-page spreads of activities that relate to the story will be used in each issue. These should emphasize the truth taught but be an activity that the child can complete." Puzzles and related items are also used in each issue. Buys 24 mss/year. Send complete ms. Length: 250-300 words. Pays 3-5¢/word.
Fiction: "Story must have logical and convincing plot with good characterization and should deal with issues facing today's teens. Dialogue must be natural. No 'put on' teen jargon or Biblical fiction. Fiction must carry a strong Christian truth which is to be inherent in the story itself." Length: 1,000-1,200 words.
Fillers: "We have several columns which deal with self-image, marriage, teen leadership in the church, and other related teen topics. These fillers should meet the same criteria for content as nonfiction." Length: 250-300 words.

YOUTH UPDATE, St. Anthony Messenger Press, 1615 Republic St., Cincinnati OH 45210. (513)241-5615. Editor: Carol Ann Morrow. 75% freelance written. Monthly newsletter of faith life for teenagers. Designed to attract, instruct, guide and challenge Catholics of high school age by applying the Gospel to modern problems/situations. Circ. 60,000. Pays when ready to print. Publishes ms an average of 4 months after acceptance. Byline given. Reports in 8 weeks. Sample copy and writer's guidelines for SAE and 1 first class stamp.
Nonfiction: Inspirational, interview/profile, practical self-help and spiritual. Buys 12 mss/year. Query. Length: 2,300-2,500 words. Pays $300. Sometimes pays expenses of writers on assignment.

Theatre, Movie, TV and Entertainment

This category's publications cover live, filmed, or videotaped entertainment, including home video, TV, dance, theatre, and adult entertainment. Besides celebrity interviews, most publications want solid reporting on trends and upcoming productions that will interest readers. For those publications with an emphasis on music and musicians, see the Music section. For markets covering video games, see Games and Puzzles.

‡AMERICAN FILM, American Film Institute, MD Publications, 3 E. 54th St., New York NY 10022. Editor: Peter Biskind. 80% freelance written. For film professionals, students, teachers, film enthusiasts, culturally oriented readers. Monthly magazine. Circ. 140,000. Buys first North American serial rights, and first and second rights to the same material. Pays kill fee. Byline given. Pays 90 days after acceptance. Sample copy $2.50. Will consider photocopied submissions. Submit material 3 months in advance. Reports in 1 month. Query. Computer printout submissions acceptable.
Nonfiction: In-depth articles on film and television-related subjects. "Our articles require expertise and first-rate writing ability." Buys informational, profile, historical and "think" pieces. No film reviews. Buys 10 unsolicited mss/year. Length: 500-4,000 words. Pays $100-1,000.
Tips: "No 'my favorite moments in films' or other 'fanzine' type pieces."

AMERICAN SQUAREDANCE, Burdick Enterprises, Box 488, Huron OH 44839. (419)433-2188. Editors: Stan and Cathie Burdick. 5% freelance written. Works with a small number of new/unpublished writers each year; eager to work with new/unpublished writers. Monthly magazine of interviews, reviews, topics of interest to the modern square dancer. Circ. 23,000. Pays on publication. Publishes ms an average of 6 months after acceptance. Byline given. Buys all rights. Submit seasonal/holiday material 3 months in advance. Computer printout submissions acceptable. Reports in 2 weeks on queries. Sample copy for 6x9 SAE; free writer's guidelines.
Nonfiction: General interest, historical/nostalgic, humor, inspirational, interview/profile, new product, opinion, personal experience, photo feature, travel. Must deal with square dance. Buys 6 mss/year. Send complete ms. Length: 1,000-1,500 words. Pays $10-35.
Photos: Send photos with ms. Reviews b&w prints. Captions and identification of subjects required.

Fiction: Subject related to square dancing only. Buys 1-2 mss/year. Send complete ms. Length: 2,000-2,500 words. Pays $25-35.

Poetry: Avant-garde, free verse, haiku, light verse, traditional. Square dancing subjects only. Buys 6 poems/year. Submit maximum 3 poems. Pays $1 for 1st 4 lines; $1/verse thereafter.

ARTSLINE, G/F Publications, Inc., 2518 Western Ave., Seattle WA 98121. (206)441-0786. Executive Editor: Sonia Grunberg. Editor: Alice Copp Smith. 80% freelance written. Monthly arts magazine serving as program magazine for seven Seattle-Tacoma theatres, concert and dance presenters. "We feature performing and visual arts, nationwide but with an emphasis on the Pacific Northwest." Circ. 73,000. Pays on acceptance. Publishes ms an average of 4 months after acceptance. Byline given. Offers 50% kill fee. Buys first North American serial rights. Submit seasonal/holiday material 6 months in advance. Simultaneous queries, and photocopied submissions OK. Computer printout submissions acceptable; prefers letter-quality to dot-matrix. Reports in 3 weeks. Sample copy for 9x12 SAE and 3 first class stamps; writer's guidelines for SAE and 1 first class stamp.

Nonfiction: Book excerpts; humor; interview/profile (arts-related only); opinion (arts-related only); photo feature (arts-related only); and performing or visual arts features. No crafts; no arts pieces of regional interest only, when region is not Pacific Northwest. Buys 24 features/year. Query with or without published clips or send complete ms. Length: 1,500-2,000 words. Pays $150-200.

Photos: Send photos with query or ms. Reviews b&w contact sheets. Pays $25-50 for 35mm or 4x5 color transparencies; $25-50 for 8x10 b&w prints. Captions and identification of subjects required. Buys one-time rights. Photo credit given.

Fillers: Jokes, anecdotes, short humor (arts-related only). Length: 150 words maximum.

Tips: "A freelancer can best break in to our publication by sending well-written material that fits our format. Feature articles are most open to freelancers. First submission from a writer new to us has to be on speculation; thereafter, we're willing to assign. Know your subject and the Northwest arts scene. Be aware of the increasing sophistication of Pacific Northwest readers and their strong support of the arts."

‡CANADIAN THEATRE REVIEW, Glendon College, 2275 Bayview Ave., Toronto, Ontario, M4N 3M6 Canada. Editor: Robert Wallace. Business Editor: Angela Fritsch. 90% freelance written. Emphasizes Canadian theater for academics and professionals. Quarterly magazine; 144 pages. Circ. 1,100. Pays on publication. Buys one-time rights. Byline given. SAE and International Reply Coupons. Reports in 10-12 weeks. Sample copy $4.

Nonfiction: Historical (theater in Canada); interview (Canadian theater figures); and photo feature (Canadian theater worldwide). Buys 50 mss/year. Length: 1,500-5,000 words. Query or submit complete ms. Fee scale on request.

Photos: State availability of photos with query or mss.

DALLAS OBSERVER, Observer Publications, Box 190289, Dallas TX 75219. (214)521-9450. Editor: Bob Walton. 80% freelance written. Weekly tabloid covering arts, lifestyle issues and entertainment. Circ. 60,000. Pays on publication. Publishes ms an average of 2 months after acceptance. Byline given. Offers 50% kill fee. Buys first serial rights. Submit seasonal/holiday material 2 months in advance. Simultaneous queries and photocopied submissions OK. Computer printout submissions acceptable; prefers letter-quality to dot-matrix. Reports in 1 month. Sample copy for $1.50, 8x10 SAE and 5 first class stamps.

Nonfiction: Interview/profile (Dallas only) and arts features. "Write intelligently about local Dallas arts and entertainment subjects." Buys 400 mss/year. Query with published clips. Length: 500-5,000 words. Pays $20-400.

Columns/Departments: Local Dallas arts and entertainment news. Buys 100 mss/year. Query with published clips. Length: 500-1,000 words. Pays $20-100.

Tips: "Freelancers can best break in to our publication with thought-provoking essays or short articles."

DANCE TEACHER NOW, SMW Communications, Inc., University Mall, Suite 2, 803 Russell Blvd., Davis CA 95616. (916)756-6222. Editor: Susan Wershing. 100% freelance written. Magazine published 9 times/year for professional teachers of stage, ballroom, and fitness dance in private studios, college departments, fitness centers, etc. Circ. 5,500. Average issue includes 6-8 feature articles, departments, and calendar sections. Pays on acceptance. Publishes ms an average of 3 months after acceptance. Byline given. Buys all rights. Submit seasonal material 6 months in advance. Computer printout submissions acceptable; "as long as the covering letter assures us the author is not shotgunning the article to a dozen publications at once." Reports in 2 months. Sample copy $2.25; free writer's guidelines.

Nonfiction: Dance techniques, legal issues, health and dance injuries, business, advertising, taxes and insurance, curricula, student/teacher relations, government grants, studio equipment, concerts and recitals, competitions, departmental budgets, etc. "The writer must choose subject matter suitable to the knowledgable, professional people our readers are." Buys 4-6 mss/issue. Query with published clips. Length: 1,000-3,000 words. Pays $100-300.

Photos: Photos to accompany articles only. Pays $20 minimum for 5x7 b&w glossy prints. Model releases required. Buys all rights.

Columns/Departments: Practical Tips (3-4 paragraphs, short items of immediate practical use to the teacher), Building Your Library, Ballroom Technique, Aerobics.

Tips: "We like complete reportage of the material with all the specifics but personalized with direct quotes and anecdotes. The writer should speak one-to-one to the reader but keep the national character of the magazine in mind. To achieve the practical quality in each article, the most important question in any interview is 'How?' We do not want personality profiles. Articles must include material of practical value to the reader. We do not want philosophical or 'artsy' articles; straightforward reporting only."

DIAL, The Magazine for Public Television, East/West Network, 34 E. 51st St., New York NY 10022. (212)888-5900. Editor: Lisa Schwarzbaum. Executive Editor: David Doty. 10% freelance written. Prefers to work with published/established writers; works with a small number of new/unpublished writers each year. Monthly magazine covering public television. "*Dial* goes to 1.2 million subscribers to public television in 13 cities: New York, Boston, Chicago, Washington D.C., Los Angeles, Dallas, Seattle, Tampa, Portland, Miami, Salt Lake City, Indianapolis and New Orleans." Pays on acceptance. Publishes ms an average of 2 months after acceptance. Byline given. Offers 25% kill fee. Buys first North American serial rights and promotional rights. Submit seasonal/holiday material 6 months in advance. Computer printout submissions acceptable; no dot-matrix. Reports in 1 month. Direct queries to editor-in-chief.

Nonfiction: "All material must have some connection with public television programming." Interview/profile; background pieces on shows. "A freelancer can best break into our publication by being aware of upcoming public television programming." Query with published clips. Length: 750-1,500 words. Pays $750-1,000. Sometimes pays the expenses of writers on assignment.

Tips: "Watch public television, read *Dial*, and get an informed sense of both. We're running shorter pieces—400-700 words."

THE DRAMA REVIEW, New York University, 721 Broadway, 6th Floor, New York NY 10003. (212)598-7589. Editor: Richard Schechner. 95% freelance written. Works with a small number of new/unpublished writers each year. "Emphasis not only on theatre but also dance, ritual, musical performance, mime, and other facets of performative behavior. For avant-garde community, students and professors of anthropology, performance studies and related fields. Political material is welcome." Quarterly magazine; 160 pages. Circ. 7,000. Pays on publication. Submit material 4 months in advance. Photocopied and previously published (if published in another language) submissions OK. Electronic submissions OK via CP/M, IBM or Macintosh, but requires hard copy also. Reports in 2 months. Publishes ms an average of 6 months after acceptance. Sample copy $5 (from MIT Press); free writer's guidelines.

Nonfiction: Ann Daly, managing editor. Buys 10-20 mss/issue. Query by letter only. Pays 2¢/word for translations and other material. Sometimes pays the expenses of writers on assignment.

Photos: Ann Daly, managing editor. Photos purchased with accompanying ms. Captions required.

Tips: "*TDR* is a place where contrasting ideas and opinions meet. A forum for writing about performances and the social, economic, and political contexts in which performances happen. The editors want interdisciplinary, intercultural, multivocal, liminal, eclectic submissions."

DRAMATICS MAGAZINE, International Thespian Society, 3368 Central Pkwy., Cincinnati OH 45225. (513)559-1996. Editor-in-Chief: Donald Corathers. 30% freelance written. For theatre arts students, teachers and others interested in theatre arts education. Magazine published monthly, September through May; 44-52 pages. Circ. 32,000. Pays on acceptance. Publishes ms an average of 3 months after acceptance. Buys first North American serial rights. Byline given. Submit seasonal/holiday material 3 months in advance. Simultaneous, photocopied and previously published submissions OK. Computer printout submissions acceptable; prefers letter-quality to dot-matrix. Reports in 4 weeks. Sample copy $2; free writer's guidelines.

Nonfiction: How-to (technical theatre); informational; interview; photo feature; humorous; profile; and technical. Buys 30 mss/year. Submit complete ms. Length: 750-3,000 words. Pays $30-150.

Photos: Purchased with accompanying ms. Uses b&w photos and color transparencies. Query. Total purchase price for ms includes payment for photos.

Fiction: Drama (one-act plays). No "plays for children, Christmas plays, or plays written with no attention paid to the playwriting form." Buys 5-9 mss/year. Send complete ms. Pays $50-200.

Tips: "The best way to break in is to know our audience—drama students and teachers and others interested in theatre—and to write for them. Writers who have some practical experience in theatre, especially in technical areas, have a leg-up here, but we'll work with anybody who has a good idea. Some freelancers have become regular contributors. Others ignore style suggestions included in our writer's guidelines."

EMMY MAGAZINE, Suite 800, Academy of Television Arts & Sciences, Suite 700, 3500 W. Olive, Burbank CA 91505-4628. (213)506-7885. Editor and Publisher: Hank Rieger. Managing Editor: Lori Kimball. 100% freelance written. Works with a small number of new/unpublished writers each year. Bimonthly magazine on television—a "provocative, critical—though not necessarily fault-finding—treatment of television and its effects on society." Circ. 10,000. Pays on publication. Publishes ms an average of 3 months after acceptance. Byline given. Offers 20% kill fee. Buys first North American serial rights. Computer printout submissions acceptable; no dot-matrix. Reports in 3 weeks on queries; 1 month on mss. Free sample copy.

Nonfiction: Provocative and topical articles, nostalgic, humor, interview/profile, opinion—all dealing with television. Buys 40 mss/year. Query with published clips. Length: 2,000-3,000 words. Pays $500-800. Sometimes pays expenses of writers on assignment.

Columns/Departments: Opinion or point-of-view columns dealing with TV. Buys 18-20 mss/year. Query with published clips. Length: 800-1,500 words. Pays $200-400.

Tips: "Query with thoughtful description of what you wish to write about. Or call. In either case, we can soon establish whether or not we can do business. The most frequent mistake made by writers in completing an article for us is that they misread the magazine and send fan-magazine items."

FANGORIA: Horrors in Entertainment, Starlog Group, 475 Park Ave. South, 8th Floor, New York NY 10016. (212)689-2830. Editors: David McDonnell, Anthony Timpone. 80% freelance written. Works with a small number of new/unpublished writers each year. Published 10 times/year. Magazine covering horror films, TV projects and literature and those who create them. Pays on publication. Byline given. Buys first North American serial rights with option for second serial (reprint) rights to same material (for reprinting in annual *Best of Anthology* for additional fee). Also will buy second serial (reprint) rights to certain other material. Submit seasonal/holiday material 6 months in advance. Simultaneous queries OK. Computer printout submissions acceptable; prefers letter-quality to dot-matrix. Reports in 6 weeks. Publishes ms an average of 3 months after acceptance. "We provide an assignment sheet (deadlines, info) to writers, thus authorizing stories queried that we're buying." Sample copy $3; writers' guidelines for SASE.

Nonfiction: Book excerpts, interview/profile of movie directors, makeup FX artists, screenwriters, producers, actor- noted-horror novelists and others—with genre credits. No "think" pieces, opinion pieces, reviews, or sub-theme overviews (i.e., vampire in the cinema). Buys 100 mss/year. Query with published clips. Length: 1,000-3,000 words. Pays $100-225. Rarely pays the expenses of writers on assignment. Avoids articles on science fiction films—see listing for sister magazine *Starlog* in science fiction magazine section.

Photos: State availability of photos. Reviews b&w and color transparencies and prints. "No separate payment for photos provided by film studios." Captions or identification of subjects required. Buys all rights.

Columns/Departments: Monster Invasion (news about new film productions; must be exclusive, early information; also mini-interviews with novelists, filmmakers). Query with published clips. Length: 300-500 words. Pays $25-35. "Also have a *small* need for 300-500 word horror novel/genre book reviews for Nightmare Library Section."

Tips: "Other than recommending that you study one or several copies of *Fangoria*, we can only describe it as a horror film magazine consisting primarily of interviews with technicians and filmmakers in the field. Be sure to stress the interview subjects' words—not your own opinions. We're very interested in small, independent filmmakers working outside of Hollywood. These people are usually more accessible to writers, and more cooperative. *Fangoria* is also sort of a *de facto* bible for youngsters interested in movie makeup careers and for young filmmakers. We are devoted only to *reel* horrors—the fakery of films, the imagery of the horror fiction of a Stephen King or a Peter Straub—we do not want nor would we *ever* publish articles on real-life horrors, murders, etc. A writer must *like* and *enjoy* horror films and horror fiction to work for us. If the photos in *Fangoria* disgust you, if the sight of (*stage*) blood repells you, if you feel 'superior' to horror (and its fans), you aren't a writer for us and we certainly aren't the market for you. *Fangoria*'s frequency has increased over the last two years and, with an editorial change reducing staff written articles, this has essentially doubled the number of stories we're buying. In 1987, we expect such opportunities only to increase for freelancers."

FILM QUARTERLY, University of California Press, Berkeley CA 94720. (415)642-6333. Editor: Ernest Callenbach. 100% freelance written. Eager to work with new/unpublished writers. Quarterly. Buys all rights. Byline given. Pays on publication. Publishes ms an average of 3 months after acceptance. Query; "sample pages are very helpful from unknown writers. We must have hard-copy printout and don't care how it is produced, but we cannot use dot-matrix printouts unless done on one of the new printers that gives type-quality letters."

Nonfiction: Articles on style and structure in films, articles analyzing the work of important directors, historical articles on development of the film as art, reviews of current films and detailed analyses of classics, book reviews of film books. Must be familiar with the past and present of the art; must be competently, although not necessarily breezily, written; must deal with important problems of the art. "We write for people who like to think and talk seriously about films, as well as simply view them and enjoy them. We use no personality pieces or reportage pieces. Interviews usually work for us only when conducted by someone familiar with most of a filmmaker's work. (We don't use performer interviews.)" Length: 6,000 words maximum. Pay is about 2¢/word.

Tips: "*Film Quarterly* is a specialized academic journal of film criticism, though it is also a magazine (with pictures) sold in bookstores. It is read by film teachers, students, and die-hard movie buffs, so unless you fall into one of those categories, it is very hard to write for us. Currently, we are especially looking for material on independent, documentary, etc. films not written about in the national film reviewing columns."

‡HOME VIEWER, The Video Entertainment Magazine, Home Viewer Publications Inc., 11 N. 2nd St., Philadelphia PA 19106. (215)629-1588. Editor: Bruce Apar. 50% freelance written. Prefers to work with published/established writers; works with a small number of new/unpublished writers. A monthly magazine covering video home entertainment. "Editorial premise is that VCR programs represent ultimate personalization of popular culture." Circ. 120,000. Pays after acceptance. Publishes ms an average of 5 months after acceptance. Byline given sometimes. Submit seasonal/holiday material 6 months in advance. Simultaneous and photocopied submissions OK. Computer printout submissions acceptable; double-spacing required; prefers letter-quality to dot-matrix. Reports in 1 month on queries; 2 weeks on mss. Free sample copy.
Nonfiction: Paula Parisi, managing editor. Book excerpts; essays; general interest; historical/nostalgic; how-to (use video equipment); humor; interview/profile (entertainment personalities); new product (audio and video); opinion; personal experience; photo features; technical; travel—any subject related to home video entertainment and information. Buys 50 mss/year. Query with published clips. Length: 100-1,500 words. Sometimes pays expenses of writers on assignment. State availability of photos with submissions.
Photos: Reviews contact sheets, transparencies and prints. Offers $25-100/photo. Captions, model releases, and identification of subjects required.
Columns/Department: Kids View (video for kids of all ages); Music View (music video reviews and interviews); Video First (programs produced first and foremost for home viewing. Buys 25 mss/year. Query with published clips. Length: 800 words. Pays $35-200.
Fillers: Paula Parisi, fillers editor. Facts, gags to be illustrated by cartoonist and newsbreaks. Buys 25/year. Length: 500 words maximum. Pays $25-100.
Tips: Sections most open to freelancers are: *Reviewer* section, individual program views; *Video Illustrated*, upfront news; and *Featurette* section, mini-interviews, who's news views and commentary.

HORIZON, The Magazine of the Arts, Boone, Inc., Drawer 30, Tuscaloosa AL 35402. Editor: Gray Boone. Managing Editor: Kellee Reinhart. 70% freelance written. An arts magazine published 10 times per year. "We publish articles on latest trends and important events in the arts world—visual arts, architecture, dance, music, film, television, literature, video, theater and photography. We also publish travel articles with an arts' slant. Our audience is affluent." Circ. 65,000. Pays on publication. Publishes ms an average of 3 months after acceptance. Byline given. Offers 20% kill fee. Buys first North American serial rights. Submit seasonal/holiday material 6 months in advance. Computer printout submissions acceptable; prefers letter-quality to dot-matrix. Reports in 1 month. Sample copy $4; writer's guidelines for SAE with 1 first class stamp.
Nonfiction: Book excerpts, interview/profile, photo feature, travel and short items on timely events. No historical articles without a timely peg, personal opinion, academic essays, or non-arts related articles. Buys 50 mss/year. Query with published clips. Length 1,000-3,000 words. Pays $200-700. Sometimes pays the expenses of writers on assignment.
Photos: State availability of photos with submissions. Reviews 35mm transparencies. Identification of subjects required. Buys one-time rights.
Columns/Department: Jennifer Graham, column/department editor. Cross Country (short items about timely and important arts events), 250 words; and Discovery (article in which a well-known artist in any field of the arts names an up-and-coming artist as someone to watch out for), 1,000 words. Buys 25 mss/year. Query with published clips. Pays $25-300.
Tips: "Our feature articles section is most open to freelancers. We get bogged down in the academic style of writing and that is discouraged. Stories should flow smoothly, include interesting information—such as anecdotes, little-known facts, etc.—and have a clear lead, which the story follows. The style should be lively."

MOVIE COLLECTOR'S WORLD, The Marketplace For Film & Video Collectors, 151 E. Birch St., Annandale MN 55302. (612)274-5230. Editor: Jon E. Johnson. 90% freelance written. Eager to work with new/unpublished writers. Bi-weekly tabloid covering film-collecting and home video: reviews, profiles, features and technical subjects. "We strive to serve the varied interests of our readers, ranging from film and video enthusiasts to still and poster collectors." Circ. 10,000. Pays on publication. Publishes ms an averge of 3 months after acceptance. Byline given. Buys first serial rights and second serial (reprint) rights. Submit seasonal/dated material 3 months in advance. Photocopied submissions OK. Computer printout submissions OK "if close to double-spaced." Reports in 3 weeks. Free sample copy and writer's guidelines.
Nonfiction: Book excerpts; expose (investigative or extensive profile-type submissions); how-to; new product (uses and technical review); opinion (in the form of reviews or commentary); technical subjects ("one very popular feature we ran was on Cinemascope"). "We'd like to see more historical retrospective-type pieces on films. For instance our stories on *The Thin Man* series and *Ma and Pa Kettle* were two recent favorites." No personal experience/first person articles other than interview, profile or general interest. "We do not need very elementary pieces on 'buying your first VCR' or humorous commentary." Send complete ms or query. Pays 3¢/word or $100 maximum.
Photos: State availability of photos with query or ms. Pays $3-5 for 8x10 b&w prints. Model release required. Buys one-time rights.

Columns/Departments: Book (film/video-related topics) and tape/disc reviews. Send ms or query. Pays $5 minimum for short reviews, word rates for longer pieces.

Tips: "*MCW* uses freelance material for nearly its entire content, and as a result it is very easy for a freelancer to break into the publication, provided his/her material suits our needs and they know what they're writing about. Once writers get a feel for what *MCW* is, and we get an idea of their work, they tend to become one of our 'family' of regular contributors. The most open areas of *Movie Collector's World* are interviews and profiles, reviews and technical/how-to pieces. All areas/sections are open to new, different and fresh writers wishing to express their feelings, expertise and knowledge as it relates to the movie/video/television/personality world. Writers who know and care about their subject should have no problem when it comes to writing for *MCW* (providing it suits our needs). We actually encourage unsolicited submissions. A look at your wares just might land you a quicker sale than if there has to be a lot of counseling, advising or hand-holding involved. With a bi-weekly schedule we work quick."

‡THE OPERA COMPANION, 40 Museum Way, San Francisco CA 94114. (415)626-2741. Editor: James Keolker, Ph.D. 25% freelance written. A magazine published 14 times yearly covering "opera in particular, music in general. We provide readers with an indepth analysis of 14 operas per year—the personal, philosophical, and political contest of each composer and his works." Circ. 8,000. Pays on acceptance. Publishes ms an average of 2 months after acceptance. Byline given. Buys first rights. Photocopied submissions OK. Computer printout submissions acceptable; prefers letter-quality to dot-matrix. Reports in 1 week on queries; 1 month on mss. Free sample copy and writer's guidelines.

Nonfiction: Essay, historical/nostalgic, humor and interview/profile (opera composers, singers, producers and designers). No Master's or Doctoral theses. Buys 10mss/year. Query with published clips. Length: 500-5,000 words. Pays $50-250.

Fillers: Anecdotes and short humor. Buys 25/year. Length: 150-500 words. Pays $50-250.

Tips: "Be pointed, pithy in statement, accurate in research. Avoid florid, excessive language. Writers must be musically sensitive, interested in opera as a continuing vocal art. Enthusiasm for the subject is important. Contact us for which operas/composers we will be featuring each year. It is those areas of research, anecdote, analysis and humor, we will be filling first."

PERFORMING ARTS IN CANADA, 2nd Fl., 52 Avenue Rd., Toronto, Ontario M5R 2G2 Canada. (416)921-2601. Editor: Mary Ann Pathy. 80% freelance written. Prefers to work with published/established writers; works with a small number of new/unpublished writers each year. Quarterly magazine for professional performers and general readers with an interest in Canadian theatre, dance, music, opera and film. Covers "all five major fields of the performing arts (music, theatre, opera, film and dance), modern and classical, plus articles on related subjects (technical topics, government arts policy, etc.)." Circ. 80,550. Pays 1 month following publication. Publishes ms an average of 3 months after acceptance. Byline given. Offers 30-50% kill fee. Buys first serial rights. Reports in 3-6 weeks. Computer printout submissions acceptable; no dot-matrix. SAE, with IRCs. Sample copy $1.

Nonfiction: "Lively, stimulating, well-researched articles on Canadian performing artists or groups. We tend to be overstocked with theatre pieces; most often in need of good classical music articles." No nonCanadian, nonperforming arts material. Buys 30-35 mss/year. Query. Length: 1,500-2,000 words. Pays $150-200. Sometimes pays the expenses of writers on assignment.

Tips: "Query preferably with an outline. Writers new to this publication should include clippings. A writer must look at the research put into an article, the open viewpoints and access to photos to accompany the article, as well as new up-to-date ideas."

‡PRE-VUE, Box 31255, Billings MT 59107. Publisher: Virginia Hansen. "We are the cable-TV guide for Montana, and also for satellite 'dish' owners and members of the industry nationwide." Weekly magazine; 32-48 pages. Circ. 50,000. Pays on acceptance. Publishes ms an average of 2 months after acceptance. Byline given. Buys first and second rights to the same material. Query. Electronic submissions OK if Editwriter 7500; prefers standard ms form. Computer printout submissions acceptable; prefers letter-quality to dot-matrix. Reports in 2 months.

Nonfiction: "Subject matter is general, but must relate in some way to television or our reading area (Montana). For the national satellite edition, we would like articles which tell of the newest advances in the industry or what is happening with the satellites, including legislation concerning them. We would like articles to have a beginning, middle and end; in other words, popular magazine style, heavy on the hooker lead." Informational, how-to, interview, profile, humor and historical. Feature length: 500-750 words. Pays 4¢/word minimum.

Market conditions are constantly changing! If this is 1988 or later, buy the newest edition of Writer's Market *at your favorite bookstore or order directly from* Writer's Digest Books.

Photos: 8½x10½ 4-color photos for covers purchased with mss or on assignment. Pays $10. B&w for inside pages, $3-5. Captions required.
Tips: "We're looking for work from experienced writers. We prefer writing that is short and peppy, or very informative or humorous."

SATELLITE DISH MAGAZINE, Your Complete Satellite TV Entertainment Guide, Satellite Publications, Inc., 460 Tennessee Ave., Box 8, Memphis TN 38101. (901)521-1580. Editor: Connie White Mills. 90% freelance written. Eager to work with new/unpublished writers. Biweekly national magazine with TV/movie entertainment news, features, reviews and personality profiles. "We are looking for two basic styles: the lively entertainment feature on current or upcoming TV (satellite/pay/cable/network) programming; and the in-depth, informative article, usually written in first person, about an issue and its relation to the satellite TV or movie/film industry." Circ. 150,000. Pays on publication. Publishes ms an average of 2 months after acceptance. Byline given. Offers negotiable kill fee. Buys first North American serial and second serial (reprint) rights. Submit seasonal/holiday material 3 months in advance. Previously published submissions "sometimes" OK. Electronic submissions OK via IBM or Digital. Computer printout submissions acceptable; no dot-matrix. Reports in approximately 2 months. Free sample copy and writer's guidelines.
Nonfiction: General interest; historical/nostalgic; interview/profile; opinion (as it relates to a topic or issue); personal experience (as it relates to a topic or issue); technical (satellite TV news, issues). "We also recommend specialized writing on any of the satellite TV programming categories: Adult Programming, Business News, Children's Programming, Consumer Events, Cultural Information, Education, Entertainment Specials, Ethnic Programming, Family Programming, Health, Movies, Music, News, Public Affairs, Public Broadcasting, Religion, Science, Sports, Unique Variety Programmings and Women's Programming. This could be a piece on an upcoming program, or a specific category or subject and how it relates to satellite television." Query with published clips or send complete ms. Length: 800-2,000 words. Pays $150-1,000. Sometimes pays the expenses of writers on assignment.
Photos: State availability of photos and/or send photos with query or mss. Pays $50 minimum for color transparencies; $25 minimum for 8x10 b&w prints; $50 minimum for 8x10 color prints. Captions required. Buys one-time rights.
Columns/Departments: Film/Movie Reviews (on movies premiering on the pay/cable/satellite networks); Books (as they relate to TV/movies); Celebrity/People (on people as they relate to TV/movies). Buys 50-100 mss/year. Query with published clips or send complete ms. Length: 1,000-1,500 words. Pays $150-750.
Tips: "Personality profiles and movie reviews are most open to freelancers."

‡Satellite ORBIT, CommTek Publishing, 9440 Fairview Ave., Boise ID 83701. (208)322-2800. Editor: Rick Ardinger. 75% freelance written. A monthly guide for the Satellite TV viewer, featuring profiles and interviews with film and TV stars and previews of upcoming TV productions. Circ. 350,000. Pays on acceptance. Publishes ms an average of 2 months after acceptance. Byline given. Offers 30% kill fee. Buys first North American serial rights. Submit seasonal/holiday material 3 months in advance. Photocopied submissions OK. Electronic submissions OK, but requires hard copy also. Computer printout submissions acceptable; prefers letter-quality to dot-matrix. Reports in 2 weeks on queries; 3 weeks on manuscripts. Sample copy $5.
Nonfiction: Interview/profile and television. Buys 75 mss/year. Query with published clips. Length: 1,500-2,000 words. Pays 400-1,200 for assigned articles; pays $350-500 for unsolicited articles. Sometimes pays the expenses of writers on assignment.
Photos: State availability of photos with submission. Reviews contact sheets and transparencies. Identification of subjects required.
Columns/Departments: Satellite Watch (information about satellite launches) and Program Review (preview of upcoming programs on satellite TV), both 1,500 words. Query with published clips. Pays $350-700.
Tips: "Features are most open to freelancers. Most writing is assigned; we like to see clips of the writer's work before we assign."

SOAP OPERA DIGEST, 254 W. 31st St., New York NY 10001. Executive Editor: Meredith Brown. 25% freelance written. Prefers to work with published/established writers; works with a small number of new/unpublished writers each year. Biweekly magazine; 144 pages. Circ. 750,000. Pays on acceptance. Publishes ms an average of 2 months after acceptance. Buys all rights. Submit seasonal/holiday material 4 months in advance of issue date. Computer printout submissions acceptable. Reports in 1 month.
Nonfiction: Lynn Davey, managing editor, freelance material. "Articles only directly about daytime and nighttime personalities or soap operas." Interview (no telephone interviews); nostalgia; photo features (must be recent); profiles; special interest features: health, beauty, with soap opera personalities and industry news, with a strong interest in nighttime soaps. "We are a 'newsy' magazine—not gossipy, and are highly interested in timely news stories. No poorly written material that talks down to the audience." Buys 2-3 mss/issue. Query with clips of previously published work. Length: 1,000-2,000 words. Pays $200 and up. Sometimes pays the expenses of writers on assignment.
Photos: State availability of photos with query. Captions preferred. Buys all rights.

Tips: "Writers must be good at in-depth personality profiles. Pack as much info as possible into a compact length. Also want humor pieces."

STARWEEK MAGAZINE, Toronto Star Newspapers, Ltd., 1 Yonge St., Toronto, Ontario M5E 1E6 Canada. (416)869-4936. Editor: John Bryden. "We are backlogged with submissions and prefer not to receive unsolicited submissions at this time."

TV GUIDE, Radnor PA 19088. Editor (National Section): David Sendler. Editor (Local Sections): Roger Youman. Managing Editor: R.C. Smith. 70% freelance written. Prefers to work with published/established writers; works with a small number of new/unpublished writers each year; eager to work with new/unpublished writers. Weekly. Circ. 17.1 million. Study publication. Query to Andrew Mills, assistant managing editor. Publishes ms an average of 2 months after acceptance. Computer printout submissions acceptable; prefers letter-quality to dot-matrix.
Nonfiction: Wants offbeat articles about TV people and shows. This magazine is not interested in fan material. Also wants stories on the newest trends of television, but they must be written in clear, lively English. Length: 1,000-2,000 words.
Photos: Uses professional high-quality photos, normally shot on assignment, by photographers chosen by *TV Guide*. Prefers color. Pays $350 day rate against page rates—$450 for 2 pages or less.

‡VCR, The Home Video Monthly, Falsoft, Inc., The Falsoft Bldg., 9509 U.S. Hwy 42, Box 385, Louisville KY 40059. (502)228-4492. Editor: Lawrence C. Falk. Managing Editor: Kevin Nickols. "*VCR*, The Home Video Monthly, is a magazine devoted to the new generation of home viewer: those who use their video recorder as an entertainment appliance instead of an electronic gadget." Estab. 1986. Circ. 80,600. Pays on publication. Publishes ms an average of 3 months after acceptance. Byline given. Buys first serial rights or all rights. Submit seasonal/holiday material 5 months in advance. Simultaneous and photocopied submissions OK. Electronic submissions OK via disk: ASCII on MS-or PC-DOS, but requires hard copy also. Computer printout submissions acceptable; prefers letter-quality to dot-matrix. Reports in 2 weeks on queries; 1 month on mss. Sample copy for 9x12 SAE with 6 first class stamps; writer's guidelines for 8½x14 SAE with 1 first class stamp.
Nonfiction: Jutta Kapfhammer, articles editor. Essays, historical/nostalgic, how-to, humor, interview/profile and photo feature. "No highly technical video-related articles. Read the magazine, follow the style." Buys 60 mss/year. Query with or without published clips, or send complete ms. Length: 1,500-10,000 words. Pays $50/page maximum. Sometimes pays expenses of writers on assignment.
Photos: State availability of photos with submission. Reviews contact sheets, transparencies and prints. Additional payment for photos accepted with ms. Identification of subjects required. Buys first serial rights.
Columns/Departments: Remember Them (interviews, etc. with TV and movie personalities of the past) and Video Gold (featuring a classic TV series, including a top 10 list and a complete episode guide). Buys 50 mss/year. Query with published clips. Length: 1,500-2,500 words.

‡VIDEO, 460 W. 34th St., New York, NY 10001. (212)947-6500. Editor: Doug Garr. Managing Editor: Stan Pinkwas. 75% freelance written. Prefers to work with published/established writers; works with a small number of new/unpublished writers each year. A monthly magazine covering home videos. Circ. 340,000. Pays on acceptance. Publishes ms an average of 2 months after acceptance. Byline given. Buys all rights. Electronic submissions OK; "please call first." Requires hard copy also. Computer printout submissions acceptable; prefers letter-quality to dot-matrix. Reports in 2 weeks on queries; 1 month on manuscripts.
Nonfiction: Buys 80 mss/year. Query with published clips. Pays $300-1,000. Sometimes pays the expenses of writers on assignment.
Tips: The entire feature area is open to freelancers. Write a brilliant query and send an unpublished copy of the submission if it's been previously published.

‡VIDEOMANIA, "The Newspaper For Video Nuts", Legs Of Stone Publishing Co., 115 Stanton St., Ripon WI 54971. Editor: Robert Katerzynske. 25% freelance written. Eager to work with new/unpublished writers. A monthly tabloid for the home video hobbyist. "Our readers are very much 'into' home video: they like reading about it—including both video hardware and software. A large number also collect video (movies, vintage TV, etc.)." Circ. 2,000. Pays on publication. Publishes ms an average of 3 months after acceptance. Byline given. Buys all rights; may reassign. Submit seasonal/holiday material 4 months in advance. Computer printout submissions acceptable; prefers letter-quality to dot-matrix. Reports in 3 weeks on mss. Sample copy $1.50.
Nonfiction: Book excerpts, exposé, general interest, historical/nostalgic, how-to, humor, interview/profile, new product, opinion, personal experience, photo feature, technical and travel. "All articles should deal with video and/or film. We always have special holiday issues in November and December." No "*complicated technical pieces.*" Buys 24 mss/year. Send complete ms. Length: 500-2,500 words. Pays $2.50 maximum. "Contributor copies given for mss deemed interesting but not as 'newsworthy' as others."

Photos: Send photos with submissions. Reviews contact sheets and 3x5 prints. Offers no additional payment for photos accepted with ms. Model releases and identification of subjects required. Buys all rights; may reassign.

Fiction: Adventure, horror and humorous. "We want short, video-related fiction only an occasional basis. No pornographic stories." Buys 5 mss/year. Send complete ms. Length: 500-2,500 words. Pays $2.50 maximum plus copies.

Tips: "Write in a plain, easy-to-understand style. We're not looking for a highhanded, knock-em-dead writing style . . . just something good! We want more short video, film and book reviews by freelancers."

VIDEO TIMES MAGAZINE, Publications International, Ltd., 3841 W. Oakton St., Skokie IL 60076. (312)676-3470. Editoral Director: David J. Hogan. Acquisitions Editor: Jeff Mintz. 90% freelance written. Prefers to work with published/established writers. Monthly magazine covering all software available for videotape and videodisc players. "We explore the movies and other aspects of entertainment and information available for video. Our audience watches a lot of pre-recorded tape. We provide both information (what's new) and ideas. We specialize in movie themes and in video tape reviews." Circ. 150,000. Pays on acceptance. Publishes ms an average of 2 months after acceptance. Byline given on features and keynote reviews; staff block credit for Calendar (short) reviews. Rights bought depend on material. Submit seasonal/holiday material 4 months in advance. Photocopied submissions OK. Computer printout submissions acceptable. Reports in 1 month. Sample copy for $1.95; free writer's guidelines.

Nonfiction: Buys 50 feature mss/year. Query with published clips. Length: 750-1,500 words. Pays up to 20¢/word. Flat fee by assignment preferable.

Photos: State availability of photos. Wants color transparencies and b&w prints "as big as possible." Identification of subjects required. "We only buy photo stills from movies."

Fillers: Anecdotes and "stories behind the movies: casting, problems, script changes, etc." Length: 50-100 words. Pays $20 per anecdote. Query with published clips.

Tips: "We need people who can accurately critique material being made specifically for video. We especially want people who watch a lot of videotape/disc—and think about it as its own medium. All areas, except signed columns, are open to freelancers. To write features, a freelancer must have a strong and proven grasp of film, or subject matter. Query first with cover story ideas. Anecdotes are basically strong research. We have 35 steady freelancers whom we try to keep busy. It is very hard to break into a review pool. Reviews most often are assigned to those who appreciate a certain type of movie (horror, etc.)."

X-IT, A general arts and entertainment magazine, Image Design, Box 102, St. John's, Newfoundland A1C 5H5 Canada. (709)753-8802. Editor: Ken J. Harvey. Managing Editor: Beth Fiander. 100% freelance written. Eager to work with new/unpublished writers. A triannual entertainment magazine concentrating on new ideas and thoughts in arts and literature (written and visual) for the general public. Circ. 3,000. Pays on publication. Publishes ms an average of 3 months after acceptance. Byline given. Buys one-time rights. Submit seasonal/holiday material 2 months in advance. Simultaneous, photocopied, and previously published submissions OK. Computer printout submissions acceptable; no dot matrix. Reports in 3 weeks on queries; 1 month on mss. Sample copy $3 and 2 IRCs.

Nonfiction: All nonfiction is assigned by the editor. Query. Sometimes pays the expenses of writers on assignment.

Fiction: Adventure, erotica, experimental, fantasy, horror, humorous, mystery, science fiction and suspense. "We are open to practically all areas of literature. Our only demand is quality." Buys 12 mss/year. Send complete ms. Length: 1,500-4,800 words. Pays $10-150.

Poetry: Allela English, poetry editor. Avant-garde, free verse, light verse and traditional. Buys 30 poems/year. Submit maximum 10 poems. Length: open. Pays $10-50.

Fillers: Jokes and short humor. Buys 12/year. Length: "preferably short." Pays $5-25.

Tips: "Send along a short bio with submissions and a cover letter describing how work would fit in with the publication. Fiction and poetry are most open to freelancers. We need fillers."

__ *Travel, Camping, and Trailer*

Travel agencies and tour companies constantly remind consumers of the joys of traveling. But it's usually the travel magazines that tell potential travelers about the positive and negative aspects of possible destinations. Publications in this category tell campers and tourists the where-tos and how-tos of travel. Publications that buy how-to camping and travel material with a conservation angle are listed in the Nature, Conservation, and ecology classification.

Regional publications are frequently interested in travel and camping material with a local angle. Hunting and fishing and outdoor publications that buy camping how-to material will be found in the Sports category. Those dealing with automobiles or other vehicles maintained for sport or as a hobby can be found in the Automotive and Motorcycle category. Many magazines in the In-Flight category are also in the market for travel articles and photos.

AAA WORLD, Hawaii/Alaska, AAA Hawaii, 730 Ala Moana Blvd., Honolulu HI 96813. (808)528-2600. Editor: Thomas Crosby. 15% freelance written. Bimonthly magazine of travel, automotive safety and legislative issues. Orientation is toward stories that benefit members in some way. Circ. 20,000. Pays on publication. Publishes ms an average of 4 months after acceptance. Byline given. Buys one-time rights. Submit seasonal/holiday material 4 months in advance. Photocopied and previously published submissions OK. Computer printout submissions acceptable. Reports in 1 week on queries; 1 month on mss. Free sample copy.
Nonfiction: How-to (auto maintenance, safety, etc.); and travel (tips, destinations, bargains). Buys 6 mss/year. Send complete ms. Length: 1,500 words. Pays $150 maximum. Sometimes pays the expenses of writers on assignment.
Photos: State availability of photos. Reviews b&w contact sheet. Pays $10-25. Captions required. Buys one-time rights.
Tips: "Find an interesting, human interest story that affects AAA members."

ACCENT, Meridian Publishing Inc., 1720 Washington, Box 10010, Ogden UT 84409. Editor: Robyn C. Walker. (801)394-9446. 60-70% freelance written. Works with a small number of new/unpublished writers each year. A monthly inhouse travel magazine distributed by various companies to employees, customers, stockholders, etc. "Readers are predominantly upscale, mainstream, family oriented." Circ. 90,000. Pays on acceptance. Publishes ms an average of 1 year after acceptance. Byline given. Buys first rights, second serial (reprint) rights and nonexclusive reprint rights. Simultaneous, photocopied and previously published submissions OK. Computer printout submissions are acceptable; dot-matrix submissions are acceptable if readable. Reports in 6 weeks. Sample copy $1 and 9x12 SAE; writer's guidelines for business size SAE and 1 first class stamp.
Nonfiction: "We want upbeat pieces slanted toward the average traveler, but we use some exotic travel. Resorts, cruises, hiking, camping, health retreats, historic sites, sports vacations, national or state forests and parks are all featured. No articles without original color photos, except with travel tips. We also welcome pieces on travel tips and way to travel." Buys 40 mss/year. Query. Length: 1,200 words. Pays 15¢/word.
Photos: Send photos with ms. Pays $35 for color transparencies; $50 for cover. Captions and model releases required. Buys one-time rights.
Tips: "Write about interesting places. We are inundated with queries for stories on California and the southeastern coast. Super color transparencies are essential. Most rejections are because of poor quality photography or the writer didn't study the market. We are using three times as many domestic pieces as foreign because of our readership."

‡ADVENTURE MAGAZINE, American Adventure, 12910 Totem Lake Blvd., Kirkland WA 98034. (206)821-7766. Editor: Pam Sather. "We are backlogged with submissions and prefer not to receive unsolicited submissions at this time."

ADVENTURE ROAD, Citicorp Publishing, 641 Lexington Ave., New York NY 10022. (212)888-9450. Editor: Deborah C. Thompson. A bimonthly magazine for members of the Amoco Motor Club, the majority of whom are professional college-educated, moderately affluent, middle-aged and enthusiastic about travel. "*Adventure Road* conveys information on domestic destinations, general vacation planning as well as car care and club benefits. Circ. 1.5 million. Pays on acceptance. Byline given. Offers 25% kill fee. Buys first rights. Submit seasonal/holiday material at least 6 months in advance. Reports in 1 month on queries; 3 weeks on mss. Sample copy for 8½x10 SAE and 4 first class stamps; writer's guidelines for business size SAE and 1 first class stamp.
Nonfiction: Book excerpts; how-to (travel-related); photo feature; and travel (restricted to domestic destinations). Buys 35 mss/year ("commissioned; rarely, if ever unsolicited"). Query with published clips. Length: 1,500-2,200 words. Pays $400-800.
Tips: "Freelancers can best break into our publication by writing a literate, well-conceived query letter and providing exciting clips. We are looking for destinations or kinds of trips that are classics, appealing to a broad number of people, as well as an occasional offbeat story on a genuine heartfelt American travel experience. Major features are most open to new freelancers, although we usually use writers already known to us. Although our articles tend to be seasonal, we do like to provide our readers with material that they will be able to use in making plans for future trips."

Close-up

Robert Scott Milne
Travel writer, Editor
Travelwriter Market Letter

Robert Scott Milne lives the travel writer's dream. As a writer, he has published articles in *The Atlantic, The New York Times* and other prestige markets. His book, *Opportunities in Travel Careers* (National Textbook Company) is an important guide for those seeking opportunities in the travel industry, and is now in its third edition.

Milne began writing articles and getting published in 1954, but did not go fulltime until 1972. "For sixteen years I worked as an associate editor, first at *Collier's Encyclopedia*, then at *Encyclopedia Americana*. During this time I was moonlighting travel articles. The turning point came in 1972 when I left *Americana*, obtained an office, and became a fulltime travel writer. It was pretty scary at first, waiting for dilatory editors to send checks for articles, wondering if I would be able to pay the rent. I suggest that other writers who depend on a nonwriting job *keep* the job, meanwhile building up their freelance output *and* income until they can safely go fulltime as a writer."

Milne's diverse background has served him well in his work. He majored in languages—French, Spanish, German and English—in college. "Languages help the travel writer," Milne says, "to understand better the foreign milieu in which he travels and which he intends to write about."

During World War II, Milne served as a naval intelligence officer at Pearl Harbor and in Washington, and as a naval attache in the U.S. Embassy in Athens. "This," Milne relates, "taught me to seek information through many channels and with great persistence, checking various sources against each other. In my editorial jobs I learned the importance of accuracy and brevity, and as an editor buying from writers I learned the publisher's point of view."

Milne edits and publishes *Travelwriter Marketletter*, known as *the* market guide for travel writers. Although his newsletter is not a market for writers, he is always ready to offer advice on travel writing. "The most important qualities for a travel writer are strong curiosity and great persistence. You also have to be able to withstand the 'tribulations' of travel writing, such as having to describe a Florida beach from a five-minute visit, fully-clothed, when there's no time for a swim."

Milne advises writers interested in travel-writing assignments to concentrate on "convincing an editor that you either know all about the subject or can find out all about it, and that you can write an article consonant with the magazine's authority. You have to speak for the magazine."

Robert Scott Milne calls travel writing "the best job in the world. When it's your *business* to travel and report, you delve deeply, get to know more people, and derive more from travel. And the feeling I have when I am creating a story is really great. I'm telling people about something wonderful that *they* too can do."

—Michael A. Banks

AL MUFTAH, The Magazine for Saudi-American Bank's Visa Gold Card Holders in the Middle East, Age Communications Ltd., Parkway House, Sheen Lane, London SW14 8LS England. Editor: Joseph R. Yogerst. Assistant Editor: Jules MacMahon. 80% freelance written. Prefers to work with published/established writers. A bimonthly magazine covering all aspects of luxury travel and consumer goods. Circ. 10,000. Pays on publication. Publishes ms an average of 1 year after acceptance. Buys first Middle East rights in both English and Arabic. Byline given. Submit seasonal/holiday material at least 6 months in advance. Simultaneous queries, and photocopied or previously published submissions OK as long as they have not or will not appear in the Middle East. Computer printout submissions acceptable; prefers letter-quality to dot-matrix. Send SAE with IRC. Reports in 2 months.
Nonfiction: Each issue includes at least four "VISA Gold Destinations" around the world, covering popular travel destinations outside the Middle East. "A luxury or up-market slant is essential, because an estimated 80 percent of our readers are millionaires." *Al Muftah* also carries regular features on charter yachting, private aircraft, high-speed rail and air travel, luxury motoring, exotic ocean cruises, equestrian sports, interior design, property rental and investment, fashion, jewelry and dining. "In 1986-87 we will have a special need for articles on national cultures i.e. cuisine, fashion and fine arts such as dance, music, theatre, painting and design. We want just about anything that could appeal to a millionaire. We also run occasional articles on exclusive private clubs, be it an 18-hole country club in Florida or a beach and tennis club in Tahiti." Length: 1,500-2,000 words. Pays minimum £80 Sterling (estimated $120) per 1,000 words. Query or send complete ms. Buys 60 mss/year.
Photos: State availability of photos. Captions required. Pays minimum of £20 for 35mm or larger format color or transparencies; pays £150 for cover photos. Buys first Middle East rights.
Tips: "We receive far too many destination stories and not nearly enough on luxury travel, fashion, property and food. Also, we need articles on fine art such as music, dance, theatre and painting. Think like a millionaire—where would you go and what would you buy if you had a million dollars?"

ASU TRAVEL GUIDE, ASU Travel Guide, Inc., 1325 Columbus Ave., San Francisco CA 94133. (415)441-5200. Editor: Kathleen Nevin. 20% freelance written. Quarterly guidebook covering international travel features and travel discounts for well-traveled airline employees. Circ. 40,000. Pays on acceptance. Publishes ms an average of 18 months after acceptance. Byline given. Offers kill fee. Buys first North American serial rights, first and second rights to the same material, and second serial (reprint) rights to material originally published elsewhere. Makes work-for-hire assignments. Submit seasonal/holiday material 6 months in advance. Simultaneous queries and simultaneous, photocopied and previously published submissions OK. Computer printout submissions acceptable; prefers letter-quality to dot-matrix. Reports in 1 month. Send SASE for writer's guidelines. Unsolicited ms or queries without SASE will not be acknowledged. No telephone queries.
Nonfiction: International travel articles "similar to those run in consumer magazines." Not interested in amateur efforts from inexperienced travelers or personal experience articles that don't give useful information to other travelers. Buys 16-20 mss/year. Destination pieces only; no "Tips On Luggage" articles. "We will be accepting fewer manuscripts and relying more on our established group of freelance contributors." Length: 1,200-1,500 words. Pays $200.
Photos: "Interested in clear, high-contrast photos; we prefer not to receive material without photos." Reviews 5x7 and 8x10 b&w prints. "Payment for photos is included in article price; photos from tourist offices are acceptable."
Tips: "Query with samples of travel writing and a list of places you've recently visited. We appreciate clean and simple style. Keep verbs in the active tense and involve the reader in what you write. Avoid 'cute' writing, excess punctuation (especially dashes and ellipses), coined words and stale cliches. Any article that starts with the name of a country followed by an exclamation point is immediately rejected. The most frequent mistakes made by writers in completing an article for us are: 1) Lazy writing; using words to describe a place that could describe any destination—i.e. 'There is so much to do in (fill in destination) that whole guidebooks have been written about it.' 2) Including fare and tour package information—our readers make arrangements through their own airline."

AWAY, c/o ALA, 888 Worcester St., Wellesley MA 02181. (617)237-5200. Editor: Gerard J. Gagnon. For "members of the ALA Auto & Travel Club, interested in their autos and in travel. Ages range approximately 20-65. They live primarily in New England." Slanted to seasons. 5-10% freelance written. Quarterly. Circ. 163,000. Buys first serial rights. Pays on acceptance. Publishes ms an average of 3 months after acceptance. Submit seasonal material 6 months in advance. Reports "as soon as possible." Although a query is not mandatory, it may be advisable for many articles. Computer printout submissions acceptable; no dot-matrix. Free sample copy.
Nonfiction: Articles on "travel, tourist attractions, safety, history, etc., preferably with a New England angle. Also, car care tips and related subjects." Would like a "positive feel to all pieces, but not the chamber of commerce approach." Buys general seasonal travel, specific travel articles, and travel-related articles; outdoor activities, for example, gravestone rubbing; historical articles linked to places to visit and humor with a point. "Would like to see more nonseasonally oriented material. Most material now submitted seems suitable only for

our summer issue. Avoid pieces on hunting and about New England's most publicized attractions, such as Old Sturbridge Village and Mystic Seaport." Length: 800-1,500 words, "preferably 1,000-1,200." Pays approximately 10¢/word.

Photos: Photos purchased with mss. Captions required. B&w glossy prints. Pays $5-10/b&w photo, payment on publication based upon which photos are used. Not buying color at this time.

Tips: "We have decided to sharply limit purchases of articles and photographs from outside sources; we will now publish more staff-produced material. The most frequent mistakes made by writers in completing an article for us are spelling, typographical errors and questionable statements of facts, which require additional research by the editorial staff."

BIKEREPORT, Bikecentennial, Inc., The Bicycle Travel Association, Box 8308, Missoula MT 59807. (406)721-1776. Editor: Daniel D'Ambrosio. 75% freelance written. Works with a small number of new/unpublished writers each year; eager to work with new/unpublished writers. Bimonthly bicycle touring magazine for Bikecentennial members. Circ. 18,000. Pays on publication. Publishes ms an average of 8 months after acceptance. Byline given. Buys first serial rights. Submit seasonal/holiday material 3 months in advance. Simultaneous queries and photocopied submissions OK. Electronic submissions OK on CP/M Morrow or MS/DOS, but requires hard copy also. Computer printout submissions acceptable; no dot-matrix. Reports in 2 weeks on queries; 1 month on mss. Publishes ms an average of 8 months after acceptance. Sample copy and guidelines for $1 postage. Include short bio with manuscript.

Nonfiction: Historical/nostalgic (interesting spots along bike trails); how-to (bicycle); humor (touring); interview/profile (bicycle industry people); personal experience ("my favorite tour"); photo feature (bicycle); technical (bicycle); travel ("my favorite tour"). Buys 20-25 mss/year. Query with published clips or send complete ms. Length: 800-2,500 words. Pays 3¢/word.

Photos: Bicycle, scenery, portraits. State availability of photos. Model releases and identification of subjects required.

Fiction: Adventure, experimental, historical, humorous. Not interested in anything that doesn't involve bicycles. Query with published clips or send complete ms. "I'd like to see more good fiction and essays." Length: 800-2,500 words. Pays 3¢/word.

Tips: "We don't get many good essays. Consider that a hint. But we are still always interested in travelogs."

‡THE CAMPER TIMES, (formerly *The Virginia Camper*), Royal Productions, Inc., Box 6294, Richmond VA 23230. (804)270-5653. Editor: David A. Posner. 50% freelance written. Prefers to work with published/established writers; works with a small number of new/unpublished writers each year. A quarterly tabloid. "We supply the camping public with articles and information on outdoor activities related to camping. Our audience is primarily families that own recreational vehicles." Circ. 35,000. Pays on publication. Publishes ms an average of 2 months after acceptance. Byline given. Buys one-time rights, second serial (reprint) rights or simultaneous rights. Submit seasonal/holiday material 2 months in advance. Simultaneous, photocopied and previously published submissions OK. Electronic submissions OK via Apple II Plus, but requires hard copy also. Computer printout submissions acceptable. Reports in 1 month. Free sample copy and writer's guidelines.

Nonfiction: How-to and travel; information on places to camp and fishing articles. Also "tourist related articles. Places to go, things to see. Does not have to be camping related." Buys 25 mss/year. Query with or without published clips, or send complete ms. Length: 100-1,000 words. Pays $20-100 for unsolicited articles. Sometimes pays the expenses of writers on assignment.

Photos: State availability of photos with submission. Reviews contact sheets and prints. Offers $1-5/photo. Identification of subjects required. Buys one-time rights.

Columns/Departments: RV Doctor (helpful hints on repairing RVs). Buys 12 mss/year. Query. Length: 100-500 words. Pays $20-50.

Fillers: Anecdotes, facts, gags to be illustrated by cartoonist, newsbreaks and short humor. Buys 25/year. Length: 10-500 words. Pays $5-20.

Tips: "Best approach is to call me. All areas of *The Camper Times* are open to freelancers. We will look at all articles and consider for publication."

CAMPERWAYS, 1108 N. Bethlehem Pike, Box 460, Spring House PA 19477. (215)643-2058. Editor-in-Chief: Karen Kane. 75% freelance written. Prefers to work with published/established writers. Emphasis on recreational vehicle camping and travel. Monthly (except Dec. and Jan.) tabloid. Circ. 35,000. Pays on publication. Publishes ms an average of 4 months after acceptance. Buys first, simultaneous, second serial (reprint) or regional rights. Byline given. Submit seasonal/holiday material 3-4 months in advance. Simultaneous, photocopied and previously published submissions OK. Computer printout submissions acceptable; prefers letter-quality to dot-matrix. Reports in 1 month. Sample copy $2; free writer's guidelines.

Nonfiction: Historical (when tied in with camping trip to historical attraction or area); how-to (selection, care, maintenance of RVs, accessories and camping equipment); humor; personal experience; and travel (camping destinations within 200 miles of New York-DC metro corridor). No "material on camping trips to destinations outside stated coverage area." Buys 80-100 unsolicited mss/year. Query. Length: 1,000-2,000 words. Pays $40-85.

Photos: "Good photos greatly increase likelihood of acceptance. Don't send snapshots, Polaroids. We can't use them." Photos purchased with accompanying ms. Captions required. Uses 5x7 or 8x10 b&w glossy prints. Pays $5/photo published.

Columns/Departments: Camp Cookery (ideas for cooking in RV galleys and over campfires—should include recipes). Buys 10 mss/year. Query. Length: 500-1,500 words. Pays $25-50.

Tips: "Articles should focus on single attraction or activity or on closely clustered attractions within reach on the same weekend camping trip rather than on types of attractions or activities in general. We're looking for little-known or offbeat items. Emphasize positive aspects of camping: fun, economy, etc. We want feature items, not shorts and fillers. Acceptance is based on quality of article and appropriateness of subject matter. The most frequent mistakes made by writers in completing an article for us are failure to follow guidelines or failure to write from the camper's perspective."

CAMPING CANADA, CRV Publishing Canada Ltd., Suite 202, 2077 Dundas St. East, Mississauga, Ontario L4X 1M2 Canada. (416)624-8218. Editor: Peter Tasler. A magazine published 7 times/year, covering camping and RVing. Circ. 100,000. Pays on publication. Byline given. Buys first rights. Submit seasonal/holiday material 3 months in advance. Computer printout submissions acceptable; no dot-matrix. Reports in 2 months. Free sample copy and writer's guidelines.

Nonfiction: General interest; historical/nostalgic (sometimes); how-to; new product; personal experience; and photo feature; technical; and travel. No material unrelated to Canada and RVing. Buys 50 mss/year. Query. Length: 1,000-2,000 words. Pays $150-300.

Photos: Send photos with query or manuscript. Reviews contact sheets, negatives, transparencies (send duplicates) and prints. Identification of subjects required. Buys first serial rights.

CAMPING TODAY, Official Publication of National Campers & Hikers Association, T-A-W Publishing Co., 9425 S. Greenville Road, Greenville MI 48838. (616)754-9179. Editors: David and Martha Higbie. 80% freelance written. Prefers to work with published/established writers. The monthly official membership publication of the NCHA, "the largest nonprofit camping organization in the United States and Canada. Members are heavily oriented toward RV travel, both weekend and extended vacations. A small segment is interested in backpacking. Concentration is on activities of members within chapters, conservation, wildlife, etc." Circ. 30,000. Pays on publication. Publishes ms an average of 6 months after acceptance. Byline given. Buys one-time rights. Submit seasonal/holiday material 3 months in advance. Simultaneous, photocopied, and previously published submissions OK. Computer printout submissions acceptable; prefers letter-quality to dot-matrix. Reports in 1 month. Sample copy and writer's guidelines for SAE.

Nonfiction: Humor (camping or travel related); interview/profile (interesting campers); new product (RV's and related equipment); technical (RV's); and travel (camping, hiking and RV travel). Buys 12-24 mss/year. Send complete ms. Length: 750-1,000 words. Pays $75-100.

Photos: Send photos with accompanying query or ms. Reviews color transparencies and 5x7 b&w prints. Pays $25 maximum for color transparencies. Captions required. Sometimes pays the expenses of writers on assignment.

Tips: "Freelance material on RV travel, RV technical subjects and items of general camping and hiking interest throughout the United States and Canada will receive special attention. Color cover every month."

CHARTERING MAGAZINE, Chartering Inc., 830 Pop Tilton's Place, Jensen Beach FL 33457. (305)334-2003. Editor: Antonia Thomas. 25-60% freelance written. Prefers to work with published/established writers. "*Chartering* is a people-oriented travel magazine with a positive approach. Our focus is yacht charter vacations." Circ. 40,000. Pays on publication. Publishes ms an average of 3 months after acceptance. Buys first North American serial rights. Submit seasonal/holiday material at least 5 months in advance. Simultaneous queries and simultaneous and photocopied submissions, and previously published work (on rare occasion) OK. Electronic submissions OK via Apple II series, Apple Macintosh. Computer printout submissions acceptable; prefers letter-quality to dot-matrix. Reports in 2-4 weeks. Writer's guidelines for #SAE and 1 first class stamp.

Nonfiction: General interest (worldwide, charter boat-oriented travel); historical/nostalgic (charter vacation oriented); how-to (bareboating technique); interview/profile (charter brokers, charter skippers, positive); new product (would have to be a new type of charter); opinion; personal experience (charter boat related, worldwide, positive people-oriented travel); photo feature (charter boat, worldwide, positive, people-oriented travel); technical (bareboat technique; charter boat IRS; charter boat documentation); travel (charter vacation-oriented); and ancillary topics such as fishing, scuba or underwater photography. Special issues will focus on the Caribbean, diving, and sportsfishing. Buys 50-85 mss/year. Query with published clips or send complete ms. Length: 600-3,000 words. Pays $50-350. Rarely pays expenses of writers on assignment.

Photos: State availability of photos or send photos with query or ms. Pays with article for b&w and color negatives, color transparencies (35mm), and b&w and color prints (3x5 or larger), plus buys cover photos. Requires model releases and identification of subjects. Buys one-time rights.

Columns/Departments: Cruising areas, bareboat techniques (all facets), sail training, facilities. Buys 12-20/year. Query with published clips or send complete ms. Length: 500-1,200 words.
Tips: "We are happy to look at the work of any freelancer who may have something appropriate to offer within our scope—travel with a charter vacation orientation. We prefer submissions accompanied by good, professional quality photography. The best first step is a request for editorial guidelines, accompanied by a typed letter and work sample. *Chartering* will be looking for more articles of 300-600 words."

‡**CHEVRON USA ODYSSEY,** H.M. Goushā, Box 6227, San Jose CA 95150. (408)296-1060. Editor: Mark Williams. 75% freelance written. Prefers to work with published/established writers. A quarterly magazine. "We are a travel- and recreation-oriented publication published on contract for the Chevron Travel Club and its members. We want positive, upbeat descriptions of places and activities." Circ. 450,000. Pays on acceptance. Publishes ms an average of 6 months after acceptance. Byline given. Offers 25% kill fee. Buys first North American serial rights. Submit seasonal/holiday material 1 year in advance. Photocopied submissions OK. Computer printout submissions acceptable; prefers letter-quality to dot-matrix. Reports in 6 weeks on queries; 2 months on manuscripts. Sample copy for 9x12 SAE with $1.24 postage; free writer's guidelines.
Nonfiction: How-to (on crafts, family activities, hobbies, etc), travel and recreational activities. No personal accounts of vacation experiences, fiction, poetry. Buys 35 mss/year. Query with published clips, or send complete ms. Length: 750-1,600 words. Pays $150-500 for assigned articles; pays $100-400 for unsolicited articles.
Photos: State availability of photos with submissions. Reviews 35mm and larger color transparencies. Offers $125-400/photo. Identification of subjects required. Buys one-time rights. "We work mainly on a stock basis with established photographers."
Columns/Departments: Americana (humorous and anecdotes on geography, language, history, travel); Family Activities (crafts and hobbies, unusual forms of recreation, such as boomerangs); and Travel Tips (featurettes on trends such as travel for the disabled or computers for travel); all 700-800 words. Buys 10 mss/year. Query with published clips. Pays $100-200.
Fillers: Anecdotes. Buys 20/year. Length: 200 words maximum. Pays $25 maximum.
Tips: "We advise writers to revise and rewrite to an acceptable professional level *before* submitting articles to us. Most manuscripts we see are closer to rough drafts and are rejected or returned for rewriting. All sections are open to anyone capable of producing high quality magazine features. We plan to give more emphasis to the South and Southwest and less to the Northeast; the West is our primary area of interest."

‡**COAST MAGAZINE, The Weekly Vacationers Guide,** Resort Publications, Ltd., 5000 N. Kings Highway, Box 2448, Myrtle Beach SC 29577. (803)449-5415. Editorial Director: Mary Miller. Published 38 times/year covering tourism. "We reach more than one million readers/tourists. Our slant is vacation articles, beach, North/South Carolina orientation with coastal information, fiction." Circ. 29,000. Pays on acceptance. Byline given. Buys one-time rights (regional). Submit seasonal/holiday material at least 2 months in advance. Simultaneous queries, and simultaneous, photocopied, and previously published submissions OK. Reports in 2 weeks on queries; 1-2 months on mss. Free sample copy and writer's guidelines.
Nonfiction: Expose (airlines); historical/nostalgic (low country, South); new product (beach, tourist-related); personal experience (tourist) and articles on music and beach music. Buys 10 mss/year. Send complete ms. Length: 400-1,000 words. Pays $30 minimum.
Photos: John Pinson, photo editor. Send photos with ms. Pays $50-100 for b&w or 4-color (cover photos) transparencies; $50 minimum for b&w and color prints. Model releases and identification of subjects required. Buys one-time rights (regional).
Fiction: Adventure (ocean, lake, hunting); historical (low country history, South Carolina and North Carolina); humorous (fishing, beach, tourist) and romance (Southern-oriented). No religious, ethnic or erotic material. Buys 2-3 mss/year. Send complete ms. Length: 1,000 words maximum.
Fillers: Bill Marjenhoff, fillers editor. Clippings, jokes, gags, anecdotes and short humor.
Tips: "Freelancer can best break in to our publication by submitting resort-oriented, and Southern historical material."

DISCOVERY, 3701 West Lake Ave., Glenview IL 60025. Editor: Elizabeth Brewster. A quarterly travel magazine for Allstate Motor Club members. Circ. 1,300,000. Buys first North American serial rights. 75% freelance written. Prefers to work with published/established writers. Pays on acceptance. Publishes ms an average of 8 months after acceptance. Computer printout submissions acceptable; no dot-matrix. Submit seasonal queries 8-14 months in advance to allow for photo assignment. Reports in 2-5 weeks. Sample copy for 9x12 SAE and $1 postage; free writer's guidelines.
Nonfiction: "The emphasis is on North America and its people." Emphasizes automotive travel, offering a firsthand look at the people and places, trends and activities that help define the American character. "We're looking for polished magazine articles that are people-oriented and promise insight as well as entertainment—not narratives of people's vacations. Destination articles must rely less on the impressions of writers and more on the observations of people who live or work or grew up in the place and have special attachments." Recent

articles include "Yellowstone in Winter" (Winter 1985-86) and "Las Vegas, Mecca to the Masses" (Spring 1986). Query. "Submit a thorough proposal suitable for *Discovery*. It must be literate, concise and enthusiastic. Accompany query with relevant published clips and a resume." Buys 15-20 unsolicited mss/year. Length: 1,500-2,000 words, plus a 500 word sidebar on other things to see and do. Rates vary, depending on assignment and writer's credentials; usual range is $350-850. Sometimes pays the expenses of writers on assignment.
Photography: Color transparencies (35mm or larger). Pays day rate. For existing photos, rates depend on use. Photos should work as story; captions required. Send transparencies by registered mail. Buys one-time rights.
Tips: "No personal narratives, mere destination pieces or subjects that are not particularly visual. We have a strong emphasis on photojournalism and our stories reflect this. The most frequent mistakes made by writers in completing an article for us are not writing to assignment, resulting in a weak focus or central theme; poor organization and a lack of development which diminishes the substance of story. Word precision frequently is the difference between a dull and an exciting story. Writers will benefit by studying several issues of the publication before sending queries."

ENDLESS VACATION, Endless Vacation Publications, Inc., Box 80260, Indianapolis IN 46280. (317)848-0500. Editor: Helen A. Wernle. Prefers to work with published/established writers. A bimonthly magazine covering travel destinations, activities and issues that enhance the lives of vacationers. Circ. 500,000. Pays on publication. Publishes ms an average of 3 months after acceptance. Byline given. Buys first-serial rights. Simultaneous and photocopied submissions OK. Computer printout submissions acceptable; prefers letter-quality to dot-matrix. Reports in 1 month on queries; 3 weeks on manuscripts. Sample copy $1; writer's guidelines for SAE with 1 first class stamp.
Nonfiction: Manuscript Editor. Travel. Buys 18 mss/year (approx). Query with published clips. Length: 1,200-2,000 words. Pays $250-600 for assigned articles; pays $150-600 for unsolicited articles. Sometimes pays the expenses of writers on assignment. State availability of photos with submissions. Reviews 4x5 transparencies and 35mm slides. Offers $100-300/photo. Model releases and identification of subjects required. Buys one-time rights.
Columns/Departments: Gourmet on the Go (culinary topics of interest to travelers whether they are dining out or cooking in their condominium kitchens; no reviews of individual restaurants). Buys 4 mss/year. Query with published clips. Length: 800-1,200 words. Pays $100-250. Sometimes pays the expenses of writers on assignment.
Tips: "Articles must be packed with pertinent facts and applicable how-to's. Information—addresses, phone numbers, dates of events, costs—must be current and accurate. We encourage a literary approach—stories can be written in narrative, anecdote, dialogue, descriptive, first-person or other more unusual styles. A writer should realize that we require first-hand knowledge of the subject and plenty of practical information. For further understanding of *Endless Vacation's* direction, the writer should study the table of contents from several issues."

EUROPE FOR TRAVELERS!, Europe Incorporated, 408 Main St., Nashua NH 03060. (603)888-0633. Editor: Carol Grasso. 80% freelance written. "We are looking for the 'right' writers. Whether they are published or unpublished, established or new, is immaterial." Semi-annual magazine on Europe for traveling Americans. "Our publication is nonpolitical and nonreligious including various ways and places for traveling with spirit and zest; lots of practicalities, hotel and restaurant fare, etc." Estab. 1985. Circ. 5,000. Pays on publication. Publishes ms an average of 5 months after acceptance. Byline given. No kill fee. Buys first North American serial rights, one-time rights, first serial rights, or second serial (reprint rights). Submit seasonal/holiday material 6 months in advance. Simultaneous queries, and simultaneous, photocopied, and previously published submissions OK. Computer printout submissions acceptable; prefers letter-quality to dot-matrix. Reports in 1 month on queries; 6 weeks on mss. Sample copy $2 and 73¢ postage; writer's guidelines with SAE and 22¢ postage.
Nonfiction: Mostly destination pieces. Also how-to (open to proposals); light humor (but not satire or sarcasm); and personal experience. No religious, political, highly technical or complaint-type articles. Buys 12 mss/year. Query (with published clips, preferred), or send complete ms. Any length up to 2,000 words. Pays $10-100.
Columns/Departments: Prefers complete sample column for consideration. No specific length. Pays $10-40.
Fillers: Buys 8/year. Pays $1-10.
Tips: "If a writer reads our publication and likes it—our outlook and our style—and feels his writing is compatible to our needs, he should try sending us a submission. Hands-on travel experience in Europe is mandatory. Submit complete package: manuscripts, photos, maps, etc. Manuscript should be a photocopy. We return photos but request SASE with sufficient postage. For feature articles, the more complete, in terms of illustrative photos both black and white and color, and maps, which enhance the story, the more likely we are to accept it."

FAMILY MOTOR COACHING, 8291 Clough Pike, Cincinnati OH 45244-2796. (513)474-3622. Editor: Pamela Wisby. Associate Editor: Maura Basile. 75% freelance written. Emphasizes travel by motorhome, and

motorhome mechanics, maintenance and other technical information. Monthly magazine; 190-260 pages. Circ. 50,000. Pays on acceptance. Buys first-time, 12 months exclusive rights. Byline given. Phone queries discouraged. Submit seasonal/holiday material 5 months in advance. Computer printout submissions acceptable; prefers letter-quality to dot-matrix. SASE. Reports in 2 months. Sample copy $2; free writer's guidelines.
Nonfiction: Motorhome travel and living on the road; travel (various areas of country accessible by motor coach); how-to (modify motor coach features); bus conversions; and nostalgia. Buys 20 mss/issue. Query. Length: 1,000-2,000 words. Pays $50-200.
Photos: State availability of photos with query. Offers no additional payment for b&w contact sheet(s) 35mm or 2¼x2¼ color transparencies. Captions required. B&w glossy photos should accompany nontravel articles. Buys first rights.
Tips: "Keep in mind, stories must have motorhome angle or connection; inclusion of information about FMCA members enhances any travel article. Stories about an event somewhere should allude to nearby campgrounds, etc. The stories should be written assuming that someone going there would be doing it by motorhome. We need more articles from which to select for publication. We need geographic balance and a blend of travel, technical and incidental stories. No first-person accounts of vacations."

FAR EAST TRAVELER, Largest Hotel Magazine in the Far East, Far East Reporters, Inc., 4-28, 1-chome, Moto-Azabu, Minato-ku 106, Tokyo, Japan. (03)452-0705. Managing Editor: Julia Nolet. "We are backlogged with submissions and prefer not to receive unsolicited submissions at this time."

‡FRANCE TODAY, Le Californien Publishing Co. Inc., 1051 Divisadero, San Francisco CA 95115. (415)921-5100. Editor: Anne Prah-Perochon. 80% freelance written. A quarterly magazine covering contemporary France: culture, arts, business, travel, food and wine, etc. for a "sophisticated group of well-traveled Americans interested in modern-day France—French thought, culture and lifestyle." Circ. 50,000. Pays on publication. Publishes ms an average of 4 months after acceptance. Byline given. Offers 10% kill fee. Buys first rights and makes work-for-hire assignments. Submit seasonal/holiday material 6 months in advance. Simultaneous, photocopied, and previously published submissions OK. Electronic submissions OK via Eagle PC—IBM compatible. Computer printout submissions acceptable. Reports in 1 month on queries. Free writer's guidelines.
Nonfiction: Essays, general interest, historical/nostalgic; how-to (travel with children, start a business in France, become a French citizen); humor, new product; opinion; personal experience; photo feature; and travel. Buys 30 mss/year. Query with or without published clips, or send complete ms. Length: 500-3,000 words. Pays $50-400 for assigned articles; pays $50-300 for unsolicited articles.
Photos: Send photos with submission. Reviews contact sheets, negatives, transparencies and prints. Offers $30-200/photo. Buys one-time rights.
Columns/Departments: Impressions (cross-cultural experience related to France or Franco-American relationships), 1,000-1,500 words. Pays $100-200.
Tips: "Writers should be advised that our readers have traveled many times to France and that we receive many travel articles. Preference is given to articles that combine various aspects of French life—art and society, fashion and business, etc. All areas are open at this time. There are greater opportunities for lifestyle, business, current events and political or socio-political articles."

GREAT EXPEDITIONS, Canada's Adventure and Travel Magazine, Box 46499, Station G, Vancouver, British Columbia V6R 4G7 Canada. Editor: Marilyn Marshall. 90% freelance written. Eager to work with new/unpublished writers. Bimonthly magazine covering adventure and travel "for people who want to discover the world around them (archaeology to climbing volcanoes); basically a how-to *National Geographic*. We focus on travel (not tourism) and adventure—a mix of Canadian and world content. We are much like a society or club—we provide services besides the basic magazine—and encourage articles and information from our readers." Circ. 3,000. Pays on publication. Publishes ms an average of 6 months after acceptance. Byline given. Buys first rights or second (reprint) rights to material originally published elsewhere. Submit seasonal/holiday material 6 months in advance. Simultaneous queries, and simultaneous, photocopied and previously published submissions OK. Computer printout submissions acceptable; prefers letter-quality to dot-matrix. SASE; IRCs outside of Canada. Reports in 1 month. Publishes ms an average of 6 months after acceptance. Sample copy $2; free writer's guidelines.
Nonfiction: Book reviews (travel and adventure); how-to (travel economically, do adventure trips); humor (on travel or adventure); interview/profile (travel or adventure-related); personal experience (travel or adventure); travel (economy and budget, exotic-*not* touristic!). No tourism articles. Buys 30 mss/year. Query or send complete ms. Length: 1,000-3,000 words. Pays $35 maximum.
Photos: "It is important to send photos with the manuscript. Otherwise we are reluctant to accept pieces (humor, how-to's and book reviews excepted)." Pays $10 for any photo used on the cover. "Color reproduced in b&w for magazine." Captions required. Buys one-time rights.
Columns/Departments: Viewpoint—opinion on travel, adventure, outdoor recreation, environment. Photography—for the traveler, adventurer: equipment techniques. Health—for travelers and adventurers: how to

keep healthy, be healthy. Money—best buys, best countries to visit. Length: 400-800 words. Pays $25 maximum.

Tips: "Best to send for a copy—we are rather different from most magazines because we are a network of travelers and adventurers and rely on this network for our information. We have a yearly article and photo contest. Prizes are $50 for best article and $25 for best photo."

‡GUIDE TO THE FLORIDA KEYS, Humm's, Crain Communications Inc., Box 330712, Miami FL 33133. (305)665-2858. Editor: William A. Humm. 80% freelance written. A quarterly travel guide to the Florida Keys. Circ. 50,000. Pays on publication. Byline given. Buys first rights and second serial (reprint) rights. Submit seasonal/holiday material 6 months in advance. Previously published submissions OK. Computer printout submissions acceptable. Reports in 2 weeks on queries; 3 weeks on manuscripts. Free sample copy.

Nonfiction: General interest, historical/nostalgic, personal experience and travel, all for the Florida Keys area. Buys 30-40 mss/year. Send complete ms. Length: 500-1,500 words. Pays $4.80/column inch. Sometimes pays the expense of writers on assignment.

Photos: State availability of photos with submission. Reviews negatives, 35mm and 2x4 transparencies, and 5x7 and 8x10 prints. Offers $40-100/photo. Captions and model releases required. Buys one-time rights.

Columns/Departments: Fishing and Diving (primarily about the Florida Keys), 500-1,500 words. Pays $4.80/column inch.

HIDEAWAYS GUIDE, Hideaways International, 15 Goldsmith St., Littleton MA 01460. Editor: Mark T. Hufford. Managing Editor: Betsy Browning. 25% freelance written. Magazine published 2 times/year—January, July. Also publishes 4 quarterly newsletters. Features travel/leisure real estate information for upscale, affluent, educated, outdoorsy audience. Deals with unique vacation opportunities: vacation home renting, buying, exchanging, yacht/houseboat charters, country inns and small resorts. Circ. 10,000. Pays on publication. Publishes ms an average of 4 months after acceptance. Byline given. Offers negotiable kill fee. Buys first North American serial rights, one-time rights and second serial (reprint) rights. Submit seasonal/holiday material 3 months in advance. Previously published submissions OK. Computer printout and disk submissions compatible with Wordstar program OK; no dot-matrix printouts. Reports in 3 weeks on queries; 4 weeks on mss. Sample copy $10; free writer's guidelines.

Nonfiction: How-to (with focus on personal experience: vacation home renting, exchanging, buying, selling, yacht and house boat chartering); travel (intimate out-of-the-way spots to visit). Articles on "learning" vacations: scuba, sailing, flying, cooking, shooting, golf, tennis, photography, etc. Buys 10 mss/year. Query. Length: 800-1,500 words. Pays $50-100.

Photos: State availability of photos with query letter or ms or send photos with accompanying query or ms. Reviews b&w prints. Pays negotiable fee. Captions and identification of subjects required. Buys one-time rights.

Tips: "The most frequent mistakes made by writers in completing an article for us is that they are too impersonal with no photos and not enough focus or accomodations."

THE ITINERARY MAGAZINE, "The" Magazine for Travelers with Physical Disabilities, Whole Person Tours, Inc., Box 1084, Bayonne NJ 07002. (201)858-3400. Editor: Robert S Zywicki. Managing Editor: Elizabeth C. Zywicki. 50-60% freelance written. Works with established and new writers. A bimonthly magazine covering travel for the disabled. Circ. 5,000 +. Pays on publication. Publishes ms an average of 6 months after acceptance. Buys first North American serial rights, first rights, one-time rights, second serial (reprint) rights, all rights, makes work-for-hire assignments. Submit seasonal/holiday material 6 months in advance. Simultaneous, photocopied and previously published submissions OK. Computer printout submissions acceptable. Reports in 1 month on queries; 2 months on manuscripts. Sample copy for 9x12 SAE with 4 first class stamps; writer's guidelines for #10 SAE with 1 first class stamp.

Nonfiction: How-to, interview/profile, new product, personal experience, photo feature and travel (especially adventure/wilderness/sports related travel for persons with disabilities). Special issues will feature accessible travel articles for Thanksgiving/Christmas time; accessible travel in South America; accessible travel in the Orient. No articles that do not deal with travel for the disabled. Buys 18-24 mss/year. Query with or without published clips, or send complete ms. Length: 750-2,000 words. Pays $100-300 for assigned articles; pays $50-150 for unsolicited articles. Sometimes pays the expenses of writers on assignment. Photos: Send photos with submission. Reviews contact sheets and prints. Offers no additional payment for photos accepted with ms. Captions, model releases and identification of subjects required. Buys one-time rights. Sometimes pays the expenses of writers on assignment.

Columns/Departments: Book Reviews (only on travel for the disabled), 300-500 words. Buys 6-10 mss/year. Query. Pays $25-50.

Tips: "Be disabled or a relative, friend or co-worker of the disabled. Be aware of the needs of the disabled in travel-related situations. Describe the venues, sightseeing, etc. The areas most open to freelancers are travelogues featuring access data for the disabled, how-to features for travelers with disabilities, and reports on hotels, transportation, etc."

JOURNAL OF CHRISTIAN CAMPING, Christian Camping International, Box 646, Wheaton IL 60189. Editor: Charlyene Wall. 75% freelance written. Prefers to work with published/established writers. Emphasizes the broad scope of organized camping with emphasis on Christian camping. "Leaders of youth camps and adult conferences read our magazine to get practical help in ways to run their camps." Bimonthly magazine; 32-48 pages. Circ. 6,000. Pays on acceptance. Publishes ms an average of 2 months after acceptance. Buys all rights. Pays 25% kill fee. Byline given. Computer printout submissions acceptable; prefers letter-quality to dot-matrix. Reports in 6 weeks. Sample copy $2.50; writer's guidelines for SASE.

Nonfiction: General interest (trends in organized camping in general and Christian camping in particular); how-to (anything involved with organized camping from motivating staff, to programming, to record keeping, to camper follow-up); inspirational (limited use, but might be interested in practical applications of Scriptural principles to everyday situations in camping, no preaching); interview (with movers and shakers in camping and Christian camping in particular; submit a list of basic questions first); and opinion (write a letter to the editor). Buys 30-50 mss/year. Query required. Length: 600-2,500 words. Pays 5¢/word.

Photos: Send photos with ms. Pays $10/5x7 b&w contact sheet or print; price negotiable for 35mm color transparencies. Buys all rights. Captions required.

Tips: "The most frequent mistake made by writers in completing an article for us is that they have not read the information in the listing and send articles unrelated to our readers."

LOOKOUT, The Magazine For Living in Spain, Lookout Publications, Puebla Lucia, Fuengirola, (Malaga), Spain. (52)460916. Editor: Ken Brown. Features Editor: Mark Little. 50-60% freelance written. A monthly magazine for the expatriate living in Spain. "We cover all aspects of life in Spain, to help Britons and Americans living there understand and enjoy their adopted country." Circ. 24,000. Pays on publication. Publishes ms an average of 4 months after acceptance. Byline given. Buys one-time rights. Submit seasonal/holiday material 6 months in advance. Photocopied submissions and previously published submissions OK. Reports in 2 weeks on queries; 6 weeks on manuscripts. Free sample copy and writer's guidelines.

Nonfiction: General interest, historical/nostalgic, humor, interview/profile, personal experience, photo feature and travel. "No travel brochure fluff or 'What I did on my holiday in Spain'." Buys 60 mss/year. Send complete ms. Length 1,500-3,500 words. Pays $150-250.

Photos: State availability of photos with submission. Reviews 35mm transparencies. Offers no additional payment for photos accepted with ms. Captions required.

Columns/Departments: Books (reviews of nonfiction books related to Spain), 500-1,500 words. Last Page (humor articles with a Spanish slant), 900 words. Buys 30 mss/year. Query. Length: 500-1,500 words. Pays $30-100.

Tips: The area of our publication most open to freelancers are well-researched travel articles on a specific destination in Spain, but avoid any travel brochure clichés (remember, our readers live in Spain and know it much better than your average holidaymaker); interviews and profiles of Americans and Britons living in Spain who are involved in some unique activity there; and humor articles with a Spanish slant.

MICHIGAN LIVING, AAA Michigan, 17000 Executive Plaza Drive, Dearborn MI 48126. (313)336-1211. Editor: Len Barnes. 50% freelance written. Emphasizes travel and auto use. Monthly magazine; 48 pages. Circ. 860,000. Pays on acceptance. Publishes ms an average of 4 months after acceptance. Buys first North American serial rights. Pays 100% kill fee. Byline given. Submit seasonal/holiday material 3 months in advance. Reports in 4-6 weeks. Buys 50-60 unsolicited mss/year. Free sample copy and writer's guidelines.

Nonfiction: Travel articles on U.S. and Canadian topics, but not on California, Florida or Arizona. Send complete ms. Length: 200-1,000 words. Pays $75-300.

Photos: Photos purchased with accompanying ms. Captions required. Pays $350 for cover photos; $25-150 for color transparencies; total purchase price for ms includes payment for b&w photos.

Tips: "In addition to descriptions of things to see and do, articles should contain accurate, current information on costs the traveler would encounter on his trip. Items such as lodging, meal and entertainment expenses should be included, not in the form of a balance sheet but as an integral part of the piece. We want the sounds, sights, tastes, smells of a place or experience so one will feel he has been there and knows if he wants to go back."

THE MIDWEST MOTORIST, AAA Auto Club of Missouri, 12901 North Forty Dr., St. Louis MO 63141. (314)851-3315. Editor: Michael J. Right. Managing Editor: Jean Kennedy. 70% freelance written. Bimonthly magazine on travel and auto-related topics. Primarily focuses on travel throughout the world; prefers stories that tell about sights and give solid travel tips. Circ. 347,000. Pays on acceptance. Publishes ms an average of 8 months after acceptance. Byline given. Not copyrighted. Buys one-time rights, simultaneous rights (rarely), and second serial (reprint) rights. Submit seasonal/holiday material 6-8 months in advance. Simultaneous queries, and simultaneous, photocopied and previously published submissions OK. Computer printout submissions acceptable as long as they are readable and NOT ALL CAPS. Reports in 1 month. Sample copy for 9x12 SAE and 4 first class stamps. Free writer's guidelines.

Nonfiction: General interest; historical/nostalgic; how-to; humor (with motoring or travel slant); interview/

profile; personal experience; photo feature; technical (auto safety or auto-related); and travel (domestic and international), all travel-related or auto-related. March/April annual European travel issue; September/October annual cruise issue. No religious, philosophical arguments or opinion not supported by facts. Buys 30 mss/year. Query with published clips. Length: 500-2,000 (1,500 preferred). Pays $50-200.

Photos: State availability of photos. Prefers color slides and b&w with people, sights, scenery mentioned. Reviews 35mm transparencies and 8x10 prints. Payment included in ms. Captions, model releases and identification of subjects required. Buys one-time rights.

Tips: "Query should be informative and entertaining, written with as much care as the lead of a story. Feature articles on travel destinations and tips are most open to freelancers."

‡**MOTORHOME**, TL Enterprises, Inc., 29901 Agoura Rd., Agoura CA 91301. (818)991-4980. Editor: Bob Livingston. Managing Editor: Gail Harrington. 60% freelance written. A monthly magazine covering motorhomes. "Motorhome is exclusively for motorhome enthusiasts. We feature road tests on new motorhomes, travel locations, controversy concerning motorhomes, how-to and technical articles relating to motorhomes." Circ. 120,000. Pays on acceptance. Publishes ms an average of 4 months after acceptance. Byline given. Buys first North American serial rights. Submit seasonal/holiday material 8 months in advance. Electronic submissions OK via Hayes Smartcom II. Computer printout submissions acceptable. Reports in 3 weeks on queries; 2 months on mss. Free sample copy and writer's guidelines.

Nonfiction: General interest; historical/nostalgic; how-to (do it yourself for motorhomes); humor; new product; photo feature; and technical. Buys 80 mss/year. Query with published clips. Length: 1,000-2,500 words. Pays $175-600 for assigned articles; pays $50-400 for unsolicited articles. Sometimes pays expenses of writers on assignment.

Photos: Send photos with submission. Reviews contact sheets and 35mm/120/4x5 transparencies. Offers no additional payment for photos accepted with ms. Captions, model releases and identification of subjects required. Buys one-time rights.

Tips: "If a freelancer has an idea for a good article it's best to send a query and include possible photo locations to illustrate the article. We prefer to assign articles and work with the author in developing a piece suitable to our audience. We are in a very specialized field with very enthusiastic readers who appreciate articles by authors who actually enjoy motorhomes. The following areas are most open: Travel—places to go with a motorhome, where to stay, what to see etc; we prefer not to use travel articles where the motorhome is secondary and How-to—personal projects on author's motorhomes to make travel easier, etc., unique projects, accessories. Also articles on unique personalities, motorhomes, humorous experiences."

‡**NATIONAL GEOGRAPHIC TRAVELER**, National Geographic Society, 17th and M Sts. NW, Washington DC 20036. (202)857-7721. Editor: Joan Tapper. 90% freelance written. A quarterly travel magazine. "*Traveler* highlights mostly U.S. and Canadian subjects, but about 10% of its articles cover other foreign destinations—most often Europe, Mexico, and the Caribbean, occasionally the Pacific." Circ. 850,000. Pays on acceptance. Byline given. Offers 50% kill fee. Reports in 2 months. Sample copy $4.85; writer's guidelines for SASE.

Nonfiction: Travel. Buys 50 mss/year. Query with published clips. Length: 2,000-4,000 words. Pays $1/word. Pays expenses of writers on assignment.

Photos: Reviews transparencies and prints.

‡**NEW ENGLAND GETAWAYS**, New England Publishing Group, Inc., 21 Pocahontas Dr., Peabody MA 01960. (617)535-4186. Managing Editor: Patricia Burns Fiore. 60% freelance written. Prefers to work with published/established writers; eager to work with new/unpublished writers. A bimonthly magazine covering travel in New England. "It is designed to promote New England as a weekend and mid-week destination to residents of the entire Atlantic Seaboard. The magazine is divided into geographic sections including maps, calendar of events and feature stories to lure travelers to specific regions." Estab. 1985. Circ. 40,000. Pays on publication. Publishes an average of 2 months after acceptance. Offers kill fee. Buys all rights or makes work-for-hire assignments. Submit seasonal/holiday material 4 months in advance. Electronic submissions OK via 300 or 1200 Baud, IBM compatible (Wordstar), but requires hard copy also. Computer printout submissions acceptable; letter-quality required, not proportional. Reports in 1 month. Sample copy $3; writer's guidelines for SASE.

Nonfiction: General interest, historical/nostalgic and travel, specific for New England. "We are interested *only* in articles featuring a specific area and topic in New England." Query. Length: 1,000-2,000 words. Pays $150-300 for assigned articles. Sometimes pays expenses of writers on assignment.

Photos: State availability of photos with submission. Reviews contact sheets, 4x5 transparencies and 8x10 prints. Offers no additional payment for photos accepted with ms. Captions and model releases required. Buys all rights.

Tips: "Know and love New England. We want to entice readers to visit Cohasset and Rockport; the White Mountains of New Hampshire; Newport, R.I. and Martha's Vineyard. Specific stories within a geographical area are best: country inns of the North Shore, spring skiing in New Hampshire, resident artist on The Cape, clam chowder in Essex . . . Each geographical area includes 1-3 articles of 1,000-2,000 words per issue. We want our readers to learn something specific about each of those sections in each issue. We will be buying more freelance material due to increase in the size of magazine and possibly will change from bi-monthly to monthly.''

NEWSDAY, Melville, Long Island NY 11747. (516)454-2020. Travel Editor: Steve Schatt. Assistant Travel Editor: Barbara Shea. Travel Writer: Eileen Swift. For general readership of Sunday Travel Section. Newspaper. 50% freelance written. Weekly. Circ. 644,000. Buys all rights for the New York area only. Buys 150 mss/year. Pays on publication. Will consider photocopied submissions. Simultaneous submissions considered if others are being made outside of the New York area. Computer printout submissions acceptable; prefers letter-quality to dot-matrix. Reports in 1 month. Submit complete ms.
Nonfiction and Photos: Travel articles with strong focus and theme for Sunday Travel Section, but does not accept pieces based on freebies, junkets, discount or subsidies of any sort. Emphasis on accuracy, honesty, service, and quality writing to convey mood and flavor. Destination pieces must involve visit or experience that a typical traveler can easily duplicate. Skip diaries, ''My First Trip Abroad'' pieces or laundry lists of activities; downplay first person. Length: 600-1,500 words; prefers 800- to 1,100-word pieces. Pays 10-15¢/word. Also, regional ''Weekender'' pieces of 700-800 words plus service box, but query Eileen Swift first. ''Schedule fills up far ahead; best possibilities are for January-March.''

NORTHEAST OUTDOORS, Northeast Outdoors, Inc., Box 2180, Waterbury CT 06722. (203)755-0158. Editor: Debora Nealley. 80% freelance written. Works with a small number of new/unpublished writers each year. A monthly tabloid covering family camping in the Northeastern U.S. Circ. 14,000. Pays on publication. Publishes ms an average of 6 months after acceptance. Byline given. Offers 50% kill fee. Buys first rights, one-time rights, second serial (reprint) rights, simultaneous rights, and regional rights. Submit seasonal/holiday material 5 months in advance. Simultaneous, photocopied and previously published submissions OK. Electronic submissions OK via Kaypro II w/Perfect Writer, but requires hard copy as well. Computer printout submissions acceptable; no dot-matrix. Reports in 1 month. Sample copy for 9x12 SAE with 4 first class stamps; writer's guidelines for letter size SAE with 1 first class stamp.
Nonfiction: Book excerpts; general interest; historical/nostalgic; how-to (on camping); humor; new product (company and RV releases only); personal experience; photo feature; and travel. ''No diaries of trips, dog stories, or anything not camping and RV related. Length: 300-1,500 words. Pays $40-80 for assigned articles; pays $30-75 for unsolicited articles.
Photos: Send photos with submission. Reviews contact sheets and 5x7 prints or larger. Offers $5-10/photo. Captions and identification of subjects required. Buys one-time rights.
Columns/Departments: Mealtime (campground cooking), 300-900 words. Buys 12 mss/year. Query or send complete ms. Length: 750-1,000 words. Pays $30-75.
Fillers: Camping related anecdotes, facts, newsbreaks and short humor. Buys few fillers. Length: 25-200 words. Pays $5-15.
Tips: ''Go camping and travel in Northeastern States especially New England. Have a nice trip, and tell us about it. Travel and camping articles, especially first-person reports on private campgrounds and interviews with owners are the areas of our publication most open to freelancers.''

PACIFIC BOATING ALMANAC, Box Q, Ventura CA 93002. (805)644-6043. Editor: William Berssen. For ''Western boat owners.'' Published in 3 editions to cover the Pacific Coastal area. Circ. 25,000. Buys all rights. Buys 12 mss/year. Pays on publication. Sample copy $10.95. Submit seasonal material 3 to 6 months in advance. Reports in 1 month. Query.
Nonfiction: ''This is a cruising guide, published annually in three editions, covering all of the navigable waters in the Pacific coast. Though we are almost entirely staff-produced, we would be interested in well-written articles on cruising and trailer-boating along the Pacific coast and in the navigable lakes and rivers of the Western states from Baja, California to Alaska inclusive.'' Pays $50 minimum.
Photos: Pays $10/8x10 b&w glossy print.
Tips: ''We are also publishers of boating books that fall within the classification of 'where-to' and 'how-to.' Authors are advised not to send manuscript until requested after we've reviewed a two- to four-page outline of the projected books.''

TACOMA NEWS TRIBUNE, Tribune Publishing Co., Box 11000, Tacoma WA 98411-0008. (206)597-8650. Editor: John Komen. Managing Editor: Norm Bell. ''We are backlogged with submissions and prefer not to receive unsolicited submissions at this time.''

TEXAS HIGHWAYS MAGAZINE, Official Travel Magazine for the State of Texas, State Dept. of Highways and Public Transportation, 11th and Brazos, Austin TX 78701. (512)475-6068. Editor: Franklin T. Lively. Managing Editor: Ms. Tommie Pinkard. 90% freelance written. Prefers to work with published/established writers. A monthly tourist magazine covering travel and history for Texas only. Pays on acceptance.

Publishes ms an average of 8 months after acceptance. Byline given. Offers $50 kill fee. Not copyrighted. Buys one-time rights. Submit seasonal/holiday material 1 year in advance. Simultaneous queries and submissions OK. Computer printout submissions acceptable; no dot-matrix. Reports in 2 weeks on queries; 1 month on mss. Free sample copy and writer's guidelines.
Nonfiction: Historical/nostalgic, photo feature, travel. Must be concerned with travel in Texas. "No disaster features." Buys 75 mss/year. Query with published clips. Length: 1,200-1,600 words. Pays $400-700.
Photos: Bill Reaves, photo editor. Send photos with query or ms. Pays $80 for less than a page, $160 for a full page, $300 for cover, $200 for back cover. Accepts 4x5, 35mm color transparencies. Captions and identification of subjects required. Buys one-time rights.
Tips: Send material on "what to see, what to do, where to go in *Texas*." Material must be tourist-oriented.

‡TOURS & RESORTS, The World-Wide Vacation Magazine, World Publishing, 4349 Howard St., Skokie IL 60076. (312)679-7474. Editor/Associate Publisher: Bob Meyers. Associate Editor: Ray Gudas. 90% freelance written. A bimonthly magazine covering world-wide vacation travel features. Estab. 1985. Circ. 250,000. Pays on acceptance. Byline given. Offers $75-125 kill fee. Buys first North American serial rights. Submit seasonal/holiday material 6 months in advance. Previously published submissions acceptable dependent upon publication—local, or regional OK. Computer printout submissions acceptable; prefers letter-quality to dot-matrix. Reports in 3 weeks on queries; 6 weeks on mss. Sample copy $2.50 with 9x12 SASE.
Nonfiction: Essays, general interest, historical/nostalgic, how-to, humor, inspirational, interview/profile, personal experience, photo feature and travel. Buys 60 mss/year. Query with published clips and 6 or more ideas, or send complete ms and photos/slides. Length: 1,500-2,000 words. Pays $150-500.
Photos: State availability of photos; prefers quality color slides or photos with submission. Reviews transparencies and slides. Offers no additional payment for photos accepted with ms. Captions required. Buys one-time rights.
Columns/Departments: Travel Views (travel tips; service articles), and World Shopping (shopping guide). Buys 12 mss/year. Query with or without published clips, or send complete ms. Length: 800-1,500 words. Pays $125-250.
Tips: "Writer must include phone number for contact. Travel features and Travel Views Department are most open to freelancers."

TRAILER LIFE, TL Enterprises, Inc., 29901 Agoura Rd., Agoura CA 90301. (213)991-4980. Editor: Bill Estes. Managing Editor: Yvonne Vollert. Editorial Director: Barbara Leonard. 60% freelance written. A monthly magazine covering the RV lifestyle, and RV travel and products. "Readers of *Trailer Life* are owners of recreational vehicles who spend a median 37.8 days traveling on the road. Articles should apply to RV travel or RV products. Articles should have a distinctive focus on the needs, entertainment and issues of the RV traveler." Circ. 310,000. Pays on acceptance. Byline given. Offers 30-50% kill fee. Buys first North American serial rights. Submit seasonal/holiday material 4 months in advance. Computer printout submissions acceptable. Sample copy $2.50; free writer's guidelines.
Nonfiction: Expose, general interest, historical/nostalgic, how-to, humor, interview/profile, new product, guest editorials, personal experience, photo feature, technical and travel. Query with or without published clips, or send complete ms. Length: 1,000-2,000 words. Pays $50-500. Sometimes pays the expenses of writers on assignment, under special circumstances.
Photos: Reviews contact sheets, 35mm transparencies (or larger), and 8x10 prints. Offers no additional payment for photos accepted with ms, but also buys photos independent of articles. Captions, model releases and identification of subjects required. Buys one-time rights.
Columns/Departments: People on the Move (short RV-related people items with black-and-white photo, can include events, humorous news items), 200-500 words; and Newswire (news items specific to the RV industry/consumer or public lands), 100 words. Send complete ms. Pays $75 maximum.
Tips: "First-hand experience with recreational vehicles and the RV lifestyle makes the writer's material more appealing. Although, the writer need not own an RV, accurate information and a knowledge of the RV lifestyle will lend desired authenticity to article submissions. People on the Move, Newswire, travel features, how-to are areas most open to feelancers. Vehicle evaluations of home-built or home-modified trailers, campers or motorhomes are open to freelancers."

TRAILS-A-WAY, 9425 S. Greenville Rd., Greenville MI 48838. (616)754-9179. Editor: David Higbie. 25% freelance written. Newspaper published 11 times/year on camping in the Midwest (Michigan, Ohio, Indiana and Illinois). "Fun and information for campers who own recreational vehicles." Circ. 53,000. Pays on publication. Byline given. Buys first and second rights to the same material, and second (reprint) rights to material originally published elsewhere. Submit seasonal/holiday material 3 months in advance. Simultaneous queries and submissions OK. Computer printout submissions acceptable; no dot-matrix. Reports in 1 month. Sample copy 75¢; writer's guidelines for business size SAE and 2 first class stamps.
Nonfiction: How-to (use, maintain recreational vehicles—5th wheels, travel and camping trailers, pop-up trailers, motorhomes); humor; inspirational; interview/profile; new product (camp products); personal experi-

ence; photo feature; technical (on RVs); travel. March/April issue: spring camping; September/October: fall camping. Winter issues feature southern hot spots. "All articles should relate to RV camping in Michigan, Ohio, Indiana and Illinois—or south in winter. No tenting or backpacking articles." Buys 40-50 mss/year. Send complete ms. Length: 1,000-1,500 words. Pays $60-125.
Photos: Send photos with ms. Pays $5-10 for b&w and color prints. No slides. Captions required. Buys one-time rights.

TRANSITIONS ABROAD, (formerly *Travel & Study Abroad*), 18 Hulst Rd., Box 344, Amherst MA 01004. (413)256-0373. Editor/Publisher: Prof. Clayton A. Hubbs. 80-90% freelance written. Eager to work with new/ unpublished writers. The established (since 1977) magazine for low-budget international travel with an educational or work component. Bound magazine. Circ. 15,000. Pays on publication. Buys first rights and second (reprint) rights to material originally published elsewhere. Byline given. Written queries only. Computer printout submissions acceptable; prefers letter-quality to dot-matrix. Reports in 1 month. Publishes ms an average of 4 months after acceptance. Sample copy $3.50; writer's guidelines and topics schedule for SASE.
Nonfiction: How-to (find courses, inexpensive lodging and travel); interview (information on specific areas and people); personal experience (evaluation of courses, special interest and study tours, economy travel); and travel (what to see and do in specific areas of the world, new learning and travel ideas). Foreign travel only. No travel pieces for businessmen. Few destination ("tourist") pieces. Emphasis on interaction with people in host country. Buys 40 unsolicited mss/issue. Query with credentials. Length: 500-1,500 words. Pays $25-75.
Photos: Send photos with ms. Pays $10-15 for 8x10 b&w glossy prints, higher for covers. No color. Additional payment for photos accompanying ms, photos increase likelihood of acceptance. Buys one-time rights. Captions required.
Columns/Departments: Study/Travel Program Notes (evaluation of courses or programs); Traveler's Advisory/Resources (new information and ideas for offbeat independent travel); and Jobnotes (how to find it and what to expect). Buys 8/issue. Send complete ms. Length: 1,000 words maximum. Pays $20-50.
Fillers: Info Exchange (information, preferably first-hand. having to do with travel, particularly offbeat educational travel and work or study abroad). Buys 10/issue. Length: 1,000 words maximum. Pays $20-50.
Tips: "We like nuts and bolts stuff, practical information, especially on how to work, live and cut costs abroad. Be specific: names, addresses, current costs. We are particularly interested in educational travel and study abroad for adults and senior citizens. More and more readers want information not only on work but retirement possibilities."

TRAVEL AND LEISURE, American Express Publishing Co, 1120 6th Ave., New York NY 10036. (212)382-5600. Editor-in-Chief: Pamela Fiori. Managing Editor: John Stevens. 80% freelance written. Monthly magazine. Circ. 1,000,000. Pays on acceptance. Byline given. Offers 25% kill fee. Buys first world and foreign edition rights. Reports in 2 weeks. Sample copy $2.95. Free writer's guidelines.
Nonfiction: Monique Burns, articles editor. Travel. Buys 200 mss/year. Query. Length open. Payment varies. Sometimes pays the expenses of writers on assignment.
Photos: State availability of photos with submission. Reviews transparencies. Payment varies. Captions required. Buys one-time rights.
Tips: "Read the magazine. Regionals are a good place to start."

TRAVEL SMART, Communications House, Inc., Dobbs Ferry NY 10522. (914)693-4208. Editor/Publisher: H.J. Teison. Covers information on "good-value travel." Monthly newsletter. Pays on publication. Buys all rights. Photocopied submissions OK. Computer printout submissions acceptable. Reports in 6 weeks. Sample copy and writer's guidelines for #10 SASE with 27¢ postage.
Nonfiction: "Interested primarily in bargains or little-known deals on transportation, lodging, food, unusual destinations that won't break the bank. No destination stories on major Caribbean islands, London, New York, no travelogs, my vacation, poetry, fillers. No photos or illustrations. Just hard facts. We are not part of 'Rosy fingers of dawn . . .' School. More like letter from knowledgable friend who has been there." Query first. Length: 100-1,000 words. Pays "up to $150."
Tips: "When you travel, check out small hotels offering good prices, little known restaurants, and send us brief rundown (with prices, phone numbers, addresses) of at least 4 at one location. Information must be current. Include your phone number with submission, because we sometimes make immediate assignments."

TRAVEL-HOLIDAY MAGAZINE, Travel Magazine, Inc., 51 Atlantic Ave., Floral Park NY 11001. (516)352-9700. Editor: Scott Shane. 90% freelance written. Prefers to work with published/established writers but, works with a small number of new/unpublished writers each year. For the active traveler with time and money to travel several times a year. Monthly magazine; 100 pages. Circ. 816,000. Pays on acceptance. Publishes ms an average of 6 months after acceptance. Buys first North American serial rights. Byline given. Submit seasonal/holiday material 6 months in advance. Computer printout submissions acceptable if double-spaced; prefers letter-quality to dot-matrix. Reports in 2 months. Sample copy $1; free writer's guidelines. No phone queries.

Nonfiction: Interested in travel destination articles. Send query letter/outline; clips of previously published work *must* accompany queries. Only the highest quality writing and photography are considered by the staff. "Don't ask if we'd like to see any articles on San Francisco, France or China. Develop a specific story idea and explain why the destination is so special that we should devote space to it. Are there interesting museums, superb restaurants, spectacular vistas, etc.? Tell us how you plan to handle the piece—convey to us the mood of the city, the charm of the area, the uniqueness of the museums, etc. No food and wine, medical, photo tips, poetry or boring travelogs." Length: featurettes (800-1,300 words), $250 and up; features (1,600-1,800), $400; "Here and There" column (575 words), $150. For "Here and There" column use "any upbeat topic that can be covered succinctly (with one piece of b&w art) that's travel related and deserves special recognition. When querying, please send suggested lead and indicate 'Here and There' in the cover letter."
Photos: B&w prints $25; color converted to b&w will be paid at $25 rate; color transparencies (35mm and larger) pays $75-400 depending upon use. Pays on publication.
Tips: "Feature stories should be about major destinations: large cities, regions, etc. Featurettes can be about individual attractions, smaller cities, side trips, etc. We welcome sidebar service information. Stimulate reader interest in the subject as a travel destination through lively, entertaining and accurate writing. A good way to break in—if we're not familiar with your writing—is to send us a good idea for a featurette. Convey the mood of a place without being verbose; although we like good anecdotal material, our primary interest is in the destination itself, not the author's adventures. Do not query without having first read several recent issues. We no longer use any broadbased travel pieces. Each article must have a specific angle. We are assigning articles to the best writers we can find and those writers who develop and produce good material and will continue to work with us on a regular basis. We have also become much more service-oriented in our articles. We will be featuring regional editorial, therefore we require additional regional United States featurette length stories."

TRIP & TOUR, Allied Publications, 1776 Lake-Worth Road, Lake Worth FL 33460. Editor: Mark Adams. A bimonthly magazine with colorful features and pictorial essays on travel and leisure. Circ. 75,000. Buys simultaneous rights; first rights; and second serial (reprint) rights. Submit seasonal material 6 months in advance. Reports in 3 weeks on "holiday mss"; 3 months on mss. Sample copy $1 and SAE; free writer's guidelines for SAE.
Nonfiction: Travel, personal experience, general interest, humor, historical/nostalgic, and photo feature. Buys 50-100 mss/year. Send complete ms. Length: 400-1,000 words. Pays 5¢/published word or $25 maximum.
Fiction: Prefers humor. Buys up to 10 mss/year. Length: 400-1,000 words. Pays 5¢/word or $25 maximum.
Photos: Send photos or state availability with ms. Pays $5 for 8x10 b&w glossy prints and color transparencies. Captions preferred; identification of subjects required. Buys one-time rights.
Cartoons: Buys few. Pays $10.
Tips: "Type manuscript, double-space and *keep a copy* (we sometimes lose them). Edit yourself ruthlessly for grammar, spelling, punctuation and style. Is your story unique? No queries—we simply can't answer them. We receive thousands of manuscripts per year, so no SASE, no answer, and no apologies. Follow the rules, be *very* patient and keep trying. We want to publish you."

VISTA/USA, Box 161, Convent Station NJ 07961. (201)538-7600. Editor: Kathleen M. Caccavale. Managing Editor: Martha J. Mendez. 90% freelance written. Will consider ms submissions from *unpublished* writers but will not assign from queries. Quarterly magazine of the Exxon Travel Club. "Our publication uses articles on North American areas without overtly encouraging travel. We strive to use as literate a writing as we can in our articles, helping our readers to gain an in-depth understanding of cities, towns and areas as well as other aspects of American culture that affect the character of the nation." Circ. 900,000. Pays on acceptance. Publishes ms an average of 1 year after acceptance. Buys first North American serial rights. Query about seasonal subjects 18 months in advance. Computer printout submissions acceptable; prefers letter-quality to dot-matrix. Reports in 1 month. Sample copy for a 9x12 or larger SASE; free writer's and photographer's guidelines.
Nonfiction: General interest (geographically oriented articles on North America focused on the character of an area; also general articles related to travel and places); humor (related to travel or places); photo features (photo essays on subjects such as autumn, winter, highly photogenic travel subjects; and special interest areas) and some articles dealing with Americana, crafts and collecting. "We buy feature articles on North America, Hawaii, Mexico and the Caribbean that appeal to a national audience." No feature articles that mention driving or follow routes on a map or articles about hotels, restaurants or annual events. Uses 7-15 mss/issue. Query with outline and clips of previously published work. Length: 1,500-2,500 words. Pays $500 minimum for features. Pays the expenses of writers on assignment.
Columns/Departments: "Our new departments need submissions. Minitrips are point to point or loop driving tours of from 50 to 350 miles covering a healthy variety of stops along the way. Close Focus covers new or changing aspects of major attractions, small or limited attractions not appropriate for a feature article (800-1,000 words). American Vignettes covers anything travel related that also reveals a slice of American life, often with a light or humorous touch, such as asking directions from a cranky New Englander, or covering the phenomenon of 'talking license plates.' "

Photos: Henry M. Pedersen, art director. Send photos with ms. Pays $100 minimum for color transparencies. Captions preferred. Buys one-time rights.

Tips: "We are looking for readable pieces with good writing that will interest armchair travelers as much as readers who may want to visit the areas you write about. Articles should have definite themes and should give our readers an insight into the character and flavor of an area or topic. Stories about personal experiences must impart a sense of drama and excitement or have a strong human-interest angle. Stories about areas should communicate a strong sense of what it feels like to be there. Good use of anecdotes and quotes should be included. Study the articles in the magazine to understand how they are organized, how they present their subjects, the range of writing styles, and the specific types of subjects used. Afterwards, query and enclose samples of your best writing. We are expecting to begin accepting advertising and, as a consequence, will be looking for fillers, department shorts, and inventory articles of a general, nonseasonal nature (1,500 to 1,800 words) at least tangentially related to travel."

‡WESTERN RV TRAVELER, (formerly *California Traveler*), Recreation Publications, 2019 Clement Ave., Alameda CA 94501. (415)865-7500. Editor: Dave Preston. Managing Editor: Greg Sellers. 85% freelance written. Works with a small number of new/unpublished writers each year. A monthly magazine for Western recreational vehicle owners. Circ 30,000. Pays on publication. Publishes ms an average of 6 months after acceptance. Byline given. Buys one-time rights. Submit seasonal/holiday material 6 months in advance. Simultaneous, photocopied, and previously published submissions OK. Electronic submissions OK via disks compatible with IBM WordStar, but requires hard copy also. Computer printout submissions acceptable. Reports in several weeks on queries; several months on mss. Free sample copy and writer's guidelines.

Nonfiction: Historical/nostalgic; how-to (fix your RV); new product; personal experience (particularly travel); technical; and travel (destinations for RVs). No non-RV travel articles. Buys 36 mss/year. Query with or without published clips, or send complete ms. Length: 1,000-5,000 words. Pays $1.50/inch.

Photos: Send photos with submissions. Reviews contact sheets, negatives, transparencies and prints. Offers $5 minimum/photo. Identification of subjects required.

Tips: "RV travel/destination stories are most open to freelancers. Include all information of value to RVers, and reasons why they would want to visit the California or western location."

Union

Union members read about their union and field of work in the following publications.

‡BROTHERHOOD OF MAINTENANCE OF WAY EMPLOYES JOURNAL, 12050 Woodward Ave., Detroit MI 48203-3596. (313)868-0490. Editor: O.M. Berge. Associate Editor: R.J. Williamson. 1% freelance written. Monthly trade union magazine for railroad track workers. "Our readers are members of our union, and their work is on the railroad where they build and maintain the tracks, bridges and buildings." Circ. 110,000. Pays on publication. Publishes ms an average of 4 months after acceptance. Byline given. Buys one-time and non-exclusive rights. Submit seasonal/holiday material 4 months in advance. Simultaneous queries, and simultaneous, photocopied and previously published submissions OK. Reports in 1 month. Free sample copy.

Nonfiction: All material must relate to railroad track work. Buys 2-3 mss/year. Length: averages 2 typewritten pages. Pays average $40. No additional fee for photos with ms.

Photos: "Photos must be dynamic and sharp." Send photos with query or ms. Pays $10 for 4x5 b&w print used inside. Pays $100-200 for 4x5 or larger color transparencies used as cover. Must be vertical format. Identification of subjects required; captions preferred.

Tips: Short articles and fillers fit our format best.

OCAW REPORTER, Box 2812, Denver CO 80201. (303)987-2229. Editor: Gerald Archuleta. 5% freelance written. Official publication of Oil, Chemical and Atomic Workers International Union. For union members. Bimonthly magazine; 24-32 pages. Circ. 125,000. Not copyrighted. Buys first rights. Pays on acceptance. Publishes ms an average of 4 months after acceptance. Byline given. Computer printout submissions acceptable; prefers letter-quality to dot-matrix. Reports in 1 month. Query. Free sample copy.

Nonfiction: Labor union materials, political subjects and consumer interest articles, slanted toward workers and consumers, with liberal political view. Interview, profile, think pieces and exposes. Most material is done on assignment. "We have severe space limitations." Length: 300-600 words. Pays $50-75. Sometimes pays the expenses of writers on assignment.
Photos: No additional payment is made for 8x10 b&w glossy photos used with mss. Captions required.
Tips: "The writer has a better chance of breaking in at our publication with short articles and fillers because of severe space limitations."

Women's

Today's readers of women's magazines have more options but less time. Readers seek women's publications as diverse as their daily schedules. Magazines that also use material slanted to women's interests can be found in the following categories: Business and Finance; Child Care and Parental Guidance; Food and Drink; Hobby and Craft; Home and Garden; Lifestyles; Religious; Romance and Confession; and Sports.

‡**THE ALLURE WOMAN**, Allure, Inc., 22 E. 41 Street, New York NY 10017. (212)689-1989. Editor-in-Chief: T. Rose Murdoch. 80% freelance written. A monthly magazine for "full-figured women (size 14+) with emphasis on fashion, beauty and health." Circ. 86,000. Pays on publication. Publishes ms an average of 6 months after acceptance. Byline given. 20% kill fee. Not copyrighted. Buys first North American serial rights and second serial (reprint) rights. Submit seasonal/holiday material 6 months in advance. Reports in 4-6 weeks on queries; 6-8 weeks on mss. Writer's guidelines for business size SAE with 1 first class stamp.
Nonfiction: Book excerpts, how-to (exercise, diet, etc.), interview/profile, personal experience and travel. Buys 36 mss/year. Query with or without published clips, or send complete ms. Length: 500-1,000 words. Pays $200-500 for assigned articles. Pays $200-300 for unsolicited articles. Pays only long distance expenses of writers.
Photos: State availability of photos with submission. Reviews contact sheets, transparencies and prints. Captions, model releases and identification of subjects required. Buys one-time rights.
Columns/Departments: Wista Johnson, health editor. Nutrition (especially women's nutritional needs/diets); Fitness (as relates to women sizes 14 and above/or "full-figured"); Travel (U.S. or abroad) and General Health Feature (psychology, women's health, mental health, medicine). Buys 36 mss/year. Query or send complete ms. Length: 500-1,000 words. Pays $200-300.
Tips: "Address the specific viewpoint of 'full-figured' women in a 'thin' world as well as their particular health/fitness needs. The areas of our publication most open to freelancers are travel (unusual, off-beat cities and countries) and health."

‡**AMIT**, AMIT Women, 817 Broadway, New York NY 10003. (212)477-4720. Editor: Micheline Ratzersdorfer. 10% freelance written. Magazine published 5 times/year "concerned with Jewish and Israeli themes, i.e., Jewish art, Jewish sociology, Jewish communities around the world to an audience with an above average educational level, a commitment to Jewish tradition and Zionism and a concern for the future of the Jewish community the world over." Circ. 50,000. Pays on publication. Buys all rights. Submit seasonal material 6 months in advance. Computer printout submissions acceptable "as long as it can be read by the human eye and has adequate leading and margins for editing." Prefers letter-quality to dot-matrix. Reports in 1 month. Publishes ms an average of 3 months after acceptance. Free sample copy and writer's guidelines.
Nonfiction: General interest; historical; interview (with notable figures in Jewish and Israeli life); nostalgia; travel; and photo feature (particularly Jewish holiday photos). "We do special holiday features for all Jewish holidays." No fiction, no memoirs about "Momma's Chicken Soup" and things of that ilk; no political analyses of the Middle East unless they can stand a six-month delay until publication; no travelogues lauding non-kosher restaurants. Buys 10 unsolicited mss/year. Query. Length: 1,000-2,000 words. Pays $50 maximum.
Photos: State availability of photos. Reviews 5x7 b&w glossy prints. Offers no additional payment for photos accepted with ms. Captions preferred. Buys one-time rights.
Columns/Departments: Public Affairs (1,000-2,000 words); Life in Israel (1,000-2,000 words). Buys 5 mss/year. Query. Length: 1,000-2,000 words. Pays $50 maximum.

Poetry: Publishes rarely. Submit 3 maximum. Length: 10-50 lines. Pays $10 minimum.

Tips: "We are interested in adding to our stable of freelance writers. The best way to break in is to send a detailed query about a subject you would like to handle for the magazine. All queries will be carefully considered and answered. We've been cut from 8 to 5 issues per year for budgetary reasons, so we're buying less material. But we're still reading whatever comes in. How-to articles in our magazine fall in the categories of Jewish-oriented travel and performance of rituals or religious observance. Humorous treatments of coping with life in Israel are also enjoyed by our readers."

BRIDAL FAIR, Meridian Publishing, Inc., Box 10010, Ogden UT 84409. (801)394-9446. Editor: Marjorie H. Rice. 65% freelance written. Monthly magazine with useful articles for today's bride. Circ. 50,000. Pays on acceptance. Publishes ms an average of 8 months after acceptance. Byline given. Buys first rights, second serial (reprint) rights and non-exclusive reprint rights. Simultaneous, photocopied and previously published submissions OK. Reports in 6 weeks. Sample copy for $1 and 9x12 SAE; writer's guidelines for SASE. All requests for samples and guidelines should be addressed Attn: Editorial Assistant.

Nonfiction: "General interest articles about traditional and modern approaches to weddings. Topics include ceremony and reception planning, wedding apparel and fashion trends, the bride, groom, and other members of the wedding party. Also featured are honeymoon destinations, the newly-wed's first home, how to build a relationship and keep romance alive, and getting to know in-laws." Buys approximately 30 mss/year. Query. Length: 1,000-1,400 words. Pays 15¢/word for first rights plus non-exclusive reprint rights. Payment for second rights is negotiable.

Photos: State availability of photos with query letter. Color transparencies and 5x7 or 8x10 prints are preferred. Pays $35 for inside photo; pays $50 for cover. Captions, model releases, and identification of subjects required.

Tips: "The best way to get started as a contributor to *Bridal Fair* is to prove that you can submit a well-focused article, written cleanly per AP style, *along with* a variety of beautiful color transparencies to illustrate the story."

‡BRIDAL GUIDE, Your Planner For The Perfect Wedding, Glad Tidings, Inc., Suite 109, 5225 North Ironwood Rd., Milwaukee WI 53217. (414)963-1131. Editor: Suzanne Kresse. Managing Editor: Eveline Kohl. 25% freelance written. Prefers to work with published/established writers; works with a small number of new/unpublished writers each year. A quarterly magazine covering wedding planning and the first home. "Bridal Guide is designed to be used as a wedding planning guide and keepsake for couples soon to be married. Information about modern wedding trends is directed to brides, grooms, and parents." Circ. 250,000. Pays on acceptance. Publishes ms an average of 6 months after acceptance. Byline given. Offers up to 50% kill fee. Buys first North American serial rights, second serial (reprint) rights and all rights. Submit seasonal/holiday material 6 months in advance. Simultaneous submissions and previously published submissions OK. Computer printout submissions acceptable; no dot-matrix. Reports in 1 month on queries; 2 months on mss. Sample copy $1.50.

Nonfiction: How-to, humor, inspirational, interview/profile, personal experience, religious and travel. Buys 12 mss/year. Send complete ms. Length: 1,000-3,000 words. Pays $100-300. Sometimes pays the expenses of writers on assignment.

Photos: Send photos with submission. Reviews 2x3 transparencies and prints. Offers no additional payment for photos accepted with ms. Captions, model releases, and indentification of subjects required. Sometimes pays the expenses of writers on assignment.

Tips: "The magazine offers re-marriage features as well as the etiquette of divorce problems in wedding planning. Various aspects of the perfect wedding from selecting the big day to the Reception Festivities and Honeymoon Getaway are explained in an organized format. Features include a calendar, checklists, planning charts, ethnic customs, and unusual wedding stories. Planning the first home is highlighted with in-depth information on major purchases. The area of our publication most open to freelancers includes, how-to stories in bridal fashion, ethnic customs, religious ceremonies, remarriage, etiquette, and Honeymoons, celebrity weddings, unusual weddings, wedding planning."

BRIDE'S, Conde Nast Bldg., 350 Madison Ave., New York NY 10017. (212)880-8800. Editor-in-Chief: Barbara D. Tober. 25% freelance written. Eager to work with new/unpublished writers. A bimonthly magazine for the first- or second-time bride, her family and friends, the groom and his family and friends. Circ. 410,000. Pays on acceptance. Publishes ms an average of 2 months after acceptance. Buys all rights. Also buys first and second serial rights for book excerpts on marriage, communication, finances. Offers 20% kill fee, depending on circumstances. Buys 30 unsolicited mss/year. Byline given. Reports in 2 months. Computer printout submissions acceptable; no dot-matrix. Address mss to Features Department. Writer's guidelines for SASE.

Nonfiction: "We want warm, personal articles, optimistic in tone, with help offered in a clear, specific way. All issues should be handled within the context of marriage. How-to features on all aspects of marriage: communications, in-laws, careers, money, sex, housing, housework, family planning, religion, interfaith marriage, step-parenting, second marriage, reaffirmation of vows; informational articles on the realities of marriage, the changing roles of men and women, the kinds of troubles in engagement that are likely to become big issues in marriage; stories from couples or marriage authorities that illustrate marital problems and solutions to men and women both; book excerpts on marriage, communication, finances; and how-to features on wedding planning that offer expert advice. Also success stories of marriages of long duration. We use first-person pieces and articles that are well researched, relying on quotes from authorities in the field, and anecdotes and dialogues from real couples." Query or submit complete ms. Article outline preferred. Length: 1,000-3,000 words. Pays $300-800.

Columns/Departments: The Love column accepts reader love poems, for $25 each.

Tips: "Since marriage rates are up and large, traditional weddings are back in style, and since more women work than ever before, do *not* query us on just living together or becoming a stay-at-home wife after marriage. Send us a query or a well-written article that is both easy to read and offers real help for the bride or groom as she/he adjusts to her/his new role. No first-person narratives on wedding and reception planning, home furnishings, cooking, fashion, beauty, travel. We're interested in unusual ideas, experiences, and lifestyles. No 'I used baby pink rose buds' articles."

CHATELAINE, 777 Bay St., Toronto, Ontario M5W 1A7 Canada. Editor-in-Chief: Mildred Istona. 75% freelance written. Prefers to work with published/established writers. Monthly general-interest magazine for Canadian women, from age 20 and up. "*Chatelaine* is read by one woman in three across Canada, a readership that spans almost every age group but is concentrated among those 25 to 45 including homemakers and working women in all walks of life." Circ. over 1 million. Pays on acceptance. Publishes ms an average of 3 months after acceptance. Byline given. Free writer's guidelines. Reports within 2 weeks. All mss must be accompanied by a SASE (IRCs in lieu of stamps if sent from outside Canada). Sample copy $1.75 and postage.

Nonfiction: Elizabeth Parr, senior editor, articles. Submit a page or two outline/query first. Full-length major pieces run from 1,500 to 3,000 words. Pays minimum $1,200 for acceptable major article. Buys first North American serial rights in English and French (the latter to cover possible use in *Chatelaine*'s sister French-language edition, edited in Montreal for French Canada). "We look for important national Canadian subjects, examining any and all facets of Canadian life, especially as they concern or interest women. For all serious articles, deep, accurate, thorough research and rich detail are required. Writers new to us should query Diane Passa, Senior Editor, with ideas for upfront columns on nutrition, fitness, relationships, health, and parents and kids." Pays $350 for about 750 words. Prefers queries for nonfiction subjects on initial contact plus a resume and writing samples. Also seeks full-length personal experience stories with deep emotional impact. Pays $750. Features on beauty, food, fashion and home decorating are supplied by staff writers and editors, and unsolicited material is not considered.

Fiction: Barbara West, senior editor, fiction. Mainstream fiction of up to 3,000 words. Pays $1,500 minimum. "Upbeat stories about man/woman relationships are the ones most likely to appeal. The central character should be a woman in the 25-45 age range, and the story should deal with and resolve contemporary problems our readers relate to. Canadian settings and characters are a plus. No query necessary for fiction."

‡COSMOPOLITAN, Hearst Corp., 224 W. 57th St., New York NY 10019. Editor: Helen Gurley Brown. Managing Editor: Guy Flatley. "We are backlogged with submissions and prefer not to receive unsolicited submissions at this time."

‡DAWN, The Orange County Woman's Magazine, Dawn Media Group, Box 6189, Laguna Niguel CA 92677. (714)249-1001. Editor: Susan O'Brien. 25% freelance written. Eager to work with new/unpublished writers. Monthly magazine "published by and for the women of Orange County, California. It regularly includes research articles, book and film reviews; psychology, literature, fashion, home and dining sections, and business and fitness articles." Circ. 30,000. Pays on publication. Publishes ms an average of 4 months after acceptance. Byline given. Buys first-time rights. Submit seasonal/holiday material 4 months in advance. Simultaneous queries and photocopied and previously published submissions OK. Computer printout submissions acceptable. Reports in 6 weeks on queries; 2 months on mss. Sample copy and writer's guidelines for 8x11 SAE and $1.20 postage.

Nonfiction: General interest, historical/nostalgic, humor, personal experience, travel. "Articles should either focus on women or reflect a woman's view of the issue, e.g., women's changing roles in films." Buys 25 mss/year. Send complete ms. Length: 500-4,000 words. Pays $5-125.

Tips: "*Dawn* is not a particularly viable vehicle for freelance writers, although we anticipate expansion and may be able to use more freelance work. As a regional publication with a limited budget, we pay primarily for one major article in each issue. Our contributing writers generally are interested in developing publishing credits or wish to reach our specific audience; a few accept token payment because they enjoy the magazine. We are a good showcase for new writers, because we treat all material with care and respect, giving it the best possible presentation."

FAIRFIELD COUNTY WOMAN, NEW HAVEN COUNTY WOMAN, HARTFORD WOMAN, FCW, Inc, Chadwick & Duke, Publishers, 15 Bank St., Stamford CT 06901. (203)323-3105. Editor: Ina B. Chadwick.

Regional Editor (New Haven): Tricia Buie, 31 Whitney St., New Haven CT 06501. Regional Editor (Hartford): Joy Esterson, 15 Franklin St., Hartford CT 06114. "We are backlogged with submissions and prefer not to receive unsolicited submissions at this time."

FAMILY CIRCLE GREAT IDEAS, 488 Madison Ave., New York NY 10022. (212)593-8181. Editor: Marie T. Walsh. Managing Editor: Shari E. Hartford. 20-95% freelance written. Published 9 times/year; 128 pages. Circ. 1,000,000. Pays on acceptance. Publishes ms an average of 3 months after acceptance. Buys all rights. Submit Christmas material 4 months in advance. Computer printout submissions acceptable; no dot-matrix. Writer's guidelines free upon request with SASE. Reports in 2 weeks. Sample copy $2.25.
Nonfiction: How-to (fashion, decorating, crafts, food and beauty) and new product (for home and family). "Writers have their best chance breaking into the *Great Ideas* series with craft ideas. Craft projects are also included in the books not specifically devoted to crafts." Will also review regionally-based features. Article queries should be directed to managing editor; must be accompanied by SASE. Buys 2 mss/issue. Query. Pays $150-350.
Tips: "We do not accept fiction or poetry."

FAMILY CIRCLE MAGAZINE, 488 Madison Ave., New York NY 10022. (212)593-8000. Editor: Gay Bryant. 60% freelance written. For women. Published 17 times/year. Usually buys all rights. Pays 25% kill fee. Byline given. Pays on acceptance. Reports in 6-8 weeks. Query. "We are a *service* magazine. Query should stress how-to angle; we want articles that will help our readers. We are especially interested in writers who have a solid background in the areas they suggest."
Nonfiction: Susan Ungaro, articles editor. Women's interest subjects such as family and social relationships, children, physical and mental health, nutrition, self-improvement, travel. Service articles. For travel, interested mainly in local material. "We look for service stories told in terms of people. We want well-researched service journalism on all subjects." Length: 1,000-2,500 words. Pays $250-2,500.
Tips: Query letters should be "concise and to the point. We get some with 10 different suggestions—by the time they're passed on to all possible editors involved, weeks may go by." Also, writers should "keep close tabs on *Family Circle* and other women's magazines to avoid submitting recently run subject matter."

FARM WOMAN, Reiman Publications, Box 643, Milwaukee WI 53201. (414)423-0100. Editor: Ann Kaiser. Managing Editor: Ruth Benedict. 65% freelance written. Eager to work with new/unpublished writers. Monthly (with combined July/August issue) magazine on the interests of farm and ranch women. "*Farm Woman* is for contemporary rural women of all ages and backgrounds and from all over the U.S. and Canada. It includes a sampling of the diversity that makes up rural women's lives—love of home, family, farm, ranch, community, hobbies, enduring values, humor, attaining new skills and appreciating present, past and future all within the content of the lifestyle that surrounds agriculture and country living." Circ. 330,000. Pays on acceptance. Publishes ms an average of 1 year after acceptance. Byline given. Offers 20% kill fee. Buys first North American serial rights, one-time rights, and second serial (reprint) rights; makes some work-for-hire assignments. Submit seasonal/holiday material 4-5 months in advance. Photocopied and previously published (on occasion) submissions OK. Computer printout submissions acceptable; no dot-matrix. Reports in 1 month on queries; 4-6 weeks on mss. Sample copy $2.50; writer's guidelines for SAE and 1 first class stamp.
Nonfiction: General interest, historical/nostalgic, how-to (crafts, community projects, family relations, self-improvement, decorative, antiquing, etc.); humor; inspirational; interview/profile; personal experience; photo feature; and travel, all pertaining to a rural woman's interest. Buys 100+ mss/year. Query, or send complete ms. Length: 1,000 words maximum. Pays $40-300. Sometimes pays the expenses of writers on assignment.
Photos: Send photos with query or ms. Reviews 35mm or 2¼ transparencies. Pays $25-100 for b&w; $60-200 for color. Captions, model releases and identification of subjects required. Buys one-time rights.
Columns/Departments: Why Farm Wives Age Fast (humor), I Remember When (nostalgia), Country Decorating, and Shopping Comparison (new product comparisons). Buys 45 (maximum)/year. Query or send complete ms. Length: 500-1,000 words. Pays $55-200.
Fiction: Adventure, humorous, mainstream, suspense and western. Buys 5 (maximum) mss/year. Query or send complete ms. Length: 1,000-1,500 words. Pays $75-200.
Poetry: Avant-garde, free verse, light verse and traditional. Buys 40 poems/year. Submit maximum 6 poems. Length: 5-24 lines. Pays $25-60.
Fillers: Jokes, anecdotes, short humor and consumer news (e.g. safety, tips, etc.). Buys 40/year. Length: 40-250 words. Pays $25-40.
Tips: "Write as clearly and with as much zest and enthusiasm as possible. We love good quotes, supporting materials (names, places, etc.) and strong leads and closings. Readers relate strongly to where they live and the lifestyle they've chosen. They want to be informed and entertained, and that's just exactly why they subscribe. Readers are busy—not too busy to read—but when they do sit down, they want good writing, reliable information and something that feels like a 'reward'. How-to, humor, personal experience and nostalgia are areas most open to freelancers. Profiles, to a certain degree, are also open. We are always especially receptive to short items—250 words, 400 words and so on. Be accurate and fresh in approach."

GLAMOUR, Conde Nast, 350 Madison Ave., New York NY 10017. (212)880-8800. Editor-in-Chief: Ruth Whitney. For college-educated women, 18-35-years old. Monthly. Circ. 2.3 million; 7 million readers. Computer printout submissions acceptable "if the material is easy to read." Prefers letter-quality to dot-matrix printouts. Pays on acceptance. Pays 20% kill fee. Byline given. Reports within 5 weeks. Writer's guidelines available for SASE.

Nonfiction: Judy Coynes, articles editor. "Editorial approach is 'how-to' with articles that are relevant in the areas of careers, health, psychology, interpersonal relationships, etc. We look for queries that are fresh and include a contemporary, timely angle. Fashion, beauty, decorating, travel, food and entertainment are all staff-written. We use 1,000 word opinion essays for our Viewpoint section. Pays $500. Our His/Hers column features generally stylish essays on relationships or comments on current mores by male and female writers in alternate months. Pays $1,000 for His/Hers mss. Buys first North American serial rights." Buys 10-12 mss/issue. Query "with letter that is detailed, well-focused, well-organized, and documented with surveys, statistics and research, personal essays excepted." Reports in 5 weeks. Short articles and essays (1,500-2,000 words) pay $1,000 and up; longer mss (2,500-3,000 words) pay $1,500 minimum on acceptance.

Tips: "We're looking for sharply focused ideas by strong writers and constantly raising our standards. We are very interested in getting new writers; and we are approachable, mainly because our range of topics is so broad."

GOOD HOUSEKEEPING, Hearst Corp., 959 8th Ave., New York NY 10019. (212)262-3614. Editor-in-Chief: John Mack Carter. Executive Editor: Mina Mulvey. Managing Editor: Mary Fiore. Prefers to work with published/established writers. Monthly; 250 pages. Circ. 5,000,000. Pays on acceptance. Buys all rights. Pays 25% kill fee. Byline given. Submit seasonal/holiday material 6 months in advance. Computer printout submissions acceptable; no dot-matrix. Reports in 6 weeks. Sample copy $2. Free writer's guidelines with SASE.

Nonfiction: Joan Thursh, articles editor. How-to/informational; investigative stories; inspirational; interview; nostalgia; personal experience; and profile. Buys 4-6 mss/issue. Query. Length: 1,500-2,500 words. Pays $1,500 on acceptance for full articles from new writers. Regional Editor: Shirley Howard. Pays $250-350 for local interest and travel pieces of 2,000 words. Pays the expenses of writers on assignment.

Photos: Herbert Bleiweiss, art director. Photos purchased on assignment mostly. Some short photo features with captions. Pays $100-350 for b&w; $200-400 for color photos. Query. Model releases required.

Columns/Departments: Light Housekeeping & Fillers, edited by Rosemary Leonard. Humorous short-short prose and verse. Jokes, gags, anecdotes. Pays $25-50. The Better Way, edited by Erika Mark. Ideas and in-depth research. Query. Pays $250-500. "Mostly staff written; only outstanding ideas have a chance here."

Fiction: Naome Lewis, fiction editor. Uses romance fiction and condensations of novels that can appear in one issue. Looks for reader identification. "We get 1,500 unsolicited mss/mo.—includes poetry; a freelancer's odds are overwhelming—but we do look at all submissions." Send complete mss. Length: 1,500 words (short-shorts); novel according to merit of material; average 5,000 words short stories. Pays $1,000 minimum for fiction short-shorts; $1,250 for short stories.

Poetry: Arleen Quarfoot, poetry editor. Light verse and traditional. "Presently overstocked." Poems used as fillers. Pays $5/line for poetry on acceptance.

HYSTERIA, Little Red Media Foundation, Box 2481, Station B, Kitchener, Ontario N2H-6M3-Canada. (519)576-8094. Editor: Catherine Edwards. 75% freelance written. Works with a small number of new/unpublished writers each year. Quarterly magazine covering social, cultural and artistic/literary issues of interest to women from a feminist perspective. Circ. 1,200. Pays on acceptance. Publishes ms an average of 6 months after acceptance. Byline given. Offers 10% kill fee. Buys first North American serial rights. Simultaneous queries, and simultaneous, photocopied, and previously published submissions OK. Computer printout submissions acceptable; prefers letter-quality to dot-matrix. SASE or SAE with IRCs. Reports in 1 month on queries; 3 months on mss. Sample copy $2.50 (Canadian); free writer's guidelines.

Nonfiction: Book excerpts, expose (except not U.S. oriented; with multinational interest); humor (cartoons especially); interview/profile (of interesting and innovative women, artists, writers, other); opinion; personal experience; and photo feature (black and white only; art oriented). "We're not interested in material by or about men; aside from that, we have catholic tastes." Buys 24-30 mss/year. Query with published clips or send complete mss. Length: 1,500-5,000 words. Pays $15-50 (some extra for illustrations). Sometimes pays the expenses of writers on assignment.

Photos: State availability of photos or send photos with query or ms. Reviews 5x7 b&w prints. Pays $10 for 5x7 b&w prints. Captions required. Buys one-time rights.

Columns/Departments: Reviews (of books by and about women, especially small-press material); Film Reviews (of films available for rental by community groups—not major releases); and "She's Just Being Hysterical" (a column of personal outrage). Buys 24 mss/year. Query with published clips or send complete ms. Length: 750-2,500 words. Pays $10-25.

Fiction: Ethnic, experimental, fantasy (but not mushy fantasy); humorous; mainstream; mystery; and science fiction. "No romance, historical or religious fiction; nothing in which the heroine gets married and lives happily ever after." Buys 6 mss/year. Send complete ms. Length: 2,000-5,000 words. Pays $20-50.

Poetry: Avant-garde, free verse, haiku and traditional. Buys 25 poems/year. Submit maximum 6 poems. Length: 40 lines maximum. Pays $5.
Tips: "We are trying to develop a broader base of writers, and article features are what we need most. If someone shares our goals and interests, we are happy to work with writers developing articles, etc. The most frequent mistakes made by writers in completing an article assignment for us is writing in a chatty style more suitable for a newspaper. Although we are not opposed to newspapers, our readers are looking for a little more depth."

LADIES' HOME JOURNAL, 3 Park Ave., New York NY 10016. (212)340-9200. Editor-in-Chief: Myrna Blyth. Executive Editor: Jan Goodwin. Managing Editor: Mary Mohler. 50% freelance written. A monthly magazine covering issues of concern to women. *"Ladies' Home Journal* reflects the lives of the contemporary mainstream American woman, and gives her information she needs, and wants, to live in today's world." Circ. 5,000,000. Pays on acceptance. Publishes ms an average of 3 months after acceptance, but time may vary. Byline given. Offers 25% kill fee. Rights bought vary with submissions. Submit seasonal/holiday material 6 months in advance. Computer printout submissions acceptable; prefers letter-quality to dot-matrix. Reports in 1 month on queries; 3 weeks on manuscripts. Free writer's guidelines.
Nonfiction: Submit the following types of articles to the names listed in parentheses. Books excerpts (Mary Lou Mullen); Fashion (Lois Johnson); Beauty (Lois Johnson); Exposé (Jan Goodwin); Education (Roberta Grant); Self-improvement (Roberta Grant); Decorating, Design (Marilyn Glass); Investing/Financial (Katherine Barrett); Humor (Jeanne Curry); Consumerism (Diane Salvatore); Health/Medical (Beth Weinhouse); Interview/profile (Jan Goodwin); Relationships (Roberta Grant); Fitness/Nutrition (Lois Johnson); Opinion/political (Jan Goodwin); Career (Connie Leisure); Entertainment (Jan Goodwin); Personal experience (Jan Goodwin); Photo feature (Tamara Schneider); Religious (Eric Sherman); Family Care (Roberta Grant); Child Care (Mary Mohler); Travel (Connie Leisure); Psychology (Pam Guthrie); and Food (Jan Hazard). Query with or without published clips. Length: 3,000-4,000 words. Fees vary; average between $2,500 and $3,500. Pays the expenses of writers on assignment.
Photos: State availability of photos with submissions. Captions, model releases, and identification of subjects required. Rights bought vary with submissions.
Fiction: Mary Lou Mullen, fiction editor. "We use only solicited or agented fiction."

McCALL'S, 230 Park Ave., New York NY 10169. (212)551-9500. Editor: Elizabeth Sloan. Managing Editor: Don McKinney. 90% freelance written. "Study recent issues." Our publication "carefully and conscientiously services the needs of the woman reader—concentrating on matters that directly affect her life and offering information and understanding on subjects of personal importance to her." Monthly. Circ. 6,200,000. Pays on acceptance. Publishes ms an average of 6 months after acceptance. Pays 20% kill fee. Byline given. Buys first rights only. Computer printout submissions acceptable; no dot-matrix. Reports in 2 months. Writer's guidelines for SASE.
Nonfiction: Don McKinney, managing editor. No subject of wide public or personal interest is out of bounds for *McCall's* so long as it is appropriately treated. The editors are seeking meaningful stories of personal experience. They are on the lookout for new research that will provide the basis for penetrating articles on the ethical, physical, material and social problems concerning readers. *McCall's* buys 200-300 articles/year, many in the 1,000- to 1,500-word length. Pays variable rates for nonfiction. Mrs. Helen Del Monte and Andrea Thompson are editors of nonfiction books, from which *McCall's* frequently publishes excerpts. These are on subjects of interest to women: biography, memoirs, reportage, etc. Almost all features on food, household equipment and management, fashion, beauty, building and decorating are staff-written. Query. "All manuscripts must be submitted on speculation, and *McCall's* accepts no responsibility for unsolicited manuscripts." Sometimes pays the expenses of writers on assignment.
Columns/Departments: Child Care (edited by Andrea Thompson); short items that may be humorous, helpful, inspiring and reassuring. Pays $100 and up. Vital Signs (edited by Denise Hatfield); short items on health and medical news. Pay varies. VIP-ZIP (edited by Lucy Sullivan); high-demography regional section. Largely service-oriented, it covers travel, decorating and home entertainment.
Fiction: Kathy Koontz, department editor. "Again the editors would remind writers of the contemporary woman's taste and intelligence. Most of all, fiction can awaken a reader's sense of identity, deepen her understanding of herself and others, refresh her with a laugh at herself, etc. *McCall's* looks for stories which will have meaning for an adult reader of some literary sensitivity. *No* stories that are grim, depressing, fragmentary or concerned with themes of abnormality or violence. *McCall's* principal interest is in short stories; but fiction of all lengths is considered." Length: about 3,000 words average. Length for short-shorts: about 2,000 words. Payment begins at $1,500; $2,000 for full length stories.

Market conditions are constantly changing! If this is 1988 or later, buy the newest edition of Writer's Market at your favorite bookstore or order directly from Writer's Digest Books.

Poetry: Barbara Stoaner and Helen DelMonte, poetry editor. "There's so much wonderful poetry out there. I wish we could use more." Poets with a "very original way of looking at their subjects" are most likely to get her attention. McCall's needs poems on love, the family, relationships with friends and relatives, familiar aspects of domestic and suburban life, Americana, and the seasons. Pays $5/line on acceptance for first North American serial rights. Length: no longer than 30 lines.
Tips: "Except for humor, query first. Material is running shorter than a few years ago. There is a great demand for shorter pieces, although I wouldn't want to rule out longer pieces such as narratives, personal essays. We are much more open to very short pieces, 750 words up. We don't encourage an idea unles we think we can use it. Address submissions to Anne Cassidy, unless otherwise specified."

MADEMOISELLE, 350 Madison Ave., New York NY 10017. Kate White, executive editor, articles. 95% freelance written. Prefers to work with published/established writers. Columns are written by columnists; "sometimes we give new writers a 'chance' on shorter, less complex assignments." Directed to college-educated, unmarried working women 18-34. Circ. 1,100,000. Reports in 1 month. Buys first North American serial rights. Pays on acceptance; rates vary. Publishes ms an average of 1 year after acceptance. Computer printout submissions are acceptable "but only letter-quality, double-spaced; no dot-matrix."
Nonfiction: Particular concentration on articles of interest to the intelligent young woman, including personal relationships, health, careers, trends, and current social problems. Articles should be well-researched and of good quality. Query with published clips. Length: 1,500-3,000 words.
Art: Kati Korpijaakko, art director. Commissioned work assigned according to needs. Photos of fashion, beauty, travel. Payment ranges from no-charge to an agreed rate of payment per shot, job series or page rate. Buys all rights. Pays on publication for photos.
Fiction: Eileen Schnurr, fiction and books editor. Quality fiction by both established and unknown writers. "We are interested in encouraging and publishing new writers and welcome unsolicited fiction manuscripts. However we are not a market for formula stories, genre fiction, unforgettable character portraits, surprise endings or oblique stream of consciousness sketches. We are looking for well-told stories that speak in fresh and individual voices and help us to understand ourselves and the world we live in. Stories of particular relevance to young women have an especially good chance, but stories need not be by or from the point of view of a woman—we are interested in good fiction on any theme from any point of view." Buys first North American serial rights. Pays $1,500 for short stories (10-25 pages); $1,000 for short shorts (7-10 pages). Allow 3 months for reply. SASE required. In addition to year-round unqualified acceptance of unsolicited fiction manuscripts, *Mademoiselle* conducts a once-a-year fiction contest open to unpublished writers, male and female, 18-30 years old. First prize is $1,000 plus publication in *Mademoiselle*; second prize, $500 with option to publish. Watch magazine for announcement, usually in January or February issues, or send SASE for rules, after Jan 1.

MILITARY LIFESTYLE, (formerly *Ladycom*), Downey Communications, Inc., 1732 Wisconsin Ave. NW, Washington DC 20007. Editor: Hope M. Daniels. 90% freelance written. Works with equal balance of published and unpublished writers. For families of military men who live in the U.S. or overseas. Published 10 times a year. Magazine. Circ. 500,000. Pays on publication. Publishes ms an average of 4 months after acceptance. Buys first North American serial rights. Submit seasonal/holiday material 6 months in advance. Computer printout submissions acceptable; prefers letter-quality to dot-matrix. Reports in 8 weeks. Sample copy $1.50. Free writer's guidelines.
Nonfiction: "All articles must have special interest for military wives and their families. General interest articles are OK if they reflect situations our readers can relate to." How-to (crafts, food), humor, profiles, personal experience, personal opinion, health, home decor and travel. "Query letter should name sources, describe focus of article, use a few sample quotes from sources, indicate length, and should describe writer's own qualifications for doing the piece." Length: 800-2,000 words. Pays $200-600/article.
Photos: Purchased with accompanying ms and on assignment. Uses 5x7 or 8x10 b&w glossy prints; 35mm or larger color transparencies; stock photo fee payment for photo with accompanying ms. Captions and model releases are required. Query art director Judi Connelly.
Columns/Departments: It Seems to Me—personal experience pieces by military family members. Your Travels—highlights of life at various bases and posts and nearby cities. Also, Your Pet, Your Money and Babystyle. Query. Length: 800-1,200 words. Rates vary.
Fiction: Slice-of-life, romance and suspense. "Military family life or relationship themes only." Buys 6-8 mss/year. Query. Length: 1,500-2,500 words. Pays $200-250.
Tips: "Our ideal contributor is a military family member who can write. However, I'm always impressed by a writer who has analyzed the market and can suggest some possible new angles for us. Sensitivity to military issues is a must for our contributors, as is the ability to write good personality profiles and/or do thorough research about military family life. We don't purchase gothic fiction; hints from Heloise-type material (no one does it better than she does, anyway); Erma Bombeck imitations; Vietnam War-era fiction; and parenting advice that is too personal and limited only to the writer's own experience."

MY WEEKLY, The Magazine for Women Everywhere, D.C. Thomson & Co., Ltd., 80 Kingsway E., Dundee DD4 8SL Scotland. Editor: Stewart D. Brown. 95% freelance written. Eager to work with new/unpublished writers. Weekly entertainment magazine for women. "Entertainment means we do not lecture or try to educate our readers." Circ. 713,165. Pays on acceptance. Publishes ms an average of 6 months after acceptance. Byline given. Buys first British serial rights. Previously published submissions OK. Reports in 1 month. Free sample copy.

Nonfiction: General interest; humor (feminine, domestic); interview/profile; personal experience (sharing an emotional or dramatic experience); and photo feature. No political articles, explicit sex or anything that "attempts to lecture" the reader. Buys over 300 mss/year. Send complete ms. Length: 800-3,000 words. Pays variable rates. Sometimes pays the expenses of writers on assignment.

Photos: Send photos with ms. Reviews 2¼x2¼ transparencies. Captions, model releases and identification of subjects required. Buys one-time rights.

Fiction: Humorous; romance; serialized novels; suspense (with feminine interest); and stories dealing with *real* emotional, domestic problems. No material dealing explicitly with sex, violence or politics. Buys 150 mss/year. Send complete ms. Length: 1,500-6,000 words. Pays variable rates.

Fillers: Short humor (feminine). Length: 800-1,200 words. Pays variable rates.

Tips: "We invite our readers to meet and share the lives and experiences of interesting people—through both first person articles and the interviews our writers supply. Much of this applies to our fiction, too. If our readers read *My Weekly* to 'escape,' it's to escape not into a glossy, unreal world of actresses, millionaires, politicians, but into the 'real' world of other people dealing with the problems of 'ordinary' life with dignity, warmth and humour."

NEW WOMAN MAGAZINE, Murdoch Magazines, 215 Lexington Ave., New York NY 10016. (212)685-4790. Editor: Pat Miller. Managing Editor: Karen Walden. 70% freelance written. A monthly general interest women's magazine for ages 25-35. We're especially interested in self-help in love and work (career); we also cover food, fashion, beauty, travel, money." Circ. 1.15 million. Pays on acceptance. Publishes ms an average of 6 months after acceptance. Byline given. Offers 20% kill fee. Buys first North American serial rights and second serial (reprint) rights. Submit seasonal/holiday material 5 months in advance. Simultaneous, photocopied and previously published submissions OK. Computer printout submissions acceptable (double space and leave a wide righthand margin); prefers letter-quality to dot-matrix. Reports in 1 month on queries; 2 weeks on mss. Writer's guidelines for business size SAE with 1 first class stamp.

Nonfiction: Stephanie von Hirschberg and Donna Jackson, senior editors. Book excerpts, essays, opinion on relationships, personal experience, travel, health, relationships, career advice, money and psychology. Does one special section on Money, Careers and/or Health every year. No book or movie reviews, advice columns, fashion, food or beauty material. Buys 75-100 ms/year. Query with published clips or send complete ms. Length: 1,000-3,500 words. Pays $500-2,000. Pays the expenses of writers on assignment.

Photos: State availability of photos with submission. Offers no additonal payment for photos accepted with ms. Captions, model releases and identification of subjects required. Buys one-time rights.

Fiction: Sarah Medford (book excerpts); Donna Jackson (short stories). No unsolicited ms except through agent. Buys 6-8 mss/year. Length: 2,000-5,000 words.

Poetry: Andrea Jarrell, poetry editor. Light Verse. Buys 12 poems/year. Length: 4-40 lines. Pays $50-100.

Fillers: Rosemarie Lennon, fillers editor. Facts, newsbreaks and newspaper clips (for Briefing section). Buys 3/year. Length: 200-500 words. Pays $10-200.

Tips: "The best approach for breaking into our publication is a personal letter, with clippings of published work, telling us what you're interested in, what you really like to write about, and your perceptions of *New Woman*. It counts a lot when a writer loves the magazine, and responds to it on a personal level. Psychology and relationships articles are most open to freelancers. Best tip: *familiarity with the magazine.* We look for originality, solid research, depth, and a friendly, accessible style."

PIONEER WOMAN, Magazine of Pioneer Women/Na'amat, the Women's Labor Zionist Organization of America, Pioneer Women/Na'amat, 200 Madison Ave., New York NY 10016. (212)725-8010. Editor: Judith A. Sokoloff. 80% freelance written. Magazine published 5 times/year covering Jewish themes and issues; Israel; women's issues; Labor Zionism; and occasional pieces dealing with social, political and economic issues. Circ. 30,000. Pays on publication. Byline given. Not copyrighted. Buys first North American serial, one-time and first serial rights; second serial (reprint) rights to book excerpts; and makes work-for-hire assignments. Reports in 1 month on queries, 2 months on mss. Free sample copy and writer's guidelines.

Nonfiction: Book excerpts; expose; general interest (Jewish); historical/nostalgic; interview/profile; opinion; personal experience; photo feature; travel (Israel); art; and music. "All articles must be of interest to the Jewish community." Buys 35 mss/year. Query with clips of published work or send complete ms. Length: 2,000-2,500 words. Pays 8¢/word.

Photos: State availability of photos. Pays $10-30 for b&w contact sheet and 4x5 or 5x7 prints. Captions and identification of subjects required. Buys one-time rights.

Columns/Departments: Film and book reviews with Jewish themes. Buys 20-25 mss/year. Query with clips of published work or send complete ms. Length: 500-1,000 words. Pays 8¢/word.

Fiction: Historical/nostalgic, humorous, women-oriented, and novel excerpts. "Good intelligent fiction with

Jewish slant. No maudlin nostalgia or trite humor." Buys 3 mss/year. Send complete ms. Length: 1,200-3,000 words. Pays 8¢/word.

PLAYGIRL, 3420 Ocean Park Blvd., Santa Monica CA 90405. (213)450-0900. Executive Editor: Thomasine E. Lewis. Senior Editor: Pat McGilligan. 75% freelance written. Prefers to work with published/established writers. Monthly entertainment magazine for 20-40-year-old females. Circ. 850,000. Average issue includes 4 articles and 2 interviews. Pays 1 month after acceptance. Publishes ms an average of 3 months after acceptance. Byline given. Offers 20% kill fee. Buys all rights. Submit seasonal material 4 months in advance. Simultaneous and photocopied submissions OK, if so indicated. Computer printout submissions acceptable; prefers letter-quality to dot-matrix. Reports in 1 month on queries; in 2 months on mss. Publishes ms an average of 3 months after acceptance. Free writer's guidelines with SASE. Sample copy $5.
Nonfiction: Ruth Drizen, senior nonfiction editor. "Humor for the modern woman"; exposes (related to women's issues); interview (Q&A format with major show business celebrities); articles on sexuality; hard information on credit and finances; medical breakthroughs; relationships; coping; and careers; insightful, lively articles on current issues; and investigative pieces particularly geared to *Play Girl*. Buys 6 mss/issue. Query with clips of previously published work. Length: 2,500-4,000 words. Pays $500-1,000. Sometimes pays the expenses of writers on assignment.
Fiction: Mary Ellen Strote, fiction editor. Contemporary romance stories of 2,500 words. Send complete fiction ms. "The important thing to remember is we don't want graphic sex, and no adventure, suspense, science fiction, murder or mystery stories. We want something emotional." Pays $300 and up for fiction.
Tips: "We are not a beginner's nonfiction market. We're looking for major clips and don't really consider nonpublished writers."

‡POLITICAL WOMAN, The Non-partisan Journal for the Thinking Woman, United Resource Services, Suite 254, 4521 Campus Dr., Irvine CA 92715. (714)854-3506. Editor: Sally Corngold. Managing Editor: Cynthia K. Horrocks. 95% freelance written. "*Political Woman* is a non-partisan quarterly magazine geared to, but not totally about or for women. The purpose is to publish objective, informative articles of global significance in a sophisticated, readable style." Estab. 1985. Circ. 2,500. Pays on publication. Publishes ms an average of 2 months after acceptance. Byline given. Offers 50% kill fee. Buys one-time rights. Simultaneous submissions OK. Electronic submissions OK; requires hard copy also. Computer printout submissions acceptable. Reports within weeks. Sample copy $2; free writers's guidelines.
Nonfiction: Expose, historical/nostalgic, humor, interview/profile, personal experience, photofeature, travel (with political relevance) and political features. Buys 30-50 mss/year. Query. Length: 2,000-3,000 words. Pays $100-1,000.
Photos: State availability of photos with submission. Reviews 3x5 transparencies. Offers no additional payment for photos accepted with mss. Captions, model releases, and identification of subjects required. Buys one-time rights.
Columns/Departments: Freda Wyant and Sally Corngold, columns department editors. Facing Off (opposing views on a single topic); Profile (political figures); Election Topics; and Political Issues. Buys 30-50 mss/year. Query. Length: 2,000-3,000 words. Pays $100-1,000.
Poetry: Joan Jefts, poetry editor. Avant-garde, free verse, haiku, light verse and traditional. Buys 4-6 poems/year. Submit maximum of 1 poem. Length: 6-24 lines. Pays $25-200.
Fillers: Gary Brown, fillers editors. Anecdotes, facts, gags to be illustrated by cartoonist, newsbreaks, and short humor. Buys 20/year. Length: 50-500 words. Pays $25-300.
Tips: The area most open to freelancers are "full-length, well documented exposes. These must be footnoted and sources given."

REDBOOK MAGAZINE, 224 W. 57th St., New York NY 10019. (212)262-8284. Editor-in-Chief: Annette Capone. Managing Editor: Jennifer Johnson. Associate Editor: Judsen Culbreth. 80% freelance written. Monthly magazine; 200 pages. Circ. 3,800,000. Pays on acceptance. Publishes ms an average of 6 months after acceptance. Rights purchased vary with author and material. Computer printout submissions acceptable; prefers letter-quality to dot-matrix. Reports in 2 months. Free writer's guidelines for *Redbook* for SASE.
Nonfiction: Karen Larson, articles editor. Jean Maguire, health editor. "*Redbook* addresses young mothers between the ages of 25 and 44. More than half of *Redbook*'s readers work outside the home and have children under 18. The articles in *Redbook* entertain, guide and inspire our readers. A significant percentage of the pieces stress 'how-to,' the ways a woman can solve the problems in her everyday life. Writers are advised to read at least the last *six* issues of the magazine (available in most libraries) to get a better understanding of what we're looking for. We prefer to see queries, rather than complete manuscripts. Please enclose a sample or two of your writing as well as a stamped, self-addressed envelope." Also interested in submissions for Young Mother's Story. "We are interested in stories for the Young Mother series offering the dramatic retelling of an experience involving you, your husband or child. Possible topics might include: how you have handled a child's health or school problem, or conflicts within the family. For each 1,500-2,000 words accepted for publication as Young Mother's Story, we pay $750. Mss accompanied by a large, stamped, self-addressed enve-

lope, must be signed, and mailed to: Young Mother's Story, c/o *Redbook Magazine*. Length: articles, 2,500-3,000 words; short articles, 1,000-1,500 words. Young Mother's reports in 3-4 months." Sometimes pays the expenses of writers on assignment.

Fiction: Kathyrne Sagan, fiction editor. "Out of the 35,000 unsolicited manuscripts that we receive annually, we buy about 50 stories/year. We find many more stories that, for one reason or another, are not suited to our needs but are good enough to warrant our encouraging the author to send others. Sometimes such an author's subsequent submission turns out to be something we can use. *Redbook* looks for stories by and about men and women, realistic stories and fantasies, funny and sad stories, stories of people together and people alone, stories with familiar and exotic settings, love stories and work stories. But there are a few things common to all of them, that make them stand out from the crowd. The high quality of their writing, for one thing. The distinctiveness of their characters and plots; stock characters and sitcom stories are not for us. We look for stories with a definite resolution or emotional resonance. Cool stylistic or intellectual experiments are of greater interest, we feel, to readers of literary magazines than of a magazine like *Redbook* that tries to offer insights into the hows and whys of day-to-day living. And all the stories reflect some aspect of the experience, the interests, or the dreams of *Redbook*'s particular readership." Short-short stories (7-9 pages, 1,400-1,600 words) are always in demand; but short stories of 10-15 pages, (3,000-5,000 words) are also acceptable. Stories 20 pages and over have a "hard fight, given our tight space limits, but we have bought longer stories that we loved. *Redbook* no longer reads unsolicited novels." Manuscripts must be typewritten, double-spaced, and accompanied by SASE the size of the manuscript. Payment begins at $850 for short shorts; $1,000 for short stories.

Tips: "Shorter, front-of-the-book features are usually easier to develop with first-time contributors. It is very difficult to break into the nonfiction section, although we do buy Young Mother's stories, dramatic personal experience pieces (1,500-2,000 words), from previously unpublished writers. The most frequent mistakes made by writers in completing an article for us are 1) Poor organization. A piece that's poorly organized is confusing, repetitive, difficult to read. I advise authors to do full outlines before they start writing so they can more easily spot structure problems and so they have a surer sense of where their piece is headed. 2) Poor or insufficient research. Most *Redbook* articles require solid research and include: full, well-developed anecdotes from real people (not from people who exist only in the writer's imagination); clear, substantial quotes from established experts in a field; and, if possible, additional research such as statistics and other information from reputable studies, surveys, etc."

SAVVY, The Magazine for Executive Women, Family Media, 3 Park Ave., New York NY 10016. (212)340-9200. Editor: Wendy Reid Crisp. Managing Editor: Ann Powell. 90% freelance written. A monthly magazine. "*Savvy* articles are written for the executive women. We try to use as many women as possible for our sources. The age group of our readers falls primarily between 25 and 45 and we address both their home and office lives." Circ. 350,000. Pays 4-6 weeks after due date. Publishes ms an average of 3 months after acceptance. Byline given. Offers 15-20% kill fee. Buys first North American serial rights, and reprint rights. Submit seasonal/holiday material 4 months in advance. Photocopied submissions OK. Computer printout submissions acceptable; prefers letter-quality to dot-matrix. Reports as soon as possible. Free writer's guidelines with SASE.

Nonfiction: Book excerpts, humor, interview/profile, opinion, personal experience and travel. No limit on mss bought/year. Query with published clips. Length: 800-3,000 words ("depends on its position"). Pays $650 minimum. Pays the expenses of writers on assignment.

Columns/Departments: Money Action (how to manage, invest and save money), 1,000-1,200 words; Health (any topics pertaining to health: illnesses, cures, new findings, etc.), 1,000-1,200 words; and Career Strategies (how to handle career situations, gain ground at work, change jobs, etc.), 1,200-2,400 words. Query with published clips. Pays $650 minimum.

SELF, Conde-Nast, 350 Madison Ave., New York NY 10017. (212)880-8834. Editor: Phyllis Starr Wilson. Managing Editor: Valorie Weaver. 50% freelance written. "We prefer to work with writers—even relatively new ones—with a degree, training or practical experience in specialized areas, psychology to nutrition."Monthly magazine emphasizing self improvement of emotional and physical well-being for women of all ages. Circ. 1,077,090. Average issue includes 12-20 feature articles and 4-6 columns. Pays on acceptance. Publishes ms an average of 6 months after acceptance. Byline given. Offers 20% kill fee. Buys first North American serial rights. Submit seasonal material 4 months in advance. Simultaneous and photocopied submissions OK. Computer printout submissions acceptable; prefers letter-quality to dot-matrix. Reports in 1 month. Free (but minimal) writer's guidelines for SASE.

Nonfiction: Well-researched service articles on self improvement, mind, the psychological angle of daily activities, health, careers, nutrition, fitness, medicine, male/female relationships and money. "We try to translate major developments and complex information in these areas into practical, personalized articles." Buys 6-10 mss/issue. Query with clips of previously published work. Length: 1,000-2,500 words. Pays $700-1,800. "We are always looking for any piece that has a psychological or behavioral side. We rely heavily on freelancers who can take an article on contraceptive research, for example, and add a psychological aspect to it.

Everything should relate to the whole person." Pays the expenses of writers on assignment "with prior approval."

Photos: Submit to art director. State availability of photos. Reviews 5x7 b&w glossy prints.

Columns/Departments: Self Issues (800-1,200 words on current topics of interest to women such as nutrition and diet scams, finding time for yourself, and personal decision making); Your Health (800-1,200 words on health topics); Your Work (800-1,200 words on career topics); and Your Money (800-1,200 words on finance topics). Buys 4-6 mss/issue. Query. Pays $700-1,200.

Tips: "Original ideas backed up by research, not personal experiences and anecdotes, open our doors. We almost never risk blowing a major piece on an untried-by-us writer, especially since these ideas are usually staff-conceived. It's usually better for everyone to start small, where there's more time and leeway for re-writes. The most frequent mistakes made by writers in completing an article for us are swiss-cheese research (holes all over it which the writer missed and has to go back and fill in) and/or not personalizing the information by applying it to the reader, but instead, just reporting it."

SUNDAY WOMAN PLUS, (formerly *Sunday Woman*), The King Features Syndicate, 235 E. 45th, New York NY 10017. Editor: Merry Clark. 90% freelance written. A weekly newspaper supplement which runs in more than 80 markets in the U.S. and Canada with circulation of more than 4 million. Buys first rights, and second (reprint) rights to material originally published elsewhere. Computer printout submissions acceptable; no dot-matrix. Sample issue and writer's guidelines for SASE (8x10).

Nonfiction: Solid, reportorial articles on topics affecting the American family, their lifestyles, relationships, careers, health, money, and business. "We often run a fascinating success story about entrepreneurs." Also uses celebrity cover stories. No beauty, fashion or pet stories. Length: 1,000-1,500 words. National focus. No poetry, fiction or essays. Pays $50-500 upon acceptance. "We are happy to consider first person stories-reprints only—for Outlook column." Reports in 2 weeks. Submit previously-published pieces for second serial publication by us." Include cover letter with address, phone number, and Social Security number; not responsible for mss submitted without SASE. Manuscripts should be typed and double-spaced. "Query, short and to the point, with clips of published material." No phone calls. Sometimes pays the expenses of writers on assignment.

Tips: "I'm looking for general interest features, oriented to the American family."

TODAY'S CHRISTIAN WOMAN, 465 Gundersen Dr., Carol Stream IL 60188. Editor: Dale Hanson Bourke. 50% freelance written. Works with a small number of new/unpublished writers each year. A bimonthly magazine for Christian women of all ages, single and married, homemakers and career women. Circ. 200,000. Pays on acceptance. Publishes ms an average of 2 years after acceptance. Byline given. Buys first rights only. Submit seasonal/holiday material 9 months in advance. Computer printout submissions acceptable; prefers letter-quality to dot-matrix. Sample copy $3.50; writer's guidelines for SASE.

Nonfiction: How-to, inspirational, and opinion. Query. "The query should include writing experience, a brief description of the article, and an explanation of its value to our readers. Each issue includes an article on a woman's turning point, or a change in attitude." Pays 10¢/word.

Fiction: Humorous, religious, romance and mainstream. Query.

WOMAN BEAUTIFUL, Allied Publications, 1776 Lake Worth Rd., Lake Worth FL 33460. Editor: Mark Adams. Bimonthly magazine distributed free to beauty salon patrons featuring style and glamour for the fashion-conscious woman; general features. Circ. 30,000. Buys first rights; one-time rights; work-for-hire (rarely); and second serial (reprint) rights. Submit seasonal material 6-8 months in advance. Simultaneous, photocopied and previously published submissions OK. Computer printout submissions acceptable; prefers letter-quality to dot-matrix. Reports in 1 month on mss. Sample copy 50¢ and SAE. Writer's guidelines for SAE and 1 first class stamp.

Nonfiction: Fashion, style, lifestyle, interpersonal, humor, motivational, general interest, photo feature, and interview/profile (must include subject's picture). Buys 30-40 mss/year. Query or send complete ms. Length: 200-1,200 words. Pays 5¢/published word or $25 maximum.

Photos: Send photos or state availability with ms. Pays $5 for 8x10 b&w glossy prints or color transparencies. Captions preferred; identification of subjects required. Buys one-time rights.

Columns/Departments: Varity Fare (50-300 words offering information and advice on personal beauty care for hair skin, nails, wardrobe). Buys 10-20 mss/year. Send complete ms. Pays 5¢/word, $25 maximum.

Fillers: Uses anecdotes, facts and short humor. Buys 10-20/year. Length: 20-100 words. Pays 5¢/word, $10 maximum.

Tips: "We don't have the page space for long manuscripts. We look for short, sharp copy that gets to the point. Content is purely entertainment—personal, positive and upbeat."

WOMAN MAGAZINE, Harris Publishing, 1115 Broadway, New York NY 10010. (212)807-7100. Editor: Sherry Amatenstein. 40% freelance written. Works with a small number of new/unpublished writers each year. Magazine published 7 times/year covering "every aspect of a woman's life. Offers self-help orientation, guidelines on lifestyles, careers, relationships, finances, health, etc." Circ. 395,000. Pays on acceptance. Publishes ms an average of 5 months after acceptance. Byline given. Buys one-time rights. Photocopied and previously published submissions OK. Computer printout submissions acceptable. Reports in 3 weeks. Sample copy $1.95; writer's guidelines for letter-size SAE and 1 first class stamp.

Nonfiction: Book excerpts (most of magazine is book reprints); how-to; humor; inspirational (how I solved a specific problem); interview/profile (short, 200-1,000 words with successful or gutsy women); and personal experience (primary freelance need: how a woman took action and helped herself—emotional punch, but not "trapped housewife" material). No articles on "10 ways to pep up your marriage"—looking for unique angle. Short medical and legal updates for "Let's Put Our Heads Together" column. Buys 100 mss/year. Query with published clips or send complete ms. Length: 200-1,500 words. Pays $25-125.

Columns/Departments: Bravo Woman (1,000 word interviews with women who overcame numerous obstacles to start their own business); Woman in News (200 word pieces on successful women); and Woman Forum (controversial issues regarding women). Query with published clips or send complete ms. Length: 200-1,000 words. Pays $20-125.

Tips: "We're for all women—ones in and out of the home. We don't condescend, neither should you. Personal experience pieces are your best bet."

WOMAN'S DAY, 1515 Broadway, New York NY 10036. (212)719-6250. Editor: Rebecca Greer. 95% freelance written. 15 issues/year. Circ. over 7,000,000. Buys first and second rights to the same material. Pays negotiable kill fee. Byline given. Pays on acceptance. Computer printout submissions acceptable; no dot-matrix. Reports in 2-4 weeks on queries; longer on mss. Submit detailed queries first to Rebecca Greer, articles editor.

Nonfiction: Uses articles on all subjects of interest to women—marriage, family life, child rearing, education, homemaking, money management, careers, family health, work and leisure activities. Also interested in fresh, dramatic narratives of women's lives and concerns. "These must be lively and fascinating to read." Length: 500-3,500 words, depending on material. Payment varies depending on length, type, writer, and whether it's for regional or national use, but rates are high. *Woman's Day* has started a new page called Reflections, a full-page essay running 1,000 words. "We're looking for both tough, strong pieces and softer essays on matters real concern to women. We're looking for strong points of view, impassioned opinions. The topics can be controversial, but they have to be convincing. We look for significant issues—medical ethics and honesty in marriage—rather than the slight and the trivial."

Fiction: Contact Eileen Jordan, department editor. Uses high quality, genuine human interest, romance and humor, in lengths between 1,500 and 3,000 words. Payment varies. "We pay any writer's established rate, however."

Fillers: Neighbors and Tips to Share columns also pay $50/each for brief practical suggestions on homemaking, child rearing and relationships. Address to the editor of the appropriate section.

Tips: "We are publishing more articles and devoting more pages to textual material. We're departing from the service format once in a while to print 'some good reads.' We're more interested in investigative journalism than in the past."

THE WOMAN'S NEWSPAPER, (formerly The Woman's Newspaper of Princeton), New Jersey's largest publication for women, The Woman's Newspaper of Princeton, Inc., Box 1303, Princeton NJ 08542. (609)890-0999. Editor: Arri Parker. 100% freelance written. Eager to work with new/unpublished writers. Monthly tabloid on anything of interest to women with two editions: North Jersey and Central Jersey. Circ. 65,000. Pays on publication. Publishes ms an average of 2 months after acceptance. Byline given. Offers $50 kill fee. Buys first rights. Submit seasonal/holiday material 2 months in advance. Simultaneous queries and submissions and photocopied and previously published submissions OK. Electronic submissions OK via ASCII. Computer printout submissions acceptable. Reports in 2 weeks. Free sample copy and writer's guidelines.

Nonfiction: Expose, how-to, interview/profile, personal experience and technical. Nothing superficial or incorrect. Buys 180 mss/year. Query by phone. Length: open. Pays $100. Sometimes pays the expenses of writers on assignment.

Photos: State availability of photos. Prefers 5x5 prints. Pays $40. Captions, model releases and identification of subjects required. Buys one-time rights.

Fiction: "We accept very little fiction because most is bad. Preferred is the 'fictionalized' personal experience—most of which is good."

Tips: "I would like to receive more feature stories—people, situations, concepts—from anywhere in the country. No more true confessions."

WOMAN'S WORLD, The Woman's Weekly, Heinrich Bauer North American, Inc., 177 N. Dean St., Box 6700, Englewood NJ 07631. (201)569-0006. Editor-in-Chief: Dennis Neeld. 95% freelance written. Weekly magazine covering "controversial, dramatic, and human interest women's issues" for women across the nation. Pays on acceptance. Publishes ms an average of 8 months after acceptance. Byline given. Offers kill fee. Buys first North American serial rights. Submit seasonal/holiday material 4 months in advance. Simultaneous

queries, and simultaneous, photocopied and previously published submissions OK. Computer printout submissions acceptable; prefers letter-quality to dot-matrix. Reports in 6 weeks on queries; 1-2 months on mss. Sample copy $1 and self-addressed label; writer's guidelines for business-size SAE and 1 first class stamp.
Nonfiction: Well-researched material with "a hard-news edge and topics of national scope." Reports of 1,000 words on vital trends and major issues such as women and alcohol or teen suicide; dramatic, personal women's stories; articles on self-improvement, medicine and health topics; and the economics of home, career and daily life. Features include In Real Life (true stories); Turning Point (in a woman's life); Families (highlighting strength of family or how unusual families deal with problems); True Love (tender, beautiful, touching and unusual love stories). Other regular features are Report (1,500-word investigative news features with national scope, statistics, etc.); Scales of Justice (true stories of 1,000-1,200 words on female criminals "if possible, presented with sympathetic" attitude); Between You and Me (600-word humorous and/or poignant slice-of-life essays); and Living Today (800 words on pop psychology or coping). Queries should be addressed to Stephanie Saible, senior editor. We use no fillers, but all the Between You and Me pieces are chosen from mail. Sometimes pays the expenses of writers on assignment.
Fiction: Elinor Nauen, fiction editor. Short story, romance and mainstream of 4,500 words and mini-mysteries of 1,200-2,000 words. "Each of our stories has a light romantic theme with a protagonist no older than forty. Each can be written from either a masculine or feminine point of view. Women characters may be single, married or divorced. Plots must be fast moving with vivid dialogue and action. The problems and dilemmas, inherent in them should be contemporary and realistic, handled with warmth and feeling. The stories must have a positive resolution." Not interested in science fiction, fantasy or historical romance. No explicit sex, graphic language or seamy settings. Humor meets with enthusiasm. Pays $1,200 on acceptance for North American serial rights for 6 months. "The mini-mysteries, at a length of 1,700 words, may feature either a 'whodunnit' or 'howdunnit' theme. The mystery may revolve around anything from a theft to a murder. However, we are not interested in sordid or grotesque crimes. Emphasis should be on intricacies-of-plot rather than gratuitous violence. The story must include a resolution that clearly states the villain is getting his or her come-uppance." Pays $500 on acceptance. Pays approximately 50¢ a published word on acceptance. Buys first North American serial rights. Queries with clips of published work are preferred; accepts complete mss.
Photos: State availability of photos. "State photo leads. Photos are assigned to freelance photographers." Buys one-time rights.
Tips: "Come up with good queries. Short queries are best. We have a strong emphasis on well-researched material. Writers must send research with manuscript including book references and phone numbers for double checking. The most frequent mistakes made by writers in completing an article for us are sloppy, incomplete research, not writing to the format, and not studying the magazine carefully enough beforehand."

WOMEN IN BUSINESS, Box 8728, Kansas City MO 64114. (816)361-6621. Editor: Margaret E. Horan. 20% freelance written. Bimonthly magazine for working women in all fields and at all levels; ages 26-55; primarily members of the American Business Women's Association; national coverage. Circ. 110,000. Pays on acceptance. Publishes ms an average of 2 months after acceptance. Buys all rights. Letter-quality computer printout submissions only. Reports in 2 months. Publishes ms an average of 6 months after acceptance. Sample copy and writer's guidelines for 9x12 SAE with $1 postage.
Nonfiction: General interest, self-improvement, business trends, and personal finance. Articles should be slanted toward the average working woman. No articles on women who have made it to the top or "slice of life opinions/editorials. We also avoid articles based on first-hand experiences (the 'I' stories)." Buys 25 mss/year. Query or submit complete ms. Length: 1,000-1,500 words. Pays $100-200.
Photos: State availability of photos with query or submit with accompanying ms. Pays $50-100 for 8x10 b&w glossy contact sheet; $150-250 for cover color transparency. Captions preferred. Buys all rights. Model releases required.

WOMEN'S CIRCLE, Box 428, Seabrook NH 03874. Editor: Marjorie Pearl. 100% freelance written. Monthly magazine for women of all ages. Buys all rights. Pays on acceptance. Byline given. Publishes ms an average of 1 year after acceptance. Submit seasonal material 8 months in advance. Reports in 3 months. Sample copy $1. Writer's guidelines for SASE.
Nonfiction: Especially interested in stories about successful, home-based female entrepreneurs with b&w photos. Length: 1,000-2,000 words. Also interesting and unusual money-making ideas. Welcomes good quality crafts and how-to directions in any media - crochet, fabric, etc.

WORKING MOTHER MAGAZINE, McCall's Publishing Co., 230 Park Ave., New York NY 10169. (212)551-9412. Editor: Vivian Cadden. Executive Editor: Mary McLaughlin. 90% freelance written. Prefers to work with published/established writers; works with a small number of new/unpublished writers each year. For the working mothers in this country whose problems and concerns are determined by the fact that they have children under 18 living at home. Monthly magazine; 140 pages. Circ. 550,000. Pays on acceptance. Publishes ms an average of 4 months after acceptance. Byline given. Buys all rights. Pays 20% kill fee. Submit seasonal/

holiday material 6 months in advance. Computer printout submissions acceptable; no dot-matrix. Reports in 1 month. Sample copy $1.95; writer's guidelines for SASE.

Nonfiction: Service, humor, material pertinent to the working mother's predicament. "Don't just go out and find some mother who holds a job and describe how she runs her home, manages her children and feels fulfilled. Find a working mother whose story is inherently dramatic." Query. Buys 9-10 mss/issue. Length: 750-2,000 words. Pays $300-500. "We pay more to people who write for us regularly." Pays the expenses of writers on assignment.

Fiction: "Stories that are relevant to working mothers' lives." Length: 2,000 words (average). Pays an average of $500/story.

Tips: "The most frequent mistakes made by writers in completing an article for us are not keeping our readers (the working mother) in mind throughout the article; material in the article is not properly organized; writing style is stilted or wordy."

WORKING WOMAN, Hal Publications, Inc., 342 Madison Ave., New York NY 10173. (213)309-9800. Executive Editor: Julia Kagan. Editor: Anne Mollegen Smith. 85% freelance written. Works with a small number of new/unpublished writers each year. Monthly magazine for executive, professional and entrepreneurial women. "Readers are ambitious, educated, affluent managers, executives, and business owners. Median age is 34. Material should be sophisticated, witty, not entry-level, and focus on work-related issues." Circ. 770,000. Pays on acceptance. Publishes ms an average of 8 months after acceptance. Byline given. Offers 20% kill fee after attempt at rewrite to make ms acceptable. Buys all rights, first rights for books, and second serial (reprint) rights. Submit seasonal/holiday material 6 months in advance. Computer printout submissions acceptable only if legible; prefers letter-quality to dot-matrix. Sample copy for $2.50 and 8½x12 SAE; writer's guidelines for SAE with 1 first class stamp.

Nonfiction: Julia Kagan, executive editor. Jacqueline Johnson, book excerpts editor. Book excerpts; how-to (management skills, small business); humor; interview/profile (high level executive, political figure or entrepreneur preferred); new product (office products, computer/high tech); opinion (issues of interest to managerial, professional, entrepreneur women); personal experience; technical (in management or small business field); travel (businesswomen's guide); and other (business). No child-related pieces that don't involve work issues; no entry-level topics; no fiction/poetry. Buys roughly 200 mss/year. Query with clips of published work. Length: 250-3,000 words. Pays $50-750. Pays the expenses of writers on assignment.

Photos: State availability of photos with ms.

Columns: Management/Enterprise, Basia Hellwig; Manager's Shoptalk, Walecia Konrad; Lifestyle, Food, Fitness, Freddi Greenberg, Health, Heather Twidale; Business Watch, Michele Morris; Computers, Technology, Roxane Farmanfarmaian. Query with clips of published work. Length: 1,200-1,500 words. Pays $400.

Tips: "Be sure to include clips with queries and to make the queries detailed (including writer's expertise in the area, if any). The writer has a better chance of breaking in at our publication with short articles and fillers as we prefer to start new writers out small unless they're very experienced elsewhere. Columns are more open than features. We do not accept phone submissions."

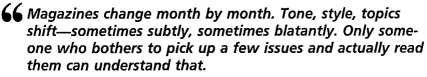

66 *Magazines change month by month. Tone, style, topics shift—sometimes subtly, sometimes blatantly. Only someone who bothers to pick up a few issues and actually read them can understand that.* **99**

Sarah Crichton, Seventeen

Trade, Technical and Professional Journals

If writing isn't your sole source of income, you've undoubtedly come across some kind of trade publication in your workplace. Almost every occupation has its own trade journal. Farmers, factory workers, nurses, musicians—everyone who is employed—can learn about other people with the same jobs and the same problems when they read their trade publications.

A trade journal can be the voice of an industry—or one of many important voices. It usually reports practices that can help or hurt a trade, provides information that isn't available elsewhere and can even influence the policies of an industry.

Trade journal readers are busy people. They want information quickly; they want specifics; and they want to be *shown* how, not told. Because the editors and readers of a trade publication already know a lot about their field, they expect the most accurate and up-to-date information.

You may be able to write for trade publications if you have training or experience in one or more occupations. Or if you've been writing for consumer magazines, you may have come across an interesting business, an innovative solution to a problem, or a fascinating employee who can offer special insights on his work. Can you write different versions of the same information for both consumer and trade publications?

Animal magazines, for example, are in the Consumer section, while farm and veterinary journals are listed here. Articles about horses may appear in all three categories—but each will have a different audience and a different slant. You'll need to "dig deeper" for facts to develop leads into articles for trade journals, but it can be worth the extra effort when you sell two or three articles instead of one.

Like consumer magazines, trade publications are affected by trends and competiton. As a result, they are becoming even more specialized, more visual and more dependent on well-written, detailed how-to articles. In general, trade journals are "sprucing up" their images and offering better pay to freelancers. Even though many trade publications are moving in the same direction as consumer magazines, don't expect their editorial requirements and practices to be the same.

Sometimes a professional or trade association relies on one person to handle their journal's production plus a variety of other tasks. A few trade journals have large staffs with contributing editors who help evaluate submissions. In any case, editors can't waste time on inappropriate, outdated or inferior submissions. If a trade journal editor says that your work does not fit his magazine's needs, do not debate his opinion. Editors with or without a staff rarely have time for correspondence not geared to the next issue.

When a trade journal editor receives a manuscript that *does* fit the magazine, he may want to contact the interviewees in the article for a number of reasons. "It would help to have source addresses and phone numbers in a cover letter," said one editor. "We often have to contact the original information source for verification or elaboration of some points." Some writers criticize editors for adding this extra material to their articles. Remember that the editor knows the audience better than you do. "The writer should not feel embarrassed or insulted that such direct follow-up may be necessary," said one editor.

The most frequent complaint of trade editors is queries that are actually computer-produced form letters. Trade journal editors want queries that show you "know your stuff" and have studied *their* magazine. Enclosing your credentials or résumé may help you land assignments. The majority of trade editors prefer to assign (and discuss) an article before it's written. Sometimes, the editor will suggest particular questions for the writer to ask when interviewing a source.

Don't forget that trade journals within a particular category often compete with one another. You'll want to know which journals are competitors and which ones have cornered the market. An editor won't want a story that his competitor has just published—unless it's a revised version with a fresh slant.

Writing for trade journals can be a good place to get started on a writing career. Editors like to find reliable freelancers for assigned articles, and they're often willing to work with writers who show promise.

Accounting

Accountants want to learn about trends and more efficient ways to do their jobs. That's why they read these trade journals. If you want to write for an accounting magazine, first find out about its readers. Are they accountants in a small firm or corporate treasurers? Reading the magazine will generally give you answers to this question. Also don't assume that an accounting practice in the United States will interest editors of Canadian trade journals.

CA MAGAZINE, 150 Bloor St., W., Toronto, Ontario M5S 2Y2 Canada. Editor: Nelson Luscombe. 10% freelance written. Works with a small number of new/unpublished writers each year. Monthly magazine for accountants and financial managers. Circ. 55,000. Pays on publication for the article's copyright. Buys all rights. Computer printout submissions acceptable; prefers letter-quality to dot-matrix. Publishes ms an average of 4 months after acceptance.
Nonfiction: Accounting, business, finance, management and taxation. Also, subject-related humor pieces and cartoons. "We accept whatever is relevant to our readership, no matter the origin as long as it meets our standards." Length: 3,000-5,000 words. Pays $100 for feature articles, $75 for departments and 10¢/word for acceptable news items. Sometimes pays the expenses of writers on assignment.

‡CASHFLOW, Coordinated Capital Resources, Inc., 1807 Glenview Rd., Glenview IL 60025. (312)998-6688. Editor: Vince DiPaolo. 20% freelance written. Magazine published monthly, covering treasury professionals in organizations or "professionals who are called upon to fulfill corporate treasury functions." Almost half hold the 'Treasurer' title and the remainder are either directly or peripherally involved in treasury activities. A good number hold CPAs or other professional designations. Circ. 13,000. Pays on publication. Byline sometimes given. Buys all rights. Electronic submissions OK if compatible with Apple WordStar. Computer printout submissions acceptable. Reports in 1 month. Publishes ms an average of 4 months after acceptance. Sample copy $6; free writer's guidelines.
Nonfiction: Material must specifically relate to the interests of treasury managers. Accepts no material "without a query first." Buys 10 mss/year. Send query and outline with clips of published work. Length: 800-2,400 words ("set by editor when assigning article"). Pays $9/published inch. Sometimes pays the expenses of writers on assignment.
Photos: Reviews b&w and color contact sheets, negatives, transparencies and prints. Model release and identification of subjects required.
Tips: "If you have a story idea that fits our audience, I want to hear about it. But *call first* before writing and submitting it. Opportunities are also available to cover news beats on a monthly basis. Contact editor for details."

CGA MAGAZINE, Suite 740, 1176 W. Georgia St., Vancouver, British Columbia V6E 4A2 Canada. (604)669-3555. 20% freelance written. Prefers to work with published/established writers. For accountants and financial managers. Magazine published 12 times/year; 72 pages. Circ. 35,000. Pays on acceptance.

Publishes ms an average of 3 months after acceptance. Buys first serial rights. Byline given. Phone queries OK. Simultaneous and photocopied submissions OK. Electronic submissions OK via CP/M, MS-DOS, PC-DOS 5¼ floppy TRSDOS, LPOS, but requires hard copy also. Computer printout submissions acceptable; prefers letter-quality to dot-matrix. Reports in 2-4 weeks. Free sample copy and writer's guidelines.

Nonfiction: "Accounting and financial subjects of interest to highly qualified professional accountants. All submissions must be relevant to Canadian accounting. All material must be of top professional quality, but at the same time written simply and interestingly." How-to, informational, academic, research, and technical. Buys 36 mss/year. Query with outline and estimate of word count. Length: 1,500-5,000 words. Pays $225-1,000.

Illustrations: State availability of photos, tables, charts or graphs with query. Offers no additional payment for illustrations.

Tips: "Fillers are not used. Frequently writers fail to include the technical information desired by professional accountants and financial managers."

‡**THE GENERAL LEDGER,** The Wethersfield Group, 78 Wethersfield St., Rowley MA 01969. (617)948-7804. Editor: Shirley E. Doherty. 25% freelance written. A monthly newsletter covering bookkeeping, accounting and taxes for bookkeepers, junior accountants and office managers. Circ. 1,000. Pays on acceptance. Publishes ms an average of 4 months after acceptance. Byline given. Buys first North American serial rights. Photocopied submissions OK. Computer printout submissions acceptable. Sample copy for #10 SAE with 1 first class stamp.

Nonfiction: How-to (on making office organization and bookkeeping easier); humor; interview/profile; new product (on forms and systems); personal experience; and technical. Special publications include a booklet containing office and bookkeeping short-cuts and ideas for organization. No-put-downs-of-accountants or CPA's. Buys 24 mss/year. Send complete ms. Length: 200-600 words. Pays 8½¢/word.

Columns/Departments: Evelyn Manzer, column/department editor. Focus (how to solve accounting problems for a specific type of business), 600 words; Quiz (bookkeeping quiz—8 questions), 200 words; and On the Lite Side (humor for office environment), 100 words. Buys 24 mss/year. Send complete ms. Pays $10-50.

Fillers: Anecdotes and facts. Length: 15-30 words. Pays $5-25.

Tips: "Informative, instructive, humorous pieces are always needed."

_____ *Advertising, Marketing and PR*

Trade journals for advertising executives, copywriters and marketing and public relations professionals are listed in this category. Those whose main interests are the advertising and marketing of specific products (such as Beverages and Bottling, and Hardware) are classified under individual product categories. Journals for sales personnel and general merchandisers can be found in the Selling and Merchandising category.

ADVERTISING AGE, 740 N. Rush, Chicago IL 60611. (312)649-5200. Managing Editor: Richard L. Gordon. Currently staff-produced. Includes weekly sections devoted to one topic (i.e., marketing in southern California, agribusiness/advertising, TV syndication trends). Much of this material is done freelance—on assignment only. Pays kill fee "based on hours spent plus expenses." Byline given "except short articles or contributions to a roundup."

ADVERTISING TECHNIQUES, ADA Publishing Co., 10 E. 39th St., New York NY 10616. (212)889-6500. Managing Editor: Loren Bliss. 30% freelance written. For advertising executives. Monthly magazine; 50 pages. Circ. 4,500. Pays on acceptance. Not copyrighted. Buys first and second rights to the same material. Reports in 1 month. Publishes ms an average of 2 months after acceptance. Sample copy $1.75.

Nonfiction: Articles on advertising techniques. Buys 10 mss/year. Query. Pays $25-50.

Close-up

H.L. Stevenson
Corporate Editor
Crain Communications

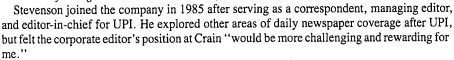

As a 31-year veteran of United Press International, H.L. Stevenson says, "In the wire services, we always wished we had more time to spend developing stories."

Writers have that chance at Crain Communications, says Stevenson, the company's corporate editor.

Crain publishes 23 quarterly, monthly and weekly business and consumer publications in the United States, plus three in Europe. Its newspapers and magazines range from *Advertising Age* and *AutoWeek* to *Florida Keys Magazine*.

Stevenson joined the company in 1985 after serving as a correspondent, managing editor, and editor-in-chief for UPI. He explored other areas of daily newspaper coverage after UPI, but felt the corporate editor's position at Crain "would be more challenging and rewarding for me."

Trade and business publications, Stevenson says, offer "a great deal of challenge and opportunity to write in-depth that no newspaper can possibly touch."

Many writers, especially those just breaking in, are not aware that the publications provide "great opportunities for investigative reporting in specialized fields for vast audiences who quickly recognize good work," he says. "Many would say the daily newspapers or the wire services are more glamorous, but there are many exciting moments in our field, too."

As corporate editor, Stevenson does not oversee production but reviews the publications and works on policy and personnel matters. He is director of Crain News Syndicate, which distributes articles from Crain publications to about 55 daily newspapers.

As a correspondent and editor, Stevenson has worked with both freelance and staff writers. Two basic traits set apart the successful writers, he says. "Be persistent and be patient. Most writers are very impatient and I don't think they're all that persistent sometimes. It takes a lot of effort."

Writers who work successfully with editors write short, well-defined inquiries and "crisp, clean, readable writing" even on technical stories. They also offer photographs or are able to recommend a good local photographer. Photographs "help *sell* the story—to the editor and the reader," he adds.

Before writing, "try to envision those questions the reader, as well as the editor, will want answered," he suggests. "Be sure you understand what the assignment is, up to and including asking the editor to give you a detailed rundown of what is expected. If you're unclear, ask!"

Writers also should evaluate their abilities. "Set up a systematic approach to the publications you want to sell material to," he says. Avoid the "scattershot approach" of submitting articles "more or less at random."

Good writers do not become self-satisfied, Stevenson says. "The most successful writers continue to develop their skills, keep up-to-date and search for new material."

—Glenda Tennant

AMERICAN DEMOGRAPHICS, American Demographics, Inc., Box 68, Ithaca NY 14851. (607)273-6343. Editor: Cheryl Russell. Managing Editor: Caroline Arthur. 25% freelance written. Works with a small number of new/unpublished writers each year. For business executives, market researchers, media and communications people, public policymakers. Monthly magazine; 60 pages. Circ. 18,000. Pays on publication. Publishes an average of 6 months after acceptance. Buys all rights. Submit seasonal/holiday material 6 months in advance. Electronic submissions OK via Apple if 5'' disk, text file. Computer printout submissions acceptable; prefers letter-quality to dot-matrix. Reports in 1 month on queries; in 2 months on mss. Include self-addressed stamped postcard for return word that ms arrived safely. Publishes ms an average of 5 months after acceptance. Sample copy $6.
Nonfiction: General interest (on demographic trends, implications of changing demographics, profile of business using demographic data); and how-to (on the use of demographic techniques, psychographics, understand projections, data, apply demography to business and planning). No anecdotal material or humor. Sometimes pays the expenses of writers on assignment.
Tips: "Writer should have clear understanding of specific population trends and their implications for business and planning. The most important thing a freelancer can do is to read the magazine and be familiar with its style and focus."

ART DIRECTION, Advertising Trade Publications, Inc., 10 E. 39th St., New York NY 10016. (212)889-6500. Editor: Loren Bliss. 10% freelance written. Emphasis on advertising design for art directors of ad agencies (corporate, in-plant, editorial, freelance, etc.). Monthly magazine; 100 pages. Circ. 12,000. Pays on publication. Buys one-time rights. Reports in 3 months. Sample copy $3.
Nonfiction: How-to articles on advertising campaigns. Pays $25 minimum.

BARTER COMMUNIQUE, Full Circle Marketing Corp., Box 2527, Sarasota FL 33578. (813)349-3300. Editor-in-Chief: Robert J. Murely. 100% freelance written. Emphasizes bartering for radio and TV station owners, cable TV, newspaper and magazine publishers and select travel and advertising agency presidents. Semiannual tabloid; 48 pages. Circ. 50,000. Pays on publication. Publishes ms an average of 3 months after acceptance. Rights purchased vary with author and material. Phone queries OK. Simultaneous, photocopied and previously published submissions OK. Computer printout submissions acceptable. Reports in 1 month. Free sample copy and writer's guidelines.
Nonfiction: Articles on "barter" (trading products, goods and services, primarily travel and advertising). Length: 1,000 words. "Would like to see travel mss on southeast U.S. and the Bahamas, and unique articles on media of all kinds. Include photos where applicable. No manuscripts on barter for products, goods and services—primarily travel and media—but also excess inventory of business to business." Pays $30-50.
Tips: "Computer installation will improve our ability to communicate."

BUSINESS MARKETING, Crain Communications, Inc., 220 E. 42nd St., New York NY 10017. (212)210-0191. Editor: Bob Donath. Monthly magazine covering the advertising, sales and promotion of business and industrial products and services for an audience in marketing/sales middle management and corporate top management. Circ. 35,000. All rights reserved. Send queries first. Submit seasonal material 3 months in advance; 1½ months in advance for spot news. Computer printout submissions without format coding acceptable. "Not responsible for unsolicited manuscripts." Sample copy $3.
Nonfiction: Expose (of marketing industry); how-to (advertise, do sales management promotion, do strategy development); interview (of industrial marketing executives); opinion (on industry practices); profile; and technical (advertising/marketing practice). "No self promotion or puff pieces." No material aimed at the general interest reader. Buys 30 mss/year. Query. Length: 1,000-2,000 words.
Photos: State availability of photos. Reviews 8x10 b&w glossy prints and color transparencies. Offers no additional payment for photos accepted with ms. Captions preferred; model release required.
Columns/Departments: Query. Length: 500-1,000 words. "Column ideas should be queried, but generally we have no need for paid freelance columnists."
Fillers: Newsbreaks. Buys 2 mss/issue. Length: 100-500 words.

CANADIAN PREMIUMS & INCENTIVES, Selling Ideas in Motivational Marketing, Maclean Hunter Publishing Company, 777 Bay St., Toronto, Ontario M5W 1A7 Canada. (416)596-5838. Editor: Ed Patrick. Publisher: Ted Wilson. 10% freelance written. Prefers to work with published/established writers. Quarterly magazine covering premium/incentive programs and promotions; incentive travel. Circ. 15,850. Pays on publication. Publishes ms an average of 2 months after acceptance. Byline given. Buys first North American serial, one-time, and first rights. Submit seasonal/holiday material 4 months in advance. Simultaneous queries OK. Computer printout submissions OK; prefers letter-quality to dot-matrix. SASE or SAE and IRCs. Reports in 1 week. Sample copy $3.
Nonfiction: Case histories of successful incentive promotions in Canada. New product and travel (incentive). Query with published clips. Length: 600-1,500 words. Pays $60-200. Sometimes pays the expenses of writers on assignment.

Photos: Pays $15-25 for 8x10 b&w prints. Captions and identification of subjects required. Buys one-time rights.

‡**THE COUNSELOR MAGAZINE**, Advertising Specialty Institute, NBS Bldg., 1120 Wheeler Way, Langhorne PA 19047. (215)752-4200. Editor: Cathy Kuczewski. For executives, both distributors and suppliers, in the ad specialty industry. Monthly magazine; 350 pages. Circ. 6,000. Pays on publication. Buys first rights only. No phone queries. Submit seasonal/holiday material 4 months in advance. Simultaneous, photocopied and previously published submissions OK. Reports in 2-3 months.
Nonfiction: Contact: Managing Editor. How-to (promotional case histories); interview (with executives and government figures); profile (of executives); and articles on specific product categories. "Articles almost always have a specialty advertising slant and quotes from specialty advertising practitioners." Buys 30 mss/year. Length: Open. Query with samples. Pays according to assigned length.
Photos: State availability of photos. B&w photos only. Prefers contact sheet(s) and 5x7 prints. Offers some additional payment for original only photos accepted with ms. Captions and model releases required. Buys one-time rights.
Tips: "If a writer shows promise, we can help him or her modify his style to suit our publication and provide leads. Writers must be willing to adapt or rewrite their material for a specific audience. If an article is suitable for 5 or 6 other publications, it's probably not suitable for us. The best way to break in is to write for *IMPRINT*, a quarterly publication we produce for the clients of ad specialty counselors. *IMPRINT* covers promotional campaigns, safety programs, trade show exhibits, traffic builders and sales incentives—all with a specialty advertising tie-in."

THE FLYING A, Aeroquip Corp., 300 S. East Ave., Jackson MI 49203. (517)787-8121. Editor-in-Chief: Wayne D. Thomas. 10% freelance written. Emphasizes Aeroquip customers and products. Quarterly magazine; 24-32 pages. Circ. 30,000. Pays on acceptance. Buys first or second rights, depending upon circumstances. Simultaneous submissions OK. Reports in 1 month.
Nonfiction: General interest (feature stories with emphasis on free enterprise, business-related or historical articles with broad appeal, human interest.) "An Aeroquip tie-in in a human interest story is helpful." No jokes, no sample copies; no cartoons, no short fillers. Buys 1 mss/issue. Query with biographic sketch and clips. Length: Not to exceed five typewritten pages. Pays $75 minimum.
Photos: Accompanying photos are helpful.
Fillers: Human interest. No personal anecdotes, recipes or "how-to" articles. "Suggest the writer contact editor by letter with proposed story outline."
Tips: "We publish a marketing-oriented magazine, with a section devoted to employee news. Despite our title, we are *not* an aviation magazine, although we do produce aerospace products."

HIGH-TECH MARKETING, Technical Marketing Corporation, 1460 Post Road East, Westport CT 06880. (203)255-9997. Editor: Philip Maher. 75% freelance written. A monthly magazine. "*HTM* is for and about the marketers of high technology." Circ. 20,000. Pays on acceptance. Publishes ms an average of 3 months after acceptance. Byline given. Offers 15% kill fee. Buys first North American serial rights. Submit seasonal/holiday material 4 months in advance. Simultaneous queries and photocopied submissions OK. Electronic submissions OK on IBM PC—Hayes Modem; MCI Mail, but requires hard copy also. Computer printout submissions acceptable; no dot-matrix. Reports in 1 month. Sample copy $3.50; free writer's guidelines.
Nonfiction: Interview/profile (prominent marketers). "We want excellent style—not technical writing. The key word is *marketing—not high tech*." Buys 45 mss/year. Query with published clips. Length: 1,000-3,000 words. Pays $200-700. Sometimes pays the expenses of writers on assignment.
Photos: State availability of photos with submission.
Tips: "We're always looking for personal profiles of high-tech marketers."

‡**HIGH-TECH SELLING, For Electronics, Telecommunications, and Other High-Tech Industries**, Bureau of Business Practice/Simon & Schuster, 24 Rope Ferry Rd., Waterford CT 06385. (800)243-0876. Editor: Laura Gardner. Managing Editor: Wayne Muller. 75% freelance written. Works with a small number of new/unpublished writers each year; eager to work with new/unpublished writers. A monthly training newsletter covering selling. Pays on acceptance. Publishes ms an average of 4 months after acceptance. Byline not given. Buys all rights. Submit seasonal/holiday material 6 months in advance. Photocopied submissions OK. Computer printout submissions acceptable; prefers letter-quality to dot-matrix. Reports in 1 week. Sample copy and writer's guidelines for SAE.
Nonfiction: How-to. Buys 50 mss/year. Query. Length: 1,000-1,500 words. Pays 10-15¢/word. Sometimes pays the expenses of writers on assignment.
Photos: Offers no additional payment for photos accepted with ms.
Tips: "Our entire publication is interview-based."

IMPRINT, The Magazine of Specialty Advertising Ideas, Advertising Specialty Institute, 1120 Wheeler Way, Langhorne PA 19047. (215)752-4200. Editor: Cathy Kuczewski. 25% freelance written. Quarterly magazine covering specialty advertising. Circ. 60,000 + . Pays on publication. Publishes ms an average of 6 months after acceptance. Byline given. Buys one-time rights. Submit seasonal/holiday material 6 months in advance. Simultaneous queries OK. Computer printout submissions acceptable; no dot-matrix. Reports in 3 months. Free sample copy.
Nonfiction: How-to (case histories of specialty advertising campaigns); and features (how ad specialties are distributed in promotions). "Emphasize effective use of specialty advertising. Avoid direct-buy situations. Stress the distributor's role in promotions. No generalized pieces on print, broadcast or outdoor advertising." Buys 10-12 mss/year. Query with clips published. Length: varied. Payment based on assigned length. "We pay authorized phone, hotel bills, etc."
Photos: State availability of 5x7 b&w photos. Pays "some extra for *original only* photos." Captions, model release and identification of subjects required.
Tips: "The most frequent mistake writers make is in their misconceptions of what specialty advertising is. Many of them do not understand the medium, or our target audience, which is the end-user and so mistakes occur. Writers are encouraged to look into the medium before attempting to write any articles. Query with a case history suggestion and writing samples. We can provide additional leads. All articles must be specifically geared to specialty advertising (and sometimes, premium) promotions."

INFORMATION MARKETING, A Direct Marketing Tool for Publishers, Communicators and Information Marketers, (formerly *The Information Age Marketing Letter*), Box 5000-WM, Davis CA 95617. Editor: Mark Nolan. 10-25% freelance written. A monthly newsletter covering advertising and marketing tips for those who deal "in information of any type." Pays on publication. Publishes ms an average of 3 months after acceptance. Byline given, sometimes depending on length of material. Buys first North American and second serial (reprint) rights. Submit seasonal/holiday material 6 weeks in advance. Simultaneous, photocopied, and previously published submissions OK. Computer printout submissions acceptable. Reports in 3 weeks. Sample copy $1.
Nonfiction: How-to (advertise or market information, press releases, etc); mail order tips, postal tips, directories available, cottage industry success stories, etc., newsletters; and new product (software, word processors). No long dissertations or editorials; only "short, pithy, impact news, tips and sources." Buys 50-100 mss/year (estimated). Recent articles: "Marketing Books Through Mail-Order" by Luther Brock, "Turning Ideas into Income" by Gordon Burgett, "My Mail-Order Trade Secrets" by Melvin Powers. Send complete ms. Length: 50-150 words. Pays $25-75.
Columns/Departments: New books department: Short reviews on books pertaining to main theme, including those on word processing, advertising techniques, salesmanship, information industry, work-at-home themes, consulting, seminars, etc. Buys 10-25 mss/year. Send complete ms. Length: 50-150 words. Pays $15-25.
Fillers: Clippings and newsbreaks. Buys 10-50/year. Length: 35-75 words. Pays $5.
Tips: "We need short items most of all. News and tips to help busy nonfiction writers and publishers: how to sell more, save money, choose 'tools', etc. The most frequent mistake made by writers in completing an article for us is too much fine writing. Our subscribers are mostly writers and publishers. They are very busy and want valuable news, tips and sources with a minimum of wasted words. Read some issues to see our style and content."

INSIDE PRINT, Voice of Print Advertising, (formerly *Magazine Age*), 6 Riverbend, Box 4949, Stanford CT 06907-0949. (203)358-9900. Editor: Robert Hogan. Managing Editor: Jenifer Howland. 30% freelance written. Monthly magazine for advertisers and advertising agencies designed "to examine how they use a wide range of publications, including consumer, business, trade, farm, newspaper, etc." Circ. 32,000. Pays on acceptance. Publishes ms an average of 3 months after acceptance. Buys all rights. Computer printout submissions acceptable. Reports in 2 weeks. Sample copy $4; writer's guidelines for SASE.
Nonfiction: "We are interested in print advertising success and failure stories. We want marketing pieces, case histories, effective use of print advertising and current trends." Buys 4 mss/issue. Query first. Will not respond to handwritten inquiries. Length: 3,000 words maximum. Pays $700 maximum.
Tips: "Find an unusual aspect of print advertising."

MORE BUSINESS, 11 Wimbledon Court, Jericho NY 11753. Editor: Trudy Settel. 50% freelance written. "We sell publications material to business for consumer use (incentives, communication, public relations)—look for book ideas and manuscripts." Monthly magazine. Circ. 10,000. Pays on acceptance. Publishes ms an average of 1 month after acceptance. Buys all rights. Computer printout submissions acceptable; no dot-matrix. Reports in 1 month.
Nonfiction: General interest, how-to, vocational techniques, nostalgia, photo feature, profile and travel. Buys 10-20 mss/year. Word length varies with article. Payment negotiable. Query. Pays $4,000-7,000 for book mss.

THE PRESS, The Greater Buffalo Press, Inc., 302 Grote St., Buffalo NY 14207. Managing Editor: Mary Lou Vogt. 100% freelance written. Works with a small number of new/unpublished writers each year. Quarterly tabloid for advertising executives at Sunday newspapers, ad agencies, retail chains and cartoonists who create the Sunday funnies. Circ. 4,000. Pays on acceptance. Publishes ms an average of 6 months after acceptance. Buys all rights. Photocopied submissions and previously published submissions OK. Computer printout submissions acceptable; prefers letter-quality to dot-matrix. Reports in 1 month. Sample copy 50¢; free writer's guidelines.
Nonfiction: Short biographies of people in advertising, retailing, business or unusual occupations. No travel/leisure or personal experience articles. Back issues sent upon written request. Buys 4-6 mss/issue. Query. Length: 800-1,500 words. Pays $100-125.
Photos: State availability of photos (with ms only). Uses 35mm transparencies or larger (color preferred). Offers no additional payment for photos accepted with ms. Captions optional. Photos are usually returned after publication. "We do not accept photographs or artwork unless they accompany a ms."

PUBLIC RELATIONS JOURNAL, Public Relations Society of America, 845 3rd Ave., New York NY 10022. (212)826-1757. Editor: Michael Winkleman. Managing Editor: Joanne Maio. 33% freelance written. Monthly trade journal covering public relations. Circ. 16,000. Pays on acceptance. Publishes ms an average of 3 months after acceptance. Byline given. Kill fee depends on why not published (0-50%). Makes work-for-hire assignments. Photocopied submissions and previously published work OK. Electronic submissions OK, but requires hard copy also. Computer printout submissions acceptable; prefers letter-quality to dot-matrix. Reports in 3 weeks. Sample copy $3; writer's guidelines for #10 SAE and 1 first class stamp.
Nonfiction: Michael Winkleman, articles editor. Book excerpts, how-to, interview/profile, new product, opinion and technical. All articles need senior level public relations angle. Buys 12-20 mss/year. Query with published clips. Length: 250-3,500 words. Pays $25-350. Pays expenses of writers on assignment.
Photos: Susan Yip, photo editor. State availability of photos with query. Reviews b&w contact sheets, and b&w 8x10 prints. Buys one-time rights.
Columns/Departments: Celia Lehrman, column/department editor. Briefings and workshops. Buys 12-20/year. Query with published clips. Length: 250-1,000 words. Pays $25-150.

SALES & MARKETING MANAGEMENT IN CANADA, Sanford Evans Communications Ltd., Suite 402, 3500 Dufferin St., Downsview, Ontario. (416)633-2020. Editor: Ernie Spear. Monthly magazine. Circ. 13,000. Pays on publication. Byline given. Buys first North American serial rights. Simultaneous queries and photocopied submissions OK. Reports in 2 weeks.
Nonfiction: How-to (case histories of successful marketing campaigns). "Canadian articles only." Buys 3 mss/year. Query. Length: 800-1,500 words. Pays $200 maximum.

SIGNCRAFT, The Magazine for the Sign Artist and Commercial Sign Shop, SignCraft Publishing Co., Inc., Box 06031, Fort Myers FL 33906. (813)939-4644. Editor: Tom McIltrot. 40% freelance written. Bimonthly magazine of the sign industry. "Like any trade magazine, we need material of direct benefit to our readers. We can't afford space for material of marginal interest." Circ. 14,500. Pays on publication. Publishes ms an average of 6 months after acceptance. Byline given. Offers negotiable kill fee. Buys first North American serial rights or all rights. Simultaneous queries, and simultaneous, photocopied, and previously published submissions OK. Computer printout submissions acceptable. Reports in 3 weeks. Free sample copy and writer's guidelines.
Nonfiction: Interviews and profiles. "All articles should be directly related to quality commercial signage. If you are familiar with the sign trade, we'd like to hear from you." Buys 20 mss/year. Query with or without published clips. Length: 500-2,000 words. Pays up to $150.

‡SIGNS OF THE TIMES, The Industry Journal since 1906, ST Publications, 407 Gilbert Ave., Cincinnati OH 45202. (513)421-2050. Editor: Tod Swormstedt. Managing Editor: Bill Dorsey. 15-30% freelance written. "We are willing to use more freelancers." Magazine published 13 times/year; special buyer's guide between November and December issue. Circ. 18,000. Pays on publication. Publishes ms an average of 3 months after acceptance. Byline given. Buys variable rights. Simultaneous queries, and simultaneous, photocopied and previously published submissions OK. Computer printout submissions acceptable; no dot-matrix. Reports in 2 weeks. Free sample copy. Writer's guidelines flexible.
Nonfiction: Historical/nostalgic (regarding the sign industry); how-to (carved signs, goldleaf, etc.); interview/profile (usually on assignment but interested to hear proposed topics); photo feature (query first); and technical (sign engineering, etc.). Nothing "nonspecific on signs, an example being a photo essay on 'signs I've seen.' We are a trade journal with specific audience interests." Buys 15-20 mss/year. Query with clips. Pays $150-250. Sometimes pays the expenses of writers on assignment.
Photos: Send photos with ms. "Sign industry-related photos only. We sometimes accept photos with funny twists or misspellings."

‡**TELEMARKETING, The Magazine of Business Telecommunications**, Technology Marketing Corporation, Graphics Plaza, Box 1229, Norwalk CT 06854. (203)846-2029. Editor: Linda Driscoll. 1% freelance written. A monthly magazine covering telecommunications and marketing via telecommunications. Emphasizes tutorial/how-to information for executives (top management) in or entering the telemarketing field. "Readers have a general understanding of the field and its benefits." Circ. 60,000. Pays on publication. Publishes ms an average of 3 months after acceptance. Byline given. Buys all rights. Computer printout submissions acceptable; prefers letter-quality to dot-matrix. Reports in 5 weeks. Free sample copy; writer's guidelines for SASE.
Nonfiction: How-to (participate in telecom/telemarketing industry); interview/profile; new product (non-commercial/advertising style); personal experience; and technical. "We need information about current technology in layman's terms/language." No interviews without queries; no broad-based "what is telemarketing" articles. Buys 5-10 mss/year. Query. Length: 500-1,400 words. Pays $15/page-$250 maximum for assigned articles.
Photos: State availability of photos with submission. Reviews contact sheets and negatives. Offers no additional payment for photos accepted with ms. Model releases and identification of subjects required. Buys one-time rights.
Columns/Departments: Telemarketing Q&A (answers to problems faced by telemarketers), 200 words. Also interested in ideas for new columns and departments. Pays $15/page-$250 maximum.
Fillers: Open to queries; request rates.
Tips: "A background in telecommunications and/or telemarketing is desired; general business management helpful. We want very *specific* ideas for articles; i.e. the *area* of telemarketing or telecommunications such as training with audio/visual materials, research of Fortune 50 companies in the field, today's hybrid PBX, etc. Research of the marketplace, i.e.; number of industry participants, future trends, No. 1 companies in the field, is most open to freelancers."

VISUAL MERCHANDISING & STORE DESIGN, ST Publications, 407 Gilbert Ave., Cincinnati OH 45202. Associate Publisher: Pamela Gramke. Editor: Ms. P.K. Anderson. 30% freelance written. Emphasizes design and merchandise presentation. Monthly magazine; 100-200 pages. Circ. 11,700. Pays on publication. Buys first and second rights to the same material. Simultaneous and previously published submissions OK. Computer printout submissions acceptable. Reports in 1 month. Publishes ms an average of 3 months after acceptance.
Nonfiction: How-to (display); informational (store design, construction, merchandise presentation); interview (display directors and shop owners); profile (new and remodeled stores); new product; photo feature (window display); and technical (store lighting, carpet, wallcoverings, fixtures). No "advertorials" that tout a single company's product or product line. Buys 24 mss year. Query or submit complete ms. Length: 500-3,000 words. Pays $250-400.
Photos: Purchased with accompanying ms or on assignment.
Tips: "Be fashion and design conscious and reflect that in the article. Submit finished manuscripts with photos or slides always. Look for stories on department and specialty store visual merchandisers and store designers (profiles, methods, views on the industry, sales promotions and new store design or remodels). The size of the publication could very well begin to increase in the year ahead. And with a greater page count, we will need to rely on an increasing number of freelancers."

Agricultural Equipment and Supplies

These specialized publications are written for people in farm-related *businesses*. Other trade journals that might use similar material are listed in the Farm category.

CUSTOM APPLICATOR, Little Publications, Suite 540, 6263 Poplar Ave., Memphis TN 38119. (901)767-4020. Editor: Tom Griffin. Managing Editor: Rob Wiley. For "firms that sell and custom apply agricultural chemicals." 50% freelance written. Circ. 17,000. Pays on publication. Buys all rights. "Query is best. The editor can help you develop the story line regarding our specific needs." Computer printout submissions acceptable; prefers letter-quality to dot-matrix.

Nonfiction: "We are looking for articles on custom application firms telling others how to better perform jobs of chemical application, develop new customers, handle credit, etc. Lack of a good idea or usable information will bring a rejection." Length: 1,000-1,200 words "with 3 or 4 b&w glossy prints." Pays 20¢/word.

Photos: Accepts b&w glossy prints. "We will look at color slides for possible cover or inside use."

Tips: "We don't get enough shorter articles, so one that is well-written and informative could catch our eyes. Our readers want pragmatic information to help them run a more efficient business; they can't get that through a story filled with generalities."

FARM SUPPLIER, Watt Publishing Co., Sandstone Bldg., Mount Morris IL 61054. (815)734-4171. Managing Editor: Marcella Sadler. For retail farm supply dealers and managers over the U.S. Monthly magazine; 64 pages. Circ. 36,000. Pays on acceptance. Byline given. Buys all rights in competitive farm supply fields. Phone queries OK. Submit seasonal material or query 2 months in advance. Computer printout submissions acceptable. Reports in 2 weeks.

Nonfiction: How-to, informational, interview, new product and photo feature. "Articles emphasizing product news and how new product developments have been profitably resold or successfully used. We use material on successful farm, feed and fertilizer dealers." No "general how-to articles that some writers blanket the industry with, inserting a word change here or there to 'customize.' " Buys 12 unsolicited mss/year.

Photos: Purchased with accompanying ms. Submit 5x7 or 8x10 b&w prints; 35mm or larger color transparencies. Total purchase price for a ms includes payment for photos.

Tips: "Because of a constantly changing industry, *FS* attempts to work only two months in advance. Freelancers should slant stories to each season in the farm industry and should provide vertical color photos whenever possible with longer features."

FERTILIZER PROGRESS, The Fertilizer Institute, 1015 18th St. NW, Washington DC 20036. (202)861-4900. Edited and published by TFI Communications. Assistant Vice President: Thomas E. Waldinger. Communications Assistant: Becki K. Weiss. 7% freelance written. Eager to work with new/unpublished writers. Bimonthly magazine covering fertilizer, farm chemical and allied industries for business and management, with emphasis on the retail market. Circ. 29,000. Pays on publication. Publishes ms an average of 3 months after acceptance. Byline given. Offers 2½¢/word kill fee for assigned stories. Buys all rights. Submit seasonal/holiday material 2 months in advance. Photocopied submissions OK. Computer printout submissions acceptable; prefers letter-quality to dot-matrix. Reports in 2 weeks on queries; 3 weeks on mss. Free sample copy.

Nonfiction: Articles on sales, services, credit, products, equipment, merchandising, production, regulation, research and environment. Also news about people, companies, trends and developments. No "highly technical or philosophic pieces; we want relevance—something the farm retail dealer can sink his teeth into." No material not related to fertilizer, farm chemical and allied industries, and the retail market. Send complete ms. Length: 400-2,500 words. Pays $35-200. Sometimes pays expenses of writers on assignment.

Photos: Send photos with ms. Pays $5-20 for 5x7 b&w and color prints. Captions and identification of subjects required.

Columns/Departments: Elements of Success (productive agronomic advice for dealers to use in selling to farmers); Fit to be Tried (ideas that really work); and Worth Repeating (agricultural-related editorial commentary). Send complete ms. Length: 500-750 words. Pays $40-60.

Tips: "Query letter to propose story idea provides best results."

___ *Art, Design and Collectibles*

The businesses of art, art administration, architecture, environmental/package design and antique collectibles are covered in these listings. Art-related topics for the general public are located in the Consumer Art category. Antiques magazines are listed in Consumer Hobby and Craft.

ANTIQUES DEALER, 1115 Clifton Ave., Clifton NJ 07013. (201)779-1600. Editor: Nancy Adams. 90% freelance written. "For antiques dealers." Monthly magazine. Circ. 7,500. Average issue includes 4 features, 6 columns. Pays on publication. Byline given. Rights purchased vary with author and material; buys all rights. Submit seasonal/holiday material 4 months in advance. Will send free sample copy to writer on request. Query first. No photocopied material. Reports in 3 weeks.

Nonfiction: "Remember that we are a trade publication and all material must be slanted to the needs and interests of antiques dealers." Only articles of national interest to dealers; may be tutorial if by authority in one specific field (open a dealership, prices of various items, locate a specific antique); otherwise of broad general interest to all dealers and news of the international antiques trade. Emphasis is currently on collectibles (20-50 years old); heirlooms (50-100 years old); as well as antiques (over 100 years old). Buys 2 mss/year. Length: minimum 500 words (2 pages double spaced); maximum 1,500 words (6 pages double-spaced). "Payment agreed upon when ms is accepted."

Photos: B&w photos only.

Fillers: How-to-run-your-shop-better and humor. Length: 500 words.

Tips: "It is more important that the writer know the subject well, as a specialist, or one interviewing a specialist, than demonstrating writing excellence. But I am also looking for good business journalists who can cover shows and interviews well. Send outline of ideas, resume and writing samples."

ART BUSINESS NEWS, Myers Publishing Co., 60 Ridgeway Plaza, Stamford CT 06905. (203)356-1745. Editor: Jo Yanow. Managing Editor: Caroline Myers Just. Monthly tabloid covering news relating to the art and picture framing industry. Circ. 24,500. Pays on publication. Byline given. Buys all rights. Submit seasonal/holiday material 2 months in advance. Photocopied and simultaneous submissions OK. Computer printout submissions acceptable; prefers letter-quality to dot-matrix. Reports in 2 months. Sample copy $2.

Nonfiction: General interest; interview/profile (of persons in the art industry); new product; articles focusing on small business people—framers, art gallery management, art trends; and how-to (occasional article on "how-to frame" accepted). Buys 8-20 mss/year. Length: 1,000 words maximum. Query first. Pays $75-250.

‡ART SHOW NEWS, The Art Conspiracy, Edgemont Branch, Box 10773, Golden CO 80401. (303)279-3817. Editor: I.J. Kuehn. 30% freelance written. A bimonthly magazine covering the visual arts, art shows, competitions, etc. Circ. 2,000. Pays on publication. Publishes ms an average of 3 months after acceptance. Buys one-time rights. Submit seasonal/holiday material 3 months in advance. Simultaneous queries and previously published work OK. Elecronic submissions OK via ASKE or any system that can translate into ASKE. Computer printout submissions acceptable; prefers letter-quality to dot-matrix. Reports in 6 weeks. Sample copy $3.50; writer's guidelines free.

Nonfiction: How to (on marketing art and art techniques in various media); interview/profile of artists; new product; personal experience (artists and marketing); photo feature (relating to artists at work). No material not related to the field of the arts and/or marketing of art. Send complete ms. Length: 600-1,200 words. Pays $10-15.

Columns/Departments: Marketing, Book Reviews, Photography, Published Arts (i.e., fantasy art). Buys 24/year. Send complete ms. Length: 700-1,100 words. Pays $10-15.

Tips: "Offer material that is informative for the working artist both in the sense of marketing strategies and in the form of techniques that will help them develop into better artists. Experiences of other artists often answer to both these needs."

‡ARTQUEST, Creative Ideas, Box 650W, Livonia NY 11487. Editor: John H. Armstrong. A bimonthly newsletter covering freelance commercial art opportunities, ideas for marketing. "*Artquest* is written by freelance artists for freelance artists. Our readers vary in experience from beginners and students to seasoned pros." Circ. 1,000+. Pays on acceptance. Byline given. Buys one-time rights. Submit seasonal/holiday material 10 months in advance. Simultaneous and photocopied submissions OK. Computer printout submissions acceptable; no dot-matrix. Reports in 2 weeks on queries; 1 month on mss. Sample copy for 1 first class stamp.

Nonfiction: How-to, humor, opinion and personal experience. Especially interested in first-person articles on proven ways (experience) to market freelance art. Special anniversary edition each September; "our largest edition with more articles. We need submission in July to plan space." No unproven suggestions or tips. Buys 6+ mss/year. Query with or without published clips, or send complete ms. Length: 200-400 words. Pays $10-20 for unsolicited articles; sometimes pays in copies by prior agreement with writer.

Photos: State availability of photos with submission. Offers no additional payment for photos accepted with ms.

Columns/Departments: Open Idea File ("How I did it and you can do it also"), 200-400 words, pays $10-20; Book/Product Reviews (content, usability of new items for commercial artists), 100-200 words, pays $10; Art Competitions (entry rules for nationwide commercial art and design contests), 100 words maximum, pays $5 to first contributor. Query or send complete ms; minimum 60 days to entry deadline for contest rules.

Fillers: Anecdotes, facts, newsbreaks. Length: 100 words maximum. Pays $5-10.

Tips: " 'Open Idea File' is most open to freelancers. We need a stimulating article on how freelance artists can make money in their own locale while gaining experience (and a portfolio of published work) to break into the national and international markets."

ARTS MANAGEMENT, 408 W. 57th St., New York NY 10019. (212)245-3850. Editor: A.H. Reiss. For cultural institutions. Published five times/year. 2% freelance written. Circ. 6,000. Pays on publication. Byline given. Buys all rights. Mostly staff-written, and especially for 1987. Computer printout submissions acceptable; no dot-matrix. Query. Reports in "several weeks."
Nonfiction: Short articles, 400-900 words, tightly written, expository, explaining how art administrators solved problems in publicity, fund raising and general administration; actual case histories emphasizing the how-to. Also short articles on the economics and sociology of the arts and important trends in the nonprofit cultural field. Must be fact-filled, well-organized and without rhetoric. Payment is 2-4¢/word. No photographs or pictures.

‡CALLIGRAPHY IDEA EXCHANGE, Calligraphy Idea Exchange, Inc., Suite 159, 2500 S. McGee, Norman OK 73072-6705. (405)364-8794. Managing Editor: Karyn L. Gilman. 85% freelance written. Eager to work with new/unpublished writers with calligraphic expertise and language skills. A quarterly magazine on calligraphy and related book arts, both historical and contemporary in nature. Circ. 2,500. Pays on publication. Publishes ms an average of 6 months after acceptance. Byline given. Offers $50 kill fee. Buys first rights. Submit seasonal/holiday material 3-4 months in advance. Photocopied submissions OK. Electronic submissions OK via IBM, but requires hard copy also. Computer printout submissions acceptable. Sample copy for 9x12 SAE with $1.28 postage; free writer's guidelines.
Nonfiction: Interview/profile, new product, opinion, and technical. Buys 50 mss/year. Query with or without published clips, or send complete ms. Length: 1,000-2,000 words. Pays $50-200 for assigned articles; pays $25-200 for unsolicited articles. Sometimes pays the expenses of writers on assignment.
Photos: State availability of photos with submission. Reviews contact sheets, negatives, transparencies and prints. Pays agreed upon cost. Captions and identification of subjects required. Buys one-time rights.
Columns/Departments: Book Reviews Viewpoint (critical), 500-1,500 words; Ms. (discussion of manuscripts in collections), 1,000-2,000 words; and Profile (contemporary calligraphic figure), 1,000-2,000 words. Query. Pays $50-200.
Tips: "*Calligraphy Idea Exchange*'s primary objective is to encourage the exchange of ideas on calligraphy, its past and present as well as trends for the future. Practical and conceptual treatments are welcomed, as are learning and teaching experiences. Third person is preferred, however first person will be considered if appropriate."

‡GLASS ART MAGAZINE, For the Business of Stained and Decorative Glass, National Business Media, Inc., Box 985, Broomfield CO 80020. (303)469-0424. Editor: Stephanie H. Walters. 50% freelance written. A monthly magazine for retail/studio owners in the stained and decorative glass business. Estab. 1985. Circ. 9,200. Pays on acceptance. Publishes ms an average of 2 months after acceptance. Byline given. Buys all rights. Submit seasonal/holiday material 3 months in advance. Photocopied submissions OK. Electronic submissions OK. Computer printout submissions acceptable; prefers letter-quality to dot-matrix. Reports ASAP. Free sample copy and writer's guidelines.
Nonfiction: How-to, interview/profile, opinion, personal experience, photo feature and technical. No fiction. Query with published clips. Length: 400-2,000 words. Pays $50-150. Pays the expenses of writers on assignment.
Photos: State availability of photos with submission or send photos with submission. Reviews 35mm or 3x5 transparencies and 5x7 b&w prints. Offers $1-25/photo. Captions and identification of subjects required. Buys all rights.
Columns/Departments: Retail (running a retail glass store), Legal (legalities involved in glass art business), Glass Art People (feature of person in the business), Profile (company) (feature of a glass art manufacturer or distributer), Finance (financial problems and solutions), and Technical Talk (technical Q&A). Buys 84 mss/year. Query with published clips. Length: 300-1,000 words. Pays $50-100.
Tips: "Features—technical and 'how-to' articles are needed. Stories that have accompanying pictures are always a *plus*."

INDUSTRIAL DESIGN, Design Publications, Inc., 330 W. 42nd St., 11th Fl., New York NY 10036. (212)695-4955. Senior Editor: Annetta Hanna. 60% freelance written. Prefers to work with published/established writers. Subject of this publication is design (of products, packaging, graphics and environments). Bimonthly magazine. Circ. 15,000. Pays on publication. Publishes ms an average of 3 months after acceptance. Byline given. Buys all rights. Phone queries OK. Computer printout submissions acceptable; prefers letter-quality to dot-matrix. Sample copy $4.50.
Nonfiction: Expose (design related); how-to (all aspects of design); interview (of important people in design); profile (corporate, showing value of design and/or how design is managed); design history; and new product. "The writer gets top pay and a bonus for hard work, extensive research, a 'how-to' sidebar, and a humorous example or two." Buys 6 unsolicited mss/year. Length: 1,800 words. Query with point-by-point outline and clips of published work. Pays $100-600. Sometimes pays the expenses of writers on assignment.
Photos: State availability of photos. Wants very good quality b&w glossy prints, four-color transparencies

and contact sheets. Offers no additional payment for photos accepted with ms. Captions required.
Departments: Portfolio (new products); Visual Communications (graphics, packaging); Environments; and News. Query with clips of published work.
Tips: "Show that you are thoroughly familiar with your topic. Read the magazine."

‡**NEAA NEWS, New England Appraisers Association Newsletter**, New England Appraisers Assocation, 5 Gill Terrace, Ludlow VT 05149. (802)228-7444. Editor: Linda L. Tucker. 75% freelance written. Works with a small number of new/unpublished writers each year. Monthly newsletter on the appraisals of antiques, art, collectibles, jewelry, coins, stamps and real estate. "The writer should be extremely knowledgeable on the subject, and the article should be written with appraisers in mind with prices quoted for objects, good pictures and descriptions of articles being written about." Circ. 1,300. Pays on acceptance. Publishes ms an average of 2 months after acceptance. Byline given, with short biography to establish writer's credibility. Not copyrighted. Buys first rights, second serial (reprint) rights, and simultaneous rights. Submit seasonal/holiday material 2 months in advance. Simultaneous and previously published submissions OK. Computer printout submissions acceptable; prefers letter-quality to dot-matrix. Reports in 1 week on queries; 3 weeks on mss. Free sample copy and writer's guidelines.
Nonfiction: Interview/profile, personal experience, technical and travel. "All articles must be geared toward professional appraisers." Query with or without published clips, or send complete ms. Length: 1,000-1,500 words. Pays $50-75.
Photos: Send photos with submission. Reviews negatives and prints. Offers no additional payment for photos accepted with ms. Identification of subjects required. Buys one-time rights.
Tips: "Interviewing members of the Association for articles, reviewing art books, shows, and large auctions are all ways for writers who are not in the field to write articles for us."

PROGRESSIVE ARCHITECTURE, 600 Summer St., Box 1361, Stamford CT 06904. Editor: John M. Dixon. 5-10% freelance written. Prefers to work with published/established writers. Monthly. Pays on publication. Publishes ms an average of 4 months after acceptance. Buys all rights for use in architectural press. Computer printout submissions acceptable; prefers letter-quality to dot-matrix.
Nonfiction: "Articles of technical professional interest devoted to architecture, interior design, and urban design and planning and illustrated by photographs and architectural drawings. We also use technical articles which are prepared by technical authorities and would be beyond the scope of the lay writer. Practically all the material is professional, and most of it is prepared by writers in the field who are approached by the magazine for material." Pays $75-300. Sometimes pays the expenses of writers on assignment.
Photos: Buys one-time reproduction rights to b&w and color photos.

Auto and Truck

These journals are geared to automobile, motorcycle, and truck dealers; service department personnel; or fleet operators. Publications for highway planners and traffic control experts are listed in the Government and Public Service category.

AMERICAN CLEAN CAR, Serving the Car & Truck Cleaning Industries, American Trade Magazines, 500 N. Dearborn, Chicago IL 60610. (312)337-7700. Editor: Renald Rooney. Associate Editor: Paul Partyka. "We are backlogged with submissions and prefer not to receive unsolicited submissions at this time."

‡**AMERICAN TRUCKER MAGAZINE**, American Trucker Marketing, Box 6366, San Bernardino CA 92412. (714)889-1167. Publisher: David Chinn. Editor: Steve Sturgess. 10% freelance written. Eager to work with new/unpublished writers. Monthly magazine for professional truck drivers, owners, management and other trucking personnel. Articles, fillers and other materials should be generally conservative and of particular interest to the readership, of an informative or entertaining nature relating to the trucking industry. Circ. 80,000. Pays on publication. Publishes ms an average of 3 months after acceptance. First-time rights requested. Submit seasonal/holiday material 3 months in advance. Electronic submissions OK via disc, CP/M or MS-DOS. Computer printout submissions acceptable. Reports in 3 weeks. Phone queries OK. Free sample copy and writer's guidelines.

Nonfiction: Realistic articles directed to trucking professionals which promote a positive image of the industry. Photo and features of outstanding rigs, truck maintenance and repair, and business aspects of trucking. 450-2,500 words. Buys 60 articles/year. Pays standard column inch rate. Sometimes pays the expenses of writers on assignment.
Photos: State availability of photos or send captioned photos with ms. Model release required.
Fiction: Realistic, "slice of life" for truckers, adventure and humor. Query. Length: 1;200-2,500 words. Buys 6/year. Pays standard column inch rate.
Tips: Freelance writers offer a balance of writing style throughout the magazine.

AUTO GLASS JOURNAL, Grawin Publications, Inc., Suite 101, 303 Harvard E., Box 12099, Seattle WA 98102-0099. (206)322-5120. Editor: Eric Cosentino. 45% freelance written. Prefers to work with published/ established writers. Monthly magazine on auto glass replacement. National publication for the auto glass replacement industry. Includes step-by-step glass replacement procedures for current model cars as well as shop profiles, industry news and trends. Circ. 4,200. Pays on acceptance. Publishes ms an average of 5 months after acceptance. No byline given. Buys all rights. Computer printout submissions acceptable; prefers letter-quality to dot-matrix. Reports in 2 weeks on queries; 1 week on mss. Sample copy for 6x9 SAE and 56¢ postage. Writer's guidelines for #10 SAE and 1 first class stamp.
Nonfiction: How-to (install all glass in a current model car); and interview/profile. Buys 22-36 mss/year. Query with published clips. Length: 2,000-3,500 words. Pays $75-250, with photos. Sometimes pays the expenses of writers on assignment.
Photos: State availability of photos. Reviews b&w contact sheets and negatives. Payment included with ms. Captions required. Buys all rights.
Tips: "Be willing to find sources for auto glass installation features."

AUTO LAUNDRY NEWS, Columbia Communications, 370 Lexington Ave., New York NY 10017. (212)532-9290. Publisher/Editor: Ralph Monti. For sophisticated carwash operators. Monthly magazine; 45-100 pages. Circ. 15,000 + . Pays on publication. Buys all rights. Submit seasonal/holiday material 2 months in advance. Computer printout submissions acceptable; no dot-matrix. Reports in 1 month.
Nonfiction: How-to, historical, humor, informational, new product, nostalgia, personal experience, technical, interviews, photo features and profiles. Buys 15 mss/year. Query. Length: 1,000-2,000 words. Pays $75-175.
Tips: "Read the magazine; notice its style and come up with something interesting to the industry. Foremost, the writer has to know the industry."

AUTO TRIM NEWS, National Association of Auto Trim Shops (NAATS), 1623 N. Grand Ave., Box 86, Baldwin NY 11510. (516)223-4334. Editor: Nat Danas. Associate Editor: Dani Ben-Ari. 25% freelance written. Monthly magazine for auto trim shops, installation specialists, customizers and restylers, marine and furniture upholsterers as well as manufacturers, wholesalers, jobbers, and distributors serving them. Circ. 8,000. Pays on publication. Byline given. Buys first rights only. Simultaneous and previously published submissions OK. Reports in 1 month. Sample copy $1.50; free writer's guidelines for SAE and 2 first class stamps.
Nonfiction: How-to, interview/profile, photo feature on customizing, restoration, convertible conversions, and restyling of motor vehicles (cars, vans, trucks, motorcycles, boats and aircraft). Query or send complete ms. Length: 500-1,000 words. Pays $50-200.
Photos: State availability of photos. Pays $5 maximum for b&w print. Reviews b&w contact sheet. Captions and identification of subjects required. Buys one-time rights.
Tips: "No material dealing with engines and engine repairs. We are an aftermarket publication."

AUTOBODY & RECONDITIONED CAR, Key Markets Publishing Co., Box 5867, Rockford IL 61125. Editor: David Mathieu. 50% freelance written. A bi-monthly magazine covering autobody repair, reconditioning and refinishing. Audience includes independent body shops; new and used car dealers and fleet operators with body shops; paint, glass and trim shops; and jobbers and manufacturers of automobile straightening equipment and refinishing supplies. Circ. 25,000. Pays on publication. Publishes manuscript an average of 3 months after acceptance. Byline given. Buys first North American serial rights and one-time rights. Submit seasonal/holiday material 3 months in advance. Simultaneous queries, and simultaneous, photocopied, and previously published (if so indicated) submissions OK. Computer printout submissions acceptable; prefers letter-quality to dot-matrix. Reports in 1 month. Sample copy $1. Writer's guidelines for business-size SAE and 1 first class stamp.
Nonfiction: Book excerpts (autobody repair, small business management); how-to (manage an autobody shop, do a specific autobody repair); interview/profile (bodyshop owner); photo feature (step-by-step repair); and technical (equipment, supplies and processes in an autobody shop). Editorial calendar will be provided with writer's guidelines. No personal experience as a customer of an autobody shop, or how *not* to run a shop. Buys 36 mss/year. Query with published clips or send complete ms. Length: 500-2,500 words. Pays $100-200 with photos.

Photos: State availability of photos and send one sample, or send photos with ms. Reviews color negatives and 4x5 transparencies, and 3½x5 b&w and color prints. Payment for photos included in payment for ms. Captions required. Buys one-time rights.
Tips: "Visit 10 autobody shops and ask the owners what they want to read about; find sources, then send in a query; or send in a letter with 10 article topics that you know you can cover and wait for an assignment. Experience in trade publication writing helps. Area most open to freelancers is technical and management how-tos. We want technical, technical, technical articles. Autobody people work with everything from laser beam measuring benches to catalytic thermoreactors. Be willing to learn about such subjects. The most frequent mistakes made by writers are not understanding the audience or the autobody business."

AUTOMOTIVE BOOSTER OF CALIFORNIA, Box 765, LaCanada CA 91011. (213)790-6554. Editor: Don McAnally. 2% freelance written. Prefers to work with published/established writers. For members of Automotive Booster clubs, automotive warehouse distributors, and automotive parts jobbers in California. Monthly. Circ. 3,400. Not copyrighted. Byline given. Pays on publication. Publishes ms an average of 1 month after acceptance. Buys first rights only.
Nonfiction: Will look at short articles and pictures about successes of automotive parts outlets in California. Also can use personnel assignments for automotive parts people in California. Query first. Pays $1.25/column inch (about 2½¢/word).
Photos: Pays $5 for b&w photos used with mss.

THE BATTERY MAN, Independent Battery Manufacturers Association, Inc., 100 Larchwood Dr., Largo FL 33540. (813)586-1409. Editor: Celwyn E. Hopkins. 40% freelance written. Emphasizes SLI battery manufacture, applications and new developments. For battery manufacturers and retailers (garage owners, servicemen, fleet owners, etc.). Monthly magazine. Circ. 5,200. Pays on acceptance. Publishes ms an average of 1 year after acceptance. Buys all rights. Byline given. Submit seasonal/holiday material 3 months in advance. Simultaneous, photocopied and previously published submissions OK. Computer printout submissions acceptable; no dot-matrix. Reports in 6 weeks. Sample copy $2.50.
Nonfiction: Technical articles. "Articles about how a company is using batteries as a source of uninterruptable power supply for its computer systems or a hospital using batteries for the same (photos with article are nice) purpose as well as for life support systems, etc." Submit complete ms. Buys 19-24 unsolicited mss/year. Recent article examples: "The Strategic Decision of Leaf vs. Envelope Battery Construction"; "Universal Batteries—Fact or Fad?" and "Acquisitions" (April 1986). Length: 750-1,200 words. Pays 6¢/word.
Tips: "Most writers are not familiar enough with this industry to be able to furnish a feature article. They try to palm off something that they wrote for a hardware store, or a dry cleaner, by calling everything a 'battery store'. We receive a lot of manuscripts on taxes and tax information (such as U.S. income tax). Since this is an international publication, we try to stay away from such subjects, since U.S. tax info is of no use or interest to overseas readers."

THE CHEK-CHART SERVICE BULLETIN, Box 6227, San Jose CA 95150. Editor: Mike Calkins. 20% freelance written. Works with a small number of new/unpublished writers each year. Emphasizes trade news and how-to articles on automobile service for professional mechanics. Monthly-newsletter; 8 pages. Circ. 20,000. Pays on acceptance. No byline. Buys all rights. Submit seasonal/holiday material 3-4 months in advance. Computer printout submissions acceptable; no dot-matrix. Reports in 2 weeks. Publishes ms an average of 3 months after acceptance. Free sample copy and writer's guidelines; mention *Writer's Market* in request.
Nonfiction: "The *Service Bulletin* is a trade newsletter, *not* a consumer magazine. How-to articles and service trade news for professional auto mechanics, also articles on merchandising automobile service. No 'do-it-yourself' articles." Also no material unrelated to car service. Buys 6 unsolicited mss/year. Query with samples. Length: 700-1,100 words. Pays $100-300.
Photos: State availability of photos with query. Offers no additional payment for photos accepted with ms. Uses 8x10 b&w glossy photos. Captions and model release required. Buys all rights.
Tips: "Be willing to work in our style. Ask about subjects we would like to have covered in the future."

COLLISION, Kruza Kaleidoscopix, Inc., Box 389, Franklin MA 02038. Editor: Jay Kruza. For auto dealers, auto body repairmen and managers, and tow truck operators. Magazine published every 5 weeks; 84 pages. Pays on acceptance. Buys all rights. Submit seasonal/holiday material 4 months in advance. Simultaneous, photocopied and previously published submissions OK. Reports in 3 weeks. Sample copy $3; free writer's guidelines and editorial schedule.
Nonfiction: Expose (on government intervention in private enterprise via rule making; also how any business skims the cream of profitable business but fails to satisfy needs of motorist); and how-to (fix a dent, a frame, repair plastics, run your business better). No general business articles such as how to sell more, do better bookkeeping, etc. Query before submitting interview, personal opinion or technical articles. "Journalism of newsworthy material in local areas pertaining to auto body is of interest." Buys 20 or more articles/year. Length: 100-1,500 words. Pays $25-125.

Photos: "Our readers work with their hands and are more likely to be stopped by photo with story." Send photos with ms. Pays $25/first, $7/each additional for 5x7 b&w prints. Captions preferred. Model release required if not news material.

Columns/Departments: Stars and Their Cars, Personalities in Auto Dealerships, Auto Body Repair Shops, Association News and Lifestyle (dealing with general human interest hobbies or pastimes). Almost anything automotive that would attract readership interest. "Photos are very important. Stories that we have purchased are: 'Post office commandeered cars to deliver help during 1906 San Francisco Quake'; 'Bob Salter has rescued 3,000 people with his tow truck'; 'Telnack's design of T-Bird and Sable set new trends in style'; 'Snow increases body shop business for Minnesota shop'; 'Race against the clock with funny wheels on frozen lake.' "

COMMERCIAL CARRIER JOURNAL, for Private Fleets & For Hire Trucking, Chilton Co., Division of American Broadcasting Co., Chilton Way, Radnor PA 19089. (215)964-4513. Editor-in-Chief: Gerald F. Standley. Managing Editor: Parry Desmond. "We are backlogged with submissions and prefer not to receive unsolicited submissions at this time."

JOBBER/RETAILER, Bill Communications, Box 5417, Akron OH 44313. Managing Editor: Sandie Stambaugh. "We are backlogged with submissions and prefer not to receive unsolicited submissions at this time."

JOBBER TOPICS, 7300 N. Cicero Ave., Lincolnwood IL 60646. (312)588-7300. Articles Editor: Jack Creighton. 10% freelance written. "A digest-sized magazine dedicated to helping its readers—auto parts jobbers and warehouse distributors—succeed in their business via better management and merchandising techniques; and a better knowledge of industry trends, activities and local or federal legislation that may influence their business activities." Monthly. Pays on acceptance. No byline given. Buys all rights. Query with outline.

Nonfiction: Most editorial material is staff-written. "Articles with unusual or outstanding automotive jobber procedures, with special emphasis on sales and merchandising; any phase of automotive parts and equipment sales and distribution. Especially interested in merchandising practices and machine shop operations. Most independent businesses usually have a strong point or two. We like to see a writer zero in on that strong point(s) and submit an outline (or query), advising us of those points and what he intends to include in a feature. We will give him, or her, a prompt reply." Length: 2,500 words maximum. Pay based on quality and timeliness of feature.

Photos: 5x7 b&w glossies or 35mm color transparencies purchased with mss.

‡MODERN TIRE DEALER, 110 N. Miller Rd., Box 5417, Akron OH 44313. (216)867-4401. Editor: Dave Burkhart. 25% freelance written. For independent tire dealers. Monthly tabloid, plus 2 special emphasis issue magazines; 50-page tabloid, 80-page special issues. Published 14 times annually. Buys all rights. Photocopied submissions OK. Computer printout submissions acceptable; no dot-matrix. Query. Reports in 1 month. Publishes ms an average of 2 months after acceptance. Free writer's guidelines.

Nonfiction: "How independent tire dealers sell tires, accessories and allied services such as brakes, wheel alignment, shocks and mufflers. The emphasis is on merchandising and management. We prefer the writer to zero in on some specific area of interest; avoid shotgun approach." Length: 1,500 words. Pays $100-250.

Photos: 8x10, 4x5, 5x7 b&w glossy prints purchased with mss.

MOTOR SERVICE, Hunter Publishing Co., 950 Lee, Des Plaines IL 60016. Editor: Jim Holloran. 25% freelance written. Monthly magazine for professional auto mechanics and the owners and service managers of repair shops, garages and fleets. Circ. 131,000. Pays on acceptance. Buys all rights. Pays kill fee. Byline given. Computer printout submissions acceptable. Publishes ms an average of 2 months after acceptance. Free sample copy.

Nonfiction: Technical how-to features in language a mechanic can enjoy and understand; management articles to help shop owners and service managers operate a better business; technical theory pieces on how something works; new technology roundups, etc. No "generic business pieces on management tips, increasing sales, employee motivation or do-it-yourself material, etc." Recent article includes "Meet GM's Self-diagnosing Computer Command Control System." Length: 1,500-2,500 words. Pays $75 for departmental material, $200-$500 for feature articles. Buys 10 mss/year, mostly from regular contributing editors. Query first. "Writers must know our market."

Photos: Photos and/or diagrams must accompany technical articles. Uses 5x7 b&w prints or 35mm transparencies. Offers no additional payment for photos accepted with ms. Captions and model releases required. Also buys color transparencies for cover use. Pays $125-200.

Tips: "We're always looking for new faces but finding someone who is technically knowledgeable in our field who can also write is extremely difficult. Good tech writers are hard to find."

MOTORCYCLE DEALERNEWS, Harcourt Brace Jovanovich Publications, #250, 1700 E. Dyer Rd., Santa Ana CA 92705. (714)250-8060. Editor: Fred Clements. 10% freelance written. A monthly magazine "with a philosophy of providing retail dealers with information they can use to be better business people." Pays on publication. Byline sometimes given. Offers negotiable kill fee. Buys all rights. Submit seasonal/holiday material 3 months in advance. Computer printout submissions acceptable; prefers letter-quality to dot-matrix. Reports in 1 month.

Nonfiction: New product and technical. No tales about riding. Buys 24 mss/year. Query with or without published clips, or send complete ms. "We prefer to discuss article possibilities by telephone." Length: 1,000-3,000 words. Pays $100 minimum; will negotiate higher payments.

Photos: State availability of photos with submission. Reviews contact sheets, negatives, transparencies and prints. Offers negotiable payment. Captions, model releases and identification of subjects required. Buys rights exclusive to our industry.

Tips: "We seek expertise in business and marketing, especially if the writer has extensive experience in the motorcycle/ATV/scooter industry. How-to articles teaching dealers good ways to market and sell their products, especially accessory items, are always sought."

O AND A MARKETING NEWS, Box 765, LaCanada CA 91011. (213)790-6554. Editor: Don McAnally. For "service station dealers, garagemen, TBA (tires, batteries, accessories) people and oil company marketing management." Bimonthly. 5% freelance written. Circ. 9,500. Not copyrighted. Pays on publication. Buys first rights only. Reports in 1 week.

Nonfiction: "Straight news material; management, service and merchandising applications; emphasis on news about or affecting markets and marketers *within the publication's geographic area of the 11 Western states.* No restrictions on style or slant. We could use straight news of our industry from some Western cities, notably Las Vegas, Phoenix, Seattle, and Salt Lake City. Query with a letter that gives a capsule treatment of what the story is about." Buys 25 mss/year. Length: maximum 1,000 words. Pays $1.25/column inch (about 2½¢ a word).

Photos: Photos purchased with or without mss; captions required. No cartoons. Pays $5.

PROFESSIONAL CARWASHING MAGAZINE, National Trade Publications, 8 Stanley Circle, Latham NY 12110. Editor: James Connell. Monthly magazine covering professional vehicle cleaning. "We are a trade magazine and serve as a communications, entertainment, and information medium for carwash owners and operators. We are also read by manufacturers and suppliers of carwash equipment, as well as their distributors." 20% freelance written. Circ. 17,000. Pays on acceptance. Byline given. Buys all rights. Submit seasonal/holiday material 4 months in advance. Simultaneous queries OK. SASE. Reports in 3 weeks. Sample copies and guidelines $2 plus 50¢ postage and handling to National Trade Publication.

Nonfiction: How-to (maintenance marketing); photo feature and technical. "All material submitted should be geared to the carwash industry. Problems of running a self-service or automatic carwash, unique or inspiring stories of success or failure, individual design of buildings, advertising and methods of marketing are good topics." No beautiful carwash stories, historic, humor, product comparisons. Buys 12-18 mss/year, but would like to buy more. Query with or without published clips. Length: 1,000-2,500 words. Pays 3-5¢/word. Sometimes pays the expenses of writers on assignment. "Payment depends on how much rewriting and follow-up needs to be done."

Photos: State availability of photos with query. Reviews 5x7 prints. Model release and identification of subjects required.

Tips: "Give us material of interests to the carwash industry, including better or unique management techniques, methods of preventative maintenance, or equipment marketing techniques, unusual design. Writers frequently give too short treatment to the subject assigned because they don't understand the industry. The writer has a better chance of breaking in at our publication with short articles and fillers because the first-time submitter will probably not understand the industry."

‡RENEWS, Kona Communications, Inc., Suite 300, 707 Lake Cook Rd., Deerfield IL 60015. (312)498-3180. Editor: Terry Haller. Managing Editor: Denise L. Rondini. 15% freelance written. Magazine published 8 times/year covering automotive engine/parts rebuilding. Emphasizes technology and management issues affecting the automotive rebuilders. Circ. 21,000. Pays on publication. Publishes ms an average of 2 months after acceptance. Byline sometimes given. Buys first rights. Photocopied submissions OK. Computer printout submissions acceptable. Reports in 1 month.

Nonfiction: Interview/profile, new product, photo feature and technical. "No articles that are too general to be helpful to our readers." Buys 8 mss/year. Query. Length: 1,000-2,500 words. Pays $75-300. Sometimes pays the expenses of writers on assignment.

Photos: Send photos with submission. Reviews contact sheets, transparencies and prints. Offers no additional payment for photos accepted with ms. Captions, model releases and identification of subjects required. Buys one-time rights.

Tips: "A strong automotive technical background or a special expertise in small business management is helpful. Technical and business management sections are most open to freelancers. Most of our writers are thoroughly experienced in the subject they write on. It is difficult for a 'generalist' to write for our audience."

SANDY CORP., 1500 W. Big Beaver Rd., Troy MI 48084. (313)649-0800. Manager of Human Resources: David Southworth. Produces material for sales and technical/automotive audiences. Works with 50-200 freelance writers. Buys all rights. Reports in 1 month on queries.
Nonfiction: Articles up to 500 words on how Chevrolet or GMC truck dealers are doing an outstanding job of selling cars and trucks, servicing cars and trucks, participating in community activities, recognizing employee achievement—can use b&w glossies of story events. Produces various publications (samples on request). Submit outline/synopsis.
Tips: "Submit only if you have good relationship with local Chevrolet or GMC truck dealership and can write copy and take pictures reflecting a professional knowledge of the business."

‡SOUTHERN MOTOR CARGO, Box 4169, Memphis TN 38104. Editor: Mike Pennington. 10% freelance written. For "trucking management and maintenance personnel of private, contract, and for-hire carriers in 16 Southern states (Ala., Ark., Del., Fla., Ga., Ky., La., Md., Miss., N.C., Okla., S.C., Tenn., Tex., Va., and W. Va.) and the District of Columbia." Special issues include "ATA Convention," October; "Transportation Graduate Directory," January; "Mid-America Truck Show," February; "Leasing or Buying?", June; and "Annual Industry Forecast, and Winterization," October. Monthly. Circ. 56,000. Buys first rights within circulation area. Pays on publication (or on acceptance in certain cases). Publishes ms an average of 2 months after acceptance. Free sample copy to sincere, interested contributors.
Nonfiction: "How a Southern trucker builds a better mousetrap. Factual newspaper style with punch in lead. Don't get flowery. No success stories. Pick one item, i.e., tire maintenance, billing procedure, etc., and show how such-and-such carrier has developed or modified it to better fit his organization. Bring in problems solved by the way he adapted this or that and what way he plans to better his present layout. Find a segment of the business that has been altered or modified due to economics or new information, such as 'due to information gathered by a new IBM process, it has been discovered that an XYZ transmission needs overhauling every 60,000 miles instead of every 35,000 miles, thereby resulting in savings of $$$ over the normal life of this transmission.' Or, 'by incorporating a new method of record keeping, claims on damaged freight have been expedited with a resultant savings in time and money.' Compare the old method with the new, itemize savings, and get quotes from personnel involved. Articles must be built around an outstanding phase of the operation and must be documented and approved by the firm's management prior to publication." Length: 1,000-3,000 words. Pays minimum 10¢/word for "feature material."
Photos: Purchased with cutlines; glossy prints. Pays $10.

SPRAY DUST MAGAZINE, The Information Source For Jersey's Auto Body Industry, Central Jersey Auto Body Association, Box 1705, Rahway NJ 07065. (201)374-3424. Editor: R. Cullen Fink. 10% freelance written. Eager to work with new/unpublished writers. Monthly magazine of news that affects auto body industry in New Jersey. "*Spray Dust* is written for the New Jersey auto body shop owner, exclusively. Articles either inform the reader on issues political or otherwise that affect his shop or instruct him on ways to improve his business. The magazine has an action slant to the degree that many pieces either imply or state a need for unification in the industry—a call to action." Circ. 2,300. Pays on publication. Publishes ms an average of 2 months after acceptance. Byline given. Buys first serial rights. Simultaneous queries and photocopied submissions OK. Electronic submissions OK via disk—IBM or compatible—Displaywriter 3 software only. Computer printout submissions acceptable; prefers letter-quality to dot-matrix. Reports in 3 weeks. Sample copy for 9x12 SAE and 5 first class stamps.
Nonfiction: Interview/profile, new product and technical. Buys 12-15 mss/year. Query with published clips. Length: 1,000-2,500 words. Pays $50-100. Sometimes pays the expenses of writers on assignment.
Photos: State availability of photos. Prefers 5x7 or larger b&w prints. Pays $5-10. Buys one-time rights.
Columns/Departments: Let's Get Down to Business (how to be a better businessman), and Advertiser Spotlight.
Tips: "We are open in all areas except Advertiser Spotlight. The best place for freelancers to begin is Let's Get Down to Business. A writer who is handy with a camera has an edge. We may be buying less freelance material in the coming year because of the poor quality of submissions in the past. We are still open to anyone, but that could change."

THE SUCCESSFUL DEALER, Kona-Cal, Inc., 707 Lake Cook Rd., Deerfield IL 60015. (312)498-3180. Editor: Denise L. Rondini. Managing Editor: R. Patricia Herron. 30% freelance written. "I will consider material from both established writers and new ones." Magazine published 6 times/year covering dealership management of medium and heavy duty trucks, construction equipment, forklift trucks, diesel engines and truck trailers. Circ. 19,000. Pays on publication. Byline sometimes given. Buys first serial rights only. Simultaneous queries, and simultaneous and photocopied submissions OK. Computer printout submissions acceptable; prefers letter-quality to dot-matrix. Reports in 2 weeks. Publication date "depends on the article; some are contracted for a specific issue, others on an as need basis."
Nonfiction: How-to (solve problems within the dealership); interview/profile (concentrating on business, not

personality); new product (exceptional only); opinion (by readers—those in industry); personal experience (of readers); photo feature (of major events); and technical (vehicle componentry). Special issues include: March-April: American Truck Dealer Convention; September-October: Parts and Service. Query. Length: open. Pays $100-150/page.

Tips: "Phone first, then follow up with a detailed explanation of the proposed article. Allow two weeks for our response. Articles should be based on real problems/solutions encoutered by truck or heavy equipment dealership personnel. I am *not* interested in general management tips."

TOW-AGE, Kruza Kaleidoscopix, Inc., Box 389, Franklin MA 02038. Editor: J. Kruza. For readers who run their own towing service business. 10% freelance written. Published every 6 weeks. Circ. 18,000. Buys all rights; usually reassigns rights. Buys about 18 mss/year. Pays on acceptance. Publishes ms an average of 4 months after acceptance. Photocopied and simultaneous submissions OK. Reports in 1-4 weeks. Computer printout submissions acceptable; prefers letter-quality to dot-matrix. Sample copy $3; free writer's guidelines.
Nonfiction: Articles on business, legal and technical information for the towing industry. "Light reading material; short, with punch." Informational, how-to, personal, interview and profile. Query or submit complete ms. Length: 200-800 words. Pays $40-100. Spot news and successful business operations. Length: 100-800 words. Technical articles. Length: 400-1,000 words.
Photos: Pays up to 8x10 b&w photos purchased with or without mss, or on assignment. Pays $25 for first photo; $7 for each additional photo in series. Captions required.

TRUCK CANADA, Sentinel Business Publications, Unit 8, 6420 Victoria Ave., Montreal, Quebec H3W 2S7 Canada. (514)731-3524. Contact: Editor. For members of the heavy trucking industry. 30% freelance-written. Monthly magazine; 40 pages. Circ. 21,500. Pays on publication. Publishes ms an average of 4 months after acceptance. Buys first Canadian rights. Phone queries OK. Submit seasonal/holiday material 3 months in advance. Photocopied submissions and previously published work (if not previously published in Canada) OK. Computer printout submissions acceptable; prefers letter-quality to dot-matrix. Reports in 3 weeks. Free sample copy and writer's guidelines for $1.48 in IRCs.
Nonfiction: General interest; historical; how-to (on truck maintenance); interview, profile and technical. Buys 18 articles/year. Query. Length: 1,500-2,500. Pays 7¢/word. Sometimes pays the expenses of writers on assignment.
Photos: "We feel articles with photos illustrating them are better accepted by readers." State availability of photos. Pays $5 for b&w contact sheets and $7.50 for color transparencies.

‡TRUCKERS' NEWS, (formerly *Farm to Market Trucker's News*), h.e.r. Publications, Ink., 1800 Nebraska St., Sioux City IA 51105. (712)258-0782. Owner: Jane Hermann. 10% freelance written. Monthly trucking newspaper for company drivers, owner/operators, owners of large and small trucking firms and persons in allied industries in the Midwest. Circ. 10,000. Pays on publication. Byline given. Not copyrighted. Buys first rights and second (reprint) rights to material originally published elsewhere. Submit seasonal/holiday material 2 months in advance. Simultaneous queries, and simultaneous, photocopied and previously published submissions OK. Computer printout submissions acceptable; no dot-matrix. Reports in 1 month. Publishes ms an average of 2 months after acceptance. Sample copy $1; free writer's guidelines.
Nonfiction: Expose, general interest, historical/nostalgic, how-to, humor, interview/profile, new product, personal experience, photo feature and technical. "Our special May Truckers' Day issue is the largest. Material should be submitted by March 15." Send complete ms. Length: 375-1,250 words. Pays $25-50. Sometimes pays the expenses of writers on assignment.
Photos: Send photos with ms. Pays $10-25 for 5x7 prints. Captions, model release and identification of subjects required.
Tips: "Good, bright features about people in transportation are always welcome, especially when accompanied by a photo."

TRUCKERS/USA, Randall Publishing Co., Box 2029, Tuscaloosa AL 35403. (205)349-2990. Editor: Claude Duncan. 25-50% freelance written. Eager to work with new/unpublished writers. Weekly tabloid for long-haul truck drivers and trucker service industry. "Most of our readers are long-haul truckers. We want stories about these drivers, their trucks, lifestyle and people who serve them, such as truck stops. We want upbeat stories." Circ. 15,000. Pays on acceptance. Publishes ms an average of 1 month after acceptance. Byline given. Offers 100% kill fee. Not copyrighted. Buys first serial rights, one-time rights, second serial (reprint) rights or simultaneous rights. Simultaneous and previously published (updated) submissions OK. Computer printout submissions acceptable; prefers letter-quality to dot-matrix. Reports in 2 weeks. Free sample copy and writer's guidelines.
Nonfiction: General interest (with trucker angle); historical/nostaglic (with trucker angle); humor (with trucker angle); interview/profile (with truckers); personal experience (with truckers); technical (re heavy-duty trucks); and crimes involving long-haul truckers. Buys 100 mss/year. Send complete ms. Length: 250-1,000 words. Pays $10-50. Sometimes pays expenses of writers on assignment.

Photos: Send photos with query or ms. Accepts b&w or color prints; commercially processed accepted if sharp quality. Pays $5. Identification of subjects required.
Fiction: Trucker-related.
Tips: "Truckers like to read about other truckers, and people with whom truckers are in frequent contact—truckstop workers, state police, etc. We're looking for localized stories about long-haul truckers. Nothing is too local if it's interesting. We encourage multiple submissions, preferrably with art. Submitting art with copy gives a definite edge. We emphasize subject matter rather than writing style, so any of the articles published can be idea leads to similar stories. We increasingly are running longer articles, which also increases our need for shorter articles to maintain our tabloid newspaper format."

WARD'S AUTO WORLD, 28 W. Adams, Detroit MI 48226. (313)962-4433. Editor-in-Chief: David C. Smith. Managing Editor: James W. Bush. Senior Editors: Jon Lowell and Richard L. Waddell. Associate Editors: Drew Winter and Michael Arnolt. 10% freelance written. Prefers to work with published/established writers; works with a small number of new/unpublished writers each year. For top and middle management in all phases of auto industry. Also includes heavy-duty vehicle coverage. Monthly magazine; 96 pages. Circ. 75,000. Pays on publication. Pay varies for kill fee. Byline given. Buys all rights. Phone queries OK. Submit seasonal/holiday material 1 month in advance. Electronic submissions OK; phone Mike Arnolt, associate editor. Computer printout submissions acceptable; check first before submitting dot-matrix. Reports in 2 weeks. Publishes ms an average of 1 month after acceptance. Free sample copy and writer's guidelines.
Nonfiction: Expose, general interest, international automotive news, historical, humor, interview, new product, nostalgia, personal experience, photo feature and technical. Few consumer type articles. No "nostalgia or personal history type stories (like 'My Favorite Car')." Buys 4-8 mss/year. Query. Length: 700-5,000 words. Pay $100-600. Sometimes pays the expenses of writers on assignment.
Photos: "We're heavy on graphics." Submit photo material with query. Pay varies for 8x10 b&w prints or color transparencies. Captions required. Buys one-time rights.
Tips: "Don't send poetry, how-to and 'My Favorite Car' stuff. It doesn't stand a chance. This is a business newsmagazine and operates on a news basis just like any other newsmagazine. We like solid, logical, well-written pieces with *all* holes filled."

_____ *Aviation and Space*

In this section are journals for aviation business executives, airport operators and aviation technicians. Publications for professional and private pilots are classified with the Aviation magazines in the Consumer Publications section.

AG-PILOT INTERNATIONAL MAGAZINE, Bio-Aeronautic Publishers, Inc., Drawer "R", Walla Walla WA 99362. (509)522-4311. Editor: Tom J. Wood. Executive Editor: Rocky Kemp. Emphasizes agricultural aerial application (crop dusting). "This is intended to be a fun-to-read, technical, as well as humorous and serious publication for the ag pilot and operator. They are our primary target." 20% freelance written. Monthly magazine; 60 pages. Circ. 12,400. Pays on publication. Publishes ms an average of 3 months after acceptance. Buys all rights. Byline given unless writer requested holding name. Computer printout submissions acceptable; prefers letter-quality to dot-matrix. Reports in 2 weeks. Sample copy $2.
Nonfiction: Expose (of EPA, OSHA, FAA or any government function concerned with this industry); general interest; historical; interview (of well-known ag/aviation person); nostalgia; personal opinion; new product; personal experience; and photo feature. "If we receive an article, in any area we have solicited, it is quite possible this person could contribute intermittently. The international input is what we desire. Industry-related material is a must. No newspaper clippings." Send complete ms. Length: 800-1,500 words. Pays $25-100. Sometimes pays the expenses of writers on assignment.
Photos: "We would like one color or b&w (5x7 preferred) with the manuscript, if applicable—it will help increase your chance of publication." Four color. Offers no additional payment for photos accepted with ms. Captions preferred, model release required.
Columns/Departments: International (of prime interest, as they need to cultivate this area—aviation/crop dusting-related); Embryo Birdman (should be written, or appear to be written, by a beginner spray pilot); The

Chopper Hopper (by anyone in the helicopter industry); Trouble Shooter (ag aircraft maintenance tips); and Catchin' The Corner (written by a person obviously skilled in the crop dusting field of experience or other interest-capturing material related to the industry). Send complete ms. Length: 800-1,500 words. Pays $25-100.
Poetry: Interested in all agri-aviation related poetry. Buys 1/issue. Submit no more than 2 at one time. Maximum length: one 10 inch x 24 picas maximum. Pays $25-50.
Fillers: Short jokes, short humor and industry-related newsbreaks. Length: 10-100 words. Pays $5-20.
Tips: "Writers should be witty and knowledgeable about the crop dusting aviation world. Material *must* be agricultural/aviation-oriented. Crop dusting or nothing! We plan a Spanish language edition to all Spanish-speaking countries."

AIR LINE PILOT, Magazine of Professional Flight Crews, Air Line Pilots Association, 535 Herndon Parkway, Box 1169, Herndon VA 22069. (703)689-4176. Editor: Esperison Martinez, Jr. 10% freelance written. Prefers to work with published/established writers; works with a small number of new/unpublished writers each year. A monthly magazine for airline pilots covering "aviation industry information—economics, avionics, equipment, systems, safety—that affects a pilot's life in professional sense." Also includes information about management/labor relations trends, contract negotiations, etc. Circ. 42,000. Pays on acceptance. Publishes ms an average of 6 months after acceptance. Offers 50% kill fee. Buys first serial rights and makes work-for-hire assignments. Submit seasonal/holiday material 6 months in advance. Computer printout submissions acceptable; no dot-matrix. Reports in 1 month. Sample copy $1; free writer's guidelines.
Nonfiction: General interest, historical/nostalgic, humor, interview/profile, photo feature and technical. Buys 20 mss/year. Query with or without published clips, or send complete ms. Length: 1,000-3,000 words. Pays $100-800 for assigned articles; pays $50-500 for unsolicited articles.
Photos: Send photos with submission. Reviews contact sheets, 35mm transparencies and 8x10 prints. Offers $10-25/photo. Identification of subjects required. Buys one-time rights.
Tips: "For our feature section, we seek aviation industry information that affects the life of a professional airline pilot from a career standpoint. We also seek material that affects his life from a job security and work environment standpoint. Historical material that addresses the heritage of the profession or the advancement of the industry is also sought. Any airline pilot featured in an article must be an Air Line Pilots Association member in good standing."

AIRPORT SERVICES MANAGEMENT, Lakewood Publications, 50 S. 9th St., Minneapolis MN 55402. (612)333-0471. Editor: Gordon Gilbert. 33% freelance written. Emphasizes management of airports, airlines and airport-based businesses. Monthly magazine. Circ. 20,000. Pays on acceptance. Publishes ms an average of 3 months after acceptance. Buys all rights. Byline given. Phone queries OK. Submit seasonal/holiday material 3 months in advance. Photocopied submissions OK but must be industry-exclusive. Computer printout submissions acceptable; prefers letter-quality to dot-matrix. Reports in 1 month. Free sample copy and writer's guidelines.
Nonfiction: How-to (manage an airport, aviation service company or airline; work with local governments, etc.); interview (with a successful operator); and technical (how to manage a maintenance shop, snow removal operations, bird control, security operations). "No flying, no airport nostalgia or product puff pieces. We don't want pieces on how one company's product solved everyone's problem (how one airport or aviation business solved its problem with a certain type of product is okay). No descriptions of airport construction projects (down to the square footage in the new restrooms) that don't discuss applications for other airports. Plain 'how-to' story lines, please." Buys 40-50 mss/year, "but at least half are short (250-750 words) items for inclusion in one of our monthly departments." Query. Length: 250-2,500 words. Pays $50 for most department articles, $150-350 for features.
Photos: State availability of photos with query. Payment for photos is included in total purchase price. Uses b&w photos, charts and line drawings.
Tips: "I rarely commission major assignments to writers unproven in writing for our audience, even if they have excellent clips from other magazines. We're using more shorter feature articles (average 2,000 words) because I find that the longer, in-depth, issue-oriented articles are better when they are staff researched and written. No 'gee-whiz' approaches. Writing style should be lively, informal and straightforward, but the *subject matter* must be as functional and as down-to-earth as possible. Trade magazines are *business* magazines that must help readers do their jobs better. Frequent mistakes are using industry vendors/suppliers rather than users and industry officials as *sources*, especially in endorsing products or approaches, and directing articles to pilots or aviation consumers rather than to our specialized audience of aviation business managers and airport managers."

‡HELICOPTERS IN CANADA, Corvus Publishing Group, Ltd., Suite 158, 1224 53rd Ave. NE, Calgary, Alberta, Canada T2E 7E2. (403)275-9457. Publisher: Paul J. Skinner. "We are backlogged with submissions and prefer not to receive unsolicited submissions at this time."

JET CARGO NEWS, The Management Journal for Air Marketing, Box 920952, #398, Houston TX 77292-0952. (713)681-4760. Editor: Rich Hall. Designed to serve international industry concerned with moving goods by air. "It brings to shippers and manufacturers spot news of airline and aircraft development, air routes, shipping techniques, innovations and rates." 50% freelance written. Works with a small number of new/unpublished writers each year. Monthly. Circ. 25,000. Buys all rights. Buys up to 50 mss/year. Pays on publication. Publishes ms an average of 2 months after acceptance. Will not consider photocopied or simultaneous submissions. Electronic submissions OK via MS-DOS 1200 Baud. Computer printout submissions acceptable; prefers letter-quality to dot-matrix. Submit seasonal material 1 month in advance. Reports in 1 month if postage is included. Submit complete ms. Will send a sample copy on request.
Nonfiction: "Direct efforts to the shipper. Tell him about airline service, freight forwarder operations, innovations within the industry, new products, aircraft, packaging, material handling, hazardous materials, computerization of shipping, and pertinent news to the industry. Use a tight magazine style. The writer must know marketing." Buys informational articles, case studies, how-to's, interviews and coverage of successful business operations. Length: 1,500 words maximum. Pays $4/inch. Sometimes pays the expenses of writers on assignment.
Photos: 8x10 b&w glossy prints purchased with and without mss; captions required. Pays $10.
Tips: A frequent mistake is missing target readers and their interests. With short articles and fillers the writer exhibits his/her initiative. "We hope to generate more case studies of successful shipping solutions. We also hope to see more wrap-ups from a variety of contributors."

Beverages and Bottling

Soft drinks and alcoholic beverages are the livelihood of people who read these publications. Manufacturers, distributors and retailers of soft drinks and alcoholic beverages rely on them. Publications for bar and tavern operators and managers of restaurants are classified in the Hotels, Motels, Clubs, Resorts and Restaurants category.

THE LIQUOR REPORTER, Smithwrite Communications, Inc., 101 Milwaukee Blvd. S., Pacific WA 98047. (206)833-9642. Editor: Robert Smith. 30-50% freelance written. Prefers to work with published/established writers. Monthly tabloid providing local news about the liquor industry, restaurants, distributing, legislature, taverns, food stores, and shops in Washington state. Circ. 11,500. Pays on publication. Publishes ms an average of 2 months after acceptance. Byline given. Offers 100% kill fee for assigned material. Not copyrighted. Buys simultaneous rights and second serial (reprint) rights. Simultaneous queries and previously published submissions OK. Electronic submissions OK if compatible with Kaypro, WordStar, CPM. Computer printout submissions acceptable; prefers letter-quality to dot-matrix. Reports in 1 month. Sample copy $1; free writer's guidelines.
Nonfiction: News and news features with emphasis on Washington state. Buys 20 mss/year. Query with published clips. Length: 150-1,000 words. Pays $2/column inch minimum. Sometimes pays the expenses of writers on assignment.
Tips: Writers have a better chance of breaking in with short, lesser-paying articles and fillers. Washington state writers preferred. "We're looking for writers in Vancouver, Bellingham, Everett, Olympia (WA) and central Washington."

‡**LIQUOR STORE MAGAZINE, The Business Magazine for the Beverage Alcohol Industry**, Jobson Publishing, 352 Park Ave. S., New York NY 10010. (212)685-4848. Editor: Christina Veiders. Managing Editor: Harvey Lederman. 35% freelance written. A magazine published 9 times/year covering beverage alcohol (wine, spirits, beer) retailing. Emphasizes business news—how owners and managers of retail outlets can improve their operations and sales. Circ. 55,000. Pays within 30 days after receipt of invoice. Publishes ms an average of 6 weeks after acceptance. Byline given sometimes. Makes work-for-hire assignments. Submit seasonal/holiday material 2 months in advance. Photocopied submissions OK. Computer printout submissions acceptable; prefers letter-quality to dot-matrix. Sample copy for 9x12 SASE; writer's guidelines for business size SASE.

Nonfiction: Interview/profile, trend, and case studies. No general business topics. Buys 12 mss/year. Query. Length: 1,500-3,000 words. Pays $300-500. Pays the expenses of writers on assignment. State availability of photos with submission.

Photos: Reviews transparencies. Offers no additional payment for photos accepted with ms. Captions and identification of subjects required. Buys all rights.

Columns/Departments: Newsline (news covering retail market in various sections of country). Query. Length: 500-800 words. Pays $75-150.

Tips: "Submit good query ideas that fit in with our editorial format. Have good track record in business writing."

MID-CONTINENT BOTTLER, 10741 El Monte, Overland Park KS 66207. (913)341-0020. Publisher: Floyd E. Sageser. 5% freelance written. Works with a small number of new/unpublished writers each year. For "soft drink bottlers in the 20-state Midwestern area." Bimonthly. Not copyrighted. Pays on acceptance. Publishes ms an average of 4 months after acceptance. Buys first rights only. Reports "immediately." Computer printout submissions acceptable. Sample copy with $1 postage; guidelines with SASE.

Nonfiction: "Items of specific soft drink bottler interest with special emphasis on sales and merchandising techniques. Feature style desired." Buys 2-3 mss/year. Length: 2,000 words. Pays $15-$100. Sometimes pays the expenses of writers on assignment.

Photos: Photos purchased with mss.

‡SOUTHERN BEVERAGE JOURNAL, Box 561107, Miami FL 33176. (305)233-7230. Features Editor: Jackie Preston. Managing Editor: Mary McMahon. 1% freelance written. A monthly magazine for the alcohol beverage industry. Readers are personnel of bars, restaurants, package stores, night clubs, lounges and hotels—owners, managers and salespersons. Circ. 23,000. Pays on publication. Byline given. Buys all rights. Submit seasonal/holiday material 3 months in advance. Computer printout submissions acceptable. Reports in 1 month.

Nonfiction: Interview/profile and success stories. No canned material. Buys 3 mss/year. Send complete ms. Length: 750-1,250 words. Pays $200 maximum for assigned articles; pays $150 maximum for unsolicited articles. Sometimes pays the expenses of writers on assignment.

Photos: State availability of photos with submission. Reviews 3x5 prints. Offers $10 maximum/photo. Identification of subjects required. Buys all rights.

‡TEA & COFFEE TRADE JOURNAL, Lockwood Book Publishing Co., 130 W. 42nd St., New York NY 10036. (212)661-5980. Editor: Jane Phillips McCabe. 50% freelance written. A monthly magazine covering the international coffee and tea market. "Tea and coffee trends are analyzed; transportation problems, new equipment for plants and packaging are featured." Circ. approximately 10,000. Pays on publication. Byline given. Makes work-for-hire assignments. Submit seasonal/holiday material 1 month in advance. Simultaneous submissions OK. Computer printout submissions acceptable; no dot-matrix. Free sample copy.

Nonfiction: Exposé, historical/nostalgic, interview/profile, new product, photo feature and technical. Special issue includes the Coffee Market Forecast and Review (January). "No consumer related submissions. I'm only interested in the trade." Buys 60 mss/year. Query. Length: 750-1,500 words. Pays $4/published inch.

Photos: State availability of photos with submission. Reviews contact sheets, negatives, transparencies and prints. Pays $4.50/published inch. Captions and identification of subjects required. Buys one-time rights.

Columns/Departments: Office Coffee Service (vending coffee industry/office coffee); Specialties (gourmet trends); and Transportation (shipping lines). Buys 36 mss/year. Query. Pays $4.50/published inch.

WINES & VINES, 1800 Lincoln Ave., San Rafael CA 94901. Editor: Philip E. Hiaring. 10% freelance written. Works with a small number of new/unpublished writers each year. For everyone concerned with the grape and wine industry including winemakers, wine merchants, growers, suppliers, consumers, etc. Monthly magazine. Circ. 5,500. Buy first North American serial rights or simultaneous rights. Pays on acceptance. Publishes ms an average of 3 months after acceptance. Submit special material (water, January; vineyard, February; Man-of-the-Year, March; Brandy, April; export-import, May; enological, June; statistical, July; marketing, September; equipment and supplies, November; champagne, December) 3 months in advance. Reports in 2 weeks. Free sample copy.

Nonfiction: Articles of interest to the trade. "These could be on grape growing in unusual areas; new winemaking techniques; wine marketing, retailing, etc." Interview, historical, spot news, merchandising technics and technical. No stories with a strong consumer orientation as against trade orientation. Author should know the subject matter, i.e., know proper grape growing/winemaking terminology. Buys 3-4 ms/year. Query. Length: 1,000-2,500 words. Pays 5¢/word.

Photos: Pays $10 for 4x5 or 8x10 b&w photos purchased with mss. Captions required.

Tips: "Ours is a trade magazine for professionals. Therefore, we do not use 'gee-whiz' wine articles."

___ *Book and Bookstore Trade*

These publications can be a market (if you know the bookstore trade) or a valuable resource. They tell you how and why certain books are successful.

AB BOOKMAN'S WEEKLY, Box AB, Clifton NJ 07015. (201)772-0020. Editor-in-Chief: Jacob L. Chernofsky. Weekly magazine; 160 pages. For professional and specialist booksellers, acquisitions and academic librarians, book publishers, book collectors, bibliographers, historians, etc. Circ. 8,500. Pays on publication. Byline given. Buys all rights. Phone queries OK. Submit seasonal or holiday material 2-3 months in advance. Simultaneous and photocopied submissions OK. Reports in 1 month. Sample copy $5.
Nonfiction: How-to (for professional booksellers); historical (related to books or book trade or printing or publishing); personal experiences; nostalgia; interviews and profiles. Query. Length: 2,500 words minimum. Pays $60 minimum.
Photos: Photos used with mss.

AMERICAN BOOKSELLER, Booksellers Publishing, Inc., 122 E. 42nd St., New York NY 10168. (212)867-9060. Editor: Ginger Curwen. 10% freelance written. This publication emphasizes the business of retail bookselling and goes to the 5,700 members of the American Booksellers Association and to more than 2,400 other readers nationwide, most of whom are involved in publishing. Monthly magazine; 48 pages. Circ. 7,800. Pays on publication. Publishes ms an average of 4 months after acceptance. Buys first serial rights. Pays 25% kill fee. Byline given. Submit seasonal/holiday material 3 months in advance. Electronic submissions OK via IBM PC, but requires hard copy also. Computer printout submissions acceptable; prefers letter-quality to dot-matrix. Reports in 3 months. Sample copy $3.
Nonfiction: General interest (on bookselling); how-to (run a bookstore, work with publishers); interview (on authors and booksellers); photo feature (on book-related events); and solutions to the problems of small businesses. Buys 2 mss/issue. Query with clips of published work and background knowledge of bookselling. Length: 750-2,000 words. Pays $75-300. Sometimes pays the expenses of writers on assignment.
Photos: State availability of photos. Uses b&w 5x7 matte prints and contact sheets. Pays $10-20. Uses 35mm color transparencies. Pays $10-50. Captions and model releases required.
Tips: "While we buy a number of articles for each issue, very few come from freelance writers. Since the focus of the magazine is on the business of bookselling, most of our contributors are booksellers who share their *firsthand* experience with our readers. 85% of these articles are assigned; the rest are unsolicited—but those come mainly from booksellers as well."

‡**The Bookdealer's PROFILE**, Gersdorf & Gersdorf, Inc., 1613 Silverwood Court, N. Fort Myers FL 33903. (813)995-0222. Editor: Antoinette G. Gersdorf. 50% freelance written. A bimonthly magazine about books and bookdealers who sell out-of-print and rare books. "We try to show the *fun* of bookdealing and book collecting." Circ. 1,000. Pays on pre-publication. Publishes ms an average of 2 months after acceptance. Byline given. Buys one-time rights. Simultaneous, photocopied and previously published submissions OK. Computer printout submissions acceptable. "Quality of writing is more important than the appearance of the ms." Reports in 1 week on queries; 2 weeks on manuscripts. Sample copy for SAE with 2 first class stamps. Free writer's guidelines.
Nonfiction: How-to, humor, interview/profile, personal experience and photo feature. "Absolutely no poetry. It's all bad!" Buys 12 mss/year. Query with or without published clips, or send complete ms. Length: 750-2,000 words. Pays $35-75. Pays in copies when bookdealers write their own stories.
Photos: Send photos with submission. Reviews prints (any size; b&w preferred). Offers $10 per photo "for cover when taken especially for the story and not provided by subject himself." Identification of subjects required. Buys one-time rights.
Columns/Department: "BookPeople" (mini-profiles on bookdealers, scouts, collectors, appraisers, etc.). "Can be in subject's own words, interview, etc. A personal slant on the dealer and his/her love of books, how they got started in the biz, advice, whatever." Photo preferred and returned intact; no extra payment. Buys "as many as we can find." Send complete ms. Length: 300-500 words. Pays $15.
Fillers: Anecdotes, facts and short humor (with literary slants). Buys as many as we can get. Length: open. Pays $2.
Tips: "Every town in America and Canada has a bookdealer, whether working in a shop or from his home. We

introduce dealers to one another. We're willing to rewrite articles with good content. We're open as to style, so long as the writer uses a human slant and even humor. We want to see more from freelancers in all areas."

BOOKSTORE JOURNAL, The How-To Magazine, Christian Booksellers Association, Box 200, Colorado Springs CO 80901. (303)576-7880. Managing Editor: Dave Somers. Monthly magazine of the Christian bookselling industry. The purpose of *Bookstore Journal* is to provide material whereby Christian booksellers can improve their professional retail skills, find information on the products they sell, and read significant news related to their industry. Circ. 7,800. Pays on publication. Byline given. Offers $100 kill fee. Buys first serial rights. Submit seasonal/holiday material 4 months in advance. Simultaneous queries OK. Reports in 1 month. Sample copy $6; free writer's guidelines.
Nonfiction: General interest (features on Christian bookstores or publishers); how-to (concerning retail management); inspirational (pertaining to how Christian books have inspired author); interview/profile (of authors/artists in the Christian industry); new product (news releases only of product with inspirational emphasis); opinion (editorials on aspects of Christian publishing and/or bookselling); and personal experience (as it relates to Christian bookselling). Buys 100 mss/year. Query with published clips. Length: 1,000-2,000 words. Pays $100-350.
Photos: State availability of photos. Reviews 5x7 b&w prints. Pays $15-25. Identification of subjects required. Buys all rights.
Tips: "Most articles are assigned to people who have expertise in business or bookstore management and can communicate clearly in writing. Freelance writers are used occasionally for reporting on industry events, for special assignments, or for interviewing selected authors, artists, suppliers, and booksellers."

COLLEGE STORE EXECUTIVE, Box 1500, Westbury NY 11590. (516)334-3030. Editor: Catherine Orobona. 3% freelance written. "Do not deal with many freelancers. Only in cases where they are very familiar with the market." Tabloid, 40 pages, published 10 times/year. Emphasizes merchandising and marketing in the college store market. Publishes 10 issues/year. Circ. 8,500. Pays on publication. Publishes ms an average of 3 months after acceptance. Byline given. Buys all rights. Submit seasonal/holiday material 3 months in advance. Photocopied submissions OK. Computer printout submissions acceptable; prefers letter-quality to dot-matrix. Reports in 1-2 months. For sample copy, use large manilla envelope only.
Nonfiction: Expose (problems in college market); general interest (to managers); how-to (advertise, manage a college store); store profile of new or remodeled location; personal experience (someone who worked for a publisher selling to bookstores); personal opinion (from those who know about the market); photo feature (on specific college bookstores in the country or outside); and technical (how to display products). No articles on typical college student or general "how-to" articles. Buys 8-10 mss/year. Query. Length: 1,000 words. Pays $2/column inch. Sometimes pays the expenses of writers on assignment.
Photos: State availability of photos with query. Pays $5 for b&w prints. Captions preferred. Buys all rights.
Tips: "No general business advice that could apply to all retail establishments—articles must deal directly with college stores. This is a good place for someone to start—but they have to understand the market." No interviews with managers on their theories of life or public relations pieces on specific products.

‡THE FEMINIST BOOKSTORE NEWS, Box 882554, San Francisco CA 94188. (415)431-2093. Editor: Carol Seajay. Managing Editor: Christine Chia. 20% freelance written. A bimonthly magazine covering feminist books and the women-in-print industry. "*Feminist Bookstore News* covers 'everything of interest' to the feminist bookstores, publishers and periodicals, books of interest to feminist bookstores, and provides an overview of feminist publishing by mainstream publishers." Circ. 450. Pays on publication. Publishes ms an average of 1 month after acceptance. Byline sometimes given. Buys one-time rights. Simultaneous and photocopied submissions OK. Electronic submissions OK via QM/WordStar, but requires hard copy also. Computer printout submissions acceptable. Reports in 3 weeks. Sample copy $4.
Nonfiction: Essays, exposé, how-to (run a bookstore); new product; opinion; and personal experience (in feminist book trade only). Special issues include Sidelines issue (May) and University Press issue (fall). No submissions that do not directly apply to the feminist book trade. Query with or without published clips, or send complete ms. Length: 250-2,000 words. Pays $10-25; may pay in copies when appropriate.
Photos: State availability of photos with submission. Model release and identification of subjects required. Buys one-time rights.
Fillers: Anecdotes, facts, newsbreaks and short humor. Length: 100-400 words. Pays $5-15.
Tips: "Have several years experience in the feminist book industry. We publish very little by anyone else."

THE HORN BOOK MAGAZINE, The Horn Book, Inc., 31 St. James Ave., Boston MA 02116. (617)482-5198. Editor: Anita Silvey. Bimonthly magazine covering children's literature for librarians, booksellers, professors, and students of children's literature. Circ. 18,000. Pays on publication. Byline given. Buys one-time rights. Submit seasonal/holiday material 6 months in advance. Simultaneous queries, and simultaneous, photocopied, and previously published submissions OK. Computer printout submissions

acceptable; no dot-matrix. Reports in 6 weeks on queries; 2 months on mss. Free sample copy; writer's guidelines for SAE with 1 first class stamp.
Nonfiction: Interview/profile (children's book authors and illustrators). Buys 20 mss/year. Query or send complete ms. Length: 1,000-2,800 words. Pays $25-250.
Tips: "Writers have a better chance of breaking into our publication with a query letter on a specific article they want to write."

INTERRACIAL BOOKS FOR CHILDREN BULLETIN, Council on Interracial Books for Children, Inc., 1841 Broadway, New York NY 10023. (212)757-5339. Managing Editor: Ruth Charnes. A magazine published 8 times/year covering children's literature/school materials. "Our publication reaches teachers, librarians, editors, authors and parents. It focuses on issues on bias/equity in children's literature and school materials." Circ. 5,000. Pays on publication. Byline given. Offers variable kill fee. Buys first North American serial rights and one-time rights. Submit seasonal/holiday material 6 months in advance. Computer printout submissions acceptable; prefers letter-quality to dot-matrix. Simultaneous queries and photocopied submissions OK. Reports in 1 month on queries; 3 months on mss. Sample copy $3.50; writer's guidelines for SAE and 1 first class stamp.
Nonfiction: Personal experience (strategies for teaching/encouraging equity); interview/profile (of authors/illustrators/teachers/others seeking bias-free children's materials); and analysis of children's materials (textbooks, literature, etc.). Buys 25 mss/year. Query. Length: 1,500-2,500 words. Pays $50-200.
Columns/Departments: Review of children's books and AV materials, resources for adults. "Our policy is that books about various groups, e.g., feminists, Third World people, older people, disabled people, etc., be reviewed by members of that group." Buys 100 mss/year. Query with or without published clips. Length: 250-350 words. Pays $10-25.
Tips: "Our goal is a society that is pluralistic and bias-free. We seek the perspectives of groups that have been oppressed by a society dominated by upper class white males. We seek documentation of that oppression in the world of children's books and school learning materials and positive ways to develop awareness of that oppression and ways to counteract it. The primary consideration in writing for the *Bulletin* is sensitivity to racism, sexism, ageism, homophobia, handicapism and other forms of injustice."

PUBLISHERS WEEKLY, 205 E. 42nd St., New York NY 10017. (212)916-1877. Editor-in-Chief: John F. Baker. Weekly. Buys first North American serial rights. Pays on publication. Computer printout submissions acceptable; prefers letter-quality to dot-matrix. Reports "in several weeks."
Nonfiction: "We rarely use unsolicited manuscripts because of our highly specialized audience and their professional interests, but we can sometimes use news items about publishers, publishing projects, bookstores and other subjects relating to books. We will be paying increasing attention to electronic publishing." No pieces about writers or word processors. Payment negotiable; generally $150/printed page.
Photos: Photos occasionally purchased with and without mss.

SMALL PRESS, Meckler Publishing Corp., 11 Ferry Ln. W., Westport CT 06880. (203)226-6967. Editor: Michael Coffee. 85% freelance written. A bimonthly magazine covering small presses and independent publishers—book and magazine—for publishers, librarians, bookstores and "desktop publishers." Circ. 7,500. Pays on publication. Publishes ms an average of 2 months after acceptance. Byline given. Buys first North American serial rights. Submit seasonal/holiday material 4 months in advance. Computer printout submissions acceptable (double-spaced); no dot-matrix. Reports in 1 month. Free sample copy.
Nonfiction: Book excerpts (on occasion); how-to; book reviews; interview/profile; new product; personal experience; and technical. Buys 36 mss/year. Query with or without published clips or send complete ms. Length: 2,000-2,500 words. Pay rates negotiable.
Photos: State availability of photos. Pays minimum $25 for 5x7 b&w prints. Identification of subjects required. Buys one-time rights.
Columns/Departments: "Columns treat the how-tos of such subjects as printing, paper, distribution, contracts, etc." Buys 36 mss/year. Query with or without published clips or send complete ms. Length: 1,800 words approximately. Fee negotiable.

WESTERN PUBLISHER, A Trade Journal, WP, Inc., Box 591012, Golden Gate Station, San Francisco CA 94159. (415)221-1964. Publisher: Tony D'Arpino. Editor: Paula von Lowenfeldt. 25% freelance written. Monthly tabloid covering publishing and book industry. Audience includes publishers, booksellers, and librarians in Western United States and Pacific Rim nations. Circ. 10,000. Pays on publication. Publishes ms an average of 1 month after acceptance. Byline given. Kill fee negotiable. Buys one-time rights. Submit seasonal/holiday material 3 months in advance; calendar: 6 months. Simultaneous queries, and simultaneous, photocopied, and previously published submissions OK. Computer printout submissions acceptable; prefers letter-quality to dot-matrix. Reports in 1 week. Sample copy $2.
Nonfiction: Book excerpts (of industry interest), general interest, historical, how-to, interview/profile, new product, opinion, personal experience, photo feature, technical, and short reviews of just published books. No

reviews over 500 words. Buys 100 mss/year. Query with or without published clips or send complete ms. Length: open. Pays negotiable rates.

Fillers: Clippings and newsbreaks. Buys 100/year. Length: 100-500 words.

Tips: "The area most open to freelancers is Western Book Round Up (review listings). A freelancer can best break in to our publication with short reviews of forthcoming books, 200-500 words; 250 words, preferred."

_____ *Brick, Glass and Ceramics*

These publications are read by manufacturers, dealers and managers of retail businesses in the industry. Other publications related to glass and ceramics are listed in the Consumer section under Art, and Hobby and Crafts.

AMERICAN GLASS REVIEW, Box 2147, Clifton NJ 07015. (201)779-1600. Editor-in-Chief: Donald Doctorow. 10% freelance written. Monthly magazine; 24 pages. Pays on publication. Byline given. Phone queries OK. Buys all rights. Submit seasonal/holiday material 2 months in advance of issue date. Reports in 2-3 weeks. Free sample copy and writer's guidelines; mention *Writer's Market* in request.

Nonfiction: Glass plant and glass manufacturing articles. Buys 3-4 mss/year. Query. Length: 1,500-3,000 words. Pays $40-50.

Photos: State availability of photos with query. No additional payment for b&w contact sheets. Captions preferred. Buys one-time rights.

BRICK AND CLAY RECORD, Cahners Plaza, 1350 E. Touhy Ave., Box 5080, Des Plaines IL 60018. (312)635-8800. Editor-in-Chief: Wayne A. Endicott. For "the heavy clay products industry." Monthly. Buys all rights. Pays on publication. Query first. Reports in 15 days.

Nonfiction: "News concerning personnel changes within companies; news concerning new plants for manufacture of brick, clay pipe, refractories, drain tile, face brick, glazed tile, lightweight clay aggregate products and abrasives; and news of new products, expansion and new building." Length: 1,500-2,000 words. Pays minimum $75/published page.

Photos: No additional payment for photos used with mss.

Fillers: "Items should concern only news of brick, clay pipe, refractory or abrasives plant operations and brick distributors. If news of personnel, should be only of top-level personnel. Not interested in items such as patio, motel, or home construction using brick; consumer oriented items; weddings or engagements of clay products people, unless major executives; obituaries, unless of major personnel; or items concerning floor or wall tile (only structural tile); of plastics, metal, concrete, bakelite, or similar products; items concerning people not directly involved in clay plant operation." Pays minimum $6 for "full-length published news item, depending on value of item and editor's discretion. Payment is only for items published in the magazine. No items sent in can be returned."

‡CERAMIC INDUSTRY, Cahners Plaza, 1350 E. Touhy Ave., Box 5080, Des Plaines IL 60018. (312)635-8800. Editor: Patricia A. Janeway. For the ceramic industry; manufacturers of glass, porcelain enamel, whiteware and advanced ceramics (electronic, industrial and high tech). Magazine; 50-60 pages. Monthly. Circ. 7,500. Buys all rights. Byline given. Buys 10-12 mss/year (on assignment only). Pays on publication. Will send free sample copy to writer on request. Reports immediately. Query first.

Nonfiction: Semitechnical, informational and how-to material purchased on assignment only. Length: 500-1,500 words. Pays $75/published page.

Photos: No additional payment for photos used with mss. Captions required.

CERAMIC SCOPE, 3632 Ashworth North, Seattle WA 98103. (206)632-7222. Editor: Michael Scott. Monthly magazine covering hobby ceramics business. For "ceramic studio owners and teachers operating out of homes as well as storefronts, who have a love for ceramics but meager business education." Also read by distributors, dealers and supervisors of ceramic programs in institutions. Circ. 8,000. Pays on publication. Byline given unless it is a round-up story with any number of sources. Submit seasonal/holiday material 5 months in advance. Computer printout submissions acceptable. Reports in 2 weeks. Sample copy $1.

Nonfiction: "Articles on operating a small business specifically tailored to the ceramic hobby field; photo feature stories with in-depth information about business practices and methods that contribute to successful studio operation."
Photos: State availability of photos or send photos with ms. Pays $5/4x5 or 5x7 glossy b&w print. Captions required.

GLASS DIGEST, 310 Madison Ave., New York NY 10017. (212)682-7681. Editor: Charles B. Cumpston. Monthly. Buys first rights only. Byline given "only industry people—not freelancers." Pays on publication "or before, if has held too long." Will send a sample copy to a writer on request. Reports "as soon as possible." Enclose SASE for return of submissions.
Nonfiction: "Items about firms in glass distribution, personnel, plants, etc. Stories about outstanding jobs accomplished—volume of flat glass, storefronts, curtainwalls, auto glass, mirrors, windows (metal), glass doors; special uses and values; and who installed it. Stories about successful glass/metal distributors, dealers and glazing contractors—their methods, promotion work done, advertising and results." Length: 1,000-1,500 words. Pays 7¢/word, "usually more. No interest in bottles, glassware, containers, etc., but leaded and stained glass good."
Photos: B&w photos purchased with mss; "8x10 preferred." Pays $7.50, "usually more."
Tips: "Find a typical dealer case history about a firm operating in such a successful way that its methods can be duplicated by readers everywhere."

GLASS MAGAZINE, For the Architectural and Automotive Glass Industries, National Glass Association, Suite 302, 8200 Greensboro Drive, McLean VA 22102. (703)442-4890. Editor: Julie Dolenga. 25% freelance written. Prefers to work with published/established writers; works with a small number of new/unpublished writers each year. A monthly magazine covering the architectural and automotive glass industries for members of the glass and architectural trades. Circ. 13,000. Pays on acceptance. Publishes ms an average of 3 months after acceptance. Byline given. Offers varying kill fee. Buys first rights only. Computer printut submissions acceptable; prefers letter-quality to dot-matrix. Reports in 2 weeks. Sample copy $4; free writer's guidelines.
Nonfiction: Interview/profile (of various glass businesses; profiles of industry people or glass business owners); and technical (about glazing processes). Buys 20 mss/year. Query with published clips. Length: 1,500 words minimum. Pays $200-600. Sometimes pays the expenses of writers on assignment.
Photos: State availability of photos. Reviews b&w and color contact sheets. Pays $15-30 for b&w; $25-75 for color. Identification of subjects required. Buys one-time rights.
Tips: "We are a growing magazine and do not have a large enough staff to do all the writing that will be required. Will need more freelancers."

GLASS NEWS, LJV Corp., Box 7138, Pittsburgh PA 15213. (412)362-5136. Managing Editor: Liz Scott. 5% freelance written. Monthly newspaper covering glass manufacturing, and glass industry news for glass manufacturers, dealers and people involved in the making, buying and selling of glass items and products. Circ. 1,650. Pays on publication. Publishes ms an average of 3 months after acceptance. Makes work-for-hire assignments. Phone queries OK. Submit seasonal material 3 months in advance. Electronic submissions OK via 300-1200 baud; contact for transmission time. Computer printout submissions acceptable; prefers letter-quality to dot-matrix. Reports in 1 month on queries; 2 months on mss. Free sample copy for 9x12 SAE and 54¢ postage.
Nonfiction: Historical (about glass manufacturers, trademarks and processes); how-to (concerning techniques of glass manufacturers); interview (with glass-related people); profile; new product (glass use or glass); and technical (glass manufacture or use). No glass dealer stories, and rarely glass crafting stories. Buys 3-5 mss/year. Query. Length: 500-10,000 words. Pays $50 minimum.
Photos: State availability of photos. Pays $25 minimum for 8x10 b&w glossy prints. Offers no additional payment for photos accepted with ms. Captions preferred; model release required. Buys one-time rights.
Fillers: Glass manufacturing-related anecdotes, short humor, newsbreaks and puzzles. Buys 5 mss/year. Pays $15 minimum.
Tips: "Get to know a lot about glass, how it is made and new developments."

Building Interiors

MODERN FLOOR COVERINGS, U.S. Business Press, Inc., 11 W. 19th St., New York NY 10011. (212)741-7210. Editor: Michael Karol. 20% freelance written. Monthly tabloid featuring profit-making ideas

on floor coverings, for the retail community. Circ. 28,000. Pays on acceptance. Pubishes ms an average of 1 month after acceptance. Byline given. Buys first rights only. Makes work-for-hire assignments. Electronic submissions OK via IBM PC. Computer printout submissions acceptable; prefers letter-quality submissions. "Better to write first. Send resume and cover letter explaining your qualifications and business writing experience." Writer's guidelines for SAE with 3 first class stamps.
Nonfiction: Interview and features/profiles. Send complete ms. Length: 1,000-10,000 words. Pays $50-250. Sometimes pays the expenses of writers on assignment.
Tips: The most frequent mistake made by writers is that "articles are too general to relate to our audience—which is mainly the floor covering retailer/specialty store."

PAINTING AND WALLCOVERING CONTRACTOR, Finan Publishing, Inc., 130 W. Lockwood, St. Louis MO 63119. (314)961-6644. Under license from the Painting and Decorating Contractors of America, 7223 Lee Hwy., Falls Church VA 22046. (703)534-1201. Publisher and Editor: Tom Finan. Executive Editor: Robert D. Richardson. 50% freelance written. Official monthly publication of the PDCA. Circ. 15,000 "with roughly 85% of that number painting contractors/owners." Emphasis on key aspects of the painting and wallcovering contracting business, aiming for complete coverage of tools, techniques, materials, and business management. Freelance by assignment only. Send resume and sample of work. Pays on publication. Publishes ms an average of 1 month after acceptance. Buys first North American serial rights. Electronic submissions OK via 5½in. floppy disks. Computer printout submissions acceptable; prefers letter-quality to dot-matrix.
Nonfiction: How-to, informational, some technical. Buys 20 mss/year. Pays $150-350. Sometimes pays the expenses of writers on assignment.
Photos: Purchased with accompanying ms. Captions required. Pays $15 for professional quality 8x10 glossy b&w prints or color slides. Model release required.
Tips: "We're looking to build long term relations with freelancers around the country. If the writer has no sample clips of the painting/wallcovering contractors, send samples showing familiarity with other aspects of the construction industry. Follow up resume/sample with phone call in 2-3 weeks. The writer sometimes has a better chance of breaking in at our publication with short articles and fillers as we need to be sure the writer understands the market we publish for—sometimes we take a chance on those with inappropriate clips. The most frequent mistake made by writers in completing an article for us is misunderstanding the reader's needs, industry and jargon."

‡REMODELING, Hanley-Wood, Inc., Suite 475, 655 15th St. NW, Washington DC 20005. (202)737-0717. Editor: Wendy Jordan. 5% freelance written. A monthly magazine covering residential and light commercial remodeling. "We cover the best new ideas in remodeling design, business, construction and products." Estab. 1985. Circ. 47,000. Pays on publication. Publishes ms an average of 3 months after acceptance. Byline given. Offers 5¢/word kill fee. Buys first North American serial rights. Photocopied submissions OK. Electronic submissions OK, but requires hard copy also. Computer printout submissions acceptable. Reports in 1 month. Free sample copy and writer's guidelines.
Nonfiction: Interview/profile, new product and technical. Buys 6 mss/year. Query with published clips. Length: 250-1,000 words. Pays 20¢/word. Sometimes pays the expenses of writers on assignment.
Photos: State availability of photos with submission. Reviews slides, 4x5 transparencies, and 8x10 prints. Offers $25-100/photo. Captions, model releases, and identification of subjects required. Buys one-time rights.
Tips: "The areas of our publication most open to freelancers are news and new product news."

WALLS & CEILINGS, 14006 Ventura Blvd., Sherman Oaks CA 91423. (213)789-8733. Editor-in-Chief: Robert Welch. Managing Editor: Don Haley. 10% freelance written. For contractors involved in lathing and plastering, drywall, acoustics, fireproofing, curtain walls, movable partitions together with manufacturers, dealers, and architects. Monthly magazine; 32 pages. Circ. 11,000. Pays on publication. Buys first North American serial rights. Byline given. Phone queries OK. Submit seasonal/holiday material 3 months in advance. Reports in 3 weeks. Sample copy $5.
Nonfiction: How-to (drywall and plaster construction and business management); and interview. Buys 5 mss/year. Query. Length: 200-1,000 words. Pays $75 maximum.
Photos: State availability of photos with query. Pays $5 for 8x10 b&w prints. Captions required. Buys one-time rights.

ALWAYS submit mss or queries with a stamped, self-addressed envelope (SASE) within your country or International Reply Coupons (IRCs) purchased from the post office for other countries.

Business Management

These publications are edited for owners of businesses and top-level business executives. They cover business trends and the general theory and practice of management. Publications that use similar material but have a less technical slant are listed in Business and Finance in the Consumer Publications section. Journals dealing with banking, investment, and financial management can be found in the Trade Finance category. Journals for middle management (including supervisors and office managers) appear in the Management and Supervision section. Those for industrial plant managers are listed under Industrial Operation and Management, and under the names of specific industries such as Machinery and Metal Trade. Publications for office supply store operators are included with the Office Environment and Equipment journals.

‡COMMON SENSE, Upstart Publishing Company, 50 Mill St., Dover NH 03820. (603)749-5071. Editor: Jean E. Kerr. 50% freelance written. A monthly newsletter covering small business and personal finance. Pays on acceptance. Publishes ms an average of 2 months after acceptance. Byline sometimes given. $20 kill fee. Buys all rights and makes work-for-hire assignments. Simultaneous, photocopied and previously published submissions OK. Computer printout submissions acceptable; prefers letter-quality to dot-matrix. Reports in 1 month. Free sample copy and writer's guidelines.
Nonfiction: How-to, interview/profile and technical. "We are looking for clear, jargon-free information. We often sell our publications in bulk to banks so must avoid subjects and stances that clearly run counter to their interests." No highly technical or pompous language, or politically contentious articles. Buys 15-20 mss/year. Query with published clips. Length: 2,500 words maximum. Pays $250 for assigned articles. "We pay with contributor's copies if there is a significant public relations benefit for the writer."
Columns/Departments: Breakthroughs (technological, medical breakthroughs or innovations, new applications for old materials or products; scientific information of interest to the business communities). Query with published clips. Length: 100-500 words. Pays $10-50.

COMMUNICATION BRIEFINGS, Encoders, Inc., 806 Westminster Blvd., Blackwood NJ 08012. (609)589-3503, 227-7371. Executive Editor: Frank Grazian. Managing Editor: Anthony Fulginiti. 15% freelance written. Prefers to work with published/established writers. A monthly newsletter covering business communication and business management. "Most readers are in middle and upper management. They comprise public relations professionals, editors of company publications, marketing and advertising managers, fund raisers, directors of associations and foundations, school and college administrators, human resources professionals, and other middle managers who want to communicate better on the job." Circ. 18,000. Pays on acceptance. Publishes ms an average of 2-3 months after acceptance. Byline given sometimes on Bonus Items and on other items if idea originates with the writer. Offers 25% kill fee. Buys one-time rights. Submit seasonal/holiday material 2 months in advance. Previously published submissions OK, "but must be rewritten to conform to our style." Computer printout submissions acceptable; prefers letter-quality to dot-matrix. Reports in 1 month. Sample copy and writer's guidelines for #10 SAE and 2 first class stamps.
Nonfiction: "Most articles we buy are of the 'how-to' type. They consist of practical ideas, techniques and advice that readers can use to improve business communication and management. Areas covered: writing, speaking, listening, employee communication, human relations, public relations, interpersonal communication, persuasion, conducting meetings, advertising, marketing, fund raising, telephone techniques, teleconferencing, selling, improving publications, handling conflicts, negotiating, etc. Because half of our subscribers are in the nonprofit sector, articles that appeal to both profit and nonprofit organizations are given top priority." *Short Items:* Articles consisting of one or two brief tips that can stand alone. Length: 40-70 words. *Articles:* A collection of tips or ideas that offer a solution to a communication or management problem or that show a better way to communicate or manage. Examples: "How to produce slogans that work," "The wrong way to criticize employees," "Mistakes to avoid when leading a group discussion," and "5 ways to overcome writer's block." Length: 150-200 words. *Bonus Items:* In-depth pieces that probe one area of communication or management and cover it as thoroughly as possible. Examples: "Producing successful special events," "How to evaluate your newsletter," and "How to write to be understood." Length:

1,300 words. Buys 30-50 mss/year. Pays $15-35 for 40- to 250-word pieces; Bonus Items, $200. Pays the expenses of writers on assignment.
Tips: "Our readers are looking for specific and practical ideas and tips that will help them communicate better both within their organizations and with outside publics. Most ideas are rejected because they are too general or too elementary for our audience. Our style is down-to-earth and terse. We pack a lot of useful information into short articles. Our readers are busy executives and managers who want information dispatched quickly and without embroidery. We omit anecdotes, lengthy quotes and long-winded exposition. The writer has a better chance of breaking in at our publication with short articles and fillers since we buy only six major features (bonus items) a year. We want queries on longer items and bonus items. Writers may submit short tips (40-70 words) without querying. The most frequent mistakes made by writers in completing an article for us are that they do not master the style of our publication and do not understand our readers' needs."

‡COMPUTERS IN BANKING, The Computer and Automation Magazine for Bank Management, Dealers Digest Inc., Suite 400, 150 Broadway, New York NY 10038. (212)227-1200. Editor: Janice Fioravante. Managing Editor: Nancy Meyers. Approximately 20-30% freelance written. Prefers to work with published/established writers. A monthly magazine covering bank automation and management. "*Computers in Banking* is for senior bank executives who make business decisions about computer and automation equipment. We cover technology but from an issues and management-oriented perspective." Circ. 34,000. Pays within 30 days of acceptance. Publishes ms an average of 2 months after acceptance. Byline sometimes given (for features). Offers 25% kill fee. Buys all rights and makes work-for-hire assignments. Photocopied submissions OK. Electronic submissions OK via IBM PC, PC-compatible or ASCII terminal, but requires hard copy also. Computer printout submissions acceptable; prefers letter-quality to dot-matrix. Sample copy for 8½x11 SAE; free writer's guidelines.
Nonfiction: How-to, interview/profile, new product, technical and event coverage. Special issues are staff written. "No one-sided, vendor-oriented pieces. We are a user-oriented magazine." Buys 24-30 mss/year. Query with published clips. Length: 2,500-4,000 words. Pays $200 for news stories, $1,000 for features. Usually pays the expenses of writers on assignment.
Photos: Send photos with submission. Reviews transparencies and any size b&w prints. Offers no additional payment for photos accepted with ms. Identification of subjects required.
Columns/Departments: Case History (one-user, one-vendor, problem/solution), 1,200 words. Buys 20 mss/year. Query with published clips. Pays $200-400. "We need short news bits for 'upfront' section, which tries to cover installations and product announcements before the official press releases."
Tips: "Writers must have a working knowledge of the computer industry and a good understanding of banking and financial matters. Our standards are very high. Writers should be willing to fill holes, answer specific questions and care about seemingly little details like what a bank paid for a computer system and when it was installed or tested. Publication is national, so focus must be broad. However, we are always looking for regional correspondents. The areas of our publication most open to freelancers are features and short news stories for 'Update' section."

‡CORPORATE MONTHLY, Anthony Publishing, Inc., 105 Chestnut St., Philadelphia PA 19106. (215)629-1611. Editor: Bruce Anthony. Managing Editor: George Ewing. 60% freelance written. Works with a small number of new/unpublished writers each year. A monthly magazine covering issues of interest to senior management. "We are a pro-business magazine read by senior management. We don't try to educate, but inform." Circ. 25,000. Pays on publication. Publishes ms an average of 2 months after acceptance. Byline given. Buys first North American serial rights. Submit seasonal/holiday material 3 months in advance. Simultaneous and photocopied submissions OK. Electronic submissions OK via IBM MS/DOS and Apple Macintosh, but requires hard copy also. Computer printout submissions acceptable; prefers letter-quality to dot-matrix. Reports in 6 weeks on queries; 4 weeks on manuscripts. Sample copy for 9x12 SAE with 70¢ postage; writer's guidelines business size SAE with 23¢ postage.
Nonfiction: Humor (short items or features); interview/profile (senior management); new product (innovative unique); and opinion. Also, interviews with CEOs and humor with business angle. Special issues include annual almanac (July). No how-to or "puff" pieces. Buys 10 mss/year. Query. Length: 1,500 words minimum. Pays $25-200; may pay with contributor copies or other premiums rather than cash but must be determined on individual basis. Sometimes pays the expenses of writers on assignment.
Photos: State availability of photos with submission. Reviews contact sheets. Offers no additional payment for photos accepted with ms. Captions, model releases and identification of subjects required. Buys one-time rights.
Fillers: Anecdotes, facts, and gags to be illustrated by cartoonist. Length: 25-100 words. Pays $5-25 with/illustration.
Tips: "Interviews and company profile features are the areas most open to freelancers. We average six features per month."

‡FARM STORE MERCHANDISING, Miller Publishing, 2501 Wayzata Blvd., Box 67, Minneapolis MN 55440. (612)374-5200. Editor: Margaret Kaeter. Associate Editor: Christopher Lynch. 25% freelance written. Eager to work with new/unpublished writers. A monthly magazine for small business owners who sell to farmers. Primary busines lines are bulk and bagged feed, animal heath products, grain storage, agriculture chemicals. Pays on publication. Publishes ms an average of 3 months after acceptance. Byline given. Offers 50% kill fee. Buys first rights or one-time rights. Submit seasonal/holiday material 3 months in advance. Photocopied and previously published submissions OK. Computer printout submissions acceptable; prefers letter-quality to dot-matrix. Reports in 1 month. Free sample copy and writer's guidelines.
Nonfiction: How-to (subjects must be business-oriented, credit, taxes, inventory, hiring, firing, etc.); interview/profile (with successful agribusiness dealers or industry leaders); opinion (on controversial industry issues); personal experiences (good or bad ways to run a business); photo features (people-oriented); and technical (how to maintain sprayers, what's the best fertilizer spreader, etc.). Buys 15 mss/year. Query. Length: 750-2,500 words. Pays $100-300 for assigned articles; pays $25-250 for unsolicited articles. Sometimes pays the expenses of writers on assignment.
Photos: Send photos with submission. Reviews contact sheets. Offers no additional payment for photos accepted with ms. Identification of subjects required. Buys one-time rights.
Columns/Departments: Inside Line (opinion pieces on highly controversial industry issues). Buys 5 mss/year. Query. Length: 1,200-2,000 words. Pays $25-300.
Tips: "The area of our publication most open to freelancers is features on successful farm store dealers. Submit two to three black and white photos. Keep the article under 2,000 words and don't get bogged down in technical details. Tell what sets their business apart and why it works. General business articles also are needed, especially if they have a rural, small-business slant."

‡FE: The Magazine for Financial Executives, Financial Executives Institute, 10 Madison Ave., Morriston NJ 07960. Editor: Robert A. Parker. 15% freelance written. A monthly magazine for corporate financial management. "*FE* is published for senior financial executives of major corporations and explores business issues without being anti-business." Estab. 1985. Circ. 19,000. Pays on acceptance. Byline given. Buys first North American serial rights. Reports in 1 week on queries; 2 weeks on mss. Sample copy $5.
Nonfiction: Analysis, based on interviews, of corporate and economic events of interest to financial executives. Buys 15 mss/year. Query with published clips; no unsolicited mss. Length: 1,500-3,000. Pays $500-1,000. Sometimes pays the expenses of writers on assignment.
Fiction: No fiction except fictional forecasts of a business or economic development or issue. Buys 2 mss/year. Query. Length: 1,500-3,000 words. Pays $500-1,000.
Tips: "Most article ideas come from editors, so the query approach is best. We use business or financial articles that follow a Wall Street Journal approach—a fresh idea, with its significance (to financial executives), quotes, anecdotes, and an interpretation or evaluation. We seek to identify business writers with top experience in different locations. We have very high journalistic standards."

‡FRANCHISE, The Magazine, Franchise Publications, Inc., 1044 Hercules, Houston TX 77058. (713)488-6827. Editor: Peggy Stein. 25% freelance written. A bimonthly magazine on franchising. Estab. 1985. Circ. 25,000. Pays on acceptance. Publishes ms an average of 1 year after acceptance. Byline given. Offers 50% kill fee. Buys first North American serial rights, second serial (reprint) rights, foreign first serial rights and makes work-for-hire assignments. Simultaneous queries and submissions, and photocopied submissions OK. Computer printout submissions acceptable; no dot-matrix. Reports in 2 weeks on queries; 1 month on mss. Sample copy for 8x11 SAE and 50¢ postage.
Nonfiction: General interest, interview/profile, and finance (as it relates to getting/investing venture capital). Nothing not directly related to franchising. Query with published clips. Length: 700-3,000 words. Pays 5¢/word.
Photos: Reviews transparencies and 5x7 prints. Pays $15-100. Identification of subjects required. Buys one-time rights. "We use color only for our cover, so chances of selling a color shot are slim."
Tips: "We are looking for writers with an upbeat informal style—not newspaper-type reporting. Dull, dry recitations of facts will not make it here. We provide information of interest to investors, financial planners, merger and acquisition analysts, venture capitalists, marketing and development firms, franchise sellers and franchise buyers.Check the subject franchise carefully. Be sure it is a legitimate franchisor and has sold at least 2 franchises. No fly-by-night promotions, please. The Better Business Bureau is a good place to start. We need articles about people behind the franchise, and articles about a unique franchise that fills a niche. For example, the Shoe Shine Co., Mail Boxes Etc. USA, Island Moped Rents, Spring-Green Lawn Care, etc. The biggies—McDonalds, et al, have been done to death."

HARVARD BUSINESS REVIEW, Soldiers Field, Boston MA 02163. (617)495-6800. Editor: Theodore Levitt. For top management in business and industry; younger managers who aspire to top management responsibilities; policymaking executives in government, policymakers in nonprofit organizations; and professional people interested in the viewpoint of business management. Published 6 times/year. Pays on

acceptance. Byline given. Buys all rights. Reports in 6 weeks.
Nonfiction: Articles on business trends, techniques and problems. *"Harvard Business Review* is *not* a news journal but seeks to inform executives about what is taking place in management. It also wants to challenge them and stretch their thinking about the policies they make, how they make them and how they administer them. It does this by presenting articles that provide in-depth analyses of issues and problems in management and, wherever possible, guidelines for thinking out and working toward resolutions of these issues and problems." Length: 2,000-8,000 words. Pays freelance market rates.

IN BUSINESS, JG Press, Inc., Box 323, Emmaus PA 18049. (215)967-4135. Editor: Jerome Goldstein. Managing Editor: Ina Pincus. 50% freelance written. Works with a small number of new/unpublished writers each year. Bimonthly magazine covering small businesses, their management and new developments for small business owners or people thinking about starting out. Circ. 60,000. Pays on publication. Publishes ms an average of 4 months after acceptance. Buys first North American serial rights. Submit seasonal material 3 months in advance. Reports in 6 weeks. Sample copy $3; free writer's guidelines.
Nonfiction: Expose (related to small business, trends and economic climate); how-to (advertise, market, handle publicity, finance, take inventory); profile (of an innovative small scale business); and new product (inventions and R&D by small businesses). "Keep how-tos in mind for feature articles; capture the personality of the business owner and the effect of that on the business operations." Buys 5 unsolicited mss/year. Query with clips of published work. Length: 1,000-2,000 words. Pays $75-200. Sometimes pays the expenses of writers on assignment.
Photos: State availability of photos. Pays $25-75. Reviews contact sheets. Captions preferred; model release required.
Tips: "Get a copy of the magazine and read it carefully so you can better understand the editorial focus. Send several specific article ideas-on-one-topic, so we can sharpen the focus. Keep in mind that the reader will be looking for specifics and transferable information."

‡THE INFORMATION REPORT, Washington Researchers Publishing, 2612 P. St. NW, Washington DC 20007. (202)333-3533. Editor: Walt Seager. 10% freelance written. A monthly newsletter for corporate intelligence gatherers. "Our audience is comprised primarily of those people within the marketing deparments of larger organizations who are charged with gathering information on their competitors, and merger, and acquisition candidates." Pays on publication. Publishes ms an average of 1 month after acceptance. Byline not given. Buys all rights. Simultaneous and photocopied submissions OK. Computer printout submissions acceptable. Reports in 1 month. Sample copy for #10 SAE with 1 first class stamp.
Nonfiction: How-to (on getting competitor intelligence from unusual sources) and information on free and low-cost information sources. Special issue features Hotlines and Recorded Messages of interest to businesspersons (May). "No long articles. Each 8-page issue contains an average of 35 articles, so all are one to three paragraph, information-packed, fast items: who, what, when, where, why, with name, address and number." Send complete ms. Length: 1 (in case of hotline telephone number)-350 words.

‡INTERNATIONAL INDUSTRY DOSSIER, Washington Researchers Publishing, 2612 P. St. NW, Washington DC 20007. (203)333-3533. Editor: Walt Seager. 10% freelance written. A monthly newsletter for corporate intelligence gatherers. "Our audience is comprised primarily of those people within the marketing departments of larger organizations who are charged with gathering information on their competitors, and on merger and acquisition candidates." Pays on publication. Byline not given. Buys all rights. Simultaneous submissions OK. Computer printout submissions acceptable. Reports in 1 month. Sample copy for #10 SAE and 1 first class stamp.
Nonfiction: How-to (on getting competitor intelligence on foreign firms or from foreign sources), and information on free and low-cost information sources. "No long articles. Each 8-page issue contains an average of 35 articles, so all are one to three paragraph information-packed, fast items. Who, what, when, where, why, with name, address, phone, cable address." Buys 50 mss/year. Send complete ms. Length: 350 words maximum. Pays $10-75 for assigned articles; pays $5-75 for unsolicited articles. May pay in copies or other premiums if contributor requests. Sometimes pays the expenses of writers on assignment.
Fillers: Facts and newsbreaks. "Because of the nature of our publication (35 articles in an 8-page newsletter), virtually all of our articles could be viewed as 'fillers.' "
Tips: "We're especially interested in sources of corporate information in countries other than the U.S. Which foreign government agencies provide what type of information on corporations? Who do you write, call? Are there any free guides or directories of information available from any government agencies? We need freelancers to dig out sources overseas from government, associations, and other sources. The techniques of information gathering are also covered in our newsletter, but this area is best left to the professional corporate intelligence gatherer. Information sources are most open to freelancers."

‡MANAGING, Graduate School of Business, University of Pittsburgh, 326 Mervis Hall, Pittsburgh PA 15260. (412)648-1644. Editor-in-Chief: Karen Hoy. Art Director: Barbara U. Dinsmore. 85% freelance written. Works with a small number of new/unpublished writers each year. Emphasizes business and management issues. Many of the readers are Graduate School of Business alumni; others are upper and middle level managers and executives in the city, tristate region and country. Magazine published two times/year (June and December); 48 pages. Circ. 5,000. Pays on acceptance. Publishes ms an average of 3 months after acceptance. Buys all rights and one-time rights. Submit seasonal/holiday material 3 months in advance. Photocopied submissions OK; previously published submissions OK, but not for full-length features. Computer printout submissions acceptable; prefers letter-quality to dot-matrix. Reports in 2 months. Free sample copy and writer's guidelines.

Nonfiction: Profile (on corporate executive to give full picture of man and his work); and business or management oriented features which stem from a regional base, but the story should have national impact. No "articles on personnel, sales or creativity." Buys 3-4 mss/issue. Length: 1,500-4,000 words. Query with samples. "Queries should include information about the author's previously published works and why he/she is qualified to handle the assignment. Prefer information on angle (direction) article will take, persons to be interviewed and subjects explored." Pays $100-400. Sometimes pays the expenses of writers on assignment.

Photos: State availability of photos. Pays $10-40 for b&w contact sheets.

Columns/Departments: Your Turn (a column on personal views toward a business or management issue written with a background in the area); Management (medium length article dealing with a particular management problem and how to solve it); and Brief Cases (short synopses of interesting management research topics with humorous twist). Buys 1/issue. Send complete ms. Length: 500-1,500 words. Pays $25 if used.

Tips: "Our magazine is not written for the average business person. It is published twice a year so articles are in-depth and are meant to be referred to by our readers. Articles *must* have an unusual slant and contain a lot of information—information our readers can't get from the popular business publications."

MAY TRENDS, George S. May International Company. 111 S. Washington St., Park Ridge IL 60068. (312)825-8806. Editor: John E. McArdle. 20% freelance written. Works with a small number of new/unpublished writers each year. For owners and managers of medium- and small-sized businesses, hospitals and nursing homes, trade associations, Better Business Bureaus, educational institutions and newspapers. Magazine published without charge 3 times a year; 28-30 pages. Circulation: 30,000. Buys all rights. Byline given. Buys 10-15 mss/year. Pays on acceptance. Publishes ms an average of 4 months after acceptance. Returns rejected material immediately. Query or submit complete ms. Computer printout submissions acceptable; prefers letter-quality to dot-matrix. Reports in 2 weeks. Will send free sample copy to writer on request for SAE with 2 first class stamps.

Nonfiction: "We prefer articles dealing with problems of specific industries (manufacturers, wholesalers, retailers, service businesses, small hospitals and nursing homes) where contact has been made with key executives whose comments regarding their problems may be quoted. We like problem solving articles, *not* success stories that laud an individual company." Focus is on marketing, economic and technological trends that have an impact on medium- and small-sized businesses, not on the "giants"; automobile dealers coping with existing dull markets; and contractors solving cost-inventory problems. Will consider material on successful business operations and merchandising techniques. Length: 2,000-3,000 words. Pays $150-250.

Tips: Query letter should tell "type of business and problems the article will deal with. We specialize in the problems of small (20-500 employees, $500,000-2,500,000 volume) businesses (manufacturing, wholesale, retail and service), plus medium and small health care facilities. We are now including nationally known writers in each issue—writers like the Vice Chairman of the Federal Reserve Bank, the U.S. Secretary of the Treasury; names like Walter Mondale and Murray Wiedenbaum; titles like the Chairman of the Joint Committee on Acreditation of Hospitals; and Canadian Minister of Export. This places extra pressure on freelance writers to submit very good articles. Frequent mistakes: 1) Writing for big business, rather than small, 2) using language that is too academic."

‡**MOBILE MANUFACTURED HOME MERCHANDISER**, RLD Group, Inc., Suite 800, 203 N. Wabash, Chicago IL 60601. (312)236-3528. Editor: Jim Mack. Managing Editor: Carrie Allen. 10% freelance written. A monthly magazine covering the mobile home industry. "Our readers are primarily retailers of mobile/manufactured homes. Our slant is to tell them, through profile stories primarily, how they can do business better and sell more." Circ. approximately 20,000. Pays on publication. Publishes ms an average of 2 months after acceptance. Byline not usually given. Not copyrighted. Buys first North American serial rights and second serial (reprint) rights. Photocopied submissions OK. Reports in 2 weeks on queries; 1 month on mss. Free sample copy and writer's guidelines.

Nonfiction: New product, personal experience, photo feature and technical. No general overview pieces or tax advice. Buys 5-10 mss/year. Query. Length: 1,000-2,000 words. Pays $150-200 for assigned articles; pays $100-200 for unsolicited articles.

Photos: State availability of photos with submission. Reviews contact sheets. Offers no additional payment for photos accepted with ms. Identification of subjects required.

Tips: "Be specific, not general. Focus on a specific area of the business."

NATION'S BUSINESS, Chamber of Commerce of the United States, 1615 H St., NW, Washington DC 20062. (202)463-5650. Editor: Robert Gray. Managing Editor: Henry Altman. 25% freelance written. Monthly magazine of useful information for business people about managing a business. Audience includes owners and managers of businesses of all sizes, but predominantly smaller to medium-sized businesses. Circ. 850,000. Pays on acceptance. Publishes ms an average of 3 months after acceptance. Byline given. Offers $150 or less kill fee. Buys all rights. Submit seasonal/holiday material 6 months in advance. Simultaneous queries, and simultaneous and photocopied submissions OK, but only for exclusive use upon acceptance. Computer printout submissions acceptable; prefers letter-quality to dot-matrix. Reports in 2 months on queries; 3 months on mss. Sample copy $2.50; free writer's guidelines.
Nonfiction: How-to (run a business); interview/profile (business success stories; entrepreneurs who successfully implement ideas); and business trends stories. Buys 40 mss/year. Query. Length: 650-2,000 words. Pays $175 minimum. Sometimes pays expenses of writers on assignment.
Tips: "Ask for guidelines and read them carefully before making any approach."

RECORDS MANAGEMENT QUARTERLY, Association of Records Managers and Administrators, Inc., Box 7070, Silver Spring MD 20907. Editor: Ira A. Penn, CRM, CSP. 10% freelance written. Eager to work with new/unpublished writers. Quarterly magazine covering records and information management. Circ. 9,000. Pays on publication. Publishes ms an average of 6 months after acceptance. Byline given. Buys all rights. Photocopied, simultaneous and previously published submissions OK. Computer printout submissions acceptable; prefers letter-quality to dot-matrix. Reports in 1 month on mss. Sample copy $8; free writer's guidelines.
Nonfiction: Professional articles covering theory, case studies, surveys, etc. on any aspect of records and information management. Buys 24-32 mss/year. Send complete ms. Length: 1,500 words minimum. Pays $25-100. Pays a "stipend"; no contract.
Photos: Send photos with ms. Does not pay extra for photos. Prefers b&w prints. Captions required.
Tips: "A writer *must* know our magazine. Most work is written by practitioners in the field. We use very little freelance writing, but we have had some and it's been good. A writer must have detailed knowledge of the subject he/she is writing about. Superficiality is not acceptable."

‡SECURITY DEALER, PTN Security Group, 101 Crossways Park West, Woodbury NY 11797. (516)496-8000. Editor: Thomas Kapinos. Managing Editor: Fay Guercio. 5% freelance written. A monthly magazine for alarm dealers and burglary and fire installers, with technical, business sales and marketing information. Circ. 21,000. Pays 3 weeks after publication. Publishes ms an average of 4 months after acceptance. Byline given sometimes. Not copyrighted. Buys first North American serial rights. Simultaneous, photocopied and previously published submissions OK. Computer printout submissions acceptable; prefers letter-quality to dot-matrix. Writer's guidelines for SAE with 39¢ postage.
Nonfiction: How-to, interview/profile and technical. No consumer pieces. Query or send complete ms. Length: 1,000-3,000 words. Pays $100-200 for assigned articles; pays $100-150 for unsolicited articles. Sometimes pays the expenses of writers on assignment.
Photos: State availability of photos with submission. Reviews contact sheets and transparencies. Offers no additional payment for photos accepted with ms. Captions and identification of subjects required.
Columns/Departments: Closed Circuit TV, and Access Control (both on application, installation, new products), 500-1,000 words. Buys 15 mss/year. Query. Pays $100-125.
Tips: "The areas of our publication most open to freelancers are technical innovations, trends in the alarm industry and crime patterns as related to the business."

‡TOP LINE, An Executive Briefing Service, 13-30 Corporation, 505 Market St., Knoxville TN 37902. (615)521-0600. Group Editor: Tom Lombardo. 33% freelance written. A quarterly magazine covering business management information for owners and CEOs of small and medium sized firms (under $100 million). Circ. 150,000. Pays on acceptance. Publishes ms an average of 2 months after acceptance. Byline given. Buys first North American serial rights. Computer printout submissions acceptable. Sample copy for 9x12 SAE and 5 first class stamps.
Nonfiction: Topics include human resources, finance and taxes, law and government, marketing strategy, trends, strictly personal. "*Top Line* offers how-to, actionable management information." Buys 8 mss/year. Query with published clips. Length: 4,000 words. Pays $250-1,500.
Tips: "Experience in business writing is a must. Each issue contains one feature article; past topics have included exporting for small companies, planning for profit, new-product development, and doing business with the government."

‡TRADESHOW AND EXHIBIT MANAGER MAGAZINE, Brentwood Publishing, a Prentice-Hall/Simon & Schuster Co., 1640 5th St., Santa Monica CA 90401. (213)395-0234. Managing Editor: Les Plesko. 75% freelance written. A monthly magazine for the tradeshow industry—for professional exhibit managers, independent show organizers and association tradeshow organizers. Estab. 1986. Circ. 12,000. Pays on acceptance and receipt of phone log and copy of phone bill. Publishes ms an average of 4 months after acceptance. Byline given. Negotiable kill fee. Makes work-for-hire assignments. Computer printout submissions acceptable. Reports in 1 week on queries.

Nonfiction: How-to, interview/profile and new product. No articles written on speculation; accepted articles by assignment only. Buys 50+ mss/year. Query. Length: 1,000 words minimum. Pays $100 minimum for assigned articles or 10-12¢ edited word. Pays the phone expenses of writers on assignment.

Tips: "Business writing experiences is helpful; particularly tradeshow experience. We provide story idea, questions, contacts and editorial assistance. Potential freelance writers should write or call—we respond to all legitimate queries. Only Feature section is open to freelancers. Clear, concise business writing is required."

‡THE TRAVEL BUSINESS MANAGER, Sontag, Annis & Associates, Inc., Suite 1501, 51 Monroe St., Rockville MD 20850. (301)294-9404. Editor: Eleanor Alexander. 40% freelance written. "Eager to work with new writers who can address our market appropriately." A biweekly newsletter covering operational, strategic, and technical issues relating to retail travel management. Pays on publication. Publishes mss an average of 2 months after acceptance. Byline given. Buys all rights. Previously published work OK. Electronic submissions OK via modem using standard ASCII character set and disk accepted. Computer printout submissions acceptable. Reports in 3 weeks on queries; 6 weeks on mss. Sample copy for SAE with 56¢ postage; writer's guidelines for #SAE with 1 first class stamp.

Nonfiction: Technical and management, with emphasis on the travel industry. No travel—"Destination pieces"—of any kind. Buys 30-40 mss/year. Query with published clips. Length: 1,000-1,800 words. Pays $200-500.

Tips: "Know the travel industry well and understand business management. This market includes retail travel agents, travel industry suppliers (such as airlines, hotel systems, and car rental vendors), corporate travel managers, and others with an interest in the travel industry. No material directed toward travelers rather than travel managers. Read the publication first to understand its orientation. Writers may best judge their ability to write for us if they can produce material that addresses its subject authoritatively—with 'The voice of Experience'—rather than on a detached or theoretical level."

VETERINARY PRACTICE MANAGEMENT, 13-30 Corporation, 505 Market St., Knoxville TN 37902. (615)521-0633. Group Editor: Thomas Lombardo. 90% freelance written. Prefers to work with published/established writers. Semiannual magazine—"a business guide to small animal practitioners." Circ. 33,000. Pays on acceptance. Publishes ms an average 3 months after acceptance. Byline given. Offers kill fee. Buys first serial rights to the same material. Simultaneous queries OK. Electronic submissions OK. Computer printout submissions acceptable; prefers letter-quality to dot-matrix. Free sample copy to experienced business writers.

Nonfiction: Elizabeth H. Dossett, associate editor. How-to, and successful business (practice) management techniques. No "how to milk more dollars out of your clients" articles. Buys 16 mss/year. Query with published clips. Pays $1,000-1,700. Pays expenses of writers on assignment.

Columns/Departments: Management Briefs, and In the Know. "Most items are written in-house, but we will consider ideas." Query with published clips.

Church Administration and Ministry

CHRISTIAN EDUCATION TODAY: For teachers, superintendents and other Christian educators, Box 15337, Denver CO 80215. Editor: Edith Quinlan. National Research Editor: Kenneth O. Gangel. 50% freelance written. Works with a small number of new/unpublished writers each year. Quarterly magazine. Pays prior to publication. Publishes ms an average of 6 months after acceptance. Byline given. Buys simultaneous rights with magazines of different circulations. Computer printout submissions acceptable; prefers letter-quality to dot-matrix. Reports in 1 month. Sample copy and writer's guidelines for $1.

Nonfiction: Articles which provide information, instruction and/or inspiration to workers at every level of Christian education. May be slanted to the general area or to specific age-group categories such as preschool, elementary, youth or adult. Simultaneous rights acceptable *only* if offered to magazines which do not have overlapping circulation. Length: 1,000-2,000 words. Payment commensurate with length and value of article to total magazine.

Tips: "Often a submitted short article is followed up with a suggestion or firm assignment for more work from that writer."

CHRISTIAN LEADERSHIP, Board of Christian Education of the Church of God, Box 2458, Anderson IN 46018-2458. (317)642-0257. Acting Editor: Kenneth G. Prunty. 15% freelance written. Works with a small number of new/unpublished writers each year. A monthly magazine (except July and August) covering local Sunday school teachers, church school administrators, youth workers, choir leaders and other local church workers. Circ. 4,160. Pays on publication. Publishes ms an average of 5 months after acceptance. Byline given. Buys first rights and second serial (reprint) rights. Submit seasonal/holiday material 4 months in advance. Simultaneous queries OK. Computer printout submissions acceptable; prefers letter-quality to dot-matrix. Reports in 4 months. Free sample copy and writer's guidelines.

Nonfiction: General interest, how-to, inspirational, personal experience, guidance for carrying out programs for special days, and continuing ministries. No articles that are not specifically related to local church leadership. Buys 90 mss/year. Send complete ms, brief description of present interest in writing for church leaders, background and experience. Length: 300-1,800 words. Pays $5-30.

Photos: Send photos with ms. Pays $10 for 5x7 b&w prints.

Tips: "How-to articles related to Sunday school teaching, program development and personal teacher enrichment or growth, with illustrations of personal experience of the authors, are most open to freelancers."

‡**THE CHRISTIAN MINISTRY, "A Practical Magazine for Thinking Clergy";** The Christian Century Foundation, 407 S. Dearborn St., Chicago IL 60605. (312)427-5380. Editor: James M. Wall. Managing Editor: Eugene C. Roehlkepartain. 95% freelance written. A bimonthly magazine covering Christian parish ministry. "We reach an audience of mainline and liberal evangelical pastors (both men and women). Most readers have college and seminary education." Circ. 12,000. Pays on publication. Publishes ms an average of 6 months after acceptance. Byline given. Offers 50% kill fee. Buys all rights. Submit seasonal/holiday material 4 months in advance. Photocopied submissions OK. Computer printout submissions acceptable; prefers letter-quality to dot-matrix. Reports in 2 weeks. Sample copy for 8½x11 SAE with 56¢ postage; writer's guidelines for legal SAE with 22¢ postage.

Nonfiction: Book excerpts (on parish ministry); essays (on technology and ministry); how-to (perform the tasks of parish ministry); humor (about church work); opinion (about parish work); personal experience (of pastors); photo feature (about churches); religious; technical (about parish work i.e., preaching, etc.); and sermons. "Each issue has a focus that is planned ahead. Writers can contact us for a current listing. No personal experience articles without a general appeal or a specific, insightful point." Buys 60 mss/year. Send complete ms. Length: 500-2,500 words. Pays $40-60 for assigned articles; pays $30-50 for unsolicited articles.

Photos: State availability of photos with submission. Reviews contact sheets and 8x10 prints, b&w only. Offers $20-50/photo. Identification of subjects required. Buys one-time rights.

Columns/Department: Reflection on Ministry (personal, reflective or inspirational meditations about parish work; can focus on what it means to be a minister or how ministry has been meaningful), 1,000 words. Buys 6 mss/year. Send complete ms. Pays $30-40.

Fillers: Anecdotes, facts, newsbreaks and short humor—useful information or funny incidents related to parish work.

Tips: "We are very open to freelance contributors. Writers should keep in mind that almost all our readers are professional clergy and that our perspective tends to be liberal Protestant. Out best articles are those that integrate a sound theological basis for very practical parish issues. 'Speech or Sermon: Is There a Difference?' 'Women in Ministry: Beyond the Barriers'; and 'Minister's Workshop' are recent practical articles about how to do the various jobs in parish work. Articles on computers in churches, pastoral care, church finances, preaching, etc. are useful. Writers should remember that we advocate women and minorities in various pastorial roles."

CHURCH ADMINISTRATION, 127 9th Ave. N., Nashville TN 37234. (615)251-2060. Editor: Gary Hardin. 15% freelance written. Works with a small number of new/unpublished writers each year. Monthly. For Southern Baptist pastors, staff and volunteer church leaders. Uses limited amount of freelance material. Pays on acceptance. Publishes ms an average of 1 year after acceptance. Byline given. Buys all rights. Computer printout submissions acceptable; no dot-matrix. Free sample copy and writer's guidelines for SAE with 2 first class stamps.

Nonfiction: "Ours is a journal for effectiveness in ministry, including church programming, organizing, and staffing; administrative skills; church financing; church food services; church facilities; communication; and pastoral ministries and community needs." Length: 1,800-2,000 words. Pays 5¢/word.

Tips: "Send query letter. Writers should be familiar with the organization and polity of Southern Baptist churches. Articles should be practical, how-to articles that meet genuine needs faced by leaders in SBC churches. Type at 54 characters per line, 25 lines per page, double-spaced. Send originals, not copies. Not responsible for manuscripts not accompanied by return postage."

‡CHURCH EDUCATOR, Creative Resources for Christian Educators, Educational Ministries, Inc., 2861-C Saturn St., Brea CA 92621. (714)961-0622. Editor: Robert G. Davidson. Managing Editor: Linda S. Davidson. 80% freelance written. Works with a small number of new/unpublished writers each year. A monthly magazine covering religious education. Circ. 5,200. Pays on acceptance. Publishes manuscript an average of 4 months after acceptance. Byline given. Buys first rights, second serial (reprint) rights, or all rights. "We prefer all rights." Submit seasonal/holiday material 4 months in advance. Simultaneous submissions OK. Computer printout submissions acceptable; prefers letter-quality to dot-matrix. Reports in 3 months. Sample copy for 9x12 SAE and 56¢ postage; free writer's guidelines.
Nonfiction: Book reviews; general interest; how-to (crafts for Church school); inspirational; personal experience; and religious. "Our editorial lines are very middle of the road—mainline Protestant. We are not seeking extreme conservative or liberal theology pieces." No testimonials. Buys 100 mss/year. Send complete ms. Length: 100-2,000 words. Pays 2-4¢/word.
Photos: Send photos with submissions. Reviews 5x7 b&w prints. Offers $5-10/photo. Captions required. Buys one-time rights.
Fiction: Mainstream, religious, and slice-of-life vignettes. Buys 15 mss/year. Send complete ms. Length: 100-2,000 words. Pays 2-4¢/word.
Fillers: Anecdotes and short humor. Buys 15/year. Length: 100-700 words. Pays 2-4¢/word.
Tips: "Send the complete manuscript with a cover letter which gives a concise summary of the manuscript. We are looking for how-to articles related to Christian education. That would include most any program held in a church. Be straightforward and to the point—not flowery and wordy. We're especially interested in youth programs. Give steps needed to carry out the program: preparation, starting the program, continuing the program, conclusion. List several discussion questions for each program."

CHURCH TRAINING, 127 9th Ave. N., Nashville TN 37234. (615)251-2843. Publisher: The Sunday School Board of the Southern Baptist Convention. Editor: Richard B. Sims. 5% freelance written. Works with a small number of new/unpublished writers each year. Monthly. For all workers and leaders in the Church Training program of the Southern Baptist Convention. Circ. 30,000. Pays on acceptance. Publishes ms an average of 18 months after acceptance. Byline given. Buys all rights. Electronic submission OK on ATEX, but requires hard copy also. Computer printout submissions acceptable; no dot-matrix. Reports in 6 weeks. Free sample copy and writer's guidelines.
Nonfiction: Articles that pertain to leadership training in the church; success stories that pertain to Church Training; associational articles. Informational, how-to's that pertain to Church Training and personal testimonies. Buys 15 unsolicited mss/year. Query with rough outline. Length: 500-1,500 words. Pays 5¢/word. Sometimes pays the expenses of writers on assignment.
Tips: "Write an article that reflects the writer's experience of personal growth through church training. Keep in mind the target audience: workers and leaders of Church Training organizations in churches of the Southern Baptist Convention. Often subjects and treatment are too general."

CIRCUIT RIDER, A Journal for United Methodist Ministers, United Methodist Publishing House, Box 801, Nashville TN 37202. (615)749-6488. Editor: J. Richard Peck. Managing Editor: Bette Prestwood. 60% freelance written. Works with a small number of new/unpublished writers each year. A monthly magazine covering professional concerns of clergy. Circ. 48,000. Pays on acceptance. Publishes ms an average of 1 year after acceptance. Byline given. Buys all rights. Submit seasonal/holiday material 6 months in advance. Photocopied submissions OK. Computer printout submissions acceptable; prefers letter-quality to dot-matrix. Reports in 3 weeks.
Nonfiction: How-to (improve pastoral calling, preaching, counseling, administration, etc.). No personal experience articles; no interviews. Buys 50 mss/year. Send complete ms. Length: 600-2,000 words. Pays $30-100. Pays the expenses of writers on assignment.
Photos: State availability of photos. Pays $25-50 for 8x10 b&w prints. Model release required. Buys one-time rights.
Tips: "Know the concerns of a United Methodist pastor. Be specific. Think of how you can help pastors."

THE CLERGY JOURNAL, Church Management, Inc., Box 1625, Austin TX 78767. (512)327-8501. Editor: Manfred Holck, Jr. 20% freelance written. Monthly (except June and December) on religion. Readers are Protestant clergy. Circ. 20,000. Pays on publication. Publishes ms an average of 4 months after acceptance. Byline given. Offers 50% kill fee. Buys all rights. Submit seasonal/holiday material 6 months in advance. Photocopied submissions OK. Computer printout submissions acceptable; prefers letter-quality to dot-matrix. Reports in 2 weeks on queries; 1 month on mss. Sample copy $2.50.
Nonfiction: How-to (be a more efficient and effective minister/administrator). No devotional, inspirational

or sermons. Buys 20 mss/year. Query. Length: 500-1,500 words. Pays $25-40. Sometimes pays expenses of writers on assignment.

KEY TO CHRISTIAN EDUCATION, Standard Publishing, 8121 Hamilton Ave., Cincinnati OH 45231. (513)931-4050. Editor-in-Chief: Virginia Beddow. 50% freelance written. Quarterly magazine; 48 pages. For "church leaders of all ages, Sunday school teachers and superintendents, ministers, Christian education professors and youth workers." Circ. 70,000. Pays on acceptance. Publishes ms an average of 2 years after acceptance. Byline given. Buys first North American serial rights. Submit seasonal/holiday material 15 months in advance. Photocopied and previously published submissions OK. Computer printout submissions acceptable; prefers letter-quality to dot-matrix. Reports in 1 month. Sample copy and writer's guidelines for a 9x12 SASE.
Nonfiction: How-to (programs and projects for Christian education); informational; interview; opinion; and personal experience. Buys 10 mss/issue. Query or submit complete ms. Length: 700-2,000 words. Pays $20-60.
Photos: Purchased with accompanying ms. Submit prints. Pays $5-25 for any size glossy finish b&w prints. Total price for ms includes payment for photos. Model release required.
Fillers: Purchases short ideas on "this is how we did it" articles. Buys 10 mss/issue. Submit complete ms. Length: 50-250 words. Pays $5-10.
Tips: "Write for guidelines, sample issue and themes. Then write an article that fits one of the themes following the guidelines. Be practical. If the article pertains to a specific age group, address the article to that department editor."

MINISTRIES: The Magazine for Christian Leaders, Strang Communications Co., 190 N. Westmonte Dr., Altamonte Springs FL 32714. (305)869-5005. Editor: Stephen Strang. 80% freelance written. Quarterly magazine covering Pentecostal/Charismatics ministries. Includes practical articles to help church leaders. Circ. 24,000. Pays on publication. Publishes ms an average of 6 months after acceptance. Byline given. Buys all rights. Submit seasonal/holiday material 6 months in advance. Photocopied submissions OK. Computer printout submissions acceptable; prefers letter-quality to dot-matrix. Reports in 1 month. Sample copy $3, SAE and 1 first class stamp; writer's guidelines for SAE and 39¢ postage.
Nonfiction: Book excerpts, how-to (for pastors), and interview/profile. Writers must have personal experience in areas they are writing about. Buys 80 mss/year. Query or send complete ms. Length: 1,700-6,000 words. Pays $50-200. Sometimes pays expenses of writers on assignment.
Photos: Carolyn Kiphuth, photo editor.
Columns/Departments: E.S. Caldwell, column/department editor. For Women Only—for women in ministry; Youthful—for youth pastors; Musical Notes—for music ministers; Fire in My Bones—views and opinions; and Book Reviews. Buys 12 mss/year. Send complete ms. Length: 1,000-1,500 words. Pays $50 minimum.
Tips: "Columns are the best place to break in. We need practical, proven ideas with both negative and positive anecdotes. We have a specialized audience—pastors and leaders of Pentecostal and Charismatic churches. It is unlikely that persons not fully understanding this audience would be able to provide appropriate manuscripts."

‡PASTORAL LIFE, Society of St. Paul, Route 224, Canfield OH 44406. Editor: Jeffrey Mickler, SSP. 66% freelance written. Eager to work with new/unpublished writers. Emphasizes priests and those interested in pastoral ministry. Magazine; 64 pages. Monthly. Circ. 8,800. Buys first rights only. Byline given. Pays on acceptance. Publishes ms an average of 3 months after acceptance. Will send sample copy to writer on request. Query with a outline before submitting ms. "New contributors are expected to include, in addition, a few lines of personal data that indicate academic and professional background." Computer printout submissions acceptable; no dot-matrix. Reports in 7-10 days.
Nonfiction: "*Pastoral Life* is a professional review, principally designed to focus attention on current problems, needs, issues and all important activities related to all phases of pastoral work and life." Buys 30 unsolicited mss/year. Length: 2,000-3,400 words. Pays 3¢/word minimum.
Tips: "Projected increase in number of pages will warrant expansion of our material needs."

THE PREACHER'S MAGAZINE, Nazarene Publishing House, 6401 The Paseo, Kansas City MO 64131. (816)333-7000. Editor: Wesley Tracy. Assistant Editor: Mark D. Marvin. 15% freelance written. Works with a small number of new/unpublished writers each year. Quarterly magazine of seasonal/miscellaneous articles. "A resource for ministers; Wesleyan-Arminian in theological persuasion." Circ. 17,000. Pays on acceptance. Publishes ms an average of 9+ months after acceptance. Byline given. Buys first serial rights, second serial (reprint) rights and simultaneous rights. Submit seasonal/holiday material 9 months in advance. Simultaneous queries and photocopied submissions OK. Computer printout submissions acceptable; prefers letter-quality to dot-matrix. Free sample copy and writer's guidelines.
Nonfiction: How-to, humor, inspirational, opinion and personal experience, all relating to aspects of ministry. No articles that present problems without also presenting answers to them; things not relating to

pastoral ministry. Buys 48 mss/year. Send complete ms. Length: 700-2,500 words. Pays 3½¢/word.
Photos: Send photos with ms. Reviews 35mm color transparencies and 35mm b&w prints. Pays $25-35. Model release and identification of subjects required. Buys one-time rights.
Columns/Departments: Today's Books for Today's Preacher—book reviews. Buys 24 mss/year. Send complete ms. Length: 300-400 words. Pays $7.50.
Fillers: Anecdotes and short humor. Buys 10/year. Length: 400 words maximum. Pays 3½¢/word.
Tips: "Writers for the *Preacher's Magazine* should have insight into the pastoral ministry, or expertise in a specialized area of ministry. Our magazine is a highly specialized publication aimed at the minister. Our goal is to assist, by both scholarly and practical articles, the modern-day minister in applying Biblical theological truths."

YOUR CHURCH, The Religious Publishing Co., 198 Allendale Rd., King of Prussia PA 19406. (215)265-9400. Editor: Phyllis Mather Rice. 50% freelance written. Bimonthly magazine for ministers and churches "providing practical, how-to articles on every aspect of administering and leading church congregations." Circ. 186,000. Pays on publication. Publishes ms an average of 1 year after acceptance. Byline given. Offers 50% kill fee. Buys one-time rights. Submit seasonal/holiday material 1 year in advance. Simultaneous queries (if informed) and previously published submissions OK. Computer printout submissions acceptable; no dot-matrix. Reports in 2 months on queries; 3 months on mss. Sample copy $1.50, 9x11 SAE, and 73¢ postage; writer's guidelines for #10 SAE and 22¢ postage.
Nonfiction: How-to (administer and lead church congregations); new product (that churches can use); personal experience (working with congregations); and technical (building churches). No sermons or dissertation-type articles. Buys 60 mss/year. Query or send complete ms. Length: 1,200-3,000 words. Pays $6/typewritten ms page—$100 total maximum.
Tips: "Freelancers can best break in with articles that have *practical* value to church pastors. We are interested in how-to, readable, interesting copy that flows. We are not interested in dissertation-type articles."

Clothing

The emphasis must be on current or upcoming styles in these publications for manufacturers and retailers. Many trade journals work to eliminate misconceptions in their respective industries.

APPAREL INDUSTRY MAGAZINE, Shore Publishing, Suite 300-South, 180 Allen Rd., Atlanta GA 30328. Editor: Karen Schaffner. Managing Editor: Ray Henderson. 30% freelance written. Monthly magazine; 64-150 pages. For executive management in apparel companies with interests in equipment, fabrics, licensing, distribution, finance, management and training. Circ. 18,700. Pays on publication. Publishes ms an average of 4 months after acceptance. Byline given. Buys first serial rights. Will consider legible photocopied submissions. Computer printout submissions acceptable. Reports in 1 month. Sample copy $3; writer's guidelines for SAE with 1 first class stamp.
Nonfiction: Articles dealing with equipment, manufacturing techniques, training, finance, licensing, fabrics, quality control, etc., related to the industry. "Use concise, precise language that is easy to read and understand. In other words, because the subjects are often technical, keep the language comprehensible. Material must be precisely related to the apparel industry. We are not a retail or fashion magazine." Informational, interview, profile, successful business operations and technical articles. Buys 30mss/year. Query. Length: 3,000 words maximum. Pays 20¢/word. Sometimes pays expenses of writers on assignment.
Photos: Pays $5/photo with ms.
Tips: "Frequently articles are too general due to lack of industry-specific knowledge by the writer."

‡EARNSHAW'S, infants-girls-boys wear review, Earnshaw Publications, 393 7th Ave., New York NY 10001. (212)563-2742. Editor: Thomas Hudson. Managing Editor: Christina Gruber. 10% freelance written. A monthly magazine covering children's wear. Circ. 10,000. Pays on publication. Publishes ms an average of 2 months after acceptance. Byline given sometimes. Offers $50 kill fee. Buys first North American serial rights. Submit seasonal/holiday material 2 months in advance. Free sample copy.

Nonfiction: How-to (sell merchandise display, etc.); interview/profile; and photo feature. Articles must be related to children's wear field. Buys 6-10 mss/year. Query with published clips. Length: 1,200-3,000 words. Pays $200-300 for assigned articles; pays $200 for unsolicited articles; sometimes pays in copies or other premiums in workable agreement with individual. Sometimes pays expenses of writers on assignment.

Photos: Send photos with submission. Reviews contact sheets. Offers no additional payment for photos accepted with ms. Captions, model releases and identification of subjects required. Buys one-time rights.

Tips: "We are looking for business-oriented articles relating to issues, people, events involving the children's wear industry. Profiles of new or interesting retailers or manufacturers who are giving a fresh slant to children's wear manufacturing or retailing are most open to freelancers."

‡**KIDS FASHIONS**, Larkin-Pluznick-Larkin, 210 Boylston St., Chestnut Hill MA 02167. Editorial offices: 71 West 35th St., Suite 1600, New York NY 10001. (212)594-0880. Editor: Larry Leventhal. 20% freelance written. Works with a small number of new/unpublished writers each year. Magazine covering children's wear industry, with the emphasis on the children's wear retailer. Circ. 18,000. Pays on acceptance. Publishes ms an average of 2 months after acceptance. One byline per writer, per issue. Buys all rights. Submit seasonal/holiday material 9 months in advance. Computer printout submissions acceptable; prefers letter-quality to dot-matrix. Reports in 2 weeks. Free sample copy.

Nonfiction: Merchandising and business how-to; retailer/store profiles and survey articles on merchandising. "Knowledge of retailing and merchandising of apparel helpful, business sense a must." No previously published articles. Buys 24-30 mss/year. Query with clips only. Length: 750-2,500 words, or dependent on subject. Pays $150-300.

Photos: State availability of photos. Reviews contacts or prints. Captions and identification of subjects required. Buys one-time rights.

Tips: "We are aiming to be more business oriented—less popcorn and fluff. We like in depth, fully researched articles with lots of attribution. We are not as interested in opinion and razzle-dazzle."

TEXTILE WORLD, Suite 420, 4170 Ashford-Dunwoody Rd. NE, Atlanta GA 30319. Editor-in-Chief: Laurence A. Christiansen. Monthly. Pays on acceptance. Buys all rights.

Nonfiction: Uses articles covering textile management methods, manufacturing and marketing techniques, new equipment, details about new and modernized mills, etc., but avoids elementary, historical or generally well-known material.

Photos: Photos purchased with accompanying ms with no additional payment, or purchased on assignment.

‡**WESTERN & ENGLISH FASHIONS**, Bell Publishing, 2403 Champa, Denver CO 80205. (303)572-1777. Editor: Larry Bell. Managing Editor: Lee Darrigrand. 90% freelance written. Prefers to work with published/established writers; works with a small number of new/unpublished writers each year. For "Western and English apparel and equipment retailers, manufacturers and distributors. The magazine features retailing practices such as marketing, merchandising, display techniques, buying and selling to help business grow or improve, etc. Every issue carries feature stories on Western/English/square dance apparel stores throughout the US." Monthly magazine; 50 pages. Circ. 13,000. Pays on publication. Publishes ms an average of 3 months after acceptance. Not copyrighted. Byline given unless extensive rewriting is required. Phone queries OK. Submit seasonal/holiday material 3 months in advance. Simultaneous (to noncompeting publications), photocopied and previously published submissions OK. Computer printout submissions acceptable; no dot-matrix. No fiction or foreign material. Free sample copy and writer's guidelines.

Nonfiction: Current trends in fashion of English riding attire, square dance & western; expose (of government as related to industry or people in industry); general interest (pertaining to Western lifestyle); interview (with Western/English store owners); new product (of interest to Western/English clothing retailers—send photo); and photo feature. "We will be doing much more fashion oriented articles and layouts." Buys 20-25/year. Query with outline. Length: 800-3,600 words. Pays $50-150. Sometimes pays the expenses of writers on assignment.

Photos: "We buy photos with manuscripts. Occasionally we purchase photos that illustrate a unique display or store with only a cutline." State availability of photos. Captions required with "names of people or products and locations." Buys one-time rights.

WESTERN OUTFITTER, 5314 Bingle Rd., Houston TX 77092. (713)688-8811. Editor/Manager: Anne DeRuyter. Assistant Editor: Margaret S. Brenner. Monthly magazine for retailers of Western/English apparel, tack and horse supplies. Circ. 17,000. Pays on publication. Buys first rights. Assigned stories only. Free sample copy and writer/photographer guidelines.

Nonfiction: Interviews with outstanding retailers. "How do they promote? What type of advertising works best for them? What retailing philosophies have made them successful? What problem have they faced and solved? We also need current information on what's new in horse supplies and horse health products. Writing should be informed and business-like." No general pieces. Length: 750-1500 words. Pays $75-200, depending upon quality of article and amount of research involved. "If you have an outstanding Western/English retailer or farm/ranch dealer in your area, determine the key to their success and send us a query." Mss purchased with or without photos. Query.

Photos: "We welcome photo features on effective store displays or successful store promotions." Query. Photos must be uncluttered and have strong angles. No static photos or uninteresting mugshots. Reviews b&w contact sheets. Color used only if it's superior. Pays $50-150.

‡**YOUNG FASHIONS MAGAZINE**, Columbia Communications, 23rd Floor, 370 Lexington Ave., New York NY 10017. (212)532-9290. Editor: Marc Richards. 50% freelance written. A monthly magazine covering the children's clothing industry. "Upbeat, lively coverage of merchandising, operations and stories aimed at retailers, manufacturers and textile people." Estab. 1985. Circ. 25,000. Pays on publication. Publishes an average of 3 months after acceptance. Byline given sometimes. Buys first North American serial rights. Submit seasonal/holiday material 6 months in advance. Reports in 2 weeks. Free sample copy and writer's guidelines.

Nonfiction: How-to (business-oriented for retailers). No non-business-oriented articles. Buys 60 mss/year. Query with or without published clips. Length: 1,200-2,500 words. Pays $250-300.

Photos: State availability of photos with submission. Reviews contact sheets and transparencies. Offers no additional payment for photos accepted with ms. Captions, model releases and identification of subjects required. Buys one-time rights.

Tips: "Full-length feature articles are most open to freelancers. We're *not* geared toward children, but to adults who make and sell children's clothing. Seasonal business writers have the best chance for acceptance as retail reporting is very specialized."

Coin-Operated Machines

AMERICAN COIN-OP, 500 N. Dearborn St., Chicago IL 60610. (312)337-7700. Editor: Ben Russell. 30% freelance written. Monthly magazine; 42 pages. For owners of coin-operated laundry and dry cleaning stores. Circ. 18,000. Rights purchased vary with author and material but are exclusive to the field. Pays two weeks prior to publication. Publishes ms an average of 4 months after acceptance. Byline given for frequent contributors. Computer printout submissions acceptable; prefers letter-quality to dot-matrix. Reports as soon as possible; usually in 2 weeks. Free sample copy.

Nonfiction: "We emphasize store operation and use features on industry topics: utility use and conservation, maintenance, store management, customer service and advertising. A case study should emphasize how the store operator accomplished whatever he did—in a way that the reader can apply to his own operation. Manuscript should have a no-nonsense, business-like approach." Uses informational, how-to, interview, profile, think pieces and successful business operations articles. Length: 500-3,000 words.

Photos: Pays 6¢/word minimum. Pays $6 minimum for 8x10 b&w glossy photos purchased with mss. (Contact sheets with negatives preferred.)

Fillers: Newsbreaks and clippings. Length: open. Pays $5 minimum.

Tips: "Query about subjects of current interest. Be observant of coin-operated laundries—how they are designed and equipped, how they serve customers and how (if) they advertise and promote their services. Most general articles are turned down because they are not aimed well enough at audience. Most case histories are turned down because of lack of practical purpose (nothing new or worth reporting). A frequent mistake is failure to follow up on an interesting point made by the interviewee—probably due to lack of knowledge about the industry."

ELECTRONIC SERVICING & TECHNOLOGY, Intertec Publishing Corp., Box 12901, Overland Park KS 66212. (913)888-4664. Editor: Conrad Persson. Managing Editor: Dan Torchia. 90% freelance written. Eager to work with new/unpublished writers. Monthly magazine for professional servicers and electronic enthusiasts who are interested in buying, building, installing and repairing consumer electronic equipment (audio, video, microcomputers, electronic games, etc.) Circ. 60,000. Pays on publication. Publishes ms an average of 6 months after acceptance. Byline given. Buys all rights. Submit seasonal/holiday material 4 months in advance. Simultaneous queries OK. Computer printout submissions acceptable; prefers letter-quality to dot-matrix. Reports in 2 weeks on queries; 1 month on mss. Free sample copy and writer's guidelines.

Nonfiction: How-to (service, build, install and repair home entertainment electronic equipment); personal experience (troubleshooting); and technical (consumer electronic equipment; electronic testing and servicing equipment). "Explain the techniques used carefully so that even hobbyists can understand a how-to article." Buys 36 mss/year. Send complete ms. Length: 1,500 words minimum. Pays $100-200.

Photos: Send photos with ms. Reviews color and b&w transparencies and b&w prints. Captions and identification of subjects required. Buys all rights. Payment included in total ms package.

Columns/Departments: Marge Riggin, column/department editor. Troubleshooting Tips. Buys 12 mss/year. Send complete ms. Length: open. Pays $30-40.

Tips: "In order to writer for *ES&T* it is almost essential that a writer have an electronics background; technician, engineer or serious hobbyist. Our readers want nuts-and-bolts type of information on electronics."

PLAY METER MAGAZINE, Skybird Publishing Co., Inc., Box 24970. New Orleans LA 70184. Publisher: Carol Lally. Editor: George Sigler. 25% freelance written. "We will work with new writers who are familiar with the amusement industry." Semimonthly trade magazine, 100 pages, for owners/operators of coin-operated amusement machine companies, e.g., pinball machines, video games, arcade pieces, jukeboxes, etc. Circ. 7,500. Pays on publication. Publishes ms an average of 2 months after acceptance. Byline given. Buys all rights. Submit seasonal/holiday material 2 months in advance. Photocopied and previously published submissions OK. Electronic submissions OK via disk formatted for Kaypro C/PM DSDD, but requires hard copy also. Computer printout submissions acceptable; prefers letter-quality to dot-matrix. Query answered in 2 months. Sample copy $2; free writer's guidelines.

Nonfiction: How-to (get better locations for machines, promote tournaments, evaluate profitability of route, etc.); interview (with industry leaders); new product. "Our readers want to read about how they can make more money from their machines, how they can get better tax breaks, commissions, etc. Also no stories about *playing* pinball or video games. Also, submissions on video-game technology advances; technical pieces on troubleshooting videos, pinballs, and novelty machines (all coin-operated); trade-show coverage (query), submissions on the pay-telephone industry. Our readers don't play the games per se; they buy the machines and make money from them." Buys 48 mss/year. Submit complete ms. Length: 250-3,000 words. Pays $30-215. Sometimes pays expenses of writers on assignment.

Photos: "The photography should have news value. We don't want 'stand 'em up-shoot 'em down' group shots." Pays $15 minimum for 5x7 or 8x10 b&w prints. Captions preferred. Buys all rights. Art returned on request.

Tips: "We need feature articles more than small news items or featurettes. Query first. We're interested in writers who either have a few years of reporting/feature-writing experience or who know the coin-operated amusement industry well but are relatively inexperienced writers."

VENDING TIMES, 545 8th. Avenue, New York NY 10018. Editor: Arthur E. Yohalem. Monthly. For operators of vending machines. Circ. 14,700. Pays on publication. Buys all rights. "We will discuss in detail the story requirements with the writer."

Nonfiction: Feature articles and news stories about vending operations; practical and important aspects of the business. "We are always willing to pay for good material." Query.

Confectionery and Snack Foods

CANDY INDUSTRY, HBJ Publications, 7500 Old Oak Blvd., Cleveland OH 44130. (216)243-8100. Editor: Pat Magee. 5% freelance written. Monthly. For confectionery manufacturers. Publishes ms an average of 4 months after acceptance. Buys first serial rights. Computer printout submissions acceptable; prefers letter-quality to dot-matrix. Reports in 2 weeks.

Nonfiction: "Feature articles of interest to large scale candy manufacturers that deal with activities in the fields of production, packaging (including package design), merchandising; and financial news (sales figures, profits, earnings), advertising campaigns in all media, and promotional methods used to increase the sale or distribution of candy." Length: 1,000-1,250 words. Pays 15¢/word; "special rates on assignments."

Photos: "Good quality glossies with complete and accurate captions, in sizes not smaller than 5x7." Pays $10 b&w; $20 for color.

Fillers: "Short news stories about the trade and anything related to candy and snacks." Pays 5¢/word; $1 for clippings.

PACIFIC BAKERS NEWS, 16 Peterson Pl., Walnut Creek CA 94595. (415)932-1256. Publisher: C.W. Soward. 30% freelance written. Eager to work with new/unpublished writers. Monthly business newsletter for commercial bakeries in the western states. Pays on publication. No byline given; uses only one-paragraph news items. Computer printout submissions acceptable.
Nonfiction: Uses bakery business reports and news about bakers. Buys only brief "boiled-down news items about bakers and bakeries operating only in Alaska, Hawaii, Pacific Coast and Rocky Mountain states. We welcome clippings. We need monthly news reports and clippings about the baking industry and the donut business. No pictures, jokes, poetry or cartoons." Length: 10-200 words. Pays 6¢/word for clips and news used. ·

Construction and Contracting

Builders, architects, and contractors learn the latest news of their trade in these publications. Journals aimed at architects are included in the Art, Design and Collectibles section. Those for specialists in the interior aspects of construction are listed under Building Interiors. Also of interest would be the markets in the Brick, Glass and Ceramics section.

‡ARCHITECTURAL TECHNOLOGY, American Institute of Architects Service Corp., 1735 New York Ave N.W., Washington DC 20006. (202)626-7590. Editor: Mitchell B. Rouda. Managing Editor: James B. Gardner. 20% freelance written. A bimonthly magazine covering architectural design and practice. "We aim to help architects do better work. We emphasize the nuts and bolts of design and firm management." Circ. 46,000. Pays on publication. Publishes ms an average of 5 months after acceptance. Byline given. Offers 40% kill fee. Buys all rights. Electronic submissions OK via ASCII. Computer printout submissions acceptable. Reports in 2 months. Sample copy $7 with 9x12 SAE and 6 first class stamps; free writer's guidelines.
Nonfiction: Essays; how-to (on architectural design or management); new product; and technical (emphasizing nuts and bolts of architecture). Query. Length: 900-5,000. Pays $100-750. Sometimes pays the expenses of writers on assignment.
Photos: State availability of photos and architectural drawings with submissions. Captions, model releases, and identification of subjects required. Buys one-time rights.
Columns/Departments: Amy E. Light, products editor. Commentary (essays on the state of the architecture profession), 950 words. Buys 6 mss/year. Query. Pays $100.

AUTOMATION IN HOUSING & MANUFACTURED HOME DEALER, (formerly *Automation in Housing & Systems Building News*), CMN Associates, Inc., Box 120, Carpinteria CA 93013. (805)684-7659. Editor-in-Chief: Don Carlson. 15% freelance written. Monthly magazine; 88 pages. Specializes in management for industrialized (manufactured) housing and volume home builders. Circ. 25,000. Pays on acceptance. Publishes ms an average of 3 months after acceptance. Buys first North American serial rights. Phone queries OK. Computer printout submissions acceptable; no dot-matrix. Reports in 2 weeks. Free sample copy and writer's guidelines.
Nonfiction: Case history articles on successful home building companies which may be 1) production (big volume) home builders; 2) mobile home manufacturers; 3) modular home manufacturers; 4) prefabricated home manufacturers; or 5) house component manufacturers. Also uses interviews, photo features and technical articles. "No architect or plan 'dreams'. Housing projects must be built or under construction." Buys 15 mss/year. Query. Length: 500-1,000 words maximum. Pays $300 minimum.
Photos: Purchased with accompanying ms. Query. No additional payment for 4x5, 5x7 or 8x10 b&w glossies or 35mm or larger color transparencies (35mm preferred). Captions required.
Tips: "Stories often are too long, too loose; we prefer 500 to 750 words. We prefer a phone query on feature articles. If accepted on query, usually article will not be rejected later."

BUILDER INSIDER, Box 191125, Dallas TX 75219-1125. (214)651-9994. Editor: Mike Anderson. Monthly covering the entire north Texas building industry for builders, architects, contractors, remodelers and homeowners. Circ. 8,000. Photocopied submissions OK. Free sample copy.
Nonfiction: "What is current in the building industry" is the approach. Wants "advertising, business builders, new building products, building projects being developed and helpful building hints localized to the Southwest and particularly to north Texas." Submit complete ms. Length: 100-900 words. Pays $30-50.

‡CALIFORNIA BUILDER & ENGINEER, 4110 Transport St., Palo Alto CA 94303. Editor: David W. Woods. "For contractors, engineers, and machinery distributors in the heavy construction industry, and civic officials concerned with public works. Our coverage is limited to California, Hawaii, Nevada and western Arizona." Published twice a month. Circ. 11,500. Pays on publication. Not copyrighted. Buys first rights only. Computer printout submissions acceptable; prefers letter-quality to dot-matrix. Reports in 3 weeks. Publishes ms an average of 2 months after acceptance. Free sample copy.
Nonfiction: "We are particularly interested in knowledgeable articles on nonconstruction issues that affect both the large and small contractor in our region. For example: accounting for the contractor, labor issues, pending legislation or office automation. These articles must be written with rigid accuracy, often requiring specialized knowledge. We are also interested in job stories from Hawaii on heavy public construction. We are not interested in residential construction. Field experience or in-depth knowledge of the industry are essential in writing for us." Buys 4-5 unsolicited mss/year. Query. Length: 1,500-2,200 words. Pays $100/article.
Photos: Send photos with ms. Reviews 5x7 b&w glossy prints. Offers no additional payment for photos accompanying ms. Captions and model release required. Buys one-time rights.

‡CANADIAN CONSTRUCTION RECORD, (formerly *Engineering and Contract Record),* Southam Communications, 1460 Don Mills Road, Toronto, Ontario M3B 2X7 Canada. (416)445-6641. Editor: Gene Lethbridge. Managing Editor: Paul Lebel. 20% freelance written. Eager to work with new/unpublished writers. For contractors in engineered construction and aggregate producers. Monthly. Circ. 24,000. Buys Canadian rights. Pays on publication. Publishes ms an average of 2 months after acceptance. Electronic submissions OK via CPM, but requires hard copy also. Computer printout submissions acceptable; prefers letter-quality to dot-matrix. Free sample copy. Reports in 2 weeks. SAE and International Reply Coupons.
Nonfiction: "Job stories. How to build a project quicker, cheaper, better through innovations and unusual methods. Articles on management, technology, equipment, maintenance and management innovations. Stories are limited to Canadian projects or Canadian construction firms working on projects overseas. No company profiles." Buys 10-12 mss/year. Query. Length: 1,000-2,000 words. Pays $500-600. Sometimes pays the expenses of writers on assignment.
Photos: Color slides or prints purchased with mss. Pays $40.
Tips: "We will be emphasizing the business side of contracting."

CATERPILLAR WORLD, Caterpillar Tractor Co., 100 NE Adams AB1470, Peoria IL 61629. (309)675-5829. Editor: Tom Biederbeck. 10% freelance written. Quarterly magazine; 24-32 pages. Emphasizes "anything of interest about Caterpillar people, plants or products. The magazine is distributed to 75,000 Caterpillar people and friends worldwide. It's printed in French and English. Readers' ages, interests and education vary all over the map." Pays on publication. Publishes ms an average of 6 months after acceptance. Buys first serial rights and second serial (reprint) rights. Computer printout submissions acceptable. First submission is always on speculation. Free sample copy.
Nonfiction: "Everything should have a Caterpillar tie. It doesn't have to be strong but it has to be there." How-to (buy one piece of equipment and become a millionaire, etc.); general interest (anything that may be of interest to Cat people worldwide); humor (it's hard to find something humorous yet interesting to an international audience; we'd like to see it, however); interview (with any appropriate person: contractor, operator, legislator, etc.); products (large projects using Cat equipment; must have human interest); personal experience (would be interesting to hear from an equipment operator/writer); photo feature (on anything of interest to Cat people; should feature people as well as product); and profile (of Cat equipment users, etc.). Prints occasional lifestyle and health articles (but must apply to international audience). Written approval by the subjects of the article is a must. Query. Length: "What ever the story is worth."
Photos: "The only articles we accept without photos are those obviously illustrated by artwork." State availability of photos in query. Captions and model release required.
Tips: "The best way to get story ideas is to stop in at local Cat dealers and ask about big sales, events, etc."

CONSTRUCTION SPECIFIER, 601 Madison St., Alexandria VA 22314. (703)684-0200. Editor: Kimberly C. Smith. 50% freelance written. Works with a small number of new/unpublished writers each year. Monthly professional society magazine for architects, engineers, specification writers and project managers. Monthly. Circ. 18,000. Pays on publication. Publishes ms an average of 4 months after acceptance. Deadline: 60 days preceding publication on the 1st of each month. Buys North American serial rights. Computer printout submissions acceptable; prefers letter-quality to dot-matrix. "Call or write first." Model release, author copyright transferral requested. Reports in 3 weeks. Free sample copy.

Nonfiction: Articles on selection and specification of products, materials, practices and methods used in commercial (nonresidential) construction projects, specifications as related to construction design, plus legal and management subjects. Query. Length: 3,000-5,000 words maximum. Pays 10¢/published word (negotiable), plus art. Pays the expenses of writers on assignment.
Photos: Photos desirable in consideration for publication; line art, sketches, diagrams, charts and graphs also desired. Full color transparencies may be used. 8x10 glossies, 3¼ slides preferred. Payment negotiable.
Tips: "We will get bigger and thus will need good technical articles."

CONTRACTORS MARKET CENTER, Randall Publishing Co., Box 2029, Tuscaloosa AL 35403. (205)349-2990. Editor: Claude Duncan. 25-50% freelance written. Eager to work with new/unpublished writers. Weekly tabloid on heavy-equipment construction industry. "Our readers are contractors including road contractors, and oil and gas industry, who utilize heavy equipment. We write positive, upbeat stories about their work and their personal success. We like personal stories related to large construction projects." Circ. 18,000. Pays on acceptance. Publishes ms an average of 1 month after acceptance. Byline given. Offers 100% kill fee. Not copyrighted. Buys first serial rights, one-time rights, second serial (reprint) rights and simultaneous rights. Submit seasonal/holiday material 1 month in advance. Simultaneous and previously published (updated) submissions OK. Computer printout submissions acceptable; prefers upper and lower case letter-quality to dot-matrix. Reports in 2 weeks. Free sample copy and writer's guidelines.
Nonfiction: General interest (with construction angle); historical/nostalgic (with construction angle); humor (with construction angle); interview/profile (with contractors); personal experience (with construction angle); technical (re: heavy equipment); and business stories related to contractors. Fiction now accepted. Buys 100 mss/year. Send complete ms. Length: 250-1,000 words. Pays $10-50. Sometimes pays the expenses of writers on assignment.
Photos: Send photos with ms. Reviews b&w and color prints; commercially processed OK if sharp. Pays $5. Identification of subjects required.
Tips: "Contractors like to read about other contractors and people with whom they are in frequent contact—suppliers, government regulators, and public works developments. We're primarily looking for people-oriented features. Nothing is too local if it's interesting. Submitting art with copy gives definite edge."

FENCE INDUSTRY, 6255 Barfield Rd., Atlanta GA 30328. (404)256-9800. Editor/Associate Publisher: Bill Coker. 60% freelance written. Monthly magazine; 54-80 pages. For retailers and installers of fencing materials. Circ. 17,000. Pays on publication. Publishes ms an average of 2 months after acceptance. Buys all rights. Electronic submissions OK if floppy disks compatible with Rainbow or Digital DECmate. Computer printout submissions acceptable. Reports in 3 months. Free sample copy.
Nonfiction: Case histories, as well as articles on fencing for highways, pools, farms, playgrounds, homes and industries. Surveys and management and sales reports. Interview, profile, historical, successful business operations and articles on merchandising techniques. No how-to articles; "they generally don't apply to installers in our industry." Buys 15-20 unsolicited mss/year. Query. Length: open. Pays 10¢/word.
Photos: Pays $10 for 5x7 b&w photos purchased with mss. Captions required.

FINE HOMEBUILDING, The Taunton Press, Inc., 52 Church Hill Rd., Box 355, Newtown CT 06470. (203)426-8171. Editor: John Lively. Bimonthly magazine covering house building, construction, design for builders, architects and serious amateurs. Circ. 195,000. Pays on publication. Byline given. Offers negotiable kill fee. Buys first rights and "use in books to be published." Computer printout submissions acceptable. Reports as soon as possible. Sample copy $3.75; free writer's guidelines.
Nonfiction: Technical (unusual techniques in design or construction process). Query. Length: 2,000-3,000 words. Pays $150-900.
Columns/Departments: Reports (conferences, workshops, products or techniques that are new or unusual); Great Moments in Building History (humorous, embarrassing, or otherwise noteworthy anecdotes); and Reviews (short reviews on books of building or design). Query. Length: 300-1,000 words. Pays $75-150.

JOURNAL OF COMMERCE, Box 34080, Station D, Vancouver, British Columbia, V6J 4M8 Canada. Editor: Stefan Koehl. 20% freelance written. Prefers to work with published/established writers. Twice-weekly tabloid aimed at a general construction and development audience in western Canada. Circ. 6,900. Payment on acceptance. Publishes ms an average of 1 month after acceptance. Buys first Canadian rights. Computer printout submissions acceptable; no dot-matrix. Enclose SAE,IRCs.
Nonfiction: Specialized stories for specific audiences. Query first. Average length: 1,500 words. Pays 15¢/word (Canadian). Sometimes pays the expenses of writers on assignment.
Photos: Pays $5 for 5x7 photos.

LOG HOME AND ALTERNATIVE HOUSING BUILDER, 16 1st Ave., Corry PA 16407-1894. (814)664-8624. Editor: Harry Calhoun. 10-20% freelance written. Prefers to work with published/established writers but open to new talent. A magazine published 9 times yearly covering alternative housing, including log, dome, solar, post and beam, and underground homes. Readership consists chiefly of builder/dealers and manufacturers of these homes. Circ. 10,000. Pays on publication. Publishes ms an average of 3 months after acceptance. Byline given. Offers negotiable kill fee. Buys all rights; rights may be re-assigned to author upon request. Submit seasonal/holiday material 3 months in advance. Simultaneous submissions and previously published work OK, "if we're told of the situation." Reports in 2 weeks on queries. Computer printout submissions acceptable; prefers letter-quality to dot-matrix. Free sample copy and writer's guidelines.

Nonficton: How-to ("not how to build—our readers *are* builders; but how to make and increase sales, better market log homes, etc.") New product; technical (new or unique products for alternative housing); and feature articles. No "puff" pieces or consumer oriented articles. Buys 8-15 mss/year. Query or send complete ms. Length: 1,000-4,000 words. Pays $50-200. Pays expenses of writers on assignment (long distance phone calls).

Photos: Send photos with submission. Reviews 8x10 prints. Offers $10-30/photo. Captions or other identification of subjects required. Buys all rights; rights may be re-assigned to author upon request.

Columns/Departments: Winner's Circle (interview with a successful builder/dealer); Commercially Speaking (alternative housing in commercial projects); Focus (introducing a manufacturer to the industry); and book reviews. Query or send complete ms. Length: 500-4,000 words (varies according to department). Pays $50-250.

Tips: A freelancer can best break in to our publication with a good query or article that shows a knowledge of our slant and our readership, that's 'How to increase alternative housing sales and improve cash flow,' rather then 'How the wife and I built our log home.' Feature articles are most open to freelancers. Come up with detailed pieces on financing, sales, marketing, expanding product lives, etc.—in the log or alternative housing industry. Now and then we'll accept and publish an article over the transom, but more often we assign articles to our freelancers. When we do this we'll provide contacts, suggested slants and interview questions, and other support. If a writer has questions, he/she need only call us."

‡**LOUISIANA CONTRACTOR,** Rhodes Publishing Co., Inc., 18271 Old Jefferson Hwy., Baton Rouge LA 70817. (504)292-8980. Editor: Joyce Elson. Associate Editor: Becky Combest. 10% freelance written. Monthly magazine comprehensive covering heavy commercial, industrial and highway construction in Louisiana, one of the largest construction markets in the U.S. Circ. 6,500. Pays on publication. Publishes ms an average of 2 months after acceptance. Offers negotiable kill fee. Buys all rights. Reports in 2 weeks on queries; 2½ months on mss. Sample copy $1.50.

Nonfiction: "We are particularly interested in writers who can get clearance into a chemical plant or refinery and detail unusual maintenance jobs. Our feature articles are semitechnical to technical, balanced by a lot of name dropping of subcontractors, suppliers and key job personnel. We want quotes, and we never run a story without lots of photos either taken or procured by the writer. Stories on new methods of construction and unusual projects in the state are always wanted. Nothing from anyone unfamiliar with the construction industry in Louisiana." Buys 8-12 mss/year. Query. Length: 1,000-3,500 words. Pays negotiable rate. Sometimes pays the expenses of writers on assignment.

Photos: State availability of photos. Reviews 5x7 or 8x10 b&w glossy prints. Captions and identification of subjects required. "It is absolutely essential that a writer understand construction terms and practices."

MID-WEST CONTRACTOR, Construction Digest, Inc., 3170 Mercier, Box 766, Kansas City MO 64141. (816)931-2080. Editor: Marcia Gruver. 5% freelance written. Biweekly magazine covering the public works and engineering construction industries in Iowa, Nebraska, Kansas and western and northeastern Missouri. Circ. 8,426. Pays on publication. Publishes ms an average of 2 months after acceptance. Byline given depending on nature of article. Not copyrighted. Makes work-for-hire assignments. Computer printout submissions acceptable; prefers letter-quality to dot-matrix. Reports in 2 weeks. Free sample copy.

Nonfiction: How-to, photo feature, technical, "nuts and bolts" construction job-site features. Buys 4 mss/year. Send complete ms. Length: 175 typewritten lines, 35 character count, no maximum. Pays $75/published page. Sometimes pays expenses of writer on assignment.

Tips: "We need writers who can write clearly about our specialized trade area. An engineering/construction background is a plus if the person is also an excellent writer. The writer may have a better chance of breaking in at our publication with short articles and fillers because we have very limited space for editorial copy. The most frequent mistake made by writers is that they do not tailor their article to our specific market—the nonresidential construction market in Nebraska, Iowa, Kansas and Missouri. We are not interested in what happens in New York unless it has a specific impact in the Midwest. We will be producing more personality profiles of contractors in 1987."

P.O.B., Point of Beginning, P.O.B. Publishing Co., Box 810, Wayne MI 48184. (313)729-8400. Editor: Edwin W. Miller. 50% freelance written. Prefers to work with published/established writers. Bimonthly magazine featuring articles of a technical, business, professional and general nature for the professionals and technicians of the surveying and mapping community. Circ. 65,500+. Pays on publication. Publication date after acceptance "varies with backlog." Byline given "with short biography, if appropriate." Offers 50% kill fee.

Buys first serial rights and all rights; makes work-for-hire assignments. Submit seasonal/holiday material 4 months in advance. Simultaneous queries and photocopied submissions OK. Computer printout submissions acceptable; prefers letter-quality (with no right margin justification); no dot-matrix. Reports in 1 month. Free sample copy for 10x13 SAE and 8 first class stamps; writer's guidelines for SAE and 1 first class stamp.

Nonfiction: Jeanne M. Helfrick, associate editor. Historical/nostalgic; how-to; interview/profile; photo feature; technical (only related to surveying, mapping, construction—profession and business of); and travel (only sites of professional society meetings). Buys 12 mss/year. Submit complete ms. Length: 1,000-4,000 words. Pays $100-400.

Photos: Send captioned photos with ms. Pays $10-50 for color transparencies and prints; $5-25 for 5x7 b&w prints. Model release and identification of subjects required.

Columns/Departments: A Conversation With (interview of people in the field about their professional involvement, point of view); and Picture Profile (profile of people in the field slanted toward their special interest, talent, involvement that is unusual to the profession). Buys 6 mss/year. Query associate editor. Length: 1,000-2,500 words. Payment varies.

Tips: "If an article is good, we'll use it. The most frequent mistake made by writers is that they have not bothered to find out who the readership of our magazine is."

‡REMODELING CONTRACTOR, Maclean Hunter Publishing Co., Suite 500, 300 W. Adams St., Chicago IL 60614. (312)726-2802. Editor: Don Logay. 5% freelance written. A monthly magazine for home-improvement contractors with "business-oriented articles pertaining to remodeling, and emphasis on business ideas for contractor/readers." Circ. 42,000. Pays on publication. Publishes ms an average of 2 months after acceptance. Byline given. Buys first North American serial rights. Submit seasonal/holiday material 3 months in advance. Electronic submissions OK via IBM PC Xywrite, but requires hard copy also. Computer printout submissions acceptable; no dot-matrix. Reports in 3 weeks on queries. Sample copy for 8½x12 SAE with $1.45 postage. Free writer's guidelines.

Nonfiction: How-to (remodeling project to some degree technical) and photo feature. Buys 6 mss/year. Query with published clips. Length: 750-2,000 words. Pays $75-350 for assigned articles; Pays $200 maximum for unsolicited articles. Sometimes pays the expenses of writers on assignment.

Photos: State availability of photos with submission. Reviews contact sheets, negatives and transparencies. Offers no additional payment for photos accepted with ms. Captions and identification of subjects required.

Tips: "Get copies of the magazine. Study approach, and then call with any suggestion. It is likely that an idea will need to be more tightly focused for a trade magazine's audience." The area most open to freelancers is feature articles.

ROOFER MAGAZINE, D&H Publications, Box 06253, Ft. Myers FL 33906. (813)275-7663. Editor: Shawn Holiday. 10% freelance written. Eager to work with new/unpublished writers. Monthly magazine covering the roofing industry for roofing contractors. Circ. 16,000. Pays on publication. Publishes ms an average of 4 months after acceptance. Byline given. Buys first serial rights and second serial (reprint) rights. Submit seasonal/holiday material 4 months in advance. Simultaneous queries, and simultaneous and previously published submissions OK. Computer printout submissions acceptable; no dot-matrix. Reports in 2 weeks on queries; 1 month on mss. Sample copy and writer's guidelines for SAE and 27¢ postage.

Nonfiction: Historical/nostalgic; how-to (solve application problems, overcome trying environmental conditions); interview/profile; and technical. "Write articles directed toward areas of specific interest; don't generalize too much." Buys 7 mss/year. Query. Length: 3,000-7,000 words. Pays $125-250.

Photos: Send photos with accompanying query. Reviews 8x10 b&w prints and standard size transparencies. Identification of subjects required. Buys all rights.

Columns/Departments: Legal column (contract agreements, litigations, warranties, etc.); technology and application problems; safety; and better business articles. Buys 30-50 mss/year. Query with published clips. Length: 3,000-7,000 words. Pays $125-250.

Tips: "We prefer substantial articles (not short articles and fillers). Slant articles toward roofing contracts. Don't embellish too much. Our audience has proven itself to be educated, intelligent and demanding. The submitted freelance article should exemplify those traits. We have little use for generic articles that can appear in any business publication and give little consideration to such material submitted. The tone of articles submitted to us needs to be authoritative but not condescending. Authors of successful freelance articles know the roofing industry."

‡ST. LOUIS CONSTRUCTION NEWS & REVIEW, The Voice for the St. Louis Area Construction Industry, Finan Publishing Co., Inc., 130 W. Lockwood, St. Louis MO 63119. (314)961-6644. Editor: Robert D. Richardson. Monthly tabloid covering all aspects of St. Louis area building design and construction tailored to the management end of the industry. Circ. 11,000. Pays on publication. Byline given. Buys first rights only. Makes work-for-hire assignments. Reports in 1 month. Sample copy $2.

Nonfiction: Expose (of local, construction related practices); interview/profile (by assignment only); photo feature (with local construction emphasis); and technical. "No material unrelated to design and construction

industries." Buys 2-5 mss/year. Query with clips of published work. Length: open. Pays $40-300.
Photos: Send photos with ms. Pays variable rates for 8x10 b&w glossy prints and contact sheets. Captions and identification of subjects required. Buys one-time rights.
Tips: "Break in with some story ideas and samples of expertise and experience in a specific area. Follow professional writers' general practices. Let editors know if you have an IBM/IBM compatible PC."

‡**SHOPPING CENTER WORLD,** Communication Channels Inc., 6255 Barfield Rd., Atlanta GA 30328. (404)256-9800. Editor: Connie Brittain. 75% freelance written. A monthly magazine covering the shopping center industry. "Material is written with the shopping center developer and shopping center tenant in mind." Pays on publication. Byline given. Buys all rights. Submit seasonal/holiday material 3 months in advance. Photocopied submissions OK. Electronic submissions OK via DecMate computer system, but requires hard copy also. Computer printout submissions acceptable; prefers letter-quality to dot-matrix. Reports in 1 month. Sample copy $4.
Nonfiction: Interview/profile, new product, opinion, photo feature, and technical. Especially interested in renovation case studies on shopping centers. Buys 50 mss/year. Query with or without published clips, or send complete ms. Length: 750-3,000 words. Pays $75-500. Sometimes pays expenses of writers on assignment.
Photos: State availability of photos with submission. Reviews 4x5 transparencies, and 35mm slides. Offers no additional payment for photos accepted with ms. Model releases and identification of subjects required. Buys one-time rights.
Tips: We are always looking for talented writers to work on assignment. Send resume and published clips. Writers with real estate writing and business backgrounds have a better chance. Product overviews, renovations, and state reviews are all freelance written on an assignment basis."

WORLD CONSTRUCTION, Technical Publishing Co., 27 Paul St., London EC2A 4JU England. (01)628-7030. Editor: Greg Newton. 10% freelance written. Monthly magazine for "English speaking engineers, contractors and government officials everywhere except the U.S. and Canada." Pays on publication. Publishes ms an average of 3 months after acceptance. Byline given unless "the article is less than one page long." Buys all rights. Computer printout submissions acceptable; prefers letter-quality to dot-matrix. Reports in 1 month. Free sample copy.
Nonfiction: "How-to articles that stress how contractors can do their jobs faster, better or more economically. Articles are rejected when they tell only what was constructed, but not how it was constructed and why it was constructed in that way. No clippings from newspapers telling of construction projects." Query. Length: 1,000-6,000 words. Pays $100-200/magazine page, or 5 typed ms pages, depending on content and quality.
Photos: State availability of photos. Photos purchased with mss; uses 4x5 or larger b&w glossy prints.
Tips: "At the present time we are most interested in articles dealing with construction projects in overseas locations, or application of computer technology to construction."

Data Processing

These publications give computer professionals more data about their trade. While they are not as changeable as computer magazines for consumers, some companies have ceased publishing data processing trade journals. Consumer publications are listed under Personal Computing.

ABSOLUTE REFERENCE, The Journal For 1-2-3 And Symphony Users, Que Publishing, Inc., 7999 Knue Rd., Indianapolis IN 46250. (317)842-7162. Editor-in-Chief: T.L. Solomon. Managing Editor: P.J. Schemenaur. 100% freelance written. Eager to work with new/unpublished writers. Monthly newsletter covering 1-2-3 and symphony applications, tips, and macros. "Que Publishing is a sister company to Que Corp., one of the world's leading publishers of microcomputer books. Our audience uses *AR* on the job to solve problems that involve Lotus spreadsheet or integrated software use. These readers work for Fortune 500 companies, as well as small businesses." Circ. 6,900. Payment initiated within 14 days of acceptance. Publishes ms an average of 3 months after acceptance. Byline given. Buys all rights. Submit seasonal/holiday

material 2 months in advance. Photocopied submissions OK. Electronic submissions OK via MS-DOS or PC DOS 5¼" disks but requires hard copyalso. Computer printout submissions acceptable. Reports in 2 weeks on queries; 1 month on mss. Sample copy $6; writer's guidelines for #10 SASE and 1 first class stamp.
Nonfiction: How-to (use 1-2-3 or Symphony). "We like to cover tax planning and tax tips using 1-2-3 or Symphony in the March issue to increase productivity on the job. " No articles on Jazz or other software that is not compatible with the IBM PC. No news. Only 1-2-3 and Symphony application articles. Buys 48 mss/year. Query should detail writer's professional experience as it relates to Lotus products or microcomputers. Length: 1,500-3,000 words. Pays 12¢/word.
Photos: "We use·program listings, tables, and PC printer images to illustrate articles. This 'art' is purchased with the article."
Columns/Departments: 1-2-3 Tips: Items on short macros to ease printing, locate files, use pointers, etc.—in short, strings of commands that save the user time and energy while working in a file. Symphony Tips are also needed, covering any streamlined approach to file usage. Macro Of The Month is a department devoted to lengthier, meatier macros covering more involved execution of file commands. Wish List items detail commands and features that readers wish Lotus had supplied in 1-2-3 or Symphony. Product Reviews focus on 1-2-3 or Symphony-related hardware or software. Buys 96 mss/year. Query on reviews; send complete ms if tip, macro, or wish list item. Length: 175-400 words (tips, wish list); 500-800 words for reviews; 700-1,000 words for macros. Pays $25 minimum for tips; 12¢/word for reviews; $50-75 for macros.
Tips: "Know 1-2-3 and/or Symphony inside-out. Test the macros; make sure your submission is complete. Suggest a title; label figures and program listings. Write subheads for text; cutlines for figures and listings. Keep in mind the business user—ranging from neophyte to 'old pro.' We use tip writers again and again and encourage them to graduate to writing articles."

‡ASHTON-TATE QUARTERLY, Ashton-Tate, 20101 Hamilton Ave., Torrance CA 90502. (213)538-7579. Editor: Patricia Matthews. 80% freelance written. A quarterly company magazine covering dBASE II, dBASE III, Framework II, and Fred and dBASE programming languages. "The *Ashton-Tate Quarterly* is designed for professional and business users of our software. Our goals are to be an essential business reference for users of Ashton-Tate software by illustrating the benefits of our products in business to increase effectiveness, productivity, and creativity and to provide insights into designing and planning business applications and systems." Estab. 1985. Circ. 15,000. Pays on acceptance. Publishes ms an average of 3 months after acceptance. Byline given. Buys all rights. Electronic submissions OK via IBM-PC, Word Star preferred—"Call, if other formats are used"—but requires hard copy also. Computer printout submissions acceptable; prefers letter-quality to dot-matrix. Reports in 1 month on queries; 6 weeks on mss. Free writer's guidelines.
Nonfiction: Book excerpts, how-to (use dBASE and Framework in business to increase productivity and effectiveness), technical and case studies of products in use. "No testimonals to Ashton-Tate software." Buys 40 mss/year. Send complete ms. Length: 1,000-3,000 words. Pays 15-20¢/word.
Photos: State availability of photos with submission. Offers no additional payment for photos accepted with ms. Model releases and identification of subjects required.
Columns/Departments: Collector's Corner (macros and other useful tips for using Framework II), 500-1,500 words; and Expert's Corner (business advice on topics of interest to our product users), 1,500-3,000 words. Buys 8 mss/year. Send complete ms. Pays15-20¢/word.
Tips: "We need technical information presented in a way that is accessible and interesting to non-technical computer users. Contact editor with article proposals. Be specific about content of articles."

BUSINESS SOFTWARE, Building Better PC Applications, M&T Publishing, 501 Galveston Dr., Redwood City CA 94063. (415)366-3600. Editor: Jim Fawcette. Managing Editor: Judy Lee. 50-60% freelance written. "Will work with new writers if technical expertise is there." Monthly magazine covering the business of computers. "We are not geared toward the prepurchasers—the people thinking about getting computers—or those just getting a start in computers. Ours is a *highly sophisticated* audience comprised of people who have been using computers in their businesses for years, who are at the leading edge of what's happening in the world of business computing and who want the leverage computers provide to them." Circ. 60,000. Pays on acceptance. Publishes ms an average of 1 month after acceptance. Byline given. Buys first serial rights plus one reprint right. Simultaneous queries and photocopied submissions OK. Electronic submissions OK on 300-1200 baud, 7-8 data bits, 1 stop bit, xmodem transfers or MCI Mail (user name: BusinessSoftware). Computer printout submissions acceptable; prefers letter-quality to dot-matrix. Reports in 4 weeks on queries; 8 weeks on mss. Free sample copy and writer's guidelines.
Nonfiction: Book excerpts; how-to (advanced tutorials on practical software use); opinion (reviews); and technical. No humor, game reviews or articles not related to business. Buys 50-75 mss/year. Query with published clips or send complete ms. Length: 750-3,500 words. Pays $75-100/published page. Sometimes pays expenses of writers on assignment.
Photos: Send photo with query or ms. Reviews b&w and color contact sheets; payment included in per-page rate. Captions, model release, and identification of subjects required. Buys one-time rights plus one reprint right.

Tips: "Query first, then call after query answered. Timeliness and technical savvy are a must with us. Feature tutorial section always open to freelancers, but note we are an *advanced* user magazine, not interested in novice, prepurchase, or other introductory material. If articles are technically competent, any length is acceptable to us. Frequent mistakes made by writers are not using enough detailed information about the application being discussed, lack of relevance or inability to relate program to business user and lack of photos, display screen, printouts, reports and sidebars. A recent change in format and editor may result in a few policy changes, but the market the magazine focuses on will remain the same."

‡THE CHRONICLE MAGAZINE, Independent Magazine for Hewlett-Packard Technical Computer Users, Wilson Publications, Inc., Box 10998, #450, Austin TX 78766. (512)250-5518. Editor: Catherine V. Warren. 70% freelance written. A monthly magazine covering Hewlett-Packard technical computers. "*The Chronicle Magazine* contains material covering the use of HP technical computers for an engineering audience. This includes HP news, tutorials, reviews and new product announcements. Writers must be technically knowledgeable about their subject." Estab. 1985. Circ. 30,000. Pays on publication. Publishes ms an average of 2 months after acceptance. Byline given. Offers negotiable percentage of promised payment as kill fee. Buys first North American serial rights. Photocopied submissions OK. Electronic submissions OK via compuserve, easylink, MCI mail. Computer printout submissions acceptable; prefers letter-quality to dot-matrix. Reports in 1 week on queries; 2 weeks on mss. Free sample copy and writer's guidelines.
Nonfiction: How-to (on hardware and software applications), new product, opinion, and technical. Submissions must be directly related to HP 1000, 9000 and series 80 computers. Buys 50+ mss/year. Query with or without published clips, or send complete ms. Length: 300-2,000. Pays $30-125 for assigned articles; pays $30-75 for unsolicited articles. Sometimes pays the expenses of writers on assignment.
Photos: State availability of photos with submission. Reviews contact sheets, negatives, transparencies and prints. Captions required.
Tips: "Understand vertical publications in general—in particular how they differ from, say, generic computer publications like *Byte*. Let us know what your expertise is and how it will make you the right person to cover the proposed topic. Write for the engineer. Tell him/her how to get the most out of hardware/software. Let readers know of unusual uses for equipment. Be technical but don't be dry (i.e. don't write in manual style)."

‡COMPAQ MAGAZINE, The Magazine for Compaq Computer Users, 3381 Ocean Dr., Vero Beach FL 32963. (305)231-6904. Managing Editor: Paul Pinella. 70% freelance written. A quarterly magazine covering application stories, software reviews and hardware analyses. "Since our readers are users of Compaq computers, writers should be Compaq users themselves or extremely familiar with these machines." Estab. 1985. Circ. 130,000+. Pays on publication. Publishes ms an average of 1 month after acceptance. Byline given. Offers 100% kill fee. Buys all rights. Submit seasonal/holiday material 3 months in advance. Electronic submissions OK via IBM PC-XT; send ASCII format. Computer printout submissions acceptable. Reports in 3 weeks on queries. Sample copy $1 with 8½x11 SAE and 3 first class stamps.
Nonfiction: Essays, general interest, interview/profile, new product, and software reviews. "Don't send anything without query and conversation with the editor." Buys 15 mss/year. Query. Length: 300-500 words. Pays $200-800. Sometimes pays the expenses of writers on assignment. State availability of photos with submission. Reviews any size transparencies and any size color or b&w prints. Offers $5-100/photo. Buys one-time rights.
Columns/Departments: Eye of the Needle (commentary on personal computer industry), 1,000 words; On the Job (short essays of interesting Compaq users), 300 words; and Newswatch (news, important events), 100-300 words. Buys 12 mss/year. Business On-Line (business software questions answered) 900 words. Query. Pays $60-200.
Tips: "Feature articles are most open to freelancers. Be familiar with the Compaq computer, and have an interesting story in mind before contacting the editor."

‡COMPUTER CONSULTANT, Schuler Communications, Inc., 208 N. Townsend St., Syracuse NY 13203. (315)472-1008. Editor: Martin McMahon. 25% freelance written. A monthly tabloid covering data processing/communication consulting. Circ. 20,000. Pays on publication. Publishes ms an average of 2 months after acceptance. Byline given. Offers 50% kill fee. Buys first North American serial rights. Submit seasonal/holiday material 3 months in advance. Simultaneous and previously published submissions OK. Electronic submissions OK via disk, ASCII format but requires hard copy also. Computer printout submissions acceptable; prefers letter-quality to dot-matrix. Reports in 1 week on queries; 2 months on mss. Sample copy for 8½x11 SAE with 4 first class stamps.
Nonfiction: John Moore, articles editor. Book excerpts, essays, expose, interview/profile, personal experience (consultant only); and technical. Buys 24-32 mss/year. Query with or without published clips, or send complete ms. Length: 250-3,000 words. Pays $50-100 for assigned articles; pays $25-75 for unsolicited articles. Sometimes pays the expenses of writers on assignment.
Photos: State availability of photos with submission.
Columns/Departments: Book (hi tech, computers, business of consultant) and Application (consultant

author only). Query with published clips. Length: 250-3,000 words. Pays $25-75.
Tips: "Never call unless we tell you to; queries longer than one page get thrown out immediately; *persist*. It will pay off. News is most open to freelancers. Consulting firms—often parts of CPA firms—are in most every city in every state. Find them and ask what they are doing, what contracts they've signed or completed. Then write us about it. We are *dying* for regional news."

COMPUTER DEALER, Gordon Publications, Inc., Box 1952, Dover NJ 07801-0952. (201)361-9060. Editor: David Shadovitz. Monthly business magazine for dealers, computer and software stores, systems houses, consultants, consumer electronics outlets and business equipment dealers. Circ. 45,000. Pays on publication. Buys all rights. Phone queries OK. Submit seasonal/holiday material 6 months in advance. Previously published submissions OK. Computer printout submissions acceptable; prefers letter-quality to dot-matrix. Reports in 2 months. Free sample copy.
Nonfiction: How-to (sell, market, etc.); interview (with computer notables and/or where market is revealed); and articles on capital formation, etc. Writers "must have a knowledge of business and the computer industry, and the ability to ferret information or restate information known in other fields in a usable, interesting and particularly applicable way to those persons engaged in selling computers and peripheral products. We prefer not to see general marketing articles." Buys 3-6 mss/issue. Query. Length: 1,000-4,000 words. Pays 10-20¢/word.
Photos: "Photos (artwork) provide and spark greater reader interest and are most times necessary to explicate text." Send photos with ms. Uses 8½x11 b&w glossy prints. Offers no additional payment for photos accepted with ms. Captions and model release required.
Columns/Departments: "Columns are solicited by editor. If writers have suggestions, please query."

COMPUTER MERCHANDISING MONTHLY, The Magazine for High Technology Retailers, C.E.S. Publishing, Suite 660, 3550 Wilshire Blvd., Los Angeles CA 90010. (213)383-5800. Editor: Mike Hogan. Managing Editor: Larry Tuck. 30% freelance written. Monthly magazine covering retailing of computers for home and small business use. "The emphasis of the magazine is to aid the growing number of computer retailers." Circ. 37,000. Pays on acceptance. Publishes ms an average of 3 months after acceptance. Buys first serial rights. Byline given. Submit seasonal/holiday material 3 months in advance. Computer printout submissions acceptable. Reports in 2 weeks. Sample copy for 9x12 SAE.
Nonfiction: Interview/profile (of industry figures); technical (simple explanation of computers, related products); merchandising suggestions; sales training promotion tips; and case histories. No articles on general topics with no relation to retailing of computers. Buys 60 mss/year. Query. Length: 1,000-2,000 words. Pays $150-450.
Tips: Submit "query which shows research of the specifics of retailing computer products—good grasp of key issues, major names, etc. It's rewarding finding someone who listens to us when we explain what we want and who consistently gives us what we ask for."

COMPUTERWORLD, 375 Cochituate Rd., Box 880, Framingham MA 01701. (617)879-0700. Editor: Terry Catchpole. 15% freelance written. Prefers to work with published/established writers. Weekly. For management level computer users chiefly in the business community, but also in government and education. Circ. 125,000. Buys all rights. Pays on publication. Publishes ms 1-2 months after acceptance. Photocopied submissions OK, if exclusive for stated period. Electronic submissions OK via Atex compability. Computer printout submissions acceptable; prefers letter-quality to dot-matrix. Reports in 1 month. Free sample copy, if request is accompanied by story idea or specific query.
Nonfiction: "*Computerworld* is written for professional users and managers of general purpose computer systems. Our audience includes those who direct, manage, supervise and program computers. Primary readers are top systems executives and their staffs, typically Fortune 1000 companies, government agencies and educational organizations. We cover news, product/service announcements and technical/management information. Emphasis is on timely, accurate information of immediate use to data processing professionals. We stress impact on users and need a practical approach. Some knowledge of business computing is required to score with us. Ask yourself: 'How do computer systems support business objectives? How are microcomputers integrated into a corporate environment? How are corporations merging voice and data communications?' Include full names, titles of people and configuration of computer systems in use. Buys 200 mss/year. Written query preferred, but brief phone calls are acceptable. Length: 1,000-6,000 words for in-depth articles and feature articles for special CW sections or publications. Payment starts at $300 for fulltime writers and goes up depending on topic, length and author. Experienced writers particularly in the computer industry, may contact the Features Director." Sometimes pays the expenses of writers on assignment.
Tips: "The most frequent mistakes made by writers in completing an article for us are not understanding the sophistication of our business users, not reading the publication before querying, and not querying."

COMPUTING CANADA, The Newspaper for Information Processing Management, Plesman Publications Ltd., #703, 2 Lansing Sq., Willowdale, Ontario M2J 5A1 Canada. (416)497-9562. Editor:

Gordon Campbell. Managing Editor: David Paddon. 10% freelance written. A biweekly tabloid covering data processing/data communications. Circ. 32,000. Pays on publication. Publishes ms an average of 2 months after acceptance. Byline given. Offers $50 kill fee. Buys first North American serial rights. Submit seasonal/holiday material 2 months in advance. Simultaneous and photocopied submissions OK. Electronic submissions OK via Model: text capture or Immedia E-mail diskette: PC or 8-in CP/M or Commodore. Computer printout submissions acceptable; prefers letter-quality to dot-matrix. Reports in 2 weeks on queries; 1 month on mss. Free sample copy and writer's guidelines.
Nonfiction: Opinion, personal experience and technical. Must have relevance to Canadians. Buys 150 mss/year. Query with published clips. Length: 400-1,500 words. Pays $75-350 (Canadian) for assigned articles; pays $50-300 for unsolicited articles; sometimes trades advertising for consultants ("*very* infrequently"). Sometimes pays the expenses of writers on assignment.
Photos: Send photos with submission. Reviews 5x7 prints. Offers $10/photo. Model releases and identification of subjects required. Buys one-time rights.

‡DATA BASE MONTHLY, For Data General and Compatible Users, Data Base Publications, 11754 Jollyville Road, Austin TX 78759. (512)250-1255. Editor: Wendell Watson. Managing Editor: Steve Knight. 50% freelance written. Works with a small number of new/unpublished writers each year. A monthly magazine covering Data General Computer Systems. "Data Base Monthly is the primary independent source of technical and market-specific information for people who use Data General computer systems or sell to the Data General market." Circ. 25,000. Pays on publication. Publishes ms an average of 3 months after acceptance. Byline given. Buys first North American serial rights and second serial (reprint) rights. Submit seasonal/holiday material 3 months in advance. Computer printout submissions acceptable; prefers letter-quality to dot-matrix. Reports in 1 month. Free sample copy and writer's guidelines.
Nonfiction: How-to, new product (computer-related), and technical all specific to Data General systems. No articles which cannot be related to Data General. Buys 25 mss/year. Query with published clips. Length: 1,000-3,500 words. Pays $100-500 for assigned articles; pays $0-500 for unsolicited articles. Sometimes pays the expenses of writers on assignment.
Photos: State availability of photos with submission. Reviews contact sheets, transparencies and 5x7 prints. Offers $0-25/photo. Captions, model releases, and identification of subjects required. Buys first serial rights.
Columns/Departments: Technical columns (instructive articles on Data General computer hardware and software, including reviews by users), 1,000-2,500 words. Query with published clips. Pays $0-300.
Tips: "Feature articles are the area of our publication most open to freelancers."

DATAMATION, Technical Publishing D & B, 875 3rd Ave., New York NY 10022. Executive Editor: Rebecca Barna. 80% freelance written. Monthly magazine for scientific, engineering and commercial data processing professionals. Circ. 150,000. Pays on publication. Byline given. Offers negotiable kill fee. Buys all rights. Submit seasonal/holiday material 3 months in advance. Photocopied and previously published submissions ("if indicated where") OK. Computer printout submissions acceptable; prefers letter-quality to dot-matrix. Reports as soon as possible on queries. Free sample copy and writer's guidelines. "Request our list of themes for the coming year."
Nonfiction: Covers all aspects of computer industry technical, managerial and sociological concerns, as well as computer industry news analysis. No general articles on computers. Buys 60 mss/year. Query with published clips. Length: 2,000-4,000 words. Pays $300-1,000/article. Pays expenses of writers on assignment.
Photos: Reviews 35mm color transparencies and 8x10 b&w prints. No extra payment for photos—included in payment for manuscript.
Tips: "The most frequent mistake made by writers is failure to read the magazine and figure out what we're about."

THE DEC PROFESSIONAL, Professional Press, Inc., 921 Bethlehem Pk., Springhouse PA 19477. (215)542-7008. Publishers: Carl B. Marbach and R.D. Mallery. 95% freelance written. Eager to work with new/unpublished writers. Bimonthly magazine covering Digital Equipment Corp. computers. "We publish highly technical, user-written articles concerning DEC equipment. We are a forum for DEC users worldwide." Circ. 92,000. Publishes ms an average of 3 months after acceptance. Byline given. Buys first North American serial rights. Electronic submissions OK via 800 or 1600 BP1 mag tape or 5¼" Rx 50 floppy for DEC Rainbow, Pro 300 or DECmate II (contact office first), but requires hard copy also. Computer printout submissions acceptable; prefers letter-quality to dot-matrix. Free sample copy and writer's guidelines.
Nonfiction: Technical (computer related). No articles "not highly technical concerning DEC computers and related topics." Send complete ms. Length: 1,500-5,000 words. Pays $100-500. Sometimes pays expenses of writers on assignment.
Tips: "Authors should be technically knowledgeable about DEC computers. Please send articles of approximately 1,500-5,000 words, preferably on an 800/1600 BPI mag tape in PIP format, or in WORD-11 or MASS-11. We also accept 5¼" Rx50 floppy disks—Rainbow 100, Professional 300 series, or DECmate II compati-

ble. In addition, we can read RT-11 (only), RX01 or RX02 8" floppies. If not available, a letter-quality hardcopy may be forwarded to the editors at Professional Press."

‡DESKTOP PUBLISHING, Producing Words and Pictures with Personal Computers, User Publications, #180, 2055 Woodside Rd., Redwood City CA 94061, (415)364-0108. Editor: Tony Bove. Managing Editor: Cheryl Rhodes. 100% freelance written. A bimonthly magazine "providing answers to specific questions about publishing applications using computers. We deliver a tightly-focused readership who expect reliable advice on how to publish with state-of-the-art tools." Estab. 1985. Circ. 25,000. Pays on publication. Publishes ms an average of 2 months after acceptance. Byline given. Buys first North American serial rights or second serial (reprint) rights. Previously published submissions OK. Electronic submissions OK via CP/M, PC-DOS, MS-DOS, Macintosh; inquire for others; hard copy not required but appreciated. Computer printout submissions acceptable; "but we require final ms on disk, or via modem after we have accepted for publication." Reports in 3 months. Sample copy $5 with 9x12 SAE and $2.40 postage, or total $7.40 without SASE; writer's guidelines for #10 SAE with $.39 postage.
Nonfiction: Historical, how-to, interview/profile, new product, opinion, personal experience and technical. Buys 80 mss/year. Complete ms preferred. Length: 1,000-10,000 words. Pays negotiable rates.
Photos: Send photos with submission. 35mm 4-color transparences and 5x7 or 8x10 b&w glossy prints. Captions, model releases, and identification of subjects required. Buys one-time rights.
Tips: "For fastest reply, send manuscript on disk and paper, include address and phone number. Give specific how-to, in-depth information. Be clear and concise in style, but be complete in giving information that the user will need to duplicate your experience. For reviews, throughly test before writing."

DR. DOBB'S JOURNAL, Software Tools for Advanced Programmers, M&T Publishing, Inc., 501 Galveston Dr., Redwood City CA 94063. (415)366-3600. Editor: Michael Swaine. Managing Editor: Vince Leone. 60% freelance written. Eager to work with new/unpublished writers. Monthly magazine on computer programming. Circ. 49,000. Pays on publication. Publishes ms an average of 9 months after acceptance. Byline given. Buys all rights. Photocopied submissions OK. Electronic submissions OK on IBM PC or ASCII, PC DOS, MS DOS, but requires hard copy also. Computer printout submissions acceptable; prefers letter-quality to dot-matrix. Reports in 1 month on queries; 9 weeks on mss.
Nonfiction: How-to and technical. Buys 48 mss/year. Send complete ms. Word length open. Pays $25-500.
Photos: Send photos with ms. Reviews 3x5 prints. Captions required. Buys all rights.
Tips: "We are happy to look at outlines or queries to see if an author is suitable. They may also obtain writer's guidelines."

HARDCOPY, The Magazine of Digital Equipment, Seldin Publishing Co., Suite D, 1061 S. Melrose, Placentia CA 92670. (714)632-6924. Editor: Leslie Frohoff. 50% freelance written. Monthly magazine covering Digital Equipment Corporation (DEC) and DEC-compatible computer equipment, software and peripherals primarily for computer-sophisticated users and equipment manufacturers looking for more information on how to sell, distribute or improve their computer products. Circ. 92,000, U.S. and Europe. Pays 30 days from acceptance. Byline given. Buys all rights to new material. Occasionally buys second (reprint) rights. Submit material 4 months in advance. Computer printout submissions acceptable. All mss must be double-spaced. Reports in 2 weeks on queries; 2 months on mss. Sample copy for 9x12 SAE and $2.30 postage; writer's guidelines for business size SAE and 1 first class stamp.
Nonfiction: How-to (sell product; computer-oriented management and business); interview/profile (DEC or DEC-compatible manufacturers); and technical (DEC computer-oriented). No noncomputer related features or computer-oriented features that do not relate in any way to Digital Equipment Corporation. Buys approximately 36 full-length (feature) mss/year, plus news items, product reviews. Query with published clips. Length: Features, 2,000-3,500 words; news items, 50-150 words; reviews, 800-1,200 words. Pays $50-600.
Photos: Pays $10-25 for 5x7 b&w prints; $25 for 35mm color transparencies. Identification of subjects required.
Tips: "We need solid technical and how-to features from contributors. Research must be thorough, and the article's main point must somehow relate to DEC. For example, a market trend article should explain how DEC's market will be affected. We suggest you query to receive direction, since our needs are very specific. Before you query, obtain a copy of the magazine and get familiar with the kinds of stories we buy. We don't like to risk holding a large slot open for a feature that doesn't work out. Frequently writers neglect the technical information and vie for style, or vice versa. We want catchy leads and tags as well as a fact-filled body. 'Padding' is also unacceptable."

IBM PC UPDATE, New Techniques For Professionals, Que Publishing, Inc., a division of MacMillan Publishing, 7999 Knue Rd., Indianapolis IN 46250. (317)842-7162. Editor: T.L. Solomon. 100% freelance written. Works with a small number of new/unpublished writers each year. Monthly newsletter about IBM PCs and PC-compatible microcomputers. "*Update* is a techniques-oriented journal specializing in providing practical, hands-on information to increase business user productivity." Pays on acceptance. Publishes ms an average of 3 months after acceptance. Byline given. Offers $50 kill fee. Buys all rights. Submit seasonal/holiday material 3 months in advance. Electronic submissions OK on WordStar; ASC II files, 5¼" disk only, IBM format, but requires hard copy also. Computer printout submissions acceptable. Reports in 1 month. Free sample copy and writer's guidelines.

Nonfiction: How-to and technical. Buys 150 mss/year. Query. Length: 2,000-4,000 words. Pays $240-480.

Columns/Departments: Inside WordStar, Inside 1-2-3, Inside dBase, Inside Framework, and Inside Symphony. Buys 60/year. Query. Length: 2,000-4,000 words. Pays $350-450.

Tips: "Writers must have solid IBM-compatible mircocomputer background. The ability to explain procedurally and logically often complex instructions is a must. New applications and techniques are welcomed additions. Stick with areas you know best. Superficiality and fluff are not welcome. We will buy less review material as the number of products in the market continues to increase. We'll be focusing on products of major impact only."

‡JOURNAL OF INFORMATION SYSTEMS MANAGEMENT, Auerbach Publishers, Inc., 1 Penn Plaza, New York NY 10001. Editor: Peggy Burns. Managing Editor: Joan Dorfmann. 100% freelance written. A quarterly magazine covering information systems management. "Our journal provides those charged with responsibility for MIS mangement with practical, timely, how-to information addressing problems associated with coordinating line functions, managing technologies, interacting with users, and dealing with corporate management." Circ. 10,000. Pays on acceptance. Publishes ms an average of 6 months after acceptance. Byline given (includes capsule biography). Buys all rights. Simultaneous submissions OK. Computer printout submissions acceptable; prefers letter-quality to dot-matrix. Reports in 2 weeks on queries; 2 months on mss. Free sample copy and writer's guidelines.

Nonfiction: How-to; interview/profile (query); case study (query); and MIS-related issues. Upcoming theme issues include Data Communications, Trends in System Design and Development, Trends in Personal Computing, and Managing End-User Computing. "We do not publish informal or jocular essays, nor do we publish elementary, theoretical, or purely academic material." Buys 20 mss/year. Query or send complete ms. Length: 1,000-6,000 words. Pays $500 maximum.

Columns: Each issue of the journal contains 8-10 of the following columns: Strategic Planning, Managing Micros, Managing End-User Computing, Staff Development, Office Automation, Data Center Operations, Systems Development, Data Communications, MIS Economics, Technology Outlook, Security and Privacy, EDP Auditing, The User Interface, Data Management, In Practice: A Consultant's Viewpoint, Corporate Issues in MIS Management, On MIS: A View from the Top, MIS Industry Trends Analysis, Software Solutions, and Book Review. "We will accept column material with a more informal, opinion-oriented slant than our regular articles." Buys 40 mss/year. Query. Length: 1,000-3,000 words. Pays $100.

Tips: "Writers should keep in mind that our readers possess a high level of sophistication in both technical and management areas. As managers of the MIS function, they have many responsibiilties that pit them against myriad problems for which they need direct, practical advice. We welcome knowledgeable writers who can help our readers by telling them something they can use, something they do not already know. We discourage submissions that are too basic in scope or too theoretical to be of practical value to MIS managers in their work environment. All areas are equally open to freelancers. We encourage long-term associations with writers who can produce valuable material for us."

JOURNAL OF SYSTEMS MANAGEMENT, 24587 Bagley Road, Cleveland OH 44138. (216)243-6900. Publisher: James Andrews. 100% freelance written. Prefers to work with published/established writers; works with a small number of new/unpublished writers each year. Monthly. For systems and procedures and management people. Pays on publication. Publishes ms an average of 3 months after acceptance. Byline given. Buys all rights. Computer printout submissions acceptable; prefers letter-quality to dot-matrix. Reports "as soon as possible." Free sample copy.

Nonfiction: Articles on case histories, projects on systems, forms control, administrative practices and computer operations. No computer applications articles, humor or articles promoting a specific product. Query or submit ms in triplicate. Length: 3,000-5,000 words. Pays $25 maximum.

Tips: Frequent mistakes made by writers are choosing the wrong subject and being too specific regarding a product.

‡MICRO CORNUCOPIA, The Micro Technical Journal, Micro Cornucopia Inc., 155 NW Hawthorne, Bend OR 97701. (503)382-8048. Editor: David J. Thompson. A bimonthly magazine offering in-depth technical coverage of micro computers. Circ. 10,000. Pays on publication. Publishes ms an average of 2 months after acceptance. Byline given. Offers $25 kill fee. Buys first rights. Submit seasonal/holiday material 3 months in advance. Electronic submissions OK via MS-DOS/PC-DOS/CP/M. Computer printout submissions acceptable; prefers letter-quality to dot-matrix. Reports in 1 month on queries; 2 months on mss. Sample copy $3; free writer's guidelines.

Nonfiction: Gary Entsminger, articles editor. How-to (published article examples—How to write a PROLOG interpreter. How to build a 68000 computer); new product; personal experience and technical. Buys 60 mss/ year. Query with or without published clips, or send complete ms. Length: 2,000-5,000 words. Pays $75 minimum for assigned articles; pays $25 minimum for unsolicited articles. May pay other premiums in addition to fee.

Photos: State availability of photos with submission. Offers no additional payment for photos accepted with ms. Buys one-time rights.

‡MINI, The Magazine for IBM Systems 34/36/38 Decision Makers, Para Research, Inc., 85 Eastern Ave., Box 61, Gloucester MA 01930. (617)283-3438. Editor: Marlene Comet. 10% freelance written ("would like more.") A bimonthly magazine covering IBM Systems 34/36/38 computers. "Our readers are general or financial managers using IBM minicomputers, mostly for accounting purposes. They are not computer professionals." Circ. 34,000. Pays on publication. Publishes ms an average of 4 months after acceptance. Byline given. Offers 10¢/word kill fee. Buys first North American serial rights, first rights, one-time rights, second serial (reprint) rights or simultaneous rights. Simultaneous, photocopied and previously published submissions OK. Computer printout submissions acceptable; prefers letter-quality to dot-matrix. Reports in 1 week on queries; 2 weeks on mss. Free sample copy.

Nonfiction: Book excerpts, how-to, new product, personal experience and technical. Buys 5-10 mss/year. Query. Length: 2,000-5,000 words. Pays $500-1,500. Sometimes pays the expenses of writers on assignment.

Photos: State availability of photos with submission. Captions, model releases and identification of subjects required. Buys one-time rights.

MINI-MICRO SYSTEMS, Cahners Publishing Co., 275 Washington St., Newton MA 02158. (617)964-3030. Editor-in-Chief: George Kotelly. 25% freelance written. Monthly magazine covering minicomputer and microcomputer industries for manufacturers and users of computers, peripherals and software. Circ. 137,000. Pays on publication. Byline given. Publishes ms an average of 3 months after acceptance. Buys all rights. Simultaneous queries and photocopied submissions OK. Computer printout submissions acceptable; prefers letter-quality to dot-matrix. Reports in 1 month on queries. Free sample copy; writer's guidelines for 4x9 SAE and 1 first class stamp.

Nonfiction: Articles about highly innovative applications of computer hardware and software "firsts". Buys 60-100 mss/year. Query with published clips. Length: 500-2,500 words. Pays $70-100/printed page, including illustrations. Sometimes pays expenses of writers on assignment.

Photos: Send line art, diagrams, photos or color transparencies.

Tips: "The best way to break in is to be affiliated with a manufacturer or user of computers or peripherals."

‡NETWORK WORLD, C W Communications, Inc., Box 9171, 375 Cochituate Rd., Framingham MA 01701. (617)879-0700. Editor: Bruce Hoard. Features Editor: Steve Moore. 10% freelance written. A weekly tabloid covering data, voice and video communications (including news and features on communications management, hardware and software, services, education, technology and industry trends) for management-level users of communications systems. Estab. 1985. Circ. 60,000. Pays on publication. Byline given. Offers negotiable kill fee. Buys all rights. Submit seasonal/holiday material 2 months in advance. Electronic submissions OK if IBM PC-compatible. Computer printout submissions acceptable; prefers letter-quality to dot-matrix. Reports in 1 month. Free sample copy and writer's guidelines.

Nonfiction: Exposé; general interest; how-to (build a strong communications staff, evaluate vendors, choose a value-added network service); humor; interview/profile; new product; opinion; and technical. Editorial calender available. "Our readers are users: avoid vendor-oriented material." Buys 20-40 mss/year. Query with published clips. Length: 500-2,500 words. Pays $100 minimum-negotiable for assigned articles; pays $100 for unsolicited articles.

Photos: Send photos with submission. Reviews 35mm and 4x5 transparencies and b&w prints (prefers 8x10 but can use 5x7). Captions, model releases and identification of subjects required. Buys one-time rights.

Fiction: Adventure, humorous, mainstream, slice-of-life vignettes and suspense. "We want literate, technically correct stories that entertain while illustrating an issue, problem or trend that affects our readership. No obtrusive styles or 'purple prose'." Buys 4-5 mss/year. Query with published clips. Length: 500-1,500 words. Pays $100 minimum-negotiable maximum.

Tips: "Exclusive stories about the first users of new communications products or services have the best chance of being published. We look for accessible treatments of technology. It's OK to dig into technical issues as long as the article doesn't read like an engineering document. Feature section is most open to freelancers. Be informative, stimulating, controversial and technically accurate."

NEWS/34-38, For Users of IBM Systems 34/36/38, Duke Corporation, Suite 210, 295 E. 29th St., Loveland CO 80537. (303)667-4132. Editor: David A. Duke. Managing Editor: David Bernard. 40% freelance written. "We need experienced computer-literate writers." A technically-oriented monthly magazine for data

processing users of IBM Systems 34/36/38. Circ. 25,000. Pays on publication. Publishes ms an average of 4 months after acceptance. Byline given. Buys all rights. Submit seasonal/holiday material 3 months in advance. Simultaneous queries OK. Electronic submissions OK on PC Crosstalk, WordStar and IBM System/36, but requires hard copy also. Computer printout submissions acceptable. Reports in 1 month. Free sample copy.
Nonfiction: How-to (use Systems 34/36/38); interviews (with users); new product (review); opinion; personal experience (as a DP manager); and technical (tips and techniques). No fluff. Buys 50-100 mss/year. Query with or without published clips. Length: 1,000-5,000 words. Pays $100-500. Sometimes pays expenses of writers on assignment.
Photos: State availability of photos. Send photos with query or ms. Pays $5-10 for b&w prints; $5-20 for color transparencies. Captions, model release, and identification of subjects required. Buys all rights.
Columns/Departments: Technical Tips. Buys 12 mss/year. Query. Length: 50-500 words. Pays $10-100.
Fillers: Newsbreaks. Buys 25/year. Length: 50-500 words. Pays $10-100.
Tips: "We are a very targeted magazine going to a technically-oriented audience. Our writers *must* have a working knowledge of the IBM Systems 34/36/38 computers. Tutorial topics, user stories and management topics are most open to freelancers. We are interested in short feature stories as preferred by our readers. Also, all articles must have immediate benefit to our readers (i.e., if a technique is described, the code must be included so readers can implement the procedure immediately)."

‡**OFFICE MANAGEMENT & AUTOMATION**, Plesman Publications Ltd., Suite 703, 2 Lansing Sq., Willowdale, Ontario M2J 5A1 Canada. (416)497-9562 or 1-800-387-5012. Editor: Gordon Campbell. Managing Editor: Barry Conway. 50% freelance. A monthly tabloid covering business management and computer applications. "Stories about managing technology and people effectively, with a Canadian and end-user focus." Estab. 1985. Circ. 51,000. Pays 30 days after acceptance. Byline given. Buys first North American serial rights and other rights. Submit seasonal/holiday material 2 months in advance. Photocopied and previously published submissions sometimes OK. Electronic submissions OK; call for details. Computer printout submissions acceptable; no dot-matrix. Reports in 2 weeks. Sample copy for 9x12 SAE with 4 first class stamps; writer's guidelines for letter-size SAE with 1 first class stamp.
Nonfiction: Book excerpts, essays, exposé, general interest, how-to (on business computer applications for business), humor, inspirational, interview/profile, new product, opinion, personal experience, photo feature and technical. "No articles lacking 'hard' facts, 'realistic understanding of business' or articles full of advice, non-attributed quotes, etc." Buys 60 mss/year. Query with published clips, resume, or send complete ms. Length: 1,600-2,500 words. Pays $0-350; up to $1,000 for cover story (with photos). Sometimes pays the expenses of writers on assignment.
Photos: State availability of photos with submission; send photos with submission. Reviews contact sheets, 4x5 transparencies (for covers), and 8x10 prints. Offers $0-500/photo. Captions, model releases, and identification of subjects required. Buys one-time rights and other rights.
Columns/Departments: Compleat Manager (humorous, oratorical, analytical, podium); Quarterly Report (legal, finance/accounting, management consulting); and Connexions (insider's report, consumer's report, etc.). Buys 12 mss/year. Query with or without published clips or send complete ms. Length: 800-1,200 words.
Tips: "Send a resume outlining education and experience, especially business and writing education/experience. We are looking for professional writers interested in realistic, humane stories about people and their changing offices in Canada. Vendor hype or generalities are not wanted."

UNIX/WORLD, Multiuser, Multitasking System, Tech Valley Publishing, 444 Castro St., Mountain View CA 94041. (415)940-1500. Publisher/Editorial Director: Robert A. Billhimer. 75% freelance written. Prefers to work with published/established writers. Monthly magazine directed exclusively to the multiuser, multitasking computer industry. Readers are employed in management, engineering, and software development. Circ. 30,000+. Pays 30 days after publication. Publishes ms an average of 4 months after acceptance. Byline given. Offers kill fee. Buys first North American serial rights and second (reprint) rights. Simultaneous queries OK. Electronic submissions OK if compatible with 300/1200 baud ASCII format, UUCP (UNIX) or via PC/MS DOS format diskettes with ASCII files, but requires hard copy also. Computer printout submissions acceptable. Reports in 1 month. Sample copy $3. Free writer's guidelines.
Nonfiction: Book excerpts; how-to (technical articles on the Unix system or the C language); new products; technical overviews; and product reviews. Query with published clips. Length: 2,500-5,000 words. Pays $50-500. Sometimes pays the expenses of writers on assignment.
Photos: Send photos with queries. Reviews b&w contact sheets. Identification of subjects required. Buys all rights.
Columns/Departments: Wizzard's Grabbag (tips and techniques to ease the programmer's burden). Buys 40 mss/year. Send complete ms. Length: 500-1,500 words. Pays $50.

Dental

Writers can't just use their observations gleaned from the dentist's chair to write for these journals. Articles must be slanted for dentists, technicians, dental office managers and dental laboratory staff.

CONTACTS, Box 407, North Chatham NY 12132. Editor: Joseph Strack. 80% freelance written. Prefers to work with published/established writers. Bimonthly. For laboratory owners, managers, and dental technician staffs. Circ. 1,200. Pays on acceptance. Publishes ms an average of 5 months after acceptance. Byline given. Buys first serial rights and second serial (reprint) rights. Reports in 2 weeks. Free sample copy.
Nonfiction: Writer should know the dental laboratory field or have good contacts there to provide technical articles, how-to, and successful business operation articles. Query. Length: 1,500 words maximum. Pays 5¢/word. Willing to receive suggestions for columns and departments for material of 400-1,200 words. Payment for these negotiable.

DENTAL ECONOMICS, Box 3408, Tulsa OK 74101. Editor: Dick Hale. "We are backlogged with submissions and prefer not to receive unsolicited submissions at this time."

‡GENERAL DENTISTRY, Journal of the Academy of General Dentistry, AGD, Suite 1200, E. Chicago Ave., Chicago IL 60611. (312)440-4344. Editor: William W. Howard, D.M.D. Managing Editor: Terrance Stanton. 5% freelance written. A bimonthly magazine covering dentistry. "We are primarily a scientific journal. We do, however, publish columns and articles on practice marketing and management and on issues affecting the general dentist." Circ. 49,000. Pays on acceptance. Byline given. Offers 33% kill fee. Buys all rights. Submit seasonal/holiday material 6 months in advance. Computer printout submissions acceptable; prefers letter-quality to dot-matrix. Reports in 2 weeks on queries; 3 weeks on mss. Sample copy $5.
Nonfiction: Interview/profile, opinion, photo feature and technical. Articles must stand up to a 4-month lead time. Buys 12 mss/year. Query. Length: 500-4,000 words. Pays $100-500. Sometimes pays in copies, but only to authors of true scientific papers. Sometimes pays the expenses of writers on assignment.
Photos: State availability of photos with submission. Reviews 5x7 prints. Offers no additional payment for photos accepted with ms. Captions and identification of subjects required. Buys all rights; negotiation possible.
Columns/Departments: Marketing Your Practice (marketing techniques in ethical, professional way), 1,400 words; and Spirit of AGD (outstanding achievements by AGD members), 1,700 words. Buys 10 mss/year. Query. Pays $100-550.
Tips: "Understand the problems of the dentist who wants to achieve a secure future while maintaining the dignity of his profession. Nonscientific subjects are most open. Our organization is commited to continuing education, and articles that emphasize or highlight it will be considered."

PROOFS, The Magazine of Dental Sales and Marketing, Box 3408, Tulsa OK 74101. (918)835-3161. Publisher: Joe Bessette. Editor: Mary Elizabeth Good. 10% freelance written. Magazine published 10 times/year; combined issues July/August, November/December. Pays on publication. Byline given. Computer printout submissions acceptable; prefers letter-quality to dot-matrix. Reports in 2 weeks. Free sample copy.
Nonfiction: Uses short articles, chiefly on selling to dentists. Must have understanding of dental trade industry and problems of marketing and selling to dentists and dental laboratories. Query. Pays about $75.
Tips: "The most frequent mistakes made by writers are having a lack of familiarity with industry problems and talking down to our audience."

‡RDH, The National Magazine for Dental Hygiene Professionals, Stevens Publishing Corp., 225 N. New Rd., Waco TX 76714. (817)776-9000. Editor: Sandra A. Pemberton. 55% freelance written. Eager to work with new/unpublished writers. A monthly magazine covering information relevant to dental hygiene professionals as business-career oriented individuals. "Dental hygienists are highly trained, licensed professionals; most are women. They are concerned with ways to develop rewarding careers, give optimum service to patients and to grow both professionally and personally." Circ. 63,210. Usually pays on publication; sometimes on acceptance. Publishes ms an average of 8 months after acceptance. Byline given. Seldom offers kill fee.

Buys first serial rights. Computer printout submissions acceptable; no dot-matrix. Reports in 3 weeks on queries; 2 months on mss. Sample copy for 9x11 SAE; writer's guidelines for SAE with 1 first class stamp.
Nonfiction: Essays, general interest, interview/profile, personal experience, photo feature and technical. "We are interested in any topic that offers broad reader appeal, especially in the area of personal growth (communication, managing time, balancing career and personal life). No undocumented clinical or technical articles; how-it-feels-to-be-a-patient articles; product-oriented articles (unless in generic terms); anything cutesy-unprofessional." Length: 1,500-3,000 words. Pays $100-350 for assigned articles; pays $50-200 for unsolicited articles. Sometimes pays expenses of writers on assignment.
Photos: Send photos with submission. Reviews 3x5 prints. Model releases required. Buys one-time rights.
Tips: "Freelancers should have a feel for the concerns of today's business-career woman—and address those interests and concerns with practical, meaningful and even motivational messages. We want to see good-quality manuscripts on both personal growth and lifestyle topics. For clinical and/or technical topics, we prefer the writers be members of the dental profession. New approaches to old problems and dilemmas will always get a close look from our editors. *RDH* is also interested in manuscripts for our feature section. Other than clinical information, dental hygienists are interested in all sorts of topics—finances, personal growth, educational opportunities, business management, staff/employer relations, communication and motivation, office rapport and career options. Other than clinical/technical articles, *RDH* maintains an informal tone that readers can identify with easily. Writing style can easily be accommodated to our format."

SMILE MAGAZINE, Atlantic Marketing Group, Inc., Box 493, Rockland ME 04841. (207)594-8866. Publisher: Wayne Mates. 75% freelance written. Works with a small number of new/unpublished writers each year. Quarterly magazine on orthodontics. Profiles of orthodontic patients and proper dental hygiene. Circ. 8,000. Pays on acceptance. Publishes ms an average of 6 months after acceptance. Byline given. Buys first North American serial rights. Submit seasonal/holiday material 2 months in advance. Simultaneous queries, and simultaneous, photocopied, and previously published submissions OK. Computer printout submissions acceptable. Reports in 1 month. Sample copy $1 and 75¢ postage; writer's guidelines for #10 SAE and 1 first class stamp.
Nonfiction: Humor (orthodontist related); personal experience; photo feature (unique braces situations); and travel (related to newsletter). Query. Length: 1,000-2,500 words. Pays $50-200.
Photos: Send photos with query. Reviews 5x7, 8x10 color transparencies and 5x7, 8x10 b&w prints. Pays $20-75. Captions, model release, and identification of subjects required. Buys one-time rights.
Fiction: Humorous, orthodontist related.

TIC MAGAZINE, Box 407, North Chatham NY 12132. (518)766-3047. Editor: Joseph Strack. 75% freelance written. Prefers to work with published/established writers. Monthly magazine for dentists, dental assistants and oral hygienists. Pays on acceptance. Publishes ms an average of 4 months after acceptance. Byline given. Buys first serial rights and second serial (reprint) rights. Reports in 2 weeks.
Nonfiction: Uses articles (with illustrations, if possible) as follows: 1) lead feature: dealing with major developments in dentistry of direct, vital interest to all dentists, 2) how-to pieces: ways and means of building dental practices, improving professional techniques, managing patients, increasing office efficiency, etc., 3) special articles: ways and means of improving dentist-laboratory relations for mutual advantage, of developing auxiliary dental personnel into an efficient office team; of helping the individual dentist to play a more effective role in alleviating the burden of dental needs in the nation and in community, etc., and 4) general articles: concerning any phase of dentistry or dentistry-related subjects of high interest to the average dentist. Especially interested in profile pieces (with b&w photographs) on dentists who have achieved recognition/success in nondental fields—business, art, sport, etc. "Interesting, well-written pieces are a sure bet." No material written for patients instead of dentists or "humorous" pieces about pain. Query. Length: 800-3,200 words. Pays 5¢ word/minimum.
Photos: Photo stories: 4-10 pictures of interesting developments and novel ideas in dentistry. B&w only. Pays $10 photo/minimun.
Tips: "We can use fillers of about 500 words or so. They should be pieces of substance on just about anything of interest to dentists."

66 *Valuing ideas above craft is a serious problem. A badly written piece is a badly written piece, no matter how good the ideas may be.* **99**

Mary Lou Redding, The Upper Room

Drugs, Health Care and Medical Products

THE APOTHECARY, Health Care Marketing Services, 153 2nd St., Box AP, Los Altos CA 94022. (415)941-3955. Editor: Jerold Karabensh. Publication Director: Janet Goodman. 100% freelance written. Prefers to work with published/established writers. Magazine published 6 times/year about pharmacy. *"The Apothecary* aims to provide practical information to community retail pharmacists." Circ. 60,000. Pays on acceptance. Publishes ms an average of 5 months after acceptance. Byline given. Buys all rights. Submit seasonal material 8 months in advance. Simultaneous queries and photocopied submissions OK. Computer printout submissions acceptable; prefers letter-quality to dot-matrix. Reports in 6 weeks on queries; 5 months on mss. Free sample copy.
Nonfiction: How-to (e.g., manage a pharmacy); opinion (of registered pharmacists); and health-related feature stories. "We publish only those general health articles with some practical application for the pharmacist as businessman. No general articles not geared to our pharmacy readership; no fiction." Buys 6 mss/year. Query with published clips. Length: 750-3,000 words. Pays $100-350.
Columns/Departments: Commentary (views or issues relevant to the subject of pharmacy or to pharmacists). Send complete ms. Length: 750-1,000 words. "This section is unpaid; we will take submissions with byline."
Tips: "Submit material geared to the *pharmacist* as *business person*. Write according to our policy, i.e., business articles with emphasis on practical information for a community pharmacist. We suggest reading several back issues and following general feature story tone, depth, etc. Stay away from condescending use of language. Though our articles are written in simple style, they must reflect knowledge of the subject and reasonable respect for the readers' professionalism and intelligence."

CANADIAN PHARMACEUTICAL JOURNAL, 101-1815 Alta Vista Dr., Ottawa, Ontario K1G 3Y6 Canada. (613)523-7877. Editor: Jean-Guy Cyr. Assistant Editors: Mary MacDonald and Catherine Partington. 20% freelance written. Works with a small number of new/unpublished writers each year. Monthly journal, 48 pages, for pharmacists. Circ. 12,000. Pays on acceptance. Publishes ms an average of 3 months after acceptance. Buys first serial rights. Computer printout submissions acceptable; no dot-matrix. Reports in 2 months. Free sample copy and writer's guidelines.
Nonfiction: Relevant to Canadian pharmacy. Publishes exposes (pharmacy practice, education and legislation); how-to (pharmacy business operations); historical (pharmacy practice, Canadian legislation, education); and interviews with and profiles on Canadian and international pharmacy figures. Length: 200-400 words (for news notices); 800-1,200 words (for articles). Query. Payment is contingent on value; usually 18¢/word. Sometimes pays expenses of writers on assignment.
Photos: B&w (5x7) glossies purchased with mss. Pays $25 first photo; $5 for each additional photo. Captions and model release required.
Tips: "Query with complete description of proposed article, including topic, sources (in general), length, payment requested, suggested submission date, and whether photographs will be included. It is helpful if the writer has read a *recent* (1986) copy of the journal; we are glad to send one if required. The letter should describe the proposed article thoroughly. References should be included where appropriate (this is vital where medical and scientific information is included). Send 3 copies of each ms. Author's degree and affiliations (if any) should be listed; author's writing background should be included (in brief form)."

DRUG TOPICS, 680 Kinderkamack Rd., Oradell NJ 07649. (201)262-3030. Editor: Valentine Cardinale. Executive Editor: Ralph M. Thurlow. Semimonthly magazine for retail drug stores and wholesalers and manufacturers. Circ. 80,000 + . Pays on acceptance. Byline given only for features. Buys all rights. Computer printout submissions acceptable.
Nonfiction: News of local, regional, state pharmaceutical associations, legislation affecting operation of drug stores, news of pharmacists and store managers in civic and professional activities, etc. No stories about manufacturers. Query on drug store success stories which deal with displays, advertising, promotions and selling techniques. Length: 1,000 words maximum. Pays $10 and up for leads, $75 and up for short articles, $100-300 for feature articles, "depending on length and depth."
Photos: May buy photos submitted with mss. May buy news photos with captions only. Pays $20/b&w used, $50/4 color.

‡HEALTH FOODS RETAILING, Communication Channels, Inc., 6255 Barfield Rd., Atlanta GA 30328. (404)256-9800. Editor: D.J. Caulfield. 25% freelance written. Eager to work with new/unpublished writers. A monthly magazine covering the health and natural foods industry primarily for retailers. Circ. 11,017. Pays on publication. Publishes ms an average of 2 months after acceptance. Makes work-for-hire assignments. Submit seasonal/holiday material 6 months in advance. Computer printout submissions acceptable; prefers letter-quality to dot-matrix. Reports in 3 weeks. Free sample copy.
Nonfiction: Interview/profile on retail operations in the health and natural food industry. "We do not use features on manufacturing firms." Buys 15 mss/year. Query with published clips. Length: 500-2,000 words. Pays $75-250 for assigned articles; pays $50-160 for unsolicited articles. Sometimes pays expenses of writers on assignment.
Photos: State availability of photos with submissions. Reviews contact sheets and 2x2 transparencies. Offers $10-20/ photo (interior use, not cover). Model releases and identification of subjects required. Buys one-time rights.
Tips: "An understanding of how to communicate basic retailing concepts is more important than a knowledge of the health and natural foods industry. Strong journalistic talent should be a given. It's better to query first, rather than sending a full manuscript. Our major feature section provides the only area for freelance participation; all else is generated by staff. Contributors should realize that as a business publication, *Health Foods Retailing* is more apt to use articles which support assertions with strong, preferably statistical, analysis. We also require generic articles, not promotional efforts for individual operations."

HOME HEALTH CARE BUSINESS, J.B. Lippincott Co., East Washington Sq., Philadelphia PA 19105; Editorial offices: 454 Morris Ave., Springfield NJ 07081. (201)564-9400. Editor: Laurie Cassak. Bimonthly magazine for pharmacists involved in the home health care and DME markets. Circ. 8,000. Pays on publication. Buys all rights. Photocopied and simultaneous submissions OK. Free sample copy and writer's guidelines.
Nonfiction: Articles about existing home health care centers or opportunities for proprietors; new technologies in the home care field; and helpful hints for the pharmacist engaged in serving the booming consumer/home health care field. "It is essential to understand your reading audience. Articles must be informative but not extremely technical." No human interest stories. Buys informational, how-to, interview and photo articles. Query. Length: 1,000-1,500 words.
Photos: Photos purchased with accompanying ms with no additional payment. Captions optional.

RX HOME CARE, The Journal of Home Health Care and Rehabilitation, Brentwood Publishing Corporation, a Prentice-Hall company, 1640 5th St., Santa Monica CA 90401. (213)395-0234. Managing Editor: Dana Bigman. 40% freelance written. Monthly magazine covering home health care equipment supply. "The journal addresses the durable medical equipment and helath care supply needs of patients being cared for at home. The primary audience is medical supply dealers. The secondary audience is physical therapists, occupational therapists, nurses, physicians, and other medical professionals in the home health care field." Circ. 15,000. Pays on acceptance. Publishes ms an average of 6 months after acceptance. Byline given. Buys all rights and makes work-for-hire assignments. Submit seasonal/holiday material 6 months in advance. Computer printout submissions acceptable; prefers letter-quality to dot-matrix. Reports in 2 months on queries; 6 months on manuscript. Sample copy $5 with 9x12 SAE and 2 first class stamps; writer's guidelines for letter-size SAE with 1 first class stamp.
Nonfiction: How-to (market durable medical equipment); and technical (on use of non-invasive therapies in the home). "No general articles on health-related topics that are not geared specifically to our readership." Buys 50 mss/year. Query with published clips. Length: 1,000-2,000 words. Pays 10-12¢/word. Pays expenses of writers on assignment.
Photos: State availability of photos with submission. Reviews 3x5 b&w prints. Captions and identification of subjects required. Buys one-time rights.
Tips: "Writers must conform to our style, which is based on the American Medical Association stylebook. A medical background is not necessary to write for *RX Home Care*, but it is helpful when tackling technical equipment-related topics. All submissions are reviewed by an editorial advisory board of industry professionals."

ALWAYS submit mss or queries with a stamped, self-addressed envelope (SASE) within your country or International Reply Coupons (IRCs) purchased from the post office for other countries.

Education

Professional educators, teachers, coaches and school personnel—as well as other people involved with training and education—read the journals classified here. One of the main reasons why your favorite educational journal may not be listed is that *Writer's Market* includes only magazines that *pay* for articles. Many journals for educators are nonprofit forums for professional advancement; writers contribute articles in return for a byline and a few contributor's copies. Education-related publications for students are included in the Career, College and Alumni, and Teen and Young Adult sections of Consumer Publications.

THE AMERICAN SCHOOL BOARD JOURNAL, National School Boards Association, 1680 Duke St., Alexandria VA 22314. (703)838-6722. Editor: Gregg Downey. 10% freelance written. "We have no preference for published/unpublished writers; it's the quality of the article and writing that count." Monthly magazine; 52 pages. Emphasizes public school administration and policymaking for elected members of public boards of education throughout U.S. and Canada, and high-level administrators of same. Circ. 42,000. Pays on acceptance. Publishes ms an average of 3 months after acceptance. Buys all rights. Phone queries OK. Photocopied submissions OK. Computer printout submissions acceptable; prefers letter-quality to dot-matrix. Reports in 2 months. Free sample copy and guidelines.
Nonfiction: Publishes how-to articles (solutions to problems of public school operation including political problems). "No material on how public schools are in trouble. We all know that; what we need are *answers*." Buys 20 mss/year. Query. Length: 400-2,000 words. Payment for feature articles varies, "but never less than $100."
Photos: B&w glossies (any size) purchased on assignment. Captions required. Pays $10-50. Model release required.
Tips: "Can you lend a national perspective to a locally observed school program? Do you prefer writing for a general audience on a specific, knowledgeable-on-this-issue audience?"

ARTS & ACTIVITIES, Publishers' Development Corporation, Suite 200, 591 Camino de la Reina, San Diego CA 92108. (619)297-5352. Editor: Dr. Leven C. Leatherbury. Managing Editor: Maryellen Bridge. 95% freelance written. Eager to work with new/unpublished writers. Monthly (except July and August) art education magazine covering art education at levels from preschool through college for educators and therapists engaged in arts and crafts education and training. Circ. 22,042. Pays on publication. Publishes ms an average of 6 months after acceptance. Byline given. Not copyrighted. Buys first serial rights. Submit seasonal/holiday material 4 months in advance. Photocopied submissions OK. Computer printout submissions acceptable; prefers letter-quality to dot-matrix. Reports in 8 weeks. Sample copy for 9x12 envelope and $2 postage; writer's guidelines for business size SAE and 1 first class stamp.
Nonfiction: Historical/nostalgic (arts activities history); how-to (classroom art experiences, artists' techniques); interview/profile (of artists); opinion (on arts activities curriculum, ideas on how to do things better); personal experience ("this ties in with the how-to—we like it to be *personal*, no recipe style"); and articles on exceptional art programs. Buys 50-80 mss/year. Length: 200-2,000 words. Pays $35-150. Sometimes pays the expenses of writers on assignment.
Tips: "Frequently in unsolicited manuscripts writers obviously have not studied the magazine to see what style of articles we publish. The best way to find out if his/her writing style suits our needs is for the author to submit a manuscript on speculation. We are starting to incorporate articles dealing with the performing arts (dance, drama) in addition to our usual editorial focus on visual arts."

BRITISH JOURNAL OF SPECIAL EDUCATION, 12 Hollycroft Ave., London NW3 7QL England. Editor: Margaret Peter. 40% freelance written. Prefers to work with published/established writers; works with a small number of new/unpublished writers each year. Quarterly. Circ. 6,000. Pays token fee for commissioned articles. Publishes ms an average of 9 months after acceptance. Buys first British rights. SAE, IRCs. Writer's guidelines 60¢ in IRCs.
Nonfiction: Articles on the education of all types of handicapped children. "The aim of this journal of the National Council for Special Education is to provide articles on special education and handicapped children that will keep readers informed of practical and theoretical developments not only in education but in the many oth-

er aspects of the education and welfare of the handicapped. While we hope that articles will lead students and others to further related reading, their main function is to give readers an adequate introduction to a topic which they may not have an opportunity to pursue further. References should therefore be selective and mainly easily accessible ones. It is important, therefore, that articles of a more technical nature (e.g., psychology, medical, research reviews) should, whenever possible, avoid unnecessary technicalities or ensure that necessary technical terms or expressions are made clear to nonspecialists by the context or by the provision of brief additional explanations or examples. No jargon-filled articles with insubstantial content. Send query that summarizes the proposed content of the article in some detail, i.e., up to 500 words." No material not related to education. Length: 2,200-3,300 words. Payment by arrangement for commissioned articles only. Sometimes pays the expenses of writers on assignment.
Tips: "It's not easy for freelancers to break in unless they are practitioners and specialists in special education. If they have the appropriate specialized knowledge and experience, then articles in easily understood, jargon-free language are welcome, provided the depth of analysis and description are also there. Do not describe projects in a different context to that in the United Kingdom."

CHILDBIRTH EDUCATOR, American Baby, 575 Lexington Ave., New York NY 10022. (212)752-0755. Editor: Marsha Rehns. Managing Editor: Trisha Thompson. 80% freelance written. Works with a small number of new/unpublished writers each year. Quarterly magazine providing prenatal education. "Our audience is teachers of childbirth and baby care classes. Articles should have a firm medical foundation." Circ. 22,000. Pays on acceptance. Publishes ms an average of 6 months after acceptance. Byline given. Offers 25% kill fee. Buys first serial rights for articles and second serial (reprint) rights for book excerpts. Submit seasonal/holiday material 5 months in advance. Simultaneous queries and submissions OK. Computer printout submissions acceptable; no dot-matrix. Reports in 2 months. Free sample copy.
Nonfiction: Book excerpts (obstetrics, child care, teaching, neonatology); how-to (teaching techniques); and technical (obstetrics; child-rearing, neonatology). Buys 24 mss/year. Query with outline, lead and published clips. Length: 1,500-2,500 words. Pays $300-500. Pays expenses of writers on assignment.
Fillers: Newsbreaks. Buys 10/year. Length: 250-750 words. Pays $50-100. No byline.
Tips: "Queries should include a detailed outline, first paragraph, and writer's background. Articles should be serious and directed to an intelligent, specially trained reader. Frequently articles are too superficial in medical terms or lacking practical advice in teaching terms."

‡CHRISTIAN EDUCATORS JOURNAL, Christian Educators Journal Association, 3854 44th SE, Grand Rapids MI 49508. (209)599-2265. Managing Editor: Lorna Van Gilst. 5% freelance written. Works with a small number of new/unpublished writers each year. A quarterly magazine covering Christian day school education. "The general purpose of the *Journal* is to foster the continuing improvement of education theory and practice in Christian schools." Pays on publication. Publishes ms an average of 1 year after acceptance. Byline given. Not copyrighted. Buys first or second serial (reprint) rights. Submit seasonal/holiday material 4 months in advance. Previously published submissions OK. Computer printout submissions acceptable; prefers letter-quality to dot-matrix. Reports in 6 weeks. Sample copy for 8½x11 SAE with 73¢ postage; free writer's guidelines.
Nonfiction: Essays. No material directed to Sunday school teachers. Buys 5 mss/year. Send complete ms. Length: 600-1,200 words. Pays $10-15. Sometimes pays the expenses of writers on assignment.
Photos: State availability of photos with submission. Reviews prints. Offers no additional payment for photos accepted with ms. Identification of subjects required. Rights returned to sender after use if requested.
Poetry: Education-oriented, especially Christian day school education. Pays $5-10.
Tips: "The potential writer should carefully consider the statement of purpose inside the front cover as well as special focus topics listed on back cover."

CLASSROOM COMPUTER LEARNING, 19 Davis Dr., Belmont CA 94002. Editor: Holly Brady. 50% freelance written. Works with a small number of new/unpublished writers each year. Monthly magazine published during school year emphasizing elementary through high school educational computing topics. Circ. 83,000. Pays on acceptance. Publishes ms an average of 8 months after acceptance. Buys all rights or first serial rights. Submit seasonal/holiday material 6 months in advance. Photocopied submissions OK. Electronic submissions OK; "we prefer Apple but we can accommodate others." Computer printout submissions acceptable; prefers letter-quality to dot-matrix. SASE. Reports in 2 months. Writer's guidelines with SAE and 1 first class stamp; sample copy for SAE and 70¢ postage.
Nonfiction: "We publish manuscripts that describe innovative ways of using computers in the classroom as well as articles that discuss controversial issues in computer education." How-to (specific computer-related activities for children in one of three segments of the school population: Kindergarten-5, 6-9, or 10-12); interviews; and featurettes describing fully developed and tested classroom ideas. Recent article example: "Artificial Intelligence: What's In It For Educators?" (January 1986). Buys 50 mss/year. Query. Length: 600 words or less for classroom activities; 1,000-1,500 words for classroom activity featurettes; 1,500-2,500 words for major articles. Pays $25 for activities; $100-150 for featurettes; varying rates for longer articles. Educational Software Reviews: Assigned through editorial offices. "If interested, send a letter telling us of your areas of in-

terest and expertise as well as the microcomputer(s) you have available to you." Pays $100 per review. Sometimes pays expenses of writers on assignment.
Photos: State availability of photos with query. Also interested in series of photos for posters showing real world use of computers and innovative computer art.
Tips:"The talent that goes in to writing our shorter hands-on pieces is different from that required for features (e.g., interviews, issues pieces, etc.) Write whatever taps your talent best. A frequent mistake is taking too 'novice' or too 'expert' an approach. You need to know our audience well and to understand how much they know about computers. Also, too many manuscripts lack a definite point of view or focus or opinion. We like pieces with clear, strong, well thought out opinions."

COACHING REVIEW, Coaching Association of Canada, 333 River Rd., Ottawa, Ontario K1L 8B9 Canada. (613)748-5624. Editor: Steve Newman. 40% freelance written. Bimonthly magazine in separate English and French issues; 80 pages. For volunteer, community and paid coaches, high school and university sports personnel. Circ. 10,000. Offers on acceptance. Publishes ms an average of 3 months after acceptance. Buys first North American serial rights. Pays 50-75% kill fee. Byline given unless author requests otherwise. Phone queries OK. Submit seasonal/holiday material 3 months in advance. Electronic submissions OK on Macintosh/Micom. Computer printout submissions acceptable; prefers letter-quality to dot-matrix. Reports in 3 weeks. Free sample copy.
Nonfiction: How-to (coach-related of a general interest to all sports); humor (in coaching situations); inspirational (coaching success stories); interview (with top successful coaches); and new product (new ideas and ways of coaching). Wants "authoritative original material on coaching topics." Does not want sports stories with little or no relevance to coaching. Buys 20-30 unsolicited mss/year. Query with complete ms. Length: 1,500-2,500 words. Pays up to $300. Pays expenses of writers on assignment.
Photos: State availability of photos. Pays $5-25 for b&w contact sheets; $15-30 for slide size color transparencies. Captions required. Buys one-time rights.
Tips:"The freelancer can best break in with short articles and fillers so we can appraise the quality of writing and then give an assignment."

COMPUTERS IN EDUCATION, Moorshead Publications, 1300 Don Mills Rd., Don Mills, Toronto, Ontario M3B 3M8 Canada. (416)445-5600. Editor: Roger Allan. 80% freelance written. Eager to work with new/unpublished writers. Magazine published 10 times/year; 48-216 pages. Articles of interest to teachers, computer consultants and administrators working at the kindergarten to 13 level. Circ. 18,000. Pays on publication. Publishes ms an average of 2 months after acceptance. Byline given. Buys first serial rights, first North American serial rights, one time rights, second serial (reprint) rights, and all rights. Phone queries OK. Photocopied submissions OK. Electronic submissions OK on WordStar, but requires hard copy also. Computer printout submissions acceptable; prefers letter-quality to dot-matrix. Free sample copy and writer's guidelines with SASE or IRC.
Nonfiction: Use of computers in education and techniques of teaching using computers; lesson plans, novel applications, anything that is practical for the teacher. Does not want overviews, "Gee Whizzes," and reinventions of the wheel. Length 700-2,000 words. Pays 6-10¢/word.
Photos: Photos and/or artwork all but mandatory. Pays extra for photos. Captions required.
Tips:"We are looking for practical articles by working teachers. Nothing too general, no overviews, or the same thing that has been said for years."

CURRICULUM REVIEW, Curriculum Advisory Service, 517 S. Jefferson St., Chicago IL 60607. (312)939-3010. Editor-in-Chief: Irene M. Goldman. 80% freelance written. A multidisciplinary magazine for kindergarten-12 principals, department heads, teachers, curriculum planners and superintendents; published 6 times/year. Circ. 10,000. Each issue includes articles in the areas of language arts/reading, mathematics, science, social studies, and the educational uses of computers. A separate feature section varies from issue to issue. Pays on publication. Publishes ms an average of 6 months after acceptance. Byline given. Buys all rights. Photocopies and multiple queries OK, but no multiple submissions. Computer printout submissions acceptable; prefers letter-quality to dot-matrix. Reports in 6 weeks on queries; 4 months on mss.
Nonfiction: Charlotte H. Cox, articles editor. How-to articles should consider primarily an audience of secondary educators and describe successful teaching units or courses with practical applications. Articles of interest to kindergarten-8 educators also welcome. Focus should be on innovative or practical programs, teaching units, new curriculum trends, and controversial or stimulating ideas in education. "While we need articles in all four areas (language arts/reading, math, science, social studies), math and science are especially welcome." Buys 45 mss/year. Length: 1,000-2,000 words. Query. Pays $25-100.
Photos: State availability of photos with query. Prefers 35mm color transparencies or 8x10 b&w or color prints. Model release required. Buys all rights with ms; no additional payment.
Columns/Departments: 600 book reviews/year on an assigned basis with educational vita; textbook, supplements, media, and computer software selection in language arts/reading, mathematics, science and social studies. Emphasizes secondary level. "We are looking for new and lively treatments of educational topics. De-

scription of specific teaching units or courses are welcome if they have broad implications for other schools. Use fresh, descriptive, plain language—no educationalese." Length: 300-600 words. Pays $20-50.
Tips: "Schedule of featured topics available upon request. The writer has a better chance of breaking in with short articles and fillers since we tend to invite submissions for feature articles to be sure that we have a choice available for feature deadlines."

‡EARLY YEARS/K-8, The Professional Magazine, Early Years, Inc., 325 Post Rd. W, Box 3330, Westport CT 06880. (203)454-1020. Editor: Allen Raymond. 90% freelance written. "We prefer material from classroom teachers." A monthly magazine covering teaching of kindergarten through eighth grades. Pays on publication. Byline given. Buys all rights. Submit seasonal/holiday material 6 months in advance. Computer printout submissions acceptable; prefers letter-quality to dot-matrix. Reports in 6 weeks on mss. Sample copy $2 with 9x12 SAE; writer's guidelines for #10 SAE with 1 first class stamp.
Nonfiction: Patricia Broderick, articles editor. Classroom curriculum material. Send complete ms. Length: 1,200-1,500 words. Pays $35 maximum.
Photos: Offers no additional payment for photos accepted with ms. Model releases and identification of subjects required.
Columns/Departments: Patricia Broderick, column department editor. Send complete ms. Length: 1,100 word maximum. Pays $25 maximum.
Tips: "Manuscripts should be specifically oriented to a successful teaching strategy, idea, project or program. Broad overviews of programs or general theory manuscripts are not usually the type of material we select for publication. Because of the definitive learning level we cover (pre-school through grade eight) we try to avoid presenting general groups of unstructured ideas. We prefer classroom tested ideas and techniques."

INSTRUCTOR MAGAZINE, 545 5th Ave., New York NY 10017. (212)503-2888. Editor-in-Chief: Leanna Landsmann. 30% freelance written. Eager to work with new/unpublished writers, "especially teachers." Monthly magazine; 180 pages. Emphasizes elementary education. Circ. 255,000. Pays on acceptance. Publishes ms an average of 1 year after acceptance. Buys all rights or first North American serial rights. Submit seasonal/holiday material 6 months in advance. Photocopied submissions OK. Computer printout submissions acceptable; prefers letter-quality to dot-matrix. Reports in 6-8 weeks. Free writer's guidelines; mention *Writer's Market* in request.
Nonfiction: How-to articles on elementary classroom practice—practical suggestions as well as project reports, opinion pieces on professional issues, and current first-person stories by teachers about the teaching experience. Query. Length: 750-2,500 words. Pays $15-100 for short items; $100-350 for articles and features. Send all queries to Marge Scherer, managing editor/editorial. No poetry.
Tips: "The most frequent mistake writers make is writing to a general audience rather than teachers. We'll be looking for writing that considers the increasing ethnic diversity of classrooms and the greater age-range among elementary teachers."

‡JOURNAL OF CAREER PLANNING & EMPLOYMENT, College Placement Council, Inc., 62 Highland Ave., Bethlehem PA 18017. (215)868-1421. Managing Editor: Patricia A. Sinnott. 25% freelance written. Published Nov., Jan., March, and May. A magazine for career development professionals who counsel and/or hire prospective college students, graduating students, employees, and job-changers. Circ. 4,000. Pays on acceptance. Publishes ms an average of 4 months after acceptance. Byline given. Buys first rights. Photocopied submissions OK. Computer printout submissions acceptable; no dot-matrix. Reports in 1 month on queries; 2 months on mss. Free sample copy and writer's guidelines.
Nonfiction: Book excerpts, how-to, humor, interview/profile, opinion, personal experience, photo feature, new techniques/innovative practices and current issues in the field. No articles that speak directly to job candidates. Buys 7-10 mss/year. Query with published clips, or send complete ms. Length: 2,000-4,000 words. Pays $200-400.
Tips: "A freelancer can best break into our publication by sending query with clips of published work, by writing on topics that aim directly at the Journal's audience—professionals in the career planning, placement and recruitment field and by using an easy-to-read, narrative style rather than a formal, thesis style. The area of our publication most open to freelancers is nonfiction feature articles only. Make sure that the topic is directly relevant to the career planning and employment field and that the style is crisp and easy to read."

LEARNING 86, 1111 Bethlehem Pike, Springhouse PA 19477. Editor: Maryanne Wagner. 45% freelance written. Published monthly during school year. Emphasizes elementary and junior high school education topics. Circ. 200,000. Pays on acceptance. Buys all rights. Submit seasonal/holiday material 6 months in advance. Photocopied submissions OK. Computer printout submissions acceptable. Reports in 3 months. Sample copy $3; free writer's guidelines.
Nonfiction: "We publish manuscripts that describe innovative, practical teaching strategies or probe controversial and significant issues of interest to kindergarten to 8th grade teachers." How-to (classroom management, specific lessons or units or activities for children—all at the elementary and junior high level, and hints

for teaching in all curriculum areas): personal experience (from teachers in elementary and junior high schools); and profile (with teachers who are in unusual or innovative teaching situations). Strong interest in articles that deal with discipline, teaching strategy, motivation and working with parents. Recent articles example: "Classroom Rights and Discipline . . . A Simple and Effective System" (March 1986); "Motivating Students to Learn: What You Can Do" (March 1986); "Helping Your Students Deal with a Death" (April 1986). Buys 250 mss/year. Query. Length: 1,000-3,500 words. Pays $50-350.

Photos: State availability of photos with query. Model release required. "We are also interested in series of photos that show step-by-step projects or tell a story that will be of interest to children."

‡LOLLIPOPS, The Magazine for Early Childhood Educators, Good Apple, Inc., 1204 Buchanan, Box 299, Carthage IL 62321. (212)357-3981. Editor: Jerry Aten. 20% freelance written. A magazine published 5 times a year providing easy-to-use, hands-on practical teaching ideas and suggestions for early childhood education. Circ. 14,500. Pays on publication. Months until publication vary. Buys all rights. Submit seasonal/holiday material 6 months in advance. Computer printout submissions acceptable; prefers letter-quality to dot-matrix. Sample copy for SAE with 3 first class stamps; writer's guidelines for SAE with 2 first class stamps.

Nonfiction: How-to (on creating usable teaching materials). Buys varying number of mss/year. Query with or without published clips, or send complete ms. Length: 200-1,000 words. Pays $25-100 for assigned articles; pays $10-30 for unsolicited articles. Writer has choice of cash or Good Apple products worth twice the contract value.

Photos: State availability of photos with submission. Reviews contact sheets and transparencies. Offers $10 minimum/photo. Model releases and identification of subjects required. Buys all rights.

Columns/Departments: Accepts material dealing with the solving of problems encountered by early childhood education. Buys varying number of mss/year. Query with published clips. Length: varies. Pays $25-100.

Fiction: Adventure and fantasy (for young children). Query with published clips.

Poetry: Light verse. Buys varying number of poems/year.

Tips: "I'm always looking for something that's new and different—something that works for teachers of young children."

‡MEDIA PROFILES: The Career Development Edition, Olympic Media Information, 550 1st St., Hoboken NJ 07030. (201)963-1600. Editor: Walt Carroll. For colleges, community colleges, libraries, corporate training directors, manpower specialists, education and training services, career development centers, audiovisual specialists and administrators. Serial in magazine format, published every 2 months. Circ. 1,000. Buys all rights. Pays on publication. "Send resume of your experience in human resource development to introduce yourself." Enclose $5 for writer's guidelines and sample issue (refunded with first payment upon publication). Electronic submissions OK if PC DOS. Reports in 2 months.

Nonfiction: "Reviews of instructional films, filmstrips, videotapes, sound/slide programs and the like. We have a highly specialized, rigid format that must be followed without exception. Besides job training areas, we are also interested in the areas of values and personal self-development, upward mobility in the world of work, social change, futuristics, management training, problem solving and adult education. Tell us, above all, about your experience with audiovisuals, and what audiovisual hardware you have access to." Buys 200-240 mss/ year. Query. Pays $15/review.

Tips: "Reviewing a film is not the art of sparkling, creative composition. We aim to tell prospective renters or purchasers of off-the-shelf AV programs all they have to know and only what they want to know about a film or tape . . . so they're aware if an entire program may (or may not) be of value to their company. Our purpose is to be accurate, analytical and unbiased. Rather than reviews, we are writing 'profiles'."

‡MEDIA PROFILES: The Health Sciences Edition, Olympic Media Information, 550 1st St., Hoboken NJ 07030. (201)963-1600. Publisher: Walt Carroll. 100% freelance written. For hospital education departments, nursing schools, schools of allied health, paramedical training units, colleges, community colleges, local health organizations. Serial, in magazine format, published every 2 months. Circ. 1,000 +. Buys all rights. Buys 240 mss/year. Electronic submissions OK on PC DOS only. Computer printout submissions acceptable. Pays on publication. "Sample copies and writer's guidelines sent on receipt of resume, background, and mention of audiovisual hardware you have access to. Enclose $5 for writer's guidelines and sample issue. (Refunded with first payment upon publication)." Reports in 1 month. Query.

Nonfiction: "Reviews of all kinds of audiovisual media. We are the only review publication devoted exclusively to evaluation of audiovisual aids for hospital and health training. We have a highly specialized, definite format that must be followed in all cases. Samples should be seen by all means. Our writers should first have a background in health sciences; second, have some experience with audiovisuals; and third, follow our format precisely. Writers with advanced degrees and teaching affiliations with colleges and hospital education departments given preference. We are interested in reviews of media materials for nursing education, in-service education, continuing education, personnel training, patient education, patient care and medical problems. We will assign audiovisual aids to qualified writers and send them these to review for us. Unsolicited mss not welcome." Pays $15/review.

MOMENTUM, National Catholic Educational Association, 1077 30th St., NW, Washington DC 20007. Editor: Patricia Feistritzer. 10% freelance written. Quarterly magazine; 56-64 pages. For Catholic administrators and teachers, some parents and students, in all levels of education (preschool, elementary, secondary, higher). Circ. 15,500. Pays on publication. Buys first serial rights. Submit material 3 months in advance. Reports in 3 months. Free sample copy.
Nonfiction: Articles concerned with educational philosophy, psychology, methodology, innovative programs, teacher training, research, financial and public relations programs and management systems—all applicable to nonpublic schools. Book reviews on educational/religious topics. Avoid general topics or topics applicable *only* to public education. "We look for a straightforward, journalistic style with emphasis on practical examples, as well as scholarly writing and statistics. All references must be footnoted, fully documented. Emphasis is on professionalism." Buys 28-36 mss/year. Query with outline. Length: 1,500-2,000 words. Pays 2¢/word.
Photos: Pays $7 for b&w glossy photos purchased with mss. Captions required.

PHI DELTA KAPPAN, Box 789, Bloomington IN 47402-0789. Editor: Robert W. Cole Jr. 2% freelance written. Monthly magazine; 72 pages. For educators—teachers, kindergarten-12 administrators and college professors. All hold BA degrees; one-third hold doctorates. Circ. 140,000. Buys all rights. Pays on publication. Publishes ms an average of 6 months after acceptance. Reports in 2 months. Free sample copy.
Nonfiction: Feature articles on education—emphasizing policy, trends, both sides of issues, controversial developments. Also informational, how-to, personal experience, inspirational, humor, think articles and expose. "Our audience is scholarly but hard-headed." Buys 5 mss/year. Submit complete ms. Length: 500-4,000 words. Pays $100-750. "We pay a fee only occasionally, and then it is usually to an author whom *we* seek out. We do welcome inquiries from freelancers, but it is misleading to suggest that we buy very much from them."
Photos: Pays average photographer's rates for b&w photos purchased with mss, but captions are required. Will purchase photos on assignment. Sizes: 8x10 or 5x7 preferred.

SCHOOL ARTS MAGAZINE, 50 Portland St., Worcester MA 01608. Editor: David W. Baker. 85% freelance written. Monthly, except June, July and August. Serves arts and craft education profession, kindergarten-12, higher education and museum education programs. Written by and for art teachers. Pays on publication. Publishes ms an average of 2 months "if timely; if less pressing, can be 1 year or more" after acceptance. Buys first serial rights and second serial (reprint) rights. Computer printout submissions acceptable; prefers letter-quality to dot-matrix. Reports in 3 months. Free sample copy.
Nonfiction: Articles, with photos, on art and craft activities in schools. Should include description and photos of activity in progress as well as examples of finished art work. Query or send complete ms. Length: 600-1,400 words. Pays $20-100.
Tips: "We prefer articles on actual art projects or techniques done by students in actual classroom situations. Philosophical and theoretical aspects of art and art education are usually handled by our contributing editors. Our articles are renewed and accepted on merit and each is tailored to meet our needs. Keep in mind that art teachers want practical tips, above all. Our readers are visually, not verbally, oriented. Write your article with the accompanying photographs in hand." The most frequent mistakes made by writers are "bad visual material (photographs, drawings) submitted with articles, or a lack of complete descriptions of art processes; and no rationale behind programs or activities. It takes a close reading of School Arts to understand its function and the needs of its readers. Some writers lack the necessary familiarity with art education."

SCHOOL SHOP, Prakken Publications, Inc., Box 8623, Ann Arbor MI 48107. Editor: Alan H. Jones. 100% freelance written. Eager to work with new/unpublished writers. A monthly (except June and July) magazine covering issues, trends and projects of interest to industrial, vocational, technical and technology educators at the secondary and post secondary school levels. Special issue in April deals with varying topics for which mss are solicited. Circ. 45,000. Buys all rights. Pays on publication. Publishes ms an average of 8 months after acceptance. Byline given. Prefers authors who have direct connection with the field of industrial and/or technical education. Submit seasonal material 6 months in advance. Simultaneous queries, and simultaneous, photocopied, and previously published submissions OK. Computer printout submissions acceptable; prefers letter-quality to dot-matrix. Reports in 6 weeks. Free sample copy and writer's guidelines.
Nonfiction: Uses articles pertinent to the various teaching areas in industrial education (woodwork, electronics, drafting, machine shop, graphic arts, computer training, etc.). "The outlook should be on innovation in educational programs, processes or projects which directly apply to the industrial/technical education area." Buys general interest, how-to, opinion, personal experience, technical and think pieces, interviews, humor, and coverage of new products. Buys 135 unsolicited mss/year. Length: 200-2,000 words. Pays $25-150.
Photos: Send photos with accompanying query or ms. Reviews b&w and color prints. Payment for photos included in payment for ms.
Columns/Departments: Shop Kinks (brief items which describe short-cuts or special procedures relevant to the industrial arts classroom). Buys 30 mss/year. Send complete ms. Length: 20-100 words. Pays $15 minimum.

Tips: "We are most interested in articles written by industrial, vocational and technical educators about their class projects and their ideas about the field. We need more and more technolgy-related articles."

TEACHER UPDATE, Ideas for Teachers, Teacher Update, Inc., Box 205, Saddle River NJ 07458. (201)327-8486. Editor: Nicholas A. Roes. 100% freelance written. Eager to work with new/unpublished writers. Monthly (except July and August) newsletter covering early childhood education for preschool teachers. Circ. 10,000. Pays on acceptance. Publishes ms an average of 4 months after acceptance. Byline given. Offers 100% kill fee. Buys all rights. Submit seasonal/holiday material 4 months in advance. Simultaneous queries, and simultaneous, photocopied, and previously published submissions OK. Computer printout submissions acceptable; prefers letter-quality to dot-matrix. Reports in 6 weeks on queries. Sample copy and writer's guidelines for SASE.
Nonfiction: How-to (suggestions for classroom activities). Query. Pays $20/published page.
Columns/Departments: Special Days and Free Materials. Buys 15 mss/year. Query. Pays $20/published page.
Poetry: Children's poems, fingerplays, etc. Buys 6-10/year. Pays $20/published page.
Tips: "Submit original ideas and make sure submissions are in the *Teacher Update* format."

TEACHING AND COMPUTERS, The Magazine for Elementary Teachers, Scholastic, Inc., 730 Broadway, New York NY 10003. (212)505-3051. Editor: Mary Dalheim. 80% freelance written. Eager to work with new/unpublished writers if they are educators. Monthly magazine covering computers and education, especially how to incorporate the computer into the teacher's everyday curriculum. Circ. 50,000. Pays on acceptance. Publishes ms an average of 7 months after acceptance. Byline given. Offers variable kill fee. Buys all rights. Submit seasonal/holiday material 7 months in advance. Simultaneous queries OK. Computer printout submissions acceptable. Reports in 3 weeks. Sample copy for 8½x11 SASE; writer's guidelines for #10 envelope and 1 first class stamp.
Nonfiction: How-to (use computers in the classroom); new product; opinion (on computers). No book reviews. Buys 40 mss/year. Send complete ms. Length: 500-2,000 words. Pays $50-300.
Fiction: Short stories and plays about computers for children in grades kindergarten-8. Buys 4 mss/year. Send complete ms. Length: 2,000 words maximum. Pays $50-300.

TODAY'S CATHOLIC TEACHER, 26 Reynolds Ave., Ormond Beach FL 32074. (904)672-9974. Editor-in-Chief: Ruth A. Matheny. 40-50% freelance written. Works with a small number of new/unpublished writers each year. For administrators, teachers and parents concerned with Catholic schools, both parochial and CCD. Circ. 65,000. Pays after publication. Publishes ms an average of 2 months after acceptance. Byline given. Buys all rights. Phone queries OK. Submit seasonal/holiday material 3 months in advance. Computer printout submissions acceptable; prefers letter-quality to dot-matrix. Sample copy $3; free writer's guidelines for SASE; mention *Writer's Market* in request.
Nonfiction: How-to (based on experience, particularly in Catholic situations, philosophy with practical applications); interview (of practicing educators, educational leaders); personal experience (classroom happenings); and profile (of educational leader). Buys 40-50 mss/year. Submit complete ms. Length: 800-2,000 words. Pays $15-75.
Photos: State availability of photos with ms. Offers no additional payment for 8x10 b&w glossy prints. Buys one-time rights. Captions preferred;model release required.
Tips: "We prefer articles based on the author's own expertise, and/or experience, with a minimum of quotations from other sources. We use many one-page features."

Electricity

These publications are edited for electrical engineers; electrical contractors; and others who build, design, and maintain systems connecting and supplying homes, businesses, and industries with power. Publications for appliance servicemen and dealers can be found in the Home Furnishings and Household Goods classification.

ELECTRIC LIGHT & POWER, Technical Publishing Co., 1301 S. Grove Ave., Barrington IL 60010. (312)381-1840. Editor: Robert A. Lincicome. Managing Editor: Robert W. Smock. 1% freelance written.

Monthly tabloid covering engineering and operations for electric utility executives, managers and engineers. Circ. 42,500. Pays on publication. Publishes ms an average of 2 months after acceptance. Byline given. Buys first serial rights. Submit seasonal/holiday material 4 months in advance. Simultaneous queries OK. Computer printout submissions acceptable; prefers letter-quality to dot-matrix. Reports in 3 weeks.

Nonfiction: Technical. "No general electricity articles or pieces discussing benefits of electrification, lighting, industrial, commercial or residential uses of electricity." Buys 5-7 mss/year. Query. Length: 4,000 words maximum. Pays $25-200/published page.

Photos: Send photos or copies of photos with ms.

Tips: "Writers must be familiar with electric utility technology and engineering, finance, regulation and operations."

‡ELECTRICAL APPARATUS, The Magazine of the Electrical Aftermarket, Barks Publications, Inc., 400 N. Michigan Ave., Chicago IL 60611-4198. (312)321-9440. Editor: Horace B. Barks. Associate Editor: Kevin N. Jones. Uses very little freelance material. A monthly magazine for persons working electrical maintenance, chiefly in industrial plants, who install and service electrical motors, tranformers, generators, and related equipment. Circ. 15,000. Byline given. Buys all rights unless other arrangements made. Electronic submissions OK via CP/M disk, or modem. Computer printout submissions acceptable. Reports in 1 week on queries; 1 month on mss. Sample copy $4.

Nonfiction: Elsie Dickson, articles editor. Technical. Buys very few mss/year. Query essential, along with letter outlining credentials. Length: no minimum or maximum. "Some articles lend themselves to serialization, so we set no limit." Pays $250-400/article installment. Pays the expenses of writers on assignment by advance arrangement.

Photos: Send photos with submission. "Photos are important to most articles. We prefer 35mm color slides, but sometimes use color or b&w prints." Offers additional payments, depending on quality and number. Captions and identification of subjects required. Buys one-time rights. "If we reuse photos, we pay residual fee."

Columns/Departments: Address to editor of department. Electrical Manager (items on managing businesses, people), 150-600 words; and Electropix (photo of interest with electrical slant), brief captions. "We are interested in expanding these departments." Pays $25-100.

Tips: "Queries are essential. Technical expertise is absolutely necessary, preferably an E.E. degree, or practical experience. We are also book publishers and some of the material in *EA* is now in book form, bringing the authors royalties."

PUBLIC POWER, 2301 M St. NW, Washington DC 20037. (202)775-8300. Editor: Vic Reinemer. 20% freelance written. Prefers to work with published/established writers. Bimonthly. Not copyrighted. Pays on publication. Publishes ms an average of 3 months after acceptance. Byline given. Electronic submissions readable on IBM PC OK, but requires hard copy also. Computer printout submissions acceptable. Free writer's guidelines.

Nonfiction: Features on municipal and other local publicly-owned electric systems. Payment negotiable. Sometimes pays the expenses of writers on assignment.

Photos: Uses b&w and glossy color prints, and slides.

SUNSHINE SERVICE NEWS, Florida Power & Light Co., Box 29100, Miami FL 33102. (305)552-3887. Editor: L.A. Muniz, Jr. 5% freelance written. Monthly employee newspaper for electrical utility. Circ. 15,000. Pays on publication. Publishes ms an average of 3 months after acceptance. Buys first serial rights. Not copyrighted. Computer printout submissions acceptable. Free sample copy.

Nonfiction: Company news, employee news, general interest, historical, how-to, humor and job safety. Company tie-in preferred. Query. Pays $50-150.

Electronics and Communication

Listed here are publications for electronics engineers, radio and TV broadcasting managers, electronic equipment operators, and builders of electronic communications systems and equipment (including stereos, television sets, radio-TV broadcasting, and cable broadcasting systems). Journals for professional announcers or communicators can be found under Journalism and Entertainment and the Arts; those for electric appliance retailers are in Home Furnishings and Household Goods; publications on computer design and data processing systems are listed in Data Processing. Magazines on personal computers appear in the Consumer/Personal Computing section. Publications for electronics enthusiasts or stereo hobbyists can be found in Science or Music in the Consumer Publications section.

ANSWER LINE, On Page Enterprises, Box 439, Sudbury MA 01776. Editor: Stanley J. Kaplan. Managing Editor: Bette Sidlo. 5% freelance written. Eager to work with new/unpublished writers. Bimonthly newsletter focusing on telephone answering services for professional and medical offices, sales and service centers as well as small business people who need telephones monitored when they are not in. Circ. 50,000 initially. Pays on acceptance. Publishes ms an average of 4 months after acceptance. Buys all rights. Phone queries OK. Submit seasonal/holiday material 3 months in advance. Computer printout submissions acceptable; prefers letter-quality to dot-matrix. Reports in 2 weeks. Free sample copy and writers' guidelines.
Fillers: Clippings, jokes, gags, anecdotes, short humor and newsbreaks. "We are particularly interested in anecdotes in the first person narrative, stories of people and their *positive* answering service experiences and newsbreaks on various developments in business communications as they relate to telephone answering service applications. We particularly seek seasonal material." Buys 5-10 mss/year. Length: 75-150 words. Pays $25-40 minimum.
Tips: "Our acceptance is often based more on subject matter and details of story than on writer's style. We look for original ideas. Submissions should be geared to telephone answering service clients with emphasis on the advantages of retaining such service. Submit nothing on answering machines—they compete with our customers' services."

‡AV BUSINESS COMMUNICATIONS, Incorporating the Communications Journal, Maclean Hunter, 5th Floor, 777 Bay St., Toronto, Ontario M5W 1A7 Canada. (416)596-5878. Editor: Don Long. 20% freelance written. A magazine appearing 10 times a year covering the audio-visual industry. "Our objective is to provide a non-technical overview of the audio-visual industry—news, new products, profiles, etc." The audience is managers of corporate communications in selected Canadian industrial, commercial and financial companies. Circ. 10,322. Pays on acceptance. Publishes ms an average of 2 months after acceptance. Byline given. Offers 50% kill fee. Buys first North American serial rights. Submit seasonal/holiday material 3 months in advance. Simultaneous and photocopied submissions OK. Computer printout submissions acceptable. Reports in 1 month on queries; 2 weeks on mss. Sample copy for 8½x11 SAE with 2 first class stamps; free writer's guidelines.
Nonfiction: Interview/profile, opinion and technical. All submissions must have a Canadian angle. Buys 20 mss/year. Query with published clips. Length: 200-1,200 words. Pays $100-400 for assigned articles; pays $50-200 for unsolicited articles. Sometimes pays the expenses of writers on assignment.
Photos: State availability of photos with submission. Reviews contact sheet. Offers $25-150 maximum/photo. Captions, model releases, and identification of subjects required. Buys one-time rights.
Columns/Departments: Newsline (regional, national and international events and trends with a Canadian angle), 600-800 words; and Clips (capsulized information in contracts awarded, personnel changes, calendar events, etc.), 100 words or less. Query. Length: 100-800 words. Pays $25-100.
Tips: "*AV Business Communications* is directed to a business audience. Readers expect information specific to their needs. Our readers have a broad range of skills and knowledge levels. Therefore, submissions must contain sufficient background material for those less familiar with a topic, yet within the interest of more experienced readers. We prefer brief, factual reporting; stories that get right to the point and always answer the question 'What's in it for me?' "

‡AV VIDEO, Montage Publishing, Suite 314, 25550 Hawthorne Blvd., Torrance CA 90505. (213)373-9993. Editor: Sam Stalos. Managing Editor: Ed Reid. 25% freelance written. Eager to work with new/unpublished writers. A monthly mgazine covering audiovisual and video technology and techniques. "We aim to inform readers who use audiovisuals, video and computer graphics in their professional capacities in business, industry, and government." Circ. 41,500. Pays on acceptance. Publishes ms an average of 1 year after acceptance. Byline given. Offers 50% kill fee. Buys first rights or all rights. Simultaneous and photocopied submissions OK. Electronic submissions OK via 300 baud, 8 bits/word, 1 stop bit, no parity, but requires hard copy also. Computer printout submissions acceptable; prefers letter-quality to dot-matrix. Reports in 2 months. Free sample copy and writer's guidelines.
Nonfiction: How-to. "In every issue we attempt to publish a wide variety of articles relating to all aspects of audiovisual productions as well as developments in video, interactive video and computer graphics. We wel-

come all informed, well-written articles pertaining to slides, video, overheads, multi-image, interactive, computer graphics and all attendant applications. No chest thumping. Keep the adjective-to-noun ratio below 50 percent. Nothing related to company profile, personnel or promotion material." Buys 12-20 mss/year. Query with or without published clips, or send complete ms. Pays $200-400 for assigned articles; pays $50-400 for unsolicited articles. Sometimes pays the expenses of writers on assignment.

Photos: Send photos with submission. Reviews negatives, transparencies and prints. Offers no additional payment for photos accepted with ms. Model releases and identification of subjects required. Buys one-time rights.

Tips: "Freelancers should have some direct contact with the industry. Academic research and interview/reportage articles written by professional writers are of less interest to us than pieces written by professionals in our industry who want to share a view, idea or technique with others in the field. The magazine will continue to change with the industry and as the use of computer graphics and video continues to expand, so will our coverage of those fields."

BROADCAST ENGINEERING, Box 12901, Overland Park KS 66212. Editor: Jerry Whitaker. "We are backlogged with submissions and prefer not to receive unsolicited submissions at this time."

‡BROADCAST MANAGEMENT/ENGINEERING, 295 Madison Ave., New York NY 10017. (212)685-5320. Editor: David Hawthorne. 10% freelance written. For broadcast executives, general managers, chief engineers and program directors of radio and TV stations. Monthly. Circ. 33,372. Buys all rights. Byline given unless "article is used as backup for staff-written piece, which happens rarely." Buys 15-20 mss/year. Pays on publication. Reports in 1 month. Query. Electronic submissions OK if compatible with Televideo Systems CPM. Computer printout submissions acceptable; prefers letter-quality to dot-matrix.

Nonfiction: Articles on technical trends and business trends affecting broadcasting. Particularly interested in equipment applications by broadcasters in the production of radio and television programs. Emphasis on "competitive advantage. No product puff pieces. No general management pieces or general information stories. Our readers are interested in details." Length: 1,200-3,000 words. Pays $200-300.

Tips: "To break in demonstrate a knowledge of the industry we serve. Send for an editorial schedule and sample copy of the magazine; then suggest an idea which demonstrates an understanding of our needs. Pictures, graphs, charts, schematics and other graphic material a must."

BROADCAST TECHNOLOGY, Box 420, Bolton, Ontario L0P 1A0 Canada. (416)857-6076. Editor-in-Chief: Doug Loney. 50% freelance written. Bimonthly magazine; 72 pages. Emphasizes broadcast engineering. Circ. 7,000. Pays on publication. Byline given. Buys all rights. Phone queries OK.

Nonfiction: Technical articles on developments in broadcast engineering, especially pertaining to Canada. Query. Length: 500-1,500 words. Pays $100-300.

Photos: Purchased with accompanying ms. B&w or color. Offers no additional payment for photos accepted with ms. Captions required.

Tips: "Most of our outside writing is by regular contributors, usually employed full-time in broadcast engineering. The specialized nature of our magazine requires a specialized knowledge on the part of a writer, as a rule."

BROADCASTER, 7 Labatt Ave., Toronto, Ontario M5A 3P2 Canada. (416)363-6111. Editor: Colin Wright. "We are backlogged with submissions and prefer not to receive unsolicited submissions at this time."

CABLE COMMUNICATIONS MAGAZINE, Canada's Authoritative International Cable Television Publication, Ter-Sat Media Publications Ltd., 4 Smetana Dr., Kitchener, Ontario N2B 3B8 Canada. (519)744-4111. Editor: Udo Salewsky. 33% freelance written. Prefers to work with published/established writers. Monthly magazine covering the cable television industry. Circ. 6,300. Pays on acceptance. Publishes ms an average of 2 months after acceptance. Byline given. Buys all rights. Submit seasonal/holiday material 1 month in advance. Photocopied submissions OK. Electronic submissions OK via IBM PC, but requires hard copy also. Computer printout submissions acceptable; no dot-matrix. Reports in 2 weeks on queries; 1 month on mss. Free writer's guidelines; $2 IRCs for sample copy.

Nonfiction: Expose, how-to, interview/profile, opinion, technical articles, and informed views and comments on topical, industry related issues. Also, problem solving-related articles, new marketing and operating efficiency ideas. No fiction. Buys 50 mss/year. Query with published clips or send complete ms. Length: 1,000-4,000 words. Pays $200-800. Pays expenses of writers on assignment.

Columns/Departments: Buys 48 items/year. Query with published clips or send complete ms. Length: 1,000-1,500 words. Pays $200-300.

Tips: "Forward manuscript and personal resume. We don't need freelance writers for short articles and fillers. Break in with articles related to industry issues, events and new developments; analysis of current issues and events. Be able to interpret the meaning of new developments relative to the cable television industry and their potential impact on the industry from a growth opportunity as well as a competitive point of view. Material should be well supported by facts and data. Insufficient research and understanding of underlying issues are frequent mistakes.''

CABLE MARKETING, The Marketing/Management Magazine for Cable Television Executives, Jobson Publishing, 352 Park Ave. South, New York NY 10010. (212)685-4848. Editor: Ellis Simon. 10% freelance written. Prefers to work with published/established writers. Monthly magazine for cable industry executives dealing with marketing and management topics, new trends and developments and their impact. Circ. 15,000. Pays on publication. Publishes ms an average of 2 months after acceptance. Byline given. Buys first North American serial rights. Photocopied submissions OK. Computer printout submissions acceptable; prefers letter-quality to dot-matrix. Reports in 1 month. Free sample copy.
Columns/Departments: Cable Tech (technology, engineering and new products); and Cable Scan (news items and marketing featurettes mostly about cable system activities and developments). Buys 20 mss/year. Query with published clips. Length: 200-3,000 words. Pays $50-500. Pays the expenses of writers on assignment.
Tips: "Learn something about the cable TV business before you try to write about it. Have specific story ideas. Have some field of expertise that you can draw upon (e.g., marketing, management or advertising). Short articles and fillers give us a chance to better assess a writer's real abilities without exposing us to undue risk, expense, aggravation, etc. on a feature. Not interested in reviews of programming. Editorial focus is on the *business* of cable television. We are considering reducing our acceptance of freelance material to allow us to hire an additonal staff writer.''

‡CABLE TELEVISION BUSINESS MAGAZINE, Cardiff Publishing Co., 6430 S. Yosemite St., Englewood CO 80111. (303)694-1522. Editor: Jill Marks. Managing Editor: Chuck Moozakis. 20% freelance written. Prefers writers with telecommunications background, Semimonthly magazine about cable television for CATV system operators and equipment suppliers. Circ. 15,000. Pays on publication. Publishes ms an average of 3 months after acceptance. Byline given. Makes work-for-hire assignments. Phone queries OK. Electronic submissions OK via Apple III, Word Juggler software, but requires hard copy also. Computer printout submissions acceptable. Reports in 2 weeks on queries; 1 month on mss. Free sample copy.
Nonfiction: Expose (of industry corruption and government mismanagement); historical (early days of CATV); interview (of important people in the industry); profiles (of people or companies); how-to (manage or engineer cable systems); new product (description and application); and case history. "We use articles on all aspects of cable television from programming through government regulation to technical pieces. We use both color and black and white photos, charts and graphs. A writer should have some knowledge of cable television, then send a letter with a proposed topic." No first person articles. Buys 5 mss/year. Query. Length: 1,800-3,500 words. Pays $100/page of magazine space. Sometimes pays expenses of writers on assignment.
Photos: State availability of photos. Reviews 35mm color transparencies. Pays $50/page of magazine space for contact sheets. Offers no additional payment for photos accepted with ms. Captions required.
Tips: "The most frequent mistake made by writers in completing an article for us is not being specific enough about what the story topic really means to cable management—i.e., dollars and cents, or operational strategy. Freelancers are only used for major features.''

‡CHANNELS, of Communications, C.C. Publishing, Inc., Suite 812, 19 W. 44th St., New York NY 10036. (212)302-2680. Editor: Les Brown. Managing Editor: Peter Ainslie. 50% freelance written. A magazine published 10 times/year covering the business/art/technology/social influences of electronic media. "Our audience is comprised primarily of professionals in the industry." Circ. 30,000. Pays on acceptance. Publishes ms an average of 2 months after acceptance. Byline given. Offers 25% kill fee. Buys worldwide serial rights or second serial (reprint) rights. Sample copy $3.95.
Nonfiction: Book excerpts, essays, exposé and interview/profile. Buys approximately 50 mss/year. Query with published clips. Length: variable. Pays variable rates. Sometimes pays the expenses of writers on assignment.

‡DVORAK DEVELOPMENTS, Freelance Communications, Box 717, Arcata CA 95521. (707)826-0102. Editor: Randy Cassigham. Managing Editor: Michele Wolf. 10% freelance written. A quarterly newsletter covering business productivity/word processing. "We promote the adoption of the Dvorak keyboard for typewriters and computers. Emphasizes current research studies, case studies, and product overviews (reviews). Readers include individuals, governmental officials, and small and large businesses." Circ. 1,500+. Pays on acceptance. Publishes ms an average of 2 months after acceptance. Byline given. Offers 33% kill fee. Buys first rights; rarely reprint rights. Photocopied submissions OK; previously published materials accepted rarely. Electronic submissions OK via disks in IBM PC format but requires hard copy also. Computer printout submissions acceptable. Reports in 2 weeks. Sample copy and writer's guidelines for 6x9 SAE with 39¢ postage.
Nonfiction: Interview/profiles (if especially interesting Dvorak user); technical (application notes/case studies); how-to (typically a case study on how a company/agency solved a conversion problem); product overviews (detailed description of a Dvorak-related product/review); book reviews (books which significantly deal

with the Dvorak). "We do *not* want to see anything that tries to convice the reader that Dvorak is superior to Qwerty—our readers already believe that. We do not generally care to see stories about an *individual's* experience in changing from Qwerty to Dvorak." Buys 10-15 mss/year. Query, preferably with a recent clip. Length: 200-1,000 words. Pays 10¢/published word. Expenses must be negotiated in advance.

Photos: State availability of photos. Reviews b&w proofs or prints. Offers no additional payment for photos accepted with ms. Captions, model releases, and identification of subjects required. Buys one-time rights.

Tips: "If writers know a lot about the Dvorak, or a specific Dvorak application, they can probably write for us. We desire to get the wider viewpoint a freelancer can provide. Sections most open to freelancers: case studies. There are a lot of Dvorak users out there that we don't know about. We want to hear about them."

‡**INFORMATION TODAY**, Learned Information Inc., 143 Old Marlton Pike, Medford NJ 08055. (609)654-6266. Publisher: Thomas H. Hogan. Editor: Bev Smith. 25% freelance written. A tabloid for the users and producers of electronic information services, published 11 times per year. Circ. 10,000. Pays on publication. Publishes ms an average of 1 month after acceptance. Byline given. Buys first rights. Submit seasonal/holiday material 2 months in advance. Computer printout submissions acceptable; prefers letter-quality to dot-matrix. Reports in 2 weeks. Sample copy for 8x12 SAE with 5 first class stamps.

Nonfiction: Book reviews; interview/profile and new product (dealing with information industry); technical (dealing with computerized information services); and articles on library technology, artificial intelligence, database and Videotex services. Buys approximately 50 mss/year. Query with published clips or send complete ms on speculation. Length: 500-1,500 words. Pays $80-200.

Photos: State availability of photos with submission.

Tips: "We look for clearly-written, informative articles dealing with the electronic delivery of information. Writing style should not be jargon-laden or heavily technical."

LASERS & APPLICATIONS, High Tech Publications, Inc., 23868 Hawthorne Blvd., Torrance CA 90505. (213)378-0261. Editor: Tom Farre. 20% freelance written. Prefers to work with published/established writers (high technical content is essential); works with a small number of new/unpublished writers each year. Monthly technical magazine of laser and optical industry for engineers and designers. Circ. 30,000. Pays on acceptance. Publishes ms an average of 2 months after acceptance. Byline given. Offers 25% kill fee. Buys all rights. Electronic submissions OK via Easilink, Crosstalk or Move-it, but call first. Computer printout submissions acceptable. Reports in 1 month. Sample copy $4.

Nonfiction: "We stress new applications of lasers and laser processes in medical, electronics, metalworking, communication, printing, military and other fields. Articles describe how a laser was used to perform a task better or cheaper; and what kind of laser and operating conditions used; and what the prognosis is for selling lasers based on this process. We are particularly interested in applications of lasers in foreign countries." Query with published clips. Length: 250-1,500 words. Pays $100-200. Sometimes pays the expenses of writers on assignment.

MASS HIGH TECH, Mass Tech Times, Inc., 755 Mt. Auburn St., Watertown MA 02172. (617)924-2422. Editor: Alan R. Earls. Managing Editor: Patrick Porter. 10-20% freelance written. "Interested in queries, samples, proposals especially from writers in the New England region." Bimonthly trade tabloid covering feature news of electronics, computers, biotech, systems analysis, etc., for high-tech professionals in New England; strong regional angle preferred. Circ. 30,000. Pays on publication. Publishes ms an average of 1 month after acceptance. Byline given. Not copyrighted. Buys first North American serial rights. Submit seasonal/holiday material 1 month in advance. Simultaneous queries, and simultaneous, photocopied, and previously published submissions OK "if not in our immediate market." Electronic submissions OK via 300 and/or 1200 baud, Hayes or X modem protocols. Computer printout submissions acceptable; prefers letter-quality to dot-matrix. Reports in 1 month. Sample copy for 9x12 SAE and 5 first class stamps.

Nonfiction: Book excerpts; historical (technology); humor; interview/profile; new product; opinion (qualified scientist); personal experience; and photo feature (needs technical orientation and strong Boston area orientation). Also, Op/Ed pieces of up to 1,200 words relevant to concerns of New England technology firms and employees. "Material should inform without over simplifying. A light, amusing approach is OK." Increasingly oriented toward news and analysis of items impacting market area. Buys 50 mss/year. Send complete ms. Length: 400-1,200 words. Pays $50-250.

Photos: Send photos with ms. Pays $25 for 5x7 b&w prints. Captions and identification of subjects required (if appropriate). Buys one-time rights.

Columns/Departments: Buys 50 mss/year. Query with idea or send one sample ms. Length: 300-900 words. Pays $50 and up.

Fillers: Anecdotes, short humor and newsbreaks. Buys 100 mss/year. Length: 25-100 words. Pays $10 and up.

Tips: "Know the Boston and New England high-tech scene or have knowledgeable contacts. Material should be plausible to trained professionals. Trends in magazine publishing that freelance writers should be aware of include the need for more sophisticated graphics—photos or drawings are often available free from their corporate subjects (in our market)."

‡**MICROELECTRONICS JOURNAL**, Benn Electronics Publications Ltd., Box 28, Luton LU72 0ED England. 0582-417438. Publishing Director: Philip Rathkey. 90% freelance written. Eager to work with qualified new/unpublished writers. For electronics engineers engaged in research design, production, applications, sales in commercial or government organizations, academics (teaching, research) and higher degree students. "Writer must be active in the microelectronics industry (including academics or higher degree students) and have either an original observation to make or be able to inform/update readers on the state-of-the-art in a specialty area, or on the activities of an organization." Bimonthly magazine; 84 pages. Circ. 1,500. Pays on publication. Publishes ms an average of 4 months after acceptance. Buys all rights. Phone queries OK. Submit seasonal/holiday material 3 months in advance. Photocopied submissions OK. Accepts previously published work only if first English translation of foreign language paper. Computer printout submissions acceptable. Send SAE and IRCs. Reports in 3 weeks to US. Free sample copy and writer's guidelines.
Nonfiction: Expose (technical critique of manufacturers' products, of government, commercial, trade); general interest (state-of-the-art technical/marketing articles); how-to (on new designs, applications, production, materials, technology/techniques); interview (of eminent captain of industry or government politician); nostalgia (concerning how microelectronics companies got started or techniques were invented); personal opinion (on any relevant technical/commercial subject); profile and short notes (of company research activities, university research activities); new product (assessment and evidence of product's importance); photo feature (must include write-up explaining its technical/commercial significance); and technical (on integrated circuit technology and systems, memories, microprocessors, optoelectronics, infra-red, hybrid integrated circuits, microwave solid state devices, CCD and SAW techniques, semiconductor materials and chemicals, semiconductor production equipment and processing techniques, and automatic test techniques and equipment). Buys 10-30 mss/year. Query or submit complete ms. Length: 4,000-6,000 words. Pays $25/published page including diagrams, photos, etc. plus 25 free reprints of your article.
Photos: Prefers b&w 6½x4½ prints unless color is technically essential. Offers no additional payment for photos accepted with ms. Captions required.
Tips: "Writers must be experienced industry professionals. Nonspecialist staff increasingly involved in typesetting. It is important that manuscripts be submitted without ambiguities and with correct punctuation, layout, explanation of abbreviations, acronyms, etc."

MICROWAVES & RF, 10 Mulholland Dr., Hasbrouck Height NJ 07604. (201)393-6285. Editor: Barry E. Manz. 70% freelance written. Eager to work with new/unpublished writers. Monthly magazine; 200 pages. Emphasizes radio frequency design. "Qualified recipients are those individuals actively engaged in microwave and RF research, design, development, production and application engineering, engineering management, administration or purchasing departments in organizations and facilities where application and use of devices, systems and techniques involve frequencies from HF through visible light." Circ. 60,500. Pays on publication. Publishes ms an average of 6 months after acceptance. Buys all rights. Phone queries OK. Photocopied submissions OK. Electronic submissions OK via 300 Baud or ASCii files on 5.25. disk. Computer printouts acceptable "if legible." Reports in 3 weeks. Free sample copy and writer's guidelines; mention *Writer's Market* in request.
Nonfiction: "We are interested in material on research and development in microwave and RF technology and economic news that affects the industry." How-to (circuit design), new product, opinion, and technical. Buys 70 mss/year. Query. Pays $50/published page.
Fillers: Newsbreaks. Pays $10 minimum.

MICROWAVE SYSTEMS NEWS & COMMUNICATIONS TECHNOLOGY (MSN & CT), EW Communications, Inc., 1170 E. Meadow Dr., Palo Alto CA 94303. (415)494-2800. Editor: Alexander E. Braun. Managing Editor: Cedric R. Braun. Monthly magazine covering developments in the microwave industry: communications, radar, avionics, monolithic integration, testing, etc. "*MSN* reaches an audience composed primarily of electrical engineers, who are interested in solving design problems and in the latest developments in the microwave industry." Circ. 55,000. Pays on publication. Byline given. Buys all rights. Submit seasonal/holiday material 3 months in advance. Computer printout submissions acceptable; prefers letter-quality to dot-matrix. Reports in 2 weeks. Sample copy for legal size SAE and $3 postage; free writer's guidelines.
Nonfiction: Technical. "No PR-hype or marketing articles." Buys 96 mss/year. Query. Length: 3,500-4,000 words. Pays $200 minimum.
Photos: Send photos with query. Reviews 8x10 b&w and color prints. Payment for photos included in payment for ms. Captions and identification of subjects required.
Tips: "Since our publication goes to a very specialized audience, prospective authors should have a solid technical writing background and possibly an engineering degree. Query first—always. We are always looking for the latest technical developments in the microwave industry. If the proposed article is solid, it'll sell itself."

MULTICHANNEL NEWS, A Fairchild Business Publication, Fairchild Publications, #450, 300 S. Jackson St., Denver CO 80209. (303)393-6397. Editor: Thomas P. Southwick. Managing Editor: Stewart Schley. 10% freelance written. Weekly newspaper/tabloid covering cable and pay television with hard news only. "We invite stringer queries for markets outside New York, Los Angeles, Washington, Atlanta and Denver." Circ. 15,000. Pays on publication. Publishes ms an average of 1 week after acceptance. Byline given. Buys one-time rights. Photocopied submissions OK. Electronic submissions OK. Computer printout submissions acceptable; no dot-matrix. Reports in 2 weeks on queries. Sample copy $1.

Nonfiction: New product and technical on local cable system news or involvement. Articles by assignment only. Wants news articles; no features. Query, then follow up letter with phone call. Length: 1,000 words maximum. Pays by column inch. Sometimes pays the expenses of writers on assignment.

Tips: "A freelancer can break into our publication with hard, breaking news about cable and/or pay TV. Use AP and UPI news style."

ON PAGE, On Page Enterprises, Box 439, Sudbury MA 01776. Editor: Stanley J. Kaplan. Managing Editor: Bette Sidlo. 5% freelance written. Eager to work with new/unpublished writers. Monthly newsletter about "the beeper industry (radio pocket paging) for professionals, medical people, sales people, small businessmen, municipal employees and any person whose job takes him/her away from the telephone and who must maintain communications." Circ. 100,000. Pays on acceptance. Publishes ms an average of 4 months after acceptance. Buys all rights. Submit seasonal material 3 months in advance. Phone queries OK. Computer printout submissions acceptable; prefers letter-quality to dot-matrix. Reports in 2 weeks. Free sample copy and writer's guidelines.

Fillers: Clippings, jokes, gags, anecdotes, short humor and newsbreaks. "We are particularly interested in anecdotes for our On Page Forum column in the first person narrative, stories of people and their beeper experiences, and newsbreaks on a variety of communication subjects of interest to people who use beepers. We especially look for seasonal freelance contributions." Buys 5-10 mss/year. Length: 75-150 words. Pays $25-40.

Tips: "Our selection is based more on subject matter and details than on the writer's style. A strong originality is of greatest concern here. Submissions should be geared to beeper-users (e.g., subject matter must be related to communications or mobility). No sarcasm or comments insulting those who carry or use a beeper." ·

PRO SOUND NEWS, International News Magazine for the Professional Sound Production Industry. P.S.N. Publications, Inc., 2 Park Ave., New York NY 10016. (212)213-3444. Editor: Randolph P. Savicky. 20% freelance written. Works with a small number of new/unpublished writers each year. Monthly tabloid covering the recording, sound reinforcement, TV and film sound industry. Circ. 14,500. Pays on publication. Publishes ms an average of 1 month after acceptance. Byline given. Buys first serial rights. Simultaneous queries, and photocopied and previously published submissions OK. Electronic submissions OK via IBM PC, but requires hard copy also. Computer printout submissions acceptable; prefers letter-quality to dot-matrix. Reports in 2 weeks.

Nonfiction: Query with published clips. Pays 10¢/word.

PROMOTION NEWSLETTER, Radio and TV, Drawer 50108, Lighthouse Point FL 33064. (305)426-4881. Editor: William N. Udell. 8% freelance written. Monthly newsletter covering promotional activities of radio and television stations. Circ. 580. Pays on acceptance. Publishes ms an average of 1 month after acceptance. Byline may or may not be given. Not copyrighted. Buys one-time rights and nonexclusive reprints; makes work-for-hire assignments. Submit seasonal/holiday material 3 months in advance. Simultaneous queries, and simultaneous and photocopied submissions OK. Computer printout submissions acceptable; prefers letter-quality to dot-matrix. Reports in 2 weeks on queries; 1 month on mss. Free sample copy (while available).

Nonfiction: How-to; interview/profile (of promotional director of a busy station); and photo feature. "We are interested in all promotional activities of radio and TV stations and unusual examples of successful promotional events. We are also looking for special material for all holidays." No "fan" material. Query or send complete ms. Length: 100-500 words, sometimes more. Pays $15-150. Sometimes pays the expenses of writers on assignment.

Photos: Reprints of ads and other material acceptable. Send photos with ms. Pays $5 minimum for b&w contact sheets and prints. Identification of subjects required. Buys one-time rights.

Fillers: Clippings and newsbreaks. Length: 100-500 words. Pays $15-150.

Tips: "The type of material we print seldom requires lengthy detail or hype. A frequent mistake is writing for general ('fan') consumption—these readers are professional business operators. No fluff."

SATELLITE DEALER, The Magazine for the Home Satellite Systems Industry, CommTek Publishing Co., Box 53, Boise ID 83707. (208)322-2800. Editor: Howard Shippey. Executive Editor: Bruce Kinnaird. 75% freelance written. Monthly magazine covering the satellite television industry. Circ. 19,000. Pays on acceptance. Publishes ms an average of 2 months after acceptance. Byline given. Offers 33% kill fee. Buys first North American serial rights, one-time rights, all rights, first serial rights, and second serial (reprint) rights. Electronic submissions OK "we have a Vax 11/785 VMS Version 4.2", but requires hard copy also. Computer printout submissions acceptable. Reports in 5 weeks on queries. Free sample copy and writer's guidelines.

Nonfiction: Book excerpts (possible from new releases in industry); expose (on government communications

policy); how-to (on installation of dishes); humor (if there is an angle); interview/profile (on industry leaders and exceptional dealers); personal experience (from TVRO dealers); photo feature (of unusual dish installations); technical (on radio theory as it pertains to satellite TV); and marketing. Special issues include trade show editions. "We print articles concerning the home satellite television industry. We also touch on SMATV (private cable). Everything we print must in some way be valuable to the satellite television dealer's business. Marketing techniques, installation tips, legal explanations and how-to or technical articles are examples of material we often use. All articles should be analytical in nature. No introductory articles on how great this industry is." Buys at least 120 mss/year. Query with published clips and state availability of photos. Length: 1,200-2,000 words. Pays $200-500. Sometimes pays expenses of writers on assignment.
Photos: State availability of photos with query. Prefers unusual installations, interesting dishes, i.e., landscaped, painted. Reviews contact sheets, and 4x5 and 35mm color transparencies. Pays $10-50 for 8x10 b&w prints; $25-150 for 8x10 color prints. Captions and identification of subjects required. Buys negotiable rights.
Tips: "Well thought out and written queries preferred. Exhibit knowledge of either satellite TV or retail sales and a command of the English language. Quality work gets published, regardless of length (within reason). Not grasping the total picture, usually because of incomplete research, is the most frequent mistake made by writers. No phone queries."

‡**TELECOMMUNICATIONS**, Horizon House-Microwave, Inc., 610 Washington St., Dedham MA 02026. (617)326-8220. Executive Editor: Charles E. White. Managing Editor: Stephen Hardy. 10% freelance written. Prefers to work with published/established writers. Monthly magazine for "individuals, or members of companies, institutions, agencies, and governments who are users of telecom systems, subsystems, equipment, and services. Recognized and respected as the authoritative periodical in the field; presents a balanced mix of feature articles, technical and application notes, special reports, industry news and products, and service information." Circ. 75,000. Pays on publication. Publishes ms an average of 2 months after acceptance. Byline given. Buys all rights. Simultaneous queries OK. Reports in 1 month. Sample copy for 9x12 SAE. Free author's guide.
Nonfiction: New product; technical; feature articles ("treating various communications' disciplines from a managerial and end user standpoint rather than exhaustive design analysis"). Material should not "be overly theoretical and should employ simple equations only when needed for clarity." Drawings, graphs, etc., should be included. Buys 6-9 unsolicited mss/year. Query. Pays fixed rate. Sometimes pays the expenses of writers on assignment.
Photos: "Photos should be glossy b&w prints not exceeding 8½x11 inches."
Columns/Departments: Telecom News (items of newsworthy interest), Washington DC, Wall St. Update, Calendar. Query.

‡**VIDEO MANAGER, The Magazine for Decision Makers**, Knowledge Industry Publications, Inc., 701 Westchester Ave., White Plains NY 10604. Editor: Fred Schmidt. 85% freelance written. Eager to work with new/unpublished writers. A monthly tabloid covering non-broadcast, private, industrial television. "Our readers are managers of audiovisual, video and communications departments. We stress management, rather than technical and applications stories." Circ. 25,000. Pays on publication. Publishes ms an average of 4 months after acceptance. Byline given. Buys first rights. Computer printout submissions acceptable; prefers letter-quality to dot-matrix. Reports in several weeks on queries. Sample copy available.
Nonfiction: Book excerpts, essays, interview/profile, new product and personal experience. No articles on non-professional activities. Buys 36 mss/year. Query with published clips. Length: 1,500-3,000 words. Pays $50. Sometimes pays the expenses of writers on assignment.
Photos: State availability of photos with submission. Reviews contact sheets, 35mm transparencies and prints. Offers no additional payment for photos accepted with ms. Captions and identification of subjects required.
Columns/Departments: Production Focus (review, how produced, of videotape, non-broadcast, industrial), 1,500 words; Video Manager in Profile (biographic and department information) in detail (standard questionnaire). Buys 70 mss/year. Pays variable rate.

VIDEO SYSTEMS, Box 12901, Overland Park KS 66212. (913)888-4664. Publisher: Duane Hefner. Editor: Tom Cook. 80% freelance written. Monthly magazine. "International magazine for qualified persons engaged in professional applications of nonbroadcast audio and video who have operating responsibilities and purchasing authority for equipment and software in the video systems field." Circ. 30,000. Pays on acceptance. Buys all rights. Submit seasonal/holiday material 2 months in advance. Photocopied submissions OK. Reports in 2 months. Free sample copy and writer's guidelines.
Nonfiction: General interest (about professional video); how-to (use professional video equipment); historical (on professional video); new product; and technical. No consumer video articles. Buys 2-6 unsolicited mss/year. Submit complete ms. Length: 1,000-3,000 words. Pays $250.
Photos: State availability of photos with ms. Pay varies for 8x10 b&w glossy prints; $100 maximum for 35mm color transparencies. Model release required.

Energy

Oil, gas, and solar energy topics are covered in addition to energy conservation for industry professionals. Electric energy publications are listed in the Electricity category.

ALTERNATIVE ENERGY RETAILER, Zackin Publications, Inc., Box 2180, Waterbury CT 06722. (203)755-0158. Editor: John Florian. Monthly magazine on selling alternative energy products—chiefly solid fuel burning appliances. "We seek detailed how-to tips for retailers to improve business. Most freelance material purchased is about retailers and how they succeed." Circ. 14,000. Pays on publication. Offers 10% kill fee. Buys first North American serial rights. Submit seasonal/holiday material 4 months in advance. Reports in 2 weeks on queries. Sample copy for 8½x11 SAE; writer's guidelines for business-size SAE.
Nonfiction: How-to (improve retail profits and business know-how); and interview/profile (of successful retailers in this field). No "general business articles not adapted to this industry." Buys 40 mss/year. Query. Length: 1,000 words. Pays $200.
Photos: State availability of photos. Pays $25 maximum for 5x7 b&w prints. Reviews color slide transparencies. Identification of subject required. Buys one-time rights.
Tips: "A freelancer can best break into our publication with features about readers (retailers). Stick to details about what has made this person a success."

BAROID NEWS BULLETIN, Box 1675, Houston TX 77251. Editor-in-Chief: Virginia Myers. 50% freelance written. "We will purchase quality manuscripts that meet our needs regardless of who writes them." Emphasizes the petroleum industry for a cross-section of ages, education and interests, although most readers are employed by the energy industries. Quarterly magazine; 36 pages. Circ. 20,000. Pays on acceptance. Publishes ms an average of 1 year after acceptance. Buys first North American serial rights. Byline given. Submit seasonal/holiday material 1 year in advance. Computer printout submissions acceptable; prefers letter-quality to dot-matrix. Reports in 2 months. Free sample copy and writer's guidelines.
Nonfiction: General interest and historical. No travel articles or poetry. Buys 12 mss/year. Complete ms preferred. Length: 1,000-3,000 words. Pays 8-10¢/word. Sometimes pays expenses of writers on assignment.
Photos: "Photos may be used in the publication, or as reference for illustration art." Submit b&w prints. No additional payment for photos accepted with ms. Captions preferred. Buys first North American serial rights.
Tips: "We generally publish historical non-fiction written in anecdotal or narrative style. We expect interesting as well as factual articles. Manuscripts accompanied by good quality photos or illustrations stand a much better chance of acceptance. We review on speculation only—no assignments."

BUTANE-PROPANE NEWS, Butane-Propane News, Inc., 338 E. Foothill Blvd., Box 419, Arcadia CA 91006. (818)357-2168. Editor: Brian Knowles. 1-5% freelance written. A monthly magazine covering the LP-gas industry from well head to retailer. "*BPN* is directed mainly at LP-gas (propane) retailers. New markets, creative load-building, clever advertising and marketing campaigns, solving regulatory problems, safety and operations management are among the top concerns of our readers." Circ. 17,500. Pays on publication. Byline given. Not copyrighted. Buys one-time rights. Simultaneous submissions OK. Computer printout submissions acceptable; no dot-matrix. Reports in 1 week on queries, 2-4 weeks on manuscripts. Free sample copy.
Nonfiction: Interview/profile (with top LP-gas marketers only); new product (equipment that uses propane); technical and application of propane stories. No generalized philosophical pieces, preachments or general financial management articles. Buys 2-4 mss/year. Query. Length: 200-600 words. Pays $90/published page including photos. Pays the expenses of writers on assignment.
Photos: Send photos with submission. Reviews contact sheets and transparencies. Offers no additonal payment for photos accepted with ms. Captions and identification of subjects required. Buys one-time rights.
Tips: "*BPN*'s readers are technically knowledgeable on LP-gas and its myriad applications so the neophyte is unlikely to contribute much in this area. What is of interest is unusual uses of LP-gas (propane) in rural applications, or even in urban applications. Unusual and successful local marketing programs are also of interest. Unique advertising campaigns are newsworthy."

FUEL OIL NEWS, Hunter Publishing Co., Box 280, Colonia NJ 07067. (201)381-7279. Editor: George Schultz. 10% freelance written. Prefers to work with published/established writers. Monthly magazine about the home heating oil market. Circ. 17,000. Pays on publication. Publishes ms an average of 3 months after acceptance. Byline given. Offers $75 kill fee. Makes work-for-hire assignments. Phone queries OK. Submit sea-

sonal material 3 months in advance. Simultaneous, photocopied and previously published submissions OK. Computer printout submissions acceptable. Reports in 2 months. Free sample copy and writer's guidelines. **Nonfiction:** Interview (industry); profile (of industry leaders); how-to (on industry methods of delivering fuel or servicing equipment); and technical. No general business articles or new product information. Buys 2 mss/issue. Query. Length: 1,000-3,000 words. Pays $70-200. "Articles should be geared to helping fuel oil dealers maintain viability in the marketplace or to some aspect of home heating or oil delivery." Sometimes pays expenses of writers on assignment.
Photos: State availability of photos. Pays $25 maximum for b&w contact sheets. Captions preferred; model release required. Buys all rights.
Tips: "A writer should be familiar with some aspect of the industry we serve."

FUEL OIL AND OIL HEAT, 389 Passaic Ave., Fairfield NJ 07006. Editor: Paul Geiger. "We are backlogged with submissions and prefer not to receive unsolicited submissions at this time."

NATIONAL PETROLEUM NEWS, 950 Lee St., Des Plaines IL 60016. (312)296-0770. Editor: Marvin Reid. 3% freelance written. Prefers to work with published/established writers. For businessmen who make their living in the oil marketing industry, either as company employees or through their own business operations. Monthly magazine; 80 pages. Circ. 18,000. Rights purchased vary with author and material. Usually buys all rights. Pays on acceptance if done on assignment. Publishes ms an average of 2 months after acceptance. "The occasional freelance copy we use is done on assignment." Computer printout submissions acceptable; prefers letter-quality to dot-matrix. Query.
Nonfiction: Don Larson, news editor. Material related directly to developments and issues in the oil marketing industry and "how-to" and "what-with" case studies. Informational, and successful business operations. "No unsolicited copy, especially with limited attribution regarding information in story." Buys 3-4 mss/year. Length: 2,000 words maximum. Sometimes pays the expenses of writers on assignment.
Photos: Pays $150/printed page. Payment for b&w photos "depends upon advance understanding."

‡**OCEAN INDUSTRY**, Gulf Publishing Co., Box 2608, Houston TX 77001. (713)529-4301. Editor: Robert E. Snyder. Associate Editors: Maretta Tubb, Ken Edmiston and Charles McCabe. 5% freelance written. "We prefer to work directly with technical experts, if the freelancer is one; that's OK. Our readers are generally engineers and company executives in companies with business dealings with off-shore petroleum interests in exploration, drilling and production." Monthly magazine. Circ. 34,000. Pays on publication. Buys all rights. Pays kill fee: "If we assign an article and it is not used, we pay full rate on estimated length." Byline given. Phone queries OK. Photocopied and previously published submissions OK. Computer printout submissions acceptable. Reports in 2 months. Publishes ms an average of 3 months after acceptance. Free sample copy and writer's guidelines.
Nonfiction: Technical and equipment and operations oriented articles relating to hydrocarbon exploration and development, diving and ROVs, electronics, instruments for oil field and offshore applications. No oceanographic, fisheries, aquaculture or mariculture material. Buys 5-10 mss/year. Query. Length: 300-1,500 words. Pays $50-150/published page.
Photos: "Technical concepts are easier to understand when illustrated." State availability of photos with query. No additional payment for 5x7 or 8x10 glossy b&w or color prints. Captions required. Buys all rights.
Tips: "We are going toward more special reports written by experts in their fields. We find freelancers do not make good middle men."

PETROLEUM INDEPENDENT, 1101 16th St. NW, Washington DC 20036. (202)857-4775. Editor: Joe W. Taylor. 5% freelance written. Prefers to work with published/established writers. For "college educated men and women involved in high risk petroleum ventures. Our readers drill 90% of all the exploratory oil wells in this country. They pit themselves against the major oil companies, politicians, and a dry hole rate of 9 out of 10 to try to find enough petroleum to offset imports. They are in a highly competitive, extremely expensive business and look to this magazine to help them change the political landscape, read about their friends and the activities of the Independent Petroleum Association of America, and be entertained. Contrary to popular opinion, they are not all Texans. They live in almost every state and are politically motivated. They follow energy legislation closely and involve themselves in lobbying and electoral politics." Bimonthly magazine. Circ. 15,000. Pays on acceptance. Publishes ms an average of 3 months after acceptance. Computer printout submissions acceptable. Buys all rights. Byline given "except if part of a large report compiled in-house." Reports in 2 weeks. Sample copy $2.
Nonfiction: "Articles need not be limited to oil and natural gas—but must tie in nicely." Expose (bureaucratic blunder); informational; historical (energy-related; accurate; with a witty twist); humor (we look for good humor pieces and have found few); and interview (with energy decision makers. Center with questions concerning independent petroleum industry. Send edited transcript plus tape); opinion; profile (of Independent Petroleum Association of America members); and photo feature. Buys 5-10 mss/year. Query with brief outline. Length: 750-3,000 words. Pays $100-500. Longer articles on assignment; pay negotiable. Sometimes pays the

expenses of writers on assignment.

Photos: Reviews unusual color transparencies of oil exploration and development. No marketing or refining. Purchased with or without accompanying ms or on assignment. Pay negotiable. Always looking for unusual 4 color material covers.

Tips: "Call first, then send outline and query. Don't write with a particular slant. Write as if for a mainstream publication."

PIPELINE & GAS JOURNAL, Box 1589, Dallas TX 75221. (214)691-3911. Editor-in-Chief: Dean Hale. 8% freelance written. Works with a small number of new/unpublished writers each year. Emphasizes energy transportation (oil, natural gas, refined petroleum products and coal slurry) by pipeline. Monthly magazine; 100 pages. Circ. 28,000. Pays on publication. Publishes ms an average of 6 months after acceptance. Buys all rights. Phone queries OK. Photocopied submissions OK. Electronic submissions OK via 5.25-in. DSDD disk, in ASCII, but requires hard copy also. Computer printout submissions acceptable "if sharp, dark and capitals and lower case." Reports in 10 weeks. Free sample copy.

Nonfiction: Technical. Pipeline construction reports. "We will furnish 'checklist' on details." Pipeline maintenance/repair reports. Inquire first. No articles on management. Buys 5-6 mss/year. Query. Length: 800-1,500 words. Pays minimum $50/printed page. Sometimes pays the expenses of writers on assignment.

Photos: State availability of photos with query. No additional payment for 8x10 b&w glossy prints and 5x7 or 8x10 color glossy prints. Captions required. Buys all rights. Model release required.

Tips: "We don't use fillers."

PIPELINE & UNDERGROUND UTILITIES CONSTRUCTION, Oildom Publishing Co. of Texas, Inc., Box 22267, Houston TX 77027. Editor: Oliver Klinger. Managing Editor: Chris Horner. 10% freelance written. Monthly magazine covering oil, gas, water, and sewer pipeline construction for contractors and construction workers who build pipelines. Circ. 13,000. No byline given. Not copyrighted. 10% freelance written. Buys first North American serial rights. Simultaneous queries and photocopied submissions OK. Computer printout submissions acceptable. Reports in 2 weeks on queries; 3 weeks on mss. Sample copy for $1 and 9x12 SAE.

Nonfiction: How-to. Query with published clips. Length: 1,500-2,500 words. Pays $100/printed page "unless unusual expenses are incurred in getting the story."

Photos: Send photos with ms. Reviews 5x7 and 8x10 prints. Captions required. Buys one-time rights.

Tips: "We supply guidelines outlining information we need." The most frequent mistake made by writers in completing articles is unfamiliarity with the field.

PIPELINE DIGEST, Universal News, Inc., Box 55225, Houston TX 77055. (713)468-2626. Editor: Thelma Marlowe. Semimonthly magazine of the worldwide pipeline construction industry for individuals and companies involved in construction and operation of pipelines (gas, oil, slurry, water) worldwide. Includes design and engineering projects and updated listings of projects proposed, awarded and under construction. Circ. 9,500. Pays on publication. Byline given. Previously published submissions OK. Reports in 2 weeks on queries; 2 months on mss.

Nonfiction: Interview/profile (of people in industry); and new product. All material must relate to the oil and gas industry. Query with published clips. Length: 250-1,000 words. Pays negotiable fee.

Engineering and Technology

Engineers and professionals with various specialties read the publications in this section. Publications for electrical engineers are classified under Electricity; journals for electronics engineers are classified under the Electronics and Communication heading. Magazines for computer professionals are listed in the Trade/Data Processing section. For magazines on personal computing, see the Consumer/Personal Computing section.

‡DESIGN GRAPHICS WORLD, Communication Channels, Inc., 6255 Barfield Rd., Atlanta GA 30328. (404)256-9800. Editor: James J. Maivald. 10% freelance written. Works with a small number of new/unpublished writers each year. A monthly magazine covering design graphics in the architecture, engineering and construction community. Circ. 37,000. Pays on publication. Publishes ms an average of 2 months after acceptance. Byline given. 10% kill fee. Buys all rights. Submit seasonal/holiday material 3 months in advance. Computer printout submissions acceptable; no dot-matrix. Reports in 1 month on queries; 2 weeks on mss. Free sample copy and writer's guidelines.

Nonfiction: How-to, interview/profile, new product and technical. "Articles should be knowledgeable, informative and written for professional architects, engineers and designers." No product sales information, brand- or product-specific information features. Buys 8 mss/year. Query with published clips. Length: 500-2,000 words. Pays $50-500 for assigned articles; pays $50-375 for unsolicited articles. Sometimes pays the expenses of writers on assignment.

Photos: Send photos with submission. Reviews 2x2 transparencies and 5x7 prints. Offers no additional payment for photos accepted with ms. Identification of subjects required. Buys all rights.

Tips: "Writers should be capable of dropping consumer-prose writing styles and adopt more technical language and usage."

GRADUATING ENGINEER, McGraw-Hill, 1221 Avenue of the Americas, New York NY 10020. (212)512-4123. Editor: Howard Cohn. Published September-March "to help graduating engineers make the transition from campus to the working world." Circ. 90,000. Pays on acceptance. Byline given. Buys first North American serial rights. Reports in 2 weeks. Free sample copy for 9x12 SAE and $1 postage. No printed writer's guidelines.

Nonfiction: General interest (on management, human resources); high technology; and careers. Special issues include Minority, Women and Computer. Buys 100 mss/year. Query. Length: 2,000-3,000 words. Pays $300-500.

Photos: State availability of photos, illustrations or charts. Reviews 35mm color transparencies, 8x10 b&w glossy prints. Captions and model release required.

LASER FOCUS MAGAZINE, the Magazine of Electro-Optics Technology, 119 Russell St., Littleton MA 01460. (617)486-9501. Publisher/Editor-in-Chief: Dr. Morris Levitt. Managing Editor: Richard Mack. Less than 10% freelance written. A monthly magazine for physicists, scientists and engineers involved in the research and development, design, manufacturing and applications of lasers, laser systems and all other segments of electro-optical technologies. Circ. 45,000. Pays on publication. Publishes ms an average of 6 months after acceptance. Byline given unless anonymity requested. Buys all rights. Computer printout submissions acceptable; prefers letter-quality to dot-matrix. Sample copy on request.

Nonfiction: Lasers, laser systems, fiberoptics, optics, imaging, and other electro-optical materials, components, instrumentation and systems. "Each article should serve our reader's need by either stimulating ideas, increasing technical competence or improving design capabilities in the following areas: natural light and radiation sources, artificial light and radiation sources, light modulators, optical materials and components, image detectors, energy detectors, information displays, image processing, information storage and processing, subsystem and system testing, support equipment and other related areas." No "flighty prose, material not written for our readership, or irrelevant material." Query first "with a clear statement and outline of why the article would be important to our readers." Pays $30/printed page. Sometimes pays expenses of writers on assignment.

Photos: Send photos with ms. Reviews 8x10 b&w glossies or 4x5 color transparencies.

Tips: "The writer has a better chance of breaking in at our publication with short articles since shorter articles are easier to schedule, but must address more carefully our requirements for technical coverage. We use few freelancers that are independent professional writers. Most of our submitted materials come from technical experts in the areas we cover. The most frequent mistake made by writers in completing articles for us is that the articles are too commercial, i.e. emphasize a given product or technology from one company. Also articles are not the right technical depth, too thin or too scientific."

‡MACHINE DESIGN, Penton/IPC, 1111 Chester, Cleveland OH 44114. (216)696-7000. Editor: Ronald Khol. Executive Editor: Robert Aronson. 1-2% freelance written. Works with a small number of new/unpublished writers each year. A bimonthly magazine covering technical developments in products or purchases of interest to the engineering community. Circ. 180,000. Pays on publication. Publishes ms an average of 2 months after acceptance. Byline sometimes given. Buys first rights. Computer printout submissions acceptable; prefers letter-quality to dot-matrix. Reports in 1 month. Free sample copy.

Nonfiction: General interest; how-to (on using new equipment or processes); and new product. No non-technical submissions. Buys 10-15 mss/year. Query. Length and payment for articles must be negotiated in advance. Sometimes pays the expenses of writers on assignment.

Photos: State availability of photos with submission. Offers negotiable payment. Captions, model releases, and identification of subjects required.

Columns/Departments: Design International (international news), captions; Backtalk (technical humor) and Personal Computers in Engineering (use of personal computers), both have negotiable word length. Buys 50-200 items/year. Query. Pays $20 minimum.

Tips: "The departments of our publication most open to freelancers are Back Talk, News Trends and Design International. Those without technical experience almost never send in adequate material."

THE MINORITY ENGINEER, An Equal Opportunity Career Publication for Professional and Graduating Minority Engineers, Equal Opportunity Publications, Inc., 44 Broadway, Greenlawn NY 11740. (516)261-8917. Editor: James Schneider. 50% freelance written. Magazines published 4 times/year (fall, winter, spring, summer) covering career guidance for minority engineering students and professional minority engineers. Circ. 16,000. Pays on publication. Publishes ms an average of 3 months after acceptance. Byline given. Buys first North American serial rights. "Deadline dates: fall, July 1; winter, September 1; spring, December 15; summer, April 1." Simultaneous, photocopied, and previously published submissions OK. Electronic submissions OK, but requires hard copy also. Computer printout submissions acceptable; prefers typed mss; no dot-matrix. Sample copy and writer's guidelines available on request.
Nonfiction: Book excerpts; articles (on job search techniques, role models); general interest (on specific minority engineering concerns); how-to (land a job, keep a job, etc.); interview/profile (minority engineer role models); new product (new career opportunities); opinion (problems of ethnic minorities); personal experience (student and career experiences); and technical (on career fields offering opportunities for minority engineers). "We're interested in articles dealing with career guidance and job opportunities for minority engineers." Query or send complete ms. Length: 1,250-3,000 words.
Photos: Prefers 35mm color slides but will accept b&w. Captions and identification of subjects required. Buys all rights.
Tips: "Articles should focus on career guidance, role model and industry prospects for minority engineers. Prefer articles related to careers, not politically or socially sensitive."

‡NSBE JOURNAL, National Society of Black Engineers Official Publication, Journals, Inc., Suite 3, 1240 S. Broad St., New Orleans LA 70125. (504)822-3533. Editor: Bill Bowers. Copy Editor: Sonya Stinson. 90% freelance written. A bimonthly magazine covering engineering, science studies and careers. "The majority of our readers are college students in engineering and other technical fields. Readership also includes professional engineers and academic personnel." Estab. 1985. Circ. 15,000. Pays on acceptance. Publishes ms an average of 2 months after acceptance. Byline given. Buys all rights. Photocopied and previously published submissions OK. Computer printout submissions acceptable. Reports in 2 weeks. Free sample copy and writer's guidelines.
Nonfiction: Historical/nostalgic, how-to, inspirational, interview/profile, photo feature, technical and travel. No highly technical articles on engineering projects, products, etc. Buys 50 mss/year. Query. Length: 3,500 words maximum. Pays $150. Sometimes pays the expenses of writers on assignment.
Photos: Send photos wth submission. Reviews contact sheets. Model releases and identification of subjects required.
Columns/Departments: NSBE Updates (trivia, news on outstanding students and professional engineers, statistical information). Buys 15 mss/year. Query. Length: 150 words maximum. Pays $150.

THE ONTARIO TECHNOLOGIST, Ontario Association of Certified Engineering Technicians and Technologists, Suite 253, 40 Orchard View Blvd., Toronto, Ontario M4R 2G1 Canada. (416)488-1175. Editor: Ruth M. Klein. Bimonthly professional association journal covering technical processes and developments in engineering for association members, educational institutions, government and industry. Circ. 14,634. Pays in membership dues or subscription fee. Byline given. Buys first serial rights. Submit seasonal/holiday material 2 months in advance. Photocopied and previously published submissions OK. Reports in 1 month. Free sample copy and writer's guidelines.
Nonfiction: New product and technical (manpower news). Buys 4 mss/year. Query with published clips. Length: 500-1,500 words. Pays 25¢/word.
Photos: State availability of photos. Pays $25 maximum for 8x10 b&w prints. Captions and identification of subjects required. Buys one-time rights.

THE WOMAN ENGINEER, An Equal Opportunity Career Publication for Graduating Women and Experienced Professionals, Equal Opportunity Publications, Inc., 44 Broadway, Greenlawn NY 11740. (516)261-8917. Editor: Anne Kelly. 60% freelance written. Magazine published 4 times/year (fall, winter, spring, summer) covering career guidance for women engineering students and professional women engineers. Circ. 16,000. Pays on publication. Publishes ms 3-12 months after acceptance. Byline given. Buys first North American rights. Simultaneous queries and submissions OK. Computer printout submissions acceptable. Free sample copy and writer's guidelines.
Nonfiction: "Interested in articles dealing with career guidance and job opportunities for women engineers. Looking for manuscripts showing how to land an engineering position and advance professionally. Wants features on job-search techniques, engineering disciplines offering career opportunities to women, problems facing women engineers—and how to cope with such problems, in addition to role-model profiles of successful

women engineers." Query. Length: 1,500-2,500 words. Sometimes pays the expenses of writers on assignment.
Photos: Prefers color slides but will accept b&w. Captions, model release and identification of subjects required. Buys all rights.
Tips: "We will be looking for shorter manuscripts (800-1,000 words) on job-search techniques or career opportunities for women engineers."

Entertainment and the Arts

The business of the entertainment/amusement industry (arts, film, dance, theatre, etc.) is covered by these publications. Journals that focus on the people and equipment of various music specialities are listed in the Trade Music section.

AMUSEMENT BUSINESS, Billboard Publications, Inc., Box 24970, Nashville TN 37202. (615)748-8120. Managing Editor: Tim O'Brien. 25% freelance written. Works with a small number of new/unpublished writers each year. Weekly tabloid; 32-108 pages. Emphasizes hard news of the amusement and mass entertainment industry. Read by top management. Circ. 15,000. Pays on publication. Publishes ms an average of 3 weeks after acceptance. Byline sometimes given; "it depends on the quality of the individual piece." Buys all rights. Submit seasonal/holiday material 3 weeks in advance. Phone queries OK. Computer printout submissions acceptable; no dot-matrix.
Nonfiction: How-to (case history of successful advertising campaigns and promotions); interviews (with leaders in the areas we cover highlighting appropriate problems and issues of today, i.e. insurance, alcohol control, etc.); new product; and technical (how "new" devices, shows or services work at parks, fairs, auditoriums and conventions). Likes lots of financial support data: grosses, profits, operating budgets and per-cap spending. Also needs in-depth looks at advertising and promotional programs of carnivals, circuses, amusement parks, fairs: how these facilities position themselves against other entertainment opportunities in the area. No personality pieces or interviews with stage stars. Buys 500-1,000 mss/year. Query. Length: 400-700 words. Pays $3/published inch. Sometimes pays the expenses of writers on assignment.
Photos: State availability of photos with query. Pays $3-5 for 8x10 b&w glossy prints. Captions and model release required. Buys all rights.
Columns/Departments: Auditorium Arenas; Fairs, Fun Parks; Food Concessions; Merchandise; Promotion; Shows (carnival and circus); Talent; Tourist Attractions; and Management Changes.
Tips: "Submission must contain the whys and whos, etc. and be strong enough that others in the same field will learn from it and not find it naive. We will be increasing story count while decreasing story length."

BILLBOARD, The International News Weekly of Music and Home Entertainment, 1515 Broadway, New York NY 10036. (212)764-7300. 9107 Wilshire Blvd., Beverly Hills CA 90210. (213)273-7040. Editor-in-Chief: Samuel Holdsworth. Special Issues Editor: Ed Ochs. L.A. Bureau Chief: Sam Sutherland. Albums: Sam Sutherland. (All Los Angeles.) Pro Equipment: Steve Dupler. Deputy Editor: Irv Lichtman. Radio/TV Editor: Kim Freeman. Black Music: Nelson George. Executive/Classical Editor: Is Horowitz. Video Editor: Tony Seideman. Review-Singles/Campus Editor: Nancy Erlich. (All New York.) International Editor: Peter Jones (London). Weekly. Pays on publication. Buys all rights.
Nonfiction: "Correspondents are appointed to send in spot amusement news covering phonograph record programming by broadcasters and record merchandising by retail dealers." Concert reviews, interviews with artists, and stories on video software (both rental and merchandising).

BOXOFFICE MAGAZINE, RLD Publishing Corp., Suite 710, 1800 N. Highland Ave., Hollywood CA 90028. (213)465-1186. Editor: Harley W. Lond. 5% freelance written. Monthly business magazine about the motion picture industry for members of the film industry: theater owners, film producers, directors, financiers and allied industries. Circ. 14,000. Pays on publication. Publishes ms an average of 2 months after acceptance.

Byline given. Buys one-time rights. Phone queries OK. Submit seasonal material 2 months in advance. Simultaneous, photocopied and previously published submissions OK. Computer printout submissions acceptable; no dot-matrix. Reports in 1 month. Sample copy $1.

Nonfiction: Expose, interview, nostalgia, profile, new product, photo feature and technical. "We are a general news magazine about the motion picture industry and are looking for stories about trends, developments, problems or opportunities facing the industry. Almost any story will be considered, including corporate profiles, but we don't want gossip or celebrity stuff." Buys 1-2 mss/issue. Query with published clips. Length: 1,500-2,500 words. Pays $75-150.

Photos: State availability of photos. Pays $10 minimum for 8x10 b&w prints. Captions required.

Tips: "Request a sample copy (for $1 to cover postage) indicating you read about *Boxoffice* in *Writer's Market*. Write a clear, comprehensive outline of the proposed story and enclose a resume and clip samples. We welcome new writers but don't want to be a classroom. Know how to write."

THE ELECTRIC WEENIE, Box 882, Honolulu HI 96728. (808)395-9600. Editor: Tom Adams. 20% freelance written. Monthly magazine covering "primarily radio, for 'personalities' worldwide (however, mostly English speaking). We mail flyers mainly to radio people, but obviously no one is excepted if he/she wants a monthly supply of first-rate gags, one liners, zappers, etc." Circ. 1,500. Pays on publication. Publishes ms an average of 6 months after acceptance. No byline given. Buys all rights. Submit seasonal/holiday material 6 months in advance. Computer printout submissions acceptable; prefers letter-quality to dot-matrix. Sample copy $5, business size SAE and 1 first class stamp.

Fillers: Jokes, gags, short humor, one liners, etc. "*Short* is the bottom line." Uses 300/month. Pays $1/gag used.

Tips: "We like to receive in multiples of 100 if possible; not mandatory, just preferred. And a little 'spicy' doesn't hurt."

THE HOLLYWOOD REPORTER, Verdugo Press, 6715 Sunset Blvd., Hollywood CA 90028. (213)464-7411. Publisher: Tichi Wilkerson. Editor: Marcia Borie. Emphasizes entertainment industry, film, TV and theatre and is interested in everything to do with financial news in these areas. 15% freelance written. Daily entertainment trade publication: 25-100 pages. Circ. 25,000. Publishes ms an average of 1 month after acceptance. Send queries first. Reports in 1 month. Sample copy $1.

Tips: "Short articles and fillers fit our format best. The most frequent mistake made by writers in completing an article for us is that they are not familiar with our publication."

THE LONE STAR COMEDY MONTHLY, Lone Star Publications of Humor, Suite #103, Box 29000, San Antonio TX 78229. Editor: Lauren Barnett. "Less than 1" percent freelance written. Monthly comedy service newsletter for professional humorists—DJs, public speakers, comedians. Includes one-liners and jokes for oral expression. Pays on publication "or before." Publishes ms an average of 4 months after acceptance. Byline given if 2 or more jokes are used. Buys all rights, exclusive rights for 6 months from publication date. Submit seasonal/holiday material 1 month in advance. Photocopied submissions OK. Computer printout submissions acceptable; no dot-matrix. Reports in 1 month. Inquire for update on prices of sample copies. Writer's guidelines for business size SAE and 1 first class stamp.

Fillers: Jokes, gags and short humor. Buys 20-60/year. Length: 100 words maximum. "We don't use major features in *The Lone Star Comedy Monthly*." Inquire for update on rates. "Submit several (no more than 20) original gags on one or two subjects only."

Tips: "For the next several months, we will be generating nearly all of our humor in-house. However, this may change by early 1987. Writers should inquire (with SASE) before submitting material."

‡MIDDLE EASTERN DANCER, Mideastern Connection, Inc., Box 1572, Casselberry FL 32707. (305)831-7475. Editor: Karen Kuzsel. Managing Editor: Tracie Harris. 60% freelance written. Eager to work with new/unpublished writers. A monthly magazine covering Middle Eastern dance and culture (belly dancing). "We provide the most current news and entertainment information available in the world. We focus on the positive, but don't shy away from controversy. All copy and photos must relate to Middle Eastern dance and cultural activities. We do not get into politics." Circ. 2,000. Pays on acceptance. Publishes ms an average of 4 months after acceptance, usually sooner, but it depends on type of article and need for that month. Byline given. Buys first rights, simultaneous rights or second serial (reprint) rights. Submit seasonal/holiday material 3 months in advance. Simultaneous, photocopied and previously published submissions OK, unless printed in another belly dance publication. Computer printout submissions acceptable; prefers letter-quality to dot-matrix. Reports in 2 weeks on queries; 3 weeks on mss. Sample copy for 9x12 SAE with 73¢ postage; writer's guidelines for #10 SAE with 1 first class stamp.

Nonfiction: Essays; general interest; historical/nostalgic; how-to (on costuming, putting on shows, teaching and exercises); humor; inspirational; interview/profile; personal experience; photo features; travel (to the Middle East or related to dancers); and reviews of seminars, movies, clubs, restaurants, and museums. Special issues include costuming (March); and anniversary issue (October). No politics. Buys 60 mss/year. Query. Pays

$20 maximum for assigned articles; pays $10 maximum for unsolicited articles. May provide free advertising in trade. Sometimes pays the expenses of writers on assignment.

Photos: Send photos with submission. Offers no additional payment for photos accepted with ms. Identification of subjects required. Buys one-time rights.

Columns/Departments: Critics Corner (reviews of books, videotapes, records, movies, clubs and restaurants, museums and special events); Helpful Hints (tips for finding accessories and making them easier or for less); Putting on the Ritz (describes costume in detail with photo), and Personal Glimpses and Profiles (provides insights of benefit to other dancers). Query. Pays $5 maximum.

Fiction: Open to fiction dealing with belly dancers as subject.

Poetry: Avant-garde, free verse, haiku, light verse and traditional. Buys 5 poems/year. Submit maximum 3 poems. Pays $5 maximum.

Tips: "It's easy to break in if you stick to belly dancing related information and expect little or no money (advertising instead). Although we are the 2nd largest in the world in this field, we're still small."

PERFORMANCE, 1020 Currie St., Fort Worth TX 76107. (817)338-9444. Publisher: Don Waitt. 25% freelance written. The international trade weekly for the touring entertainment industry. "*Performance* publishes tour routing information, updated on a weekly basis. These itineraries, along with box office reports, street news, industry directories, live performance reviews and industry features are of interest to our readers." Weekly magazine; also publishes industry directories once a month. Circ. 20,000. Publishes ms an average of 1 month after acceptance. Buys all rights. Phone queries OK. Submit seasonal/holiday material 2 months in advance. Simultaneous submissions OK. Computer printout submissions acceptable; prefers letter-quality to dot-matrix. Reports in 1 month. Sample copy and writer's guidelines $3.

Nonfiction: "This is a trade publication, dealing basically with the ins and outs of booking live entertainment. We are interested in adding freelancers from major cities around the U.S. to provide us with hard news and spot information on sound, lighting and staging companies, clubs, ticketing, concert venues, promoters, booking agents, personal managers, and college news relevant to the live entertainment industry. We also publish interviews and overviews of touring in the major cities." Interviews, opinion and profile. Needs many short news items, much like a newspaper.

Photos: State availability of photos with ms. B&w photos only. Captions preferred. Buys all rights.

Tips: "You won't make a fortune writing for *Performance*, and you may have to wait awhile for the paycheck; on the other side of the coin, though, there are some benefits to writing for the magazine such as free access to many club shows and area concerts, backstage passes, invites to music related press conferences and parties, and the opportunity to gather information and interviews for possible use in higher-paying consumer publications."

‡TOURIST ATTRACTIONS & PARKS MAGAZINE, Kane Communications, Inc., Suite 226, 401 N. Broad St., Philadelphia PA 19108. (215)925-9744. Editor: Chuck Tooley. A bimonthly magazine covering mass entertainment and leisure facilities. Emphasizes management articles. Circ. 19,600. Pays on publication. Buys all rights. Computer printout submissions acceptable; prefers letter-quality to dot-matrix. Reports in 3 weeks. Sample copy for 9x12 SAE with $1.50 postage.

Nonfiction: Interview/profile and new product. Buys 10 mss/year. Query. Length: 1,000-2,500 words. Pays $50-250 for assigned articles; sometimes payment arranged individually with publisher. Sometimes pays expenses of writers on assignment.

Photos: State availability of photos with submission. Captions and model releases required.

Tips: "Inquire about covering trade shows for us, such as C.M.A."

VANTAGE POINT: ISSUES IN AMERICAN ARTS, American Council for the Arts, 570 7th Ave., New York NY 10018. Editor: Bill Keens. Published 5 times/year as 16-page editorial supplement in *Horizon Magazine*. Bimonthly magazine. Circ. 3,500. Pays on publication. Byline given. Buys first North American serial rights. No telephone queries. Simultaneous queries and simultaneous and photocopied submissions OK. Reports in 6 weeks. Free sample copy if interested in query or submission—otherwise $2.50, 9x12 SAE and $1 postage.

Nonfiction: Features, profiles, essays and interviews. Buys 12 mss/year. Length: 500-3,000 words. Pays $100-250.

Tips: "*Vantage Point* focuses on contemporary issues (social, political, economics and artistic) as they affect the art community on all levels. Readers include high level art executives, trustees, patrons, members of the corporation, foundation and education communities, artists and elected government officials."

Market conditions are constantly changing! If this is 1988 or later, buy the newest edition of Writer's Market *at your favorite bookstore or order directly from* Writer's Digest Books.

Farm

Today's farm publication editor wants more than rewrites of USDA and extension press releases. Farm magazines reflect this, and the successful freelance farm writer turns his attention to the business end of farming.

Do you need to be a farmer to write about farming? The general consensus is yes, and no, depending on the topic. For more technical articles, most editors feel that writers should have a farm background or some technical farm education. But there are writing opportunities for the general freelancer, too.

The following listings for farm publications are divided into five categories, each specializing in a different aspect of farm publishing: crops and soil management; dairy farming; general interest farming and rural life (both national and local); livestock; and miscellaneous. Be sure to write for sample copies and writer's guidelines. As more and more farmers experience financial problems, some of the publications that serve them are struggling for survival too.

Crops and Soil Management

‡ONION WORLD, Columbia Publishing, 111C S. 7th Ave., Box 1467, Yakima WA 98907. (509)248-2452. Editor: D. Brent Clement. 90% freelance written. A monthly magazine covering "the world of onion production and marketing" for onion growers and shippers. Circ. 5,500. Pays on publication. Publishes ms an average of 1 month after acceptance. Byline given. Not copyrighted. Buys first North American serial rights. Submit seasonal/holiday material 1 month in advance. Simultaneous submissions OK. Computer printout submisions acceptable; prefers letter-quality to dot-matrix. Reports in several weeks. Sample copy for 8½x11 SAE with 90¢ postage.
Nonfiction: General interest, historical/nostalgic and interview/profile. Buys 60 mss/year. Query. Length: 1,200-1,500 words. Pays $75-100 for assigned articles.
Photos: Send photos with submission. Offers no additional payment for photos accepted with ms unless cover shot. Captions and identification of subjects required. Buys all rights.
Tips: "Writers should be familiar with growing and marketing onions. We use a lot of feature stories on growers, shippers and others in the onion trade—what they are doing, their problems, solutions, marketing plans, etc."

POTATO GROWER OF IDAHO, Harris Publishing, Inc., Box 981, Idaho Falls ID 83402. (208)522-5187. Editor: Steve Janes. 25% freelance written. Emphasizes material slanted to the potato grower and the business of farming related to this subject—packing, shipping, processing, research, etc. Monthly magazine; 48-96 pages. Circ. 18,000. Pays on publication. Buys first North American serial rights. Byline given. Phone queries OK. Submit seasonal/holiday material 3 months in advance. Simultaneous queries, and photocopied and previously published submissions OK. Computer printout submissions acceptable. Reports in 1 month. Sample copy $1, 8½x11 SAE, and 37¢ postage; writer's guidelines for 5½x7 SAE and 1 first class stamp.
Nonfiction: Expose (facts, not fiction or opinion, pertaining to the subject); how-to (do the job better, cheaper, faster, etc.); informational articles; interviews ("can use one of these a month, but must come from state of Idaho since this is a regional publication; on unique personalities in the potato industry, and telling the nation how Idaho grows potatoes"); all types of new product articles pertaining to the subject; photo features (story can be mostly photos, but must have sufficient cutlines to carry technical information); and technical (all aspects of the industry of growing, storage, processing, packing and research of potatoes in general, but must relate to the Idaho potato industry). Buys 5 mss/year. Query. Length: 1,000-2,000 words. Pays $15-100.
Photos: B&w glossies (any size) purchased with mss or on assignment; use of color limited. Query if photos are not to be accompanied by ms. Pays $5 for 5x7 b&w prints; $10-50 for 35mm color slides. Captions, model release, and identification of subjects required. Buys one-time rights.
Columns/Departments: Buys 2 mss/year. Query. Length: 750-1,000 words. Pays $20-35.
Fillers: Newsbreaks. Buys 5/year. Length: 50-500 words. Pays $5-15.
Tips: "Choose one vital, but small aspect of the industry; research that subject and slant it to fit the readership

and/or goals of the magazine. All articles on research must have a valid source for foundation. Material must be general in nature about the subject or specific in nature about Idaho potato growers. Write a query letter, noting what you have in mind for an article; be specific." Articles on advancement in potato-growing methods or technology are most open to freelancers.

SINSEMILLA TIPS, Domestic Marijuana Journal, New Moon Publishing, 217 SW 2nd, Box 2046, Corvallis OR 97339. (503)757-2532 or 757-8477. Editor: Thomas Alexander. 50% freelance written. Quarterly magazine tabloid covering the domestic cultivation of marijuana. Circ. 10,000. Pays on publication. Publishes ms an average of 2 months after acceptance. Byline given. "Some writers desire to be anonymous for obvious reasons." Buys first serial rights and second serial (reprint) rights. Submit seasonal/holiday material 2 months in advance. Electronic submissions OK on Osborne 1, HP110, "both have most protocals, but notify in advance." Requires hard copy also. Computer printout submissions acceptable. Reports in 2 months. Sample copy $5.
Nonfiction: Book excerpts and reviews; expose (on political corruption); general interest; how-to; interview/profile; opinion; personal experience; and technical. Send complete ms. Length: 500-2,000 words. Pays $25-100. Sometimes pays the expenses of writers on assignment.
Photos: Send photos with ms. Pays $10-20 for b&w prints. Captions optional; model release required. Buys all rights.
Tips: "Sometimes we have too many major articles—usually we hold over to next issue. Writers may have a better chance with short articles and fillers."

SOYBEAN DIGEST, Box 41309, 777 Craig Rd., St. Louis MO 63141-1309. (314)432-1600. Editor: Gregg Hillyer. 75% freelance written. Emphasizes soybean production and marketing. Monthly magazine. Circ. 200,000. Pays on acceptance. Buys all rights. Byline given. Phone queries OK. Submit seasonal material 2 months in advance. Reports in 3 weeks. Sample copy $3; mention *Writer's Market* in request.
Nonfiction: How-to (soybean production and marketing); and new product (soybean production and marketing). Buys over 100 mss/year. Query or submit complete ms. Length: 1,000 words. Pays $50-350.
Photos: State availability of photos with query. Pays $25-100 for 5x7 or 8x10 b&w prints, $50-275 for 35mm color transparencies, and up to $350 for covers. Captions and/or ms required. Buys all rights.

‡TOBACCO REPORTER, Suite 300, 3000 Highwoods Blvd., Box 95075, Raleigh NC 27625. Editor: Anne Shelton. 5% (by those who *know* the industry) freelance written. International business journal for tobacco producers, processors, warehousemen, exporters, importers, manufacturers and distributors of cigars, cigarettes and other tobacco products. Monthly. Buys all rights. Pays on publication. Computer printout submissions acceptable; no dot-matrix. Publishes ms an average of 2 months after acceptance.
Nonfiction: Uses exclusive original material on request only. Pays 10-15¢/word.
Photos: Pays $25 for photos purchased with mss.
Fillers: Wants clippings on new tobacco product brands, smoking and health, and the following relating to tobacco and tobacco products: job promotions, honors, equipment, etc. Pays $5-10/clipping on use only.

Dairy Farming

‡BUTTER-FAT, Fraser Valley Milk Producers' Cooperative Association, Box 9100, Vancouver, British Columbia V6B 4G4 Canada. (604)420-6611. Editor: C.A. Paulson. Managing Editor: T.W. Low. Eager to work with new/unpublished writers. 50% freelance written. Monthly magazine emphasizing this dairy cooperative's processing and marketing operations for dairy farmers and dairy workers in British Columbia. Circ. 3,500. Pays on acceptance. Publishes ms an average of 4 months after acceptance. Byline given. Buys first rights and first and second rights to the same material. Makes work-for-hire assignments. Phone queries preferred. Submit seasonal material 4 months in advance. Simultaneous, photocopied and previously published submissions OK. Computer printout submissions acceptable. Reports in 1 week on queries; in 1 month on mss. Free sample copy and writer's guidelines.
Nonfiction: Interview (character profile with industry leaders); local nostalgia; opinion (of industry leaders); and profile (of association members and employees).
Photos: Reviews 5x7 b&w negatives and contact sheets. Offers $10/published photo. Captions required. Buys all rights.
Columns/Departments: "We want articles on the people, products, business of producing, processing and marketing dairy foods in this province." Query first. Buys 3 mss/issue. Length: 500-1,500 words. Pays 7¢/word.
Fillers: Jokes, short humor and quotes. Buys 5 mss/issue. Pays $10.
Tips: "Make an appointment to come by and see us!"

DAIRY GOAT JOURNAL, Box 1808, Scottsdale AZ 85252. Editor: Kent Leach. 10% freelance written. Monthly for breeders and raisers of dairy goats. Pays on publication. Publishes ms an average of 8 months after acceptance. Buys first serial rights. Computer printout submissions acceptable; prefers letter-quality to dot-matrix. Reports in 1 month. Free sample copy.

Nonfiction: Uses articles, items and photos that deal with dairy goats and the people who raise them; goat dairies and shows. How-to articles up to 1,000 words. Buys 12-25 unsolicited mss/year. Query. Pays by arrangement. Sometimes pays the expenses of writers on assignment.

Photos: Buys 5x7 or 8x10 b&w photos for $1-15.

Tips: "In query give the thrust or point of the article, what illustrations may be available, how soon it might be finished—and if payments are expected, state how much or if negotiable."

THE DAIRYMAN, Box 819, Corona CA 91718. (714)735-2730. Editor: Dennis Halladay. 10% freelance written. Monthly magazine dealing with large herd commercial dairy industry. Circ. 33,000. Pays on acceptance or publication. Publishes ms an average of 2 months after acceptance. Byline given. Buys first North American serial rights. Submit seasonal material 3 months in advance. Photocopied submissions OK. Computer printout submissions acceptable. Reports in 2 weeks. Free sample copy; writer's guidelines with legal size SAE and 1 first class stamp.

Nonfiction: Humor, interview/profile, new product, opinion, and industry analysis. Special issues: Computer issue (February); herd health issues (July and August); and A.I. and breeding issue (November). No religion, nostalgia, politics or 'mom and pop' dairies. Query or send complete ms. Length: 300-5,000 words. Pays $10-200.

Photos: Send photo with query or ms. Reviews b&w contact sheets and 35mm or 2¼x2¼ transparencies. Pays $10-25 for b&w; $25-60 for color. Captions, model release, and identification of subjects required. Buys one-time rights.

Columns/Departments: Herd health, taxes and finances, insurance, dairy safety, economic outlook for dairying. Buys 40/year. Query or send complete ms. Length: 300-1,000 words. Pays $25-100.

Tips: "Pretend you're an editor for a moment; now would you want to buy a story without any artwork?; neither would I. Writers often don't know modern commercial dairying and they forget they're writing for an audience of *dairymen*. Publications are becoming more and more specialized . . . you've really got to know who you're writing for and why they're different."

General Interest Farming and Rural Life

National

ACRES U.S.A., A Voice for Eco-Agriculture, Acres U.S.A., Box 9547, Kansas City MO 64133. (816)737-0064. Editor: Charles Walters, Jr. Monthly tabloid covering biologically sound farming techniques. Circ. 16,000. Pays on acceptance. Byline sometimes given. Buys all rights. Submit seasonal/holiday material 3 months in advance. Computer printout submissions acceptable. Reports in 1 month. Sample copy $2.

Nonfiction: Expose (farm-related); how-to; and case reports on farmers who have adopted eco-agriculture (organic). No philosophy on eco-farming or essays. Buys 80 mss/year. Query with published clips. Length: open. Pays 6¢/word.

Photos: State availability of photos. Reviews b&w photos only. Top quality photos only. Pays $6 for b&w contact sheets, negatives and 7x10 prints.

Tips: "We need on-scene reports of farmers who have adopted eco-farming—good case reports. We must have substance in articles and need details on systems developed. Read a few copies of the magazine to learn the language of the subject."

AGWAY COOPERATOR, Box 4933, Syracuse NY 13221. (315)477-6231. Editor: Jean Willis. 2% freelance written for farmers. Works with a small number of new/unpublished writers each year. Published 9 times/year. Pays on acceptance. Publishes ms an average of 6 months after acceptance. Time between acceptance and publication varies considerably. Usually reports in 1 week. Computer printout submissions acceptable; no dot-matrix.

Nonfiction: Should deal with topics of farm or rural interest in the Northeastern U.S. Length: 1,200 words maximum. Pays $100, usually including photos.

Tips: "We prefer an Agway tie-in, if possible. Fillers don't fit into our format. We do not assign freelance articles."

BUYING FOR THE FARM, Elmbrook Publishing, Inc., 21100 W. Capitol Dr., Pewaukee WI 53072. (414)783-5157. Editor: H. Lee Schwanz. 15% freelance written. Prefers to work with published/established writers. A monthly farming and ranching magazine "concentrating on ways farmers can save money on inputs for crops and livestock production. Prices are compared for classes of inputs." Circ. 25,000. Pays on acceptance. Publishes ms an average of 2 months after acceptance. Byline given. Offers negotiable kill fee. Buys all rights. Submit seasonal/holiday material 2 months in advance. Simultaneous queries OK. Computer printout submissions acceptable; prefers letter-quality to dot-matrix. Reports in 2 weeks. Sample copy and writer's guidelines for $1.

Nonfiction: Articles related to purchasing for the farm. Buys 50 mss/year. Query with farm writing credentials. Length: 400-800 words. Pays $100-300. Sometimes pays the expenses of writers on assignment.

Photos: Reviews b&w contacts and negatives. Buys one-time rights.

Tips: "We do farmer experience articles and want wide geographical distribution. Writers frequently don't write for the specific type of articles used in *Buying*. We have a unique format."

COUNTRY JOURNAL, (formerly *Blair and Ketchum's Country Journal*), Box 870, Manchester Center VT 05255. Editor: Tyler Resch. Managing Editor: David D. Sleeper. 90% freelance written. Works with a small number of new/unpublished writers each year. Monthly magazine featuring country living for people who live in rural areas or who are thinking about moving there. Circ. 320,000. Average issue includes 8-10 feature articles and 10 departments. Pays on acceptance. Publishes ms an average of 1 year after acceptance. Byline given. Buys first North American serial rights. Submit seasonal material 1 year in advance. Photocopied submissions OK. Computer printout submissions acceptable, prefers letter-quality; "dot-matrix submissions are acceptable if double-spaced." Reports in 1 month. Sample copy $2.50; writer's guidelines for SASE.

Nonfiction: Book excerpts; general interest; opinion (essays); profile (people who are outstanding in terms of country living); how-to; issues affecting rural areas; and photo feature. No historical or reminiscence. Query with published clips. Length: 2,000-3,500 words. Sometimes pays the expenses of writers on assignment.

Photos: Stephen R. Swinburne, photo editor. State availability of photos. Reviews b&w contact sheets, 5x7 and 8x10 b&w glossy prints and 35mm or larger color transparencies. Captions, model release, and identification of subjects required. Buys one-time rights.

Columns/Departments: Listener (brief articles on country topics, how-to's, current events and updates). Buys 15 mss/year. Query with published clips. Length: 200-400 words. Pays approx. $75.

Poetry: Free verse, light verse and traditional. Buys 1 poem/issue. Pays $2.50/line.

Tips: "Be as specific in your query as possible and explain why you are qualified to write the piece (especially for how-to's and controversial subjects). The writer has a better chance of breaking in at our publication with short articles."

FARM & RANCH LIVING, Reiman Publications, 5400 S. 60th St., Greendale WI 53129. (414)423-0100. Managing Editor: Bob Ottum. 80% freelance written. Eager to work with new/unpublished writers. A bimonthly lifestyle magazine aimed at families engaged full time in farming or ranching. "*F&RL* is *not* a 'how-to' magazine—it deals with people rather than products and profits." Circ. 260,000. Pays on acceptance. Publishes ms an average of 1 year after acceptance. Byline given. Offers 25% kill fee. Buys first serial rights and one-time rights. Submit seasonal/holiday material 6 months in advance. Previously published submissions OK. Computer printout submissions acceptable. Reports in 6 weeks. Sample copy $2; writer's guidelines for business size SAE and 1 first class stamp.

Nonfiction: Interview/profile, photo feature, historical/nostalgic, humor, inspirational and personal experience. No how-to articles or stories about "hobby farmers" (doctors or lawyers with weekend farms), or "hard-times" stories (farmers going broke and selling out). Buys 50 mss/year. Query first with or without published clips; state availability of photos. Length: 1,000-3,000 words. Pays $150-500 for text-and-photos package. Pays expenses of writers on assignment.

Photos: Scenic. Pays $20-40 for b&w photos; $75-200 for 35mm color slides. Buys one-time rights.

Fillers: Clippings, jokes, anecdotes and short humor. Buys 150/year. Length: 50-150 words. Pays $20 minimum.

Tips: "In spite of poor farm economy, most farm families are proud and optimistic, and they especially enjoy stories and features that are upbeat and positive. *F&RL*'s circulation continues to increase, providing an excellent market for freelancers. A freelancer must see *F&RL* to fully appreciate how different it is from other farm publications . . . ordering a sample is strongly advised (not available on newsstands). Query first—we'll give plenty of help and encouragement if story looks promising, and we'll explain why if it doesn't. Photo features (about interesting farm or ranch families); Most Interesting Farmer (or Rancher) I've Ever Met (human interest profile); and Prettiest Place in the Country (tour in text and photos of an attractive farm or ranch) are most open to freelancers. We can make separate arrangements for photography if writer is unable to provide photos."

FARM COMPUTER NEWS, Meredith Corp., 1716 Locust, Des Moines IA 50336. (515)284-2127. Editor: Gary Vincent. Bimonthly magazine covering farm computerization. "Our readers are farmers who own or are interested in owning a microcomputer." Circ. 16,000. Pays on acceptance. Byline sometimes given. Buys all rights. Submit seasonal/holiday material 3 months in advance. Computer printout submissions acceptable; prefers letter-quality to dot-matrix. Reports in 2 weeks on queries; 3 months on mss. Free sample copy.

Nonfiction: Interview/profile (farmers using computers); and technical (direct applications to farming). Buys 50-60 mss/year. Query with published clips. Pays $200-400.

FARM FUTURES, The Farm Business Magazine, AgriData Resources, 330 E. Kilbourn, Milwaukee WI 53202. (414)278-7676. Editor: Claudia Waterloo. 40% freelance written. Eager to work with new/unpublished writers. Circ. 160,000. Pays on publication. Publishes ms an average of 2 months after acceptance. Byline given. Offers negotiable kill fee. Buys first serial rights only. Simultaneous queries, and photocopied and previously published submissions OK; no simultaneous submissions. Electronic submissions OK; inquire about requirements. Reports in 1 month. Free sample copy and writer's guidelines.
Nonfiction: Practical advice and insights into managing commercial farms, farm marketing how-to's, financial management, use of computers in agriculture, and farmer profiles. Buys 35 mss/year. Query with published clips. Length: 250-2,000 words. Pays $35-400. Sometimes pays the expenses of writers on assignment.
Tips: "The writer has a better chance of breaking in at our publication with short articles and fillers since our style is very particular; our stories are written directly to farmers and must be extremely practical. It's a style most writers have to 'grow into.' The most frequent mistakes made by writers in completing an article for us are lack of thoroughness and good examples; language too lofty or convoluted; and lack of precision—inaccuracies. Our magazine is growing—we'll be needing more freelance material."

FARM INDUSTRY NEWS, Webb Publishing, 1999 Shepard Rd., St. Paul MN 55116. (612)690-7284. Editor: Joseph Degnan. Managing Editor: Kurt Lawton. 5% freelance written. Works with a small number of new/unpublished writers each year. Magazine published 10 times/year in 16 Midwest and Mideast states. Covers product news, high technology, buying information. "We treat high volume farmers as purchasing agents rather than producers. Our stories provide farmers with in-depth information on new products they may consider buying, new developments in agriculture and on other farmers who have invented their own equipment." Circ. 300,000. Pays on acceptance. Publishes ms an average of 2 months after acceptance. Byline given. Buys one-time rights. Computer printout submissions acceptable. Reports in 3 weeks. Free sample copy and writer's guidelines.
Nonfiction: Interview/profile, new product and technical. No production stories, fiction or poetry. "Please study the publication before submitting stories." Query or send complete ms. Length: 500-1,500 words. Pays $50-400. Sometimes pays the expenses of writers on assignment.
Photos: Reviews b&w contact sheets, 35mm color transparencies or 8x10 b&w prints. Payment depends on use and is included with ms. Captions and indentification of subjects required.
Tips: "Read the magazine, then query with specific idea and contacts. Good photographs showing a product and human involvement help in selling an article." Phone queries OK.

HIGH PLAINS JOURNAL, "The Farmers Paper", High Plains Publishers, Inc., Box 760, Dodge City KS 67801. (316)227-7171. Editor: Galen Hubbs. 5% freelance written. Weekly tabloid with news, features and photos on all phases of farming and livestock production. Circ. 58,000. Pays on publication. Publishes ms an average of 1 month after acceptance. Byline given. Not copyrighted. Buys first serial rights. Submit seasonal/holiday material 1 month in advance. Simultaneous queries and photocopied submissions OK. Computer printout submissions acceptable; prefers letter-quality to dot-matrix. Reports in 3 weeks on queries; 1 month on mss. Sample copy for $1 and SAE with 3 first class stamps; writer's guidelines for SAE and 1 first class stamp.
Nonfiction: General interest (agriculture); how-to; interview/profile (farmers or stockmen within the High Plains area); and photo feature (agricultural). No rewrites of USDA, extension or marketing association releases. Buys 50-60 mss/year. Query with published clips. Length: 10-40 inches. Pays $1/column inch. Sometimes pays the expenses of writers on assignment.
Photos: State availability of photos. Pays $5-10 for 4x5 b&w prints. Captions and complete identification of subjects required. Buys one-time rights.
Tips: "Limit submissions to agriculture. Stories should not have a critical time element. Stories should be informative with correct information. Use quotations and bring out the human aspects of the person featured in profiles. Frequently writers do not have a good understanding of the subject. Stories are too long or are too far from our circulation area to be beneficial. Too many writers are just seeking a way to make additional income."

THE NATIONAL FUTURE FARMER, Box 15130, Alexandria VA 22309. (703)360-3600. Editor-in-Chief: Wilson W. Carnes. 15% freelance written. Prefers to work with published/established writers. Bimonthly magazine for members of the Future Farmers of America who are students of vocational agriculture in high school, ranging in age from 14-21 years; major interest in careers in agriculture/agribusiness and other youth interest subjects. Circ. 476,500. Pays on acceptance. Buys all rights. Byline given. Submit seasonal/holiday material 4 months in advance. Computer printout submissions acceptable; prefers letter-quality to dot-matrix. Usually reports in 1 month. Free sample copy and writer's guidelines.
Nonfiction: How-to for youth (outdoor-type such as camping, hunting, fishing); and informational (getting money for college, farming; and other help for youth). Informational, personal experience and interviews are used only if FFA members or former members are involved. Buys 15 unsolicited mss/year. Query or send complete ms. Length: 1,000 words maximum. Pays 4-6¢/word.

Photos: Purchased with mss (5x7 or 8x10 b&w glossies; 35mm or larger color transparencies). Pays $7.50 for b&w; $30-40 for inside color; $100 for cover.
Tips: "Find an FFA member who has done something truly outstanding that will motivate and inspire others, or provide helpful information for a career in farming, ranching or agribusiness. We are also very interested in stories on the latest trends in agriculture and how those trends may affect our readers. We're accepting manuscripts now that are tighter and more concise. Get straight to the point."

NEW HOLLAND NEWS, (formerly *Sperry New Holland News*), Sperry New Holland, Inc., 500 Diller Ave., New Holland PA 17557. Editor: Gary Martin. 50% freelance written. Prefers to work with published/established writers; works with a small number of new/unpublished writers each year. Magazine published 8 times/year on agriculture; designed to entertain and inform farm families. Pays on acceptance. Publishes ms an average of 1 year after acceptance. Byline usually given. Offers negotiable kill fee. Buys first North American serial rights, one-time rights, and second serial (reprint) rights. Submit seasonal/holiday material 6 months in advance. Simultaneous queries and previously published submissions OK. Computer printout submissions acceptable; prefers letter-quality to dot-matrix. Reports in 1 month. Free sample copy and writer's guidelines.
Nonfiction: "We need strong photo support for short articles up to 800 words on farm management, farm human interest and agricultural research." Buys 16-20 mss/year. Query. Length: 800 words. Pays $400-700. Sometimes pays the expenses of writers on assignment.
Photos: Send photos with query when possible. Reviews color transparencies. Pays $25-200. Captions, model release, and identification of subjects required. Buys one-time rights.
Tips: "The writer must have an emotional understanding of agriculture and the farm family and must demonstrate in the article an understanding of the unique economics that affect farming in North America. We want to know about the exceptional farm managers, those leading the way in use of new technology, new efficiencies—but always with a human touch. Successful writers keep in touch with the editor as they develop the article."

SUCCESSFUL FARMING, 1716 Locust St., Des Moines IA 50336. (515)284-2897. Managing Editor: Loren Kruse. 3% freelance written. Prefers to work with published/established writers. Magazine of farm management published for top farmers 14 times/year. Circ. 605,000. Buys all rights. Pays on acceptance. Publishes ms an average of 2 months after acceptance. Reports in 2 weeks. Computer printout submissions acceptable; no dot-matrix. Sample copy for SAE and 5 first class stamps.
Nonfiction: Semitechnical articles on the aspects of farming with emphasis on how to apply this information to one's own farm. "Most of our material is too limited and unfamiliar for freelance writers, except for the few who specialize in agriculture, have a farm background and a modern agricultural education." Recent article example: "Check these financial ratios before you expand" (March, 1986). Buys 25 unsolicited mss/year. Query with outline. Length: about 1,500 words maximum. Pays $250-600. Sometimes pays the expenses of writers on assignment.
Photos: Jim Galbraith, art director. Prefers 8x10 b&w glossies to contacts; color should be transparencies, not prints. Buys exclusive rights. Assignments are given, and sometimes a guarantee, provided the editors can be sure the photography will be acceptable.
Tips: "We are looking for more farm business stories rather than production stories. A frequent mistake made by writers in completing articles is that the focus of the story is not narrow enough and does not include enough facts, observations, examples, and dollar signs. Short articles and fillers are usually specific and to the point."

Local

AcreAGE, Malheur Publishing Co., Box 130, Ontario OR 97914. (503)889-5387. Editor: Marie A. Ruemenapp. 20% freelance written. Eager to work with new/unpublished writers. Monthly tabloid covering anything and everything relating to farming and ranching for all rural boxholders in southern Idaho and eastern Oregon. Circ. 42,000. Pays on publication. Publishes ms an average of 3 months after acceptance. Byline given. Buys first serial rights; some exceptions are made; query first. Computer printout submissions acceptable; prefers letter-quality to dot-matrix. Reports in 3 weeks. Sample copy $1.
Nonfiction: General interest (on farming and ranching); how-to (install fence, irrigate, plant, harvest, etc.); interview/profile (of leaders in agriculture); and personal experience (better ways to farm and ranch). No nostalgic pieces. "About 50% of our articles are technical pieces about such things as ag chemicals, irrigation, etc. These pieces are difficult for writers lacking a good ag background and proximity to a university or research center specializing in such work. No manuscripts on 'how nice (or bad) it is to be a farmer or rancher.' " Buys 24 mss/year. Query or send complete ms. Length: 1,200 words maximum. Pays $1/inch.
Photos: Pays $5-7.50 for 5x7 (minimum) b&w glossy prints. Buys some color slides as cover photos (prefer these with ms). Identification of subjects required.
Tips: "Avoid telling the obvious, e.g., 'Holsteins are a breed of cow that gives lots of milk.' Writers will have

better luck breaking in with human interest features (farm-ranch oriented). Past articles have included a power hang-glider (ultralight) pilot who used his machine to check irrigation lines; Landsat satellites for water and crop management; an old-time threshing bee; and a farmer who collects antique farm machinery. The majority of our articles deal with farming and ranching in the southern Idaho, eastern Oregon region. We are a regional publication. The farmers and ranchers in this area have different agricultural practices than their counterparts in other areas of the country. Writers frequently forget this.''

‡**AG REVIEW**, Farm Resource Center, 16 Grove St., Putnam CT 06260. (203)928-7778. Editor: Lucien Laliberty. Associate Editor: Liz Cabelus. 50% freelance written. A monthly magazine covering Northeast (New England, New York and Pennsylvania) agriculture for dairy, beef, cash and field crop farms: reporting and analyzing trends, research and product developments, and innovative problem-solving. Circ. 6,000. Pays on publication. Publishes ms an average of 2 months after acceptance. Byline given. Offers 50% kill fee. Buys one-time rights, second serial (reprint) rights or simultaneous rights. Submit seasonal/holiday material 4 months in advance. Photocopied and previously published submissions OK. Computer printout submissions acceptable. Reports in 1 month on queries; 6 weeks on mss. Free sample copy and writer's guidelines.
Nonfiction: Essays (current events or agricultural developments or researched techniques); how-to (solving specific farm products, appropriate to Northeast); and new product (unusual innovations, home adaptions). Writer's guidelines lists theme issues. "No blow-by-blow reports of conferences or meetings; gardening; or description of how some farmer runs his farm if it's ordinary stuff." Buys 10 mss/year. Query with or without published clips, or send complete ms. Length: 500-20,000 words (5,000 words more likely; 20,000 would be printed in parts in several issues). Pays $25-300; sometimes pays in Farm Resource Center data management or marketing services. Sometimes pays the expenses of writers on assignment.
Photos: State availability or send photos with submission. Reviews transparencies or 3x5 minimum prints. Offers $5-10/photo. Captions and identification of subjects required. Buys one-time rights.
Columns/Departments: Farm Innovator (farmers who have developed innovative products or markets or techniques that will inspire readers), 1,000-2,000 words. Buys 3-6 mss/year. Query or send complete ms. Pays $25-100.
Fiction: Humorous and slice-of-life vignettes, agricultural- or rural-related. Send complete ms. Length: 500-1,500 words. Pays $25-100.
Tips: "We're happy to consider work by unpublished writers. We're wide open to freelancers. We have too few articles on computers, sheep, hogs, and vegetable crops."

‡**CALIFORNIA FARMER, The Magazine for Commercial Agriculture**, California Farmer Publishing Co., 731 Market St., San Francisco CA 94103. (415)495-3340. Editor: Len Richardson. Managing Editor: Richard Smoley. 60% freelance written. Magazine published semimonthly: once a month in July, August, December covering California agriculture. "We cover all issues of interest to the state's commercial farmers, including production techniques, marketing, politics, and social and economic issues." Circ. 56,000. Pays on acceptance. Publishes ms an average of 1 month after acceptance. Byline given. Offers $100 kill fee. Buys first North American serial rights or makes work-for-hire assignments. Submit seasonal/holiday material 3 months in advance. Photocopied and previously published submissions OK. Electronic submissions OK, only ASCII text by modem through MCI Mail. Computer printout submissions acceptable, "must be double-spaced"; prefers letter-quality to dot-matrix. Reports in 1 month. Free writer's guidelines.
Nonfiction: How-to (agricultural, livestock); interview/profile; technical (agricultural: weed and pest control; crop and livestock management; cultural and irrigation practices; financial involvement and marketing of farm products.) No "It happened to me"-type stories. Buys 75 mss/year. Query with published clips. Length: 1,000-3,000 words. Pays $100-400 for assigned articles; pays $50-300 for unsolicited artcles. Pays expenses of writers on assignment.
Photos: Send photos with submission. Reviews 35mm color transparencies and b&w prints (any size). Captions and identification of subjects required. Buys one-time rights.
Tips: "We will give preference to writers with a demonstrated knowledge of California agriculture, but we will consider material from and occasionally give assignments to good writers with an ability to research a story, get the facts right and write in a smooth, easy-to-understand style. We are most interested in stories about technical innovations in farming as they relate to California agriculture. Stories should be clear, concise, and above all, accurate. We especially welcome pictures of California farmers as illustration."

‡**COASTAL PLAINS FARMER MAGAZINE**, Specialized Agricultural Publications, Inc., Suite 300, 3000 Highwoods Blvd., Raleigh NC 27625. (919)872-5040. Editor: Sid Reynolds. A monthly magazine covering agriculture and rural living. "Primarily, *Coastal Plains Farmer* is a business-of-farming magazine with 70 percent of its content devoted to concise how-to and bottom-line articles. Twenty percent of the content deals with the real, ever-present needs of rural communities, from state legislation and its impact on education, rural health, retirement, and the many topics that are as much a part of farming as field work. The remaining 10 percent of the *Coastal Plains Farmer* is devoted to the human aspects of farming and living in the rural Coastal Plains areas." Circ. 96,000. Pays on acceptance. Byline sometimes given; "depends on significance." Buys

first North American serial rights. Submit seasonal/holiday material 3 months in advance. Simultaneous queries OK. Computer printout submissions acceptable. Reports in 2 weeks on queries; 2 months on mss. Sample copy and writer's guidelines free.

Nonfiction: How-to (specific money slant on farm techniques in sandy-textured soils); humor (on rural life in the Coastal Plains); and interview/profile (on farmers in the Coastal Plains). No one-source articles. Query with published clips. Length: 100-2,500 words. Pays $25-500.

Photos: Send photos with query or ms. Pays $15-500 for 5x7 color transparencies; $10-100 for 5x7 b&w prints. Captions and identification of subjects required; model releases sometimes required.

Columns/Departments: Machine Shop (farmers in the Coastal Plains who have adapted machinery for a specific function); Bottomline (farm financial management tips or legislative information). Buys 5 mss/year. Query. Length: 100-1,000 words. Pays $25-100.

Tips: "It helps to have practical experience in farming."

‡FARM FOCUS, Box 128 Yarmouth, Nova Scotia, Canada B5A 4B1. Editor: Heather Jones. 60% freelance written. Works with a small number of new/unpublished writers each year. Bimonthly magazine read by farmers, people in agribusiness, and in government agricultural agencies. "It is the only farm and agricultural paper that is distributed throughout Atlantic Canada." Circ. 11,500. Pays on publication. Publishes ms an average of 1 month after acceptance. Buys first or second rights. Computer printout submissions acceptable; no dot-matrix. SAE and International Reply Coupons.

Nonfiction: "Any American developments that could have an impact on the Canadian agricultural scene." No "re-writes on agricultural bulletins, scientific papers." Buys 100 unsolicited mss/year. Send complete ms. Length: 800-1,400 words. Pays 3-7¢/word.

Photos: Pays $5 for 5x7 b&w prints. Sometimes pays the expenses of writers on assignment.

Tips: "At the present time it is not easy for a freelance writer to break into the limited field we service, but copy on any government policies that would affect agriculture, new innovations in agriculture, or about individuals or groups that have been successful by flying in the face of tradition, would be of interest. Articles should be as concise as possible and written so the layman can understand them."

FLORIDA GROWER & RANCHER, 723 E. Colonial Dr., Orlando FL 32803. Editor: Frank Abrahamson. "We are backlogged with submissions and prefer not to receive unsolicited submissions at this time."

IOWA REC NEWS, Suite 48, 8525 Douglas, Urbandale IA 50322. (515)276-5350. Editor: Karen Tisinger. Managing Editor: David Strabala. 15% freelance written. Emphasizes energy issues for residents of rural Iowa. Monthly magazine. Circ. 125,000. Pays on publication. Publishes ms an average of 3 months after acceptance. Buys first serial rights and second serial (reprint) rights. Not copyrighted. Simultaneous, photocopied and previously published submissions OK. Computer printout submissions acceptable.

Nonfiction: General interest, historical, humor, farm issues and trends; rural lifestyle trends, energy awareness features, and photo feature. Buys approximately 12 unsolicited mss/year. Send complete ms. Pays $40-60.

Tips: "The easiest way to break into our magazine is: research a particular subject well, include appropriate attributions to establish credibility, authority and include a couple paragraphs about the author. Reading and knowing about farm people is important. Stories that touch the senses or can improve the lives of the readers are highly considered, as are those with a strong Iowa angle. We prefer to tailor our articles to Iowa REC readers and use our staff's skills. Freelancers have the advantage of offering subject matter that existing staff may not be able to cover. Often, however, many articles lack evidence of actual research—they provide lots of information but do not include any sources to give the story any credibility. (Rarely is the author a renowned expert on the subject he's written about.) Inclusion of nice photos is also a plus. The most frequent mistakes made by writers are: lots of typos in copy, uncorrected; story too long, story too biased; no attribution to any source of info; and not relevant to electric consumers, farmers."

MAINE ORGANIC FARMER & GARDENER, Maine Organic Farmers & Gardeners Association, Box 2176, Augusta ME 04330. (207)622-3118. Editor: Pam Bell, Box 53, South Hiram ME 04080. 30% freelance written. Prefers to work with published/established writers; works with a small number of new/unpublished writers each year. Bimonthly magazine covering organic farming and gardening for urban and rural farmers and gardeners and nutrition-oriented, environmentally concerned readers. "*MOF&G* promotes and encourages sustainable agriculture and environmentally sound living. Our primary focus is organic sustainable farming, gardening and forestry, but we also deal with local, national and global environmental issues." Circ. 15,000. Pays on publication. Publishes ms an average of 6 months after acceptance. Byline given. Buys first North American serial rights, one-time rights, first serial rights, or second serial (reprint) rights. Submit seasonal/holiday material 4 months in advance. Simultaneous queries, and simultaneous, photocopied, and previously published submissions OK. Computer printout submissions acceptable. Reports in 5 weeks. Sample copy $1.50; free writer's guidelines.

Nonfiction: Historical/nostalgic (farming); how-to (farm, garden [organically], forestry, woodlot management and rural skills); interview/profile (farmers, gardeners, government or other ag people); personal experience (with livestock, plants, trees, energy [renewable], gardens, farms); photo feature; technical (renewable energy, alternative agriculture, organic horticulture); and nutrition and the food system. Also first person experience, interview, or documented report dealing with environmental problem and/or solution. Buys 20 mss/year. Query with published clips or send complete ms. Length: 1,000-3,000 words. Pays $40-130. Sometimes pays expenses of writers on assignment.

Photos: State availability of photos with query; send photos with ms. Reviews contact sheets and negatives. "We usually work from negatives. Many of our assignment writers send exposed films, and we process and print." Pays $5 for 5x7 b&w prints. Captions, model releases, and identification of subjects required. Buys one-time rights.

Tips: "Freelance writers interviewing organic farmers and gardeners, or commercial farmers who are looking for a more organic way should be mindful that interview and profile articles are more than human interest pieces for our readers—they are the backbone of our how-to information. Our readers want to know how-to but they also want to enjoy the reading. And they want to know who the teacher is. We don't want impersonal how-to articles that sound like Extension bulletins or textbooks. We are hiring a staff writer and thus will use ⅓ fewer freelance manuscripts and definitely fewer reprint articles."

‡**N.D. REC MAGAZINE**, N.D. Association of RECs, Box 727, Mandan ND 58554. (701)663-6501. Editor-in-Chief: Leland Ulmer. Managing Editor: Dennis Hill. Monthly magazine covering rural electric program and rural North Dakota lifestyle. "Our magazine goes to the 70,000 North Dakotans who get their electricity from rural electric cooperatives. We cover rural lifestyle, energy conservation, agriculture, farm family news and other features of importance to this predominantly agrarian state. Of course, we represent the views of our statewide association." Circ. 74,000. Pays on publication; "acceptance for assigned features." Byline given. Buys first North American serial rights. Submit seasonal/holiday material 6 months in advance. Simultaneous queries OK. Computer printout submissions acceptable; prefers letter-quality to dot-matrix. Reports in 2 weeks. Sample copy for 9x12 SAE with $1.37 postage.

Nonfiction: Dennis Hill, managing editor. Expose (subjects of ND interest dealing with rural electric, agriculture, rural lifestyle); historical/nostalgic (ND events or people only); how-to (save energy, weatherize homes, etc.); interview/profile (on great leaders of the rural electric program, agriculture); and opinion (why family farms should be saved, etc.). No fiction that does not relate to our editorial goals. Buys 10-12 mss/year. Length: open. Pays $35-300.

Photos: Dennis Hill, managing editor. "We need 5x7 b&w glossy prints for editorial material. Transparencies needed for cover, ag/rural scenes only—ND interest." Pays $25 maximum for 35mm color transparencies; $5 minimum for 5x7 b&w prints. Captions and identification of subjects required. Buys one-time rights.

Columns/Departments: Dennis Hill, managing editor. Guest Spot: Guest opinion page, preferably about 700-850 words, about issues dealing with agriculture, rural social issues and the rural electric program. Buys 12 mss/year. Length: 700-1,000 words. Pays $35-75.

‡**NEW ENGLAND FARM BULLETIN**, New England Farm & Home Assn., Box 147, Cohasset MA 02025. Editor-in-Chief: V.A. Lipsett. Managing Editor: M.S. Maire. 5% freelance written. A biweekly newsletter covering New England farming. Circ. 11,000. Pays on publication. Publishes ms an average of 2 months after acceptance. Byline given. Buys first North American serial rights. Submit seasonal/holiday material 6 months in advance. Photocopied submissions OK. Computer printout submissions acceptable; prefers letter-quality to dot-matrix. Reports in 1 week.

Nonfiction: Essays (farming/agriculture); general interest; historical/nostalgic; how-to; humor; interview/profile (possibly, of New England farm); personal experience; and technical. All articles must be related to New England farming. Buys 6-12 mss/year. Query or send complete ms. Length: 500-2,500 words. Pays 5-10¢/word.

Tips: "We would probably require the writer to live in New England or to have an unmisstakable grasp of what New England is like; must also know farmers." Especially interested in general articles on New England crops/livestocks, specific breeds, crop strains and universal agricultural activity in New England.

THE OHIO FARMER, 1350 W. 5th Ave., Columbus OH 43212. (614)486-9637. Editor: Andrew Stevens. 10% freelance written. For Ohio farmers and their families. Biweekly magazine; 50 pages. Circ. 93,000. Usually buys all rights. Pays on publication. Publishes ms an average of 2 months after acceptance. Will consider photocopied submissions. Reports in 2 weeks. Computer printout submissions acceptable; prefers letter-quality to dot-matrix. Sample copy $1; free writer's guidelines.

Nonfiction: Technical and on-the-farm stories. Buys informational, how-to, and personal experience. Buys 5-10 mss/year. Submit complete ms. Length: 600-700 words. Pays $15.

Photos: Photos purchased with ms with no additional payment, or without ms. Pays $5-25 for b&w; $35-100 for color. 4x5 b&w glossies; and transparencies or 8x10 color prints.

Tips: "We are now doing more staff-written stories. We buy very little freelance material."

‡PENNSYLVANIA FARMER, Harcourt Brace Jovanovich Publications, 704 Lisburn Rd., Camp Hill PA 17011. (717)761-6050. Editor: John Vogel. 20% freelance written. A bimonthly farm business magazine "oriented to providing readers with ideas to help their businesses and personal lives." Circ. 68,000. Pays on publication. Publishes ms an average of 3 months after acceptance. Byline sometimes given. Buys one-time rights. Submit seasonal/holiday material 3 months in advance. Simultaneous submissions OK. Reports in 2 weeks. Free writer's guidelines.
Nonfiction: Humor, inspirational, and technical. No stories without a strong tie to modern-day farming. Buys 15 mss/year. Query. Length: 500-1,000 words. Pays $25-100. Sometimes pays the expenses of writers on assignment.
Photos: Send photos with submission. Reviews contact sheets, 35mm transparencies and 5x7 prints. Offers no additional payment for photos accepted with ms. Captions and identification of subjects required. Buys one-time rights.
Columns/Departments: Lynn Tilton, column/department editor. Country Air (humorous, first-person accounts of farm happenings), 600 words. Buys 18 mss/year. Send complete ms. Pays $25.

WALLACES FARMER, Suite 501, 1501 42nd Street, W. Des Moines IA 50265. (515)224-6000. Editor: Monte N. Sesker. 2% freelance written. Semimonthly magazine for Iowa farmers and their families. Buys Midwest states rights (Nebraska, Minnesota, Wisconsin, Illinois, Missouri, South Dakota and Iowa). Pays on acceptance. Publishes ms an average of 2 weeks after acceptance. Computer printout submissions acceptable; prefers letter-quality to dot-matrix. Reports in 2 weeks.
Nonfiction: Occasional short feature articles about Iowa farming accompanied by photos. Buys 10 unsolicited mss/year. Query. Length: 500-1,000 words. Pays 4-5¢/word.
Photos: Photos purchased with or without mss. Should be taken on Iowa farms. Pays $7-15 for 5x7 b&w; $50-100 for 4x5, 2¼x2¼ color transparencies. See recent issue covers for examples.
Tips: "We are moving toward more staff-produced articles."

WYOMING RURAL ELECTRIC NEWS, 340 West B St., Casper WY 82601. (307)234-6152. Editor: Gale Eisenhauer. 10% freelance written. Works with a small number of new/unpublished writers each year; eager to work with new/unpublished writers. For audience of rural people, some farmers and ranchers. Monthly magazine; 20 pages. Circ. 58,500. Not copyrighted. Byline given. Pays on publication. Publishes ms an average of 3 months after acceptance. Buys first serial rights. Will consider photocopied and simultaneous submissions. Submit seasonal material 2 months in advance. Computer printout submissions acceptable; prefers letter-quality to dot-matrix. Reports in 1 month. Free sample copy with SAE and 3 first class stamps.
Nonfiction and Fiction: Wants energy-related material, "people" features, historical pieces about Wyoming and the West, and things of interest to Wyoming's rural people. Buys informational, humor, historical, nostalgia and photo mss. Submit complete ms. Buys 12-15 mss/year. Length for nonfiction and fiction: 1,200-1,500 words. Pays $25-50. Buys some experimental, western, humorous and historical fiction. Pays $25-50. Sometimes pays the expenses of writers on assignment.
Photos: Photos purchased with accompanying ms with additional payment, or purchased without ms. Captions required. Pays up to $50 for cover photos. Color only.
Tips: "Study an issue or two of the magazine to become familiar with our focus and the type of freelance material we're using. Submit entire manuscript. Don't submit a regionally set story from some other part of the country and merely change the place names to Wyoming. Photos and illustrations (if appropriate) are always welcomed."

Livestock

BEEF, The Webb Co., 1999 Shepard Rd., St. Paul MN 55116. (612)690-7374. Editor-in-Chief: Paul D. Andre. Senior Managing Editor: Warren Kester. 5% freelance written. Prefers to work with published/established writers. Monthly magazine for readers who have the same basic interest—making a living feeding cattle or running a cow herd. Circ. 125,000. Pays on acceptance. Publishes ms an average of 4 months after acceptance. Buys all rights. Byline given. Phone queries OK. Submit seasonal material 3 months in advance. Computer printout submissions acceptable. Reports in 2 months. Free sample copy and writer's guidelines.
Nonfiction: How-to and informational articles on doing a better job of producing, feeding cattle, market building, managing, and animal health practices. Material must deal with beef cattle only. Buys 8-10 mss/year. Query. Length: 500-2,000 words. Pays $25-300. Sometimes pays the expenses of writers on assignment.
Photos: B&w glossies (8x10) and color transparencies (35mm or 2¼x2¼) purchased with or without mss. Query or send contact sheet caption and/or transparencies. Pays $10-50 for b&w; $25-100 for color. Model release required.
Tips: "Be completely knowledgeable about cattle feeding and cowherd operations. Know what makes a story. We want specifics, not a general roundup of an operation. Pick one angle and develop it fully. The most frequent mistake is not following instructions on an angle (or angles) to be developed."

THE CATTLEMAN MAGAZINE, Texas & Southwestern Cattle Raisers Association, 1301 W. 7th St., Ft. Worth TX 76102. (817)332-7155. Editor: Dale Segraves. Managing Editor: Don C. King. Emphasizes beef cattle production and feeding. "Readership consists of commercial cattlemen, purebred seedstock producers, cattle feeders and horsemen in the Southwest." Monthly magazine; 170 pages. Circ. 22,500. Pays on acceptance. Publishes ms an average of 6 months after acceptance. Byline given. Buys all rights. Computer printout submissions acceptable; prefers letter-quality to dot-matrix. Reports in 3 weeks. Sample copy $1.50; writer's guidelines for business size SAE and 1 first class stamp.
Nonfiction: Need informative, entertaining feature articles on specific commercial ranch operations, cattle breeding and feeding, range and pasture management, profit tips, and university research on beef industry. "We feature various beef cattle breeds most months." Will take a few historical western-lore pieces. Must be well-documented. No first person narratives or fiction or articles pertaining to areas outside the Southwest or outside beef cattle ranching. Buys 24 mss/year. Query. Length: 1,500-2,000 words. Pays $75-200. Sometimes pays the expenses of writers on assignment.
Photos: Photos purchased with or without accompanying ms. State availability of photos with query or ms. Pays $15-25 for 5x7 b&w glossies; $100 for color transparencies used as cover. Total purchase price for ms includes payment for photos. Captions, model release, and identification of subjects required.
Fillers: Cartoons.
Tips: "Submit an article dealing with ranching in the Southwest. Too many writers submit stories out of our general readership area. Economics may force staff writers to produce more articles, leaving little room for unsoliticed articles."

LIMOUSIN WORLD, Limousin World, Inc., 6408 S. College Ave., Fort Collins CO 80525. Editor: Wes Ishmael. Managing Editor: Louise Kello. 10% freelance written. "Eager to work with any writers, veteran or new, who can do the job for us." A monthly magazine on the Limousin breed of beef cattle for people who breed and raise them. Circ. 13,000. Pays on acceptance. Publishes ms an average of 2 months after acceptance. Byline given. Buys negotiable rights. Submit seasonal/holiday material 2 months in advance. Simultaneous queries, and photocopied and previously published submissions OK. Computer printout submissions acceptable; prefers letter-quality to dot-matrix. Reports in 2 weeks. Sample copy and writer's guidelines for $2.40.
Nonfiction: How-to (beef herd management equipment); interview/profile (interesting Limousin breeders); new product (limited); and travel (Limousin oriented). "Write interesting, informative, entertaining articles on farm and ranch operations where Limousin breeding has an influence. Management, feeding, breeding, profit producing methods, university research and interesting people are all good topics. Queries should be made on subject for herd features before doing. Short human interest articles on well-known popular personalities who are also breeding Limousin are used." Special issue on Herd Reference. No inflammatory or controversial articles. Query. Length: open. Pays $25-200. Sometimes pays the expenses of writers on assignment.
Photos: Send photos with query or ms. Pays $5-25 for 5x7 and 8x10 b&w prints; $25-100 for 5x7 and 8x10 color prints. Captions and model release required. Buys first-time rights.
Tips: "Our readers are in the cattle breeding and raising business for a living so writing should be directed to an informed, mature audience. What we need are articles geared toward the Limousin breed of cattle specifically."

‡POLLED HEREFORD WORLD, 4700 E. 63rd St., Kansas City MO 64130. (816)333-7731. Editor: Ed Bible. For "breeders of Polled Hereford cattle—about 80% registered breeders, 5% commercial cattle breeders; remainder are agribusinessmen in related fields." Monthly. Circ. 13,000. Not copyrighted. Buys "no unsolicited mss at present." Pays on publication. Photocopied submissions OK. Computer printout submissions acceptable; prefers letter-quality to dot-matrix. Submit seasonal material "as early as possible: 2 months preferred." Reports in 1 month. Query first for reports of events and activities. Query first or submit complete ms for features. Free sample copy. No writer's guidelines.
Nonfiction: "Features on registered or commercial Polled Hereford breeders. Some on related agricultural subjects (pastures, fences, feeds, buildings, etc.). Mostly technical in nature; some human interest. Our readers make their living with cattle, so write for an informed, mature audience." Buys informational articles, how-to's, personal experience articles, interviews, profiles, historical and think pieces, nostalgia, photo features, coverage of successful business operations, articles on merchandising techniques, and technical articles. Length: "varies with subject and content of feature." Pays about 5¢/word ("usually about 50¢/column inch, but can vary with the value of material").
Photos: Purchased with mss, sometimes purchased without mss, or on assignment; captions required. "Only good quality b&w glossies accepted; any size. Good color prints or transparencies." Pays $2 for b&w, $2-25 for color. Pays $25 for color covers.

SHOW RING MAGAZINE, Box 1399, Albany TX 76430. (915)762-2242. Editor: Mike Martinson. Assistant Editor: Carol Lackey. Approximately 50% freelance written. "We need submissions." A national monthly magazine covering the livestock industry (cattle, sheep and swine) with focus on major livestock shows and sales, as well as the purebred breeding industry. Audience includes families and 4-H and FFA groups. "The emphasis of our editorial content is directed toward youth livestock activities, such as state and national livestock shows, youth livestock events, and breeders of livestock for youth." Circ. 5,000. Pays on publication. Publishes ms an average of 2 months after acceptance. Byline given. Not copyrighted. Buys first rights. Submit seasonal/holiday material 3 months in advance. Simultaneous queries OK. Computer printout submissions acceptable; prefers letter-quality to dot-matrix. Reports in 1 month. Sample copy $1.50.

Nonfiction: General interest (anything on livestock industry); historical/nostalgic (how things have changed in livestock shows or sales); how-to (clip a calf, exhibit an animal); humor (pertaining to livestock); interview/profile (story about prominent ranch or farm "check with us before writing"); new product (any new livestock product); opinion (about any current happening in livestock industry); personal experience (with livestock, exhibiting animals, etc.; 4-H or FFA experience); photo feature; and technical (on embryo transplants, artificial insemination, etc.). Special issues include Show Pig issues (April-October); Sire issue (May); Directory of Agriculture (June/July). Buys 10 mss/year. Query. Length: 500-2,500 words. Pays at least $25-100. Sometimes pays the expenses of writers on assignment.

Photos: State availability of photos. Pays $5/3x5 b&w and color prints. Captions and identification of subjects required. Buys one-time rights.

Fiction: "We will not use much fiction. We might be interested if it is humorous or a special story for Christmas, etc. It must pertain to livestock." Buys 1-3 mss/year. Query. Length: 500 words. Pays $25-100.

Tips: "We especially need articles on young people having good experiences showing livestock. How-to articles are also very popular with our readers."

SIMMENTAL SHIELD, Box 511, Lindsborg KS 67456. Publisher/Editor: Chester Peterson Jr. 30% freelance written. Eager to work with new/unpublished writers. Official publication of American Simmental Association. Readers are breeders of purebred cattle and/or commercial cattlemen. Monthly; 124 pages. Circ. 7,000. Buys all rights. Pays on publication. Publishes ms an average of 3 months after acceptance. Computer printout submissions acceptable. Submit material 4 months in advance. Reports in 1 month. Free sample copy $1.50.

Nonfiction and Fillers: Farmer experience and management articles with emphasis on ideas used and successful management ideas based on cattleman who owns Simmental. Research: new twist to old ideas or application of new techniques to the Simmental or cattle business. Wants articles that detail to reader how to make or save money or pare labor needs. Buys informational, how-to, personal experience, interview, profile, humor and think articles. January is AI issue; July is herd sire issue; December is brood cow issue. Query first or submit complete ms. Rates vary. Sometimes pays the expenses of writers on assignment.

Photos: Photos purchased with accompanying ms with no additional payment. Interest in cover photos; accepts 35mm if sharp, well exposed.

Tips: "Articles must involve Simmental and/or beef breeding cattle. Be conversant with our lingo and community."

Miscellaneous

‡AMERICAN BEE JOURNAL, Dadant and Sons, Inc., 51 S. 2nd St., Hamilton IL 62341. (217)847-3324. Editor: Joe Graham. 20% freelance written. Works with a small number of new/unpublished writers each year. Monthly magazine about beekeeping for hobbyist beekeepers, commercial beekeepers and researchers. Circ. 20,000. Average issue includes 8-10 nonscientific articles and 1-2 scientific articles by researchers. Pays on publication. Publishes ms an average of 2 months after acceptance. Byline given. Buys first serial rights. Submit seasonal material 2 months in advance. Previously published submissions OK, if so indicated. Computer printout submissions acceptable; prefers letter-quality to dot-matrix. Reports in 2 weeks. Free sample copy.

Nonfiction: General interest (articles that deal with beekeeping management; honey packing and handling; bee diseases; other products of the hive such as royal jelly, pollen and beeswax; pesticide hazards to honeybees; and occasional articles on beekeeping as a business). No general information about beekeeping. Buys 20-40 unsolicited mss/year. Send complete ms. Length: 1,200-1,500 words. Pays $2\frac{1}{2}$¢/word minimum.

Photos: Send photos with ms. Pays $5 minimum for 5x7 b&w glossy prints. Captions and model release required.

Fillers: Newsbreaks. Buys 1-2 mss/issue. Pays $2\frac{1}{2}$¢/word minimum.

THE SUGAR PRODUCER, Harris Publishing, Inc., 520 Park, Box 981, Idaho Falls ID 83402. (208)522-5187. Editor: Steve Janes. 25% freelance written. Bimonthly magazine covering the growing, storage, use and by-products of the sugar beet. Circ. 19,000. Pays on publication. Publishes ms an average of 3 months after acceptance. Buys one-time rights. Byline given. Phone queries OK. Photocopied and previously published submissions OK. Computer printout submissions acceptable. Reports in 1 month. Free sample copy and writer's guidelines.

Nonfiction: "This is a trade magazine, not a farm magazine. It deals with the business of growing sugar beets, and the related industry. All articles must tell the grower how he can do his job better, or at least be of interest to him, such as historical, because he is vitally interested in the process of growing sugar beets, and the industries related to this." Expose (pertaining to the sugar industry or the beet grower); how-to (all aspects of growing, storing and marketing the sugar beet); interview; profile; personal experience; and technical (material source must accompany story—research and data must be from an accepted research institution). Query or send complete ms. Length: 750-2,000 words. Pays 3¢/word.
Photos: Purchased with mss. Pays $5 for any convenient size b&w; $10 for color print or transparency; $25 for color shot used on cover. Captions and model release required.

‡UNITED CAPRINE NEWS, Double Mountain Press, Drawer A, Rotan TX 79546. (915)735-2278. Editor: Kim Pease. Managing Editor: Jeff Klein. 80% freelance written. A monthly tabloid covering dairy pygmy and angora goats. Circ. 5,000. Pays on publication. Publishes ms an average of 3 months after acceptance. Byline given. Buys first rights, and makes work-for-hire assignments. Computer printout submissions acceptable; prefers letter-quality to dot-matrix. Reports in 1 month. Sample copy $1.
Nonfiction: Interview/profile, new product, photo feature and technical—articles directed to all phases of goat keeping: management, showing, breeding and products. Buys 50 mss/year. Send complete ms. Length: open. Pays 25¢/column inch.
Photos: Send photos with submission. Reviews 5x7 prints. Offers 25¢/column inch. Captions required. Buys first rights.
Fillers: Facts and newsbreaks. Buys 25/year. Pays 25¢/column inch.
Tips: "We will consider any articles of an informative nature relating to goats that will benefit professional goat breeders. Most acceptable would be features on goat dairies or farms, technical data on health care and state-of-art topics related to breeding and genetics."

Finance

These magazines deal with banking, investment and financial management. Publications that use similar material but have a less technical slant are listed in Consumer Publications under Business and Finance.

BANKING TODAY, Florida Bankers Association, Box 536847, Orlando FL 32853. (305)896-0441. Editor: William Piping Seaparke. 90% freelance written. "We look at all submissions." A monthly magazine covering financial services. "A regional magazine, *Banking Today* is primarily written for executives and personnel in financial occupations giving them information useful to them in their business and personal lives." Circ. 6,300. Pays on publication. Publishes ms an average of 6 months after acceptance. Byline given. Offers 25% kill fee. Buys all rights (with working loan-back agreements for credit to the publication). Submit seasonal/holiday material 3 months in advance. Photocopied submissions OK. Computer printout submissions acceptable; prefers letter-quality to dot-matrix. Reports in 4 months. Sample copy $2.
Nonfiction: General interest (on banking); historical/nostalgic (on banking); how-to (on banking); humor (cartoons); interview/profile (financial executives with b/w photos); technical (banking); and occasionally travel. No submissions not dealing with financial executives in the Southeast. Query or send complete ms. Length determined on assignment. Pays $25-100. Pays the expenses of writers on assignment (if pre-agreed in writing).
Photos: Send photos with submission. Reviews b&w glossy prints. Offers $10/photo (no color). Model releases and identification of subjects required. Buys all rights.
Columns/Departments: Success Stories (must tell how a person devised a contribution to his organization); VIP Bio-Sketch (introduce a banker of note to the Southeastern market). Buys 24 mss/year. Query or send complete ms. Length: 250-600 words. Pays $25.
Tips: "Small publications, magazines, such as the one I manage, often do not have the budget to be able to afford the large amount of postage it would take to return unsolicited submissions that arrive without self-addressed, stamped envelopes. SASE: it's important. I don't speak for every editor, I'm certain, but I reject all

submissions that arrive with cover letters beginning, Dear William. Unless I'm on a first-name basis with a freelancer, or until I have placed myself on that basis, I find casual reference to me by him or her offensively discourteous. Another turnoff for me is the freelancer that proceeds to give me instructions as to how to read his material and not to change anything without his agreement. I would never purposely change the meaning of any writer's words, but I will correct what needs to be corrected and reformat to the specifications of my publication. A third turnoff for me involves calls from writers at public relations agencies. Such agencies should not ask to speak to the editor, or anyone else about when we are going to use their news releases. They should either subscribe to the publication or check the copy in the local library. We may begin a tearsheet subscription service at cost in the future. I am interested in receiving submissions from freelancers when they submit usable material in the proper way, and I am interested in receiving the news releases of public relations agencies that might be of interest to readers of the publications I edit, but I do wish them to take a little of their time to make certain they do not waste a lot of my time. Freelancers should check appropriate source books to determine what kind of material editors are looking for. If you don't, you're missing a good chance to make a friend of some editor, such as myself, who might truly be in need of your freelance efforts, done correctly for his publication."

BENEFITS CANADA, Pension Fund Investment and Employee Benefit Management, Maclean Hunter Ltd., 777 Bay St., Toronto, Ontario M5W 1A7 Canada. (416)596-5958. Editor: John Milne. 5% freelance written. Works with a small number of new/unpublished writers each year. Magazine published 10 times/year covering investment management, pension fund administration and employee benefits industry for experts in the field. Circ. 14,000. Pays on acceptance. Publishes ms an average of 2 months after acceptance. Byline given. Buys first North American serial rights. Computer printout submissions acceptable; no dot-matrix. Reports in 2 weeks on queries; 1 month on mss. Free sample copy.
Nonfiction: Interview/profile and opinion (of people in pension fund, investments or employee benefits); and technical (investment or employee benefit administration). Query with published clips or send complete ms. Length: 1,000-2,200 words. Pays $125-300. Sometimes pays the expenses of writers on assignment.

‡BIOTECHNOLOGY INVESTMENT OPPORTUNITIES, High Tech Publishing Co., 10 Ridge Rd., Ridge NY 11961. (516)924-6168. Editor: Philip T. DiPeri. 10% freelance written. Monthly newsletter covering investment opportunities in high technology aimed at "sophisticated, well-informed investors seeking calculated-risk investments. Identifies and analyzes emerging investment opportunities in genetic engineering; follows trends and conditions having significant impact on the development and commercial application of leading-edge biotechnology research. Emphasis is on new enterprise formation, capital formation, emerging markets and applications." Circ. 1,000. Pays on publication. Byline given. Buys all rights. Simultaneous queries and simultaneous, photocopied and previously published submissions OK. Computer printout submissions acceptable. Reports in 2 weeks. Publishes ms an average of 1 month after acceptance. Sample copy for business-size SAE and 1 first class stamp.
Nonfiction: Interview/profile (high technology, capital providers, firms, idea/research/patent generators); new product (potential commercialization of research concepts and ideas); technical (new patents with commercial possibilities, related instrumentation); and current research efforts in various high technology areas. Special issues include bimonthly supplements providing in-depth reporting of important aspect of investing in genetic engineering and high technology. Buys 150 mss/year. Send complete ms. Length: 25-500 words. Pays "competitive" rates.
Columns/Departments: New patents (in genetic engineering with commercial possibilities); new applications (of biotech processes and products); and people (briefs on the principal players in biotechnology). Buys 100 mss/year. Send complete ms. Length: 25-500 words. Pays "competitive" rates.
Fillers: Newsbreaks. Buys 10/year. Length: 25-500 words. Pays "competitive" rates.
Tips: "Submit completed manuscript or, if extensive investigation or research is needed, query first. We're looking for newsletter-style writing with a high proportion of nouns and verbs over adjectives and adverbs."

CANADIAN BANKER, The Canadian Bankers' Association, Box 348, 2 First Canadian Place, Toronto, Ontario, M5X 1E1 Canada. Editor: Brian O'Brien. "We are backlogged with submissions and prefer not to receive unsolicited submissions at this time."

‡CAPITAL CLUB MONTHLY, The Newsletter for Active Entrepreneurs, Venture Magazine, Inc., Suite 1500, 521 Fifth Ave., New York NY 10175. (212)682-7373. Editor: Steven M. Cohen. 80% freelance written. Prefers to work with published/established writers; works with a small number of new/unpublished writers each year. A monthly newsletter covering venture capital investments. "We cover the informal investor and his approach to venture investing." Estab. 1985. Circ. 5,000. Pays on publication. Publishes ms an average of 2 months after acceptance. Byline given. Buys first serial rights. Makes work-for-hire assignments. Simultaneous submissions OK. Electronic submissions OK via disk only, IBM compatible, DOS 2.0 or higher. Computer printout submissions acceptable; no dot-matrix. Reports in 2 weeks on queries and mss. Free sample copy.
Nonfiction: How-to invest in private companies. "Articles must demonstrate in-depth knowledge of venture

capital." Buys 30 mss/year. Query with published clips, or send complete ms. Length: 250-1,500 words. Pays $75-300 for assigned articles; pays $50-300 for unsolicited articles. Pays the expenses of writers on assignment.

Photos: State availability of photos, or send photos with submission. Offers $10/photo. Identification of subjects required. Buys one-time rights.

Tips: "Articles from entrepreneurs about how they raised money are especially welcome."

‡CFO, The Magazine for Chief Financial Officers, CFO Publishing Corp., 268 Summer St., Boston MA 02210. (617)542-0660. Editor: Neil Goldhirsh. Managing Editor: Julia Homer. 90% freelance written. A monthly magazine covering areas of interest to CFOs of small to midsized companies. Estab. 1985. Circ. 212,000. Pays 2 weeks after acceptance. Publishes ms an average of 2 months after acceptance. Byline given. Offers 20-30% kill fee. Buys first North American serial rights or makes work-for-hire assignments. Submit seasonal/holiday material 3 months in advance. Electronic submissions OK via IBM/Hayes. Computer printout submissions acceptable; prefers letter-quality to dot-matrix. Reports in 2 weeks on queries; 1 week on mss. Sample copy $3; free writer's guidelines.

Nonfiction: How-to (related to CFO's job); new product (short pieces on office technologies, new financial services); and technical (reviews of office technologies). "Stories should have practical application to CFO's varied responsibilities. We don't use news features; puff pieces on a company, or stories focused on an operations or marketing problem—the focus must be finance." Buys 40 mss/year. Query with published clips. Length: 1,500-4,000 words. Pays $450-2,000 for assigned features; $100-150 for short pieces. Pays the expenses of writers on assignment.

Columns/Departments: Bill Souder, Leslie Schultz, column/department editors. Law, Taxes, Finance, Cash Management, Real Estate, Management, Insurance and Benefits. All columns should address the implications of a new development on business tactics—how-to focus; 1,000-2,000 words. Buys 60 mss/year. Query with published clips. Pays $250-900.

Tips: "Talk to one of the editors; supply us with an idea. *News Developments* and *Bottom Line* are most open to freelancers. *Bottom Line* is specific operational tips that reduce expenses in travel, telephone, shipping, transporation, inventory management, office systems procurement, purchasing."

‡EXECUTIVE FINANCIAL WOMAN, Suite 1400, 500 N. Michigan Ave., Chicago IL 60611. (312)661-1700. Editor: Lawrence R. Quinn. 30% freelance written. Prefers to work with published/established writers; works with a small number of new/unpublished writers each year. Bimonthly magazine for members of the National Association of Bank Women and paid subscribers covering banking, insurance, financial planning, diversified financials, credit unions, thrifts, investment banking and other industry segments. Circ. 30,000. Publishes ms an average of 1 month after acceptance. Byline given. Buys all rights. Submit seasonal material 3 months in advance. Simultaneous queries and photocopied submissions OK. Computer printout submissions acceptable; prefers letter-quality to dot-matrix. Reports in approximately 1 month. Sample copy $4.

Nonfiction: "We are looking for articles in the general areas of financial services, career advancement, businesswomen's issues and management. Because the financial services industry is in a state of flux at present, articles on how to adapt to and benefit from this fact, both personally and professionally, are particularly apt." Query with resume and clips of published work. Length: 1,000-4,000 words. Pays variable rates. Pays expenses of writers on assignment.

Photos: "Photos and other graphic material can make an article more attractive to us." Captions and model release required.

Tips: "We're looking for writers who can write effectively about the people who work in the industry and combine that with hard data on how the industry is changing. We're interested in running more Q&As with top executives in the industry, both men and women."

‡FINANCIAL PRODUCT NEWS, The Magazine for Personal Investment Advisors, Snyder Associates, Inc., Suite 202, 1483 Chain Bridge Rd., McLean VA 22108. (703)448-0322. Editor: Richard Stolz. Managing Editor: Tom Goldsmith. 15% freelance written. A monthly tabloid on magazine stock. "We are a news publication covering financial 'products' mutual funds, limited partnerships, insurance of interest to people who either sell or recommend these products. Stories concern individual products as well as broader industry and regulatory trends." Estab. 1985. Circ. 40,000. Pays on acceptance or within 30 days of acceptance. Byline given sometimes "if article is substantial enough." Offers 50% kill fee. Buys all rights. Computer printout submissions acceptable; prefers letter-quality to dot-matrix. Free sample copy.

Nonfiction: Interview/profile, new product, technical (financial) and news. Buys approximately 50 mss/year. Query. Length: 750-2,000 words. Pays $200-1,500. Sometimes pays expenses of writers on assignment.

Photos: State availability of photos with submission.

FINANCIAL WORLD, The News Magazine for Investors, Financial World Partners, 1450 Broadway, New York NY 10008. (212)869-1616. Editor: Roger B. Harris. 25% freelance written. Prefers to work with published/established writers. Biweekly magazine on investing for professionals and high net worth individuals. "Our objective is to enlighten and instruct our readers about investment opportunities presented by today's multifaceted financial markets. We seek to cover every type of investment vehicle and related subjects of investor interest." Circ. 140,000. Pays on publication. Publishes ms an average of 1 month after acceptance. Byline given. Offers variable kill fee. Submit seasonal/holiday material 1 month in advance. Simultaneous queries and photocopied submissions OK. Computer printout submissions acceptable. Reports in 1 month. Free sample copy.

Nonfiction: Interview/profile and technical. Buys 12 mss/year. Query with published clips or send complete ms. Length: 1,200-2,000 words. Pays $25-750. Sometimes pays the expenses of writers on assignment.

Tips: "We like clear, informed, well-reported financial stories. Send us an excellent piece in our field."

FUTURES MAGAZINE, 219 Parkade, Cedar Falls IA 50613. (319)677-6341. Publisher: Merrill Oster. Editor-in-Chief: Darrell Jobman. 20% freelance written. Prefers to work with published/established writers. Monthly magazine; 124-140 pages. For private, individual traders, brokers, exchange members, agribusinessmen, bankers, anyone with an interest in futures or options. Circ. 75,000. Buys all rights. Byline given. Pays on publication. Publishes ms an average of 6 months after acceptance. Photocopied submissions OK. Computer printout submissions acceptable; no dot-matrix. Reports in 1 month. Free sample copy.

Nonfiction: Articles analyzing specific commodity futures and options trading strategies; fundamental and technical analysis of individual commodities and markets; interviews, book reviews, "success" stories; and news items. Material on new legislation affecting commodities, trading, any new trading strategy ("results must be able to be substantiated"); and personalities. No "homespun" rules for trading and simplistic approaches to the commodities market. Treatment is always in-depth and broad. Informational, how-to, interview, profile, technical. "Articles should be written for a reader who has traded commodities for one year or more; should not talk down or hypothesize. Relatively complex material is acceptable." No get-rich-quick gimmicks, astrology articles or general, broad topics. Buys 30-40 mss/year. Query or submit complete ms. Length: 1,500 words optimum. Pays $50-1,000, depending upon author's research and writing quality. "Rarely" pays the expenses of writers on assignment.

Tips: "Writers must have a solid understanding and appreciation for futures or options trading. We will have more financial and stock index features as well as new options contracts that will require special knowledge and experience. The writer has a better chance of breaking in at our publication with short articles and fillers since they can zero in on a specific idea without having to know the whole broad area we cover. Fluffy leads or trying to describe whole trading world instead of targeting key issues are frequent mistakes made by writers. More articles on trading options and on financial institution's use of futures/options will be published in 1987."

ILLINOIS BANKER, Illinois Bankers Association, Suite 1100, 205 W. Randolph, Chicago IL 60606. (312)984-1500. Director of Publications: Cindy L. Altman. Production Assistant: Anetta Gauthier. Editorial Assistant: Bobbie McDonald. 50% freelance written. Eager to work with new/unpublished writers. Monthly magazine about banking for top decision makers and executives, bank officers, title and insurance company executives, elected officials and individual subscribers interested in banking products and services. Circ. 3,000. Pays on publication. Publishes ms an average of 4 months after acceptance. Byline given. Buys first serial rights. Phone queries OK. Submit material by the 1st of the month prior to publication. Simultaneous submissions OK. Computer printout submissions acceptable; no dot-matrix. Reports in 2 weeks. Free sample copy and writer's guidelines.

Nonfiction: Interview (ranking government and banking leaders); personal experience (along the lines of customer relations); and technical (specific areas of banking). "The purpose of the publication is to educate, inform and guide its readers in the activities and projects of their banks and those of their fellow bankers, while keeping them aware of any developments within the banking industry and other related fields. Any clear, fresh approach geared to a specific area of banking, such as agricultural bank management, credit, lending, marketing and trust is what we want." Buys 4-5 unsolicited mss/year. Send complete ms. Length: 825-3,000 words. Pays $50-100.

Fillers: Jokes, anecdotes and financial puzzles. Buys 8 mss/year. Pays $15-50.

INDEPENDENT BANKER, Independent Bankers Association of America, Box 267, Sauk Centre MN 56378. (612)352-6546. Editor: Norman Douglas. 15% freelance written. Works with a small number of new/unpublished writers each year. Monthly magazine for the administrators of small, independent banks. Circ. 10,000. Pays on acceptance. Publishes ms an average of 3 months after acceptance. Byline given. Not copyrighted. Buys all rights. Computer printout submissions acceptable. Reports in 1 week. Free sample copy and writer's guidelines.

Nonfiction: How-to (banking practices and procedures); interview/profile (popular small bankers); technical (bank accounting, automation); and banking trends. "Factual case histories, banker profiles or research pieces of value to bankers in the daily administration of their banks." No material that ridicules banking and finance or puff pieces on products and services. Buys 12 mss/year. Query. Length: 2,000-2,500 words. Pays $300 maximum.

Tips: "In this magazine, the emphasis is on material that will help small banks compete with large banks and large bank holding companies. We look for innovative articles on small bank operations and administration."

‡OTC REVIEW, OTC Review, Inc., 110 Pennsylvania Ave., Oreland PA 19075. (215)887-9000. Editor: Robert Flaherty. Executive Editor: Michael Woods. 50% freelance written. A monthly magazine covering publicly owned companies whose stocks trade in the over-the-counter market. "We are a financial magazine covering the fastest-growing securities market in the world. We study the management of companies traded over-the-counter and act as critics reviewing their performances. We aspire to be 'The Shareholder's Friend.' " Circ. 27,000. Pays on publication. Publishes ms an average of 2 months after acceptance. Byline given. Buys first rights or second (serial) rights. Sample copy for 8½x11 SAE with 5 first class stamps.
Nonfiction: New product and technical. Buys 30 mss/year. "We must know the writer first as we are fussy about whom we publish. A letter of introduction with resumé and clips is the best way to introduce yourself. Financial writing requires specialized knowledge and a feel for people as well, which can be a tough combination to find." Query with published clips. Length: 300-1,500 words. Pays $150-750 for assigned articles; pays $50-350 for unsolicited articles. Offers copies or premiums for guest columns by famous money managers who are not writing for cash payments, but for the showcase for their ideas and approach. Sometimes pays the expenses of writers on assignment.
Photos: Send photos with submission. Reviews contact sheets, negatives, transparencies and prints. Offers no additional payment for photos accepted with ms. Identification of subjects required.
Columns/Departments: Pays $25-75 for assigned items only.
Tips: "Anyone who enjoys analyzing a business and telling the story of the people who started it, or run it today, is a potential *OTC Review* contributor. But to protect our readers and ourselves, we are fussy about who writes for us. Business writing is an exciting area and our stories reflect that. If a writer relies on numbers and percentages to tell his story, rather than the individuals involved, the result will be numbingly dull."

Fishing

NATIONAL FISHERMAN, Diversified Communications, 21 Elm St., Camden ME 04843. (207)236-4342. "We are backlogged with submissions and prefer not to receive unsolicited submissions at this time."

PACIFIC FISHING, Special Interest Publications, 1515 NW 51st St., Seattle WA 98107. (206)789-5333. Editors: Ken Talley and Kris Freeman. 50% freelance written. Eager to work with new/unpublished writers. Monthly business magazine for commercial fishermen and others in the West Coast commercial fishing industry. *Pacific Fishing* views the fisherman as a small businessman and covers all aspects of the industry, including harvesting, processing and marketing. Circ. 10,000. Pays on publication. Publishes ms an average of 2 months after acceptance. Byline given. Offers 10-15% kill fee on assigned articles deemed unsuitable. Buys one-time rights. Queries highly recommended. Computer printout submissions acceptable; prefers letter-quality to dot-matrix. Reports in 1 month. Sample copy and writer's guidelines for SAE and 1 first class stamp.
Nonfiction: Interview/profile and technical (usually with a business hook or slant). "Articles must be concerned specifically with *commercial* fishing. We view fishermen as small businessmen and professionals who are innovative and success-oriented. To appeal to this reader, *Pacific Fishing* offers four basic features: technical, how-to articles that give fisherman hands-on tips that will make their operation more efficient and profitable; practical, well-researched business articles discussing the dollars and cents of fishing, processing and marketing; profiles of a fisherman, processor or company with emphasis on practical business and technical areas; and in-depth analysis of political, social, fisheries management and resource issues that have a direct bearing on West Coast commercial fishermen." Buys 20 mss/year. Query noting whether photos are available, and enclosing samples of previous work. Length: 1,500-3,000 words. Pays 7-10¢/word. Sometimes pays the expenses of writers on assignment.
Photos: "We need good, high-quality photography, especially color, of West Coast commercial fishing. We prefer 35mm color slides. Our rates are $125 for cover; $25-75 for inside color; $15-35 for b&w and $10 for table of contents."
Tips: "Because of the specialized nature of our audience, the editor strongly recommends that freelance writers query the magazine in writing with a proposal. We enjoy finding a writer who understands our editorial needs and satisfies those needs, a writer willing to work with an editor to make the article just right. Most of our

shorter items are staff written. Our freelance budget is such that we get the most benefit by using it for feature material. The most frequent mistakes made by writers are not keeping to specified length and failing to do a complete job on statistics that may be a part of the story."

Florists, Nurseries and Landscaping

Readers of these publications may be involved in growing, selling, or servicing flowers, plants and trees. Magazines geared to consumers interested in gardening are listed in the consumer Home and Garden section.

FLORIST, Florists' Transworld Delivery Association, 29200 Northwestern Hwy., Box 2227, Southfield MI 48037. (313)355-9300. Editor-in-Chief: William P. Golden. Managing Editor: Susan L. Nicholas. 5% freelance written. For retail florists, floriculture growers, wholesalers, researchers and teachers. Monthly magazine; 128 pages. Circ. 25,000. Pays on acceptance. Buys one-time rights. Pays 10-25% kill fee. Byline given "unless the story needs a substantial rewrite." Phone queries OK. Submit seasonal/holiday material 4 months in advance. Simultaneous, photocopied, and previously published submissions OK. Computer printout submissions acceptable. Reports in 1 month.
Nonfiction: How-to (more profitably run a retail flower shop, grow and maintain better quality flowers, etc.); general interest (to floriculture and retail floristry); and technical (on flower and plant growing, breeding, etc.). Buys 5 unsolicited mss/year. Query with published clips. Length: 1,200-3,000 words. Pays 20¢/word.
Photos: "We do not like to run stories without photos." State availability of photos with query. Pays $10-25 for 5x7 b&w photos or color transparencies. Buys one-time rights.
Tips: "Send samples of published work with query. Suggest several ideas in query letter."

FLOWER NEWS, 549 W. Randolph St., Chicago IL 60606. (312)236-8648. Editor: Lauren C. Oates. For retail, wholesale florists, floral suppliers, supply jobbers and growers. Weekly newspaper; 32 pages. Circ. 14,500. Pays on acceptance. Byline given. Submit seasonal/holiday material at least 2 months in advance. Photocopied and previously published submissions OK. Reports "immediately."
Nonfiction: How-to (increase business, set up a new shop, etc.; anything floral related without being an individual shop story); informational (general articles of interest to industry); and technical (grower stories related to industry, but not individual grower stories). Submit complete ms. Length: 3-5 typed pages. Pays $10-25.
Photos: "We do not buy individual pictures. They may be enclosed with manuscript at regular manuscript rate (b&w only)."

‡FLOWERS &, The beautiful magazine about the business of flowers, Suite #260, 12233 W. Olympic Blvd., Los Angeles CA 90064. (213)826-5253. Editor: Marie Moneysmith. Managing Editor: Jane Siblering. 40% freelance written. A monthly magazine for the retail floristry industry. "We are essentially a small business magazine." Circ. approximately 28,000. Pays on acceptance. Publishes ms an average of 4 months after acceptance. Byline given. Offers 20% kill fee. Buys first North American serial rights and second serial (reprint) rights. Submit seasonal/holiday material 4 months in advance. Simultaneous submissions OK. Electronic submissions OK via IBM. Computer printout submissions acceptable; prefers letter-quality to dot-matrix. Reports in 1 month on queries; 3 months on mss. Sample copy for 8½x11 SAE; writer's guidelines for #10 SAE with 1 first class stamp.
Nonfiction: Book excerpts; historical/nostalgic; how-to (improve business, strengthen advertising, put out a newsletter, etc.); interview/profile; new product; opinion; and technical. "No articles not geared specifically to the floral industry; no articles about flowers (these are written in-house)." Buys 20 mss/year. Query with published clips. Length: 1,000-3,000 words. Pays $250-500. Sometimes pays the expenses of writers on assignment.
Photos: Reviews contact sheets and 4x5 transparencies. Offers $25-100/photo. Captions, model releases, and identification of subjects required. Buys one-time rights.

Tips: "Features are most open to freelancers. Think like a small-businessowner. How can you help them solve day-to-day problems? Come up with good, timely topics, make sure they apply to retail floristry, and write a to-the-point query letter, describing the problem and how you'll approach it in an article."

GARDEN SUPPLY RETAILER, Miller Publishing, Box 67, Minneapolis MN 55440. (612)374-5200. Editor: Kay Melchisedech Olson. 15% freelance written. Prefers to work with published/established writers but "quality work is more important than experience of the writer." Monthly magazine for lawn and garden retailers. Circ. 40,000+. Pays on acceptance in most cases. Publishes ms an average of 4 months after acceptance. Buys first serial rights, and occasionally second serial (reprint) rights. Previously published submissions "in different fields" OK as long as not in overlapping fields such as hardware, nursery growers, etc. Computer printout submissions acceptable; prefers letter-quality to dot-matrix. Reports in 2 weeks on rejections, acceptance may take longer. Sample copy $2.
Nonfiction: "We aim to provide retailers with management, merchandising, tax planning and computer information. No technical advice on how to care for lawns, plants and lawn mowers. Articles should be of interest to *retailers* of garden supply products. Stories should tell retailers something about the industry that they don't already know; show them how to make more money by better merchandising or management techniques; address a concern or problem directly affecting retailers or the industry." Buys 10-15 mss/year. Send complete ms or rough draft plus clips of previously published work. Length: 800-1,000 words. Pays $150-200.
Photos: Send photos with ms. Reviews color negatives and transparencies, and 5x7 b&w prints. Captions and identification of subjects required.
Tips: "We will not consider manuscripts offered to 'overlapping' publications such as the hardware industry, nursery growers, etc. Query letters outlining an idea should include at least a partial rough draft; lists of titles are uninteresting. We seldom use filler material and would find it a nuisance to deal with freelancers for this. Freelancers submitting articles to our publication will find it increasingly difficult to get acceptance as we will be soliciting stories from industry experts and will not have much budget for general freelance material."

INTERIOR LANDSCAPE INDUSTRY, The Magazine for Designing Minds and Growing Businesses, American Nurseryman Publishing Co., Suite 545, 111 N. Canal St., Chicago IL 60606. (312)782-5505. Editor: Brent C. Marchant. 10% freelance written. "Willing to work with freelancers as long as they can fulfill the specifics of our requirements." Monthly magazine on business and technical topics for all parties involved in interior plantings, including interior landscapers, growers and allied professionals (landscape architects, architects and interior designers). "We take a professional approach to the material and encourage our writers to emphasize the professionalism of the industry in their writings." Circ. 10,000. Pays on publication. Publishes ms an average of 5 months after acceptance. Byline given. Buys all rights. Submit material 2 months in advance. Electronic submissions OK on diskettes suitable for IBM PC. Computer printout submissions acceptable; prefers letter-quality to dot-matrix. Reports in 2 weeks on queries; 1 week on mss. Free sample copy.
Nonfiction: How-to (technical and business topics related to the audience); interview/profile (companies working in the industry); personal experience (preferably from those who work or have worked in the industry); photo feature (related to interior projects or plant producers); and technical. No shallow, consumerish-type features. Buys 30 mss/year. Query with published clips. Length: 3-15 ms pages double spaced. Pays $2/published inch. Sometimes pays expenses of writers on assignment.
Photos: Send photos with query. Reviews b&w contact sheet, negatives, and 5x7 prints; standard size or 4x5 color transparencies. Pays $5-10 for b&w; $15 for color. Identification of subjects required. Buys all rights.
Tips: "Demonstrate knowledge of the field—not just interest in it. Features, especially profiles, are most open to freelancers. We anticipate greater coverage of the design professions, specifically as they relate to interior landscaping, during 1987."

‡WEEDS TREES & TURF, HBJ Publications, 7500 Old Oak Blvd., Cleveland OH 44130. (216)243-8100. Editor: Jerry Roche. Managing Editor: Ken Kuhajda. 30% freelance written. Prefers to work with published/established writers; works with a small number of new/unpublished writers each year; eager to work with new/unpublished writers. Monthly magazine on landscape, lawn and golf course maintenance. Circ. 46,000. Pays on receipt. Publishes ms an average of 3 months after acceptance. Byline sometimes given. 10% kill fee. Buys all rights. Submit seasonal/holiday material 3 months in advance. Reports in 2 weeks on queries; 3 weeks on mss. Free sample copy and writer's guidelines.
Nonfiction: How-to, interview/profile, and new product, all industry specific. No submissions not covered in these three categories. Buys 12 mss/year. Query. Length: 1,000-2,500 words. Pays $250-400 for assigned articles; pays $100-250 for unsolicited articles. Sometimes pays the expenses of writers on assignment.
Photos: Send photos with submission. Reviews 2¼, 35mm, 4x5 transparencies and 5x7 prints. Offers no additional payment for photos accepted with ms. Buys all rights.
Tips: "The writer should note the conversational style of staff-written and freelance articles. We will be focusing more on outdoor power equipment selection and maintenance."

Food Products, Processing and Service

In this section are journals for food wholesalers, processors, warehouses, caterers, institutional managers and suppliers of grocery store equipment. Publications for grocery store operators are classified under Groceries. Journals for food vending machine operators can be found under Coin-Operated Machines.

FOOD PEOPLE, Olson Publications, Inc., Box 1208, Woodstock GA 30188. (404)928-8994. Editor: Mark W. Pryor. 80% freelance written. Monthly tabloid covering the retail food industry. "We write news and 'news features' about food stores, wholesalers and brokers in the Sunbelt and food manufacturers nationwide." Circ. 28,000. Pays on publication. Publishes ms an average 1 month after acceptance. Byline given. Buys all rights. Submit seasonal/holiday material 6 weeks in advance. Photocopied submissions OK. Computer printout submissions acceptable; prefers letter-quality to dot-matrix. Reports in 1 month. Sample copy $1.
Nonfiction: Interview/profile (of major food industry figures); photo feature (of food industry conventions, expos and meetings); and news of store/warehouse openings, ad campaigns, marketing strategies, important new products and services. "Articles should be informative, tone is upbeat. Do not send recipes or how-to shop articles; we cover food as a *business*." Buys 120-180 mss/year. Query or send complete ms. Length: 200-1,000 words. Pays $2/published inch. Sometimes pays the expenses of writers on assignment.
Photos: "Photos of people. Photos of displays, or store layouts, etc., that illustrate points made in article are good, too. But stay away from storefront shots." State availability of photos with query or send photos with ms. Pays $10 plus expenses for b&w contact sheets and 5x7 b&w prints; and $30 plus expenses for color transparencies. Captions required. Buys one-time rights.
Columns/Departments: Coast-to-Coast (1-2 paragraph newsbriefs from the Mid-Atlantic, South, West, and Pacific West). Send complete ms. Pays $10.
Tips: "Begin with an area news event—store openings, new promotions. Write that as news, then go further to examine the consequences. Talk with decision makers to get 'hows' and 'whys.' Because we are news-oriented, we have short deadlines for a monthly. We look for contributors who work well quickly and who *always* deliver."

‡MEAT PLANT MAGAZINE, 9701 Gravois Ave., St. Louis MO 63123. (314)638-4050. Editor: Tony Nolan. 10% freelance written. Prefers to work with published/established writers; works with a small number of new/unpublished writers each year. For meat processors, locker plant operators, freezer provisioners, portion control packers, meat dealers and food service (food plan) operators. Monthly. Pays on publication. Publishes ms an average of 6 months after acceptance. Computer printout submissions acceptable. Reports in 2 weeks.
Nonfiction and Fillers: Buys feature-length articles and shorter subjects pertinent to the field. Length: 1,000-1,500 words for features. Pays 5¢/word. Sometimes pays the expenses of writers on assignment.
Photos: Pays $5 for photos.

‡PRODUCE NEWS, 2185 Lemoine Ave., Fort Lee NJ 07024. Editor: Gordon Hochberg. 10-15% freelance written. Works with a small number of new/unpublished writers each year. For commercial growers and shippers, receivers and distributors of fresh fruits and vegetables, including chain store produce buyers and merchandisers. Weekly. Circ. 8,800. Pays on publication. Publishes ms an average of 1 month after acceptance. Deadline is Tuesday afternoon before Thursday press day. Computer printout submissions acceptable; no dot-matrix. Free sample copy and writer's guidelines.
Nonfiction: News stories (about the produce industry). Buys profiles, spot news, coverage of successful business operations and articles on merchandising techniques. Query. Pays minimum of $1/column inch for original material. Sometimes pays the expenses of writers on assignment.
Photos: B&w glossies. Pays $8-10 for each one used.
Tips: "Stories should be trade-oriented, not consumer-oriented. As our circulation grows in the next year, we are interested in stories and news articles from all fresh fruit-growing areas of the country."

QUICK FROZEN FOODS INTERNATIONAL, E.W. Williams Publishing Co., 80 8th Ave., New York NY 10011. (212)989-1101. Editor: John M. Saulnier. 20% freelance written. Quarterly magazine covering frozen foods around the world—"every phase of frozen food manufacture, retailing, food service, brokerage, transport, warehousing, merchandising. Especially interested in stories from Europe, Asia and emerging nations." Circ. 13,500. Pays on publication. Publishes ms an average of 3 months after acceptance. Byline given. Offers kill fee; "if satisfactory, we will pay promised amount. If bungled, half." Buys all rights, but will relinquish any rights requested. Submit seasonal/holiday material 6 months in advance. Photocopied submissions OK "if not under submission elsewhere." Computer printout submissions acceptable; prefers letter-quality to dot-matrix. Sample copy $1 and SAE.

Nonfiction: Book excerpts; general interest; historical/nostalgic; interview/profile; new product (from overseas); personal experience; photo feature; technical; and travel. No articles peripheral to frozen food industry such as taxes, insurance, government regulation, safety, etc. Buys 20-30 mss/year. Query or send complete ms. Length: 500-4,000 words. Pays 3¢/word or by arrangement. "We will reimburse postage on articles ordered from overseas." Sometimes pays the expenses of writers on assignment.

Photos: "We prefer photos with all articles." State availability of photos or send photos with accompanying ms. Pays $7 for 5x7 b&w prints (contact sheet if many shots). Captions and identification of subject required. Buys all rights. Release on request.

Columns/Departments: News or analysis of frozen foods abroad. Buys 20 columns/year. Query. Length: 500-1,500 words. Pays by arrangement.

Fillers: Newsbreaks. Length: 100-500 words. Pays $5-20.

Tips: "We are primarily interested in feature materials, 1,000-3,000 words with pictures. Always query (though we will buy unsolicited manuscripts if they are suitable). A freelancer visited Poland before the crackdown and reported on the state of frozen foods in stores—turned out to be a scoop. Same reporter did the same on recent trip to Israel. Another did the same for China; all queried in advance. A frequent mistake is submitting general interest material instead of specific industry-related stories."

THE WISCONSIN RESTAURATEUR, Wisconsin Restaurant Association, 122 W. Washington, Madison WI 53703. (603)251-3663. Editor: Jan La Rue. 10% freelance written. Eager to work with new/unpublished writers. Emphasizes restaurant industry for restaurateurs, hospitals, institutions, food service students, etc. Monthly magazine (December/January combined). Circ. 3,600. Pays on acceptance. Publishes ms an average of 3 months after acceptance. Buys all rights or one-time rights. Pays 10% kill fee. Byline given. Phone queries OK. Submit seasonal/holiday material 2-3 months in advance. Previously published OK; "indicate where." Computer printout acceptable. Reports in 3 weeks. Sample copy and writer's guidelines with large postpaid envelope.

Nonfiction: Expose, general interest, historical, how-to, humor, inspirational, interview, nostalgia, opinion, profile, travel, new product, personal experience, photo feature and technical articles pertaining to restaurant industry. "Needs more in-depth articles. No features on nonmember restaurants." Buys 1 ms/issue. Query with "copyright clearance information and a note about the writer in general." Length: 700-1,500 words. Pays $10-20.

Photos: Fiction and how-to mss stand a better chance for publication if photos are submitted. State availability of photos. Pays $15 for b&w 8x10 glossy prints. Model release required.

Columns/Departments: Spotlight column provides restaurant member profiles. Buys 6/year. Query. Length: 500-1,500 words. Pays $5-10.

Fiction: Experimental, historical and humorous stories related to food service only. Buys 12 mss/year. Query. Length: 1,000-3,000 words. Pays $10-20.

Poetry: Uses all types of poetry, but must have food service as subject. Buys 6-12/year. Submit maximum 5 poems. Length: 10-50 lines. Pays $5-10.

Fillers: Clippings, jokes, gags, anecdotes, newsbreaks and short humor. No puzzles or games. Buys 12/year. Length: 50-500 words. Pays $2.50-7.50.

Government and Public Service

Below are journals for people who provide governmental services, either in the employ of local, state, or national governments or of franchised utilities. Journals for city managers, politicians, civil servants, firefighters, police officers, public administrators, urban transit managers and utilities managers are also listed in this section. Journals for professionals in world affairs can be found in the International Affairs section. Publications for lawyers are in the Law category. Journals for teachers and school administrators can be found in Education. Those for private citizens interested in politics, government, and public affairs are classified with the Politics and World Affairs magazines in the Consumer Publications section.

‡AMERICAN FIRE JOURNAL, The Western Source for the Progressive Fire and Rescue Service, Fire Publications, Inc., Suite 7, 9072 E. Artesia Blvd., Bellflower CA 90706. (213)866-1664. Editor: Carol Carlsen. 75% freelance written. A monthly magazine covering the fire service. "Our readers are fire service professionals, generally at the management level. We try to pay respect to the long and rich traditions of America's firefighters while advocating that they keep up with the latest technology in the field." Pays on publication. Publishes ms an average of 6 months after acceptance. Byline given. Offers 50% kill fee, but rarely makes assignments. Buys first rights. Submit seasonal/holiday material 3 months in advance. Computer printout submissions acceptable; prefers letter-quality to dot-matrix. Reports in 1 month. Sample copy $2; free writer's guidelines.
Nonfiction: How-to (on firefighting techniques); interview/profile (of various fire departments around the country); opinion (guest editorials—non-paid); photo feature (of fire scenes); and technical (on fire science). Buys 84 mss/year. Send complete ms. Length ranges from news shorts to 5-part series. Pays $1.50/published inch. Pays premiums other than cash to fire department members or training officers writing on company time about in-house programs.
Photos: Send photos with submission. Reviews contact sheets, negatives and prints (b&w prints preferred except for cover photos, which are color). Offers $4-30/photo. Captions and identification of subjects required. Buys one-time rights, then photos may be used again from morgue, though photographer may also re-sell.
Columns/Departments: Hot Flashes (news from the fire service), 100-300 words; and Innovations (new ideas in tactics, equipment uses or tricks-of-the-trade), 400-800 words (with photos). Buys 24 mss/year. Send complete ms. Pays $1.50/inch.
Fillers: Anecdotes, facts and cartoons. Buys 12/year. Length: open. Pays $5-1.50/inch.
Tips: "Generally, our contributors are members of or involved with the fire service in some way. Our readers are mostly command-level officers, and they are very knowledgeable about the subject, so writers need to be experts in their fields in order to show them something new. We're always looking for good fireground action photos with accompanying description of the fire dept. tactics used. Non-firefighters may break in with articles on management, health and fitness, stress reduction, finance, etc., if they can be related to firefighters."

‡CHIEF FIRE EXECUTIVE, The Management Magazine for Fire Service Leaders, Firehouse Communications, 33 Irving Place, New York NY 10003. (212)475-5400. Editor: William S. Porter. Associate Editor: Gloria Sturzenacker. 25% freelance written. A bimonthly magazine for fire service managers. Pays on publication. Publishes ms an average of 4 months after acceptance. Byline given. Offers negotiable kill fee. Buys first North American serial rights. Photocopied submissions OK. Electronic submissions OK via MS-DOS 2.1; requires hard copy also. Computer printout submissions acceptable; prefers letter quality to dot-matrix. Reports in 1 month. Sample copy $5 with 10x13 SAE and $1.75 postage; writer's guidelines for letter size SAE and 1 first class stamp.
Nonfiction: Book excerpts, expose, how-to, interview/profile and technical. Buys 10 mss/year. Query with published clips. Length: 250-3,000 words. Pays $0-400. May negotiate payment to writers with contributor copies or premiums rather than cash. Sometimes pays the expenses of writers on assignment.
Photos: State availability of photos with submission. Reviews contact sheets, transparencies and prints. Offers no additional payment for photos accepted with ms. Identification of subjects required. Buys one-time rights.
Tips: *Chief Fire Executive* "concentrates on the management concerns of fire service leaders, both emergency and nonemergency, and seeks out unusual, innovative techniques which can serve as an example to others."

FIREHOUSE MAGAZINE, Firehouse Communications, Inc., 33 Irving Pl., New York NY 10003. (212)935-4550. Editor: Dennis Smith. Executive Editor: John D. Peige. 85% freelance written. Works with a small number of new/unpublished writers each year. Monthly magazine covering fire service and emergency medical service. "*Firehouse* covers major fires nationwide, controversial issues and trends in the fire service, the latest firefighting equipment and methods of firefighting, historical fires, firefighting history and memorabilia." Fire-related books, firefighters with interesting avocations, fire safety education, hazardous materials incidents and the emergency medical services are also covered. Circ. 115,000. Pays on publication. Publishes ms an average of 2 months after acceptance. Byline given. Buys first North American serial rights. Submit seasonal/holiday material 4 months in advance. Simultaneous queries and previously published submissions OK.

Computer printout submissions acceptable; prefers letter-quality to dot-matrix. Reports in 2 weeks. Sample copy for SAE with 7 first class stamps; free writer's guidelines.

Nonfiction: Book excerpts (of recent books on fire, EMS, and hazardous materials); historical/nostalgic (great fires in history, fire collectibles; the fire service of yesteryear); how-to (fight certain types of fires, buy and keep equipment, run a fire department); interview/profile (of noteworthy fire leader; centers, commissioners); new product (for firefighting, EMS); personal experience (description of dramatic rescue; helping one's own fire department); photo feature (on unusual apparatus, fire collectibles, a spectacular fire); technical (on almost any phase of firefighting; techniques, equipment, training, administration); and trends (controversies in the fire service). No profiles of people or departments that are not unusual or innovative, reports of nonmajor fires, articles not slanted toward firefighters' interests. Buys 100 mss/year. Query or send complete ms. Length: 500-3,000 words. Pays $50-400.

Photos: Jon Nelson, photo editor. Send photos with query or ms. Pays $15-45 for 8x10 b&w prints; $30-200 for color transparencies and 8x10 color prints. Captions required. Buys one-time rights.

Columns/Departments: Command Post (for fire service leaders); Training (effective methods); Book Reviews; Fire Safety (how departments teach fire safety to the public); Communicating (PR, dispatching); Arson (efforts to combat it); Doing Things (profile of a firefighter with an interesting avocation; group projects by firefighters); and Family Things (activities involving firefighters' families). Query or send complete ms. Length: 750-1,000 words. Pays $100-300.

Fillers: Clippings, jokes, gags, anecdotes, short humor and newsbreaks. Buys 20/year. Length: 50-100 words. Pays $5-15.

Tips: "Read the magazine to get a full understanding of the subject matter, the writing style and the readers before sending a query or manuscript. Send photos with manuscript or indicate sources for photos. Be sure to focus articles on firefighters."

FOREIGN SERVICE JOURNAL, 2101 E St. NW, Washington DC 20037. (202)338-4045. Editor: Stephen R. Dujack. 80% freelance written. "No preference for published vs. unpublished writers as long as the writer has some expertise." For Foreign Service personnel and others interested in foreign affairs and related subjects. Monthly (July/August combined). Pays on publication. Publishes ms an average of 3 months after acceptance. Byline given. Buys first North American serial rights. Electronic submissions OK via Wang 8 in. floppy disk, modem—please call, but requires hard copy also. Computer printout submissions acceptable; prefers letter-quality to dot-matrix.

Nonfiction: Uses articles on "international relations, internal problems of the State Department and Foreign Service, diplomatic history and articles on Foreign Service experiences. Much of our material is contributed by those working in the fields we reach, Informed outside contributions are welcomed, however." Query. Buys 5-10 unsolicited mss/year. Length: 1,000-4,000 words. Pays 2-6¢/word.

Tips: The most frequent mistakes made by writers in completing an article for us are that the items are not suitable for the magazine, and they don't query.

FOUNDATION NEWS, The Magazine of Philanthropy, Council on Foundations, 1828 L St. NW, Washington DC 20036. (202)466-6512. Editor: Arlie Schardt. Managing Editor: Kathleen Hallahan. 50% freelance written. Prefers to work with published/established writers. Bimonthly magazine covering the world of philanthropy, nonprofit organization and their relation to current events. Read by staff and executives of foundations, corporations, hospitals, colleges and universities and various nonprofit organizations. Circ. 15,000. Pays on acceptance. Publishes ms an average of 5 months after acceptance. Byline given. Offers negotiable kill fee. Not copyrighted. Buys all rights. Submit seasonal/holiday material 5 months in advance. Simultaneous queries and previously published submissions OK. Computer printout submissions acceptable; prefers letter-quality to dot-matrix. Reports in 6 weeks.

Nonfiction: Book excerpts, expose, general interest, historical/nostalgic, how-to, humor, interview/profile and photo feature. Special issue on the role of religion in American life and how religious giving affects social welfare, culture, health conditions, etc. Buys 25 mss/year. Query. Length: 500-3,000 words. Pays $200-2,000. Sometimes pays the expenses of writers on assignment.

Photos: State availability of photos. Pays negotiable rates for b&w contact sheet and prints. Captions and identification of subjects required. Buys one-time rights; "some rare requests for second use."

Columns/Departments: Buys 12 mss/year. Query. Length: 900-1,400 words. Pays $100-500.

Tips: "In 1987 we anticipate more emphasis on what nonprofits are doing, how they are faring and what kinds of interesting new pursuits they've started."

THE GRANTSMANSHIP CENTER NEWS, The Grantsmanship Center, 1031 S. Grand Ave., Los Angeles CA 90015. (213)749-4721. Editor: Norton J. Kiritz. 10% freelance written. Emphasizes fundraising, philanthropy, grants process and nonprofit management for professionals in government, foundations and nonprofit organizations. Bimonthly magazine; 88 pages. Circ. 14,000. Pays on publication. Publishes ms an average of 4 months after acceptance. Makes assignments on a work-for-hire basis. Pays variable kill fee. Byline given. Simultaneous, photocopied, and previously published submissions OK. Computer printout submissions accepta-

ble; prefers letter-quality to dot-matrix. Reports in 2 months. Sample copy $4.65.
Nonfiction: Expose, general interest, how-to and interview. "Familiarity with the field is an asset." Buys 1-2 mss/issue. Query with published clips. Length: 1,500-10,000 words. Pays $50-350.
Photos: State availability of photos. Uses b&w contact sheets and color transparencies. Offers no additional payment for photos accepted with ms. Captions preferred; model release required. Buys all rights.
Tips: "The most frequent mistake made by writers in completing an article for us is ignoring the special concerns of our readership."

LAW AND ORDER, Hendon Co., 1000 Skokie Blvd., Wilmette IL 60091. (312)256-8555. Editor: Bruce W. Cameron. 90% freelance written. Prefers to work with published/established writers. Monthly magazine covering the administration and operation of law enforcement agencies, directed to police chiefs and supervisors. Circ. 26,000. Pays on publication. Publishes ms an average of 6 months after acceptance. Byline given. Buys first North American serial rights. Submit seasonal/holiday material 3 months in advance. Photocopied submissions OK. No simultaneous queries. Computer printout submissions acceptable; prefers letter-quality to dot-matrix. Reports in 1 month. Sample copy for 9x12 SAE.
Nonfiction: General police interest; how-to (do specific police assignments); new product (how applied in police operation); and technical (specific police operation). Special issues include Buyers Guide (January); Communications (February); Training (March); International (April); Administration (May); Small Departments (June); Police Science (July); Equipment (August); Weapons (September); Mobile Patrol (November); and Working with Youth (December). No articles dealing with courts (legal field) or convicted prisoners. No nostalgic, financial, travel or recreational material. Buys 20-30 mss/year. Length: 2,000-3,000 words. Pays $100-300.
Photos: Send photos with ms. Reviews transparencies and prints. Identification of subjects required. Buys all rights.
Tips: "*L&O* is a respected magazine that provides up-to-date information that chiefs can use. Writers must know their subject as it applies to this field. Case histories are well received. We are upgrading quality for editorial—stories *must* show some understanding of the law enforcement field. A frequent mistake is not getting photographs to accompany article."

MARINE CORPS GAZETTE, Professional Magazine for United States Marines, Marine Corps Association, Box 1775, Quantico VA 22134. (703)640-6161. Editor: Col. John E. Greenwood, USMC (Ret.). Managing Editor: Joseph D. Dodd. 5% freelance written. "Will continue to welcome and respond to queries, but will be selective due to large backlog from Marine authors." Monthly magazine. "*Gazette* serves as a forum in which serving Marine officers exchange ideas and viewpoints on professional military matters." Circ. 33,000. Pays on publication. Publishes ms an average of 6 months after acceptance. Byline given. Buys first North American serial rights; change to all rights under consideration. Computer printout submissions acceptable. Reports in 3 weeks on queries; 2 months on mss. Sample copy $1; free writer's guidelines.
Nonfiction: Historical/nostalgic (Marine Corps operations only); and technical (Marine Corps related equipment). "The magazine is a professional journal oriented toward hard skills, factual treatment, technical detail—no market for lightweight puff pieces—analysis of doctrine, lessons learned goes well. A very strong Marine Corps background and influence are normally prerequisites for publication." Buys 4-5 mss/year from non-Marine Corps sources. Query or send complete ms. Length: 2,500-5,000 words. Pays $200-400; short features, $50-100.
Photos: "We welcome photos and charts." Payment for illustrative material included in payment forms. "Photos need not be original, nor have been taken by the author, but they must support the article."
Columns/Departments: Book Reviews (of interest and importance to Marines); and Ideas and Issues (an assortment of topical articles, e.g., opinion or argument, ideas of better ways to accomplish task, reports on weapons and equipment, strategies and tactics, etc., also short vignettes on history of Corps). Buys 60 book review and 120 Ideas and Issues mss/year, most from Marines. Query. Length: 500-1,500 words. Pays $25-50 plus book for 750-word book review; $50-100 for Ideas and Issues.
Tips: "Book reviews or short articles (500-1,500 words) on Marine Corps related hardware or technological development are the best way to break in. Sections/departments most open to freelancers are Book Reviews and Ideas & Issues sections—query first. We are not much of a market for those outside U.S. Marine Corps or who are not closely associated with current Marine activities."

PLANNING, American Planning Association, 1313 E. 60th St., Chicago IL 60637. (312)955-9100. Editor: Sylvia Lewis. 25% freelance written. Emphasizes urban planning for adult, college-educated readers who are regional and urban planners in city, state or federal agencies or in private business or university faculty or students. Monthly. Circ. 25,000. Pays on publication. Publishes ms an average of 3 months after acceptance. Buys all rights or first rights. Byline given. Photocopied and previously published submissions OK. Computer printout submissions acceptable; prefers letter-quality to dot-matrix. Reports in 2 months. Free sample copy and writer's guidelines.

Nonfiction: Expose (on government or business, but on topics related to planning, housing, land use, zoning); general interest (trend stories on cities, land use, government); historical (historic preservation); how-to (successful government or citizen efforts in planning; innovations; concepts that have been applied); and technical (detailed articles on the nitty-gritty of planning, zoning, transportation but no footnotes or mathematical models). Also needs news stories up to 500 words. "It's best to query with a fairly detailed, one-page letter. We'll consider any article that's well written and relevant to our audience. Articles have a better chance if they are timely and related to planning and land use and if they appeal to a national audience. All articles should be written in magazine feature style." Buys 2 features and 1 news story/issue. Length: 500-2,000 words. Pays $50-600. "We pay freelance writers and photographers only, not planners."

Photos: "We prefer that authors supply their own photos, but we sometimes take our own or arrange for them in other ways." State availability of photos. Pays $25 minimum for 8x10 matte or glossy prints and $200 for 4-color cover photos. Captions preferred. Buys one-time rights.

‡POLICE PRODUCT NEWS, Hare Publications, 6200 Yarrow Dr., Carlsbad CA 92008. (619)438-2511. Editor: Kim Dallas. 100% freelance written. A monthly magazine covering topics related to law enforcement officicals. "Our audience is strictly law enforcement officials, detectives and specialized enforcement divisions." Circ. 40,000. Pays on acceptance. Publishes ms an average of 6 months after acceptance. Buys all rights. Submit seasonal/holiday material 2 months in advance. Photocopied submissions OK. Computer printout submissions acceptable; prefers letter-quality to dot-matrix. Reports in 2 weeks on queries; 3 months on mss. Sample copy $5; free writer's guidelines.

Nonfiction: General interest, humor, inspirational, personal experience and technical. "No articles that focus on how bad the law enforcement is, or what a terrible job these people do for a living—no degrading material on the subject of Law Enforcement." Buys 100 mss/year. Query or send complete ms. Length: 2,000-4,000 words. Pays $200-400 for unsolicited articles.

Photos: Send photos with submission. Reviews transparencies. Offers no additional payment for photos accepted with ms. Captions required. Buys all rights.

Columns/Departments: The Beat (first-person accounts of law enforcement activity); The Arsenal (weapons and ammunition used in the line of duty); and Officer Survival (skills used in high risk situations). Buys 75 mss/year. Send complete ms. Length: 1,000-1,500 words. Pays $100 maximum.

Fillers: Newsbreaks. Buys 5-10/year. Length: 500-1,000 words. Pays $25 maximum.

Tips: "Get quotes from legitimate police officers for qualification of information. Have local police chief or captain review manuscript for technical accuracy. Include bio on author. Talk to police departments and get to know how they work, talk, eat and sleep. This basic foundation of understanding is essential to this market." Features are most open to freelancers. "Get associated with local police department before attempting to address topics. Know the language policemen use. Pick up references which have common police codes and ammunition information in them."

POLICE TIMES, The Chief of Police Magazine, American Police Academy, 1100 NE 125th St., North Miami FL 33161. (305)891-1700. Editor: Gerald Arenberg. Managing Editor: Donna Shepherd. 80% freelance written. A monthly tabloid covering "law enforcement (general topics) for men and women engaged in law enforcement and private security, and citizens who are law and order concerned." Circ. 55,000. Pays on acceptance. Byline given. Offers 50% kill fee. Buys second serial (reprint) rights. Submit seasonal/holiday material 4 months in advance. Simultaneous, photocopied and previously published submissions OK. Computer printout submissions acceptable; prefers letter-quality to dot-matrix. Sample copy for 8x11 SAE with 3 first class stamps; writer's guidelines for SASE with 1 first class stamp.

Nonfiction: Book excerpts; essays (on police science); exposé (police corruption); general interest; historical/nostalgic; how-to; humor; interview/profile; new product; personal experience (with police); photo feature; and technical—all police-related. "We produce a special edition on police killed in the line of duty. It is mailed May 15 so copy must arrive six months in advance. Photos required." No anti-police materials. Buys 50 mss/year. Send complete ms. Length: 200-3,000 words. Pays $5-50 for assigned articles; pays $5-25 for unsolicited articles. Sometimes pays the expenses of writers on assignment.

Photos: Send photos with submission. Reviews 5x6 prints. Offers $5-25/photo. Identification of subjects required. Buys all rights.

Columns/Departments: Legal Cases (lawsuits involving police actions); New Products (new items related to police services); and Awards (police heroism acts). Buys variable number of mss/year. Send complete ms. Length: 200-1,000 words. Pays $5-25.

Fillers: Anecdotes, facts, newsbreaks and short humor. Buys 100/year. Length: 50-100 words. Pays $5-10. Fillers are usually humorous stories about police officer and citizen situations. Special stories on police cases, public corruptions, etc. are most open to freelancers.

SUPERINTENDENT'S PROFILE & POCKET EQUIPMENT DIRECTORY, Profile Publications, 220 Central Ave., Box 43, Dunkirk NY 14048. (716)366-4774. Editor: Robert Dyment. 60% freelance written. Prefers to work with published/established writers. Monthly magazine covering "outstanding" town, village, county and city highway superintendents and Department of Public Works Directors throughout New York state only. Circ. 2,500. Publishes ms an average of 3 months after acceptance. Pays within 90 days. Byline given for excellent material. Buys first serial rights. Submit seasonal/holiday material 3 months in advance. Simultaneous queries OK. Computer printout submissions acceptable. Reports in 2 weeks on queries; 1 month on mss. Sample copy for 9x12 SAE and 3 first class stamps.

Nonfiction: John Powers, articles editor. Interview/profile (of a highway superintendent or DPW director in NY state who has improved department operations through unique methods or equipment); and technical. Special issues include winter maintenance profiles. No fiction. Buys 20 mss/year. Query. Length: 1,500-2,000 words. Pays $125 for a full-length ms. "Pays more for excellent material. All manuscripts will be edited to fit our format and space limitations." Pays the expenses of writers on assignment.

Photos: John Powers, photo editor. State availability of photos. Pays $5-10 for b&w contact sheets; reviews 5x7 prints. Captions and identification of subjects required. Buys one-time rights.

Poetry: Buys poetry if it pertains to highway departments. Pays $5-15.

Tips: "We are a widely read and highly respected state-wide magazine, and although we can't pay high rates, we expect quality work. Too many freelance writers are going for the expose rather than the meat and potato type articles that will help readers. We use more major features than fillers. Frequently writers don't read sample copies first. We will be purchasing more material because our page numbers are increasing."

TRANSACTION/SOCIETY, (incorporating *Worldview*), Rutgers University, New Brunswick NJ 08903. (201)932-2280, ext. 83. Editor: Irving Louis Horowitz. 10% freelance written. Prefers to work with published/established writers. For social scientists (policymakers with training in sociology, political issues and economics). Published every 2 months. Circ. 45,000. Buys all rights. Byline given. Pays on publication. Publishes ms an average of 6 months after acceptance. Will consider photocopied submissions. No simultaneous submissions. Electronic submissions OK; "manual provided to authors." Computer printout submissions acceptable; prefers letter-quality to dot-matrix. Reports in 1 month. Query. Free sample copy and writer's guidelines.

Nonfiction: Michele Teitelbaum, articles editor. "Articles of wide interest in areas of specific interest to the social science community. Must have an awareness of problems and issues in education, population and urbanization that are not widely reported. Articles on overpopulation, terrorism, international organizations. No general think pieces." Payment for articles is made only if done on assignment. *No payment for unsolicited articles.*

Photos: Joan DuFault, photo editor. Pays $200 for photographic essays done on assignment or accepted for publication.

Tips: "Submit an article on a thoroughly unique subject, written with good literary quality. Present new ideas and research findings in a readable and useful manner. A frequent mistake is writing to satisfy a journal, rather than the intrinsic requirements of the story itself. Avoid posturing and editorializing."

VICTIMOLOGY: An International Journal, Box 39045, Washington DC 20016. (703)528-8872. Editor-in-Chief: Emilio C. Viano. "We are the only magazine specifically focusing on the victim, on the dynamics of victimization; for social scientists, criminal justice professionals and practitioners, social workers and volunteer and professional groups engaged in prevention of victimization and in offering assistance to victims of rape, spouse abuse, child abuse, incest, abuse of the elderly, natural disasters, etc." Quarterly magazine. Circ. 2,500. Pays on publication. Buys all rights. Byline given. Reports in 2 months. Sample copy $5; free writer's guidelines.

Nonfiction: Expose, historical, how-to, informational, interview, personal experience, profile, research and technical. Buys 10 mss/issue. Query. Length: 500-5,000 words. Pays $50-150.

Photos: Purchased with accompanying ms. Captions required. Send contact sheet. Pays $15-50 for 5x7 or 8x10 b&w glossy prints.

Poetry: Avant-garde, free verse, light verse and traditional. Length: 30 lines maximum. Pays $10-25.

Tips: "Focus on what is being researched and discovered on the victim, the victim/offender relationship, treatment of the offender, the bystander/witness, preventive measures, and what is being done in the areas of service to the victims of rape, spouse abuse, neglect and occupational and environmental hazards and the elderly."

‡THE VOLUNTEER FIREMAN, A Fire Service Publication, Publico, Inc., Suite 112, 7504 E. Independence Blvd., Charlotte NC 28212. (704)535-8200. Editor: Pattie Toney. Managing Editor: Martha Tatum. 75% freelance written. Eager to work with new/unpublished writers. Quarterly magazine for volunteer fire fighters nationwide covering fire safety/protection, news of saves and special fire ground situations. Circ. 20,000. Pays on publication. Publishes ms an average of 9 months after acceptance. Byline given. Buys first North American serial rights. Photocopied submissions OK. Computer printout submissions acceptable. Reports within 90 days. Sample copy for 9x12 SAE and 3 first class stamps; writer's guidelines for $1, 9x12 SAE, and 2 first class stamps.

Nonfiction: Expose; general interest; historical/nostalgic; how-to (raise funds for volunteer fire departments); humor; interview/profile; new product; opinion; personal experience; photo feature; and technical.

"We want 'glamour' articles. We want good, exciting and honest news. No mom 'n' pop, picnic news, etc." Length: 200-1,500 words. Pays $10-105.

Photos: Send photos with ms. Pays $5-25 for 5x7 b&w prints. Captions, model release and identification of subjects required.

Columns/Departments: News, features and product reviews. Buys 8-10 ms/year. Length: 100-750 words. Pays $5-52.50.

Fillers: Clippings, anecdotes, short humor and newsbreaks. Buys 20/year. Length: 25-100 words. Pays $1.75-10.

Tips: "Writers should keep our readership in mind. Most of our articles need to relate to blue-collar type workers. They are not concerned with Dow-Jones, etc. but how they can raise enough money for that new pumper. Volunteer fire fighters are highly interested in ways to save other people's lives while not harming their own."

YOUR VIRGINIA STATE TROOPER MAGAZINE, Box 2189, Springfield VA 22152. (703)451-2524. Editor: Kerian Bunch. 90% freelance written. Biannual magazine covering police topics for troopers, police, libraries, legislators and businesses. Circ. 10,000. Pays on acceptance. Publishes ms an average of 3 months after acceptance. Byline given. Buys first North American serial rights and all rights on assignments. Submit seasonal/holiday material 2 months in advance. Simultaneous and photocopied submissions OK. Computer printout submissions acceptable; prefers letter-quality to dot-matrix. Reports in 1 month. Writer's guidelines for SAE and 1 first class stamp.

Nonfiction: Book excerpts; expose (consumer or police-related); general interest; nutrition/health; historical/nostalgic; how-to (energy saving); humor; interview/profile (notable police figures); opinion; personal experience; technical (radar); and other (recreation). Buys 40-45 mss/year. Query with clips or send complete ms. Length: 2,500 words. Pays $250 maximum/article (10¢/word). Sometimes pays expenses of writers on assignment.

Photos: Send photos with ms. Pays $25 maximum/5x7 b&w glossy print. Captions and model release required. Buys one-time rights.

Fiction: Adventure, humorous, mystery, novel excerpts and suspense. Buys 4 mss/year. Send complete ms. Length: 2,500 words minimum. Pays $250 maximum (10¢/word) on acceptance.

Tips: "The writer may have a better chance of breaking in at our publication with short articles and fillers due to space limitations."

‡THE WASHINGTON TROOPER, Grimm Press and Publishing Co., Inc. Communications Dateline, Box 1523, Longview WA 98632. (206)577-8598. Editor: Ron Collins. Managing Editor: Bruce D. Grimm. 10% freelance written. Works with a small number of new/unpublished writers each year. A quarterly law enforcement magazine covering legislation, traffic and highway safety "for members of the Washington State Patrol Troopers Association, state legislators, educators, court officials, and civic minded individuals in the State of Washington." Circ. 3,500. Pays on publication. Publishes ms an average of 3 months after acceptance. Byline given. Buys all rights. Submit seasonal/holiday material 6 months in advance. Simultaneous queries and submissions OK. Computer printout submissions OK; prefers letter-quality to dot-matrix. Reports in 6 weeks on queries; 3 months on mss. Sample copy $3.50; writer's guidelines for #10 SAE and 39¢ postage.

Nonfiction: Marjorie F. Grimm, articles editor. Exposé (on state of Washington government or traffic); interview/profile (Washington state troopers); new products; opinion (on law enforcement or traffic and highway safety); and technical (police equipment). Buys 12-20 mss/year. Query or send complete ms. Length: 500-3,500 words. Pays $5-75.

Photos: State availability of photos with query letter or manuscript. Reviews contact sheets and transparencies. Pays $5-25. Model releases, and identification of subjects required.

Fillers: Short humor and newsbreaks. Buys 15/year. Length: 50-250 words. Pays $5-15.

Tips: "Writers must be familiar with goals and objectives of the Washington State Patrol and with law enforcement in general in the Pacific Northwest. The areas of our publication that are most open to freelancers are feature articles depicting life in the State of Washington familiar to a Washington state trooper."

❝ On smaller—or company—publications like mine, we often handle several other magazines as well. In effect, we have several deadlines each month. ❞

Ed Rabinowitz, **Volkswagen's World**

Groceries

Owners and operators of retail food stores read these publications. Journals for food whole-salers, packers, warehousers and caterers are classified with the Food Products, Processing, and Service journals. Publications for food vending machine operators can be found in the Coin-Operated Machines category.

CANADIAN GROCER, Maclean-Hunter Ltd., Maclean Hunter Building, 777 Bay St., Toronto, Ontario M5W 1A7 Canada. (416)596-5772. Editor: George H. Condon. 8% freelance written. Prefers to work with published/established writers. Monthly magazine about supermarketing and food retailing for Canadian chain and independent food store managers, owners, buyers, executives, food brokers, food processors and manufacturers. Circ 16,000. Pays on publication. Publishes ms an average of 2 months after acceptance. Byline given. Buys first Canadian rights. Phone queries OK. Submit seasonal material 2 months in advance. Previously published submissions OK. Computer printout submissions acceptable; prefers letter-quality to dot-matrix. Reports in 1 month. Sample copy $4.
Nonfiction: Interview (Canadian trendsetters in marketing, finance or food distribution); technical (store operations, equipment and finance); and news features on supermarkets. "Freelancers should be well versed on the supermarket industry. We don't want unsolicited material. Writers with business and/or finance expertise are preferred. Know the retail food industry and be able to write concisely and accurately on subjects relevant to our readers: food store managers, senior corporate executives, etc. A good example of an article would be 'How a Six Store Chain of Supermarkets Improved Profits 2% and Kept Customers Coming.' " Buys 14 mss/year. Query with clips of previously published work. Pays 21¢/word. Sometimes pays the expenses of writers on assignment.
Photos: State availability of photos. Pays $ 10-25 for 8x10 b&w glossy prints. Captions preferred. Buys one-time rights.
Tips: "Suitable writers will be familiar with sales per square foot, merchandising mixes and direct product profitability."

‡FANCY FOOD & CANDY, Catering to the Gourmet Industry, Talcott Publishing, Inc., Suite 409, 2700 River Rd., Des Plaines IL 60018. (312)824-7440. Editor: Clark H. Flint. 60% freelance written. A trade magazine covering specialty food and confections. Published 9 times a year. Circ. 24,000. Pays on publication. Publishes an average of 2 months after acceptance. Byline given sometimes. Buys all rights. Submit seasonal/holiday material 2 months in advance. Computer printout submissions acceptable; prefers letter-quality to dot-matrix. Sample copy $4.
Nonfiction: Interview/profile and new product. Buys 50 mss/year. Query with published clips. Length: 1,500-4,000 words. Pays $200-250 for assigned articles. Sometimes pays expenses of writers on assignment.
Photos: Send photos with submission. Reviews transparencies and prints. Offers no additional payment other than for film and development for photos accepted with ms. Captions and identification of subjects required. Buys all rights.
Columns/Departments: Points West, Wine & Spirits Review, Coffee, Industry News and Buyer's Mart. Buys 24 mss/year. Query with published clips. Length: 2,000-3,000 words. Pays $100-200.
Tips: Multi-source product category overviews are most open to freelancers.

HEALTH FOODS BUSINESS, Howmark Publishing Corp., 567 Morris Ave., Elizabeth NJ 07208. (201)353-7373. Editor: Mary Jane Ditmar. Editorial Director: Alan Richman. 40% freelance written. Eager to work with new/unpublished writers if competent and reliable. For owners and managers of health food stores. Monthly magazine; 75-100 pages. Circ. 11,000. Pays on publication. Publishes ms an average of 4 months after acceptance. Byline given "if story quality warrants it." Buys first serial rights and first North American serial rights; "also exclusive rights in our trade field." Phone queries OK. "Query us about a good health food store in your area. We use many store profile stories." Simultaneous and photocopied submissions OK if exclusive to their field. Previously published work OK, but please indicate where and when material appeared previously. Computer printout submissions acceptable if double-spaced and in upper and lower case; no dot-matrix. Reports in 1 month. Sample copy $5; plus $2 for postage and handling.
Nonfiction: Expose (government hassling with health food industry); how-to (unique or successful retail operators); informational (how or why a product works; technical aspects must be clear to laymen); historical (natural food use); interview (must be prominent person in industry or closely related to the health food

industry or well-known or prominent person in any arena who has undertaken a natural diet/lifestyle); and photo feature (any unusual subject related to the retailer's interests). Buys 1-2 mss/issue. Query for interview and photo features. Will consider complete ms in other categories. Length: long enough to tell the whole story without padding. Pays $50 and up for feature stories, $75 and up for store profiles.

Photos: "Most articles must have photos included"; negatives and contact sheet OK. Captions required. No additional payment.

Tips: "A writer may find that submitting a letter with a sample article he/she believes to be closely related to articles read in our publication is the most of expedient way to determine the appropriateness of his/her skills and expertise."

PROGRESSIVE GROCER, Progressive Grocer Co., 1351 Washington Blvd., Stamford CT 06902. (203)325-3500. Editor: Ed Walzer. Editorial Director: Larry Schaeffer. 3% freelance written. Monthly magazine covering the retail food industry. "We provide analyses of trends, merchandising ideas and innovations, statistical data, company profiles—all retailer oriented. Audience runs gamut from top executive to department managers." Circ. 87,000. Pays on publication. Publishes ms an average of 3 months after acceptance. Byline given. Buys all rights. Computer printout submissions acceptable; no dot-matrix. Submit seasonal/holiday material 3 months in advance. Simultaneous queries and photocopied submissions OK. Reports in 1 month. Free sample copy.

Nonfiction: General interest, how-to (set up or operate a particular department in supermarket); interview/profile (executive level); and photo feature (interesting store format). No puff pieces or anything in excess of 8 typewritten, double-spaced pages. Buys 3 mss/year. Send complete ms. Length: 500-1,500 words. Pays $200 maximum magazine page. Sometimes pays expenses of writers on assignment.

Photos: State availability of photos with ms. Pays $100 maximum for b&w contact sheets; $300 maximum for color contact sheets. Captions, model release and identification of subjects required.

WHOLE FOODS, Informing and Educating Whole Food Retailers, WFC Inc., 195 Main St., Metuchen NJ 08840. Publisher: Howard Wainer. Editor: Marsha Parker Cox. 10% freelance written. Prefers to work with published/established writers. Monthly magazine edited for health food retailers, wholesalers and manufacturers serving the industry. Byline given on articles and columns; photocredits also. Pays on publication. Publishes ms an average of 4 months after acceptance. Buys first North American serial rights or one-time rights. Submit seasonal material 3 months in advance. Photocopied submissions OK. Computer printout submissions acceptable; no dot-matrix. Reports in 3 months on queries; 1 month on mss. Sample copy $4; writer's guidelines for 5x7 SAE with 1 first class stamp. "Good freelancers wanted."

Nonfiction: Editorial content targets product knowledge and aids retailers in making responsible and profitable inventory selection through nutritional education, market awareness and merchandising expertise. Feature articles explain products, including manufacturing procedures, proper storage and preparation, as well as nutritional benefits. Industry members speak out about the industry issues in the Debate department. Calendar, book reviews, industry news and product showcase are written in-house. No consumer-oriented pieces other than one-subject consumer tearouts (i.e., "Everything You Need To Know About Tofu . . . or Sprouts . . ."). Not interested in undocumented, unreferenced, experiential pieces unless company or store profile of success (or specifics about failure). Wants "higher quality, compact, documentable work. Testimonials/healing stories *not* wanted." Send complete ms. Length 500-2,000 words. Pays $100 minimum.

Photos: Send photos with ms. Reviews contact sheets, transparencies and 5x7 prints. Offers $5 minimum. Requires captions, model release and identification of subjects. Provide captions and model release if appropriate.

Tips: "We are in the market for qualified freelancers who submit on-target pieces which do not require considerable editing, retyping, etc. Writer should read three issues of the magazine and have observed the operation of a health food store prior to beginning any work. Industry exclusive a must for all submissions. We will provide list of competitors' magazines."

Grooming Products and Services

AMERICAN SALON EIGHTY-SEVEN, 747 3rd Ave., New York NY 10017. (212)418-4100. Editor: Jody Bynre. Monthly for beauty salon owners and operators. Pays on publication. Buys all rights. Computer printout submissions acceptable; prefers letter-quality to dot-matrix.

Nonfiction: Profiles, how-to and management. Technical material is mainly staff written. "We are not interested unless material is directly related to the needs of beauty salon professionals."

MODERN SALON, Vance Publishing, 400 Knightsbridge Pkwy., Lincolnshire IL 60069. (312)634-2600. Editor: Mary Atherton. Managing Editor: Arlene Tolin. 10% freelance written. Monthly magazine covering hairdressing. "Articles slanted toward small business owners, especially owners of beauty salons, are most appropriate." Circ. 100,000. Pays 6 weeks after acceptance or upon publication, whichever comes first. Publishes ms an average of 2 months after acceptance. Buys first North American serial rights. Submit seasonal/holiday material 4 months in advance. Simultaneous queries and photocopied submissions OK. Computer printout submissions acceptable; prefers letter-quality to dot-matrix. Reports in 3 weeks on queries; 2 months on mss. Sample copy $3.
Nonfiction: How-to (increase business); interview/profile (with a successful salon owner); and business advice and tax tips. No photo tearsheet, opinion pieces, or anything *not* based on research. Buys 20 mss/year. Query with published clips. Length: 1,500-3,500 words. Pays $150-250.
Photos: State availability of photos with query. Pays $5-30 for b&w prints. Captions, model release and identification of subjects required. Buys all rights.
Tips: "The most frequent mistakes made by writers in completing an article assignment for us are inadequate research and insufficient tailoring to salon industry." Major features are staff-written.

‡NATIONAL BEAUTY SCHOOL JOURNAL, Milady Publishing Corp., 3839 White Plains Rd., Bronx NY 10467. (212)881-3000. Editor: Mary Jane Tenerelli. Managing Editor: Mary Healy. 75% freelance written. Works with a small number of new/unpublished writers each year. A monthly magazine covering cosmetology education. "Articles must address subjects pertinent to cosmetology education (i.e. articles which will assist the instructor in the classroom or the school owner to run his business)." Circ. 6,500 schools. Pays on publication. Publishes ms an average of 2 months after acceptance. Byline given. Buys first rights. Submit seasonal/holiday material 3 months in advance. Simultaneous submissions, photocopied submissions, and previously published submissions OK. Computer printout submissions acceptable; prefers letter-quality to dot-matrix. Free sample copy with writer's guidelines.
Nonfiction: Book excerpts, essays, historical/nostalgic, how-to (on doing a haircut, teaching a technique) humor, inspirational, interview/profile, new product, personal experience, photo feature and technical. No articles geared to the salon owner or operator instead of the cosmetology school instructor or owner. Buys 24 mss/year. Query with or without published clips, or send complete ms. Length: 500-3,000 words. Pays $150 if published. Sometimes pays the expenses of writers on assignment.
Photos: Send photos with submissions. Reviews 5x7 prints. Offers no additional payment for photos accepted with ms. Identification of subjects required. Buys all rights.
Columns Departments: Buys 6 mss/year; willing to start new departments. Length: 500-1,000 words. Pays $150.
Fiction: Humorous and slice-of-life vignettes. No fiction relating to anything other than the classroom or the beauty school business. Send complete ms. Length: 500-3,000 words. Pays $150.
Fillers: Facts, gags to be illustrated by cartoonist and newsbreaks. Length: 250-500 words. Pays $150.
Tips: "Talk to school owners and instructors to get a feel for the industry. All areas of our publication are open. Write in clear, simple language."

Hardware

Journals for general hardware wholesalers and retailers, and retailers of miscellaneous special hardware items are listed in this section. Journals specializing in the retailing of hardware for a certain trade, such as plumbing or automotive supplies, are classified with the other publications for that trade.

CHAIN SAW AGE, 3435 N.E. Broadway, Portland OR 97232. Editor: Ken Morrison. 1% freelance written. "We will consider any submissions that address pertinent subjects and are well-written." For "mostly chain saw dealers (retailers); small businesses—usually family-owned, typical ages, interests and education." Monthly. Circ. 18,000. Pays on acceptance or publication. Publishes ms an average of 4 months after acceptance. Will consider photocopied submissions. Query first. Computer printout submissions acceptable; no dot-matrix. Free sample copy.

Nonfiction: "Must relate to chain saw use, merchandising, adaptation, repair, maintenance, manufacture or display." Buys informational articles, how-to, personal experience, interview, and profiles, inspirational, personal opinion, photo feature, coverage of successful business operations, and articles on merchandising techniques. Buys very few mss/year. Length: 500-1,000 words. Pays $20-50 "2½¢/word plus photo fees." Sometimes pays the expenses of writers on assignment.

Photos: Photos purchased with or without mss, or on assignment. For b&w glossies, pay "varies." Captions required.

Tips: Frequently writers have an inadequate understanding of the subject area. "We may be in a position to accept more freelance material on an assignment basis."

HARDWARE MERCHANDISER, The Irving-Cloud Publishing Co., 7300 N. Cicero, Lincolnwood IL 60646. (312)674-7300. Editor: Howard E. Kittelberger. Monthly tabloid covering hardware, home center and hardlines market for owners and managers of hardware stores, home centers and executives of businesses serving them. Circ. 65,000. Pays on acceptance. Buys first North American serial rights. Reports in 1 month on queries. Free sample copy.

Nonfiction: Profile (of hardware business). Buys 10 mss/year. Query or send complete ms "on speculation; enough to tell the story."

Photos: Send photos with ms. Reviews 35mm or larger color transparencies. "Photos are paid for as part of article payment."

Home Furnishings and Household Goods

Readers rely on these publications to learn more about the home furnishings trade. Included in this section are magazines that focus on specific aspects of home furnishings such as glassware and water beds. Magazines geared to consumers interested in home furnishings are listed in the Consumer Home and Garden section.

CHINA GLASS & TABLEWARE, Ebel-Doctorow Publications, Inc., Box 2147, Clifton NJ 07015. (201)779-1600. Editor-in-Chief: Amy Stavis. 60% freelance written. Works with a small number of new/unpublished writers each year. Monthly magazine for buyers, merchandise managers and specialty store owners who deal in tableware, dinnerware, glassware, flatware and other tabletop accessories. Pays on publication. Publishes ms an average of 2 months after acceptance. Buys one-time rights. Byline given. Phone queries OK. Submit seasonal/holiday material 3 months in advance. Computer printout submissions acceptable. Reports in 3 weeks. Free sample copy and writer's guidelines; mention *Writer's Market* in request.

Nonfiction: General interest (on store successes, reasons for a store's business track record); interview (personalities of store owners; how they cope with industry problems; why they are in tableware); and technical (on the business aspects of retailing china, glassware and flatware). "Bridal registry material always welcomed." No articles on how-to or gift shops. Buys 2-3 mss/issue. Query. Length: 1,500-3,000 words. Pays $40-50/page. Sometimes pays the expenses of writers on assignment.

Photos: State availability of photos with query. No additional payment for b&w contact sheets or color contact sheets. Captions required. Buys first serial rights.

Fillers: Clippings. Buys 2/issue. Pays $3-5.

Tips: "Show imagination in the query; have a good angle on a story that makes it unique from the competition's coverage and requires less work on the editor's part for rewriting a snappy beginning."

‡DRAPERIES & WINDOW COVERINGS, The Magazine for the American Window Coverings Industry, L.C. Clark Publishing Co., Box 13079, North Palm Beach FL 33408. (305)627-3393. Editor: Katie Renckens. 20% freelance written. A monthly magazine on home furnishing and hard and soft window cover-

ings for retailers of window covering products. Circ. 25,000. Pays on publication. Publishes ms an average of 2 months after acceptance. Byline given. Offers $50 kill fee. Buys all rights and makes work-for-hire assignments. Free sample copy.
Nonfiction: How-to (on selling, installing or making window coverings) and interview/profile (of successful window covering retailers). Buys 20 mss/year. Query with published clips; no unsolicited mss. Length: 1,000-3,000 words. Pays $200-500. Pays expenses of writers on assignment.
Photos: State availability of photos with submission. Offers $10-25/photo. Captions and identification of subjects required. Buys all rights.

ENTRÉE, Fairchild, 7 E. 12th St., New York NY 10003. (212)741-4009. Editor: Terence Murphy. 30% freelance written. Monthly feature magazine covering "better food preparation and presentation products (i.e.: gourmet cookware, small electrical appliances, tabletop, etc.) wherever they are sold, including department stores, mass merchants, specialty shops. Also covers gift food products such as coffee and chocolate." Circ. 15,000. Average issue includes 5-11 features, 2 columns, a calendar, news and 50% advertising. Pays on publication. Publishes ms an average of 2½ months after acceptance. Byline given. Kill fee varies. Buys all rights. Phone queries OK. Computer printout submissions acceptable; no dot-matrix. Reports in 6 weeks on queries; 1 week on mss. Sample copy $2.
Nonfiction: Corporate profiles (of major retailers and manufacturers); new product ("hot product categories"); photo feature; and technical (cookware and specialty food in terms retailers can apply to their businesses). No first person, humor, cartoons and unsolicited stories on obscure retailers or general pieces of any kind such as accounting or computer stories. Buys 2-3 mss/issue. Query. Length: 1,500-3,000 words. Pays $250-400. Sometimes pays the expenses of writers on assignment.
Photos: Jodee Stringham, art director. Always looking for illustrations and photographs.
Tips: "We're much more interested in experienced *trade* writers rather than experienced consumer magazine writers. We've rejected stories from successful consumer writers because they simply don't meet the requirements of a *business* magazine. *Entrée* is actively searching for qualified, experienced trade writers. We use two to three freelancers every issue and now wish to establish a core of regular writers we can rely on. Our problem is that, while writers are in abundance, experienced *trade* writers are not. We need a writer who can thoroughly analyze a market, whether it be cutlery, drip coffee makers, food processors or cookware. We need someone who can do in-depth profiles of major retailers or manufacturers. Most important, we're not particularly interested in hearing queries. Frequently writers do not have enough business information or understanding. We'd rather interview qualified writers who can accept *our* assignments month after month. A typical feature pays $400."

FLOORING MAGAZINE, 7500 Old Oak Blvd., Cleveland OH 44130. Editor: Dan Alaimo. 5% freelance written. Prefers to work with published/established writers. Monthly magazine for floor covering retailers, wholesalers, contractors, specifiers and designers. Circ. 22,000. Pays on acceptance. Publishes ms an average of 3 months after acceptance. No byline or credit given. Buys all rights. Computer printout submissions acceptable; prefers letter-quality to dot-matrix. Writer's guidelines for SASE.
Nonfiction: Will be mostly staff-written in 1987. Will not be buying a significant number of manuscripts. However, has frequent need for correspondents skilled in 35mm photography for simple, local assignments.

‡FLOTATION SLEEP INDUSTRY, The Journal for the Waterbed Trade, Hester Communications, Inc., Suite 250, 1700 E. Dyer Rd., Santa Ana CA 92705. (714)549-4834. Editor: Kurt Indrik. Managing Editor: Leslie Holden. "We will use no unsolicited material in 1987."

GIFTS & DECORATIVE ACCESSORIES, 51 Madison Ave., New York NY 10010. (212)689-4411. Editor-in-Chief: Phyllis Sweed. "We are backlogged with submissions and prefer not to receive unsolicited submissions at this time."

GIFTWARE BUSINESS, 1515 Broadway, New York NY 10036. (212)869-1300. Editor: Rita Guarna. 10% freelance written. Monthly for "merchants (department store buyers, specialty shop owners) engaged in the resale of giftware, china and glass, and decorative accessories." Monthly. Circ. 37,500. Buys all rights. Byline given "by request only." Pays on publication. Publishes ms an average of 2 months after acceptance. Will consider photocopied submissions. Computer printout submissions acceptable; prefers letter-quality to dot-matrix.
Nonfiction: "Retail store success stories. Describe a single merchandising gimmick. We are a tabloid format—glossy stock. Descriptions of store interiors are less important than sales performance unless display is outstanding. We're interested in articles on aggressive selling tactics. We cannot use material written for the consumer." Buys coverage of successful business operations and merchandising techniques. Query or submit complete ms. Length: 750 words maximum.
Photos: Purchased with mss and on assignment; captions required. "Individuals are to be identified." Reviews b&w glossy prints (preferred) and color transparencies.

Tips: "All short items are staff produced. The most frequent mistake made by writers is that they don't know the market. As a trade publication, we require a strong business slant, rather than a consumer angle."

‡GIFTWARE NEWS,Talcott Corp., 112 Adrossan, Box 5398, Deptford NJ 08096. (609)227-0798. Editor: Anthony DeMasi. 50% freelance written. A monthly magazine covering gifts, collectibles, and tabletops for giftware retailers. Circ. 41,000. Pays on publication. Publishes ms an average of 2 months after acceptance. Byline given. Buys all rights. Submit seasonal/holiday material 4 months in advance. Reports in 2 months on mss. Sample copy $1.50.
Nonfiction: How-to (sell, display) and new product. Buys 50 mss/year. Send complete ms. Length: 1,500-2,500 words. Pays $150-250 for assigned articles; pays $75-100 for unsolicited articles.
Photos: Send photos with manuscript. Reviews 4x5 transparencies and 5x7 prints. Offers no additional payment for photos accepted with ms. Identification of subjects required.
Columns/Departments: Tabletop, Wedding Market and Display—all for the gift retailer. Buys 36 mss/year. Send complete ms. Length: 1,500-2,500 words. Pays $75-200.

HAPPI, (*Household and Personal Products Industry*), Box 555, 26 Lake St., Ramsey NJ 07446. Editor: Hamilton C. Carson. 5% freelance written. For "manufacturers of soaps, detergents, cosmetics and toiletries, waxes and polishes, insecticides, and aerosols." Circ. 15,000. Not copyrighted. Pays on publication. Publishes ms an average of 2 months after acceptance. Will consider photocopied submissions. Submit seasonal material 2 months in advance. Query. Computer printout submissions acceptable.
Nonfiction: "Technical and semitechnical articles on manufacturing, distribution, marketing, new products, plant stories, etc., of the industries served. Some knowledge of the field is essential in writing for us." Buys informational interview, photo feature, spot news, coverage of successful business operations, new product articles, coverage of merchandising techniques and technical articles. No articles slanted toward consumers. Query with published clips. Buys 3 to 4 mss a year. Length: 500-2,000 words. Pays $10-200. Sometimes pays expenses of writers on assignment.
Photos: 5x7 or 8x10 b&w glossies purchased with mss. Pays $10.
Tips: "The most frequent mistakes made by writers are unfamiliarity with our audience and our industry; slanting articles toward consumers rather than to industry members."

HOME FURNISHINGS, Box 581207, Dallas TX 75258. (214)741-7632. Editor: Tina Berres Filipski. 20% freelance written. "We don't buy much unsolicited material. Hardly ever use a writer I don't know." Biannual magazine for home furnishings retail dealers, manufacturers, their representatives and others in related fields. Circ. 18,000. Pays on acceptance. Publishes ms an average of 2 months after acceptance. Buys first serial rights. Computer printout submissions acceptable; no dot-matrix.
Nonfiction: Informational articles about retail selling; success and problem solving stories in the retail business; economic and legislative-related issues, etc. "No profiles of people out of our area. No trite, over-used features on trends, lighthearted features." Query. Length: open; appropriate to subject and slant. Particularly interested in articles related to Sunbelt furniture retailing. Photos desirable. Sometimes pays the expenses of writers on assignment.

HOME LIGHTING & ACCESSORIES, Box 2147, Clifton NJ 07015. (201)779-1600. Editor: Peter Wulff. 5-10% freelance written. For lighting stores/departments. Monthly magazine. Circ. 7,000. Pays on publication. Publishes ms an average of 4-6 months after acceptance. Buys all rights. Submit seasonal/holiday material 6 months in advance. Computer printout submissions acceptable; no dot-matrix. Free sample copy.
Nonfiction: How-to (run your lighting store/department, including all retail topics); interview (with lighting retailers); personal experience (as a businessperson involved with lighting); profile (of a successful lighting retailer/lamp buyer); and technical (concerning lighting or lighting design). Buys 10 mss/year. Query. Pays $60/published page.
Photos: State availability of photos with query. Offers no additional payment for 5x7 or 8x10 b&w glossy prints. Pays additional $90 for color transparencies used on cover. Captions required.
Tips: "We don't need fillers—only features."

MART, Business Ideas For Today's Retailers and Distributors, Gordon Publications, Inc., Box 1952, Dover NJ 07801. (201)361-9060. Editor: Bob Ankosk. Associate Editor: Al Stewart. 20% freelance written. Monthly tabloid on consumer electronics, and major appliances retailing; readership includes wholesale distributors, and manufacturing district managers and representatives. Circ. 65,000. Pays on acceptance. Publishes ms an average of 1 month after acceptance. Byline given. Offers $50 kill fee. Buys all rights. Submit seasonal/holiday material 5 months in advance. Computer printout submissions acceptable; prefers letter-quality to dot-matrix. Reports in 1 month. Sample copy $3; free writer's guidelines.
Nonfiction: Industry trends, interview/profile and new product roundups. Buys 50 mss/year. Query with published clips. Length: 800-2,000 words. Pays $100-350. Sometimes pays the expenses of writers on assignment.

Tips: "Writers frequently miss getting facts of particular interest to retailers: store volume, selling area, percentage of sales in major appliances, in consumer electronics, etc. Say something to an electronics/major appliance retailer that will somehow help his business."

‡**NATIONAL HOME CENTER NEWS**, Lebhar-Friedman, Inc., 425 Park Ave., New York NY 10022. (212)371-9400. Editor: Wyatt Kash. 6% freelance written. Prefers to work with published/established writers. Biweekly tabloid covering "business news in the $65 billion retail building supply and do-it-yourself home improvement industry." Circ. 34,000. Pays on publication. Publishes ms an average of 1 month after acceptance. Byline given in some cases. Rights purchased are negotiable. Submit seasonal/holiday material 1 month in advance. Simultaneous queries, and simultaneous and photocopied submissions acceptable. Computer printout submissions acceptable, "as long as the copy is easily read and edited. Letter-quality submissions preferred to dot-matrix. We have no ability, however, to receive stories via computer, or wire. (We *do* use facsimile machines.)" Reports in 2 weeks.
Nonfiction: "We use very little freelance material. Please write first. Query editor on possible story ideas concerning specific retail building supply/home center companies, housing, home improvements and home improvement products." No how-to stories on running a business or on do-it-yourself projects. "We're looking for business stories on actual companies or on trends regarding home improvement products sales and merchandising of interest to retailers and wholesalers of those products."
Tips: "Readers are responding increasingly to 'market intelligence' information in the business (trade) publishing field. They value news, analysis with a human interest twist far more now than 'how-to,' 'did you know?' articles. Their time is more valuable than ever. Articles must propel the reader quickly, and *deliver*. If a writer has written business analysis stories like what is published in our publication, or the subject matter is one that is familiar, then the writer will have more appeal to us."

RAYTHEON MAGAZINE, Raytheon Company, 141 Spring St., Lexington MA 02173. (617)862-6600, ext. 2415. Editor-in-Chief: Robert P. Suarez. 90% freelance written. Prefers to work with published/established writers. Quarterly magazine for Raytheon stockholders, employees, customers, suppliers, plant city officials, libraries and interested persons. "Ours is a company publication that strives to avoid sounding like a company publication. All stories must involve some aspect of Raytheon or its products." Circ. 200,000. Pays on acceptance. Publishes ms an average of 3 months after acceptance. Byline given. Computer printout submissions acceptable; prefers letter-quality to dot-matrix. Free sample copy.
Nonfiction: General interest, humor, interview/profile, new product, nostalgia, photo feature, technical and travel. "This is a corporate publication designed to illustrate the breadth of Raytheon Company in a low key manner through six general-interest articles per issue. Photos are used liberally, top quality and exclusively color. Stories are by assignment only." Buys 4 mss/issue. Query with clips of published work, stating specialties, credentials and other publication credits. Length: 800-1,500 words. Pays $750-1,000/article. Pays the expenses of writers on assignment.
Tips: "Submit resume and magazine-style writing samples. We are looking for established writers who are capable of crisp, interesting magazine journalism. We are not looking to promote Raytheon, but rather to inform our audience about the company, very subtly. Heavy marketing style or house organ writing is of no interest to us. A frequent mistake made by writers is not taking the time to truly understand what they're writing about and who the audience is."

UNFINISHED FURNITURE MAGAZINE, United States Exposition Corp., 1850 Oak St., Northfield IL 60093. (312)446-8434. Editor: Lynda Utterback. 50% freelance written. Bimonthly magazine for unfinished furniture retailers, distributors and manufacturers throughout the U.S., Canada, England, Australia and Europe. Circ. 6,000. Pays on publication. Publishes ms an average of 2 months after acceptance. Byline given. Buys all rights. Submit seasonal/holiday material 6 months in advance. Simultaneous queries, and simultaneous and photocopied submissions OK. Computer printout submissions acceptable. Reports in 3 weeks on queries; 1 month on mss. Free sample copy and writer's guidelines.
.**Nonfiction:** How-to, interview/profile, new product, personal experience and technical (as these relate to the unfinished furniture industry). Production distribution, marketing, advertising and promotion of unfinished furniture and current happenings in the industry. Buys 10 unsolicited mss/year. Send complete ms. Length: 2,000 words. Pays $50-100.
Photos: Pays $5 for b&w photos.
Tips: "We look for professionals in the field (i.e., accountants to write tax articles) to write articles. A frequent mistake made by writers in completing an article for us is not understanding the audience."

The double dagger before a listing indicates that the listing is new in this edition. New markets are often the most receptive to freelance contributions.

Hospitals, Nursing and Nursing Homes

In this section are journals for nurses; medical and nonmedical nursing home personnel; clinical and hospital staffs; and laboratory technicians and managers. Journals publishing technical material on new discoveries in medicine and information for physicians in private practice are listed in the Medical category. Publications that report on medical trends for the consumer are in the Health and Science categories.

‡AMERICAN JOURNAL OF NURSING, 555 West 57th St., New York NY 10019. (212)582-8820. Editor: Mary B. Mallison, RN. 2% freelance written. Eager to work with new/unpublished writers. Monthly magazine covering nursing and health care. Circ. 330,000. Pays on publication. Publishes ms an average of 6 months after acceptance. Byline given. Simultaneous queries OK. Computer printout submissions acceptable; prefers letter-quality to dot-matrix. Reports in 3 weeks on queries, 4 months on mss. Sample copy $3; free writer's guidelines.
Nonfiction: How-to, satire, new product, opinion, personal experience, photo feature and technical. No material other than nursing care and nursing issues. "Nurse authors mostly accepted for publication." Query. Length: 1,000-1,500 words. Pays $20 minimum/published page. Pays the expenses of writers on assignment.
Photos: Forbes Linkhorn, art editor. Reviews b&w and color transparencies and prints. Model release and identification of subjects required. Buys variable rights.
Columns/Departments: Buys 12 mss/year. Query with or without clips of published work.

HOSPITAL GIFT SHOP MANAGEMENT, Creative Age Publications, 7628 Densmore Ave., Van Nuys CA 91406. (818)782-7232. Editor: Barbara Feiner. 25% freelance written. Works with a small number of new/unpublished writers each year. Monthly magazine covering hospital gift shop management. "*HGSM* presents practical and informative articles and features to assist in expanding the hospital gift shop into a comprehensive center generating large profits." Circ. 15,000 + . Pays on acceptance. Publishes ms an average of 4 months after acceptance. Byline given. Buys first North American serial rights. Submit seasonal/holiday material 8 months in advance. Computer printout submissions acceptable; dot-matrix OK "if readable and double-spaced." Reports in 1 month. Sample copy and writer's guidelines for $4 postage.
Nonfiction: How-to, interview/profile, photo feature, and-management-themed articles. "No fiction, no poetry, no first-person 'I was shopping in a gift shop' kinds of pieces." Buys 12-25 mss/year. Length: 750-2,500 words. Pays $10-100. Query first.
Photos: State availability of photos with query. "If you are preparing a gift shop profile, think of providing gift shop photos." Reviews 5x7 color or b&w prints; payment depends on photo quality and number used. Captions, model release, and identification of subjects required.
Fillers: Cartoons only. Buys 12/year. Pays $20.
Tips: "A freelancer's best bet is to let us know you're out there. We prefer to work on assignment a lot of the time, and we're very receptive to freelancers—especially those in parts of the country to which we have no access. Call or write; let me know you're available. Visit your nearby hospital gift shop—it's probably larger, more sophisticated than you would imagine. I've noticed that query letters are becoming sloppy and lack direction. I wouldn't mind finding writers who can communicate well, explain story ideas in a one-page letter, spell correctly, and wow me with original ideas. Make your query letter stand out. Convince me that your story is going to be exciting. A boring query usually yields a boring story."

HOSPITAL SUPERVISOR'S BULLETIN, Bureau of Business Practice, 24 Rope Ferry Rd., Waterford CT 06386. Editor: Janice Endresen. 40% freelance written. Works with a small number of new/unpublished writers each year. For non-medical hospital supervisors. Semimonthly newsletter; 8 pages. Circ. 8,000. Pays on acceptance. Publishes ms an average of 4 months after acceptance. Buys all rights. No byline. Submit seasonal/holiday material 6 months in advance. Photocopied submissions OK. Computer printout submissions acceptable; prefers letter-quality to dot-matrix. Reports in 1 month. Free sample copy and writer's guidelines.
Nonfiction: Publishes interviews with non-medical hospital department heads. "You should ask supervisors to pinpoint current problems in supervision, tell how they are trying to solve these problems and what results

they're getting—backed up by real examples from daily life." Also publishes interviews on people problems and good methods of management. People problems include the areas of training, planning, evaluating, counseling, discipline, motivation, supervising the undereducated, getting along with the medical staff, dealing with change, layoffs, etc. No material on hospital volunteers. "We prefer six- to eight-page typewritten articles. Articles must be interview-based." Pays 12¢/word after editing.

Tips: "Often stories lack concrete examples explaining general principles. I want to stress that freelancers interview supervisors (not high-level managers, doctors, or administrators) of non-medical departments. Interviews should focus on supervisory skills or techniques that would be applicable in any hospital department. The article should be conversational in tone: not stiff or academic. Use the second person to address the supervisor/reader."

‡LICENSED PRACTICAL NURSE, Official Publication of the National Federation of LPN's, Publico, Box 10350, Charlotte NC 28212. (704)535-8200. Editor: John T. Kerr. 40% freelance written. A quarterly magazine on nursing for members of the National Federation of LPN's. Circ. 10,000. Pays on publication. Byline given. Offers 100% kill fee. Buys first North American serial rights. Submit seasonal/holiday material 3 months in advance. Photocopied submissions OK. Reports in 1 month. Sample copy for 9x12 SAE and 3 first class stamps; free writer's guidelines.

Nonfiction: Book excerpts/reviews; historical/nostalgic; how-to (improve basic skills, new methods, etc.); humor; opinion/topics of controversy (such as life support systems, unionization, etc.); personal experience; photo feature; non-technical medical news; nurse/doctor and nurse/patient situations; legal liabilities of nurses; tax update for nurses; nursing ethics; care for the elderly; and continuing education. Special Convention Issue mid-summer each year. No highly technical articles or articles devoted to RN situations that would have no bearing on LPN's. Buys 16 mss/year. Query. Length: 300-1,500 words. Pays $15-125.

Photos: State availability of photos, or send photos with query or ms if available. Reviews b&w and color contact sheets. Pays $10-25 for 5x7 b&w prints; $10-75 for 5x7 color prints and color transparencies. Captions, model release, and identification of subjects required. Buys one-time rights.

Fillers: Clippings, anecdotes, short humor and newsbreaks. Buys 20/year. Length: 50-200 words. Pays $2.50-10.

Tips: "First choice is given to LPN writers, then nurse writers, then all others. Articles are chosen because of their value to LPNs in LPN work situations. Content must be invigorating and readable. Dull, technical material will not be accepted."

‡MEDICENTER MANAGEMENT, Brentwood Publishing Corp., Box 2178, Santa Monica CA 90406. (213)395-0234. Editor: Martin H. Waldman. Managing Editor: Rebecca Morrow. 40% freelance written. A monthly magazine covering freestanding ambulatory health care centers. Circ. 12,000. Pays on acceptance. Publishes ms an average of 3 months after acceptance. Byline given. Makes work-for-hire assignments. Photocopied submissions OK. Computer printout submissions acceptable; prefers letter-quality to dot-matrix. Reports in 2 weeks. Sample coy for 8½x11 SAE with 3 first class stamps; writer's guidelines for letter size SAE with1 first class stamp.

Nonfiction: Essays, how-to (associated with the business of running a medicenter), interview/profile, new product and technical. Buys 35 mss/year. Query with published clips. Length: 1,500-3,000 words. Pays 10-12¢/word. Sometimes pays the expenses of writers on assignment.

Photos: Send photos with submission. Reviews prints. Offers no additional payment for photos accepted with ms. Model releases and identification of subjects required. Buys all rights.

Columns/Departments: Profile (a telephone interview or visit to an ambulatory care center resulting in a feature-type profile of the facility), 2,000-2,500 words. Buys 12 mss/year. Query with published clips. Pays 10-12¢/word.

Tips: "We are looking to build up our national freelancing network. Writers based outside of California are especially desirable. A background in business and/or light medical writing coupled with a willngness to learn about an exciting new field are ideal qualifications. Most often we assign industry interview articles that are equipment-related. Do some research, talk to ambulatory care center operators in your area. The types of centers we cover include birthing centers, urgent care centers, surgical centers, mobile diagnostic and treatment units, radiological screening units, ophthalmology centers and immediate care centers."

66 *When I discover an editor that responds rapidly and efficiently to my queries or mss, I cherish her, praise her, hug her, take her into my heart.* **And I write for her!** **99**

Cork Millner

Hotels, Motels, Clubs, Resorts, Restaurants

These publications offer trade tips to hotel and restaurant management, and owners, managers and operators of these establishments. Journals for manufacturers and distributors of bar and beverage supplies are listed in the Beverages and Bottling category. For publications slanted to food wholesalers, processors and caterers, see Food Products, Processing and Service.

BARTENDER, Bartender Magazine Publishing Corp., Box 593, Livingston NJ 07039. (201)227-4330. Publisher: Raymond P. Foley. Editor: Jaclyn M. Wilson. Emphasizes liquor and bartending for bartenders, tavern owners and owners of restaurants with liquor licenses. 100% freelance written. Prefers to work with published/established writers; eager to work with new/unpublished writers. Bimonthly magazine; 50 pages. Circ. 80,000. Pays on publication. Publishes ms an average of 3 months after acceptance. Buys first serial rights, first North American serial rights, one-time rights, second serial (reprint) rights, all rights, and simultaneous U.S. rights. Byline given. Phone queries OK. Submit seasonal/holiday material 3 months in advance. Simultaneous, photocopied, and previously published submissions OK. Computer printout submissions acceptable; prefers letter-quality to dot-matrix. Reports in 2 months. Sample copies $2.50.
Nonfiction: General interest, historical, how-to, humor, interview (with famous ex-bartenders); new products, nostalgia, personal experience, unique bars, opinion, new techniques, new drinking trends, photo feature, profile, travel and bar sports or bar magic tricks. Send complete ms. Length: 100-1,000 words. Sometimes pays the expenses of writers on assignment.
Photos: Send photos with ms. Pays $7.50-50 for 8x10 b&w glossy prints; $10-75 for 8x10 color glossy prints. Caption preferred and model release required.
Columns/Departments: Bar of the Month; Bartender of the Month; Drink of the Month; New Drink Ideas; Bar Sports; Quiz; Bar Art; Wine Cellar Tips of the Month (from prominent figures in the liquor industry); One' For The Road (travel); Collectors (bar or liquor-related items); Photo Essays. Query. Length: 200-1,000 words. Pays $50-200.
Fillers: Clippings, jokes, gags, anecdotes, short humor, newsbreaks and anything relating to bartending and the liquor industry. Length: 25-100 words. Pays $5-25.
Tips: "To break in, absolutely make sure that your work will be of interest to all bartenders across the country. Your style of writing should reflect the audience you are addressing. The most frequent mistake made by writers in completing an article for us is using the wrong subject."

‡CATERING TODAY, The Professional Guide to Catering Profits, ProTech Publishing and Communications, Inc., Box 222, Santa Claus IN 47579. (812)937-4464. Editor: Mary Jeanne Schumacher. Managing Editor: Danny Bolin. 50% freelance written. A monthly magazine for the off-premise and on-site catering industry covering food trends, business and management advice and features on successful caterers. Estab. 1985. Circ. 36,000. Pays on publication. Publishes ms an average of 2 months after acceptance. Byline given. Offers 10-30% kill fee. Buys all rights. Submit seasonal/holiday material 3 months in advance. Simultaneous, photocopied and previously published submissions OK. Computer printout submissions acceptable; prefers letter-quality to dot-matrix. Reports in 2 weeks on queries; 3 weeks on mss. Free sample copy and writer's guidelines.
Nonfiction: How-to (on ice carving, garnishes, cooking techniques, etc); interview/profile; new product; and photo feature. No fillers, humor, poetry or fiction. Buys 35-40 mss/year. Query with published clips. Length varies. Pays 8¢/word.
Photos: Send photos with submission. Reviews contact sheets, negatives, 4x5 transparencies, and 5x7 prints. Offers $5-10/photo. Captions required.
Tips: "Write from a viewpoint that a caterer/business person can understand, appreciate and learn from. Submissions should be neat, accurate and not flowery or wordy. Areas of our publication most open to freelancers are food trends and uses, equipment reviews, and feature length profiles of caterers."

FLORIDA HOTEL & MOTEL JOURNAL, The Official Publication of the Florida Hotel & Motel Association, Accommodations, Inc., Box 1529, Tallahassee FL 32302. (904)224-2888. Editor: Mrs. Jayleen Woods. 10% freelance written. Monthly magazine for managers in the lodging industry (every licensed hotel, motel and resort in Florida). Circ. 6,500. Pays on publication. Publishes ms an average of 2 months after acceptance. Byline given. Offers $50 kill fee. Buys all rights and makes work-for-hire assignments. Submit seasonal/holiday material 3 months in advance. Photocopied submissions OK. Computer printout submissions acceptable; no dot-matrix. Reports in 1 month. Sample copy for 9x12 SAE and 4 first class stamps; writer's guidelines for business size SAE and 1 first class stamp.

Nonfiction: General interest (business, finance, taxes); historical/nostalgic (old Florida hotel reminiscences); how-to (improve management, housekeeping procedures, guest services, security and coping with common hotel problems); humor (hotel-related anecdotes); inspirational (succeeding where others have failed); interview/profile (of unusual hotel personalities); new product (industry-related and non brand preferential); photo feature (queries only); technical (emerging patterns of hotel accounting, telephone systems, etc.); travel (transportation and tourism trends only—no scenics or site visits); and property renovations and maintenance techniques. Buys 10-12 mss/year. Query with clips of published work. Length: 750-2,500 words. Pays $75-250 "depending on type of article and amount of research." Sometimes pays the expenses of writers on assignment.

Photos: Send photos with ms. Pays $25-100 for 4x5 color transparencies; $10-15 for 5x7 b&w prints. Captions, model release and identification of subjects required.

Tips: "We prefer feature stories on properties or personalities holding current membership in the Florida Hotel and Motel Association. Memberships and/or leadership brochures are available (SASE) on request. We're open to articles showing how Mom and Dad management copes with inflation and rising costs of energy systems, repairs, renovations, new guest needs and expectations. The writer may have a better chance of breaking in at our publication with short articles and fillers because the better a writer is at the art of condensation, the better his/her feature articles are likely to be."

HOTEL AND MOTEL MANAGEMENT, Harcourt Brace Jovanovich, Inc., 7500 Old Oak Blvd., Cleveland OH 44130. (216)243-8100. Editor: Michael Deluca. Managing Editor: Robert Nozar. 25% freelance written. Prefers to work with published/established writers. Monthly newsmagazine about hotels, motels and resorts in the continental U.S. and Hawaii for general managers, corporate executives, and department heads (such as director of sales; food and beverage; energy; security; front office; housekeeping, etc.) Circ. 41,000. Pays on acceptance. Publishes ms an average of 2 months after acceptance. Byline given. Buys first North American serial rights. No phone queries. Computer printout submissions acceptable; prefers letter-quality to dot-matrix. Reports in 3 weeks on queries; do not send mss. Free sample copy.

Nonfiction: "A how-to, nuts-and-bolts approach to improving the bottom line through more innovative, efficient management of hotels, motels and resorts in the continental U.S. and Hawaii. Articles consist largely of specific case studies and interviews with authorities on various aspects of the lodging market, including franchising, financing, personnel, security, energy management, package tours, telecommunications, food service operations, architecture and interior design, and technological advances. We use freelance coverage of spot news events (strikes, natural disasters, etc.). Query with published clips. Write a query letter outlining your idea and be specific." Length: 800-1,000 words. Sometimes pays expenses of writers on assignment.

Photos: State availability of b&w photos. Captions preferred. Buys one-time rights.

Tips: "The writer may have a better chance of breaking in at our publication with short articles and fillers because we are a newsmagazine that covers an industry of people who don't have time to read longer articles. We need 'hands on' articles which explain the topic."

INNKEEPING WORLD, Box 84108, Seattle WA 98124. Editor/Publisher: Charles Nolte. 75% freelance written. Emphasizes the hotel industry worldwide. Published 10 times a year; 12 pages. Circ. 2,000. Pays on acceptance. Publishes ms an average of 3 months after acceptance. Buys all rights. No byline. Submit seasonal/holiday material 1 month in advance. Computer printout submissions acceptable; prefers letter-quality to dot-matrix. Reports in 1 month. Sample copy and writer's guidelines for SASE.

Nonfiction: Main topics: Managing—interview with successful hotel managers of large and/or famous hotels/resorts (length: 600-1,200 words); Marketing—interviews with hotel marketing executives on successful promotions/case histories (length: 300-1,000 words); Lodging Classics—stories of famous or highly-rated hotels/inns/resorts, domestic and overseas listing of hotels available from the publisher (length: 300-1,000 words); Bill of Fare—outstanding hotel restaurants, menus and merchandising concepts (length: 300-1,000 words); and The Concierge—interviews with the world's most experienced about their experience in guest relations (length: 300-1,000 words). Pays $100 minimum or 15¢/word (whichever is greater) for main topics. Other topics—advertising, creative packages, cutting expenses, frequent guest profile, guest comfort, guest relations, hospitality, ideas, interior design, landscape design, public relations, reports and trends, sales promotion, special guestrooms, staff relations. Length: 50-500 words. Pays 15¢/word.

‡LODGING HOSPITALITY MAGAZINE, Penton Publishing, 1100 Superior Ave., Cleveland OH 44114. (216)696-7000. Editor: Edward Watkins. Managing Editor: Loretta Ivany. 25% freelance written. A monthly magazine covering the lodging industry. "Our purpose is to inform lodging management of trends and events which will affect their properties and the way they do business. Audience: owners and managers of hotels, motels, resorts." Circ. 44,000. Pays on acceptance. Publishes ms an average of 2 months after acceptance. Byline given. Buys first rights. Submit seasonal/holiday material 2 months in advance. Reports in 1 month.
Nonfiction: General interest, how-to, interview/profile and travel. Special issues include technology (January); interior design (April); foodservice (May); investments (June); franchising (July); marketing (September); and state of the industry (December). "We do *not* want personal reviews of hotels visited by writer, or travel pieces. All articles are geared to hotel executives to help them in their business." Buys 25 mss/year. Query. Length: 700-2,000 words. Pays $150-600. Pays the expenses of writers on assignment.
Photos: State availability of photos with submission. Reviews contact sheets and transparencies. Offers no additional payment for photos accepted with ms. Captions and identification of subjects required. Buys one-time rights.
Columns/Departments: Budget Line, Suite Success, Resort Report, Executive on the Spot, Strategies Marketwatch, Report from Washington, Food for Profit, Technology Update—all one-page reports of 700 words. Buys 25 mss/year. Query. Pays $150-250.

‡PIZZA TODAY, The Professional Guide To Pizza Profits,, ProTech Publishing and Communications, Inc., Box 114, Santa Claus IN 47679. (812)937-4464. Editor: Grace Brown. Managing Editor: Danny Bolin. 50% freelance written. A monthly magazine for the pizza industry, covering trends, features of successful pizza operators, business and management advice, etc. Circ. 30,000. Pays on publication. Publishes ms an average of 2 months after acceptance. Byline given. Offers 10-30% kill fee. Buys all rights and negotiable rights. Submit seasonal/holiday material 3 months in advance. Simultaneous, photocopied and previously published submissions OK. Computer printout submissons acceptable; prefers letter-quality to dot-matrix. Reports in 2 weeks on queries; 3 weeks on manuscripts. Free sample copy and writer's guidelines.
Nonfiction: Interview/profile, new product, entrepreneurial slants, time management, pizza delivery and employee training. No fillers, fiction, humor or poetry. Buys 40-60 mss/year. Query with published clips. Length: 750-2,500 words. Pays 8¢/word.
Photos: Send photos with submission. Reviews contact sheets, negatives, 4x5 transparencies and 5x7 prints. Offers $5-10/photo. Captions required.

RESORT & HOTEL MANAGEMENT MAGAZINE,(formerly *Resort Management Magazine*), Western Specialty Publications, Inc., Box A, Del Mar CA 92014. (699)755-7431. 80% freelance written. Works with a small number of new/unpublished writers each year. A magazine published 8 times/year covering the hotel/resort and condo/timeshare industries. "We do not reach motels or motor lodges." Pays on publication. Publishes ms an average of 6 months after acceptance. Byline given. Offers $50 kill fee. Buys all rights. Submit all material 2 months in advance. Simultaneous queries and photocopied and previously published submissions OK. Computer printout submissions acceptable. Reports in 3 months. Sample copy $5.
Nonfiction: Book excerpts, expose, general interest, historical/nostalgic, how-to, humor, inspirational, interview/profile, new product, opinion, personal experience, photo feature, technical and travel. Especially interested in state-of-the-art technology and management methods, industry megatrends and instant cost saving devices. Buys 6 mss/year. Query with clips of published work. Length: 500-2,000 words. Pays $50-100.
Photos: Kaaren Slen, associate publisher. Send photos with accompanying query or ms. "Won't return without SASE." Pays $5-10 for b&w and color prints; $10-20 for b&w transparencies; $10-25 for color transparencies. Buys all rights.
Tips: "We recommend the writer query before sending submissions." Anticipates becoming a monthly publication.

RESTAURANT HOSPITALITY, Penton IPC, Penton Plaza, 1111 Chester Ave., Cleveland OH 44114. (216)696-7000. Editor: Stephen Michaelides. 30% freelance written. Prefers to work with published/established writers. Monthly magazine covering the foodservice industry for owners and operators of independent restaurants, hotel foodservices, executives of national and regional restaurant chains and foodservice executives of schools, hospitals, military installations and corporations. Circ. 120,000. Average issue includes 10-12 features. Pays on acceptance. Publishes ms an average of 5 months after acceptance. Byline given. Buys exclusive rights. Query first. Computer printout submissions acceptable; prefers letter-quality to dot-matrix. Reports in 1 week. Sample copy for 9x12 SAE and $1.54 postage.
Nonfiction: General interest (articles that advise operators how to run their operations profitably and efficiently); interview (with operators); and profile. Stories on psychology, consumer behavior, managerial problems and solutions, how-to's on buying insurance, investing (our readers have a high degree of disposable income), design elements and computers in foodservice. No restaurant reviews. Buys 30 mss/year. Query with clips of previously published work and a short bio. Length: 500-1,500 words. Pays $100/published page. Pays the expenses of writers on assignment.

Photos: Send color photos with manuscript. Captions required.
Columns/Departments: "We are accepting 100-150 word pieces with photos (slides preferred; will accept b&w) for our Restaurant People department. Should be light, humorous, anecdotal." Byline given. Pays $75.
Tips: "We're accepting fewer queried stories but assigning more to our regular freelancers. We need new angles on old stories, and we like to see pieces on emerging trends and technologies in the restaurant industry. Our readers don't want to read how to open a restaurant or why John Smith is so successful. We'll be publishing short, snappy profiles—way more than in the past—with fewer major features."

‡TEXAS FOOD & SERVICE NEWS, Texas Restaurant Association, Box 1429, Austin TX 78767. (512)444-6543. Editor: Kim Goodwin. 25% freelance written. Prefers to work with published/established writers. Magazine published 10 times/year about the Texas food service industry for restaurant owners and operators. Circ. 5,500. Pays on acceptance. Publishes ms an average of 3 months after acceptance. Byline given. Not copyrighted. Buys first and second rights to the same material, and second (reprint) rights to material originally published elsewhere. Written queries preferred. Submit seasonal material 2 months in advance. Simultaneous queries, and photocopied and previously published submissions OK. Accepts electronic submissions; requires hard copy. "Call us." Computer printout submissions acceptable; prefers letter-quality to dot-matrix. Reports in 1 month. Free sample copy.
Nonfiction: Interview, profile, how-to, humor and personal experience. "The magazine spotlights many general categories (economy, energy, labor relations, new products and staff editorials) in short columns. Therefore, we appreciate getting good, terse articles with a how-to-improve-your-business slant. These we prefer with sharp, black and white photos. All articles should be substantiated with plenty of facts or specific examples. Avoid too much vocabulary. Opt for shorter sentences and shorter words." No restaurant critiques. Buys 10 mss/year. Query. Length: 1,000-1,500 words. Pays $15-50. Sometimes pays the expenses of writers on assignment.
Photos: State availability of photos. Pays $10-20 for b&w contact sheet; $10-50 for b&w and color negatives. Buys one-time rights.
Columns/Departments: Send complete ms.
Tips: "All of our readers are business people seeking to improve their operations. We like to feature specific areas of food service, such as employee relations; serving health food, computers and eating out trends. The magazine adopts a professional approach to the food service industry. In other words, articles must contain ideas and information that will make money. We want more submissions by restaurant industry experts."

‡VACATION INDUSTRY REVIEW, Worldex Corp., Box 431920, South Miami FL 33243. (305)667-0202. Managing Editor: George Leposky. 50% freelance written. A bimonthly magazine covering leisure lodgings (timeshare resorts, RV parks, condo hotels, etc.). Circ. 2,500. Pays on acceptance. Publishes ms an average of 2-4 months after acceptance. Byline given. Buys all rights and makes work-for-hire assignments. Submit seasonal/holiday material 4 months advance. Photocopied submissions OK. Electronic submissions OK, but requires hard copy with floppy disk. Computer printout submissions acceptable; prefers letter-quality to dot-matrix. Reports in 1 month. Sample copy $1; free writer's guidelines.
Nonfiction: How-to, interview/profile, new product, opinion, personal experience, technical and travel. No consumer travel or real estate related material. Buys 15 mss/year. Query with published clips. Length: 1,000-2,500 words. Pays $75-175. Pays the expenses of writers on assignment, if previously arranged. Send photos with submission. Reviews contact sheets, 35mm transparencies, and 5x7 prints. Offers no additional payment for photos accepted with ms. Captions and identification of subjects required. Buys one-time rights.
Tips: "We want articles about the business aspect of the vacation industry: entrepreneurship, project financing, design and construction, sales and marketing, operations, management—in short, anything that will help our readers plan, build, sell and run a quality vacation property that satisfies the owners/guests while earning a profit for the proprietor. Our destination pieces are trade-oriented, reporting the status of tourism and the development of various kinds of leisure lodging facilities in a city, region or country. You can discuss things to see and do in the context of a resort located near an attraction, but that shouldn't be the main focus or reason for the article."

66 *Writers shouldn't worry about editors stealing their ideas. Ideas are everywhere; it's the execution of the idea they are selling.* **99**

R.W. Gardner, Ohio Business

Industrial Operation and Management

Industrial plant managers, executives, distributors and buyers read these journals. Subjects include equipment, supplies, quality control and production engineering. Some industrial management journals are also listed under the names of specific industries, such as Machinery and Metal Trade. Publications for industrial supervisors are listed in Management and Supervision.

‡**APPLIANCE MANUFACTURER, For Managers in Business/Office, Consumer & Commercial Appliances,** Cahners Publishing Co., 1350 E. Touhy Ave., Des Plaines IL 60018. (312)635-8800. Editor: Walter J. Maczka. 5% freelance written. A monthly magazine covering design for manufacturing in high-volume automated manufacturing industries. Circ. 34,000. Pays on publication. Publishes ms an average of 4 months after acceptance. Byline given sometimes. Buys all rights. Simultaneous submissions OK. Computer printout submissions acceptable; prefers letter-quality to dot-matrix. Reports in 3 weeks. Free sample copy.
Nonfiction: How-to; interview/profile (sometimes); new product; and technical. Buys 12 mss/year. Send complete ms. Length: open. Pays $50/published page.
Photos: Captions and identification of subjects required.

‡**CHEMICAL BUSINESS,** Schnell Publishing Company, 100 Church St., New York NY 10007-2694. (212)732-9820. Editor: Arthur Kavaler. Managing Editor: J. Robert Warren. 70% freelance written. A monthly magazine covering chemicals and related process industries such as plastics, paints, some minerals, essential oils, soaps, detergents. Publishes features on the industry, management, financial and (Wall Street) marketing, shipping and storage, labor, environment international, and company profiles. Circ. 45,000. Pays on acceptance. Publishes ms an average of 3 months after acceptance. Byline given. Offers $100 kill fee. Buys all rights. Call before submitting seasonal/holiday material. Photocopied submissions and previously published book excerpts OK. Computer printout submissions acceptable; prefers letter-quality to dot-matrix. Free sample copy and writer's guidelines.
Nonfiction: No broad, general industrial submissions on how-to. Buys 60 mss/year. Query. Length: 2,000-3,000 words. Pays $400 for assigned articles. Pays the expenses of writers on assignment.
Photos: Send photos with submission. Reviews contact sheets, negatives, and 35mm, 70mm ("almost any size") transparencies. No pay for company photos; offers $10-25/photo taken by writer. Model releases required. Buys all rights.

COMPRESSED AIR, 253 E. Washington Ave., Washington NJ 07882. Editor/Publications Manager: S.M. Parkhill. 75% freelance written. Emphasizes general industrial/technology subjects for engineers and managers. Monthly magazine; 48 pages. Circ. 150,000. Buys all rights. Publishes ms an average of 2 months after acceptance. Computer printout submissions acceptable; no dot-matrix. Reports in 6 weeks. Free sample copy, editorial schedule; mention *Writer's Market* in request.
Nonfiction: "Articles must be reviewed by experts in the field." Buys 48 mss/year. Query with published clips. Pays negotiable fee. Sometimes pays expenses of writers on assignment.
Photos: State availability of photos in query. Payment for 8x10 glossy color photos is included in total purchase price. Captions required. Buys all rights.
Tips: "We are presently looking for freelancers with a track record in industrial/technology writing. Editorial schedule is developed well in advance and relies heavily on article ideas from contributors. Resume and samples help. Writers with access to authorities preferred; and prefer interviews over library research. The magazine's name doesn't reflect its contents. We suggest writers request sample copies."

INDUSTRIAL CHEMICAL NEWS, McGraw-Hill, 1221 Ave. of the Americas, New York NY 10020. (212)512-2500. Editor: Irvin Schwartz. Managing Editor: Susan Neale. "We are backlogged with submissions and prefer not to receive unsolicited submissions at this time."

‡INDUSTRIAL MANAGEMENT, Clifford/Elliot Ltd., 277 Lakeshore Rd., E., Oakville, Ontario, Canada L6J 6J3. (416)842-2884. Editor: Carol Radford. Managing Editor: Jackie Roth. 35% freelance written. Works with a small number of new/unpublished writers each year. Monthly magazine for Canada's manufacturing industries providing "management information and innovations in the areas of industrial and labor relations, product development, new production technology, motivation, communications, etc." Circ. 27,000. Pays on acceptance. Publishes ms an average of 2 months after acceptance. Byline given. Offers 50% kill fee. Buys first North American serial rights. Simultaneous queries and photocopied submissions OK. Computer printout submissions acceptable; prefers letter-quality to dot-matrix. Reports in 2 weeks on queries, 1 month on mss. Free sample copy and writer's guidelines.
Nonfiction: How-to (management, productivity improvement, problem solving); interview/profile (industry leaders); new product. "All articles must have a manufacturing management angle and must be written by Canadian freelancers." Buys 15-20 mss/year. Query. Length: 1,000-3,000. Pays $400-800. Sometimes pays the expenses of writers on assignment.

INSULATION OUTLOOK, National Insulation Contractors Association, Suite 410, 1025 Vermont NW, Washington DC 20005. (202)783-6278. Editor: Dixie M. Lee. 10-20% freelance written. Prefers to work with published/established writers; works with a small number of new/unpublished writers each year. Monthly magazine about general business, commercial and industrial insulation for the insulation industry in the United States and abroad. Publication is read by engineers, specifiers, owners, contractors and energy managers in the industrial and commercial insulation field. There is also representative distribution to public utilities, and energy-related industries. Pays on publication. Publishes ms an average of 4 months after acceptance. Byline given. Buys first rights only. Phone queries OK. Written queries should be short and simple, with samples of writing attached. Submit seasonal material 6 months in advance. Simultaneous, photocopied and previously published submissions OK. Computer printout submissions acceptable. Sample copy $2; free writer's guidelines. "Give us a call. If there seems to be compatibility, we will send a free issue sample so the writer can see directly the type of publication he or she is dealing with."
Nonfiction: Articles on the technical aspects of insulation; case studies. Sometimes pays the expenses of writers on assignment.
Columns/Departments: Query. Pays $50-300.

‡MANUFACTURING SYSTEMS, The Management Magazine of Integrated Manufacturing, Hitchcock Publishing Co., 25 W 550 Geneva Rd., Wheaton IL 60188. (312)665-1000. Editor: Tom Inglesby. Senior Editor: Mary Emrich. 10-15% freelance written. A monthly magazine covering computers/information in manufacturing for upper and middle-level management in manufacturing companies. Circ. 131,000. Pays on acceptance. Publishes ms an average of 2 months after acceptance. Byline given. Offers 35% kill fee. Buys all rights. Submit seasonal/holiday material 4 months in advance. Simultaneous and photocopied submissions OK. Electronic submissions OK via Kaypro, Eagle 1600, IBM-PC/AT; prefers hard copy also. Computer printout submissions acceptable; prefers letter-quality to dot-matrix. Reports in 2 weeks. Free sample copy.
Nonfiction: Book excerpts, essays, general interest, interview/profile, new product, opinion, technical, case history—applications of system. "Each issue emphasizes some aspect of manufacturing. Editorial schedule available, usually in September, for next year." No humor or negative ("manufacturing is dying-type") articles. Buys 6-8 mss/year. Query with or without published clips, or send complete ms. Length: 500-2,500 words. Pays $150-600 for assigned articles; pays $100-500 for unsolicited articles. Sometimes pays limited, pre-authorized expenses of writers on assignment.
Photos: State availability of photos with submission. Reviews contact sheets, negatives, 2x2 and larger transparencies and 5x7 and larger prints. Offers no additional payment for photos accepted with ms. Captions and identification of subjects required. Buys one-time rights.
Columns/Departments: Forum (VIP-to-VIP, bylined by manufacturing executive), 1,000 words maximum; and Manufacturing Management (consultant's columns, bylined by manufacturing consultant), 500-600 words. Buys 1-2 mss/year. Query. 500-1,000 words. Sometimes pays $100-200. "These are *rarely* paid for but we'd consider ghost written pieces bylined by 'name.' "
Fillers: Barbara Dutton, fillers editor. Anecdotes, facts, gags to be illustrated by cartoonist and newsbreaks. Buys 3-6/year. Length: 25-100 words. Pays $10-50.
Tips: "We are interested in direct efforts to apply computers to manufacturing productivity—concepts (just-in-time), zero defects, Japanese management methods, *statistical* quality control or newest whizz-bang hardware/software (artificial intelligence, super computer, robots). Features are the most open area. We will be happy to provide market information and reader profile on request."

‡OCCUPATIONAL HEALTH & SAFETY MAGAZINE, Stevens Publishing, 225 N. New Road, Box 7573, Waco TX 76714. (817)776-9000. Editor: Carolyn L. Aydelotte. Managing Editor: Sheri Poore. 80% freelance written. Works with a small number of new/unpublished writers each year. A monthly magazine covering health and safety in the workplace. Circ. 93,000. Pays on acceptance. Publishes ms an average of 8 months after acceptance. Byline given. Buys first serial rights and first North American serial rights. Submit seasonal/

holiday material 6 months in advance. Simultaneous submissions OK. Electronic submissions OK via IBM compatible, WordStar or Word Plus. Computer printout submissions acceptable; prefers letter-quality to dot-matrix. Reports in 1 month on queries; 2 months on mss. Free sample copy with writer's guidelines.

Nonfiction: Exposé; how-to (for health/safety professionals); interview/profile; new product and technical. Subjects of interest include product liability; dusts in the workplace; interviews with health and safety personnel of interest to general readers; and employee assistance programs. No unsubstantiated material; no advertorials; no first-person articles. Length 1,200-5,000 words. Payment varies. Sometimes pays the expenses of writers on assignment.

Photos: Reviews contact sheets, negatives, 4x5 transparencies and prints. Captions, model releases and identification of subjects required.

Tips: "Writers can judge whether their expertise will suit our needs by taking note of the technical quality of material in our magazine, and by keeping in mind that we will consider anything occupational-health or safety related."

PLANT MANAGEMENT & ENGINEERING, MacLean Hunter Bldg; 777 Bay St., Toronto, Ontario M5W 1A7 Canada. Editor: Ron Richardson. 5% freelance written. Prefers to work with published/established writers. For Canadian plant managers and engineers. Monthly magazine. Circ. 26,000. Pays on acceptance. Publishes ms an average of 2 months after acceptance. Buys first Canadian rights. Computer printout submissions acceptable; prefers letter-quality to dot-matrix. Reports in 3 weeks. Sample copy with SAE only.

Nonfiction: How-to, technical and management technique articles. Must have Canadian slant. No generic articles that appear to be rewritten from textbooks. Buys fewer than 20 unsolicited mss/year. Query. Pays 12¢/word minimum. Sometimes pays the expenses of writers on assignment.

Photos: State availability of photos with query. Pays $25-50 for b&w prints; $50-100 for 2¼x2¼ or 35mm color transparencies. Captions preferred. Buys one-time rights.

Tips: Query first by letter. "Read the magazine. Know the Canadian readers' special needs. Case histories and interviews only—no theoretical pieces. We will probably be buying even less freelance material because of more staff writers."

PRODUCTION ENGINEERING, Penton Plaza, Cleveland OH 44114. (216)696-7000. Editor: Donald E. Hegland. Executive Editor: John McRainey. 50% freelance written. Prefers to work with published/established writers. For "men and women in production engineering—the engineers who plan, design and improve manufacturing operations." Monthly magazine; 100 pages. Circ. 95,000. Pays on publication. Publishes ms an average of 2 months after acceptance. Buys exclusive first North American serial rights. Byline given; "if by prior arrangement, an author contributed a segment of a broader article, he might not be bylined." Phone queries OK. Photocopied submissions OK, if exclusive. Computer printout submissions acceptable; prefers letter-quality to dot-matrix. Reports in 2 weeks. Free sample copy and writer's guidelines.

Nonfiction: How-to (engineering, data for engineers); personal experience (from *very* senior production or manufacturing engineers only); and technical (technical news or how-to). "We're interested in solid, hard hitting technical articles on the gut issues of manufacturing. Not case histories, but no-fat treatments of manufacturing concepts, innovative manufacturing methods, and state-of-the-art procedures. Our readers also enjoy articles that detail a variety of practical solutions to some specific, everyday manufacturing headaches." Buys 2-3 mss/issue. Query. Length: 800-3,000 words. Pays $100-300.

PURCHASING EXECUTIVE'S BULLETIN, Bureau of Business Practice, 24 Rope Ferry Rd., Waterford CT 06386. (203)442-4365. Editor: Claire Sherman. Managing Editor: Wayne Muller. For purchasing managers and purchasing agents. Semimonthly newsletter; 4 pages. Circ. 5,500. Pays on acceptance. Buys all rights. Submit seasonal/holiday material 3 months in advance. Reports in 2 weeks. Free sample copy and writer's guidelines.

Nonfiction: How-to (better cope with problems confronting purchasing executives); and direct interviews detailing how purchasing has overcome problems and found better ways of handling departments. No derogatory material about a company; no writer's opinions; no training or minority purchasing articles. "We don't want material that's too elementary (things any purchasing executive already knows)." Buys 2-3 mss/issue. Query. Length: 750-1,000 words.

Tips: "Make sure that a release is obtained and attached to a submitted article."

SEMICONDUCTOR INTERNATIONAL, Cahners Publishing Co., 1350 E. Touhy Ave., Box 5080, Des Plaines IL 60018. (312)635-8800. Editor: Donald E. Swanson. 5% freelance written. Monthly magazine covering semiconductor industry processing, assembly and testing technology subjects for semiconductor industry processing engineers and management. "Technology stories that cover all phases of semiconductor product manufacturing and testing are our prime interest." Circ. 35,134. Pays on publication. "News items are paid for upon acceptance." Publishes ms an average of 6 months after acceptance. Byline given. Buys all rights and makes work-for-hire assignments. Computer printout submissions acceptable; no dot-matrix. Reports in 1 month.

Nonfiction: Technical and news pertaining to the semiconductor industry in the U.S. and overseas. No "articles that are commercial in nature or product oriented." Buys 50 mss/year (including feature articles and news). Query with "your interest and capabilities" or send complete ms. Length: 2,500 words maximum.

Photos: State availability of photos or send photos with ms. Reviews 8x10 b&w prints and 35mm color transparencies. Captions and identification of subjects required.

Columns/Departments: "News of the semiconductor industry as it pertains to technology trends is of interest. Of special interest is news of the semiconductor industry in foreign countries such as Japan, England, Germany, France, and the Netherlands." Buys 30-40 mss/year. Query. Length: 200-1,500 words. Pays 15¢/word for accepted, edited copy.

Tips: "The most frequent mistake made by writers in completing an article for us is lack of understanding of the semiconductor fabricating industry."

‡**WASTE AGE**, National Solid Wastes Management Association, 1730 Rhode Island Ave. NW, Washington DC 20036. Editor: Joe Salimando. 10% freelance written. A monthly magazine for businessmen and municipal officials who manage organizations which remove and dispose of wastes. Circ. 30,000. Pays on acceptance. Byline sometimes given. Offers 50% kill fee. Buys all rights. Electronic submissions OK via IBM Voluswriter software, but requires hard copy also. Computer printout submissions acceptable; prefers letter-quality to dot-matrix. Reports in 3 weeks on queries.

Nonfiction: Historical/nostalgic, interview/profile, photo feature, technical and case studies. Buys 15 mss/year. Must query. Length: 700-3,000 words. Pays $300 minimum. Sometimes pays the expenses of writers on assignment.

Photos: State availability of photos with submission. Reviews contact sheets. Identification of subjects required. Buys one-time rights.

Columns/Departments: Safety (protecting waste industry workers), and Your Image (promotion ideas—for refuse and hazardous waste). Query. Length: 300-1,000 words. Pays $300-450.

WEIGHING & MEASUREMENT, Key Markets Publishing Co., Box 5867, Rockford IL 61125. (815)399-6970. Editor: David M. Mathieu. For users of industrial scales and meters. Bimonthly magazine; 32 pages. Circ. 15,000. Pays on acceptance. Buys all rights. Pays 20% kill fee. Byline given. Reports in 2 weeks. Free sample copy.

Nonfiction: Interview (with presidents of companies); personal opinion (guest editorials on government involvement in business, etc.); profile (about users of weighing and measurement equipment); and technical. Buys 25 mss/year. Query on technical articles; submit complete ms for general interest material. Length: 750-2,500 words. Pays $45-125.

Insurance

COMPASS, Marine Office of America Corporation (MOAC), 180 Maiden Lane, New York NY 10038. (212)440-7720. Editor: Irene E. Lombardo. 75% freelance written. Prefers to work with published/established writers. Semiannual magazine of the Marine Office of America Corporation. Magazine is distributed to persons in marine insurance (agents, brokers, risk managers) and the media. Circ. 8,000. Pays half on acceptance, half on publication. Publishes ms an average of 6 months after acceptance. Byline given. Offers $250 kill fee. Not copyrighted. Buys first North American serial rights. Does not accept previously published work or unsolicited mss. Query first. Simultaneous queries OK. Computer printout submissions acceptable; no dot-matrix. Reports in 4 weeks on queries. Free sample copy and writer's guidelines.

Nonfiction: General interest, historical/nostalgic and technical. "Historical/nostalgia should relate to ships, trains, airplanes, balloons, bridges, sea and land expeditions, seaports and transportation of all types. General interest includes marine and transportation subjects; fishing industry; and environmental events—improvements relating to inland waterways, space travel and satellites. Articles must have human interest. Technical articles may cover energy exploration and development—offshore oil and gas drilling, developing new sources of electric power and solar energy; usages of coal, water and wind to generate electric power; and special cargo handling such as containerization on land and sea. Articles must not be overly technical and should have reader interest." No book excerpts, first-person, exposes, how-to, humor or opinion. Buys 8 mss/year. Query with or without published clips. Length: 1,500-2,000 words. Pays $1,000 maximum. Sometimes pays the expenses of writers on assignment.

Photos: Robert A. Cooney, photo editor. (212)838-6200. State availability of photos. Reviews b&w and color transparencies and prints. Captions and identification of subjects required. Buys one-time rights.

Tips: "We want profiles of individuals connected with marine, energy, and transportation fields who are unusual. Send a brief outline of the story idea to editor mentioning also the availability of photographs in b&w and color. All articles must be thoroughly researched and original. Articles should have human interest through the device of interviews. We only publish full-length articles—no fillers."

‡INSURANCE REVIEW, Insurance Information Institute, 110 William St., New York NY 10038. (212)669-9200. Editor: Colleen Katz. Managing Editor: Joseph Burns. 100% freelance written. A monthly magazine covering property and casualty insurance for agents, brokers, insurers, educators, lawyers, financial analysts and journalists. Circ. 80,000. Pays on acceptance. Publishes ms an average of 2 months after acceptance. Byline given. Offers 25% kill fee. Buys first North American serial rights; rights returned to author 90 days after publication. "We retain right to reprint." Electronic submissions OK via IBM PC Word Perfect, but requires hard copy also. Reports in 1 month. Free sample copy and writer's guidelines.

Nonfiction: How-to (improve agency business), humor, interview/profile, opinion, photo feature, technical, travel and business articles with insurance information. Buys 180 mss/year. Query with published clips. Length: 750-2,500 words. Pays $150-1,000 for assigned articles. Pays expenses of writers on assignment.

Photos: Send photos with submission. Reviews contact sheets and transparencies. Captions, model releases and identification of subjects required.

Columns/Departments: By Line (analysis of one line of business p/c), Analysis (financial aspects of p/c industry), and Discoveries (travel pieces on a city). Query. Length: 750-1,200 words. Pays $200-350.

Fillers: Anecdotes, facts, gags to be illustrated by cartoonist, newsbreaks and short humor. Buys 50/year. Length: 75-500 words. Pays $25-100.

Tips: "Become well-versed in issues facing the insurance industry. Find interesting people to write about. Profile successful agents or brokers."

PROFESSIONAL AGENT MAGAZINE, Professional Insurance Agents, 400 N. Washington St., Alexandria VA 22314. (703)836-9340. Editor/Publisher: Janice J. Artandi. 25% freelance written. Monthly magazine covering insurance/small business for independent insurance agents. Circ. 40,000. Pays on acceptance. Byline given. Buys exclusive rights in the industry. Computer printout submissions acceptable. Reports ASAP. Sample copy for SAE.

Nonfiction: Insurance management for small businesses and self-help. Special issues on life insurance and computer interface. Buys 24 mss/year. Query with published clips or send complete ms. Length: 1,000-3,000 words. Pays $100-500.

Photos: State availability of photos. Pays $35-200 for 5x7 b&w prints; $50-300 for 35mm color transparencies. Captions, model release, and identification of subjects required. Buys one-time rights.

‡PULSE, Transamerica Occidental Life Insurance Corp., 10th floor, 1149 S. Broadway, Los Angeles CA 90015. (213)741-7226. Editor: Paul A. Sergios. Managing Editor: Stephanie Burchfield. 20% freelance written. A monthly company magazine covering products and developments in life insurance. "*Pulse* contains information for Transamerica's 10,000-member selling force, emphasizing trends in life insurance industry, selling techniques of products, and profiles on top sellers." Circ. 10,000. Pays on acceptance. Publishes ms an average of 1 month after acceptance. Byline given. Offers 25% kill fee. Buys one-time rights. Simultaneous, photocopied, and previously published submissions OK. Electronic submissions OK via Xywrite software. Computer printout submissions acceptable; prefers letter-quality to dot-matrix. Reports in 2 weeks on queries; 1 month on mss. Free sample copy and writer's guidelines.

Nonfiction: Interview/profile, new product and sales techniques. Articles must deal directly with the life insurance industry, or sales techniques. Query with published clips. Length: open. Pays $250-500; sometimes pays in copies to very new writers seeking portfolio material.

Photos: Reviews contact sheets. Offers $25-100. Model releases and identification of subjects required. Buys one-time rights.

Tips: "Keep abreast of current trends in life insurance sales, new product introduction and cross-competitive offerings. A strong marketing orientation and extensive knowledge of today's financial services marketplace is preferred in freelancers. Research the local Transamerica branch in your area and look for newsworthy subject matter. Areas most open to freelancers are profiles of Transamerica's top sellers—usually not sought out but occasionally, if the author has done the research; new product introductions—read industry trades and keep track of competitors; and selling techniques—having been a line person always helps."

_____ _International Affairs_

These publications cover global relations, international trade, economic analysis and philosophy for business executives and government officials involved in foreign affairs. Consumer publications on related subjects are listed in Politics and World Affairs.

FOREIGN AFFAIRS, 58 E. 68th St., New York NY 10021. (212)734-0400. Editor: William G. Hyland. 100% freelance written. For academics, businessmen (national and international), government, educational and cultural readers especially interested in international affairs of a political nature. Published 5 times/year. Circ. 90,000. Pays on publication. Publishes ms an average of 3 months after acceptance. Buys all rights. Pays kill fee. Byline given. Photocopied submissions OK. Electronic submissions OK via 8" disk: Wang; Modem (300-1200 baud), but requires hard copy also. Computer printout submissions acceptable; prefers letter-quality to dot-matrix. Reports in 6 weeks. Submit complete ms. Sample copy $5 postpaid.
Nonfiction: "Articles dealing with international affairs; political, educational, cultural, economic, scientific, philosophical and social sciences. Develop an original idea in depth, with a strong thesis usually leading to policy recommendations. Serious analyses by qualified authors on subjects with international appeal." Buys 25 unsolicited mss/year. Submit complete ms. Length: 5,000 words. Pays approximately $500.
Tips: "We like the writer to include his/her qualifications for writing on the topic in question (educational, past publications, relevant positions or honors), and a clear summation of the article: the argument (or area examined), and the writer's policy conclusions."

JOURNAL OF DEFENSE & DIPLOMACY, Defense and Diplomacy, Inc., 6819 Elm St., McLean VA 22101. (703)448-1338. Editor: Lois M. Blake. 50% freelance written. "Publication credentials not necessary for consideration." Monthly publication covering international affairs and defense. "The *Journal* is a sophisticated, slick publication that analyzes international affairs for decision makers—heads of state, key government officials, defense industry executives—who have little time to pore through all the details themselves." Circ. 20,000. Pays on publication. Publishes ms an average of 3 months after acceptance. Byline given. Offers 10% kill fee. Buys first rights and second serial (reprint) rights. Simultaneous queries, and simultaneous, photocopied, and previously published submissions OK. Computer printout submissions acceptable; prefers letter-quality to dot-matrix. Reports in 1 month on queries; 2 months on mss. Sample copy $5 (includes postage); writer's guidelines for business size envelope and 1 first class stamp.
Nonfiction: Book excerpts, general interest (strategy and tactics, diplomacy and defense matters), interview/profile, opinion and photo feature. "Decision-makers are looking for intelligent, straightforward assessments. We are looking for clear, concise writing on articles with international appeal. While we have accepted articles that deal with U.S. decisions, there is always an international aspect to the subject." No articles that focus solely on the United States. Buys 24 mss/year. Send complete ms. Length: 2,000-4,000 words. Pays $250. Sometimes pays the expenses of writers on assignment.
Photos: Reviews color and b&w photos. No additional payment is offered for photos sent with ms.
Columns/Departments: Speaking Out (1,000 to 3,000-word "point of view" piece analyzing any current topic of widespread interest); Materiel (a technical discussion of current and upcoming weapons systems); Books (reviews of books on world politics, history, biography and military matters); interview ("We constantly need interviews with important international figures. We are always looking for the non-U.S. interview."). Buys 12 mss/year. Query with published clips. Length: 1,500-3,000 words. Pays $100-250.
Tips: "We depend on experts in the field for most of the articles that we use. As long as a manuscript demonstrates that the writer knows the subject well, we are willing to consider anyone for publication. The most frequent mistake made by writers in completing an article for us is writing in too technical or too official a style. We want to be very readable. We are looking for writers who are able to digest complex subjects and make them interesting and lively. We need writers who can discuss complicated and technical weapons systems in clear non-technical ways."

THE NATIONAL REPORTER, Box 647, Ben Franklin Station, Washington DC 20044. (202)328-0178. Editor: John Kelly. 30% freelance written. Bimonthly magazine covering the CIA, IMF, World Bank, foreign policy and corporations. Circ. 6,000. Pays on publication. Publishes ms an average of 2 months after acceptance. Byline given. Buys all rights. Submit seasonal/holiday material 1 month in advance. Photocopied and previously published submissions OK. Computer printout submissions acceptable; no dot-matrix. Reports in 2 weeks on queries; 3 weeks on mss. Free sample copy and writer's guidelines.

Nonfiction: Expose (government and U.S. corporation), humor, interview/profile, personal experience and photo feature. No "right wing" articles. Buys 10 mss/year. Send complete ms. Length: 2,500-5,000 words. Pays $50 maximum.

Columns/Departments: News Not In the News (important stories ignored by the mainstream media). Buys 10 mss/year. Send complete ms. Length: 1,000 words maximum. Pays $20 maximum.

Fiction: Experimental, historical and novel excerpts. Buys 2 mss/year. Send complete ms. Length: 1,500 words maximum. Pays $25 minimum.

Poetry: Avant-garde and free verse. Buys 7 poems/year. Submit 5 poems maximum. Line length open. Pays $25 maximum.

Fillers: Rose Audette, editor. Clippings, jokes, gags, anecdotes, short humor and newsbreaks. Buys 20/year. Length: 500 maximum. Pays $10 maximum.

Tips: "We want well written and fully documented materials."

PROBLEMS OF COMMUNISM, U.S. Information Agency, P/PMP, Room 402, 301 4th St., Washington DC 20547. (202)485-2230. Editor: Paul A. Smith Jr. Works with a small number of new/unpublished writers each year. For scholars and decision makers in all countries of the world with higher education and a serious interest in foreign area studies and international relations. Circ. 29,300 (English language); 5,600 (Spanish language). Not copyrighted. Pays 20% kill fee. Byline given. Pays on acceptance. Publishes ms an average of 2 months after acceptance. Usually buys all rights. Photocopied submissions OK. Computer printout submissions acceptable; prefers letter-quality to dot-matrix. Reports in 3 months. Free sample copy.

Nonfiction: "*Problems of Communism* is one of a very few journals devoted to objective, dispassionate discourse on a highly unobjective, passionately debated phenomenon: communism. It is maintained as a forum in which qualified observers can contribute to a clearer understanding of the sources, nature and direction of change in the areas of its interest. It has no special emphasis or outlook and represents no partisan point of view. Standards of style are those appropriate to the field of international scholarship and journalism. We use intellectually rigorous studies of East/West relations, and/or related political, economic, social and strategic trends in the U.S.S.R., China and their associated states and movements. Length is usually 5,000 words. Essay reviews of 1,500 words cover new books offering significant information and analysis. Emphasis throughout *Problems of Communism* is on original research, reliability of sources and perceptive insights. We do not publish political statements or other forms of advocacy or apologetics for particular forms of belief." Buys 60-70 mss/year. Query or submit complete ms. Pays $600/article; $300/essay reviews.

Photos: Pays minimum $45 for b&w glossy prints.

Jewelry

AMERICAN JEWELRY MANUFACTURER, 8th Floor, 825 7th Ave., New York NY 10019. (212)245-7555. Editor: Steffan Aletti. 5% freelance written. For jewelry manufacturers, as well as manufacturers of supplies and tools for the jewelry industry; their representatives, wholesalers and agencies. Monthly. Circ. 5,000. Buys all rights (with exceptions). Publishes ms an average of 5 months after acceptance. Byline given. Will consider photocopied submissions. Computer printout submissions acceptable. Submit seasonal/holiday material 3 months in advance. Reports in 1 month. Free sample copy and writer's guidelines.

Nonfiction: "Topical articles on manufacturing; company stories; economics (e.g., rising gold prices). Story must inform or educate the manufacturer. Occasional special issues on timely topics, e.g., gold; occasional issues on specific processes in casting and plating. We reject material that is not specifically pointed at our industry; e.g., articles geared to jewelry retailing or merchandising, not to manufacturers." Informational, how-to, interview, profile, historical, expose, successful business operations, new product, merchandising techniques and technical. Buys 5-10 unsolicited mss/year. Query. Length: open. Payment "usually around $50/printed page."

Photos: B&w photos purchased with ms. 5x7 minimum.

Tips: "The most frequent mistake made by writers in completing an article for us is unfamiliarity with the magazine—retail or merchandising oriented articles are sent in. Query first; we have accepted some general business articles, but not many."

CANADIAN JEWELLER, 777 Bay St., Toronto, Ontario M5W 1A7 Canada. Editor: Simon Hally. Monthly magazine for members of the jewelry trade, primarily retailers. Circ. 6,000. Pays on acceptance. Buys first Canadian serial rights.
Nonfiction: Wants "stories on the jewelry industry internationally." Query. Length: 200-2,000 words. Pays $40-500.
Photos: Reviews 5x7 and 8x10 b&w prints and 35mm and 2¼x2¼ color transparencies. "We pay more if usable photos accompany ms. Payment is based on space used in the book including both text and photos."

THE DIAMOND REGISTRY BULLETIN, 30 W. 47th St., New York NY 10036. Editor-in-Chief: Joseph Schlussel. 15% freelance written. Monthly newsletter. Pays on publication. Buys all rights. Submit seasonal/holiday material 1 month in advance. Simultaneous and previously published submissions OK. Computer printout submissions acceptable; prefers letter-quality to dot-matrix. Reports in 3 weeks. Sample copy $5.
Nonfiction: Prevention advice (on crimes against jewelers); how-to (ways to increase sales in diamonds, improve security, etc.); and interview (of interest to diamond dealers or jewelers). Submit complete ms. Length: 50-500 words. Pays $10-150.
Tips: "We seek ideas to increase sales of diamonds."

THE ENGRAVERS JOURNAL, Davis, Farrell & Associates, Inc., Box 318, 26 Summit St., Brighton MI 48116. (313)229-5725. Co-Publisher and Managing Editor: Michael J. Davis. 15% freelance written. Works with a small number of new/unpublished writers each year. A bimonthly magazine covering the recognition and identification industry (engraving, marking devices, awards, jewelry, and signage.) "We provide practical information for the education and advancement of our readers, mainly retail business owners." Pays on acceptance. Publishes ms an average of 1 year after acceptance. Byline given "only if writer is recognized authority." Buys all rights (usually). Query with published clips and resume. Photocopied and previously published submissions OK. Computer printout submissions OK. Computer printout submissions acceptable; prefers letter-quality to dot-matrix. Reports in 2 weeks. Free writer's guidelines; sample copy to "those who send writing samples with inquiry."
Nonfiction: General interest (industry-related); how-to (small business subjects, increase sales, develop new markets, use new sales techniques, etc.); interview/profile; new product; photo feature (a particularly outstanding signage system); and technical. No general overviews of the industry. Buys 12 mss/year. Query with writing samples "published or not," or "send samples and resume to be considered for assignments on speculation." Length: 1,000-5,000 words. Pays $75-250, depending on writer's skill and expertise in handling subject.
Photos: Send photos with query. Reviews 8x10 prints. Pays variable rate. Captions, model release and identifiction of subjects required.
Tips: "Articles should always be down to earth, practical and thoroughly cover the subject with authority. We do not want the 'textbook' writing approach, vagueness, or theory—our readers look to us for sound practical information."

WATCH AND CLOCK REVIEW, 2403 Champa St., Denver CO 80205. (303)296-1600. Managing Editor: Jayne L. Barrick. 20% freelance written. The magazine of watch/clock sales and service. Monthly magazine; 68 pages. Circ. 16,000. Pays on publication. Buys first rights only. Byline given. Submit seasonal/holiday material 3 months in advance. Reports in 3 weeks. Free sample copy.
Nonfiction: Articles on successful watch/clock manufacturers and retailers, merchandising and display, and profiles of industry leaders. Buys 15 mss/year. Query. Length: 1,000-2,000 words. Pays $100-250.
Photos: Submit photo material with accompanying ms. No additional payment for b&w glossy prints. Captions preferred; model release required. Buys first serial rights.
Columns/Departments: Buys 7 mss/issue. Pays $150-200. Open to suggestions for new columns/departments.
Tips: "Brevity is helpful in a query. Find the right subject—an interesting clock shop, a jewelry store with unique watch displays, a street clock of antiquarian interest, etc."

ALWAYS submit mss or queries with a stamped, self-addressed envelope (SASE) within your country or International Reply Coupons (IRCs) purchased from the post office for other countries.

Journalism

Journalism magazines cover the business and creative ends of writing. Even if you never send a query to one, you'll see how other writers approach their work and learn about new marketing strategies and markets. Journalism magazine editors need writers whose experiences will be an inspiration to new writers. They also need writers who can report new trends and markets for *their* readers. Both paying and nonpaying markets of the writing trade are included here.

THE AMERICAN SCREENWRITER, Grasshopper Productions, Inc., Box 67, Manchaca TX 78652. (512)282-2749. Editor: Gerald J. LePage. 25% freelance written. Eager to work with new/unpublished writers. A bimonthly newsletter covering scriptwriting for the screen and TV. "We address scriptwriters who ask for help through our script evaluation program. We aim at writers who are struggling to find their place in the market." Circ. 100 and growing. Pays by arrangement with author. Foreign publication residuals guaranteed. Publishes ms an average of 2 months after acceptance. Byline given. Buys all rights. Submit seasonal/holiday material 2 months in advance. Simultaneous queries OK. Reports in 1 month. Sample copy $1.25; writer's guidelines for SAE and 1 first class stamp.
Nonfiction: Book excerpts, interview/profile, and personal experience related to scriptwriting. "No sophisticated material that oozes of past films which require reader having seen them." Query with published clips. Length: 300-500 words. Pays 2-10¢/word; interviews pay $50; pays $30/article.
Tips: "We welcome journalists with screenwriter interview material. We want 'visual' writing—short, comprehensive articles that bring home a problematical point in less than five minute's reading. Suggest writers study publication."

BOOK ARTS REVIEW, The Center for Book Arts, 626 Broadway, New York NY 10012. (212)460-9768. Managing Editor: Bryan R. Johnson. "Staff written only."

BOOK DEALERS WORLD, American Bookdealers Exchange, Box 2525, La Mesa CA 92041. (619)462-3297. Editorial Director: Al Galasso. Senior Editor: Cynthia Schubert. 50% freelance written. Quarterly magazine covering writing, self-publishing and marketing books by mail. Circ. 20,000. Pays on publication. Publishes ms an average of 3 months after acceptance. Byline given. Buys first serial rights and second serial (reprint) rights to material originally published elsewhere. Simultaneous and previously published submissions OK. Computer printout submissions acceptable; no dot-matrix. Reports in 1 month. Sample copy for $1.
Nonfiction: Book excerpts (writing, mail order, direct mail, publishing); how-to (home business by mail, advertising); and interview/profile (of successful self-publishers). Positive articles on self-publishing, new writing angles, marketing, etc. Buys 10 mss/year. Send complete ms. Length: 1,000-1,500 words. Pays $25-50.
Columns/Departments: Print Perspective (about new magazines and newsletters); Small Press Scene (news about small press activities); and Self-Publisher Profile (on successful self-publishers and their marketing strategy). Buys 20 mss/year. Send complete ms. Length: 250-1,000 words. Pays $5-20.
Fillers: Clippings. Fillers concerning writing, publishing or books. Buys 6/year. Length: 100-250 words. Pays $3-10.
Tips: "Query first. Get a sample copy of the magazine."

‡BOOKS AND RELIGION, Editorial Office, The Divinity School, Duke University, Durham NC 27706. (919)684-3569. Publisher: Dennis Campbell. Editor: Christopher Walters-Bugbee. 75% freelance written. Works with a small number of new/unpublished writers each year. Tabloid published monthly except July and August, reviewing religion—ecumenically conceived—and related fields. Circ. 15,000. "We do not pay for reviews. Reviewer keeps book." Publishes ms an average of 1 month after acceptance. Byline given. Submit seasonal/holiday material 3 months in advance. Reports in 1 month. Sample copy available from: *Books and Religion*, The Divinity School, Duke University, Durham NC 27706.
Nonfiction: Book reviews. "Submit qualifications for reviewing serious works." Pays the expenses of writers on assignment.
Fiction: Query. "Only religious thematic material, broadly understood and not longer than 2,000 words." Purchases first serial rights and second serial rights for both excerpts.

BYLINE, Box 130596, Edmond OK 73013. (405)348-3325. Executive Editor/Publisher: Marcia Preston. Managing Editor: Kathryn Fanning. 90% freelance written. Eager to work with new/unpublished writers. Monthly magazine for writers and poets. "We stress encouragement of beginning writers." Publishes ms an average of 6 months after acceptance. Byline given. Buys first North American serial rights. Reports within 1 month. Sample copy $3; writer's guidelines for SASE.

Nonfiction: How-to, humor, inspirational, personal experience, *all* connected with writing and selling. Read magazine for special departments. Buys approximately 60 mss/year. Prefers queries; will read complete mss. Length: 50-2,000 words. Pays $5-100; usual rate for features is $35, on acceptance.

Fiction: Mysteries or general fiction connected (at least remotely) with writers or writing. Send complete ms: 1,000-3,000 words. Pays $50 on acceptance.

Poetry: Any style, on a writing theme. Preferred length: 4-36 lines. Pays $3-5 on publication plus free issue.

CALIFORNIA PUBLISHER, Suite 1040, 1127 11th St., Sacramento CA 95814. (916)443-5991. Editor: Jackie Nava. 5% freelance written. Monthly tabloid read by publishers, journalism teachers, editors and managers in newspaper publishing in California. Publishes ms an average of 2 months after acceptance. Byline given. Buys first and second (reprint) rights. Computer printout submissions acceptable; prefers letter-quality to dot-matrix.

Nonfiction: In-depth stories or articles designed to inform and amuse California newspaper publishers. Sample topics include: newsprint shortage, changing role of papers, historical profiles on California journalism greats, success stories, role of minorities in the newspaper field, profiles on California newspapers, and technological advances. No general humorous material. "If it isn't specific to *California* journalism, we don't want it." Query. Length: 2,000 words maximum. Pays $25-30.

Photos: Reviews b&w glossy prints.

Tips: "Go on; query us. Stories used will be read by all the newspaper publishers who count in the state of California. We'd like to showcase first effort, good writing talent."

CANADIAN AUTHOR & BOOKMAN, Canadian Authors Association, 24 Ryerson Ave., Toronto, Ontario M5T 2P3 Canada. Editor: Anne Osborne. 100% freelance written. Prefers to work with published/established writers. "For writers—all ages, all levels of experience." Quarterly magazine; 32 pages. Circ. 5,000. Pays on publication. Publishes ms an average of 6 months after acceptance. Buys first Canadian rights. Byline given. Written queries only. Computer printout submissions acceptable; prefers letter-quality to dot-matrix. Sample copy $4.50.

Nonfiction: How-to (on writing, selling; the specifics of the different genres—what they are and how to write them); informational (the writing scene—who's who and what's what); interview (on writers, mainly leading ones, but also those with a story that can help others write and sell more often); and opinion. No personal, lightweight writing experiences; no fillers. Query with immediate pinpointing of topic, length (if ms is ready), and writer's background. Length: 800-1,500 words. Pays $25/printed page.

Photos: "We're after an interesting-looking magazine, and graphics are a decided help." State availability of photos with query. Offers $5/photo for b&w photos accepted with ms. Buys one-time rights.

Poetry: High quality. "Major poets publish with us—others need to be as good." Buys 40 poems/year. Pays $5.

Tips: "We dislike material that condescends to its reader and articles that advocate an adversarial approach to writer/editor relationships. We agree that there is a time and place for such an approach, but good sense should prevail. If the writer is writing to a Canadian freelance writer, the work will likely fall within our range of interest."

CANADIAN WRITER'S JOURNAL, Ronald J. Cooke Ltd., 58 Madsen Ave., Beaconsfield, Quebec H9W 4T7 Canada. (514)697-9315. Editor: Ronald S. Cooke. 50% freelance written. "We will accept well-written articles for and by young or experienced writers." A bimonthly digest-size magazine for writers. Circ. 3,000. Pays on publication. Byline given. Buys one-time rights. "We seldom use anything pertaining to holidays." Computer printout submissions acceptable; no dot-matrix. Reports in 2 weeks on queries; 1 month on mss. Sample copy $2.

Nonfiction: How-to articles for writers. Buys 30-35 mss/year. Query. Length: 500-1,000 words. "Would welcome an article on writing plays."

Tips: "We prefer short, how-to articles; 1,000 words is our limit and we prefer 700 words."

CHILDREN'S LITERATURE, The Children's Literature Foundation, Box 370, Windham Center CT 06280. (203)456-1900. Editor: Francelia Butler. Managing Editor: John C. Wandell. 90% freelance written. Annual; 250 pages. Circ. 3,500. Pays in reprints. Publishes ms an average of 1 month after acceptance. Byline given. Phone queries OK. Submit seasonal/holiday material 1 year in advance. Reports in 1 month.

Nonfiction: Scholarly or critical articles *only*—not creative work. Manuscripts must conform to MLA Handbook. Uses 20 mss/issue. Query or send complete ms. Length: 5,000 words.

Photos: State availability of photos. Uses 4x5 or 8x10 b&w glossy prints. Captions and permission to publish required.

Columns/Departments: Book review articles (send to Prof. John Cech, University of Florida, Gainesville FL 32611). Uses 20/year. Query. Length: 3,000 words. Open to suggestions for new columns/departments. **Tips:** "This is a scholarly journal."

THE CHRISTIAN WRITER, The Professional Writing Magazine for Christians, Box 5650, Lakeland FL 33807. (813)644-3548. Editor: Thomas A. Noton. Associate Editor: Jana Huss. 50% freelance written. Prefers to work with published/established writers. Monthly writing magazine aimed at a Christian audience. "We reach Christians who desire to write or are writers. Our aim is to help create the professional approach to this craft." Circ. 10,000. Publishes ms an average of 4 months after acceptance. Acquires first serial rights; no reprints. Submit seasonal/holiday material 4 months in advance. Simultaneous queries and photocopied submissions OK. Computer printout submissions acceptable. Reports in 1 month on queries; 6 weeks on mss. Sample copy $2.50. Writer's guidelines require #10 SAE with 1 first class stamp.
Nonfiction: How-to (specifics on authoring, selling, related subjects); humor (some); inspirational (limited); interview/profile (top Christian authors); new product (electronic writing); and personal experience (some). Material on conferences, workshops, clubs, etc. for annual Service Guide issue. "We receive too many 'this is my life' articles. We want more specific articles helping others overcome specialized problems in authoring." Buys 36-50 mss/year. Query with writing credits. Length: 800-2,500 words. Pays $10 minimum for fillers to $200 for feature articles. Payment depends on need and article. Sometimes pays expenses of writers on assignment.
Tips: "We're looking for freelancers who have answers for specific problems in writing, marketing, querying, rewriting, or editing. We are only interested in professionalism as it applies to the craft of writing. Although we use the Christian influence, we do not deal with it directly. We deal with the craft, its problems and answers. Attention to the style of the regular columnists will give a freelance author a 'feel' for what we like."

‡**CHRISTIAN WRITERS NEWSLETTER,** Suite 9C, 300 E. 34th St., New York NY 10016. (212)686-5737. Editor: William H. Gentz. 50% freelance written. A bimonthly newsletter. "We are an opportunity for the sharing of information, inspiration, markets, and resources for writers who are interested primarily in writing for Christian-oriented markets." Circ. 500. Pays on acceptance. Publishes ms an average of 4 months after acceptance. Byline given. Buys first North American serial rights and second serial (reprint) rights. Submit seasonal/holiday material 4 months in advance. Photocopied submissions and previously published submissions OK. Computer printout submissions acceptable; no dot-matrix. Reports in 1 week on queries; 2 weeks on mss. Sample copy for #10 SAE with 1 first class stamp.
Nonfiction: Book excerpts, how-to, humor, inspirational, interview/profile, opinion (does not mean letters to the editor), personal experience and religious. No material that does not conern writers. Buys 12 mss/year. Send complete ms. Length: 300-1,000 words. Pays $10-25 for assigned articles; pays $5-20 for unsolicited articles.
Columns/Departments: Buys 6 assigned mss/year. Send complete ms. Pays $25-30.
Poetry: Free verse, light verse and traditional. No poetry not on the subject of the newsletter—Christian writing or related interests. Buys 4 mss/year. Submit maximum 3 poems. Length: 4-20 lines. Pays $5-10.
Fillers: Anecdotes and short humor. Buys 5/year. Length: 15-30 words. Pays $5.
Tips: "Most of our material comes from subscribers who are currently writing for Christian publications and understand the craft and the market. Others are welcome, but they must write on the subject of the publication—*articles* that tell how you do it, what makes for success, how you deal with failures, rejections, etc., in the Christian writing marketplace."

COLLEGE MEDIA REVIEW, Dept. of Journalism, Ball State University, Munice IN 47306. Contact: Lillian Lodge-Kopenhaver, Dept. of Communication, Florida International University, North Miami FL 33181. 100% freelance written. Eager to work with new/unpublished writers. Quarterly magazine for members of College Media Advisers and staffs, editors and faculty advisers of college publications, journalism professors, and others interested in student communication media. Circ. 1,200. Acquires all rights. No payment. Publishes ms an average of 5 months after acceptance. Photocopied submissions OK. Computer printout submissions acceptable; prefers letter-quality to dot-matrix. Reports in 5 months. Sample copy $2.50; free writer's guidelines.
Nonfiction: Articles by, about and of interest to college publications advisers, staffs and editors. Articles should focus on editing, advising and producing college newspapers, yearbooks and magazines and operating electronic media, including radio, television and cable. "We like to use articles reporting research in publications and journalism skills and well-thought-out opinion and essays on issues in the student media. Legal research specifically is welcome. Articles should be in a readable style with adequate attribution but without overuse of footnotes." Topical subjects of interest include increasing income, reducing costs, promoting publications, use of new technology, censorship cases at private colleges, tips on purchasing new equipment, how-to articles, and advances in techniques and resources. Query or submit complete ms. Submit 2 copies of all mss. Length: 3,000 words maximum.
Photos: B&w glossy photos used with ms. Captions required.

COLUMBIA JOURNALISM REVIEW, 700 Journalism Bldg., Columbia University, New York NY 10027. (212)280-5595. Managing Editor: Gloria Cooper. "We welcome queries concerning media issues and performance. *CJR* also publishes book reviews. We emphasize in-depth reporting, critical analysis and good writing. All queries are read by editors."

‡**THE COMICS JOURNAL, THE Magazine of News and Criticism**, Fantagraphics, Inc., 4359 Cornell Rd., Agoura CA 91301. (818)706-7606. Editor: Gary G. Groth. Managing Editor: Thomas J. Heintjes. 90% freelance written. A monthly magazine covering the comic book industry. "Comic books can appeal intellectually and emotionally to an adult audience, and can express ideas that other media are inherently incapable of." Circ. 9,500. Pays on publication. Publishes ms an average of 2 months after acceptance. Byline given. Buys first rights. Submit seasonal/holiday material 5 months in advance. Photocopied submissions OK. Computer printout submissions acceptable; prefers letter-quality to dot-matrix. Reports in 2 weeks. Sample copy $3.50.
Nonfiction: Essays, exposé, historical/nostalgic, interview/profile, opinion and magazine reviews. Buys 120 mss/year. Send complete ms. Length: 500-3,000 words. Pays 1.5¢/word; writers may request trade for merchandise. Pays the expenses of writers on assignment.
Photos: Send photos with submission. Offers no additional payment for photos accepted with ms. Identification of subjects required. Buys one-time rights.
Columns/Departments: Opening Shots (brief commentary, often humorous), 1,000 words; Executive Forum (written by publishers offering opinions on various subjects), 3,000 words; The Comics Library (graphic review), and Ethics (examining the ethics of the comic-book industry), both 3,000 words. Buys 60 mss/year. Send complete ms. Pays 1.5¢/word.
Tips: "Have an intelligent, sophisticated, critical approach to writing about comic books."

CREATIVE YEARS, Coronado Publishers, #40, 2490 SW 14th Dr., Gainesville FL 32608. (904)373-7445. Editor: Eloise Cozens Henderson. Associate Editor: Mary Onkka. 20% freelance written. Bimonthly magazine for new and unpublished writers. Circ. 2,000. Pays on publication. Publishes ms an average of 9 months after acceptance. Acquires one-time rights. Submit seasonal/holiday material 3 months in advance. Simultaneous submissions OK. Reports in 3 weeks on queries; 3 months on mss. Sample copy $2; writer's guidelines for SASE.
Nonfiction: General interest, historical/nostalgic, interview, humor, inspirational, opinion and personal experience. "We have an overload of writer's advice. We now feature experiences and articles by disabled people, i.e., 'Profiles in Courage.' " No obscenity, profanity, or liquor/drug related articles. Buys 30 mss/year. Length: 450-500 words. Send complete ms. Pays presently in copies only.
Fiction: Humorous, historical and religious. No obscenity, profanity, liquor/drug related mss. Buys 30 mss/year. Length: 450-500 words. Send complete ms. Pays in copies only.
Poetry: Light verse, traditional. No far out, agnostic, atheist, etc. poetry. Buys 12 poems/year. Pays in copies only.
Tips: "We use mostly material of beginning writers. We especially need Biblical quiz and other puzzle material. We are also seeking short articles about old times in sports (Babe Ruth, Ty Cobb, etc.)."

CROSS-CANADA WRITERS' QUARTERLY, The Canadian Literary Writer's Magazine, Cross-Canada Writers, Inc., Box 277, Station F, Toronto, Ontario M4Y 2L7 Canada. (416)690-0917. Editor: Ted Plantos. Associate Editor: Susan Ioannou. 80% freelance written. Prefers to work with published/established writers. A quarterly literary writer's magazine covering Canadian writing within an international context. Circ. 2,500. Pays on publication. Publishes ms an average of 1 year after acceptance. Byline given. Buys first North American serial rights. Submit seasonal/holiday material 6 months in advance. Photocopied submissions OK. Computer printout submissions acceptable. Reports in 3 weeks on queries; 2 months on mss. Sample copy $3.95, 9x12 SAE, and 85¢ Canadian postage or 2 IRCs.
Nonfiction: Essays, articles on literary aesthetics and interview/profile (established authors, editors, publishers—in-depth with photos). "Articles and interviews must have depth, be thought-provoking and offer insights into the creative and working processes of literature." No how-to's for beginners, or on nonliterary kinds of writing. Buys 4-10 mss/year. Query or send complete ms. "Each case is different. With an interview, a query could save time and work. A straight article we would have to read."
Photos: State availability of accompanying photos with query or send photos with ms, 5x7 b&w prints. Captions, model release, and identification of subjects required. Buys one-time rights.
Fiction: Contact the editor. Mainstream. No slight material—mere anecdotes rather than fully developed stories. Buys 4-8 mss/year. Send complete ms. Length: 1,000-3,000 words. Payment on publication.
Poetry: Poetry Editor. Free verse, haiku and traditional (if well-done). No concrete poetry, "diary excerpts" merely, highly obscure private poems or doggerel. Buys 40-50 poems/year. Submit maximum 10 poems. Length: 100 lines maximum "in exceptional cases." Offers $5/poem as payment.

Tips: "The writer should submit a sample to us. The most frequent mistakes made by writers in completing an article for us are misunderstanding of slant, and missing the opportunity for in-depth analysis. We want greater emphasis on literary essays on the aesthetics of writing."

DUSTBOOK, SMALL PRESS REVIEW, Box 100, Paradise CA 95969. Editor: Len Fulton. Associate Editor: Ellen Ferber. Monthly for "people interested in small presses and magazines, current trends and data; many libraries." Circ. 3,000. Byline given. "Query if you're unsure." Reports in 2 months. Free sample copy.
Nonfiction: News, short reviews, photos, short articles on small magazines and presses. Uses how-to, personal experience, interview, profile, spot news, historical, think, photo, and coverage of merchandising techniques. Accepts 50-200 mss/year. Length: 100-200 words.
Photos: Uses b&w glossy photos.

EDITOR & PUBLISHER, 11 W. 19th St., New York NY 10011. Editor: Robert U. Brown. 10% freelance written. Weekly magazine; 60 pages. For newspaper publishers, editors, executives, employees and others in communications, marketing, advertising, etc. Circ. 29,000. Pays on publication. Publishes ms an average of 2 weeks after acceptance. Buys first serial rights. Computer printout submissions acceptable; prefers letter-quality to dot-matrix. Sample copy.
Nonfiction: John P. Consoli, managing editor. Uses newspaper business articles and news items; also newspaper personality features and printing technology. Query.
Fillers: "Amusing typographical errors found in newspapers." Pays $5.

THE EDITORIAL EYE, Focusing on Editorial Standards and Practices, Editorial Experts, Inc., Suite 400, 85 S. Bragg St., Alexandria VA 22312. (703)642-3040. Editor: Bruce Boston. Managing Editor: Eleanor Johnson. 5% freelance written. Prefers to work with published/established writers. Monthly professional newsletter on editorial subjects: writing, editing, proofreading, and levels of editing. "Our readers are professional publications people. Use journalistic style." Circ. 1,800. Pays on acceptance. Publishes ms an average of 3 months after acceptance. Byline given. Kill fee determined for each assignment. Buys first North American serial rights. "We retain the right to use articles in our training division and in an anthology of collected articles." Submit seasonal/holiday material 3 months in advance. Computer printout submissions acceptable; prefers letter-quality to dot-matrix. Reports in 1 month. Sample copy for SASE and 39¢ postage; writer's guidelines for SAE and 1 first class stamp.
Nonfiction: Editorial problems, issues, standards, practices, and techniques; publication management; publishing technology; style, grammar and usage. No word games, vocabulary building, language puzzles, or jeremiads on how the English language is going to blazes. Buys 10 mss/year. Query. Length: 300-1,000. Pays $25-50.
Tips: "We seek mostly lead articles written by people in the publications field about the practice of publications work. Our style is journalistic with a light touch (not cute). We are interested in submissions on the craft of editing, levels of edit, editing by computer, publications management, indexing, lexicography, usages, proofreading. Our back issue list provides a good idea of the kinds of articles we run."

‡EDITORS' FORUM, Editors' Forum Publishing Company, Box 1806, Kansas City MO 64141. (913)236-9235. Editor: Jay H. Lawrence. Managing Editor: William R. Brinton. 20% freelance written. Works with a small number of new/unpublished writers each year. A monthly newsletter geared toward communicators, particularly those involved in the editing and publication of newsletters and company publications. Circ. 700. Pays on publication. Publishes ms an average of 3 months after acceptance. Byline given. Offers 25% kill fee. Not copyrighted. Buys first North American serial rights, second serial (reprint) rights, and makes work-for-hire assignments. Photocopied submissions OK. Previously published submissions OK depending on content. Computer printout submissions acceptable; no dot-matrix. Reports in 2 weeks on queries. Sample copy and writer's guidelines for # 10 SAE with 39¢ postage.
Nonfiction: How-to on editing and writing, etc. "With the advent of computer publishing, *EF* is running a regular high tech column on desk top publishing, software, etc. We can use articles on the latest techniques in computer publishing. Not interested in anything that does not have a direct effect on writing and editing newsletters. This is a how-to newsletter." Buys 22 mss/year. Query. Length: 250-1,000 words. Pays $20/page maximum.
Photos: State availability of photos with submission. Reviews contact sheets. Offers $5/photo. Captions, model releases and identification of subjects required. Buys one-time rights.
Tips: "We are necessarily interested in articles pertaining to the newsletter business. That would include articles involving writing skills, layout and makeup, the use of pictures and other graphics to brighten up our reader's publication, and an occasional article on how to put out a good publication inexpensively."

‡FICTION WRITERS MONTHLY, Romantic Times Publishing Group, 163 Joralemon St., Box 1234, Brooklyn Heights NY 11201. (718)237-1097. Editor: Donna Meyer. 85% freelance written. A monthly magazine covering fiction writing techniques, marketing and news. "We are a straightforward, nuts-and-bolts, how-to write publication for writers of popular fiction. Our goals are to make writing easier, more fun, and more profitable for our readers as well as to remind them that they are not alone in their strange desire to write publishable popular fiction." Circ. 1,200. Publishes ms an average of 3 months after acceptance. Byline given. Buys first rights, one-time rights, second serial (reprint) rights, or simultaneous rights. Submit seasonal/holiday material 3 months in advance. Simultaneous, photocopied, and previously published submissions OK. Electronic submissions OK via IBM-PC XT with Perfect Writer. Computer printout submissions acceptable; prefers letter-quality to dot-matrix. Reports in 2 months. Sample copy $5.

Nonfiction: Book excerpts (on how to write); Essays ("one writer's opinion" on some aspect of popular fiction publishing); how-to (on writing popular fiction); humor (on fiction writing or a publishing experience); inspirational ("I did it, so can you"); interview/profile (with authors); new product (computers for authors); opinion; personal experience (about writing); travel (specifically for writers); and research for writers. No fiction. We publish articles about popular fiction, but not fiction itself. Buys 60 mss/year. Query or send complete ms. Length: 500-2,000 words. Pays in contributor copies.

Photos: Send photos with submission. Reviews contact sheets and 5x7 b&w prints. Offers no additional payment for photos accepted with ms. Identification of subjects required. Buys one-time rights.

Columns/Departments: One Writer's Opinion (essay/opinion on any aspect of popular fiction writing and/or publishing); and The Research Report (new or unusual research sources—historical or contemporary—for popular fiction writers). Buys 24 mss/year. Send complete ms. Length: 500-1,000 words. Payment in copies.

Fillers: Anecdotes, facts, gags to be illustrated by cartoonist, newsbreaks and short humor. Buys 4-20/year. Length: 25-100 words. Pays in contributor's copies.

Tips: "The whole magazine except Market Update is open. New writers who have just made their first sale should send details to the First Sale section of our gossip column. It's great publicity. The best way to break in is with a good nuts and bolts how-to-write piece. Be specific. Use examples and a lively, inspiring, 'I did it, so can you' style."

FOLIO: The Magazine for Magazine Management, 6 River Bend, Box 4949, Stamford CT 06907. Editor-in-Chief: J. Hanson. "We are backlogged with submissions and prefer not to receive unsolicited submissions at this time."

FREELANCE WRITER'S REPORT, Cassell Communications Inc., Box 9844, Fort Lauderdale FL 33310. (305)485-0795. Editor: Dana K. Cassell. 15% freelance written. Prefers to work with published/established writers. Monthly newsletter covering writing and marketing advice for freelance writers. Pays on publication. Publishes ms an average of 6 months after acceptance. Byline given. Buys one-time rights. Submit seasonal/holiday material 2 months in advance. Simultaneous queries, and simultaneous, photocopied, and previously published submissions OK. Computer printout submissions OK; no dot-matrix. Reports in 1 month. Sample copy $2.50.

Nonfiction: Book excerpts (on writing profession); how-to (market, write, research); interview (of writers or editors); new product (only those pertaining to writers); photojournalism; promotion and administration of a writing business. No humor, fiction or poetry. Buys 36 mss/year. Query or send complete ms. Length: 500 words maximum. Pays 10¢/edited word.

Tips: "Write in terse newsletter style, eliminate flowery adjectives and edit mercilessly. Send something that will help writers increase profits from writing output—must be a proven method."

‡GEM'S NEWSLETTER FOR AUTHORS, Box 1417, Marietta GA 30061. (404)433-8091. Editor: (Mrs.) H.C. McGarity. 1% freelance written. Semiannual 4-page newsletter, primarily with market listings. "Publishes news of interest to writers, mostly who's buying/not buying or news of who's been published, poetry contests, etc." Circ. 300. Pays on acceptance. Publishes ms in "next issue." Byline given. Buys one-time rights. Simultaneous submissions OK. Computer printout submissions acceptable; prefers letter-quality to dot-matrix. Reports in 1 week on queries; 1 month on mss. Sample copy $1; free writer's guidelines.

Nonfiction: Opinion (current condition/trend of writing). No how-to-write articles. Buys 2-3 mss/year. Query. Length: 400-1,000 words. Pays 3-5¢/word.

‡GOOD NEWS, for Christians In The Media Or For Those Interested In The Media As A Ministry, Crown Creations Associates, Box 11626, St. Paul MN 55111-0626. Editor: Steven Mark Deyo. 50% freelance written. Works with a small number of new/unpublished writers each year. A quarterly newsletter "addressing Christianity in the news profession, and examining how Christians go about their jobs in journalism. It treats ethics, union dynamics, news issues, constitutional rights, media law and history and profiles Christians who exhibit excellence in their news profession." Circ. 500. Pays on publication. Publishes ms an average of 6 months after acceptance. Byline given. Buys first rights or second serial (reprint) rights. Submit seasonal/holiday material 6 months in advance. Photocopied and previously published submissions OK, originals and clips preferred. Electronic submissions OK via Apple Macintosh, standard modem procedure; but requires hard copy also. Computer printout submissions acceptable; prefers letter-quality to dot-matrix. Reports in 1 month on queries; 8 weeks on mss. Sample copy for # 10 SASE; writer's guidelines for # 10 SASE.

Nonfiction: Essays, exposé, general interest, historical, how-to, humor, inspirational, interview/profile, opinion, personal experience, photo feature, religious and travel. "No articles from folks who aren't journalists or who haven't professionally interviewed/profiled journalist(s). Articles must tie in a living Christian faith." Buys 6-8 mss/year. Query with or without published clips, or send complete ms. Length: 200-800 words. Pays up to 4 copies. Sometimes pays the expenses of writers on assignment.

Photos: Send photos with submission. Reviews contact sheets and 5x7 prints. Offers no additional payment for photos accepted with ms. Buys one-time rights.

Columns/Departments: News File (news rundown of issues/events involving Christianity in journalism), 20-100 words; Bureau Report (Christian-in-Media profile: professionalism on location), 200-800 words; and How Will They Hear . . .? (profile of coverage of Christian news angle missed by secular press), 200-800 words. Buys 6-8 mss/year. Query.

Fillers: Anecdotes, facts and newsbreaks. Acquires 10-20/year. Length: 20-100 words. Pays up to 2 copies.

Tips: "Be as professional as the journalist you profile. Be true to a scriptural Christian faith; use spiritual discernment. Go for issues where the church can have a particular answer the secular press seems to be missing. Be open to seeking out the moral/ethical/religious angle in news events that secular journalists pass by."

THE INKLING LITERARY JOURNAL, Inkling Publications, Inc., Box 128, Alexandria MN 56308. (612)762-2020. Editor: Marilyn Bailey. Associate Editor: Betty Ulrich. Managing Editor: John Hall. 30% freelance written. Monthly journal providing advice, guidance and inspiration for writers and poets. "The *Inkling* is both informative and motivational, providing a forum for writers. Well-written articles and timely market news are the main criteria." Circ. 3,000. Pays on publication. Publishes ms an average of 2 months after acceptance. Byline given. Buys first North American serial rights. Submit seasonal/holiday material 4 months in advance. Simultaneous queries OK. Electronic submissions OK if compatible with TRS 80 model III-DOS, MS-DOS or IBM PC-DOS. Computer printout submissions acceptable; prefers letter-quality to dot-matrix. Reports in 1 month on queries; 6 weeks on mss. Sample copy $2; writer's guidelines for business size SAE and 1 first class stamp.

Nonfiction: How-to (on the business and approach to writing); motivational; interview/profile; opinion; and personal experience. Buys 30-40 mss/year. Send complete ms. Length: 500-1,500 words. Pays $15-50.

Poetry: Avant-garde, free verse, haiku, light verse and traditional. "The *Inkling* runs two poetry contests each year—spring and fall: Winner and 2nd place cash prizes and two honorable mentions." Buys 20-30 poems/year. Submit maximum 3 poems. Length: 25 lines maximum. Pays $4-15.

Tips: "Articles must be *well* written and slanted toward the business (or commitment) of writing and/or being a writer. Interviews with established writers should be in-depth, particularly reporting interviewee's philosophy on writing, how (s)he got started, how (s)he 'does it.' Tape interviews, transcribe, then edit. Monthly 'theme' emphasizes a particular genre or type of writing. Opinion pieces (researched and authoritative) on any of the monthly themes welcomed. (Theme schedule available with guidelines.)"

JOURNALISM EDUCATOR, School of Journalism, University of North Carolina, Chapel Hill NC 27514. (919)962-4084. Editor: Thomas A. Bowers. 100% freelance written. Quarterly for journalism professors, administrators, and a growing number of professional journalists in the U.S. and Canada. Published by the Association for Education in Journalism and Mass Communication. Founded by the American Society of Journalism School Administrators. Does not pay. Byline given. Publishes ms an average of 10 months after acceptance. Computer printout submissions acceptable. Electronic submissions OK via AEJMC Forum or CompuServe.

Nonfiction: "We do accept some unsolicited manuscripts dealing with our publication's specialized area—problems of administration and teaching in journalism education. Because we receive more articles than we can use from persons working in this field, we do not need to encourage freelance materials, however. A writer, generally, would have to be in journalism/communications teaching or in some media work to have the background to write convincingly about the subjects this publication is interested in. The writer also should become familiar with the content of recent issues of this publication." Nothing not directly connected with journalism education at the four-year college and university level. Length: 2,500 words maximum. No payment.

JOURNALISM QUARTERLY, School of Journalism, Ohio University, Athens OH 45701. (614)594-5013. Editor: Guido H. Stempel III. 100% freelance written. Eager to work with new/unpublished writers. "We have 150-175 writers represented each year." For members of the Association for Education in Journalism and Mass Communication and other academicians and journalists. Quarterly. No payment. Publishes ms an average of 8 months after acceptance. Usually acquires all rights. Circ. 4,200. Photocopied submissions OK. Computer printout submissions acceptable; no dot-matrix. Reports in 3 months. Free writer's guidelines.

Nonfiction: Research in mass communication. Recent article includes "Understanding and Recall of TV News." No essays or opinion pieces. Length: 4,000 words maximum. Submit complete ms in triplicate. No payment.

Tips: "Query letters don't really help either the author or me very much. We can't make commitments on the basis of query letters, and we are not likely to reject or discourage the manuscript either, unless it is clearly outside our scope. Do a good piece of research. Write a clear, well-organized manuscript."

PHILATELIC JOURNALIST, 154 Laguna Court, St. Augustine Shores FL 32086-7031. (904)797-3513. Editor: Gustav Detjen, Jr. 25% freelance written. Bimonthly for "journalists, writers and columnists in the field of stamp collecting. *The Philatelic Journalist* is mainly read by philatelic writers, professionals and amateurs, including all of the members of the Society of Philaticians, an international group of philatelic journalists." Circ. 1,000. Not copyrighted. Pays on publication. Publishes ms an average of 30 days after acceptance. Free sample copy. Submit seasonal material 2 months in advance. Photocopied submissions OK. Computer printout submissions acceptable. Reports in 2 weeks. Query.
Nonfiction: "Articles concerned with the problems of the philatelic journalist, how to publicize and promote stamp collecting, how to improve relations between philatelic writers and publishers and postal administrations. Philatelic journalists, many of them amateurs, are very much interested in receiving greater recognition as journalists, and in gaining greater recognition for the use of philatelic literature by stamp collectors. Any criticism should be coupled with suggestions for improvement." Buys profiles and opinion articles. Length: 250-500 words. Pays $15-30.
Photos: Photos purchased with ms. Captions required.

PRO/COMM, The Professional Communicator, published by Women in Communications, Inc., Box 9561, Austin TX 78766. (512)346-9875. Managing Editor: Barbara A. Johnston. 50% freelance written, mostly by WICI members and without pay. Works with a small number of new/unpublished writers each year; eager to work with new/unpublished writers. Published bimonthly; 32-40 pages. Circ. 12,000. Publishes ms an average of 3 months after acceptance. Byline given. Buys first serial rights and second serial (reprint) rights. Photocopied and previously published submissions OK. Accepts electronic submissions via disk or modem. "Check with editor for current system requirements." Computer printout submissions acceptable; no dot-matrix. Reports in 1 month. Sample copy: first copy free, subsequent copies $2 each.
Nonfiction: General interest (media, freedom of information, legislation related to communications); how-to (improve graphics, take better photos, write a better story, do investigative reporting, sell ideas, start a magazine or newspaper, improve journalism education, reach decision-making jobs, etc.); personal experience (self-improvement, steps to take to reach management level jobs); profile (people of interest because of their work in communications); and technical (advancements in print or electronic media). Query. Length: 1,000-1,500 words.
Photos: Offers no additional payment for photos accepted with mss. State availability of photos with query. Uses b&w photos. Captions required.
Tips: "The writer may have a better chance of breaking in at our publication with short articles. We welcome an easy-to-read, comfortable, informative style rather than a dry, pedantic approach to the subject. Areas open for other copy vary in size, so fillers appropriate to our sphere of interest are often useful."

PUBLISHED!, Platen Publishing Co., 14240 Bledsoe St., Sylmar CA 91342. (818)367-9613. Editor: Patricia Begalla. 100% freelance written. Eager to work with new/unpublished writers. A monthly magazine covering the writing profession. "We cater to all writers, with emphasis on the talented beginner. Articles on the craft of writing are emphasized." Estab. 1985. Circ. 5,000. Pays on acceptance. Publishes ms an average of 6 months after acceptance. Buys first rights and second serial (reprint) rights. Submit seasonal/holiday material 6 months in advance. Simultaneous, photocopied and previously published submissions OK. Computer printout submissions acceptable; prefers letter-quality to dot-matrix. Reports in 30-45 days. Sample copy for 9x12 SAE with 4 first class stamps; writer's guidelines for #10 SAE with 1 first class stamp.
Nonfiction: Book excerpts, general interest (few), how-to (on writing), humor, interview/profile (of writers), and travel. No sex, politics, religious or science fiction. Buys 120 mss/year. Query with or without published clips, or send complete ms. Length: 100-900 words. Pays 6¢/word.
Fiction: Short stories complete on 2 pages, 1,500 words maximum. Any subject except explicit sex or pornography. Buys 12 short stories/year. 6¢/word for original material; 4¢/word for reprints.
Photos: Send photos with submission. Offers $10/photo. Identification of subjects required. Buys one-time rights.
Columns/Departments: Query with or without published clips or send complete ms. Length: 300-900 words. Pays 6¢/word for original material; 4¢/word for reprints.
Poetry: Avant-garde, free verse, haiku, light verse and traditional. Buys 24 poems/year. Submit maximum 2 poems. Length: 5-20 lines. Pays $10.
Fillers: Anecdotes, facts and short humor. Buys 20/year. Length: 50-100 words. Pays $5-10.
Tips: "Articles on the craft of writing—written by established and successful pros are always needed. We would like to see more articles on the craft of writing. Many of our subscribers are beginners, and ask for constructive help in their chosen trade. Seasoned professionals have been very supportive by contributing articles that serve to help the less experienced author. We also want stories about well known writers . . . their lifestyles, work habits, research methods, etc. We like pieces that inspire and encourage the serious beginner—how-to

tips, little-known but lucrative markets, information that provides knowledge and support for the fledging author."

‡**PUBLISHER'S REPORT**, National Association of Independent Publishers, Box 850, Moore Haven FL 33471. (813)946-0283. Editor: Ailsa Dewing. 10% freelance written. Bimonthly newsletter for independent publishers, small press and self-publishers with how-to articles on all aspects of publishing. Estab. 1985. Circ. 350. Publishes ms an average of 6 months after acceptance. Byline given. Buys one-time rights. Submit seasonal/holiday material 6 months in advance. Computer printout submissions acceptable; prefers letter-quality to dot-matrix. Reports in 3 weeks on queries. Sample copy $2 with SAE and 39¢ postage.
Nonfiction: How-to. Buys 6 mss/year. Send complete ms. Length: 250 words. Payment in contributor copies.

RISING STAR, Star/Sword Publications, 47 Byledge Rd., Manchester NH 03104. (603)623-9796. Editor: Scott E. Green. "We are backlogged with submissions and prefer not to receive unsolicited submissions at this time."

THE ROMANTIST, F. Marion Crawford Memorial Society, Saracinesca House, 3610 Meadowbrook Ave., Nashville TN 37205. (615)292-9695 or 226-1890. Editors: John C. Moran, Don Herron and Steve Eng. 100% freelance written. "Writers' backgrounds not an issue; their grasp of their material, and skill at imparting it, is." Annual magazine emphasizing modern romanticism; especially fantastic literature and art. Circ. 300, controlled. All rights retained but permission always is given an author for reprints. Publishes ms an average of 1 year after acceptance. Byline given. Photocopied poems, simultaneous submissions and previously published submissions not desired. Reports in 1 month. Writer's guidelines with SASE.
Nonfiction: Solid articles or bibliographies on fantasy, horror and other romantic authors (or artists or composers). No articles without querying first.
Poetry: Traditional; very little free verse. "We prefer rhymed and metered poems, but no homespun doggerel-lite; prefer the tradition of Swinburne, Poe, Noyes, De la Mare, Millay, Masefield, Clark Ashton Smith; especially weird or fantastic verse." Poetry submissions should be double-spaced. Uses 15 unsolicited poems/year.
Tips: Closed currently to poetry.

ST. LOUIS JOURNALISM REVIEW, 8606 Olive Blvd., St. Louis MO 63132. (314)991-1699. Editor/Publisher: Charles L. Klotzer. 50% freelance written. Prefers to work with published/established writers. Works with a small number of new/unpublished writers each year; eager to work with new/unpublished writers. Monthly tabloid newspaper critiquing St. Louis media, print, broadcasting, TV and cable primarily by working journalists and others. Also covers issues not covered adequately by dailies. Occasionally buys articles on national media criticism. Circ. 9,000. Buys all rights. Byline given. Computer printout submissions acceptable.
Nonfiction: "We buy material which analyzes, critically, St. Louis metro area media and, less frequently, national media institutions, personalities or trends." No taboos. Payment depends. Sometimes pays the expenses of writers on assignment.

‡**SAN FRANCISCO REVIEW OF BOOKS**, Box 33-0090, San Francisco CA 94133. Editor: Arnie Williams. 60% freelance written. For a college-educated audience interested in books and publishing. Quarterly magazine; 32 pages. Circ. 5,000. Acquires all rights. Byline given. Uses about 180 mss/year. Payment in contributors copies and subscription. Publishes ms an average of 3 months after acceptance. Sample copy $1.50. No photocopied or simultaneous submissions. Reports on material accepted for publication in 4-6 weeks. Query for nonfiction; submit complete ms for book reviews.
Nonfiction: Book reviews and articles about authors, books and their themes. "No glib, slick writing. Primarily serious; humor occasionally acceptable. No restrictions on language provided it is germane to the book or article." Interviews, profiles, historical and think articles. Length: 1,200 words maximum for reviews; 2,000 words maximum for articles.

‡**SCAVENGER'S NEWSLETTER**, 519 Ellinwood, Osage City KS 66523. (913)528-3538. Editor: Janet Fox. 25% freelance written. Eager to work with new/unpublished writers. A monthly newsletter covering markets for science fiction/fantasy/horror materials especially with regard to the small press. Circ. 300. Publishes ms an average of 8 months after acceptance. Byline given. Not copyrighted. "Copyright symbol printed with author's name on publication." Buys one-time rights. Submit seasonal/holiday material 2 months in advance. Simultaneous, photocopied and previously published submissions OK. Computer printout submissions acceptable; prefers letter-quality to dot-matrix. Reports in 2 weeks. Sample copy 60¢; writer's guidelines for #10 SASE.
Nonfiction: Essays; general interest; how-to (write, sell, publish sf/fantasy/horror); humor; interview/profile (writers, artists in the field); and opinion. Buys 12-15 mss/year. Send complete ms. Length: 1,000 words maximum. Pays $2.

Poetry: Avant-garde, free verse, haiku, light verse and traditional. All related to science fiction/fantasy/horror genres or to writing. Buys 24 poems/year. Submit maximum 3 poems. Length: 10 lines maximum. Pays $1.

SCIENCE FICTION CHRONICLE, Algol Press, Box 4175, New York NY 10163. (718)643-9011. Editor: Andrew Porter. 5% freelance written. Works with a small number of new/unpublished writers each year. Monthly magazine about science fiction and fantasy publishing for readers, editors, writers, et al., who are interested in keeping up with the latest developments and news in science fiction and fantasy. Publication also includes market reports, UK news, letters, reviews, columns. Circ. 3,800. Buys first serial rights. Pays on publication. Publishes ms an average of 2 months after acceptance. Makes work-for-hire assignments. Phone queries OK. Submit seasonal/holiday material 4 months in advance. Computer printout submissions acceptable; prefers letter-quality to dot-matrix. Reports in 1 week. Sample copy $2.
Nonfiction: Interviews, new product and photo feature. No articles about UFOs, or "news we reported six months ago." Buys 15 unsolicited mss/year. Send complete ms. Length: 200-2,000 words. Pays 1-5¢/word.
Photos: Send photos with ms. Pays $5-15 for 4x5 and 8x10 b&w prints. Captions preferred. Buys one-time rights.
Tips: "News of publishers, booksellers and software related to is most needed from freelancers."

SHORT STORY REVIEW CLUB, Trouvere Company, Rt. 2, Box 290, Eclectic AL 36024. Editor: Brenda Williamson. 95% freelance written. Triannual short story writer's club. Newsletter published with critiquing of short stories by members. Estab. 1985. Circ. 75. Byline given. Buys one-time rights. Computer printout submissions acceptable; prefers letter-quality to dot-matrix. Reports in 1 month. Sample copy $3; writer's guidelines for 25¢ and #10 SAE and 1 first class stamp.
Nonfiction: How-to (about short story writing). Buys 10 mss/year. Send complete ms. Length: 500-1,500 words. Pays "sometimes."
Fiction: Adventure, condensed novels, confession, erotica, ethnic, experimental, fantasy, historical, horror, humorous, mainstream, mystery, novel excerpts, religious, romance, science fiction, serialized novels, suspense and western—any short story. Buys 25 mss/year. Send complete ms. Length: 500-3,000 words. Pays $5-50.
Tips: "Articles are accepted from both subscribers and nonsubscribers. Short stories are only accepted from members."

WAYSTATION, for the SF Writer, (formerly *Empire*), c/o Unique Graphics, 1025 55th St., Oakland CA 94608. (415)655-3024. Editor: Millea Kenin. 99% freelance written. Prefers to work with published/established writers; works with a small number of new/unpublished writers each year. Quarterly magazine covering writing, editing and publishing science fiction and fantasy. "*Waystation*'s aim is to assist, entertain and inform science fiction and fantasy writers." Circ. 1,500. Pays on publication. Publishes ms an average of 6 months after acceptance. Byline given. Buys first English language serial rights, and occasionally second serial (reprint) rights. Simultaneous queries and photocopied submissions OK if simultaneous are so identified. "We are completely receptive to computer printout submissions as long as they are *not* dot-matrix with dots visible to the naked eye. Such printouts will be returned unread." Reports in 1 month or less. Sample copy $2.50, payable to Unique Graphics. Guidelines available for SAE with 39¢ postage.
Nonfiction: Expose (of publishing industry); how-to (on specific writing and marketing techniques and skills for science fiction and fantasy); humor (about the science fiction writer's life; "If you find any, send it to us"); interview/profile (of writers, editors, agents, publishers, filmmakers involved in the SF genre); personal experience ("how I wrote and sold science fiction, fantasy or horror fiction"); and technical (science fact with application to science fiction). "We use articles about writing, editing and publishing *science fiction and fantasy*; our material is written by professional science fiction writers for would-be professional science fiction writers. We are not interested in general articles for the beginning writer, nor articles on coping with failure as a writer. We take a practical nuts-and-bolts approach." Buys 32 mss/year. Query with proposal if you have not previously written for *Waystation*. Length: 1,000-3,500 words. Offers contributor copies as payment and a one-year subscription. Pay negotiable to regular contributors.
Fiction: Crazy Diamonds. "Each issue contains one story which has failed to sell elsewhere and three critiques of the story by professional science fiction writers. We use no other fiction." Buys 4 mss/year. Length: 3,500 words maximum, shorter preferred. Offers contributor copies as payment and subscription.
Poetry: "Short humorous or serious verse about the act of writing science fiction or the science fiction writer's life."
Tips: "If you have not seen a copy of *Waystation* and are not closely involved with the science fiction genre, it is better to query with a proposal rather than submitting an unsolicited article. If she/he is not a big-name science fiction writer, she/he must have specific knowledge of interest to writers in this genre or specific *successful*, relevant experiences to share. We're tightening up on relevance; absolutely no general how-to-write stuff will be accepted except if solicited."

WDS FORUM, Writer's Digest School, 9933 Alliance Rd., Cincinnati OH 45242. (513)984-0717. Editor: Kirk Polking. 100% freelance written. Bimonthly newsletter covering writing techniques and marketing for students of courses in fiction and nonfiction writing offered by Writer's Digest School. Circ. 11,000. Pays on acceptance. Publishes ms an average of 6 months after acceptance. Byline given. Pays 25% kill fee. Buys first serial rights and second serial (reprint) rights. Submit seasonal/holiday material 4 months in advance. Simultaneous, photocopied, and previously published submissions OK. Electronic submissions OK, but requires hard copy also. Computer printout submissions acceptable; no dot-matrix. Reports in 3 weeks. Free sample copy.
Nonfiction: How-to (write or market short stories, articles, novels, poetry, etc.); and interviews (with well-known authors of short stories, novels and books). Buys 15 mss/year. Phone or written query. Length: 500-1,000 words. Pays $10-25.
Photos: Pays $5-10 for 8x10 b&w prints of well-known writers to accompany mss. Captions required. Buys one-time rights.

WEST COAST REVIEW OF BOOKS, Rapport Publishing Co., Inc., 6331 Hollywood Blvd., Hollywood CA 90028. (213)464-2662. Editor: D. David Dreis. Bimonthly magazine for book consumers. "Provocative articles based on specific subject matter, books and author retrospectives." Circ. 80,000. Pays on publication. Byline given. Offers kill fee. Buys one-time rights and second serial (reprint) rights to published author interviews. Sample copy $2.
Nonfiction: General interest, historical/nostalgic, and profile (author retrospectives). "No individual book reviews." Buys 25 mss/year. Query. Length: open.
Tips: "There must be a reason (current interest, news events, etc.) for any article here. Example: 'The Jew-Haters' was about anti-semitism which was written up in six books; all reviewed and analyzed under that umbrella title. Under no circumstances should articles be submitted unless query has been responded to." No phone calls.

THE WRITER, 120 Boylston St., Boston MA 02116. Editor-in-Chief/Publisher: Sylvia K. Burack. Managing Editor: Elizabeth Preston. Monthly. Pays on acceptance. Buys first serial rights. Uses little freelance material. Computer printout submissions acceptable; no dot-matrix. Sample copy $2.
Nonfiction: Articles of instruction for writers. Length: about 2,000 words. Pays on acceptance.

WRITERS CONNECTION, 10601 S. De Anza Blvd., Cupertino CA 95117. (408)973-0227. Editor: Jon Kennedy. 60% freelance written. Monthly magazine covering writing and publishing with strong Bay area/northern California emphasis for northern California writers. Circ. 2,500. Pays on publication. Publishes ms an average of 6 months after acceptance for articles, much less for column updates. Byline given. Buys first serial rights or second serial (reprint) rights. Submit seasonal/holiday material 2 months in advance. Simultaneous queries, and simultaneous, photocopied, and previously published submissions OK. Computer printout submissions acceptable; prefers letter-quality to dot-matrix. Prefers telephone queries. Sample copy and writer's guidelines $2.
Nonfiction: Book excerpts (on writing/publishing); how-to (write and publish, market writing); inspirational (overcoming writer's block, "staying the course"); interview/profile (writers and publishers with how-to slant); new product (books, videotapes, etc. on writing and publishing); and travel writing. "All types of writing from technical to romance novels and article writing are treated." Submit material for California writers conferences by January each year. No personal experience or profiles without a strong how-to slant. Buys 36 mss/year. Query, preferably by telephone, between 11 a.m. and noon. Length: 100-2,500 words. Pays $12-80; "pay is in credit for Writers Connection memberships, seminars, subscriptions and advertising only."
Columns/Departments: Markets/Jobs Update and self-publishing. Buys 24 mss/year. Send complete ms. Length: 100-300 words. Pays $12-25 in subscriptions, ads, or credits on seminars or memberships.
Tips: "Find and report on new markets freelancers can break into, new ways to succeed in the business. We use far more short column items, and we generally have a backlog of features awaiting use."

WRITER'S DIGEST, 9933 Alliance Rd., Cincinnati OH 45242. (513)984-0717. Submissions Editor: Sharon Rudd. (Please note that anything submitted to *Writer's Digest* is automatically considered for publication in *Writer's Yearbook*, so there's no point in submitting to each individually.) 90% freelance written. Monthly magazine about writing and publishing. "Our readers write fiction, poetry, nonfiction, plays and all kinds of creative writing. They're interested in improving their writing skills, improving their sales ability, and finding new outlets for their talents." Circ. 200,000. Pays on acceptance. Publishes ms an average of 1 year after acceptance. Buys first North American serial rights for one-time editorial use, microfilm/microfiche use, and magazine promotional use. Pays 20% kill fee. Byline given. Submit seasonal/holiday material 8 months in advance. Previously published and photocopied submissions OK. No unsolicited electronic submissions. "We're able to use electronic submissions only for accepted pieces and will discuss details if we buy your work. We'll accept computer printout submissions, of course—but they *must* be readable. That's the rule behind any submission to any magazine. We strongly recommend letter-quality. If you don't want your manuscript returned, indicate that on the first page of the manuscript or in a cover letter." Reports in 1 month. Sample copy $2.50; writer's guidelines for SASE.

Close-up

Janet Burroway
Author

©Jerry Blankenship

"She looked into his blue eyes, and she was flooded with the most magnificent affection she had ever felt," says author Janet Burroway as she tells how some writers might describe a character.

"That won't do it. We don't believe it; we don't care," she points out, because the writer has generalized how the character feels. The scene needs *significant detail*—a concept Burroway explores in her book *Writing Fiction* (Little, Brown and Company) and in her own writing.

"Every writer's problem is to learn how to use detail," says Burroway, the author of six novels, two poetry books, and two children's books. "If the detail implies an idea or a judgment as well as giving information, then it's more likely to be significant.

"The understanding and believing in the use of significant detail make the reader believe whatever else you say," says Burroway.

For her latest novel *Cutting Stone*, she designed a costume (in words) to mark one character's arrival. The costume *per se* isn't important, she says. "What matters is how the character feels about herself and what the character is trying to do with that costume—to startle and make people admire her when she steps off the train." It took an hour and a half to write the seven lines, recalls Burroway, who scanned four costume books as part of the writing process.

"Surely the more you write, the easier it gets?" she once asked her freshman English professor.

"It doesn't get easier; it gets better," he replied.

Now as Florida State University's foundation professor of English literature and writing, she demonstrates what makes good writing: thoroughness, self-criticism, tenacity at the typewriter.

One significant detail writers face in their lives is the struggle to find time to write, Burroway says. She skips vacations and writes whenever she can get to the word processor.

"Very few writers I know want yachts; what they want is time to write."

When Burroway writes, she focuses on the story, not on the selling of it. Writing a story to fill a magazine's needs doesn't work for Burroway, whose work has appeared in American and British magazines, such as *Ms.*, *The Atlantic*, *Newstatesman* and *Story Quarterly*. "There is a very thin line between market and audience," she observes. "I don't like to think of the market, but I am very happy to think of my audience.

"What I've got to do is to make readers feel in their stomachs what's happening in the story," says Burroway, who has also written British television drama.

Cutting Stone began as a film script. After writing 120 pages, Burroway decided she needed to take her audience inside the characters' minds—a depth of involvement more suited to a novel than to a film. All writers must decide which form—novel, play or poem—can best express a particular idea. If an idea is suited to two forms, such as a novel and film, "the form that has the best chance is the one you can write best," says Burroway. With significant detail, in either case.

—Paula Deimling

Nonfiction: "Our mainstay is the how-to article—that is, an article telling how to write and sell more of what you write. For instance, how to write compelling leads and conclusions, how to improve your character descriptions, how to become more efficient and productive. We like plenty of examples, anecdotes and $$$ in our articles—so other writers can actually see what's been done successfully by the author of a particular piece. We like our articles to speak directly to the reader through the use of the first person voice. Don't submit an article on what five book editors say about writing mysteries. Instead, submit an article on how you cracked the mystery market and how our readers can do the same. But don't limit the article to your experiences; include the opinions of those five editors to give your article increased depth and authority." General interest (about writing); how-to (writing and marketing techniques that work); humor (short pieces); inspirational; interview and profile (query first); new product; and personal experience (marketing and freelancing experiences). "We can always use articles on fiction and nonfiction technique, and solid articles on poetry or scriptwriting are always welcome. No articles titled 'So You Want to Be a Writer,' and no first person pieces that ramble without giving a lesson or something readers can learn from in the sharing of the story." Buys 90-100 mss/year. Queries are preferred, but complete mss are OK. Length: 500-3,000 words. Pays 10¢/word minimum. Sometimes pays expenses of writers on assignment.

Photos: Used only with interviews and profiles. State availability of photos or send contact sheet with ms. Pays $25 minimum for 5x7 or larger b&w prints. Captions required.

Columns/Departments: Chronicle (first person narratives of writing adventures; length: 1,200-1,500 words; pays 10¢/word); The Writing Life (length: 50-800 words; pays 10¢/word); Tip Sheet (short, unbylined items that offer solutions to writing- and freelance business-related problems that writers commonly face; pays 10¢/word); and My First Sale (an "occasional" department; a first person account of how a writer broke into print; length: 1,000 words; pays 10¢/word). "For First Sale items, use a narrative, anecdotal style to tell a tale that is both inspirational and instructional. Before you submit a My First Sale item, make certain that your story contains a solid lesson that will benefit other writers." Buys approximately 200 articles/year for Writing Life section, Tip Sheet and shorter pieces. Send complete ms.

Poetry: Light verse about "the writing life"—joys and frustrations of writing. "We are also considering poetry other than short light verse—but related to writing, publishing, other poets and authors, etc." Buys 2/issue. Submit poems in batches of 1-8. Length: 2-20 lines. Pays $10-50/poem.

Fillers: Anecdotes and short humor, primarily for use in The Writing Life column. Uses 2/issue. Length: 50-200 words. Pays 10¢/word.

WRITER'S INFO, Rhyme Time/Story Time, Box 2377, Coeur d'Alene ID 83814. (208)667-7511. Editor: Linda Hutton. 90% freelance written. Eager to work with new/unpublished writers. Monthly newsletter on writing. "We provide helpful tips and advice to writers, both beginners and old pros." Estab. 1985. Circ. 200. Pays on acceptance. Publishes ms an average of 6 months after acceptance. Byline given. Buys first North American serial rights and second serial (reprint) rights. Submit seasonal/holiday material 9 months in advance. Simultaneous queries, and simultaneous, photocopied, and previously published submissions OK. Computer printout submissions acceptable; prefers letter-quality to dot-matrix. Reports in 1 month. Sample copy for #10 SAE and 2 first class stamps; writer's guidelines for # 10 SAE and 2 first class stamps.

Nonfiction: How-to, humor and personal experience, all related to writing. No interviews or re-hashes of articles published in other writers magazines. Buys 50-75 mss/year. Send complete ms. Length: 300 words. Pays $1-10.

Poetry: Free verse, light verse and traditional. No avant-garde or shaped poetry. Buys 40-50/year. Submit maximum 6 poems. Length: 4-20 lines. Pays $1-10.

Fillers: Jokes, anecdotes and short humor. Buys 3-4/year. Length: 100 words maximum. Pays $1-10.

Tips: "Tell us a system that worked for you to make a sale or inspired you to write. All departments are open to freelancers."

WRITER'S LIFELINE, Box 1641, Cornwall, Ontario K6H 5V6 Canada. Contact: Editor. 95% freelance written. Eager to work with new/unpublished writers. Bimonthly magazine "aimed at freelance writers of all ages and interests." Buys first serial rights. SAE and IRCs.

Nonfiction: "Articles on all aspects of writing and publishing, also book reviews." Send complete ms. Length: 500 words maximum. Payment: 3 free issues in which article appears. Publishes ms an average of 2 months after acceptance.

Fiction: Must be tied in to writing and publishing. Poetry published. Payment: 3 free issues in which story or poem appears.

Tips: "Writer should show evidence of his qualification to write on subject. All articles should be pegged to current concerns of writers: self-publishing, hitting local markets, anecdotes of new writer breaking in, and preparing book reviews are among articles we have published recently."

‡**WRITER'S NEWSLETTER**, Writer's Studio, 1530 7th St., Rock Island IL 61201. (309)788-3980. Editor: Betty Mowery. A bimonthly newsletter/club publication prepared for the help and exposure of writers. Circ. 350. Byline given. Not copyrighted. Acquires first rights. Submit seasonal/holiday material 3 months in advance.

Simultaneous submissions OK. Computer printout submissions acceptable; prefers letter-quality to dot-matrix. Reports in 1 week. Free sample copy; writer's guidelines for SAE with 1 first class stamp.
Nonfiction: Essay, general interest, inspirational, interview/profile, personal experience and anything else pertaining to writing. Buys 12 mss/year. Send complete ms. Length: 500 words maximum. Pays in copies.
Fiction: Adventure, experimental, fantasy, historical, humorous, mainstream, mystery, romance and slice-of-life vignettes. No erotica. Buys 12 mss/year. Send complete ms. Length: 500 words minimum. Pays copies.
Poetry: Avant-garde, free verse, haiku, light verse and traditional. Buys 36 poems/year. Submit maximum 5 poems. Length: 20 lines maximum. Pays in copies.
Fillers: Anecdotes, facts and short humor. Buys 6/year. Length: 250 words maximum. Pays in copies.

WRITERS WEST, An American Forum, Box 16097, San Diego CA 92116. (619)278-6108. Editor: Francis X. Feighan. Managing Editor: Douglas K. Emry. 90% freelance written. Works with a small number of new/unpublished writers each year. A bimonthly magazine for the professional writer and the informed, literate public. Circ. 2,500. Pays on acceptance. Publishes ms an average of 4 months after acceptance. Byline given. Buys first North American serial rights, and second serial (reprint) rights. Simultaneous queries, and simultaneous, photocopied, and previously published submissions OK except for poetry and fiction, which must be previously unpublished. Computer printout submissions acceptable. Reports in 2 weeks. Sample copy $2; writer's guidelines for SAE and 1 first class stamp.
Nonfiction: Expose; interview/profile (well-known authors, writing-related personalities); and opinion (writing related). "*Writers West* would like to see articles of a general literary nature, such as: Major Authors Who Wrote for Copies; Style-Past & Present Forms; History & Development of the American Short Story; Effects on Literacy of Teaching Philosophy to Children; The Literary Society—A Profile. No elementary how-tos or how great it is being a writer." Buys 24 mss/year. Query or send complete ms. Length: 2,500 words maximum. "Token payment and/or copies."
Photos: "Photos with articles are welcome—preferably with the subject in his/her working environment, or head shots. Include the photographer's credit line." State availability of photos. Reviews 5x7 and larger b&w prints. Payment included in payment for ms. Identification of subjects required. Buys one-time rights.
Fiction: Dona Cameron, fiction editor. "Will consider anything of quality. No trials and tribulations of being a writer." Buys 12 mss/year. Send complete ms; include short biography. Length: 3,000 words maximum.
Poetry: E.I.V. von Heitlinger, poetry editor. May be any subject in any style, 50 lines maximum. No hardcore pornography, but tasteful erotica will be considered. Looking for well-crafted, tight, polished poems of clarity and force of vision. Token payment and/or copies.
Tips: "Writers' most frequent mistakes are misjudging (or *not* judging) WW's intended market: the professional writer (who is *not* interested in how to budget time in order to write), and the informed, literate public. A writer can break in any category. WW has published first-time writers; professional treatment of the subject matter is the deciding factor. *Writers West* wants to publish material which reflects the high literary standards set by quality publications such as *The Atlantic*. A copy of the magazine should be obtained for guidance in selecting material for submission."

WRITER'S YEARBOOK, 9933 Alliance Rd., Cincinnati OH 45242. Submissions Editor: Sharon Rudd. Anything submitted to *Writer's Yearbook* is automatically considered for publication in *Writer's Digest* so there's no point in submitting to each individually. 90% freelance written. Newsstand annual for freelance writers, journalists and teachers of creative writing. "We provide how-to features and information to help our readers become more skilled at writing and successful at selling their writing." Buys first North American serial rights and (occasionally) reprint rights. Pays 20% kill fee. Byline given. Pays on acceptance. Publishes ms an average of 6 months after acceptance. "Writers should query in spring with ideas for the following year." Send detailed query or outline of what you have in mind. Previously published (book reprints) and high-quality photocopied submissions OK. Computer printout submissions acceptable; prefers letter-quality to dot-matrix. "If you don't want your manuscript returned, indicate that on the first page of the manuscript or in a cover letter."
Nonfiction: "We want articles that reflect the current state of writing in America. Trends, inside information and money-saving and money-making ideas for the freelance writer. We try to touch on the various facets of writing in each issue of the *Yearbook*—from fiction to poetry to playwriting, and any other endeavor a writer can pursue. How-to articles—that is, articles that explain in detail how to do something—are very important to us. For example, you could explain how to establish mood in fiction, how to improve interviewing techniques, how to write for and sell to specialty magazines, or how to construct and market a good poem. We are also interested in the writer's spare time—what she/he does to retreat occasionally from the writing wars; where and how to refuel and replenish the writing spirit. 'How Beats the Heart of a Writer' features interest us, if written warmly, in the first person, by a writer who has had considerable success. We also want interviews or profiles of well-known bestselling authors, always with good pictures. Articles on writing techniques that are effective today are always welcome." Recent article example: " 'Megatrends': Where the Magazine Market is headed in 1986," by Greg Daugherty. Buys 10-15 mss/year. Length: 750-4,500 words. Pays 10¢/word minimum. Sometimes pays expenses of writers on assignment.

Photos: Interviews and profiles must be accompanied by high-quality photos. Reviews b&w photos only, depending on use; pays $20-50/published photo. Captions required.

___ Laundry and Dry Cleaning

Some journals in the Coin-Operated Machines category are also in the market for material on laundries and dry cleaning establishments.

AMERICAN DRYCLEANER, 500 N. Dearborn St., Chicago IL 60610. (312)337-7700. Editor: Earl V. Fischer. 20% freelance written. "We prefer to work regularly with widely scattered photo-reporters who need little direction, but always open to unsolicited submissions from newcomers." For professional drycleaners. Monthly. Circ. 28,000. Buys first North American serial rights or in some cases industry-exclusive simultaneous rights. Pays on publication. Publishes ms an average of 3 months after acceptance. Will send free sample copy to writers with specific queries. Reports "promptly." Computer printout submissions acceptable; prefers letter-quality to dot-matrix.
Nonfiction: Articles on all aspects of running a drycleaning business. "These can be narratives about individual drycleaners and how they are handling, say, advertising, counter service, customer relations, cleaning, spot removal, pressing, inspection, packaging, paperwork, or general business management; interpretive reports about outside developments, such as new fabrics and fashions or government regulations affecting drycleaners; or how-to articles offering practical help to cleaners on any facet of their business. The important thing is that the reader find practical benefit in the article, whichever type submitted." No basic advertising and public relations material. "We have regulars for this who know our industry." Pays a minimum of 6¢/published word. Recent article example: "Updated plant perks along at '65,000 pounds per drum' " (February 1986).
Photos: Photos purchased with mss; quality 8x10 or 5x7 b&w glossies. Photos should help tell story. Pays $6 minimum.
Tips: "We are happy to receive and frequently publish unsolicited manuscripts. If an advance query is made, it would help to get a theme sentence or brief outline of the proposed article. Also helpful would be a statement of whether (and what sort of) photos or other illustrations are available. Anyone with the type of article that our readers would find helpful can break into the publication. The most frequent mistake made by writers in completing an article for us is writing too superficially on too many aspects of a business. It's better to probe for the really unusual and adaptable practical ideas in practice and find out all about them. Also too many photos are meaningless or their significance is not explained. Find a successful drycleaner—one with unusually satisfied customers, for example, or one that seems to be making a lot of money. Find out what makes that cleaner so successful. Tell us about it in specific, practical terms, so other cleaners will be able to follow suit. Articles should help our readers operate their drycleaning businesses more successfully; the appropriateness and practical value of information given are more important than writing style. We prefer *short* reports about *small* cleaning companies doing *one thing* well enough for others to want to know about it and how they might do the same. Reports can range from less than 250 words up to any length the writer can justify. Our editorial space is steadily increasing; staff help is not. We're glad to use anything suitable for publication (new writers are always welcome)."

INDUSTRIAL LAUNDERER, Suite 613, 1730 M St. NW, Washington DC 20036. (202)296-6744. Editor: David A. Ritchey. "We are backlogged with submissions and prefer not to receive unsolicited submissions at this time."

✝ The double dagger before a listing indicates that the listing is new in this edition. New markets are often the most receptive to freelance contributions.

Law

While all of these publications deal with topics of interest to attorneys, each has a particular slant. Be sure that your subject is geared to the specific market—lawyers in a single region, students, paralegals, etc. Publications for law enforcement personnel are listed under Government and Public Service.

‡**ABA JOURNAL**, American Bar Association, 750 N. Lake Shore Dr., Chicago IL 60611. (312)988-5000. Editor: Larry Bodine. Associate Editor: Robert Yates. 35% freelance written. Prefers to work with published/established writers. Monthly magazine covering law and laywers. "The content of the *Journal* is designed to appeal to the association's diverse membership with emphasis on the general practitioner." Circ. 350,000. Pays on acceptance. Publishes ms an average of 2 months after acceptance. Byline given. "Editor works with writer until article is in acceptable form." Buys all rights. Submit seasonal/holiday material 3 months in advance. Simultaneous queries, and simultaneous and photocopied submissions OK. Electronic submissions OK via ABA/net (the lawyer's computer network). Computer printout submissions acceptable; no dot-matrix. Contact associate editor about electronic submissions. Reports in 3 weeks. Free sample copy and writer's guidelines.
Nonfiction: Book excerpts; general interest (legal); how-to (law practice techniques); interview/profile (law firms and prominent individuals); and technical (legal trends). "The emphasis of the *Journal* is on the practical problems faced by lawyers in general practice and how those problems can be overcome. Articles should emphasize the practical rather than the theoretical or esoteric. Writers should avoid the style of law reviews, academic journals or legal briefs and should write in an informal, journalistic style. Short quotations from people and specific examples of your point will improve an article." Special issues have featured women and minorities in the legal profession. Buys 30 mss/year. Query with published clips or send complete ms. Length: 1,000-3,000 words. Pays $300-800. Pays expenses of writers on assignment.
Tips: "Write to us with a specific idea in mind and spell out how the subject would be covered. Full length profiles and feature articles are always needed. We look for practical information. Don't send us theory, philosophy or wistful meanderings. Our readers want to know how to win cases and operate their practices more efficiently. We need more writing horsepower on lifestyle, profile and practice pieces for lawyers. If the New York Times or Wall Street Journal would like your style, so will we."

THE ALTMAN & WEIL REPORT TO LEGAL MANAGEMENT, Altman & Weil Publications, Inc., Box 472, Ardmore PA 19003. (215)649-4646. Editor: Robert I. Weil. 15-20% freelance written. Works with a small number of new/unpublished writers each year. Monthly newsletter covering law office purchases (equipment, insurance services, space, etc.). Circ. 2,200. Pays on publication. Publishes ms an average of 6 months after acceptance. Byline given. Buys all rights; sometimes second serial (reprint) rights. Photocopied and previously published submissions OK. Computer printout submissions acceptable; no dot-matrix. Reports in 1 month on queries; 6 weeks on mss. Sample copy for business size SAE and 1 first class stamp.
Nonfiction: How-to (buy, use, repair); interview/profile; and new product. Buys 6 mss/year. Query. Submit a sample of previous writing. Length: 500-2,500 words. Pays $125/published page.
Photos: State availability of photos. Reviews b&w prints; payment is included in payment for ms. Captions and model release required. Buys one-time rights.

BARRISTER, American Bar Association Press, 750 N. Lake Shore Dr., Chicago IL 60611. (312)988-6056. Editor: Anthony Monahan. 70% freelance written. Prefers to work with published/established writers; works with a small number of new/unpublished each year. For young lawyers who are members of the American Bar Association concerned about practice of law, improvement of the profession and service to the public. Quarterly magazine; 64 pages. Circ. 155,000. Pays on acceptance. Publishes ms an average of 3 months after acceptance. Buys all rights, first serial rights, second serial (reprint) rights, or simultaneous rights. Photocopied submissions OK. Letter-quality submissions preferred. Reports in 6 weeks. Free sample copy.
Nonfiction: "As a magazine of ideas and opinion, we seek material that will help readers in their interrelated roles of attorney and citizen; major themes in legal and social affairs." Especially needs expository or advocacy articles; position should be defended clearly in good, crisp, journalistic prose. "We would like to see articles on issues such as the feasibility of energy alternatives to nuclear power, roles of women and minorities in law, the power and future of multinational corporations; national issues such as gun control; and aspects of

the legal profession such as salary comparisons, use of computers in law practice." No humorous court reporter anecdote material or political opinion articles. Buys 15 unsolicited mss/year. Length: 3,000-4,000 words. Query with a working title and outline of topic. "Be specific." Pays $450-750. Sometimes pays the expenses of writers on assignment.

Photos: Donna Tashjian, photo editor. B&w photos and color transparencies purchased without accompanying ms. Pays $35-150.

Tips: "We urge writers to think ahead about new areas of law and social issues: sexual habits, work habits, corporations, etc. We would like to receive profiles of young lawyers with national impact."

CALIFORNIA LAWYER, The State Bar of California, 555 Franklin St., San Francisco CA 94102. (415)561-8286. Editor: Jonathan R. Maslow. Associate Editor: Tom Brom. 80% freelance written. Monthly magazine of law-related articles and general interest subjects of appeal to attorneys. Circ. 100,000. Pays on acceptance. Publishes ms an average of 3 months after acceptance. Byline given. Buys all rights. Simultaneous queries, and simultaneous and photocopied submissions OK. Computer printout submissions acceptable; prefers letter-quality to dot-matrix. Reports in 2 weeks on queries; 3 weeks on mss. Sample copy for 8½x11 SAE and $1.50 postage; writer's guidelines for SAE and 1 first class stamp.

Nonfiction: General interest, historical, opinion, technical, and personal effectiveness. "We are interested in concise, well-written and well-researched articles on recent trends in the legal profession, legal aspects of issues of current concern, as well as general interest articles of potential appeal and benefit to the state's lawyers. We would like to see a description or outline of your proposed idea, including a list of possible information sources." Buys 36 mss/year. Query with published clips if available. Length: 2,000-3,000 words (features). Pays $500-700.

Photos: Jan Leonard, photo editor. State availability of photos with query letter or manuscript. Reviews prints. Identification of subjects required.

Columns/Departments: Business of Practice; After Hours; Profile; Money; and Effectiveness. Buys 100/year. Query with published clips if available. Length: 1,000-1,500 words. Pays $300-400.

Tips: "Trends in magazine publishing that freelance writers should be aware of include shorter articles, more emphasis on individual magazine styles; stricter guidelines for libel and fact checking."

COMPUTER USER'S LEGAL REPORTER, Computer Law Group, Inc., 191 Post Rd. W., Westport CT 06880. (203)227-1360. Editor: Charles P. Lickson. 10% freelance written. Prefers to work with published/established writers or "experts" in fields addressed. Monthly newsletter featuring legal issues and considerations facing users of computer and processed data. "The *Computer User's Legal Reporter* is written by a fully qualified legal and technical staffer for nonlawyer readers. It features brief summaries on developments in such vital areas as computer contracts, insurance, warranties, crime, proprietary rights and privacy. Each summary is backed by reliable research and sourcework." Circ. 1,000. Pays on publication. Publishes ms an average of 1 month after acceptance. Offers 50% kill fee. Buys first North American serial rights. Simultaneous queries, and simultaneous, photocopied, and previously published submissions OK. Computer printout submissions acceptable; prefers letter-quality to dot-matrix. Reports in 2 weeks. Sample copy $5 with #10 SAE and 5 first class stamps.

Nonfiction: Book excerpts; expose; how-to (protect ideas, etc.); humor (computer law . . . according to Murphy); interview/profile (legal or computer personality); and technical. No articles not related to computers or high-tech and society. Buys 12 mss/year. Query with published clips. Length: 250-1,000 words. Pays $50; $150 for scenes.

Columns/Departments: Computer Law . . . according to Murphy (humorous "laws" relating to computers, definitions, etc.). The editor buys all rights to Murphyisms which may be included in his book, *Computer Law . . . According to Murphy.* Buys 16 mss/year. Length: 25-75 words. Pays $10-50.

Tips: "Send materials with a note on your own background and qualifications to write what you submit. We invite intelligently presented and well-argued controversy within our field."

‡THE LAWYER'S PC, A Newsletter for Lawyers Using Personal Computers, Shepard's/McGraw-Hill, Inc.; editorial office at Box 1108, Lexington SC 29072. (803)359-9941. Editor: Robert P. Wilkins. Managing Editor: Daniel E. Harmon. 40% freelance written. A biweekly newsletter covering computerized law firms. "Our readers are lawyers who want to be told how a particular microcomputer program or type of program is being applied to a legal office task, such as timekeeping, litigation support, etc." Circ. 4,000. Pays end of the month of publication. Publishes ms an average of 4 months after acceptance. Byline given. Buys first North American serial rights and the right to reprint. Submit seasonal/holiday material 5 months in advance. Electronic submissions OK via IBM PC-compatible computers, preferably with WordPerfect software. Computer printout submissions acceptable; prefers letter-quality to dot-matrix. Reports in 1 month on queries; 2 months on mss. Sample copy for 9x12 SAE with 56¢ postage.

Nonfiction: How-to (applications articles on law office computerization) and software reviews written by lawyers who have no compromising interests. No general articles on why lawyers need computers or reviews of products written by public relations representatives or vending consultants. Buys 30-35 mss/year. Query.

Length: 500-2,500 words. Pays $25-125. Sometimes pays the expenses of writers on assignment.
Tips: "Most of our writers are lawyers. If you're not a lawyer, you need to at least understand why general business software may not work well in a law firm. If you understand lawyers' specific computer problems, write an article describing how to solve one of those problems, and we'd like to see it."

LEGAL ECONOMICS, The Magazine of Law Office Management, A Magazine of the Section of Economics of Law Practice of the American Bar Association, Box 11418, Columbia SC 29211. Managing Editor/Art Director: Delmar L. Roberts. 10% freelance written. For the practicing lawyer. 8 issues/year. Magazine; 80-100 pages. Circ. 27,000. Rights purchased vary with author and material. Usually buys all rights. Byline given. Pays on publication. Publishes ms an average of 8 months after acceptance. Computer printout submissions acceptable. Query. Free writer's guidelines; sample copy $6 (make check payable to American Bar Association). Returns rejected material in 90 days, if requested.
Nonfiction: "We assist the practicing lawyer in operating and managing his or her office by providing relevant articles and departments written in a readable and informative style. Editorial content is intended to aid the lawyer by conveying management methods that will allow him or her to provide legal services to clients in a prompt and efficient manner at reasonable cost. Typical topics of articles include fees and billing; word processing developments; microcomputer applications; client/lawyer relations; office equipment; compensation of partners and associates; legal data base research; and use of paralegals." No elementary articles on a whole field of technology, such as, "why you need word processing in the law office." Pays $75-300.
Photos: Pays $30-60 for b&w photos purchased with mss; $50-75 for color; $100-125 for cover transparencies.
Tips: "We occasionally publish thematic issues, such as one issue exclusively on computer hardware and another on software. Each issue has a theme in that 2 or more articles focus on a given topic."

LOS ANGELES LAWYER, Los Angeles County Bar Association, Box 55020, Los Angeles CA 90055. (213)627-2727, ext. 265. Editor: Susan Pettit. 100% freelance written. Prefers to work with published/established writers. Monthly (except for combined July/August issue) magazine covering legal profession with "journalistic and scholarly articles of interest to the legal profession." Circ. 17,000. Pays on acceptance. Publishes ms an average of 2 months after acceptance. Byline given. Buys first serial rights only. Submit seasonal/holiday material 4 months in advance. Simultaneous queries and photocopied submissions OK. Computer printout submissions acceptable; prefers letter-quality to dot-matrix. Reports in 1 month on queries; 2 months on mss. Sample copy $1.50; free writer's guidelines.
Nonfiction: How-to (tips for legal practitioners); humor; interview (leading legal figures); opinion (on area of law, lawyer attitudes or group, court decisions, etc.); travel (very occasionally); and consumer-at-law feature articles on topics of interest to lawyers. No first person, nonlegal material. Buys 22 mss/year. Query with published clips. Length: 4,000-4,500 words for feature (cover story); 2,000-2,750 words for consumer article. Pays $500-600 for cover story, $200-225 for consumer article. Sometimes pays the expenses of writers on assignment.
Tips: "Writers should be familiar with the Los Angeles legal community as the magazine has a local focus."

THE NATIONAL LAW JOURNAL, New York Law Publishing Company, 111 8th Ave., New York NY 10011. (212)741-8300. Editor: Timothy Robinson. Managing Editor: David Pike. 15% freelance written. Weekly newspaper for the legal profession. Circ. 40,000. Pays on publication. Publishes ms an average of 2 months after acceptance. Byline given. Offers $75 kill fee. Buys all rights. Simultaneous queries OK. Electronic submissions OK on 300 or 1200 baud. Computer printout submissions acceptable; prefers letter-quality to dot-matrix. Reports in 3 weeks on queries; 5 weeks on mss. Sample copy $2.
Nonfiction: Expose (on subjects of interest to lawyers); and interview/profile (of lawyers or judges of note). "The bulk of our freelance articles are 2,000-2,500 word profiles of prominent lawyers, or trend stories relating to the legal profession. We also buy a steady stream of short, spot-news stories on local court decisions or lawsuits; often, these come from legal affairs writers on local newspapers. No articles without a legal angle." Buys 60 mss/year. Query with published clips or send complete ms. Length: 1,500-3,000 words. Pays $300-500. Sometimes pays the expenses of writers on assignment.
Columns/Departments: "For those who are not covering legal affairs on a regular basis, the best way into *The National Law Journal* is probably through our Exhibit A feature. Every week we print a sort of reporter's notebook on some proceeding currently underway in a courtroom. These stories come from all around the country and range from gory murder trials to a night in small claims court. They usually run about 1,000 words and are stylistically quite flexible. We also use op-ed pieces on subjects of legal interest, many of which come from freelancers. Writers interested in doing an op-ed piece should query first." Pays $150.

ONTARIO LAWYERS WEEKLY, The Newspaper for the Legal Profession in Ontario, Butterworth (Canada) Inc., 2265 Midland Ave., Scarborough, Ontario M1P 4S1 Canada. (416)292-1421. Editor: D. Michael Fitz-James. 40% freelance written. "We will work with any *talented* writer of whatever experience level." A weekly tabloid covering law and legal affairs for a "sophisticated up-market readership of lawyers and accountants." Circ. 10,000. Pays on publication. Publishes ms an average of 1 month after acceptance. Byline given. Offers 50% kill fee. Usually buys all rights. Submit seasonal/holiday material 1 month in advance. Simultaneous queries and submissions, and photocopied submissions OK. Accepts electronic submissions via 1200 baud. "Call for specs." Computer printout submissions acceptable; prefers letter-quality to dot-matrix. SAE and IRC. Reports in 1 month. Sample copy $1.50 Canadian funds and 8½x11 SAE.

Nonfiction: Book reviews; expose; general interest (law); historical/nostalgic; how-to (professional); humor; interview/profile (lawyers and judges); opinion; technical; news; and case comments. "We try to wrap up the week's legal events and issues in a snappy informal package with lots of visual punch. We especially like news stories with photos or illustrations. We are always interested in feature or newsfeature articles involving current legal issues, but contributors should keep in mind our audience is trained in English/Canadian Common law—not U.S. law. That means most U.S. constitutional or criminal law stories will generally not be accepted. Contributors should also keep in mind they're writing for *lawyers* and they don't need to reduce legal stories to simple-minded babble often seen in the daily press." Special Christmas issue. No routine court reporting or fake news stories about commercial products. Buys 200-300 mss/year. Length: 700-1,500 words. Pays $25 minimum, negotiable maximum (have paid up to $250 in the past). Payment in Canadian dollars. Sometimes pays the expenses of writers on assignment.

Photos: State availability of photos with query letter or ms. Reviews b&w contact sheets, negatives, and 5x7 prints. Identification of subjects required. Buys one-time rights.

Columns/Departments: Buys 90-100 mss/year. Send complete ms. Length: 500-1,000 words. Pays negotiable rate.

Fillers: Clippings, jokes, gags, anecdotes, short humor and newsbreaks. Length: 50-200 words. Pays $10 minimum.

Tips: "Freelancers can best break into our publication by submitting news, features, and accounts of unusual or bizarre legal events. We'll be expanding our coverage from Ontario to National Canadian-marketplace. A frequent mistake made by writers is forgetting that our audience is intelligent and learned in law. They don't need the word 'plaintiff' explained to them." No unsolicited mss returned without SASE.

THE PARALEGAL, The Publication for the Paralegal Profession, Paralegal Publishing Corp./National Paralegal Association, 10 S. Pine St., Box 629, Doylestown PA 18901. (215)348-5575. Editor: William Cameron. 90% freelance written. Works with a small number of new/unpublished writers each year; eager to work with new/unpublished writers. Bimonthly magazine covering the paralegal profession for practicing paralegals, attorneys, paralegal educators, paralegal associations, law librarians and court personnel. Special and controlled circulation includes law libraries, colleges and schools educating paralegals, law schools, law firms and governmental agencies, etc. Circ. 4,000. Byline given. Buys all rights. Simultaneous queries, and simultaneous, photocopied, and previously published submissions OK. Computer printout submissions acceptable; prefers letter-quality to dot-matrix. Reports in 2 weeks on queries; 1 month on mss. Writer's guidelines and suggested topic sheet for business-size SAE.

Nonfiction: Book excerpts, expose, general interest, historical/nostalgic, how-to, humor, interview/profile, new product, opinion, personal experience, photo feature, technical and travel. Suggested topics include the paralegal (where do they fit and how do they operate within the law firm in each specialty); the government; the corporation; the trade union; the banking institution; the law library; the legal clinic; the trade or professional association; the educational institution; the court system; the collection agency; the stock brokerage firm; and the insurance company. Articles also wanted on paralegals exploring "Where have they been? Where are they now? Where are they going?" Query or send complete ms. Length: 1,500-3,000 words. Pays variable rates. Ask amount when submitting ms or other material to be considered.

Photos: Send photos with query or ms. Captions, model release, and identification of subjects required.

Columns/Departments: Case at Issue (a feature on a current case from a state or federal court which either directly or indirectly affects paralegals and their work with attorneys, the public, private or governmental sector); Humor (cartoons, quips, short humorous stories, anecdotes and one-liners in good taste and germane to the legal profession); and My Position (an actual presentation by a paralegal who wishes to share with others his/her job analysis). Query.

Fillers: Clippings, jokes, gags, anecdotes, short humor and newsbreaks.

THE PENNSYLVANIA LAWYER, Pennsylvania Bar Association, 100 South St., Box 186, Harrisburg PA 17108. (717)238-6715. Executive Editor: Francis J. Fanucci. Editor: Donald C. Sarvey. 20% freelance written. Prefers to work with published/established writers. Magazine published 7 times/year as a service to the legal profession. Circ. 26,000. Pays on acceptance. Publishes ms an average of 5 months after acceptance. Byline given. Buys negotiable serial rights; generally first rights, occasionally one-time rights or second serial (reprint) rights. Submit seasonal/holiday material 5 months in advance. Simultaneous submissions or queries will be considered, but the practice is not encouraged. If the submission or query is a simultaneous one, it should be so noted. Computer printout submissions acceptable; prefers letter-quality to dot-matrix. Reports in 2 weeks. Free sample copy.

Nonfiction: General interest, how-to, humor, interview/profile, new product, and personal experience. All features *should* relate in some way to Pennsylvania lawyers or the practice of law in Pennsylvania. Buys 12 mss/year. Query. Length: 800-2,500 words. Pays $75-350. Sometimes pays the expenses of writers on assignment.

STUDENT LAWYER, American Bar Association, 750 N. Lake Shore Dr., Chicago IL 60611. (312)988-6048. Editor: Lizanne Poppens. Associate Editor: Sarah Hoban. 95% freelance written. Works with a small number of new/unpublished writers each year. Monthly (September-May) magazine; 48-56 pages. Circ. 40,000. Pays on publication. Buys first serial rights and second serial (reprint) rights. Pays negotiable kill fee. Byline given. Submit seasonal/holiday material 4 months in advance. Photocopied submissions OK. Computer printout submissions acceptable; prefers letter-quality to dot-matrix. Reports in 6 weeks. Publishes ms an average of 3 months after acceptance. Sample copy $2; free writer's guidelines.
Nonfiction: Expose (government, law, education and business); profiles (prominent persons in law-related fields); opinion (on matters of current legal interest); essays (on legal affairs); interviews; and photo features. Recent article example: "The Growing Power of Private Police" (February 1986). Buys 5 mss/issue. Query. Length: 3,000-5,000 words. Pays $250-600 for main features. Covers some writer's expenses.
Columns/Departments: Briefly (short stories on unusual and interesting developments in the law); Legal Aids (unusual approaches and programs connected to teaching law students and lawyers); Esq. (brief profiles of people in the law); End Note (very short pieces on a variety of topics; can be humorous, educational, outrageous); Pro Se (opinion slot for authors to wax eloquent on legal issues, civil rights conflicts, the state of the union); and Et Al. (column for short features that fit none of the above categories). Buys 4-8 mss/issue. Length: 250-1,000 words. Pays $75-250.
Fiction: "We buy fiction only when it is very good and deals with issues of law in the contemporary world or offers insights into the inner workings of lawyers. No mystery or science fiction accepted."
Tips: "*Student Lawyer* actively seeks good new writers. Legal training definitely not essential; writing talent is. The writer should not think we are a law review; we are a feature magazine with the law (in the broadest sense) as the common denominator. Past articles concerned gay rights, prison reform, the media, pornography, capital punishment, and space law. Find issues of national scope and interest to write about; be aware of subjects the magazine—and other media—have already covered and propose something new. Write clearly and well."

VERDICT MAGAZINE, Legal Journal of the Association of Southern California Defense Counsel, American Lifestyle Communications, Inc., 123 Truxtun Ave., Bakersfield CA 93301. (805)325-7124. Editor: Sharon Muir. Managing Editor: Steve Walsh. A quarterly magazine covering defense law (corporate). Circ. 5,000. Pays on publication. Byline given. Buys first North American serial rights. Submit seasonal/holiday material 4 months in advance. Photocopied submissions OK. Computer printout submissions acceptable. Reports in 2 months. Sample copy for $2.50, 9x12 SAE and $2 postage; free writer's guidelines.
Nonfiction: How-to (corporate defense law); interview/profile; personal experience; and technical. Buys 12 mss/year. Send complete ms. Length: 1,500-3,000 words. Pays $20-35.
Photos: Send photos with ms. Pays $5-10 for 3x5 b&w prints. Captions required. Buys all rights.
Columns/Departments: Buys 4 mss/year. Send complete ms. Length: 500-750 words. Pays $15-20.
Fiction: Historical and mystery. Buys 4 mss/year. Send complete ms. Length: 1,500-3,000 words. Pays $20-35.

Leather Goods

SHOE SERVICE, SSIA Service Corp., Box 123, La Grange IL 60525. (312)482-8010. Editor: Mark Paulson. 50% freelance written. Monthly magazine for business people who own and operate small shoe repair shops. Circ. 6,500. Pays on publication. Publishes ms an average of 3 months after acceptance. Byline given. Buys first serial rights, first North American serial rights, and one-time rights. Submit seasonal/holiday material 3 months in advance. Simultaneous queries, and photocopied and previously published submissions OK. Computer printout submissions acceptable; prefers letter-quality to dot-matrix. Reports in 6 weeks. Sample copy $1.
Nonfiction: How-to (run a profitable shop); interview/profile (of an outstanding or unusual person on shoe repair); and business articles (particularly about small business practices in a service/retail shop). Buys 12-24 mss/year. Query with published clips or send complete ms. Length: 500-2,000 words. Pays 5¢/word.

Photos: "Quality photos will help sell an article." State availability of photos. Pays $10-30 for 8x10 b&w prints. Uses some color photos, but mostly uses b&w glossies. Captions, model release, and identification of subjects required.

Tips: "Visit some shoe repair shops to get an idea of the kind of person who reads *Shoe Service*. Profiles are the easiest to sell to us if you can find a repairer we think is unusual."

Library Science

AMERICAN LIBRARIES, 50 E. Huron St., Chicago IL 60611. (312)944-6780. Editor: Arthur Plotnik. 5-10% freelance written. Works with a small number of new/unpublished writers each year. Magazine published 11 times/year for librarians. "A highly literate audience. They are for the most part practicing professionals with a down-to-earth interest in people and current trends." Circ. 42,500. Buys first North American serial rights. Publishes ms an average of 4 months after acceptance. Pays negotiable kill fee. Byline given. Will consider photocopied submissions if not being considered elsewhere at time of submission. Computer printout submissions acceptable; prefers letter-quality to dot-matrix. Submit seasonal material 6 months in advance. Reports in 10 weeks.

Nonfiction: "Material reflecting the special and current interests of the library profession. Nonlibrarians should browse recent journals in the field, available on request in medium-sized and large libraries everywhere. Topic and/or approach must be fresh, vital, or highly entertaining. Library memoirs and stereotyped stories about old maids, overdue books, fines, etc., are unacceptable. Our first concern is with the American Library Association's activities and how they relate to the 42,000 reader/members. Tough for an outsider to write on this topic, but not to supplement it with short, offbeat or significant library stories and features." No fillers. Pays expenses of writers on assignment.

Photos: "Will look at all good black and white, well-lit photos of library situations, and at color transparencies and bright prints for possible cover use." Buys 10-15 mss/year. Pays $25-200 for briefs and articles. Pays $25-75 for b&w photos.

Tips: "You can break in with a sparkling, 300-word report on a true, offbeat library event, use of new technology, or with an exciting photo and caption. Though stories on public libraries are always of interest, we especially need arresting material on academic and school libraries."

CHURCH MEDIA LIBRARY MAGAZINE, 127 9th Ave. N., Nashville TN 37234. (615)251-2752. Editor: Floyd B. Simpson. Quarterly magazine; 50 pages. For adult leaders in church organizations and people interested in library work (especially church library work). Circ. 16,000. Pays on publication. Buys all rights, first serial rights and second serial (reprint) rights. Byline given. Phone queries OK. Submit seasonal/holiday material 14 months in advance. Previously published submissions OK. Reports in 1 month. Free sample copy and writer's guidelines.

Nonfiction: "We are primarily interested in articles that relate to the development of church libraries in providing media and services to support the total program of a church and in meeting individual needs. We publish how-to accounts of services provided, promotional ideas, exciting things that have happened as a result of implementing an idea or service; human interest stories that are library-related; and media education (teaching and learning with a media mix). Articles should be practical for church library staffs and for teachers and other leaders of the church." Buys 10-15 mss/issue. Query. Pays 5¢/word.

EMERGENCY LIBRARIAN, Dyad Services, Box 46258, Stn. G, Vancouver, British Columbia V6R 4G6 Canada. Co-Editors: Carol Ann Haycock and Ken Haycock. Bimonthly magazine. Circ. 4,500. Pays on publication. Photocopied submissions OK. No multiple submissions. SAE and IRCs. Reports in 6 weeks. Free writer's guidelines.

Nonfiction: Emphasis is on improvement of library service for children and young adults in school and public libraries. Also annotated bibliographies. Buys 3 mss/issue. Query. Length: 1,000-3,500 words. Pays $50.

Columns/Departments: Five regular columnists. Also Book Reviews (of professional materials in education, librarianship). Query. Length: 100-300 words. Payment consists of book reviewed.

SCHOOL LIBRARY JOURNAL, 205 E. 42nd. St., New York NY 10017. Editor: Lillian N. Gerhardt. For librarians in schools and public libraries. Magazine published 10 times/year; 88 pages. Circ. 43,000. Buys all rights. Pays on publication. Reports in 6 months.

Nonfiction: Articles on library services, local censorship problems, and how-to articles on programs that use books, films or microcomputer software. Informational, personal experience, interview, expose, and successful business operations. "Interested in history articles on the establishment/development of children's and young adult services in schools and public libraries." Buys 24 mss/year. Length: 2,500-3,000 words. Pays $100 and up, depending on length.

WILSON LIBRARY BULLETIN, 950 University Ave., Bronx NY 10452. (212)588-8400. Editor: Milo Nelson. 80% freelance written. Monthly (September-June) for professional librarians and those interested in the book and library worlds. Circ. 30,000. Pays on publication. Publishes ms an average of 2 months after acceptance. Buys first North American serial rights. Sample copies may be seen on request in most libraries. "Manuscript must be original copy, double-spaced; additional photocopy or carbon is appreciated." Computer printout submissions acceptable; prefers letter-quality to dot-matrix. Deadlines are a minimum 2 months before publication. Reports in 3 months.
Nonfiction: Uses articles "of interest to librarians throughout the nation and around the world. Style must be lively, readable and sophisticated, with appeal to modern professionals; facts must be thoroughly researched. Subjects range from the political to the comic in the world of media and libraries, with an emphasis on the human as well as the technical aspects of any story. No condescension: no library stereotypes." Buys 30 mss/year. Send complete ms. Length: 2,500-6,000 words. Pays about $100-400, "depending on the substance of article and its importance to readers." Sometimes pays the expenses of writers on assignment.
Tips: "The best way you can break in is with a first-rate black and white photo and caption information on a library, library service, or librarian who departs completely from all stereotypes and the commonplace. Libraries have changed. You'd better first discover what is now commonplace."

____ *Lumber and Woodworking*

B.C. LUMBERMAN MAGAZINE, Box 34080, Station D, Vancouver, British Columbia V6J 4M8 Canada. (604)731-1171. Editorial Director: Brian Martin. 60% freelance written. Monthly magazine; 75 pages. For the logging and saw milling industries of western Canada and the Pacific Northwest of the United States. Circ. 8,500. Pays on acceptance. Publishes ms an average of 2 months after acceptance. Buys first Canadian serial rights. Submit seasonal/holiday material 2 months in advance. Reports in 2 weeks.
Nonfiction: How-to (technical articles on any aspect of the forest industry); general interest (anything of interest to persons in forest industries in western Canada or U.S. Pacific Northwest); interview (occasionally related to leading forestry personnel); and technical (forestry). No fiction or history. Buys 8 mss/issue. Query first with published clips. Length: 1,500 words average. Pays 15¢/word (Canadian).
Photos: State availability of photos with query. Pays $5-25 for b&w negatives and $50-80 for 8x10 glossy color prints. Captions required. Buys first Canadian rights.

NORTHERN LOGGER AND TIMBER PROCESSOR, Northeastern Loggers' Association, Box 69, Old Forge NY 13420. (315)369-3078. Editor: Eric A. Johnson. 40% freelance written. Monthly magazine of the forest industry in the northern U.S. (Maine to Minnesota and south to Virginia and Missouri). "We are not a purely technical journal, but are more information oriented." Circ. 13,000. Pays on publication. Publishes ms an average of 3 months after acceptance. Byline given. Buys all rights. Submit seasonal/holiday material 3 months in advance. Photocopied and previously published submissions OK. "Any computer printout submission that can be easily read is acceptable." Reports in 2 weeks. Free sample copy.
Nonfiction: Expose, general interest, historical/nostalgic, how-to, interview/profile, new product and opinion. "We only buy feature articles, and those should contain some technical or historical material relating to the forest products industry." Buys 12-15 mss/year. Query. Length: 500-2,500 words. Pays $25-125.
Photos: Send photos with ms. Pays $20-35 for 35mm color transparencies; $5-15 for 5x7 b&w prints. Captions and identification of subjects required.
Tips: "We accept most any subject dealing with this part of the country's forest industry, from historical to logging, firewood, and timber processing."

ROSEBURG WOODSMAN, Roseburg Forest Products Co., c/o Hugh Dwight Advertising, Suite 101, 4905 SW Griffith Dr., Beaverton OR 97005. Editor: Shirley P. Rogers. 99% (but most rewritten) freelance written. Prefers to work with published/established writers. Monthly magazine for wholesale lumber distributors and other buyers of forest products, such as furniture manufacturers. Emphasis on wood products, especially company products. Publishes a special Christmas issue. Circ. 8,000. Pays on publication. Publishes ms an average of 1 year after acceptance. Buys first serial rights or one-time rights. No byline given. Submit seasonal material 6 months in advance. Computer printout submissions acceptable; prefers letter-quality to dot-matrix. Reports in 1 week. Free sample copy and writer's guidelines.

Nonfiction: Features on the "residential, commercial and industrial applications of wood products, such as lumber, plywood, prefinished wall paneling, and particleboard, particularly Roseburg Lumber Co. products. We are no longer looking for stories on hobbyists or individual craftsmen. No 'clever,' 'wise' or witty contributions unless they tell a fascinating story and are well-illustrated. No fillers, isolated photos or inadequately illustrated articles." Buys 25-30 mss/year. Query or submit complete ms. Length: 250-500 words. Pays $50-$100. Pays expenses of writers on assignment.

Photos: "Photos are essential. Good pictures will sell us on a story." Rarely uses b&w photos or color prints. Prefers color transparencies or 35mm slides. Pays $25-50/color transparency used, more for cover photo. Photos purchased only with ms.

Tips: "Since everything is rewritten to our style, the writer's style is not vitally important. However, there should be some expertise regarding forest products terms, and an absolute dedication to accuracy. I sometimes hire a freelancer 'on assignment' at a higher rate. Send letter specifying experience, publications, types of stories and geographic area covered."

TREE TRIMMERS LOG, A Newsletter For Today's Tree Trimmer, Tree Trimmers Log, Box 833, Ojai CA 93023. (805)646-9688. Editor: D. Keith. Eager to work with new/unpublished writers. Trade newsletter on tree trimming published 10 times/year. Circ. 400. Pays on acceptance. Publishes ms an average of 2 months after acceptance. Byline given. Offers 25% kill fee. Buys first serial rights. Submit seasonal/holiday material 2 months in advance. Simultaneous queries, and simultaneous, photocopied, and previously published submissions OK. Computer printout submissions acceptable. Reports in 1 month. Free sample copy and writer's guidelines.

Nonfiction: Historical/nostalgic (trees, older trimmer reminiscings); how-to (run small businesses, maintain equipment, be more efficient in work); humor; interview/profile (of a trimmer with a slant: singing trimmer, community concerned trimmer, etc.); new product; personal experience (if you're a working trimmer); photo feature (rescue action); and technical (taking care of equipment, climbing gear). No "cuteness." Buys 12-15 mss/year. Query or send complete ms. Length: 50-800 words. Pays $5-25.

Photos: State availability of photos. Reviews b&w contact sheets and b&w 3½x5 prints. Pays $5 for contact sheets; $5-10 for prints. Identification of subjects required. Buys first serial rights.

Columns/Departments: Chain Saw (or equipment) Corner and First Aid (50-150 words). "We're open to suggestions." Buys 10/year. Query. Length: 150-350 words. Pays $10.

Fillers: Clippings, jokes, anecdotes, short humor, puzzles, newsbreaks and cartoons. Buys 20/year. Pays $5.

Tips: "Submit a query for an interview with a tree trimmer, a local college horticulturist (trees), etc. Find someone unique, with a good story to tell, or who can offer tips to his fellow trimmers. Being writers, we work with and encourage writers. Our prices are low now, but we invite writers to grow with us."

Machinery and Metal

‡CANADIAN MACHINERY & METALWORKING, 777 Bay St., Toronto, Ontario M5W 1A7 Canada. (416)596-5714. Editor: Nick Hancock. 25% freelance written. Monthly. Buys first Canadian rights. Pays on acceptance. Query. Publishes ms an average of 6 weeks after acceptance.

Nonfiction: Technical and semitechnical articles dealing with metalworking operations in Canada and in the U.S., if of particular interest to Canadian readers. Accuracy and service appeal to readers is a must. Pays minimum 25¢/word.

Photos: Purchased with mss and with captions only. Pays $10 minimum for b&w features.

CUTTING TOOL ENGINEERING, 464 Central Ave., Northfield IL 60093. (312)441-7520. Publisher: John William Roberts. Editor: Larry Teeman. 25% freelance written. Prefers to work with published/established writers. For metalworking industry executives and engineers concerned with the metal-cutting/metal-removal/abrasive machining function in metalworking. Bimonthly. 25% freelance written. Circ. 38,775. Pays on publication. Publishes ms an average of 6 months after acceptance. Byline given. Buys all rights. Electronic submissions OK on IBM PC, but requires hard copy also. Computer printout submissions acceptable; no dot-matrix. Call Larry Teeman before querying or submitting ms. Will send free sample copy on request.

Nonfiction: "Intelligently written articles on specific applications of all types of metal cutting tools, mills, drills, reamers, etc. Articles must contain all information related to the operation, such as feeds and speeds, materials machined, etc. Should be tersely written, in-depth treatment. In the Annual Diamond/Superabrasive Directory, published in June, we cover the use of diamond/superabrasive cutting tools and diamond/superabrasive grinding wheels." Length: 1,000-2,500 words. Pays "$35/published page, or about 5¢/published word."
Photos: Purchased with mss. 8x10 b&w glossies preferred.
Tips: "The most frequent mistake made by writers in completing an article for us is that they don't know the market."

MODERN MACHINE SHOP, 6600 Clough Pike, Cincinnati OH 45244. Editor: Ken Gettelman. 25% freelance written. Monthly. Pays 1 month following acceptance. Publishes ms an average of 6 months after acceptance. Byline given. Electronic submissions OK if IBM compatible, but requires hard copy also. Computer printout submissions acceptable; prefers letter-quality to dot-matrix. Reports in 5 days.
Nonfiction: Uses articles dealing with all phases of metal working manufacturing and machine shop work, with photos. No general articles. "Ours is an industrial publication, and contributing authors should have a working knowledge of the metalworking industry." Buys 10 unsolicited mss/year. Query. Length: 800-3,000 words. Pays current market rate. Sometimes pays the expenses of writers on assignment.
Tips: "The use of articles relating to computers in manufacturing is growing."

Maintenance and Safety

‡CLEANING MANAGEMENT, The Magazine for Today's Building Maintenance Housekeeping Executive, Harris Communications, 1550 Rockfield Blvd., Irvine CA 92718. (714)770-5008. Editor: R. Daniel Harris Jr. Monthly magazine covering building maintenance/housekeeping operations in large institutions such as hotels, schools, hospitals, etc., as well as commercial and industrial, recreational and religious buildings, stores and markets. For managers with on-staff cleaning operations, contract cleaning service companies, and professional carpet cleaning companies. Circ. 34,000. Pays on publication. Byline given. Offers "full payment, if article has been completed." Buys all rights. Submit seasonal/holiday material 3 months in advance. Simultaneous queries and photocopied submissions OK. Reports in 1 month. Free sample copy and writer's guidelines.
Nonfiction: How-to (custodial operations); interview/profile (of custodial managers); opinion (of custodial managers); personal experience (on-the-job). Special issues include: March—Carpet Care; April and June—Floor Care; May—Exterior Building Maintenance; September—Office Cleaning. Buys 5-6 mss/year. Query. Length: 1,000-2,000 words. Pays $100-300.
Photos: State availability of photos. Pays $5-15 for 8x10 b&w prints; $20-75 for 4x5 color transparencies. Captions, model release, and identification of subjects required.
Tips: "We want writers familiar with our field or who can pick it up quickly."

EQUIPMENT MANAGEMENT, 7300 N. Cicero Ave., Lincolnwood IL 60646. (312)588-7300. Editor: Greg Sitek. 10% freelance written. "We are always interested in material related to the equipment industry." Monthly magazine; 76-110 pages. Circ. 55,000. Pays on publication. Publishes ms an average of 4 months after acceptance. Rights purchased vary with author and material; usually buys all rights. Computer printout submissions acceptable; prefers letter-quality to dot-matrix. Reports in 1 month. Free sample copy.
Nonfiction: "Our focus is on the effective management of equipment through proper selection, careful specification, correct application and efficient maintenance. We use job stories, technical articles, safety features, basics and shop notes. No product stories or 'puff' pieces." Buys 12 mss/year. Query with outline. Length: 2,000-5,000 words. Pays $25/printed page minimum, without photos. Sometimes pays the expenses of writers on assignment.
Photos: Uses 35mm and 2¼x2¼ or larger color transparencies with mss. Pays $50/printed page when photos are furnished by author.
Tips: "Know the equipment, how to manage it and how to maintain, service, and repair it."

‡PEST CONTROL MAGAZINE, 7500 Old Oak Blvd., Cleveland OH 44130. (216)243-8100. Editor: Jerry Mix. For professional pest control operators and sanitation workers. Monthly magazine; 68 pages. Circ. 15,000. Buys all rights. Buys 12+ mss/year. Pays on publication. Submit seasonal material 2 months in advance. Reports in 30 days. Query or submit complete ms.

Nonfiction and Photos: Business tips, unique control situations, personal experience (stories about 1-man operations and their problems) articles. Must have trade or business orientation. No general information type of articles desired. Buys 3 unsolicited mss/year. Length: 4 double-spaced pages. Pays $150 minimum. Regular columns use material oriented to this profession. Length: 8 double-spaced pages. No additional payment for photos used with mss. Pays $50-150 for 8x10 color or transparencies.

SANITARY MAINTENANCE, Trade Press Publishing Co., 2100 W. Florist Ave., Milwaukee WI 53209. (414)228-7701. Managing Editor: Don Mulligan. Associate Editor: Susan M. Netz. 7-8% freelance written. Prefers to work with published/established writers, although all will be considered. A monthly magazine for the sanitary supply industry covering "trends in the sanitary supply industry; offering information concerning the operations of janitor supply distributors and building service contractors; and helping distributors in the development of sales personnel." Circ. 13,756. Pays on publication. Publishes ms an average of 5 months after acceptance. Byline given. Buys first North American serial rights. Photocopied submissions OK. Computer printout submissions acceptable; prefers letter-quality to dot-matrix. Free sample copy and writer's guidelines.
Nonfiction: How-to (improve sales, profitability as it applies to distributors, contractors); and technical. No product application stories. Buys 8-12 mss/year. Query with published clips. Length: 1,500-3,000 words. Pays $75-200.
Photos: State availability of photos with query letter or ms. Reviews 5x7 prints. Payment for photos included in payment for ms. Identification of subjects required.
Tips: Articles on sales and financial information for small businesses are open to freelancers.

SERVICE BUSINESS, Published Quarterly for the Self-Employed Professional Cleaner, Service Business Magazine, Inc., Suite 345, 1916 Pike Place, Seattle WA 98101. (206)622-4241. Publisher/Editor: William R. Griffin. 80% freelance written. Quarterly magazine covering technical and management information relating to cleaning and self-employment. "We cater to those who are self-employed in any facet of the cleaning and maintenance industry who seek to be top professionals in their field. Our readership is small but select. We seek concise, factual articles, realistic but definitely upbeat." Circ. 5,000. Pays between acceptance and publication. Publishes ms an average of 3 months after acceptance. Byline given. Buys first serial rights, second serial (reprint) rights, and all rights; makes work-for-hire assignments. Submit seasonal/holiday material 4 months in advance. Simultaneous queries and previously published work (rarely) OK. Computer printout submissions acceptable; prefers letter-quality to dot-matrix. Reports in 3 months. Sample copy $3, 9x7½ SAE and 3 first class stamps; writer's guidelines for business size SAE and 1 first class stamp.
Nonfiction: Expose (safety/health business practices); how-to (on cleaning, maintenance, small business management); humor (clean jokes, cartoons); interview/profile; new product (must be unusual to rate full article—mostly obtained from manufacturers); opinion; personal experience; and technical. Special issues include "What's New?" (Feb. 10). No "wordy tomes written off the top of the head, obviously without research, and needing more editing time than was spent on writing." Buys 40 mss/year. Query with or without published clips. Length: 500-3,000 words. Pays $5-80. ("Pay depends on amount of work, research and polishing put into article much more than on length.") Sometimes pays the expenses of writers on assignment.
Photos: State availability of photos or send photos with ms. Pays $5-25 for "smallish" b&w prints. Captions, model release, and identification of subjects required. Buys one-time rights and reprint rights. "Magazine size is 8½x7—photos need to be proportionate."
Columns/Departments: "Ten regular columnists now sell four columns per year to us. We are interested in adding a Safety & Health column (related to cleaning and maintenance industry). We are also open to other suggestions—send query." Buys 36 columns/year; department information obtained at no cost. Query with or without published clips. Length: 500-1,500 words. Pays $15-85.
Fillers: Jokes, gags, anecdotes, short humor, newsbreaks and cartoons. Buys 40/year. Length: 3-200 words. Pays $1-20.
Tips: "A freelancer can best break into our publication with fairly technical articles on how to do specific cleaning/maintenance jobs; interviews with top professionals covering this and how they manage their business; and personal experience. Our readers demand concise, accurate information. Don't ramble. Write only about what you know and/or have researched. Editors don't have time to rewrite your rough draft. Organize and polish before submitting."

Market conditions are constantly changing! If this is 1988 or later, buy the newest edition of Writer's Market *at your favorite bookstore or order directly from* Writer's Digest Books.

Management and Supervision

This category includes trade journals for middle management business and industrial managers, including supervisors and office managers. Journals for business executives and owners are classified under Business Management. Those for industrial plant managers are listed in Industrial Operation and Management.

CONSTRUCTION SUPERVISION & SAFETY LETTER, (CL) Bureau of Business Practice, 24 Rope Ferry Rd., Waterford CT 06386. (203)442-4365. Editor: DeLoris Lidestri. 80% freelance written. "I'm *willing* to work with a few new writers if they're willing to follow guidelines carefully." Semimonthly newsletter; 4 pages. Emphasizes all aspects of construction supervision. Buys all rights. Publishes ms an average of 4 months after acceptance. Phone queries OK. Submit seasonal material at least 4 months in advance. Reports in 6 weeks. Free sample copy and writer's guidelines.
Nonfiction: Publishes solid interviews with construction managers or supervisors on how to improve a single aspect of the supervisor's job. Buys 100 unsolicited mss/year. Length: 360-720 words. Pays 10-15¢/word.
Photos: Purchased with accompanying ms. Pays $10 for head and shoulders photo of person interviewed. Total purchase price for ms includes payment for photo.
Tips: "A writer should call before he or she does anything. I like to spend a few minutes on the phone exchanging information."

EMPLOYEE RELATIONS AND HUMAN RESOURCES BULLETIN, Bureau of Business Practice, 24 Rope Ferry Rd., Waterford CT 06386. Supervisory Editor: Barbara Kelsey. 75% freelance written. Works with a small number of new/unpublished writers each year. For personnel, human resources and employee relations managers on the executive level. Semimonthly newsletter; 8 pages. Circ. 3,000. Pays on acceptance. Publishes ms an average of 3 months after acceptance. Buys all rights. No byline. Phone queries OK. Submit seasonal/holiday material 6 months in advance. Photocopied submissions OK. Computer printout submissions acceptable; prefers letter-quality to dot-matrix. Reports in 1 month. Free sample copy and writer's guidelines.
Nonfiction: Interviews about all types of business and industry such as banks, insurance companies, public utilities, airlines, consulting firms, etc. Interviewee should be a high level company officer—general manager, president, industrial relations manager, etc. Writer must get signed release from person interviewed showing that article has been read and approved by him/her, before submission. Some subjects for interviews might be productivity improvement, communications, compensation, government regulations, safety and health, grievance handling, human relations techniques and problems, etc. No general opinions and/or philosophy of good employee relations or general good motivation/morale material. Buys 3 mss/issue. Query. Length: 700-2,000 words. Pays 10¢/word after editing. Sometimes pays the expenses of writers on assignment.

THE FOREMAN'S LETTER, Bureau of Business Practice, 24 Rope Ferry Rd., Waterford CT 06386. (203)442-4365. Editor: Carl Thunberg. 50% freelance written. Works with a small number of new/unpublished writers each year. Semimonthly. For industrial supervisors. Pays on acceptance. Publishes ms an average of 3 months after acceptance. Buys all rights. Interested in regular stringers (freelance). Computer printout submissions acceptable. Comprehensive guidelines available.
Nonfiction: Interested primarily in direct in-depth interviews with industrial supervisors in the U.S. and Canada. Subject matter would be the interviewee's techniques for becoming a more effective manager, bolstered by illustrations out of the interviewee's own job experiences. Slant would be toward informing readers how to solve a particular supervisory problem. "Our aim is to offer information which readers may apply to their own professional self improvement. No copy that focuses on the theme that 'happy workers are productive workers.' " Buys 15-20 unsolicited mss/year. Length: 600-1,200 words. Pays 8¢-14½¢/word "after editing for all rights."
Photos: Buys photos submitted with mss. Captions needed for identification only. Head and shoulders, any size b&w glossy from 2x3 up. Pays $10.
Tips: "Study our editorial guidelines carefully. Emulate the style of sample issues. Write a how-to article fo-

cusing on one specific topic. A new freelancer should be willing to rewrite submissions if necessary. Editor will offer suggestions. An effort will be made to cultivate freelancers who comply the *closest* to editorial guidelines."

HIGH-TECH MANAGER'S BULLETIN, TEM, Bureau of Business Practice, 24 Rope Ferry Rd., Waterford CT 06386. (203)442-4365. Editor: Isabel Will Becker. 50-75% freelance written. "I work with both new or established writers, and am always looking for fresh talent." Bimonthly newsletter for technical supervisors wishing to improve their managerial skills in high technology fields. Pays on acceptance. Publishes ms on average of 6 weeks after acceptance. No byline given. Buys all rights. Computer printout submissions acceptable; prefers letter-quality to dot-matrix. Reports in 2 weeks on queries, 6 weeks on mss. Free sample copy and writer's guidelines.
Nonfiction: How-to (solve a supervisory problem on the job); and interview (of top-notch supervisors and managers). "Sample topics could include: how-to increase productivity, cut costs, achieve better teamwork, and help employees adapt to change." No filler or non-interview based copy. Buys 72 mss/year. Query first. "Strongly urge writers to study guidelines and samples." Length: 750-1,000 words. Pays 8-14¢/word. Sometimes pays the expenses of writers on assignment "under unusual circumstances.
Tips: "We need interview-based articles that emphasize direct quotes. Each article should include a reference to the interviewee's company (location, size, products, function of the interviewee's department and number of employees under his control). Define a problem and show how the supervisor solved it. Write in a light, conversational style, talking directly to technical supervisors who can benefit from putting the interviewee's tips into practice."

LE BUREAU, Suite 1000, 1001 de Maisonneuve W., Montreal, Quebec H3A 3E1 Canada. (514)845-5141. Editor: Paul Saint-Pierre, C.Adm. "We are backlogged with submissions and prefer not to receive unsolicited submissions at this time."

MANAGE, 2210 Arbor Blvd., Dayton OH 45439. (513)294-0421. Editor-in-Chief: Douglas E. Shaw. 60% freelance written. Quarterly magazine; 40 pages. For first-line and middle management and scientific/technical managers. Circ. 75,000. Pays on acceptance. Buys North American magazine rights with reprint privileges; book rights remain with the author. Reports in 1 month. Free sample copy and writer's guidelines.
Nonfiction: "All material published by *Manage* is in some way management oriented. Most articles concern one or more of the following categories: communications, cost reduction, economics, executive abilities, health and safety, human relations, job status, labor relations, leadership, motivation and productivity and professionalism. Articles should be specific and tell the manager how to apply the information to his job immediately. Be sure to include pertinent examples, and back up statements with facts and, where possible, charts and illustrations. *Manage* does not want essays or academic reports, but interesting, well-written and practical articles for and about management." Buys 6 mss/issue. Phone queries OK. Submit complete ms. Length: 600-2,000 words. Pays 5¢/word.
Tips: "Keep current on management subjects; submit timely work."

‡MANAGEMENT DIGEST, Allied Publications, 1776 Lake Worth Rd., Lake Worth FL 33460. (305)582-2099. Editor: Mark Adams. 50% freelance written. A monthly magazine sold to client businesses nationwide for distribution to their customers as a promotion/public relations tool. Covers creative management, career development and business humor. "*Management Digest* provides executives and managers with perspectives on the 'human element' in business life." Estab. 1985. Circ. 20,000. Pays on acceptance. Publishes ms an average of 3 months after acceptance. Byline given (except for some fillers). Buys first rights, one-time rights, second serial (reprint rights) or makes work-for-hire assignments. Submit seasonal/holiday material 8 months in advance. Simultaneous, photocopied, and previously published submissions OK. Computer printout submissions acceptable. Reports in one month. Sample copy and writer's guidelines for 9x12 SAE with 50¢ postage.
Nonfiction: Book excerpts (management strategies and techniques); essays (on humor and opinion); general interest (business); historical/nostalgic (biographical or industry-oriented); how-to (on improving communication skills, management styles); humor (of fewer than 600 words in length); personal experience (in a business or management situation); photo feature; technical (for the lay reader only, such as "coping with your PC"); and travel (for the business traveler). "We're rarely interested in market forecasts, economics or short range trends. We're interested in the business world in a broader context and the individual manager's place in it." Buys 40 mss/year. Query with or without published clips, or send complete ms. Length: 200-1,200 words. Pays 5¢/word-$25. May pay in copies rather than cash at writer's request.
Photos: Send photos with submission. Reviews prints. Offers $5 minimum. Captions, and identification of subjects required. Buys one-time rights.
Fillers: Anecdotes, facts and short humor. Buys 10-20/year. Length: 20-100 words. Pays 5¢-$10.
Tips: Freelancers have the best chance of selling short nonfiction—"essays offering fresh perspectives on

classical business concerns, especially self-evaluation and improvement, human relations, communication, career advancement, office humor and anecdotes."

PERSONNEL ADVISORY BULLETIN, Bureau of Business Practice, 24 Rope Ferry Rd., Waterford CT 06386. (203)442-4365, ext. 355. Editor: Laura Gardner. 75% freelance written. Emphasizes all aspects of personnel practitioners for personnel managers in all types and sizes of companies, both white collar and industrial. Semimonthly newsletter; 8 pages. Pays on acceptance. Publishes ms an average of 4 months after acceptance. Buys all rights. Phone queries OK. Submit seasonal/holiday material 4 months in advance. Computer printout submissions acceptable; no dot-matrix. Reports in 2 weeks. Free sample copy and writer's guidelines for SAE and 1 first class stamp.
Nonfiction: Interviews with personnel managers or human resource professionals on topics of current interest in the personnel field. No articles on hiring and interviewing, discipline, or absenteeism/tardiness control. Buys 30 mss/year. Query with brief, specific outline. Length: 1,000-1,500 words.
Tips: "We're looking for concrete, practical material on how to solve problems. We're providing information about trends and developments in the field. We don't want filler copy. It's very easy to break in. Just query by phone or letter (preferably phone) and we'll discuss the topic. Send for guidelines first, though, so we can have a coherent conversation."

PRODUCTIVITY IMPROVEMENT BULLETIN, PIB, Bureau of Business Practice, 24 Rope Ferry Rd., Waterford CT 06386. (203)442-4365. Editor: Shelley Wolf. 75% freelance written. Eager to work with new/unpublished writers. Semimonthly newsletter covering productivity improvement program and techniques of interest to middle management. Pays on acceptance. Publishes ms an average of 4 months after acceptance. No byline given. Buys all rights. Computer printout submissions acceptable; prefers letter-quality to dot-matrix. Reports in 2 weeks on queries; 1 month on mss. Free sample copy and writer's guidelines.
Nonfiction: Interviews with middle managers from business or industry detailing how they solved a particular productivity problem. "Our intent is to offer readers a 'success story' for consideration, then show them how they can put these proven techniques into practice in their own company. Stories *must* combine case-study information with how-to advice, organized into a series of 'steps to follow.' " No articles on general management theory. Buys 50 mss/year. Query. Length: 1,000-1,300 words. Pays 10-15¢/word "after editing."
Columns/Departments: "Personal Productivity column uses interview-based copy explaining specific measures managers can take to increase their personal effectiveness." Buys 12 mss/year. Query. Length: 800-1,000 words. Pays 10-15¢/word.
Tips: "All articles *must* cover a 'problem/solution/how-to/results' format as described in the writer's guidelines. Be willing to rewrite, if necessary. Topics should be well focused. (Check with us before doing the write-up. We like to talk to freelancers.) Writing should be conversational; use the 'you' approach and speak directly to the readers. Use subheads and questions to guide the reader through your piece. Articles on activities of a specific company are subject to its approval."

SALES MANAGER'S BULLETIN, The Bureau of Business Practice, 24 Rope Ferry Rd., Waterford CT 06386. Editor: Paulette S. Withers. 25-50% freelance written. Newsletter published twice a month; 8 pages. For sales managers and salespeople interested in getting into sales management. Pays on acceptance. Publishes ms an average of 6 months after acceptance. Written queries only except from regulars. Submit seasonal/holiday material 6 months in advance. Original submissions only. Buys all rights. Computer printout submissions acceptable; prefers letter-quality to dot-matrix. Reports in 2 weeks. Free sample copy and writer's guidelines only when accompanied by SASE.
Nonfiction: How-to (motivate salespeople, cut costs, create territories, etc.); interview (with working sales managers who use innovative techniques); and technical (marketing stories based on interviews with experts). No articles on territory management, saving fuel in the field, or public speaking skills. Break into this publication by reading the guidelines and sample issue. Follow the directions closely and chances for acceptance go up dramatically. One easy way to start is with an interview article ("Here's what sales executives have to say about . . ."). Query is vital to acceptance; "send a simple postcard explaining briefly the subject matter, the interviewees (if any), slant, length, and date of expected completion, accompanied by a SASE." Length: 800-1,500. Pays 10-15¢/word.
Tips: "Freelancers should always request samples and writer's guidelines, accompanied by SASE. Requests without SASE are discarded immediately. Examine the sample, and don't try to improve on our style. Write as we write. Don't 'jump around' from point to point and don't submit articles that are too chatty and with not enough real information. The more time a writer can save the editors, the greater his or her chance of a sale and repeated sales, when queries may not be necessary any longer."

SECURITY MANAGEMENT, American Society for Industrial Security, Suite 1200, 1655 N. Fort Myer Dr., Arlington VA 22209. (703)522-5800. Publisher: Mary Alice Crawford. Managing Editor: Pamela Blumgart. 10% freelance written. Monthly professional magazine of the security industry (i.e., protecting assets from loss). Circ. 25,000. Pays on publication. Call publisher to discuss payment arrangement. Publishes ms an average of 4 months after acceptance. Byline given. Buys all rights. Submit seasonal/holiday material 6 months in advance. Simultaneous queries OK. Computer printout submissions acceptable; prefers letter-quality to dot-matrix. Reports in 3 weeks on queries; 10 weeks on mss. Free sample copy and writer's guidelines.

Nonfiction: Mary Alice Crawford, articles editor. Book excerpts, how-to, interview/profile, opinion, personal experience, photo feature and technical. Case studies, analytical pieces and new approaches to persistent security problems such as access control and computer security. No humor. "Send a coherent outline query." Buys 5-10 mss/year. Query or outline *only*, with or without published clips. Length: 1,500-5,000 words. Payment negotiable; no payment for unsolicited mss.

Photos: State availability of photos. Reviews b&w and color contact sheets and prints, and color transparencies.

Fillers: Cecily Roberts, fillers editor. Clippings, anecdotes and newsbreaks. Buys variable number/year. Length: 50-200 words.

SECURITY MANAGEMENT: PROTECTING PROPERTY, PEOPLE & ASSETS, Bureau of Business Practice, 24 Rope Ferry Rd., Waterford CT 06386. Editor: Alex Vaughn. 75% freelance written. Eager to work with new/unpublished writers. Semimonthly newsletter; 8 pages. Emphasizes security for industry. "All material should be slanted toward security directors, preferably industrial, but some retail and institutional as well." Circ. 3,000. Pays on acceptance. Buys all rights. Phone queries OK. Photocopied submissions OK. Computer printout submissions acceptable; prefers letter-quality to dot-matrix. Reports in 2 weeks. Free sample copy and writer's guidelines.

Nonfiction: Interview (with security professionals only). "Articles should be tight and specific. They should deal with new security techniques or new twists on old ones." Buys 2-5 mss/issue. Query. Length: 750-1,000 words. Pays 10¢/word.

‡SHOPPING CENTERS TODAY, International Council of Shopping Centers, 665 Fifth Ave., New York NY 10022. (212)421-8181. Editor: Mark Westerbeck. 15% freelance written. A monthly tabloid covering the shopping center industry with an emphasis on retailing but including a broad range of development, management, financial and regional issues. No slant-straight-newsjournalism. "Audience is membership of ICSC, essentially: developers, retailers, property managers, financers, suppliers, lawyers, academicians, and government officials." Circ. 17,000. Pays on acceptance. Publishes ms an average of 3 months after acceptance. Byline given. Buys first North American serial rights or simultaneous rights. Submit seasonal/holiday material 2 months in advance. Simultaneous and previously published submissions OK. Computer printout submissions acceptable; prefers letter-quality to dot-matrix. Reports in 2 weeks on queries; 3 weeks on mss. Free sample copy.

Nonfiction: Essays, exposé, general interest, humor, interview/profile, new product and photo feature. No promotional items on firms or people. Buys 20 mss/year. Query with published clips. Length: 500-2,000 words. Pays $150-500. Sometimes pays the expenses of writers on assignment.

Photos: State availability of photos with submission. Reviews contact sheets, transparencies, and prints. Offers $50-250/photo. Identification of subjects required. Buys one-time rights.

Columns/Departments: The Last Stop (humor or feature-like look at shopping center industry), 1,000 words. Buys 6 mss/year. Query with published clips. Pays $300-500.

Fillers: Anecdotes, facts, and newsbreaks. Length: 50-150 words. Pays $25-150.

SUPERVISION, 424 N. 3rd St., Burlington IA 52601. Publisher: Michael S. Darnall. Editorial Supervisor: Doris J. Ruschill. Editor: Barbara Boeding. 95% freelance written. Prefers to work with published/established writers; works with a small number of new/unpublished writers each year. Monthly magazine; 24 pages. For first-line foremen, supervisors and office managers. 8½x11 inches. Circ. 8,630. Pays on publication. Publishes ms an average of 1 year after acceptance. Buys all rights. Reports in 3 weeks. Free sample copy and writer's guidelines; mention *Writer's Market* in request.

Nonfiction: How-to (cope with supervisory problems, discipline, absenteeism, safety, productivity, goal setting, etc.); and personal experience (unusual success story of foreman or supervisor). No sexist material written from only a male viewpoint. Include biography and/or byline with ms submissions. Author photos used. Buys 12 mss/issue. Query. Length: 1,500-1,800 words. Pays 4¢/word.

Tips: "We are particularly interested in writers with first-hand experience—current or former supervisors who are also good writers. Following AP stylebook would be helpful." Uses no advertising.

TRAINING, The Magazine of Human Resources Development, Lakewood Publications, 50 S. Ninth St., Minneapolis MN 55402. (612)333-0471. Editor: Jack Gordon. Managing Editor: Chris Lee. 10% freelance written. A monthly magazine covering training and employee development in the business world. "Our core readers are managers and professionals who specialize in employee training and development (e.g., corporate training directors, VP-human resource development, etc.). We have a large secondary readership among managers of all sorts who are concerned with improving human performance in their organizations. We take a businesslike approach to training and employee education." Circ. 52,000. Pays on acceptance. Publishes ms an average of 3 months after acceptance. Byline sometimes given. Offers $25 kill fee. Buys first North American serial rights and second serial (reprint) rights. Simultaneous, photocopied and previously published submissions OK. Computer printout submissions acceptable; no dot-matrix. Reports in 2 weeks on queries; 6 weeks on mss. Sample copy for 9x11 SAE with 4 first class stamps. Writer's guidelines for letter size SAE with 1 first class stamp.

Nonfiction: Essay; exposé; how-to (on training, management, sales, productivity improvement, etc.); humor; interview/profile; new product; opinion; photo feature; and technical (use of audiovisual aids, computers, etc.). "No puff, no 'testimonials' or disguised ads in any form, no 'gee-whiz' approaches to the subjects." Buys 10-12 mss/year. Query with or without published clips, or send complete ms. Length: 200-3,000 words. Pays $50-500.

Photos: State availability of photos or send with submission. Reviews contact sheets and prints. Offers no additional payment for photos accepted with ms. Identification of subjects required. Buys one-time rights and reprint rights.

Columns/Departments: Training Today (news briefs, how-to tips, reports on pertinent research, trend analysis, etc.), 200-800 words. Buys 6 mss/year. Query or send complete ms. Pays $50-75.

Tips: "We almost never give firm assignments to unfamiliar writers, so you have to be willing to hit us with one or two on spec to break in. Short pieces for our Training Today section involve least investment on your part, but also are less likely to convince us to assign you a feature. Don't tell us what an important person you are and what a huge favor you're doing us by allowing us to review your article. Let the manuscript do the talking. When studying the magazine, freelancers should look at our staff-written articles for style, approach and tone. Do not concentrate on articles written by people identified as consultants, training directors, etc."

UTILITY SUPERVISION, (United States), Bureau of Business Practice, 24 Rope Ferry Rd., Waterford CT 06386. (203)442-4365. Editor: DeLoris Lidestri. 80% freelance written. "I'm willing to work with a few new writers if they're willing to follow guidelines carefully." Semimonthly newsletter; 4 pages. Emphasizes all aspects of utility supervision. Pays on acceptance. Publishes ms an average of 4 months after acceptance. Buys all rights. Phone queries OK. Submit seasonal material 4 months in advance. Reports in 6 weeks. Free sample copy and writer's guidelines.

Nonfiction: Publishes how-to (interview on a single aspect of supervision with utility manager/supervisor concentrating on how reader/supervisor can improve in that area). Buys 100 mss/year. Query. Length: 360-750 words. Pays 10-15¢/word.

Photos: Purchased with accompanying ms. Pays $10 for head and shoulders photo of person interviewed. Total purchase price for ms includes payment for photo.

Tips: "A writer should call before he or she does anything. I like to spend a few minutes on the phone exchanging information."

WAREHOUSING SUPERVISOR'S BULLETIN, WSB, Bureau of Business Practice, 24 Rope Ferry Rd., Waterford CT 06386. (203)442-4365. Editor: Isabel Will Becker. 75-100% freelance written. "I work with a wide variety of writers and am always looking for fresh talent." Biweekly newsletter covering traffic, materials handling and distribution for warehouse supervisors "interested in becoming more effective on the job." Pays on acceptance. Publishes ms an average of 3 months after acceptance. No byline given. Buys all rights. Computer printout submissions acceptable; prefers letter-quality to dot-matrix. Reports in 2 weeks on queries; 6 weeks on mss. Free sample copy and writer's guidelines.

Nonfiction: How-to (increase efficiency, control or cut costs, cut absenteeism or tardiness, increase productivity, raise morale); and interview (of warehouse supervisors or managers who have solved problems on the job). No descriptions of company programs, noninterview articles, textbook-like descriptions or union references. Buys 50 mss/year. Query. "A resume and sample of work are helpful." Length: 800-1,200 words. Pays 8-14¢/word.

Tips: "Interview-based articles must emphasize direct quotes. They should also include a reference to the interviewee's company (location, size, products, function of the interviewee's department and number of employees under his control). Focus articles on one problem, and get the interviewee to pinpoint the best way to solve it. Write in a light, conversational style, talking directly to warehouse supervisors who can benefit from putting the interviewee's tips into practice."

ALWAYS submit mss or queries with a stamped, self-addressed envelope (SASE) within your country or International Reply Coupons (IRCs) purchased from the post office for other countries.

Marine Industries and Water Navigation

BOATING INDUSTRY, 850 3rd Ave., New York NY 10022. Editor-in-Chief/Publisher: Charles A. Jones. Editor: Olga Badillo. 15% freelance written. Monthly for boating retailers and distributors. Circ. 27,200. Pays on publication. Publishes ms an average of 3 months after acceptance. Byline given. Buys all rights. Best practice is to check with editor first on story ideas for go-ahead. Submit seasonal material 4 months in advance. Reports in 2 months.
Nonfiction: Business-oriented pieces about marine management. Interested in good column material, too. Buys 10-15 mss/year. Query. Length: 1,500-4,000 words. No clippings. Pays 9-15¢/word.
Photos: B&w glossy photos purchased with mss; "also some color."

‡**BOATING PRODUCT NEWS, The Newspaper for the Marine Industry**, Whitney Communications Corp., 850 3rd Ave., New York NY 10022. (212)715-2729. Editor: James Pavia. 20% freelance written. A monthly newspaper covering the "business end of the marine industry for distributors, dealers, manufacturers, marina owners and retailers." Circ. 27,000. Pays on publication. Publishes ms an average of 2 months after acceptance. Byline given. Buys first rights, simultaneous rights and all rights. Submit seasonal/holiday material 3 months in advance. Simultaneous and previously published submissions OK. Computer printout submissions acceptable; prefers letter-quality to dot-matrix. Reports in several months. Free sample copy and writer's guidelines.
Nonfiction: Interview/profile, new product, photo feature, technical and feature and news stories. Buys 40-45 mss/year. Query with published clips. Length: 500 words. Pays $6/printed inch. Sometimes pays the expenses of writers on assignment. State availability of photos with submission.
Photos: Reviews contact sheets and 3x5 prints. Offers $20 minimum/photo. Identification of subjects required. Buys one-time rights.

SEAWAY REVIEW, The Business Magazine of the Great Lakes/St. Lawrence System, The Seaway Review Bldg., 221 Water St., Boyne City MI 49712. Publisher: Jacques LesStrang. Managing Editor: Michelle Cortright. 10% freelance written. Prefers to work with published/established writers. "For the entire Great Lakes/St. Lawrence region maritime community, executives of companies that ship via the Great Lakes, traffic managers, transportation executives, federal and state government officials and manufacturers of maritime equipment." Quarterly magazine. Circ. 16,000. Pays on publication. Publishes ms an average of 3 months after acceptance. Buys first North American serial rights. Submit seasonal material 2 months in advance. Photocopied submissions OK. Electronic submissions OK via 1200 Baud/MS DOS. Computer printout submissions acceptable. Reports in 3 weeks. Sample copy $5.
Nonfiction: Articles dealing with Great Lakes shipping, shipbuilding, marine technology, economics of 8 states in the Seaway region (Michigan, Minnesota, Illinois, Indiana, Ohio, New York, Pennsylvania and Wisconsin), and Canada (Ontario, Quebec), port operation, historical articles dealing with Great Lakes shipping, current events dealing with commercial shipping on lakes, etc. No subjects contrary to our editorial statement. Submit complete ms. Length: 1,000-4,000 words. "Pay varies with value of subject matter and knowledgeability of author, $50-300." Pays expenses of writers on assignment.
Photos: State availability of photos with query. Pays $10-50 for 8x10 glossy b&w prints; $10-100 for 8x10 glossy color prints or transparencies. Captions required. Buys one-time rights. Buys "hundreds" of freelance photos each year for photo file.
Fillers: Clippings and spot news relating to ports and the Great Lakes. Buys 3/issue. Length: 50-500 words. Pays $5-50.

‡**THE WORK BOAT**, H.L. Peace Publications, Box 2400, Covington LA 70434. (504)893-2930. Publisher/Editor: Harry L. Peace. Managing Editor: Chip Edgan. Monthly. Buys all rights. Pays on acceptance. Query. Reports in 1 month. Sample copy $3; writer's guidelines for SASE.
Nonfiction: "Articles on waterways, river terminals, barge line operations, work boat construction and design, barges, offshore oil vessels and tugs. Best bet for freelancers: one-angle article showing in detail how a barge line, tug operator or dredging firm solves a problem of either mechanical or operational nature. This market is semitechnical and rather exacting. Such articles must be specific, containing firm name, location,

officials of company, major equipment involved, by brand name, model, power, capacity and manufacturer; with color or b&w photos." Length: 1,000-2,000 words. Pays $150 minimum.
Photos: 5x5 or 5x7 b&w; 4x5 color prints only. No additional payment for photos accompanying ms. Captions and model release required. Buys one-time rights.

Medical

Through these journals, physicians and mental health professionals learn how other professionals help their patients and manage their medical practices efficiently. Listed here are publications for physicians and health professionals also reporting on new discoveries in medicine and health care plans. Journals for nurses, laboratory technicians and other medical workers are included with the Hospitals, Nursing and Nursing Home journals. Publications for druggists and drug wholesalers and retailers are grouped with the Drugs and Health Care Products journals. Publications that report on medical trends for the consumer can be found in the Health and Science categories.

AMERICAN MEDICAL NEWS, American Medical Association, 535 N. Dearborn St., Chicago IL 60610. (312)645-5000. Editor: Dick Walt. Executive Editor: Barbara Bolsen. 5-10% freelance written. "Prefers writers already interested in the health care field—not clinical medicine." Weekly tabloid providing nonclinical information for physicians—information on socio-economic, political, and other developments in medicine. "*AMN* is a specialized publication circulating to physicians, covering subjects touching upon their profession, practices, and personal lives. This is a well-educated, highly sophisticated audience." Circ. 375,000 physicians. Pays on acceptance. Publishes ms an average of 2 months after acceptance. Byline given. Offers variable kill fee. Buys all rights. Rights sometimes returnable on request after publication. Simultaneous queries OK. Computer printout submissions acceptable. Reports in 3 weeks. Free sample copy and writer's guidelines.
Nonfiction: Carol Brierly Golin, articles editor. Interview/profile (occasional); opinion (mainly from physicians); and news and interpretive features. Special issues include "Year in Review" issue published in January. No clinical articles, general-interest articles physicians would see elsewhere, or recycled versions of articles published elsewhere. Buys 100 mss/year. Query. Length: 1,200-2,000 words. Pays $400-700 for features; $150 for opinions and short news items. "We have limited travel budget for freelancers; we pay minimal local expenses."

‡AORN JOURNAL, The Official Publication for The Association of Operating Room Nurses, 10170 E. Mississippi Ave., Denver CO 80321. (303)755-6300. Editor: Pat Palmer. A monthly magazine covering nursing issues. Circ. 37,000. Pays on publication. Publishes ms an average of 6 months after acceptance. Byline given. Buys all rights. Reports in 2 weeks on queries; 6 weeks on manuscripts. Writer's guidelines for #10 SAE with 1 first class stamp.
Nonfiction: Surgical nursing. Length: 8-15 typed pages. Pays $5-25/published page.
Photos: Send photos with submission. Offers no additional payment for photos accepted with ms. Captions required. Buys one-time rights.
Columns/Departments: Ambulatory surgery, ethics, and legislation (on medical/nursing issues). Buys 24 mss/year. Query. Pays $50-100.

APA MONITOR, 1200 17th St. NW, Washington DC 20036. (202)955-7690. Editor: Jeffrey Mervis. Associate Editor: Kathleen Fisher. 5% freelance written. Monthly 64-page newspaper for psychologists and other social scientists and professionals interested in behaviorial sciences and mental health area. Circ. 80,000. Pays on acceptance. Publishes ms an average of 3 months after acceptance. Buys first serial rights. Computer printout submissions acceptable; no dot-matrix. Sample copy $2.40 and large SASE.
Nonfiction: News and feature articles about issues facing psychology both as a science and a mental health profession; political, social and economic developments in the behaviorial science area. Interview, profile and

occasional historical pieces. No personal views or reminiscences. Buys no mss without query. Length: 300-3,000 words. Pays expenses of writers on assignment.

Tips: "Our writers need to be longtime readers or science writers to strike the proper balance for reaching both the top scientists and practitioners in the country and the beginning graduate student."

CARDIOLOGY WORLD NEWS, Medical Publishing Enterprises, Box 1548, Marco Island FL 33937. (813)394-0400. Editor: John H. Lavin. 75% freelance written. Monthly magazine covering cardiology and the cardiovascular system. "We need news articles *for doctors* on any aspect of our field—diagnosis, treatment, risk factors, etc." Estab. 1985. Pays on acceptance. Publishes ms an average of 2 months after acceptance. By-line given "for special reports and feature-length articles." Offers 20% kill fee. Buys first North American serial rights. Photocopied submissions OK. Computer printout submissions acceptable; no dot-matrix. Reports in 1 month. Sample copy $1; free writer's guidelines.

Nonfiction: New product and technical (clinical). No fiction, profiles of doctors or poetry. Query with published clips. Length: 250-1,500 words. Pays $50-300; $50/column for news articles. Pays expenses of writers on assignment.

Photos: State availability of photos with query. Pays $50/published photo. Rough captions, model release, and identification of subjects required. Buys one-time rights.

Columns/Departments: Send complete ms. Length: 250-1,000 words. Pays $50-150.

Fillers: Anecdotes. Buys 4-6/year. Length: 100-250 words. Pays $25.

Tips: "Submit written news articles of 250-500 words on speculation with basic source material (not interview notes) for fact-checking. We demand clinical or writing expertise for full-length feature. Clinical cardiology conventions/symposia are the best source of news and feature articles."

‡CONTEMPORARY DIALYSIS & NEPHROLOGY MAGAZINE, The News & Issues Magazine of the Renal Care Field, Fisher Publications, Inc., Suite D, 17901 Ventura Blvd., Encino CA 91316. (818)344-4200. Editor: David Anast. 5-10% freelance written. Works with a small number of new/unpublished writers each year. A monthly magazine covering kidney dialysis, kidney transplantation, kidney disease and government regulations. "We are the only news-oriented journal in the renal care field; Contemporary Dialysis and Nephrology, publishes the latest business, government, industry, association, professional, scientific, clinical, dialysis and nephrology news that is crucial for keeping renal care professionals informed and up-to-date." Circ. approximately 16,500. Pays 2 months after acceptance. Publishes ms an average of 6 months after acceptance. Byline usually given. Offers 10-50% kill fee if applicable. Buys first rights and first worldwide rights. Photocopied submissions and previously published submissions OK. Reports in 1-2 months. Sample copy for 8½x11 SAE with $1.19 postage; free writer's guidelines.

Nonfiction: Exposé, general interest, interview/profile, opinion, photo feature, technical and government regulation of the industry (renal). Also, first person news accounts of Washington, DC-oriented actions/incidents, investigative pieces. No humor, cartoons, how-to, personal experience of patients, essays, religious or travel submissions. Buys 1-12 mss/year. Query with published clips. Length: 500-3,000 words. Pays 6-10¢/word for assigned articles. Pays the expenses of writers on assignment depending on what the expenses are; must be preapproved, except in special circumstances. Reviews prints. Captions and identification of subjects required. Buys all rights.

Columns/Department: Governmental Affairs (government regulation of kidney dialysis and the kidney transplantation field; reporting on one particular event of newsworthy value); 500-2,000 words. Buys 1-3 mss/year. Query with published clips. Pays 6-10¢/words.

Tips: "If you can write crisp, clean, nonwordy (defogged), authoritative copy that reads like a hard news article, you may be interested in querying *CD&N*. Always check with the editor first before submitting a finished manuscript; I hate to have writers duplicate topics we've already covered, and receive nothing in return for their efforts."

DIAGNOSTIC IMAGING, Miller Freeman, 500 Howard St., San Francisco CA 94105. Publisher: Thomas Kemp. Editor: Peter Ogle. 10% freelance written. Monthly news magazine covering radiology, nuclear medicine and ultrasound for physicians in diagnostic imaging professions. Circ. 24,000. Average issue includes 4-5 features. Pays on acceptance. Publishes ms an average of 2 months after acceptance. Byline given. Buys all rights. No phone queries. "Written query should be well written, concise and contain a brief outline of proposed article and a description of the approach or perspective the author is taking." Submit seasonal material 1 month in advance. Simultaneous and photocopied submissions OK. Electronic submissions OK on Apple II, IBM PC, and MacIntosh, but requires hard copy also. Computer printout submissions acceptable; prefers letter-quality to dot-matrix. Reports in 2 weeks. Free sample copy.

Nonfiction: "We are interested in topical news features in the areas of radiology, magnetic resonance imaging, nuclear medicine and ultrasound, especially news of state and federal legislation, new products, insurance, regulations, medical literature, professional meetings and symposia and continuing education." Buys 10-12 mss/year. Query with published clips. Length: 1,000-2,000 words. Pays 22¢/word minimum.

Photos: Reviews 5x7 b&w glossy prints and 35mm and larger color transparencies. Offers $20 for photos accepted with ms. Captions required. Buys one-time rights.

‡**EMERGENCY, The Journal of Emergency Services**, 6200 Yarrow Drive, Box 159, Carlsbad CA 92008. (619)438-2511. Editor: Kim Dallas. 100% freelance written. A monthly magazine covering pre-hospital services and emergency care. "Our readership is primarily composed of EMTs, Paramedics and ambulance attendants. We prefer a professional, semi-technical approach on pre-hospital subjects." Circ. 35,000. Pays on acceptance. Publishes ms an average of 6 months after acceptance. Byline given. Buys all rights. Submit seasonal/holiday material 3 months in advance. Photocopied submissions OK. Computer printout submissions acceptable; prefers letter-quality to dot-matrix. Reports in 4 weeks on queries, 2 months on manuscripts. Sample copy $5; free writers guidelines.

Nonfiction: Exposé, general interest, how-to, interview/profile, opinion, personal experience, photo feature and semi-technical. "We do not publish cartoons, color *print* photos, term papers or overly-scientific manuscripts." Buys 100 mss/year. Query with or without published clips, or send complete ms. Length 1,000-4,000 words. Pays $0-350.

Photos: Send photos with submission. Reviews color transparencies and b&w prints. Offers no additional payment for photos accepted with ms. Offers $5-25/photo without ms. Captions and identification of subjects required.

Columns/Departments: Open Forum (opinion, brief personal experience), 1,000-500 words. Medical insight (pre-hospital care topics, different injuries, etc.), 2,000-1,000 words; and Trauma Primer (pre-hospital care topics, type and care of trauma), 2,000-1,000 words. Buys 30 mss/year. Query or send complete ms. Length: 500-2,000 words. Pays $0-150.

Poetry: Free verse and traditional. "Prefers very high quality." Publishes about 4/year. Submit maximum 5 poems. Length 10-30 lines. No payment for poetry.

Fillers: Anecdotes, facts and newsbreaks. Buys 10/year. Length: 500 words. Pays $0-50.

Tips: "Writing style for features and departments should be knowledgeable and thorough with a clear theme or story line to maintain reader interest and enhance comprehension. We appreciate a short, one paragraph biography on the author."

FACETS, American Medical Association Auxiliary, Inc., 535 N. Dearborn St., Chicago IL 60610. (312)645-4470. Editor: Kathleen T. Jordan. Works with both established and new writers; welcomes well-written, well-researched articles from either. For physicians' spouses. 30% freelance written. Magazine published 6 times/year; 32 pages. Circ. 90,000. Pays on acceptance. Publishes ms an average of 6 months after acceptance. Buys first rights. Simultaneous, photocopied and previously published submissions OK. Computer printout submissions acceptable; prefers letter-quality to dot-matrix. Reports in 6 weeks. Free sample copy and writer's guidelines.

Nonfiction: All articles must be related to the experiences of physicians' spouses. Current health issues; financial topics; physicians' family circumstances; business management; volunteer leadership how-to's. Buys 20 mss/year. Query with clear outline of article—what points will be made, what conclusions drawn, what sources will be used. No personal experience or personality stories. Length: 1,000-2,500 words. Pays $300-800. Pays expenses of writers on assignment.

Photos: State availability of photos with query. Uses 8x10 glossy b&w prints and 2¼x2¼ color transparencies.

Tips: Uses "articles only on specified topical matter; with good sources, not hearsay or personal opinion. Since we use only nonfiction and have a limited readership, we must relate factual material."

GENETIC ENGINEERING NEWS, The Source of Bioprocess/Biotechnology News, Mary Ann Liebert, Inc., 157 E. 86th St., New York NY 10028. (212)722-3708. Managing Editor: John Sterling. 80% freelance written. Prefers to work with published/established writers. Tabloid published 10 times/year featuring articles on industry and research in areas of biotechnology such as recombinant DNA and hybridoma technology. Circ. 18,000. Pays on acceptance. Publishes ms an average of 6 weeks after acceptance. Byline given. Buys all rights. Computer printout submissions acceptable; prefers letter-quality to dot-matrix. Reports in 6 weeks on queries; 1 month on mss. Writer's guidelines for SAE and 1 first class stamp.

Nonfiction: Interview/profile (of corporate executives, academicians or researchers); new product; technical (any articles relating to biotechnology with emphasis on application); and financial (Wall Street analysis, etc.—of new companies). No company personnel changes or rewritten press releases. Buys 150 mss/year. Query with published clips. Length: 1,000-1,200 words. "All negotiable." Sometimes pays the expenses of writers on assignment.

Photos: Send photos with ms. Pays negotiable fee for b&w contact sheets. Identification of subjects required.

Tips: "The writer may have a better chance of breaking in at our publication with short articles and fillers, but because biotechnology is a complex area covering molecular biology and economics, and because our readers are primarily professionals in the field, our writers tend to have had some experience writing on biotech before writing for *GEN*. Writers submitting queries *must* be extremely knowledgeable in the field and have direct access to hard news. The most frequent mistake made by writers in completing an article for us is a lack of clarity; writers often fail to develop and explain ideas fully, clearly and accurately. Accuracy is essential."

GERIATRIC CONSULTANT, Medical Publishing Enterprises, Box 1548, Marco Island FL 33937. (813)394-0400. Editor: John H. Lavin. 70% freelance written. Bimonthly magazine covering medical care of the elderly. "We're a clinical magazine directed to doctors and physician assistants. All articles must *help* these health professionals to help their elderly patients. We're too tough a market for nonmedical beginners." Circ. 105,000. Pays on acceptance. Publishes ms an average of 2 months after acceptance. Byline given. Offers 20% kill fee. Buys first North American serial rights. Simultaneous queries OK. Computer printout submissions acceptable; no dot-matrix. Reports in 1 month. Sample copy for $1; free writer's guidelines.
Nonfiction: How-to (diagnosis and treatment of health problems of the elderly) and technical/clinical. No fiction or articles directed to a lay audience. Buys 20 mss/year. Query. Length: 750-3,000 words. Pays $100-300. Pays expenses of writers on assignment.
Photos: State availability of photos. (Photos are not required.) Model release and identification of subjects required. Buys one-time rights.
Fillers: Anecdotes. Buys 6-8/year. Length: 250 words. Pays $25 maximum.
Tips: "Many medical meetings are now held in the field of geriatric care. These offer potential sources and subjects for us."

THE JOURNAL, Addiction Research Foundation of Ontario, 33 Russell St., Toronto, Ontario M5S 2S1 Canada. (416)595-6053. Editor: Anne MacLennan. 50% freelance written. Prefers to work with published/established writers. Monthly tabloid covering addictions and related fields around the world. "*The Journal* alerts professionals in the addictions and related fields or disciplines to news events, issues, opinions and developments of potential interest and/or significance to them in their work, and provides them an informed context in which to judge developments in their own specialty/geographical areas." Circ. 26,000. Pays on publication. Publishes ms an average of 3 months after acceptance. Byline given. Kill fee negotiable. Not copyrighted. Buys first serial rights and second serial (reprint) rights. Computer printout submissions acceptable. SAE with Canadian postage; IRC. Reports in 2 months on queries; 3 months on mss. Free sample copy and writer's guidelines.
Nonfiction: Only. Query with published clips or send complete ms. Length: 1,000 words maximum. Pays 18¢/word minimum. Sometimes pays the expenses of writers on assignment.
Photos: Terri Etherington, production editor. State availability of photos. Pays $10-35 for 5x7 or 8x10 b&w prints. Captions, model release, and identification of subjects required. Buys one-time rights.
Columns/Departments: Under contract.
Tips: "A freelancer can best break in to our publication with six years reporting experience, preferably with medical/science writing background. We rarely use untried writers."

‡THE MAYO ALUMNUS, Mayo Clinic, 200 SW 1st St., Rochester MN 55905. (507)284-2511. Editor: Mary Ellen Landwehr. 10% freelance written. "We usually use our own staff for writing, and only occasionally use freelancers." For physicians, scientists and medical educators who trained at the Mayo Clinic. Quarterly magazine; 48 pages. Circ. 12,000. Pays on acceptance. Publishes ms an average of 3 months after acceptance. Buys all rights. Previously published submissions OK. Computer printout submissions acceptable; prefers letter-quality to dot-matrix. Reports in 2 months. Free sample copy; mention *Writer's Market* in request. No writer's guidelines available at this time.
Nonfiction: "We're interested in seeing interviews with members of the Mayo Alumni Association—stories about Mayo-trained doctors/educators/scientists/researchers who are interesting people doing interesting things in medicine, surgery or hobbies of interest, etc." Query with clips of published work. Length: 1,000-3,000 words. Pays 15¢/word, first 1,500 words. Maximum payment is $275. Sometimes pays the expenses of writers on assignment.
Photos: "We need art and must make arrangements if not provided with the story." Pays $50 for each color transparency used. State availability of photos with query. Captions preferred. Buys all rights.
Tips: "I usually keep a file of freelance writers, and when I need an alumni covered in a certain area of the country, I contact a freelancer from that area. Those who suit my needs are the writers in the right place at the right time or those who have a story about an interesting alumnus."

MD MAGAZINE, New Horizons for the Physician, MD Publications, 30 E. 60th St., New York NY 10022. (212)355-5432. Editor: A.J. Vogl. Managing Editor: Barbara Guidos. 80% freelance written. Monthly magazine on culture/travel; a general interest magazine for physicians, covering all aspects of human experience. Circ. 140,000. Pays on acceptance. Publishes ms an average of 6 months after acceptance. Byline given. Offers 33⅓% kill fee. Buys first North American serial rights and second serial (reprint) rights. Submit seasonal/holiday material 4 months in advance. Photocopied and previously published submissions OK. Computer printout submissions acceptable; prefers letter-quality to dot-matrix. Reports in 1 month. Sample copy $2; free writer's guidelines.
Nonfiction: Sharon AvRutuick, articles editor. Book excerpts, general interest, historical/nostalgic, interview/profile, photo feature and travel. Buys 100+ mss/year. Query with published clips. Length: 1,000-3,000 words. Pays $350-700. Rarely pays expenses of writers on assignment.

Photos: Doris Brautigan, photo editor. Send photos with ms. Reviews b&w and color transparencies (35mm or larger) and 8x10 prints and b&w contact sheets. Payment varies. Captions and identification of subjects required. Pays $60-175 for b&w photos; $100-225 for color. Buys one-time rights.
Columns/Departments: Buys 50+ mss/year. Query with published clips. Length: 1,000-1,500 words. Pays $300-350.
Tips: "It is fresh ideas and writing that make things and people come alive."

MEDICAL ECONOMICS, Medical Economics Co., Inc., 680 Kinderkamack Rd., Oradell NJ 07649. (201)262-3030. Editor: Don L. Berg. Managing Editor: Richard Service. Less than 5% freelance written. Biweekly magazine covering topics of nonclinical interest to office-based private physicians (MDs and DOs only). "We publish practice/management and personal/finance advice for office-based MDs and osteopaths." Circ. 167,000. Pays on acceptance. Publishes ms an average of 3 months after acceptance. Byline given. Offers 25% of full article fee as kill fee. Buys all rights and first serial rights. Computer printout submissions acceptable. Reports in 2 months on queries; 3 weeks on mss. Sample copy for $3 and 9x12 SASE.
Nonfiction: Contact Lilian Fine, chief of Outside Copy Division. How-to (office and personnel management, personal-money management); personal experience (only involving MDs or DOs in private practice); and travel (how-to articles). No clinical articles, hobby articles, personality profiles or office design articles. Buys 8-10 mss/year. Query with published clips. Length: 1,500-3,000 words. Pays $750-1,800. "The payment level is decided at the time go-ahead is given after query."
Photos: Contact Lilian Fine, chief of Outside Copy Division. State availability of photos. Pays negotiable rates for b&w contact sheets and for 35mm color slides. Model release and identification of subjects required. Buys one-time rights.
Tips: "How-to articles should fully describe techniques, goals, options and caveats—in terms that are clear and *realistic* for the average physician. Use of anecdotal examples to support major points is crucial. Our full-time staff is quite large, and therefore we buy only freelance articles that are not already assigned to staff writers. This puts a premium on unusual and appealing subjects."

THE MEDICAL POST, 777 Bay St., Toronto, Ontario M5W 1A7 Canada. Editor: Derek Cassels. "We are backlogged with submissions and prefer not to receive unsolicited submissions at this time."

MEDICAL TIMES, Romaine Pierson Publishers, Inc., 80 Shore Rd., Port Washington NY 11050. (516)883-6350. Editors: A.J. Bollet, M.D., and A.H.Bruckheim, M.D. Executive Editor: Susan Carr Jenkins. 100% freelance written. "Anyone with a good (i.e., applicable) idea and a well-written query letter will be considered for assignment." Monthly magazine covering clinical medical subjects for primary care physicians in private practice. Circ. 120,000. Pays on acceptance. Publishes ms an average of 1 year after acceptance. Byline given. Buys all rights and makes work-for-hire assignments. Submit seasonal/holiday material 6 months in advance. Simultaneous queries OK. Computer printout submissions acceptable; no dot-matrix. Reports in 1 month on queries; 2 months on mss. Sample copy $5; writer's guidelines for business size SASE.
Nonfiction: "We accept only clinical medical and medico-legal material. It is useless to send us any material that is not related directly to medicine. No first person accounts or interviews. We publish articles on the diagnosis and treatment of diseases." Buys 100 mss/year (95% from physicians). Query. Length: 500-2,500 words. Pays $25-300. Sometimes pays the expenses of writers on assignment.
Photos: State availability of photos. Pays variable rates for 2x2 b&w and color transparencies, and 4x5 or 8x10 b&w and color prints. Model release and identification of subjects required.
Fillers: Anecdotes. "Must be true, unpublished and medically oriented." Buys 25/year. Length: 25-200 words.
Tips: "A query letter is a must. 99% of our material is 'invited.' The writer must have a medical or health-related background and be able to write on technical subjects for a sophisticated audience."

‡MEDICAL WORLD NEWS, HEI Publishing, Suite 112, 7676 Woodway, Houston TX 77063. (713)780-2299. Editor: Annette Oestreicher. Managing Editor: Don Gibbons. 20% freelance written. Works with a small number of new/unpublished writers each year. A biweekly magazine covering the clincial, social, political, and economic aspects of medicine for doctors. Circ. 160,000. Pays on publication. Publishes ms an average of 3 weeks after acceptance. Byline sometimes given. Offers up to 50% kill fee. Buys all rights. Computer printout submissions acceptable; prefers letter-quality to dot-matrix. Free sample copy and writer's guidelines.
Nonfiction: "All stories must have at least two sources and news style. No single-source articles. Buys 100 mss/year. Query with published clips. Length: 200-4,000 words. Pays $80-1,800. Sometimes pays the expenses of writers on assignment.
Photos: State availability of photos with submission. Offers $20/photo. Identification of subjects required. Buys one-time rights.

THE NEW PHYSICIAN, 1910 Association Dr., Reston VA 22091. Editor: Renie Schapiro. 20% freelance written. For medical students, interns and residents. Published 9 times/year; 56 pages. Circ. 50,000. Buys first serial rights. Buys 6-12 mss/year. Pays on publication. Publishes ms an average of 3 months after acceptance. Will consider simultaneous submissions. Computer printout submissions acceptable. Reports in 3 months. Free sample copy.

Nonfiction: "Articles on social, political, economic issues in medicine/medical education. Our readers need more than a superficial, simplistic look into issues that affect them. We want skeptical, accurate, professional contributors to do well-researched, comprehensive, incisive reports and offer new perspectives on health care problems." Not interested in material on "my operation," or encounters with physicians, or personal experiences as physician's patient, investment/business advice for physicians, or highly technical or clinical material. Humorous articles and cartoons for physicians-in-training welcome. Query or send complete ms. Length: 500-3,500 words. Pays $50-500 with higher fees selected investigative pieces. Sometimes pays expenses of writers on assignment.

Tips: "Our magazine demands real sophistication on the issues we cover because we are a professional journal for readers with a progressive view on health care issues and a particular interest in improving the health case system. Those freelancers we publish reveal in their queries and ultimately in their manuscripts a willingness and an ability to look deeply into the issues in question and not be satisfied with a cursory review of those issues."

‡NURSINGLIFE, The magazine for professional growth and fulfillment, Springhouse Corp., 1111 Bethlehem Pike, Springhouse PA 19477. (215)646-8700. Editorial Director: Maryanne Wagner. Managing Editor: Tony DeCrosta. 75% freelance written. A bimonthly magazine that "addresses all the needs of nurses—clinical, psychological, legal, etc." Circ. 200,000. Pays on publication. Byline given. Offers variable kill fee. Buys all rights and makes work-for-hire assignments. Simultaneous and photocopied submissions OK. Computer printout submissions acceptable. Reports in 6 weeks. Free sample copy and writer's guidelines.

Nonfiction: Book excepts (of interest to nurses); how-to (showing nurses how to be better at their jobs); interview/profile (with nurse experts); new product; legal; ethical; management; psychology; timely topics; personal experience and technical. "Specific articles cover subjects such as how to avoid legal risks in the operating room, how to use emergency drugs correctly, and how to use teamwork for better patient care. 'Difficult Person' articles are first-person narratives by nurses describing the most difficult person they've ever worked with. Practical solutions are important; a good story isn't enough." No fiction, poetry or personal experience articles that simply vent frustration but don't offer advice other nurses can use. Buys 30-40 mss/year. Query with or without published clips, or send complete ms. Length: 750-2,500 words. Pays $200. Pays expenses of writers on assignment.

Photos: State availability of photos with submission. Reviews contact sheets and transparencies. Captions, model releases and identification of subjects required. Buys one-time rights.

Tips: "Call with your idea—we'll give you immediate yes or no. The area of our publication most open to freelancers is Difficult Person feature. We're always looking for clinical advances or other health care trends related to nursing."

‡NURSINGWORLD JOURNAL, Prime National Publishing Corp., 470 Boston Post Rd., Weston MA 02193. (617)849-2702. Editor: Ira Alterman. 50% freelance written. A monthly tabloid covering nursing for professional nurses. Circ. 40,000. Pays on publication. Byline given. Buys all rights. Computer printout submissions acceptable; prefers letter-quality to dot-matrix. Reports in 1 month on queries; 2 months on manuscripts. Sample copy $2; free writer's guidelines.

Nonfiction: General interest, historical/nostalgic, how-to and technical. Buys 20-50 mss/year. Send complete ms. Length: 500-2,000 words. Pays $50-100.

Photos: Send photos with submission. Reviews contact sheets and prints. Offers no additional payment for photos accepted with ms. Captions, releases and identification of subjects required.

‡O & P PRACTICE NEWSLETTER, Orthotics & Prosthetics (Art. Limbs & Braces), Lexel Publishing Company, Inc., 2304 E. Fletcher Ave., Box 350282, Tampa FL 33695-0282. (813)971-0108. Director: Les Bauer. Editor: Dottie Gifford. 60% freelance written. Lexel Publishing produces approximately 25 newsletters for orthotists & prosthetists, orthopedic doctors, physical therapists, and other medical professionals. Material is technical and educational with some fillers. Circ. 15,000. Pays on publicaton. Publishes ms an average of 4 months after acceptance. Byline sometimes given. Offers negotiable kill fee. Buys one-time rights, second serial (reprint) rights; simultaneous rights, and makes work-for-hire assignments. Submit seasonal/holiday material 3 months in advance. Simultaneous submissions, photocopied submissions and previously published submissions OK. Computer printout submissions acceptable; prefers letter-quality to dot-matrix. Reports in 1 month on queries; 2 months on manuscripts. Sample copy and writer's guidelines for #10 SAE with 1 first class stamp.

Nonfiction: Interview/profile, new product, personal experience, photo feature and technical. No vague and general health-related stories. Buys 3-6 mss/year. Query with or without published clips, or send complete ms.

Length: 400-2,500 words. Pays $50-300. Sometimes pays the expenses of writers on assignment.
Photos: Send photos with submission. Reviews prints. Offers $3-30 per photo. Model releases and identification of subjects required. Buys one-time rights.
Columns/Departments: P.O. Box (Dear P.O.)—(a write-in column from doctors, nurses, patients, etc., with appropriate answers.) "We need humorous letters and answers relating to common problems within doctors' offices and hospitals—one humorous letter per month." Buys 6 mss/year. Send complete ms. Length: 100 words maximum. Pays $5-35.
Fillers: Anecdotes, facts, gags to be illustrated by cartoonist, and short humor. Buys 4-6/year. Length: 100 words. Pays $5-50.
Tips: "Interview a local orthotist, or prosthetist, or their patients. Read orthopedic trade journals and orthotic and prosthetic trade publications. Case histories are perfect if they are specific and educational. Condensations of product announcements are easy ways to be featured in our newsletter. The easiest way to help us is with humorous letters from doctors for our P.O. Box (Dear P.O.) column, or cartoons depicting the same kinds of situations within the medical field. Past questions for our column have covered computer problems, a brace to keep the head down during a golf swing, or patients spending money from insurance payments meant for doctors. Detailed serous case histories are best."

‡PERINATAL PRESS, Perinatal Press, Inc., 52nd and F Sts., Sacramento CA 95819. (916)733-1750. Executive Editor: J.M. Schneider, M.D. Managing Editor: D.F. Bulger, M.S. A newsletter published 10 times per year for perinatal health care providers. Circ. 5,000. Pays on publication. Publishes ms an average of 8 months after acceptance. Byline given. Buys first North American serial rights. Reports in 3 weeks on queries; 6 weeks on mss. Sample copy $3.
Nonfiction: How-to, humor, opinion, technical and review articles. Buys 4-6 mss/year. Query. Pays $75-150 for assigned articles. May pay with premiums rather than cash for short pieces, such as book reviews.
Photos: State availability of photos with submission. Reviews 3x5 prints. Offers no additional payment for photos accepted with ms. Captions required. Buys one-time rights.
Poetry: "Have never used poetry before but would *consider* for publication. Must be about perinatal health care—for professionals. Would offer $25.
Tips: "Feature articles are most open to freelancers. We have a *professional audience* and need well written articles with nonsexist language, and family-centered care philosophy."

THE PHYSICIAN AND SPORTSMEDICINE, McGraw-Hill, 4530 W. 77th St., Edina MN 55435. (612)835-3222. Managing Editor: Douglas Benson. Executive Editor: Frances Munnings. Monthly magazine covering medical aspects of sports and exercise. "We look in our feature articles for subjects of practical interest to our physician audience." Circ. 130,000. Pays on acceptance. Byline given. Buys one-time rights. Submit seasonal/holiday material 6 months in advance. Simultaneous queries OK. Reports in 2 weeks. Sample copy for $3; free writer's guidelines.
Nonfiction: Interview/profile (persons active in this field); and technical (new developments in sports medicine). Query. Length: 250-2,500 words. Pays $400-750.
Photos: Marty Duda, photo editor. State availability of photos. Pays ASTM rates for color transparencies. Buys one-time rights.

PODIATRY MANAGEMENT, 401 N. Broad St., Philadephia PA 19108. (215)925-9744. Publisher: Scott C. Borowsky. Editor: Barry Block, D.P.M. Managing Editor: M.J. Goldberg. Business magazine published 8 times/year for practicing podiatrists. "Aims to help the doctor of podiatric medicine to build a bigger, more successful practice, to conserve and invest his money, to keep him posted on the economic, legal and sociological changes that affect him." Circ. 11,000. Pays on publication. Byline given. Buys first North American serial rights and second serial (reprint) rights. Submit seasonal/holiday material 4 months in advance. Simultaneous queries, and simultaneous, photocopied and previously published submissions OK. Send mss to Dr. Block, 225 E. 64th St., New York NY 10021. Reports in 2 weeks. Sample copy $2; free writer's guidelines.
Nonfiction: General interest (taxes, investments, estate planning, recreation, hobbies); how-to (establish and collect fees, practice management, organize office routines, supervise office assistants, handle patient relations); interview/profile; and personal experience. "These subjects are the mainstay of the magazine, but offbeat articles and humor are always welcome." Buys 25 mss/year. Query. Length: 1,000-2,500 words. Pays $150-350.
Photos: State availability of photos. Pays $10 for b&w contact sheet. Buys one-time rights.

‡PRIVATE PRACTICE, Box 12489, Oklahoma City OK 73157. Executive Editor: Brian Sherman. 80% freelance written. Eager to work with new/unpublished writers. For "medical doctors in private practice." Monthly. Buys first North American serial rights. "If an article is assigned, it is paid for in full, used or killed." Byline given "except if it was completely rewritten or a considerable amount of additional material is added to the article." Pays on publication. Publishes ms an average of 4 months after acceptance. Query. "Computer printout submissions acceptable; prefers letter-quality to dot-matrix.

Nonfiction: "Articles that indicate importance of maintaining freedom of medical practice or which detail outside interferences in the practice of medicine, including research, hospital operation, drug manufacture, etc. Straight reporting style. No cliches, no scare words, no flowery phrases to cover up poor reporting. Stories must be actual, factual, precise and correct. Copy should be lively and easy to read. We also publish travel and leisure." No general short humor, poetry or short stories. "Please, no first person humor or other type of personal experiences with your doctor—i.e., my account of when my doctor told me I needed my first operation, etc." Buys 50-60 unsolicited mss/year. Length: up to 2,500 words. Pays "usual minimum $150."

Photos: Photos purchased with mss only. B&w glossies, 8x10. Payment "depends on quality, relevancy of material, etc."

Tips: "The article we are most likely to buy will be a straight report on some situation where the freedom to practice medicine has been enhanced, or where it has been intruded on to the detriment of good health."

RESIDENT & STAFF PHYSICIAN, Romaine Pierson Publishers, Inc., 80 Shore Rd., Port Washington NY 11050. (516)883-6350. Editor: Alfred Jay Bollet, M.D. Managing Editor: Anne Mattarella. 5% freelance written. Monthly journal covering clinical medicine and practice management for residents and staff physicians. "*Resident & Staff Physician* goes to hospital-based physicians throughout the country, including practically all residents and the full-time hospital staff responsible for their training." Circ. 100,000. Pays on acceptance. Publishes ms an average of 1 year after acceptance. Byline given. Buys all rights. "However, we may grant permission to reprint if requested by the writer." Submit seasonal/holiday material 1 year in advance. Photocopied submissions OK. Reports in 3 weeks on queries; 4 months on mss. Sample copy for $8; free writer's guidelines.

Nonfiction: Historical/nostalgic (medical); medical humor; medical practice management. No case reports. Buys 2 mss/year. Query. Length: 6-8 typewritten pages. Pays $200-300.

Photos: State availability of photos. "Payment is included in manuscript payment." Captions, model-release and identification of subjects required. Buys all rights.

Columns/Departments: Medical Mixups (terms patients mix up, e.g., Cadillacs in the eyes instead of cataracts). Buys 5-10 mss/year. Send complete ms. Length: 50 words. Pays $25 maximum.

Fillers: Jokes, anecdotes, short humor and newsbreaks. Buys 5/year. Length: 25-500 words. Pays $25-$100.

Tips: "A freelancer can best break in to our publication with filler items or humorous anecdotes. Keep the audience in mind. Jokes about high doctor fees are *not* funny to doctors."

‡SOUTH FLORIDA MEDICAL REVIEW, Review Business Publications, 100 N.E. 7th St., Miami FL 33132. (305)377-3721. Editor: Avram Goldstein. 25% freelance written. Prefers to work with published/established writers. A biweekly tabloid for MDs, DOs and health care administrators covering health industry news in Dade, Broward, and Palm Beach counties and statewide. Emphasizes stories of interest to practicing physicians and administrators and executives at hospitals, HMOs, nursing homes and home health agencies; regulatory, legal, financial, competitive, ethical and other issues. Estab. 1985. Circ. 15,000. Pays on publication. Publishes ms an average of 5 months after acceptance. Byline given. Offers variable kill fee. Buys first rights or all rights. Submit seasonal/holiday material 6 weeks in advance. Simultaneous submissions OK. Electronic submissions OK via standard modem transmission, 300 or 1200 baud, 1200: 8 data bits, 1 stop bit, no parity, ½ duplex; prefers hard copy also. Computer printout submissions acceptable; prefers letter-quality to dot-matrix. Reports in 2 weeks. Sample copy for $2 and 8½x11 SAE.

Nonfiction: Essays, exposé, historical/nostalgic, humor, interview/profile, opinion, personal experience and photo feature. "No consumer how-to, excessively clinical articles, or breaking news that could be too quickly dated by our deadlines." Query with published clips. Length: 300-2,000 words. Pays $25-175. Sometimes pays expenses of writers on assignment.

Photos: Send photos with submission. Pays variable rate. Identification of subjects required. Buys one-time rights.

Columns/Departments: Managing Your Practice (helps doctors run their businesses), 750-1,000 words; Opinions (contributions from experts on variety of subjects of interest to readers) 800-1,200 words. Buys 10 ms/year. Query, or send complete ms. Pays variable rate.

Tips: "Areas most open to freelancers are news columns and features on subjects of interest to health professionals—especially topics involving malpractice, legal issues, socioeconomic trends, personality pieces—all with a South Florida angle.

‡STRATEGIC HEALTH CARE MARKETING, Health Care Communications, 211 Midland Ave., Box 594, Rye NY 10580. (914)967-6741. Editor: Michele von Dambrowski. 20% freelance written. "Will only work with unpublished writer on a 'stringer' basis initally." A monthly newsletter covering health care services marketing in a wide range of settings including hospitals and medical group practices, home health services and urgent care centers. Emphasizing strategies and techniques employed within the health care field and relevant applications from other service industries. Pays on publication. Publishes ms an average of 2 months after acceptance. Byline sometimes given. Offers 25% kill fee. Buys first North American serial rights. Simultaneous and photocopied submissions OK. Computer printout submissions acceptable; no dot-matrix. Reports in 1 month.

Sample copy for 9x12 SAE and 56¢ postage; guidelines sent with sample copy only.
Nonfiction: How-to, interview/profile, new product and technical. Buys 9 mss/year. Query with published clips. Length: 700-2,000 words. Pays $50-250. Sometimes pays the expenses of writers on assignment with prior authorization.
Photos: State availability of photos with submissions. (Photos, unless necessary for subject explanation, are rarely used.) Reviews contact sheets. Offers $10-30/photo. Captions and model releases required. Buys one-time rights.
Fillers: Facts and newsbreaks. Buys 6/year. Length: 50-250 words. Pays $10-50.
Tips: "Writers with prior experience on business beat for newspaper or newsletter will do well. This is not a consumer publication—the writer with knowledge of both health care and marketing will excel. Interviews or profiles are most open to freelancers. Absolutely no unsolicited manuscripts; any received will be returned or discarded unread."

SURGICAL ROUNDS, Romaine Pierson Publishers, Inc., 80 Shore Rd., Port Washington NY 11050. (516)883-6350. Editor: Mark M. Ravitch, M.D. Executive Editor: Roxane Cafferata. Monthly magazine for surgeons and surgical specialists throughout the country, including interns and residents, all surgical faculty in medical schools, plus full-time hospital and private practice surgeons and operating room supervisors. Circ. 70,000. Pays on acceptance. Byline given. Buys all rights. Reports in 1 month. Sample copy $5; free writer's guidelines.
Nonfiction: How-to (practical, everyday clinical applications). "Articles for 'The Surgeon's Laboratory' should demonstrate a particular procedure step-by-step and be amply and clearly illustrated with intraoperative color photographs and anatomical drawings." Buys 80 mss/year. Query with published clips. Length: 1,500-2,000 words. Pays $150-400.

Mining and Minerals

GOLD PROSPECTOR, Gold Prospectors Association of America, Box 507, Bonsall CA 92003. (619)728-6620. Editor: Steve Teter. 60% freelance written. Eager to work with new/unpublished writers. Bimonthly magazine covering gold prospecting and mining. "*Gold Prospector* magazine is the official publication of the Gold Prospectors Association of America. The GPAA is an international organization of more than 100,000 members who are interested in recreational prospecting and mining. Our primary audience is people of all ages who like to take their prospecting gear with them on their weekend camping trips, and fishing and hunting trips. Our readers are interested not only in prospecting, but camping, fishing, hunting, skiing, backpacking, etc. And we try to carry stories in each issue pertaining to subjects besides prospecting." Circ. 150,000. Pays on publication. Publishes ms an average of 6 months after acceptance. Byline given. Buys first North American serial rights and second serial (reprint) rights. Submit seasonal/holiday material 6 months in advance. Simultaneous queries and photocopied and previously published submissions OK. Computer printout submission acceptable; no dot-matrix. Reports in 3 weeks. Sample copy $1; free writer's guidelines.
Nonfiction: Historical/nostalgic; how-to (prospecting techniques, equipment building, etc.); humor; new product; personal experience; technical; and travel. "One of our publishing beliefs is that our audience would rather experience life than watch it on television—that they would like to take a rough and tumble chance with the sheer adventure of taking gold from the ground or river after it has perhaps lain there for a million years. Even if they don't, they seem to enjoy reading about those who do in the pages of *Gold Prospector* magazine." Buys 75-100 mss/year. Query with or without published clips if available or send complete ms. Length: 1,000-3,000 words. Pays $25-100.
Photos: State availability of photos with query or ms. Pays $2.50-$10 for 3½x5 b&w prints; $5-25 for 3½x5-color prints. Captions, model release, and identification of subjects required. Buys all rights.
Columns/Departments: Precious metals market report, mining news, and dowsing report. Buys 15-25/year. Query with or without published clips if available or send complete ms. Length: 500-1,000 words. Pays $25-100.
Fillers: Clippings and anecdotes. Buys 25/year. Length: 50-100 words. Pays $5-15.
Tips: "We need manuscripts that accurately describe prospecting techniques, outdoor camping trips and information, and rock hounding techniques, etc."

ROCK PRODUCTS, Maclean-Hunter Publishing Corp., 300 W. Adams, Chicago IL 60606. (312)726-2802. Editor: Richard S. Huhta. Monthly magazine of the nonmetallic mining industry for producers of cement,

lime, sand, gravel, crushed stone and lightweight gypsum aggregate. Circ. 23,000. Pays on publication. Byline given. Buys first serial rights. Reports in 2 weeks.
Nonfiction: Technical (maintenance and cement). "All pieces must relate directly to our industry. No general business articles." Buys 5-6 mss/year. Query. Length: 2,000-4,000 words. Pays variable fee.
Photos: No restrictions. Color transfer a plus. No additional fee for ms accompanied by photos.

Music

‡**THE CHURCH MUSICIAN**, 127 9th Ave. N., Nashville TN 37234. (615)251-2961. Editor: William Anderson. 30% freelance written. Works with a small number of new/unpublished writers each year; eager to work with new/unpublished writers. Southern Baptist publication for Southern Baptist church music leaders. Monthly. Circ. 20,000. Buys all rights. Pays on acceptance. Publishes ms an average of 1 year after acceptance. No query required. Reports in 2 months. Free sample copy.
Nonfiction: Leadership and how-to features, success stories and articles on Protestant church music. "We reject material when the subject of an article doesn't meet our needs. And they are often poorly written, or contain too many 'glittering generalities' or lack creativity." Length: maximum 1,300 words. Pays up to 4¢/word.
Photos: Purchased with mss; related to mss content only. "We use only b&w glossy prints."
Fiction: Inspiration, guidance, motivation and morality with Protestant church music slant. Length: to 1,300 words. Pays up to 3¹/₂¢/word.
Poetry: Church music slant, inspirational. Length: 8-24 lines. Pays $5-15.
Fillers: Short humor. Church music slant. No clippings. Pays $5-15.
Tips: "I'd advise a beginning writer to write about his or her experience with some aspect of church music; the social, musical and spiritual benefits from singing in a choir; a success story about their instrumental group; a testimonial about how they were enlisted in a choir—especially if they were not inclined to be enlisted at first. A writer might speak to hymn singers—what turns them on and what doesn't. Some might include how music has helped them to talk about Jesus as well as sing about Him. We would prefer most of these experiences be related to the church, of course, although we include many articles by freelance writers whose affiliation is other than Baptist. A writer might relate his experience with a choir of blind or deaf members. Some people receive benefits from working with unusual children—retarded, or culturally deprived, emotionally unstable, and so forth. Photographs are valuable here."

CLAVIER, A Magazine for Pianists and Organists, The Instrumentalist Co., 200 Northfield Rd., Northfield IL 60093. (312)446-5000. Editor: Barbara Kreader. 95% freelance written. A magazine published 10 times a year covering keyboard teaching and performance. Circ. 20,000. Pays on publication. Publishes ms an average of 1 year after acceptance. Byline given. Buys all rights. Submit seasonal/holiday material 6 months in advance. Computer printout acceptable; prefers letter-quality to dot-matrix. Reports in 1 week on queries; 2 months on manuscripts. Free sample copy and writer's guidelines.
Nonfiction: Essays, historical/nostaglic; how-to (on teaching, keeping a small business running, etc.); humor, interview/profile; personal experience and photo feature. Query with published clips. Length: 1,000-3,000 words. Pays $20-45/printed magazine page.
Photos: Send photos with submission. Reviews contact sheets, negatives, transparencies, and prints. Offers no additional payment for photos accepted with ms; offers $10-20/photo if by major photographers. Captions, model releases and identification of subjects required.
Tips: "Articles should be of interest and direct practical value to our readers, who are studio teachers of piano and organ, church organists, or harpsichordists. Topics may include pedagogy, technique, performance, ensemble playing, and accompanying. Material should be covered clearly and thoroughly but without repetition and unnecessary digressions."

‡**FLUTE TALK**, The Instrument Publishing Co., 200 Northfield Rd., Northfield IL 60093. (312)446-5000. Editor: Polly Hansen. 70% freelance written. Magazine published 10 times/year covering flute performance. Circ. 9,000. Pays on publication. Publishes ms an average of 6 months after acceptance. Byline given. Buys all rights. Submit seasonal/holiday material 4 months in advance. Computer printout submissions acceptable; no dot-matrix. Reports in several weeks. Free sample copy and writer's guidelines.
Nonfiction: How-to (execute certain flute techniques); humor; inspirational; interview/profile; opinion; personal experience; photo feature; and technical (flute repair). "Writing must be educational, but upbeat. A

thorough knowledge of flute playing and/or music teaching is necessary." March issue contains listing of flute master classes held in the summer. No unsolicited performance guides or interviews duplicating those already featured. Buys 25 mss/year. Send complete ms. Length: 500-3,000 words. Pays $20-200. Sometimes pays the expenses of writers on assignment.

Photos: Send photos with submission. Reviews contact sheets, 2x2 transparencies and 8x10 prints—for cover only. Identification of subjects required. "For cover photos we pay photographer and buy all rights; for photos within an article, we don't pay and will accept any size."

Columns/Departments: Book Review (review of recently published flute texts), 500-750 words; and Record Reviews (review of recently released flute recordings), 500 words. Buys 6 mss/year. Query with published clips. Length: 250-750 words. Pays $20-45.

Fillers: Anecdotes, facts, gags to be illustrated by cartoonist, newsbreaks and short humor. Buys 20/year. Length: 125-375 words. Pays $15 maximum.

Tips: "We look for highly informative, knowledgeable, and fun to read articles related to flute performance. It is easy to be published in *Flute Talk* if the article is well-written and applicable. Do *not* send single spaced manuscripts. If a photocopy is sent make sure the copy is dark. Submissions should not be under consideration by another publication. Most open to freelancers are articles related to flute techniques such as breath control, finger technique, tonguing exercises with music included, alternate fingering charts, trill charts, etc. Also book, concert, and record reviews. Because *Flute Talk* is read by both professional flutists and amateurs, we present material for a wide range of ability levels. General interest regarding flute related topics are therefore applicable."

‡**THE INSTRUMENTALIST**, Instrumentalist Publishing Company, 200 Northfield Rd., Northfield IL 60093. (312)446-5000. Managing Editor: Anne Driscoll. Approximately 95% freelance written. A monthly magazine covering instrumental music education for school band and orchestra directors, as well as performers and students. "We publish some general interest articles, but primarily written for and by those involved in music education." Circ. approximately 20,000. Pays on publication. Byline given. Buys all rights. Submit seasonal/holiday material 4 months in advance. Photocopied submissions OK. Computer printout submissions acceptable; prefers letter-quality to dot-matrix. Reports in 2 months. Sample copy $2; free writer's guidelines.

Nonfiction: Book excerpts (rarely); essays (on occasion); general interest (on occasion, music); historical/nostalgic (music); how-to (teach, repair instruments); humor (on occasion); interview/profile (performers, conductors, composers); opinion; personal experience; photo feature; and travel. Buys 35-40 mss/year. Send complete ms. Length: 750-1,750 words. Pays $25-45/published page.

Photos: State availability of photos with submission. Reviews slides and 5x7 prints. Payment varies. Captions and identification of subjects required. Buys variable rights.

Columns/Departments: Challenge (opinions on issues facing music educators), 500-750 words; Personal Perspective (advice and ideas from experienced educators and performers), 500-750 words; Idea Exchange ('how-to's' from educators), 250-500 words; My 2¢ Worth (opinions and humorous viewpoints), 250-500 words. Buys 12-15 mss/year. Send complete ms. Length: 250-500 words. Pays $30-45.

Fillers: Anecdotes and short humor. Buys 12-15/year. Length: 250 words maximum. Pays $25-45.

Tips: "Know the music education field, specifically band and orchestra. Interviews with performers should focus on the person's contribution to educating, opinions about it, experience, etc. Interviews and features on performers and groups are probably most accessible to non-musicians."

MUSIC CONNECTION MAGAZINE, The Alternative Music Trade Publication, Connection Publications, Suite 201, 6640 Sunset Blvd., Hollywood CA 90028. (213)462-5772. Executive Editor: J. Michael Dolan. Senior Editor: Bud Scoppa. 80% freelance written. A biweekly magazine covering the entire music industry for musicians and trade executives. Circ. 40,000. Pays on publication. Publishes ms an average of 2 months after acceptance. Byline given. Makes work-for-hire assignments. Submit seasonal/holiday material 6 weeks in advance. Simultaneous queries and photocopied submissions OK. Computer printout submissions acceptable; prefers letter-quality to dot-matrix. Reports in 1 month on queries; 2 months on mss. Sample copy for $2; 9x12 SAE and 2 class stamps; writer's guidelines for 9x12 SAE and 2 first class stamps.

Nonfiction: Expose (dealing with major music industry companies or organizations); interview/profile (personalities of interest in popular music); technical (new technological developments in instruments and musical computers); how-to (breaking into the industry, cutting records, etc.); and historical (dealing with the historical background of the music and record industry). Special issues include: Recording Studios, Video, Nightclubs, and Year-End Review. "All articles must deal with factual and timely occurences and personalities in the music industry." Buys 120 mss/year. Query with resume and published clips. Length: 800-2,500 words. Pays $30-150. Sometimes pays expenses of writers on assignment.

Photos: Attention: photo editor. Send photos with accompanying query or ms. Payment negotiable. Identification of subjects required. Buys all rights.

Columns/Departments: Bruce Duff, review editor/club rep. Concert and Nightclub Reviews (acts playing southern California); Record Reviews (recent release LPs, EPs, singles and cassettes); and News & Local Notes (noteworthy happenings in the popular music industry). Buys 500 mss/year. Query with resume and published clips. Length: 100-800 words. Pays $5-40.

Fiction: Bud Scoppa, editor. Humorous (dealing with the music business and the trials of getting accepted); and mainstream (pertaining to the record industry and the nightclub scene). "We do not want to see anything which is irrelevant to popular music." Buys 1-2 mss/year. Query with resume and published clips. Length: 750-2,500 words. Pays $25-100.

Fillers: Ken Kerner, associate editor. Clippings, gags, anecdotes and newsbreaks. Buys 5/year. Length 30-300 words. Pays $5-25.

Tips: "Previous experience in the music industry and proven background as a professional writer in related publications are very important. Send as complete a resume as possible, including samples of previously published work, and a cover letter dicussing your musical interests. Feature stories, interviews, and news-article writing are the areas where we most often use freelancers. It is important to take an authoritative and knowledgeable music industry slant when writing these articles. There is no substitute for intensive research when writing a piece for any publication. It becomes painfully obvious to the informed reader when the writer is unsure of his subject matter."

MUSIC & SOUND OUTPUT, The Magazine For Performers and Producers, Testa Communications, Inc., 220 Westbury Ave., Carle Place NY 11514. (516)334-7880. Editor: Chris Clark. Managing Editor: David Browne. 10% freelance written. Monthly magazine of contemporary music and recording. Audience is mostly working musicians. Prefers technical versus sociological slant in coverage of rock, jazz, R&B, country, pop, blues, and ethnic music. Circ. 78,000. Pays on publication. Publishes ms an average of 3 months after acceptance. Byline given. Offers 10-20% kill fee. Buys all rights. Photocopied submissions OK. Computer printout submissions acceptable; prefers letter-quality to dot-matrix. Reports in 2 weeks. Sample copy for $2.50.

Nonfiction: Interview/profile (music performers, producers, engineers); technical (recording, and live sound, query first); and reviews of records. No mss written from a fan's point of view, i.e., features on performers without getting an interview. Buys 10-20 mss/year. Query with published clips. Length: 250-3,000 words. Pays $25-500. Sometimes pays expenses of writers on assignment.

Photos: State availability of photos. Prefers exclusive photos. Reviews color transparencies and 8x10 b&w prints. Pays $50-300 for color; $20-200 for b&w. Identification of subjects required. Buys one-time rights.

Columns/Departments: Record reviews (any genre). Buys 10-20 mss/year. Send complete ms. Length: 200-500 words. Pays $20-50.

Tips: "A huge pile of music-related clips is always impressive. We are seeking writers with experience in the music industry as a performer or with extensive technical background in recording. Areas most open to freelancers include record reviews and short (500-1,000 words), profiles of new bands, established musicians with a new direction, producers, engineers and innovators."

OPERA NEWS, 1865 Broadway, New York NY 10023. Editor: Robert Jacobson. 75% freelance written. Monthly magazine (May-November); biweekly (December-April). For all people interested in opera; opera singers, opera management people, administrative people in opera, opera publicity people, and artists' agents; people in the trade and interested laymen. Circ. 120,000. Pays on publication. Buys first serial rights only. Pays negotiable kill fee. Byline given. Computer printout submissions acceptable; prefers letter-quality to dot-matrix. Sample copy $2.50.

Nonfiction: Most articles are commissioned in advance. In summer, uses articles of various interests on opera; in the fall and winter, articles that relate to the weekly broadcasts. Emphasis is on high quality in writing and an intellectual interest in the opera-oriented public. Informational, how-to, personal experience, interview, profile, humor, historical, think pieces, personal opinion and opera reviews. Query; no telephone inquiries. Length: 2,500 words maximum. Pays 13¢/word for features; 10¢/word for reviews.

Photos: Pays minimum of $25 for photos purchased on assignment. Captions required.

SYMPHONY MAGAZINE, American Symphony Orchestra League, 633 E St., NW, Washington DC 20004. (202)628-0099. Editor: Robin Perry Allen. Associate Editor: Chester Lane. 60% freelance written. Prefers to work with published/established writers; works with a small number of new/unpublished writers each year. Bimonthly magazine covering symphony orchestras in North America and the classical music industry for members of the association, including managers, conductors, board members, musicians, volunteer association members, music businesses, schools, libraries, etc. Circ. 15,500. Pays on publication. Publishes ms an average of 2 months after acceptance. Byline given. Pays negotiable kill fee. Buys all rights (sometimes negotiable). Simultaneous queries, and photocopied and previously published submissions OK. Electronic submissions OK but requires hard copy also. Computer printout submissions acceptable; no dot-matrix. Reports in 1 month. Free sample copy.

Nonfiction: How-to (manage, fundraising, marketing) for symphony orchestra administrative personnel; interview/profile (conductors, philanthropists, managers and personalities in the field); technical (budgeting, tour planning); and "thoughtful, reflective looks at the state of the classical music industry." Buys 25 mss/year. Query with published clips. Length: 1,500-3,000 words. Pays $50-400. Sometimes pays the phone expenses of writers on assignment.

Photos: "We prefer b&w action shots and informal shots." State availability of photos. Captions required.
Tips: "If he or she knows about issues and personalities in the classical music world, and can relate in an original and literate manner, there is a high possibility that we could use his or her contribution."

Office Environment and Equipment

AMERICAN OFFICE DEALER, (formerly *Western Office Dealer*), 41 Sutter St., San Francisco CA 94104. Editor: Jan Stafford. 5% freelance written. Works with a small number of new/unpublished writers each year; eager to work with new/unpublished writers. Monthly magazine; 60-70 pages. Circ. 20,000. Byline given. Pays on acceptance. Publishes ms an average of 3 months after acceptance. Buys first serial rights. Submit seasonal (merchandising) material 4 months in advance. Computer printout submissions acceptable; prefers letter-quality to dot-matrix. Reports in 1 week. Sample copy $2.
Nonfiction: "Our main interest is in how retailers of stationery and office products can do a better selling job. We use how-to-do-it merchandising articles showing dealers how to sell more stationery and office products to more people at a greater profit. Seasonal merchandising articles always welcome, if acceptable." Informational, how-to, personal experience, interview, and successful business operations. "We only want material pertaining to successful merchandising activities." Buys 12 mss/year. Query or submit complete ms. Length: 1,000-1,500 words. Pays $100-200.
Photos: Send photos with ms. Pays $15 for b&w photos used with mss; 3x5 minimum. Captions required.
Tips: "Readers prefer specific, real-life examples as a way of illustrating the topic or business practice under discussion. We seek simple, easy-to-understand business stories."

GEYER'S OFFICE DEALER, 51 Madison Ave., New York NY 10010. (212)689-4411. Editor: Robert D. Rauch. 20% freelance written. For independent office equipment and stationery dealers, and special purchasers for store departments handling stationery and office equipment. Monthly. Buys all rights. Pays kill fee. Byline given. Pays on publication. Publishes ms an average of 3 months after acceptance. Computer printout submissions acceptable; prefers letter-quality to dot-matrix. Reports "immediately."
Nonfiction: Articles on dealer efforts in merchandising and sales promotion; programs of stationery and office equipment dealers. Problem-solving articles related to retailers of office supplies, social stationery items, office furniture and equipment and office machines. Must feature specified stores. Query. Length: 300-1,000 words. Pays $125 minimum but quality of article is real determinant.
Photos: B&w glossies are purchased with accompanying ms with no additional payment.

‡**MARKING INDUSTRY MAGAZINE,** Marking Devices Publishing Co., 2640 N. Halsted, Chicago IL 60614. (312)528-6600. Editor: David Hachmeister. 25% freelance written. Prefers to work with published/established writers. Monthly magazine for manufacturers and dealers of marking products. Pays on acceptance. Publishes ms an average of 2 months after acceptance. Byline given. Rights purchased vary. Simultaneous queries, and simultaneous, photocopied and previously published submissions OK. Electronic submissions OK via D-Base III, Smartcom, IBM PC-XT. Computer printout submissions acceptable; prefers letter-quality to dot-matrix. Reports in 2 weeks. Free sample copy and writer's guidelines.
Nonfiction: How-to, inspirational, interview/profile, new product and technical. "We publish a promotional quarterly for which we need cartoons, jokes and fillers. Nothing controversial." Buys 12-18 mss/year. Query with clips of published work. Length: 4,000 words maximum. Pays $25 minimum. Pays expenses of writers on assignment.
Photos: State availability of photos. Buys one-time rights.
Fillers: Jokes and short humor. Buys 20/year. Pays $30 minimum.

‡**MODERN OFFICE TECHNOLOGY,** Penton Publishing, 1111 Chester Ave., Cleveland OH 44114. (216)696-7000. Editor: Lura K. Romei. Managing Editor: Vickie Friess. 5-10% freelance written. A monthly magazine covering office automation. "We serve corporate management and corporate personnel, financial management, administrative and operating management, systems and information management, managers and supervisors of support personnel, and purchasing." Circ. 156,500. Pays on publication. Publishes ms an

average of 6 months after acceptance. Byline given. Buys first and one-time rights. Photocopied submissions OK. Electronic submissions OK via disk only, Kaypro II, IBM compatible; requires hard copy also. Computer printout submissions acceptable. Reports in 3 weeks. Free sample copy and writer's guidelines.
Nonfiction: New product, opinion and technical. Buys 8 mss/year. Query with or without published clips, or send complete ms. Length: open. Pays $250-500 for assigned articles; pays $250-400 for unsolicited articles. Pays writers with contributor copies or other premiums rather than a cash on request. Pays expenses of writers on assignment.
Photos: Send photos with submission. Reviews contact sheets, 4x5 transparencies and prints. Offers no additional payment for photos accepted with ms. Captions and identification of subjects required. Buys one-time rights.
Columns/Departments: Reader's Soapbox (opinions on office-related subjects), 750 words. Buys 3 mss/year. Send complete ms. Pays $75-150.
Tips: "Our readers are always looking for better ways to do the things they have to do daily. Any off-the-beaten-track material has a fairly good chance of being seriously considered. Features, certainly, is our most open area. We're looking for depth, clarity, and applicability to office management."

‡**OFFICE SYSTEMS ERGONOMICS REPORT**, The Koffler Group, 3029 Wilshire Blvd., Santa Monica CA 90403. (213)453-1844. Editor: Kathy Potosnak. Managing Editor: Richard Koffler. 5% freelance written. "We will review all submissions." A bimonthly covering computers and human factors: "objective, practical advice on how computers can/should be used by people." Circ. 1,000. Pays on publication. Publishes ms an average of 2 months after acceptance. Byline given. Offers negotiable kill fee. Buys all rights. Simultaneous, photocopied and previously published submissions OK. Electronic submissions OK via ASCII. Computer printout submissions acceptable. Free sample copy.
Nonfiction: Book excerpts, essays, exposé, general interest, humor, interview/profile, new product, opinion, personal experience and technical. Buys 6-10 mss/year. Query with or without published clips, or send complete ms. Length: open. Pays negotiable rates.
Photos: Send photos with submission. Reviews contact sheets. Offers no additional payment for photos accepted with ms. Captions and model releases required. Buys one-time rights.
Tips: "Writers who can objectively review an issue and related scientific research and then provide practical advice on the topic for managers will suit our needs. Continued emphasis will be placed on usable information with a *firm* basis in research."

Paint

AMERICAN PAINT & COATINGS JOURNAL, American Paint Journal Co., 2911 Washington Ave., St. Louis MO 63103. (314)534-0301. Editor: Chuck Reitter. 10% freelance written. Weekly magazine; 78 pages. For the coatings industry (paint, varnish, lacquer, etc.); manufacturers of coatings, suppliers to coatings industry, educational institutions, salesmen. Circ. 7,300. Publishes ms an average of 3 months after acceptance. Pays on publication. Pays kill fee "depending on the work done." Buys all rights. Phone queries OK. Simultaneous and photocopied submissions OK. Computer printout submissions acceptable. Reports in 3 weeks. Free sample copy and writer's guidelines.
Nonfiction: Informational, historical, interview, new product, technical articles and coatings industry news. Buys 2 mss/issue. Query before sending long articles; submit complete ms for short pieces. Length: 75-1,200 words. Pays $5-100. Sometimes pays expenses of writers on assignment.
Photos: B&w (5x7) glossies purchased with or without mss or on assignment. Query. Pays $3-10.

AMERICAN PAINTING CONTRACTOR, American Paint Journal Co., 2911 Washington Ave., St. Louis MO 63103. (314)534-0301. Editor: Paul Stoeckein. 10% freelance written. Monthly magazine; 80 pages. For painting and decorating contractors, in-plant maintenance painting department heads, architects and paint specifiers. Circ. 13,000. Publishes ms an average of 2 months after acceptance. Buys all rights. Submit seasonal/holiday material 2 months in advance. Reports in 1 month. Free sample copy.
Nonfiction: Historical, how-to, humor, informational, new product, personal experience, interviews, photo features and profiles. Buys 10-15 unsolicited mss/year. "Freelancers should be able to write well and have some understanding of the painting and decorating industry. We do not want general theme articles such as 'How to Get More Work Out of Your Employee' unless they relate to a problem within the painting and decorating industry." Length: 1,000-2,500 words. Pays $150-225.

Photos: B&w and color purchased with mss or on assignment. Captions required. Send prints or transparencies.
Tips: "We are not looking for anything but well-researched, major features. The most frequent mistakes made by writers are that articles tend to be too generic and brief—often they do not become familiar with the magazine's content and writing style before submitting manuscripts."

Paper

‡BOXBOARD CONTAINERS, Maclean Hunter Publishing Co., 300 W. Adams St., Chicago IL 60606. (312)726-2802. Editor: Charles Huck. Managing Editor: William Turley. A monthly magazine covering box and carton manufacturing for corrugated box, folding carton, setup box manufacturers internationally. Emphasizes technology and management. Circ. 13,000. Pays on publication. Byline given. Buys first North American serial rights. Submit seasonal/holiday material 2 months in advance. Photocopied submissions OK. Electronic submissions OK via XY Write/IBM PC, but requires hard copy also. Computer printout submissions acceptable; no dot-matrix. Reports in 1 month. Free sample copy.
Nonfiction: How-to, interview/profile, new product, opinion, personal experience, photo feature and technical. Buys 10 mss/year. Query. Length: 2,000-6,000 words. Pays $75-350 for assigned articles; pays $50-200 for unsolicited articles. Sometimes pays the expenses of writers on assignment.
Photos: Send photos with submission. Reviews 35mm, 4x5 and 6x6 transparencies and 8x10 prints. Offers no additional payment for photos accepted with ms. Captions, model releases and identification of subjects required. Buys one-time rights.
Tips: Features are most open to freelancers.

PAPERBOARD PACKAGING, 7500 Old Oak Blvd., Cleveland OH 44130. (216)243-8100: Editor: Mark Arzoumanian. 10% freelance written. Works with a small number of new/unpublsihed writers each year. Monthly. For "managers, supervisors, and technical personnel who operate corrugated box manufacturing, folding carton converting and rigid box companies and plants." Circ. 15,000. Pays on publication. Publishes ms an average of 2 months after acceptance. Buys all rights. Photocopied submissions OK. Submit seasonal material 3 months in advance. Computer printout submissions acceptable; no dot-matrix. Sample copy on request.
Nonfiction: "Application articles, installation stories, etc. Contact the editor first to establish the approach desired for the article. Especially interested in packaging systems using composite materials, including paper and other materials." Buys technical articles. Query. Length: open. Pays "$75/printed page (about 1,000 words to a page), including photos." Sometimes pays the expenses of writers on assignment.
Photos: "Will not pay photography costs, but will pay cost of photo reproductions for article."
Tips: "Writing style is not as much a concern to me as individual's knowledge of my industry and objective in writing article in first place. My company is cracking down on use of freelancers. Budgets are being cut; I'll probably use *very* few in 1987. Nature of publication (trade) automatically means limited use of freelancers because of specialized field."

PULP & PAPER CANADA, Southam Communications Ltd., Suite 201, 310 Victoria Ave., Montreal, Quebec H3Z 2M9 Canada. (514)487-2302. Editor: Peter N. Williamson. Managing Editor: Graeme Rodden. 5% freelance written. Prefers to work with published/established writers. Monthly magazine. Circ. 8,488. Pays on acceptance. Publishes ms "as soon as possible" after acceptance. Byline given. Offers kill fee according to prior agreement. Buys first North American serial rights. Submit seasonal/holiday material 2 months in advance. Computer printout submissions acceptable; prefers letter-quality to dot-matrix. Reports in 2 weeks on queries; 3 weeks on mss. Sample copy $5 (Canada), $7 (other countries); free writer's guidelines.
Nonfiction: How-to (related to processes and procedures in the industry); interview/profile (of Canadian leaders in pulp and paper industry); and technical (relevant to modern pulp and/or paper industry). No fillers, short industry news items, or product news items. Buys 10 mss/year. Query with or without published clips or send complete ms. Articles with photographs (b&w glossy) or other good quality illustrations will get priority review. Length: 1,500-2,000 words (with photos). Pays $140 (Canadian funds)/published page, including photos, graphics, charts, etc. Sometimes pays the expenses of writers on assignment.

Pets

Listed here are publications for professionals in the pet industry, wholesalers, manufacturers, suppliers, retailers, owners of pet specialty stores, pet groomers, aquarium retailers, distributors and those interested in the fish industry. Publications for pet owners are listed in the Animal section of Consumer Publications.

PET AGE, The Largest Circulation Pet Industry Trade Publication, H.H. Backer Associates, Inc., 207 S. Wabash Ave., Chicago IL 60604. (312)663-4040. Editor: Karen M. Long. 10-20% freelance written. Prefers to work with published/established writers. Monthly magazine about the pet industry for pet retailers and industry. Circ. 16,000. Pays on acceptance. Publishes ms an average of 6 months after acceptance. Byline given. Buys first serial rights. Submit seasonal/holiday material 3 months in advance. Computer printout submissions acceptable; prefers letter-quality to dot-matrix. Reports in 6 weeks. Sample copy $2.50; free writer's guidelines.
Nonfiction: Profile (of a successful, well-run pet retail operation); how-to; interview; photo feature; and technical—all trade-related. Query first with published clips. Buys 12 mss/year. "Query as to the name and location of a pet operation you wish to profile and why it would make a good feature. No general retailing articles or consumer-oriented pet articles." Length: 1,500-2,500 words. Pays $75-200. Sometimes pays the expenses of writers on assignment.
Photos: State availability of photos. Reviews 5x7 b&w glossy prints, contact sheets and color transparencies. Captions and identification of subjects required.
Columns/Departments: Fish Care, Retailing, Government Action, Tax & Finance, Bird Care, New Products and Industry News. Query with published clips. Length: 1,000-1,500 words.
Tips: "We are interested in profiling successful, imaginative and/or unique retailing operations. Focus should be on the aspects that make the business successful: history/background of business and owners; description of service/products, sales and marketing strategies, advertising and promotional activities, etc. You must be able to provide 8-10 good b&w photos."

THE PET DEALER, Howmark Publishing Corp., 567 Morris Ave., Elizabeth NJ 07208. (201)353-7373. Editorial Director: Alan Richman. 15% freelance written. Monthly magazine; 80 pages. Emphasizes merchandising, marketing and management for owners and managers of pet specialty stores, departments, and pet groomers and their suppliers. Circ. 11,000. Pays on publication. Publication "may be many months between acceptance of a manuscript and publication." Byline given. Phone queries OK. Submit seasonal/holiday material 3 months in advance. Computer printout submissions acceptable; no dot-matrix. Reports in 1 week. Free sample copy and writer's guidelines.
Nonfiction: How-to (store operations, administration, merchandising, marketing, management, promotion and purchasing). Consumer pet articles—lost pets, best pets, humane themes—*not* welcome. Emphasis is on *trade* merchandising and marketing of pets and supplies. Buys 8 unsolicited mss/year. Length: 800-1,200 words. Pays $50-100.
Photos: Submit photo material with ms. No additional payment for 5x7 b&w glossy prints. "Six photos with captions required." Buys one-time rights.
Tips: "We're interested in store profiles outside the New York, New Jersey, Connecticut and Pennsylvania metro areas. Photos are of key importance. Articles focus on new techniques in merchandising or promotion. Submit query letter first, with writing background summarized; include samples. We seek one-to-one, interview-type features on retail pet store merchandising. Indicate the availability of the proposed article, your willingness to submit on exclusive or first-in-field basis, and whether you are patient enough to await payment on publication."

PETS/SUPPLIES/MARKETING, Harcourt Brace Jovanovich Publications, 1 E. 1st St., Duluth MN 55802. (218)723-9303. Publisher/Editor: David Kowalski. 10% freelance written. Monthly magazine. For independent pet retailers, chain franchisers, livestock and pet supply wholesalers, and manufacturers of pet products. Circ. 14,200. Pays on publication. Buys first rights only. Phone queries OK. Submit seasonal/holiday material 4 months in advance. Photocopied submissions OK. Computer printout submissions acceptable. Reports in 2 months. Free writer's guidelines. Sample copy $5.
Nonfiction: How-to (merchandise pet products, display, set up window displays, market pet product line); interviews (with pet store retailers); opinion (of pet industry members or problems facing the industry); photo

features (of successful pet stores or effective merchandising techniques and in-store displays); profiles (of successful retail outlets engaged in the pet trade); and technical articles (on more effective pet retailing, e.g., building a central filtration unit, constructing custom aquariums or display areas). Business management articles must deal specifically with pet shops and their own unique merchandise and problems. Length: 1,000-2,000 words. Buys 1-2 mss/issue. Query. Pays 10¢/word. Sometimes pays the expenses of writers on assignment.

Photos: Purchased with or without mss or on assignment. "We prefer 5x7 or 8x10 b&w glossies. But we will accept contact sheets and standard print sizes. For color, we prefer 35mm Kodachrome transparencies or 2¼x2¼." Pays $10 for b&w; $25 for color. Captions and model release required.

Columns/Departments: Suggestions for new columns or departments should be addressed to the editor. No clippings, please.

Tips: "We want articles which stress professional retailing, provide insight into successful shops, and generally capture the excitement of an exciting and sometimes controversial industry. All submissions are read. However, an initial query could save time and energy and ensure a publishable article."

Photography

AMERICAN CINEMATOGRAPHER, A.S.C. Holding Corp., Box 2230, Hollywood CA 90078. (213)876-5080. Editor: George Turner. 75% freelance written. Monthly magazine; 112 pages. An international journal of film and video production techniques "addressed to creative, managerial, and technical people in all aspects of production. Its function is to disseminate practical information about the creative use of film and video equipment, and it strives to maintain a balance between technical sophistication and accessibility." Circ. 35,000. Pays on publication. Publishes ms an average of 8 months after acceptance. Buys all rights. Phone queries OK. Simultaneous and photocopied submissions OK. Computer printout submissions acceptable "provided they are adequately spaced."

Nonfiction: Jean Turner, assistant editor. Descriptions of new equipment and techniques or accounts of specific productions involving unique problems or techniques; historical articles detailing the production of a classic film, the work of a pioneer or legendary cinematographer or the development of a significant technique or type of equipment. Also discussions of the aesthetic principles involved in production techniques. Recent article example: "Tales From Silverado," (July, 1985). Length: 1,500 to 5,000 words. Pays according to position and worth. Negotiable. Sometimes pays the expenses of writers on assignment.

Photos: B&w and color purchased with mss. No additional payment.

Tips: "No unsolicited articles. Call first. Doesn't matter whether you are published or new. Queries must describe writer's qualifications and include writing samples."

FUNCTIONAL PHOTOGRAPHY, The Magazine of Visual Documentation and Communication for the Scientific, Technical & Medical Image Maker, PTN Publishing Corp., 101 Crossways Park West, Woodbury NY 11797. Senior Editor: David A. Silverman. 70% freelance written. Bimonthly magazine of scientific/medical/technical image producers (doctors, R&D, scientific personnel). Circ. 33,000. Pays on publication. Publishes ms an average of 6 months after acceptance. Byline given. Not copyrighted. Computer printout submissions acceptable; letter-quality or double strike dot-matrix. Prefers no dot-matrix. Reports in 6 weeks. Sample copy $2; writer's guidelines for #10 SAE and 1 first class stamp.

Nonfiction: How-to, photo feature (related to our market), and technical. "Articles must be of instructive value for our particular type of technical reader." Buys 10-20 mss/year. Query with published clips. Pays $150-200.

Photos: Send photos with query. Reviews prints. Captions, model release and identification of subjects required. Buys one-time rights.

PHOTOFLASH, Models & Photographers Newsletter, Box 7946, Colorado Springs CO 80933. Managing Editor: Ron Marshall. 20% freelance written. Prefers to work with published/established writers; also works with a small number of new/unpublished writers each year. Quarterly newsletter of photographic modeling and glamour photography "for models, photographers, publishers, picture editors, modeling agents, advertising agencies, and others involved in the interrelated fields of modeling and photography." Pays on publication. Publishes ms an average of 3 months after acceptance. Byline given. Buys first North American serial rights and second serial (reprint) rights. Submit seasonal/holiday material 6 months in advance. Simultaneous queries, and simultaneous, photocopied and previously published submissions OK. "If previously published, please tell us when and where." Computer printout submissions acceptable; prefers letter-quality to dot-matrix. Reports in 2 months on queries; 4 months on mss. Sample copy $5.

Nonfiction: Interview/profile (of established and rising professionals in the field, especially models); photo feature; and technical (illustrating/explaining photographic and modeling techniques). Send complete ms. "We prefer photo-illustrated text packages."

Photos: Send photos with ms. "Payment is for the complete photo-text package; it includes a credit line, contributor copies and $15-25 depending on quality, completeness, etc. of the submissions." Reviews 8x10 b&w prints. Captions and model release required.

PHOTO LAB MANAGEMENT, PLM Publishing, Inc., 1312 Lincoln Blvd., Santa Monica CA 90406. (213)451-1344. Editor: Carolyn Ryan. Associate Editor: Arthur Stern. 75% freelance written. Monthly magazine covering process chemistries, process control, process equipment and marketing/administration for photo lab owners, managers and management personnel. Circ. over 13,000. Pays on publication. Publishes ms an average of 5 months after acceptance. Byline and brief bio given. Buys first North American serial rights. Submit seasonal/holiday material 6 months in advance. Computer printout submissions acceptable; no dot-matrix. Reports on queries in 6 weeks. Free sample copy and writer's guidelines for business size SAE and 1 first class stamp.

Nonfiction: Personal experience (lab manager); technical; and management or administration. Buys 40-50 mss/year. Query with brief biography. Length: 1,200-1,800 words. Pays $60/published page.

Photos: Reviews 35mm color transparencies and 4-color prints suitable for cover. "We're looking for outstanding cover shots of photofinishing images."

Tips: "Our departments are written in-house and we don't use 'fillers'. Send a query if you have some background in the industry or a willingness to dig out information and research for a top quality article that really speaks to our audience. The most frequent mistakes made by writers in completing an article for us are on the business management side—taking a generic rather than a photo lab approach."

PHOTOLETTER, Photosource International, Pine Lake Farm, Osceola WI 54020. (715)248-3800. Editor: Angela Larson. Managing Editor: H.T. White. 20% freelance written. A monthly newsletter on marketing photographs. "The *Photoletter* pairs photobuyers with photographers' collections." Circ. 1,532. Pays on acceptance. Publishes ms an average of 3 months after acceptance. Byline given. Buys one-time rights and simultaneous rights. Submit seasonal/holiday material 3 months in advance. Simultaneous, photocopied, and previously published submissions OK. Electronic submissions OK via MCI Mail, or NewsNet. Computer printout submissions acceptable; prefers letter-quality to dot-matrix. Reports in 2 weeks on queries. Sample copy $3; no writer's guidelines.

Nonfiction: Lori Johnson, articles editor. How-to market photos and personal experience in marketing photos. "Our readers expect advice in how-to articles." No submissions that do not deal with selling photos. Buys 6 mss/year. Query. Length: 300-850 words. Pays $50-100 for unsolicited articles.

Columns/Departments: Jeri Engh, columns department editor. "We would welcome column ideas. Length: 350 words. Pays $45-75.

Fillers: Facts. Buys 20/year. Length: 30-50 words. Pays $10.

Tips: "Columns are most open to freelancers. Bring an *expertise* on marketing photos or some other aspect of aid to small business persons."

‡PHOTOVIDEO, (formerly *Photo Video Retailer*), Maclean Hunter, 5th Fl., 777 Bay St. Toronto, Ontario M5W 1A7 Canada. (416)596-5878. Editor: Don Long. 20% freelance written. A magazine published 9 times a year for photo and video retailers, and professional photographers. "We seek to provide information to the trade to help in making better business decisions—news, products, trends, how-to etc." Circ. 16,500. Pays on acceptance. Publishes ms an average of 2 months after acceptance. Byline given. Offers 50% kill fee. Buys first North American serial rights. Submit seasonal/holiday material 3 months in advance. Simultaneous and photocopied submissions OK. Computer printout submissions acceptable; prefers letter-quality to dot-matrix. Reports in 1 month on queries; 2 weeks on manuscripts. Sample copy for 8½x11 SAE with IRCs.

Nonfiction: Professional how-to, interview/profile, opinion, photo feature (professionally oriented) and technical. No non-Canadian submissions. Buys 20 mss/year. Query with published clips. Length 200-1,200 words. Pays $100-400 for assigned articles; pays $50-200 for unsolicited articles. Sometimes pays the expenses of writers on assignment.

Photos: State availability of photos with submission. Reviews contact sheets. Offers $25-150/photo. Captions, model releases, and identification of subjects required. Buys one-time rights.

Columns/Departments: News and Comment (regional, national and international events), 600-800 words; and What's Coming Up (Calendar, minimum lead time of 2 months), 100 words. Query. Length: 100-800 words. Pays $25-100.

Tips: "Content is a carefully balanced package for both retailer and professional about photo and video. It covers such areas as profiles of successful businesses, new technology, professional techniques, marketing and merchandising ideas, advertising and promotion, business and association news, and economic and market trends.

Our readers must have a broad range of skills and knowledge levels. Therefore, submissions must contain sufficient background material for those less familiar with a topic, yet maintain the interest of more experienced readers.

PHOTO WEEKLY, Billboard Publications, Inc., 1515 Broadway, New York NY 10036. (212)764-7415. Editor: Willard Clark. Weekly photography tabloid featuring industry news for photographic retailers and photofinishers. Circ. 15,000. Pays on acceptance. Byline given. Buys one-time rights.

THE PROFESSIONAL PHOTOGRAPHER, Serving the Entire Professional Market, Professional Photographers of America, Inc., 1090 Executive Way, Des Plaines IL 60018. (312)299-8161. Editor: Alfred DeBat. 80% freelance written. Monthly magazine of professional portrait, commercial and industrial photography. Describes the technical and business sides of professional photography—successful photo techniques, money-making business tips, legal considerations, selling to new markets, and descriptions of tough assignments and how completed. Circ. 36,000. Publishes ms an average of 9 months after acceptance. Byline given. Buys one-time rights. Submit seasonal/holiday material 6 months in advance. Simultaneous queries, and photocopied and previously published submissions OK. Computer printout submissions acceptable; prefers letter-quality to dot-matrix. Reports in 2 months. Sample copy $3.25; free writer's guidelines.
Nonfiction: How-to. Professional photographic techniques: How I solved this difficult assignment, How I increased my photo sales, How to buy a studio . . . run a photo business etc. Special issues include February: Portrait Photography; April: Wedding Photography; May: Commercial Photography; and August: Industrial Photography. Buys 8-10 ms/issue. Query. Length: 1,000-3,000 words. "We seldom pay, as most writers are PP of A members and want recognition for their professional skills, publicity, etc."
Photos: State availability of photos. Reviews 35mm color transparencies and 8x10 prints. Captions and model release required. Buys one-time rights.

THE RANGEFINDER, 1312 Lincoln Blvd., Santa Monica CA 90406. (213)451-8506. Editor: Arthur C. Stern. Associate Editor: Carolyn Ryan. Monthly magazine; 80 pages. Emphasizes professional photography. Circ. 55,000. Pays on publication. Publishes ms an average of 3 months after acceptance. Byline given. Buys first North American serial rights. Phone queries OK. Submit seasonal material 4 months in advance. Computer printout submissions acceptable; prefers letter-quality to dot-matrix. Reports in 6 weeks. Sample copy $2.50; writer's guidelines for SASE.
Nonfiction: How-to (solve a photographic problem; such as new techniques in lighting, new poses or set-ups); profile; and technical. "Articles should contain practical, solid information. Issues should be covered in depth. Look thoroughly into the topic." No opinion or biographical articles. Buys 5-7 mss/issue. Query with outline. Length: 800-1,200 words. Pays $60/published page.
Photos: State availability of photos with query. Captions preferred; model release required. Buys one-time rights.
Tips: "Exhibit knowledge of photography. Introduce yourself with a well-written letter and a great story idea."

STUDIO PHOTOGRAPHY, PTN Publishing Corp., 101 Crossways Park West, Woodbury NY 11797. (516)496-8000. Editor: Mark Zacharia. 65% freelance written. Monthly magazine. Circ. 65,000. Pays on publication. Publishes ms an average of 6 months after acceptance. Not copyrighted. Buys first serial rights only. Submit seasonal/holiday material 5 months in advance. Computer printout submissions acceptable; prefers letter-quality to dot-matrix. Reports in 6 weeks.
Nonfiction: Interview, personal experience, photo feature, communication-oriented, technical and travel. No business-oriented articles. Buys 2-3 mss/issue. Length: 1,700-3,000 words. Pays $75 minimum. Sometimes pays expenses of writers on assignment.
Photos: State availability of photos with query. Photos and article in one package.
Columns/Departments: Point of View (any aspect of photography dealing with professionals only). Buys 1/issue. Length: 1,700 words minimum.
Tips: "No handwritten queries will even be looked at. We look for professional quality in writing. No original transparencies, only fine quality duplicates. Submit photos with all articles. Only people with definite ideas and a sense of who they are need apply for publication. Read the magazine and become familiar with it before submitting work. Write for sample copy, editorial schedule, and writer/photographer's guidelines."

TECHNICAL PHOTOGRAPHY, PTN Publishing Corp., 101 Crossways Park West, Woodbury NY 11797. Senior Editor: David A. Silverman. 60% freelance written. Monthly magazine; 64 pages. Publication of the "on-staff (in-house) industrial, military and government still, video and AV professional who must produce (or know where to get) visuals of all kinds." Circ. 60,000. Pays on publication. Publishes ms an average of 4 months after acceptance. Buys first North American serial rights. Byline given. Computer printout submissions acceptable; prefers letter-quality or double-strike dot-matrix. Reports in 6 weeks. Sample copy $2; guidelines for #10 envelope and 1 first class stamp.

Nonfiction: How-to; interview; photo feature; profile (detailed stories about in-house operations); and technical. "All manuscripts must relate to industrial, military or government production of visuals." Buys 50 mss/year. Query. Length: "as long as needed to adequately cover the subject matter." Pays $150-200.
Photos: Offers no additional payment for photos purchased with ms. Query. Captions, model release, and subject identification required.

Plumbing, Heating, Air Conditioning, Refrigeration

Plumbers and repairmen learn how to do a better job from these publications. Publications for fuel oil dealers who also install heating equipment are classified with the Energy journals.

CONTRACTOR MAGAZINE, 1301 S. Grove Ave., Barrington IL 60010. Editor: John A. Schweizer. 15% freelance written. For mechanical contractors and wholesalers. Bimonthly newspaper; 50 (11x15) pages. Circ. 46,100. Pays on publication. Publishes ms an average of 3 months after acceptance. Buys first serial rights. Photocopied submissions OK. No simultaneous submissions. Computer printout submissions acceptable; prefers letter-quality to dot-matrix. Reports in 1 month. Sample copy $3.
Nonfiction: Articles on materials, use, policies, and business methods of the air conditioning, heating, plumbing, piping, solar, energy management, and contracting industry. Topics covered include interpretive reports, how-to, informational, interview, profile, think articles, expose, spot news, successful business operations, merchandising techniques and labor. Buys 12 mss/year. Query or submit complete ms. Pays $300 maximum. Pays expenses of writers on assignment.
Photos: 5x7 b&w glossies purchased with or without ms. Pays $10. Captions required.
Tips: "We are looking more for news than for features. We're backlogged with features."

DISTRIBUTOR, The Voice of Wholesaling, Technical Reporting Corp., Box 479, Wheeling IL 60090. (312)537-6460. Editorial Director: Steve Read. Managing Editor: James Butschli. 35% freelance written. Bimonthly magazine on heating, ventilating, air conditioning and refrigeration. Editorial material shows "executive wholesalers how they can run better businesses and cope with personal and business problems." Circ. 10,000. Pays on publication. Publishes ms an average of 2 months after acceptance. Byline given. Buys onetime rights. Submit seasonal/holiday material 3 months in advance. "We want material exclusive to the field (industry)." Photocopied submissions OK. Computer printout submissions acceptable; prefers letter-quality to dot-matrix. Reports in 2 weeks. Sample copy $4.
Nonfiction: How-to (run a better business, cope with problems); and interview/profile (the wholesalers). No flippant or general approaches. Buys 6 mss/year. Query with or without published clips or send complete ms. Length: 1,000-3,000 words. Pays $100-250 (10¢ a word). Sometimes pays the expenses of writers on assignment.
Photos: State availability of photos or send photos with query or ms. Pays $10-25 for color contact sheets; $15-30 for 35mm color transparencies; and $15-30 for 5x7 color prints. Captions and identification of subjects required.
Tips: "Know the industry—come up with a different angle on an industry subject (one we haven't dealt with in a long time). Wholesale ideas, profiles and interviews are most open to freelancers."

DOMESTIC ENGINEERING MAGAZINE, Construction Industry Press, 135 Addison Ave., Elmhurst IL 60126. Editor: Stephen J. Shafer. Managing Editor: David J. Hanks. 30% freelance written. Prefers to work with published/established writers. Monthly magazine; 100 pages. Emphasizes plumbing, heating, air conditioning and piping for contractors, and for mechanical contractors in these specialties. Gives information on management, marketing and merchandising. Circ. 40,000. Pays on acceptance. Buys all rights. Simultaneous, photocopied and previously published submissions OK. Computer printout submissions acceptable; prefers letter-quality to dot-matrix. Reports in 1 month. Sample copy $10.

Nonfiction: How-to (some technical in industry areas). Expose, interview, profile, personal experience, photo feature and technical articles are written on assignment only and should be about management, marketing and merchandising for plumbing and mechanical contracting businessmen. Buys 12 mss/year. Query. Pays $25 minimum. Sometimes pays the expenses of writers on assignment.

Photos: State availability of photos. Pays $10 minimum for b&w prints (reviews contact sheets) and color transparencies.

‡EXPORT, 386 Park Ave. S., New York NY 10016. Editor: R. Weingarten. For importers and distributors in 167 countries who handle hardware, air conditioning and refrigeration equipment and related consumer hardlines. Bimonthly magazine; 60-80 pages in English and Spanish editions. Circ. 38,500. Buys first rights and second (reprint) rights to material originally published elsewhere. Byline given. Buys about 10 mss/year. Pays on acceptance. Publishes ms an average of 5 months after acceptance. Reports in 1 month. Query.

Nonfiction: News stories of products and merchandising of air conditioning and refrigeration equipment, hardware and related consumer hardlines. Informational, how-to, interview, profile and successful business operations. Length: 1,000-3,000 words. Pays $300 maximum.

Tips: "One of the best ways to break in here is with a story originating outside the U.S. or Canada. Our major interest is in new products and new developments—but they must be available and valuable to overseas buyers. We also like company profile stories. Departments and news stories are staff-written."

‡HEATING/PIPING/AIR CONDITIONING, 2 Illinois Center, Chicago IL 60601. (312)861-0880. Editor: Robert T. Korte. Monthly. Buys all rights. Pays on publication. Query. Reports in 2 weeks.

Nonfiction: Uses engineering and technical articles covering design, installation, operation, maintenance, etc., of heating, piping and air conditioning systems in industrial plants and large buildings. Length: 3,000-4,000 words maximum. Pays $30/printed page.

Tips: "Query to have facts and an in-depth analysis of unique approaches. Be able to communicate with top level engineers first. Non-engineering trained freelancers really have very little chance of acceptance."

HEATING, PLUMBING, AIR CONDITIONING, 1450 Don Mills Rd., Don Mills, Ontario M3B 2X7 Canada. (416)445-6641. Editor: Ronald H. Shuker. 20% freelance written. Monthly. For mechanical contractors; plumbers; warm air and hydronic heating, refrigeration, ventilation, air conditioning and insulation contractors; wholesalers; architects; consulting and mechanical engineers who are in key management or specifying positions in the plumbing, heating, air conditioning and refrigeration industries in Canada. Circ. 14,500. Pays on publication. Publishes ms an average of 3 months after acceptance. Computer printout submissions acceptable; prefers letter-quality to dot-matrix. Reports in 2 months. For a prompt reply, "enclose a sheet on which is typed a statement either approving or rejecting the suggested article which can either be checked off, or a quick answer written in and signed and returned." Free sample copy.

Nonfiction: News, technical, business management and "how-to" articles that will inform, educate, motivate and help readers to be more efficient and profitable who design, manufacture, install, sell, service, maintain or supply all mechanical components and systems in residential, commercial, institutional and industrial installations across Canada. Length: 1,000-1,500 words. Pays 10-20¢/word. Sometimes pays expenses of writers on assignment.

Photos: Photos purchased with ms. Prefers 5x7 or 8x10 glossies.

Tips: "Topics must relate directly to the day-to-day activities of *HPAC* readers in Canada. Must be detailed, with specific examples, quotes from specific people or authorities—show depth. We specifically want material from other parts of Canada besides southern Ontario. Not really interested in material from U.S. unless specifically related to Canadian readers' concerns. We primarily want articles that show *HPAC* readers how they can increase their sales and business step-by-step based on specific examples of what others have done."

SNIPS MAGAZINE, 407 Mannheim Rd., Bellwood IL 60104. (312)544-3870. Editor: Nick Carter. 2% freelance written. Monthly. For sheet metal, warm air heating, ventilating, air conditioning and roofing contractors. Publishes ms an average of 3 months after acceptance. Buys all rights. "Write for detailed list of requirements before submitting any work."

Nonfiction: Material should deal with information about contractors who do sheet metal, warm air heating, air conditioning, ventilation and roofing work; also about successful advertising campaigns conducted by these contractors and the results. Length: "prefers stories to run less than 1,000 words unless on special assignment." Pays 5¢ each for first 500 words, 2¢ each for additional word.

Photos: Pays $2 each for small snapshot pictures, $4 each for usable 8x10 pictures.

WOOD 'N ENERGY, Energy Publications, Inc., Box 2008, Laconia NH 03247. (603)528-4285. Editor: Jason Perry. 10% freelance written. Works with a small number of new/unpublished writers each year. Monthly magazine covering wood, coal and solar heating (residential). "*Wood 'n Energy* is mailed to retailers, distributors and manufacturers of wood, coal and solar heating equipment in the U.S. and Canada. A majority of our readers are small businessmen who need help in running their businesses and want to learn secrets to prospering in a field that has seen better days when oil embargoes were daily happenings." Circ. 32,000. Pays on publication. Publishes ms an average of 2 months after acceptance. Byline given. Buys one-time rights and all rights. Submit seasonal/holiday material 4 months in advance. Simultaneous queries OK. Electronic submissions OK if compatible with TRS-80, Model III or IV, but requires hard copy also. Computer printout submissions acceptable; prefers letter-quality to dot-matrix. Reports in 2 weeks. Sample copy $2.50.

Nonfiction: Interview/profile (of stove dealers, manufacturers, others); photo feature (of energy stores); and technical (nuts and bolts of stove design and operation). Special issue includes Buyers Guide/Retailers Handbook (annual issue with retail marketing articles, "how to run your business," accounting. "The best times of year for freelancers are in our fall issue (our largest) and also in February and March." No "how wonderful renewable energy is" and experiences with stoves. "This is a *trade* book." Buys 25 mss/year. Query with or without published clips or send complete ms. Pays $25-300. Sometimes pays expenses of writers on assignment.

Photos: State availability of photos or send photos with query or ms. Pays $35 minimum for b&w contact sheets; $125 maximum for color contact sheets. Identification of subjects required. Buys one-time rights.

Columns/Departments: Reports (energy news; potpourri of current incentives, happenings); Regulations (safety and standard news); and Retailers Corner (tips on running a retail shop). "We are also looking for freelancers who could serve in our 'network' around the country. If there's a law passed regulating wood-stove emissions in their town, for example, they could send us a clip and/or rewrite the story. These pay $50 or so, depending on the clip. Contact editor on an individual basis (over the phone is OK) for a green light." Query with or without published clips. Length: 150-500 words. Pays $35-150.

Tips: "Short, hot articles on retailers (500 words and photographs) are desperately needed. We're looking for serious business articles. Freelancers who know the ins and outs of running a business have an excellent shot at being published."

WOODHEAT '88, Energy Publications, Inc., Box 2008, Laconia NH 03247. (603)528-4285. Editor: Jason Perry. 40% freelance written. An annual buyer's guide and sourcebook on wood heat, published in August. Circ. 175,000. Pays on variable schedule. Publishes ms an average of 6 months after acceptance. Byline given. Offers variable kill fee. Buys variable rights. Simultaneous queries and submissions OK. Computer printout submissions acceptable; prefers letter-quality to dot-matrix. Reports in 1 month.

Nonfiction: How-to (installation, etc.); interview/profile (of those in the field, retailers, consumers); new product (new wood energy products); photo feature (of stove installations and/or energy efficient homes); and technical (details on buying and installing). No personal experiences with wood stoves. Buys 5-8 mss/year. Query. Length: 100-2,550 words. Pays $50-500. Pays expenses of writers on assignment.

Photos: State availability of photos with query or ms. Uses all types. Pays $35-250. Captions, model release, and identification of subjects required. Buys variable rights.

Columns/Departments: Reports (potpourri of energy news, wood heat news). Buys 0-10 mss/year. Query. Length: 150-400 words. Pays $35-100.

Tips: "Articles in the magazine must appeal to both current owners and buyers. Personality is a plus in any article; we'd like features on someone who has invented a better burning stove or someone who is handcrafting masonry fireplaces, for example. Article ideas are formulated by mid-January, so query letters should be on hand at that time. Be specific with story ideas. Shorter articles on a wide range of energy issues—in a section called Reports—can be accepted until May. These must be accompanied by a photo. Writing should be spicy, interesting and short. All areas are open to freelancers. We find that freelancers score better with articles with local slants. With 15 million households having wood stoves, there are bound to be many stories to tell."

> **❝** *How do I approach the task of rewriting? Usually with great reluctance. But if an editor's suggestions and my own second thoughts seem to make sense, then I will set to work with renewed enthusiasm and a conviction that improvement is a worthwhile goal.* **❞**
>
> *Robert Bloch*

Printing

These magazines are geared for printers and publishers in various types of plants.

GRAPHIC ARTS MONTHLY, Technical Publishing Co., 875 Third Ave., New York NY 10022. (212)605-9574. Editor: Roger Ynostroza. Managing Editor: Peter Johnston. 15% freelance written. Prefers to work with published/established writers. A monthly magazine covering the printing industry. Circ. 80,000. Pays on publication. Publishes ms an average of 3 months after acceptance. Byline given. Buys all rights. Submit seasonal/holiday material 3 months in advance. Simultaneous queries OK. Computer printout submissions acceptable; prefers letter-quality to dot-matrix. Reports in 1 month. Free sample copy and writer's guidelines for SAE and 2 first class postage stamps.
Nonfiction: New product, photo feature and technical. Buys 15 mss/year. Query. Pays 10¢/word.
Photos: State availability of photos with query or ms. Captions required.
Fillers: Cartoons. Buys 50/year. Pays $15 minimum.
Tips: "The writer may have a better chance of breaking in at our publication with short articles and fillers since a very technical and specialized field means that major features need to be tailored specifically to the audience while shorter pieces can be more general. The most frequent mistakes made by writers in completing an article for us are that topic and writing style are usually much too general to be of direct benefit to our readership. Many freelance writers seem to want to adapt one topic to several different fields and publications. Also, case-study stories are often success-story descriptions that benefit and interest only the subject company, not the bulk of the readership."

HIGH VOLUME PRINTING, Innes Publishing Co., Box 368, Northbrook IL 60062. (312)564-5940. Editor: Bill Esler. 20-25% freelance written. Eager to work with new/unpublished writers. Bimonthly magazine for book, magazine printers, large commercial printing plants with 20 or more employees. Aimed at telling the reader what he needs to know to print more efficiently and more profitably. Circ. 26,000. Pays on publication. Publishes ms an average of 6 months after acceptance. Byline given. Buys first and second serial rights. Simultaneous queries OK. Computer printout submissions acceptable; prefers letter-quality to dot-matrix. Reports in 2 weeks. Writer's guidelines, sample articles provided.
Nonfiction: How-to (printing production techniques); new product (printing, auxiliary equipment, plant equipment); photo feature (case histories featuring unique equipment); technical (printing product research and development); shipping; and publishing distribution methods. No product puff. Buys 12 mss/year. Query. Length: 700-3,000 words. Pays $50-300. Sometimes pays the expenses of writers on assignment.
Photos: Send photos with ms. Pays $25-100 for 3x5 and larger b&w prints; $25-150 for any size color transparencies and prints. Captions, model release, and identification of subjects required.
Tips: "Feature articles covering actual installations and industry trends are most open to freelancers. Be familiar with the industry, spend time in the field, and attend industry meetings and trade shows where equipment is displayed."

IN-PLANT PRINTER, Innes Publishing, Box 368, Northbrook IL 60062. (312)564-5940. Editor: Kraig J. Debus. 20% freelance written. Works with a small number of new/unpublished writers each year. Bimonthly magazine covering in-house print shops. Circ. 38,000. Pays on publication. Publishes ms an average of 2 months after acceptance. Byline "usually" given. Buys first and second rights. Submit seasonal/holiday material 2 months in advance. Photocopied and previously published submissions OK. Electronic submissions OK via IBM-PC, must be on disk. Computer printout submissions OK; prefers letter-quality to dot-matrix. Reports in 2 weeks. Free sample copy and writer's guidelines.
Nonfiction: Book excerpts, how-to and case history. "More electronic printing articles, we need experts in this area to write technical articles. No nebulous management advice; undetailed stories lacking in concrete information. No human interest material." Buys 18 mss/year. Query or send complete ms. Length: 1,500-3,000 words. Pays $100-250. Pays expenses of writers on assignment.
Photos: Send photos with ms. "No additional payment is made for photos with ms, unless negotiated." Captions required. Buys all rights.

IN-PLANT REPRODUCTIONS & ELECTRONIC PUBLISHING, North American Publishing Co., 401 N. Broad St., Philadelphia PA 19108. (215)238-5300. Editor: Maria Martino. Assistant Editor: Denise Wallace. 15-20% freelance written. Prefers to work with published/established writers. Works with a small number of

new/unpublished writers each year; eager to work with new/unpublished writers. Monthly magazine about in-plant printing management and electronic publishing for printing departments in business, government, education and industry. These graphic arts facilities include art, composition, camera, platemaking, press, and finishing equipment, xerographic and other business communications systems. Circ. 40,000. Pays on publication. Publishes ms an average 6 months after acceptance. Byline given. Buys first North American serial rights or all rights. Phone queries OK. Computer printout submissions acceptable; prefers letter-quality to dot-matrix. Reports in 1 month. Sample copy $5. Sometimes pays the expenses of writers on assignment.
Nonfiction: Interview, profile, how-to and technical. Buys 4 mss/issue. Query. Length: 500-2,500 words. Pays $75-200.

INSTANT AND SMALL COMMERCIAL PRINTER, (formerly *Instant Printer*), Innes Publishing, 425 Huehl Rd., Bldg. 11B, Northbrook IL 60062. (312)564-5940. Editor: Daniel Witte. Bimonthly magazine covering the instant/retail and smaller commercial printing industry for owners/operators of print shops. "We are primarily concerned with ways to be successful, ways to make lots of money, new markets and processes, technological innovations. Basically we try to focus on the needs and concerns of the entrepreneurial type." Circ. 24,000. Pays on publication. Byline given. Buys first North American serial rights with option for future use. Submit seasonal/holiday material 6 months in advance. Photocopied and previously published submissions OK. Reports in 2 weeks on queries; 1 month on mss. Sample copy $3; free writer's guidelines.
Nonfiction: Book excerpts (primarily on small business-related or graphic arts-related topics); general interest (anything about marketing, promotion, management); how-to (focus on more efficient ways to do everyday things printers do; and technical, business, financial); interview/profile (case histories of successful printers with angle on unique or special services); personal experience (any small printer who has tried marketing some new or unique service, successful or not); technical (any printing-related topic). Buys 18-25 mss/year. Query with or without published clips or send complete ms. Pays $200 maximum.
Photos: State availability of photos. Pays $50 maximum for b&w contact sheets, slides or 3x5 prints; $100 maximum for color contact sheets, slides or 3x5 prints. Captions, model release and identification of subjects required. Buys all rights.
Columns/Departments: Promotion—about advertising/promotion techniques used by instant printers (with samples), and Computers—information about computers and software for instant printers. Buys 12 mss/year. Query with or without published clips or send complete ms. Length: 1,000 words maximum. Pays $75 maximum.
Fillers: Clippings, anecdotes, newsbreaks, and printing or marketing hints. Pays $10 maximum.
Tips: "I would suggest reading copies of our magazine, as well as related graphic arts magazines, for style."

PLAN AND PRINT, 9931 Franklin Ave., Box 879, Franklin Park IL 60131. (312)671-5356. Editor-in-Chief: James C. Vebeck. 50% freelance written. Prefers to work with published/established writers. Works with a small number of new/unpublished writers each year; eager to work with new/unpublished writers. Monthly magazine for computer-aided design users, commercial reproduction companies, in-plant reproduction, printing, drafting and design departments of business and industry and architects. Circ. 27,000. Pays on publication. Publishes ms an average of 6 months after acceptance. Buys all rights. Byline given. Submit seasonal/holiday material 6 months in advance. Computer printout submissions acceptable; no dot-matrix. Reports in 2 weeks. Free sample copy and writer's guidelines.
Nonfiction: How-to (how certain problems may have been solved; new methods of doing certain kinds of reprographics and/or design/drafting/computer-aided design work); and technical (must relate to industry). "Strong interest in computer-aided design." Buys 60 mss/year. Query with published clips. Length: 250-5,000 words. Pays $75-400. Sometimes pays expenses of writers on assignment.
Photos: State availability of photos with query. Pays $5-10 for 8x10 b&w glossy prints. Captions and model release required. Buys all rights.
Columns/Departments: Open to suggestions for new columns/departments.
Poetry: Light verse related to the industry. Buys 6/year. Length: 4-12 lines. Pays $8 maximum.

‡PRINTING VIEWS, For the Midwest Printer, Midwest Publishing, 8328 N. Lincoln, Skokie IL 60077. (312)539-8540. Editor: Ed Schwenur. 10% freelance written. Prefers to work with published/established writers. Monthly magazine about printing and graphic arts for Midwest commercial printers, typographers, platemakers, engravers and other trade people. Circ. 15,000. Average issue includes 3-4 articles. Pays on publication. Publishes ms an average of 2 months after acceptance. Byline given. Buys one-time rights. Phone queries OK. Reports in 2 weeks. Sample copy $1.50.
Nonfiction: Interview (possibly with graphic arts personnel); new product (in graphic arts in a Midwest plant); management sales success in Midwest printing plant; and technical (printing equipment). Buys 8 mss/year. Query with published clips of previously published work—"We will entertain query letters; no unsolicited manuscripts." Length: 2-9 typed pages. Pays $200. Sometimes pays the expenses of writers on assignment.
Photos: State availability of photos. Reviews b&w contact sheets. Offers additional payment for photos accepted with ms. Captions preferred. Buys one-time rights.

‡QUICK PRINTING, The Information Source for Commercial Copyshops and Printshops, Coast Publishing, 3255 South U.S. 1, Ft. Pierce FL 33482. (305)465-9450. Publisher: Robert Schweiger. Editor: Douglas E. Roorbach. 75% freelance written. A monthly magazine covering the quick printing industry. "Our articles tell quick printers how they can be more profitable. We want figures to illustrate points made." Circ. 28,000+. Pays on acceptance. Publishes ms an average of 4 months after acceptance. Byline given. Buys first North American serial rights, all rights. Submit seasonal/holiday material 4 months in advance. Photocopied submissions OK. Rarely uses previously published submissions. Electronic submissions OK via IBM PC-compatible, Word Star or MultiMate WP. Computer printout submissions acceptable; prefers letter-quality to dot-matrix. Reports in 2 weeks. Sample copy $3; writer's guidelines for #10 SAE with 1 first class stamp.
Nonfiction: How-to (on marketing products better or accomplishing more with equipment); new product; opinion (on the quick printing industry); personal experience (from which others can learn); technical (on printing). No generic business articles, or articles on larger printing applications. Buys 50 mss/year. Send complete ms. Length: 500-1,500 words. Pays $75.
Photos: State availability of photos with submission. Reviews transparencies and prints. Offers no payment for photos. Captions and identification of subjects required.
Columns/Departments: Viewpoint/Counterpoint (opinion on the industry); QP Profile (shop profiles with a marketing slant); and Management (how to handle employees and/or business strategies), all 500-1,500 words; and Postscript 250-500 words. Buys 10 mss/year. Send complete ms. Pays $75.
Tips: "Show a knowledge of the industry. Try visiting your local quick printer for an afternoon to get to know about us. When your articles make a point, back it up with examples, statistics, and dollar figures. We need good material in all areas, but avoid the shop profile. Technical articles are most needed, but they must be accurate. No puff pieces for a certain industry supplier."

SCREEN PRINTING, 407 Gilbert Ave., Cincinnati OH 45202. (513)421-2050. Editor: Tamas S. Frecska. 25-30% freelance written. Works with a small number of new/unpublished writers each year. Monthly magazine; 150 pages. For the screen printing industry, including screen printers (commercial, industrial and captive shops), suppliers and manufacturers, and ad agencies and allied professions. Circ. 11,000. Pays on publication. Publishes ms an average of 3 months after acceptance. Byline given. Buys all rights. Electronic submissions OK on IBM PC, XT; submit in ASCII. Prefer hard copy accompany electronic submission. Computer printout submissions acceptable; prefers letter-quality to dot-matrix. Reporting time varies. Free writer's guidelines.
Nonfiction: "Since the screen printing industry covers a broad range of applications and overlaps other fields in the graphic arts, it's necessary that articles be of a significant contribution, preferably to a specific area of screen printing. Subject matter is fairly open, with preference given to articles on administration or technology; trends and developments. We try to give a good sampling of technical business and management articles; articles about unique operations. We also publish special features and issues on important subjects, such as material shortages, new markets and new technology breakthroughs. While most of our material is nitty-gritty, we appreciate a writer who can take an essentially dull subject and encourage the reader to read on through concise, factual, 'flairful' and creative, expressive writing. Interviews are published after consultation with and guidance from the editor." Interested in stories on unique approaches by some shops. No general, promotional treatment of individual companies. Buys 6-10 unsolicited mss/year. Length: 1,500-3,500 words. Pays minimum of $150 for major features. Sometimes pays the expenses of writers on assignment.
Photos: Cover photos negotiable; b&w or color. Published material becomes the property of the magazine.
Tips: "If the author has a working knowledge of screen printing, assignments are more readily available. General management articles are rarely used."

SOUTHERN GRAPHICS, Cody Publications, Box 2028, Kissimmee FL 32742. (305)846-2800. Editor: George Meyer. 10-20% freelance written. Monthly magazine covering commercial printing and graphic arts. "We write about people and trends in the industry and ideas that will affect the effective management and marketing of commercial printing houses in the South." Circ. 10,000. Pays on acceptance. Publishes ms an average of 2 months after acceptance. Byline given. Offers 20% kill fee. Buys one-time rights. Submit seasonal/holiday material 2 months in advance. Simultaneous queries, and simultaneous, photocopied, and previously published submissions OK. Electronic submissions OK, but requires hard copy also. "Call for details." Computer printout submissions acceptable; prefers letter-quality to dot-matrix. Reports in 2 weeks. Free sample copy and writer's guidelines.
Nonfiction: Book excerpts, historical/nostalgic, humor, interview/profile, new product, personal experience, technical, and anything to do with print communication—products, trends, etc. No religious or extremist politics. Buys 3-5 mss/year. Query with or without published clips or send complete ms. Length: 800-3,000 words. Pays $50-300. Sometimes pays the expenses of writers on assignment.
Photos: State availability of photos or send photos with query or ms. Pays $20-30. Identification of subjects required.
Tips: "We offer a readership that gives freelancers excellent exposure in the publishing industry. By

recognizing the eclectic gathering of styles in the book, the writer will know that clarity and content matter above all else. Regional topics and regional writers will have an advantage."

THE TYPOGRAPHER, Typographers International Association, Suite 101, 2262 Hall Pl. NW., Washington DC 20007. (202)965-3400. Editor: Geoff Lindsay. 10% freelance written. Eager to work with new/unpublished writers. Bimonthly tabloid of the commercial typesetting industry for owners and executives of typesetting firms. Circ. 10,000. Pays on publication. Publishes ms an average of 2 months after acceptance. Byline given. Buys one-time rights. Simultaneous queries, and simultaneous, photocopied, and previously published submissions OK. Electronic submissions OK via standard protocols, but requires hard copy also. Computer printout submissions acceptable; prefers letter-quality to dot-matrix. Reports in 1 week. Free sample copy.
Nonfiction: Book excerpts, historical/nostalgic, how-to, interview/profile, new product, opinion, personal experience, photo feature and technical. "All articles should relate to typesetting management." No opinion pieces. Buys 20 mss/year. Query with published clips. Length: 1,000-2,000 words. Pays $50-150.
Photos: State availability of photos. Pays $20-35 for 5x7 b&w prints. Captions and identification of subjects required.

Real Estate

‡APARTMENT AGE, the voice of the industry, Apartment Association of Greater Los Angeles, 551 S. Oxford Ave., Los Angeles CA 90020. (213)384-4131. Editor: Kevin B. Postema. 10% freelance written. Works with a small number of new/unpublished writers each year. A monthly magazine covering rental housing, geared toward apartment house owners/operators/managers/investors. Circ. 36,300. Pays on publication. Publishes ms an average of 2 months after acceptance. Byline given. Buys all rights. Simultaneous queries OK. Computer printout submissions acceptable; prefers letter-quality to dot-matrix. Reports in 1 month. Free sample copy and writer's guidelines for business-size SAE and 1 first class stamp.
Nonfiction: Historical/nostalgic; how-to (apartment maintenance); humor; personal experience; property management; finance; investing; property management; finance; investing; and legal/political. Query. Length: 500-1,000 words. Pays $125-250. Sometimes pays the expenses of writers on assignment.

‡AREA DEVELOPMENT MAGAZINE, 525 Northern Blvd., Great Neck NY 11021. (516)829-8990. Editor-in-Chief: Tom Bergeron. 40% freelance written. Prefers to work with published/established writers. Emphasizes corporate facility planning and site selection for industrial chief executives worldwide. Monthly magazine; 110-190 pages. Circ. 33,000. Pays when edited. Publishes ms an average of 2 months after acceptance. Buys first rights only. Byline given. Photocopied submissions OK. Computer printout submissions acceptable; prefers letter-quality to dot-matrix. Reports in 1-3 weeks. Free sample copy and writer's guidelines.
Nonfiction: How-to (case histories of companies; experiences in site selection and all other aspects of corporate facility planning); historical (if it deals with corporate facility planning); interview (corporate executives and industrial developers); and related areas of site selection and facility planning such as taxes, labor, government, energy, architecture and finance. Buys 8-10 mss/yr. Query. Pays $30-40/ms page; rates for illustrations depend on quality and printed size. Sometimes pays the expenses of writers on assignment.
Photos: State availability of photos with query. Prefer 8x10 or 5x7 b&w glossy prints. Captions preferred.
Tips: "Articles must be accurate, objective (no puffery) and useful to our industrial executive readers. Avoid any discussion of the merits or disadvantages of any particular areas or communities. Writers should realize we serve an intelligent and busy readership—they should avoid 'cute' allegories and get right to the point."

‡BUSINESS FACILITIES, Business Facilities Publishing Co., 121 Monmouth St., Box 2060, Red Bank NJ 07701. (201)842-7433. Editor: Eric Peterson. Managing Editor: Dora Hatras. 20% freelance written. Prefers to work with published/established writers. A monthly magazine covering economic development and commercial and industrial real estate. "Our audience consists of corporate site selectors and real estate people; our editorial coverage is aimed at providing news and trends on the plant location and corporate expansion field." Circ. 32,000. Pays on publication. Publishes ms an average of 3 months after acceptance. Byline given. Buys all rights. Photocopied and previously published submissions OK. Computer printout submissions acceptable; prefers letter-quality to dot-matrix. Reports in 2 weeks. Free sample copy and writer's guidelines.
Nonfiction: General interest, how-to, interview/profile and personal experience. No news shorts and no clippings; feature material only. Buys 12-15 mss/year. Query. Length: 1,000-3,000 words. Pays $200-1,000

for assigned articles, pays $200-600 for unsolicited articles. Sometimes pays the expenses of writers on assignment.

Photos: State availability of photos with submission. Reviews contact sheets, negatives, transparencies and 8x10 prints. Payment negotiable. Captions and identification of subjects required. Buys one-time rights.

Tips: "First, remember that our reader is a corporate executive responsible for his company's expansion and/or relocation decisions and our writers have to get inside that person's head in order to provide him with something that's helpful in his decision-making process. And second, the biggest turnoff is a telephone query. We're too busy to accept them and must require that all queries be put in writing. Submit major feature articles only; all news departments, fillers, etc., are staff prepared. A writer should be aware that our style is not necessarily dry and business-like. We tend to be more upbeat and a writer should look for that aspect of our approach."

CANADIAN REAL ESTATE, The Canadian Real Estate Association, 99 Duncan Mill Rd., Don Mills, Ontario, M3B 1Z2 Canada.(416)445-9910. Editor: Shirley A. Taylor. 5% freelance written. Bimonthly real estate newspaper. Circ. 65,000. Pays on publication. Publishes ms an average of 2 months after acceptance. Byline given. Buys all rights. Simultaneous and previously published submissions OK. Computer printout submissions acceptable; no dot-matrix. Reports in 2 weeks on queries; 1 month on mss. Sample copy for 9x12 SAE.

Nonfiction: How-to (make sales and operate a successful real estate business); interview/profile; personal experience; photo feature. No articles on other than real estate subjects. Recent article example: "Here's How Bigger Businesses Are Built." Buys 10 unsolicited mss/year. Send complete ms. Length: 1,000-2,500 words. Pays variable fee; "depends on quality."

Photos: Send photos with ms. Reviews 5x7 b&w prints. Captions required. Buys one-time rights.

Tips: "The most frequent mistakes made by writers in completing an article for us are spelling errors, not checking facts and submitting material unsuited to the Canadian real estate industry."

COMMUNITY DEVELOPMENT PUBLICATIONS, Suite 100, 8555 16th St., Silver Spring MD 20910. (301) 588-6380. "We use clips only."

‡FINANCIAL FREEDOM REPORT, 1831 Fort Union Blvd., Salt Lake City UT 84121. (801)943-1280. Chairman of the Board: Mark O. Haroldsen. Managing Editor: Carolyn Tice. 25% freelance written. Eager to work with new/unpublished writers. For "professional and nonprofessional investors, and would-be investors in real estate—real estate brokers, insurance companies, investment planners, truck drivers, housewives, doctors, architects, contractors, etc. The magazine's content is presently expanding to interest and inform the readers about other ways to put their money to work for them." Monthly magazine; 72 pages. Circ. 50,000. Pays on publication. Publishes ms an average of 3 months after acceptance. Buys all rights. Phone queries OK. Simultaneous submissions OK. Accepts electronic submissions via Macintosh Apple. Computer printout submissions acceptable; prefers letter-quality to dot-matrix. Reports in 2 weeks. Sample copy $3; free writer's guidelines.

Nonfiction: How-to (find real estate bargains, finance property, use of leverage, managing property, developing market trends, goal setting, motivational); and interviews (success stories of those who have relied on own initiative and determination in real estate market or related fields). Buys 25 unsolicited mss/year. Query with clips of published work or submit complete ms. Length: 1,500-3,000 words. "If the topic warranted a two- or three-parter, we would consider it." Pays 5-10¢/word. Sometimes pays the expenses of writers on assignment.

Photos: Send photos with ms. Uses 8x10 b&w matte prints. Offers no additional payment for photos accepted with ms. Captions required.

Tips: "We would like to find several specialized writers in our field of real estate investments. A writer would need to have had some hands-on experience in the real estate field."

‡PROPERTIES MAGAZINE, 4900 Euclid Ave., Cleveland OH 44103. (216)431-7666. Editor: Gene Bluhm. 0-15% freelance written. Monthly. Buys first rights. Pays on publication. Publishes ms an average of 3 months after acceptance. Query. Computer printout submissions acceptable; prefers letter-quality to dot-matrix.

Nonfiction: Wants articles of real estate, construction news value and personality profiles. Interested primarily in articles relating to northeastern Ohio. Length: up to 900 words. Sometimes pays the expenses of writers on assignment.

Photos: Buys photographs with mss.

‡REAL ESTATE INFORMATION NETWORK, 70 S. Broadway, Box 257, New York NY 10960. (914)358-2335. Editor James Clyde. An on-line service for real estate and mortgage banking. "We cover market personalities, profiles of successful firms new deals, tax law and investment in real estate, legislation, community profiles and market trends. Pays on publication. Publishes ms an average of 2 months after acceptance. Byline given. Offers 100% kill fee. Buys second serial (reprint) rights, all rights, and makes work-for-hire assignments. Submit seasonal/holiday material 3 months in advance. Previously published submissions OK. Electronic submissions OK; consult guidelines. Computer printout submissions acceptable. Reports in 3 weeks on manuscripts. Writer's guidelines for SASE with 1 first class stamp.

Nonfiction: How-to, humor, interview/profile, new product and technical. Buys 60 mss/year. Send complete ms. Length 75-250 words. Pays $50-100 for assigned articles; pays $25-50 for unsolicited articles. Pays in copies or other premiums for first submission. Sometimes pays the expenses of writers on assignment.

Columns Departments: Send complete ms. Length: 75-250 words. Pays $25-50.

Fillers: Glen V. Carvella, fillers editor. Anecdotes, facts and newsbreaks. Pays $25.

Tips: "Material submitted by disk or modem is ready for publication. An eye to the appearance of material on the computer screen is as important as content."

‡REAL ESTATE PROFIT, Catalyst Communications, 1252 Randol Ave., San Jose CA 95126. (408)998-3121. Editor/Publisher: Wm. Barrie Moore. Managing Editor: Patricia A. Bina. 80% freelance written. A monthly tabloid covering industrial, investment and commercial real estate. Estab. 1986. Circ. 30,000. Pays on publication. Publishes ms an average of 3 months after acceptance. Byline given. Offers 50% kill fee. Buys first North American serial rights, one-time rights, second serial (reprint) rights or simultaneous rights. Submit seasonal/holiday material 2 months in advance. Simultaneous, photocopied and previously published submissions OK. Electronic submissions OK via IBM. Computer printout submissions acceptable; prefers letter-quality to dot-matrix. Reports in 2-3 weeks. Sample copy $1 with 9x12 SAE and 4 first class stamps. Writer's guidelines for #10 SASE.

Nonfiction: Book excerpts; essays; historical/nostalgic (real estate); how-to (syndicate investment properties); humor (real estate related); interview/profile (real estate, financial); new product (real estate, financial); personal experience (real estate related); photo feature (development or real estate related) and technical (financial, real estate or computer). Buys 60 mss/year. Send complete ms. Length: 500-3,500 words. Pays $25-300. Sometimes pays the expenses of writers on assignment.

Photos: Send photos with submission. Reviews contact sheets and 5x7 or 8x10 prints. Offers $5-50/photo. Captions, model releases and identification of subjects required. Buys one-time rights.

Columns/Departments: Tax Shelters, Estate Building, Tax-Preferred Exchange, Financing, Syndicating and Developing. Submissions should be "well-documented and written for the highly sophisticated investor or real estate professional." Buys 100 mss/year. Send complete ms. Length: 600-1,200 words. Pays $30-100.

Fiction: Adventure, experimental, historical, horror, humorous, mainstream, mystery, science fiction, serialized novel and suspense. Stories must be themed around real estate subjects and characters. Buys 10-12 mss/year. Query. Length: 600-3,000 words. Pays $25-250.

Poetry: Avant-garde, free verse, haiku, light verse and traditional. (All real estate oriented). Buys 20-30 poems/year. Submit maximum 5 poems. Length: 4-80 lines. Pays $5-25.

Fillers: Anecdotes, facts, gags to be illustrated by cartoonist, and short humor. All real estate related. Buys 100/year. Length: 10-200 words. Pays $5-25.

Tips: "We are looking for continuing writers and columnists. The writer should offer challenging and creative fresh ideas for real estate professionals and investors. Our readers are highly sophisticated professionals who know the basics. Think of your work as being on the graduate level. Make sure your work is well documented and up-to-date. Each column or article should tackle one topic and guide the reader from starting premise to conclusion. Be positive. Be active. Be aggressive. As a new publication, we are looking for a wide scope of input from a broad national base. Our primary areas will cover real estate syndication, developing, tax shelters, financial planning, broker estate building, international real estate, creative finance, investment counseling, new technology for real estate, new investment areas, etc."

‡REAL ESTATE SALESPEOPLE, The Infinity Group, Suite 201, 2531 W. Dunlap Ave., Phoenix AZ 85021. (800)824-6864 toll free (in Arizona, 861-0881). Editor: Allan B. Starr. Managing Editor: Jeff Burger. 60% freelance written. A bimonthly magazine for residential real estate salespeople. Estab. 1985. Circ. 60,000. Pays on acceptance. Byline given usually. Offers 25% kill fee. Buys first rights and "we retain right to resell to other publishers, in which case we split income 50/50 with writer. Writer also retains right to resell material (and to keep all resulting income)." Submit seasonal/holiday material 5 months in advance. Photocopied and computer printout submissions acceptable. Reports in 1 month. Sample copy for 9x12 SAE with $1.24 postage; writer's guidelines for SAE with 1 first class stamp.

Nonfiction: Book excerpts, essays, exposé, general interest, how-to, humor, interview/profile, new product, opinion and personal experience. "Our articles are colorful, cogent, anecdotal and people-oriented." Buys 35 mss/year. Query with or without published clips, or send complete ms. Length: 100-3,000 words. Pays $25-600. Sometimes pays expenses of writers on assignment.

Photos: State availability of photos with submission or send photos with submission. Reviews contact sheets, 35mm, 2¼x4x5, and 8x10 prints. Offers $25-400/photo. Identification of subjects required. Buys one-time rights or all rights.

Columns/Departments: People Watch, Marketplace, Buying Time, Pro-file and Star Builders. Buys 12 mss/year. Send complete ms. Length: 100-1,000 words. Pays "competitive negotiable rates."

Fillers: Anecdotes for Once Upon a Sale. Length: 25-100 words. Pays $10-100.
Tips: "Query first with ideas for features that suit our audience. Features plus brief items for People Watch, Marketplace and Once Upon a Sale departments are most open to freelancers."

‡SOUTHWEST REAL ESTATE NEWS, Communication Channels, Inc., Suite 240, 18601 LBJ Freeway, Mesquite TX 75150. (214)270-6651. Associate Publisher/Editor: Jim Mitchell. Managing Editor: Sheryl Roberts. 40% freelance written. Prefers to work with published/established writers. Monthly tabloid newspaper about commercial and industrial real estate for professional real estate people, including Realtors, developers, mortgage bankers, corporate real estate executives, architects, contractors and brokers. Circ. 17,000. Average issue includes 4 columns, 20-50 short news items, 2-5 special articles and 10 departments. Pays on publication. Publishes ms an average of 2 months after acceptance. Byline given. Buys all rights. Phone queries OK. Submit seasonal/holiday material 2 months in advance. Photocopied submissions OK. Computer printout submissions acceptable; dot-matrix only if it has ascenders and descenders. Prefers letter-quality. Reports in 4-6 weeks. Free sample copy and writer's guidelines.
Nonfiction: "We're interested in hearing from writers in major cities in the states that we cover, which are TX, OK, CO, NM, LA, AZ, AR, NV and CA. We are particularly interested in writers with newspaper experience or real estate background. Assignments are made according to our editorial schedule which we will supply upon request. Most open to freelancers are city reviews and special articles. Contact the staff to discuss ideas first. No unsolicited material." Buys 3-5 mss/issue. Query. Pays $100-500.
Columns/Departments: Offices, Shopping Centers, Industrials, Multiplexes, Leases, Sales and Purchases, Mortgage and Financial, Realty Operations, Residentials, and People in the News. No newspaper clippings. Buys 3 mss/issue. Query. Length: 1,000-5,000 words. Pays $75-100.
Tips: "Call us and submit a sample of previous work."

Resources and Waste Reduction

PUMPER PUBLICATIONS, Eastern Pumper, Midwest Pumper and Western Pumper, COLE Inc., Drawer 220, Three Lakes WI 54562. (715)546-3347. Editors: Bob Kendall and Pete Lawonn. 5% freelance written. A monthly tabloid covering the liquid waste hauling industry (portable toilet renters, septic tank pumpers, industrial waste haulers, chemical waste haulers, oil field haulers, and hazardous waste haulers). "Our publication is read by companies that handle liquid waste and manufacturers of equipment." Circ. 15,000. Pays on publication. Publishes ms an average of 1 month after acceptance. Byline given. Offers negotiable kill fee. Buys first serial rights. Submit seasonal/holiday material 3 months in advance. Simultaneous queries, and simultaneous, photocopied, and previously published submissions OK. Computer printout submissions acceptable; prefers letter-quality to dot-matrix. Reports in 1 month. Free sample copy.
Nonfiction: Expose (government regulations, industry problems, trends, public attitudes, etc.); general interest (state association meetings, conventions, etc.); how-to (related to industry, e.g., how to incorporate septage or municipal waste into farm fields, how to process waste, etc.); humor (related to industry, especially septic tank pumpers or portable toilet renters); interview/profile (including descriptions of business statistics, type of equipment, etc.); new product; personal experience; photo feature; and technical (especially reports on research projects related to disposal). "We are looking for quality articles that will be of interest to our readers; length is not that important. We publish trade journals. We need articles that deal with the trade. Studies on land application of sanitary waste are of great interest." Query or send complete ms. Pays 7½¢/word. Sometimes pays expenses of writers on assignment.
Photos: Send photos with query or ms. Pays $10-15 for b&w and color prints. "We need good contrast." Captions "suggested" and model release "helpful." Buys one-time rights.
Tips: "We hope to expand the editorial content of our monthly publications. We also have publications for sewer and drainage cleaners with the same format as *The Pumpers*; however, the *Cleaner* has a circulation of 23,000. We are looking for the same type of articles and pay is the same."

RESOURCE RECYCLING, Journal of Recycling, Reuse and Waste Reduction, Resource Recycling, Inc., Box 10540, Portland OR 97210. (503)227-1319. Editor: Jerry Powell. 20% freelance written. Works with a small number of new/unpublished writers each year. Bimonthly magazine covering recycling of paper, metals, glass, etc. for recycling processors. "*Resource Recycling* provides thorough assessments of trends and developments in waste recovery." Circ. 3,000 in 20 countries. Pays on publication. Publishes ms an average of 11 months after acceptance. Byline given. "We don't assign manuscripts." Buys first North American serial rights, one-time rights, first serial rights, and second serial (reprint) rights. "No seasonal material in our trade." Simultaneous queries, and simultaneous, photocopied, and previously published submissions OK. Computer printout submissions acceptable. Reports in 1 month. Sample copy $1.24; writer's guidelines for SASE.

Nonfiction: Historical/nostalgic, interview/profile, new product, photo feature and technical. No nontechnical or opinion articles. Buys 15-20 mss/year. Query with published clips. "Queries should include a step-by-step outline of the proposed manuscript." Length: 1,500-3,000 words. Pays $100-250. Sometimes pays expenses of writers on assignment.

Photos: State availability of photos. Pays $5-10 for b&w contact sheets, negatives and prints. Identification of subjects required. Buys one-time rights.

Tips: "A freelancer can best break into our publication with overviews of one recycling aspect in one state (e.g., oil recycling in Alabama). We can supply lists of sources, data, etc. Write with enough sophistication on the subject for our professional audience."

WATER WELL JOURNAL, Water Well Journal Publishing Co., 6375 Riverside Dr., Dublin OH 43017. (614)761-3222. Publisher: Jay H. Lehr. Editor: Anita B. Stanley. 10% freelance written. Monthly magazine about water well drilling and ground water for contractors, suppliers, and manufacturers of equipment. Circ. 34,000. Pays on publication. Publishes ms an average of 3 months after acceptance. Byline given. Makes work-for-hire assignments. Submit seasonal material 6 months in advance. Photocopied submissions OK. Computer printout submissions acceptable. Reports in 1 month. Sample copy $1; free writer's guidelines.

Nonfiction: Interview, photo feature and technical. "We need major articles such as personality profiles of drillers and articles on pollution problems. We have special issues on pump and pump installation and rural water districts." No general articles on ground water. Buys 1 issue. Query. Pays $50/typeset page.

Fillers: Gloria Swanson, fillers editor. Clippings. Buys 1 ms/issue.

Tips: The most frequent mistake made by writers in submitting an article to us is not knowing enough about the industry.

Selling and Merchandising

Sales personnel and merchandisers interested in how to sell products successfully consult these journals. Journals in nearly every other category of this Trade Journal section also buy sales-related material if it is slanted to the specialized product or industry they deal with, such as clothing or paint. Publications for advertising and marketing professionals can be found under Advertising, Marketing and PR.

THE AMERICAN SALESMAN, 424 N. 3rd St., Burlington IA 52601. Publisher: Michael S. Darnall. Editorial Supervisor: Doris J. Ruschill. Editor: Barbara Boeding. 95% freelance written. Prefers to work with published/established writers; works with a small number of new/unpublished writers each year. Monthly magazine; 32 pages, (5½x8½). For distribution through company sales representatives. Circ. 2,612. Pays on publication. Publishes ms an average of 4 months after acceptance. Buys all rights. Free sample copy and writer's guidelines; mention *Writer's Market* in request.

Nonfiction: Sales seminars, customer service and follow-up, closing sales, sales presentations, handling objections, competition, telephone usage and correspondence, managing territory, and new innovative sales concepts. No sexist material, illustration written from only a salesperson's viewpoint. No ms dealing with supervisory problems. Query. Length: 900-1,200 words. Pays 3¢/word. Uses no advertising. Follow AP Stylebook. Include biography and/or byline with ms submissions. Author photos used.

ART MATERIAL TRADE NEWS, The Journal of All Art, Craft, Engineering and Drafting Supplies, Communication Channels Inc., 6255 Barfield Rd., Atlanta GA 30328. (404)256-9800. Editor: Jeffrey

Abugel. 30% freelance written. Monthly magazine on art materials. "Our editorial thrust is to bring art materials retailers, distributors and manufacturers information they can use in their everyday operations." Circ. 12,000. Pays on publication. Publishes ms an average of 3 months after acceptance. "All assigned manuscripts are published." Buys first serial rights. Submit seasonal/holiday material 3 months in advance. Photocopied submissions OK. Computer printout submissions acceptable; prefers letter-quality to dot-matrix. Reports in 6 weeks. Sample copy for 9x12 SAE and $1 postage; writer's guidelines for 4x9½ SAE and 1 first class stamp.

Nonfiction: How-to (sell, retail/wholesale employee management, advertising programs); interview/profile (within industry); and technical (commercial art drafting/engineering). "We encourage a strong narrative style where possible. We publish an editorial 'theme' calendar at the beginning of each year." Buys 36-40 mss/year. Query with published clips. Length: 2,500-3,000 words (prefers 2,500 words). Pays 10¢/word and expenses with prior approval.

Photos: State availability of photos. Pays $10 maximum for b&w contact sheets. Identification of subjects required.

Columns/Departments: Business Talk (the impact of current economic or political events on art materials business). Buys 12-15 mss/year. Query with published clips. Length: 1,000-2,000 words. Pays $75-200.

Tips: "A current, solid background in any one of these areas helps—commercial art, retail selling, wholesale selling, business finance, employee management, interviewing or advertising. We frequently need filler items relating to the art industry. We appreciate clean, concise copy. We do a lot of dealer profiles throughout U.S. They must be written in good conversational tone with complete, accurate background information."

CONVENIENCE STORE NEWS, BMT Publications, Inc., 254 W. 31st St., New York NY 10001. (212)594-4120. Editor: Denise Melinsky. 30% freelance written. Prefers to work with published/established writers. Tabloid published 16 times/year. For convenience store chain executives, middle management and owner/operators; franchisors and franchisees; convenience store managers, wholesalers, distributors, service merchandisers, food brokers and manufacturers involved in the food retailing and convenience store business. Circ. 85,000. Pays on publication. Publishes ms an average of 3 months after acceptance. Buys all rights. Phone queries OK. Query for submission of seasonal/holiday material. Electronic submissions OK via Tandy 2000 or IBM compatible, but requires hard copy also. Computer printout submissions acceptable; prefers letter-quality to dot-matrix. Reports on queries in 2 weeks. Free sample copy and writer's guidelines.

Nonfiction: General interest, how-to, interview, profile and photo feature. Interested in news about convenience stores and chains and oil retailers who operate convenience stores, their personnel, operations and product mix trends, promotions and legislative activities on all levels of government that affect the operations of these businesses. Buys 90 unsolicited mss/year. Query. Pays $3/column inch or negotiated fee, in some cases. Pays expenses of writers on assignment.

Photos: Send photos with ms. Pays $5 for b&w glossy prints; $35 for contact sheet and negatives, "provided at least one photo is used." Captions required.

Columns/Departments: Store Managers section. Buys 16-20 mss/issue. Query. Length: 4 double-spaced pages maximum. Pays $3/column inch or negotiated fee, in some cases.

Fillers: Newsbreaks ("in our industry only"). Length: 1-2 pages, double-spaced.

Tips: "We need more in-depth features. The most frequent mistake made by writers in completing an article for us is not getting correct or complete information—a result of not knowing the industry. Most of our articles follow a newspaper style—lead first and short, punchy sentences."

‡DEALER COMMUNICATOR, Fichera Publications, Box 4639, Margate FL 33063. (305)971-4360. Editor: Dave Kaiser. Publisher: Mike Fichera. 20% freelance written. A monthly magazine covering personnel and news developments for the graphic arts industry. Circ. 10,000. Pays on publication. Byline given. Not copyrighted. Buys one-time rights. Simultaneous and photocopied submissions OK. Reports in 1 week on queries.

Nonfiction: Interview/profile. Buys a varying number of mss/year. Query with published clips. Length: 500-1,000 words. Pays 3-7¢/word. Sometimes pays the expenses of writers on assignment.

Photos: State availability of photos with submissions. Offers $5-10/photo. Captions required.

Fillers: Facts and newsbreaks. Buys a varying number/year. Length: 10-50 words. Pays $1-1.50.

Tips: "Find out what local printing/graphic arts dealers are doing and what is news in the area."

‡FAIR TIMES, Independent Dealers Association, Box 455, Arnold MO 63010. (314)464-2616. Editor: Georgia Goodridge. 20-90% freelance written. A monthly tabloid covering fairs, celebrations and indoor expositions for vendors who travel North America working these various events. Byline given. Buys first rights. Submit seasonal/holiday material 3 months in advance. Photocopied and previously published submissions OK. Free sample copy and writer's guidelines.

Nonfiction: How-to, interview/profile and new product. Special issues include an annual fair directory and semi-annual flea market directory. No submissions unrelated to selling at events. Query. Length: 400-750 words. Pays $2.50/column inch; may offer premiums instead of cash. Sometimes pays the expenses of writers on assignment.

Photos: Send photos with submission. Reviews contact sheets. Offers $5/photo. Captions required. Buys one-time rights.
Columns/Departments: 3 columns monthly (must deal with vending at events in North America). Query with published clips. Length: 400-750 words. Pays $3/column inch.

INFO FRANCHISE NEWSLETTER, 11 Bond St., St. Catharines, Ontario L2R 4Z4 Canada or 728 Center St., Box 550, Lewiston NY 14092. (716)754-4669. Editor-in-Chief: E.L. Dixon, Jr. Managing Editor: Caroline McCaffery. Monthly newsletter; 8 pages. Circ. 5,000. Pays on publication. Buys all rights. Photocopied submissions OK. Reports in 1 month.
Nonfiction: "We are particularly interested in receiving articles regarding franchise legislation, franchise litigation, franchise success stories, and new franchises. Both American and Canadian items are of interest. We do not want to receive any information which is not fully documented or articles which could have appeared in any newspaper or magazine in North America. An author with a legal background who could comment upon such things as arbitration and franchising or class actions and franchising, would be of great interest to us." Expose, how-to, informational, interview, profile, new product, personal experience and technical. Buys 10-20 mss/year. Length: 25-1,000 words. Pays $10-300.

OPPORTUNITY MAGAZINE, 6 N. Michigan Ave., Chicago IL 60602. Managing Editor: Jack Weissman. 33% freelance written. Eager to work with new/unpublished writers. Monthly magazine "for anyone who is interested in making money, full or spare time, in selling or in an independent business program." Circ. 190,000. Pays on publication. Buys all rights. Byline given. Submit seasonal/holiday material 6 months in advance. Free sample copy and writer's guidelines.
Nonfiction: "We use articles dealing with sales techniques, sales psychology or general self-improvement topics." How-to, inspirational, and interview (with successful salespeople selling products offered by direct selling firms, especially concerning firms which recruit salespeople through *Opportunity Magazine*). Articles on self-improvement should deal with specifics rather than generalities. Would like to have more articles that deal with overcoming fear, building self-confidence, increasing personal effectiveness, and other psychological subjects. Submit complete ms. Buys 35-50 unsolicited mss/year. Length: 250-900 words. Pays $20-35.
Photos: State availability of photos with ms. Offers no additional payment for 8x10 b&w glossy prints. Captions and model release required. Buys all rights.
Tips: "Many articles are too academic for our audience. We look for a free-and-easy style in simple language which is packed with useful information, drama and inspiration. Check the magazine before writing. We can't use general articles. The only articles we buy deal with material that is specifically directed to readers who are opportunity seekers—articles dealing with direct sales programs or successful ventures that others can emulate. Try to relate the article to the actual work in which the reader is engaged. Look for fresh approaches. Too many people write on the same or similar topics."

PRIVATE LABEL, The Magazine for House Brands and Generics, E.W. Williams Publishing Co., 80 8th Ave., New York NY 10011. (212)989-1101. Managing Editor: Mark Edgar. 10% freelance written. Bimonthly magazine covering food and nonfood private label and generic products. Circ. 25,000. Pays on acceptance. Publishes ms an average of 1 month after acceptance. Byline given. Offers 50-100% kill fee, depending on circumstances. Buys first serial rights and second serial (reprint) rights. Submit seasonal/holiday material 4 months in advance. Photocopied submissions OK if not under submission elsewhere. Computer printout submissions acceptable; no dot-matrix. Reports in "weeks." Sample copy $1 and SAE.
Nonfiction: Book excerpts (if segments are appropriate); general interest; historical/nostalgic; how-to; interview/profile; personal experience; photo feature; and travel. "We use feature articles showing how retailers promote, buy, display, sell, and feel about their store brands (private label and generic products). We're always interested in coverage of areas more than 300 miles from New York. No articles on peripheral topics such as taxes, insurance, safety, etc." Buys 30-40 mss/year. Query or send complete ms. Length:

66 *Writers who have not worked with us before impress us most with clips from other publications and with a written query that shows they have studied our magazine.* **99**

William B. McMorris **Boys' Life**

500-4,000 words. Pays 5¢/word; "flat fee by special arrangement." Sometimes pays expenses of writers on assignment.
Photos: "We prefer articles with photos." Send photos with ms. Reviews contact sheets (if large selection). Pays $10 minimum for 5x7 b&w prints. Captions and identification of subjects required. Buys all rights; "release on request."
Tips: "We are wide open to freelancers who can line up store permission (preferably headquarters) for feature articles on philosophy, purchase, consumer attitudes, retailer attitudes, display and promotion of private label and generic products."

PROFESSIONAL SELLING, 24 Rope Ferry Rd., Waterford CT 06386. (203)442-4365. Editor: Paulette S. Withers. 33% freelance written. "No unsolicited/unqueried material." Works with a small number of new/unpublished writers each year. Bimonthly newsletter for sales professionals covering industrial or wholesale sales. "*Professional Selling* provides field sales personnel with both the basics and current information that can help them better perform the sales function." Pays on acceptance. Publishes ms an average of 6 months after acceptance. No byline given. Buys all rights. Submit seasonal/holiday material 4 months in advance. Computer printout submissions acceptable; prefers letter-quality to dot-matrix. Reports in 2 weeks. Sample copy and writer's guidelines for business size SAE and 1 first class stamp.
Nonfiction: How-to (successful sales techniques); and interview/profile (interview-based articles). "We buy only interview-based material." Buys 12-15 mss/year. No unsolicited manuscripts; written queries only. Length: 800-1,000 words.
Tips: "Only the lead article is open to freelancers. That must be based on an interview with an actual sales professional. Freelancers may occasionally interview sales managers, but the slant must be toward field sales, *not* management."

‡**SELLING DIRECT**, Communication Channels, Inc., 6255 Barfield Rd., Atlanta GA 30328. (404)256-9800. Publisher: William Hood. Editor: Robert Rawls. 20% freelance written. For independent businessmen and women who sell door-to-door, store-to-store, office-to-office and by the party plan method as well as through direct mail and telephone solicitation; selling products and services. Monthly magazine; 50-100 pages. Circ. 500,000. Pays on publication. Buys all rights. Byline given. Submit seasonal/holiday material 3 months in advance. Electronic submissions OK if compatible with Decmate or Decmate II. Computer printout submissions acceptable. Reports in 3 months. Publishes ms an average of 1 year after acceptance. Free sample copy and writer's guidelines.
Nonfiction: How-to (sell better; increase profits); historical (related to the history of various kinds of sales pitches, anecdotes, etc.); and inspirational (success stories, "rags to riches" type of stories)—with no additional payment. Buys 30 unsolicited mss/year. Query or submit complete ms. Length: 500-1,500 words. Pays 10¢/word.
Photos: Photos purchased with accompanying ms.
Columns/Departments: Ideas Exchange (generated from our readers). Submit complete ms. Open to suggestions for new columns/departments.
Fillers: Jokes, gags, anecdotes and short humor. Buys 2/issue. Length: 150-500 words. Pays $10 for each published item.
Tips: No general articles on "How to be a Super Salesperson." Writers should concentrate on one specific aspect of selling and expand on that.

SOUND MANAGEMENT, Radio Advertising Bureau, 304 Park Ave. S., New York NY 10010. (212)254-4800. Editor-in-Chief: Daniel Flamberg. Editor: Susan Galardi. 15% freelance written. A monthly magazine covering radio sales and marketing. "We write practical business and how-to stories for the owners and managers of radio stations on topics geared toward increasing ad sales and training salespeople." Circ. 10,000. Pays on publication. Publishes ms an average of 4 months after acceptance. Byline given. Buys one-time rights, exclusive rights for the field or makes work-for-hire assignments. Submit seasonal/holiday material 3 months in advance. Previously published submissions OK. Free sample copy and writer's guidelines.
Nonfiction: Essays, how-to, interview/profile and personal experience. No articles on disc jockeys or radio programming. Buys 5-10 mss/year. Query with published clips. Length: 400-750 words. Pays $350-650 for assigned articles; pays $50-150 for unsolicited articles. May pay contributor copies for republished items.
Photos: State availability of photos with submission. Reviews contact sheets, negatives and transparencies. Captions, model releases, and identification of subjects required. Buys one-time rights.
Tips: "Our cover story is most open to freelancers, but proven experience in writing about media advertising and marketing is necessary, with strong interviewing and critical writing skills."

‡**WATERBED MAGAZINE**, Bobit Publishing, 2500 Artesia Blvd., Redondo Beach CA 90278. (213)376-8788. Editor: Kathy Drake. 10% freelance written. A monthly magazine covering waterbeds and accessories for waterbed specialty shop owners, furniture stores, sleep shops and waterbed manufacturers,

distributors. Circ. 9,200. Pays on acceptance. Publishes ms an average of 2 months after acceptance. Byline given. Buys first rights or second serial (reprint) rights. Submit seasonal/holiday material 3 months in advance. Photocopied and previously published submissions OK. Computer printout submissions acceptable; no dot-matrix. Reports in 2 weeks. Free sample copy.

Nonfiction: Book excerpts; essays (health benefits of waterbeds); historical/nostalgic; how-to (business management, display techniques, merchandising tips); humor (if in good taste); interview/profile; new product; personal experience; photo feature; technical; and general features depicting waterbeds in a positive way. "Convention issue published in April or May prior to the Waterbed Manufacturer's Association Convention is extra large. We need more manuscripts then." No articles depicting waterbeds in a negative manner. "The goal of the waterbed industry and the magazine is to get away from the sexy, hippie image associated with waterbeds in the past." Buys 25-30 mss/year. Query with published clips. Length: 1,000-5,000 words. Pays $60-250 for assigned articles; pays $50-200 for unsolicited articles. Pays expenses of writers on assignment.

Photos: Send photos with submission. Reviews contact sheets, transparencies and 8x10 prints. Offers $10-25/photo. Captions and identification of subjects required. Buys one-time rights.

Tips: "We need profiles on successful waterbed retailers in all parts of the country. If a large, full-line furniture store in your area also sells waterbeds, we are interested in profiles on those stores and owners as well. We are also always looking for interviews with doctors, chiropractors and other health professionals who recommend waterbeds for their patients. Most of our freelance articles concern business management. We need articles on obtaining credit, display techniques, merchandising, how to be a successful salesperson, attracting new customers, creating effective advertising, how to put together an attractive store window display, hiring employees, etc. Anything that could benefit a salesperson or store owner."

Sport Trade

AEROBICS & FITNESS JOURNAL, The Journal of the Aerobics and Fitness Association of America, Aerobics and Fitness Association of America, Suite 802, 15250 Ventura Blvd., Sherman Oaks CA 91403. (818)905-0040. Editor: Peg Angsten, R.N. Managing Editor: Harlyn Enholm. 80% freelance written. Eager to work with new/unpublished writers. Bimonthly magazine covering aerobic exercise and sports, health and fitness education. "We need timely, in-depth informative articles on health, fitness, aerobic exercise, sports nutrition, sports medicine and physiology." Circ. 20,000. Pays on publication. Publishes ms an average of 6 months after acceptance. Byline given. Offers $50 kill fee. Buys first North American serial rights, and simultaneous rights (in some cases). Submit seasonal/holiday material 4 months in advance. Simultaneous queries and simultaneous, photocopied, and previously published submissions OK. Electronic submissions OK via either Macintosh 512K or IBM PCXT. Computer printout submissions acceptable; prefers letter-quality to dot-matrix. Reports in 2 weeks. Sample copy for $1 or SAE with 6 first class stamps; writer's guidelines for SAE.

Nonfiction: Book excerpts (fitness book reviews); expose (on nutritional gimmickry); historical/nostalgic (history of various athletic events); humor (personal fitness profiles); inspirational (sports leader's motivational pieces); interview/profile (fitness figures); new product (plus equipment review); opinion (on clubs); personal experience (successful fitness story); photo feature (on exercise, fitness, new sport); and travel (spas that cater to fitness industry). No articles on unsound nutritional practices, popular trends or unsafe exercise gimmicks. Buys 18-25 mss/year. Query. Length: 800-2,500 words. Pays $65-280. Sometimes pays expenses of writers on assignment.

Photos: Sports, action, fitness, aerobic competitions and exercise classes. Pays $30-60 for 8x10 b&w prints; $35-100 for color transparencies. Captions, model release, and identification of subjects required. Buys one-time rights; other rights purchased depend on use of photo.

Columns/Departments: Fitness Industry News, shorts on health and fitness, and profiles on successful fitness figures. Buys 50 mss/year. Query with published clips or send complete ms. Length: 50-150 words. Pays 1¢/word.

Poetry: Buys 2 poems/year. Submit maximum 1 poem. Length: 20-80 lines. Pays $20-50.

Fillers: Cartoons, clippings, jokes, short humor and newsbreaks. Buys 12/year. Length: 75-200 words. Pays $20-50.

Tips: "Cover an athletic event, get a unique angle, provide accurate and interesting findings, and write in an intellectual manner. We are looking for new health and fitness reporters and writers. *A&F* is a good place to get started. I have generally been disappointed with short articles and fillers submissions due to their lack of force. Cover a topic with depth."

AMERICAN BICYCLIST, 80 8th Ave., New York NY 10011. (212)206-7230. Editor: Konstantin Doren. 40% freelance written. Prefers to work with published/established writers. Monthly magazine for bicycle sales and service shops. Circ. 11,025. Pays on publication. Publishes ms an average of 4 months after acceptance. Only staff-written articles are bylined, except under special circumstances. Buys all rights. Computer printout submissions acceptable; no dot-matrix.
Nonfiction: Typical story describes (very specifically) unique traffic-builder or merchandising ideas used with success by an actual dealer. Articles may also deal exclusively with moped sales and service operation within conventional bicycle shops. Emphasis on showing other dealers how they can follow similar pattern and increase their business. Articles may also be based entirely on repair shop operation, depicting efficient and profitable service systems and methods. Buys 12 mss/year. Query. Length: 1,000-2,800 words. Pays 9¢/word, plus bonus for outstanding manuscript. Pays expenses of writers on assignment.
Photos: Reviews relevant b&w photos illustrating principal points in article purchased with ms; 5x7 minimum. Pays $8/photo. Captions required. Buys all rights.
Tips: "A frequent mistake made by writers is writing as if we are a book read by consumers instead of professionals in the bicycle industry."

AMERICAN FIREARMS INDUSTRY, AFI Communications Group, Inc., 2801 E. Oakland Park Blvd., Ft. Lauderdale FL 33306. 10% freelance written. "Work with writers specifically in the firearms trade." Monthly magazine specializing in the sporting arms trade. Circ. 30,000. Pays on publication. Publishes ms an average of 4 months after acceptance. Buys all rights. Computer printout submissions acceptable. Reports in 2 weeks.
Nonfiction: R.A. Lesmeister, articles editor. Publishes informational, technical and new product articles. No general firearms subjects. Query. Length: 900-1,500 words. Pays $100-150. Sometimes pays the expenses of writers on assignment.
Photos: Reviews 8x10 b&w glossy prints. Manuscript price includes payment for photos.

AMERICAN HOCKEY MAGAZINE, Amateur Hockey Association of the United States, 2997 Broadmoor Valley Rd., Colorado Springs CO 80906. (303)576-4990. Publisher: Hal Trumble. Managing Editor: Mike Schroeder. 80% freelance written. Monthly magazine covering hockey in general (with amateur/youth hockey emphasis) for teams, coaches and referees of the Amateur Hockey Association of the U.S., ice facilities in the U.S. and Canada, buyers, schools, colleges, pro teams, and park and recreation departments. Circ. 35,000. Pays on publication. Publishes ms an average of 1 month after acceptance. Byline given. Buys first serial rights; makes work-for-hire assignments. Phone queries OK. Submit seasonal/holiday material 4 months in advance. Photocopied and previously published submissions OK. Reports in 1 month. Sample copy $2.
Nonfiction: General interest, profile, new product and technical. Query. Length: 500-3,000 words. Pays $50 minimum.
Photos: Reviews 5x7 b&w glossy prints and color slides. Offers no additional payment for photos accepted with ms. Captions preferred. Buys one-time rights.
Columns/Departments: Rebound Shots (editorial); Americans in the Pros (U.S. players in the NHL); College Notes; Rinks and Arenas (arena news); Equipment/Sports Medicine; Referees Crease; Coaches Playbook; For the Record; and Features (miscellaneous). Query.

BICYCLE BUSINESS JOURNAL, Box 1570, 1904 Wenneca, Fort Worth TX 76101. Editor: Levy Joffrion. Works with a small number of new/unpublished writers each year. 10% freelance written. Monthly. Circ. 10,000. Pays on acceptance. Publishes ms an average of 3 months after acceptance. Buys all rights. Computer printout submissions acceptable.
Nonfiction: Stories about dealers who service what they sell, emphasizing progressive, successful sales ideas in the face of rising costs and increased competition. Also includes moped dealerships. Length: 3 double-spaced pages maximum. Sometimes pays the expenses of writers on assignment.
Photos: B&w glossy photo a must; vertical photo preferred. Query.
Tips: "We are requesting greater professionalism and more content and research in freelance material."

CORPORATE FITNESS & RECREATION, The Journal for Employee Health and Services Programs, Brentwood Publishing Corp., (a Prentice-Hall Company), 825 S. Barrington Ave., Los Angeles CA 90049. (213)826-8388. Editor: Martin H. Waldman. Managing Editor: Dana Bigman. 60% freelance written. Bimonthly magazine on employee fitness and recreation. "Our readers are directors of on-site employee fitness and recreation programs." Circ. 12,000. Pays on acceptance. Publishes ms an average of 6 months after acceptance. Byline given. Buys all rights. Submit seasonal/holiday material 6 months in advance. Computer printout submissions acceptable; prefers letter-quality to dot-matrix. Reports in 1 month on queries; 2 months on mss. Free sample copy and writer's guidelines.
Nonfiction: How-to (plan, implement, supervise, and evaluate employee health and wellness programs); interview/profile (of on-site corporate fitness and recreation programs and facilities); technical (regarding sports medicine, exercise, physiology, and lifestyle improvements—stress management; smoking cessation, employee assistance program, etc.); and analysis of studies conducted on the benefits of employee fitness

programs. "No general articles on health-related topics that are not geared specifically to our readership." Buys 30 mss/year. Query with published clips. Length: 1,000-2,000 words. Pays $100-240. Pays expenses of writers on assignment.

Columns/Departments: Sports Medicine: Prevention and Treatment of injuries incurred by participants in employee fitness and recreation programs. Writers should have exercise physiology background. Buys 6 mss/year. Query with published clips. Length: 1,500-2,000 words. Pays $150-240.

Tips: "Queries with clips are appreciated. Submissions should conform to American Medical Association style and be written clearly and concisely. A medical or exercise physiology background is not necessary, but is helpful when tackling technical subjects. All submissions are reviewed by an editorial advisory board of industry professionals."

FISHING TACKLE RETAILER, B.A.S.S. Publications, 1 Bell Rd., Montgomery AL 36141. (205)272-9530. Editor: Dave Ellison. 80% freelance written. Prefers to work with published/established writers. Magazine published 10 times/year, "designed to promote the economic health of retail sellers of freshwater and saltwater angling equipment." Circ. 22,000. Byline usually given. Publishes ms an average of 1 year after acceptance. Buys all rights. Submit seasonal/holiday material 6 months in advance. Computer printout submissions acceptable; no dot-matrix. Reports in 6 weeks. Sample copy $2; writer's guidelines for standard size SAE and 1 first class stamp.

Nonfiction: How-to (merchandising and management techniques); technical (how readers can specifically benefit from individual technological advances); and success stories (how certain fishing tackle retailers have successfully overcome business difficulties and their advice to their fellow retailers). Articles must directly relate to the financial interests of the magazine's audience. Buys 100 mss/year. Query with published clips. Length: 50-3,000 words. Pays $10-600. Sometimes pays expenses of writers on assignment.

Photos: State availability of photos. Payment included with ms.

Columns/Departments: Retail Pointers (200-300 words) and Profit Strategy (750-900 words)—how-to tips, should be accompanied by illustration. Buys variable number mss/year.

Tips: "Long stories are usually assigned to writers with whom we have an established relationship. The writer has a better chance of breaking in at our publication with short, lesser-paying articles and fillers."

‡GOLF COURSE MANAGEMENT, Golf Course Superintendents Association of America, 1617 St. Andrews, Lawrence KS 66046. (913)841-2240. Editor: Clay Loyd. Monthly magazine covering golf course and turf management. Circ. 17,000. Byline given. Buys all rights. Submit seasonal/holiday material 6 months in advance. Simultaneous queries and submissions OK. Reports in 2 weeks on queries; 1 month on mss. Free sample copy and writer's guidelines.

Nonfiction: Book excerpts, historical/nostalgic, interview/profile, personal experience and technical. "All areas that relate to the golf course superintendent—whether features or scholarly pieces related to turf/grass management. We prefer all submissions to be written *simply*." Special issues include January "conference issue"—features on convention cities used each year. Buys 20 mss/year. Query with clips of published work. Length: 1,500-3,000 words. Pays $100-300.

Photos: Send photos with ms. Pays $50-250 for color, 4x5 transparencies preferred. Captions, model release and identification of subjects required. Buys one-time rights.

Tips: "Call communications department (913)841-2240, offer idea, follow with outline and writing samples. Response from us is immediate."

GOLF SHOP OPERATIONS, 5520 Park Ave., Trumbull CT 06611. (203)373-7000. Editor: Nick Romano. 5% freelance written. Works with a small number of new/unpublished writers each year. Magazine published 6 times/year for golf professionals and shop operators at public and private courses, resorts, driving ranges and golf specialty stores. Circ. 13,000. Pays on publication. Publishes ms an average of 2 months after acceptance. Byline given. Submit seasonal material (for Christmas and other holiday sales, or profiles of successful professionals with how-to angle emphasized) 3 months in advance. Photocopied submissions OK. Computer printout submissions acceptable; prefers letter-quality to dot-matrix. Reports in 1 month. Sample copy free.

Nonfiction: "We emphasize improving the golf retailer's knowledge of his profession. Articles should describe how pros are buying, promoting merchandising and displaying wares in their shops that might be of practical value. Must be aimed only at the retailer." How-to, profile, successful business operation and merchandising techniques. Buys 6-8 mss/year. Phone queries preferred. Pays $165-200. Sometimes pays expenses of writers on assignment.

Photos: "Pictures are mandatory with all manuscript submissions." Captions required.

Tips: "I'm less inclined to assign anything unless the person can handle a camera. The profile pieces must have decent photos. We're really looking for the freelancers that understand the golf business. This helps us in that we won't have to rewrite a lot or have the writer go back and ask the obvious questions."

POOL & SPA NEWS, Leisure Publications, 3923 W. 6th St., Los Angeles CA 90020. (213)385-3926. Editor-in-Chief: J. Field. 40% freelance written. Semimonthly magazine emphasizing news of the swimming

pool and spa industry for pool builders, pool retail stores and pool service firms. Circ. 12,000. Pays on publication. Publishes ms an average of 1 month after acceptance. Buys all rights. Photocopied submissions OK. Computer printout submissions acceptable. Reports in 2 weeks.
Nonfiction: Interview, new product, profile and technical. Phone queries OK. Length: 500-2,000 words. Pays 8-10¢/word. Sometimes pays expenses of writers on assignment.
Photos: Pays $8 per b&w photo used.

‡**SAILBOARD NEWS**, The International Trade Journal of Boardsailing, Sports Ink Magazine, Inc., Box 159, Fair Haven VT 05743. (802)265-8153. Editor: Mark Gabriel. 50% freelance written. Works with a small number of new/unpublished writers each year. Monthly boardsailing trade glossy tabloid. Circ. 19,000. Pays 30 days after publication. Publishes ms an average of 2 weeks after acceptance. Byline given. Buys one-time rights. Submit seasonal/holiday material 3 weeks in advance. Simultaneous queries OK. Electronic submissions OK via MacIntosh or Easylink. Computer printout submissions acceptable. Reports in 3 weeks. Free sample copy and writer's guidelines.
Nonfiction: Regional retail reports, book excerpts, expose, general interest, historical/nostalgic, how-to, humor, inspirational, interview/profile, new product, opinion, photo feature, technical, travel. Buys 50 mss/year. Send complete ms. Length: 750 words minimum. Pays $50-200.
Photos: Send photos with ms. Reviews b&w negatives and 8x10 prints. Identification of subjects required.
Columns/Departments: Buys 12 mss/year. Query with published clips or send complete ms.

‡**SKI BUSINESS**, 537 Post Rd., Darien CT 06820. Managing Editor: Nancy Coveney. 70% freelance written. Works with a small number of new/unpublished writers each year. Tabloid magazine published 11 times/year. For ski retailers, both alpine and cross-country markets; also covers sailboard industry. Circ. 18,000. Byline given, except on "press releases and round-up articles containing passages from articles submitted by several writers." Pays on publication. Buys first rights plus reprint rights for promotional use and republication in special editions. Submit seasonal material 3 weeks in advance. Electronic submissions OK via 300 or 1200 baud, eight data bits, no parity, full duplex. Computer printout submissions acceptable; no dot-matrix. Reports in 1 month. Publishes ms an average of 2 months after acceptance. Free sample copy available to qualified writers.
Nonfiction: Will consider ski shop profiles; mss about unique and successful merchandising ideas; unique, successful programs that introduce skiing to the public; and ski area equipment rental operations. "All material should be slanted toward usefulness to the ski shop operator. Always interested in in-depth interviews with successful retailers." Uses round-ups of preseason sales and Christmas buying trends across the country from September to December. Would like to see reports on what retailers in major markets are doing. Buys about 100 mss/year. Query first. Pays $50-250. Pays expenses of writers on assignment.
Photos: Photos purchased with accompanying mss. Buys 5x7 b&w glossy photos. Pays minimum of $35/photo; more for color and 35mm transparencies.
Tips: "We are most interested in retailer profiles of successful ski shop operators, with plenty of advice and examples for our readers. We anticipate a shift in editorial direction to more closely meet the needs of retailers, which will require more retailer-oriented pieces."

THE SPORTING GOODS DEALER, 1212 N. Lindbergh Blvd., St. Louis MO 63132. (314)997-7111. President/Chief Executive Officer: Richard Waters. Editor: Steve Fechter. 20% freelance written. Prefers to work with published/established writers. For members of the sporting goods trade: retailers, manufacturers, wholesalers, and representatives. Monthly magazine. Circ. 27,000. Buys second serial (reprint) rights. Buys about 15 mss/year. Pays on publication. Computer printout submissions acceptable; no dot-matrix. Publishes ms an average of 3 months after acceptance. Query. Sample copy $4 (refunded with first ms).
Nonfiction: "Articles about specific sporting goods retail stores, their promotions, display techniques, sales ideas, merchandising, timely news of key personnel; expansions, new stores, deaths—all in the sporting goods trade. Specific details on how individual successful sporting goods stores operate. What specific retail sporting goods stores are doing that is new and different. We would also be interested in features dealing with stores doing an outstanding job in retailing of exercise equipment, athletic footwear, athletic apparel, baseball, fishing, golf, tennis, camping, firearms/hunting and allied lines of equipment. Query on these." Successful business operations and merchandising techniques. Does not want to see announcements of doings and engagements. Length: open. Rates negotiated by assignment. Also looking for material for the following columns: Terse Tales of the Trade (store news); Selling Slants (store promotions); and Open for Business (new retail sporting goods stores or sporting goods departments). All material must relate to specific sporting goods stores by name, city, and state; general information is not accepted.
Photos: Pays minimum of $3.50 for sharp clear b&w photos; size not important. These are purchased with or without mss. Captions optional, but identification requested.
Fillers: Clippings. These must relate directly to the sporting goods industry. Pays 2¢/published word.
Tips: "The writer has to put himself or herself in our readers' position and ask: Does my style and/or expertise help retailers run their business better?"

SPORTS MERCHANDISER, W.R.C. Smith Publishing Co., 1760 Peachtree Rd. NW, Atlanta GA 30357. (404)874-4462. Editor: Eugene R. Marnell. 5% freelance written. Monthly tabloid; 100 pages. For retailers and wholesalers of sporting goods in all categories; independent stores, chains, specialty stores, and department store departments. Circ. 30,000. Pays on publication. Publishes ms an average of 3 months after acceptance. Buys all rights. Submit seasonal/holiday material 6 months in advance. Computer printout submissions acceptable; prefers letter-quality to dot-matrix. Reports in 4 months.
Nonfiction: Articles telling how retailers are successful in selling a line of products, display ideas, successful merchandising programs, inventory operations, and advertising program successes. No articles on business history. Query to be one-page with card (reply) enclosed. Letters to state full name of contact, address, etc. and describe type of business relative to volume, inventory and positioning in local market. Tell particular slant author believes most interesting. Length: 1,000-2,000 words. Pays $75-175.
Photos: State availability of photos with query. Offers no additional payment for 5x7 or 8x10 b&w prints. Captions required. Buys all rights.
Tips: "The retail order season is almost six months opposite the retail buying season (i.e., consumer buying). Lead time for ordering is six months—sometimes more on hardgoods and softgoods. Other products have full-year ordering cycle. The writer has a better chance of breaking into our publication with short, lesser-paying articles because they provide greater detail information on a specific element of store, operator, etc. A query will help everyone."

SPORTSTYLE, Fairchild Publications, Inc., 7 E. 12th St., New York NY 10003. (212)741-5995. Editor: Mark Sullivan. A bimonthly tabloid covering the sporting goods industry for sporting goods retailers and manufacturers of athletic footwear, apparel and equipment. Circ. 30,000. Pays on publication. Byline given. Offers negotiable kill fee. Computer printout submissions acceptable. Reports in 1 month. Free sample copy.
Nonfiction: "We run business stories only and use a lot of retailer profiles and occasionally manufacturer profiles." Buys 25 mss/year. Query. Length: 2,000 words. Pays $5/column inch.

SWIMMING POOL AGE & SPA MERCHANDISER, Communication Channels, Inc., 6255 Barfield Rd., Atlanta GA 30328. (404)256-9800. Editor: Terri Simmons. 30% freelance written. Works with a small number of new/unpublished writers each year. Monthly tabloid emphasizing pool, spa and hot tub industry. Circ. 15,000. Pays on publication. Publishes ms an average of 3 months after acceptance. Buys all rights. Phone queries OK. Submit seasonal/holiday material 3 months in advance. Electronic submissions OK on DecMate disk or diskette, but requires hard copy also.
Nonfiction: How-to (installation techniques, service and repairs, tips, etc.); interview (with people and groups within the industry); photo feature (pool/spa/tub construction or special use); technical (should be prepared with expert within the industry); industry news; and market research reports. Also, comparison articles exploring the same type of products produced by numerous manufacturers. Buys 5-10 unsolicited mss/year. Mss must be double-spaced on *white* paper. Query. Length: 250-2,500 words. Pays 10¢/word. Sometimes pays the expenses of writers on assignment.
Photos: Purchased with accompanying ms or on assignment. Query or send contact sheet. Will accept 35mm transparencies of good quality. Captions required.
Tips: "If a writer can produce easily understood technical articles ontaining unbiased, hard facts, we are definitely interested. We will be concentrating on technical and how-to articles because that's what our readers want."

WOODALL'S CAMPGROUND MANAGEMENT, Woodall Publishing Co., Suite 205, 11 North Skokie Highway, Lake Bluff IL 60044. (312)295-7799. Editor: Mike Byrnes. 66% freelance written. Works with a small number of new/unpublished writers each year. A monthly tabloid covering campground management and operation for managers of private and public campgrounds throughout the U.S. Circ. 17,200. Pays after publication. Publishes ms an average of 4 months after acceptance. Byline given. Buys all rights. Submit seasonal/holiday material 4 months in advance. Simultaneous queries OK. Computer printout submissions acceptable; prefers letter-quality to dot-matrix. Reports in 2 weeks on queries; 6 weeks on mss. Free sample copy and writer's guidelines.
Nonfiction: How-to, interview/profile and technical. "Our articles tell our readers how to maintain their resources, manage personnel and guests, market, develop new campground areas and activities, and interrelate with the major tourism organizations within their areas. 'Improvement' and 'profit' are the two key words." Buys 48+ mss/year. Query. Length: 500 words minimum. Pays $50-200. Sometimes pays expenses of writers on assignment.
Photos: Send contact sheets and negatives. "We pay for each photo used."
Tips: "Contact us and give us an idea of your ability to travel and your travel range. We sometimes have assignments in certain areas. The best type of story to break in with is a case history type approach about how a campground improved its maintenance, physical plant or profitability."

__ *Stone and Quarry Products*

CONCRETE CONSTRUCTION MAGAZINE, 426 South Westgate, Addison IL 60101. Editorial Director: Ward R. Malisch. Monthly magazine, 80 pages average, for general and concrete contractors, architects, engineers, concrete producers, cement manufacturers, distributors and dealers in construction equipment and testing labs. Circ. 82,000. Pays on acceptance. Bylines used only by prearrangement with author. Buys all rights. Photocopied submissions OK. Reports in 2 months. Free sample copy and writer's guidelines.
Nonfiction: "Our magazine has a major emphasis on cast-in-place and precast concrete. Prestressed concrete is also covered. Our articles deal with tools, techniques and materials that result in better handling, better placing, and ultimately an improved final product. We are particularly firm about not using proprietary names in any of our articles. Manufacturer and product names are never mentioned; only the processes or techniques that might be of help to the concrete contractor, the architect or the engineer dealing with the material. We do use reader response cards to relay reader interest to manufacturers." No job stories or promotional material. Buys 8-10 mss/year. Submit query with topical outline. Pays $200/2-page article. Prefers 1,000-2,000 words with 2-3 illustrations.
Photos: Photos used only as part of complete ms.
Tips: "Condensed, totally factual presentations are preferred."

CONCRETE INTERNATIONAL: DESIGN AND CONSTRUCTION, American Concrete Institute, 22400 W. Seven Mile Rd., Detroit MI 48219. (313)532-2600. Editor: Robert Wilde. "We are backlogged with submissions and prefer not to receive unsolicited submissions at this time."

‡DIMENSIONAL STONE, Dimensional Stone Institute, Inc., Suite D, 17901 Ventura Blvd., Encino CA 91316. (818)344-4200. Editor: Jerry Fisher. 25% freelance written. A bimonthly magazine covering dimensional stone use for managers of producers, importers, contractors, fabricators and specifiers of dimensional stone. Estab. 1985. Circ. 13,300. Pays on publication. Publishes ms an average of 2 months after acceptance. Byline given. Buys first rights or second serial (reprint) rights. Photocopied submissions and previously published submissions OK. Computer printout submissions acceptable; prefers letter-quality to dot-matrix. Sample copy available.
Nonfiction: Interview/profile and technical, only on users of dimensional stone. Buys 6-7 mss/year. Send complete ms. Length: 1,000-3,000 words. Pays $100 maximum. Sometimes pays the expenses of writers on assignment.
Photos: Send photos with submission. Reviews any size prints. Offers no additional payment for photos accepted with ms. Identification of subjects required.
Tips: "Articles on outstanding uses of dimensional stone are most open to freelancers."

‡MINE AND QUARRY, Ashire Publishing Ltd., 42 Gray's Inn Rd., London WC1X 8LR England. Editor: Kim Burridge. Monthly magazine; for senior management at mines and quarries. 80 pages. Circ. 4,600. Buys all rights. Phone queries OK. Submit seasonal/holiday material 2 months in advance. Simultaneous, photocopied and previously published submissions OK. Computer printout submissions acceptable. SAE and IRCs. Reports in 2 months. Free sample copy and writer's guidelines.
Nonfiction: Technical and new product articles related to the industry. Buys 10 mss/year. Submit complete ms. Length: 200-1,000 words. Pays $10-20.
Photos: B&w glossy prints and color transparencies purchased with or without mss. Captions required. Send contact sheet, prints or transparencies.

STONE IN AMERICA, American Monument Association, 6902 N. High St., Worthington OH 43085. (614)885-2713. Managing Editor: Bob Moon. Monthly magazine for the retailers of upright memorials in the U.S. and Canada. Circ. 2,600. Pays on acceptance. Buys interment industry rights. Phone queries preferred. Reports in 1 month. Free sample copy and writer's guidelines.
Nonfiction: How-to (run a monument business); informational (major news within the industry, monuments as an art form); profile (successful retailers); and technical. Buys 30-40 mss/year. Length: 1,500-2,000 words. Query. Pays $100-400.
Photos: Pays $20-50 for 5x7 or 8x10 b&w glossy prints.

——— *Toy, Novelty and Hobby*

‡CREATIVE PRODUCT NEWS, Box 584, Lake Forest IL 60045. (312)234-5052. Editor: Linda F. Lewis. 2% freelance written. Works with a small number of new/unpublished writers each year. Monthly tabloid for retailers of crafts, needlework and art materials for fine art, hobby art and doll house miniatures. Circ. 34,000. Pays on acceptance. Publishes ms an average of 6 months after acceptance. Byline given. Buys first North American serial rights. Submit seasonal/holiday material 6 months in advance. Simultaneous queries and photocopied submissions OK. Computer printout submissions acceptable; dot-matrix "if good quality." Reports in 1 month. Free sample copy.
Nonfiction: "We need only one thing: packages containing 4-6 photos and 200- to 500-word descriptions. Topic should be demonstration of a new art or craft technique; photos must show finished article, supplies used and procedure." Buys 12 mss/year. Query with clips of published work. Pays $50. Sometimes pays the expenses of writers on assignment.
Tips: "Our total concern is what's new. Submit only ideas that are truly new. We are only interested in submissions from writers with expertise in our industry."

MODEL RETAILER MAGAZINE, Clifton House, Clifton VA 22024. (703)830-1000. Editor: Geoffrey Wheeler. 40% freelance written. Monthly magazine "for hobby store owners—generally well-established small business persons, fairly well educated, and very busy." Circ. 6,300. Pays on publication. Byline given. Buys one-time rights. Phone queries OK (no collect calls), but prefers written queries. Submit seasonal/holiday material 3 months in advance. Photocopied and previously published submissions OK. Computer printout submissions acceptable; prefers letter-quality to dot-matrix. Reports in 3 weeks. Free writer's guidelines and sample copy.
Nonfiction: Retailer profiles; articles on store management, marketing, merchandising, advertising; and photo feature (if photos tie in with marketing techniques or hobby store operation, etc.). No company profiles, 'human interest' stories, self-publicity articles, or reports on trade shows. ("We do those ourselves"). Buys 2-4 mss/issue. Query. Length: 1,200-2,500 words. Pays for complete manuscript package of: main copy, side bars (if needed), working headline, and illustrative material (if needed). Range: $125-350, depending on length and degree of specialization.
Photos: "Photos that illustrate key points and are of good quality will help the article, particularly if it concerns business operation. Photos are paid for as part of total package."

‡PLAYTHINGS, Geyer-McAllister, 51 Madison Ave., New York NY 10010. (212)689-4411. Editor: Frank Reysen, Jr. Managing Editor: Barbara McClorey. A monthly merchandising magazine covering toys and hobbies aimed mainly at mass market toy retailers. Circ. 15,000. Pays on acceptance. Publishes ms an average of 3 months after acceptance. Byline sometimes given. Buys one-time rights. Submit seasonal/holiday material 3 months in advance. Simultaneous and photocopied submissions OK. Reports in 2 weeks. Free sample copy.
Nonfiction: Interview/profile, photo feature and retail profiles of toy and hobby stores and chains. Annual directory, May. Buys 10 mss/year. Query. Length: 900-2,500 words. Pays $100-350. Sometimes pays the expenses of writers on assignment.
Photos: Send photos with submission. Captions and identification of subjects required. Buys one-time rights.
Columns/Departments: Buys 5 mss/year. Query. Pays $50-100.

‡SOUVENIRS & NOVELTIES MAGAZINE, Kane Communications, Inc., Suite 226, 401 N. Broad St., Philadelphia PA 19108. (215)925-9744. Editor: Chuck Tooley. A magazine published 7 times/year for resort and gift industry. Circ. 20,000. Pays on publication. Byline given. Buys all rights. Computer printout submissions acceptable; prefers letter-quality to dot-matrix. Reports in 3 weeks. Sample copy for 6x9 SAE with $1 postage.
Nonfiction: Interview/profile and new product. Buys 6 mss/year. Query. Length: 700-1,500 words. Pays $25-175 for assigned articles. Sometimes pays the expenses of writers on assignment.
Photos: State availability of photos with submission. Captions, model releases and identification of subjects required.

THE STAMP WHOLESALER, Box 706, Albany OR 97321. Executive Editor: Kyle Jansson. 80% freelance written. Newspaper published 28 times/year; 32 pages. For philatelic businessmen; many are part-time and/or retired from other work. Circ. 6,400. Pays on publication. Byline given. Buys all rights. Computer printout submissions acceptable; prefers letter-quality to dot-matrix. Reports in 10 weeks. Free sample copy.
Nonfiction: How-to information on how to deal more profitably in postage stamps for collections. Emphasis

on merchandising techniques and how to make money. Does not want to see any so-called "humor" items from nonprofessionals. Buys 60 ms/year. Submit complete ms. Length: 1,000-1,500 words. Pays $35 and up/article.

Tips: "Send queries on business stories. Send manuscript on stamp dealer stories. We need stories to help dealers make and save money."

Transportation

INBOUND LOGISTICS, (formerly *Inbound Traffic Guide*), Thomas Publishing Co., 1 Penn Plaza, 26th Fl., New York NY 10019. (212)290-7336. Editor: Richard S. Sexton. 50% freelance written. Bimonthly magazine covering the transportation industry. *"Inbound Logistics* is distributed to people who buy, specify, or recommend inbound freight transportation services and equipment. The editorial matter provides basic explanations of inbound freight transportation, directory listings, how-to technical information, trends and developments affecting inbound freight movements, and expository, case history feature stories." Circ. 45,000. Pays on publication. Publishes ms an average of 3 months after acceptance. Byline given. Buys all rights. Simultaneous queries, and simultaneous and photocopied submission OK. Computer printout submissions acceptable; no dot-matrix. Reports in 2 weeks. Free sample copy and writer's guidelines.

Nonfiction: How-to (basic help for traffic managers) and interview/profile (transportation professionals). Buys 15 mss/year. Query with published clips. Length: 750-1,000 words. Pays $300-1,200. Pays expenses of writers on assignment.

Photos: Paula J. Slomer, photo editor. State availability of photos with query. Pays $100-500 for b&w contact sheets, negatives, transparencies and prints; $250-500 for color contact sheets, negative transparencies and prints. Captions and identification of subjects required.

Columns/Departments: Viewpoint (discusses current opinions on transportation topics). Query with published clips.

Tips: "Have a sound knowledge of the transportation industry; educational how-to articles get our attention."

Travel

These publications are by and for people who help other people travel. Travel professionals learn about trends, tours and types of transportation for their customers through trade journals. Magazines about vacations and travel for general readers are listed under Travel in the Consumer section.

AMERICAS, Organization of American States, Editorial Offices, General Secretariat Bldg., 1889 F. St. NW, Washington DC 20006. Managing Editor: A.R. Williams. 70% freelance written. Official cultural organ of Organization of American States. Audience is persons interested in inter-American topics. Editions published in English and Spanish. Bimonthly. Circ. 75,000. Buys first publication and reprint rights. Byline given. Pays on publication. Publishes ms an average of 6 months after acceptance. Computer printout submissions acceptable; prefers letter-quality to dot-matrix. "They have *got* to be readable." Free sample copy. Queries preferred. Articles received on speculation only. Include cover letter with writer's background. Reports in 3 months. Not necessary to enclose SASE.

Nonfiction: Articles of general New World interest on travel, history, art, literature, theatre development, archeology, travel, etc. Emphasis on modern, up-to-date Latin·America. Taboos are religious and political themes or articles with noninternational slant. Photos required. Buys 36 unsolicited mss/year. Length: 2,500 words maximum. Pays $200 minimum.

Tips: "Send excellent photographs in both color and b&w, address an international readership, not a local or national one. We want something more critically insightful than a Sunday newspaper travel section piece. We read everything that comes in over the transom. We'll publish anything that's good, and we don't much care if the author has been published before or not. In fact, we're getting weary of published authors who don't write very well and whose careers seem to have been propelled along by talented editors providing the authors with marvelous clips."

BUS TOURS MAGAZINE, The Magazine of Bus Tours and Long Distance Charters, National Bus Trader, Inc., Box 349B, Rt. 3, (Theater Rd.), Delavan WI 53115. (414)728-2691. Editor: Larry Plachno. Editorial Assistant: Dianna Woss. 80% freelance written. Eager to work with new/unpublished writers. Bimonthly magazine for bus companies and tour brokers who design or sell bus tours. Circ. 9,306. Pays as arranged. Publishes ms an average of 1 year after acceptance. Byline given. Not copyrighted. Buys rights as arranged. Submit seasonal/holiday material 9 months in advance. Simultaneous queries OK. Computer printout submissions acceptable; prefers letter-quality to dot-matrix. Reports in 1 month. Free sample copy and writer's guidelines.

Nonfiction: Historical/nostalgic, how-to, humor, interview/profile, new product, professional, personal experience, and travel; all on bus tours. Buys 10 mss/year. Query. Length: open. Pays negotiable fee. Sometimes pays the expenses of writers on assignment.

Photos: State availability of photos. Reviews 35mm transparencies and 6x9 or 8x10 prints. Caption, model release, and identification of subjects required.

Columns/Departments: Bus Tour Marketing; and Buses and the Law. Buys 15-20 mss/year. Query. Length: 1-1½ pages.

Tips: "Most of our feature articles are written by freelancers under contract from local convention and tourism bureaus. Specifications sent on request. Writers should query local bureaus regarding their interest. Writer need not have extensive background and knowledge of bus tours."

BUS WORLD, Motor Coach Photo-Feature Magazine, Sunrise Enterprises, Box 39, Woodland Hills CA 91365. (818)710-0208. Editor: Ed Stauss. 75% freelance written. Eager to work with new/unpublished writers. Quarterly trade journal covering the transit and intercity bus industries. *"Bus World* is edited to inform and entertain people who have an interest in buses—bus owners, managers, drivers, enthusiasts and historians. With extensive photographic coverage, *Bus World* describes the function and lore of the bus industry including intercity, transit, tour and charter." Circ. 7,000. Pays on publication. Publishes ms an average of 4 months after acceptance. Byline given. Buys first North American serial rights. Electronic submissions OK on IBM PC DOS, but requires hard copy also. Computer printout submissions acceptable; prefers letter-quality to dot-matrix. Reports in 3 weeks. Sample copy $1; writer's guidelines for SAE and 1 first class stamp.

Nonfiction: "Author must show an understanding of the bus industry. Coverage includes descriptions of new vehicles, surveys of operating systems, first person experiences with transit and intercity operations, and reviews of historic equipment and systems. Primary coverage is North America." No tourist or travelog viewpoints. Buys 8-12 mss/year. Query. Length: 500-2,000 words. Pays $20-100.

Photos: Photos should be sharp and clear. State availability of photos. "We buy photos with manuscripts under one payment." Reviews 35mm color transparencies and 8x10 b&w prints. Captions required. Buys one-time rights.

Fillers: Cartoons. Buys 4-6/year. Pays $10.

Tips: "Be employed in or have a good understanding of the bus industry. Be enthusiastic about buses—their history and future—as well as current events. Acceptable material will be held until used and will not be returned unless requested by sender. Unacceptable and excess material will be returned only if accompanied by suitable SASE."

CANADIAN RV DEALER, Suite 202, 2077 Dundas St. E., Mississauga, Ontario L4X 1M2 Canada. (416)624-8218. Editor: Peter Tasler. 20% freelance written. Published 7 times/year "to better the development and growth of Canada's recreational vehicle and camping accessory dealers." Circ. 8,000. Pays on publication. Publishes ms an average of 2 months after acceptance. Byline given. Buys first serial rights. Reports in 2 months. Free sample copy and writer's guidelines.

Nonfiction: All features must pertain to the Canadian RV dealer and marketplace. Will consider occasional U.S. pieces if applicable to Canada or unusual slant. Would also consider dealer-slanted humor. Self-help management-type articles also OK. Query first.

GO GREYHOUND, The Greyhound Corp., Greyhound Tower - 1810, Phoenix AZ 85077. (602)248-5714. Editor: Donald L. Behnke. 10% freelance written. Eager to work with new/unpublished writers. Quarterly in-house publication for Greyhound shareholders, employees and other interested individuals. Circ. 200,000. Pays on acceptance. Publishes ms an average of 6 months after acceptance. No byline given. Buys one-time rights. Submit seasonal/holiday material 9 months in advance. Simultaneous queries, and simultaneous and photocopied submissions OK. Computer printout submissions acceptable; no dot-matrix. Reports in 3 months. Sample copy and writer's guidelines for 9x12 manila envelope and 4 first class stamps.

Nonfiction: Juanita Soto, assistant editor. Travel (to places reached by Greyhound bus). "We review features about historic, scenic or entertainment attractions that can be reached by Greyhound bus." No personal experience stories. Buys 4 mss/year. Query or send complete ms. Length: 500-800 words. Pays $350 maximum with color pictures.

Photos: "Articles must be accompanied by a minimum of 12 good quality color transparencies from which we may choose to illustrate the story." Payment included with purchase of ms. Reviews 35mm and larger color transparencies and 5x7 color prints.

Tips: "Follow our writer's guidelines. We must see accompanying transparencies. We require excellent color pictures for the travel stories. Articles submitted without required transparencies will not be considered. Do not send personal experience travel on bus. Travel articles which read like guided tours, with bits and pieces of personal perspective, are ideal for *Go Greyhound*."

LEISURE WHEELS MAGAZINE, Murray Publications Ltd., Box 7302, Station "E", Calgary, Alberta, Canada T3C 3M2. (403)263-2707. Editor: Murray Gimbel. 75% freelance written. Works with a small number of new/unpublished writers each year; eager to work with new/unpublished writers. Bimonthly magazine covering Canadian recreational vehicle travel. Circ. 47,700. Pays on publication. Publishes ms an average of 2 months after acceptance. Byline given. Buys second serial (reprint) rights. Submit seasonal/holiday material 2 months in advance. Computer printout submissions acceptable; prefers letter-quality to dot-matrix. Sample copy 75¢; free writer's guidelines.

Nonfiction: Travel and outdoor leisure-time hobbies. Buys 12 mss/year. Query with published clips. Length: 1,000-2,000 words. Pays $135-200. Sometimes pays the expenses of writers on assignment.

Photos: State availability of photos. Pays $15-25 for 5x11 color prints; $10-20 for b&w 5x11 prints. Identification of subjects required. Buys one-time rights.

Columns/Departments: Buys 12 mss/year. Query with or without published clips. Length: 750-1,000 words. Pays $110-150.

Fiction: Adventure and humorous (relating to travel). Buys 6 mss/year. Query with or without published clips. Length: 1,000-1,500 words. Pays $135-150.

Fillers: Jokes and anecdotes. Buys 6 mss/year. Length: 500-700 words. Pays $50-70.

NATIONAL BUS TRADER, The Magazine of Bus Equipment for the United States and Canada, Rt. 3, Box 349B (Theater Rd.), Delavan WI 53115. (414)728-2691. Editor: Larry Plachno. 25% freelance written. Eager to work with new/unpublished writers. Monthly magazine for manufacturers, dealers and owners of buses and motor coaches. Circ. 7,354. Pays on either acceptance or publication. Publishes ms an average of 6 months after acceptance. Byline given. Not copyrighted. Buys rights "as required by writer." Simultaneous queries, and simultaneous, photocopied, and previously published submissions OK. Computer printout submissions acceptable; prefers letter-quality to dot-matrix. Reports in 1 month. Free sample copy.

Nonfiction: Historical/nostalgic (on old buses); how-to (maintenance repair); new products; photo feature; and technical (aspects of mechanical operation of buses). "We are finding that more and more firms and agencies are hiring freelancers to write articles to our specifications. We are more likely to run them if someone else pays." No material that does *not* pertain to bus tours or bus equipment. Buys 3-5 unsolicited mss/year. Query. Length: varies. Pays variable rate.

Photos: State availability of photos. Reviews 5x7 or 8x10 prints and 35mm transparencies. Captions, model release, and identification of subjects required.

Columns/Departments: Bus maintenance; Buses and the Law; Regulations; and Bus of the Month. Buys 20-30 mss/year. Query. Length: 1-1½ pages. Pays variable rate.

Tips: "We are a very technical publication. Writers should submit qualifications showing extensive background in bus vehicles. We're very interested in well-researched articles on older bus models and manufacturers, or current converted coaches. Write or phone editors with article concept or outline for comments and approval."

THE OVERNIGHTER, The Overnighter, Inc., Box 408310, Chicago IL 60640. (312)545-1558. Editor: Philip W. Sunseri. Managing Editor: Eugene B. Biondi. 60% freelance written. Eager to work with new/unpublished writers. Quarterly magazine covering airline crewmembers (flight attendants and pilots). Circ. 7,000. Pays on publication. Publishes ms an average of 3 months after acceptance. Byline given. Buys first serial rights. Submit seasonal/holiday material 6 months in advance. Photocopied and previously published submissions OK. Computer printout submissions acceptable; prefers letter-quality to dot-matrix. Reports in 4 weeks. Sample copy for $1.50, 6x9 SAE and 4 first class stamps; free writer's guidelines.

Nonfiction: General interest, historical/nostalgic, how-to, humor, interview/profile, opinion, personal experience, photo feature and travel. "We are especially looking for articles of 1,000-2,000 words on travel, industry-related issues, and interviews for a highly mobile and diversified airline crewmember." No articles

related to sex or religion. Buys 12 mss/year. Send complete ms. Length: 250-2,500 words. Pays $10-25.
Photos: Send photos with ms. Pays $5-10 for b&w negatives and prints. Captions required. Buys one-time rights.
Columns/Departments: Book Reviews; Health (airline crewmember related); Industry Trends; City Streets (interesting areas of different cities); and Travel Tips. Buys 8-10/year. Send complete ms. Length: 500-2,500 words. Pays $10-25.
Fiction: Condensed novels, confession, historical, mainstream, novel excerpts, romance and suspense. No sex- or religion-related fiction. Buys 4 mss/year. Send complete ms. Length: 1,000-2,500 words. Pays $10-25.
Fillers: Clippings, anecdotes, short humor and newsbreaks. Buys 15-25/year. Length: 100-500 words. Pays $5-25.
Tips: "Get to know the airline industry as it relates to the crewmember. Understand the lifestyle of the pilot and flight attendant. All articles *must* relate to the airline crewmember."

‡PACIFIC TRAVEL NEWS, Official Airline Guides, 100 Grant Ave., San Francisco CA 94108. (415)781-8240. Associate Publisher/Editorial: Donald Langley. Managing Editor: James Gebbie. 5-10% freelance written. A monthly magazine covering travel in Asia/South Pacific written strictly for the travel trade, the area of coverage is from Hawaii west to Pakistan. Circ. 24,000. Pays on publication. Offers variable kill fee. Buys first rights. Submit seasonal/holiday material 6 months in advance. Simultaneous, photocopied and previously published submissions OK. Free sample copy and writer's guidelines.
Nonfiction: Travel. Buys 6-10 mss/year. Query. Length: 1,000-1,500 words. Pays $150-175.
Photos: State availability of photos with submission. Reviews transparencies. Offers $35/b&w; $75/color; $150/cover photo. Captions and identification of subjects required.

RV BUSINESS, TL Enterprises, Inc., 29901 Agoura Rd., Agoura CA 91301. (818)991-4980. Editor: Michael Schneider. Managing Editor: Sheryl Harris. 60% freelance written. Prefers to work with published/established writers. Monthly magazine covering the recreational vehicle and allied industries for people of the RV industry—dealers, manufacturers, suppliers, park management, legislators and finance experts. Circ. 25,000. Pays on acceptance. Publishes ms an average of 4 months after acceptance. Byline given. Offers 50% kill fee. Buys first North American serial rights. Submit seasonal/holiday material 6 months in advance. Photocopied submissions OK. Electronic submissions OK (call first), but requires hard copy also. Computer printout submissions acceptable; prefers letter-quality to dot-matrix. Reports in 3 weeks on queries; 6 weeks on mss. Sample copy for 9x12 SAE and 3 first class stamps; writer's guidelines for business size SAE and 1 first class stamp.
Nonfiction: Expose (carefully done and thoroughly researched); historical/nostalgic (companies, products or people pertaining to the RV industry itself); how-to (deal with any specific aspect of the RV business); interview/profile (persons or companies involved with the industry—legislative, finance, dealerships, park management, manufacturing, supplier); new product (no payment for company promo material—Product Spotlight usually requires interview with company spokesperson, first-hand experience with product. Specifics and verification of statistics required—must be factual); opinion (controversy OK); personal experience (must be something of importance to readership)—must have a point: it worked for me, it can for you; or this is why it didn't work for me); photo feature (4-color transparencies required with good captions; photo coverage of RV shows, conventions and meetings not appropriate topics for photo feature); and technical (photos required, 4-color preferred). General business articles may be considered. Buys 75 mss/year. Query with published clips. Send complete ms—"but only read on speculation." Length: 1,000-2,000 words. Pays variable rate up to $500. Sometimes pays expenses of writers on assignment.
Photos: State availability of photos with query or send photos with ms. Reviews 35mm transparencies and 8x10 b&w prints. Captions, model release, and identification of subjects required. Buys one-time or all rights; unused photos returned.
Columns/Departments: Guest editorial; News (50-500 words maximum, b&w photos appreciated); and RV People (color photos/4-color transparencies; this section lends itself to fun, upbeat copy). Buys 100-120 mss/year. Query or send complete ms. Pays $10-200 "depending on where used and importance."
Tips: "Query. Phone OK; letter preferable. Send one or several ideas and a few lines letting us know how you plan to treat it/them. We are always looking for good authors knowledgable in the RV industry or related industries. Change of editorial focus requires more articles that are brief, factual, hard hitting, business oriented and in-depth. Will work with promising writers, published or unpublished."

THE STAR SERVICE, Sloane Travel Agency Reports, Box 15610, Fort Lauderdale FL 33318. (305)472-8794. Executive Editor: Charles Kulander. 100% freelance written. Eager to work with new/unpublished writers. Editorial manual sold to travel agencies on subscription basis. Pays 15 days prior to publication. Buys all rights. "Write for instruction sheet and sample report form. Initial reports sent by a new correspondent will be examined for competence and criticized as necessary upon receipt; but once established, a correspondent's submissions will not usually be acknowledged until payment is forwarded, which can often be several months, depending on immediate editorial needs." Computer printout submissions acceptable; prefers letter-quality to dot-matrix. Query. Writer's guidelines for SAE and 1 first class stamp.

Nonfiction: "Objective, critical evaluations of worldwide hotels and cruise ships suitable for North Americans, based on inspections. Forms can be provided to correspondents so no special writing style is required, only perception, experience and judgment in travel. No commercial gimmick—no advertising or payment for listings in publication is accepted." With query, writer should "outline experience in travel and writing and specific forthcoming travel plans, and time available for inspections. Leading travel agents throughout the world subscribe to *Star Service*. No credit or byline is given correspondents due to delicate subject matter often involving negative criticism of hotels. We would like to emphasize the importance of reports being based on current experience and the importance of reporting on a substantial volume of hotels, not just isolated stops (since staying in a hotel is not a requisite) in order that work be profitable for both publisher and writer. Experience in travel writing and/or travel industry is desirable." Buys 4,000 reports/year. Length: "up to 350 words, if submitted in paragraph form; varies if submitted on printed inspection form." Pays $15/report (higher for ships) used. Higher rates of payment and of guaranteed acceptance of set number of reports will be made after correspondent's ability and reliability have been established. Sometimes pays the expenses of writers on assignment.

‡THE TRAVEL AGENT, Fairchild Publishing-Capitol Cities/ABC, 2 W. 46th St., New York NY 10036. (212)575-9000. Editor: Richard S. Kahn. Managing Editor: Eileen Zitnak. 2% freelance written. A business/news magazine for the travel industry published twice weekly. Circ. 41,000. Pays on acceptance. Publishes ms an average of 2 months after acceptance. Byline given. Offers 100% kill fee. Buys first rights. Submit seasonal/holiday material 6 months in advance. Simultaneous, photocopied and previously published submissions OK "but not when it involves competing publications in the travel field." Electronic submissions OK via 1200 Baud/7 data/even parity/1 stop bit/linefeeds required; disk; MS-DOS 5¼ inch. Computer print-out submissions acceptable; prefers letter-quality to dot-matrix. Reports in 1 month. Sample copy for 8½x11 SAE with 2 first class stamps. Free writer's guidelines.

Nonfiction: How-to (on running a travel agency), humor, interview/profile, new product and technical. No personal travel experiences. Buys 200 mss/year. Query with or without published clips, or send complete ms. Length: 500-1,500 words. Pays $50-100 for assigned articles; pays $50 for unsolicited articles. Sometimes pays the expenses of writers on assignment.

Photos: Send photos with submission. Reviews transparencies. Offers $5-10/photo. May pay with premiums rather than cash if photos are used on cover without accompanying story. Captions and identification of subjects required. Buys one-time rights.

TRAVELAGE WEST, Official Airline Guides, Inc., 100 Grant Ave., San Francisco CA 94108. Executive Editor: Donald C. Langley. 5% freelance written. Weekly magazine for travel agency sales counselors in the western U.S. and Canada. Circ. 30,000. Pays on publication. Byline given. Buys all rights. Offers kill fee. Submit seasonal/holiday material 2 months in advance. Computer printout submissions acceptable. Reports in 1 month. Free writer's guidelines.

Nonfiction: Travel. "No promotional approach or any hint of do-it-yourself travel. Emphasis is on news, not description. No static descriptions of places, particularly resort hotels." Buys 40 mss/year. Query. Length: 1,000 words maximum. Pays $1.50/column inch.

Tips: "Query should be a straightforward description of the proposed story, including (1) an indication of the news angle, no matter how tenuous, and (2) a recognition by the author that we run a trade magazine for travel agents, not a consumer book. I am particularly turned off by letters that try to get me all worked up about the 'beauty' or excitement of some place. Authors planning to travel might discuss with us a proposed angle before they go; otherwise their chances of gathering the right information are slim."

❝ Rejection is part of any creative art. To overcome, I immediately get back to the keyboard and work harder. Then I think of Hemingway, F. Scott Fitzgerald, Jack London, all of whom were rejected hundreds of times. ❞

Cork Millner

Veterinary

MODERN VETERINARY PRACTICE, American Veterinary Publications, Inc., Drawer KK, 300 E. Canon Perdido, Santa Barbara CA 93101. 5% freelance written. Monthly magazine, 90 pages; for graduate veterinarians. Circ. 22,000. Pays on publication. Publishes ms an average of 3 months after acceptance. Buys all rights. Phone queries OK. Submit seasonal/holiday material 3 months in advance. Computer printout submissions acceptable; prefers letter-quality to dot-matrix. Reports in 1 month. Sample copy $2.75.
Nonfiction: How-to (clinical medicine, new surgical procedures, business management); informational (business management, education, government projects affecting practicing veterinarians, special veterinary projects); interviews (only on subjects of interest to veterinarians; query first); and technical (clinical reports, technical advancements in veterinary medicine and surgery). Buys 12-15 unsolicited mss/year. Submit complete ms, but query first on ideas for pieces other than technical or business articles. Pays $50 for first published page; $25 for each additional page.
Photos: B&w glossies (5x7 or larger) and color transparencies (5x7) used with mss. No additional payment.
Tips: "Contact practicing veterinarians or veterinary colleges. Find out what interests the clinician and what new procedures and ideas might be useful in a veterinary practice. Better yet, collaborate with a veterinarian. Most of our authors are veterinarians or those working with veterinarians in a professional capacity. Knowledge of the interests and problems of practicing veterinarians is essential."

VETERINARY COMPUTING, American Veterinary Publications, Inc., Drawer KK, Santa Barbara CA 93102. (800)235-6947 CA, AK or HI (805)963-6561. Editors: Jean Yamamura and Paul Pratt, VMD. 75% freelance written. Prefers to work with published/established writers. Monthly magazine insert covering computer applications in veterinary medicine and practice management. "Our readers are veterinary practitioners who have computers or are thinking about buying them. They are looking for information on the best and most cost-effective ways to purchase and use computers in their practices." Pays on publication. Publishes ms an average of 4 months after acceptance. Byline given. Buys all rights. Submit seasonal/holiday material 3 months in advance. Simultaneous queries and photocopied submissions OK. Electronic submissions OK if 5¼" single-sided disks with an MS DOS WordStar, or any ASCII file, but requires hard copy also. Computer printout submissions acceptable; prefers letter-quality to dot-matrix. Reports in 3 weeks on queries; 1 month on mss. Publishes ms an average of 4 months after acceptance. Sample copy for 9x12 SAE and 3 first class stamps; free writer's guidelines.
Nonfiction: How-to, new product, book and software reviews, and computer-user tips. No profiles or overly philosophical articles. "We want concrete, practical, usable pieces about how practitioners can most effectively use computers in their businesses." Buys 12-24 mss/year. Query or send complete ms (on short articles). Length: 150-2,000 words. Pays $10 (for short tips; $50/first published page, $25 for succeeding full pages for longer articles; printed page equals 3 typed double-spaced pages).
Tips: "Make submissions concise, practical, and usable in plain, nontechnical language. We are especially interested in material on how to use canned software such as Lotus 1-2-3, dBase II and WordStar in a veterinary or similar professional practice. Reviews/articles about canned software and money-saving computer tips are the areas most open to freelancers in our publication. The writer may have a better chance of breaking in short articles and fillers, though length does not matter as much as practicality. The most frequent mistakes made by writers are lack of depth and lack of how-to information (telling what a vet does with the computer without telling how)."

VETERINARY ECONOMICS MAGAZINE, 9073 Lenexa Dr., Lenexa KS 66215. (913)492-4300. Editor: Mike Sollars. 50% freelance written. Prefers to work with published/established writers. Monthly magazine for all practicing veterinarians in the U.S. Buys exclusive rights in the field. Pays on publication. Publishes ms an average of 3 months after acceptance. Computer printout submissions acceptable; prefers letter-quality.
Nonfiction: Uses case histories telling about good business practices on the part of veterinarians. Also, articles about financial problems, investments, insurance and similar subjects of particular interest to professionals. "We reject articles with superficial information about a subject instead of carefully researched and specifically directed articles for our field." Pays negotiable rates. Pays expenses of writers on assignment.

Scriptwriting

"Don't touch the TV screen." You probably heard that warning when you were growing up. But today, for scriptwriters and interactive videodisk users, *touching* is important, though in different ways, for each medium. What all of the following media share is the need for scripts that touch the audience. The dialogue, the characters or narrators, and the setting must create an atmosphere where the audience wants to listen. Media that involve the audience (in a participatory way) more readily hold the audience's attention. Some interactive disk programs, for instance, require that the viewer touch a button *on the screen* to activate them. The writer for stage and screen, on the other hand, must subtly press the audience to feel, think and react emotionally. Some people learn how to write for industry, schools, stage and screen through nonpaying internships or entry-level jobs. The experience can pay off as you gradually switch from understudy to centerstage (at the typewriter or word processor). Before writing a script, ask yourself these questions:

- Who will be your audience?
- What is the purpose of your script?
- Under what circumstances or at what place will the script be produced?
- Who will be paying the bill for the script and its production?
- Will there be producers or companies interested in the script?

Go ahead—touch the screen. Put words on paper. Until you write a script, nobody will be watching *you*.

Business and Educational Writing

"I want to be intrigued in the first ten pages," points out one producer. Most unsolicited scripts or the leads of one-page queries don't do that. Because of the high costs of producing audiovisual materials, producers need scripts that will intrigue their clients and eventually the viewers.

Today's corporations and schools often rely on video to instruct students and employees. People are also using video in their homes to learn new skills like golfing or gourmet cooking. "The expanding home and educational video market provides an excellent opportunity for writers who can produce interesting material with a strong visual slant," says one production manager. "We see this market expanding greatly in the next few years."

An important consideration in writing an instructional script is to design it so an audience might enjoy (and learn from) a second viewing of the film. Especially in the home video market, customers will rent—but not buy—videocassettes that don't have lasting value.

As for nonlinear interactive videodisks, the viewer can learn a skill at his own pace. Such programs enable users to learn a particular aspect of a skill by selecting it on a menu, then touching the screen or appropriate button as directed by the scriptwriter through a computer. In some cases, the viewer is not even aware that the sequence of the film is controlled by a computer (as activated by the viewer). For scriptwriters interested in interactive scripting, knowledge of this field and computer programs is essential.

Some companies, when they contract to have a video program produced, will provide the scriptwriter to work with the audiovisual production company. In addition to pursuing freelance scriptwriting opportunities, the *experienced* scriptwriter might want to contact companies about such possible assignments, especially if you *know* the industry you'd be writing for.

"Your script must meet customer needs more than ever before," points out one educational film producer. The advice certainly isn't new, but with increased competition among media and media firms, those that please the customer get "top billing."

"Clients want choices," says another producer. With the options of film, video, and multi-image productions becoming more affordable, business and education representatives want to choose which medium will best serve their audiences and organization's goals.

To be more competitive in the marketplace, some companies are expanding the media services they offer. Scriptwriters must likewise broaden the range of assignments they handle.

With companies entering the software and cable markets, there is an additional need for freelancers. A square (□) to the left of a listing denotes firms interested in cable TV scripts. Reading each *Writer's Market* listing will tell you what a company wants or doesn't want in scripts.

Become familiar with the particular firm you plan to query. What else have they produced? Arrange for a screening that will help you define their audiences, formats and style. Contact local producers directly. Write to out-of-town firms for a list of their clients in your area. If they are interested in your writing, you may be able to view their AV material at a local company or school that uses it. Be sure that your script idea fits with a company's established image. A résumé that establishes you as a writer and writing samples that prove it are very important in this business. Read carefully the market listings detailing how to make initial contact with a production company. Meeting deadlines and doing quality work are essential.

A.V. MEDIA CRAFTSMAN, INC., Suite 600, 110 E. 23rd St., New York NY 10010. (212)228-6644. President: Carolyn Clark. Produces audio visual training material for corporations and educational material for publishers. Works with New York area writers only. Contracts scripts for 10-15 projects per year. Query with samples and resume. Call later. Samples and resumes kept on file.
Needs: "Most of our projects are 10-15 minute training scripts with related study materials for corporations and educational publishers. We create multi-screen presentations for conferences as well." Produces slide shows, sound filmstrips, videos, multiscreen shows, multimedia kits, overhead transparencies, tapes and cassettes. Pays $350-500 per project.
Tips: "Accept changes, do accurate research, and enjoy the subject matter. Send resume and cover letter. State special areas of interest (ie., economics, science, fashion, health, etc.)."

ADMASTER, INC., 95 Madison Ave., New York NY 10016. (212)679-1134. Director: Charles Corn. Produces sales and training material. Purchases 50-75 scripts/year. Works with 5-10 writers/year. Buys all rights. No previously published material. Reports in 1 month. Free catalog.
Needs: Charts, film loops (16mm), films (35 and 16mm), filmstrips (sound), multimedia kits, overhead transparencies, slides, tapes and cassettes. "We need material for multi-media industrial and financial meetings." Submit synopsis/outline, complete script or resume. Makes outright purchase of $250-500.
Tips: "We want local writers only."

ANIMATION ARTS ASSOCIATES, INC., 1100 E. Hector St., Conshohocken PA 19428. (215)825-8530. Contact: Harry E. Ziegler, Jr. For government, industry, engineers, doctors, scientists, dentists, general public, military. 100% freelance written. Buys average 12 scripts/year.
Needs: Produces 3½-minute 8mm and 16mm film loops; 16mm and 35mm films (ranging from 5-40 minutes); 2¼x2¼ or 4x5 slides; and teaching machine programs for training, sales, industry and public relations. Also produces software—motion picture scripts for training sales promotion and recruitment films. Submit software to Michael Levanios, general manager. Send resume of credits for motion picture and filmstrip pro-

ductions and software. "The writer should have scriptwriting credits for training, sales, promotion and public relations." Payment dependent on client's budget.
Tips: "Send us a resume listing writing and directing credits for films and sound/slide programs."

ARZTCO PICTURES, INC., 15 E. 61st St., New York NY 10021. (212)753-1050. President/Producer: Tony Arzt. Produces material for industrial, education, and home viewing audiences (TV specials and documentaries). 80% freelance written. 75% of scripts produced are unagented submissions. Buys 8-10 scripts/year. Buys all rights. Previously produced material OK ("as sample of work only"). Computer printout submissions acceptable; prefers letter-quality to dot-matrix. SASE, "however, we will only comment in writing on work that interests us." Reports in 3 weeks.
Needs: Business films, sales, training, promotional, educational. "Also interested in low-budget feature film scripts." 16mm and 35mm films, videotapes and cassettes, and software. Submit synopsis/outline or completed script and resume. Pays in accordance with Writers Guild standards.
Tips: "We would like writers to understand that we cannot find time to deal with each individual submission in great detail. If we feel your work is right for us, you will definitely hear from us. We're looking for writers with originality, skill in turning out words, and a sense of humor when appropriate. We prefer to work with writers available in the New York metropolitan area."

AUDIO-VIDEO CORP., 213 Broadway, Menands (Albany) NY 12204. (518)449-7213. Manager of Production Services: Tony Scardillo. Produces material for TV commercial audiences, and sales and informational film screenings. "We purchase 20 scripts annually, with our need increasing." Buys first serial rights. Query with samples or submit resume. Reports in 6 weeks.
Needs: Scripts for 10 to 30 minute programs for audiences ranging from educational, business and consumer groups to nonprofit organizations. "At least half of the material is of a humorous nature, or is otherwise informative and thought-provoking. We seek imagination, motivation, experience, and after receiving numerous responses from this listing, we would prefer to narrow down our writers' file to those in the New York State-New England area. Menands is a suburb of Albany, New York and we will be providing production services to our offices across the rest of the state. While our market primarily encompasses the Northeast, our requirements span a spectrum of subjects. With our recent expansion, we need access to a pool of freelance writers experienced in producing film scripts that are creative and practical." Produces videotapes, multimedia kits and slide sets. Pays $30-80/minute of finished program.
Tips: "The realities of budgets in the current economy naturally restrict production extravaganzas. It is essential to come up with a clever, concise script that lends itself well to the location and studio budget priorities of the project. Having a visual sense is a bonus and sometimes essential for a 'fresh' approach, but inexperience in this realm should not be a restraint to a good writer."

A/V CONCEPTS CORP., 30 Montauk Blvd., Oakdale NY 11769. (516)567-7227. Contact: P. Solimene or K. Brennan. Produces material for elementary-high school students, either on grade level or in remedial situations. 100% freelance written. Works with a small number of new/unpublished writers each year. Buys 25 scripts/year from unpublished/unproduced writers. Employs both filmstrip and personal computer media. Computer printout submissions acceptable. Reports on outline in 1 month; on final scripts in 6 weeks. Buys all rights.
Needs: Interested in original educational computer (disk-based) software programs for Apple plus, 48k. Main concentration in language arts, mathematics and reading. "Manuscripts must be written using our lists of vocabularly words and meet our readability formula requirements. Specific guidelines are devised for each level. Length of manuscript and subjects will vary according to grade level for which material is prepared. Basically, we want material that will motivate people to read." Pays $100 and up.
Tips: "Writers must be highly creative and highly disciplined. We are interested in mature content materials."

BARR FILMS, 3490 E. Foothill Blvd., Pasadena CA 91107. (213)793-6153. Contact: Don Barr or Mark Chodzko. "Produces material for all age levels; grades kindergarten through college level as well as in the public library market to the same age span and adult audience. We also have interest in materials aimed at business and industry/management training programs." 20% freelance written. 100% of scripts produced are unagented submissions. Query with samples. Computer printout submissions acceptable. "We will assign projects to qualified writers. We require previous experience in film writing and want to see samples of films previously written and completed for sale in the market." Buys 2-4 scripts/year. Reports in 1 month. Catalog $1.
Needs: "We produce and distribute 16mm films in all curriculum and subject areas. We prefer a semi-dramatic form of script that entertains and provides information. Avoid excess verbiage—we produce films, not books. The length of our films is 15-24 minutes. We will also consider pure informational subjects with voice over narration. Fees are entirely negotiable. We will accept film treatments and/or completed visual and dialogue scripts. Inquire prior to sending your materials to us."
Tips: "Meet the producer, share previous films, talk film, and be available. Your script must meet customer needs more than ever before."

SAMUEL R. BLATE ASSOCIATES, 10331 Watkins Mill Dr., Gaithersburg MD 20879-2935. (301)840-2248. President: Samuel R. Blate. Produces audiovisual material for business and nearby Washington, D.C. government. "We work with two to six writers per year—it varies as to business conditions and demand." Buys first rights when possible. Electronic submissions OK via CP/M-80, SSDD, Kaypro II. Computer printout submissions acceptable; prefers letter-quality to dot-matrix. Reports in 1 week on queries; 2 weeks on submissions.
Needs: Filmstrips (silent and sound), multimedia kits, slides, and tapes and cassettes. Especially needs short AV productions produced for specific client needs. Query with samples. Payment "depends on type of contract with principal client." Pays expenses of writers on assignment.
Tips: "Writers must have a strong track record of technical and aesthetic excellence. Clarity is not next to divinity—it is above it."

BOARD OF JEWISH EDUCATION OF NEW YORK, 426 W. 58th St., New York NY 10019. (212)245-8200. Director, Division of Multimedia and Materials Development: Yaakov Reshef. Produces material for Jewish schools, youth groups, temples and synagogues; for audience from kindergarten to old age. Buys 12-15 scripts/year. Submit outline/synopsis. Reports in 3 months. Buys first rights or all rights.
Needs: General, educational and informational. "Generally, length is up to 20-25 minutes maximum; most material is geared to 10-12 years old and up. Jewish background needed." Produces sound filmstrips, video 16mm films, tapes and cassettes, and slide sets. Pays 10-15% royalty or $1,000 minimum/outright purchase.

‡BURNS MEDIA, 5550 Main St., Amherst NY 14221. (716)632-1632. President: Jim Burns. Produces material for business, government and consumers. Buys all rights. Reports in 3 weeks.
Needs: Scripts for corporate marketing, employee relations, internal communications, and videotape productions. Produces videotapes. Query with samples. Makes outright purchase.
Tips: "Prior experience with writing scripts for productions described above is a prerequisite. We look for a command of writing in marketing/promotional language and style."

ALDEN BUTCHER PRODUCTIONS, 6331 Hollywood Blvd., Hollywood CA 90028. (213)467-6045. President: Alden Butcher. Produces material for commercial/industrial and entertainment audiences. Contracts for 20 scripts/year. Deals mainly with local clients. Uses *only* local writers. Buys all rights. Computer printout submissions acceptable.
Needs: "Our needs depend upon contracts closed." Produces multimedia slide shows, film and video programs. Looks for "the ability to easily communicate with an industrial client and translate that into a script that meets their communication objectives the first time." Query with samples and resume. Pays "according to production budget on an individual basis."
Tips: "Clients are looking more and more for a production company to provide creative approaches as a part of a bidding process. Often it is important for a writer to volunteer to be involved in this speculative process prior to writing the actual script. This way they can help develop the style and approach."

CABSCOTT BROADCAST PRODUCTION, INC., 517 7th Ave., Lindenwold NJ 08021. (609)346-3400. Contact: Larry Scott/Anne Foster. Produces industrial and broadcast material. 10% freelance written. Works with a small number of new/unpublished writers each year. Buys 10-12 scripts/year. Buys all rights. No previously produced material. Electronic submissions OK via Apple MacIntosh or Apple III, but requires hard copy also. Computer printout submissions acceptable; prefers letter-quality to dot-matrix. Reports in 1 month. Free catalog.
Needs: Tapes and cassettes and video. Query with samples. Makes outright purchase. Sometimes pays expenses of writers on assignment.

CATHEDRAL FILMS, INC., Suite I, 5310 Derry, Agoura CA 91301. (818)991-3290. Contact: Scott Miller. Produces material for church and school audiences. Works with variable number of writers/year. Buys all rights and AV rights. Previously produced material OK "except from other AV media." Reports in 1 month on queries; 2 months on mss. Catalog for SAE and 54¢ postage.
Needs: Various Christian, religious, educational and/or dramatic material. All ages. Produces 16mm films, sound filmstrips and video. Submit synopsis/outline or complete script. Pays variable rates.

CLEARVUE, INC., 5711 N. Milwaukee Ave., Chicago IL 60646. (312)775-9433. President: W.O. McDermed. Produces material for educational market—grades kindergarten-12. 90% freelance written. Prefers to work with published/established writers; works with a small number of new/unpublished writers each year. Buys 20-50 scripts/year from previously unpublished/unproduced writers. Buys all rights. Previously produced material OK. Electronic submissions OK, but requires hard copy also. Computer printout submissions acceptable; prefers letter-quality to dot-matrix. Reports in 2 weeks on queries; 3 weeks on submissions. Free catalog.
Needs: Filmstrips (silent), filmstrips (sound), multimedia kits, and slides. "Our filmstrips are 35 to 100

frames—8 to 30 minutes for all curriculum areas." Query. Makes outright purchase, $100-5,000. Sometimes pays the expenses of writers on assignment.

Tips: "Our interests are in filmstrips and video for the elementary and high school markets on all subjects."

‡COMPASS FILMS, 6 Florence Ln., Newton NJ 07860. Executive Producer: Robert Whittaker. Produces material for educational, industrial and general adult audiences. Specializes in Marine films, stop motion and special effects with a budget . . . and worldwide filming in difficult locations. 60% freelance written. Works with 4 writers/year. Buys 2-4 scripts/year from unpublished/unproduced writers. 60% of scripts are unagented submissions. Query with samples or submit resume. Computer printout submissions acceptable. Reports in 6 weeks. Buys all rights.

Needs: Scripts for 10- to 30-minute business films, and general documentary and theatrical feature films. "We would like to consider theatrical stories for possible use for feature films. We also would like to review writers to develop existing film treatments and ideas with strong dialogue." Also needs (ghost writers) editors and researchers. Produces 16mm and 35mm films. Payment negotiable, depending on experience. Sometimes pays expenses of writers on assignment.

Tips: Writer/photographers receive higher consideration "because we could also use them as still photographers on location and they could double-up as rewrite men and ladies. Experience in videotape editing supervision an asset. We are producing more high 'fashion-tech' industrial video."

‡COMPRENETICS, INC., Suite 102, 1448 Fifteenth St., Santa Monica CA 90404. (213)395-9238. President: Ira Englander. 10% freelance written. Prefers to work with published/established writers. "Target audience varies, however, programs are designed for health care audiences only. This ranges from entry level health workers with minimal academic background to continuing education programs for physicians and health professionals. In the cultural area, all levels." Produces material for video—creatively adapting subject matter treatments. Buys approximately 10-20 scripts/year. All scripts are unagented submissions. Query with samples or submit resume. Computer printout submissions acceptable; prefers letter-quality to dot-matrix. Reports in 1 month. Buys all rights. Sometimes pays the expenses of writers on assignment.

Needs: "Films are generally 10 to 20 minutes in length and tend to have a dramatic framework. Subject topics include all educational areas with emphasis on health and medical films, manpower and management training and multi-cultural education. Our staff normally does subject matter research and content review which is provided for the writer who is then required to provide us with an outline or film treatment for review. Due to the extensive review procedures, writers are frequently required to modify through three or four drafts before final approval." Produces sound filmstrips, 16mm films, and tapes and cassettes. Pays $1,000-5,000.

‡COMPRO PRODUCTIONS, Suite 114, 2080 Peachtree Ind. Court, Atlanta GA 30341. (404)455-1943. Producers: Nels Anderson and Steve Brinson. Audience is general public and specific business audience. Buys 10-25 scripts/year. Buys all rights. No previously produced material. No unsolicited material; submissions will not be returned because "all work is contracted."

Needs: "We solicit writers for corporate films/video in the areas of training, point purchase, sales, how-to, benefit programs, resorts and colleges." Produces 16-35mm films and videotapes. Query with samples. Makes outright purchase or pays cost per minute.

CONCEPT 80's, 3409 West Chester Pike, Newtown Square PA 19073. (215)353-5900. Marketing Manager/Producer: Jim Higgins, Jr. Produces material for primarily corporate audiences—approximately 75% technical/industrial, 25% consumer organizations—mostly management, sales force or distributors. Buys 20-25 scripts/year. Buys all rights. No previously produced material. Computer printout submissions acceptable. Reports in several weeks. Catalog for SAE with 1 first class stamp.

Needs: Charts, silent and sound filmstrips, multimedia kits, overhead transparencies, slides, videotape presentations, and multi-image. "Most projects develop, are produced and delivered within 4-6 weeks." Query with samples or submit resume. Pays by outright purchase, $200-1,000.

Tips: "Writers should have written for audiovisual or print at least 10-20 successful scripts for blue chip corporations."

CONDYNE/THE OCEANA GROUP, 75 Main St., Dobbs Ferry NY 10522. (914)693-5944. Vice President: Yvonne Heenan. Produces material for legal market, and business and CPA markets. Works with 10-20 writers/year; buys 20 scripts/year. Buys all rights. No previously produced material. Electronic submissions OK via IBM PC. Dot-matrix submissions acceptable. Reports in 2 weeks on queries; 2 months on submissions. Catalog for 7x10 SAE and 3 first class stamps.

Needs: Tapes and cassettes, and video (Betamax). "We are looking for video, ½ hour to one hour length—preview in ½" Beta II, practical, how-to for legal market (lawyers in practice, law students)." Query with samples, submit synopsis/outline, resume or preview tape and synopsis/outline. No phone calls accepted. All submissions must be in writing. Pays royalty or makes outright purchase; $250-500 for audio scripts, depending on qualifications; 10% royalty.

Tips: "We are especially interested in original software programs for lawyers and interactive videodisks (legal how-to) and video."

CONSOLIDATED/MEDIA, Box 6834, Jacksonville FL 32205. (904)389-4541. Vice President: Donald E. Barton. Produces material for various audiences. 70% freelance written. Buys 4 scripts/year from unpublished writers. 100% of scripts are unagented submissions. Works with average of 6 writers/year. Buys all rights. Computer printout submissions acceptable; prefers letter-quality to dot-matrix. Reports in 1 month.
Needs: Sports films, health care, TV commercials, documentary and sales—motivation, material—16mm films and video tapes. Query with samples. Also produces scripts for videos. Pays $850-5,000. Pays expenses of writers on assignment.

CORONADO STUDIOS, #600, 3550 Biscayne Blvd., Miami FL 33137. (305)573-7250. President: Fred L. Singer. Produces material for the general public, various specialized audiences. Buys 50 commercials/year; 15 corporate films/year. "We commission custom scripts that have no value to anyone but our clients." Computer printout submissions acceptable. Reports in 2 weeks on queries; 1 month on submissions.
Needs: "We will need an indeterminate number of scripts for commercials and corporate films." Produces 16mm films and video tapes. Query with samples. Pays by outright purchase; "depends on nature of job."

CORPORATE COMMUNICATIONS, INC., 2950 E. Jefferson Ave., Detroit MI 48207. (313)259-3585. Administrative Manager: Patrick Longe. Produces commercial and industrial material. Works with 15-20 writers/year. Buys all rights. No previously published materal.
Needs: Films (16 and 35mm), multimedia kits and slides. Send resume and samples for reference. Pays per project.

CP FILMS, INC., 4431 N. 60th Ave., Omaha NE 68104. (402)453-3200. President: G. Pflaum. Produces religious education material. 100% freelance written. Eager to work with new/unpublished writers. Works with 4 writers/year. Buys 2-3 scripts/year from previously unpublished/unproduced writers. Buys one-time rights, simultaneous, second serial and first serial rights. Accepts previously produced material. Electronic submissions OK via TRS-80 Scripsit. Computer printout submissions acceptable; prefers letter-quality to dot-matrix. Reports in 1 month. Free catalog.
Needs: Tapes and cassettes (video and audio). Produces video scripts for religious education, classroom education, and one person teleplays. Will accept material from other mediums (radio, short story, stage) if author interested in adapting to video play. Submit complete script on detailed video treatment. Pays royalty; 6-10% on wholesale price of video cassette.
Tips: "The educational video market requires the production of material be budgeted at no more than $10-20,000 for production costs."

THE CREATIVE ESTABLISHMENT, 115 W. 31st St., New York NY 10001. (212)563-3337. Vice President, Creative Services: Dale Wilson. Produces material for business meetings and corporate management audiences. 45% freelance written. Prefers to work with published/established writers; works with a small number of new/unpublished writers each year. 95% of scripts produced are unagented submissions. Works with approximately 25 writers/year. Buys all rights. Electronic submissions OK. Computer printout submissions acceptable; prefers letter-quality to dot-matrix. "We don't return unsolicited material; material is held on file. Writing assignments are always specific to project. We cannot predict future needs."
Needs: Multi-image, live shows, videotapes and films. Submit samples and resume. Pays by outright purchase. Sometimes pays the expenses of writers on assignment.
Tips: "We would like all our writers to be able to communicate with us through computer modem."

NICHOLAS DANCY PRODUCTIONS, INC., 333 W. 39th St., New York NY 10018. (212)564-9140. President: Nicholas Dancy. Produces media material for corporate communications, general audiences, employees, members of professional groups, members of associations and special customer groups. 60% freelance written. Prefers to work with published/established writers. Buys 5-10 scripts/year; works with 5-10 writers/year. None of scripts are unagented submissions. Buys all rights. Reports in 1 month. Electronic submissions OK. Computer printout submissions acceptable; prefers letter-quality to dot-matrix.
Needs: "We use scripts for videotapes or films from 5 minutes to 1 hour for corporate communications, sales, orientation, training, corporate image, medical and documentary." Format: videotape, 16mm films and slide tape. Query with resume. "No unsolicited material. Our field is too specialized." Pays by outright purchase of $800-5,000. Pays expenses of writers on assignment.
Tips: "Writers should have a knowledge of business and industry and professions, an ability to work with clients and communicators, a fresh narrative style, creative use of dialogue, good skills in accomplishing research, and a professional approach to production. New concept trends are important in business video—rock music formats are declining in interest. We're looking for new areas."

□**NORM DREW ENTERTAINMENT FEATURES**, Suite 608-L, Laurier House, 1600 Beach Ave., Vancouver, British Columbia V6G 1Y6 Canada. Contact: Norm Drew. Produces material for advertising, training and entertainment. "I create, produce, and distribute educational and entertainment features in animated film/video, book, comic strip AV slide, or puppet forms." 75% freelance written. Works with a small number of new/unpublished writers each year. Buys 10% of scripts/year from previously unpublished writers. Buys all rights. Computer printout submissions acceptable; no dot-matrix. Send SAE with IRC for guidelines.
Needs: Looking for fresh, original ½ or 1 hour TV special animated feature script for our cartoon characters, CHIKA, and THE BUSH BABIES. Produces scripts for video; and humor and animation for cable TV. Uses both contemporary themes and traditional values. Query first with resume. Do not send scripts. Pays negotiable fee.
Tips: "We forsee an increased need for interactive slide and videodisk programming."

DUBOIS/RUDDY, 2145 Crooks, Troy MI 48084. (313)643-0320. Vice President: Chris Ruddy. Produces material for corporations. Works with 20-30 writers/year. Buys all rights. No previously produced material. Query with resume. No scripts.
Needs: Multi-image and film production. Makes outright purchase; payment negotiable.
Tips: "We will use local writers only. Call and make an appointment."

THE DURASELL CORPORATION, 360 Lexington Ave., New York NY 10017. President: Albert A. Jacoby. Produces AV and video multi-media sales and marketing corporation material for sales presentations, meetings, and training programs—primarily for consumer package goods companies. 100% freelance written. Does not buy scripts from unpublished/unproduced writers. All scripts produced are unagented submissions. Buys 30-50 scripts/year; works with 6-10 writers/year. Buys all rights. Computer printout submissions acceptable; prefers letter-quality to dot-matrix.
Needs: Video, meetings, slides and tapes. Send letter and resume. Pays by outright purchase. ("Freelancer sets fee.")

EDUCATIONAL IMAGES LTD., Box 3456, Elmira NY 14905. (607)732-1090. Executive Director: Dr. Charles R. Belinky. Produces material (sound filmstrips, multimedia kits and slide sets) for schools, kindergarten through college and graduate school, public libraries, parks, nature centers, etc. Also produces science-related software material. Buys 50 scripts/year. Buys all AV rights. Computer printout submissions OK. Free catalog.
Needs: Slide sets and filmstrips on science, natural history, anthropology and social studies. "We are looking primarily for complete AV programs; we will consider slide collections to add to our files. This requires high quality, factual text and pictures." Query with a meaningful sample of proposed program. Pays $150 minimum.
Tips: The writer/photographer is given high consideration. "Once we express interest, follow up. Potential contributors lose many sales to us by not following up on initial query. Don't waste our time and yours if you can't deliver."

EDUCATIONAL INSIGHTS, 19560 S. Ranch Way, Dominquez Hills CA 90220. (213)637-2131. Director of Development: Dennis J. Graham. Educational publisher. 30% freelance written. Averages 50 titles/year. Buys 6 scripts/year from unpublished/unproduced writers. 90% of scripts are unagented submissions. Pays 5% minimum royalty; buys some mss outright. No advance. Simultaneous and photocopied submissions OK. Computer printout submissions acceptable; prefers letter-quality to dot-matrix. Reports in 1 month. Free catalog.
Needs: Educational areas. Query or submit outline/synopsis and sample chapters or script.

EFC, INC., 5101 F Backlick Rd., Box 1017, Annandale VA 22003. (703)750-0560. Vice President/Script Development: Ruth Pollak. Produces dramatic and documentary film and video for commercial, government, broadcast, schools and communities. 80% freelance written. Buys scripts from published/produced writers only. 50% of scripts produced are unagented submissions. Buys all rights. Computer printout submissions acceptable; prefers letter-quality to dot-matrix. Reports in 1 month.
Needs: Strong dramatic screenplays, especially for family/children audience. Query with samples. Makes outright purchase or pays by commercial arrangement. Pays expenses of writers on assignment.

EFFECTIVE COMMUNICATION ARTS, INC., 221 W. 57th St., New York NY 10019. (212)333-5656. Vice President: W.J. Comcowich. Produces films, videotapes and interactive videodisks for physicians, nurses and medical personnel. Prefers to work with published/established writers. 80% freelance written. Buys approximately 2 scripts/year. Electronic submissions OK via direct modem or MCI mailbox. Computer printout submissions acceptable; prefers letter-quality to dot-matrix. Buys all rights. Reports in 1 month.
Needs: Multimedia kits, 16mm films, television shows/series, videotape presentations, and interactive vi-

□*Open box preceding a listing indicates a cable TV market.*

deodisks. Currently interested in about 15 films, videotapes for medical audiences; 6 interactive disks for medical audience, 3 interactive disks for point-of-purchase. Submit complete script and resume. Makes outright purchase or negotiates rights. Pays expenses of writers on assignment.
Tips: "Videotape scripts on technical subjects are becoming increasingly important. Explain what the film accomplishes—how it is better than the typical."

EMC CORP., 300 York Ave., St. Paul MN 55101. Editor: Eileen Slater. Produces material for children and teenagers in the primary grades through high school. "We sell strictly to schools and public libraries." Software submissions accepted; educational (most subject areas). 100% freelance written by published/produced writers. All scripts produced are unagented submissions. Buys 2-3 scripts/year. Buys world rights. Electronic submissions OK via Apple IIC, TRS-80 III. Computer printout submissions acceptable; prefers letter-quality to dot-matrix. Catalog for 9x12 SASE.
Needs: Career education, consumer education, and special education (as related to language arts especially). "No standard requirements, due to the nature of educational materials publishing." No religious topics. Query with resume and one or more samples of previously produced work. No unsolicited manuscripts accepted. Payment varies.

MARTIN EZRA & ASSOCIATES, 48 Garrett Rd., Upper Darby PA 19082. (215)352-9595 or 9596. Producer: Martin Ezra. Produces material for business, industry and education. Works with 4-5 writers/year. Buys all rights and first rights. Reports in 3 weeks.
Needs: Educational and informational work. Film loops, films, silent filmstrips, videotapes, sound filmstrips, multimedia kits, slides, and tapes and cassettes. Query with samples or submit complete script "in writing only." Payment varies with project.

FIRE-PREVENTION THROUGH FILMS, INC., Box 11, Newton Highlands MA 02161. (617)965-4444. Manager: Julian Olansky. Produces material for audiences involved with fire prevention and general safety: grades kindergarten through 12; colleges and universities; laboratories; industry and home safety. 50% freelance written. Works with a small number of new/unpublished writers each year. Purchases 1-3 scripts/year. "We work with several local script writers on a yearly basis." Buys all rights. No previously produced material. Computer printout submissions acceptable; prefers letter-quality to dot-matrix. Reports in 3 weeks. Free catalog.
Needs: Films (16mm). "We will need scripts for films dealing with general safety in an office setting (20 minutes.) Will consider any script dealing with fire prevention and/or general safety (20 minute film or less)." Query with or without samples. Makes outright purchase.

FLIPTRACK LEARNING SYSTEMS, Division of Mosaic Media, Inc., 999 Main, Glen Ellyn IL 60137. (312)790-1117. Publisher: F. Lee McFadden. Produces training media for microcomputer equipment and business software. Works with a small number of new/unpublished writers each year. 40% freelance written. Buys 5 courses/year; 2-3 from unpublished/unproduced writers. All courses published are unagented submissions. Works with 8-10 writers/year. Buys all rights. Electronic submissions OK via IBM PC, Hayes modem, prefers WordStar or Multimate; requires hard copy also. Computer printout submissions OK. Reports in 3 weeks. Free product literature.
Needs: Computer courses on disk, video or audio geared to the adult or mature student in a business setting and to the first-time microcomputer user. Produces audio, video, CBT and reference manuals. Query with resume and samples if available. Pays negotiable royalty; makes some outright purchases. Sometimes pays expenses of writers on assignment.
Tips: "We would like to move from primarily audio-based courseware into audio and computer-based-training. We prefer to work with Chicago-area and mid-western writers."

FLORIDA PRODUCTION CENTER, 150 Riverside Ave., Jacksonville FL 32202. (904)354-7000. Vice President: L.J. Digiusto. Produces audiovisual material for general, corporate and government audiences. Buys all rights. No previously produced material.
Needs: Films (16mm), filmstrips (silent and sound), multimedia kits, overhead transparencies, slides, tapes and cassettes, teaching machine programs, and videos. Query with samples and resume. Makes negotiable outright purchase.

PAUL FRENCH & PARTNERS, INC., Rt. 5, Gabbettville Rd., LaGrange GA 30240. (404)882-5581. Contact: Gene Byrd. 20% freelance written. Computer printout submissions acceptable. Reports in 2 weeks. Buys all rights.
Needs: Wants to see multi-screen scripts (all employee attitude related) and/or multi-screen AV sales meeting scripts or resumes. Produces silent and sound filmstrips, video tapes and cassettes, and slides. Query or submit resume. Pays in outright purchase of $500-5,000. Payment is in accordance with Writers Guild standards.

FRIED PRODUCTIONS, 768 Farmington Ave., Farmington CT 06032. (203)674-8221. President: Joel Fried. Executive Producer: Roy Shaw. Production Assistant: David Shearer. "We produce programs that are

aimed at the high school/college/cable TV market." Buys all rights. Query; "tell us what your idea is and why you can write on this particular subject." Electronic submissions OK. Computer printout submissions acceptable.
Needs: "Education is very important to us. You should be familiar with the market and what subjects are of interest to today's students. We are open to any good idea. Original script ideas for cable production also of interest." Buys 20-40 scripts. Subjects include vocational education and academics, chemistry, career awareness, physics and biology, horticulture, sex education—just about any area. Produces videotapes, 6mm sound filmstrips, overhead transparencies, slides, study prints, teaching machine programs, and multimedia kits. Pays by cash and/or royalty.
Tips: "Let us hear your ideas. All queries are answered."

‡□GATEWAY PRODUCTIONS INC., 304 E. 45th St., New York NY 10017. (212)286-0770. Produces material for corporate communications, over-the-air commercial television, cable and the international business community. Buys "non-theatrical rights under corporation client's name."
Needs: "Scripts are developed through research of each client's needs. Length is usually 10-30 minutes. Subject matter and style vary." Produces 16mm films and video. Submit resume. Payment is "based on overall production budget and negotiation of flat fee."
Tips: Interested in "strong visualization capability, fresh concepts, research capability, client rapport and especially professionalism. Most people who write for us come to us through referrals and are actually working in the New York metropolitan area."

GESSLER PUBLISHING CO., INC., Gessler Educational Software, 900 Broadway, New York NY 10003. (212)673-3113. President: Seth C. Levin. Produces material for students learning ESL and foreign languages. 50% freelance written. Eager to work with new/unpublished writers. Buys about 60-75 scripts/year. 100% of scripts are unagented submissions. Prefers to buy all rights, but will work on royalty basis. Do not send disk submission without documentation. Electronic submissions OK on Apple IIe/c, C-64/128, IBM PC/PCjr; requires hard copy also. Computer printout submissions acceptable; prefers letter-quality to dot-matrix. Reports in 3 weeks on queries; 2 months on submissions.
Needs: Filmstrips "to create an interest in learning a foreign language and its usefulness in career objectives; also culturally insightful filmstrips on French, German, Italian and Spanish speaking countries." Produces sound filmstrips, multimedia kits, overhead transparencies, games, realia, tapes and cassettes, computer software. Also produces scripts for videos. Submit synopsis/outline or software with complete documentation, introduction, objectives. Makes outright purchase and pays royalties.
Tips: "Be organized in your presentation; be creative but keep in mind that your audience is primarily junior/senior high school students. We will be looking for new filmstrips, videotapes, software and videodisks which can be used in foreign language and ESL classes."

GRIFFIN MEDIA DESIGN, 802 Wabash Ave., Chesterton IN 46304. (219)926-8602. Assistant Administrator: C. Rogers. Produces variety of business and industrial accounts, specifically for the development of advertising, public relations, training programs, marketing, conventions, etc. "We may buy as few as 10 to 50 projects per year." Buys all rights. No previously produced material. Reports on queries in 3 weeks. Catalog for 9x12 SAE and 2 first class stamps.
Needs: Films, filmstrips (sound), multimedia kits, overhead transparencies, slides, and tapes and cassettes. Query with samples. Makes outright purchase.
Tips: "Potential contributors should make themselves known. It's just as hard for businesses to find good writers as it is for good writers to find work."

HAYES SCHOOL PUBLISHING CO., INC., 321 Pennwood Ave., Wilkinsburg PA 15221. (412)371-2373. 2nd Vice President: Clair N. Hayes, III. Produces material for school teachers, principals, elementary through high school. Also produces charts, workbooks, teacher's handbooks, posters, bulletin board material, educational software, and liquid duplicating books (grades kindergarten through 12). 25% freelance written. Prefers to work with published/established writers; works with a small number of new/unpublished writers each year. Buys 5-10 scripts/year from unpublished/unproduced writers. 100% of scripts produced are unagented submissions. Buys all rights. Electronic submissions OK via Apple IIe. Computer printout submissions acceptable; prefers letter-quality to dot-matrix. Catalog for 3 first class stamps.
Needs: Educational material only. Particularly interested in educational material for high school level. Query. Pays $25 minimum.

ICOM INC., 278 N. 5th St., Columbus OH 43215. (614)224-4400. President: Phil Yoder. Produces material for corporate customers, sales people and employees. Buys 40 scripts/year. Buys all rights. Electronic submissions OK via IBM PC WordStar or 8" WordStar. Computer printout submissions acceptable; no dot-matrix except for rough drafts. Reports in 2 weeks on query; 1 month on submissions.
Needs: Multimedia kits, slides, videotape presentations, and multi-image. Currently interested in hi-tech, business and sales presentations; training programs. Submit resume. Makes outright purchase $300-2,000.

IDEAL SCHOOL SUPPLY CO., 11000 S. Lavergne Ave., Oak Lawn IL 60453. (312)425-0800. Vice President, Marketing: Barbara Stiles. Produces material for preschool, primary and elementary students. "The majority of our product line comes from outside sources, most of them practicing classroom teachers. Occasionally these products are edited by freelance talent." 0-5% freelance written. Buys 25 scripts/year from unpublished/unproduced writers. 98% of scripts are unagented submissions. Computer printout submissions acceptable; no dot-matrix. Free catalog.
Needs: Style, length and format vary according to grade level and subject matter of material. Produces manipulatives, games, models, printed material, multimedia kits and cassette programs. Other freelance needs are for occasional writing, editing, and proofreading educational copy in the form of product directions, manuscript, packaging, etc. Writers and editors are also used for some special development projects. Query with resume which will be filed for future reference.

‡IMAGE INNOVATIONS, INC., 14 Buttonwood Dr., Somerset NJ 08873. President: Mark A. Else. Produces material for business, education and general audiences. 100% freelance written. "Credentials and reputation means much—published or unpublished." Buys 15-20 scripts/year from previously unpublished/unproduced writers. All scripts produced are unagented submissions. Computer printout submissions acceptable; prefers letter-quality to dot-matrix. Reports in 2 weeks.
Needs: Subject topics include education, sales and public relations. Produces sound filmstrips, 16mm films, multimedia kits, 1 inch and ¾-inch video, and tapes and cassettes. Query with samples. Pays in outright purchase of $500-5,000. Sometimes pays the expenses of writers on assignment.

IMAGE MEDIA, 1362 LaSalle Ave., Minneapolis MN 55403. (612)872-0578. Creative Director: A.M. Rifkin. Query with samples. Reports in 2 weeks. Rights purchased "depend on project."
Needs: Produces silent and sound filmstrips, 16mm films, tapes and cassettes and slides. Pays in outright purchase.

‡IMAGES, INC., 1662 Stockton St., Jacksonville FL 32204. (904)388-3300. Vice President of Production: Mark Grandin. Audience is the clients and employees of corporations. Works with 10 writers annually; buys 3-5 scripts/year. Buys all rights. No previously produced material. Reports on queries in 1 month.
Needs: "We produce corporate business communications for Fortune 500 companies. Subjects include corporate culture, employee motivation, training, marketing, public relations and direct sales presentations." Produces sound filmscripts, multimedia kits, slides, tapes, cassettes, and multi-image film and video tape. Query with samples. Payment negotiated on a per job basis.

IMPERIAL INTERNATIONAL LEARNING CORP., 329 E. Court St., Kankakee IL 60901. (815)933-7735. Editor: Patsy Gunnels. Material intended for kindergarten through grade 12 audience. 60% freelance written. Prefers to work with published/established writers; works with a small number of new/unpublished writers each year. Buys 2-4 scripts/year from unpublished/unproduced writers. Buys all rights. No previously produced material. Electronic submissions OK via Apple, IBM PC, TRS-80, Commodore 64, with at least 48K. Computer printout submissions acceptable. Reports in 2 weeks on queries; 1 month on submissions. Free catalog.
Needs: "Supplemental learning materials of various lengths in the areas of reading, math, social studies, and science with emphasis on using the microcomputer or videotape programs." Produces silent filmstrips, tapes and cassettes, and microcomputer and videotape. Query with samples or submit complete script and resume. Pays negotiable rates.
Tips: "We are interested in software, interactive videodisks, and videotape programs that meet curricular needs in the math, science, language arts, social studies, and special education classroom."

INDUSTRIAL MEDIA, INC., 6660 28th St. SE, Grand Rapids MI 49506. (616)949-7770. Contact: Ed Anderson. Produces instructional aids for vocational schools and industrial in-plant training programs. 50% freelance written. Buys 1 script/year from unpublished/unproduced writers. 2 scripts are unagented submissions. Buy all rights "usually, but other arrangements are possible." Computer printout submissions acceptable; prefers letter-quality to dot-matrix. Catalog for 1 first class stamp.
Needs: Slide/cassette and video presentations coordinated with student workbooks and instruction guides for industrial training. "We specialize in materials for training industrial equipment maintenance personnel and apprentices. Topics of particular interest to our customers include: Industrial electricity, electronics, hydraulics, mechanical maintenance, blueprint reading, welding, safety, and management skills for plant supervisors. We will consider any topic with broad application in manufacturing training. We prefer to work with writers who can develop an entire, self-contained package, complete with performance objectives, script, workbooks, instruction guide and testing materials." Pays expenses of writers on assignment.

INSIGHT! INC., 100 E. Ohio St., Chicago IL 60611. (312)467-4350. President: Neal Cochran. Produces material for all audiences, depending on type of client. 90% freelance written. Buys scripts from produced writers

only. All scripts produced by contract. Buys over 200 scripts/year from more than 30 writers. Buys all rights. Electronic submissions OK via modem ASCOM CP/M or 5¼" disk Apple II+ or Eagle II. Computer printout submissions acceptable.
Needs: "Our needs depend on contracts awarded to Insight! Films, videotapes, filmstrips and, most important, industrial shows of all types." Produces 16mm films, multimedia and "book" shows. No educational materials. Concentrates entirely on film, video and shows. Query with samples. Pays by outright purchase.

INSTRUCTOR BOOKS, 545 5th Ave., New York NY 10176. Director: Judy Cohn. "U.S. and Canadian school supervisors, principals, and teachers purchase items in our line for instructional purposes." 50% freelance written. Buys 6 scripts/year from unpublished/unproduced writers. Most scripts produced are unagented submissions. Buys all rights. Writer should have "experience in preparing materials for elementary students, including suitable teaching guides to accompany them, and demonstrate knowledge of the appropriate subject areas, or demonstrate ability for accurate and efficient research and documentation." Computer printout submissions acceptable; no dot-matrix. Free catalog.
Needs: Elementary curriculum enrichment—all subject areas. Display material, copy and illustration should match interest and reading skills of children in grades for which material is intended. Production is limited to printed matter: resource handbooks, teaching guides and idea books. Length: 6,000-12,000 words. Query. Standard contract, but fees vary considerably, depending on type of project. Sometimes pays the expenses of writers on assignment.
Tips: "Writers who reflect current educational practices can expect to sell to us."

INTERAND CORPORATION, 3200 W. Peterson Ave., Chicago IL 60659. Currently staff written.

☐**INTERNATIONAL MEDIA SERVICES INC.**, 718 Sherman Ave., Plainfield NJ 07060. (201)756-4060. President/General Manager: Stuart Allen. Produces varied material depending on assignment or production in house; includes corporate, public relations, sales, radio/TV, CATV, teleconferencing/CCTV, etc. 60-75% freelance written. 90% of scripts produced are unagented submissions. "We normally issue assignments to writers in the freelance market who specialize in appropriate fields of interest." Buys all rights. No previously produced material. Computer printout submissions acceptable. Reporting time varies depending on job requirements and specifications.
Needs: Charts, dioramas, 8/16mm film loops, 16/35mm films, silent and sound filmstrips, kinescopes, multimedia kits, overhead transparencies, phonograph records, slides, tapes and cassettes, television shows/series, and videotape presentations. "We routinely hire writers from a freelance resource file." Cable TV needs include educational and entertainment marketplaces. Query with or without samples, or submit synopsis/outline and resume. "All work must be copyrighted and be original unpublished works." Pays in accordance with Writers Guild standards, negotiated contract or flat rate.
Tips: "We are not responsible for unsolicited material and recommend not submitting complete manuscripts for review without prior arrangement."

☐**PAUL S. KARR PRODUCTIONS**, 2949 W. Indian School Rd., Box 11711, Phoenix AZ 85017. Utah Division: 1024 N. 250 E., Box 1254, Orem UT 84057. (801)226-8209, (602)266-4198. Produces film and videos for industry, business and education. *"Do not submit material unless requested."* Buys all rights. Works on coproduction ventures that have been funded.
Needs: Produces 16mm films and videos. Query. Payment varies.
Tips: "One of the best ways for a writer to become a screenwriter is to create a situation with a client that requires a film or video. He then can assume the position of an associate producer, work with an experienced professional producer in putting the production into being, and in that way learn about filmmaking and chalk up some meaningful credits."

KEN-DEL PRODUCTIONS, INC., 111 Valley Rd., Wilmington DE 19804-1397. (302)655-7488. President: Ed Kennedy. Produces material for "elementary, junior high, high school and college level, as well as interested organizations and companies."
Needs: "Topics of the present (technology, cities, traffic, transit, pollution, ecology, health, water, race, genetics, consumerism, fashions, communications, education, population control, waste, future sources of food, undeveloped sources of living, food, health, etc.); topics of the future; how-to series (everything for the housewife, farmer, banker or mechanic, on music, art, sports, reading, science, love, repair, sleep—on any subject); and material handling." Produces sound filmstrips; 8mm, 16mm, and 35mm films; 16mm film loops; phonograph records; prerecorded tapes and cassettes; slides and videotapes in ¾" U-matic, ½" VHS, ½" BETA cassettes. Query.

KIMBO EDUCATIONAL-UNITED SOUND ARTS, INC., 10-16 N. 3rd Ave., Box 477, Long Branch NJ 07740. (201)229-4949. Contact: James Kimble or Amy Laufer. Produces materials for the educational market (early childhood, special education, music, physical education, dance, and preschool children 6 months and up). 50% freelance written. Buys approximately 12-15 scripts/year; works with approximately 12-15 writers/year. Buys 5 scripts/year from unpublished/unproduced writers. Most scripts are unagented submissions. Buys all rights or first rights. Previously produced material OK "in some instances." Reports in 1 month. Free catalog.

Needs: "For the next two years we will be concentrating on general early childhood movement oriented products, new albums in the fitness field and more. Each will be an album/cassette with accompanying teacher's manual and, if warranted, manipulatives." Phonograph records and cassettes; "all with accompanying manual or teaching guides." Query with samples and synopsis/outline or completed script. Pays 5-7% royalty on lowest wholesale selling price, and by outright purchase. Both negotiable. Sometimes pays expenses of writers on assignment.

Tips: "We look for creativity first. Having material that is educationally sound is also important. Being organized is certainly helpful. Fitness is growing rapidly in popularity and will always be a necessary thing. Children will always need to be taught the basic fine and gross motor skills. Capturing interest while reaching these goals is the key."

☐**KOCH/MARSCHALL PRODUCTIONS, INC.,** 1718 N. Mohawk St., Chicago IL 60614. (312)664-6482. Executive Producer: Salley E. Marschall. Produces material for general library audience, high school or college, and mass audience. 20% freelance written. "We read more than a hundred scripts a year. We may buy one a year. We work with one writer at a time." Buys all rights. No previously produced material. Reports in 2 months on queries; 3 months on submissions.

Needs: Produces 16 and 35mm films. "We are looking for feature film ideas that have comedic potential. These can be historical, comtemporary, musical, theatrical, European, American, romantic, thrilling, and/or mysterious." Produces feature-length comedy material for cable TV. "We negotiate payment with each writer."

Tips: "We are looking for original, innovative, nonexploitational, nonderivative screenplays. No first drafts, no student theses. Screenplays must be intelligent, provocative and exciting. Writers must be well-educated, experienced in film writing, and compatible with a team of filmmakers."

DETRICK LAWRENCE, 580 Tremon St., Box 1722, Duxbury MA 02331. (617)934-6561. Executive Producer: Gordon Massingham. Produces television, educational and corporate material. Works with two writers regularly. Purchases average of seven scripts, most of which are commissioned. Buys all rights. No previously produced material. Reports in 3 weeks on queries; 5 weeks on submissions.

Needs: Film (16, 35mm); filmstrips (sound); slides; and tapes and cassettes. Query. Makes outright purchase or option.

Tips: "We look for a proven record of success, timeliness and accuracy."

BRIEN LEE & COMPANY, 2025 N. Summit Ave., Milwaukee WI 53202. (414)277-7600. President/Creative Director: Brien Lee. Produces custom audiovisual material for business; industry; arts/nonprofit; advertising and public relations agencies; business associations; and special entertainment oriented projects. Buys average 5 scripts/year. Buys all rights. Computer printout submissions acceptable; disk OK if compatible. Reports in 1 month, sometimes leading to an interview and an assignment.

Needs: "We need people who understand what AV is all about . . . words, pictures, sound. Motivational, informational, clear-cut, straightforward . . . writing that is literate, but never so good it could stand on its own without the pictures or sound. It is usually writing for one narrator, plus additional voices and/or characters. No hype." Produces videotapes, multi-image presentations, and mixed media presentations, slide-sound programs and interactive video. Submit example of scripting ability as well as a resume.

Recent Production: AVL, Milwaukee Journal.

WILLIAM V. LEVINE ASSOCIATES, INC., 31 E. 28th St., New York NY 10016. (212)683-7177. President: William V. Levine. Presentations for business and industry. 15% freelance written. Prefers to work with published/established writers. Buys 4 scripts/year. Firm emphasizes "creativity and understanding of the client's goals and objectives." Will interview writers after submission of resume and/or sample AV scripts. Specifically seeks writers with offbeat or humorous flair. Previously produced material OK. Buys all rights. "We prefer New York City area based writers only."

Needs: Business-related scripts *on assignment* for specific clients for use at sales meetings or for desk-top presentations. Also uses theme-setting and inspirational scripts with inherent messages of business interest. Produces sound and silent filmstrips, 16mm films, multimedia kits, tapes and cassettes, slide sets and live industrial shows. Also produces scripts for video. Query with resume. Pays $500-2,500. Sometimes pays the expenses of writers on assignment.

J.B. LIPPINCOTT CO., Audiovisual Media Department, East Washington Sq., Philadelphia PA 19105. (215)238-4200. Contact: H.M. Eisler. Produces materials for nursing students and medical students. Buys 15-25 scripts/year. Works with approximately 25 writers/year. Buys all rights. Disk submissions OK if compatible

with IBM PC and Apple II. Reports in 2 weeks on queries; 1 month on submissions. Free catalog.
Needs: "High-level instruction in medical/surgical topics for pre-service and in-service professional education." Produces 16mm films, sound filmstrips, slides (rarely), video materials and computer software. Query. Pays negotiable rate.

‡**LITTLE SISTER PICTURES INC.**, 1986 Palmerston Place, Los Angeles CA 90027. (213)668-1559. Vice President, Production: Rupert Macnee. Produces material for business and industry, home video, educational, training and instructional audience. Buys all rights. Computer printout submissions acceptable. Reports in 1 month on queries; 2 months on submissions.
Needs: Videotape presentations. "We are looking for ideas to develop for the home video market, typically one hour programs that can be produced for less than $100,000. Also interested in comedy and music programming." Query. Pays in accordance with Writers Guild standards.
Tips: "Writers should be aware of the move towards home video, the one-on-one feel, a modular approach to information, interactive programming."

‡**LYONS STUDIOS, INC.**, 715 Orange St., Box 8860, Wilmington DE 19899. (302)654-6146. Contact: Philip A. Gable. Produces material for business and industry. 20% freelance written. Prefers to work with published/established writers. Buys 1-9 scripts/year from unpublished/unproduced writers. 99% of scripts produced are unagented submissions. Computer printout submissions acceptable; prefers letter-quality to dot-matrix. Reports in 2 weeks. Buys all rights.
Needs: Subject topics include "business/industrial presentations—both educational and motivational." Produces multimedia presentations, video programs and collateral materials. Submit completed script with resume. Pays in outright purchase of $200-$1,000. Sometimes pays the expenses of writers on assignment.
Tips: "Submit complete scripts with description of objectives, audience, time and budget required. We want honest estimates of time and budget needs; clean, terse style—conversational copy."

MARSHFILM ENTERPRISES, INC., Box 8082, Shawnee Mission KS 66208. (816)523-1059. President: Joan K. Marsh. Produces material for elementary and junior/senior high school students. Also produces software and filmstrips. 100% freelance written. Works with a small number of new/unpublished writers each year. Buys 8-16 scripts/year. All scripts produced are unagented submissions. Buys all rights. Computer printout submissions acceptable; prefers letter-quality to dot-matrix.
Needs: 50 frame; 15 minutes/script. Sound filmstrips. Query only. Pays by outright purchase of $250-500/script.

MARYLAND PUBLIC TELEVISION, 11767 Bonita Ave., Owings Mills MD 21117. (301)337-4052. Head Writer: Dick George. Produces material "for general public audience; sometimes a specialized audience; people who get college credit by watching our telecourses, farmers who watch Farm Day, our agricultural news show, etc. The vast majority of our scripts are staff-written; however, when our staff is too busy to take on a new project, we do occasionally buy freelance material, perhaps 3 times a year." Buys all rights. No previously produced material. Reports in 2 months.
Needs: Films (16mm) and video. "We do documentaries and instructional shows on many different subjects. Right now I need comedy sketches for Crabs, a local comedy show produced and aired live. We don't take outside submissions unless I've commissioned them." Send resume and samples, etc. Make outright purchase; approximately $100/script minute, with exceptions.
Tips: Send resume and samples. "I'm *not* looking for program ideas—I'm in occasional need of writers to develop *our* program ideas."

ED MARZOLA & ASSOCIATES, Bldg. B-173, 5555 Melrose Ave., Hollywood CA 90028-3197. Vice President: William Case. Produces material for worldwide broadcast. Reports in 2 weeks.
Needs: "We now produce television programs and feature-length films for theatrical release." Produces 35mm films and videotaped presentations. "We negotiate each case individually." Query with samples or submit resume. Pays according to Writers Guild standards.

THE MEDIA GROUP, LTD., 5989 Tahoe Dr. SE, Grand Rapids MI 49506. (616)956-9503. Producer: Kenneth Schmidt. "We work primarily with two excellent industrial writers." 40% freelance written. Approximately 120 finished pages/year. Prefers to work with published/established writers. Buys 4 scripts/year from previously unpublished/unproduced writers. 100% of scripts produced are unagented submissions. Buys all rights. No previously produced material. Electronic submissions OK. Computer printout submissions acceptable; prefers letter-quality to dot-matrix. Catalog for 8x10 SAE and 53¢ postage.
Needs: Produces film/tape projects entirely. Industrial—corporate identification; educational, instructive (some interactive disk and tape). Promotional/sales, and occasionally commercial scripts. Style is mainly taking technical information and presenting it understandably to a select audience, but varies with project. Length: between 6-20 pages (average). Films (16 and 35mm), tapes and cassettes and interactive disk, tape. Query with

samples. Submit synopsis/outline, completed script and resume. Pays by outright purchase—$100/finished page (generally), more for more involved writing. Pays expenses of writers on assignment.
Tips: "Our writers need industrial writing background—technically and production-oriented, and in instructive design. Our clients want direct contact with our freelance writers for meetings. Writers should be immediately available for meetings with clients. Interactive is on the upswing in training. A good understanding of technical flow-charting and instructive design is essential in that area. We incorporate media tools (digital video effects, computer graphics) into our programs. Writers should have basic understanding of how to write for such elements."

MEDIA LEARNING SYSTEMS, INC., 1532 Rose Villa St., Pasadena CA 91106. (818)449-0006. President: Jim Griffith. Produces "custom" material for corporate, industrial, educational, and product promotional audience. 50% freelance written. Buys 12 scripts/year. Buys 1-2 scripts/year from unpublished/unproduced writers. All scripts are unagented submissions. Buys all rights. No previously produced material. Computer printout submissions acceptable. Reports in 1 month.
Needs: Video and video disks. Also produces scripts for video and video disks for kindergarten through grade 12 learning programs. Sometimes pays expenses of writers on assignment.
Tips: "We are seeking generic, curriculum-oriented educational scripts suitable for interactive video disk development."

MERIWETHER PUBLISHING LTD. (Contemporary Drama Service), Box 457, Downers Grove IL 60515. Editor: Arthur Zapel. "We publish how-to materials in book, filmstrip, game and audio cassette formats. We are interested in materials for high school and college level students only." 95% freelance written. Works with a small number of new/unpublished writers each year; eager to work with new/unpublished writers. Buys 40-60 scripts/year from unpublished/unproduced writers. 95% of scripts are unagented submissions." Computer printout submissions acceptable; no dot-matrix.
Needs: Filmstrips, game and audio cassettes. Christian activity book mss also accepted. We will consider elementary level religious materials and plays. Query. Pays royalty; buys some mss outright. Sometimes pays the expenses of writers on assignment.
Tips: "We publish a wide variety of speech contest materials for high school students. We are publishing more reader's theatre scripts and musicals based on classic literature or popular TV shows provided the writer includes letter of clearance from the copyright owner."

MILADY PUBLISHING CORPORATION, 3839 White Plains Rd., Bronx NY 10467. (212)881-3000. Business Education Editor: Harry Moon. Produces occupational educational material for students. 50% freelance written. Eager to work with new/unpublished writers. Buys 6-8 scripts/year from previously unpublished/unproduced writers. 100% of scripts produced are unagented submissions. Buys all rights. No previously produced material. Computer printout submissions acceptable; prefers letter-quality to dot-matrix. Reports in 2 weeks on queries; 1 month on submissions.
Needs: Charts, filmstrips (sound), overhead transparencies, slides, tapes and cassettes and video slides. Query. Makes outright purchase. Payment depends on the size and nature of project. "We have some royalty arrangements in so far as print materials are concerned."
Tips: "We will be looking for a number of new text/software programs for business education (IBM PC, TRS 80, Apple IIe compatible)."

‡BENJAMIN MORSE INC., 16 Aberdeen St., Boston MA 02215. (617)262-1550. President: Brian Higgins. Produces material for industry and education. 100% freelance written. Prefers to work with published/established writers. Buys 5 scripts/year from previously unpublished/unproduced writers. All scripts produced are unagented submissions. Electronic submissions OK, but requires hard copy also. Computer printout submissions acceptable; prefers letter-quality to dot-matrix. Reports in 2 weeks. Buys all rights. Free catalog.
Needs: Produces business presentations, speaker-support slides, models, multimedia kits, overhead transparencies, tapes and cassettes, slides, study prints and special effects. Query with samples and resume. Does not return unsolicited material—"cannot handle volume." Pays "depending on job."
Tips: Especially interested in "someone who writes for 'the ear' and not 'the eye.' "

MOTIVATION MEDIA, INC., 1245 Milwaukee Ave., Glenview IL 60025. (312)297-4740. Executive Producer: Frank Stedronsky. Produces customized material for salespeople, customers, corporate/industrial employees and distributors. 90% freelance written. Buys 100 scripts/year from unpublished/unproduced writers. Prefers to work with published/established writers. All scripts produced are unagented submissions. Buys all rights. Computer printout submissions acceptable. Reports in 1 month.
Needs: Material for all audiovisual media—particularly marketing-oriented (sales training, sales promotional, sales motivational) material. Produces sound filmstrips, 16mm films, multimedia sales meeting programs, videotapes, cassettes, and slide sets. Software should be AV-oriented. Query with samples. Pays $150-5,000. Pays the expenses of writers on assignment.

MRC FILMS & VIDEO, Div. McLaughlin Research Corp., 71 W. 23rd St., New York NY 10010. (212)989-1754. Executive Producer: Larry Mollot. "We are backlogged with submissions and prefer not to receive unsolicited submissions at this time."

MULTI-MEDIA PRODUCTIONS, INC., Box 5097, Stanford CA 94305. Program Manager: Mark Vining. Produces audiovisual instructional material for secondary (grades 9-12) schools. 100% freelance written. Prefers to work with published writers, but can work with small number of promising unpublished writers. Buys 20 programs/year; 10-15 from unpublished/unproduced writers. All scripts produced are unagented submissions. Buys all rights. Computer printout submissions acceptable; prefers letter-quality to dot-matrix. Reports in 6 weeks. Free catalog.
Needs: Sound filmstrip or already produced video material suitable for general high school social studies curricula: history, biography, sociology, psychology, student health, anthropology, archeology and economics. "Style should be straightforward, lively, objective and interactive." Approximate specifications (filmstrip): 50 frames, 10-15 minutes/program part; 1- or 2-part programs. Video: 10-40 minutes per program. Writer supplies script, slides for filmstrip, and teacher's manual (per our format). Pays royalties quarterly, based on 15% of return on each program sold. "Programs with a central academic theme sell best. Program subjects should adhere to secondary curricula and to student-interactive instructional methods." Query with samples.
Recent Production: *The Louisiana Purchase* (sound filmstrip).
Tips: "We are looking for programs that engage the viewer with their controversy, timeliness, and appropriateness to curricula. Sound filmstrips still do best when they challenge the student by presenting conflicting viewpoints or by directly inviting the student to participate in the program. We want to add significantly to our sound filmstrip line and move into distribution of video materials applicable to the educational market. Submit queries and we will offer our suggestions."

MULTIVISION INTERNATIONAL INC., 340 W. Huron, Chicago IL 60610. (312)337-2010. Creative Director: Michael Knab. "Most of our work is motivational/corporate image/employee communications." Buys about 50 scripts/year. Buys variable rights. Electronic disk submissions via Exxon System OK. Computer printout submissions acceptable; no dot-matrix. Reports in 2 weeks.
Needs: 16 and 35mm films, models, multimedia kits, slides, tapes and cassettes, videotape presentations, and all print. Query with samples or submit synopsis/outline. Pays in royalty or outright purchase.
Tips: "We look for quality writing and imagination."

BURT MUNK & COMPANY, 666 Dundee Rd., Northbrook IL 60062. (312)564-0855. President: Burton M. Munk. Produces material for industrial, sales training, product information, and education (schools). 100% freelance written. Works with approximately 10 writers/year. All scripts are unagented submissions. "We deal directly with writers but do not receive submissions of scripts." Buys all rights. Electronic submissions OK via Apple II Plus or Apple IIe, 64K, DOS 3.3. Does not return material; "all our work is 'made to order' for specific client needs—we are a custom house."
Needs: Sound filmstrips, slides, tapes and cassettes, 16mm films and videotapes. Also produces scripts for video. Open for software ideas. "We will contact individual writers who seem suitable for our projects." Makes outright purchase. Sometimes pays expenses of writers on assignment.
Tips: "We have published one very successful software program and are open for more. We will accept unsolicited ideas in disk form (Apple II Plus, 64K, DOS 3.3)."

HENRY NASON PRODUCTIONS, INC., 555 W. 57th St., New York NY 10019. (212)757-5437. President: Henry Nason. Produces custom audiovisual presentations for corporate clients. 90% freelance written. Buys all rights. Computer printout submissions acceptable; prefers letter-quality to dot-matrix. Reports in 1 month.
Needs: Usually 10- to 15-minute scripts on corporate subjects, such as sales, marketing, employee benefits, products, systems, public affairs, etc. Usually freestanding audiovisual modules. "The style should be clear and relaxed, well-researched and organized. Writers must live in the New York City area." Produces slide, multimedia presentations and video scripts. Query with samples or contact for personal interview. Pays an average of 8-10% of production budget. Sometimes pays expenses of writers on assignment.

□**NETWORK COMMUNICATIONS LTD.**, 14524 85th Ave., Edmonton, Alberta T5R 3Z4 Canada. (403)489-1044. President: R. Schwartz. Produces material for advertising, cable TV, government, etc. 50% freelance written. 100% of scripts are unagented submissions. Computer printout submissions acceptable; prefers letter-quality to dot-matrix. Reports in 3 weeks.
Needs: Produces cable programs, industrial films and TV commercials (35mm, 16mm or videotape). Submit resume and sample concept or script. Pays by hourly rate, percentage of budget dependent upon project. Sometimes pays expenses of writers on assignment.

NYSTROM, 3333 N. Elston Ave., Chicago IL 60618. (312)463-1144. Editorial Director: Darrell A. Coppock. Produces material for school audiences (kindergarten through 12th grade). Computer printout and disk submissions OK. Free catalog.

Needs: Educational material on social studies, earth and life sciences, career education, reading, language arts and mathematics. Produces charts, sound filmstrips, models, multimedia kits, overhead transparencies and realia. Required credentials depend on topics and subject matter and approach desired. Query. Pays according to circumstances.

OCEAN TELEVISION, Suite 6, 7110 Bonita Dr., Miami Beach FL 33141. President: Richard H. Stewart. Produces ocean-related material for broad and narrow cast audience. Works with 8 writers/year. Buys all rights and first serial rights. Previously produced material OK. Reports in 1 month.
Needs: Tapes and cassettes. Query with samples.

OUR SUNDAY VISITOR, INC., Religious Education Dept., 200 Noll Plaza, Huntington IN 46750. (219)356-8400. Director of Religious Education: Joseph Laiacona. Produces material for students (kindergarten through 12th grade), adult religious education groups and teacher trainees. "We are very concerned that the materials we produce meet the needs of today's church." Free catalog.
Needs: "Proposals for projects should be no more than 2 pages in length, in outline form. Programs should display up-to-date audiovisual techniques and cohesiveness. Broadly speaking, material should deal with religious education, including liturgy and daily Christian living, as well as structured catechesis. It must not conflict with sound Catholic doctrine, and should reflect modern trends in education." Produces educational books, charts, sound filmstrips and multimedia kits. "Work-for-hire and royalty arrangements possible."

PHOTO COMMUNICATION SERVICES, INC., 6410 Knapp NE, Ada MI 49301. (616)676-1499. President: Michael Jackson. Produces commercial, industrial, sales, training, etc. material. 95% freelance written. Buys 25% of scripts from unpublished/unproduced writers. 95% of scripts produced are unagented submissions. Buys all rights and first serial rights. Electronic submissions OK via IBM PC format (disk), 300, 1200 or 2400 Baud Modem, or on the Source, I.D. #BBH782 or MCI Mail I.D. 247-7996 or EasyLink Box No. 62909611. Computer printout submissions acceptable. Reports in 1 month on queries; 2 weeks on scripts. Writer's guidelines for SASE.
Needs: Multimedia kits, slides, tapes and cassettes, and video presentations. Primarily interested in 35mm multimedia, 1-24 projectors and video. Query with samples or submit completed script and resume. Pays in outright purchase or by agreement.

□**PHOTOGRAPHIC ILLUSTRATION COMPANY**, 2220 W. Magnolia Blvd., Burbank CA 91505. (818)849-7345. Executive Producer: Shelly Schiner. Produces material for corporate and public audience. 50% freelance written. Buys 10+ scripts/year. Buys all rights. No previously produced material. Electronic submissions OK via IBM Displaywriter. Computer printout submissions acceptable; prefers letter-quality to dot-matrix. Reports "as requested." Catalog for SAE.
Needs: Charts, films, silent and sound filmstrips and multimedia kits, overhead transparencies, slides, tapes and cassettes, videotape presentations, multimedia, video and film.

PREMIER VIDEO FILM & RECORDING CORP., 3033 Locust, St. Louis MO 63103. (314)531-3555. Secretary/Treasurer: Grace Dalzell. Produces material for the corporate community, religious organizations, political arms, and hospital and educational groups. 100% freelance written. Prefers to work with published/established writers. Buys 50-100 scripts/year. All scripts are unagented submissions. Buys all rights; "very occasionally the writer retains rights." Previously produced material OK; "depends upon original purposes and markets." Computer printout submissions acceptable; prefers letter-quality to dot-matrix. Reports "within a month or as soon as possible."
Needs: "Our work is all custom produced with the needs being known only as required." 35mm film loops, super 8mm and 35mm films, silent and sound filmstrips, multimedia kits, overhead transparencies, phonograph records, slides, and tapes and cassettes. Produces TV, training and educational scripts for video. Submit complete script and resume. Pays in accordance with Writers Guild standards or by outright purchase of $100 or "any appropriate sum." Sometimes pays the expenses of writers on assignment.
Tips: "Always place without fail *occupational pursuit*, name, address and phone number in upper right hand corner of resume. We're looking for writers with creativity, good background and a presentable image."

□**PRIMALUX VIDEO**, 30 W. 26th St., New York NY 10010. (212)206-1402. Director: M. Clarke. Produces industrial and training material; promotional pieces. 70% freelance written. Buys 10 scripts/year; works with 2 writers/year. Buys all rights. No previously produced material. Computer printout submissions acceptable.
Needs: Television show/series and videotape presentations. Produces scripts for video and fashion show material for cable TV. Query with samples. Pays royalty or by outright purchase. Pays expenses of writers on assignment.

BILL RASE PRODUCTIONS, INC., 955 Venture Ct., Sacramento CA 95825. (916)929-9181. President: Bill Rase. Produces material for business education and mass audience. Buys 20 scripts maximum/year. Buys all rights. Reports "when an assignment is available."

Needs: Produces silent and sound filmstrips, multimedia kits, slides, cassettes, videotapes and video productions. Submit resume, sample page or two of script, and description of expertise. Pays negotiable rate in 30 days.

Tips: "Call and ask for Bill Rase personally. Must be within 100 miles and thoroughly professional."

REGENTS PUBLISHING CO., 2 Park Ave., New York NY 10016. (212)889-2780. Acquisitions Editor: John Chapman. "We are backlogged with submissions and prefer not to receive unsolicited submissions at this time."

RHYTHMS PRODUCTIONS, Whitney Bldg., Box 34485, Los Angeles CA 90034. President: R.S. White. "Our audience is generally educational, with current projects in elementary early childhood." 50% freelance written. Buys 6 scripts/year from unpublished/unproduced writers. 50% of scripts are unagented submissions. Computer printout submissions acceptable; prefers letter-quality to dot-matrix.

Needs: Phonograph records; video scripts for children's stories and music. "For our phonograph records, we accept only fully produced tapes of a professional quality. If tapes are sent, include return postage." Query. "We need to know a writer's background and credits and to see samples of his work."

SAVE THE CHILDREN, 54 Wilton Rd., Westport CT 06880. (203)226-7272. Producer: Joseph Loya. Produces 16mm films, tapes and cassettes, 2¼x2¼ slides, posters and displays. 30% freelance written. Prefers to work with published/established writers. 100% of scripts produced are unagented submissions. Generally buys all rights, "but it depends on project. We use work only written for specific assignments." Electronic submissions OK. Computer printout submissions acceptable; prefers letter-quality to dot-matrix.

Needs: General (radio and TV); and education (high school, college and adult). Also produces scripts for video. Sometimes pays the expenses of writers on assignment. Pays $250-500 minimum/assignment.

SAXTON COMMUNICATIONS GROUP LTD., 6th Floor, 96 Morton St., New York NY 10014. (212)645-4500. Produces material for industrial, consumer and sales audiences, AV presentations and meetings.

Needs: "We work with more than ten outside writers regularly. We buy copy and scripts for approximately thirty projects a year." Submit resume.

SCIENCE RESEARCH ASSOCIATES, 155 N. Wacker, Chicago IL 60606. (312)984-7390. Script Coordinator: Corey Cather. Produces instructional video scripts for IBM data-processing community. "We do instructional design work on new training topics. Our products are designed in-house. We require our freelance writers to develop scripts to our specifications and detailed designs." Does not buy *completed* scripts. 100% freelance written. Works with 10-15 writers/year. 100% of scripts produced are unagented submissions. Prefers to work with published/established writers. Buys all rights. No previously produced material. Computer printout submissions acceptable; prefers letter-quality to dot-matrix. Reports in 2 weeks. Free writer's guidelines.

Needs: Videotape presentations. Currently interested in developing "data processing training videotapes on IBM software products. Tapes will be 10-15 minutes and will have 50-100% animation." Submit treatment and 3 drafts of script/storyboards. Set fee to be determined prior to agreement. Pays expenses of writers on assignment.

SCOTT RESOURCES, INC., Box 2121, Fort Collins CO 80522. (303)484-7445. Produces material for public and private school audiences, kindergarten through grade 12. Supplemental math and science materials. 90% freelance written. Works with 3-5 authors/year. Buys 3-5 scripts/year from unpublished/unproduced writers. 100% of scripts are unagented submissions. Electronic submissions OK. Computer printout submissions acceptable. Free math and science catalog.

Needs: Looking for written or AV material and computer software in earth science/geology and elementary/junior high mathematics. Also produces scripts for videos. Query with samples. Will negotiate equitable royalty.

SCREENSCOPE, INC., 4330 Yuma NW, Washington DC 20016. (202)364-0055. President: Marilyn Weiner. Produces material for schools, industry, television and theatre. Buys 20 scripts/year. Buys all rights. Reports in 1 month.

Needs: "For education we need a script which can communicate to many grade levels. Style, format, length, etc. are discussed with producer and client." Produces 16mm and 35mm films and slides. Submit resume. Pays by outright purchase.

SEVEN OAKS PRODUCTIONS, 9145 Sligo Creek Pkwy., Silver Spring MD 20901. (301)587-0030. Production Manager: M. Marlow. 80% freelance written. Produces material for students, civic and professional groups, and PTA chapters. Buys 10-20 scripts from 10 writers/year. 65% of scripts are unagented submissions.

Buys all rights or first rights, but rights purchased are negotiable. Computer printout submissions acceptable; prefers letter-quality to dot-matrix. Reports in 4 months.
Needs: Educational, medical, safety and general entertainment material. "We look for clarity in style, imagination with the ability to get information across and accomplish objectives, the ability to meet deadlines and to dig if necessary to get sufficient information to make the script better than another on the same subject. Writers should know the film format." Produces 16mm films, video disk computer active programs, multimedia kits, phonograph records, tapes and cassettes, and slide sets. Query only first; will keep on file. Will not return unsolicited material. Payment negotiable according to project.

SIMMONS PRODUCTIONS, 660 Main St., Woburn MA 01801. (617)933-6377. Producer: Russ Chapman. Produces material for private corporations—their employees, sales people or potential customers. 100% freelance written. Works with a small number of new/unpublished writers each year. Buys 25 scripts/year from previously unpublished/unproduced writers. All scripts produced are unagented submissions. Buys all rights. Computer printout submissions acceptable. Reports in 2 weeks on queries; 1 week on submissions. Free brochure.
Needs: "Our slide shows vary in length from 3 to 25 minutes. Format is generally narration, sometimes interspersed with testimonials from clients, etc. Videotape scripts are more complex, obviously including dialogue. Our clients are a wide variety of companies from the private sector: computer companies, electronics manufacturers, food handlers, colleges." Produces video, multi image, films and slides. Query with samples. Buys by outright purchase. Sometimes pays the expenses of writers on assignment.
Tips: "Send us a sample of your work, then follow up with a phone call. We would prefer writers with a background in the visual media and an ability to write a 'visual' script."

PHOEBE T. SNOW PRODUCTIONS, INC., 240 Madison Ave., New York NY 10016. (212)679-8756. Creative Director: Deborah R. Herr. Produces material for corporate uses, sales force, in-house training, etc. 90% freelance written. Buys 20-40 scripts/year from published/produced writers only. All scripts produced are unagented submissions. Buys all rights. Computer printout submissions acceptable; prefers letter-quality to dot-matrix. Reports in 2 weeks on queries; 1 month on mss.
Needs: 16mm films, sound filmstrips and slides. Query with samples and resume. Pays by outright purchase.
Tips: "Have some understanding of AV for corporations. This is not the educational field. We're looking for creative writers who work with speed and can take direction. Be aware of short deadlines and some low budgets."

SOUTH CAROLINA EDUCATIONAL TELEVISION NETWORK, Drawer L, Columbia SC 29250. (803)758-7261. Director for State Agencies: Ms. Sandra V. Pedlow. Produces material for the general public; training and career development for business and industry; college courses; and on-going adult education in fields of medicine and technical education. Works only with freelancers in the South Carolina area. 15% freelance written. Works with a small number of new/unpublished writers each year. Buys 25 scripts/year from previously unpublished/unproduced writers. 99% of scripts produced are unagented submissions. Computer printout submissions acceptable; prefers letter-quality to dot-matrix. Buys all rights. Query or submit resume. Reports in 2 weeks.
Needs: "The Division of Continuing Education works in all media. Since, as a state agency, we work with other state agencies of varying needs, style, format, length, etc. are determined for each individual project." Produces 16mm films, multimedia kits, slides, videotape, live in-studio television productions, teleconferences and related printed materials for training programs. Payment "depends on funding governed by South Carolina state law guidelines." Pays expenses of writers on assignment.
Tips: "If possible, come in for an interview and bring in samples of previous work."

SPENCER PRODUCTIONS, INC., 234 5th Ave., New York NY 10001. (212)697-5895. General Manager: Bruce Spencer. Produces material for high school students, college students and adults. Occasionally uses freelance writers with considerable talent.
Needs: 16mm films, prerecorded tapes and cassettes. Satirical material only. Query. Pay is negotiable.

□**SPINDLER PRODUCTIONS,** 1501 Broadway, New York NY 10036. (212)730-1255. Creative Directors: Richard Cardran and Victor Spindler. Produces material for corporations, ad agencies and upper end of consumer audience. 90% freelance written. Buys 10-20 scripts/year; works with 4-10 writers/year. All scripts are unagented submissions. Buys all rights. No previously produced material. Electronic submissions OK via TRS 80, Tandy 2000, Telex/Easy Link, 300 Baud, 1 stopbit, 8 bit, no parity. Level 2 or 3 telecopy computer printout submissions acceptable. Reports in 2 weeks. Catalog for 9x12 SAE and 1 first class stamp.
Needs: TV commercials, industrials, training films, charts, film loops, 16 and 35mm films, multimedia kits, overhead transparencies, slides, tapes and cassettes, teaching machine programs, videotape presentations, and AV presentations. Produces scripts for video—commercials, industrials, training and corporate. Produces material for cable TV (informercials). Query with sample scripts preferably of used/published material or submit

outline/synopsis or completed script and resume. Pays by outright purchase. Pays the expenses of writers on assignment.

SPOTTSWOOD STUDIOS, 2524 Old Shell Rd., Box 7061, Mobile AL 36607. (205)478-9387. Co-owner: M.W. Spottswood. "We normally work for sponsors (but not always) who seek public attention." Buys 1-2 scripts. Buys all rights. Computer printout submissions acceptable. Reports in 2 weeks.
Needs: Business, religious and general. Produces 16mm films and 8mm loops, sound filmstrips, videotape and slide sets. Query with resume and samples. Pays by outright purchase.

AL STAHL ANIMATED, 1600 Broadway, New York NY 10019. (212)265-2942. President: Al Stahl. Produces industrial, sales promotion, educational and television commercial material. Buys first rights. Query. Free catalog.
Needs: "We specialize in making movies from slides and in converting slide shows and multimedia (three or more screens) into a one-screen movie." Produces 8mm and 16mm films, and multimedia kits. Pays by outright purchase.

□**E.J. STEWART, INC.**, 525 Mildred Ave., Primos PA 19018. (215)626-6500. "Our firm is a television production house providing programming for the broadcast, industrial, educational and medical fields. Government work is also handled." 50% freelance written. Buys 50 scripts/year; buys 5% of scripts/year from unpublished/unproduced writers. Buys all rights. Computer printout submissions acceptable. Reports "when needed."
Needs: "We produce programming for our clients' specific needs. We do not know in advance what our needs will be other than general scripts for commercials and programs depending upon requests that we receive from clients." Cable television material. Videotapes. Submit resume only. Pays in negotiable outright purchase. Sometimes pays expenses of writers on assignment.
Tips: "A trend in the audiovisual field freelance writers should be aware of is interactive laser disk programming."

TALCO PRODUCTIONS, 279 E. 44th St., New York NY 10017. (212)697-4015. President: Alan Lawrence. Vice President: Marty Holberton. Produces variety of material for motion picture theatres, TV, radio, business, trade associations, non-profit organizations, etc. Audiences range from young children to senior citizens. 20-40% freelance written. Buys scripts from published/produced writers only. All scripts produced are unagented submissions. Buys all rights. No previously published material. Computer printout submissions acceptable; prefers letter-quality to dot-matrix. Reports in 3 weeks on queries.
Needs: Films (16-35mm); filmstrips (sound); phonograph records; slides; radio tapes and cassettes; and videotape. "We maintain a file of writers and call on those with experience in the same general category as the project in production. We do not accept unsolicited manuscripts. We prefer to receive a writer's resume listing credits. If his/her background merits, we will be in touch when a project seems right." Makes outright purchase/project and in accordance with Writer's Guild standards (when appropriate). Sometimes pays the expenses of writers on assignment.

TEL-AIR INTERESTS, INC., 1755 N.E. 149th St., Miami FL 33181. (305)944-3268. President: Grant H. Gravitt. Produces material for groups and theatrical and TV audiences. Buys all rights. Submit resume.
Needs: Documentary films on education, travel and sports. Produces films and videotape. Pays by outright purchase.

□**TELEMATION PRODUCTIONS, INC. AND TELEMATION INTERACTIVE**, 7700 E. Iliff Ave., Denver CO 80231. (303)751-6000. Corporate Sales: Jim Anderson (Telemation Productions, Inc). Senior/Producer: Richard Schneider (Telemation Interactive). "Telemation is a major video production firm with studios in Denver, Chicago, Phoenix and Seattle. We will forward contacts to the appropriate telemation facility from Denver." Produces material for corporate and industrial video. 90% freelance written. Prefers to work with published/established writers. 100% of scripts produced are unagented submissions. Buys all rights. No previously produced material. Electronic submissions OK via Hayes 1200sm or IBM-XT, IBM-AT, but requires hard copy also. Computer printout submissions acceptable; prefers letter-quality to dot-matrix.
Needs: Video tape; interactive video disk programs for the corporate and industrial market—marketing, sales, training, product rollout, etc. Submit all interactive video programming to Richard Schneider. Produces material—from entertainment to documentary to educational—for cable TV. Query with samples and resume. "All work is done on assignment. We do not accept unsolicited scripts—assignments only." Makes outright purchase. Pays expenses of writers on assignment.
Tips: "Only writers with solid corporate and industrial video experience should contact us. Also, location near one of Telemation's facilities is important. We have a growing need for script writers in the area of corporate and industrial video or film."

‡TELETECHNIQUES, INC., 1 W. 19th St., New York NY 10011. (212)206-1475. Contact: Michael Temmer. Works with 3-4 writers/year. Buys all rights. Sometimes accepts previously produced material. Reports in 2 months.
Needs: Material for industrials and TV programs. Produces 35 and 16mm films and videos. Query with samples. Writers are paid in accordance with Writers Guild standards by royalty or outright purchase.
Tips: "Contributors should be flexible and have a knowledge of the video and film media."

TELSTAR, INC., 366 N. Prior Ave., St. Paul MN 55104. Editor: Dr. Victor Kerns. Produces video material for adult, college-level audience, in industry and continuing education. Buys video recording rights. Produces instructional videotapes not intended for broadcast.
Needs: Education (curricular materials for small group or independent study); business (training and development material); and communication skills. Looks for "the ability to chapterize/pace the instruction." Query. Pays $100 plus royalties.

FRANCIS THOMPSON, INC., 231 E. 51st St., New York NY 10022. (212)759-4558. Vice President: Byron McKinney. Produces films for varied audiences. Commissions scriptwriting only.

TROLL ASSOCIATES, 320 Rt. 17, Mahwah NJ 07430. (201)529-4000. Contact: M. Schecter. Produces material for elementary and high school students. Buys approximately 200 scripts/year. Buys all rights. Reports in 3 weeks. Free catalog.
Needs: Produces silent and sound filmstrips, multimedia kits, tapes and cassettes, and (mainly) books. Query or submit outline/synopsis. Pays royalty or by outright purchase.

TUTOR/TAPE, 107 France St., Toms River NJ 08753. President: Richard R. Gallagher. Produces and publishes cassettes, filmstrips, software and visual aids including slides and transparencies for the college market. 50% freelance written. Most scripts produced are unagented submissions. Buys average 5 scripts/year. "We are the largest publisher of prerecorded educational cassettes for the college market. We are capable of handling everything from writer to recording to packaging to marketing in a totally vertically integrated production-marketing publishing organization." Computer printout submissions acceptable. Reports in 1 week.
Needs: 10 to 25 page scripts for 15 to 30 minute educational messages on college topics, including business, management, marketing, personnel, advertising, accounting, economics and other related material. We also seek remedial and study skills material useful to college students and suitable for audio presentation. Send brief synopsis or short outline stating credentials, education or experience. Pays 15% royalty or by outright purchase.
Tips: "Writers should submit material relevant to students in college who need assistance in passing difficult courses, or interesting material which supplements college textbooks and enhances class work."

UNIVERSITY OF WISCONSIN STOUT TELEPRODUCTION CENTER, 800 S. Broadway, Menomonie WI 54751. (715)232-2624. Production Manager/TV Coordinator: Tim Fuhrmann. Produces instructional TV programs for primary, secondary, post secondary and specialized audiences. 10% freelance written. Buys scripts from published/produced writers only. All scripts produced are unagented submissions. "We produce ITV programs for national, regional and state distribution to classrooms around the U.S. and Canada." Buys all rights. Computer printout submissions acceptable; prefers letter-quality to dot-matrix.
Needs: "Our clients fund programs in a 'series' format which tend to be 8-12 programs each." Produces only with one-inch broadcast quality. "I need materials from writers who have experience in writing instructional TV. I have an immediate need for writers with secondary teaching experience who can write a secondary level chemical abuse series. Only the 'pros' need apply. We also have a need for writers in Wisconsin and Minnesota whom we can call on to write one or multi-program/series in instructional television." Query with resume and samples of TV scripts.
Recent Production: *Story Lords* (2nd grade reading comprehension agency: Wisconsin Educational Communications Board). Sometimes pays the expenses of writers on assignment.
Tips: "Freelance writers should be aware of the hardware advances in broadcast and nonbroadcast. There are new avenues for writers to pursue in adult learning, computer assisted programming and interactive programming."

VISUAL HORIZONS, 180 Metro Park, Rochester NY 14623. (716)424-5300. President: Stanley Feingold. Produces material for general audiences. Buys 5 programs/year. Reports in 5 months. Free catalog.
Needs: Business, medical and general subjects. Produces silent and sound filmstrips, multimedia kits, slide sets and videotapes. Query with samples. Payment negotiable.

□WREN ASSOCIATES, INC., 208 Bunn Dr., Princeton NJ 08540. Copy Department Head: Barbara Kram. Produces material for employees and sales people, and various sales and corporate presentations for Fortune 500 corporate clients. 20% freelance written. Buys 30-40 scripts/year from previously produced writers only.

All scripts produced are unagented submissions. Buys all rights. No previously published material. Electronic submissions OK over CompuServe network, on IBM/Compaq, MS word, and Kaypro II. Computer printout submissions acceptable. Reports in 3 weeks. Catalog for #10 SAE and 1 first class stamp. .
Needs: Produces 8mm film loops, 16mm films, sound filmstrips, multimedia kits, slides (multiprojector shows); tapes and cassettes, television shows/series (corporate networks); videotape presentations; interactive video on a project-by-project basis for clients and video scripts for industrial specialists on assignment. Produces scripts for cable TV medical network. "We need freelance writers who can assimilate technical or business-oriented subject matter (e.g., telecommunications services, automotive). They must be able to present this material in a clear, entertaining presentation that *sells* the product," Query with samples. Pays $400-7,000/job. Sometimes pays expenses of writers on assignment. .
Tips: "Freelance writers should be aware of interactive video disk, tape trend. It's the coming wave in training and P.O.P. sales."

ZELMAN STUDIOS LTD., 623 Cortelyou Rd., Brooklyn NY 11218. (718)941-5500. General Manager: Jerry Krone. Produces material for business, education and fund-raising audiences. Reports in 1 month. Buys all rights.
Needs: Produces film loop, silent and sound filmstrips, films, videotapes, audiocassettes and slides. Query with samples and resume. Pays by outright purchase "by agreement, based on talent and turnaround."

ZM SQUARED, Box C-30, Cinnaminson NJ 08077. (609)786-0612. Contact: Pete Zakroff. "We produce AVs for a wide range of clients including education, business, industry and labor organizations." Buys 10 scripts/year; works with 4-5 writers/year. Buys all rights. No previously produced material. Electronic submissions OK via Apple system. Computer printout submissions acceptable. Reports in 2 weeks on queries; 1 month on submissions. Free catalog.
Needs: Silent filmstrips, kinescopes, multimedia kits, overhead transparencies, slides, tapes and cassettes, and videotape presentations. Query with or without samples. Pays 3-10% royalty or by outright purchase $150-750.

Playwriting

"What is important is that playwrights think about the world today," stress script editors and directors. A musical may be set in Charlemagne's time (*Pippin*) or a play may recreate the days of Mozart (*Amadeus*), but productions must be about *today*. "Arthur Miller's *The Crucible*, though set during the witch trials centuries ago, showed audiences what was going on in America in 1952," said Samuel French, Inc. editor Lawrence Harbison.

Today, though, playwrights might want to avoid historical plays. With the high costs of salaries, costumes, and sets, producers look for small cast plays. If additional characters don't contribute significantly to the story line, don't include them.

Producers continue to look for scripts with "substantial roles for women." Samuel French, for instance, needs scripts with numerous female roles since the majority of amateur theatre performers are women.

Reading and attending current plays is the best way to know what producers are buying. Too many playwrights' knowledge of theatre comes from reading the classics—"plays by dead Europeans," said Harbison. Knowing both classic and current plays is essential for playwrights. Many scriptwriters begin working for theatres or companies as interns or volunteers. Spend time on and off stage and backstage whenever possible. You must learn the idiosyncrasies of the medium and this learning can occur in New York or at regional theatres on the West Coast or Midwest.

One misconception among amateur theatres is that what succeeds in New York will be successful with their audiences. "What succeeds in New York is novelty," pointed out the Samuel French editor. "What succeeds with amateur theatre audiences is generally that which is familiar."

Don't write off "regional" theatres as minor league. They are often more "professional" than Broadway—and there are more opportunities for new playwrights there, said Harbison.

Attendance at any theatre production gives you insights into how audiences react to particular moments and types of characters. The Theatre Development Fund (Suite 2110, 1501 Broadway, New York, NY 10036) enables playwrights to get reduced tickets. Audience Extras (163 W. 23rd St., New York, NY 10011; 1540 N. Highland Ave., Los Angeles, CA 90028; and 1169 Market St., San Francisco, CA 94103) is a source for getting inexpensive tickets after you've paid an annual membership fee. When contacting these organizations, be willing to follow their guidelines. In many cities, high school and college students can get discounts on tickets.

We've heard playwrights stress the importance of getting your work on the stage, but make sure that the production doesn't make your play untouchable for producers and publishers. "If a play is produced Off-Off Broadway under what is called the Actors Equity Showcase Code, the showcase actors have a hold on their roles for three years," said Harbison, "which means a subsequent professional producer must either book them in for his production or pay them off to the tune of three weeks' rehearsal salary—neither of which will he probably do."

Staged readings and productions of your play by colleges or community theatres will enable you to make revisions based on your audiences' reactions, possibly making it more sellable.

"The big question with so many places isn't money," said one playwright. "What it boils down to is what kinds of rights are they going to want to retain to your work. That's the thing the playwright has to be very, very careful about."

Organizations like New Dramatists (424 W. 44th St., New York, NY 10036) sponsor readings and encourage new talent. "We offer script-in-hand readings of our members' plays, panel discussions, writer studios, free theatre tickets, a national script distribution service and exchanges with theatres," said literary assistant Richard LeComte, assistant to the director of Script Development and Marketing.

Aspiring playwrights should also consider joining The Dramatists Guild (234 W. 44th St., New York, NY 10036). You need not have sold a script to be a member. Guild members receive the monthly *Dramatists Guild Newsletter* and *The Dramatists Guild Quarterly*; both contain information about marketing plays.

The International Society of Dramatists publishes *The Dramatist's Bible*, *Plays & Playwrights*, and a newsletter, *The Globe* (ISD Fulfillment Center, Box 3470, Fort Pierce, FL 22448). The *Dramatists Sourcebook* (Theatre Communications Group, 355 Lexington Ave., New York, NY 10017) lists theatres that consider unsolicited playscripts, play publishers, agents, fellowships, festivals and contests, conferences and workshops, and playwriting opportunities in film, radio and video. A useful directory is the *Theatre Directory* (Theatre Communications Group) listing nearly 275 professional nonprofit theatres. The Alliance of Resident Theatres—New York (formerly the Off-Off Broadway Alliance) will provide general information to playwrights and consultations only for members. The Alliance (Room 315, 325 Spring St., New York NY 10013) also has information on its 85 member theatres.

Professional format

Many aspiring playwrights incorrectly use the format of *published* plays as a guideline for typing their unpublished manuscript. In books of plays for the general reader, the publisher puts as many words on a page as possible with a minimum amount of white space. Manuscripts you send to publishers, producers and actors should be as readable as possible, separating parenthetical remarks from dialogue in the reader's visual field. An example of proper manuscript format is available in *Guidelines*, available for $3, postpaid, from Samuel French, Inc., 45 W. 25th St., New York, NY 10010. Pica type is preferred by people who evaluate manuscripts.

Put your name, address, *and phone number* on the title page. Place your script in a two- or three-ring binder; some publishers don't like some of the newer clamped binders.

In mailing your submission, don't forget to enclose a self-addressed, stamped envelope with enough postage for the return of the script. (Most producers won't return scripts at their own expense.) Sometimes the evaluation of unsolicited scripts will take six months to a year so don't badger a producer into a quick response that would probably be *no*. Also, if a producer says he reviews only queries, write a query for your completed script. Some playhouses, to review more playwrights' work, will only consider queries with outlines/synopses of plays. Make sure that your submission is appropriate to the theatre or company to which you send it.

ACADEMY THEATRE, 1137 Peachtree St. NE, Atlanta GA 30309. (404)873-2518. Artistic Director: Frank Wittow. Produces 10 plays/year. 20% freelance written. 5% of scripts produced are unagented. Plays performed in Academy Theatre—415 seats thrust stage, and in Academy Lab Theatre, 100 seats, flexible stage. Professional productions tour the Southeast for elementary, high school, college and community audiences. Works with 2-5 unpublished/unproduced writers annually. Submit complete ms. "We accept synopses of scripts." Computer printout submissions acceptable; prefers letter-quality to dot-matrix. Reports in 4 months. Buys negotiable rights. Pays negotiable royalty.
Needs: "Full length plays, one acts, children's plays, adaptations, translations, original plays of contemporary significance, plays that go beyond the conventions of naturalism; Transformational plays: actors playing multiple roles. Prefer small cast; unit set. Follow standard playwright submission guidelines and standard preparation of script." No sitcom love affairs, triangles; plays with very large casts. Special programs: "Academy Playwrights Lab is an ongoing program of workshop productions of previously unproduced full length and one act plays by Southeastern playwrights. Deadline is open. The Atlanta New Play Project is sponsored each June by the Community of Atlanta theatres. The project includes staged readings, workshops, full productions as plays in progress with a forum for discussion of new works. Southeastern playwrights are specifically desired for this project."
Tips: "Lack of funding in the arts will cause us to seek plays that do not depend for their success on production costs. A perfect script for the Academy is one that utilizes a small cast and simple set and which, more importantly, is structurally innovative, linguistically dangerous, and/or attentive to the darker psychological aspects of man in his society."

ACTORS THEATRE OF LOUISVILLE, 316 West Main St., Louisville KY 40202. (502)584-1265. Artistic Director: Jon Jory. Produces/publishes approximately 35 new plays of varying lengths/year. Professional productions are performed for subscription audience from diverse backgrounds. Submit complete ms for one-act plays; agented submissions only for full-length plays. Reports in 6-9 months on submissions. No computer printout submissions. Buys production (in Louisville only) rights. Offers variable royalty.
Needs: "We accept only one-act plays—unsolicited. No children's shows or musicals. We produce both full-lengths and one-acts."

ALASKA REPERTORY THEATRE, Suite 201, 705 W. 6th Ave., Anchorage AK 99501. (907)276-2327. Artistic Director: Robert J. Farley. Produces 4-5 plays/year. Professional plays performed for Alaskan audiences. No unsolicited scripts; synopsis and letter of inquiry *only*. Reports in 5 months. Pays 3%+ royalty "depending on work."
Needs: Produces all types of plays.

AMAS REPERTORY THEATRE, INC., 1 E. 104th St., New York NY 10029. (212)369-8000/8001. Artistic Director: Rosetta LeNoire. Produces 6 plays/year. 1 or 2 scripts produced are unagented submissions. "AMAS is a professional, off-off-Broadway showcase theatre. We produce three showcase productions of original musicals each season; these are presented for a sophisticated New York theatre audience. A number have gone on to commercial productions, the best known of which is *Bubbling Brown Sugar*. We also present two children's theatre productions and one summer tour." Query with synopsis or submit complete script with cassette tape of score or of partial score. Computer printout submissions acceptable; prefers letter-quality to dot-matrix. Reports in 2 months. "Be prepared to wait at least one year or more between acceptance and production. Our standard contract calls for a small percentage of gross and royalties to AMAS, should the work be commercially produced within a specified period."
Needs: "*Musicals only*; in addition, all works will be performed by multi-racial casts. Musical biographies are especially welcome. Cast size should be under 15 if possible, including doubling. Because of the physical space, set requirements should be relatively simple."

Tips: "AMAS is dedicated to bringing all people—regardless of race, creed, color or religion—together through the creative arts. In writing for AMAS, an author should keep this overall goal in mind."

‡**THE AMERICAN LINE**, Suite 5C, 810 W. 18 3rd St., New York NY 10033. (212)795-3104. Artistic Director: Richard Hoehler. Produces 3 plays/year. Query with synopsis. Reports in 2 months. Rights and payment negotiable.
Needs: "Contemporary straight plays (one-act or full lengths) that make a point. Simple sets; small casts. No period pieces or verse."

‡**AMERICAN MUSIC THEATER FESTIVAL**, Suite 905, 1617 JFK Blvd., Philadelphia PA 19103. Artistic Director: Eric Salzman. Produces 5 music theatre works/year. Stages professional music theatre and opera productions during an annual fall festival. Intended for all audiences (no children's theatre.) "For the most part, audiences are upscale theatre-goers. We produce these music theatre productions in different Center City Philadelphia theatres." Submit complete ms and cassette tape of music. Reports in 9 months. Pays royalty or fee; "amount not available for publication". Submissions will not be reviewed without a SASE.
Needs: "The American Music Theater Festival produces an annual festival entirely devoted to music theatre in all its forms: musical comedy, music drama, opera and experimental work. We produce only music theatre. We prefer small casts and orchestras with minimum sets, but we do produce large, mainstage music theatre works as well. We are seeking librettists and composers who are taking risks in the field. Our primary purpose is to become a center of vitality for this art form by providing support for artists doing important new work in the field."

‡**AMERICAN STAGE FESTIVAL**, Box 225, Milford NH 03055. Artistic Director: Larry Carpenter. "The ASF is a central New England professional theatre (professional equity company) with a 3 month summer season (June-August) for audience of all ages, interests, education and sophistication levels. Query with synopsis. Produces musicals (20%) and nonmusicals (80%) (5 are mainstage and 10 are children's productions); 40% are originals. Royalty option and subsequent amount of gross: optional. Reports in 3 months.
Needs: "The Festival can do comedies, musicals and dramas. However, the most frequent problems come from plays not fitting into the resident acting company system (all men, all young, for example) and/or that are bolder in language and action than a general mixed audience will accept. We have a 40 foot proscenium stage with 30 foot wings, but no fly system. Festival plays are chosen to present scale and opportunities for scenic and costume projects far beyond the 'summer theater' type of play." Length: Mainstage: 2-3 acts; children's productions: 50 minutes.
Recent Productions: *Corpse*, by Gerald Mood.
Tips: Writers could improve submissions with "dramatic action, complexity, subplot and a unique statement. Try to get a staged reading of the script before submitting the play to us. Our audiences prefer plays that deal with human problems presented in a conventional manner."

AMERICAN THEATRE ARTS, Dept. W, 11305 Magnolia Blvd., North Hollywood CA 91601. Submit to Director of Play Development: Pamela Bohnert. Artistic Director: Don Eitner. Produces 5 plays/year. 10-15% freelance written. Plays performed in 75 seat Equity Waiver theatres for the general public. Works with 1-2 unpublished/unproduced writers annually. No unsolicited scripts. Query with resume, synopsis and SASE. Please include complete cast description and set requirements. Reports in 2 months. If script is requested, reports in 4 months. Minimum royalty $100. If show goes to full Equity production, percentage is worked out with author in compliance with Dramatist Guild guidelines.
Needs: No restrictions as to genres, topics or styles.

‡**AN CLAIDHEAMH SOLUIS/CELTIC ARTS CENTER**, 5651 Hollywood Blvd., Hollywood CA 90028. (213)462-6844. Artistic Director: B. Heron. Produces 6 plays/year. Equity waiver. Query and synopsis. Reports in 6 weeks. Rights acquired varies. Pays $25-50.
Needs: Scripts of celtic interest (Scottish, Welsh, Irish, Cornish, Manx, Breton). "This can apply to writer's background or subject matter. We are particularly concerned with works that relate to the survival of cultures and nature traditions."

‡**ARAN PRESS**, 1320 S. 3rd St., Louisville KY 40208. (502)636-0115. Publishes a varying number of professional theatre, community theatre, college and university theatre, dinner theatre and summer stock plays. Query. Reports in 3 weeks. Acquires stage production rights. Pays 10% royalty on book; or 50% of standard royalty (i.e. half of $35 or $50 per performance).
Needs: "Anything the writer deems suitable for one or more of our five targeted markets." No children's plays.

ARENA STAGE, 6th and Maine Ave. SW, Washington DC 20024. (202)554-9066. Artistic Director: Zelda Fichandler. Produces 8 plays/year. 100% freelance written. Works with 1-4 unpublished/unproduced writers an-

Close-up

Sallie Bingham
Playwright

"I acted once in college. It was terrifying. I never acted again," says Sallie Bingham of her onstage theatre experience. "It was definitely beyond me." It is difficult to imagine Bingham feeling anything to be beyond her. She is a busy woman, serving as the director of the National Book Critics Circle; she is also the founder of the Kentucky Foundation for Women and the publisher of the Louisville-based literary magazine, *The American Voice*.

Although she may never act again, Bingham is still involved with the theatre. She mails out four to five plays per week, with the aim of seeing one of her plays produced per year. "I haven't quite succeeded, but I've come close—about a play every two years."

When asked why she turned to playwriting after having had numerous books and short stories published, she replies, "Playwriting is, at the moment, open to women writers and directors. Workshops and contests all over the country are devoting time and money to plays by women. This is not true of publishing. In addition, I felt the need to develop my ability to write about conflict. The theatre has forced me in this direction. And I was ready to collaborate after twenty-five years of working alone."

Bingham believes that the collaborative effort between writer and actor is something aspiring playwrights should consider. Some writers are protective of their characters; allowing another person to interpret them for an audience can sometimes prove difficult. "It is exciting and enabling," says Bingham. "It can also be highly frustrating at times, when an actor has an entirely different concept, or no concept, of the character. This is one of the dangers of releasing your characters to allow another person to bring them to life. Acting is a highly subjective art . . . the interpretation draws on years of experience, both in and out of the theatre."

Having written for both print and the stage, Bingham has noticed other differences between the two. "In fiction, I can depend on establishing a mood which will obliquely convey some of what I am trying to say. Small details carry weight. On the stage, everything must be bolder, bigger, even more obvious. Conflict cannot be hinted at. It must be seen. This leads to a greater dependence on action, rather than on words alone. And the action must mean something. Simply getting up for another cup of coffee means nothing."

When she first wrote for the theatre, Bingham was involved in all aspects of producing the play—taking part in casting, preliminary discussions and rehearsals. As she became more experienced, she cut back on that involvement. "It's important to let go early and let the director and actors take over. The script must work without the playwright's presence or interpretation. Otherwise the script is not ready, really, for production."

Bingham recommends beginning playwrights see every play they can find, "without worrying about whether it is 'good' or not. The easiest way to begin [playwriting] is with monologues and one-acts, gradually building up to a full-length play. But some short-cuts, such as two character plays, should be avoided.

"No one learns anything from talking, reading handbooks, taking classes—though the last may help in terms of loneliness. The only way is to see plays, think about plays, recast your ideas in terms of the visual. Then write, write, write."

—Sheila Freeman

nually in "Play Lab," a play development project. Stages professional productions in Washington for intelligent, educated, sophisticated audiences using resident Equity company. Virtually none of the scripts produced are unagented submissions. Works with 2-4 unpublished/unproduced writers annually. Prefers query and synopsis plus the first 10 pages of dialogue, or agented submissions. Reports in 4 months. "We obtain an option to produce for one year or other term; percentage of future earnings." Pays 5% royalty. Computer printout submissions acceptable "as long as they are easily readable; no dot-matrix."
Needs: Produces classical, contemporary European and American plays; new plays, translations and adaptations without restrictions. No sitcoms, blank verse, pseudo-Shakespearean tragedies, movies-of-the-week, or soap operas.
Tips: "We can consider large casts, though big plays are expensive and must justify that expense artistically. Be theatrical. Navel-gazing is of little interest. Plays with relevance to the human situation—which cover a multitude of dramatic approaches—are welcome here."

THE ARKANSAS ARTS CENTER CHILDREN'S THEATRE, Box 2137, MacArthur Park, Little Rock AR 72203. (501)372-4000. Artistic Director: Bradley Anderson. Produces 5 mainstage plays, 3 tours/year. Mainstage season plays performed at The Arkansas Arts Center for Little Rock and surrounding area; tour season by professional actors throughout Arkansas and surrounding states. Mainstage productions perform to family audiences in public performances; weekday performances for local schools of grades 3 through senior high school. Tour audiences generally the same. Works with 1 unpublished/unproduced writer annually. Submit complete script. Computer printout submissions acceptable; prefers letter-quality to dot-matrix. Reports in several months. Buys negotiable rights. Pays $250-1,500 or negotiable commission.
Needs: Original adaptations of classic and contemporary works. Also original scripts. "This theatre is defined as a children's theatre; this can inspire certain assumptions about the nature of the work. We would be pleased if submissions did not presume to condescend to a particular audience. We are not interested in 'cute' scripts. Submissions should simply strive to be good theatre literature."
Recent Title: *Great Expectations* (Dickens).
Tips: "We would welcome scripts open to imaginative production and interpretation. Also, scripts which are mindful that this children's theatre casts adults as adults and children as children. Scripts which are not afraid of contemporary issues are welcome."

ART CRAFT PUBLISHING CO., Box 1058, Cedar Rapids IA 52406. (319)364-6311. Publisher: C. McMullen. Publishes plays for the junior and senior high school market. Query with synopsis. Reports in 6 weeks. Acquires amateur rights only. Makes outright purchase for $100-1,500 or pays royalty.
Needs: One- and three-acts—preferably comedies or mystery comedies. Currently needs plays with a larger number of characters for production within schools. No "material with the normal 'taboos'—controversial material."

ARTREACH TOURING THEATRE, 3936 Millsbrae Ave., Cincinnati OH 45209. (513)351-9973. Director: Kathryn Schultz Miller. Produces 4 plays/year to be performed in area schools and community organizations. "We are a professional company. Our audience is primarily young people in schools and their families." Submit complete ms. Reports in 6 weeks. Buys exclusive right to produce for 9 months. Pays $4/show (approximately 150 performances).
Needs: Plays for children and adolescents. Serious, intelligent plays about contemporary life or history/legend. "Limited sets and props. Can use scripts with only 2 men and 2 women; 45 minutes long. Should be appropriate for touring." No cliched approaches, camp or musicals.
Tips: "We look for opportunities to create innovative stage effects using few props, and we like scripts with good acting opportunities."

ARTS CLUB THEATRE, 1585 Johnston St., Vancouver, British Columbia V6H 3R9 Canada. (604)687-5315. Artistic Director: Bill Millerd. Produces 14 plays/year. Plays peformed in three theatres seating 500, 200 and 225, for a diverse adult audience. Stock company operating on a year round basis. Tours British Columbia and does occasional national tours as well.
Needs: Full-length plays for adult audiences. Comedies and plays about concerns of the region. Well-made plays as opposed to experimental; realistic over fantasy. "We are interested in plays that are well-suited to our 200 seat intimate space. Such plays usually are one-set, and have limited number of characters (not more than 8) and have a strong story line. We are also interested in plays for our 500 seat theatre, and in musical revues for our cabaret theatre."
Recent Production: *It's Snowing On Saltspring*, by Nicola Cavendish (an adult Christmas fantasy-farce situated on an island close to Vancouver).
Tips: "The Arts Club recently embarked on a program of new play development under the title *Playwrights' 86*. We will be developing and producing local playwrights under the aegis of this program for the next two years, and will be concentrating on this program in terms of new play production."

ASOLO STATE THEATRE, Postal Drawer E, Sarasota FL 33578. (813)355-7115. Artistic Director: John Ulmer. Produces 7 plays/year. 80% freelance written. About 50% of scripts produced are unagented submissions. A LORT theatre with an intimate performing space. "We play to rather traditional middle class audiences." Works with 2-4 unpublished/unproduced writers annually. "We do not accept unsolicited scripts. Writers must send us a letter and synopsis with self-addressed stamped postcard." Computer printout submissions acceptable; no dot-matrix. Reports in 5 months. Negotiates rights. Negotiates payment.
Needs: Play must be *full length*. "We do not restrict ourselves to any particular genre or style—generally we do a good mix of classical and modern works."
Tips: "We have no special approach—we just want well written plays with clear, dramatic throughlines. Don't worry about trends on the stage. Write honestly and write for the stage, not for a publication."

AT THE FOOT OF THE MOUNTAIN THEATER, 2000 S. 5th St., Minneapolis MN 55454. (612)375-9487. Artistic Director: Phyllis Jane Rose. 60% freelance written. 2-4 scripts are unagented submissions. "Plays will be performed in our 'black box' theatre by a professional acting company. Plays submitted to our *Broadcloth Series* (a sampler of new scripts by women writers) will be given staged readings by our professional ensemble. Multimedia Crosscultural Alliance of Women is a group of women of color interested in producing work written and performed by people of color." Works with 4-6 unpublished/unproduced writers annually. Submit complete script. Computer printout submissions acceptable; no dot-matrix. Reports in 6 months. Pays $10-30/performance. Submissions returned with SASE.
Needs: All genres: full-length plays, one acts, and musicals by women. Encourages experimental plays. "We are mainly interested in plays by and about women and prefer to produce plays with predominantly female casts. Plays with a feminist approach to the world; plays which work at creating new forms." No sexist or racist plays.
Tips: "The theatre prefers small casts and simple sets."

RAN AVNI/JEWISH REPERTORY THEATRE, 344 E. 14th St., New York NY 10003. (212)674-7200. Artistic Director: Ran Avni. "We are an Equity non-profit theatre, Mini-contract." Produces 5 plays/year. Query with synopsis. Reports in 1 month. Pays $25-50/performance.
Needs: "Plays in English that relate to the Jewish experience."

‡BACKSTAGE THEATRE, Box 297, Breckenridge CO 80424. (303)453-0199. Artistic Director: Allyn Mosher. Produces 2-5 plays/year. Plays performed semi-professionally for resort community, tourist market. Submit query and synopsis or complete ms. Reports in 3 weeks. Pays $20-40/performance.
Needs: Comedies, mysteries and small cast musicals. Cast should be of fewer than 10, single-level sets.
Tips: "Writers should be aware of theatrical multiple roles in plays like *The Dining Room* and *Greater Tuna*. Avoid sterile TV-like situations."

BAKER'S PLAY PUBLISHING CO., 100 Chauncy St., Boston MA 02111. Editor: John B. Welch. 80% freelance written. Plays performed by amateur groups, high schools, children's theatre, churches and community theatre groups. "We are the largest publisher of chancel drama in the world." 90% of scripts are unagented submissions. Works with 2-3 unpublished/unproduced writers annually. Submit complete script. Submit complete cassette of music or musical submissions. Computer printout submissions acceptable. Publishes 18-25 straight plays and musicals; all originals. Pay varies; outright purchase price to split in production fees. Reports in 4 months.
Needs: "We are finding strong support in our new division—plays for young adults featuring contemporary issue-oriented dramatic pieces for high school production."

MARY BALDWIN COLLEGE THEATRE, Mary Baldwin College, Staunton VA 24401. (703)886-6277. Artistic Director: Dr. Virginia R. Francisco. Produces 5 plays/year. 10% freelance written. 0-1% of scripts are unagented. Works with 0-1 unpublished/unproduced writers annually. An undergraduate women's college theatre with an audience of students, faculty, staff and local community (adult, conservative). Query with synopsis. Electronic submissions OK via IBM-PC DOS Text File, Word Perfect, Word Star, or Multimate File. Computer printout submissions acceptable; prefers letter-quality to dot-matrix. Reports in 3 months. Buys performance rights only. Pays $10-50/performance.
Needs: Full-length and short comedies, tragedies, musical plays, particularly for young women actresses, dealing with women's issues both contemporary and historical. Experimental/studio theatre not suitable for heavy sets. Cast should emphasize women. No heavy sex; minimal explicit language.
Tips: "A perfect play for us has several roles for young women, few male roles, minimal production demands, a concentration on issues relevant to contemporary society, and elegant writing and structure."

‡BERKELEY JEWISH THEATRE, 1414 Walnut St., Berkeley CA 94709. (415)849-0498. Artistic Director: Barbara Damashek. Produces 4 plays and 6 staged readings/year. Plays performed in an Equity Waiver theatre, 100 seats at Berkeley Jewish Community Center. "Will move end of this year to new 200 seat theatre and caba-

ret space in redesigned Durkee building in west Berkeley." Submit complete ms. Reports in 1 month. Acquires production rights. Pays $35-50/performance.
Needs: Plays for main stage and cabaret in all genres which embody and express the variety of experience of the American Jewish diaspora.
Tips: "Writers should have a sound general knowledge of American Jewish culture and the problems confronting the largest Jewish community outside of the State of Israel. Avoid the models for plays set by Broadway, Hollywood or television, or risk ruining one's talent and integrity."

BERKSHIRE THEATRE FESTIVAL, INC., E. Main St., Stockbridge MA 01262. Artistic Director: Josephine R. Abady. 25% original scripts. Produces 7-8 plays a year (4 are mainstage and 4 are second spaces). Submissions by agents only.

BROADWAY PLAY PUBLISHING, INC., 357 W. 20th St., New York NY 10011. (212)627-1055. Publishes 15-20 plays/year. 10% of scripts published are unagented submissions. Works with 5 unpublished/unproduced writers annually. Query with synopsis. Computer printout submissions acceptable. Reports on submitted mss in 3 months. Buys stock, amateur, acting edition publishing rights. Pays 10% on book royalty; 90% stock; 80% amateur.
Needs: New contemporary full-length American plays—use of language. No autobiography, domestic realism, adaptations or translations. Musicals must be accompanied by cassette. No one-acts.

GERT BUNCHEZ AND ASSOCIATES, INC., 7730 Carondelet, St. Louis MO 63105. President: Gert Bunchez. "We feel that the time is propitious for the return of stories to radio. It is our feeling that it is not necessary to 'bring back' old programs and that there certainly should be contemporary talent to write mystery, detective, suspense, children's stories, soap operas, etc. We syndicate radio properties to advertisers and stations. Requirements are plays with sustaining lead characters, 5 minutes to 30 minutes in length, suitable for radio reproduction. Disclaimer letter must accompany scripts."

CAPITAL REPERTORY COMPANY, Box 399, Albany NY 12201. (518)462-4531. Artistic Directors: Peter Clough and Bruce Bouchard. Stages 6 productions/season. 33% freelance written. "We are a professional regional theatre with a subscriber audience (broad mix)." 50% of scripts are unagented submissions. Works with 5-10 unpublished/unproduced writers annually. Submit complete ms. Reports in 3 months. Makes outright purchase. Computer printout submissions acceptable; no dot-matrix. All genres, topics, styles, lengths, etc. are needed.
Tips: Send "bound, typed, clean manuscripts."

‡CARROLL COLLEGE, Helena MT 59625. (406)442-3450. Director of Theater: Jim Bartruff. Produces 4-6 plays/year. "We produce plays in an educational theatre with amateurs for college and community audiences." Submit query and synopsis or complete ms. Reports in 2 weeks. Pays $10-50/performance.
Needs: American standards, musicals, classics, and original scripts. "We are a small group with limited space and production budgets. Gear plays for college students learning the various crafts of the theatre."
Tips: "As a church-related college, we do dismiss certain titles due to language, topic, theme, etc."

‡CASA MANANA MUSICALS, INC., 3101 W. Lancaster, Box 9054, Fort Worth TX 76107. (817)332-9319. Producer/General Manager: Bud Franks. Produces 12 plays/year. "All performances are staged at Casa Manana Theatre and are community funded." Query. Computer printout submissions acceptable. No disk submissions. Reports in 2 months. Produces summer musicals (uses Equity people only), Theatre for Youth and new plays. Theater-in-the-round or proscenium.
Needs: Scripts of all kinds.

‡THE CAST THEATRE, 804 N. El Centro Ave., Los Angeles CA 90038. (213)462-9872. Producing Artistic Director: Ted Schmitt. Equity Waiver (professional) production either in The CAST Theatre or in The-CAST-at-the-Circle, the two theatres in the complex. The productions are meant for general audience. Submit complete ms. Reports in 4 months. Offers $100-500 advance against royalties.
Needs: "Any style, type, or genre of playscript and musicals (tape of score must accompany book and lyrics for consideration). We look for both comedies and dramas with substance and compelling ideas, that deal with human relationships and with the indomitability of the human spirit. Because of limited staging, we cannot consider elaborate concepts and are inclined to favor limbo or one-unit settings." Maximum cast: 18. No "comedies that smack of TV sit-com situations and writing."

‡CENTER FOR PUPPETRY ARTS, 1404 Spring St. NW, Atlanta GA 30309. (404)873-3089. Artistic Director: Luis Q. Barroso. Produces 4 plays/year. Professional puppet theatre. Adult audiences. Submit query and synopsis, or submit complete ms. Reports in 6 weeks. Negotiates rights. Pays $15-50/performance.
Needs: Plays that can be produced with puppets or a combination of actors and puppets. Playwright should be "adventurous, willing to deal with the uniqueness of puppetry."

Tips: "Puppetry is becoming an accepted form of theatre, not just for children but also for adults. Writers should acquaint themselves with the different types of puppets (marionette, rod, hand, shadows) and begin to write meaningful scripts for this unique art form."

THE CHANGING SCENE THEATER, 1527½ Champa St., Denver CO 80202. Director: Alfred Brooks. Year-round productions in theatre space. Cast may be made up of both professional and amateur actors. For public audience; age varies, but mostly youthful and interested in taking a chance on new and/or experimental works. No limit to subject matter or story themes. Emphasis is on the innovative. "Also, we require that the playwright be present for at least one performance of his work, if not for the entire rehearsal period. We have a small stage area, but are able to convert to round, semi-round or environmental. Prefer to do plays with limited sets and props." 1-act, 2-act and 3-act. Produces 8-10 nonmusicals a year; all are originals. 90% freelance written. 65% of scripts produced are unagented submissions. Works with 3-4 unpublished/unproduced writers annually. "We do not pay royalties or sign contracts with playwrights. We function on a performance share basis of payment. Our theatre seats 76; the first 50 seats go to the theatre; the balance is divided among the participants in the production. The performance share process is based on the entire production run and not determined by individual performances. We do not copyright our plays." Send complete script. Reporting time varies; usually several months.
Recent Title: *Hostages*, by Mary Guzzy.
Tips: "We are experimental: open to young artists who want to test their talents and open to experienced artists who want to test new ideas/explore new techniques. Dare to write 'strange and wonderful' well-thought-out scripts. We want upbeat ones. Consider that we have a small performance area when submitting."

CHILDREN'S RADIO THEATRE, 1314 14th St. NW, Washington DC 20005. (202)234-4136. Director of Production: Joan Bellsey. Produces 6 plays/year. 50% freelance written. "Children's Radio Theatre produces plays for children and their families." 100% of scripts are unagented submissions. Works with 1 unpublished/unproduced writer annually.
Needs: "Commissions writers for specific radio projects and does not produce unsolicited material. Writer must send a sample script with SASE. Reports in 3 months. Produces half-hour radio plays covering a wide range of topics including fairy tales, folk tales, musicals, adaptations, and original works. Contact Children's Radio Theatre before sending any material."

CIRCLE IN THE SQUARE THEATRE, 1633 Broadway, New York NY 10019. (212)307-2700. Artistic Director: Theodore Mann. Literary Advisor: Robert Pesola. Produces 3 plays/year. Theatre for subscription audience and New York theatre-going public. Query with 1-page synopsis only. Reports in 3 months. Pays royalty.
Tips: "We produce classics, revivals, full-length new plays and musicals."

CIRCLE REPERTORY CO., 161 Avenue of the Americas, New York NY 10013. (212)691-3210. Associate Artistic Director: Rod Marriott. Produces 5 mainstage plays. 5 Projects in Progress/year. Accepts unsolicited mss full length plays only; we no longer produce one-acts.

CIRCUIT PLAYHOUSE/PLAYHOUSE ON THE SQUARE, 51 S. Cooper, Memphis TN 38104. (901)725-0776. Artistic Director: Jackie Nichols. Produces 2 plays/year. 100% freelance written. Professional plays performed for the Memphis/Mid-South area. Member of the Theatre Communications Group. 100% of scripts are unagented submissions. Works with 1 unpublished/unproduced writer annually. A play contest is held each fall. Submit complete ms. Computer printout submissions acceptable. Reports in 3 months. Buys "percentage of royalty rights for 2 years." Pays $500-1,000 in outright purchase.
Needs: All types; limited to single or unit sets. Cast of 20 or fewer.
Tips: "Each play is read by three readers through the extended length of time a script is kept. Preference is given to scripts for the southeastern region of the U.S."

I.E. CLARK, INC., Saint John's Rd., Box 246, Schulenburg TX 78956. (409)743-3232. Publishes 15 plays/year for educational theatre, children's theatre, religious theatre, regional professional theatre, amateur community theatre. 20% freelance written. 3-4 scripts produced are unagented submissions. Works with 2-3 unpublished/unproduced writers annually. Submit complete script. Computer printout submissions acceptable; prefers letter-quality to dot-matrix. Reports in 6 months. Buys all available rights; "we serve as an agency as well as a publisher." Pays standard book and performance royalty, "the amount and percentages dependent upon type and marketability of play."
Needs: "We are interested in plays of all types—short or long. We seldom publish musicals. We prefer that a play has been produced (directed by someone other than the author); photos and reviews of the production are helpful. No limitations in cast, props, staging, etc.; however, the simpler the staging, the larger the market. Plays with more than one set are difficult to sell. So are plays with only one or two characters. We insist on literary quality. We like plays that give new interpretations and understanding of human nature. Correct spelling, punctuation and grammar (befitting the characters, of course) impress our editors."

Tips: "Entertainment value and a sense of moral responsibility seem to be returning as essential qualities of a good play script. The era of glorifying the negative elements of society seems to be fading rapidly. Literary quality, entertainment value and good craftsmanship rank in that order as the characteristics of a good script in our opinion. 'Literary quality' means that the play must say something; preferably something new and important concerning man's relations with his fellow man; and these 'lessons in living' must be presented in an intelligent, believable, and—perhaps—poetic manner."

THE CLEVELAND PLAY HOUSE, Box 1989, Cleveland OH 44106. (216)795-7010. Acting Artistic Director: William Rhys. Plays performed in professional LORT theatre for the general public. Produces 8 musicals (12%) and nonmusicals (88%) a year; 25% are originals. 25% freelance written. Very few scripts produced are unagented submissions. "Cleveland Play House is a long-standing resident company performing in three theatres presenting an eclectic season of commercial plays, musicals, and contemporary and traditional classics with occasional American and world premieres." Works with 2-3 unpublished/unproduced writers annually. Submit letter of inquiry and synopsis. Computer printout submissions acceptable; prefers letter-quality to dot-matrix. Buys stock rights and sometimes first class options. Payment varies. Reports in 6 months.
Needs: "No restrictions. Vulgarity and gratuitous fads are not held in much esteem. Cast size should be small to moderate. Plays intended for arena stages are not appropriate. Musicals should be geared for actors, not singers. One-act plays are rarely performed."

COACH HOUSE PRESS, INC., Box 458, Morton Grove IL 60053. (312)967-1777. President: David Jewell. Primarily publisher of children's plays. 100% freelance written. Most scripts published are unagented submissions. Works with 3-5 unpublished/unproduced writers annually. Publishes production scripts and trade paperback originals. Averages 3-8 plays/year. Works with 3-5 unpublished writers annually. Pays 5-15% royalty on book receipts; 50% on performance royalty. Simultaneous and photocopied submissions OK. Electronic submissions OK by special arrangement via ASCII, but requires hard copy also. Computer printout submissions acceptable; prefers letter-quality to dot-matrix. Reports in 3 weeks on queries; 2 months on mss.
Needs: Drama—plays for children's theatre and over-60 adult theatre. Books on theatre production. Publishes for theatre producers and recreation specialists.
Recent Title: *The Land of Everywhere* by Josh White III and Robert C. Williams.
Tips: "The trend to greater respect for young people is leading toward more intelligent and challenging scripts for children's theatre. A script which has received first-rate production(s) enhances its value to us, because it's more likely the author has tested and strengthened the script with the help of audience response."

CONTEMPORARY DRAMA SERVICE, 885 Elkton Dr., Colorado Springs CO 80907. Editor: Arthur L. Zapel. Publishes 25-35 plays & musicals/year; 1-act plays, 3-act plays. Both originals and adaptations. 95% freelance written. Plays performed with amateur performers for age level junior high to adult. "We publish mostly drama but also some how-to books on theatre and speech." 40% of scripts are unagented submissions. Works with 30 unpublished/unproduced writers annually. Letter quality computer printout submissions OK; no dot-matrix. Reports in 1 month. Catalog for $1 postage.
Needs: "We prefer scripts that can be produced in schools or churches where staging materials are limited. In the church field we are looking for chancel drama for presentation at various holidays: Thanksgiving, Mother's Day, Christmas, Easter, etc. School drama materials can be speech and drama contest plays and monologues, reader's theatre adaptations, drama rehearsal scripts, and musicals. Emphasis on humor. We like a free-and-easy style. Nothing too formal. We publish elementary material only for church school." Submit synopsis or complete script. Pays negotiable royalty up to 10%.
Recent Titles: *Bicycles Built for Two* by Peg Kehret (musical).
Tips: "The current use of comedy as part of socio-drama is important to us. We like message plays if they are handled with a light touch. We prefer scripts that require a minimum of set design, staging and props—scripts suitable for performance by non-professional groups."

THE CRICKET THEATRE, 528 Hennepin Ave., Minneapolis MN 55403. (612)333-5241. Artistic Director: Sean Michael Dowse. Produces 4 plays, main stage; 2-3 plays, Works-in-Progress; musicals and nonmusicals. 40% are originals. 20% freelance written. Produces plays by living American playwrights and foreign theatre companies. Audiences consist of adults and students. 25-40% of scripts are unagented submissions. Submit complete ms. "Must include SASE." Reports in 6 months minimum. Buys production rights for selected dates. Only full-length plays will be considered for production.
Needs: "There are no content or form restrictions for scripts of the main season. For Works-in-Progress, any kind of a script is welcomed provided there is a spark of a good play in it. Works-in-Progress presentations are readings, staged readings and stage 2 productions. The focus is on the text and not the fully staged, polished performance as with the main season. All Works-in-Progress playwrights are brought to Minneapolis to join in the play's rehearsal and revision process. Works-in-Progress cannot use plays currently under option or that have had full professional productions. Such plays will be considered only for the main season." No children's plays or large Broadway-type musicals. Cast limit: 9.

Tips: "Trends in the American stage freelance writers should be aware of include the drift from naturalism; the tendency not to give unsolicited manuscripts much attention; the passing of programs to develop new playwrights; the tendency to search for the next hit; and the boredom of two-character plays."

CROSSROADS THEATRE COMPANY, 320 Memorial Parkway, New Brunswick NJ 08901. (201)249-5625. Artistic Director: Lee Richardson. Produces 6 plays/year. Regional theatre that stages Equity professional productions. Query with synopsis. Computer printout submissions acceptable. Reports in 6 months. Returns rights to percentage of future productions. Pays royalty.
Needs: "We need plays involving minority experiences by any writer." Black (Afro-American, African, Caribbean) and interracial plays are preferred. Productions should be suited to a 150-seat theatre.
Tips: "We look for well-crafted scripts that deal with minorities in a non-traditional form, providing a new perspective or insight. Cast size and scenic requirements figure prominently in selection process."

DELAWARE THEATRE COMPANY, Box 516, Wilmington DE 19899. (302)658-6448. Artistic Director: Cleveland Morris. Produces 5 plays/year. 10% freelance written. "Plays are performed as part of a five-play subscription season in a 300-seat auditorium. Professional actors, directors and designers are engaged. The season is intended for a general audience." 10% of scripts are unagented submissions. Works with 1 unpublished/unproduced writer every two years. Query with synopsis. Computer printout submissions acceptable; prefers letter-quality to dot-matrix. Reports in 6 months. Buys variable rights. Pays 5% (variable) royalty.
Needs: "We present comedies, dramas, tragedies and musicals. All works must be full-length and fit in with a season composed of standards and classics. All works have a strong literary element. Plays with a flair for language and a strong involvement with the interests of classical humanism are of greatest interest. Single-set, small-cast works are likeliest for consideration."

DENVER CENTER THEATRE COMPANY, 1050 13th St., Denver CO 80204. (303)893-4200. Artistic Director: Donovan Marley. Produces 12 plays/year. Professional regional repertory (LORT-B) plays performed in the only major regional theatre in the Rocky Mountain West. Also, professional tours possible, both regionally and nationally. Submit complete ms. Computer printout submissions acceptable; no dot-matrix. Reports in 2 months. Negotiates rights. Negotiates royalty.
Needs: "Full-length comedies and dramas. The Denver Center Theatre Company is especially eager to see plays of regional interest."

DODD, MEAD & CO., 79 Madison Ave., New York NY 10016. Senior Editor: Allen T. Klots. "We're only interested in playwrights after professional production, who promise to contribute to the literature of the theatre." Royalty negotiated. Buys book rights only. Reports in 1 month.

DORSET THEATRE FESTIVAL, Box 519, Dorset VT 05251. (802)867-2223. Artistic Director: Jill Charles. Produces 6 plays/year. 20% freelance written. A professional (equity) theatre, season June-September or October. Audience is sophisticated, largely tourists and second-home owners from metropolitan New York and Boston areas. Query with synopsis and 5-10 pages dialogue; submit through agent. Computer printout submissions acceptable; prefers letter-quality to dot-matrix. Reports in 2 months. Negotiates rights. Negotiates rate; minimum $250 for 11 performances.
Needs: Full length plays (2 acts); any genre, but should have broad audience appeal; generally realistic, but *not* "kitchen dramas." Will consider musicals; must have accompanying cassette. Cast less than 10; single or unit (flexible) settings preferred. "We produce one new play each season and also have a new play reading series of 5 new scripts. We lean toward *positive* plays, whether comedy or drama. No family melodrama."
Tips: "Best time to submit plays is from September to January. (Plays received after March 1 may not be read until fall). Trends on the American stage that freelance writers should be aware of include small casts—stay away from kitchen drama."

THE DRAMATIC PUBLISHING CO., 311 Washington St., Woodstock IL 60098. (815)338-7170. Publishes about 30 new shows a year. 60% freelance written. 40% of scripts published are unagented submissions. "Current growth market is in plays and small cast musicals for stock and community theatre." Also has a large market for plays and musicals for children and for amateur theatre (i.e., junior highs, high schools, colleges, churches and other theatre groups). Works with 4-8 unpublished/unproduced writers annually. Reports in 2-6 months. Buys stock and amateur theatrical rights. Pays by usual royalty contract, 10 free scripts and 40% discount on script purchases.
Tips: "Avoid stereotype roles and situations. Submit cassette tapes with musicals whenever possible. Always include SASE if script is to be returned. Only one intermission (if any) in a show running up to two hours."

EAST WEST PLAYERS, 4424 Santa Monica Blvd., Los Angeles CA 90029. (213)660-0366. Artistic Director: Mako. 90% freelance written. Produces 5-6 plays/year. Professional plays performed in an Equity waiver house for all audiences. Works with 2-3 unpublished/unproduced writers annually. Query with synopsis or submit complete ms. Reports in 3 weeks on query and synopsis; 2 months on mss. "High majority" of scripts produced are unagented submissions. Buys standard Dramatist's Guild contract rights. Pays $200 in outright purchase or 2-6% of house receipts (ticket prices vary).

Needs: "We prefer plays dealing with Asian-American themes. The majority of the important roles should be playable by Asian-American actors; our acting company is 98 percent Asian." No fluff, TV sitcom-type material.

Tips: "East West Players was founded by a group of Asian-American actors weary of playing stereotypes in theatre and film. Submitting writers should bear this in mind and refrain from wallowing in 'exoticism.' There appears to be a minor burgeoning of interest in Asian-American writers and themes—witness David Henry Hwang's success on the East Coast, the continuing success and influence of East West Players on the West Coast and establishment theatres developing Asian American material (e.g., The Mark Taper Forum in Los Angeles working on a stage adaptation of Maxine Hong Kingston's works), etc."

ELDRIDGE PUBLISHING CO., Drawer 216, Franklin OH 45005. (513)746-6531. Editor/General Manager: Nancy Vorhis. 100% freelance written. Plays performed in high schools and churches; some professional—but most are amateur productions. Publishes plays for all age groups. Publishes 12-15 plays/year; 2% musicals; 100% originals. All scripts produced are unagented submissions. Works with 12-15 unpublished/unproduced writers annually. Send synopsis or complete script. Computer printout submissions acceptable; prefers letter-quality to dot-matrix. Buys all rights "unless the author wishes to retain some rights." Pays $100-125 for 1-act plays; $350 for 3-acts. Also royalty contracts for topnotch plays. Reports in 60 days.

Needs: "We are looking for good comedies and dramatic works which will appeal to community theatre, high school, junior-high age groups and some elementary. We do not publish anything which can be suggestive. Most of our plays are published with a hanging indentation—2 ems. All stage, scenery and costume plots must be included." No run-of-the-mill plots. Length: 1-acts from 25-30 minutes; 2-acts of around 2 hours; and skits of 10-15 minutes.

Recent Title: *Amelia, Once More* by David Muschell.

Tips: "We're interested in seeing plays reflecting today's non-nuclear families, that is Mom and Dad divorced, remarried, etc., and how this affects teens. Doesn't have to be serious or depressing but rather light and, for lack of a better word, coping. A perfect script would be one that is suitable for schools, churches and community groups to perform (nothing suggestive), is light, yet has good characterization and action. The dialog would be quick and witty. Overall, the play would have something to say. We receive a lot of scripts with little stage action, which may be OK for TV when cameras focus in on a character, but impossible on stage."

THE EMPTY SPACE, 95 S. Jackson St., Seattle WA 98104. (206)587-3737. Artistic Director: M. Burke Walker. Produces 6 plays/year. 100% freelance written. Professional plays for subscriber base and single ticket Seattle audience. 1 script is unagented submission. Works with 5-6 unpublished/unproduced writers annually. Query with synopsis before sending script. Computer printout submissions OK; prefers letter-quality to dot-matrix. Response in 3 months. LOA theatre.

Needs: "Other things besides linear, narrative realism; but we are interested in that as well; no restriction on subject matter. Generally we opt for broader, more farcical comedies and harder-edged, uncompromising dramas. We like to go places we've never been before." No commercial musicals.

‡THE ENSEMBLE STUDIO THEATRE, 549 W. 52nd St., New York NY 10019. (212)247-4982. Artistic Director: Curt Dempster. Literary Manager: D.S. Moynihan. Produces 15-20 plays/year for off-off Broadway theatre. 100-seat house, 60-seat workshop space. Submit complete ms. Reports in 3 months. Standard production contract (letter of agreement with AEA). Pays $80-1,000.

Needs: Full-lengths and one-acts with strong dramatic actions and situations. No musicals, verse-dramas or elaborate costume dramas.

Tips: Submit work September through April.

ETOBICOKE CHILDREN'S THEATRE, Box 243, Etobicoke, Ontario M9C 1Z1 Canada. (416)626-1963. Artistic Director: Mary E. Miller. Produces 5 plays/year. 50% freelance written. Plays are produced professionally with nonunion performers for children, families and seniors. Performed on tour to schools, libraries, senior citizen's homes, community centers, etc. Produces 1 unagented submission each year. Works with 1 unpublished/unproduced writer annually. Computer printout submissions acceptable; prefers letter-quality to dot-matrix. Reports in 2 months. Rights revert to author.

Needs: "For children—must be entertaining plot plus underlying social or moral values. Any 'lessons' must be learned through what happens, rather than by what is said. For seniors—must be highly entertaining; variety format is good." Length: 45-50 minutes. Cast limited to 3-5 performers. "Plays must require no definite set. Props and costumes must fit into the back of a station wagon." Query with synopsis or submit complete ms. SAE with IRCs. Pays $10-20 for 30-80 performances.

Tips: "Trends in Canadian stage and screen that freelance writers should be aware of include 'money is tight'—material must sell—and that a cast of two or three is about all that is being produced by children's touring companies."

‡**EUREKA THEATRE**, 2730 16th St., San Francisco CA 94103. (415)558-9811. Artistic Director: Tony Taccone. Produces 6 plays/year. Produces professional plays under Equity LOA contract for Bay area subscription audience. Accepts agented submissions only. Reports in 6 months. Rights purchased negotiated with agent. Pays 5% minimum royalty.
Needs: Full-length and one-acts—dramas and comedies, some with music—new plays, translations, adaptions, etc. No children's theatre.
Tips: "The Eureka Theatre has a decidedly progressive political bias and is primarily interested in plays that consciously support that concern. We are much more interested in plays which explore social relationships then domestic relationships."

‡**RICHARD FICARELLI**, 5037 Macbeth Lane SW, Ft. Meyers FL 33908. Freelance staff. Produces 1-2 plays/year. Plays are Equity productions performed in NY, Broadway and off-Broadway theatres. Submit query and synopsis. Reports in 6 weeks. Acquires DGA (standard) rights. Pays standard royalty.
Needs: Situation comedies *only*. Prefers cast of fewer than 14. No dramas.

THE FIREHOUSE THEATRE, 514 S. 11th St., Omaha NE 68102. (402)346-6009. Artistic Director: Dick Mueller. Produces 7 plays/year. Has produced 4 unagented submissions in 14 years. Computer printout submissions acceptable; prefers letter-quality to dot-matrix.
Needs: "We produce at the Firehouse Dinner Theatre in Omaha. Our interest in new scripts is the hope of finding material that can be proven here at our theatre and then go on from here to find its audience." Submit complete ms. Reporting times vary; depends on work load. Buys negotiable rights. Pays $100/week or negotiable rates.
Tips: "We are a small theatre. Certainly size and cost are a consideration. Quality is also a consideration. We can't use heavy drama in this theatre. We might, however, consider a production if it were a good script and use another theatre."

‡**FLORIDA STUDIO THEATRE**, 1241 N. Palm Ave., Sarasota FL 33577. (813)366-9017. Artistic Director: Richard Hopkins. Produces 5 established scripts and 3 new plays/year. "*FST* is a professional not-for-profit theatre." Plays are produced in 165-seat theatre for a subscription audience (primarily). *FST* operates under a small professional theatre contract of Actor's Equity. Submit query and synopsis. Reports in 1 month. Pays $200 for workshop production of new script.
Needs: Contemporary plays ("courageous and innovative"). Prefers casts of no more than 8, and single sets.

SAMUEL FRENCH, INC., 45 W. 25th St., New York NY 10010. Editor: Lawrence Harbison. 100% freelance written. "We publish about 80-90 new titles a year. We are the world's largest publisher of plays. 10-20% are unagented submissions. In addition to publishing plays, we occasionally act as agents in the placement of plays for professional production—eventually in New York. Pays on royalty basis. Submit complete ms (bound). "Always type your play in the standard, accepted stageplay manuscript format used by all professional playwrights in the U.S. If in doubt, send $3 to the attention of Lawrence Harbison for a copy of guidelines. We require a minimum of two months to report."
Needs: "We are willing at all times to read the work of freelancers. As publishers, we prefer simple-to-stage, light, happy romantic comedies or mysteries. If your work does not fall into this category, we would be reading it for consideration for agency representation. No 25-page 'full-length' plays; no children's plays to be performed *by* children; no puppet plays; no adaptations of public domain children's stories; no verse plays; no large-cast historical (costume) plays; no seasonal and/or religious plays; no 'high school' plays; no television, film or radio scripts; no translations of foreign plays."
Recent Title: *Snacks* by Leonard Gershe (light romantic comedy).

GEORGETOWN PRODUCTIONS, 7 Park Ave., New York NY 10016. Producers: Gerald Van De Vorst and David Singer. Produces 1-2 plays/year for a general audience. Works with 2-3 unpublished/unproduced writers annually. Dramatist Guild membership required. Submit complete ms only. Standard Dramatists Guild contract.
Needs: Prefers plays with small casts and not demanding more than one set. Interested in new unconventional scripts dealing with contemporary issues, comedies, mysteries, musicals or dramas. No first-drafts; outlines; 1-act plays.
Tips: "The current trend is toward light entertainment, as opposed to meaningful or serious plays."

GEVA THEATRE, 75 Woodbury Blvd., Rochester NY 14607. (716)232-1366. Literary Director: Ann Patrice Carrigan. Produces 6 plays/year. Works with 1-4 unpublished/unproduced writers annually. Query with synopsis. Reports in 6 months. Buys theatre options for 1st- and 2nd-class productions; percentage of author royalties 5 to 10 years from closing production at GeVa Theatre. Pays 5% royalty. Computer printout submissions acceptable; no dot-matrix.
Needs: "Plays done here run 2-2½ hours. We do one classical piece of world literature, one American classic,

three relatively current plays that have made an impact in resident professional theatres across the country and one new work. Those works are normally comedies and dramas in a realistic/impressionist style. We now have a play reading series—a four-day workshop process—for new writers." Limited to cast of 6 actors, 1-3 set changes. "The priority at GeVa is for scripts that touch people's heads and emotions through vital characterization and a significant storyline. We look for scripts that challenge through entertaining audiences. We are interested in scripts that would stretch the company artistically and the audience imaginatively. We would not be interested in a play whose theme, characterization and structure are not of a piece."

Tips: "Many scripts that come in are scripts for television. The writing is bald and the structure is episodic, and there is the definite logic and texture of a television movie. Writers have to make television writing work in terms of theatre. Often, they do not. People should be writing according to what they are thinking, feeling and responding to rather than *trends*."

‡GOLDEN ROD PUPPETS, 218 Northeast Ave., Swannanoa NC 28778. (704)686-5386. Puppeteer: Hobey Ford. Produces 3 plays/year. Professional productions for tours. Plays are performed solo, using a variety of puppetry techniques, puppeteer in full view. Plays and variety shows are performed at festivals, libraries, elementary schools, theatres, company parties and hotel lobbies for kindergarden through sixth grade, family audiences and adult audiences. Submit query and synopsis or letters of interest for collaboration on special projects. Reports in 1 month. Acquires full rights. Pays .06% royalty or makes outright purchase for $50-500.

Needs: Narratives introducing action, with musical background. Plot unfolds through puppet action. No dialogues, or limited to a puppet narrator. Also character skits with one character, action and dialogue, comedy. 10 characters maximum. Scenery limited or suggested by music or sound. Characters go into audience and play off environment. "I produce plays, skits and do storytelling, 5 minutes, 10 minutes, 30 minutes and 45 minutes; plays must be simple, written for puppet action, one or two characters at a time. Short animated character storytelling pieces needed. Educational, ecological or cultural themes." No "sing-song-ish" scripts, preachy scripts, negative comedy, or overtly political plays requiring elaborate staging or more than puppeteer.

Tips: "I am looking for a steady collaborator(s), willing to explore new ways of staging puppetry for a solo puppeteer. Golden Rod Puppets have innovative highly artistic puppets and staging techniques. I see a deterioration of the well-crafted story. I think writers go wrong when they forget the importance of good dialogue that builds the plot, and the art of the storyteller that is essential to most forms of theater. Writers should write what they know and feel most strongly about; then ask themselves very honestly what is essential and interesting for their audience."

HONOLULU THEATRE FOR YOUTH, Box 3257, Honolulu HI 96801. (808)521-3487. Artistic Director: John Kauffman. Produces 6 plays/year. 50% freelance written. Plays are professional productions in Hawaii, primarily for youth audiences (youth aged 2 to 20). Most scripts are unagented submissions. 80% of scripts are unagented submissions. Works with 2 unpublished/unproduced writers annually. Computer printout submissions acceptable; prefers letter-quality to dot-matrix. Reports in 3 months. Buys negotiable rights.

Needs: Contemporary subjects of concern/interest to young people; adaptations of literary classics; fantasy including space, fairy tales, myth and legend. "HTY wants well-written plays, 60-90 minutes in length, that have something worthwhile to say and that will stretch the talents of professional adult actors." Cast not exceeding 8; *no* technical extravaganzas; *no* full-orchestra musicals; simple sets and props, costumes can be elaborate. No plays to be enacted by children or camp versions of popular fairytales. Query with synopsis. Pays $1,000-2,500.

Tips: "Young people are intelligent and perceptive, if anything more so than lots of adults, and if they are to become fans and eventual supporters of good theatre, they must see good theatre while they are young. Trends on the America stage that freelance writers should be aware of include a growing awareness that we are living in a world community. We must learn to share and understand other people and other cultures."

WILLIAM E. HUNT, 801 West End Ave., New York NY 10025. Interested in reading scripts for stock production, off-Broadway and even Broadway production. "Small cast, youth-oriented, meaningful, technically adventuresome; serious, funny, far-out. Must be about people first, ideas second. No political or social tracts." No 1-act, anti-Black, anti-Semitic or anti-Gay plays. "I do not want 1920, 1930 or 1940 plays disguised as modern by 'modern' language. I do not want plays with 24 characters, plays with 150 costumes, plays about symbols instead of people. I do not want plays which are really movie or television scripts." Works with 2-3 unpublished/unproduced writers annually. Pays royalties on production. Off-Broadway, 5%; on Broadway, 5%, 7½% and 10%, based on gross. No royalty paid if play is selected for a showcase production. Reports in "a few weeks." Must have SASE or script will not be returned.

Tips: "Production costs and weekly running costs in the legitimate theatre are so high today that no play (or it is the very rare play) with more than six characters and more than one set, by a novice playwright, is likely to be produced unless that playwright will either put up or raise the money him or herself for the production."

‡HUNTINGTON PLAYHOUSE, 28601 Lake Rd., Bay Village OH 44140. (216)871-8333. Artistic Director: Bud Binns. Produces 7 plays/year. Stages amateur productions at own theatre for an adult community audi-

ence. Submit complete ms. Reports in 2 months. Pays $35-40/performance; $75-100/performance on musical.
Needs: Musicals and straight comedies. No dramas.

ILLUSION THEATER, Suite 704, 528 Hennepin Ave., Minneapolis MN 55403. (612)339-4945. Artistic Director: Michael Robins. Produces 3-9 plays/year. 90% freelance written. 2-3 scripts are unagented submissions. Works with 1-2 unpublished/unproduced writers annually. "We are a professional acting company performing usually in a studio space seating approximately 300 people. Occasionally productions tour to colleges and high schools. Audience is generally between ages 18-40." Query with synopsis. Letter quality submissions are preferred. Reports in 1 month. "Work we do with playwrights is collaborative. Agreements pertaining to rights are made on an individual basis depending on the project." Pays fee plus royalty.
Needs: "Our plays range from adaptations of works of literature (*Spring Awakening, Orlando*) to plays created around the history of the acting company's grandparents (*Becoming Memories*) to plays dealing with social issues. The resident company is six actors although the theatre does hire additional artists when needed." Playwrights should send general business letter introducing themselves and their work and include resume if possible.
Tips: "The theatre is not interested in children's plays, religious plays, or plays suitable for the commercial dinner theatre type audiences. Also not interested in plays that are sexist or abusive towards a specific group of people. Our theatre most frequently works with playwrights to collaborate on plays. While the theatre is interested in reading manuscripts to get a sense of the playwright's writing ability and style, the theatre rarely commissions works already complete."

INDIANA REPERTORY THEATRE, 140 W. Washington, Indianapolis IN 46204. (317)635-5277. Artistic Director: Tom Haas. Produces 10 full-length, 9 90-minute cabarets/year. Plays are professional productions, LORT B and C contracts, in 3 theatres. Mainstage seats 600, Upperstage seats 250, Cabaret seats 150. Subscription audience composed of cross section of Indianapolis community. Query with synopsis. Reports in 3 months. Retains rights for first- or second-class production with 60 days after production closes; retains percent on subsequent productions elsewhere. Pays 5% royalty; $500-1,000 nonrefundable advance over royalties.
Needs: "On our Mainstage we produce exclusively classics, with a heavy emphasis on American work, adaptations of classic work or new translations of classic work; also produce one musical yearly (often new musical). Upperstage produces new work of a smaller scale. Cabaret produces exclusively small cast (5 or less) satirical musicals. Prefer under 10 casts, staging which can be adapted—that is, not rigidly realistic; prefer one set or unit set which can be adapted. We tend to be attracted to plays that display an acute interest in using language vigorously, that exhibit an awareness of political thinking without being imitative of political situations. We are interested in epic proportion and in plays that speak very directly to concerns of 1980s. No TV scripts, movie scripts or things that rely on dated techniques like flashbacks; plays which depend on excessive profanity or explicit sexual behavior; one acts."

INVISIBLE THEATRE, 1400 N. 1st Ave., Tucson AZ 85719. (602)882-9721. Artistic Director: Susan Claassen. Produces 5-7 plays/year. 10% freelance written. Semiprofessional regional theatre for liberal, college-educated audiences. Plays performed in 78 seat non-Equity theatre with small production budget. "During 85-86 season we gave staged-readings to five unagented scripts, four of them selected from our 1985 AZ New Play Contest." Works with 1-5 unpublished/unproduced writers annually. Query with synopsis. Computer printout submissions acceptable; prefers letter-quality to dot-matrix. Reports in 6 months. Buys non-professional rights. Pays 10% of royalty.
Needs: "Two act plays, generally contemporary, some historical, comedies, drama, small musicals, wide range of topics. Limited to plays with small casts of 10 or less, strong female roles, simple sets, minimal props." No large musicals, complex set designs, casts larger than 15.
Tips: "Trends in the American stage that will affect the types of scripts we accept include social issues—social conscience—i.e. South Africa, coming to terms with elderly parents, overcoming effects of disease, family relationships, things that the average person can relate to and think about. Challenges we can all relate to, common experiences, because people enjoy people. Our audiences include some older, somewhat conservative, members (although *not* rigid or dogmatic) as well as younger, more liberal groups. We try to have broad appeal—mixing experimental with comedy and drama throughout the year."

‡JANUS THEATRE CO., INC., 124 W. Coronado Rd., Phoenix AZ 85003. (602)258-2727. Artistic Director: Steven C. Schemmel. Produces 4-5 plays/year. Plays performed for community theatre. Mixed audience, all ages. Submit complete ms. Reports in 2 months. Pays $25-50/performance.
Needs: All types of plays—half of season deals with homosexual (male-female) themes. Cast of six to twelve.

LAMB'S PLAYERS THEATRE, 500 Plaza Blvd., Box 26, National City CA 92050. (619)474-3385. Artistic Director: Robert Smyth. Produces 8 plays/year. 15% freelance written. A professional non-Equity resident company with a year-round production schedule. Audience is varied; high percentage of family and church interest. Works with 1-2 unpublished/unproduced writers annually. Submit synopsis or script with application for Fieldstead New Plays Award. Computer printout submissions acceptable. Reports in 4 months. Buys first production rights, touring option. Pays $500-5,000.

Needs: "We produce a wide variety of material which, while not necessarily 'religious' in nature often reflects a broad-based Christian perspective." Prefers smaller cast (2-10); adaptable staging (arena stage). "We are not interested in material that is 'preachy,' or material that's intention is to shock or titillate with sex, violence or language."

Tips: "Trends freelance writers should be aware of include productions which offer hope without being cliche or sentimental; productions needing small cast and imaginative yet inexpensive sets; and an interest in presentational style pieces—acknowledgment and/or interaction with the audience."

LILLENAS PUBLISHING CO., Box 527, Kansas City MO 64141. (816)931-1900. Editor, Lillenas Drama Resources: Paul Miller. Publishes 4 collections composed of 25 short plays/year (total). 98% freelance written. All scripts published are unagented submissions. "Because we are a religious music and play publisher, most of our works will be performed by churches and church-related schools." Submit query and synopsis or complete ms. "Both are acceptable when the writer is aware of our market." Works with 25 unpublished/unproduced writers annually. Reports in 2 months. "On short plays that become a part of a collection (Christmas, Easter, Mother's Day, etc.) we obtain first rights; on full length plays (or serious one-act plays and sketches) we negotiate with the author. Generally, the work is copyrighted in the author's name." Pays 10% royalty on full length plays and collections by one author, no advance; or pays in outright purchase from $5/double-spaced, typed ms page. Computer printout submissions acceptable; no dot-matrix. Write for a copy of contributor's guidelines and current need sheets.

Needs: *Full-length plays:* "This is a new venture; we are looking for Biblical and contemporary themes. Prefer characterization and thought over settings and large casts." *Short plays and skits:* Primarily seasonal. Children and teen actors (some adults OK). "We are interested in chancel drama, reader's theatre, and choral speaking pieces, as well as traditional staged scripts." Stylistic concerns: "Thorough knowledge of proper script format; complete listing of cast, prop, and set requirements; approximate timing. Likes to have a summary paragraph for the reader. Taboos—'good guys' drinking and smoking; put-down of church." No short plays and skits dealing with "the real meaning of Christmas;" a secular approach to Easter and Christmas (Santa Claus, Easter Bunny), fantasy; "religious themes that drip with sentimentality and the miraculous;" plots that depend on the coincidental and plots that have too many subthemes. "We want one strong idea."

Tips: "We are distributed in 10,000 Christian bookstores in North America and other areas of the English-speaking world. We also deal with musicals that have religious themes (again, both Biblical and contemporary)."

LOS ANGELES THEATRE CENTER, 514 S. Spring St., Los Angeles CA 90013. (213)627-6500. Artistic Producing Director: Bill Bushnell. Produces 15-20 plays/year. 90% freelance written. A professional theatre for a multicultural metropolitan audience. 10% of scripts are unagented submissions. Works with 3-5 unproduced writers annually. Query with synopsis plus 10 pages of script. *No unsolicited ms.* Send script inquiries to Mame Hunt, literary manager. Reports in 6 months. Buys first production rights, options to extend and move, subsidiaries. Pays 4-7% royalty. Computer printout submissions acceptable; no dot-matrix.

Needs: Plays with social or political awareness preferred. 10 actors maximum. No "television scripts or movies pretending to be theatre."

Tips: "The most important and exciting new work in the theatre is non-naturalistic. It takes risks with its subject matter and form and, therefore, it is dramatic writing that cannot be easily transferred to another form, i.e., television or film."

‡LUNCHBOX THEATRE, Box 9027, Bow Valley Sq. II, Calgary, Alberta T2P 2W4 Canada. (403)265-4292. Artistic Director: Bartley Bard. Produces 8 plays/year. 12.5% freelance written. Varying number of scripts produced are unagented submissions. Professional company performs at lunchtime for downtown workers, shoppers, school groups—everyone. Submit complete ms. Reports in 2 months. Pays $25 and up/performance. Returns scripts once or twice a year. "In the meantime, we mail out letters."

Needs: One-acts only. "Must be 40-50 minutes in length. Emphasis on fast-paced comedies. Small cast plays given more consideration. Generally, *one* set. No 'dead baby' plays, plays containing overt physical violence, 'prairie dramas' or 'kitchen sink dramas.' "

THE MAC-HAYDN THEATRE, INC., Box 204, Chatham NY 12037. (518)392-9292 (summer). Producers: Lynne Haydn, Linda MacNish. Produces 6-15 plays/year. "This is a resort area, and our audiences include rural residents and summer residents from the metropolitan New York City and Albany areas who demand professional quality productions." Reports in 8 months. Buys exclusive rights to stage production.

Needs: "We are interested in musicals which are wholesome family entertainment; these should be full-length musicals, although we might consider one-act musicals in the future. There is no limitation as to topic, so long as the object is to entertain. We will consider original material as well as adaptations, but any adaptations of

copyright material must include proper clearances. We are most interested in legitimate music for trained voices; no rock or fad music. We are looking for scripts which have a story to tell, and which build to a climax; no vignettes, slice of life or character study. We prefer a fast pace and good emotional content, and the score should extend the action, not cause it to stop. We are not interested in political muck-raking or controversy unless it has high entertainment value, and we will not consider obscenity, nudity or bad writing." Submit complete ms; we can only consider a complete script and written score, and would prefer that at least a piano tape be included on the score. Pays $25-100/performance.
Recent Production: *Pal Joey* by Rodgers and Hart.

MAGIC THEATRE, INC., Bldg. D, Fort Mason, San Francisco CA 94123. (415)441-8001. General Director: John Lion. Administrative Director: Marcia O'Dea. Dramaturge: Martin Esslin. "Oldest experimental theatre in California." For public audience, generally college-educated. General cross-section of the area with an interest in alternative theatre. Plays produced in the off-Broadway manner. Cast is part Equity, part non-Equity. Produces 7 plays/year. 50% of scripts produced are unagented submissions. Works with 4-6 unpublished/unproduced writers annually. Submit complete ms.
Needs: "The playwright should have an approach to his writing with a specific intellectual concept in mind or specific theme of social relevance. We don't want to see scripts that would be television or 'B' movies-oriented. 1- or 2-act plays considered. We pay $500 advance against 5% of gross."

‡MAGNUS THEATRE COMPANY, 137 N. May St., Thunder Bay, Ontario P7C 3N8 Canada. (807)623-5818. Artistic Director: Brian Richmond. Produces 6 plays/year. Professional stock theatre produced in 197-seat facility, and performed for a demographically-diverse general audience. Acquires first production rights within one year; second production and touring rights (Canada) for the following 9-12 months. Pays 8-10% royalty.
Needs: "Fairly general in genres, but with a particular emphasis on new plays, must be full-length. Smaller (i.e. up to seven) casts are viewed favorably; some technical limitations, always, always, budget limitations. No one act plays or plays with very large casts, multiple settings, plays which are specifically American in theme or content."
Tips: Thunder Bay is very earthy, lunch-bucket city, and we try to reflect that sensibility in our choice of plays. Beyond that, however, Magnus has gained a national reputation for its commitment to the development and production of new plays, including, where possible, workshops. Scripts should be universal (i.e. accessible to Canadian audiences) in theme; should be produceable within realistic budget limitations.

MANHATTAN THEATRE CLUB, 321 E. 73 St., New York NY 10021. Literary Manager: Molly Fowler. Produces 10 plays/year. All freelance written. A few of scripts produced are unagented submissions. A two-theatre performing arts complex classified as off-Broadway, using professional actors. "We present a wide range of new work, from this country and abroad, to a subscription audience. We want plays about contemporary problems and people. Comedies are welcome. No verse plays or historical dramas or large musicals. Very heavy set shows or multiple detailed sets are out. We prefer shows with casts not more than 15. No skits, but any other length is fine." Computer printout submissions acceptable; no dot-matrix. Query with synopsis. Reports in 6 months. Payment is negotiable.

‡MERIDIAN GAY THEATRE, Box 294, Village Station, New York NY 10014. (212)279-4200. Artistic Director: Terry Helbing. Produces 4-5 mainstage plays and 10-15 staged readings/year. Plays are performed off-off-Broadway to a general audience interested in gay/lesbian themed plays. Submit query and synopsis or complete ms. Obtains New York rights only. pays 6% royalty or $20-25/performance.
Needs: Plays with gay and lesbian major characters or themes of any length or style. "We have a small theatre and budget which makes scripts with small casts and minimal set requirements more likely to be considered."

MIDWEST PLAY LAB PROGRAM, The Playwrights Center, 2301 Franklin Ave. E., Minneapolis MN 55406. (612)332-7481. Executive Director: Joan Patchen. 100% freelance written. "Midwest Play Lab is a 2-week developmental workshop for new plays. The program is held in Minneapolis-St. Paul and is open by script competition to playwrights who have an association with the 13 midwestern states or are a member of the Playwrights' Center. It is an extensive two-week workshop focusing on the development of a script and the playwright. Six plays are given staged readings at the site of the workshop." Works with 60 unpublished/unproduced writers annually. In most cases writers should be a member of the Playwrights' Center. Announcements of playwrights by mid-April. Computer printout submissions acceptable; prefers letter-quality to dot-matrix.
Needs: "We are interested in playwrights with talent, ambitions for a professional career in theatre and scripts which could benefit from an intensive developmental process involving professional dramaturges, directors and actors. A playwright needs to be affiliated with the Midwest (must be documented if they no longer reside in the Midwest) or be a Center member; MPL accepts scripts after first of each year. Full lengths only. No produced materials—"a script which has gone through a similar process which would make our work redundant

(O'Neill Conference scripts, for instance)." Submit complete ms or work in progress. Pays a small stipend; room per diem and travel.

Tips: "We do not buy scripts. We are a service organization that provides programs for developmental work on scripts for members."

‡BRUCE E. MILLAN/DETROIT REPERTORY THEATRE, 13103 Woodrow Wilson, Detroit MI 48238. (313)868-1347. Artistic Director: Bruce E. Millan. Produces 4-5 plays/year. 50% freelance written. 50% of scripts produced are unagented submissions. Plays performed professionally. "Our audience is mixed: 60% black, 40% white; mostly middle class professionals with college backgrounds." Works with 0-1 unpublished/unproduced writers annually. Submit complete ms. Computer printout submissions acceptable. Reports in 6 months. Pays for production plus $15-25/performance.

Needs: "We interracially cast without bloodline or sex distinctions when and where possible." No one-acts or musicals. Special consideration to Michigan playwrights.

NASHVILLE ACADEMY THEATRE, 724 2nd Ave. S., Nashville TN 37210. (615)254-9103. Artistic Director: Scot Copeland. Produces both amateur and professional productions in a studio situation and in a 696-seat theatre. Age groups performed for are: kindergarten through 4th grade, 5th grade through 8th, and 9th grade to adult. Produces 4 musicals (15%) and nonmusicals (85%); 15% are originals. 15% freelance written. 25% of scripts produced are unagented submissions. "We are considered a family theatre. Although we select plays for different age groups, we feel that any age should enjoy any play we do on some level. In the past we have produced murder mysteries, Shakespeare, plays of the supernatural, fairy tales, *The Mikado,* dance-drama, musical comedy, serious drama, chamber theatre, contemporary children's drama—almost anything you can think of." Reports in 2 months. Buys exclusive performance rights for middle Tennessee, one year prior to and during their production. Pays $10-35/performance. Works with 1 unpublished/unproduced writer annually. Computer printout submissions acceptable; no dot-matrix.

Needs: "We prefer a variety of styles and genres. Length is usually limited to one hour. We are interested in quality new scripts of the old fairy tales for our younger audiences. There is no limit on topics. Interested in musicals also." Wants a richness of language and mood in their productions. No intermissions. Fluid and fast moving. Must have at least some literary merit. No or little obscenity. Cast size: 5-10 players. No limits in staging.

NATIONAL ARTS CENTRE-ENGLISH THEATRE CO., Box 1534, Station B, Ottawa, Ontario K1P 5W1 Canada. (613)996-5051. Theatre Producer: Andis Celms. Produces and/or presents 12 plays/year. 0-5% freelance written. Works with 1-2 unpublished/unproduced writers annually. All scripts produced are agented submissions. Professional productions performed in the theatre and studio of the National Arts Centre (also, workshop productions in a new theatre space). Audience ranges from young/middle-aged professionals (especially civil servants) to students. Computer printout submissions acceptable; prefers letter-quality to dot-matrix.

Tips: "Our 'mainstage' audience likes a solid, well-written play with an intelligent story line and no coarse language. Our 'workshop' audience likes to be challenged, both in language and structure, but not abused. We are interested in the smaller cast, 'human interest' style of theatre and film. For example, last season we produced *Children of a Lesser God.* Our audience likes the combination of having heard of the play and being moved by the emotions."

‡NECESSARY ANGEL THEATRE, 761 Queen St. W., Toronto, Ontario M6J 1G1 Canada (416)365-0533. Artistic Director: Richard Rose. Produces 4 plays/year. Plays are Equity productions in various Toronto theatres and performance spaces for an urban audience between 20-45 years of age. Submit complete ms. Reports in 1 month. Obtains various rights "based on the manuscript (original, translation, adaptation) and the playwright (company member, etc.)." Pays 10% royalty.

Needs: "We are open to new theatrical ideas, environmental pieces, unusual acting styles, and large casts. The usual financial constraints exist, but they have never eliminated a work to which we felt a strong commitment." No "vacuous TV-influenced sit-coms and melodramas."

Tips: "Necessary Angel Theatre has a full-time dramaturge and all submissions are considered for a series of one day readings and/or one week workshops leading to productions within the company season. Playwrights should be aware of the interdisciplinary approach to performance (music, dance, visual arts, theatre) in which the essence of a piece is revealed in visual and aural images which support the text."

‡NEDERLANDER ORGANIZATION, INC., 1564 Broadway, New York NY 10036. (212)730-8200. Artistic Director: James M. Nederlander. Produces 3 or more plays/year. Plays are performed for a general audience on Broadway, London West End, and national tours. Agented submissions only; referrals from established producers also accepted. Obtains first-class Broadway and touring rights. "We also expect to obtain movie and TV rights on most projects." Payment negotiated according to Dramatists Guild guidelines.

Needs: Musicals, comedies, and dramas suitable for first-class Broadway production. Material must be suitable for staging in proscenium theatres. Musicals should not be submitted without demo tape of at least 6-8 songs; no musical projects should be sent without finished script. No one-act plays. No cabaret or musical revues.

Tips: "Good common sense should be used as to the commercial viability of a project. Scripts which have received successful showcase or regional productions are of special interest, as are projects which have placed well in award competitions. Reviews, etc., should be included with the manuscript. Multimedia projects are increasingly important, when the writing supports the spectacle. There's also a trend toward new-wave vaudeville and dramatically cohesive one- or two-person shows."

THE NEW AMERICAN THEATER, 118 N. Main St., Rockford IL 61101. (815)963-9454. Producing Director: J.R. Sullivan. Produces 6 mainstage plays in ten-month season. "The New American Theater is a professional resident theatre company performing on a thrust stage with a 270-seat house. It is located in a predominantly middle class midwestern town with significant minority populations." Submit complete ms March through June with replies in 6 months. Buys negotiable rights. Pays royalty based on number of performances. No limitations, prefer serious themes, contemporary pieces. Open to format, etc. No opera.

Tips: "We look for 'well made' plays exploring past and present American and international social themes. We produce at least 1 premiere each season."

‡THE NEW CONSERVATORY CHILDREN'S THEATRE COMPANY AND SCHOOL, Suite 205, 1537 Franklin St., San Francisco CA 94109. (415)441-0564. Artistic Director: Ed Decker. Produces 4-5 plays/year. "The New Conservatory is a children's theatre school (ages four to nineteen) which operates year-round. Each year we produce several plays, for which the older students (usually eleven and up, but younger depending on the readiness of the child) audition. These are presented to the general public at the Macondray Theatre at the Unitarian Center in San Francisco (130 seats). Our audience is approximately age ten to adult." Send query and synopsis. Reports in 1 month. Pays 5% royalty.

Needs: "We emphasize works in which children play *children*, and prefer relevant and controversial subjects, although we also do musicals. We have a commitment to new plays. Examples of our shows are: Mary Gail's *Nobody Home* (world premiere; about latchkey kids) and Brian Kral's *Special Class* (about disabled kids). As we are a non-profit group on limited budget, we tend not to have elaborate staging; however, our staff is inventive—includes choreographer and composer. Write innovative theatre that explores topics of concern/interest to young people, that takes risks. We concentrate more on ensemble than individual roles, too. We do *not* want to see fairytales or trite rehashings of things children have seen/heard since the age of two. However, we are not averse to fantasy/fable/parable in themselves, and have done an adapation of George Orwell's *Animal Farm*. See theatre as education, rather than 'children are cute'."

Tips: "It is important for young people and their families to explore and confront issues relevant to growing up in the '80's. Theatre is a marvelous teaching tool that can educate while it entertains."

NEW PLAYS INCORPORATED, Box 273, Rowayton CT 06853. (203)866-4520. Publisher: Patricia Whitton. Publishes average 4 plays/year. Publishes plays for producers of plays for young audiences and teachers in college courses on child drama. Query with synopsis. Reports in 2 months. Agent for amateur and semi-professional productions, exclusive agency for script sales. Pays 50% royalty on productions; 10% on script sales. Free catalog on request.

Needs: Plays for young audiences with something innovative in form and content. Length: usually 45-90 minutes. "Should be suitable for performance by adults for young audiences." No skits, assembly programs, improvisations or unproduced manuscripts.

‡NEW PLAYWRIGHTS' THEATRE, 31 Water Street, Ashland OR 97520. (503)482-9236. Artistic Director: Bradford O'Neil. Produces 12 new plays/year. "We facilitate our own black box theatre in Ashland with an in-house acting company of ten non-Equity actors. Guest actors and directors are hired with each season. Our audience is both local and out of state." Submit complete ms. Plays 5% royalty.

Needs: Full-length, naturalistic, surrealistic and contemporary. Emphasis is placed on excellent writing (dialogue, structure, and plotting). Single set plays preferred. Will not read plays with casts of more than eight. No children's material or " 'martini' farces—'I'm home, honey, where's my martini?' "

THE NEW PLAYWRIGHTS' THEATRE OF WASHINGTON, 1742 Church St. NW, Washington DC 20036. (202)232-4527. Contact: Literary Manager. Produces 5 musicals and straight plays and 16 readings/year. 100% freelance written. 15% of scripts produced are unagented submissions. "Plays are produced in professional productions in the 125-seat New Playwrights' Theatre in the Dupont Circle area of the city for a subscription audience as well as large single-ticket buying followers. Works with varying number of writers annually; 30% unpublished, 65% unproduced. Prefers synopsis plus 20 pages of finished script, "typed to form, suitably bound." All musicals must be accompanied by cassette tape recording of songs in proper order. Reports in 2 weeks on synopsis; 6-8 months on scripts. "Rights purchased and financial arrangements are individually negotiated." SASE, acknowledgement postcard. No rights requested on readings; buys 7% of playwright's future royalties for 7 years, and first production credit requested for plays or musicals offered as full productions. Pays 6% royalty against a $300/week minimum.

Needs: "All styles, traditional to experimental, straight plays to musicals and music-dramas, revues and cabaret shows, and full-lengths only. No verse plays, children's plays, puppet plays or film scripts. Staging: performance space adaptable."

Tips: "We prefer a strong plot line, be the play realistic, expressionistic or non-realistic, with a positive outlook on life. We prefer not to receive, but will accept plays of the 'theatre of the infirm.' Would like to find some good, new, funny plays; nothing too far out, surrealistic or avant garde. We will absolutely not accept adaptations or plays written by other than American citizens."

NEW TUNERS THEATRE, (formerly New Tuners Theatre/Performance Community), 1225 W. Belmont Ave., Chicago IL 60657. (312)929-7367. Artistic Director: Byron Schaffer, Jr. Produces 3-4 new musicals/year. 66% freelance written. "Nearly all" scripts produced are unagented submissions. Plays performed in a small off-Loop theatre seating 148 for a general theatre audience, urban/suburban mix. Submit complete ms and cassette tape of the score, if available. Reports in 6 months. Buys exclusive right of production within 80 mile radius. "Submit first, we'll negotiate later." Pays 5-10% of gross. "Authors are given a stipend to cover a residency of at least two weeks." Computer printout submissions acceptable; prefers letter-quality to dot-matrix.

Needs: "We're interested in traditional forms of musical theatre as well as more innovative styles. We have less interest in operetta and operatic works, but we'd look at anything. At this time, we have no interest in non-musical plays unless to consider them for possible adaptation—please send query letter first. We are also seeking comic sketches and songs for a 'New Faces' type revue. Our primary interest is in comedic and up-tempo songs, but we will also consider ballads. Cassette tapes of songs should be sent, if possible. Our production capabilities are limited by the lack of space, but we're very creative and authors should submit anyway. The smaller the cast, the better. We are especially interested in scripts using a younger (35 and under) ensemble of actors. We mostly look for authors who are interested in developing their script through workshops, rehearsals and production. No interest in children's theatre. No casts over 15. No one-man shows."

Tips: "Freelance writers should be aware that musical theatre can be more serious. The work of Sondheim and others who follow demonstrates clearly that musical comedy can be ambitious and can treat mature themes in a relevant way. Probably 90 percent of what we receive would fall into the category of 'fluff.' We have nothing against fluff. We've had some great successes producing it and hope to continue to offer some pastiche and farce to our audience; however, we would like to see the musical theatre articulating something about the world around us, rather than merely diverting an audience's attention from that world."

NORTHLIGHT THEATRE, (formerly Northlight Repertory Theatre), 2300 Green Bay Rd., Evanston IL 60201. (312)869-7732. Artistic Director: Michael Maggio. "We are a LORT-D theatre with a subscription audience using professional artistic personnel. Our season runs from September through June. We are committed to developing new plays, translations and adaptations from other literary forms. We produce significant new scripts and second productions from an international repertoire." Audience is primarily college educated, 35-65 years old, with a broad range of socio-economic backgrounds. Query with synopsis. Computer printout submissions acceptable. Reports in 3 months. Produces 5 mainstage plays a year; 40% are unproduced originals developed inhouse. Rights purchased vary.

Needs: "New plays and small production music theatre. Plays may vary in genre and topic. Full-length and prefer a cast size of 8 or less without doubling. Though accessibility is an issue, we rate substance as a higher concern for our audience. We have a 298-seat house with a small, extended apron proscenium stage allowing for some use of multiple sets but only the suggestion of levels, e.g. a second story home, etc. Our budget and other resources restrict very elaborate staging but we are fortunate to have very talented and creative designers. Solely commercial work or dinner theatre material is not appropriate for our audiences. Trends on the American stage that freelance writers should be aware of include adaptations from other literary forms and new translations of foreign work. We emphasize work which speaks to the human condition and is often contemporary."

Recent Title: *West Memphis Mojo* by Martin Jones.

ODYSSEY THEATRE ENSEMBLE, 12111 Ohio Ave., Los Angeles CA 90025. (213)826-1626. Artistic Director: Ron Sossi. Produces 12 plays/year. Plays performed in a 3-theatre facility. "All three theatres are Equity waiver; Odyssey 1 and 2 each have 99 seats, while Odyssey 3 has 72-90 seats. We have a subscription audience of 1,800 who subscribe to a six-play season, and are offered a discount on our remaining non-subscription plays. Remaining seats are sold to the general public." Query with synopsis, cast breakdown and 8-10 pages of sample dialogue to Literary Manager: Jon Lewis. Scripts must be securely bound. Reports in 1 month on queries; 6 months on scripts. Buys negotiable rights. Pays 5-7% royalty or $25-35/performance. "We will *not* return scripts without SASE."

Needs: Full-length plays only with "either an innovative form or extremely provocative subject matter. We desire more theatrical pieces that explore possibilities of the live theatre experience. We are seeking full-length musicals. We are not reading one-act plays or light situation comedies."

OLD GLOBE THEATRE, Box 2171, San Diego CA 92112. (619)231-1941. Artistic Director: Jack O'Brien. Produces 12 plays/year. "We are a LORT B professional house. Our plays are produced for a single ticket and subscription audience of 250,000, a large cross section of southern California, including visitors from the LA area." Submit complete ms through agent only. Reports in 2 months. Buys negotiable rights. Pays 6-10% royalty.
Needs: "We are looking for contemporary, realistic, theatrical dramas and comedies and request that all submissions be full-length plays at this time." Prefers smaller cast and single sets, and "to have the playwright submit the play he has written rather than to enforce any limitations. No musicals or large cast historical dramas."
Tips: "Get back to theatricality. I am tired of reading screenplays."

O'NEILL THEATER CENTER'S NATIONAL PLAYWRIGHTS CONFERENCE/NEW DRAMA FOR TELEVISION PROJECT, Suite 901, 234 W. 44th St., New York NY 10036. (212)382-2790. Artistic Director: Lloyd Richards. Develops staged readings of 12 stage plays, 3-4 teleplays/year for a general audience. "We accept unsolicited mss with no prejudice toward either represented or unrepresented writers. Our theatre is located in Waterford, Connecticut and we operate under an Equity LORT(C) Contract. We have 3 theatres: Barn-250 seats, Amphitheatre-300 seats, Instant Theater-150." Submit complete bound ms. Decision by late April. "We have an option on the script from time of acceptance until 60 days *after* the four-week summer conference is completed. After that, all rights revert back to the author." Pays small stipend plus room, board and transportation. Computer printout submissions acceptable. "Interested writers should send us a self-addressed-stamped #10 envelope and request our updated guidelines in September prior to the following summer's conference. We accept script submissions from Sept. 15-Dec. 1 of each year. Conference takes place during four weeks in July each summer."
Needs: "We do staged readings of new American plays. We use modular sets for all plays, minimal lighting, minimal props and no costumes. We do script-in-hand readings with professional actors and directors."

ORACLE PRESS, LTD., 5323 Heatherstone Dr., Baton Rouge LA 70820. (504)766-5577. Artistic Director: Cj Stevens. Publishes 10-15 plays/year. 90% freelance written. 90% of scripts produced are unagented submissions. Plays performed by college, high school and other amateur groups. Works with 20-30 unpublished/unproduced writers annually. Query with synopsis. Computer printout submissions acceptable; prefers letter-quality to dot-matrix. Reports in 6 weeks. Copyright in name of playwright; performance rights referred to playwright. Pays 10% royalty.
Needs: "Production must be playable *on stage*. Will not publish gratuitous filth or obscenity."
Tips: "The trend which we find deplorable is that of writing everything for Broadway; hence, small casts, limited sets. College and high school groups frequently desire just the opposite."

JOSEPH PAPP, PRODUCER, New York Shakespeare Festival/Public Theater, 425 Lafayette St., New York NY 10003. (212)598-7129. Plays and Musicals Department—Director: Gail Merrifield. Literary Manager: Bill Hart. Executive Assistant: Elizabeth Holloway. 90% freelance written. Interested in full-length plays and musical works. No restriction as to style, form, subject matter. New works produced year-round on five stages at the Public Theater complex. 3 scripts are unagented submissions. Works with 10 unpublished/unproduced writers annually. Unsolicited material accepted. Electronic submissions OK via VHS, but requires hard copy also. Computer printout submissions acceptable; prefers letter-quality to dot-matrix. Standard options and production agreements. Reports in 2 months.

PEOPLE'S LIGHT & THEATRE COMPANY, 39 Conestoga Rd., Malvern PA 19355. (215)647-1900. Producing Director: Danny S. Fruchter. Produces 6 full-length, several one-act plays/year. "LORT D Actors' Equity plays are produced in Malvern 30 miles outside Philadelphia in 350-seat main stage and 150-seat second stage. Our audience is mainly suburban, some from Philadelphia. We do a 6-show subscription season." Query with synopsis and cast list. Computer printout submissions acceptable; prefers letter-quality to dot-matrix. Reports in 10 months. Buys "rights to production in our theatre, sometimes for local touring." Pays 2-5% royalty.
Needs: "We will produce anything that interests us." Prefers single set, maximum cast of 12 (for full length), fewer for one act. No musicals, mysteries, domestic comedies.
Tips: "Freelance writers should be aware of trend away from naturalistic family drama and toward smaller cast size."

‡ERIC PETERSON, OLDCASTLE THEATRE COMPANY, Box 1555, Bennington VT 05201. (802)447-0564. Artistic Directors: Shelli DuBoff, Richard Howe. Produces 7 plays/year. Plays are performed in a small (104 seat) theatre on a former estate now used by Southern Vermont College, by a professional theatre company (in a season from April through October) for general audiences, including residents of a three-state area and tourists during the vacation season. Submit complete ms. Pays "by negotiation with the playwright. As a not-for-profit theatre company, we do not have large sums available."
Needs: Produces classics, musicals, comedy, drama, most frequently American works. Usual performance

time is 2 hours. "With a small stage, we limit to small cast and simple props, though we usually do prefer designed sets and appropriate costumes. Since our audiences are usually a mix of ages from children to elderly and of all interests, we probably could not use material that was of too narrow a scope, or prejudiced as to be hurtful to any of our audience."

‡**THE PHILADELPHIA COMPANY.** Suite 735, Bourse Building, 21 S. 5th St., Philadelphia PA 19108. (215)592-8333. Artistic Director: Sara Garonzik. Produces 4 plays/year. Professional productions. Submit resume, synopsis and complete ms. Reports in 1 month. Payment negotiated.
Needs: Plays must be written by Americans. No children's plays, musicals, or lightweight commercial pieces, such as mysteries, situation comedies, etc.
Workshops: Lynn Thomson, project director. Produces 2-3 workshops of new scripts/year. Pays $500. Write for deadline information and requirements.
Tips: "I find so many new plays evidence little or no understanding of dramatic action (and by this I don't mean heavy external action, such as muggings and deaths), and have no story to tell. The scope of the plays are small—they're case studies, not plays. Often writers don't distinguish between the nature of theatre and that of film."

‡**PIER ONE THEATRE**, Box 894, Homer AK 99603. (907)235-7333. Artistic Director: Lance Petersen. Produces 5-8 plays/year. "Plays to various audiences for various plays—e.g. children's, senior citizens, adult, family, etc. Plays are produced on Kemai Peninsula." Submit complete ms. Reports in 2 months. Acquires live performance rights. Pays $25-125/performance.
Needs: "No restrictions—willing to read *all* genres." No stock reviews, hillbilly, or sit-coms.
Tips: "Don't start your play with a telephone conversation. New plays ought to be risky business; they ought to be something the playwright feels is terriby-important."

PIONEER DRAMA SERVICE, 2171 S. Colorado Blvd., Box 22555, Denver CO 80222. (303)759-4297. Publisher: Shubert Fendrich. 10% freelance written. Plays are performed by high school, junior high and adult groups, colleges, churches and recreation programs for audiences of all ages. "We are one of the largest full-service play publishers in the country in that we handle straight plays, musicals, children's theatre and melodrama." Publishes 10 plays/year; 40% musicals and 60% straight plays. 100% of scripts published are un-agented submissions. Query only; no unsolicited manuscripts. Computer printout submissions acceptable; prefers letter-quality to dot-matrix. Buys all rights. Makes outright purchase or pays 10% royalty on copy sales; 50% of production royalty and 50% of subsidiary rights with some limitations on first-time writers. Reports in 30-60 days.
Needs: "We use the standard 1-act and 2-act format, 2-act musicals, religious drama, comedies, mysteries, drama, melodrama and plays for children's theater (plays to be done by adult actors for children)." Length: 1-acts of 30-45 minutes; 2-act musicals and 2-act comedies up to 90 minutes; and children's theatre of 1 hour. Prefer many female roles, one simple set.
Recent Title: *Luann* by Eleanor and Ray Harder (musical based on the Greg Evans comic strip).
Tips: "Pioneer Drama Service is beginning to recognize developmental drama and contemporary issues in current children's theatre as a worthwhile direction for new plays. We are also exploring the religious theatre market. Plays with a cross-market appeal (i.e., schools, community theatre, semi- and professional theatres), with one set, many female roles, two act structure are ideal for our needs."

PLAYERS PRESS, INC., Box 1132, Studio City CA 91604. Senior Editor: Robert W. Gordon. "We deal in all areas and handle works for film, television as well as theatre. But all works must be in stage play format for publication." Also produces scripts for video, and material for cable television. 80% freelance written. 10-12 scripts are unagented submissions. Works with 1-10 unpublished/unproduced writers annually. Submit complete ms. "Must have SASE or play will not be returned, and two #10 SASE for update and correspondence. All submissions must have been produced and should include a flyer and/or program with dates of performance." Reports in 3 months. Buys negotiable rights. "We prefer all area rights." Pays variable royalty "according to area; approximately 10-75% of gross receipts." Also pays in outright purchase of $100-25,000 or $5-5,000/performance.
Needs: "We prefer comedies, musicals and children's theatre, but are open to all genres. We will rework the ms after acceptance. We are interested in the quality, not the format."

PLAYS, The Drama Magazine for Young People, 120 Boylston, Boston MA 02116. Editor: Sylvia K. Burack. Publishes approximately 75 1-act plays each season to be performed by junior and senior high, middle grades, lower grades. Can use comedies, farces, melodramas, skits, mysteries and dramas, plays for holidays and other special occasions, such as Book Week; adaptations of classic stories and fables; historical plays; plays about other lands; puppet plays; folk and fairy tales; creative dramatics; and plays for conservation, ecology or human rights programs. Mss should follow the general style of *Plays*. Stage directions should not be typed in capital letters or underlined. No incorrect grammar or dialect. Characters with physical defects or speech impediments should not be included. Desired lengths for mss are: Junior and Senior high—20 double-spaced ms pages (25 to 30 minutes playing time). Middle Grades—12 to 15 pages (15 to 20 minutes playing time). Lower Grades—6 to 10 pages (8 to 15 minutes playing time). Pays "good rates on acceptance." Reports in 2-3 weeks. Sample copy $3; send SASE for manuscript specification sheet.

‡**PLAYWRIGHTS FUND OF NORTH CAROLINA, INC.**, Box 646, Greenville NC 27835. (919)758-3628. Artistic Director: Christine Rusch. Literary Director: Jeffry Scott Jones. Produces 10 workshop productions/year. Productions are usually staged readings in non-traditional theatre space for purposes of script development. "We do about eight new one-acts each season at the Best Lunch Theatre Ever and Downtown, Downstairs (Sept.-May), with selected longer work at annual PFNC Southeastern Playwrights' Conference (June). Our audiences are intelligent, sensitive folks who love informal theatre. Each of our plays is followed by a post-performance discussion with the playwright, director, cast and audience." Produces plays by Southeastern writers only. Submit query and synopsis or complete ms. "We request program/publishing credit for works we've done." Pays $75, travel and per diem so playwight can attend.
Needs: One-acts written by playwrights residing in the Southeastern U.S. (North Carolina, South Carolina, Virginia, West Virginia, Tennessee, Kentucky, Florida, Georgia, District of Columbia, Maryland); "we look for fresh, vivid language, structured action, manifested values. Most of our productions are staged readings. If we can't *do* it (and we like the play), we'll *read* it. We are not currently able to accept scripts from outside the Southeastern U.S. region."
Tips: "Our focus is on helping the playwright to develop his/her work to its fullest literary potential. We read and provide written response to everything, so be patient. We also have annual PFNC Competition for NC Playwrights (deadline Oct. 1)."

‡**RAFT THEATRE**, 432 W. 42nd St., New York NY 10036. (212)947-8389. Artistic Director: Martin Zurla. Produces 5 plays/year. Plays performed are professional: showcase (AEA), with mini-contract, off-Broadway; intended for general audiences. Submit complete ms. Computer printout submissions OK. Reports in 4 months. Pays on year option and royalty (on individual basis).
Needs: "We have *no* restrictions on content, theme, style or length. Prefer scripts that have six or *fewer* characters and limited set and scene changes (due to performing space); and scripts that are typed in professional play-script format (theme, structure, format, etc.)."
Tips: "We are looking for writers that respect their craft and present their work in like manner. We prefer works that set their own trends and not those that follow other trends. We normally look for scripts that deal with human issues and cover a wide scope and audience, and not the so-called commercial property."

‡**A.M. RAYCHEL**, Suite 200, 750 8th Ave., New York NY 10036. Artistic Director: A.M. Raychel. Produces 4 plays/year, mostly Equity showcase productions, occasional off-Broadway and staged readings. Submit query and synopsis or complete ms. Reports in 2 months. Pays $35 maximum.
Needs: Strong statements on relevant social issues. Likes experimental formats, theatre cabaret style and film techniques. Prefers 10 or less characters. No traditional, conventional, historical, light comedy or sitcom-like plays.
Tips: "Narrative elements must be minimal. Use of stylized movement and gesture, sound space/time freedom all enhance productions—make stronger use of *theatrical* possibilities."

READ MAGAZINE, 245 Long Hill Rd., Middletown CT 06457. (203)347-7251. Senior Editor: Edwin A. Hoey. 10% freelance written. For junior high school students. Biweekly magazine; 32 pages. Circ. 500,000. Rights purchased vary with author and material. May buy second serial (reprint) rights or all rights. Byline given. Buys 10 mss/year. Pays on publication. Sample copy and writer's guidelines for SASE. Will consider photocopied submissions. No simultaneous submissions. Reports in 6 weeks. Submit complete ms.
Drama and Fiction: First emphasis is on plays; second on fiction with suspense, adventure or teenage identification themes. "No preachy material. Plays should have 12 to 15 parts and not require complicated stage directions, for they'll be used mainly for reading aloud in class. Remember that we try to be educational as well as entertaining." No kid detective stories or plays. No obscenity. Pays $50 minimum.

‡**SAIDYE BRONFMAN CENTRE**, 5170 Cote St. Catherine Rd., Montreal, Quebec H3W 1M7 Canada. (514)739-2301. Director: Harry Gulkin. Coordinator of Performing Arts: Jane Needles. Produces 5-7 plays/year. Professional theatre company. Plays performed in 350 seat theatre. Submit complete ms. Reports in 2 months. Rights negotiated. Pays 4-5% royalty ("approximately, depending on the work").
Needs: Plays with Jewish themes or characters. Small cast. "Themes should be current or daily problems, but we are not specific in our requirements, as plays take many forms."
Tips: "Trends seem to be going towards the intimate play, with a theme that affects everyone, especially child-abuse, drug-abuse, medical problems, etc., although there are a number of historical plays that are surfacing showing a deep interest in past history."

THE SHAKESPEARE THEATRE AT THE FOLGER, 301 E. Capitol St. SE, Washington DC 20003. (202)547-3230. Artistic Producer: John Neville-Andrews. Produces 5 plays/year. 3% freelance written. A LORT D regional theatre for general audience, classically oriented. Works with 1—if any at all—unpublished/unproduced writers annually. Computer printout submissions acceptable; no dot-matrix. Reports in 3 months. Negotiates rights. Negotiates payment.
Needs: Classics, new adaptations, and translations of classics only. Query with synopsis; submit through agent.
Tips: "We look for universal ideas and as far as translations and adaptations go—clear, literate scripts that are ture to the spirit and intention of the original."

‡SHAW FESTIVAL CANADA, Box 774, Niagara-on-the-Lake, Ontario L0S 1J0 Canada. Artistic Director: Christopher Newton. Produces 10 plays/year. 4% freelance written. "Professional summer festival operating three theaters (Festival: 845 seats, Court House: 370 seats and Royal George: 250 seats). We also host some music and some winter rentals. Mandate is based on the works of G.B. Shaw and his contemporaries." No scripts are unagented submissions. Works with 2 unpublished/unproduced writers annually. Submit complete ms. Computer printout submissions acceptable; no dot-matrix. Reports in 6 months. "We prefer to hold rights for Canada and northeastern U.S., also potential to tour." Pays 5-6% royalty. SASE or SAE and IRCs.
Needs: We operate an acting ensemble of up to 75 actors, this includes 12 actors/singers and have sophisticated production facilities. We run a winter season in Toronto for the production of new works. During the summer season (April-October) the Academy of the Shaw Festival organizes several workshops of new plays."

‡RICHMOND SHEPARD THEATRE STUDIOS, 6468 Santa Monica Blvd., Hollywood CA 90038. (213)462-9399. Artistic Director: Richmond Shepard. Produces 4 new plays/year. Has Equity waiver in Hollywood for the general public. "Our shows are reviewed by all the Los Angeles press and have won many awards. Several have been subsequently published and/or optioned for further production." Prefers query and synopsis "but will accept complete ms." Reports in 2 months. Acquires perpetual residual rights for first production. Pays royalty of 6% of gross after initial production has recouped its investment. Must enclose SASE for reply.
Needs: Small casts, few sets preferred. Use *play form* in your writing. No "illiterate soap operas or plays with much exposition. Familiar plays we have produced include *Travesties* by Tom Stoppard; *Cold Storage* by Ron Ribman and *Entertaining Mr. Sloane* by Joe Orton—shows that show a little intellect and wit."

SOHO REPERTORY THEATRE, 80 Varick St., New York NY 10013. (212)925-2588. Co-Artistic Directors: Jerry Engelbach and Marlene Swartz. Produces 4-10 full productions and 8-10 staged readings/year. 25% freelance written. Performances at the Greenwich House Theatre, Greenwich Village. "The audience is well-educated, mature and composed of regular theatregoers. Our playwrights have usually been produced, and some published, previously." All scripts are unagented submissions. Works with 5-10 unpublished/unproduced writers annually, including productions and staged readings. Query with description of the play and how it will work as a live theatre piece. "We prefer that queries/descriptions be submitted by a director interested in staging the play, but will accept author queries, too." Computer printout submissions acceptable; prefers letter-quality to dot-matrix. Reports in 90 days. Rights for full-length plays: percentage of author's royalties on future earnings; credit in published script and on future programs; for staged readings: none. Pays $100 and up for limited run performance rights. Pays $500 and up for future right to option.
Needs: "Unusual plays not likely to be seen elsewhere; including rarely produced classics; revivals of superior modern works; new plays that utilize contemporary theatre techniques; and musicals and mixed media pieces that are noncommercial. Writers should keep in mind that our stage is a thrust, not a proscenium." Desires "full-length works that are physical, three-dimensional and that use heightened language, are witty and sophisticated, and that demonstrate a high quality of dramatic craft. No sitcoms, featherweight pieces for featherbrained audiences, drawing room plays, pedantic political pieces, works that do not require the audience to think, or pieces more suited to television or the printed page than to the live stage."
Tips: "We go our own way and are not influenced by 'trends,' 'fads' or other commercial, nonartistic considerations. An ideal script for Soho Rep is highly literate, witty, and dramatically sound, and has plenty of scope for imaginative, physically active staging that breaks the fourth wall."

‡SOUTH COAST REPERTORY, Box 2197, Costa Mesa CA 92628. (714)957-2602. Dramaturge: Jerry Patch. Literary Manager: John Glore. Produces 6 plays/year on mainstage, 5 on second stage. A professional non-profit theatre; a member of LORT and TCG. "We operate in our own facility which houses a 507-seat mainstage theatre and a 161-seat second stage theatre. We have a combined subscription audience of 24,000." Submit query and synopsis; manuscripts considered if submitted by agent. Reports in 4 months. Acquires negotiable rights. Pays negotiable royalty (usually 5%).
Needs: "We produce mostly full-lengths but will consider one-acts. Our only iron-clad restriction is that a play be well-written. We prefer plays that address contemporary concerns and are dramaturgically innovative.

A play whose cast is larger than fifteen-twenty will need to be extremely compelling and its cast size must be justifiable."
Tips: "We don't look for a writer to write for us—he or she should write for him or herself. We look for honesty and a fresh voice. We're not likely to be interested in writers who are mindful of *any* trends. Originality and craftsmanship are the most important qualities we look for."

SOUTHEASTERN ACADEMY OF THEATRE AND MUSIC INC., DBA ACADEMY THEATRE, 1137 Peachtree St. NE, Atlanta GA 30309. (404)873-2518. Artistic Director: Frank Wittow. Produces 12-18 plays/year; mainstage subscription series theatre for youth, first stage studio new play series, school of performing art, and lab theatre series. Query and/or synopsis or agented submissions. Reports in 6 months. Buys "usually sole and exclusive right to produce play within a 100-mile radius of the metro Atlanta area for up to 3 years." Pays 5% royalty or $5-100/performance.
Needs: "Full-length, small cast shows which provide interesting challenges for actors. Plays which deal with new approaches to naturalism, transformational plays. One-acts considered for lab theatre (minimal royalty)." Cast: 12 maximum. Minimal or simple sets. "Deal with basic, honest emotions. Delve into social issues in a subtle manner. Provide thought-provoking material which deals with the human condition and allows for greater self-awareness." No frivolous, light comedies.
Tips: "The Academy Theatre is devoted to exploring human behavior, through physical and emotional involvement, for the purpose of greater self-awareness, for the purpose of making people more social, more able to live with each other."

STAGE ONE: The Louisville Children's Theatre, 721 W. Main St., Louisville KY 40202. (502)589-5946. Producing Director: Moses Goldberg. Produces 6-7 plays/year. 20% freelance written. 15-20% of scripts produced are unagented submissions (excluding work of Playwright-in-Residence). Plays performed by an Equity company for young audiences aged 4-18; usually does different plays for different age groups within that range. Submit complete ms. Computer printout submissions acceptable. Reports in 4 months. Pays negotiable royalty or $25-50/performance.
Needs: "Good plays for young audiences of all types: adventure, fantasy, realism, serious problem plays about growing up or family entertainment." Cast: ideally, 10 or less. "Honest, visual potentiality, worthwhile story and characters are necessary. An awareness of children and their schooling is a plus." No "campy material or anything condescending to children. No musicals unless they are fairly limited in orchestration."

‡STAGES REPERTORY THEATRE, Suite 101, 3201 Allen Pkwy., Houston TX 77019. (713)527-0240. Artistic Director: Ted Swindley. Produces 12 adult, 5 children's plays/year. Non-profit professional company, operating in two theatres (one arena and one thrust). "We also tour with children's programs in the Houston area. Adult audience is a fairly eclectic urban mix, tending, we hope, towards the adventurous. Our children's shows are for four to eleven, mostly school groups. All scripts should be accompanied by resume, SASE, and one-page synopsis including casting and technical requirements. No unbound scripts. Reports in 3 months. Rights and payment negotiated."
Needs: "Our Mainstage programming tends towards new off-Broadway works, (renovated) classics and towards thought-provoking, issue oriented theatre. Our children's programming focuses on works that parents will enjoy as much as kids and we're always looking for children's scripts that lend themselves to the creation of educational materials for distribution to the teachers." Small-scale production requirements preferable.

CHARLES STILWILL, Managing Director, Community Playhouse, Box 433, Waterloo IA 50704. (319)235-0367. Plays performed by Waterloo Community Playhouse with a volunteer cast. Produces 13 plays (7 adult, 6 children's); 1-3 musicals and 7-12 nonmusicals/year; 1-4 originals. 17% freelance written. Most scripts produced are unagented submissions. Works with 1-4 unpublished/unproduced writers annually. "We are one of few community theatres with a commitment to new scripts. We do at least one and have done as many as four a year. We are the largest community theatre per capita in the country. We have 3,000 season members." Average attendance at main stage shows is 3,000; at studio shows 1,500. "We try to fit the play to the theatre. We do a wide variety of plays. Looking for good plays with more roles for women than men. Our public isn't going to accept nudity, too much sex, too much strong language. We don't have enough Black actors to do all-Black shows." Theatre has done plays with as few as two characters, and as many as 98. "On the main stage, we usually pay between $300 and $500. In our studio, we usually pay between $50 and $300. We also produce children's theatre. We are looking for good adaptations of name children's shows and very good shows that don't

Market conditions are constantly changing! If this is 1988 or later, buy the newest edition of Writer's Market *at your favorite bookstore or order directly from* Writer's Digest Books.

necessarily have a name. We produce children's theatre with both adult and child actors. We also do a small (2-6 actors) cast show that tours the elementary schools in the spring. This does not have to be a name, but it can only be about 35 minutes long." Send synopsis or complete script. Computer printout submissions acceptable. "Reports negatively within 11 months, but acceptance takes longer because we try to fit a wanted script into the balanced season."
Recent Title: *Time Bomb* by Betty Jane Wylie (world premiere).

‡STUDIO THEATRE, Box 301, Lindenhurst NY 11757. (516)226-1838. Artistic Director: Marcey Levin. Produces 8+ plays/year. Plays are performed for a regional general audience for a maximum of 18 performances in a 150 seat house, thrust stage, with limited wing space. Submit query and synopsis, or complete script. Reports in 2 months. Pays $10-15/performance.
Needs: Contemporary drama and comedy, one-act or full-length, with a strong social, political, psychological or emotional statement (impressionistic, absurdist, nontraditional). Should have 5 or fewer characters with minimal scenic requirements. No musicals, romance, or "living room" drama or comedy.
Workshops: Plays in Process "is interested in experimental and developmental styles in any form with strong thematic structure. We like to challenge ourselves and our audience with non-traditional styles."
Tips: "Today's writers should be sensitive to a more theatre-wise and knowledgable audience."

‡THEATER LUDICRUM, INC., Suite 83, 64 Charlesgate E., Boston MA 02215. (617)424-6831. Contact: Director. Produces 2-3 plays/year. Plays are performed in a small, non-Equity theatre in Boston. "Our audience includes minority groups (people of color, gays, women)." Submit complete ms. Reports in 2 weeks. Rights revert to author after production. Pays $15-30/performance.
Needs: "As a small theater with a small budget, we look for scripts with minimal sets, costumes, props and expense in general. We are interested in scripts that emphasize the word and acting."

‡THEATER OF THE OPEN EYE, 270 W. 89th St., New York NY 10024. (212)769-4143. Artistic Director: Amie Brockway. Produces 3-4 full-length plays/year plus a series of readings and workshop productions of one acts. "The Open Eye is a professional, Equity LOA, 115-seat, off-off Broadway theater. Our audiences include a broad spectrum of ages and backgrounds." Submit complete ms in clean, bound copy with SASE for its return. Reports in 3-6 months. Playwright fee for mainstage: $500.
Needs: "Theatre of the Open Eye is particularly interested in one-act and full-length plays that take full advantage of the live performance situation. We tend not to do totally realistic plays. We especially like plays that appeal to young people and adults alike."

‡THEATRE ON THE MOVE, Box 462, Islington, Ontario M9A 4X4 Canada. (416)622-1423. Executive Director: Anne Hines. Produces 5 plays/year for families and young audiences—elementary and high schools and special venues (museums, etc.). Uses professional, adult union actors. Submit query and synopsis or complete ms. Reports in 2 months. Acquires exclusive rights to Ontario, usually for a minimum of 1 year. Pays royalty, or commission for works-in-progress.
Needs: Musicals or dramas for small casts (limit 4 actors) which deal with current topics of interest to children and families. Uncomplicated, 'tourable' sets.
Tips: "Our shows have to educate the audience about some aspect of modern life, as well as entertain. The trend is away from fairy-tales, etc."

‡THEATRE RHINOCEROS, 2926 16th St., San Francisco CA 54103. (415)552-4100. Artistic Director: Kris Gannon. Produces 6-10 plays/year. Professional productions of plays written by and relevant to gay and lesbian people. Submit complete ms. Reports in 3 months. Acquires production rights—some subsidiary rights for unproduced scripts. Pays $20-30/performance.
Needs: We encourage submission of scripts that are experimental and visual in presentation. Full-length scripts preferred. "Smaller casts and single sets work best for us."

THEATRE THREE, 2800 Routh, Dallas TX 75201. (214)871-2933. Artistic Director: Norma Young. Produces 11-12 plays/year. 8% freelance written. 3 scripts produced are unagented submissions. Plays in an arena house to a general audience using professional actors. Works with approximately 2 unpublished/unproduced writers annually. Produces a new play festival that includes staged readings of up to 10 new plays. Submit complete script. Computer printout submissions acceptable. Replies in several months. Buys performance/staged reading rights for productions at Theatre Three only. Pays 6% royalty or honorarium for readings.
Needs: Full-length plays. "We produce a wide range of genre including musicals. Our house is inappropriate for spectacle-type shows. Multiset and large cast shows can be cost prohibitive."

THEATRE VIRGINIA, Boulevard & Grove Ave., Richmond VA 23221. (804)257-0840. Artistic Director: Terry Burgler. Produces 7 plays/year. LORT company. 10-15% freelance written. Submit complete script. Computer printout submissions acceptable; prefers letter-quality to dot-matrix. Reports in 5 months. Buys negotiable rights, "but usually we share in future earnings from the property, if we produce the premiere." Pays royalty.

Tips: "We look for someone whose writing reflects an understanding of the theatre; whose writing reflects an awareness, an accurate ear and eye for people; whose writing reflects an honest understanding of whatever plot/situation they've concocted, and an understanding of what those things mean in human terms, theatrical terms, historical terms and sociological terms. We look for someone who is honestly addressing the issues of their piece, rather than someone who is attempting to address what they think we'd like."

‡THEATREWORKS, University of Colorado, Box 7150, Colorado Springs CO 80933. (303)593-3232. Producing Director: Whit Andrews. Produces 4 full-length plays/year and two new one-acts. "New full-length plays produced on an irregular basis. Casts are semi-professional and plays are produced at the university." Submit query and synopsis. (One-act plays are accepted as competition entries—submit complete ms. Two one-act competition winners receive full production, cash awards and travel allowances.) Acquires exclusive regional option for duration of production. Full rights revert to author upon closing. Pays $300-1,200.

Needs: Full lengths and one-acts—no restrictions on subject. "Cast size should not exceed 20; stage area is small with limited wing and fly space. Theatreworks is interested in the exploration of new and inventive theatrical work. Points are scored by imaginative use of visual image. Static verbosity and staid conventionalism not encouraged." No formulaic melodrama or children's plays.

Tips: "Too often, new plays seem far too derivative of television and film writing. We think theatre is a medium which an author must specifically attack. The standard three act form would appear to be on the way out. Economy, brevity and incisiveness favorably received."

‡THEATREWORKS/USA, 131 W. 86th St., New York NY 10021. (212)595-7500. Artistic Director: Jay Hamick. Associate Artistic Director: Barbara Pasternack. Produces 3 new plays/season. Produces professional musicals that primarily tour but also play (TYA contract) at an off-Broadway theatre for a young audience. Submit query and synopses or complete ms. Reports in 6 months. Buys all rights. Pays 6% royalty; offers $1,500 advance against future royalties for new, commissioned plays.

Needs: Musicals and plays with music. Historical/biographical themes (ages 9-15), classic literature, fairy tales, and issue-oriented themes suitable for young people ages 9-15. Five person cast, minimal lighting. "We like well-crafted shows with good dramatic structure—a protagonist who wants something specific, an antagonist, a problem to be solved—character development, tension, climax, etc. No Saturday afternoon special-type shows, shows with nothing to say or 'kiddy' theatre shows."

Tips: "Writing for kids is just like writing for adults—only better (clearer, cleaner). Kids will not sit still for unnecessary exposition and overblown prose. Long monologues, soliloquies and 'I Am' songs and ballads should be avoided. Television, movies, video make the world of entertainment highly competitive. Theatre should and must give audiences something they can't get in other mediums. It needs to be real, honest, entertaining and well-crafted—how else can you compete with special effects, stunt men, MTV?"

‡UNIVERSITY OF MINNESOTA, DULUTH THEATRE, 10 University Dr., Duluth MN 55812. (218)726-8562. Artistic Director: Richard Durst. Produces 13 plays/year. Plays are performed at the University Theatre, American College Theatre Festival and the Minnesota Repertory Theatre (summer). Submit query and synopsis only. Reports in 3 weeks. Acquires performance rights. Pays $35-100/performance.

Needs: All genres. Prefers younger casting requirements and single set or unit setting shows. No previously produced work or one act plays.

Tips: "We are a very active undergraduate theatre program that is very interested in producing new work. We annually produce a new play for the American College Theatre Festival in which there are several major playwriting awards."

‡VICTORIAN THEATRE, 4201 Hooker, Denver CO 80211. (303)433-5050. Artistic Director: Sterling Jenkins. Produces 5-6 plays/year. Plays are produced at Victorian Theatre, a non-profit, semi-professional organization with a widely varied general audience in Denver. The historic theatre seats 90 people. Agented submissions are preferred; submit query and synopsis, or complete ms. Reports in 3 months. Requires regional exclusivity. Pays $30-40/performance.

Needs: Prefers modern two-act comedies and dramas. No topic restriction. "We have a small, intimate proscenium stage with a trap door, limited wings and no fly space." Prefer simple one-set plays. No large scale musicals or multi-setting, three-act dramas.

Tips: "Because of television, audiences are used to action packed variety in entertainment and have shortening attention spans. Comic relief is an asset in even the most serious drama. Audiences are looking more than ever for escape from stress of life."

‡VILLAGE PERFORMERS THEATRE, 98-A, 3rd Ave., New York NY 10003. (212)473-8835. Artistic Director: Reena Heenan. Produces 6-10 plays/year. Plays performed off-off Broadway at 98-A 3rd Avenue theatre. Submit complete ms. Reports in 2 months. Pays royalty.

Needs: All genres, prefers two acts, occasionally uses one acts. Cast under 12. Wants new plays by new playwrights.

VIRGINIA STAGE COMPANY, 108 E. Tazewell St., Norfolk VA 23510. (804)627-6988. Artistic Director: Charles Towers. Produces 7 plays/year. 20% freelance written. 10% of scripts produced are unagented submissions. A professional regional theatre serving the one million people of the Hampton Roads area. Plays are performed in LORT C proscenium mainstage or LORT D flexible second stage. Works with 2 unpublished/unproduced writers annually. Query with synopsis; "sample scene or dialogue may be included." Negotiates rights and payment.
Needs: "Primarily full-length dramas and comedies which address contemporary issues within a study of broader themes and theatricality. A small cast and limited staging is preferable but not necessary. Material must be inherently theatrical in use of language, staging or character. We do not want to see material which offers simplistic solutions to complex concerns, is more easily suited for television or film or whose scope is *limited to* specific contemporary topical issues."

WEST COAST PLAYS, Suite 809, 849 S. Broadway, Los Angeles CA 90014. (213)622-6727. Editor: Robert Hurwitt. Publishes 14 plays/year (2 volumes, 7 plays each). 100% freelance written. ½-¾ of scripts published are unagented submissions. Plays are for general audience, professional use (through theatres), and academic use (some volumes get used as texts). Works with 7 unpublished/unproduced writers annually. "Half to three-fourths of the writers we publish each year (up to 14) may be previously unpublished." Submit complete script. Reports in 6 months. Buys one-time publication rights with right to reprint. Pays royalty: .7% of list price on first 2,000 copies sold; 1.4% after that. Advance on royalties from $50 for a one-act to $100 for a full-length play. Computer printout submissions acceptable; no dot-matrix.
Needs: All types: one-acts, full-length plays; children's plays, experimental, epic or realistic; musical, comedy, drama, Third World, women's, gay, straight. "We try to cover the spectrum of what is most exciting in new plays from the Western U.S. We *only* publish plays that have had their first U.S. production in the western United States, roughly anywhere from Denver to Hawaii." No scripts that have not yet had a full-scale production.

‡WOMEN'S THEATRE PROJECT, 203 N. Howell, St. Paul MN 55104. (612)647-1953. Artistic Director: Carolyn Levy. Produces 2-3 plays/year. Plays performed in small (140 seat) Black Box theatre. Professional production for general public. Submit complete ms. Reporting time varies. Pays 5-10% royalty or $500-1,000.
Needs: "New plays by women about issues of importance to women, hopefully with good roles for women although they do *not* need to be plays with all women casts. We are interested in good characters, interesting forms and styles, risk-taking ventures into new ideas and forms."
Tips: "We want to make our audiences think and ask questions. We don't solve problems or prescribe solutions, we raise issues."

WOOLLY MAMMOTH THEATRE COMPANY, 1317 G St. NW, Washington DC 20005. (202)393-3939. Artistic Director: Howard Shalwitz. Literary Manager: Neil Steyskal. Produces 5-6 plays/year. 100% freelance written. Produces professional productions for the general public in Washington, DC. 3-4 scripts are unagented submissions. Works with 1-2 unpublished/unproduced writers annually. Query with synopsis. Reports in 2 weeks on synopsis; 6 weeks on scripts. Buys first and second class production rights. Pays 5% royalty.
Needs: "We look for plays that depart from the traditional categories in some way. Apart from an innovative approach, there is no formula. One-acts are not used." Cast limit of 8; no unusually expensive gimmicks.

‡WORCESTER FOOTHILLS THEATRE COMPANY, Box 236, Worcester MA 01602. (617)754-4018. Artistic Director: Marc P. Smith. Produces 5-6 plays/year. A regional theatre serving a community of 160,000; multigenerational audience. "We produce plays that demonstrate high literary quality, appealing to a broad segment of the general population." Query with synopsis. Reports in 2 months. Standard professional contract negotiated with play agent. Pays $25/performance.
Needs: "No theme is untouchable, no thought unthinkable when put into the healthy context of a family discussion." No experimental avant-garde; material offensive to a general audience; large-cast musicals.
Tips: "We are in the process of constructing a new theatre which will seat 350, opening 1987."

ALWAYS submit mss or queries with a stamped, self-addressed envelope (SASE) within your country or International Reply Coupons (IRCs) purchased from the post office for other countries.

Screenwriting

Scriptwriters can write for audiences in their own communities and around the world. There are more opportunities today than just five years ago. While the term "screenwriting" might prompt you to think of movies shown at a theatre, the scriptwriter this year will probably find more success in writing for the TV screen. Even if writing movies for the box office is your goal, you might want to turn your attention first to television.

Made-for-TV movies, TV shows, and docudramas are outlets for scriptwriters, although the field is a difficult one to break in to. Most producers want material that has been registered with the Writers Guild of America. "In our business, writers think if they have an idea, that is enough for a show," said one TV show producer. "We won't consider anything without funds or set talent."

The cable television market provides a wealth of opportunity for the scriptwriter, depending on whether the writer contacts cable pay channels or local cable franchises. Cable TV producers will have to give audiences *more* in view of the home video competition, said one producer. Pay cable firms are producing more material lately. Producers either approach cable companies with ideas, or companies are subcontracting with producers for films.

Watch what each cable channel is producing *before* you query one with your ideas. You'll be competing against scriptwriters with track records when you try to crack the national cable market, so follow each company's guidelines and develop ideas that mass audiences will be interested in. Cable networks that serve special-interest audiences, on the other hand, need more specialized material. Producers that consider cable TV material are indicated in this book with the symbol (□). Consult cable TV trade journals, *The New York Times*, and *Variety* to keep up with the latest trends.

The best opportunities for new scriptwriters are in their hometowns. As cable companies vied for each city's franchise in the last few years, the firms began offering local programming (public access) as a selling point. As a result, citizens can receive production studio training and can produce shows using their local cable company's facilities for little or no charge. An estimated 1,100 U.S. cities have one or more community video centers.

Local access programming focuses more on nonfiction than fiction, although citizens are not restricted to doing only community service material. Citizen groups, colleges, art agencies and community theatres can produce original screenplays using public access facilities. Of course, persons interested in producing such a project would first have to discuss it with the staff at their local cable center.

You may want to enroll in a training class for public access production—to find out what the requirements are—before approaching the cable company or a local group about producing a script. Keep in mind, though, that the citizen, not the cable company, would be the producer for public access programs. If, for instance, you want to make a documentary about drunken driving, you could approach your local Alcoholism Council for feedback and perhaps active involvement in the production of your script.

Industry sources believe the home video market will be creating a demand for more how-to and feature films. Of course, producers will then be looking for more scriptwriters. As the prices of video cassette recorders continue to decrease, more consumers are buying them. And as the price of cassettes also drops (due to the greater volume), the emphasis will shift more from the rental of films to purchase.

Fiction on film has always outsold nonfiction at box offices and in video stores, but now people will be turning more often to video tapes to learn facts about a subject or to learn a skill (while continuing to enjoy cassette movies).

One consideration that producers will be watchful of (in reading scripts) is whether it will have a lasting value for viewers. A cooking film, for instance, that teaches the viewer how to make one dish is less useful than one that teaches a variety of cooking skills. Producers want a film to be so useful and so interesting that viewers will return to the film much as they would a how-to book.

Two-hour movies (fiction, again) produced for video store distribution rather than movie-house distribution are another trend that will affect scriptwriters. Hollywood films for theatre distribution cost an estimated $10 million to $40 million to produce. The made-for-video-only films are being produced at a cost of $50,000, for a drama to $1 million for an action film. Whereas the Hollywood scriptwriter needs a script "package" that sometimes includes a major star's agreement to be in the film, video movies will rely more on the script and on good but lesser-known actors. Good stories and catchy packaging will attract video movie fans to these films.

Also, if you have extensive writing credits, you might approach producers of cinema-distributed films. It's a good idea to register your script with the Writers Guild of America (8955 Beverly Blvd., Los Angeles 90048, or 555 W. 57th St., New York, New York 10019) prior to submitting it. Some producers seek only scripts submitted through agents. (See Author's Agents listings for more information.)

Format for the screenplay calls for a typed, single-spaced (triple-spaced between the dialogue of different characters) manuscript. Set margins at 15 and 75 (pica) or 18 and 90 (elite) and allow 125-150 pages for a two-hour feature film (90 pages for 90 minutes).

BONIME ASSOCIATES, LTD., 279 E. 44th St., New York NY 10017. (212)490-2910. President: Andrew Bonime. Produces "feature motion pictures. We develop high quality, moderate- to high-budget feature film projects. We either purchase scripts, book manuscripts, or hire writers on the average of six projects per year (includes rewrites of presently owned material)." 100% freelance written. Works with 1-2 unpublished/unproduced writers annually. Buys theatrical motion picture rights. "We accept only material submitted through recognized agents. Pays in accordance with Writers Guild standards."
Tips: "We are always looking for new writing talent, but because of sheer time and volume and because of legal reasons, we cannot accept unsolicited material or any material that does not come through recognized agents. We're interested in writers who have an understanding of motion picture technique for writing scripts, ability to create character—drama or comedy—and an understanding of the visual process of film. Freelance writers should be aware of personal/character relationships and unusual concepts."

☐**THE CHAMBA ORGANIZATION,** 230 W. 105th St., #2-A, New York NY 10025. President: St. Clair Bourne. Produces material for "the activist-oriented audience; the general audience (PG), and in the educational film market we aim at high school and adult audiences, especially the so-called 'minority' audiences. Assignments are given solely based upon our reaction to submitted material. The material is the credential." 100% freelance written. 100% of scripts produced are unagented submissions. Buys 2-4 scripts/year. Works with 3 unpublished/unproduced writers annually. Computer printout submissions acceptable; prefers letter-quality to dot-matrix.
Needs: "I concentrate primarily on feature film projects and unique feature-length documentary film projects. We prefer submission of film treatments first. Then, if the idea interests us, we negotiate the writing of the script." Also needs scripts for music videos and material (film) for cable television. Query with a brief description of plot, thumbnail descriptions of principal characters and any unusual elements. Payment negotiable according to Writers Guild standards.
Tips: Trends in screen include "a critical examination of traditional American values and dissatisfaction with 'yuppie ideology'."

☐**CHRISTIAN BROADCASTING NETWORK,** Virginia Beach VA 23463. (804)424-7777. Executive Producer, Program Development: David Freyss. Produces material for a general mass audience as well as Christian audiences. Second largest cable network in the nation. Producer of *700 Club*. 20% freelance written. 60% of scripts produced are unagented submissions. "We are planning over 12 different programs: some one-shot, some series, women's programs, dramas based on Bible characters and holiday shows. Mostly staff-written but will consider freelance treatments." Buys negotiable rights. Works with 5 unpublished/unproduced writers annually. Previously produced material OK. Computer printout submissions acceptable; prefers letter-quality to dot-matrix. Send to Tom Rogeberg, Director of Operations, CBN Cable Network. Reports in 2 weeks.
Needs: Secular and Christian. Dramatic, service, educational, children's, feature films, informational shows,

film adaptations of books. Query and request release form to submit an idea or script. Buys some ideas outright; flat fee for treatment, outline or script.
Tips: "We're looking for writers with strong television/film background who have screenwriting experience. A basic belief in the *Bible* is necessary."

CINE/DESIGN FILMS, INC., 255 Washington St., Denver CO 80203. (303)777-4222. Producer/Director: Jon Husband. Produces educational material for general, sales training and theatrical audiences. 75% freelance written. 90% of scripts produced are unagented submissions. "Original solid ideas are encouraged." Computer printout submissions acceptable. Rights purchased vary.
Needs: "Motion picture outlines in the theatrical and documentary areas. We are seeking theatrical scripts in the low-budget area that are possible to produce for under $1,000,000. We seek flexibility and personalities who can work well with our clients." Produces 16mm and 35mm films. Send an 8-10 page outline before submitting ms. Unbound scripts will be returned unread. Pays $100-200/screen minute on 16mm productions. Theatrical scripts negotiable.

□**CINETUDES**, 295 W. 4th St., New York NY 10014. (212)924-0400. Contact: Director of Development. Produces material for television, scripts for video and material for cable television. Works with 20 writers/year. 50% freelance written. 5 scripts are unagented submissions. Works with 5 unpublished/unproduced writers annually. Query with samples or submit resume only. Reports in 2 weeks. Buys all rights.
Needs: Feature length screenplays (theatrical/television); theatrical shorts; children's programming. "We look for the willingness to listen and past experience in visual writing." Produces 16mm and 35mm films and videotape. Pays by outright purchase or pays daily rates.

□**DA SILVA ASSOCIATES**, 137 E. 38th St., New York NY 10016. Creative Director: Raul da Silva. 10% freelance written. Produces material for entertainment audiences. Must work with published/established writers. 50% of scripts produced are unagented submissions. Rights purchased vary. "If possible, we share profits with writers, particularly when resale is involved." Computer printout submissions acceptable; prefers letter-quality to dot-matrix.
Needs: "We produce both types of material: on assignment and proprietary." Produces video (entertainment only—drama, comedy, and documentaries); 35mm films, phonograph records, tapes and cassettes. Also produces material for cable TV (drama/comedy). "Generally we work on assignment only. We have a selection of writers known to us already." Cannot handle unsolicited mail/scripts. Submit resume. Open to credit sheets. Pays in accordance with Writers Guild standards. Pays expenses of writers on assignment.
Tips: "We are planning several series, both drama and documentary."

□**DILLY INTERNATIONAL PRODUCTIONS**, 1349 McMillan, Cincinnati OH 45206. (513)861-7065. Contact: Millard Segal. Produces material for a general TV audience. Buys all rights. Reports "immediately or takes option."
Needs: Magazine-format shows—visually interesting. "You must know the structure of TV scripting. Take college courses to learn before submitting." Submit treatment. Negotiates royalty; buys some scripts outright for a negotiable rate; "guaranteed deal for a series."
Tips: "There is not much money in writing for cable TV now, but in a couple of years there will be."

□**DSM PRODUCERS**, Suite 1204, 161 W. 54th St., New York NY 10019. (212)245-0006. Produces material for consumer, trade and executive audiences. 96% freelance written. Previously produced material OK. Computer printout submissions acceptable; prefers letter-quality to dot-matrix. Reports in 1 month.
Needs: Phonograph records, tapes and cassettes. Currently interested in commercial material for all segments of the music industry i.e., record acts; commercials/film/radio-television/industrial/trade. Produces material for cable television. Submit cassette/video or completed script and resume. Pays in royalty or in accordance with Writers Guild standards.

□**ETERNAL WORD TELEVISION NETWORK**, 5817 Old Leeds Rd., Birmingham AL 35210. (205)956-9537. Director of Programming: Dick Stephen. Produces material with a Catholic focus on everyday living. "Spiritual growth network which also airs family entertainment. Support comes from donations. Founded by Mother Angelica who has an active book ministry." Computer printout submissions acceptable; no dot-matrix. Reports in 4 months.
Needs: "We would like to see scripts in all forms and formats: drama, talk shows, panel discussions and original ideas." Half-hour programs or specials for cable television with uplifting, inspirational themes. Submit synopsis/outline of script. "May hold the script for up to 1 year."
Tips: "We want scripts that promote strong social values, or with religious themes."

GOLDSHOLL DESIGN & FILM, INC., 420 Frontage Rd., Northfield IL 60093. (312)446-8300. President: M. Goldsholl. Query. Buys all rights.
Needs: Scripts for corporate industrial public relations films. Also interested in original screenplays and short

stories to be made into screenplays. "Describe your material before sending it. Do not send 'fantasy' scripts!" Produces sound filmstrips, 16mm and 35mm films, multimedia kits, tapes and cassettes, and 35mm slide sets. Pays 5-10% of budget.
Tips: "Write your ideas clearly. Know the visual world."

‡IN-SYNC, Box 61, Grand Blanc, MI 48439. (313)694-3391. Contact: Story Department. Estab. 1985. Produces films for young people ages 13 to 24. "As a growing company we are increasing inhouse production every year. We add three more pictures annually. Since we are a newly formed company, a writer has a very good chance with us." Negotiates purchase of rights on an individual basis. Accepts previously produced material "if non-theatrically produced." Reports in 5 weeks on submissions.
Needs: Youth-oriented feature-length screenplays (at least 80 pages). Subjects include friendships, psycho-thrillers, action/adventure, and science fiction. No pornography. Screenplays must be properly formatted, including a 3 page treatment (double-spaced), and a topic sentence. Produces 35mm films. Submit synopsis/outline and 2 copies of completed script. Payment is negotiated on an individual basis, according to Writers Guild standards.
Tips: "There are presently new waves of youth-oriented films, such as *The Breakfast Club* and *Pretty in Pink*, that represent a new market, aside from the unintelligent R-rated teenage films. Producers are now seeking this type of profitable story."

□LEE MAGID PRODUCTIONS, Box 532, Malibu CA 90265. (213)858-7282. President: Lee Magid. Produces material for all markets, teenage-adult; commercial—even musicals. 90% freelance written. 70% of scripts produced are unagented submissions. Buys 20 scripts/year; works with 10 writers/year. Works with "many" unpublished/unproduced writers. Buys all rights. Previously produced material OK. Electronic submissions acceptable via VHS video or cassette/audio. Reports in 6 weeks.
Needs: Films, sound filmstrips, phonograph records, television shows/series, videotape presentations. Currently interested in film material, either for video (television) or theatrical. "We deal with cable networks, producers, live-stage productions, etc. Market is still questionable as to monies to be paid." Works with musicals for cable TV. Prefers musical forms for video comedy. Submit synopsis/outline and resume. Pays in royalty, in outright purchase, in accordance with Writers Guild standards, or depending on author.
Tips: "We're interested in comedy material."

□MEDIACOM DEVELOPMENT CORP., Box 1926, Simi Valley CA 93062. (818)991-5452 or (213)552-9988. Director/Program Development: Felix Girard. 80% freelance written. Buys 10-20 scripts annually from unpublished/unproduced writers. 50% of scripts produced are unagented submissions. Query with samples. Computer printout submissions acceptable. Reports in 1 month. Buys all rights or first rights.
Needs: Produces charts; sound filmstrips; 16mm films; multimedia kits; overhead transparencies; tapes and cassettes; slides and videotape with programmed instructional print materials, broadcast and cable television programs. Publishes software ("programmed instruction training courses"). Negotiates payment depending on project.
Tips: "Send short samples of work. Especially interested in flexibility to meet clients' demands, creativity in treatment of precise subject matter. We are looking for good, fresh projects (both special and series) for cable and pay television markets. A trend in the audiovisual field that freelance writers should be aware of is the move toward more interactive video disk/computer CRT delivery of training materials for corporate markets."

‡MERIWETHER PUBLISHING LTD., 885 Elkton Dr., Colorado Springs, CO 80907. (303)594-4422. Editor: Arthur L. Zapel. Produces material for high school speech, drama and English classes, and some religious material. Buys 30 scripts/year. Buys all rights and filmstrip rights. Accepts previously produced material. Reports in 3 weeks on queries; 6 weeks on submissions. Catalog for 8½x11 SAE with $1 postage.
Needs: "We are always looking for good scripts relating to the communication arts—speech, drama, and English. Scripts can be related to literature or stage." Produces slides, tapes, cassettes, and sound and silent filmstrips. Audiovisual scripts should not exceed 30 minutes. Scripts must be typewritten in audiovisual format. Query with samples; submit synopsis/outline and resume. Offers 10% royalty or makes outright purchase of $150-750.

□NICKELODEON MTV NETWORKS, INC., 1133 Avenue of the Americas, New York NY 10036. (212)944-4250. Manager of Program Services and Commercial Clearance: Ann Sweeney. Produces material for age-specific audience aged 2 to 15. Now in 18 million homes. Buys negotiable rights. Reports in 1 month.
Needs: "Full channel children's programming for cable TV. Value filled, non-violent material desired." Submit resume and programming ideas (2-3 page explanations). Phone first for information and release forms. Pays variable rate.

□PACE FILMS, INC., 411 E. 53rd Ave., New York NY 10022. (212)755-5486. President: R. Vanderbes. Produces material for a general theatrical audience. Buys all rights. Reports in 2 months.

Close-up

Paul Haggis
Executive Producer
"Facts of Life"

"A good writer should be able to write anything—comedy, drama, suspense. We tend to pigeonhole ourselves, and then we're surprised when others do the same to us," says Paul Haggis, executive producer for the NBC sitcom, "The Facts of Life." Haggis has first-hand knowledge of the successful writer's need for versatility. He has been a freelance writer, staff writer, story editor and executive script consultant. In addition to his duties as a series producer, Haggis is also a freelance writer of screenplays.

Haggis came to Hollywood eight years ago from Ontario, Canada. It was three years before he landed a writing assignment for a television series. Soon afterwards he sold two screenplays. He has written for animated series such as "Dingbat and the Creeps," "Plastic Man" and "Scooby Doo," and for prime time series such as "Three's Company" and "Love Boat." He worked as a writer for the Canadian sitcom "Hangin' In," and was story editor for "Diff'rent Strokes" and "One Day at a Time." Two years ago he joined "The Facts of Life."

"In comedy, the executive producer is almost always a writer. Being a freelancer, staff writer, story editor and producer are all gradient steps in a learning process that *should* teach you the skills you need to run a show. But if you're not a good writer, all the technical ability and political savvy don't amount to much. And there are many freelancers in our business who prefer to stay freelancers—there's a lot to be said for the freedom," says Haggis.

When questioned about the diversity of his writing experience, Haggis reveals the reason for his flexibility. "In order to keep 'the spark' you have to keep trying new forms, new genres. The people who know me from my suspense work can't imagine me writing comedy."

When reading sample scripts, Haggis doesn't insist that they be written specifically for "The Facts of Life." "A great sample script is going to get someone's attention. It doesn't have to be for a specific show—you can send me a 'Family Ties' script, or a 'Night Court,' or an 'All in the Family'—as long as I know the characters, and the style of comedy is more or less similar to our show. But the script *must* be submitted by a literary agent."

Haggis emphasizes the importance of an agent when marketing scripts. "Selling the agent on your work is a first step. The agent will then send your sample script to me. I'll read it and if it is truly innovative and hilariously funny, I'll run all the way to your house and beg you to write for me. If it's not, it goes in a big pile. All you have to be is great, it's no harder or easier than that. Don't necessarily send out your first attempt at writing a sitcom. You usually get one shot to really impress a producer; make the first one count."

Haggis understands the problems freelancers face. "There's a lot of competition for writing assignments," he says, "but you can't look at the competition. You have to believe in your talent and keep working on your craft and keep writing new sample scripts. An ideal writer has a limitless imagination, a peculiar sense of humor, an eye for the absurdity of everyday life—and the ability and craftsmanship to put it into dramatic form. Ideal writers will never buy the lie that the audience is any less bright or sophisticated than they are."

—Sheila Freeman

Needs: Theatrical motion pictures. Produces 35mm films, cable tapes and cassettes. Query with samples; submit synopsis/outline or completed script. Pays in accordance with Writers Guild standards.

PAULIST PRODUCTIONS, Box 1057, Pacific Palisades CA 90272. (213)454-0688. Contact: Story Department. 100% freelance written. *Family Specials* are geared toward senior high school students. Buys 4-6 half-hour scripts/year. WGA membership required. Computer printout submissions acceptable; no dot-matrix.
Needs: "We are looking for longer form one- to three-hour television specials and theatrical releases on people who have acted boldly on their moral convictions regarding human and/or Christian values." Submit complete script through agent only. "We are not interested in unsolicited manuscripts."
Tips: "Watch our *Family Specials* enough so that you have a strong sense of the sort of material we produce. We look for wit, originality of theme and approach, an unsentimental, yet strong and positive manner of approaching subject matter—intelligent, literate, un-cliché-ridden writing."

□**RESTON TELEVISION THEATER,** Box 3615, Reston VA 22090. (703)437-0764. Executive Producer: Sharon Cohen. 100% freelance written. Produces material for local cable and PBS audience. Buys 1-2 scripts/year. 100% of scripts are unagented submissions. "We negotiate with playwright on the basis of a percentage of resulting sales." Reports in 1 month on queries; 4 months on submissions.
Needs: "Original scripts—no adaptations. Production requirements should be simple (no car chases). Playing time may be 30-90 minutes. All scripts considered within the limits of good taste." Submit complete script.
Tips: "We aren't interested in trends. We're only interested in good stories, well-told."

□**TELEVISION PRODUCTION SERVICES CORP.,** 381 Horizon Dr., Edison NJ 08817. (201)287-3626. Executive Director/Producer: R.S. Burks. Produces video music materials for major market distributor networks, etc. Buys 50-100 scripts/year. Buys all rights. Computer printout submissions OK; prefers letter-quality to dot-matrix printouts. Reports in 2 weeks.
Needs: "We do video music for record companies, MTV, HBO, etc. We use treatments of story ideas from the groups management. We also do commercials for over the air broadcast and cable." We are now doing internal-in-house video for display on disco or internally distributed channels. Submit synopsis/outline or completed script, and resume; include return envelope and postage.
Tips: Looks for rewrite flexibility and availability. "We have the capability of transmission electronically over the phone modem to our printer or directly onto disk for storage."

‡**THEME SONG: A Musical and Literary Production House,** 396 Watchogue Rd., Staten Island NY 10314. (718)698-4178. Produces material for theatre (stage/screen); radio; television (entertainment/educational documentary). Buys 50 scripts/year. Buys first rights. Previously published material OK, if a revision is sought. Reports in 1 month. "I'll answer each query individually. We enjoy newsworthy subjects and investigative/collaborative themes."
Needs: Phonographs records, tapes and cassettes and ¾" video tape. Query. Pays negotiable royalty.
Tips: "I am interested in political lyrics/songs and in concrete criticism of American life and ways of improving our condition; also international themes or cooperative themes."

UNITED JEWISH APPEAL/FEDERATION OF JEWISH PHILANTHROPIES, 130 E. 59th St., New York NY 10022. (212)980-1000. Director of Campaign Communications: Martin Irom. Produces material for people interested in Jewish topics and a Jewish audience. Produces scripts for video. 80% freelance written. 2-3 scripts are unagented submissions. Works with 10 unpublished/unproduced writers annually. Buys negotiable rights. Previously produced material OK. Computer printout submissions acceptable; prefers letter-quality to dot-matrix. Reports in 1 month.
Needs: Audiovisual materials for group showing, scripts for commercial TV and radio programs. "Writer must be well-versed in Judaic tradition and customs." Produces slides/sound shows, video, radio, films. Query with sample or resume and sample of script from a completed program. Does not return samples. Buys scripts outright for $100-500; "varies with length and requirement of the script."
Tips: "Unique ideas are welcome here. New angles on holidays are always of interest. Additional per diem freelance writing assignments for news release work and the like is also available."

□*Open box preceding a listing indicates a cable TV market.*

Gag Writing

If you find your dedication to humor far exceeds the occasional wry remark at the dinner table, and you believe your sense of humor is something others will want to share, gag writing can be a satisfying hobby that can add a few extra dollars to your bank account. Collaboration between gag writers and cartoonists, or comedy writers and comedians isn't unusual. Keep in mind, though, that to comedians and cartoonists, humor is a business—but few writers can live by humor writing alone.

The professional approach is essential. Sending carbon copies of jokes, handwritten gags, or cards bent by repeated submissions will reveal the amateur gag writer. Type each of your gags or jokes on a separate sheet of paper or on an index card. Submit gags in batches of 10 to 20; always include a SASE.

Keep careful records of your submissions. Individual cards can easily become separated, so include your name and address on the back of each card. Include a code number in the upper left corner. A master card in your files should list the text of each joke, its code number, where and when it has been submitted, and any response it received. You may also want to keep a file with a submission sheet for each market you've approached. Include the submission date and the code number of each gag sent to that particular market. If you've mailed more than one batch to the same market, keep a separate sheet for each mailing. Number each sheet and write the same number on the back of your return envelope. When your gags are returned, matching the number on the envelope with the number on the submission sheet should make it easier to check your returned material.

Many buyers may hold a gag for a year while trying to find a market for it. If you're dealing with cartoonists who accept simultaneous submissions, be sure to inform them if a gag they are holding has been sold. If you're dealing with comedians, do not make simultaneous submissions. Wait until you receive a response or your material is returned before sending the gag to another entertainer. Since you may not be sure your material has reached a comedian, you should politely state in your cover letter that if you have not been contacted within four months, you'll assume that the comedian is not buying gags and you will market your material elsewhere.

Before choosing to write for a comedian or a cartoonist, decide which type of presentation is best for your ideas. Comedians need one-liners they can enhance with just the right facial expression and tone of voice. Cartoonists need material appropriate for visual gags, in which the humor relies on the combination of words and illustration.

If you're interested in writing gags for a cartoonist, your submission does not require an elaborate drawing, or even a paragraph setting up the situation. A simple statement like "Woman says to man" will usually be sufficient. Cartoonists like to illustrate without seeing another person's interpretation of the gag. A truly funny line should set an artist's imagination to work without any additional help from the writer.

Captions should be simple and the humor universal. You can get extra mileage out of a gag by first directing it toward a specific audience and focusing on cartoonists who deal with that market; then alter the gag to appeal to a more general audience and send it to cartoonists who specialize in that market.

Study cartoonists' work in books and magazines. You'll see that most cartoonists use timely gags that focus on the audiences' newest crazes. Avoid submitting gags that insult people's religions or nationalities; you're hoping to entertain an audience, not insult them.

Gag writers working with cartoonists are paid after the cartoonist receives a check from the publication. Magazines may pay from $10 to $300 per cartoon. The writer usually earns 25%

commission on the selling price. The commission may go as high as 50% if the cartoonist submits a sketch and sells only the writer's gag line, not the finished cartoon.

Comedians generally buy their material one-liner at a time, though some do buy entire monologues. Payment rates for this type of writing vary greatly. Comedians may pay $10 for a one-liner, but some pay more, others less.

Though comedians are invited to be listed in *Writer's Market*, some decline because they lack the time or staff to handle unsolicited material. Others choose not to be listed because they don't want their audiences to know they don't write all their own material. But don't let the lack of a listing keep you from submitting to a favorite comedian.

Familiarize yourself with a comedian's style and subject matter, and compose several jokes tailored to that performer. Send your material to the comedian in care of the theater, nightclub or TV station where he or she is performing. Remember not to send simultaneous submissions. There is plenty of coincidental duplication of jokes; don't complicate the problem by sending the same material to different comedians. Some entertainers are hesitant to look at an unfamiliar writer's material, fearing they'll be accused of stealing ideas. It may take years to establish contacts for comedy writing, but if your material proves to be audience-pleasing, comedians will want your gags.

If you should hear a joke very similar to one of your own, don't panic. Many jokes and stories are in the public domain and may be used by anyone. Jokes and stories that are truly your own, derived from your own life experiences, may be submitted for copyright protection (see Appendix).

Cartoonists and comedians are not the only markets humor writers should consider. Read Sol Saks' *The Craft of Comedy Writing* (Writer's Digest Books) for information on humor writing for TV, radio, film and theatre. Many of the listings in *Writer's Market* will consider humorous material. Some greeting card companies are interested in humorous verse and many magazines buy short humor, anecdotes and jokes as fillers. When it comes to selling, don't limit your sense of humor; there are lots of markets that could use a good laugh.

EDOUARD BLAIS, 2704 Parkview Blvd., Minneapolis MN 55422. (612)588-5249. Holds 250 gags/year. Works with 10-15 gagwriters/year. Prefers to work with published/established writers. Sells to men's, sports, fitness, health, education, family, outdoor, camping and fishing publications. Recently sold material to *Dash*, *Nutrition Health Review*, and *Sun*. Buys 25-50% of the gags received from freelance writers. Submit gags on 3x5 slips; 10-12 in one batch. Reports in 1 week. Sells cartoons for $10-50; pays gagwriters $2-12. Pays 25% commission. Writer's guidelines for SASE.
Needs: Erotic, women's magazines; health, fitness, hobbies, education, family, outdoors, camping, and fishing gags, etc. Looks for sight gags—no captions, or a minimum amount of words. "I accept gags I feel match up well with my style of drawing."
Tips: "I would especially like to receive gags on family—especially young married couples, not necessarily dealing with sex (that's OK, too), but all aspects of young family life. Gag writers should be aware of what's going on in all phases of society, the style of language being used, and new developments (like fast food, microwave, G-spot, etc.)."

DAN BORDERS, 191 Alton Rd., Galloway OH 43119. (614)878-3528. Holds 35 gags/year. Works with 7 gagwriters/year. Sells to computer magazines of all kinds, trade journals, many general interest and electronic gags. Has sold material to *Computer World*, *Info World*, *Dr. Dobb's Journal*, *Radio-Electronics* and *Reader's Digest*. Eager to work with new/unpublished writers. Buys 25% of the gags received from freelance writers. Submit gags on 3x5 cards or slips. Submit 15 gags in one batch. Sells cartoons for $25-50. Pays 25% commission.
Needs: Electronics and computer gags, and environment, family and angel gags. No "girlie gags." Looks for humorists with dry humor.
Tips: "Many computer magazines are buying computer cartoons. Also electronic 'toons' are selling well. I am always ready to see good, well-thought-out ideas."

BILL BOYNANSKY, Apt. 13/20, Ansonia Hotel, 2109 Broadway, New York NY 10023. Works with 35-60 gagwriters/year. Holds over 1,000 gags/year; sells between 800-900 cartoons/year. Submit 15-20 gags at one time. Reports in 3 days to 2 months. Pays "25% for regular, 35% for captionless; all others—regular payment."

Needs: General, male, female, sexy, girlie, family, children's, adventure and medical. "No overdone girlie gags, overdone family gags, TV, parking the car, woman nagging husband, etc. Prefer to see captionless gag ideas on all subject matters, but no beginners; only those who know their business. I prefer to deal with cartoonists by letter or phone because it saves me time."

ASHLEIGH BRILLIANT, 117 W. Valerio St., Santa Barbara CA 93101. Sold about 315 cartoons last year. Self-syndicated and licensed to publications and manufacturers worldwide. Reports in 2 weeks. Pays $25.
Needs: "My work is so different from that of any other cartoonist that it must be carefully studied before any gags are submitted. Any interested writer not completely familiar with my work should first send $2 and SASE for my catalog of 1,000 copyrighted examples. Otherwise, their time and mine will be wasted."

LEONARD BRUCE, AKA "LEO", Leoleen-Durak Creations, Suite 226, Box 2767, Jackson TN 38302. (901)668-1205. Holds 20 gags/month. Works with 4 gagwriters/year. Works with a small number of new/unpublished writers each year; eager to work with new/unpublished writers. Sells to newspapers, charity publications, space publications, science fiction and science fiction movie magazines, comic book publications, and animal care publications. Submit gags on 3x5 cards. Submit 12 gags in one batch. Pays 10% commission. Buys first serial rights. Reports in 2 weeks.
Needs: Looking for gags on science fiction movie themes, comic book hero themes, themes on computers, space travel, UFOs, life on other planets, "aliens" trying to cope with our world. Also a Berry's World theme; one guy in crazy situations. No political, foreign affairs or white collar themes. Will consider gags for cartoon strips: Leotoons (science fiction "alien" themes); Fred (space exploration themes); and It's a Mad World (crazy situations in our insane world). Looks for offbeat gags, weird humor, "taking normal situations and turning them into 'sight gags' or word gags. As an example: Berry's World or Herman gag themes."
Tips: "I look for quality and good typing ability in a gagwriter. Gagwriters should be aware that gags *have* to be very funny or the whole cartoon doesn't work or sell. The gag is the main reason a cartoon sells nowadays. We are a 2 person operation and the gagwriter should have patience in working with me on the artistic and financial part of the business. Also the gag writer should work *with* the artist to help 'sell' his gags also in strip form. I would especially like to receive gags on alien life and science fiction."

DON COLE, Box 917, Dover NJ 07801. (201)328-9153. Holds 25-50 gags/year. Sells to general interest publications; also trade journals. Working on humorous comic strip. Works with 26 gagwriters/year. Buys 5% of the gags received from freelance writers. Submit gags on 3x5 slips; about 12 (or 1 ounce) per batch. Reports in 3 days. Sells cartoons for $10-500; pays gagwriters $2.50-62.50. Pays 25% commission.
Needs: General; trade journal; comic strip; or single panel gags; "*anything* funny." No off-color gags. Especially wants "topical humor, satire, anything funny, or a general audience or related to a trade." No unsolicited resumes, correspondence, or analysis of writer's work.
Tips: "Send *original* work only. No gags from old magazines or cartoon books. Each gag based on its own merit."

THOMAS W. DAVIE, 28815 4th Place S, Federal Way WA 98003. Buys 75 gags/year. Works with 10 gagwriters/year. Has sold to *Medical Economics*, *Sports Afield*, King Features, *Chevron U.S.A.*, *Rotarian*, *Saturday Evening Post*, *Ladies' Home Journal*, *Playgirl* and *Boys' Life*. Buys 30% of the gags received from freelance writers. Gags should be typed on 3x5 slips. Prefers batches of 5-25. Sells cartoons for $10-450. Pays 25% commission. Reports in 1 month. No IRC.
Needs: General gags, medicals, mild girlies, sports (hunting and fishing), business and travel gags. No pornography.
Tips: "I'm often overstocked—please don't flood me with gags."

ED DAVIS, 69 Wind Whisper Court, The Woodlands TX 77380. (713)363-9264. "We are backlogged with submissions and prefer not to receive unsolicited submissions at this time."

LEE DeGROOT, Box 115, Ambler PA 19002. Pays 25% on sales.
Needs: Interested in receiving studio greeting card ideas. "I draw up each idea in color before submitting to greeting card publishers, therefore, giving the editors a chance to visualize the idea as it would appear when printed . . . and thus increasing enormously the chances of selling the idea."

NORM DREW, Laurier House, Suite 608-L, 1600 Beach Ave., Vancouver, British Columbia V6G 1Y6 Canada. Holds 500 gags a year. Sells to general urban magazines and daily and weekly newspapers, trade journals, TV, film, greeting card and novelty companies. Submit 3x5 cards or slips; 12-20 in a batch. Reports in 1 week on submissions. Works with both published and new writers. Works with 25 gagwriters/year. Buys 10-15% of the gags received from freelance writers. Sells cartoons for $10-1,500; pays gagwriters 25%. General gags: 25-40% reprint. Makes outright purchase for Chika, Bush Babies. SAE with IRCs.

Needs: Comic strips, gags, or TV animation scripts. Query first. Do *not* send scripts. Subjects include urban lifestyles, consumer angst, TV viewers, bicycling, photography, home video, media trades—TV, radio, press, entertainment—film, stock market, apartment living, travel, hobbies: model building, model railroads, short-wave radio, collectors: stamps, coins, and flea market hunters, gardening. Young urbans, senior citizens, and contemporary kids views, foibles. No puns, porn, prurience, 'sick' subjects; no religion, racial, or stereotypes. No weak play-on-words or illustrated "jokes". "I look for fresh, original, healthy humor, astute eye for contemporary urban foibles; subtle, classy observations; accurate inside knowledge of the subject; visual irony, imminent victim gags; good visual situation sense; fresh, zany, slightly irreverent, sassy approach; attuned to current absurdities, timeless universal human frailties. Condense punchline to its punchiest minimal. I may reword/restage gag for stronger visual impact. Gag writer still will get 25%."

DAVE GERARD, Box 692, Crawfordsville IN 47933. (317)362-3373. Holds 100 gags/year. Sells 10-20 freelance cartoons per month for magazines and periodicals. Recently sold material to *National Enquirer*, *D.A.C. News*, *Wall Street Journal*, *Good Housekeeping*, *Better Homes & Gardens*, *Medical Economics*, and King Features' Laff-A-Day. Works with 10 writers annually. Submit gags on 3x5 cards; 10 in one batch. Reports in 2 weeks. Sells cartoons for $50-300. Pays 25% commission.

Needs: General interest and sports, business, family and upbeat gags on pertinent and timely topics, like taxes, inflation, computers, etc. No "prisoners hanging on wall, kings and queens, talking animals, or put-down humor. I will be frank if material is not what I like. No erotic material."

Tips: "I like good sight gag material and short captions; also no-caption gags. Writers should be aware that subject matter changes along with the lifestyles of Americans, which, of course, change yearly. Gagwriting is stuck, in many cases, on old material. Do not like gags which are one-liners and need no cartoon."

‡GLASSMAN, Box 46664, Los Angeles CA 90046. Buys 75 gags/year. Buys 50% of gags from freelance writers. Has performed on talk shows, at nightclubs and at conventions. Will be performing on talk shows, at comedy clubs, and at one night comedy concerts in the next year. Submit gags in one-time form typed on 8½x11 paper. No limit to number submitted on one subject. Reports in 2 weeks. Pays $15 minimum/line. Pays after the gag is performed (in a workshop situation).

Needs: Will specify slant and topic. "I like as many one liners on that specific subject as I can get." Material must be acceptable on network TV.

MEL HELITZER, Scripps Hall, Ohio University, Athens OH 45701. (614)594-5608. Buys 100-150/year. Uses gags as a master of ceremonies at banquets. Works with 5-6 gagwriters/year. Eager to work with new/unpublished writers. Buys 1% of the gags received from freelance writers. Submit gags on 3x5 cards; 10 or more in a batch. Reports in 1 week. Pays gagwriters $5-10. Pays on acceptance.

Needs: University-related material from professor's point of view. Subjects include faculty, administration, students and curriculum. Short one-liners or one-paragraph ancedotes. No student drugs, sex or alcohol. "No blue language, but doubles entendres are OK."

CHARLES HENDRICK JR., Old Fort Ave., Kennebunkport ME 04046. (207)967-4412. Buys several gags/year; sold 50-60 cartoons last year. Prefers to work with published/established writers. Sells to newspapers, magazines and local markets. Works with 6 gagwriters/year. Buys 5-10% of the gags received from freelance writers. Submit 8 gags at a time. Sells cartoons for $25-200. Pays 50% of net commission or negotiates commission. Reports in 1 month.

Needs: General family, trade (hotel, motel, general, travel, vacationers), safe travel ideas—any vehicle, and medical. Gags must be clean; no lewd sex. Mild sex OK.

WAYNE HOGAN, Box 842, Cookeville TN 38503. "We are backlogged with submissions and prefer not to receive unsolicited submissions at this time."

DAVID R. HOWELL, Box 170, Porterville CA 93258. (209)781-5885. Holds 100+ gags/year. Sells to magazines, trade journals, etc. Has sold material to *True Detective*, *TV Guide*, *National Enquirer*, *Woman's World*, King Features, *Cartoons*, etc. Works with 30-40 gagwriters/year. Prefers to work with published/established writers. Buys 5% of gags received from freelance writers. Submit gags on 3x5 cards or slips; 6-12 in one batch. Reports in 1 week. Sells cartoons for $25-300; pays gagwriters $6.25-75. Pays 25% commission.

Needs: Cars, medical, farm, computer, specific topics. "No politics, sex, taboo topics. No old stuff. I need fresh, original approaches."

FRED ("FREJAC") JACKSON III, 70 Illinois, Pontiac MI 48053. Holds 150 gags/year. Works with 100 gagwriters/year. Sells cartoons to book companies (mostly cartoons to illustrate textbooks), girlie magazines, computer magazines, general interest magazines, religious publications, business publications, women's pub-

lications, children's magazines, farm magazines. Has sold to *Ahoy!*, *Woman's World*, *Radio-Electronics*, *Computerworld*, *Prentice-Hall Books*, *Wallace's Farmer*, *Creative Computing*, and others. Works with 100 gagwriters/year. Holds 5% of the gags received from freelance writers. Submit gags on 3x5 slips. Sells cartoons for $10-100. Pays 25-35% commission; 35% for captionless and major market sales. Reports in 1 month. "I hold unsold gags indefinitely until sold."
Needs: Girlie (both X-rated and softcore), captionless computer, office, general, business, humor through youth, animals, family, farm, captionless, cable and pay TV, the sciences, electronics gags. "No old, tired gags, please. I've seen them all before."
Tips: "I need a constant supply of computer, girlie and humor through family gags. Most gags I receive are unfunny, stale and unoriginal. I look for gags that are very visual, clever sight gags. Girlie gags get top priority."

REAMER KELLER, 4500 S. Ocean Blvd., Palm Beach FL 33480. (305)582-2436.
Needs: Prefers general and visual gags. Pays 25%.

MILO KINN, 1413 SW Cambridge St., Seattle WA 98106. Holds approximately 200 gags/year; sells 100-200 cartoons/year. Has sold to *Medical Economics*, *Machine Design*, *American Machinist*, *Infoworld*, *Review of the News*, *Charlton* and many farm publications and trade journals, etc. Works with 8-10 writers annually. Buys 25% of the gags received from freelance writers. Sells cartoons for $15-100 "and up, on occasion." Pays 25% commission.
Needs: Medical, machinist, dental, farm, male slant, girlie, woman, captionless, adventure and family gags. Sells girlie, farm, medical, office, factory, crime and general cartoons.
Tips: "There seems to be fewer markets. Computers seem to be out."

"FRANK" LENGEL, 900 Karlaney Ave., Cayce SC 29033. (803)791-1558. Holds 200 gags/year. Sells to trade journals and general interest. Recent sales to *Saturday Evening Post*, *Diversion*, *National Enquirer*, *Kiwanis* and *The Optimist*. Works with 50 gagwriters/year. Eager to work with new/unpublished writers. Buys 5% of the gags received from freelance writers. Submit on 3x5 slips. But "also would look at a gag submitted on a brown paper bag if it's a gem!" Reports in 1 week. Sells cartoons for $15-300; pays gagwriters $5-100. Pays 33⅓% commission "upon receipt of my check from the publication." Submit seasonal material 4-6 months in advance.
Needs: General interest, family, business, medical, sex. "I will look at almost anything if it is fresh and funny." Rarely considers word-play or multi-panel cartoons.
Tips: "Be cognizant of the difference between a gag for a cartoon and a joke. Jokes are for comedians, gags, for cartoonists. I see far too many recycled jokes that were originally sent to comedians. Also, don't feel pressured to send me a certain number of gags. I would rather review a couple of good gags than a couple dozen 'junk' gags written to stuff an envelope. I welcome new talent because I think I get original material from new writers, but want to continue hearing from 'the regulars' also."

LO LINKERT, 1333 Vivian Pl., Port Coquitlam, British Columbia V3C 2T9 Canada. Works with 20 gagwriters/year. Has sold to most major markets. Prefers batches of 10-15 gags. Sells cartoons for $50-600; pays gagwriters $20-100. Pays 25% commission. Returns rejected material in 1 week. Enclose SAE and 30¢ U.S. postage.
Needs: Clean, general, topical, medical, family, office, outdoors gags; captionless, pro woman sophisticated ideas. "Make sure your stuff is funny. No spreads." Wants "action gags—not two people saying something funny. No puns, dirty sex, drugs, drunks, racial or handicapped. Religion gags must be in good taste."
Tips: "I look for a gagwriter who sends few, but great, gags. I hate to be swamped by one writer who dumps bundles of gags on me."

ART McCOURT, Box 210346, Dallas TX 75211. (214)339-6865. Began selling cartoons in 1950. Works with 15 gagwriters/year. Sells 700 cartoons/year to general/family, medical, farm and male magazines. Has sold material to *Ford Times*, *Furrow*, *Agway Coop*, *Medical Management*, McNaught Syndicate, *National Enquirer*, *American Legion* and King Features. Prefers to work with published/established writers; works with a small number of new/unpublished writers each year. Buys 50% of the gags received from freelance writers. Submit 15-20 gags at one time on 3x5 cards or slips. Sells cartoons for $10-340. Pays 25% commission. Reports in 2 days.
Needs: Family/general, medical (no gripes about doctors' bills), male, computers, hunting, fishing, and farm gags. "Something unique and up-to-date." No "crowds, ghouls, TV, mothers-in-law, talking animals or desert islands."
Tips: "I look for original, crisp wordage and fresh approach with minimal descriptions. Don't just send a punchline that has no background. Read the newspapers; be topical. Writers shouldn't be impatient; gags can make the rounds for several years."

THERESA McCRACKEN, 910 Constitution NE, Washington DC 20002. (202)547-1373. Holds 100 gags/year. Sells mostly to trade journals, but also to some general interest city magazines and newspapers. Recently sold material to *Creative Computing*, *Computer World*, *Physician's Management*, *Journal of AMA*, *Training*, *Chemtech*. Works with 10 gagwriters/year. Buys 5% of the gags received from freelance writers. Sells cartoons for $10-100; pays gagwriters $2.50-25. Submit gags on 3x5 cards or slips; 10-20 in one batch. Pays 25% commission.

Needs: "Since I sell mostly to trade journals in one batch, I prefer to receive 10 to 20 gags on one subject so I can do several cartoons for one market all at the same time. I don't care what the subject is since I live near the Library of Congress and am able to search for publications that deal with just about any imaginable interest. Nothing sexist (i.e., no bad woman-driver gags), or racist gags."

Tips: "I really like cartoons where the humor is in the drawing as opposed to the caption. At any rate, I also prefer short captions. My humor is similar to that of Gary Larson. 'In jokes' in a profession are also welcomed. Be aware of what's going on in the world by reading a good newspaper everyday."

ROBERT MAKINSON, GPO Box 3341, Brooklyn NY 11202. (718)855-5057. Began buying jokes in 1979; bought 175 last year. "I publish *Latest Jokes* and *Jokes by Contributors*. Jokes are used by comedians, disc jockeys and public speakers." Works with 20 jokewriters/year. Works with a small number of new/unpublished writers each year. Buys 5% of jokes received from freelance writers. Submit jokes on 3x5 slips in batches of 10-20. Makes outright purchase of $1/joke. Reports in 2 weeks.

Needs: "I want jokes that relate to current trends but which do *not* mention the names of current famous personalities."

Tips: "The jokes I buy are strong enough to make an audience laugh out loud and do not sound too similar to jokes I've heard before. The characteristics I look for in a jokewriter is the ability to distinguish between a simply clever statement, and a statement which is unique and surprising. Would like to receive jokes on new trends and which make use of modern words and phrases. Lines for public speakers also wanted—introductions, opening remarks, heckler squelchers, etc."

REX F. MAY (BALOO), Box 2239, West Lafayette IN 47906. (317)463-3689. Holds 500 gags/year. Works with 15 gagwriters/year. Sells to general interest and some girlie magazines. Has sold material to *Good Housekeeping*, *National Enquirer*, *Hustler*, *Cavalier*, *Woman's World*, *Wall Street Journal*, King Features, *Medical Economics*, *Saturday Evening Post*, *Easyriders*, *Datamation*, *Leadership*, *New Woman*, *Changing Times* and *Christian Science Monitor*. Buys less than 1% of the gags received from freelance writers. Submit gags on 3x5 slips; no more than 100 in a batch. Sells cartoons for $15-300; pays gagwriters $3.75-75. Pays 25% commission. Reports in 2 weeks.

Needs: "I don't need many gags. A top gagwriter myself, I write 15,000 gags a year for many top cartoonists. I still use gags by others if they fit my style. You probably should look my style over before you submit. I don't do much background or use many props. It's a very simple style. What I want is general-to-weird material. I sell weird non-girlie stuff to the girlie magazines, so don't send standard girlies. Simplicity and shortness of caption are the way to go."

Tips: "I'm currently acting as a gag-agent for selected gagwriters. That is, I select certain gags they send me to rewrite and try to sell as my own gags. When I sell, I pay them 50% of what I get. So gagwriters should let me know when sending if they want me to consider the gags as an agent, or just as a cartoonist. (As an agent, I'll handle *any* kind of good gag.) Cartoonists be aware that I have plenty of gags on hand. Especially interested in writing for syndicated features, panel or strip. It takes me about three years currently, to try a cartoon from the top to the bottom markets, so be patient."

RAY MORIN, 140 Hamilton Ave., Meriden CT 06450. (203)237-4500. "We are backlogged with submissions and prefer not to receive unsolicited submissions at this time."

THOMAS PRISK, Star Rt., Box 52, Michigamme MI 49861. Holds 300 "and up" gags/year. Worked with more than 130 writers last year. Sells to trade journals, newsletters, magazines, etc. Published in *The Bulletin of The Atomic Scientists*, Charlton Publications, *Computerworld*, *Medical Economics*, *Creative Computing*, etc. Holds with the *Saturday Evening Post*, *National Enquirer*, *Good Housekeeping*, etc. Submit gags on 3x5 slips, 10 or more to a batch. Pays 25% commission. Reports in 3 weeks. "Foreign writers, use only American postage; I don't have the time or patience for the postal coupons."

Needs: Medical, dental, computer, office, captionless and with short captions. "I would also like to see religious gags with the Christian slant and much more off-beat humor." No porn or racial prejudice slants.

Tips: "Include blank slip with gags for comments. Unless gags are legibly handwritten, they should be typed out. The gags I hold are slanted to my style and market needs. Rejected gags are not necessarily considered unsalable. I look for off-beat material that takes an old or popular theme and gives it a special twist. SASE *must* be included in each batch and in *all* inquiries if a response is desired. If requested, a held gag will be returned to the writer, otherwise, I will hold it until sold, or until I reconsider the gag and return it at a later date."

ART REYNOLDS, Box 226, Vader WA 98593. (206)295-3736. Began selling cartoons in 1977. Sells to general interest magazines and trade magazines. Has sold material to Creative Communications Publishers, *The*

Gag Writing **937**

Northern Logger & Timber Processor, Timber/West Magazine, Loggers World Magazine and *Christian Logger Magazine*. Submit gags on 3x5 cards; 10-15 in one batch. Pays 25% commission. Reports in 1 week.
Needs: General and family gags that appeal to *Saturday Evening Post, Saturday Review, Good Housekeeping* and *Better Homes & Gardens*. Also gags with outdoor emphasis. No overworked themes or sex and girlie-girlie gags. "Inquire with SASE. I look for fresh, short and snappy, and funny gags."
Tips: "Try your gag idea on your family before submitting. If you don't get a favorable response from them, you probably won't from me either."

DAN ROSANDICH, Pilgrim Route, Box 101A, Houghton MI 49931. (906)482-6234. Holds estimated 250 gags/year. "I have had my cartoons published in local papers, newsletters, reprinted work in college textbooks, and send my cartoons to the most obscure trade journals up to the large circulation general-family publications. A California distributor sells my reprints overseas and in South America." Sold material to *National Enquirer, The Star, Physician's Management, Medical Economics,* King Features, *Laff-A-Day, American Medical News,* National Catholic News Service, *Espionage, Official Detective Stories.* Works with 15-25 gagwriters/year. Prefers to work with published/established writers; eager to work with new/unpublished writers. Buys 20-25% of the gags received from freelance writers. Submit 3x5 slips or cards (prefers 3x5 slips). "I'd like to see a good supply of gags submitted to make my own conclusions on a writer's consistency." Sells cartoons for $10-200; pays gagwriters $2.50-50. Pays 25%. "I would also buy ideas outright at $1 per gag. The writers should specify this in the submission—I would buy a lot if I saw good material."
Needs: "Anyone considering sending gags should be aware of the fact that I currently work with several excellent gagwriters, but I'm wide open to newcomers if they can show exceptional work. The field of men's magazines is declining in its use of gag cartoons, probably due to several economic factors, so withhold work in this category. I'd love to find the writer who specializes in captionless themes. I sell to a dozen or so agricultural magazines on a monthly basis so am open to farm gags of any kind. I also appreciate seeing timely ideas relating to computers, family and banking gags. I'd like health and medical material; keep the doctor in mind with medicals."

TER SCOTT, Box 305, Lake Nebagamon WI 54849. (715)374-2525. Holds 100-300 gags/year. Works with 15-30 gagwriters/year. Sells to trade journals, newspapers and advertisers. Submit gags on 3x5 slips; 10-25 in one batch. Sells cartoons for $25-100. Pays 25% commission plus occasional bonuses. Reports in 2 weeks.
Needs: "I will look at anything but hardcore, girlies and racial prejudice and prefer general, religious, farm, sales and trade journal material. I provide a list of markets and currently submit cartoons to my regular gagwriters as these accounts become stocked or change often. I always need topical and seasonal material for Classified Comics newspaper strip, sales magazines, and ideas for greeting cards (nothing risque), magazines and trade journals (in subjects such as salesmanship, business) and general family humor, etc."
Tips: "Forget resumes, fancy paper, etc. Humor is what I need. Readable 3x5 cards are fine. Also, I'd like to see a batch on one subject like farming, sales, etc., making sure to pick on the right folks. For instance, a farm magazine shouldn't pick on farmers, they're the heros and the audience. Sales people look at their sales journal and want to see their customers or procedures picked on not *themselves*. Gags rejected are humor that should be for standup comedians, those submitted on anything other than usual 3x5 cards and those with postage due. Submissions without SASE will not be responded to."

JOSEPH SERRANO, Box 725, Capitola CA 95010. Has sold to most major and middle markets. Pays 25% commission.
Needs: General and topical material.

GODDARD SHERMAN, 1214 McRee Dr., Valdosta GA 31602. Holds 200 gags/year. Sells to general, medical and youth publications. Has sold material to *National Enquirer, Saturday Evening Post, Boys' Life, Medical Economics, Modern Maturity* and *Woman's World.* Submit gags on 3x5 slips; 15-20 gags in one batch. Reports in 2 weeks. Pays 33⅓% commission.
Needs: Prefers captionless gags, or very short captions; funny action in picture. No overly technical settings. Avoid overworked themes, such as invention of wheel, natives boiling missionaries, desert islands, etc.

JOHN W. SIDE, 335 Wells St., Darlington WI 53530. Interested in "small-town, local happening gags with a general slant." Pays 25% commission. Sample cartoon $1. Returns rejected material "immediately."

STEWART SLOCUM, (signs work Stewart), 18 Garretson Road, White Plains NY 10604. (914)948-6682. Holds about 50 gags/year. Works with 20 gagwriters/year. Sells to general interest, women's and sports publications. Recently sold material to *McCalls, Family Circle, Better Homes & Gardens, New Woman, National Enquirer, Golf Journal,* Kings Features. Sells up to half of the gags held from freelance writers. Submit gags on 3x5 slips; 10-15 in one batch. Sells cartoons for $15-325; pays gagwriters $3.75-81.50. Pays 25% commission. Reports in 2 days.
Needs: General, family, women-in-business, computer and sports gags. The best markets for cartoons/gags

in 1987 will be women's magazines and publications that publish general and business humor.
Tips: "I would especially like to receive gags on women in family and business situations, and on golf, baseball, and important holidays."

SUZANNE STEINIGER, 9373 Whitcomb, Detroit MI 48228. (313)838-5204. Holds 100+ gags/year. Sells to farm magazines, sex-type periodicals, women's and general interest magazines and Charlton Publications. Works with 3-4 gagwriters/year. Prefers to work with published/established writers. Buys 30% of the gags received from freelance writers. Submit gags on 3x5 cards or 3x5 slips. Submit 30 or more gags in one batch. Pays 25% commission. Reports in 1 week.
Needs: "For the present I would like to see gags *National Lampoon* style. I guess you could say general interest, but I'm looking for crazy *new* ideas. I like to see everything except detailed scenes. Writers should simplify their words and scenes. I am working on a cartoon strip. I will not say what the strip is about for fear of someone accidentally getting the same idea. I am looking for a patient writer, someone I can discuss my idea with and someone to *help*. I do like gags that are funny and less detailed. For example, a writer should say 'man to woman in restaurant' instead of 'man in crowded restaurant, waiter looking surprised to the woman next to him.' There should be less confusion. I like quick and simple gags the best. I would especially like to receive greeting card ideas in 1987."
Tips: "Today the gags are funnier visually. The scene should have fewer props. Fewer props made the great comics such as the Marx Brothers very funny and popular, not to mention Peanuts. There should be fewer details and more concentration on the joke, the entire *gag*. I like writers who do a good job of writing and leave the drawing to us (cartoonists)."

FRANK TABOR, 2817 NE 292nd Ave., Camas WA 98607. (206)834-3355. Began selling cartoons in 1947. Holds 200 gags/year. Works with 20 gagwriters/year. Sells to trade journals. Recently sold material to *American Medical News, American Machinist, Management Accounting, Computing, Chesapeake Bay, Tooling & Production, True Detective, Espionage.* Works with a small number of new/unpublished writers each year. Buys 5% of the gags received from freelance writers. Submit gags on 3x5 slips; 10-20 in one batch. Sells cartoons for $7.50-150; pays gagwriters $2-25. Pays 25-30% commission. Reports in 2 days.
Needs: Police; detective; fishing; health and fitness; prison situations; salesman; medical (must be funny for the doctor—no gags on big doctor bills); industrial (shop gags OK); office and accounting and flower shop gags. "Cartoon spreads are wide open." No gags on subjects not listed above. "I receive too much material written for the general markets and not nearly enough gags on the subjects I ask for. I look for situations in which the cartoon carries the punch; I don't care for the one-liner or illustrated joke. I need trade gags by writers who know or who will study the trade they're writing about. General gags should be on current subjects such as technology, terrorism, foreign relations and foreign agents."
Tips: "Not enough writers are trying to write for the trades. They're too easily won over by the big rates at the major markets. I have lots of trades paying $35 to $225, and they're begging for cartoons. I am interested in reviewing ideas on strips and panels for syndication."

ISSAM TEWFIK, #701, 2400 Carling Ave., Ottawa, Ontario K2B 7H2 Canada. (613)828-5239. Holds 300 gags/year. Sells to general interest magazines, trade journals, men's and women's publications and newspapers. Has sold material to *Hospital Supervisor Bulletin* and *Accent on Living.* Works with 20 gagwriters/year. Eager to work with new/unpublished writers. Buys 20% of the gags received from freelance writers. Submit gags on 3x5 slips. Submit 10 or more gags in one batch. Sells cartoons for $25-100; pays gagwriters $3-10. Pays 25% commission. Reports in 1 week.
Needs: General, family, erotic, sports, law, military, insurance, medical, computers, children, detective, cars, old age, management, outdoor, money, trucking, etc. Prefers gags that are slanted towards a specific subject and a magazine. Research the magazine and slant towards its requirements. "I will consider eagerly a well conceived strip or panel with well-defined characters and theme (e.g., family, animal, professional, children and single people)."
Tips: "Identify a need either in a specific magazine or a syndicate and let us work together to produce something marketable. Slanting to the different publications is the key to success."

BOB THAVES, Box 67, Manhattan Beach CA 90266. Pays 25% commission. Returns rejected material in 1-2 weeks. May hold unsold gags indefinitely.
Needs: Gags "dealing with anything except raw sex. Also buys gags for syndicated (daily and Sunday) panel, Frank & Ernest. I prefer offbeat gags for that, although almost any general gag will do."

Market conditions are constantly changing! If this is 1988 or later, buy the newest edition of Writer's Market *at your favorite bookstore or order directly from* Writer's Digest Books.

MARVIN TOWNSEND, 631 W. 88th St., Kansas City MO 64114. "During 1987 I will be doing all of my own gags—unless something really outstanding is sent to me."

BARDULF UELAND, Halstad MN 56548. Has sold to over 90 different publications. Works with 12 gagwriters/year. Submit 12-15 gags/batch. Pays 30% commission. Reports in 1-3 days, but holds unsold gags indefinitely unless return is requested.
Needs: General, family, education. No sex.

JOSEPH F. WHITAKER, 2522 Percy Ave., Orlando FL 32818. (305)298-8311. Holds 100 gags/year. Works with 6-7 gagwriters/year. Sells all types of gags. Recently sold material to *Star*, *National Enquirer*, *National Catholic News*, McNaught Syndicate and women's magazines. Prefers to work with published/established writers; works with a small number of new/unpublished writers each year. Buys 60% of the gags received from freelance writers. Submit gags on 3x5 slips; 10-15 in one batch. Sells cartoons for $10-300. Pays 25% commission. Reports in 2 weeks.
Needs: All types of gags. The best markets for cartoons/gags in 1987 will be syndicates, girlie, women, farm, advertising and insurance.
Tips: "I look for captionless gags."

MARTIN YOUNG, Box 7415, Orlando FL 32854. (305)898-0690. Holds 250-300 gags/year. Works with 15 gagwriters/year. Sells to men's and women's, general interest magazines, trade journals and newspapers. Recently sold material to M.A.D.D. (Mothers Against Drunk Drivers), *Saturday Evening Post*, *Charisma*, Atari Computer, *Orlando Sentinel*, *Florida Singles*, and Florida Right to Life. Buys 75% of the gags received from freelance writers. Submit gags on 3x5 cards; 15-20 gags in one batch. Sells cartoons for $5-125. Pays 25% of cartoon sale. Reports in 3 days.
Needs: Computer (home/office); religious (no anti-religious); dieting; *Saturday Evening Post* type; hospital/doctor/nurse; family humor; humor through youth; school/teachers/kids; and off-the-wall general gags. No political or sex gags, no overworked gags or cliches. "Only send funniest material. I currently have a cartoon single-panel called Wit and Wisdumb, it's witty, silly sayings from every area of life."
Tips: "I very much like *strong, very funny*, straight-to-the-point gags. I have been getting too many weak, overworked themes. Try to be original. Gagwriters should keep up with the times. Their gags will reflect how current they are on what's happening in the world around them. Characteristics that I look for in a gagwriter include that they be honest, friendly, and will try to please me with their material. I would like gag writers to send along a resume with their first inquiry. I want to know upfront if I'm working with a long time professional or a novice. I will willingly work with both. I have been selling cartoons long enough to know what sells and what doesn't. I would be willing to work with cartoonists on cartoon strips, or single panels."

> **❝** *I always have more projects on the back burner than I can find time to get through the typewriter. I do try to vary the kinds of writing—if I have just finished a novel, I may next try a nonfiction book or article* **❞**
>
> **L. Sprague de Camp**

If you've ever spent an hour at a greeting card rack—trying to choose just the right card for a special person—you have some idea of the task faced by greeting card publishers as they consider ideas for cards. One publisher estimates his firm receives 200,000 submissions per year . . . and buys only 200. Though numbers such as these may be discouraging, writers who can deliver the old messages—messages of love, sympathy, or best wishes—in new ways are much in demand.

"Think always of the sending situation, of both the person buying the card and its intended recipient," advises Ken Illingworth of Sunrise Publications, Inc. Note any unique occasions when you think you'd like to send or receive a card. Cards that were considered unconventional—or a little risqué—several years ago are growing in popularity. Many companies are producing cards that celebrate job promotions, diets, even divorces. Humorous and insult cards are growing in popularity, though there is a wide demand for the more sentimental verses.

Some companies note a trend toward cards that appeal to men, following closely on the heels of cards that appealed to women only. Although the industry estimates that 80 to 90 percent of greeting cards are bought by women, you'll usually have the best luck with cards that appeal to both women and men, and that can be sent by either.

Many companies prefer unrhymed verses and everyday language. If you do decide to use rhyme, keep your verses short and don't use overworked rhyming words. Reading your verses and puns aloud can help you determine if the rhythms flow smoothly. When writing for a company that sells boxed assortments, avoid using the actual words _we_ and _I_. These two words place limits on a card's sending potential, restricting the number of people who can send it. But do keep in mind the from-me-to-you sending situation that is unique to greeting cards; it will help you shape your messages.

If a company you're interested in writing for offers guidelines or a market list, send for these before submitting your card ideas. Submission requirements and definitions of the different types of cards may vary slightly from company to company. These guidelines will acquaint you with the company's preferences and requirements. Always include a SASE with your request.

Greeting card companies usually acquire all rights to the verses they buy. A writer may be able to negotiate rights if presenting a complete concept for a "promotion series." Such a series incorporates an original character or a special theme in greeting cards and subsidiary product lines. Many companies also require writers to provide a release form, guaranteeing the material submitted is original and has not been sold elsewhere. If a company provides you with a release form, be sure you understand the terms before signing it.

To submit conventional greeting card material, type or neatly print your verses on 4x6 or 3x5 slips of paper or index cards. Don't assume that including your name and address in a cover letter will be sufficient information for your card ideas. The usual submission is 5 to 15 cards, and they can easily become separated from your cover letter; you should type your name and address on the back of each. To avoid sending duplicate submissions to the same publisher, also include an identification code on each card. Establish a master card for each idea and keep track of where and when it was submitted and its purchase or return date. Some writers find it useful to begin their code with a letter signifying the type of card, such as B for birthday or A for anniversary. Larry Sandman's _A Guide to Greeting Card Writing_ (Writer's Digest Books) suggests following this code with the first letter of each of the first three words of your verse. Keep all the cards you submit to a company in one batch, and assign the batch a submission number. Write this number on the back of your return SASE to help you match up your verses as they are returned to you.

To submit humorous or studio card ideas, fold sheets of paper into card dummies about the size and shape of an actual card, or use index cards. Unless your idea relies on a visual gag, or you are artistically inclined, it's best not to sketch in a design for your card. For ideas that use attachments—such as a Valentine's day "key to your heart" with an actual key attached to the card—try to include the item on your dummy. For mechanical card ideas, many of which use pop-ups or sliding parts, you must make a workable mechanical dummy. Though these types of cards are extra work for the writer, most companies pay more for attachment and mechanical card ideas.

Before submitting your card ideas to a company, always consider their latest lines of cards. In addition to the market lists and guidelines many companies offer, study the card racks. Notice the types of cards people are exclaiming over and buying. You may find clerks in card stores have some valuable observations on the kinds of cards that are most popular with the customers. If you are an aspiring greeting card writer, not only will this research help you sell your work, but you'll have fun while learning your customers' needs.

AMBERLEY GREETING CARD CO., Box 36159, Cincinnati OH 45236. (513)489-2775. Editor: Ned Stern. 90% freelance written. Bought 250 freelance ideas/samples last year; receives an estimated 25,000 submissions annually. Reports in 1 month. Material copyrighted. Buys all rights. Pays on acceptance. Writer's guidelines for business size SAE and 1 first class stamp. Market list is regularly revised.
Needs: Humorous, informal, sensitive and studio. No seasonal material or poetry. Prefers unrhymed verses/ideas. Humorous cards sell best. Pays $40/card idea.
Tips: "Amberley publishes specialty lines, primarily novelty and humorous studio greeting cards. We accept freelance ideas, including risque and nonrisque. Make it short and to the point. Nontraditional ideas are selling well."

‡AMERICAN GREETINGS, 10500 American Rd., Cleveland OH 44144. (216)252-7300. Contact: Director-Creative Recruitment. No unsolicited material. "We like to receive a letter of inquiry describing education or experience, or a resume first. We will then screen those applicants and request samples from those that interest us."

‡ARGUS COMMUNICATIONS, 1 DLM Park, Allen TX 75002. (214)248-6300. Editor: Martee Phillips. 80% freelance written. Buys 350-400 sentiments for line, and 200-300 for test. Bought 300 freelance ideas/samples last year; receives an estimated 4,000 submissions annually. Submit seasonal/holiday material 1 year in advance. Reports in 3 weeks. Purchases right for card, poster and postcards. Pays on acceptance. Submission guidelines available for business size SASE. Market letter is regularly revised and sent to writers on a mailing list.
Needs: Humorous, informal, sensivity, studio, and unique "lifestyle" concepts. No long, traditional sentiments. Prefers unrhymed verses/ideas. Pays $50-100, or may negotiate for a total concept. Smaller test fee paid if submission is held for testing.
Other Production Lines: Postcards, posters and promotions.
Tips: "Greeting cards are a personalized, 'me-to-you' form of communication that express a wish for the recipient, a greeting, or an expression of endearment. Cards that focus solely on the sender tend to do poorly. Concentrate on warm humor that supports the relationship. Writers should be mindful of less use of captioned cards. Cartoon line work, photos and special themes sell best to us."

ARTFORMS CARD CORPORATION, 725 County Line Rd., Dearfield IL 60015. (312)272-9844. Editor: Ms. Bluma K. Marder. 50% freelance written. Bought 85 freelance ideas/samples last year; receives an estimated 1,000-1,500 submissions annually. Submit ideas in batches of 10. Submit seasonal/holiday material 6 months in advance. Reports in 3 weeks. Buys all rights. Catalog $1.50. Market list available for SASE.
Needs: Conventional; humorous; informal; inspirational; sensitivity; studio; messages for Jewish greeting cards such as Bar/Bat Mitzvah, Jewish New Year; Chanukah; and Passover; wedding, engagement, confirmation, new home, new baby, bridal shower, baby shower, terminally ill, friendship, sympathy, anniversary, get well and birthday. No insults or risque greetings. "Both rhymed and unrhymed. Brief, two-lines are best." Length: 2 lines minimum, 4 lines maximum. Pays $15-25/card idea.
Other Product Lines: Gift wrap for Chanukah and year 'round use.

Tips: "Do research on Judaism so greeting is not questionable to a religious market; also, if Biblical quotes are used, make sure references are correct. We look for simple messages that pertain directly to subject matter. The shorter the message—the better. It is not necessary for the message to rhyme. Humorous cards are selling well. We will be expanding from Judaic market only to general market."

CAROLYN BEAN PUBLISHING, LTD., 120 2nd St., San Francisco CA 94105. (415)957-9574. Chief Executive Officer: Lawrence Barnett. 90% freelance written. Bought 800 freelance ideas/samples last year; receives an estimated 10,000-15,000 submissions annually. Submit seasonal/holiday material 18 months in advance. Buys exclusive card rights; negotiates others. Pays on acceptance or publication. Reports in 6 weeks. Writer's guidelines for SASE and 49¢ postage.
Needs: Conventional holiday and occasions; humorous; informal; studio; general, occasion-oriented messages. Looks for sophisticated, witty and/or sensitive material. Prefers unrhymed verses/ideas. Occasion-oriented and humor cards sell best. Pays $15-30. "These terms are negotiable."
Tips: Sympathy card ideas are difficult to find.

‡BLACK IS MORE THAN BEAUTIFUL, INC., (BMB INC.), Suite 3, 1815 N. Gramercy Pl., Los Angeles CA 90028. (213)405-7756. Editor: Phill Wilson. Submit seasonal/holiday material 18 months in advance. Reports in 6 weeks. Retains right to use material on specific product. Pays on publication. Free market list. Market list is regularly revised.
Needs: Announcements, conventional, humorous, inspirational, invitation, sensitivity and soft line. "For all types of greeting cards, please remember that our market is the Black consumer." Pays $100 maximum/card idea.
Other Product Lines: Bumper stickers, calendars, gift books, greeting books, plaques, postcards, posters and promotions. "These products would be licensed and paid for as a royalty (3-7%)."
Tips: "We have found that a large percentage of our customers like very traditional greeting cards with wordy verses."

BLUE MOUNTAIN ARTS, INC., Dept. WM, Box 1007, Boulder CO 80306. Contact: Editorial Staff. Buys 50-75 items/year. Reports in 3-5 months. Buys all rights. Pays on publication.
Needs: Inspirational (without being religious); and sensitivity ("primarily need sensitive and sensible writings about love, friendships, families, philosophies, etc.—written with originality and universal appeal"). Pays $150.
Other Product Lines: Calendars, gift books and greeting books. Payment varies.
Tips: "Get a feel for the Blue Mountain Arts line prior to submitting material. Our needs differ from other card publishers; we do not use rhymed verse, preferring instead a more honest person-to-person style. We use unrhymed, sensitive poetry and prose on the deep significance and meaning of life and relationships. A very limited amount of freelance material is selected each year, either for publication on a notecard or in a gift anthology, and the selection prospects are highly competitive. But new material is always welcome and each manuscript is given serious consideration."

BRILLIANT ENTERPRISES, 117 W. Valerio St., Santa Barbara CA 93101. Contact: Editorial Dept. Buys all rights. Submit words and art in black on 5½x3½ horizontal, thin white paper in batches of no more than 15. Reports "usually in 2 weeks." Catalog and sample set for $2.
Needs: Postcards. Messages should be "of a highly original nature, emphasizing subtlety, simplicity, insight, wit, profundity, beauty and felicity of expression. Accompanying art should be in the nature of oblique commentary or decoration rather than direct illustration. Messages should be of universal appeal, capable of being appreciated by all types of people and of being easily translated into other languages. Since our line of cards is highly unconventional, it is essential that freelancers study it before submitting." No "topical references, subjects limited to American culture or puns." Limit of 17 words/card. Pays $40 for "complete ready-to-print word and picture design."

CONTENOVA GIFTS, 1239 Adanac St., Vancouver, British Columbia V6A 2C8 Canada. (604)253-4444. Editor: Jeff Sinclair. 100% freelance written. Bought over 100 freelance ideas/samples last year; receives an estimated 10,000 submissions annually. Submit ideas on 3x5 cards or small mock-ups in batches of 10. Reports same day received. Buys world rights. Pays on acceptance. Current needs list for SAE and IRC. Do *not* send U.S. postage stamps.
Needs: Humorous and studio. Both risque and nonrisque. "Short gags with good punch work best." Birthday, belated birthday, get well, anniversary, thank you, congratulations, miss you, new job, etc. Seasonal ideas needed for Christmas by March; Valentine's Day by September. Prefers unrhymed verses/ideas. Risque and birthday cards sell best. Pays $50.
Tips: "Not interested in play-on-words themes. We do not like to follow trends but set them. We're leaning toward more 'cute risque' and no longer using drinking themes. Put together your best ideas and submit them. One great idea sent is much better than 20 poor ideas filling an envelope."

CRABWALK, INC., 648 Broadway, New York NY 10012. (212)260-1901. Editor: Alan Gabay. Seasonal/holiday material should be submitted 1 year in advance. Reports in 2 months. Not copyrighted. Pays on acceptance. Market list for #10 envelope and 22¢ postage. Market list is regularly revised.
Needs: Humorous, informal, sensitivity, soft line, and studio cards. Pays $30-50.
Other Product Lines: Calendars, gift books, postcards, promotions, pads and gift matches.

CURRENT, INC., Box 2559, Colorado Springs CO 80901. (303)594-4100. Editor: Nancy McConnell. 10-15% freelance written. Bought 100 freelance sentiments or manuscripts last year and a half; receives an estimated 500 submissions annually. Buys 2 or 3 children's book manuscripts/year. Submit seasonal/holiday material 18 months in advance. Reports in 3-5 weeks. Buys all rights. Pays on acceptance. "Flat fee only; no royalty." Pays approximately $100-300 for 1,500-word children's ms. Writer's guidelines for business size SAE and 1 first class stamp.
Needs: All occasion and woman-to-woman cards; short 1-2 line puns for all occasions not too risque; short children's stories, and children's activity books. Pays $15/sentiment.
Tips: "We pick up trends and create our own. We suggest that writers keep abreast of what's selling at retail. Don't send traditional greeting card verse or off-color humor. Fresh puns for holidays such as Christmas and Easter, are difficult to get. Read our direct mail catalog."

‡**CURTIS-SWANN, INC.,** 50 Dorman Ave., San Francisco CA 94124. Reports in 1 month. Pays on acceptance. Free market list and writer's guidelines. Market list regularly revised.
Needs: All everyday and seasonal sending situations, humorous and traditional ideas. Pays $50-75/card idea.

DRAWING BOARD GREETING CARDS, INC., 8200 Carpenter Freeway, Dallas TX 75247. (214)637-0390. Editorial Director: Jimmie Fitzgerald. Submit ideas on 3x5 cards, typed, with name and address on each card. Reports in 2 weeks. Pays on acceptance.
Needs: Conventional, informal, inspirational, everyday and seasonal cards. Pays $50-100 per idea for humor or studio.
Other Product Lines: Calendars. Pays $200-600.

D. FORER & CO., INC., 105 E. 73rd St., New York NY 10021. (212)879-6600. Editor: Barbara Schaffer. Reports in 2 weeks. Pays on acceptance. One-time market list for SAE and 1 first class stamp.
Needs: Humorous, studio. Pays $20.

FREEDOM GREETING CARD CO., Box 715, Bristol PA 19007. (215)945-3300. Editor: J. Levitt. 100% freelance written. Submit seasonal/holiday material 1 year in advance. Reports in 1 month. Material copyrighted. Buys greeting card rights. Pays on acceptance. Writer's guidelines for SASE.
Needs: Announcements, conventional, inspirational, juvenile, sensitive and soft line. Pays per card idea; $10 minimum for 2-8 line card verses.

‡**THE GREEN TIGER PRESS, INC.,** 1061 India St., San Diego CA 92101. (619)238-1001. Does not plan to buy freelance material this year.

LEANIN' TREE PUBLISHING CO., Box 9500, Boulder CO 80301. (303)530-1442. Contact: Editor. Submit verses (not more than 15) on 3x5 cards. Reports in 3 months. May hold good verses indefinitely. Pays $35 on publication; $10 for reuse. Market list and verse writer guidelines for SASE.
Needs: Birthday, friendship, get well, anniversary, thank you, sympathy, wedding, romantic love, Christmas, Valentine's, Easter, Mother's Day, Father's Day and all-occasion Christian.
Tips: "We publish western, Christian and contemporary friendship (not studio) cards. Humor preferred in western card line. Please do not send art suggestions. Become familiar with our card lines before submitting."

MAINE LINE CO., Box 418, Rockport ME 04856. (207)236-8536. Editor: Marjorie MacClennen. Buys 200-400 freelance ideas/samples per year. Submit photocopies (1 idea per page); submissions not returned. Reports in 2 months. Submit seasonal/holiday material 1 year in advance. Material copyrighted. Buys greeting card rights. Pays on acceptance. Writer's guidelines for business size SAE and 3 first class stamps. Market list is regularly revised and issued one time only.
Needs: Humorous, invitations, seasonal, and holiday cards for modern women. No juvenile or religious material. Pays $50/card idea.
Other Product Lines: Postcards and notepad ideas.
Tips: "Don't submit traditional-type material. Study our guidelines. We want greeting card copy with particular appeal to contemporary women of all ages, from all walks of life. Prose is better than verse; humor based on realities of life rather than on word-play most likely to be accepted. Copy that speaks, beneath the humor, a universal truth which women recognize, or copy which articulates attitudes, experiences, and feelings shared by many, many women is most likely to be accepted. Copy that is suggestive, clever and tasteful is OK, but not

necessary. Birthday cards and women-to-women friendship cards dealing with women's concerns are always needed. There is a demand for freelance copy from people who have an interesting perspective on modern life, expressed in a unique way, understood by many. Writers need not submit any visuals with copy but may suggest visuals. Lack of drawing ability does not decrease chances of having copy accepted; however, we also seek people who can both write and illustrate. Writers who have a contemporary illustrative style are invited to send samples or tearsheets to illustrate copy they're submitting.''

ALFRED MAINZER, INC., 27-08 40th Ave., Long Island City NY 11101. (718)392-2627. Art Director: Arwed Baenisch. 15% freelance written. Bought 200 freelance ideas/samples last year. Buys all rights.
Needs: Conventional, inspirational, informal and juvenile. All types of cards and ideas. Traditional material. All seasonals and occasionals wanted. Payment for card ideas negotiated on individual basis only.

OATMEAL STUDIOS, Box 138, Rochester VT 05767. (802)767-3325. Editor: Helene Lehrer. 90% freelance written. Buys 200-400 greeting card lines/year. Bought over 350 freelance ideas/samples last year. Pays on acceptance. Reports in 6 weeks. Current market list for self-addressed, business size envelope and 1 first class stamp.
Needs: Birthday, friendship, anniversary, get well cards, etc. Also Christmas, Chanukah, Mother's Day, Father's Day, Easter, Valentine's Day, etc., and humorous invitations. Humorous material (clever and *very* funny) year-round. "Humorous tongue-in-cheek-type humor, conversational in tone and format, sells best for us." Pays $50.
Tips: "The greeting card market has become more competitive with a greater need for creative and original ideas. We are looking for writers who can communicate situations, thoughts, and relationships in a funny way and apply them to a birthday, get well, etc., greeting. We suggest that a writer send for our guidelines to get a clear picture of the type of humor we're looking for."

PARAMOUNT CARDS, INC., Box 1225, Pawtucket RI 02862. Editorial Director: Dolores Riccio. Submit ideas in batches of no more than 15. Reports in 1 month. Buys all rights. Pays on acceptance. Send SASE for instruction sheet with seasonal reading dates.
Needs: Contemporary me-to-you messages, general or cute/clever, rhymed or unrhymed, short or long, for all everyday and seasonal titles. Address humorous and studio card ideas and studio promotions to Duff Orlemann, Humor Director.
Other Product Lines: Promotions.
Tips: "Study the market; use conversational, contemporary language; avoid limitations and heavy sentiment; experiment with natural, new ways of saying what greeting card buyers want to say."

‡PAWPRINTS, Box 446, Jaffrey NH 03452. Editor: Marcy Tripp. 10% freelance written. Bought 70 freelance ideas/samples last year; receives an estimated 1,000 submissions annually. Submit seasonal/holiday material 1 year in advance. Reports in 1 month. Buys reproduction rights. Pays on acceptance.
Needs: Conventional, humorous, sensitivity and soft line. "Witty, humorous, anthropomorphic animal cards aimed at a bright, fun-loving audience sell best for us. Card ideas with the right mix of word-play, humor and appropriateness to an occasion—like a birthday—are difficult to get." Prefers unrhymed verses/ideas. Pays $50-100.
Tips: "Keep it fun, clean and witty. The trend is back to romance—away from-the-off-color."

RED FARM STUDIO, Box 347, 334 Pleasant St., Pawtucket RI 02862. (401)728-9300. Editor: Mary M. Hood. Reports in 2 weeks. Buys all rights. Pays on acceptance. Market list for #10 SASE.
Needs: Conventional, inspirational, sensitivity, and soft line cards. "We cannot use risque or insult humor." Pays $3 per line of copy.
Tips: "Write verses that are direct and honest. Flowery sentiments are not in fashion right now. It is important to show caring and sensitivity, however."

‡RED/ETERKARDZ, Box 231015, Pleasant Hill CA 94523. (415)365-7906. Editor: Ed Kennedy. Buys 30-60 freelance sentiments annually. Bought 30 freelance ideas/samples last year; receives an estimated 117 submissions annually. Submit seasonal/holiday material 1 year in advance. Reports in 3 weeks. Pays on acceptance. Free market list. Market list available to writer on mailing list basis.
Needs: Conventional, humorous, informal, juvenile, sensitivity and soft line. Uses both rhymed and unrhymed verse, but uses more unrhymed. Pays $50-150.
Other Product Lines: Calendars (pays $300-500); and posters (pays $75-200).
Tips: "Write 'me to you' messages that appeal to as many people as possible—material that is positive, fun, clever. Be aware of the increase in working women, short term relationships, cohabitation, mobility i.e., 'changing roles', and 'individual lifestyles'."

REED STARLINE CARDS CO., Box 26247, Los Angeles CA 90026. (213)663-3161. Editor: Barbara Stevens. 100% freelance written. Purchases 200 ideas and artwork/year; receives an estimated 150,000-

200,000 submissions annually. Pays on acceptance. Buys international rights. Submit seasonal/holiday material 6 months (for season 2 years ahead publishing) in advance. Reports in 2 months on submissions. Guidelines for SAE. Market list is regularly revised.

Needs: Humorous and studio cards. "Birthday group cards sell best for us." No verse or jingles-type material; prefers unrhymed verses/ideas. Pays $40 minimum/card idea.

Tips: It is difficult to get card ideas for odd categories such as leaving, congratulations, thank you and anniversaries.

‡RENAISSANCE GREETING CARDS, Box 126, Springvale ME 04083. (207)324-4153. Editor: Ronnie Sellers. Purchase minimal freelance submissions. 5% freelance written. Bought 20-50 freelance ideas/samples last year; receives 1,000-1,500 submissions annually. Submit seasonal/holiday material at least 9 months in advance. Reports in 2 months, longer on seasonal submissions. (Ceramic and other gift products, cards, stationery, gift wrap copyrighted). Pays on acceptance or publication, "probably acceptance with writers." Market list for business-size SAE with 1 first class stamp. Market list regularly revised.

Needs: "Most interested in humorous submissions. Always interested in receiving inspirational, but not heavily religious cards." Sensitivity cards are also important. "We publish 'upbeat' positive and sincere greetings that enhance relationships." No off-color material or 'put down' material. Usually pays flat fee of $25-50 (per accepted written submission), more if provided with illustrations or graphics.

Other Product Lines: Calendars, gift books, greeting books, postcards, posters and puzzles. Payment negotiable.

Tips: "Address the specific occasions for which greeting cards are sent (Birthday, Get Well, Friendship, etc.). Be original but be sincere. Be clever but stay upbeat and positive. We are a contemporary card company. Our customers expect written context that is more 'original' than that normally associated with the traditional publishers. Write material that will appeal to younger, 'baby boom' audience. We are interested in expanding our humor lines—no slang or off-color. We prefer occasion-oriented but are open to other ideas."

ROCKSHOTS, INC., 632 Broadway, New York NY 10012. (212)420-1400. Editor: Tolin Greene. "We buy 75 greeting card verse (or gag) lines annually." Submit seasonal/holiday material 1 year in advance. Reports in 1 month. Buys use for greeting cards. Writer's guidelines for SAE and 1 first class stamp.

Needs: Humorous ("should be off-the-wall, as outrageous as possible, preferably for sophisticated buyer"); soft line; combination of sexy and humorous come-on type greeting ("sentimental is not our style"); and insult cards ("looking for cute insults"). No sentimental or conventional material. "Card gag can adopt a sentimental style, then take an ironic twist and end on an off-beat note." Pays up to $50. Prefers gag line on 8x11 paper with name, address, and phone and social security numbers in right corner.

Tips: "Think of a concept that would normally be too outrageous to use, give it a cute and clever wording to make it drop-dead funny and you will have commercialized a non-commercial message. It's always good to mix sex and humor. Our emphasis is definitely on the erotic. Hard-core eroticism is difficult for the general public to handle on greeting cards. The trend is toward 'light' sexy humor, even cute sexy humor. 'Cute' has always sold cards, and it's a good word to think of even with the most sophisticated, crazy ideas. Remember that your gag line will probably be illustrated by a cartoonist, illustrator or photographer. So try to think visually. If no visual is needed, the gag line *can* stand alone, but we generally prefer some visual representation."

‡ROUSANA CARDS, 28 Sager Place, Hillside NJ 07205. (201)373-1000. Editor: Janice E. Thurmond. 80% freelance written. Bought the majority of line freelance ideas/samples last year. Submit seasonal/holiday material 9 months in advance. Reports in 2 weeks. Material not copyrighted. Pays on acceptance.

Needs: Announcements, conventional, humorous, informal, inspirational, invitations, juvenile, sensitivity, soft line, and studio. Conventional cards sell best. Humor/studio cards are difficult to find. No risque material. Pays $35 minimum for ideas and prose; pays $2/line for traditional verse.

Tips: "Keep verses general, yet to the point. Be mindful of the trend of shorter verses."

‡SANDPIPER STUDIOS, Box 1007, Boulder CO 80306. Contact: Dept. W. "We are just beginning to accept freelance material for publication consideration." Reports in 3-5 months. Buys exclusive, worldwide publication rights. Pays on publication. Market list for business size SAE with 1 first class stamp.

Needs: Humorous and studio cards. Pays $150.

Tips: "We want writing that is unique, clever, original, and written in a contemporary style. Illustrations are not necessary, unless they are crucial to the point. No rewrites of old jokes or existing material; we want fresh, new ideas. We strongly recommend that writers send for a copy of our market letter and needs list."

SUNRISE PUBLICATIONS, INC., Box 2699, Bloomington IN 47402. (812)336-9900. Product Manager: Ken Illingworth. 100% freelance written. Bought 100 freelance ideas/samples last year; receives an estimated 2,000 submissions annually. Reports in 1 month. Acquires greeting card rights only. Pays on acceptance. Free writer's guidelines. Market list is regularly revised.

Needs: Conventional, humorous, informal and juvenile. No "off-color humor or lengthy poetry." Prefers unrhymed verses/ideas. "We like short one- or two-line captions, sincere or clever. Our customers prefer this to lengthy rhymed verse. Submit ideas for birthday, get well, friendship, wedding, baby congrats, sympathy, thinking of you, anniversary, belated birthday, thank yous, office, fun and love, health and exercise." Pays $20 per card idea.

Tips: "Think always of the sending situation and both the person buying the card and its intended recipient. Most card purchasers are aged between 18 and 45 years, and are female."

VAGABOND CREATIONS, INC., 2560 Lance Dr., Dayton OH 45409. (513)298-1124. Editor: George F. Stanley, Jr. 30% freelance written. Buys 30-40 ideas annually. Submit seasonal/holiday material 6 months in advance. Reports in 1 week. Buys all rights. Sometimes copyrighted. Pays on acceptance. Writer's guidelines for business size SAE. Market list issued one time only.

Needs: Cute, humorous greeting cards (illustrations and copy) often with animated animals or objects in people-situations with short, subtle tie-in message on inside page only. No poetry. Pays $10-25/card idea.

WARNER PRESS, INC., Box 2499, Anderson IN 46018. (317)644-7721. Editor: Jane H. Wendt. 85% freelance written. Buys $3,000-4,000 worth of freelance material/year. Submit seasonal/holiday material 9 months in advance. Reports in 5 weeks. Prefers to buy all rights. Pays on acceptance. Writer's guidelines for business size SASE. Market list is regularly revised.

Needs: Announcements, conventional, informal, inspirational, juvenile, sensitivity and verses of all types with contemporary Christian message and focus. No off-color humor. "Cards with a definite Christian perspective that is subtly stressed, but not preachy, sell best for us." Uses both rhymed and unrhymed verses/ideas "but we're beginning to move away from 'sing-song' rhyme, toward contemporary prose." Pays $5-40 per card idea.

Other Product Lines: Pays $60-150 for calendars; $30-100 for greeting books; $15-30 for plaques; $5-10 for postcards; $10-50 for posters; $20-50 for short meditations; negotiates payment for coloring books and children's books.

Tips: "Try to avoid use of 'I' or 'we' on card verses. A majority of what we purchase is for box assortments. An estimated 75% of purchases are Christian in focus; 25% good conventional verses. Religious card ideas that are not preachy are difficult to find. The market is moving away from the longer verses in a variety of card types, though there is still a market for good inspirational verses (i.e., like Helen Steiner Rice)."

CAROL WILSON FINE ARTS, INC., Box 17394, Portland OR 97217. (503)281-0780. Editor: Gary Spector. 75% freelance written. Purchases 100 freelance designs annually. Submit seasonal/holiday material 1 year in advance. Reports in 3 weeks. Buys negotiable rights. Payment to be discussed.

Needs: Announcements, conventional, humorous, informal, inspirational, invitations, juvenile, sensitivity, soft line. "We are particularly interested in expanding the humorous part of our line with work that is laugh-out-loud funny. Birthday cards are always an important category. Cards should be 'personal'—ask yourself 'Is this a card that someone would buy for a specific person?' Keep in mind that the majority of card buyers are women between the ages of 20 and 40." Pays $35 and up per card idea. Royalties to be discussed.

Other Product Lines: Calendars, gift-books, postcards and posters.

Tips: "Schedule work time daily even if ideas don't seem to be flowing well. Think of people you know and try to invent cards to send to them."

> **❝ Don't wait for inspiration to come to you—rush out and grab it by the throat, capture it in notes which await your attention whenever you're free to use them. ❞**
>
> **Robert Bloch**

Thousands of editors, staff columnists for newspapers and magazines, established free-lancers, and beginning writers hope to be syndicated. It's one of the most competitive areas a writer can venture into. Rumors of wealth aside, the major advantage of syndication is that a syndicate's marketing efforts can expose a writer's name to millions of readers. But even those accepted by a syndicate have no guarantee that their exposure will be long-lived. The success of a column depends on the response it draws from readers. If reader interest wanes, the syndicate loses subscribers. And a syndicate will drop a column that fails to make money, even a once-popular column.

Before you approach a syndicate, be ready to prove you can regularly turn out material that will appeal to readers. Study the writers currently syndicated, not just in your local daily newspaper, but in papers from other cities as well. Check back issues of newspapers at the library and see how successful columnists keep up with current events and change their approach to reflect social changes. Study the structure of their columns—notice how they lead into a topic, support their position, summarize and close. You'll find that syndicated material is short (500-1,000 words), concise and carefully documented. Since syndicates sell primarily to newspapers, that terse newspaper style is appropriate even for features.

For your own column, choose a subject that interests you, one that you know well. Don't make the mistake of imitating a well-known columnist. Newspapers already have an Art Buchwald, a William F. Buckley and an Ellen Goodman; they don't need any more. It will also be to your advantage if you have some experience in writing a column for a newspaper. You don't have to be a regular staffer. Columns written free of charge for a local paper will prove that you can produce work on a steady basis, but be sure your tearsheets support your proposal when you approach a syndicate. Clips of a local society column won't prove you can write political commentary.

Most syndicate editors prefer a query with approximately six sample columns and SASE. If you're dealing with a specialized subject, mention any training or experience that qualifies you to deal with such material. If you have never written a column for a newspaper, be sure to mention any writing experience you do have.

Syndicates handle not only regular columns, but also one-shot features, puzzles, fillers and newsbreaks. Some sell only specialized material, such as health, religious or business articles, so be sure your material fits the syndicate you're querying.

Writers are usually paid 40-60% on the syndicate's gross receipts for each column. Syndicates may also offer a salary, or pay a flat fee for a one-shot item. They usually acquire all rights to accepted material; copyright is in the syndicate's name. The writer cannot reuse such material without the syndicate's permission.

Some writers choose to self-syndicate, but this option calls for investing your time and money in marketing and distributing your work. Payment is usually whatever the newspaper is willing to pay. Small papers pay as little as $5 for a column, while larger dailies may pay up to $15-$20. You may find it necessary to negotiate with some newspapers, offering your material free of charge for a trial period, then agreeing on a fee for later columns if you receive a favorable response.

Self-syndicators must provide their own copyright protection, as many newspapers are not copyrighted. It's less expensive to copyright columns as a collection, rather than individually. More information on copyright can be found in Rights and the Writer in the Appendix of this edition of *Writer's Market*.

For more information on syndicates and syndication markets, consult the *Editor and Publisher Syndicate Directory* (11 W. 19th St., New York NY 10011), and the *Ayer Directory of Publications* in your library.

‡**AP NEWSFEATURES**, 50 Rockefeller Plaza, New York NY 10020. (212)621-1500. Assistant General Manager: Dan Perkes.
Nonfiction: Buys column ideas "dealing with all areas that can be expanded into book form. Do not buy single features."

ARKIN MAGAZINE SYNDICATE, 761 NE 180th St., North Miami Beach FL 33162. Editor: Joseph Arkin. 20% freelance written by writers on contract; 70% freelance written by writers on a one-time basis. "We regularly purchase articles from several freelancers for syndication in trade and professional magazines." Submit complete ms. Previously published submissions OK, "if all rights haven't been sold." Computer printout submissions acceptable; no dot-matrix. Reports in 3 weeks. Buys all North American magazine and newspaper rights.
Needs: Magazine articles (nonfiction; 750-2,200 words, directly relating to business problems common to several (not just one) business firms, in different types of businesses); and photos (purchased with written material). "We are in dire need of the 'how-to' business article." Will not consider article series. Pays 3-10¢/word; $5-10 for photos; "actually, line drawings are preferred instead of photos." Pays on acceptance.
Tips: "Study a representative group of trade magazines to learn style, needs and other facets of the field."

‡**ARTHUR'S INTERNATIONAL**, Box 10599, Honolulu HI 96816. (808)955-4969. Editor: Marvin C. Arthur. Syndicates to newspapers and magazines. Computer printout submissions acceptable; prefers letter-quality to dot-matrix. Reports in 1 week. SASE must be enclosed. Buys all rights.
Needs: Fillers, magazine columns, magazine features, newspaper columns, newspaper features and news items. "We specialize in timely nonfiction and historical stories, and columns, preferably the unusual. We utilize humor. Travel stories utilized in 'World Traveler'." Buys one shot features and article series. "Since the majority of what we utilize is column or short story length, it is better to submit the article so as to expedite consideration and reply. Do not send any lengthy manuscripts." Pays 50% of net sales; salary on some contracted work and flat rate on commissioned work. Currently Marv, by Marvin C. Arthur (informative, humorous, commentary); Humoresque, by Don Alexander (humorous); and World Spotlight, by Don Kampel (commentary).

THE ARTISTS AND WRITERS SYNDICATES, 1034 National Press Building, Washington DC 20045. (202)882-8882. Associate Editor: David Steitz. 100% written by writers on contract. Purchases 2 or 3 freelance features annually. Syndicates to newspapers—U.S. and Canada. Electronic submissions OK via IBM PC compatible, Hayes modem. Computer printout submissions acceptable. Reports in 2 weeks. Writer's guidelines for SASE.
Needs: Newspaper columns (weekly preferred, illustrated). Must be popular subject. "Quality of writing must be first-rate." Query with published clips or photocopies of unpublished work. Pays 50% commission.
Tips: "This is a very difficult field to enter. We suggest trying newspaper syndication only after succeeding (and establishing a good track record) with a newspaper—or two or three newspapers."

AUTHENTICATED NEWS INTERNATIONAL, ANI, 29 Katonah Ave., Katonah NY 10536. (914)232-7726. Editor: Sidney Polinsky. Syndication and Features Editor: Helga Brink. Supplies book review material to national magazines, newspapers, and house organs in the United States and important countries abroad. Buys exclusive and non-exclusive rights. Previously published submissions OK "at times." Reports in 3 months.
Nonfiction and Photos: Can use photo material in the following areas: hard news, photo features, ecology and the environment, science, medical, industry, education, human interest, the arts, city planning, and pertinent photo material from abroad. 750 words maximum. Prefers 8x10 b&w glossy prints, color transparencies (4x5 or 2¼x2¼, 35mm color). Where necessary, model releases required. Pays 50% royalty.

BUDDY BASCH FEATURE SYNDICATE, 771 West End Ave., New York NY 10025. (212)666-2300. Editor/Publisher: Buddy Basch. 10% written by writers on contract; 5% freelance written by writers on a one-time basis. Buys 10 features/year; works with 3-4 previously unpublished writers annually. Syndicates to print media: newspapers, magazines, house organs, etc. Computer printout submissions acceptable; no dot-matrix. Reports in 2 weeks or less. Buys first North American serial rights.
Needs: Magazine features, newspaper features, and one-shot ideas that are really different. "Try to make them unusual, unique, real 'stoppers', not the usual stuff." Will consider one-shots and article series on travel, entertainment, human interest—"the latter, a wide umbrella that makes people stop and read the piece. Different, unusual and unique are the key words, not what the *writer* thinks is, but has been done nine million times before." Query. Pays 20-50% commission. Additional payment for photos $10-50. Currently syndicates It Takes a Woman, by Frances Scott (woman's feature), Travel Whirl and Scramble Steps.
Tips: "Never mind what your mother, fiance or friend thinks is good. If it has been done before and is old hat, it has no chance. Do a little research and see if there are a dozen other similar items in the press—and don't just try a very close 'switch' on them. You don't fool anyone with this. There are fewer and fewer newspapers, with more and more people vying for the available space. But there's *always* room for a really good, different feature or story. Trouble is few writers (amateurs especially) know a good piece, I'm sorry to say."

Writer's DIGEST

THE WORLD'S LEADING MAGAZINE FOR WRITERS

How would you like to get:

- up-to-the-minute reports on new markets for your writings.
- professional advice from editors and writers about what to write and how to write it to maximize your opportunities for getting published.
- in-depth interviews with leading authors who reveal their secrets of success.
- expert opinion about writing and selling fiction, nonfiction, poetry and scripts.
- …all at a $7.00 discount?

(See other side for details.)

BUSINESS FEATURES SYNDICATE, Box 9844, Ft. Lauderdale FL 33310. (305)485-0795. Editor: Dana K. Cassell. 100% freelance written by writers on a one-time basis. Buys about 100 features/columns a year. Syndicates to trade journal magazines, business newspapers and tabloids. Computer printout submissions acceptable; no dot-matrix. Buys exclusive rights while being circulated. Writer's guidelines for business size SAE and 1 first class stamp. Reports in 1 month.
Needs: Fillers, magazine columns, magazine features, newspaper columns, newspaper features and news items. Buys single features and article series on generic business, how-to, marketing, merchandising, security, management and personnel. Length: 250-2,500 words. Query or submit complete ms. Pays 50% commission. Sometimes pays 50% on photos. Currently syndicates Retail Market Clinic, Security Patrol, The Printing Buyer's Advisor.
Tips: "We need nonfiction material aimed at the independent retailer or small service business owner. Material must be written for and of value to more than one field, for example: jewelers, drug store owners, and sporting goods dealers. We aim at retail trade journals; our material is more how-to business oriented than that bought by other syndicates."

CHRONICLE FEATURES, Suite 1009, 870 Market St., San Francisco CA 94102. (415)777-7212. Editor/General Manager: Stuart Dodds. Buys 3 features/year. Syndicates to daily newspapers in the U.S. and Canada. Reports in 1 month. Buys first North American serial and second serial (reprint) rights.
Needs: Newspaper columns and features. "In choosing a column subject, the writer should be guided by the aspirations and lifestyle of today's newspaper reader. We look for originality of expression and, in special fields of interest, a high degree of expertise." Preferred length: 500-750 words. Submit complete ms. Pays 50% revenue from syndication. Offers no additional payment for photos or artwork accompanying ms. Currently syndicates The Nuclear Age, by Lewis Rothlein (op-ed page column); Bizarro, by Dan Piraro (cartoon panel); and Naturally, by Sharon Cadwallader (food).

‡COLUMBIA FEATURES, INC., 36 W. 44 St., New York NY 10036. (212)840-1812. Editor: Joseph M. Boychuk. Syndicates to newspapers. Reports in 1 month. Buys all rights.
Needs: Magazine columns, magazine features, newspaper columns and newspaper features. Submit complete ms. Pays 50% of gross sales. Currently syndicates Rex Reed (movie review); Young Ideas, by Dick Young (sports); and Antique Wise, by Dorothy Hammond (antiques).

CONTINUUM BROADCASTING NETWORK/GENERATION NEWS, INC., Suite 46, 345 W. 85th St., New York NY 10024. Submit material to: 3546 84th St., Jackson Heights NY 11372. (212)713-5208. Executive Editor: Donald J. Fass. Associate Editor: Stephen Vaughn. Broadcast Feature Producer: Deanna Baron. 60% freelance written. 45% written by writers on contract; 5% freelance written by writers on a one-time basis. Buys 300 features/interviews/year. Works with 25-30 previously unpublished writers annually. Syndicates to newspapers and radio. Computer printout submissions acceptable; no dot-matrix. Buys all rights. Writer's guidelines for business size SAE and 2 first-class stamps. Reports in 5 weeks.
Needs: Newspaper columns (all kinds of weekly regular features for newspapers); radio broadcast material (90-second and 2½-minute regular daily radio features: lifestyle, comedy, music and interview—scripts as well as taped features); 30-minute and 60-minute specials. One-shot features for radio only-for 30- and 60-minute specials; scripts and completed productions. Query with 1 or 2 clips of published work only and 1 page summary on proposed articles. Demo tape and/or full script for broadcast; not necessary to query on tapes, but return postage must be provided. Pays 25-50% commission or $25-175, depending on length. Offers no additional payment for photos accompanying ms. Currently syndicates The World of Melvin Belli, Getting It Together (weekly youth-oriented music and lifestyle column); Keeping Fit (daily series); Rockweek and Backstage (weekly entertainment series).
Tips: "We seek a unique or contemporary concept with broad appeal that can be sustained indefinitely and for which the writer already has at least some backlog. Unique health, fitness, lifestyle, music, entertainment and trivia material will be emphasized, with a decrease in pop psychology, child psychology, history, seniors and parenting material."

‡THE CRICKET LETTER, INC., Box 527, Ardmore PA 19003. (215)789-2480. Editor: J.D. Krickett. 10% written by writers on contract; 10% freelance written by writers on a one-time basis. Works with 2-3 previously unpublished writers annually. Syndicates to trade magazines and newspapers. Computer printout submissions acceptable; prefers letter-quality to dot-matrix. Reports in 3 weeks. Buys all rights.
Needs: Magazine columns, magazine features, newspaper columns, newspaper features, and news items—all tax and financial-oriented (700-1,500 words); newspaper columns, features and news items directed to small business. Query with clips of published work. Pays $50-500. Currently syndicates Hobby/Business, by Mark E. Battersby (tax and financial); Farm Taxes, by various authors (farm taxes); and Small Business Taxes, by Mark E. Battersby (small business taxes).

‡CROWN SYNDICATE, INC., Box 99126, Seattle WA 98199. President: L.M. Boyd. Buys countless trivia items and cartoon and panel gag lines. Syndicates to newspapers, radio. Reports in 1 month. Buys first North American serial rights. Free writer's guidelines.
Needs: Filler material used weekly, items for trivia column, gaglines for specialty comic strip (format guidelines sent on request). Pays $1-5/item, depending on how it's used, i.e., trivia or filler service or comic strip. Offers no additional payment for photos accompanying ms. Currently syndicates puzzle panels and comic strips, by Crown contributors (daily strip).

EDITORIAL CONSULTANT SERVICE, Box 524, West Hempstead NY 11552. Editorial Director: Arthur A. Ingoglia. 40% written by writers on contract; 15% freelance written by writers on a one-time basis. "We work with 75 writers in the U.S. and Canada." Previously published writers only. Adds about 3 new columnists/ year. Syndicates material to an average of 60 newspapers, magazines, automotive trade and consumer publications, and radio stations with circulation of 50,000-575,000. Computer printout submissions acceptable; letter-quality submissions preferred. Buys all rights. Writer's guidelines for SASE. Reports in 3 weeks.
Needs: Magazine and newspaper columns and features; news items; and radio broadcast material. Prefers carefully documented material with automotive slant. Also considers automotive trade features. Will consider article series. No horoscope, child care, lovelorn or pet care. Query. Author's percentage varies; usually averages 50%. Additional payment for 8x10 b&w and color photos accepted with ms. Submit 2-3 columns. Currently syndicates Let's Talk About Your Car, by R. Hite.
Tips: "Emphasis is placed on articles and columns with an automotive slant. We prefer consumer-oriented features, i.e., how-to save money on your car, what every woman should know about her car, how-to-get more miles per gallon, etc."

FICTION NETWORK, Box 5651, San Francisco CA 94101. (415)391-6610. Editor: Jay Schaefer. 100% freelance written by writers who have signed contracts; 100% freelance written by writers on a one-time basis. Syndicates fiction to newspapers and regional magazines. Buys 100 features/year. Works with 25 previously unpublished writers annually. Computer printout submissions acceptable; letter-quality only. Reports in 3 months. Buys first serial rights. Sample catalog of syndicated stories $4; writer's guidelines for SAE with 1 first class stamp.
Needs: All types of fiction (particularly holiday) under 2,000 words. "We specialize in quality literature." Submit complete ms; do not send summaries or ideas. "Send one manuscript at a time; do not send second until you receive a response to the first." Pays 50% commission. Syndicates short fiction only; authors include Alice Adams, Ann Beattie, Max Apple, Andre Dubus, Bobbie Ann Mason, Joyce Carol Oates and others.
Tips: "We seek and encourage previously unpublished authors. Keep stories short, fast-paced and interesting."

FIRST DRAFT, Box 191107, Dallas TX 75219. (800)772-0722. Editor: Sheri Rosen. 75% written by writers on contract; 25% freelance written by writers on a one-time basis. Buys 60 articles/year. Syndicates to corporate and organizational employee publications. Electronic submissions OK—ASCII compatible or MCI Mail. Computer printout submissions acceptable. Reports in 2 months. Buys all rights. Writer's guidelines for business size SAE and 2 first class stamps.
Nonfiction: News items of 500 words (the effect of what's happening in the world on working people and businesses). May be universal or limited by industry. Buys one-shot features. Query with published clips or submit complete ms. Pays flat rate of $100 on acceptance.
Tips: "Most freelancers we use are business writers or former company publication editors."

GENERAL NEWS SYNDICATE, 147 W. 42nd St., New York NY 10036. (212)221-0043. 100% freelance written; 100% freelance written by writers on a one-time basis. Works with 12 writers/year; average of 3 previously unpublished writers annually. Syndicates to an average of 12 newspaper and radio outlets averaging 20 million circulation; buys theatre and show business people columns (mostly New York theatre pieces). Computer printout submissions acceptable; prefers letter-quality to dot-matrix. Reports in 3 weeks. Buys one-time rights.
Needs: Entertainment-related material.

‡GLOBAL PRESS REVIEW, 1307 4th St., NE, Washington DC 20002. (202)543-9428. Editor: Diane Sherwood. 50% written by writers on contract; 50% freelance written by writers on a one-time basis. Works with 12 previously unpublished writers annually. Syndicates to domestic and foreign news and features publications, independent journals, specialized newsletters, and electronic and print information services—both domestic and overseas. Send photocopies of ideas or mss which do not need to be returned. Electronic submissions OK via MSDOS or CPM or MCI (electronic) Mail Box #216-0456. Computer printout submissions acceptable; prefers letter-quality to dot-matrix. Reports "as soon as possible." Buys negotiable rights.
Needs: Reports on significant international events, trends and prognostications, top thinkers and influential organizations, cutting edge ideas and "best" tools for good living, appropriate- and high-tech, information age

technology, social experiments, women's affairs, bio-regionalism, and innovative barter/trade arrangements. Also book reviews, interviews. One-shot features and article series. Pays $200-800 on acceptance.

DAVE GOODWIN & ASSOCIATES, Drawer 54-6661, Surfside FL 33154. Editor: Dave Goodwin. 70% written by writers on contract; 10% freelance written by writers on a one-time basis. Buys about 25 features a year from freelancers. Works with 2 previously unpublished writers annually. Rights purchased vary with author and material. May buy first rights or second serial (reprint) rights or simultaneous rights. Will handle copyrighted material. Electronic submissions OK via IBM PC. Computer printout submissions acceptable; prefers letter-quality to dot-matrix. Query or submit complete ms. Reports in 3 weeks.
Nonfiction: "Money-saving information for consumers: how to save on home expenses; auto, medical, drug, insurance, boat, business items, etc." Buys article series on brief, practical, down-to-earth items for consumer use or knowledge. Rarely buys single features. Currently handling Insurance for Consumers. Length: 300-5,000 words. Pays 50% on publication. Submit 2-3 columns.

HARRIS & ASSOCIATES PUBLISHING DIVISION, 615 Carla Way, La Jolla CA 92037. (615)488-3851. President: Dick Harris. 50% written by writers on contract; 25% freelance written by writers on a one-time basis. Works with 10 previously published writers annually. Rights purchased vary with author and material. Buys first North American serial rights. Does not purchase many mss per year since material must be in special style. Pays on acceptance. Reports in less than 1 month.
Nonfiction: Material on driver safety and accident prevention. Not necessary to query. Send sample of representative material. Pays 15¢/word minimum.
Photos: Action, unposed, 8x10 b&w photos are purchased without features or on assignment. Captions are required. Pays $25 minimum/photo.
Humor: Humor for modern women (not women's lib); humor for sports page. "We like to look at anything in our special interest areas. Golf and tennis are our specialties. We'll also look at cartoons in these areas. Will buy or contract for syndication. Everything must be short, terse, with humorous approach."
Tips: "Submit *good* photos or art with text."

HERITAGE FEATURES SYNDICATE, 214 Massachusetts Ave. NE, Washington DC 20002. (202)543-0440. Managing Editor: Andy Seamans. 95% freelance written by writers on a one-time basis. Buys 3 columns/year. Works with 1-2 previously unpublished writers annually. Syndicates to over 100 newspapers with circulations ranging from 2,000-630,000. Works with previously published writers. Computer printout submissions acceptable. Buys first North American serial rights. Reports in 3 weeks.
Needs: Newspaper columns (practically all material is done by regular columnists). One-shot features. "We purchase 750-800 word columns on political, economic and related subjects." Query. Pays $50 minimum. Currently syndicates nine columnists, including For the Record by Herb Schmertz; Fed Up, by Don Feder; and The Answer Man, by Andy Seamans.
Tips: "We have no plans in the foreseeable future to add to our regular catalog of columnists."

HISPANIC LINK NEWS SERVICE, 1420 N St. NW, Washington DC 20005. (202)234-0280. Editor/Publisher: Charles A. Ericksen. 50% freelance written by writers on contract; 20% freelance written by writers on a one-time basis. Buys 156 columns and features/year. Works with 50 writers/year; 5 previously unpublished writers. Syndicates to 200 newspapers and magazines with circulations ranging from 5,000 to 300,000. Computer printout submissions acceptable; prefers letter-quality to dot-matrix. Reports in 2 weeks. Buys second serial (reprint) or negotiable rights. Free writer's guidelines.
Needs: Magazine columns, magazine features, newspaper columns, newspaper features. One-shot features and article series. "We prefer 650-700 word op/ed or features, geared to a general national audience, but focus on issue or subject of particular interest to Hispanic Americans. Some longer pieces accepted occasionally." Query or submit complete ms. Pays $25-150. Currently syndicates Hispanic Link, by various authors (opinion and/or feature columns).
Tips: "This year we would especially like to get topical material and vignettes relating to Hispanic presence and progress in the United States. Provide insights on Hispanic experience geared to a general audience. Eighty-five to ninety percent of the columns we accept are authored by Hispanics; the Link presents Hispanic viewpoints, and showcases Hispanic writing talent to its 200 subscribing newspapers and magazines. Copy should be submitted in English. We syndicate in English and Spanish."

HOLLYWOOD INSIDE SYNDICATE, Box 49957, Los Angeles CA 90049. (714)678-6237. Editor: John Austin. 10% written by writers on contract; 40% freelance written by writers on a one-time basis. Purchases entertainment-oriented mss for syndication to newspapers in San Francisco, Philadelphia, Detroit, Montreal, London, and Sydney, etc. Works with 2-3 previously unpublished writers annually. Pays on acceptance "but this is also negotiable because of delays in world market acceptance and payment." Previously published submissions OK, if published in the U.S. and Canada only. Computer printout submissions acceptable; prefers letter-quality to dot-matrix. Reports in 6 weeks. Buys first rights or second serial (reprint) rights.

Needs: News items (column items concerning entertainment—motion picture—personalities and jet setters for syndicated column; 750-800 words). Also considers series of 1,500-word articles; "suggest descriptive query first. We are also looking for off-beat travel pieces (with pictures) but not on areas covered extensively in the Sunday supplements. We can always use pieces on 'freighter' travel but not luxury cruise liners. We also syndicate nonfiction book subjects—sex, travel, etc., to overseas markets. No fiction." Query or submit complete ms. Pay negotiable.

Tips: "Study the entertainment pages of Sunday (and daily) newspapers to see the type of specialized material we deal in. Perhaps we are different from other syndicates, but we deal with celebrities. No 'I' journalism such as 'when I spoke to Cloris Leachman.' Many freelancers submit material from the 'dinner theatre' and summer stock circuit of 'gossip type' items from what they have observed about the 'stars' or featured players in these productions—how they act off stage, who they romance, etc. We use this material."

HYDE PARK MEDIA, 7158 Lee St., Chicago IL 60648. (312)967-7666. Editor: Anthony DeBartolo. 75% freelance written by writers on a one-time basis. Syndicates to area newspapers and magazines. Computer printout submissions acceptable; prefers letter-quality to dot-matrix. Reports in 3 weeks. Buys first and second serial rights.

Needs: Unusual, off-beat magazine features (1,500-3,000 words) and newspaper features (750-1,500 words). Buys single (one-shot) features. Query with published clips or complete manuscript. No phone queries. Pays 50% commission on sale.

Tips: "No more submissions from Indiana housewives wanting to be columnists. We *ain't* Santa Claus."

‡INFORMATIONAL FEATURES SYNDICATE, 6066 Civic Terrace Ave., Newark CA 94560. (415)790-3883. Editor: Daniel Danielson. Estab. 1986. 80% of features purchased from writers. Syndicates to newspapers, magazines, television and radio. Reports in 1 month. Buys all rights, first North American serial rights, and second serial (reprint) rights. Writer's guidelines for SASE.

Needs: Magazine features; newspaper columns (anything to do with health, self-help, psychology, sports, business management); newspaper features; radio broadcast material (anything to do with break-throughs in medicine or science that would improve quality of life); TV material; cartoons and comics. Buys one-shot features and article series. "We consider all types of articles, especially that where the author has an exclusive angle." Query with clips of published work, or submit complete ms. Pays author 50%. Additional payment for photos accepted with ms. Currently syndicates Successful Parenting, by Dr. Katherine Kersey (parenting advice); Fitness for Life, by Dr. Garth Fisher (health advice); and Successful Management, by Dr. Warren Bennis (business management advice).

INTERCONTINENTAL MEDIA SERVICES, LTD., Box 75009, Washington DC 20013. (202)775-1113. Editor: Dr. Edward von Rothkirch. Buys 500 features, 1,200 syndicated columns/year. Syndicates primarily to newspapers, some magazines. "In addition we syndicate six radio programs and are now going into three to six TV vignettes." Reports in 1 month. Buys all rights when available. Writer's guidelines for SAE and 1 first class stamp.

Needs: Newspaper columns (travel, collectibles, medical—500 to 700 words); newspaper features (travel, unusual subjects—1,500 words); news items (political backgrounders on foreign countries and personalities); radio broadcast material (travel, book reviews, science—length 2-3 minutes). One-shot (sometimes) and article series. "We will consider 400-1,500 words on foreign politics or personalities, travel to out-of-the-way or unusual places, collectibles of all kinds, science or medical subjects." Submit complete ms. Pays 50% of net received from clients; $50-500 (special) flat rate. Pays $25-100 for photos. Currently syndicates Magic Carpet, by Edward R'Church (travel).

Tips: "If the material is well-prepared, the approach is new or different, and there is a substantial segment of potential readers that have an interest in the subject, there is a good chance for syndication. The writer should indicate what the market potential is for the material."

INTERNATIONAL ECO FEATURES SYNDICATE, Box 69193, W. Hollywood, Los Angeles CA 90069. Director: Janet Bridgers. 100% freelance written by writers on a one-time basis. Syndicates to newspapers. Works with approximately 5 previously unpublished writers annually. Electronic submissions OK, but "we prefer contact by mail first;" hard copy also required. Computer printout submissions acceptable; prefers letter-quality to dot-matrix. Reports in 2 months. Buys first worldwide serial rights. Writer's guidelines for business size SASE.

Needs: Newspaper columns specializing in environment, ecology and animal rights. Op-ed articles, 800-1,000 words; features, 1,000-2,000 words with photos. Electronic submissions OK, but query with clips of published work. Pays 50% commission. "We will ask a higher price from newspapers when photos are accepted with manuscripts."

Tips: "We specialize in material about ecology, the environment and animal rights. We are not interested in material that is not about these subjects. We are *particularly* interested in op-eds on regional environmental issues."

Close-up

Vicki Williams
Syndicated Columnist

"King Features was the first syndicate I approached, and they bought the column," recalls Vicki Williams. "Most proposals probably come from journalists rather than factory workers, which was what I was at the time. Their executive editor flew to Indiana to meet me to see if I was 'for real.' " Since that meeting in September, 1984, the high school graduate who worked as a file clerk, an assembly line worker, and a part-time bartender has rapidly become one of the most imitated of syndicated columnists—and is simply referred to by some in syndicate circles as "the Indiana housewife."

"As a political columnist, I think my column appeals particularly to 'average citizens,' " she says. "They seem to feel a rapport with a writer of my background. But I think it is presumptuous for columnists to write as if they have inside information on what 'the people' think. What I write are my opinions, period. Some will agree and some will disagree, and some who agreed with today's column may disagree with tomorrow's."

Williams had been writing for years before trying to sell to a publication. "It was my best subject in school, but it was only in my 30's that I began to think I might actually sell my writing. Most of my writing was in the form of journal writing. Then I specialized in what I called my 'rural ramblings,' which I sold to regional, country-oriented publications. Very personal, introspective writing is probably the easiest to do at first."

Finding and researching an unusual slant for a topic were things Williams learned to do early in her writing career. Her first sale was to the *Harley Davidson Enthusiast*. She says she knew nothing about motorcycles and had never ridden one, but with a little research, her article "The Value of a Harley Davidson as a Farm Vehicle" sold the first time it was submitted. "I also sold an article, from a mother's point of view, to *Sports Illustrated*," she says, another example of her success with taking an unusual approach to a publication's usual topics.

The magazine freelance work also helped her choose the idea for the column she now writes. "I always got the most response from political and controversial social commentary pieces, so I concluded there was the most interest in that type of writing." Luckily, it was also the sort of material she wanted to write.

Williams convinced her local paper to try her column for 90 days in exchange for a subscription. "They were nervous about taking on an untried columnist," she says. She draws upon that experience when asked if she has advice to offer writers interested in syndication.

"The local paper is the best place to start. Even if you have to write for them for nothing for a certain period, it's worth it. You prove you can consistently come up with creative ideas, meet deadlines, and attract a positive audience. You will also find out whether you like to do this sort of writing week after week. Once you've written for a local paper for a year or two, you have a much greater chance of appealing to a syndicate."

Aware that some writers may be reluctant to write without payment, or to start a one- or two-year stint with a local paper, she adds, "At this point you need *them* more than they need you. You have to look at it as an investment you are willing to make in yourself."

—Sheila Freeman

INTERNATIONAL MEDICAL TRIBUNE SYNDICATE, 257 Park Ave. S., 19th Floor, New York NY 10010. (212)674-8500. Editor: Ken Senerth. 50% freelance written; 10% freelance written by writers on a one-time basis. Buys about 100 articles/year. Works with a few previously unpublished writers annually. Syndicates to small- and medium-sized newspapers, daily and weekly; magazines; computer news service; specialty publications in the health field. Electronic submissions OK, but query first. Computer printout submissions acceptable; prefers letter-quality to dot-matrix. Reports in 1 month. Buys all rights.
Needs: Fillers (250-400 words on medical or health developments); newspaper features (750-1,000 words—relatively complete treatment of an area of medicine or health); news items (straight news story filed within one week of event covered, etc., average 500 words). One-shot features on any topic in medicine and health. "Topics that we would especially like to get material on this year include up-to-date medical advances that can tell people how best to stay healthy." Length: 750-1,000 words. Query with published clips or submit complete ms. "Call with idea." Pays 20¢/word. Offers kill fee if assigned story. Offers no additional payment for photos accompanying ms.
Tips: "Our syndicate is an excellent opportunity for freelancers, but clear, concise and *lively* writing is a must. Strongly suggest query first, by mail or phone."

INTERPRESS OF LONDON AND NEW YORK, 400 Madison Ave., New York NY 10017. (212)832-2839. Editor: Jeffrey Blyth. 50% freelance written by writers on contract; 50% freelance written by writers on a one-time basis. Works with 3-6 previously unpublished writers annually. Buys British and European rights mostly, but can handle world rights. Will consider photocopied submissions. Previously published submissions OK "for overseas." Computer printout submissions acceptable; prefers letter-quality to dot-matrix. Pays on publication, or agreement of sale. Reports immediately or as soon as practicable.
Nonfiction: "Unusual stories and photos for British and European press. Picture stories, for example, on such 'Americana' as a five-year-old evangelist; the 800-pound 'con-man'; the nude-male calendar; tallest girl in the world; interviews with pop celebrities such as Yoko Ono, Michael Jackson, Bill Cosby, Tom Selleck, Cher, Priscilla Presley, Cheryl Tiegs, Eddie Murphy, Liza Minelli, also news of stars on such shows as "Dynasty"/"Dallas"; cult subjects such as voodoo, college fads, anything amusing or offbeat: Extracts from books such as Earl Wilson's *Show Business Laid Bare*, inside-Hollywood type series ('Secrets of the Stuntmen'). Real life adventure dramas ('Three Months in an Open Boat,' 'The Air Crash Cannibals of the Andes'). No length limits—short or long, but not too long. Query or submit complete ms. Payment varies; depending on whether material is original, or world rights. Pays top rates, up to several thousand dollars, for exclusive material."
Photos: Purchased with or without features. Captions required. Standard size prints. Pay $50 to $100, but no limit on exclusive material.
Tips: "Be alert to the unusual story in your area—the sort that interests the American tabloids (and also the European press)."

KING FEATURES SYNDICATE, INC., 235 E. 45th St., New York NY 10017. (212)682-5600. Editor: James D. Head. 10% freelance written. Syndicates material to newspapers. Works with 10 previously unpublished writers annually. Submit "brief cover letter with samples of feature proposals." Previously published submissions OK. Computer printout submissions acceptable. Reports in 3 weeks. Buys all rights.
Needs: Newspaper features and columns. No travel, wine or general humor columns; restaurant, theatre or movie reviews; or fad-oriented subjects. Pays "revenue commission percentage" or flat fee. Special single article opportunity is Sunday Woman Plus, a weekly supplement distributed nationally. Buys one-time rights to articles on beauty, health, grooming, fashion, coping, money management for women, career guidance, etc. Query with SASE to Merry Clark, senior editor.
Tips: "Be brief, thoughtful and offer some evidence that the feature proposal is viable. Read newspapers—lots of them in big and small markets—to find out what already is out there. Don't try to buck established columns which newspapers would be reluctant to replace with new and untried material."

‡MIKE LeFAN FEATURES, 1802 S. 13th St., Temple TX 76501. (817)773-4768. Editor: Mike LeFan. 100% freelance written. Buys 40-50 filler items/year. Syndicates to newspapers, and to some magazines or newspaper magazine sections. Reports in 3 weeks. Electronic submissions OK via WordStar, CP/M-80 compatible, 5¼" SSDD disk; modem 300 or 1200 baud. Requires hard copy also. Computer printout submissions acceptable; prefers letter-quality to dot-matrix. Buys first North American rights and second serial (reprint) rights. Submit seasonal material 3 months in advance.
Needs: (Fillers up to 100 words, showing how to get more for your money). Especially needs seasonal material. *No* household hints. Submit complete ms. Pays $3/filler. Currently syndicates More for Your Money, and HMOs and Your Health.
Tips: "Talent will help any writer get syndicated, but persistence is absolutely vital. It's also necessary to study the markets and your competition. There's a trend toward material geared to so-called senior citizens, or at least the over-55 crowd."

LOS ANGELES TIMES SYNDICATE, Times-Mirror Square, Los Angeles CA 90053. Vice President/Editor: Don Michel. Special Articles Editor: Dan O'Toole. Syndicates to U.S. and worldwide markets. Usually buys first North American serial rights and world rights, but rights purchased can vary. Submit seasonal material six weeks in advance. Material ranges from 800-2,000 words.
Needs: Reviews continuing columns and comic strips for U.S. and foreign markets. Send columns and comic strips to Don Michel. Also reviews single articles, series, magazine reprints, and book serials. Send these submissions to Dan O'Toole. Recent special projects include Yeager: An Autobiography, Fit for Life, and Elvis and Me. Send complete mss. Pays 50% commission. Offers no additional payment for photos accompanying ms. Currently syndicates Erma Bombeck, Art Buchwald, Dr. Henry Kissinger, William Pfaff, Paul Conrad and Lee Iacocca.
Tips: "We're dealing with fewer undiscovered writers but still do review material."

‡MINORITY FEATURES SYNDICATE, Box 421, Farrell PA 16146. (412)962-2522. Editor: Sally Foglia. Reports in 5 weeks. 50% written by freelance on contract; 25% freelance written by writers on a one-time basis. Works with 5 previously unpublished writers annually. Buys first North American serial rights. Computer printout submissions acceptable; no dot-matrix. Reports in 5 weeks. Writer's guidelines for 44¢ postage.
Needs: Fillers, magazine features, newspaper features. Also needs comic book writers for Bill Murray Productions. Query with published clips. Pays open commission. Pays $25 minimum for photos. Currently syndicates Sonny Boy, Those Browns and The Candyman, by Bill Murray (newspaper features).
Tips: "We are getting into the comic book market. Writers should write for guidelines."

NATIONAL NEWS BUREAU, 2019 Chancellor St., Philadelphia PA 19103. (215)569-0700. Editor: Harry Jay Katz. "We work with more than 200 writers and buy over 1,000 stories per year." Syndicates to more than 1,000 publications. Reports in 2 weeks. Buys all rights. Writer's guidelines for 9x12 SAE and 54¢ postage.
Needs: Newspaper features; "we do many reviews and celebrity interviews. Only original, assigned material." One-shot features and article series; film reviews, etc. Query with clips. Pays $5-200 flat rate. Offers $5-200 additional payment for photos accompanying ms.

NEW YORK TIMES SYNDICATION SALES CORP., 200 Park Ave., New York NY 10166. (212)972-1070. Vice President/Editorial Director: Paula Reichler. 20% written by writers on contract; 50% freelance written by writers on a one-time basis. Syndicates approximately "three books per month plus numerous one-shot articles." Also included in foreign newspapers and magazines. Buys first serial rights, first North American serial rights, one-time rights, second serial (reprint) rights, and all rights. Computer printout submissions acceptable; no dot-matrix.
Needs: Wants magazine and newspaper features; magazine and newspaper columns; and book series. "On syndicated articles, payment to author is 50% of net sales. We only consider articles that have been previously published. Send tearsheets of articles published." Submit approximately 12 samples of articles. Photos are welcome with books and articles. "Topics that we would especially like to get material on this year include fitness and holiday themes."
Tips: "Topics should cover universal markets and either be by a well-known writer or have an off-beat quality. Quizzes are welcomed if well researched."

NEWS FLASH INTERNATIONAL, INC., 2262 Centre Ave., Bellmore NY 11710. (516)679-9888. Editor: Jackson B. Pokress. 25% written by writers on contract; 10% freelance written by writers on a one-time basis. Supplies material to Observer newspapers and overseas publications. Works with 1-10 previously unpublished writers annually. "Contact editor prior to submission to allow for space if article is newsworthy." Photocopied submissions OK. Computer printout submissions acceptable; no dot-matrix. Pays on publication.
Nonfiction: "We have been supplying a 'ready-for-camera' sports page (tabloid size) complete with column and current sports photos on a weekly basis to many newspapers on Long Island, as well as pictures and written material to publications in England and Canada. Payment for assignments is based on the article. Payments vary from $20 for a feature of 800 words. Our sports stories feature in-depth reporting as well as book reviews on this subject. We are always in the market for good photos, sharp and clear, action photos of boxing, wrestling, football, baseball and hockey. We cover all major league ball parks during the baseball and football seasons. We are accredited to the Mets, Yanks, Jets and Giants. During the winter we cover basketball and hockey and all sports events at the Nassau Coliseum."
Photos: Purchased on assignment; captions required. Uses "good quality 8x10 b&w glossy prints; good choice of angles and lenses." Pays $7.50 minimum for b&w photos.
Tips: "Submit articles which are fresh in their approach on a regular basis with good quality black and white glossy photos if possible; include samples of work. We prefer well-researched, documented stories with quotes where possible."

‡NEWSLINK AFRICA, Suite 411, London International Press Centre, 76 Shoe Lane, Fleet St., London EC4 England. Tel. (01)353-0186. Telex: 23862 (Attn: Newsafrica). Managing Editor: Shamlal Puri. 60% freelance written. Buys about 300 features/year (200 written inhouse). "We work with very few previously unpublished writers annually, but we like to encourage writers (whether published or unpublished) to provide copy on African affairs. So, if they are unpublished on Africa (but have written generally), we are prepared to give them a break provided they have the potential." Computer printout submissions acceptable; prefers letter-quality to dot-matrix. Syndicates to magazines, newspapers, radio, reference libraries. Reports in 3 months. Buys all rights.

Needs: Fiction, fillers, magazine columns, magazine features, newspaper columns, newspaper features, radio broadcast material. "We concentrate on African affairs or how world events affect Africa, and are (reportedly) the only syndicate dealing in African affairs exclusively in Britain, Europe and Canada. We look at events in Africa as Africans would do. We do not like 'injecting' Western influence or values into our output. Our agency is run by Africans whose sole motive is dissemination of news and information. We are not backed by any multi-national or political party. We'd prefer specialists in African affairs. We try to avoid academic writing style—simplicity is the main prerequisite." One-shot features and article series (about 1,000-2,000 words). "Topics should include Africa (economics, commerce, politics, social scene or any topic having a bearing on Africa)." Query with clips of published work or submit complete ms. "Material accepted on speculation also. Enclose IRC/check for return postage. Work accepted purely on merit. Our payments start from 5-200 pounds sterling for 1,000 words." Currently syndicates African Culture Series, by T. Ankrah.

Photos: "We prefer negatives to make more prints. Send negative with each print."

Tips: Encourages objectivity, sticking to details and simple language. "You must know your subject well. In our field, we prefer specialists in African affairs."

‡PACHECO AUTOMOTIVE NEWS SERVICE, Box 6691, Concord CA 94524. (415)228-7821. Editor: Bob Hagin. 40% written by writers on contract; 5% freelance written by writers on a one-time basis. Buys 1 feature/month. Syndicates to 45 U.S. and Canadian daily papers; KCBS San Francisco—2 hours/week. Works with 3 previously unpublished writers annually. Computer printout submissions acceptable. Reports in 1 week. Buys all rights.

Nonfiction: Newspaper features—auto-related only. Query only. Does not return material. Pays $25 minimum guarantee; $10 additional minimum payment for photos. Currently syndicates Auto Feature, Collectible Car, Road Test, Motor Sports.

PHOTO ASSOCIATES NEWS SERVICE, INC., Box 306, Flushing NY 11358. (212)619-1700/(718)961-0909. Editor-in-Charge: Rick Moran. Freelance Editor: R.J. Maiman. "We worked with 30 writers last year handling 450 stories for a variety of domestic and international magazines and newspapers." Prefers electronic submissions via phone; 300 Baud or MCI Mail (Telex 75-0809—photo UD; MC/ Mail 217-8611). Computer printout submissions acceptable. Query with resume, published clips and SASE. "Also enclose a list of story ideas that you think we would want." Responds within 10 days with writer's guidelines.

Needs: "Our big emphasis is on articles with illustrations or photos. Our client list includes publications in Asia, South America and Europe and virtually all of them want art to accompany stories. Topics we have been successful with in the past include entertainment, travel, pop science and psychology and public safety issues (police, fire, paramedics). All sorts of celebrity material is constantly being called for by our clients overseas, as are fresh story ideas that have not already been exploited over the wires. Pet and animal stories have also done very well in the past. Our greatest emphasis is on breaking news and headline stories, feature length, covered with a local angle, but these too must be accompanied by good photos." Pays 65% commission on sale. Payments are made once a month.

Tips: "We are supportive of both National Writers Union and ASMP members. While we prefer writers who have proven track records, we are always looking for new talent with a flair."

‡SYNDICATED WRITERS & ARTISTS INC., Suite 205, 1321 Meridian St., Indianapolis IN 46204. (317)634-4900. Editor: Eunice Trotter. Estab. 1985. 99% written by writers on contract; 1% freelance written by writers on a one-time basis. Works with 30 writers annually. Syndicates to newspapers. Reports in 6 weeks. Electronic submissions OK via compatible with most PCs and miniframes. Computer printout submissions acceptable; prefers letter-quality to dot-matrix. Buys all rights. Free writer's guidelines.

Needs: Fillers, newspaper columns, newspaper features and news items. 300 words with minority angle. Query with clips of published work. "Three different samples of your work should be submitted (10 cartoon strips or panels). Submissions should also include brief bio of writer/artists. No material is returned without a SASE. Pays author's percentage of 35-40%. Currently syndicates Into the Groove, by L. Michael Jackson (entertainment); Viewpoint, by Ken Wibecan (editorial); and Political Cartoon, by Dennis Gill (editorial).

Tips: "The kind of writing we seek has a minority angle. Previously, there was no market for material with a minority angle; we believe there now is such a market. More news instead of opinion will be required. Quality requirements."

SYNDICATED WRITERS GROUP, Box 23, Boyertown PA 19512. (215)367-9496. Editor: Daniel Grotta. 100% written by writers on contract. "Syndicated Writers Group is a unique and revolutionary syndicate in that we are the world's first interactive computerized library databank which editors may access from their own ter- · minals and select and download ready-to-publish articles and columns. We syndicate to newspapers and maga- zines." Electronic submissions OK from contract writers via disk or modem. Models I, II and IV TRS-80 35 or 40 track 5" single sided, single density; Tandy Model 100 3.5" disk; 40 or 76 track 5" or 8" CP/M format; any 5" 40 track MS-DOS disk. Modem access restricted to authorized users. Computer printout submissions pre- ferred from prospective writers. Reports in 3 months. Maintains exclusive rights for the length of the contract. Writer's guidelines with SASE. "No submissions acknowledged or returned without SASE."
Needs: "We have a need for contract writers in certain fields such as technology, medicine, pets, lifestyles, politics, computers, consumerism, etc. At present we are not interested in columns or one-shot submissions, but writers who can regularly produce individual articles that can be marketed as independent pieces. Our main sales emphasis is through our library—it functions much like a stock photo agency—and although we do repre- sent about a dozen columns, we do not wish to add any more to our roster. We are interested in finished feature articles—*no columns*—that can be periodically updated and sold for months or years to come." Pays 50% com- mission; 80% when SWG acts as agent for specific assignment; 85% for secondary rights sales, such as books, TV, etc. Maintains exclusive rights for the length of the contract. Pays additional for photos or artwork sold with manuscripts, but only top-quality stuff. At present we cannot consider any separate graphics material such as photos, cartoons, etc.
Tips: "We are looking for top quality pros, preferably with magazine or book backgrounds who are used to presenting substance with style. However, we will consider newcomers if they can impress us with their abili- ties. Our articles—most of which are 1,000 words or under—are not only informative and interesting, but en- tertaining. We want each piece to be a potential award-winner." SWG is an electronic editorial syndicate, and all our writers will be eventually connected to us by computer. We work only with writers under direct contract to us.

TEENAGE CORNER, INC., 70-540 Gardenia Ct., Rancho Mirage CA 92270. President: David J. Lavin. Buys 122 items/year for use in newspapers. Submit complete ms. Reports in 1 week. Material is not copyrighted.
Needs: 500-word newspaper features. Pays $25.

TRIBUNE MEDIA SERVICES, 64 E Concord St., Orlando FL 32801. (305)422-8181. President: Robert S. Reed. Editor: Michael Argirion. Syndicates to newspapers. Reports in 1 month. Buys all rights, first North American serial rights and second serial (reprint) rights.
Needs: Newspaper columns and features. Buys single features and article series if suitable for newspapers. Query with published clips. Pays 50% commission. Currently syndicates the columns of Mike Royko, Bob Greene, Liz Smith, Andy Rooney, Marilyn Beck, Jeff MacNelly, Eric Wilson and Mike Peters.

UNITED CARTOONIST SYNDICATE, Box 7081, Corpus Christi TX 78415. (512)855-2480. President: Pe- dro R. Moreno. 5% freelance written by writers on a one-time basis. Works with 12 cartoonists annually. Syn- dicates to newspapers, newsletters, magazines, books or book publishers, and licensing companies. Reports in · 1 week on submissions. Simultaneous submissions OK. Guidelines $5 with copies of artwork or clips of published or unpublished work.
Needs: Newspaper features (comic panel and comic strips in a family entertainment slant). Purchases single (one-shot) features and article series. Will consider meta-physical, UFOs, and human and animal interest sto- ries or articles. Query with published clips or 12-24 samples of unpublished artwork (reduced) or articles. Pays author 40%. Additional payment for photos: $10-25. Currently syndicates Brother Simon and Lucus, by Pedro R. Moreno.
Tips: "We do not accept any material that deals with sex, or put down material against anything or anybody."

WEEKLY FEATURES SYNDICATE LTD., 126 S. 8th St., St. Joseph MO 64501. (816)364-2920. Editor: Lin- da Bennett. 100% written by writers on contract. Works with 5 previously unpublished writers annually. "We have 12 overseas agencies that sell our features, plus we market all newspapers and magazines in the United States area." Reports in 1 month. Buys all rights. Writer's guidelines for 9x12 SAE.
Needs: Features on home fix-it and decoration ideas. Buys articles series. Submit complete ms. "We do not use features represented by other agents. Pays 75% commission. Pays $10-100 for photos accepted with mss. Currently syndicates Archie Richard (financial), Fred Cassel (household tips), and Yvonne Lancaster (hu- mor).

‡WORK, 907 Sand Dollar Bldg., Shell Pt. Village, Ft. Meyers FL 33908. Does not wish to receive unsolicited material. Syndicates only own material.

Services & Opportunities

Author's Agents

Some writers approach an agent the way an ailing patient approaches a doctor. "Oh, fix it and make it well," begs the patient, while the writer pleads with the agent, "Oh, fix it and make it sell."

In an ideal world, no one would ever need a doctor—or an agent. Writers would always submit polished manuscripts to the appropriate publisher, who would eagerly accept and promptly pay for them.

You can probably see at least four fallacies in this "ideal world." Writers don't always submit *polished* manuscripts to the *appropriate* publisher; instead of *accepting* and *paying* for manuscripts immediately, publishers more often reject manuscripts and are sometimes less than prompt in paying.

Literary agents try to smooth out those rough spots. In general, agents are a combination of sales representatives and business managers. Agents keep in touch with editors and buyers of subsidiary rights; they know where to sell marketable manuscripts and how to negotiate contracts; they help collect payments from publishers and keep accurate records.

Whether you're ready for an agent or not, it's a good idea to get acquainted with the variety of services they offer, the fees or commissions they charge, and the way they deal with writers and publishers.

Agents and today's market

"We are like gold diggers plowing through tons of slag in search of a nugget called a viable manuscript," says one agent. Of course agents don't decide whether or not a manuscript should be published; that's still a job for editors. Agents can only tell you if they believe your manuscript is *ready* to be submitted to a publisher.

If you've read the Book Publishers section of *Writer's Market*, you know that the publishing industry has become extremely competitive and cost-conscious. Like any other business, a publishing company that fails to make a profit will not survive. More and more book publishers will only consider manuscripts submitted through agents. That isn't fair, you mutter to yourself. Fair? Maybe not. Necessary? In many cases, yes.

Today few publishers can afford to hire a fulltime staff of editors—or even freelance readers—to go through hundreds of unsolicited manuscripts. Publishers simply receive too many manuscripts—too many *unpublishable* manuscripts—with this "open door" policy. That's why so many publishers now rely on agents.

This greater demand for agented submissions has caused an increase in the number of literary agencies. For many years, a "New York agent" was the best—if not the only—kind of agent for professional writers. Then a number of agents settled on the West Coast, primarily to work with film and TV producers. Now more and more new agencies are opening in the Midwest and other parts of the U.S. to serve the needs of writers and publishers. Some of the newer literary agencies have been started by former editors and teachers with an entrepreneurial spirit.

Fees and commissions

Literary agents have always charged a commission on the manuscripts they place with publishers or producers—in much the same way real estate agents charge a commission. The commission (usually 10%-20%) is subtracted from the author's advance and royalty payments from the publisher. In other words, the writer doesn't pay the agent a commission until the manuscript has been sold.

Agents rarely charge for general office "overhead" (the cost of utilities, secretarial service, etc.). Instead, they sometimes ask their clients to pay for specific expenses related to selling that writer's manuscripts: photocopying, long distance phone calls, messenger service, etc.

Commissions and charges for specific office expenses are regarded as perfectly acceptable in the industry. *Additional* fees—for reading or criticizing manuscripts—are becoming more common, although not uniformly accepted. Some agencies charge a *reading fee* to unpublished writers; no comments on improving the manuscript are offered in this case. Other agencies charge a *criticism fee*; they often provide several pages of detailed suggestions.

"We regard a reading fee and criticism fee interchangeably since notes from reading are used for the critique," says one new agent. Several firms that charge fees regard them as one-time payments; if the writer becomes a client, no more fees will be charged for future manuscripts. Some agencies also reimburse the writer for the original fee when the manuscript is sold. At least one agency frequently returns the fee to writers whose material is submitted before it is in professional condition.

Writer beware

Agents' fees continue to be a hotly debated topic. Previous editions of *Writer's Market* sought to protect our readers by listing only those agents who told us they charged nothing but commissions. In *Writer's Market '87*, you'll find a new policy and new listings—of both commission-only and commission- and fee-charging agents.

Why include agents who charge fees? Approximately 80% of all literary agencies now charge some kind of fee. We at *Writer's Market* believe our job is to provide you, our readers, with the most complete and up-to-date information. We can't give recommendations or make decisions for you—but we do want to help you in your search for an agent. You'll find that, in addition to new listings of agents, we've added questions you should ask an agent—and yourself—before you make any decisions.

Remember that payment of a reading or criticism fee almost never guarantees that the agency will represent you. Payment of a fee may—or may not—give you the kind of constructive criticism you need. Read the individual listings carefully. There's no way to generalize about fee-charging agencies. They may be new or established, large or small, good or bad. Some are almost apologetic about their fees. "This is a legitimate 'labor of love' on my part—not a rip-off," a new agent told us. With others, it's strictly business; time is money, and it certainly takes time to read the dozens of manuscripts delivered to many agencies each day.

How much should you pay? There are no "standard" fees. Some agencies charge criticism fees of $25-75; others charge $200 or more. Reading fees, though less common than criticism fees, are usually less than $50. One fee may apply to a complete manuscript, while another is for an outline and sample chapters. Some agents require fees from unpublished writers only. Sometimes agents refund a fee when the manuscript is sold. A few agents charge a marketing, handling or processing fee of $25-100 to all clients. Several agents offer a consultation service ($15-200/hour) to advise writers on book contracts they have received without the help of an agent. If you decide to pay a fee, be sure you *know exactly* what you'll receive in return.

What a literary agent does

Agents do many things to earn their commissions, but it's almost impossible to describe what an "average" agent does. Let's begin by considering what literary agents *don't* do.

An agent can't sell unsalable work or teach you how to write. An agent won't edit your manuscript; that's an editor's job. An agent can't defend you in a court of law (unless he or she is also an attorney). An agent won't act as your press agent, social secretary, or travel agent; you'll have to hire someone else to handle those chores. An agent can't solve your personal problems, lend you money, or be immediately and constantly available to have long discussions with you. As a rule, agents don't handle short stories, poetry or magazine articles.

As far as what an agent *can* and *will* do, each agency is different—in the services it offers, the clients it prefers, its contacts in the industry, and the style in which it conducts business. In general, an agent's tasks can be divided into those that are done *before* a sale, *during* a sale and *after* a sale.

Before the sale, the agent evaluates your manuscript and sometimes makes suggestions about revisions. If the agent wants to represent you, you'll usually receive a contract or letter of agreement specifying the agent's commission, any fees and the term of the agreement. When that's signed, the agent begins talking to editors and sending your manuscript out. Your agent can tell you about any marketing problems, give you a list of submissions, and send you copies of rejections—if you really want to know. The agent repeats this sequence until the manuscript sells, you withdraw it, or the term of your agreement expires.

During the sale, the agent negotiates with the publisher for you, offering certain rights to the publisher and usually reserving other rights for future sale. The agent examines the contract, negotiates clauses for your benefit and tries to get additional rights (like book jacket approval) for you. Your agent can explain the contract to you and make recommendations, but the final decision is always yours.

After the sale, the agent maintains a separate bank account for you, collects money from the publisher, deducts the appropriate commission and sends you the remainder. The agent examines all royalty statements and requests corrections or an audit when necessary. The agent also checks the publisher's progress on the book—including production and promotion—and makes sure your copyright has been registered. Sometimes the agent resolves conflicts you might have with your editor or publisher. If you have retained subsidiary rights to your book, the agent will continue working for additional sales—for movie, book club, foreign, or video rights, etc. Your agent could even introduce you to an editor who might be interested in your next book.

You and an agent

Not everyone needs an agent. Some writers are perfectly capable of handling the placement of their manuscripts; they enjoy being involved in all stages of selling, negotiating and checking the production of their books. Others have no interest in—or talent for—the business side of writing.

How well do you know yourself? Think carefully as you answer the following questions:
- Do you have the skills that would allow you to handle an agent's usual tasks?

- Can you take care of marketing your book, contract analysis, self-promotion?
- Can you afford to pay an agent 10%-20% of your royalties?
- Would you like working through a middleman—the agent—on all aspects of your book's future?
- Will you have more time to write if you have an agent?

No matter how much you want or "need" an agent, you'll be wasting time—and possibly money—if you and your manuscript aren't *ready* for an agent. Of the manuscripts received by agents, only one in 100 is ready to be submitted to publishers; some agents say one in 1,000 is a better estimate.

What are writers doing wrong? "Would you believe novels with only one page of dialogue?" asks a frustrated agent. "Writers who use the words 'two,' 'too,' and 'to' interchangeably? Two-hundred page manuscripts submitted in longhand, instead of being neatly typed?"

"I work closely with my clients and expect a high level of professionalism in exchange," says one agent. Other agents echo her sentiments. "Unpublished writers . . . should be business-like and unemotional about their own writing. If a writer has a mastery of the craft of writing, a mature knowledge of subject or background, an individual style, and a *theme* beneath the ability to tell a story, then a relationship between author and agent is possible" as well as eventual publication.

Getting ready

It isn't easy to meet agents' expectations; you'll have to be prepared—and so will your manuscript. You must be objective, too, as you answer the following questions:
- Have you truly *polished* your manuscript—so that it shines like a gold nugget?
- Have you studied the marketplace for buyers of your kind of writing?
- Have you talked to fellow-writers who have agents?
- Have you read all you can find about agents?
- Do you have a reasonable expectation that your manuscript is publishable?

Sounds like a lot of work, doesn't it? It is. And if you want an agent to take you seriously, you'll make every effort to:
- Get a recommendation from another writer who's a client of the agency you approach.
- Sell a short story or magazine article—anything—before contacting an agent.
- Get your writing published, even if it's in a nonpaying but reputable market.
- Win a prize in a legitimate literary or journalistic contest.
- Act like a professional writer when you correspond with an agent.

Of course you don't have to follow all these suggestions (except the last one) before you start your search. These aren't requirements; but if you can do two or more, you may be *ready* to send your work to an agent.

Contacting an agent

Few agents will look at unsolicited manuscripts. Some will consider queries only if you've been recommended by a client or an editor. But the majority will look at a query (and possibly an outline) from an unknown writer.

Apparently, many writers make some basic mistakes when approaching agents. "SASE is a must!" says one agent. "Please, no handwritten or messy typewritten queries."

Another agent agrees. "With 60-80 query letters a week pouring in, I would like to stress one thing . . . without SASE for the query, we don't bother to read the letters. Another thing, which is petty," he adds, "we don't look at letters or manuscripts that have been processed with dot-matrix. These are hard on eyes so we don't read them."

Other agents may have particular preferences, too. In addition to following the suggestions in each agent's listing, plan your query letter carefully. It should include a brief description of your manuscript, anticipated number of words or pages, whether or not you've been published, and your credentials (for nonfiction).

If the agent asks to see more of your work, consider yourself lucky—but don't assume that you now "have an agent." Just as you need to find out more about the agent, the agent has to know more about you and your writing. Many agents refer to their relationship with a client as a "marriage." Don't rush into it, and don't expect an immediate response to your query or manuscript. "In this business, patience is one of the highest virtues," says more than one agent.

On the other hand, if you receive no response—or a negative response—to your query, don't be discouraged. Continue to contact other agents. It's OK to send multiple (simultaneous) queries, but *never* send a manuscript to two agents at the same time.

How to judge an agent

A bad agent can be worse than no agent at all. We've already discussed the expectations agents have for writers. Now it's time for you to decide what *your* expectations are for an agent. When an agency indicates an interest in representing your work, don't just assume it's the right one for you. If you want to make a knowledgable decision, you'll need more information—and that means asking more questions.

You can get a basic "feel" for an agency from their response to these questions. You may (or may not) be impressed by their credentials, their commission and fee structure, or the sevices they offer. You'll also get a feeling for the agency's "tone" or "style"—which can vary from low-key and personal to high-pressure or strictly business.

While the answers to many of these questions appear in agencys' individual *Writer's Market* listings, it's a good idea to ask them again. Policies change; reporting times, commission amounts and fees may vary from those indicated here.

● What's your commission on domestic (U.S.) sales? Foreign sales? Performance (for scripts and screenplays)?
● How soon do you report on queries? On manuscripts?
● Do you charge a reading or critiquing fee? If yes—
—How much?
—What kind of feedback will I receive?
—What's the ratio of the agency's income from fees compared to income from marketing books?
—If the manuscript is accepted, will my fee be returned? Credited against my marketing expenses? Or is it a nonreturnable charge to cover reading/critiquing expenses?
● Do you charge any other fees? For marketing, etc.?
● How many clients do you represent?
● Will you provide me with lists of recent sales, titles published or clients? [*Writer's Market* asked each agency for this information; it's included in individual listings under "Recent Titles Sold." Some agents chose not to respond to this question; their listings have the notation "No information given."]
● May I contact any of your clients for referrals? [This is the most valuable information you can get, but some agents regard it as a breach of confidentiality.]
● How many agents are in your agency?
● Who will work with me and what kind of feedback can I expect—regular status reports, good news only, copies of informative letters from editors, etc.?
● Who will negotiate my contracts?
● Which subsidiary rights (foreign, performance, serial, electronic, etc.) do you market di-

rectly? Which are marketed through subagents? Which are handled by the publisher?
- Do you offer any special services—tax/legal consultation, manuscript typing, book promotion or lecture tour coordination, etc.? Which cost extra? Which are covered by the commission?
- Do you offer any editorial support? How much?
- Do you offer a written agreement? If yes—
—How long does it run?
—Which projects (or kinds of projects) are covered?
—Will (or must) all my writing be represented?
—What will be your commission on sales? Domestic? Foreign? Performance? [Even though you may know the answers to these questions, they should be specified in the agreement.]
—Which expenses am I responsible for? Are they deducted from earnings, billed directly, or paid by initial deposit?
—How can the agreement be terminated?
—After it terminates, what happens to works already sold, current submissions, etc.?
   If the agency doesn't offer a contract or written agreement of any kind, you should write a letter of your own that summarizes *your* understanding on all these issues. Ask the agent to return a signed copy to you. A few agents prefer "informal, verbal" agreements. No matter how personal a relationship you have with an agent, it is still a business matter. If the agent refuses to sign a simple letter of understanding, you may want to reconsider your choice of agencies.

Additional resources

   The search for an agent can be a frustrating and time-consuming task—especially if you don't know what you're looking for. You can learn more about agents by studying several books on the subject. Check with your library or bookstore for *Literary Agents: How to Get and Work with the Right One for You*, by Michael Larsen (Writer's Digest Books) and *Literary Agents: A Writer's Guide*, by Debby Mayer (Poet's & Writer's, Inc.; 201 W. 54th St., New York, NY 10019). *Literary Agents of North America, 3rd edition* (Author Aid/Research Associates International, 340 E. 52nd St., New York, NY 10022) is an annual directory of agents; it is indexed by individual agents, geography, subjects and specialties, size, branch offices and affiliates. The library may also have a copy of *Literary Market Place*, which includes names and addresses of agents.
   Remember that agents are not required to have any special training or accreditation. Some are members of a number of professional organizations or writers groups, depending on their special interests. In *Writer's Market* listings, we mention only three types of membership: ILAA, SAR, and WGA. Each of these organizations requires its agent members to subscribe to a code of ethics and standard practices.
- ILAA—Independent Literary Agents Association, Inc., 15th Floor, 55 5th Ave., New York, NY 10003. Founded in 1977, ILAA is a nationwide trade association of fulltime literary agents. ILAA members are generally newer, smaller agencies located in New York, Boston, San Francisco, Washington D.C., and other cities. An informative brochure, a list of members, and a copy of the ILAA Code of Ethics will be sent on request to writers who enclose a #10 SASE with 2 first class stamps. ILAA is unable to provide information on specialties of individual members.
- SAR—Society of Author's Representatives, Inc., Box 650, Old Chelsea Station, New York, NY 10113. Founded in 1928, SAR is a voluntary association of New York agents, usually the larger, older agencies. A brochure and membership list are available for SASE. Members are identified as specializing in literary or dramatic material.

● WGA—Writer's Guild of America. Agents and producers in the TV, radio and motion picture industry can become members (or signatories) of WGA by signing the guild's basic agreement, which outlines minimum standards for treatment of writers. For a list of agents who have signed the WGA agreement, send a money order for $1.30 to one of the WGA offices. If you live east of the Mississippi River, write to WGA, East, 555 W. 57th St., New York, NY 10019; west of the Mississippi, write WGA, West, 8955 Beverly Blvd., Los Angeles, CA 90048.

Remember that many agencies are in a period of transition. Some are "not yet" charging fees; some that were once "commission only" have recently begun to charge fees; and others have discontinued their previous policy of reading or criticism fees.

Always enclose SASE when submitting a query or manuscript to an agent. Be patient. Some agencies listed here for the first time may be unprepared for the number of queries received from readers of *Writer's Market*; their stated reporting times may suffer.

CAROL ABEL LITERARY AGENCY, 160 W. 87th St., New York NY 10024. (212)724-1168. President: Carol Abel. Estab. 1978. Member of ILAA. Represents 45 clients. 25% of clients are new/unpublished authors. Prefers to work with published/established writers; works with a small number of new/unpublished authors. Specializes in contemporary women's novels, biographies, thrillers, health, nutrition, medical nonfiction (diet and exercise) and history.
Will Handle: Nonfiction books, novels, and juvenile books (some young adult). Currently handles 50% nonfiction books and 50% novels. Will read—at no charge—unsolicited queries, outlines and mss. Reports in 2 weeks on queries; 6 weeks on mss. "If our agency does not respond within 2 months to your request to become a client, you may submit requests elsewhere."
Terms: Agent receives 15% commission on domestic sales; 15% on dramatic sales; and 20% on foreign sales. Charges for phone, bulk mailing, messenger and photocopying expenses. 100% of income derived from commission on ms sales.
Recent Sales: *Infidelities*, by Freda Bright (Atheneum); *Living on the Edge*, by Kathy Ketcham (Bantam); and *Scarlette Greene's Mistake*, by Barbara Ucko (St. Martins).

DOMINICK ABEL LITERARY AGENCY, INC., Suite 12C, 498 W. End Ave., New York NY 10024. (212)877-0710. President: Dominick Abel. Estab. 1975. Member of ILAA. Represents 80 clients. 5% of clients are new/unpublished writers. Prefers to work with published/established authors; works with a small number of new/unpublished authors.
Will Handle: Nonfiction books and novels. Currently handles 50% nonfiction books and 50% novels. Will read—at no charge—unsolicited queries and outlines. Reports in 2 weeks on queries. "If our agency does not respond within 2 months to your request to become a client, you may submit requests elsewhere."
Terms: Agent receives 10% commission on domestic sales; 10% on dramatic sales; and 20% on foreign sales. Charges for overseas postage, phone and cable expenses.
Recent Sales: No information given.

EDWARD J. ACTON INC., 928 Broadway, New York NY 10010. (212)675-5400. Contact: Inge Hanson. Estab. 1975. Member of ILAA. Represents 100 clients. Works with a small number of new/unpublished authors. Specializes in politics, celebrities, sports and historical romances.

66 *I've always had a great deal of confidence in my writing. Even when agents have given up on my novels, I sent them out myself and found publishers for some of them.* **99**

Walter Olesky

Will Handle: Nonfiction books and novels. Currently handles 5% magazine articles; 40% nonfiction books; 35% novels; 5% movie scripts; 5% TV scripts; 10% video production and software. Will read—at no charge—unsolicited queries and outlines. Reports in 3 weeks on queries.
Terms: Agent receives 15% commission on domestic sales; 15% on dramatic sales; and 19% on foreign sales. Charges for photocopy expenses. 100% of income derived from commission on ms sales.
Recent Sales: *An Autobiography*, by Tip O'Neill (Random House); *An Autobiography*, by Pete Rose (Warner Books); and *The Irish*, by Jason Miller (Simon & Schuster).

LEE ALLAN AGENCY, Box 18617, Milwaukee WI 53218. (414)463-7441. Agent: Lee A. Matthias. Estab. 1983. Member of WGA. Represents 18 clients. 80% of clients are new/unpublished writers. "A writer must have a minimum of one (in our judgment) salable work. Credentials are preferred, but we are open to new writers." Specializes in "screenplays for mass film audience, low to medium budget preferred, but of high quality, not exploitation; and novels of high adventure, genre fiction such as mystery and science fiction—no romance, nonfiction, textbooks, or poetry."
Will Handle: Novels (male adventure, mystery, science fiction, literary) and movie scripts (low to medium budget, mass appeal material). Currently handles 15% novels; 84% movie scripts; 1% TV scripts. Will read—at no charge—unsolicited queries and outlines, but may charge a criticism fee or service charge for work performed after the initial query-reading; does not read unsolicited mss. Must be queried first. Reports in 2 weeks on queries; 6 weeks on mss. "If our agency does not respond within 1 month to your request to become a client, you may submit requests elsewhere."
Terms: Agent receives 10% commission on domestic sales; 10% on dramatic sales; and 20% on foreign sales. Charges a reading fee; waives fee if representing writer. Charges a criticism fee; $10 above basic $25/150 pages or less; $15/each additional 150 pages. "Our critiques are a minimum of one-half page typed single spaced, up to a dozen pages. They are generally overall evaluations with some line-by-line commentary for example/illustration. Some marketing advice is offered where applicable, but nowhere promised. Agent/owner Matthias does the critique based on reader evaluation report or his own reading notes; he is a published author with a degree in film history/theory/criticism." Payment of a criticism fee does not ensure that agency will represent a writer. "Representation is based on salability as judged in our evaluation, not by critique payment."
Recent Sales: "We have sold film options for two novels and secured a staff writer position on a TV series. We specialize in screenplay marketing and dramatic rights marketing, and have only recently and in a limited fashion begun marketing books."

JAMES ALLEN LITERARY AGENT, In Association with Virginia Kidd Literary Agents, Box 278, Milford PA 18337. Agent: James Allen. Estab. 1974. Represents 40 clients. 15% of clients are new unpublished writers. Writer must have $3,000 writing income from previous year "and a track record in the area they want me to start work: story sales to genre magazines are a good background for bringing me a novel in that genre." Prefers to work with published/established authors. Specializes in mysteries ("cosies, shoot-'em-ups, general 'suspense,' espionage, both stand-alones and with series characters"), occult, horror, science fiction, contemporary and historical romance, fantasy, young adult novels, and mainstreams. No "little-kid juveniles or westerns."
Will Handle: Magazine fiction ("for novelists on my list. I am *not* looking for short-story clients."), nonfiction books, and novels. Currently handles 10% magazine fiction; 3% nonfiction books; 85% novels; and 2% movie scripts. Does not read unsolicited mss. Query with "track record" and 3 page synopsis; submissions not accompanied by SASE are thrown out. Reports in 2 weeks on queries; 10 weeks on mss. "If our agency does not respond within 4 months to your request to become a client, you may submit requests elsewhere."
Terms: Agent receives 10% commission on domestic sales; 20% on dramatic sales; and 20% on foreign sales. Charges for photocopying a booklength manuscript, airmail postage to get copies to sub-rights affiliates abroad, and Cashier's Checks if client won't take regular check. Deducted after sale. 100% of income derived from commission on ms sales.
Recent Sales: A 16-title reprint package of contemporary romantic suspense, by Elsie Lee (Zebra Books); *The Little Duke*, by Dixie McKeone (Harlequin Books); and *Soulstorm*, by Chet Williamson (Tor Books).

MARCIA AMSTERDAM AGENCY, Suite 9A, 41 W. 82nd St., New York NY 10024. (212)873-4945. Contact: Marcia Amsterdam. Estab. 1969. Member of WGA. 20% of clients are new/unpublished writers. Eager to work with new/unpublished writers. Specializes in fiction, nonfiction, young adult, TV and movies.
Will Handle: Nonfiction books, novels, juvenile books (young adult), and movie and TV scripts. Will read—at no charge—unsolicited queries, synopses and outlines. Reports in 2 weeks on queries; 1 month on mss. "If our agency does not respond within 1 month to your request to become a client, you may submit requests elsewhere."
Terms: Agent receives 15% commission on domestic sales; 15% on dramatic sales; and 15% on foreign sales. Charges for telegraph, cable, phone, and legal fees (when client agrees to them). 100% of income is derived from commission on ms sales.

Recent Sales: *The Secret Papers of Camp Get Around*, by Rose Blue (NAL); *Wait and See*, by Ruby Jean Jensen (Zebra Books); and *Right Behind the Rain*, by Joyce Sweeney (Delacorte).

APPLEGATE BYFORD AND ASSOCIATES TALENT AGENCY, Suite 214, 6305 Yucca St., Hollywood CA 90028. (213)461-2726. Head Literary Department: Arthur Dreifuss. Estab. 1983 (Agency; literary department 1986). Represents 18 clients for TV and films only. 50% of our clients are new/unpublished writers. **Will Handle:** Movie scripts and TV scripts. Currently handles 50% movie scripts and 50% TV scripts. Will read—at no charge—unsolicited queries, outlines and mss. Reports in 10 weeks on queries; 5 months on mss. "If our agency does not respond within 3 months to your request to become a client, you may submit requests elsewhere." ·
Terms: Agent receives 10% commission on domestic sales. 50% of income derived from commission on ms sales.
Recent Sales: TV and movie scripts only.

AUTHORS MARKETING SERVICES LTD., 217 Degrassi St., Toronto, Ontario M4M 2K8 Canada. (416)463-7200. Vice President: L. Hoffman. Estab. 1978. Represents 22 clients. 60% of clients are new/unpublished writers. Prefers to work with published/established authors; works with a small number of new/unpublished authors. Specializes in contemporary novels, intrigue/adventure, self-help and business.
Will Handle: Nonfiction books and novels. Currently handles 35% nonfiction books; 60% novels; and 5% consultation. Will read—at no charge—unsolicited queries and outlines. Reports in 3 weeks on queries. "If our agency does not respond within 1 month to your request to become a client, you may submit requests elsewhere."
Terms: Agent receives 15% commission on domestic (Canada and US) sales; and 20% on foreign sales. Charges a reading fee; will waive fee if representing the writer. 3% of income derived from reading fees. Sometimes offers a consultation service through which writers not represented can get advice on a contract; charges $35/hour. 5% of income derived from fees; 95% of income derived from commission on ms sales.
Recent Sales: *Barbarossa Red*, by Dennis Jones (Little Brown); *Dissolute Duke*, by Miranda Cameron (New American Library); and *Baby Games*, by Elaine Martin (Collins).

THE AXELROD AGENCY, INC., 126 5th Ave., New York NY 10011. (212)929-1704. President: Steven Axelrod. Estab. 1983. Represents 45 clients. 15% of our clients are new/unpublished writers. Specializes in hardcover and softcover mainstream and genre fiction, and software.
Will Handle: Nonfiction books, novels and software. Currently handles 45% nonfiction books; 45% novels and 10% software. Will read—at no charge—unsolicited queries, outlines and mss. Reports in 1 week on queries; 5 weeks on mss. "If our agency does not respond within 2 months to your request to become a client, you may submit requests elsewhere."
Terms: Agent receives 10% commission on domestic sales; 10% on dramatic sales; and 20% on foreign sales. 100% of income derived from commission on ms sales.
Recent Sales: *Mayflower Madam*, by Sydney Biddle Barrows, with William Novak (Arbor House); *Masterpiece Theatre* and *Nova Calendars (1986)* (Tidemark Press); and *The Gamble*, by La Vyrle Spencer (Berkley).

THE BALKIN AGENCY, 850 W. 176th St., New York NY 10033. (212)781-4198. President: Rick Balkin. Estab. 1973. Member of ILAA. "We are not accepting new clients and do not wish to receive queries or unsolicited submissions."

VIRGINIA BARBER LITERARY AGENCY, INC., 353 W. 21st St., New York NY 10011. (212)255-6515. Contact: Virginia Barber or Mary Evans. Estab. 1974. Member of ILAA. Represents 75 clients. "Sometimes we receive such an interesting query letter that we ask to read the manuscript even though the writer lists no publications at all. We have no rigid rules about prior publication. We prefer authors who have tried to publish their work, if only in little magazines or newspapers. No agent could honestly claim to prefer unpublished writers to successfully established ones. If you want to know whether or not we could be enthusiastic about, say a particular novel by an unpublished writer, the answer is emphatically 'yes'." Specializes in general adult fiction and nonfiction. "We represent only a few authors of paperback originals or category novels."
Will Handle: Nonfiction books and novels. "The large majority of our contracts involve adult books, nonfiction and fiction about 50/50." Will read—at no charge—unsolicited queries and outlines. Reports in 2 weeks on queries; 6 weeks on mss. "If our agency does not respond within 2 months to your request to become a client, you may submit requests elsewhere."
Terms: Agent receives 10% commission on domestic sales; 10% on dramatic sales; and 20% on foreign sales. 100% of income derived from commission on ms sales.
Recent Sales: "If any writer we want to represent requests information, we will gladly refer them to various editors we've worked with."

MAXIMILIAN BECKER, 115 E. 82nd St., New York NY 10028. (212)988-3887. President: Maximilian Becker. Estab. 1950. Works with a small number of new/unpublished authors.
Will Handle: Nonfiction books, novels and stage plays. Will read—at no charge—unsolicited queries, outlines and mss, but may charge a criticism fee or service charge for work performed after the initial reading. Reports in 2 weeks on queries; 3 weeks on mss.
Terms: Agent receives 15% commission on domestic sales; and 20% on foreign sales. Charges a criticism fee "if detailed criticism is requested. Writers receive a detailed criticism with suggestions—five to ten pages. No criticism is given if manuscript is hopeless."
Recent Sales: *Goering*, by David Irving (William Morrow); and *Year of the Wild Rose*, by Clara Rising (Villard Books).

THE BLAKE GROUP LITERARY AGENCY, Suite 105, 4300 N. Central Expressway, Dallas TX 75206. (214)828-2160. Director/Agent: Ms. Lee B. Halff. Estab. 1979. Member of Texas Publishers Association (TPA) and Texas Booksellers Association (TBA). Represents 30 clients. Prefers to work with published/established authors; works with a small number of new/unpublished authors.
Will Handle: Magazine fiction, nonfiction books, novels, textbooks, juvenile books, movie scripts, radio scripts, stage plays, TV scripts, syndicated material and poetry. Currently handles 13% magazine articles; 30¢ nonfiction books; 33% novels; 2% textbooks; 7% juvenile books; 2% movie scripts; 2% stage plays; 1% TV scripts; 8% poetry; and 2% science fiction. Will read submissions at no charge, but may charge a criticism fee or service charge for work performed after the initial reading. Reports in 1 week on queries; 3 months on mss. "If our agency does not respond within 3 months to your request to become a client, you may submit requests elsewhere."
Terms: Agent receives 10% commission on domestic sales; 15% on dramatic sales; and 20% on foreign sales. Sometimes offers a consultation service through which writers not represented can get advice on a contract; charges $30/hour. 100% of income derived from commission on ms sales.
Recent Sales: No information given.

BLOOM, LEVY, SHORR AND ASSOCIATES, Suite 9, 800 S. Robertson Blvd., Los Angeles CA 90035. (213)659-6160. Member of WGA. 50% of clients are new/unpublished writers. Writer must have an entertainment industry referral. Works with a small member of new/unpublished authors. Specializes in screenplays, teleplays, high concept action-adventure, romantic comedy.
Will Handle: Movie scripts and TV scripts. Currently handles 50% movie scripts and 50% TV scripts. Will read—at no charge—unsolicited queries. Reports in 1 month on queries; 6 weeks on mss.
Terms: Agent receives 10% commission on domestic sales. Charges for photocopy expenses.
Recent Sales: No information given.

THE BOOK PEDDLERS, 18326 Minnetonka Blvd., Deephaven MN 55391. (612)475-3527. Owner/Agent: Vicki Lansky. Estab. 1984. Also provides book packaging services. Represents 26 clients. 80% of clients are new/unpublished writers. Prefers to work with published/established authors.
Will Handle: Nonfiction books, novels and syndicated material. Currently handles 80% nonfiction books and 20% novels. Will read—at no charge—unsolicited queries and outlines. Does not read unsolicited mss. Reports in 2 weeks on queries; 3 weeks on mss. "If our agency does not respond within 1 month to your request to become a client, you may submit requests elsewhere."
Terms: Agent receives 15% commission on domestic sales; and 20% on foreign sales. Does not charge reading fee "at this time" (April, '86). Sometimes offers a consultation service through which writers not represented can get advice on a contract; charges $50/hour. 90% of income derived from commission on ms sales.
Recent Sales: *File Don't Pile*, by Pat Dorf (St. Martin's); *Family Bed*, by Tine Thevinin (Avery); and *With Interest*, by Jo Murphy (Dow-Jones/Irwin).

GEORGE BORCHARDT INC., 136 E. 57th St., New York NY 10022. (212)753-5785. President: George Borchardt. Estab. 1967. Member of SAR. Represents 200 clients. 1-2% of our clients are new/unpublished writers. "We do not consider new clients unless highly recommended by someone we trust." Prefers to work with published/established authors; also works with a small number of new/unpublished authors. Specializes in fiction, biography and general nonfiction of unusual interest.
Will Handle: Nonfiction books and novels. Does not read unsolicited mss.
Terms: Agent receives 10% commission on domestic sales; 10% on dramatic sales; and 20% on foreign sales (15% on British). Charges for photocopy expenses. 100% of income derived from commission on ms sales.
Recent Sales: *The Great Pretender*, by James Atlas (Atheneum); *Reagan*, by Edmund Morris (Random House); and *The Literary Text*, by Robert Alter (Simon & Schuster).

THE BRADLEY-GOLDSTEIN AGENCY, Suite 6E, 7 Lexington Ave., New York NY 10010. (718)672-7924. President: Paul William Bradley. Director: Martha Goldstein. Estab. 1985. Represents 75 clients. 50% of clients have been new/unpublished writers. Will consider taking on a small number of new/unpublished authors.

Specializes in "quality" fiction and nonfiction, biographies, politics, science, social science, business, current affairs, and the arts.
Will Handle: Nonfiction books, novels, and textbooks. Currently handles 50% nonfiction books; 40% novels; and 10% textbooks. Will read—at no charge—unsolicited query letters and outlines only. Do not send mss. Reports in 2 months on queries.
Terms: Agent receives 15% commission on domestic sales; and 20% on foreign sales. Charges for postage, photocopying, and telephone expenses. Offers a consultation service through which writers can get advice on a contract; charges $50/hour. 100% of income is derived from commission on ms sales.
Recent Sales: *F.S. Remington: A Biography*, by A. Manley and M.M. Mangum (Dutton); *The Frigate Pallada*, by Klaus Goetze (St. Martin's); and *The Compleat Clammer*, by Christopher Reaske (Nick Lyons Books).

BRANDT & BRANDT LITERARY AGENTS, INC., 1501 Broadway, New York NY 10036. (212)840-5760. Estab. 1914. Member of SAR. Represents 250 clients. Works with a small number of new/unpublished authors.
Will Handle: Nonfiction books and novels. "We read and answer letters from writers about their work only."
Terms: Agent receives 10% commission on domestic sales; 10% on dramatic sales; and 20% on foreign sales. Charge for photocopy and phone expenses. 100% of income derived from commission on manuscript sales.
Recent Sales: *The Le Baron Secret*, by Birmingham (Little, Brown); *Move Your Shadow*, by Lelyveld, (Times Books); and *Easy In the Islands*, by Shacochis (Crown).

CURTIS BROWN LTD., 10 Astor Pl., New York NY 10003. (212)473-5400. Member of SAR. Prefers to work with published/established authors; works with a small number of new/unpublished authors. Specializes in general fiction and nonfiction.
Will Handle: Nonfiction books, novels and juvenile books. Will read—at no charge—unsolicited queries and outlines accompanied by SASE; does not read unsolicited mss.
Terms: "Will explain to clients when they wish to sign."
Recent Sales: No information given.

PEMA BROWNE LTD., 185 E. 85th St., New York NY 10028. (212)369-1925. Treasurer: Perry J. Browne. Estab. 1966. Member of WGA. Represents 25 clients. 25% of clients are new/unpublished writers. "We review only new projects and require that writers have not sent manuscript to publishers or other agents." Eager to work with new/unpublished writers. Specializes in men's adventure, thrillers, mainstream, historical, regencies and contemporary romances; young adult; children's; reference; how-to and other types on nonfiction.
Will Handle: Nonfiction books, novels, juvenile books, movie scripts, TV scripts and syndicated material. Currently handles 25% nonfiction books; 25% novels; 10% juvenile books; 2% movie scripts; 2% TV scripts; 2% syndicated material; and 33% mass-market. Will read—at no charge—unsolicited queries, synopses and mss. Reports in 2 weeks on queries; 1 month on mss. "If our agency does not respond within 2 months to your request to become a client, you may submit requests elsewhere."
Terms: Agent receives 15% commission on domestic sales; 10% on dramatic sales; and 10% on foreign sales. 100% of income derived from commission on ms sales.
Recent Sales: *Death Merchant*, by Joseph R. Rosenberger (Dell); historical romance contract for Joanne Goodman (Zebra Books); and young adult contract for Charlotte St. John (Fawcett Books).

SHIRLEY BURKE AGENCY, Suite B-704, 370 E. 76th St., New York NY 10021. (861)2309. President: Shirley Burke. Estab. 1948. Represents 15 clients. 15% of our clients are new/unpublished writers. "The most important qualification for writers is talent—not how many books they've sold." Eager to work with new/unpublished writers "if I feel there is real talent there."
Will Handle: Nonfiction books and novels. Currently handles 50% nonfiction books and 50% novels. Will read—at no charge—unsolicited queries and short outlines. Reports in 2 weeks on queries.
Terms: Agent receives 10% commission on domestic sales; 20% on foreign sales.
Recent Sales: *Mozart* (McGraw-Hill); *Our Father's House* (Putnam); and *Wild Orchids*, (Warner).

CANADIAN SPEAKERS' AND WRITERS' SERVICE LIMITED, 44 Douglas Crescent, Toronto, Ontario M4W W2E Canada. (416)921-4443. President: Matie Molinaro. Estab. 1950. Represents 225 clients. 3% of clients are new/unpublished writers. Prefers to work with published/established authors; works with a small number of new/unpublished authors.
Will Handle: Magazine fiction, nonfiction books, novels, juvenile books, movie scripts, radio scripts, stage plays and TV scripts. Currently handles 70% nonfiction books; 5% novels; 5% movie scripts; 10% radio scripts; 5% stage plays; and 5% TV scripts. Does not read unsolicited mss. Reports in 3 weeks on queries; 1 month on mss. "If our agency does not respond within 1 month to your request to become a client, you may submit requests elsewhere."
Terms: Agent receives 15% commission on domestic sales; 15% on dramatic sales; and 20% on foreign sales. Charges a criticism/reading fee; $50, plus $3/one-thousand words. "Each reading/critique is handled by four

people and a composite report is sent out to the writer." Offers a consultation service through which writers not represented can get advice on a contract; charges $160/hour. 5% of income derived from fees; 95% of income derived from commission on manuscript sales. Payment of a criticism fee does not ensure that agency will represent a writers.
Recent Sales: *McLuhan Letter*, (Oxford University Press); *Ben Wicks First Treasury*, by Ben Wicks (Methuen Publishers); and *Medical Survival*, by Dr. Gifford Jones (Methuen).

RUTH CANTOR, LITERARY AGENT, Rm. 1133, 156 5th Ave., New York NY 10010. (212)243-3246. Contact: Ruth Cantor. Estab. 1952. Represents 40 clients. Writer must have "a good, sound track record in the publishing field . . . A skimpy one will sometimes get you a reading if I'm convinced that talent might be lurking in the bulrushes." Prefers to work with published/established authors; works with a small number of new/unpublished authors. Specializes in "any good trade book, fiction of quality, good, competent mysteries with new elements, juvenile books above the age of eight, up through young adult."
Will Handle: Nonfiction books, novels and juvenile books. Will read—at no charge—unsolicited queries and outlines. Reports in 1 month on queries; 2 months on mss.
Terms: Agent receives 10% commission on domestic sales; 10% on dramatic sales; and 20% on foreign sales.
Recent Sales: *The Rod of Sybil* (Harcourt); *The Players* (Warner); and *Talk Show* (Dell).

THE CARPENTER CO.,1516 W. Redwood St., San Diego CA 92101. (619)542-0951. Contact: Lee Carpenter. Estab. 1981. Prefers to work with published/established authors. Specializes in fantasy, science fiction, adventure and period (historical) for book, TV and film markets and industrial non-broadcast.
Will Handle: Novels; juvenile books; movie scripts; radio scripts (industrial only); TV scripts (industrial, MOW, mini-series) and computer programming. Currently handles 5% novels; 5% juvenile books; 80% movie scripts; and 10% TV scripts. Does not read unsolicited mss. "If our agency does not respond within 1 month to your request to become a client, you may submit requests elsewhere."
Terms: Agent receives 15% commission on domestic sales. 100% of income derived from commission on ms sales.
Recent Sales: No information given.

MARIA CARVAINIS AGENCY, INC., 235 W. End Ave., New York NY 10023. (212)580-1559. President: Maria Carvainis. Estab. 1978. Member of WGA. Represents 70 clients. 20% of clients are new/unpublished writrs. Eager to work with new/unpublished writers. Specializes in mainstream fiction, historicals, category romance, regencies, westerns, mysteries, suspense and young adult fiction, business and finance, women's issues, political biography, medicine, psychology and popular and social science.
Will Handle: Magazine articles and fiction (for clients already represented); nonfiction books; novels; young adult books; movie scripts; TV scripts; and poetry (for established poets only). Currently handles 5% magazine articles; 45% nonfiction books; 40% novels; and 10% young adult books. Will read—at no charge—unsolicited queires and short outlines accompanied by SASE. Reports in 3 weeks on queries; 3 months on mss.
Terms: Agent receives 15% commission on domestic sales; 10% on dramatic sales; and 20% on foreign sales. 100% of income derived from commission on ms sales.
Recent Sales: *Alexander's Empire* (Berkeley Publishing Group); *Chase the Heart* (William Morrow); and a major political biography to be published by Simon & Schuster.

CDS LITERARY MANAGEMENT, Box 605, Station A, Toronto, Ontario M5W 1G2 Canada. (416)223-9683. Agent: Cheryl Saurette. Estab. 1982. Represents 10 clients. 50% of clients are new/unpublished writers. Works with a small number of new/unpublished authors. Specializes in suspense novels, literary novels, and "topical mass market nonfiction."
Will Handle: Novels, movie scripts, stage plays, and TV scripts. Currently handles 50% nonfiction books; 40% novels; and 10% TV scripts. Will read submissions at no charge, but may charge a criticism fee or service charge for work performed after the initial reading. Reports in 1 month on queries; 2 months on mss. "Writers must enclose SAE with International Reply Coupons."
Terms: Agent receives 15% commission on domestic, dramatic and foreign sales. Charges a reading fee "if manuscript is over 500 pages and critique is requested." Fee will be waived if representing the writer. Charges criticism fee of $50 if service is requested by author. Writer receives "an overall evaluation of 2 to 3 typewritten pages in letter form." Charges postage and phone expenses. Offers a consultation service through which writers not represented can get advice on a contract; charges $15/hour. 10% income derived from fees; 90% of income derived from commission on ms sales.
Recent Sales: *Blood Angel*, by Alex Law (St. Martin's Press); TV script sold to Canadian production company; and project in negotiation with Donald I. Fine.

TERRY CHIZ AGENCY, Suite E, 5761 Whitnall Hwy., North Hollywood CA 91601. (818)506-0994. President: Terry Chiz. Vice President: Joann Carol. Estab. 1984. Represents 18 clients. 20% of clients are new/un-

published writers. Prefers to work with published/established authors; works with a small number of new/unpublished authors. Specializes in film and TV.
Will Handle: Novels, movie scripts and TV scripts. No romance or historical. Currently handles 20% novels; 40% movie scripts; and 40% TV scripts. Will read—at no charge—unsolicited queries and outlines. Reports in 2 weeks. "If our agency does not respond within 1 month to your request to become a client, you may submit elsewhere." Will not respond without SASE.
Terms: Agent receives 10% commission.
Recent Sales: "Film deals pending on several properties that are in book and script not for public information."

CONNIE CLAUSEN ASSOCIATES, Suite 16H, 250 E. 87 St., New York NY 10128. (212)427-6135. Contacts: Connie Clausen, Guy Kettelhack. Estab. 1976. Represents approximately 90 clients. 3% of clients are new/unpublished writers. Prefers to work with published/established authors; works with a small number of new/unpublished authors. Considers recommendations from clients and publishers. Specializes in trade nonfiction of all kinds, and some fiction.
Will Handle: Nonfiction books, and novels and juvenile books (sometimes). Handles magazine articles and fiction if client has a book. Currently handles 3% magazine articles; 90% nonfiction books; 5% novels; and 2% juvenile books. Does not read unsolicited mss. Reports in 1 month "when possible (often less)" on queries.
Terms: Agent receives 15% commission on domestic sales; 15% on dramatic sales; and 20% on foreign sales. Charges for photocopying, postage, and messenger expenses.
Recent Sales: *Robert Haas Fitness Book* (Bantam); *Divorcing a Corporation*, by Dr. Jacqueline Plumez (Villard); and *Everything to Live For*, by Susan White-Bowden (Poseidon).

HY COHEN LITERARY AGENCY, LTD., Suite 1400, 111 W. 57th St., New York NY 10019. (212)757-5237. President: Hy Cohen. Estab. 1975. Represents 20 clients. 50% of our clients are new/unpublished writers.
Will Handle: Nonfiction books and novels. Currently handles 50% nonfiction books and 50% novels. Will read—at no charge—unsolicited queries, outlines and mss, accompanied by SASE. Reports in 1 week on queries; 1 month on mss. "If our agency does not respond within 1 month to your request to become a client, you may submit requests elsewhere."
Terms: Agent receives 10% commission on domestic sales; 10% on dramatic sales; and 20% on foreign sales. Charges for "unusual" postage and phone expenses. Sometimes offers a consultation service through which writers not represented can get advice on a contract. 100% of income derived from commission on ms sales.
Recent Sales: *Explorers of the Black Box*, by Susan Allport (Norton); *Coronary Bypass Surgery: Who Needs It*, by Dr. Siegfried Kra (Norton); and *Serious Living*, by Tom Lorenz (Viking).

RUTH COHEN, INC., Box 7626, Menlo Park CA 94025. (415)854-2054. President: Ruth Cohen. Estab. 1982. member of ILAA. Represents 45-60 clients. 30% of clients are new/unpublished writers. Writers must have a book that is well written and preferably have some publishing experience. Prefers to work with published/established authors; eager to work with new/unpublished writers. Specializes in juvenile, young adult, nonfiction and genre books.
Will Handle: Nonfiction books, juvenile books (for ages 8-11 and young adult), and novels—contemporary romance, science fiction, fantasy, mystery, Western and historical romance. Currently handles 30% nonfiction books; 30% novels; and 40% juvenile books. Will read—at no charge—unsolicited queries, outlines and partial mss. Reports in 3 weeks on queries; 1 month on mss. "No multiple agency submissions. If our agency does not respond within 3 months to your request to become a client, you may submit requests elsewhere."
Terms: Agent receives 10% commission on domestic sales; 15% on dramatic sales; and 20% on foreign sales. 100% of income derived from commission on ms sales.
Recent Sales: *Boomerang Kids*, (Atlantic Monthly Press); *The Everlasting Covenant* (Little Brown); and *After the Dancing Days* (Harper & Row).

COLLIER ASSOCIATES, Suite 1003, 875 Avenue of the Americas, New York NY 10001. (212)563-4065. Manager: Oscar Collier. Estab. 1976. Member of SAR and ILAA. Represents 80 clients. Works with a small number of new/unpublished authors. Specializes in fiction trade books (war, crime, and historical novels) and nonfiction trade books on business and finance, biographies, popular psychology, math for general audience, puzzles and games, politics, exposes, medicine, nature and outdoors, history, cookbooks by highly qualified experts, nutrition, and sports.
Will Handle: Nonfiction books and novels. Will read—at no charge—unsolicited queries and outlines with SASE. Simultaneous submissions OK. Usually reports in 1 month on queries.
Terms: Agent receives 10% commission on domestic sales; 10% on dramatic sales; and 20% on foreign sales. Charges for books ordered from publishers for rights submissions, Express Mail, and copying expenses.
Recent Sales: *Paybacks*, by Christopher Britton (Donald I. Fine, Inc.); *Yup the Organization*, by James E. Wavada (Franklin Watts, Inc.); and *Love Among The Allies*, by Margot Arnold (Fawcett-Ballantine).

COLUMBIA LITERARY ASSOCIATES, INC., 7902 Nottingham Way, Ellicott City MD 21043. (301)465-1595. Contact: Linda Hayes or Kathryn Jensen. Estab. 1980. Represents 40 clients. 25% of clients are new/unpublished writers. Works with a small number of new/unpublished authors. Specializes in adult mass market, mainstream fiction and nonfiction, contemporary romance (category and single title), suspense, intrigue, cookbooks, general popular nonfiction and book series.
Will Handle: Nonfiction books, novels (open to family sagas, "blockbusters") and cookbooks. Currently handles 30% nonfiction books and 70% novels. Will read—at no charge—unsolicited queries and outlines; must include SASE for response. Reports in 3 weeks on queries; 6 weeks on mss. "If our agency does not respond within 6 weeks to your request to become a client, you may submit requests elsewhere."
Terms: Agent receives 12-15% commission on domestic sales and 20% on dramatic and foreign sales if separate from book rights. Charges writers for photocopies, shipping and phone expenses and for copies of book required for subrights sales. Sometimes offers a consultation service through which writers not represented can get advice on a contract; charges $50/hour.
Recent Sales: *Peregrine Connection* novels (Dell); *Jewish Holiday Cookbook* (Random House); and *The 60-Minute Bread Book* (Putnam).

CONNOR LITERARY AGENCY, 640 W. 153rd St., New York NY 10031. (212)491-5233. Owner: Marlene Connor. Estab. 1985. Represents 15 clients. 25% of clients are new/unpublished writers. "I would prefer that my writers have been published at some point (it shows that they have attempted to market themselves). Literary awards are also good; I would accept an author with awards who has not been published." Works with a small number of new/unpublished authors. Specializes in commercial fiction leaning toward thrillers, romantic suspense, current affairs, and horror. "I am also interested in black writers and ethnic novels. I am an expert at general nonfiction, how-to, illustrated, and self-help books. I also work with magazine tie-in books, and books that tie-in with an organization, corporation, or a TV or film production."
Will Handle: Nonfiction books, novels, illustrated, how-to and reference. Currently handles 50% nonfiction books and 50% novels. Will read—at no charge—unsolicited queries and outlines. Reports in 2 months on queries.
Terms: Agent receives 15% commission on domestic sales; and 25% on foreign sales. No criticism fee "unless the author requests a criticism after rejection, then the charge is $25. I would offer an overall critique of the work giving specific suggestions of how it might be improved. I would not bother to critique a work or to charge for the critique unless I felt the manuscript were worth-while and salvageable." Charges for photocopy, postage, telephone and messenger expenses, and special materials for presentation. Sometimes offers a consultation service through which writers can get advice on a contract; charges $75/hour. 2% of income derived from fees; 98% of income derived from commission on ms sales.
Recent Sales: *Hellfire*, by Charles Gatewood (Pocket Books) and *Investing in Antiques and Collectibles*, by Harry Rinker (Arbor House).

BILL COOPER ASSOC., INC., Suite 411, 224 W. 49th St., New York NY 10019. (212)307-1100. Contact: Nancy Frank or William Cooper. Estab. 1964. Represents 10 clients. 10% of clients are new/unpublished writers. Prefers to work with published/established authors; works with a small number of new/unpublished authors. Specializes in contemporary fiction.
Will Handle: Novels, movie scripts, stage plays, and TV scripts. Currently handles 90% novels and 10% TV scripts. Will read submissions at no charge, but may charge a criticism fee or service charge for work performed after the initial reading. Reports in 2 weeks on queries and mss.
Terms: Agent receives 15% commission on domestic sales; 15% on dramatic sales; and 20% on foreign sales. Sometimes charges a reading fee for unpublished writers. 10% of income derived from fees. Payment of a criticism fee does not ensure that agency will represent writer.
Recent Sales: No information given.

RICHARD CURTIS ASSOCIATES, INC., Suite 1, 164 E. 64th St., New York NY 10021. (212)371-9481. President: Richard Curtis. Estab.1969. Member of ILAA. Represents 75 clients. 5% of clients are new/unpublished writers. Writer must have some published work and either a finished novel or proposed nonfiction book. Prefers to work with published/established authors; works with a small number of new/unpublished authors. Specializes in commercial fiction of all genres, mainstream fiction and nonfiction.
Will Handle: Nonfiction books, novels, textbooks, juvenile books, and movie scripts. Currently handles 1% magazine articles; 1% magazine fiction; 25% nonfiction books; 65% novels; 5% textbooks; 3% juvenile books. Will read—at no charge—unsolicited queries and outlines. Reports in 2 weeks on queries; 1 month on mss. "If our agency does not respond within 1 month to your request to become a client, you may submit requests elsewhere."
Terms: Agent receives 10% commission on domestic sales; 15% on dramatic sales; and 20% on foreign sales. Charges a reading fee; 1% of income derived from reading fee. Writer receives two to four single-spaced pages of general explanation, line-by-line, and assessment of market and of author's "credentials." Work done by

book trade editors. Charges for photocopying, messengers, purchase of books for subsidiary exploitations. Offers a consultation service through which writers not represented can get advice on a contract; charges $200/hour. 1% of income derived from fees; 99% of income derived from commission on ms sales.
Recent Sales: *The Great Alone*, by Janet Dailey (Poseidon Press); *Heart of the Comet*j, by David Brin and Greg Benford (Bantam Books); and *Grania*, by Morgan Llwelyn.

D.J. ENTERPRISES, 339 S. Franklin St., Allentown PA 18102. (215)437-0723. President: Douglas J. Tomel. Estab. 1980. Member of ILAA. Represents 200 clients. 95% of clients are new/unpublished writers. Writer must send letter of reference before sending ms. Prefers to work with published/established authors. "We handle all material, except gay material."
Will Handle: Magazine articles (true-to-life stories) and movie and TV scripts. Currently handles 5% magazine articles;.90% movie scripts; and 5% TV scripts. Will read—at no charge—unsolicited queries, outlines and mss. Reports in 2 weeks on queries and mss. "If our agency does not respond within 1 month to your request to become a client, you may submit requests elsewhere."
Terms: Agent receives 10% commission on domestic, dramatic, and foreign sales. Charges for postage expenses.
Recent Sales: *A Tiger in the Streets* and *The Miracle of Melody Malone*, both in production.

LIZ DARHANSOFF AGENCY, 1220 Park Ave., New York NY 10128. (212)534-2479. Associate: Abigail Thomas. Estab. 1975. Member of ILAA. Represents 60 clients. 15% of clients are new/unpublished writers. Works with a small number of new/unpublished authors. Specializes in literary fiction.
Will Handle: Nonfiction books and novels. Currently handles 35% nonfiction books; 60% novels; and 5% juvenile books. Will read—at no charge—unsolicited queries and outlines. Reports in 2 weeks on queries. "If our agency does not respond within 2 months to your request to become a client, you may submit requests elsewhere."
Terms: Agent receives 10% commission on domestic sales and 20% on foreign sales. Charges for photocopy expenses. 100% of income derived from commission on ms sales.
Recent Sales: *Quinn's Book*, by William Kennedy (Viking/Penguin); *Walking Distance*, by Marian Thurm (Random House); and *Brain Matters*, by Bruce Dobkin (Crown).

THE JONATHAN DOLGER AGENCY, Suite 9B, 49 E. 96th St., New York NY 10128. (212)427-1853. President: Jonathan Dolger. Estab. 1980. Represents 70 clients. 25% of clients are new/unpublished writers. Writer must have been previously published if submitting fiction. Prefers to work with published/established authors; works with a small number of new/unpublished authors. Specializes in adult trade fiction and nonfiction, and illustrated books.
Will Handle: Nonfiction books, novels and illustrated books. Will read—at no charge—unsolicited queries and outlines. Reports in 1 month on queires.
Terms: Agent receives 10-15% commission on domestic sales; 10% on dramatic sales; and 20-30% on foreign sales. Charges for "standard expenses." Offers a consultation service through which writers not represented can get advice on a contract; charges a negotiable fee. 100% of income derived from commission on ms sales.
Recent Sales: Confidential.

THE DORSET GROUP, 820 W. Belmont, Chicago IL 60657. (312)871-7126. President: Elizabeth Newton. Executive Vice President: Edward K. Sachs. Estab. 1983 (US); 1977 (England). Represents 30 clients. 5% of clients are new/unpublished writers. Writers must have published fiction or nonfiction book. Prefers to work with published/established authors; works with a small number of new/unpublished authors.
Will Handle: Nonfiction books and novels. Currently handles 50% nonfiction books and 50% novels. Will read—at no charge—unsolicited queries and outlines. Reports in 2 weeks on queries; 6 weeks on mss.
Terms: Agent receives 15% commission on domestic sales; 20% on dramatic sales; and 20% on foreign sales. Charges a reading fee "if we think there is hope for the manuscript. If not, it is returned." Waives fee if representing the writer. 5% of income derived from reading fees. Charges a $25/month retainer. 1% of income derived from fees. 70% of income derived from commission on ms sales (also lectures and consults with publishers).
Recent Sales: *British Village Walks*, by Norman Saunders (White); *On Torture*, by Dr. Wagner and Dr. Rasmussen (Hans Reitzey); and *The House of Zion*, by John Schmidt (Avon).

EDUCATIONAL DESIGN SERVICES, INC., Box 253, Wantagh NY 11793. (718)539-4107/(516)221-0995. Vice-President: Edwin Selzer. President: Bertram Linder. Estab. 1979. Represents 18 clients. 90% of clients are new/unpublished writers. Eager to work with new/unpublished writers in the educational field. Specializes in educational materials aimed at the kindergarten through twelfth grade market; primarily textual materials.
Will Handle: Nonfiction books and textbooks. Currently handles 100% textbooks. Reports in 1 month on queries and mss. "If our agency does not respond within 6 weeks to your request to become a client, you may submit requests elsewhere."

Order your 1988 Writer's Market NOW!

Don't let your Writer's Market turn old on you.

You may be reluctant to give up this copy of Writer's Market. After all, you would never discard an old friend.

But resist the urge to hold onto an old Writer's Market! Like your first typewriter or your favorite pair of jeans, the time will come when this copy of Writer's Market will have to be replaced.

In fact, if you're still using this 1987 Writer's Market when the calendar reads 1988, your old friend isn't your best friend anymore. Many of the editors listed here have moved or been promoted. Many of the addresses are now incorrect. Rates of pay have certainly changed, and even the editorial needs are changed from last year.

You can't afford to use an out-of-date book to plan your marketing efforts. But there's an easy way for you to stay current—order the 1988 Writer's Market. All you have to do is complete the attached post card and return it with your payment or charge card information. Best of all, we'll send you the 1988 edition at the 1987 price—just $21.95. The 1988 Writer's Market will be published and ready for shipment in October 1987.

Make sure you have the most current marketing information—order the new edition of Writer's Market now.

To order, drop this postpaid card in the mail.

☐ YES! I want the most current edition of Writer's Market. Please send me the 1988 Writer's Market at the 1987 price—$21.95. I have included $2.00 for postage and handling. (Ohio residents add 5½% sales tax.) NOTE: 1988 Writer's Market will be ready for shipment in October 1987.

☐ Payment enclosed (Slip this card and your payment into an envelope.)

☐ Charge my: ☐ Visa   ☐ MasterCard

Account #_____ Exp. Date_____

Signature_____

Name_____

Address_____

City_____ State_____ Zip_____

(This offer expires August 1, 1988. Please allow 30 days for delivery.)

260

9933 Alliance Road
Cincinnati, Ohio 45242

Make sure you
have the current

Writer's Market has been the writer's bible for 54 years. Each edition contains hundreds of changes to give you the most current information to work with. Make sure your copy is the latest edition.

This card will get you the 1988 edition... at 1987 prices! ➡

Terms: Agent receives 15% commission on domestic sales; and 25% on foreign sales. Charges for phone, postage and delivery expenses, and retyping "if necessary"; charges $50/hour. 100% of income derived from commission on ms sales.
Recent Sales: *The American Indian* (Schoolhouse Press); *Nueva Historia de Los Estados Unidos* (Miverva Books); and *Comprehensive Social Studies* (Barrons Education Series).

PETER ELEK ASSOCIATES, Box 223, Canal St. Station, New York NY 10013. (212)431-9368. Assistant: Carol Diehl. Estab. 1979. Also provides book packaging services. Represents 15 clients. 15% of our clients are new/unpublished writers. "An applicant must be, or is clearly intending to be self-supporting through their writing." Prefers to work with published/established authors; works with a small number of new/unpublished authors. Specializes in illustrated nonfiction, current affairs, self-help (not pop-psych), contemporary biography/autobiography, food, popular culture (all for adults); and preschool and juvenile illustrated fiction, nonfiction and novelties; and contemporary adventure for adults.
Will Handle: Nonfiction books, novels and juvenile books. No category fiction. Currently handles 60% nonfiction books and 40% juvenile books. Will read—at no charge—unsolicited queries and outlines. Reports in 2 weeks on queries. "If our agency does not respond within 6 weeks to your request to become a client, you may submit requests elsewhere."
Terms: Agent receives 15% commission on domestic sales; 20% on dramatic sales; and 20% on foreign sales. Charges for manuscript retyping, "if required." Sometimes offers a consultation service through which writers not represented can get advice on a contract; charges $75/hour, $125 minimum. 5% of income derived from fees; 33⅓% of income derived from commission on ms sales ("66⅔% derived from sale of finished packaged books"). 100% income derived from sales of writers' work.
Recent Sales: *The World of Robert Bateman*, by Ramsay Derry (Random House); *Annie Bananie*, Leah Komaiko (Harper & Row Juvenile); and *The Everyday Gourmet*, by Kathleen Perry (Warner).

JOHN FARQUHARSON LTD., Suite 1914, 250 W. 57th St., New York NY 10107. (212)245-1993. Director: Jane Gelfman. Agent: Deborah Schneider. Estab. 1919 (London); 1980 (New York). Member of SAR and ILAA. Represents 125 clients. 5% of our clients are new/unpublished writers. Prefers to work published/established authors; works with a small number of new/unpublished authors. Specializes in trade fiction and nonfiction. Mysteries and some science fiction and romance. No poetry, short stories or screenplays.
Will Handle: Novels and juvenile books (few); handles magazine articles and magazine fiction for authors already represented. Currently handles 49% nonfiction books; 49% novels; and 2% juvenile books. Will read—at no charge—unsolicited queries and outlines. Reports in 3 weeks on queries.
Terms: Agent receives 10% commission on domestic sales; 10% on dramatic sales; and 20% on foreign sales. Charges for messengers, photocopying and overseas calls.
Recent Sales: *The Beans of Egypt, Maine*, by Caroline Chute (Ticknor & Fields); *The Serpent and the Rainbow*, by Wade Davis (Simon & Schuster); and *The Man Who Mistook His Wife for a Hat*, by Oliver Sacks (Summit).

FLORENCE FEILER LITERARY AGENCY, 1524 Sunset Plaza Dr., Los Angeles CA 90069. (659)652-6920/652-0945. Associate: Audrey Rugh. Estab. 1967. Represents 40 clients. 10% of clients are new/unpublished writers. Works with a small number of new/unpublished authors. "Quality is the criterion." Specializes in fiction, nonfiction, essays and screen; very little TV and no short stories.
Will Handle: Magazine articles, textbooks (for special clients), juvenile books, movie scripts, and syndicated material (for special clients). Will read—at no charge—unsolicited queries and outlines. Reports in 2 weeks on queries; 10 weeks on mss. "If our agency does not respond within 3 months to your request to become a client, you may submit requests elsewhere."
Terms: Agent receives 10% commission on domestic sales; 10% on dramatic sales; and 20% on foreign sales.
Recent Sales: *Angelic Avengers, Last Tales* and *Out of Africa*.

THE FILM/PUBLISHING GROUP, 11141 Wicks St., Sun Valley CA 91352. (818)767-5587. Director of Communications: Vincent R. Ducette. Estab. 1983. Represents 16 clients. 30% of clients are new/unpublished writers. Prefers to work with published/established authors; works with a small number of new/unpublished authors. Specializes in contemporary novels in the mainstream, romance novels, biographies and autobiographies, motion picture and television scripts, poetry collections of book length and stage plays. "Vehicles reflecting contemporary American life and interests that are commercially viable."
Will Handle: Magazine articles (of special interest to women); nonfiction books (of biographical nature); novels (of contemporary or romantic genre); juvenile books (adventurous and morally uplifting); movie scripts; stage plays; and TV scripts (television series ideas if accompanied by fully developed treatment for initial episode). Currently handles 2% magazine articles; 1% magazine fiction; 8% nonfiction books; 40% novels; 5% juvenile books; 20% movie scripts; 4% stage plays; 15% TV scripts; and 5% science fiction novels. Will read unsolicited queries and outlines at no charge, but may charge a criticism fee or service charge for work performed after the initial reading "if the ms lacks basic professional standards, or if the writer has been

unpublished thru the present." Reports in 1 week on queries. "If our agency does not respond within 1 month to your request to become a client, you may submit requests elsewhere."

Terms: Agent receives 15% commission on domestic sales; 15% on dramatic sales; and 20% on foreign sales. In some cases charges a reading fee, "when writer is unpublished non-client who agrees beforehand to an evaluation or a $100 cost defrayment fee regardless of manuscript length." 10% of income derived from reading fees. Charges a criticism fee; $100 if author requests criticism. "Our agents do the reading. Each manuscript is read by three different individuals independent of each other and their consensus is distilled and written as a constructive critique pinpointing specific instances in point within the manuscript, overall concensus of opinion, and possible markets for manuscript in present form—or when revision is complete following our suggestions. The critiques are part line-by-line, and part general, averaging five pages long." 10% of income derived from fees; 90% of income derived from commission on ms sales. Payment of criticism fee does not ensure that agency will represent a writer.

Recent Sales: *See the Woman . . .*, by J.L. Kullinger (Marquis Publications); *The Abduction*, by John Cronis (Marquis Publishers); and *Other Side of Vice*, by Lee Young (Worldwide Publishing).

FRIEDA FISHBEIN LTD., 353 W. 57th St., New York NY 10019. (212)247-4398. President: Janice Fishbein. Estab. 1925. Represents 30 clients. 50% of clients are new/unpublished writers. "We agree to represent a writer solely on the basis of a *complete* work." Eager to work with new/unpublished writers. Specializes in historical romance, historical adventure, male adventure, mysteries, thrillers, and family sagas. Books on the environment, nursing and medicine, plays and screenplays.

Will Handle: Nonfiction books, novels, textbooks, juvenile books, movie scripts, stage plays and TV scripts. No poetry or magazine articles. Currently handles 20% nonfiction books; 30% novels; 5% textbooks; 10% juvenile books; 10% movie scripts; 15% stage plays; and 10% TV scripts. Will read—at no charge—unsolicited queries and outlines. Reports in 2 weeks on queries; 6 weeks on mss. "If our agency does not respond within 2 months to your request to become a client, you may submit requests elsewhere."

Terms: Agent receives 10% commission on domestic sales; 10% on dramatic sales; and 20% on foreign sales. Charges reading fee; $60/TV script, screenplay or play; $60/50,000 words for manuscripts, $1/each 1,000 additional words. Fee will be waived if representing writer. "Our readers are part-time workers who also serve as editors at magazines and/or publishers. Our reports are always longer for larger manuscripts. The usual reader's report varies between three to five pages, and may or may not include a line-to-line critique, but it always includes an overall evaluation." 20% of income derived from fees; 80% of income derived from commission on ms sales. Payment of a criticism fee does not ensure that agency will represent a writer.

Recent Sales: *Behind You*, by Thomas Millstead (Dell Publishing); *Not A Single Blade of Grass*, by Thomas Harris (play); and *The Perfect Defense*, by Gary Bohlke (play).

THE FOLEY AGENCY, 34 E. 38th St., New York NY 10016. (212)686-6930. Partners: Joan and Joseph Foley. Estab. 1956. Represents 30 clients. 5% of clients are new/unpublished writers. Prefers to work with published/established authors; works with a small number of new/unpublished authors. Specializes in general fiction and nonfiction.

Will Handle: Nonfiction books and novels. Currently handles 60% nonfiction books, and 40% novels. Will read—at no charge—unsolicited queries and outlines if SASE is enclosed. Reports in 2 weeks on queries.

Terms: Agent receives 10% commission on domestic sales; 5-10% on dramatic sales; and 10% on foreign sales. Charges for occasional messenger fee and special phone expenses. 100% of income derived from commission on ms sales.

Recent Sales: *Autobiography*, by Roy Cohn (Random House); *Small Sacrifices*, by Ann Rule (New American Library); and *Treasury of True Crime*, by John Dunning (Arbor House).

FRANKLIN/NATHAN LITERARY AGENCY, Suite 1903, 386 Park Ave. S., New York 10016. (212)689-1842. Agents: Lynn Franklin, Ruth Nathan, and Jeff Gerecke. Estab. 1981. Represents 30 clients. 75% of clients are new/unpublished writers. Eager to work with new/unpublished writers. Specializes in general trade fiction and nonfiction (self-help, business, illustrated books).

Will Handle: Nonfiction books and novels. No category fiction. Currently handles 80% nonfiction books and 20% novels. Will read—at no charge—unsolicited queries, outlines and manuscripts. Reports in 1 week on queries; 1 month on manuscripts. "If our agency does not respond within 2 months to your request to become a client, you may submit requests elsewhere."

Terms: Agent receives 15% commission on domestic sales; 20% on dramatic sales; and 20% on foreign sales.

Recent Sales: *Treasure Hunt: Romance with American Antiques*, by Harold Sack with Max Wilk (Little Brown and Company); *Ten Shun*, by Lou Anne Johnson (St. Martin's Press); and *Think*, by Dr. Robert Anthony (Berkley).

ROBERT A. FREEDMAN DRAMATIC AGENCY, INC., Suite 2310, 1501 Broadway, New York NY 10028. (212)840-5760. President: Robert A. Freedman. Estab. 1928 (as Brandt & Brandt Dramatic Department, Inc.)

under present name since 1984. Member of SAR. Prefers to work with established authors; works with a very small number of new/unpublished authors. Specializes in plays and motion picture and television scripts.
Will Handle: Movie scripts, stage plays and TV scripts. Does not read unsolicited mss. Usually reports in 2 weeks on queries; 6 weeks on mss.
Terms: Agent receives 10% on dramatic sales; "and, as is customary, 20% on amateur rights." Charges for photocopying.
Recent Sales: "We will tell any author directly information on our sales that are relevant to his/her specific script."

SAMUEL FRENCH, INC., 45 W. 25th St., New York NY 10010. (212)206-8990. Editor: Lawrence Harbison. Estab. 1830. Member of SAR. Represents "hundreds" of clients. Prefers to work with published/established authors; works with a small number of new/unpublished authors. Specializes in plays.
Will Handle: Stage plays. Currently handles 100% stage plays. Will read—at no charge—unsolicited queries, outlines and mss. Reports in 1 week on queries; 2-8 months on mss. "Enclose SASE."
Terms: Agent receives 90% book royalties; 10% professional production royalties; and 20% amateur production royalties.
Recent Sales: No information given.

FROMMER PRICE LITERARY AGENCY INC., Suite 32E, 185 E. 85th St., New York NY 10028. (212)289-0589. President: Diana Price. Estab. 1979. Represents 60 clients. 10% of clients are new/unpublished writers. Prefers writer be published or an expert in his/her field. Prefers to work with published/established authors; works with a small number of new/unpublished authors. Specializes in mainstream adult fiction and adult non-fiction.
Will Handle: Nonfiction books and novels. Currently handles 75% nonfiction books and 25% novels. Will read—at no charge—unsolicited queries, outlines and mss. Reports in 1 week on queries; 1 month on mss. "If our agency does not respond within 2 months to your request to become a client, you may submit requests elsewhere."
Terms: Agent receives 15% commission on domestic sales; 15% on dramatic sales; and 20% on foreign sales. Charges for postage, photocopying and messenger expenses. 100% of income derived from commission on ms sales.
Recent Sales: *The Fourth Angel*, by Robin Hunter (Arbor House); *Wholefood Catalog*, by Nava Atlas (Ballantine); and *College Pursuit* ® a Game, by Cowan & Gaddine (Simon & Schuster).

MAX GARTENBERG, LITERARY AGENT, 15 W. 44th St., New York NY 10036. (212)860-8451. Contact: Max Gartenberg. Estab. 1954. Represents 30 clients. 10% of clients are new/unpublished writers. "The writer must convince me of his or her professional skills, whether through published or unpublished materials he/she has produced." Prefers to work with published/established authors; works with a small number of new/unpublished authors. Specializes in nonfiction and fiction trade books.
Will Handle: Nonfiction books and novels. Currently handles 75% nonfiction books and 25% novels. Will read—at no charge—unsolicited queries and outlines. Reports in 1 week on queries. "If our agency does not respond within 1 month to your request to become a client, you may submit requests elsewhere. SASE required."
Terms: Agent receives 10% commission on domestic sales; 10% on dramatic sales; and 15% on foreign sales. 100% of income derived from commission on ms sales.
Recent Sales: *Scaling the Ivy Wall*, by Howard Greene (Little, Brown & Co.); *Banking on Your Home*, by Robert Minton (Dow Jones-Irwin); and *The Environmental Encyclopedia*, by William Ashworth (Facts on File).

GEDDES AGENCY, Suite 7, 1509 N. Crescent Heights, Los Angeles CA 90046. (213)650-4011. Literary Department Head: Eileen Orr. Estab. 1964. Member of WGA. Represents 10 clients. 90% of our clients are new/unpublished writers. Eager to work with new/unpublished writers; yet "always looking for writers with some kind of track record. We repesent novelists, screenwriters, television writers and playwrights interested in crossing over. We specialize in material which is intelligent, well-crafted, and entertaining. We are not looking for 'fluff,' i.e., mindless youth comedies, or very, very esoteric fiction. We will consider just about anything except slasher pictures."
Will Handle: Novels, movie and TV scripts. Currently handles 20% novels; 40% movie scripts; 40% TV scripts. Will read—at no charge—unsolicited queries and outlines. Reports in 1 month.
Terms: Agent receives 10% commission on domestic sales (occasionally 15% on domestic for new authors whose work requires heavy editing); 10% on dramatic sales; and 10% on foreign sales. 50% of income derived from commission on ms sales.
Recent Sales: No information given.

LUCIANNE S. GOLDBERG LITERARY AGENTS, INC., Suite 6-A, 255 W. 84th St., New York NY 10024. (212)799-1260. Editorial Director: Cyril Hildebrand. Estab. 1974. Represents 65 clients. 10% of clients are new/unpublished writers. "Any author we decide to repesent must have a good idea, a good presentation of that idea and writing skill to compete with the market. Representation depends solely on the execution of the work whether writer is published or unpublished." Specializes in nonfiction works, "but will review a limited number of novels."

Will Handle: Nonfiction books and novels. Currently handles 75% nonfiction books and 25% novels. Will read—at no charge—unsolicited queries and outlines. Reports in 2 weeks on queries; 3 weeks on mss. "If our agency does not respond within 1 month to your request to become a client, you may submit requests elsewhere."

Terms: Agent receives 15% commission on domestic sales; 25% on dramatic sales;and 25% on foreign sales. Charges reading fee on unsolicited mss: $150/full-length ms. Criticism is included in reading. 1% of income derived from reading fees. "Our critiques run three to four pages, single-spaced. They deal with the overall evaluation of the work. Three agents within the organization read and then confer. Marketing advice is included." Payment of fee does not ensure the agency will represent a writer. Charges for phone expenses, cable fees, photocopying and messenger service after the work is sold. 80% of income derived from commission on ms sales.

Recent Sales: *IDOL: The Real Rock Hudson Story*, by Jerry Oppenheimer (Random House); *Sunny: The Life of Martha von Bulow*, by James Southwood (Simon & Schuster); and *One Big Bed*, by John Krich (McGraw-Hill).

GOODMAN ASSOCIATES LITERARY AGENTS, 500 West End Ave., New York NY 10024. Contact: Arnold or Elise Goodman. Estab. 1976. Member of ILAA. Represents 75 clients and oversees publishers and agents. 10% of clients are new/unpublished writers. Works with a small number of new/unpublished authors. Specializes in general adult trade fiction and nonfition. No fantasy, science fiction, stories, articles or computer books.

Will Handle: Nonfiction books and novels. Will read—at no charge—unsolicited queries and outlines. Reports in 1 week on queries. "If our agency does not respond within 1 month to your request to become a client, you may submit requests elsewhere."

Terms: Agent receives 15% commission on domestic sales; 15% on dramatic sales; and 20% on foreign sales. Charges for photocopying, phone, messenger, telex and cable expenses, and book purchases for subsidiary rights submissions.

Recent Sales: No information given.

IRENE GOODMAN LITERARY AGENCY, 521 5th Ave., 17th Floor, New York NY 10017. (212)688-4286. Contact: Irene Goodman, president (books) and Paul Katz, associate (scripts.) Estab. 1978. Member of ILAA. Represents 120 clients. 10% of clients are new/unpublished writers. Works with a small number of new/unpublished authors. Specializes in women's fiction (mass market, category, and historical romance), science fiction, fantasy, popular nonfiction, reference and young adult (romance and series).

Will Handle: Nonfiction books, novels, juvenile books, movie scripts, stage plays and TV scripts. Currently handles 40% nonfiction books; 40% novels; 10% movie scripts; 5% stage plays; and 5% TV scripts. Will read—at no charge—unsolicited queries. Reports in 1 week. "If our agency does not respond within 1 month to your request to become a client, you may submit requests elsewhere. However you may feel free to query other agents at any time—I am competitive, not possessive."

Terms: Agent receives 15% commission on domestic sales; 15% on dramatic sales; and 20% on foreign sales. Charges for phone, photocopy, postage, and messenger expenses. Sometimes offers a consultation service through which writers not represented can get advice on a contract.

Recent Sales: *Caitlin 7, 8 and 9*, by Diana Gregory (Bantam); *Call Down the Moon*, by Joyce Thies (Pocket); and *A Delicate Balance*, by Carol Katz (Berkley-Jove).

GRAHAM AGENCY, 311 W. 43rd St., New York NY 10036. (212)489-7730. Owner: Earl Graham. Estab. 1971. Member of SAR. Represents 35 clients. 15% of clients are new/unpublished writers. Prefers to work with published/established authors; eager to work with new/unpublished writers. Specializes in full-length stage plays and musicals.

Will Handle: Stage plays and musicals. Currently handles 100% stage plays. Will read—at no charge—unsolicited queries and outlines, and plays and musicals which we agree to consider on the basis of the letters of inquiry. Reports in 1 week on simple queries. Simultaneous submissions OK.

Terms: Agent receives 10% commission on domestic sales; 10% on dramatic sales; and 10% on foreign sales. 100% of income derived from commission on ms sales.

Recent Sales: No information given.

HAROLD R. GREENE, INC., Suite 302, 760 N. La Cienega, Los Angeles CA 90069. (213)855-0824. President: Harold Greene. Estab. 1985. Member of WGA. Represents 12 clients, primarily screenwriters. Specializes in screenplay writing and novels that are adaptable to films or TV movies.

Will Handle: Novels and movie scripts. Currently handles 5% novels and 95% movie scripts. Does not read unsolicited mss.
Terms: Agent receives 10% commission on domestic sales; 10% on dramatic sales; and 10% on foreign sales.
Recent Sales: *The Long Walk*, by George La Fountaine (Putnam); *Lifter*, by Crawford Kilian (Berkeley); and *Forever And a Day*, by Pamela Wallace (Silhouette).

THOMAS S. HART LITERARY ENTERPRISES, 20 Kenwood St., Boston MA 02124. (617)288-8512. President: Thomas Hart. Estab. 1983. Represents 27 clients. 50% of clients are new/unpublished writers. Prefers to work with published/established authors; works with a small number of new/unpublished authors. Specializes in literary and mainstream fiction, sports, fitness and natural history.
Will Handle: Nonfiction books and novels. Currently handles 5% magazine articles; 35% nonfiction books; and 60% novels. Will read—at no charge—unsolicited queries, outlines and mss. Reports in 3 weeks on queries; 1 month on mss. "If our agency does not respond within 2 months to your request to become a client, you may submit requests elsewhere."
Terms: Agent receives 10% commission on domestic sales; 15% on dramatic sales; and 20% on foreign sales. Doesn't give criticism if project is rejected. Charges for phone and photocopy expenses. Offers a consultation service through which writers not represented can get advice on a contract; charges $150/contract. Approximately 1% of income derived from fees; 99% of income derived from commission on ms sales.
Recent Sales: *Family Resemblances*, by Larry Pei (Random House); *Fields of Friendly Strife*, by John Janovy, Jr. (Viking Penguin); and *A Vanishing Species*, by Don Stop (Knopf).

HEACOCK LITERARY AGENCY, INC., Suite 14, 1523 6th St., Santa Monica CA 90401. (213)393-6227. President: Jim Heacock. Vice President: Rosalie Heacock. Estab. 1978. Member of ILAA. Represents 60 clients. 35% of clients are new/unpublished writers. Works with a small number of new/unpublished authors. Specializes in nonfiction on a wide variety of subjects—health, nutrition, diet, exercise, sports, psychology, crafts, women's studies, business expertise, pregnancy and parenting, alternative health concepts, starting a business and celebrity biographies.
Will Handle: Nonfiction books; novels (previously published by major houses); movie scripts (prefer Writer's Guild members); and TV scripts (prefer Writer's Guild members). Currently handles 85% nonfiction books; 5% novels; 5% movie scripts and 5% TV scripts. Will read—at no charge—unsolicited queries and outlines. Reports in 1 month on queries if SASE is included. "If our agency does not respond within 1 month to your request to become a client, you may submit requests elsewhere."
Terms: Agent receives 15% commission on domestic sales; 10% on dramatic sales; 25% on foreign sales (if a foreign agent is used. If we sell direct to a foreign publisher, the commission is 15%). Offers a consultation service through which writers not represented can get advice on a contract; charges $100/hour. 2% of income derived from such fees; 98% of income derived from commission on ms sales.
Recent Sales: *The Christine Craft Story*, by Christine Craft (Capra Press); *King Bidgood's in the Bathtub*, by Don and Audrey Wood (Harcourt Brace Jovanovich); *DLPA To End Chronic Pain and Depression*, by Dr. Arnold Fox (Simon & Schuster).

HEINLE + HEINLE ENTERPRISES, INC., 29 Lexington Rd., Concord MA 01742. (617)369-4858. President: Beverly D. Heinle. Estab. 1973. Represents 25 clients. 50% of clients are new/unpublished writers. Prefers previously published writers, but will consider serious new writers. Prefers to work with published/established authors; works with a small number of new/unpublished authors. Specializes in cookbooks.
Will Handle: Nonfiction and juvenile books. Currently handles 80% nonfiction and 20% juvenile books. Will read—at no charge—unsolicited queries and outlines. Reports in 2 weeks on queries. "If our agency does not respond within 2 months to your request to become a client, you may submit requests elsewhere."
Terms: Agent receives 10% commission on domestic, dramatic and foreign sales. 100% of income derived from commission on ms sales.
Recent Sales: *The Shopping Bag: Portable Art*, by Stephen Wagner and Michael Closen (Crown); *Body-sense: A Hazard-Free Exercise Program*, by Sue Luby (Faber & Faber); and *Fabulous Fruit Desserts*, by Terence Janericco (Yankee).

HHM LITERARY AGENCY, Box 1153, Rahway NJ 07065. (201)388-8167. Contact: Haes H. Monroe. Estab. 1985. Represents 20 clients. 25% of clients are new/unpublished writers. Prefers to work with published/established authors; works with a small number of new/unpublished authors.
Will Handle: Nonfiction books, novels, and juvenile books. Currently handles 10% nonfiction books; 75% novels; 15% juvenile books. Will read—at no charge—unsolicited queries, outlines and mss. Reports in 1 month on queries; 5 weeks on mss. "If our agency does not respond within 6 months to your request to become a client, you may submit requests elsewhere."
Terms: Agent receives 10% commission on domestic sales; 15% on dramatic sales; and 20% on foreign sales. Charges for phone and photocopying, messenger, cable, "other extraordinary" office expenses. 100% of income derived from commission on ms sales.
Recent Sales: No information given.

FREDERICK HILL ASSOCIATES, 2237 Union St., San Francisco CA 94123. (415)921-2910. Associate: Bonnie Nadell. Estab. 1979. Represents 60 clients. 50% of clients are new/unpublished writers. Specializes in general nonfiction (biography, history, politics, current events, architecture, cooking, the arts, etc.); mainstream fiction, young adult, genre fiction (occasionally, but not "formula" fiction).
Will Handle: Nonfiction books, novels and juvenile books. Currently handles 40% nonfiction books; 40% novels; and 20% young adult books. Will read—at no charge—unsolicited queries and outlines. Reports in 3 weeks on queries; 2 months on mss. "If our agency does not respond within 2 months to your request to become a client, you may submit requests elsewhere."
Terms: Agent receives 15% commission on domestic sales; 10% on dramatic sales; and 20% on foreign sales. Charges for overseas airmail (books, proofs only), overseas telex, cable, domestic telex. 100% of income derived from commission on ms sales.
Recent Sales: *The Broom of the System*, by David Foster Wallace (Viking); *Eddie Black*, by Walter Shapiro (Arbor House); and *Torch Rat*, by Steve Barr and John Poppy (William Morrow).

ALICE HILTON LITERARY AGENCY, (formerly Warren-Hilton Literary Agency, estab. 1969), 13131 Welby Way, North Hollywood CA 91606. (818)982-5423/982-2546. Estab. 1986. Eager to work with new/unpublished writers. Specializes in movie and TV scripts—"any good salable material with quality—although agent has a personal affection for material suitable for 'American Playhouse' or 'Masterpiece Theatre.' "
Will Handle: Movie and TV scripts only. Will read—at no charge—unsolicited queries, outlines and manuscripts. Reports in 1 month. "If our agency does not respond within 2 months to your request to become a client, you may submit requests elsewhere."
Terms: Agent receives 15% commission on dramatic sales. Charges for phone, postage and photocopy expenses. 100% of income derived from commission on ms sales.
Recent Sales: No information given.

HINTZ & FITZGERALD, INC., Suite 211, 207 E. Buffalo St., Milwaukee WI 53202. (414)273-0300. Contact: Sandy Hintz and Colleen Fitzgerald. Estab. 1978. Represents 25 clients. 30% of clients are new/unpublished writers. "Preference is given to writers with some publishing history, e.g., articles in quality publications and books. We also seriously consider anyone (new people) with a good story and writing style." Specializes in most fiction—mysteries, westerns, science fiction, fantasy, how-tos, biographies, general nonfiction, and juvenile fiction and nonfiction. No picture books.
Will Handle: Nonfiction books, novels, juvenile books, movie scripts and TV scripts. Currently handles 20% nonfiction books; 60% novels; 5% juvenile books; 10% movie scripts; and 5% TV scripts. Will read—at no charge—unsolicited queries and outlines. Reports in 2 weeks on queries; 1 month on mss. "If our agency does not respond within 2 months to your request to become a client, you may submit requests elsewhere."
Terms: Agent receives 10% commission on domestic sales. Charges for postage and phone expenses. ("This is not necessary 95 percent of time.") Sometimes offers a consultation service through which writers not represented can get advice on a contract. 100% of income derived from commission on ms sales.
Recent Sales: *Highland Laddie Gone*, by Sharyn McCrumb (Avon); *6-Book Space Series*, by Gregory Vogt (Franklin Watts); and *Nathan Phillips Book #4*, (Paperjacks Press).

JOHN L. HOCHMANN BOOKS, 320 E. 58th St., New York NY 10022. (212)319-0505. Chairman: John L. Hochmann. Estab. 1976. Represents 21 clients. 15% of clients are new/unpublished writers. Writer must have demonstrable eminence in field or previous publications for nonfiction, and critically and/or commercially successful books for fiction. Prefers to work with published/established authors; and to "develop new series for established authors of original paperback fiction."
Will Handle: Nonfiction books, novels, and textbooks. Currently handles 65% nonfiction books and 35% novels. Will read—at no charge—unsolicited queries, outlines and solicited mss. Reports in 2 weeks on queries; 6 weeks on mss.
Terms: Agent receives 15% commission on domestic sales; and 10% on foreign sales. Sometimes offers a consultation service through which writers not represented can get advice on a contract; "we have sometimes done this without charge, but if the number of inquiries increases, our policy must change." 100% of income derived from commission on ms sales.
Recent Sales: *The Bataan Nurses*, by Donald Knox (Harcourt Brace Jovanovich); *Metropolitan Seminars*, by John Canaday (Metropolitan Museum of Art); and *Dallas, The Early Years*, by Noel B. Gerson (McGraw-Hill).

INTERNATIONAL LITERATURE AND ARTS AGENCY, 50 E. 10th St., New York NY 10003. (212)475-1999. Director: Bonnie R. Crown. Estab. 1977. Represents 10 clients. 20% of clients are new/unpublished writers. Works with a small number of new/unpublished authors; eager to work with new/unpublished writers in area of specialization, and established translators from Asian languages. Specializes in translations of literary works from Asian languages, arts- and literature-related works, and "American writers who have been influenced by some aspect of an Asian culture, for example, a novel set in Japan, or a nonfiction work about a

Vietnam vet's experience in Vietnam. For details of policy, send query with SASE."
Will Handle: Novels, stage plays (related to Asia or Asian American experience), and poetry (translations of Asian classics). Currently handles 50% nonfiction books; 25% novels; and 25% classics from Asian languages. Will read—at no charge—unsolicited queries and brief outlines. Reports in 1 week on queries; 3 weeks on mss. "If our agency does not respond within 2 weeks to your request to become a client, you may submit requests elsewhere. For details of policy, send query with SASE."
Terms: Agent receives 15% commission on domestic sales; and 20% on foreign sales. Charges a reading fee to new, unpublished writers; waives fee if representing the writer. 2% of income derived from reading fees. "We do not do critiques, as such, but do give the writer a brief evaluation of marketing potential based on my reading. If a reading fee is waived there is a processing fee of $25-45. May charge for phone and photocopy expenses. 2-3% of income derived from fees; 97-98% of income is derived from commission on ms sales.
Recent Sales: *Awaiting Trespass*, by Linda Ty-Casper (Readers International).

INTERNATIONAL PUBLISHER ASSOCIATES, INC., 746 West Shore, Sparta NJ 07871. (201)729-9321. Executive Vice President: Joe DeRogatis. Estab. 1982. Represents 30 clients. 80% of clients are new/unpublished writers. Eager to work with new/unpublished writers. Specializes in all types of nonfiction.
Will Handle: Nonfiction books and novels. Currently handles 95% nonfiction books and 5% movie scripts. Will read—at no charge—unsolicited queries and outlines. Reports in 3 weeks on queries. "If our agency does not respond within 1 month to your request to become a client, you may submit requests elsewhere."
Terms: Agent receives 15% commission on domestic sales; and 20% on foreign sales. 100% of income derived from commission on ms sales.
Recent Sales: No information given.

JANUS LITERARY AGENCY, Box 107, Nahant MA 01908. (617)593-0576. Contact: Lenny Cavallaro. Estab. 1980. Represents 7 clients. 14.7% of clients are new/unpublished writers. "Will gladly consider published and/or unpublished writers." Prefers nonfiction "of popular or controversial slant."
Will Handle: Nonfiction books and novels. Currently handles 10% magazine articles; 80% nonfiction books; and 10% novels. Will read—at no charge—unsolicited queries and outlines. Must enclose SASE. Reports in 1 week on queries; 2 weeks on mss.
Terms: Agent receives 15% commission on domestic sales; and 20% on foreign sales. Charges reading fee; $50-200, to appraise ms. 11.5% of income derived from reading fees. Reading fee includes critique. "Most critiques run 1½-3 typed pages, single spaced. Some very detailed, line-by-line commentary is included. I read everything myself; hold degree in English; was formerly an English teacher; am a published author; was formerly a book critic for *New Haven Register* (newspaper)." Charges $50-100 handling fee (phone calls, postage, etc.). Sometimes offers a consultation service through which writers not represented can get advice on a contract; charges $25/hour. 20% of income derived from fees; 80% of income derived from commission on ms sales. Payment of a criticism fee does not ensure that agency will represent writer.
Recent Sales: *Protect Your Children*, by Laura Huchton (Prentice-Hall); and *Ouija: The Most Dangerous Game*, by Stoker Hunt (Harper & Row).

SHARON JARVIS AND CO., INC., 260 Willard Ave., Staten Island NY 10314. (718)273-1066. President: Sharon Jarvis. Estab. 1985 (previously known as Jarvis, Braff Ltd. Established 1979). Member of ILAA. Represents 70 clients. 20% of clients are new/unpublished writers. Prefers to work with published/established authors; works with a small number of new/unpublished authors. Considers types of genre fiction, commercial fiction and nonfiction.
Will Handle: Nonfiction books, novels and juvenile books. Currently handles 20% nonfiction books; 60% novels; and 20% juvenile books. Does not read unsolicited mss. Reports in 1 week on queries. "If our agency does not respond within 1 month to your request to become a client, you may submit requests elsewhere."
Terms: Agent receives 15% commission on domestic sales; "splits commission" on dramatic sales; and extra 10% on foreign sales. ("We have sub-agents in ten different foreign markets.") Charges reading fee; $40 for opening chapters and outline; ("fee goes to outside reader; recommended material then read by agency at no extra charge"). Critique is a one-page analysis "aimed toward agency evaluation of author's talent and marketability." Charges for photocopying. 100% of income derived from commission on ms sales.
Recent Sales: Six-book series, *Vietnam Ground Zero* by Eric Helm (Harlequin Gold Eagle); 6-book series, *S.E.A.L.S*, by Kevin Randle (Avon Books); and *Breeze Horror*, by Candace Caponegro (New American Library).

JET LITERARY ASSOCIATES, INC., 124 E. 84th St., New York NY 10028. (212)879-2578. President: J. Trupin. Estab. 1976. Represents 85 clients. 5% of clients are new/unpublished writers. Writer must have published articles or books. Prefers to work with published/established authors. Specializes in nonfiction.
Will Handle: Nonfiction books and novels. Currently handles 50% nonfiction books and 50% novels. Does not read unsolicited mss. Reports in 2 weeks on queries; 1 month on mss. "If our agency does not respond with-

in 2 months to your request to become a client, you may submit requests elsewhere."
Terms: Agent receives 15% commission on domestic sales; 15% on dramatic sales; and 25% on foreign sales. Charges for phone and postage expenses. 100% of income derived from commission on ms sales.
Recent Sales: *Imponderables*, by David Feldman (Morrow); *Stallone*, by Jeff Roijin (Pocket Books); and *Trailsman*, by Will Knott (New American Library).

ALEX KAMAROFF ASSOCIATES, Suite 417, 51 E. 42nd St., New York NY 10017. (212)421-8685. President: Alex Kamaroff. Estab. 1985. Member of ILAA. Represents 37 clients. 15% of clients are new/unpublished writers. Works with a small number of new/unpublished authors. Specializes in men's adventure, science fiction, mysteries, horror, category and historical romances, contemporary women's fiction. "Very interested in popular nonfiction ideas."
Will Handle: Nonfiction books, novels, movie scripts, and TV scripts. Currently handles 20% nonfiction books; 50% novels; 15% movie scripts; and 15% TV scripts. Will read—at no charge—unsolicited queries and outlines; no reply without SASE. Reports in 1 week on queries; 3 weeks on mss. "If our agency does not respond within 1 month to your request to become a client, you may submit requests elsewhere."
Terms: Agent receives 10% commission on domestic sales; 10% on dramatic sales; and 20% on foreign sales. Charges for phone expenses. Offers a consultation service through which writers can get advice on a contract. 100% of income derived from commission on ms sales.
Recent Sales: *Frontier Woman*, by Joan Johnston (Pocket); 3-book deal by Diana Morgan (Berkley-Jove) and *Louis Rukeyser Business Almanac* (Simon & Schuster).

KIDDE, HOYT AND PICARD LITERARY AGENCY, 335 E. 51st St., New York NY 10022. (212)755-9461. Chief Associate: Katharine Kidde. Estab. 1981. Represents 50 clients. 10% of clients are "relatively" new/unpublished writers. "We prefer that a writer be published, with at least a few pieces in magazines, but we will take on a new writer if we feel her or his writing is extraordinary." Works with a small number of new/unpublished authors. Specializes in mainstream and literary fiction; romantic fiction; some historical; more contemporary; mainstream nonfiction; and some young adult fiction.
Will Handle: Nonfiction books and young adult books. Will handle magazine articles and magazine fiction for national magazines, if also handling a book-length ms for the author. Currently handles 1% magazine articles; 2% magazine fiction; 22% nonfiction books; 70% novels; and 5% young adults books. Will read—at no charge—unsolicited queries and outlines. Reports in 1½ weeks on queries; 3 weeks on mss. "If our agency does not respond within 6 weeks to your request to become a client, you may submit requests elsewhere."
Terms: Agent receives 15% commission on domestic sales; 15% on dramatic sales; and 15% on foreign sales. Charges for phone, postage and photocopy expenses. 100% of income derived from commission on ms sales.
Recent Sales: *All That Glitters*, by Norma Seely (Doubleday); and *The All Of It*, by Jeannette Haien (Godine).

HARVEY KLINGER, INC., 301 W. 53rd St., New York NY 10019. (212)581-7068. President: Harvey Klinger. Estab. 1977. Represents 60 clients. 25% of clients are new/unpublished writers. "We seek writers demonstrating great talent, fresh writing and a willingness to listen to editorial criticism and learn." Works with a small number of new/unpublished authors. Specializes in mainstream fiction, (not category romance or mysteries, etc.), nonfiction in the medical, social sciences, autobiography and biography areas.
Will Handle: Nonfiction books and novels. Currently handles 60% nonfiction books and 40% novels. Will read—at no charge—unsolicited queries and outlines. Reports in 2 weeks on queries. "If our agency does not respond within 2 months to your request to become a client, you may submit requests elsewhere."
Terms: Agent receives 15% commission on domestic sales; 15% on dramatic sales; and 25% on foreign sales. Charges for photocopying expenses. 100% of income derived from commission on ms sales.
Recent Sales: *Soul Flame*, by Barbara Wood (Random House); *The Girl Next Door: An Autobiography*, by Jane Powell (William Morrow); and *Quarry*, by C. Terry Cline, Jr. (NAL Books).

PAUL KOHNER, INC., 9169 Sunset Blvd., Los Angeles CA 90069. (213)550-1060. Agent: Gary Salt. Estab. 1939. Represents 100 clients. Writer must have sold material in the market or category in which they are seeking representation. Prefers to work with published/established authors. Specializes in film and TV scripts and related material, and dramatic rights for published or soon-to-be published books—both fiction and nonfiction. No plays, poetry or short stories.
Will Handle: Magazine articles and nonfiction books (if they have film or TV potential); novels (only previously published or with publication deals set); movie scripts; and TV scripts. Currently handles 5% magazine articles; 12½% nonfiction books; 12½% novels; 40% movie scripts; and 30% TV scripts. Will read—at no charge—unsolicited queries only. Reports in 1 week on queries. "If our agency does not respond within 1 month to your request to become a client, you may submit requests elsewhere."
Terms: Agent receives 10% commission on dramatic sales. Charges for photocopy and binding expenses. Sometimes offers a consultation service through which film and TV writers not represented can get advice on a contract; charges varying rate. 100% of income derived from commission on ms sales.
Recent Sales: *The Hunt for Red October*, by Tom Clancy (Navel Institute Press).

BARBARA S. KOUTS, (Affiliated with Philip G. Spitzer Literary Agency), 1465 3rd Ave., New York NY 10028. (212)628-0352. Literary Agent: Barbara S. Kouts. Estab. 1980. Member of ILAA. Represents 50 clients. 75% of clients are new/unpublished writers. Eager to work with new/unpublished writers. Specializes in fiction, nonfiction and children's books.
Will Handle: Magazine fiction, nonfiction books, novels and juvenile books. Currently handles 5% magazine articles; 5% magazine fiction; 35% nonfiction books; 35% novels; and 20% juvenile books. Will read—at no charge—unsolicited queries and outlines. Reports in 3 weeks on queries; 6 weeks on mss. "If our agency does not respond within 2 months to your request to become a client, you may submit requests elsewhere."
Terms: Agent receives 10% commission on domestic sales; and 20% on foreign sales. Charges writers for photocopy expenses.
Recent Sales: *A Little Ignorance*, by Penelope Scambly Schott (Clarkson Potter); *A Man Named Thoreau*, by Robert Burleigh (Atheneum): and *The Ultimate Paper Airplane*, by Richard Kline (Simon & Schuster).

MICHAEL LARSEN/ELIZABETH POMADA LITERARY AGENTS, 1029 Jones St., San Francisco CA 94109. (415)673-0939. Contact: Mike Larsen or Elizabeth Pomada. Member of ILAA. Represents 150 clients. 50-55% of clients are new/unpublished writers. Eager to work with new/unpublished writers. "We have very catholic tastes and do not specialize. We handle literary, commercial, and genre fiction, and the full range of nonfiction books."
Will Handle: Adult nonfiction books and novels. Currently handles 75% nonfiction books and 25% novels. Will read—at no charge—unsolicited queries, the first 30 pages and synopsis of completed novels, and nonfiction book proposals. Reports in 6 weeks on queries.
Terms: Agent receives 15% commission on domestic sales; 15% on dramatic sales; and 20% on foreign sales. May charge writer for printing, postage for multiple submissions, foreign mail, foreign phone calls, galleys, books, and legal fees. Offers a separate consultation service; charges $100/hour. 100% of income derived from commission on ms sales.
Recent Sales: *The Castrated Woman: What Your Doctor Won't Tell You About Hysterectomy*, by Naomi Stokes (Franklin Watts); *Daggarspell*, by Katharine Kerr (Doubleday); and *The Pharmacist's Prescription*, by F. James Grogan (Rawson Associates).

LAW OFFICES OF ROBERT L. FENTON, P.C., Suite 390, 31800 Northwestern Hwy., Farmington Hills MI 48018. (313)855-8780. President: Robert L. Fenton. Estab. 1960. Represents 30 clients. 10% of clients are new/unpublished writers. Prefers to work with published/established authors; works with a small number of new/unpublished authors.
Will Handle: Nonfiction books and novels. Currently handles 50% nonfiction books and 50% novels. Reads solicited queries, outlines and mss for a fee. Reports in 3 weeks on queries. "If our agency does not respond within 2 months to your request to become a client, you may submit requests elsewhere."
Terms: Agent receives 15% commission on domestic sales and 15% on foreign sales. Charges a reading fee; waives fee if representing writer who has been published twice. 10% of income derived from reading fees. Critique: If both oral and written, the written is approximately 1½ pages. Charges nominal retainer to unpublished authors. Charges for phone, photocopy and postage expenses. 20% of income derived from fees.
Recent Sales: *The Congregation*, by Hal Kantor (Putnam); and *Plunderes*, by R. Greenfield and H. Margolis (Simon & Schuster).

ELIZABETH LAY, LITERARY AGENT, 9 Overman Pl., New Rochelle NY 10801. President: Elizabeth Lay. Estab. 1980. Member of ILAA. Represents 20 clients. 30% of clients are new/unpublished writers. Works with a small number of new/unpublished authors. Specializes in fiction (women's mainstream, fantasy, mysteries, historical romances and westerns) and nonfiction (of interest to women, and health and diet).
Will Handle: Nonfiction books and novels. Currently handles 50% nonfiction books and 50% novels. Will read—at no charge—unsolicited queries and outlines. Reports in 2 weeks on queries; 6 weeks on mss. "If our agency does not respond within 2 months to your request to become a client, you may submit requests elsewhere."
Terms: Agent receives 15% commission on domestic sales; 15% on dramatic sales; and 20% on foreign sales. Charges reading fee for first novel mss by unpublished writers. Fees based on length, minimum $50, maximum $200/1,000 pages. 95% of income derived from commission on ms sales.
Recent Sales: *Too Close to the Bone*, by R. Seid (Prentice Hall Press); *Full House*, by S. Singer (St. Martin's Press); and *The Snow White Syndrome*, by B. Cohen (Macmillan).

L. HARRY LEE LITERARY AGENCY, Box 203, Rocky Point NY 11778. (516)744-1188. President: L. Harry Lee. Estab. 1979. Member of WGA. Represents 135 clients. 60% of clients are new/unpublished writers. Works with a small number of new/unpublished authors; "mainly interested in screenwriters." Specializes in movies, TV (episodic, movies and sit-coms) and contemporary novels.
Will Handle: Novels, movie scripts, stage plays, and TV scripts (movies, mini-series, episodic, and sit-coms). Currently handles 10% novels; 60% movie scripts; 3% stage plays; 27% TV scripts. Will read—at no

charge—unsolicited queries and outlines; does not read material submitted without SASE. No dot-matrix. Reports in 2 weeks on queries; 6 weeks on mss. "If our agency does not respond within 3 months to your request to become a client, you may submit requests elsewhere."
Terms: Agent receives 15% commission on domestic sales; 15% on dramatic sales; and 20% on foreign sales. Charges a marketing fee; 5% of income derived from marketing fees. Charges for photocopies, line editing, proofing, typing, and postage expenses. Offers a consultation service through which writers not represented can get advice on a contract; charges $75/hour. 5% of income derived from marketing fees; 90% of income derived from commission on ms sales.
Recent Sales: "Heaven Help Us," "Turk-182," and "Tel-Star Conspiracy" (motion pictures).

LENINGER LITERARY AGENCY, INC., (See John K. Payne Literary Agency, Inc.).

THE ADELE LEONE AGENCY, INC., 26 Nantucket Pl., Scarsdale NY 10583. (914)961-2965/3085. Associate: Richard McEnroe. Estab. 1979. Represents 100 clients. 20% of clients are new/unpublished writers. Prefers to work with published/established authors; works with a small number of new/unpublished authors. Specializes in historical, gothic, regency, and contemporary romance; science fiction and fantasy, westerns, horror, war novels, military history, biography and general women's and mainstream fiction.
Will Handle: Nonfiction books and novels. Currently handles 40% nonfiction books and 60% novels. Will read—at no charge—unsolicited queries and outlines. Reports in 6 weeks on queries.
Terms: Agent receives 15% commission on domestic sales; 15% on dramatic sales; and 10% on foreign sales (unless sold direct, then 15%). 75% of income derived from commission on ms sales.
Recent Sales: *Moondust and Madness*, by Janelle Taylor (Bantam); *The Chaos Theory*, by John Briggs and David Peat (Harper and Row); and *Predators*, by Eric Sauter (Simon & Schuster).

WENDY LIPKIND AGENCY, Suite 5K, 225 E. 57th St., New York NY 10022. (212)935-1406. President: Wendy Lipkind. Estab. 1977. Member of ILAA. Represents 50 clients. 20% of clients are new/unpublished writers. Works with a small number of new/unpublished authors. Specializes in nonfiction (social history, adventure, biography, science, sports, history) and fiction ("good story telling. I do not specialize in genre mass-market fiction").
Will Handle: Nonfiction books and novels. Currently handles: 80% nonfiction books and 20% novels. Will read—at no charge—unsolicited queries and outlines. Reports in 2 weeks on queries.
Terms: Agent receives 10% commission on domestic sales; 10-15% on dramatic sales; and 20% on foreign sales. Charges $100 one-time handling fee if sells work. Charges for phone, foreign postage, photocopy, cables and messenger expenses. 100% of income derived from commission on ms sales.
Recent Sales: *The New Crowd* (Simon and Schuster); *Windstar* (Macmillan); and *American Art Deco* (Atlantic Monthly Press).

PETER LIVINGSTON ASSOCIATES, INC., 143 Collier St., Toronto, Ontario M4W 1M2 Canada. (416)928-1010. Associate: David Johnston. Estab. 1982. Member of ILAA. Represents 50 clients. 50% of our clients are new/unpublished writers. Works with a small number of new/unpublished authors. Specializes in hardcover, "front list" fiction—thrillers, mystery, and women's books—and nonfiction by leading authorities or experienced journalists. "In nonfiction, previous magazine publication and/or credentials in the field help. In fiction, short story publications help:"
Will Handle: Nonfiction books; novels (hardcover, mainstream); and movie scripts (only if by previously published or produced writers). Currently handles 5% magazine articles; 60% nonfiction books; 25% novels; 5% movie scripts; and 5% TV scripts. Will read—at no charge—unsolicited queries and outlines. Reports in 2 weeks on queries; 5 weeks on mss. "If our agency does not respond within 6 weeks to your request to become a client, you may submit requests elsewhere."
Terms: Agent receives 15% commission on domestic sales; 15% on dramatic sales; and 20% on foreign sales. Charges a reading fee to "unrecommended and previously unpublished authors" of fiction; waives fee if representing writer. 1% of income derived from reading fees. Writer receives "a brief (two to three page) critique of the manuscript for reading fee. Readings are done by inhouse agents and/or professional editors." Charges for photocopy, postage, messenger, telex, and phone expenses.
Recent Sales: *The Christkiller*, by Marcel Montecino (Arbor House); *Savant: Genius Among Us, Genius Within Us*, by Dr. Darold Treffert (Harper & Row); and *The Real Coke: The Real Story*, by T. Oliver (Random House).

THE STERLING LORD AGENCY, INC., 660 Madison Ave., New York NY 10021. (212)751-2533. Contact: Evan Marshall. Member of SAR. 10% of clients are new/unpublished writers. Works with a small number of new/unpublished authors. Specializes in adult hardcover fiction and nonfiction, and paperback fiction and nonfiction.
Will Handle: Nonfiction books and novels in all genres. Currently handles 50% nonfiction books and 50% novels. Will read—at no charge—unsolicited queries and outlines. Reports in 1 month on queries. "If our

agency does not respond within 3 months to your request to become a client, you may submit requests elsewhere."

Terms: Agent receives 10% commission on domestic sales; 10% on dramatic sales; and 20% on foreign sales. Charges for photocopy expenses.

Recent Sales: No information given.

BARBARA LOWENSTEIN ASSOCIATES, INC., Suite 714, 250 W. 57th St., New York NY 10107. (212)586-3825. President: Barbara Lowenstein. Vice President: Eileen Fallon. Estab. 1976. Member of ILAA. Represents 120 clients. 15% of clients are new/unpublished writers. Specializes in nonfiction—especially science and medical-topic books for the general public—historical and contemporary romance, bigger woman's fiction and general fiction.

Will Handle: Nonfiction books and novels. Currently handles 2% magazine articles; 55% nonfiction books; and 43% novels. Will read—at no charge—unsolicited queries and outlines. Reports in 2 weeks on queries.

Terms: Agent receives 15% commission on domestic sales; 15% on dramatic sales; and 20% on foreign sales. Charges for photocopy, foreign postage and messenger expenses. 100% of income derived from commission on ms, other dramatic and 1st serial sales.

Recent Sales: Confidential.

THE LUND AGENCY, Suite 12-14, 10000 Riverside Dr., Toluca Lake CA 91602. (818)761-0928. President: Cara Lund. Estab. 1979. Member of WGA. Represents 25 clients. 2% of clients are new/unpublished writers. Writer must be published/produced. Prefers to work with published/established authors; works with a small number of new/unpublished authors. Specializes in science fiction, horror, fantasy, true accounts and action. Particular interest in screenplays that adapt major novels of science fiction with permission of novelists.

Will Handle: Novels, movie scripts, and TV scripts. Currently handles 15% nonfiction books; 15% novels; 40% movie scripts and 40% TV scripts. Will read—at no charge—unsolicited queries and outlines. "Will answer only if interested, requires SASE. If our agency does not respond within 1 month to your request to become a client, you may submit requests elsewhere."

Terms: Agent receives 10% commission on domestic sales; 15% on dramatic sales; and 20% on foreign sales. 10% of income derived from commission on ms sales.

Recent Sales: "Our contracts have clauses which prevent release of this information."

DONALD MACCAMPBELL INC., 12 E. 41st St., New York NY 10017. (212)683-5580. Editor: Maureen Moran. Estab. 1940. Represents 50 clients. "The agency does not handle unpublished writers." Specializes in women's book-length fiction in all categories.

Will Handle: Novels. Currently handles 100% novels. Does not read unsolicited mss. Reports in 1 week on queries; 2 weeks on mss. "If our agency does not respond within 1 month to your request to become a client, you may submit requests elsewhere."

Terms: Agent receives 10% commission on domestic sales; and 20% on foreign sales. 100% of income derived from commission on ms sales.

Recent Sales: *Prisoner of Desire*, by Jennifer Blake (Ballantine); *Guadalajara*, by E. Howard Hunt (Stein & Day); and *Sweet Thunder*, by Lynne Scott-Drennan (Doubleday).

JANET WILKENS MANUS LITERARY AGENCY INC., Suite 906, 370 Lexington Ave., New York NY 10017. (212)685-9558. President: Janet Wilkens Manus. Estab. 1981. Member of ILAA. Represents 40 clients. 20% of our clients are new/unpublished writers. Prefers to work with published/established authors; works with a small number of new/unpublished authors. Specializes in general adult trade fiction and nonfiction.

Will Handle: Nonfiction books (trade oriented); novels (adult and young adult); and juvenile books. Currently handles 5% magazine articles; 5% magazine fiction; 40% nonfiction books; 45% novels; and 5% juvenile books. Will read—at no charge—unsolicited queries and outlines. Reports in 2 weeks on queries; 5 weeks on manuscripts. "If our agency does not respond within 3 months to your request to become a client, you may submit requests elsewhere."

Terms: Agent receives 15% commission on domestic sales; 15% on dramatic sales; and 20% on foreign sales. Charges for photography, messenger, overseas phone, and postage expenses.

Recent Sales: *Prime Evil*, by Judith Kelman (Berkley Books); *Take Control of Your Money: A Life Guide to Financial Freedom*, by Barbara Lee and Paula M. Siegel (Villard); and *Make the Most of a Good Thing—You!*, by Diana Shaw (Atlantic Monthly Press).

DENISE MARCIL LITERARY AGENCY, INC., 316 W. 82nd St. 5F, New York NY 10024. (212)580-1071. President: Denise Marcil. Estab. 1977. Member of ILAA. Represents 80 clients. Works with a small number of new/unpublished authors. Specializes in "solid, informative nonfiction including such areas as money, business, health, child care, parenting, self-help and how-to's and commercial fiction, especially women's fiction; also mysteries, psychological suspense and horror. We're actively seeking young adult authors."

Will Handle: Nonfiction books, novels and young adult. Currently handles 40% nonfiction books and 60%

novels (10% young adult). Will read—at no charge—unsolicited queries and outlines. Reports in 2 weeks on queries; 3 months on mss. "If our agency does not respond within 4 months to your request to become a client, you may submit requests elsewhere."
Terms: Agent receives 15% commission on domestic sales; 15% on dramatic sales; and 22½% on foreign sales. Charges a reading fee: $30/first 3 chapters and outline. Less than 5% of income derived from reading fee. Charges for disbursements only when ms sells. 95% of income derived from commission on ms sales.
Recent Sales: *Off the Wall*, by Elaine Raco Chase (Bantam); *Private Company, Personal Gold Mine*, by Douglas Forde (Viking/Penguin); and *Julio Iglesias*, by Elizabeth Garcia (Ballantine).

BETTY MARKS, Suite 9F, 176 E. 77th St., New York NY 10021. (212)535-8388. Contact: Betty Marks. Estab. 1969. Member of ILAA. Represents 35 clients. Prefers to work with published/established authors; works with a small number of new/unpublished authors. Specializes in journalists' nonfiction.
Will Handle: Nonfiction books and novels. Will read—at no charge—unsolicited queries and outlines. Reports in 1 week on queries; 6 weeks on mss. "If our agency does not respond within 6 weeks to your request to become a client, you may submit requests elsewhere."
Terms: Agent receives 10% commission on domestic sales; and 10% on foreign sales (plus 10% to foreign agent). Charges a reading fee for unpublished writers; fee will be waived if representing writer. Charges criticism fee. "Writers receive two to three page letter covering storyline, plot, characters, dialogue, language, etc." Written by agent. Charges for "extraordinary" postage, phone and messenger expenses. Offers a consultation service through which writers not represented can get advice on a contract; charges $50/hour. 95% of income derived from commission on ms sales. Payment of criticism fee does not ensure that agency will represent a writer.
Recent Sales: *The Death and Life of Dith Pran* (Elizabeth Sifton); *At Any Cost* (Pantheon); and *I, Koch* (Dodd Mead).

CLAUDIA MENZA LITERARY AGENCY, 237 W. 11th St., New York NY 10014. (212)889-6850. President: Claudia Menza. Estab. 1983. Represents 25 clients. 40% of clients are new/unpublished writers. Specializes in unique fiction and nonfiction dealing with serious subjects (i.e. political and medical issues).
Will Handle: Nonfiction books and novels. Currently handles 50% nonfiction books and 50% novels. Will read—at no charge—unsolicited queries, outlines and mss, "but prefer queries and outlines, or sample chapters, rather than entire manuscripts." Reports in 2 weeks on queires; 2 months on mss.
Terms: Agent receives 15% commission on domestic sales; 15% on dramatic sales; and 15% on foreign sales (20% if a foreign agent is also used).
Recent Sales: "Privileged information."

SCOTT MEREDITH, INC., 845 3rd Ave., New York NY 10022. (212)245-5500. Vice President and Editorial Director: Jack Scovil. Estab. 1946. Represents 2,000 clients. 10% of clients are new/unpublished writers. "We'll represent on a straight commission basis writers who've sold one or more recent books to major publishers, or several (three or four) magazine pieces to major magazines, or a screenplay or teleplay to a major producer. We're a very large agency (staff of fifty-one) and handle all types of material except individual cartoons or drawings, though we will handle collections of these as well."
Will Handle: Magazine articles, magazine fiction, nonfiction books, novels, textbooks, juvenile books, movie scripts, radio scripts, stage plays, TV scripts, syndicated material and poetry. Currently handles 5% magazine articles; 5% magazine fiction; 23% nonfiction books; 23% novels; 5% textbooks; 10% juvenile books; 5% movie scripts; 2% radio scripts; 2% stage plays; 5% TV scripts; 5% syndicated material; and 5% poetry. Will read—at no charge—unsolicited queries, outlines, and manuscripts "if from a writer with track record as described previously; charges a fee if no sales." Reports in 2 weeks.
Terms: Agent receives 10% commission on domestic sales; 10% on dramatic sales; and 20% on foreign sales. Charges "a single fee which covers multiple readers, revision assistance or critique as needed." 10% of income derived from reading fees. "When a script is returned as irreparably unsalable, the accompanying letter of explanation will usually run two single-spaced pages minimum on short stories or articles, or from 4 to 10 single-spaced pages on book-length manuscripts, teleplays, or screenplays. All reports are done by agents on full-time staff. No marketing advice is included, since, if it's salable, we'll market and sell it ourselves." Charges for telex, cables and phone expenses. 10% of income derived from fees; 90% of income derived from commission on mss sales.
Recent Sales: *Harlot's Ghost*, by Norman Mailer (Random House); *Contact*, by Carl Sagan (Simon and Schuster); and *Murder in Georgetown*, by Margaret Truman (Arbor House).

THE PETER MILLER AGENCY, INC., Suite 301, 1021 6th Ave., New York NY 10018. (212)221-8329. President: Peter Miller. Associate Agent: Lori Perkins. Estab. 1975. Represents 30 clients. 50% of clients are new/unpublished writers. Eager to work with new/unpublished writers, as well as with published/established authors (especially journalists). Specializes in celebrity books (biographies and self-help), true crime accounts, mysteries, mystery thrillers, historical fiction/family sagas, women's fiction, and "fiction with *real* motion picture potential."

Will Handle: Nonfiction books, novels and movie scripts. Currently handles 45% nonfiction books; 35% novels; and 20% movie scripts. Will read—at no charge—unsolicited queries and outlines. Reports in 2 weeks on queries; 1 month on mss. "If our agency does not respond within 1 month to your request to become a client, you may submit requests elsewhere."

Terms: Agent receives 15% commission on domestic sales; and 20-25% on foreign sales. Charges a criticism fee for unpublished writers. Fee is refunded if book sells. 5% of income derived from criticism fees. "The agency offers a reading evaluation, usually two to four pages in length, which gives detailed analysis of literary craft, commercial potential and recommendations for improving the work, if necessary. The evaluations are done by published authors." Charges for photocopy expenses. 5% of income derived from fees; 95% of income derived from commission on ms sales.

Recent Sales: *Limbo*, by Joe DeSario (Doubleday); *The Terminator*, by Randall Frakes and Bill Wisher (Bantam); and *Sneaky Exercises*, by Leslie Goldin (World Almanac).

MARVIN MOSS INC., 601-9200 Sunset, Los Angeles CA 90069. (213)274-8483. President: Marvin Moss. Estab. 1970. Member of WGA. 1% of clients are new/unpublished writers. Prefers to work with published/established authors; works with a small number of new/unpublished authors.

Will Handle: Nonfiction books, movie scripts and TV scripts. No poetry, romance or children's books. Currently handles 20% nonfiction books; 10% novels; 30% movie scripts and 40% TV scripts. Does not read unsolicited mss. Accepts no material without executed release. Reports in 6 weeks on queries.

Terms: Agent receives 10% commission on domestic sales; 10% on dramatic sales; and 20% on foreign sales. 100% of income derived from commission on ms sales.

Recent Sales: No information given.

MULTIMEDIA PRODUCT DEVELOPMENT, INC., Suite 724, 410 S. Michigan Ave., Chicago IL 60605. (312)922-3063. President: Jane Jordan Browne. Estab. 1971. Member of ILAA. Represents 100 clients. 10% of clients are new/unpublished writers. Works with a small number of new/unpublished authors. "We are generalists, taking on nonfiction and fiction that we believe will be on target for the market."

Will Handle: Nonfiction books ("new idea" books, how-to, science and biography) and novels (mainstream and genre). Currently handles 68% nonfiction books; 30% novels; and 2% juvenile books. Will read—at no charge—unsolicited queries and outlines. Reports in 3 weeks on queries. "We review manuscripts only if we solicit submission and only as 'exclusives.'"

Terms: Agent receives 15% commission on domestic sales; 15% on dramatic sales; and 20% on foreign sales. Charges for photocopying, overseas telephone calls, and postage expenses. Sometimes offers a consultation service through which writers not represented can get advice on a contract; charges $75/hour. 100% of income derived from commission on ms sales.

Recent Sales: *Herbs and Apples*, by Helen Hooven Santmyer (Harper & Row); *Little Saigon*, by T. Jefferson Parker (St. Martin's); and *Cousteau: A Biography*, by Axel Madsen (Beaufort Books).

CHARLES NEIGHBORS, INC., Suite 3607A, 7600 Blanco Rd., San Antonio TX 78216. (512)342-5324. Owner: Charles Neighbors. Estab. 1966. Represents 60 clients. 10% of clients are new/unpublished writers. Works with a small number of new/unpublished authors.

Will Handle: Nonfiction books, novels and movie scripts. Currently handles 30% nonfiction books; 60% novels; and 10% movie scripts. Will read—at no charge—unsolicited queries and outlines. Reports in 1 month on queries; 2 months on mss. "If our agency does not respond within 2 months to your request to become a client, you may submit requests elsewhere."

Terms: Agent receives 15% commission on domestic sales; 15% on dramatic sales; and 20% on foreign sales. Charges for photocopying and foreign postage expenses. 100% of income derived from commission on ms sales.

Recent Sales: *Two Point Conversion*, by Bryce Webster (Amacom); *The White Jaguar*, by William Appel (Richardson & Steirman); and *High Risk*, by Paula Paul (Harlequin).

B.K. NELSON LITERARY AGENCY, 10 E. 39th St., New York NY 10016. (212)889-0637. President: Bonita K. Nelson. Estab. 1978. Represents 15 clients. 2% of clients are new/unpublished writers. "A writer has to understand the basics of writing, not just have an idea. We want professionalism. Do the best you can do and we will work with you." Eager to work with new/unpublished writers. Specializes in how-to, computer, business books, historical romances, contemporary romance, software and game show proposals, the college educational market, and motion picture scripts of all kinds.

Will Handle: Nonfiction books, novels, movie scripts, how-to and computer applications. Currently handles 65% nonfiction books; 30% novels; and 5% textbooks. "Will read inquiries and outlines limited to 5 pages and will make a decision at point of inquiry." Does not read unsolicited mss. Reports in 1 week on queries; 2 weeks on mss. "If our agency does not respond within 3 months to your request to become a client, you may submit requests elsewhere."

Terms: Agent receives 15% commission on domestic sales; 15% on dramatic sales; and 10% on foreign sales. Charges a reading fee if the writer "wants a manuscript read, and for us to determine if it is salable." 1% of income derived from reading fees. "If the writer wants a detailed criticism against which to rewrite the book, we will then do it for a fee after having discussed the manuscript with a potential author/client." 1% of income derived from fees; 99% of income derived from commission on ms sales.

Recent Sales: *Marketing to the Fortune 500*, by Jeff Davidson (Harcourt Brace Jovanovich); *Marketer's Direct-Mail Idea Book and Workbook*, by Holtz, Herman; and *The Complete Writer's Reference*, by Holtz (Dow Jones).

NEW ENGLAND PUBLISHING ASSOCIATES, INC., Box 5, Chester CT 06412. (718)788-6641 or (203)345-4976. President: Elizabeth Frost Knappman. Estab. 1983. Represents 45-50 clients. 25% of clients are new/unpublished writers. Works with new/unpublished authors. Specializes in serious nonfiction.

Will Handle: Nonfiction books. Currently handles 100% nonfiction books. Will read—at no charge—unsolicited queries and outlines. Phone queries are OK. Reports in 1 month on queries. Simultaneous queries OK.

Terms: Agent receives 15% on domestic sales; and 10% on dramatic and foreign sales (plus 10% to co-agent). 100% of income derived from commission on ms sales.

Recent Sales: *Mafia Assassin*, by Tom Renner and Cecil Kirby (Random House); *Poisoned Blood*, by Philip Ginsburg (Scribner's); and *Dian Fossey: A Life for Gorillas*, by Jeremy Cherfas (Pantheon).

THE BETSY NOLAN LITERARY AGENCY, 215 Park Ave. S, New York NY 10003. (212)420-6000. President: Betsy Nolan. Vice President: Michael Powers. Estab. 1980. Represents 26 clients. 50% of clients are new/unpublished writers. Works with a small number of new/unpublished authors.

Will Handle: Nonfiction books and novels. Currently handles 60% nonfiction books and 40% novels. Will read—at no charge—unsolicited queries and outlines. Reports in 2 weeks on queries; 1 month on mss. "If our agency does not respond within 1 month to your request to become a client, you may submit requests elsewhere."

Terms: Agent receives 15% commission on domestic sales; and 20% on foreign sales.

Recent Sales: No information given.

NORTHEAST LITERARY AGENCY, 69 Broadway, Concord NH 03301. (603)225-9162. Sr. Editor: Vic Levine. Estab. 1973. Represents 15 clients. 20% of clients are new/unpublished writers. "We don't insist on preset criteria for representation. We're more concerned with a writer's potential . . . that is, once he or she has submitted a potentially salable manuscript." Eager to work with new/unpublished writers. Specializes in historical and contemporary romance, science fiction, mysteries, westerns, serious (non-genre) novels; nonfiction, on remedial education, environment, women's rights, health, how-to, personal memoirs, "plus just about any other salable subject (controversial topics are especially welcome)."

Will Handle: Magazine articles, magazine fiction, nonfiction books, novels, juvenile books (including picture books), movie scripts, radio scripts, stage plays, TV scripts, syndicated material, poetry collections, and computer software for Commodore C-64. Currently handles 2% magazine articles; 3% magazine fiction; 25% nonfiction books; 50% novels; 2% textbooks; 8% juvenile books; 1% movie scripts; 1% radio scripts; 1% stage plays; 2% TV scripts; and 5% poetry. Will read—at no charge—unsolicited queries and outlines. Reports in 1 week on queries; 3 weeks on mss. "If our agency does not respond within 1 month to your request to become a client, you may submit requests elsewhere."

Terms: Agent receives 15% commission on domestic sales; 20% on dramatic sales; and 20% on foreign sales. Charges reading fee: $135/manuscript or $250/one-time fee; fee waived if writer has sold to major publisher within preceding year. Fee returned following sale of first work. Charges for phone and photocopying expenses. Offers a consultation service through which writers not represented can get advice on a contract; charges $50/hour. 20% of income derived from fees; 80% of income derived from commission on ms sales.

Recent Sales: *Making the Words Stand Still*, by Don Lyman (Houghton Mifflin); *Working It Out*, by Judi Sprankle (Walker and Co.); *Putting Work In Its Place*, by Henry Ebel and Judi Sprankle (Walker and Co.).

MARY NOVIK, LITERARY AGENT, 5519 Deerhorn Ln., North Vancouver, British Columbia V7R 4S8 Canada. (604)987-4982. Owner: Mary Novik. Estab. 1982. "Writers must have done their homework and know the romance market thoroughly. Writer's novel must reflect current trends." Prefers to work with published/established authors; works with a small number of new/unpublished authors. Specializes in romance novels—those destined for publishers such as Harlequin, Silhouette, Dell, Loveswept.

Will Handle: Romance novels *only*. Currently handles 100% novels. Will read—at no charge—unsolicited queries and outlines. Reports in 1 month on queries if interested; will not respond if not interested. "If our agency does not respond within 1 month to your request to become a client, you may submit requests elsewhere."

Terms: Agent receives 10% commission on domestic sales and 20% on foreign sales. Charges no office expenses under usual circumstances. 100% of income derived from commission on ms sales.
Recent Sales: *Dare to Dream*, by Cara Colter (Silhouette Romance); *Seductive Deceiver*, by Kathy Orr (Dell Candlelight Ecstasy); and *Separate Lives*, by Caroline Jantz (Harlequin Romance).

FIFI OSCARD ASSOCIATES, 19 W. 44th St., New York NY 10036. (212)764-1100. Contact: Ivy Fischer-Stone, Literary Department. Estab. 1956. Member of SAR and WGA. Represents 108 clients. 5% of clients are new/unpublished writers. "Writer must have published articles or books in major markets or have screen credits if movie scripts, etc." Works with a small number of new/unpublished authors. Specializes in literary novels, commercial novels, mysteries and nonfiction, especially celebrity biographies and autobiographies.
Will Handle: Nonfiction books, novels, movie scripts and stage plays. Currently handles 35% nonfiction books; 35% novels; 10% movie scripts; 10% stage plays; and 10% TV scripts. Will read—at no charge—unsolicited queries and outlines. Reports in 1 week on queries if SASE enclosed. "If our agency does not respond within 1 month to your request to become a client, you may submit requests elsewhere."
Terms: Agent receives 15% commission on domestic sales; 10% on dramatic sales; and 20% on foreign sales. Charges for photocopy expenses.
Recent Sales: *Inner Tube*, by Hob Broun (Knopf); *Kaffir Boy*, by Mark Mathabane (Macmillan); and *Debbie Reynolds Autobiography* (Morrow).

THE OTTE COMPANY, 9 Goden St., Belmont MA 02178. (617)484-8505. Contact: Jane H. Otte. Estab. 1973. Represents 25 clients. 33% of clients are new/unpublished writers. Works with a small number of new/unpublished authors. Specializes in quality adult trade books.
Will Handle: Nonfiction books and novels. Currently handles 40% nonfiction books; and 60% novels. Will read—at no charge—unsolicited queries. Reports in 1 week on queries; 1 month on mss. "If our agency does not respond within 1 month to your request to become a client, you may submit requests elsewhere.
Terms: Agent receives 15% commission on domestic sales; 7½% on dramatic sales; and 10% on foreign sales plus 10% to foreign agent. Charges for photocopy, overseas phone and postage expenses. 100% of income derived from commission on ms sales.
Recent Sales: *Jack and Susan in 1913*, by Michael McDowell (Ballantine); *Eat and Run*, by Arlene E. Langseth (Holt); and *The Fourth Medium*, by Cameron Foote (Dow Jones-Irwin).

JOHN K. PAYNE LITERARY AGENCY, INC., (formerly Lenninger Literary Agency, Inc.), Suite 1101, 175 5th Ave., New York NY 10010. (212)475-6447. President: John K. Payne. Estab. 1923 (as Lenniger Literary Agency). Represents 30 clients. 20% of clients are new/unpublished writers. Prefers writers who have one or two books published, or stories and articles. Specializes in popular women's fiction, historical romance, biography, sagas and Irish background fiction/nonfiction.
Will Handle: Nonfiction books, novels, and juvenile books (young adult fiction, nonfiction). Currently publishes 20% nonfiction books and 80% novels. Charges reading fee to unpublished writers.
Terms: Agent receives 10% commission on domestic sales; 10% on dramatic sales; and 20% on foreign sales. Charges for express mail expenses. 100% of income derived from commission on ms sales (as of April, '86). Evaluation service is new.
Recent Sales: *The Will and the Way*, by Rita Clay Estrada (Harlequin); *All the Golden Promises*, by Diana Haviland (Fawcett); and *The Man Who Rode Midnight*, by Elma Kelton (Doubleday).

RAY PEEKNER LITERARY AGENCY, 3210 S. 7th St., Milwaukee WI 53215. (414)482-0629. Owner: Ray Puechner. Estab. 1973. Represents 60 clients. 5% of clients are new/unpublished writers. "New clients are usually referred by an editor or a client already on the list." Prefers to work with published/established authors. Specializes in private-eye novels (hard-boiled), westerns, quality young adult and middle-grades novels. "Film rights are handled by an associated agency: Lee Allan Agency." Currently handles 10% nonfiction books; 70% novels; and 20% juvenile books. Does not read unsolicited mss. Reports in 2 weeks on queries.
Terms: Agent receives 10% commission on domestic sales; 10% on dramatic sales; and 20% on foreign sales. 100% of income derived from commission on ms sales.
Recent Sales: *Bloody Season*, by Loren D. Estleman (Bantam Books); *Sentries*, by Gary Paulsen (Bradbury Press); and *Murder in the Wings*, by Ed Gorman (St. Martin's Press).

SIDNEY E. PORCELAIN, Box 1229, Milford PA 18337. (717)296-6420. Manager: Sidney Porcelain. Estab. 1952. Represents 20 clients. 50% of clients are new/unpublished writers. Prefers to work with published/established authors; works with a small number of new/unpublished authors. Specializes in fiction (novels, mysteries, and suspense) and nonfiction (celebrity and exposé).
Will Handle: Magazine articles, magazine fiction, nonfiction books, novels and juvenile books. Currently handles 2% magazine articles; 5% magazine fiction; 5% nonfiction books; 50% novels; 5% juvenile books; 2% movie scripts; 1% TV scripts; and 30% "comments for new writers." Will read—at no charge—unsolicited queries, outlines and mss. Reports in 2 weeks on queries; 3 weeks on mss.

Terms: Agent receives 10% commission on domestic sales; 10% on dramatic sales; and 10% on foreign sales. Sometimes offers a consultation service through which writers not represented can get advice on a contract. 10% of income derived from commission on ms sales.
Recent Sales: No information given.

AARON M. PRIEST LITERARY AGENCY, Suite 812, 565 5th Ave., New York NY 10017. (212)818-0344. Contact: Aaron Priest or Molly Freidrich.
Will Handle: Nonfiction books and novels. Currently handles 50% nonfiction books and 50% novels. Will read submissions at no charge, but may charge a criticism fee or service charge for work performed after the initial reading. Reports in 1 month on mss. "If our agency does not respond within 1 month to your request to become a client, you may submit requests elsewhere."
Terms: Agent receives 10-15% commission on domestic sales. Charges for photocopy and foreign postage expenses.
Recent Sales: *A Lesser Life, the Myth of Womens Liberation*, by Sylvia Hemlett; *Joanna's Husband—David's Wife*, by Elizabeth Harley; and *Fort Worth*, by Leonard Sanders.

SUSAN ANN PROTTER LITERARY AGENT, Suite 1408, 110 W. 40th St., New York NY 10018. (212)840-0480. Contact: Susan Protter. Estab. 1971. Member of ILAA. Represents 50 clients. 10% of clients are new/unpublished writers. Writer must have book-length project or manuscript that is ready to be sold. Works with a small number of new/unpublished authors. Specializes in self-help, health, medicine, general nonfiction, novels, science fiction, mysteries and thrillers.
Will Handle: Nonfiction books and novels. Currently handles 5% magazine articles; 60% nonfiction books; 30% novels; and 5% photography books. Will read—at no charge—unsolicited queries and outlines. "Must include SASE." Reports in 2 weeks on queries; 5 weeks on solicited mss. "If our agency does not respond within 2 months to your request to become a client, you may submit requests elsewhere."
Terms: Agent receives 15% commission on domestic sales; 15% on TV, film and dramatic sales; and 25% on foreign sales. Charges for phone, photocopying, messenger, express mail and airmail expenses. 100% of income derived from commission on ms sales.
Recent Sales: *How to Design Your Own Vitamin and Mineral Program*, by Lieberman and Bruning (Doubleday); *Less Stress in 30 Days*, by Roggenbuck and Bechtel (NAL); and *Profit and Sheen*, by James Colbert (Houghton-Mifflin).

HELEN REES LITERARY AGENCY, 308 Commonwealth Ave., Boston MA 02116. (617)262-2401. Contact: Catherine Mahar. Estab. 1982. Member of ILAA. Represents 55 clients. 25% of our clients are new/unpublished writers. Writer must have been published or be an authority on a subject. Prefers to work with published/established authors; works with a small number of new/unpublished authors. Specializes in nonfiction, biographies and business.
Will Handle: Nonfiction books and novels. Currently handles 90% nonfiction books and 10% novels. Will read—at no charge—unsolicited queries and outlines. Reports in 2 weeks on queries; 3 weeks on mss.
Terms: Agent receives 15% commission on domestic sales; and 20% on foreign sales. Occasionally charges a reading fee "for clients who are unpublished and want that service. I don't solicit this." Reading fee will be waived if representing the writer. Sometimes offers a consultation service through which writers not represented can get advice on a contract: no set fee.
Recent Sales: *States of Mind*, by Dr. Ellen Lanyer (Addison Wesley); four books on science by the Boston Museum of Science (Simon & Schuster); and two books by Rick Boyer to be published by Houghton Mifflin.

RHODES LITERARY AGENCY INC., 140 West End Ave., New York NY 10023. (212)580-1300. President: Joan Lewis. Estab. 1971. Member of ILAA.
Will Handle: Nonfiction books, novels (a limited number), and juvenile books. Will read—at no charge—unsolicited queries and outlines. Reports in 2 weeks on queries.
Terms: Agent receives 10% commission on domestic sales; and 20% on foreign sales.
Recent Sales: No information given.

ELEANOR ROSZEL ROGERS, LITERARY AGENT, 1487 Generals Hwy., Crownsville MD 21032. (301)987-8166. Agent: Eleanor Rogers. Estab. 1976. Represents 15 clients. "The only qualification a writer must meet is that I like what he sends me—either fiction or nonfiction, for adults or children . . . I have fairly catholic tastes." Eager to work with new/unpublished writers; "I'm interested in seeing what's available, without preempting myself, and am interested in working with published *and* nonpublished writers." Specializes in mainstream fiction and nonfiction. "I have no interest whatsoever in 'Harlequin-type' romances."
Will Handle: Nonfiction books, novels and juvenile books. Currently handles 50% nonfiction books; 49% novels; and 1% juvenile books. Will read—at no charge—unsolicited queries, outlines and mss. Reports in 2 weeks on queries; 3 weeks on mss. "If our agency does not respond within 2 months to your request to become a client, you may submit requests elsewhere."

Terms: Agent receives 10% commission on domestic sales and 20% on foreign sales. "I don't offer criticism unless I see weakness in a work I hope to represent." Charges for phone, postage, photocopying, and agreed upon travel expenses. 80% of income derived from commission on manuscript sales.
Recent Sales: *Maryland Houses & Gardens* by Weeks and Foster (Stemmer House); *A Promise Is To Keep*, Agle (Zondervan); and *1919*, by Klingaman (St. Martin's).

STEPHANIE ROGERS AND ASSOCIATES, 3855 Lankershim Blvd.—#218, N. Hollywood CA 91604. (818)509-1010. Owner: Stephanie Rogers. Estab. 1981. Represents 17 clients. 20% of clients are new/unpublished writers. Prefers that the writer has been produced (motion pictures or TV), his properties optioned or has references. Prefers to work with published/established authors. Specializes in screenplays—dramas (contemporary), action/adventure, romantic comedies and biographies for motion pictures and TV.
Will Handle: Novels (only wishes to see those that have been published and can translate to the screen) and movie and TV scripts (must be professional in presentation and not over 130 pages). Currently handles 10% novels; 50% movie scripts and 40% TV scripts. Does not read unsolicited mss.
Terms: Agent receives 10% commission on domestic sales; 10% on dramatic sales; and 10% on foreign sales. Charges for phone, photocopying and messenger expenses. 10% of income derived from commission on ms sales.
Recent Sales: No information given.

JACK SCAGNETTI LITERARY AGENCY, Suite 210, 5330 Lankershim Blvd., N. Hollywood CA 91601. (818)762-3871. Owner: Jack Scagnetti. Estab. 1974. Member of WGA. Represents 50 clients. 10% of clients are new/unpublished writers. Prefers to work with published/established authors.
Will Handle: Nonfiction books, novels, movie scripts, and TV scripts. Currently handles 20% nonfiction books; 10% novels; 40% movie scripts; and 30% TV scripts. Will read—at no charge—unsolicited queries and outlines. Reports in 2 weeks on queries; 1 month on mss. "If our agency does not respond within 2 months to your request to become a client, you may submit requests elsewhere."
Terms: Agent receives 10% commission on domestic sales; 10% on dramatic sales; and 15% on foreign sales. Charges for postage on multiple submissions. Offers a consultation service through which writers not represented can get advice on a contract (books only); charges $35/hour.
Recent Sales: *Superstition Gold* (Dorchester Publishing).

JOHN SCHAFFNER ASSOCIATES, INC., Suite 402, 114 E. 28th St., New York NY 10016. (212)689-6888. Contact: Timothy Schaffner or Patrick Delahunt. Estab. 1948. Member of SAR and ILAA. Represents 50-60 clients. 15% of clients are new/unpublished writers. Works with a small number of new/unpublished authors. Specializes in speculative fiction, science fiction, fantasy, celebrity bios, popular self-help, and general nonfiction and fiction.
Will Handle: Nonfiction books and novels. Currently handles 5% magazine fiction; 30% nonfiction books; 60% novels; and 5% juvenile books. Will read—at no charge—unsolicited queries and outlines with SASE or $5 for handling. Reports in 2 weeks on queries; 6 weeks on mss. "If our agency does not respond within 1 month to your request to become a client, you may submit requests elsewhere."
Terms: Agent receives 10% commission on domestic sales; 15% on dramatic sales; and 20% on foreign sales. Charges writers for "extra services," photocopy expenses, overseas courier, etc. 100% of income derived from commission on ms sales.
Recent Sales: *How to Be Funny*, by Steve Allen (McGraw-Hill); *Mary Tyler Moore*, a biography by Jason Bonderoff (St. Martins), and *Psiderweb*, by Lucius Shepard (Bantam).

THE SUSAN SCHULMAN LITERARY AGENCY, INC., 454 W. 44th St., New York NY 10036. (212)713-1633/4/5. President: Susan Schulman. Estab. 1978. Member of SAR and ILAA. 10-15% of clients are new/unpublished writers. Prefers to work with published/established authors; works with a small number of new/unpublished authors.
Will Handle: Nonfiction books, novels, movie scripts, treatments for television movies of the week, and dramatic and comedy series. Currently handles 50% nonfiction books; 20% novels; 10% movie scripts; 5% stage plays; and 10% TV scripts. Will read—at no charge—unsolicited queries and outlines. Reports in 2 weeks on queries; 6 weeks on mss. "If our agency does not respond within 1 month to your request to become a client, you may submit request elsewhere."
Terms: Agent receives 15% commission on domestic sales; 10-20% on dramatic sales; and 7½-10% on foreign sales (plus 7½-10% to co-agent). Charges a reading fee if detailed analysis requested; fee will be waived if repesenting the writer. Less than 1% of income derived from reading fees. Charges for foreign mail, special messenger or delivery services, telex and telegrams. Sometimes offers a consultation service through which writers not represented can get advice on a contract; charges $175/hour. 1% of income derived from fees; 99% of income derived from commission on ms sales. Payment of a criticism fee does not ensure that agency will represent writer.

Recent Sales: *Women Who Love Too Much*, by Robin Norwood (Jeremy Tarcher Inc.); *The Wannabee*, by David Saperstein (Bantam); and *Flies in the Water, Fish in the Air*, by Jim Arnosky (Lothrop Lee and Shepard).

JAMES SELIGMANN AGENCY, Suite 1101, 175 5th Ave., New York NY 10010. (212)477-5186. Proprietor: James F. Seligmann. Estab. 1960. Member of SAR. Represents 50 clients. 25% of clients are new/unpublished writers. Works with a small number of new/unpublished authors. Specializes in fiction ("mainstream novels and settings from 1920's to present") and nonfiction ("various topics, but especially biographies of well-known contemporary and nearly-contemporary people").
Will Handle: Nonfiction books and novels. Currently handles 30% nonfiction books and 70% novels. Will read—at no charge—unsolicited queries and outlines. Reports "usually on receipt" on queries.
Terms: Agent receives 15% commission on domestic sales and dramatic sales; 15% plus foreign agent's commission, if one is involved ("except Britain, where commissions are 10% for us and 10% for our British agent, if one is involved. If no British foreign agent, our regular 15%). Charges for office expenses "as stipulated in SAR code of ethics." 100% of income derived from commission on ms sales.
Recent Sales: *The Process of Sculpture*, by Anthony Padovano (Da Capo Press, Inc.); *The New No-Pill No-Risk Birth Control*, by Nona Aguilar (Rawson Associates); *Hefner*, by Frank Brady (Zebra Books).

SHAPIRO-LICHTMAN TALENT AGENCY, 8827 Beverly Blvd., Los Angeles CA 90048. (213)859-8877. Estab. 1969. Writer must have appropriate academic background and recommendations. Prefers to work with published/established authors.
Will Handle: Movie scripts and TV scripts. Currently handles 90% movie and TV scripts. Does not read unsolicited mss. Reports in 2 weeks on queries.
Terms: Agent receives 10% commission on domestic sales; 10% on dramatic sales; and 20% on foreign sales.
Recent Sales: No information given.

BOBBE SIEGEL, LITERARY AGENCY, 41 W. 83rd St., New York NY 10024. (212)877-4985. Associate: Richard Siegel. Estab. 1975. Represents 60 clients. 40% of clients are new/unpublished writers. "The writer must have a good project, have the credentials to be able to write on the subject and must deliver it in proper fashion. In fiction it all depends on whether I like what I read and if I feel I can sell it." Prefers to work with published/established authors; works with a small number of new/unpublished authors. "Prefer track records, but am eager to work with talent." Specializes in literary fiction, detective and suspense fiction, historicals, how-to, health, woman's subjects, fitness, beauty, feminist sports, biographies and crafts.
Will Handle: Nonfiction books and novels. Currently handles 65% nonfiction books and 35% novels. Does not read unsolicited mss. Reports in 2 weeks on queries; 2 months on mss. "If our agency does not respond within 2 months to your request to become a client, you may submit requests elsewhere."
Terms: Agent receives 15% commission on domestic sales; 10% on dramatic sales; and 10% on foreign sales. If writer wishes critique, will refer to a freelance editor. Charges for photocopying, telephone, overseas mail, express mail expenses. Sometimes offers a consultation service through which writers not represented can get advice on a contract; charges $75/hour. 70% of income derived from commission on ms sales; 30% comes from foreign representation. 100% of income derived from sales of writers' work "not enough derived from critique to mention as a percentage."
Recent Sales: *Survival in Auschwitz*, by Primo Levi (Summit); *Candlelight on Tarnished Brass*, by J.M. Dykes (Berkley); and *Sailing Lake Superior*, by Marlin Bree (Clarkson-Potter).

SINGER COMMUNICATIONS, INC., 3164 Tyler Ave., Anaheim CA 92801. (714)527-5650. Executive Vice President: Natalie Carlton. Estab. 1945. 10% of clients are new/unpublished writers. Prefers to work with published/established authors; works with a small number of new/unpublished authors. Specializes in contemporary romances, nonfiction and biographies.
Will Handle: Magazine articles and syndicated material (submit tear sheets); nonfiction books (query); and romance novels. Currently handles 5% nonfiction books; 20% novels; 75% syndicated material. Will read—at no charge—unsolicited queries and outlines; but may charge a criticism fee or service charge for work performed after the initial reading. Reports in 2 weeks on queries; 6 weeks on mss. "If our agency does not respond within 2 months to your request to become a client, you may submit requests elsewhere."
Terms: Agent receives 15% commission on domestic sales and 20% on foreign sales. Charges a reading fee to unpublished authors which will be credited on sales: 5% of income derived from reading fees. Criticism included in reading fee. "A general overall critique averages three pages. It does not cover spelling or grammar, but the construction of the material. A general marketing critique is also included." Sometimes offers a consultation service through which writers not represented can get advice on a contract. 95% of income derived from sales of writers' work; 5% of income derived from criticism services. "Payment of a criticism fee does not ensure that agency will represent a writer. The author may not be satisfied with our reply, or may need help in making the manuscript marketable."
Recent Sales: No information given.

EVELYN SINGER LITERARY AGENCY, Box 594, White Plains NY 10602. Agent: Evelyn Singer. Estab. 1951. Represents 75 clients. To be represented, writer must have $20,000 in past sales of freelance works. Prefers to work with published/established authors. Specializes in fiction and nonfiction books, adult and juvenile (picture books only if writer is also the artist).
Will Handle: Nonfiction books (bylined by authority or celebrity); novels (no romances, or pseudo-science, violence or sex); and juvenile books. Currently handles 50% nonfiction books; 25% novels; and 25% juvenile books. Does not read unsolicited mss. "If our agency does not respond within 2 months to your request to become a client, you may submit requests elsewhere."
Terms: Agent receives 10% commission on domestic sales; 15% on dramatic sales; and 20% on foreign sales. Charges for phone and expenses authorized by the author. Sometimes offers a consultation service through which writers not represented can get advice on a contract; charges $100/hour. 100% of income derived from commission on ms sales.
Recent Sales: *Chain of Vengeance*, by William Beechcroft (Dodd Mead); *Body*, by Mary Elting (Macmillan); and *Easy as Pie*, by Mike and Marcia Folsom (Clarian).

MICHAEL SNELL LITERARY AGENCY, Bridge and Castle Rd., Truro MA 02666. (617)349-3781. President: Michael Snell. Estab. 1980. Represents 100+ clients. 25% of our clients are new/unpublished writers. Eager to work with new/unpublished writers. Specializes in business books (from professional/reference to popular trade how-to); college textbooks (in all subjects, but especially business, science and psychology); and how-to and self-help (on all topics, from diet and exercise to sex and personal finance).
Will Handle: Nonfiction books and textbooks. Currently handles 80% nonfiction books; 10% novels; and 10% textbooks. Will read—at no charge—unsolicited queries and outlines. Reports in 3 weeks on queries. "If our agency does not respond within 1 month to your request to become a client, you may submit requests elsewhere."
Terms: Agent receives 15% commission on domestic sales; 15% on dramatic sales; and 15% on foreign sales. "When a project interests us, we provide a two to three page critique and sample editing, a brochure on *How to Write a Book Proposal*, and a model book proposal at no charge." Charges collaboration, ghostwriting and developmental editing fee "as an increased percentage of manuscript sale—no cash fee." Charges $100/hour. 100% of income derived from commission on sales.
Recent Sales: *Creating Excellence* (New American Library); *Playing Hardball with Soft Skills* (Bantam); and *Hidden Ladders* (Doubleday).

ELYSE SOMMER, INC., 962 Allen Ln., Box E, Woodmere LI NY 11598. Estab. 1950. Also offers book packaging services. Member of ILAA. Represents 20 clients. 20% of clients are new/unpublished writers. Prefers to work with published/established authors; works with a small number of new/unpublished authors.
Will Handle: Nonfiction books. Currently handles 99% nonfiction books. Will read—at no charge—unsolicited queries and outlines. Reports in 2 weeks on queries.
Terms: Agent receives 15% commission on domestic sales; 20% on dramatic sales; and 20% on foreign sales.
Recent Sales: No information given.

PHILIP G. SPITZER LITERARY AGENCY, 1465 3rd Ave., New York NY 10028. (212)628-0352. Member of SAR. Represents 50 clients. 10% of clients are new/unpublished writers. Prefers to work with published/established authors; works with a small number of new/unpublished authors. Specializes in general nonfiction (politics, current events, sports, biography) and fiction, including mystery/suspense.
Will Handle: Nonfiction books, novels and movie scripts. Currently handles 45% nonfiction books; 45% novels; and 10% movie scripts. Will read—at no charge—unsolicited queries and outlines. Reports in 2 weeks on queries; 5 weeks on mss. "If our agency does not respond within 1 month to your request to become a client, you may submit requests elsewhere."
Terms: Agent receives 10% commission on domestic sales; 10% on dramatic sales; and 20% on foreign sales. Charges for photocopying expenses. 100% of income derived from commission on ms sales.
Recent Sales: *The Dreams of Ada*, by Robert Mayer (Viking/Penguin); *Neon Rain*, by James Lee Burke (Henry Holt & Co.); and *The Walker Double-Cross*, by Thomas Allen and Norman Polmar (Delacorte).

ELLEN LIVELY STEELE AND ASSOCIATES, Drawer 447, Organ NM 88052. (505)382-5449. Estab. 1980. Represents 15 clients. 80% of clients are new/unpublished writers. Writer must be referred. Works with a small number of new/unpublished authors.
Will Handle: Novels, movie scripts, TV scripts and syndicated material. Currently handles 60% novels; 30% movie scripts; and 10% TV scripts. Does not read unsolicited mss. Reports in 6 weeks on mss. "If our agency does not respond within 2 months to your request to become a client, you may submit requests elsewhere."
Terms: Agent receives 10% commission on domestic sales and 5% on foreign sales. Charges for "actual charges incurred in selling work."
Recent Sales: No information given.

GLORIA STERN, Suite 3, 12535 Chandler Blvd., North Hollywood CA 91607. (818)508-6296. Contact: Gloria Stern. Estab. 1984. (Not affiliated with Gloria Stern Agency in New York City.) Represents 18 clients. 85% of clients are new/unpublished writers. Writer must query with project description or be recommended by qualified reader. Prefers to work with published/established authors; works with a number of new/unpublished authors. Specializes in novels and scripts, some theatrical material, dramas or comedy.
Will Handle: Novels, movie scripts and TV scripts (movie of the week). Currently handles 13% novels; 79% movie scripts; and 8% TV scripts. Will read submissions at charge and may charge a criticism fee or service charge for on-going consultation and editing. Reports in 2 weeks on queries; 6 weeks on mss. "If our agency does not respond within 3 months to your request to become a client, you may submit requests elsewhere."
Terms: Agent receives 10-15% commission on domestic sales; 10-15% on dramatic sales; and 18% on foreign sales. Occasionally waives fee if representing the writer. Charges criticism fee; $35/hour (may vary). "Initial report averages four or five pages with point by point recommendation. I will work with the writers I represent to point of acceptance." Charges for postage, photocopy, and long distance phone expenses. Percentage of income derived from commission on ms sales varies with sales. Payment of criticism fee usually ensures that agency will represent writer.

GLORIA STERN AGENCY, 1230 Park Ave., New York NY 10128. (212)289-7698. Agent: Gloria Stern. Estab. 1976. (Not affiliated with agent Gloria Stern of North Hollywood CA.) Member of ILAA. Represents 30 clients. 2% of clients are new/unpublished writers. Prefers to work with published/established authors; works with a small number of new/unpublished authors.
Will Handle: Nonfiction books (no how-to; must have expertise on subject); and novels ("serious mainstream", accepts very little fiction). Currently handles 90% nonfiction books and 10% novels. Will read—at no charge—unsolicited queries and outlines. Reports in 1 week on queries; 6 weeks on manuscripts. "If our agency does not respond within 2 months to your request to become a client, you may submit request elsewhere."
Terms: Agent receives 15% commission on domestic sales; and 20% on foreign sales. Charges for photocopy exenses. Offers a consultation service ("as a courtesy to some authors") through which writers not represented can get advice on a contract; charges $125.
Recent Sales: *How to Learn Math*, by Sheila Tobias (The College Board); Untitled Cookbook, by Lucy Ash (Knopf); and *Power Struggle*, by Rudolph and Ridley (Harper & Row).

STEVENS-RABINOWITZ AGENCY, Suite 271, 2265 Westwood, Los Angeles CA 90064. (213)275-0931. President: Serita Stevens. Estab. 1979. Represents 25 clients. 90% of clients are new/unpublished writers. Works with a small number of new/unpublished authors. Specializes in historical romance, romantic suspense, gothics, women's mainstream, fiction and young adult.
Will Handle: Novels and juvenile books. Will read unsolicited queries and outlines for a fee. Reports in 1 month on queries; 6 weeks on mss. "If our agency does not respond within 3 months to your request to become a client, you may submit requests elsewhere."
Terms: Agent receives 15% commission on domestic sales; 20% on dramatic sales; and 20% on foreign sales. Charges reading fee; $75/3 chapters/synopsis for unpublished wriers; includes critique. 10% of income derived from reading fees. Gives 1 page critique. "Detailed. Both overall suggestions and sometimes line-by-line." Charges for postage, phone and photocopy expenses. 15% of income derived from fees; 25% of income derived from commission on ms sales.
Recent Sales: *Heart is a Traitor*, by Laurie Grant (Leisure); *Winds of Change*, by Judith Hagar (SOS); and *Lighting and Fire*, by Serita Stevens (Leisure).

TEAL & WATT, 2036 Vista del Rosa, Fullerton CA 92631. (714)738-8333. Owner: Patricia Teal. Estab. 1978. Member of ILAA. Represents 40 clients. 20% of clients are new/unpublished writers. "Writer must have honed his skills by virtue of educational background, writing classes, previous publications. Any of these *may* qualify him to submit." Works with a small number of new/unpublished authors. Specializes in category fiction such as mysteries, romances (contemporary and historical), westerns, men's adventure, horror, etc. Also handles nonfiction in all areas, especially self-help and how-to.
Will Handle: Nonfiction books (self-help and how-to) and novels (category only). Currently handles 30% nonfiction books and 70% category novels. Will read—at no charge—unsolicited queries and outlines. No response if not accompanied by SASE. Reports in 3 weeks on queries.
Terms: 15% commission for new, unpublished writers, and 10% for published. Agent receives 10-15% commission on domestic sales; 20% on dramatic sales; and 20% on foreign sales. Sometimes charges fees. Charges for phone, postage and photocopy expenses.
Recent Sales: *Stepping Up*, by Dr. Jon Kramer (Arbor House); *The Young Girl's Guide To Sex*, by Dr. Jay Gale (Holt); and *The Exiled Heart* (NAL).

THOMPSON AND CHRIS LITERARY AGENCY, 3926 Sacramento St., San Francisco CA 94118. (415)386-2443. Partner: Teresa Chris. Estab. 1980. Represents 45 clients. 50% of clients are new/unpublished writers.

Eager to work with new/unpublished writers. Specializes in "virtually all nonfiction, fiction (mainstream, literary, science fiction, contemporary and historical romance, murder mysteries, etc.), juveniles, picture books, and young adults.
Will Handle: Nonfiction books, novels and juvenile books. Currently handles 60% nonfiction books; 30% novels; 9% juvenile books; and 1% movie scripts. Will read—at no charge—unsolicited queries, outlines and mss. Reports in 1 week on queries; 3 weeks on mss. "If our agency does not respond within 1 month to your request to become a client, you may submit requests elsewhere."
Terms: Agent receives 15% commission on domestic sales; 15-20% on dramatic sales; and 15-20% on foreign sales. Charges writers for phone expenses. 100% of income derived from commission on ms sales.
Recent Sales: *Sun Drenched Cuisines*, by M. Spieler (J.P. Tarcher); *Pumping Iron for Teenagers*, by E. Schiffer (Ballantine); and *The American Book of the Dead*, by S. Billias (Warner).

A TOTAL ACTING EXPERIENCE, Suite 300, 6736 Laurel Canyon, North Hollywood CA 91606. (818)765-7244. Agent: Dan A. Bellacicco. Estab. 1984. Member of WGA. Represents 24 clients. 70% of clients are new/unpublished writers. Will accept new and established writers. Specializes in romance, science fiction, mysteries, humor, how-to and self-help books, and audio/visual tapes on all topics.
Will Handle: Nonfiction books, novels, juvenile books, movie scripts, radio scripts, stage plays, TV scripts, syndicated material, lyricists and composers. (No heavy violence, drugs or sex.) Currently handles 2% magazine articles; 2% magazine fiction; 5% nonfiction books; 5% novels; 2% juvenile books; 50% movie scripts; 2% radio scripts; 5% stage plays; 19% TV scripts; and 8% from lyricists/composers. Will read—at no charge—unsolicited queries, outlines and mss. Reports in 2 weeks on queries; 3 months on mss. "If our agency does not respond within 3 months to your request to become a client, you may submit requests elsewhere."
Terms: Agent receives 10% commission on domestic sales; 10% on dramatic sales; and 10% on foreign sales. 100% of income derived from commission on ms sales.
Recent Sales: "Confidential."

SUSAN P. URSTADT, INC., Suite 2A, 125 E. 84 St., New York NY 10028. (212)744-6605. President: Susan P. Urstadt. Estab. 1975. Member of ILAA. Represents 35-40 clients. 5% of clients are new/unpublished writers. "Writer must demonstrate writing ability through sample, qualifications through curriculum vitae and reliability through resume or biography." Works with a small number of new/unpublished authors. Specializes in literary and commercial fiction, decorative arts and antiques, architecture, sailing, tennis, gardening, cookbooks, biography, performing arts, sports (especially horses), current affairs, lifestyle, and current living trends.
Will Handle: Nonfiction books and novels. "We look for serious books of quality with fresh ideas and approaches to current situations and trends." Currently handles 65% nonfiction books; 25% novels; and 10% juvenile books. Will read—at no charge—unsolicited queries, outlines and mss. SASE required. Reports in 1 month on queries; 6 weeks on mss. "If our agency does not respond within 1½ months to your request to become a client, you may submit requests elsewhere."
Terms: Agent receives 10% commission on domestic sales; 15% on dramatic sales; and 20% on foreign sales. Charges for phone, photocopying, foreign postage and express mail expenses. 100% of income derived from commission on ms sales.
Recent Sales: *Bravo Burning*, by Don Tate (Scribners); *How to Make $20,000 Year in Antiques*, by Bruce Johnson (Rawson); and *Fakes and Frauds in American Antiques*, by Myrna Kaye (New York Graphic Society).

RALPH VICINANZA LTD., Suite 1205, 432 Park Ave., New York NY 10016. (212)725-5133. Assistant: Anthony Chase. Estab. 1978. Represents 60 clients. Works with a small number of new/unpublished authors. Specializes in history, fantasy and thrillers.
Will Handle: Nonfiction books and novels. Currently handles 20% nonfiction books and 80% novels. Will read—at no charge—unsolicited queries and outlines. Reports in 2 weeks on queries; 5 weeks on mss. "If our agency does not respond within 6 weeks to your request to become a client, you may submit requests elsewhere."
Terms: Agent receives 10% commission on domestic sales; and 20% on foreign sales. Charges for photocopy expenses and special mailings. 100% of income derived from commission on ms sales.
Recent Sales: *Kingdom of Fear*, by Tim Underwood and Chuck Miller (NAL); *Footfall*, by Larry Niven and Jerry Pournelle (Gollancz); and *The Cat Who Walks Through Walls*, by Robert Heinlein (Hodder and Stoughton).

CARLSON WADE, Room K-4, 49 Bokee Ct., Brooklyn NY 11223. (718)743-6983. President: Carlson Wade. Estab. 1949. Represents 40 clients. 50% of clients are new/unpublished writers. Eager to work with new/unpublished writers. Will consider all types of fiction and nonfiction.
Will Handle: Magazine articles, magazine fiction, nonfiction books, and novels. Currently handles 10% magazine articles; 10% magazine fiction; 40% nonfiction books; and 40% novels. Will read submissions at no

charge, but may charge a criticism fee or service charge for work performed after the initial reading. Reports in 2 weeks. "If our agency does not respond within 1 month to your request to become a client, you may submit requests elsewhere."

Terms: Agent receives 10% commission on domestic sales; 10% on dramatic sales; and 10% on foreign sales. Charges reading fee: $1/1,000 words on short ms; $50/book. 20% of income derived from reading fee. Charges a criticism fee if ms requires extensive work. 10% of income derived from criticism fees. "Short manuscript receives 5 pages of critique, book receives 15 (single space, page by page critique)." 20% of income derived from fees; 80% of income derived from commission on ms sales. Payment of a criticism fee does not ensure that agency will represent a writer. "If a writer revises properly then we take it on. Further help is available at no cost."

Recent Sales: *Eat Away Illness* (Prentice Hall) and *Nutritional Therapy* (Prentice Hall).

MARY JACK WALD ASSOCIATES, INC., Suite 325, 799 Broadway, New York NY 10003. (212)254-7842. President: Mary Jack Wald. Estab. 1985 (previously partner in Wald-Hardy Associates, Inc.). Represents 35 authors plus subsidiary rights for publishers. 15% of authors are new/unpublished writers. Works with a small number of new/unpublished authors.

Will Handle: magazine articles (for authors we represent that have book length material); nonfiction books (no computer books); novels; juvenile books (authors and authors that are illustrators); movie scripts; and TV scripts. Currently handles 20% nonfiction books; 20% novels; 30% juvenile books; and 30% subsidiary rights including magazine, book club, TV and movie. Will read—at no charge—unsolicited queries and outlines. Reports in 1 month on queries; 6 weeks on mss.

Terms: Agent receives 15% commission on domestic sales; 15% on dramatic sales; and 15% on foreign sales (25-30% if represented by our foreign representative as sub-agent). "If extraordinary expenses are requested (large photocopying expenses, foreign phone calls, long distance trips, etc.) by the author in writing, then bill for same is forwarded to the author. Author must request and agree to these in-writing before expenses are incurred." 100% of income derived from commission on ms sales.

Recent Sales: *Youth in Chains*, by Thomas Geve (Academy Chicago Publishers); *Helen the Hungry Bear*, by Marilyn MacGregor (Four Winds); and *The Victim's Song*, by Alice R. Kaminsky (Warner Bros. Television).

JOHN A. WARE LITERARY AGENCY, 392 Central Park West, New York NY 10025. (212)866-4733. Contact: John Ware. Estab. 1978. Represents 60 clients. 50% of clients are new/unpublished writers. Writers must have appropriate credentials for authorship of proposal (nonfiction) or manuscript (fiction); no publishing track record required. "Open to good writing and interesting ideas, by 'new' or 'old' writers." Specializes in biography; investigative journalism; history; health and psychology (academic credentials required); no category fiction (except mysteries); current issues and affairs; sports; oral history; Americana and folklore."

Will Handle: Nonfiction books and novels. Currently handles 75% nonfiction books; and 25% novels. Will read—at no charge—unsolicited queries and outlines; does not read unsolicited mss. Reports in 2 weeks on queries. "If our agency does not respond within 1 month to your request to become a client, you may submit requests elsewhere."

Terms: Agent receives 10% commission on domestic sales; 10% on dramatic sales; and 20% on foreign sales. Charges only for "extraordinary" photocopy and "other such" expenses. 100% of income derived from commission on ms sales.

Recent Sales: *The Age Advantage*, by Frank Satterthwaite Ph.D (Houghton Mifflin); *Johnson in Vietnam*, by William J. Rust (Scribner's); and *Mike Singletary's Chicago Bears Book*, with Armen Keteyian (Contemporary Books).

ANN WAUGH AGENCY, Suite 5, 4731 Laurel Canyon Blvd., N. Hollywood CA 91607. (818)980-0141. Agent: Steve Jacobson. Estab. 1979. Member of SAG. Represents 15 clients. 50% of clients are new/unpublished writers. Prefers to work with published/established authors; works with a small number of new/unpublished authors. Specializes in modern romance, comedy and action adventure screenplays. No pornography or slasher screenplays.

Will Handle: Movie and TV scripts (not episodic). Currently handles 70% movie scripts and 30% TV scripts. Will read—at no charge—unsolicited queries and mss; send letter size SASE before submission to receive release form. Reports in 1 week on queries; 6 weeks on mss. "If our agency does not respond within 3 months to your request to become a client, you may submit requests elsewhere."

Terms: Agent receives 10% commission on domestic sales; 10% on dramatic sales; and 10% on foreign sales. Sometimes offers a consultation service through which writers not represented can get advice on a contract. 100% of income derived from commission on ms sales.

Recent Sales: Screenplays; Movies of the Week sold to Rastar, etc.

WIESER & WIESER, INC., 118 E. 25th St., New York NY 10010. (212)260-0860. President: Olga B. Wieser. Estab. 1976. Represents 60 clients. 10% of clients are new/unpublished writers. Prefers to work with published/established authors; works with a small number of new/unpublished authors. Specializes in literary

and mainstream fiction, serious and popular historical fiction, mass market regencies, general nonfiction, business, finance, aviation, sports, photography, Americana, cookbooks, travel books and popular medicine.
Will Handle: Nonfiction books and novels. Currently handles 70% nonfiction books and 30% novels. Will read—at no charge—unsolicited queries and outlines. Reports in 1 week on queries accompanied by SASE.
Terms: Agent receives 15% commission on domestic sales; 15% on dramatic sales; and 20% on foreign sales. Charges for photocopy, cable and overnight postage expenses. Sometimes offers a consultation service through which writers not represented can get advice on a contract; charges $75/hour. 100% of income derived from commission on ms sales.
Recent Sales: *Roman*, by Douglas C. Jones (Henry Holt & Co.); *Blind Trust*, by John Nance (William Morrow & Co.); and *Investor's Encyclopedia*, by Chet Currier & The Associated Press (Franklin Watts, Inc.).

ALAN WILLIG AND ASSOCIATES, Suite 409, 165 W. 46th St., New York NY 10036. (212)921-4460. Head, Literary Department: Jack Tantleff. Estab. 1985. Represents 25 clients. 25% of clients are new/unpublished writers. Prefers to work with published/established authors. Specializes in plays, screenplays, and television.
Will Handle: Movie scripts, radio scripts, stage plays, TV scripts and syndicated material. Will read—at no charge—unsolicited queries and outlines. Reports in 6 weeks on queries.
Terms: Agent receives 10% commission on domestic sales; 10% on sales; and 10% on foreign sales. Charges for photocopying expenses. 100% of income derived from commission on ms sales.
Recent Sales: No information given.

RUTH WRESCHNER, AUTHOR'S REPRESENTATIVE, 10 W. 74th St., New York NY 10023. (212)877-2605. Agent: Ruth Wreschner. Estab. 1981. Represents 30 clients. 80% of clients are new/unpublished writers. "In fiction, if a client is not published yet, I prefer writers who have written for magazines; in nonfiction, a person well-qualified in his field is acceptable." Prefers to work with published/established authors; works with new/unpublished authors. "I will always pay attention to a writer referred by another client." Specializes in popular medicine, health, how-to books and fiction (no pornography, screenplays or dramatic plays).
Will Handle: Magazine articles and fiction (only for commercial magazines); nonfiction books; novels; textbooks; and juvenile books (young adult). Currently handles 5% magazine articles; 85% nonfiction books; 3% novels; 3% textbooks; and 4% juvenile books. Will read—at no charge—unsolicited queries and outlines. Reports in 2 weeks on queries. "Until I am willing to represent a client and he/she has decided to work with me, clients are free to contact other agents; some writers do multiple agent submissions, but they usually state so in their query."
Terms: Agent receives 15% commission on domestic sales; and 20% on foreign sales. Charges for photocopying expenses. "Once a book is placed, I will retain some money from the second advance to cover airmail postage of books, long distance calls, etc. on foreign sales." 100% of income derived from commission on ms sales. "I may consider charging for reviewing contracts in future. In that case I will charge $25/hour plus long distance calls, if any."
Recent Sales: *Making The Best of It: How to Cope with Being Handicapped* (Epiphany/Ballantine); and *Sibling Rivalry*, (Facts on File).

ANN WRIGHT REPRESENTATIVES, INC., 136 East 57th St., New York NY 10022. (212)832-0110. Head of Literary Department: Dan Wright. Estab. 1963. Member of WGA. Represents 41 clients. 25% of clients are new/unpublished writers. "Writers must be skilled or have superior material for screenplays, stories or novels that can eventually become motion pictures or television properties." Prefers to work with published/established authors; works with a small number of new/unpublished authors. "Eager to work with any author with material that we can effectively market in the motion picture business worldwide." Specializes in themes that make good motion picture projects.
Will Handle: Novels, movie scripts, stage plays and TV scripts. Currently handles 10% novels; 75% movie scripts; and 15% TV scripts. Will read—at no charge—unsolicited queries and outlines; does not read unsolicited mss. Reports in 2 weeks on queries; 6 weeks on mss. "If our agency does not respond within 2 months to your request to become a client, you may submit requests elsewhere."
Terms: Agent receives 10% commission on domestic sales; 10% on dramatic sales; and 10% on foreign sales. Will critique only works of signed clients. Charges for photocopying expenses. 100% of income derived from commission on ms sales.
Recent Sales: No information given.

WRITERS HOUSE, INC., 21 W. 26 St., New York NY 10010. (212)685-2400. Director of New Clients: Susan Marks. Estab. 1974. Member of ILAA. Represents 140 clients. 5% of clients are new/unpublished writers. Works with a small number of new/unpublished authors. Specializes in fiction of all types, adult fiction, juvenile novels, and nonfiction books on business, parenting and popular lifestyles.
Will Handle: Nonfiction books, novels and juvenile books. Currently handles 40% nonfiction books; 30%

novels; and 30% juvenile books. Will read—at no charge—unsolicited queries and outlines. Reports in 2 weeks on queries.
Terms: Agent receives 10% commission on domestic sales; 15% on dramatic sales; and 20% on foreign sales. Charges for overseas postage, Telex, messenger, phone and photocopy expenses. 95% of income derived from commission on ms sales.
Recent Sales: *Lie Down with Lions*, by Ken Follett; *Sweet Valley Summer*, by Francine Pascal; and *The IBM Way*, by F. Buck Rodgers.

WRITER'S PRODUCTIONS, Box 630, Westport CT 06881. (203)227-8199. Agent: David L. Meth. Estab. 1981. 50% of clients are new/unpublished writers. Eager to work with new/unpublished writers. Specializes in "fiction of literary quality, unique, intriguing nonfiction and photo-essay books, works of Asian American writers about the Asian American experience, works about the Orient. No historical romances, science fiction, westerns, how-to, health works, etc."
Will Handle: Nonfiction books, novels and juvenile books. Currently handles 15% nonfiction books; 70% novels; and 15% juvenile books. Will read—at no charge—unsolicited queries, outlines and mss. Reports in 2 weeks on queries; 1 month on mss. "If our agency does not respond within 1 month to your request to become a client, you may submit requests elsewhere."
Terms: Agent receives 15% commission on domestic sales; 15% on dramatic sales; and 20% on foreign sales. 100% of income derived from commission on ms sales.
Recent Sales: *Home Made Love*, by J. California Cooper (St. Martin's Press); *The Bronx in the Innocent Years*, by Hermalyn and Ultan (Harper & Row); and *The Upper Room*, by Mary Monroe (St. Martin's Press).

THE WRITERS WORKSHOP, INC., Suite 1508, 310 Madison Ave., New York NY 10017. (212)687-1122. President: Anita Diamant. Estab. 1917. Member of SAR. Represents 100 clients. Prefers to work with published/established authors; works with a small number of new/unpublished authors. "We handle books for the adult markets."
Will Handle: Nonfiction books and novels. Currently handles 50% nonfiction books and 50% novels. Will read—at no charge—unsolicited queries and outlines; does not read unsolicited mss. Reports in 1 week on queries; 6 weeks on mss. "If our agency does not respond within 3 months to your request to become a client, you may submit requests elsewhere."
Terms: Agent receives 10-15% commission on domestic sales; and 15-20% on foreign sales. Charges for phone and messenger expenses. Sometimes offers a consultation service through which writers not represented can get advice on a contract. 99% of income derived from commission on ms sales.
Recent Sales: No information given.

BARBARA W. YEDLIN, LITERARY AGENT, Pump St., Newcastle ME 04553. (207)563-8335. Agent: Barbara W. Yedlin. Estab. 1981. Represents 3 clients. 100% of clients are new/unpublished writers. "I would like to represent writers with sustained literary talent; they must also display a professional attitude in their dealings with agents and publishers." Works with a small number of new/unpublished authors. Specializes in literary novels and short stories "of high calibre"; juvenile novels (for ages 8-12); mysteries (but no other genre writing); travel; biography and autobiography. No teenage novels, or picture books.
Will Handle: Magazine fiction, nonfiction books, novels and juvenile books. Currently handles 20% magazine fiction; 10% nonfiction books; 60% novels; and 10% juvenile books. Will read—at no charge—unsolicited queries, outlines and mss. Reports in 1 week on queries; 2 weeks on mss. "If our agency does not respond within 1 month to your request to become a client, you may submit requests elsewhere."
Terms: Agent receives 10% commission on domestic sales. Charges for postal expenses and typing of mss ($1/page). 100% of income is derived from commission on ms sales.
Recent Sales: No information given.

SUSAN ZECKENDORF ASSOCIATES, Suite 11B, 171 W. 57th St., New York NY 10019. (212)245-2928. President: Susan Zeckendorf. Estab. 1979. Member of ILAA. Represents 45 clients. 80% of clients are new writers. Eager to work with new/unpublished writers. Specializes in fiction of all kinds—literary, historical, and commercial women's, mainstream thrillers and mysteries, science, music, self-help, and parenting books.
Will Handle: Nonfiction books (by a qualified expert) and novels. Currently handles 40% nonfiction books and 60% novels. Will read—at no charge—unsolicited queries and outlines. Reports in 2 weeks on queries; 1 month on mss. "If our agency does not respond within 1 month to your request to become a client, you may submit requests elsewhere."
Terms: Agent receives 15% commission on domestic sales; 15% on dramatic (movie or TV) sales; and 20% on foreign sales. Charges for phone, photocopy and foreign postage expenses. 100% of income derived from commission on ms sales.
Recent Sales: *Riches*, by Una Mary Parker (NAL); *Jeremiah Martin*, by Robert Fowler (Dodd Mead); and *Monk's Dream, The Biography of Thelonious Monk* (Morrow).

TOM ZELASKY LITERARY AGENCY, 3138 Parkridge Crescent, Chamblee GA 30341. (404)458-0391. Agent: Tom Zelasky. Estab. 1984. Represents 6 clients. 90% of clients are new/unpublished writers. Prefers to work with published/established authors; works with a small number of new/unpublished authors. Specializes in mainstream fiction or nonfiction, categorical romance, historical romance, historical fiction, westerns, action/detective mysteries, suspense, science fiction.

Will Handle: Nonfiction books, novels, juvenile books, movie scripts, stage plays and TV scripts. Currently handles 20% nonfiction books; 60% novels; and 20% juvenile books. Will read—at no charge—unsolicited queries and outlines. "SASE is compulsory, otherwise, manuscript will be in storage and destroyed after 2 years." Reports in 3 weeks on queries; 3 months on mss. "If our agency does not respond within 3 months to your request to become a client, you may submit requests elsewhere."

Terms: Agent receives 10-15% commission on domestic sales; 10-15% on dramatic sales; and 15-25% on foreign sales. Charges a reading fee; will waive fee if representing the writer. "Reading fee is combined with criticism fee; i.e., a critique of one to three pages is mailed to writer when manuscript is rejected. I do my own reading and critique. It is usually a one to three page item, single space, citing craft skills, marketability and overall evaluation." Considering offering a consultation service.

Recent Sales: No information given.

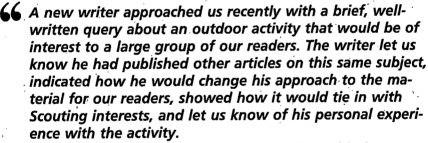

“ *A new writer approached us recently with a brief, well-written query about an outdoor activity that would be of interest to a large group of our readers. The writer let us know he had published other articles on this same subject, indicated how he would change his approach to the material for our readers, showed how it would tie in with Scouting interests, and let us know of his personal experience with the activity.*

When we asked him to amplify his ideas a bit, he gave us a sample lead, a brief, but more specific, synopsis of the article he intended to write and some more comments and questions that showed he had read our magazine carefully. Then he told us about some high quality photos he had and offered some samples. He made the sale.

Another person telephoned. He asked me how much we paid for articles and stories. When I asked him why he wanted to know, he said he was a freelance writer. He had not seen the magazine, but he had heard that we pay pretty well and thought he might do something for us. What was I in the market for?

I told him to write a query when he had read the magazine and had an idea. ”

William B. McMorris, **Boys' Life**

Contests and Awards

If the prospect of having writers judge your work sounds appealing, then you'll want to explore these listings for contests, grants, fellowships and awards. While editors sometimes judge entries in magazine contests, most contest sponsors hire professional writers to select the winning entries.

Contests enable writers to compete with one another where the same rules apply to each writer. Some competitions focus on a form (like the short story) or a subject (like human rights). For other awards, the theme or approach doesn't matter; the sole object for judges is to find _the best_—the best article, play, or first-time novel. When writing a story for a contest or applying for a fellowship, give the judges something that will stand out in their minds. Entries need images and details that are vivid and unforgettable.

Contests offer writers a variety of benefits. Aside from the monetary rewards from many writing prizes, there is satisfaction and recognition. Distinction in a playwriting contest may lead to staged readings of a script; a major book award may increase the sales of a novel.

Most of the contests listed here are annual competitions. To our knowledge, _no contest that charges the writer an entry or reading fee has been included._ Contests for both published and unpublished work are listed. Some competitions do not accept entries or nominations directly from writers; we've included them for their national or literary importance. If you feel that your writing meets the requirements of one of these competitions, tell your publisher/editor about the contest.

Some contests have very detailed instructions and requirements. In contests where writers' names must be concealed in a _titled_ envelope, putting your name on the manuscript will disqualify it from consideration. Another reason for studying contest rules is to find out if you are eligible. Not all contests are for everyone. There are contests for beginning writers and those for professionals; some contests are for college and high school students only.

Contest rules will usually state what is meant by _professional_ or _amateur_ in a particular contest, since there are numerous connotations for these terms. If the rules are not clear, however, send a self-addressed, stamped envelope and ask for clarification. Pose a simple question in the note—"Am I eligible to enter your contest if I have sold one short story to _Family Circle?_"—with _yes_ and _no_ boxes, one of which the contest director could check as a response. Don't send or expect a lengthy letter. Some contests draw thousands of entries.

This year's _Writer's Market_ includes a sampling of opportunities for writers interested in pursuing fellowships and grants for their writing projects. Fellowships may include stipends, writing residencies and/or cash awards to be used for professional advancement. Requirements and eligibilities are unique to each program. Funds for writers to practice their craft _are_ available; the key is knowing where to look. Become familiar with these two resources available in most large public libraries: _Annual Register of Grant Support_ (National Register Publishing Co., Inc., 3004 Glenview Rd., Wilmette IL 60091) and _Foundation Grants to Individuals_ (Foundation Center, 79 5th Ave., New York, NY 10003). The former is a guide to grant and fellowship support programs in government, public and private foundations, companies, professional associations, and special interest groups. A detailed subject index will lead you to writing-related programs. The Foundation Center directory lists approximately 1,000 foundations and application procedures for grants offered to individuals. Included are scholarships, fellowships, residencies, grants to needy writers, and a bibliography of other funding information.

If you don't win the first contests or fellowships you apply for, don't get discouraged. Some entries can be so close in merit that judges must reread each one numerous times. In all contests, judges weigh the *content* (what is said in the entry) and the *form* (how it is present-ed). Analyze the content and form of your writing *before* judges do.

These contests are listed by title, address, contact person and type of competition. If a con-test sounds interesting to you, send a self-addressed, stamped envelope to the contest con-tact person (if listed) for contest information and rules. Don't enter any contest without seeking this information.

AAAS PRIZE FOR BEHAVIORAL SCIENCE RESEARCH, American Association for the Advancement of Science, 1333 H. St. NW, Washington DC 20005. Assistant to the Executive Officer: Marge White. Psycholo-gy/social sciences/sociology.

AAAS-WESTINGHOUSE SCIENCE JOURNALISM AWARDS, American Association for the Advancement of Science, 1333 H St. NW, Washington DC 20005. (202)326-6525. Administrator: Grayce A. Finger. Sci-ence, technology and engineering (newspaper, magazine, radio and TV).

‡HERBERT BAXTER ADAMS PRIZE, Committee Chairman, American Historical Association, 400 A St. SE, Washington DC 20003. European history (first book).

MAUDE ADAMS PLAYWRITING COMPETITION, Stephens College, Columbia MO 65215. (314)876-7193. Artistic Director: Addison Myers. Estab. 1984-85. Full-length plays written by women, dealing with women's issues, with leading roles for women.

‡JANE ADDAMS PEACE ASSOCIATION CHILDREN'S BOOK AWARD, Jane Addams Peace Association and Women's International League for Peace and Freedom, 5477 Cedonia Ave., Baltimore MD 21206. (301)488-6987. Award Director: Annette Chotin Blank. Previously published book that promotes peace, so-cial justice, and the equality of the sexes and races.

‡ADRIATIC AWARD, International Society of Dramatists, Box 1310, Miami FL 33153. (305)756-8313. Award Director: Renee Jordon. Full-length play either unproduced professionally, *or* with one professional production (using Equity actors).

AID TO INDIVIDUAL ARTISTS FELLOWSHIP, Ohio Arts Council, 727 E. Main St., Columbus OH 43205. (614)466-2613. Contact: Susan Dickson. Nonfiction, fiction, criticism, poetry and plays. (Ohio resident, non-student).

ALBERTA NEW NOVELIST COMPETITION, Alberta Culture, Film and Literary Arts, 12th Fl., CN Tower, Edmonton, Alberta T5J 0K5 Canada. (403)427-2554. Open only to unpublished Alberta resident authors.

ALBERTA NON-FICTION AWARD, Alberta Culture, Film and Literary Arts, 12 Fl., CN Tower, Edmonton, Alberta T5J 0K5 Canada. (403)427-2554. Nonfiction book by Alberta author published in calendar year.

‡AMERICAN ASSOCIATION OF UNIVERSITY WOMEN AWARD, NORTH CAROLINA DIVISION, North Carolina Literary and Historical Association, 109 E. Jones St., Raleigh NC 27611. (919)733-7305. Award Director: Becky Myer. Previously published juvenile literature by a North Carolina author.

THE AMERICAN BOOK AWARDS, Before Columbus Foundation, Suite D, 1446 6th St., Berkeley CA 94710. (415)527-1586. Director: Gundars Strads. Previously published books by contemporary American au-thors.

AMERICAN SPEECH-LANGUAGE-HEARING ASSOCIATION (ASHA), NATIONAL MEDIA AWARD, 10801 Rockville Pike, Rockville MD 20852. (301)897-5700. Speech-language pathology and audiology (ra-dio, TV, newspaper, magazine).

AMY WRITING AWARDS, The Amy Foundation, Box 16091, Lansing MI 48901. (517)323-3181. Presi-dent: James Russell. Religious articles previously published in the secular media.

ANNUAL INTERNATIONAL SHAKESPEAREAN SONNET CONTEST, Poets Club of Chicago, Agnes Wa-thall Tatera, 2546 Atlantic St., Franklin Park IL 60131. (312)455-4771. Chairman: Agnes Wathall Tatera. "Classic" Shakespearean sonnets.

THE ANNUAL NATIONAL BIBLE WEEK EDITORIAL CONTEST, The Laymen's National Bible Committee Inc., 815 2nd Ave., New York NY 10017. (212)687-0555. Contact: Executive Director. Unpublished editorial (journalism students registered in a college or university only).

ANNUAL NATIONAL ONE ACT PLAYWRITING CONTEST, Dubuque Fine Arts Players, 1089 S. Grandview, Dubuque IA 52001. Contest Director: Cheri Kraske. Unpublished one-act plays. Submissions accepted between Nov. 1 and Dec. 31.

ANNUAL NJ POETRY CONTEST, NJIT Alumni Association, NJ Institute of Technology, Newark NJ 07102. (201)596-3441. Contest/Award Director: Dr. Herman A. Estrin. Poetry by elementary, junior high, secondary, and college students.

ANNUAL NORTH AMERICAN ESSAY CONTEST, (formerly The North American Essay Contest for Young Men and Women of Goodwill), *The Humanist Magazine*, 7 Harwood Dr., Box 146, Amherst NY 14226. (716)839-5080. Contest/Award Director: Lloyd Morain. Unpublished essay by writers age 29 or younger.

RUBY LLOYD APSEY PLAYWRITING AWARD, University of Alabama, Department of Theater and Dance, University Station, Birmingham AL 35294. (215)934-3236. Contest Director: Dr. Rick J. Plummer. Unpublished full-length plays by new American playwrights.

‡THE ARTISTS FELLOWSHIP PROGRAM, The Artists Foundation, Inc., 110 Broad St., Boston MA 02110. (617)482-8100. Award Director: Lucine Ann Folgueras. Fellowships for playwriting, poetry, fiction and nonfiction by Massachusetts residents. Published or unpublished work.

ASSOCIATION FOR EDUCATION IN JOURNALISM AWARDS, Magazine Division, Loyola College, Baltimore MD 21210. Professor of Journalism: Andrew Ciofalo. Unpublished nonfiction magazine article, research paper on magazine journalism, and magazine design by a college student.

‡THE ATHENAEUM OF PHILADELPHIA LITERARY AWARD, The Athenaeum of Philadelphia, 219 S. 6th St., Philadelphia PA 19106. (215)925-2688. Award Director: Nathaniel Burt. Nominated book by a Philadelphia resident.

BALTIMORE PLAYWRIGHTS' FESTIVAL, Baltimore Playwrights' Festival, 2201 Brookhaven Ct., Fallston MD 21047. (301)597-4709. Producer: Tim Evans. Plays by Baltimore playwrights.

BANTA AWARD, Wisconsin Library Association/Banta Foundation of the George Banta Company, Inc., 1922 University Ave., Madison WI 53705. (608)231-1513. Contact: Faith B. Miracle, Administrator, WLA. Book by a Wisconsin author published during the previous year.

‡GEORGE LOUIS BEER PRIZE, Committee Chairman, American Historical Association, 400 A St. SE, Washington DC 20003. European international history since 1895 (scholarly work).

‡ALBERT J. BEVERIDGE AWARD, Committee Chairman, American Historical Association, 400 A St. SE, Washington DC 20003. American history of U.S., Canada and Latin American (book).

‡THE BEVERLY HILLS THEATRE GUILD-JULIE HARRIS PLAYWRIGHT AWARD COMPETITION, 2815 N. Beachwood Drive, Los Angeles CA 90068. (213)465-2703. Playwright Award Coordinator: Marcella Meharg. Original full-length plays, unpublished, unproduced, and not currently under option.

BITTERROOT MAGAZINE POETRY CONTEST, Contact: Menke Katz, Editor-in-Chief, *Bitterroot*, Spring Glen NY 12483. Sponsors William Kushner Annual Awards and Heershe Dovid-Badonneh Awards for unpublished poetry.

‡IRMA SIMONTON BLACK AWARD, Bank Street College of Education, 610 W. 112th St., New York NY 10025. (212)663-7200, ext. 540. Award Director: William H. Hooks. Previously published children's book.

BLACK WARRIOR REVIEW LITERARY AWARDS, *Black Warrior Review*, The University of Alabama, Box 2936, University AL 35486. (205)348-4518. Contact: Editor. Unpublished poetry and fiction.

‡HOWARD W. BLAKESLEE AWARDS, American Heart Association, 7320 Greenville Ave., Dallas TX 75231. (214)750-5430. Award Director: Howard L. Lewis. Previously published or broadcast reports on cardiovascular diseases.

BOLLINGEN PRIZE IN POETRY OF THE YALE UNIVERSITY LIBRARY, Yale University Library, New Haven CT 06520. (203)436-0236. Secretary, Yale Administrative Committee: David E. Schoonover. American poetry (book).

‡**BOSTON GLOBE-HORN BOOK AWARDS**, Stephanie Loer, Children's Book Editor, *The Boston Globe*, Boston MA 02107. Poetry, nonfiction and illustrated book.

BOWLING WRITING COMPETITION, American Bowling Congress, Public Relations, 5301 S. 76th St., Greendale WI 53129. Director: Dave DeLorenzo, Public Relations Manager. Feature, editorial and news.

ARLEIGH BURKE ESSAY CONTEST, U.S. Naval Institute, Preble Hall, U.S. Naval Academy, Annapolis MD 21402. (301)268-6110. Award Director: James A. Barber, Jr. Essay that advances professional, literary or scientific knowledge of the naval and maritime services.

CANADA COUNCIL CHILDREN'S LITERATURE PRIZE, Canada Council, Box 1047, Ottawa, Ontario K1P 5V8 Canada. (613)237-3400. Contact: Katherine Berg. Awards to encourage published Canadian writers of children's books and illustrators of books for young people.

CANADA COUNCIL TRANSLATION PRIZES, Canada Council, Box 1047, Ottawa, Ontario K1P 5V8 Canada. (613)237-3400. Contact: Katherine Berg. The best translations of Canadian works: one for a translation from English into French and one for a translation from French into English. *The books must be written and translated by Canadians.*

‡**CANADIAN BOOKSELLERS ASSOCIATION AUTHOR OF THE YEAR AWARD**, 49 Laing St., Toronto, Ontario M4L 2N4 Canada. Contact: Board of Directors of the Association. Book by Canadian author.

MELVILLE CANE AWARD, Poetry Society of America, 15 Gramercy Park S., New York NY 10003. (212)254-9268. Contact: Award Director. Published book of poems or prose work on a poet or poetry submitted by the publisher.

RUSSELL L. CECIL ARTHRITIS WRITING AWARDS, Arthritis Foundation, 1314 Spring St. NW, Atlanta GA 30309. (404)872-7100. Contact: Public Relations Department. Medical and features (news stories, articles, and radio/TV scripts).

‡**CHICAGO FOUNDATION FOR LITERATURE AWARD**, Friends of Literature, c/o James Friend, 3415 W. Pratt, Lincolnwood IL 60645. (312)677-9218. Award Director: James Friend. Fiction and nonfiction categories. Book by current or past resident of Chicago.

CHILDREN'S SCIENCE BOOK AWARDS, New York Academy of Sciences, 2 E. 63rd St., New York NY 10021. (212)838-0230. Public Relations Director: Ann E. Collins. General or trade science books for children under 17 years.

‡**THE CHRISTOPHER AWARD**, The Christophers, 12 E. 48th St., New York NY 10017. (212)759-4050. Award Director: Peggy Flanagan. Outstanding books published during the calendar year that "affirm the highest values of the human spirit."

GERTRUDE B. CLAYTOR MEMORIAL AWARD, Poetry Society of America, 15 Gramercy Park S., New York NY 10003. (212)254-9628. Contact: Award Director. Poem in any form on the American scene or character. Members only.

COLLEGIATE POETRY CONTEST, *The Lyric*, 307 Dunton Dr. SW, Blacksburg VA 24060. Editor: Leslie Mellichamp. Unpublished poems (36 lines or less) by fulltime undergraduates in 4-year U.S. or Canadian colleges.

‡**COMMONWEALTH OF PENNSYLVANIA COUNCIL ON THE ARTS LITERATURE FELLOWSHIPS**, 216 Finance Bldg., Harrisburg PA 17120. (717)787-6883. Award Director: Peter Carnahan. Fellowships for Pennsylvania writers of fiction and poetry.

‡**COMMUNITY CHILDREN'S THEATRE OF KANSAS CITY, ANNUAL PLAYWRITING AWARD**, 8021 E. 129th Terrace, Grandview MO 64030. (816)761-5775. Award Director: E. Blanche Sellens. Unpublished play for elementary school audiences.

ALBERT B. COREY PRIZE IN CANADIAN-AMERICAN RELATIONS, Office of the Executive Director, American Historical Association, 400 A St. SE, Washington DC 20003. History, Canadian-U.S. relations or history of both countries (book).

‡**HAROLD C. CRAIN AWARD IN PLAYWRITING**, Department of Theatre Arts, San Jose State University, San Jose CA 95192. (408)277-2763. Contest Coordinator: Dr. Karl Toepfer. Full-length plays.

‡**CREATIVITY FELLOWSHIP**, Northwood Institute Alden B. Dow Creativity Center, Midland MI 48640. (517)832-4403. Award Director: Carol B. Coppage. Ten week residency for individuals in any field.

GUSTAV DAVIDSON MEMORIAL AWARD, Poetry Society of America, 15 Gramercy Park S., New York NY 10003. (212)254-9628. Contact: Award Director. Sonnet or sequence in traditional forms. Members only.

MARY CAROLYN DAVIES MEMORIAL AWARD, Poetry Society of America, 15 Gramercy Park S., New York NY 10003. (212)254-9628. Contact: Award Director. Unpublished poem suitable for setting to music. Members only.

MARIE-LOUISE D'ESTERNAUX POETRY SCHOLARSHIP CONTEST, The Brooklyn Poetry Circle, 61 Pierrepont St., Brooklyn NY 11201. (718)875-8736. Contest Chairman: Gabrielle Lederer. Poetry by students between 16 and 21 years of age.

ALICE FAY DI CASTAGNOLA AWARD, Poetry Society of America, 15 Gramercy Park S., New York NY 10003. (212)254-9628. Contact: Award Director. Manuscript in progress: poetry, prose on poetry or verse-drama. Members only.

EMILY DICKINSON AWARD, Poetry Society of America, 15 Gramercy Park S., New York NY 10003. (212)254-9628. Contact: Award Director. Poem inspired by Emily Dickinson. Members only.

‡**THE DISCOVERY/NATION 1987**, The Poetry Center of the 92nd Street YM-YWHA, 1395 Lexington Ave., New York NY 10128. (212)427-6000, ext. 176. Poetry (unpublished in book form).

‡**DOUBLEDAY/COLUMBIA FELLOWSHIP**, Doubleday and Company, Inc. and Columbia University, Doubleday and Company, Inc., 245 Park Ave., New York NY 10167. (212)953-4995. Contact: Award Director. Novel, published or unpublished.

‡**JOHN H. DUNNING PRIZE IN AMERICAN HISTORY**, Committee Chairman, American Historical Association, 400 A St. SE, Washington DC 20003. Biennial (in even-numbered years) award for U.S. history monograph/book.

‡**CLIFF DWELLERS AWARD**, Friends of Literature, c/o James Friend, 3415 W. Pratt, Lincolnwood IL 60645. (312)677-9218. Contest Director: James Friend. Fiction and nonfiction categories. For a book by a past or current resident of Chicago.

‡**DAVID JAMES ELLIS MEMORIAL AWARD**, Theatre Americana, Box 245, Altadena CA 91001. Contact: Mrs. Leone Jones. Two- or three-act plays with a performance time of about 1½-2 hours.

‡**THE RALPH WALDO EMERSON AWARD**, Phi Beta Kappa (The United Chapters of Phi Beta Kappa), 1811 Q St. NW, Washington DC 20009. (202)265-3808. Contact: Administrator, Phi Beta Kappa Book Awards. Studies of the intellectual and cultural condition of man, submitted by the publisher.

‡**EROTIC FICTION CONTEST**, Yellow Silk, Box 6374, Albany CA 94706. (415)841-6500. Award Director: Lily Pond. Erotic short stories of fine literary quality.

JOHN K. FAIRBANK PRIZE IN EAST ASIAN HISTORY, Committee Chairman, American Historical Association, 400 A St. SE, Washington DC 20003. Book on East Asian history.

NORMA FARBER FIRST BOOK AWARD, Poetry Society of America, 15 Gramercy Park S., New York NY 10003. (212)254-9628. Contact: Award Director. Book of original poetry. Publishers only.

‡**FELLOWSHIPS FOR TRANSLATORS/CREATIVE WRITERS**, National Endowment for the Arts, Literature Program, 1100 Pennsylvania Ave. NW, Washington DC 20506. (202)682-5451. Award Director: Frank Conroy. Published creative writers and translators of exceptional talent.

‡**ROBERT AND HAZEL FERGUSON MEMORIAL AWARD FOR POETRY**, Friends of Literature, c/o James Friend, 3415 W. Pratt, Lincolnwood IL 60645. (312)677-9218. Contest Director: James Friend. Book of poetry by a current or past resident of Chicago.

‡**FICTION WRITERS CONTEST**, Mademoiselle Magazine, 350 Madison Ave., New York NY 10017. Contest Director: Eileen Schnurr. Unpublished fiction by writers aged 18-30. Deadline March 15.

‡**ROBERT L. FISH MEMORIAL AWARD**, Mystery Writers of America, Inc., 150 5th Ave., New York NY 10011. (212)255-7005. Contact: Mary A. Frisque. First mystery or suspense short story published during the previous year.

CONSUELO FORD AWARD, Poetry Society of America, 15 Gramercy Park S., New York NY 10003. (212)254-9628. Contact: Award Director. Unpublished lyric. Members only.

‡**GEORGE FREEDLEY MEMORIAL AWARD**, Theatre Library Association, 111 Amsterdam Ave., New York NY 10023. (212)870-1670. Award Committee Chair: Martha R. Mahard, Harvard Theatre Collection, Harvard College Library, Cambridge MA 02138. Mary Ann Jensen. Published books related to performance in theatre.

‡**DON FREEMAN MEMORIAL GRANT-IN-AID**, Society of Children's Book Writers, Box 296 Mar Vista, Los Angeles CA 90066. To enable picture-book artists to further their understanding, training and/or work. Members only.

‡**THE CHRISTIAN GAUSS AWARD**, Phi Beta Kappa (The United Chapters of Phi Beta Kappa), 1811 Q St. NW, Washington DC 20009. (202)265-3808. Contact; Administrator, Phi Beta Kappa Book Awards. Works of literary criticism or scholarship submitted by publisher.

‡**GOLDEN KITE AWARDS**, Society of Children's Book Writers (SCBW), Box 296 Mar Vista Station, Los Angeles CA 90066. (818)347-2849. Coordinator: Sue Alexander. Calendar year published children's fiction, nonfiction and picture illustration books by a SCBW member.

‡**GOVERNOR GENERAL'S LITERARY AWARDS**, Canada Council, Box 1047, Ottawa, Ontario K1P 5V8 Canada. (613)237-3400. Award Director: Katherine Berg. All Canadian books by Canadian authors published during the previous calendar year are considered. No formal application required.

GUIDEPOSTS MAGAZINE YOUTH WRITING CONTEST, Guideposts Associates, Inc., 747 3rd Ave., New York NY 10017. Senior Editor: MaryAnn O'Roark. Memorable true experience of 1,200 words, preferably spiritual in nature. Unpublished first person story by high school juniors or seniors or students in equivalent grades overseas.

‡**CLARENCE H. HARING PRIZE**, Committee Chairman, American Historical Association, 400 A St. SE, Washington DC 20003. Book on Latin American history by Latin American author. Awarded every 5 years.

NATE HASELTINE MEMORIAL FELLOWSHIPS IN SCIENCE WRITING, Council for the Advancement of Science Writing, Inc., 618 North Elmwood, Oak Park IL 60302. Executive Director: William J. Cromie. Graduate level study in science writing programs.

ERNEST HEMINGWAY FOUNDATION AWARD, P.E.N. American Center, 568 Broadway, New York NY 10012. First-published novel or short story collection by American author.

CECIL HEMLEY MEMORIAL AWARD, Poetry Society of America, 15 Gramercy Park S., New York NY 10003. (212)254-9628. Contact: Award Director. Unpublished lyric poem on a philosophical theme. Members only.

SIDNEY HILLMAN PRIZE AWARD, Sidney Hillman Foundation, Inc., 15 Union Square, New York NY 10003. (212)242-0700. Executive Director: Joyce D. Miller. Social/economic themes related to ideals of Sidney Hillman (daily or periodical journalism, nonfiction, radio and TV).

HONOLULU MAGAZINE FICTION CONTEST, *Honolulu Magazine*, 36 Merchant St., Honolulu HI 96813. Contact: Pat Pitzer. Stories under 25 typewritten pages with a Hawaiian theme, setting and/or characters.

THE ROY W. HOWARD AWARDS, The Scripps Howard Foundation, 1100 Central Trust Tower, Cincinnati OH 45202. (513)977-3036. Public service reporting.

‡**HUMOROUS POETRY AWARD**, *POET*, Box 44021, Shreveport LA 71134. Contest/Award Director: Peggy Cooper. Estab. 1985. Poetry published during the preceding year in the *Poet*.

ILLINOIS STATE UNIVERSITY FINE ARTS PLAYWRITING AWARD, Illinois State University, Theatre Department, Normal IL 61761. (309)438-8783. Directors: Dr. John W. Kirk and Daniel Wilhelm. Previously unproduced full-length plays.

‡**INDIVIDUAL ARTIST FELLOWSHIP**, Maryland State Arts Council, 15 W. Mulberry St., Baltimore MD 21201. (301)685-6740. Award Director: Oletha De Vane. Grants to Maryland residents for completed works or works in progress.

‡**INSPIRATIONAL POETRY AWARD**, *POET*, Box 44021, Shreveport LA 71134. Contest/Award Director: Peggy Cooper. Estab. 1985. Poetry published during the preceding year in the *Poet*.

INTERNATIONAL IMITATION HEMINGWAY COMPETITION, Harry's Bar & American Grill, 2020 Avenue of the Stars, Los Angeles CA 90067. (213)277-2333. Contest/Award Director: Mark S. Grody, Grody/Tellem Communications, Inc., Suite 840, 11150 W. Olympic Blvd., Los Angeles CA 90064. (213)479-3363. Unpublished one-page parody of Hemingway.

‡**INTERNATIONAL READING ASSOCIATION PRINT MEDIA AWARD**, International Reading Association, Box 8139, 800 Barksdale Rd., Newark DE 19714. (302)731-1600. Contact: Arlene Militello, 135 Oaktree Dr., North Kingston RI 02852. Reports by professional journalists from newspapers, magazines and wire services on reading programs.

IOWA ARTS COUNCIL LITERARY AWARDS, Iowa Arts Council, State Capitol Complex, Des Moines IA 50319. (515)281-4451. Director: Iowa Arts Council. Unpublished fiction and poetry by Iowa writers (legal residents).

IOWA SCHOOL OF LETTERS AWARD FOR SHORT FICTION, Iowa School of Letters, Department of English/EPB, University of Iowa, Iowa City IA 52242. (319)353-3181. Award Director: John Leggett. Unpublished collection of short stories.

JOSEPH HENRY JACKSON/JAMES D. PHELAN LITERARY AWARDS, The San Francisco Foundation, 500 Washington St., 8th Floor, San Francisco CA 94111. (415)392-0600. Assistant Coordinator: Adrienne Krug. Jackson: unpublished, partly completed book-length fiction, nonfiction, short story or poetry by author with 3-year consecutive residency in N. California or Nevada prior to submissions. Age 20-35. Phelan: unpublished, incomplete work of fiction, nonfiction, short story, poetry or drama by California-born author. Age 20-35.

JACKSONVILLE UNIVERSITY PLAYWRITING CONTEST, College of Fine Arts, Jacksonville University, Jacksonville FL 32211. (904)744-3950. Director: Davis Sikes. Unproduced one-act and full-length plays.

‡**JAMESTOWN PRIZE**, Institute of Early American History and Culture, Box 220, Williamsburg VA 23187. (804)229-5118. Award Director: Philip D. Morgan. Book-length scholarly ms on early American history or culture.

ANSON JONES AWARD, c/o Texas Medical Association, 1801 N. Lamar Blvd., Austin TX 78701. (512)477-6704. Health (Texas newspaper, magazine—trade, commercial, association, or company—radio and TV).

MARGO JONES PLAYWRITING COMPETITION, Texas Woman's University, Department of Music & Drama, Box 23865, Denton TX 76204. (817)383-3586. Contest Chairman: Richard Rodean. Biennial. Unproduced plays for or about women.

‡**JUNIOR AND SENIOR AWARDS**, International Society of Dramatists, Box 1310, Miami FL 33153. Award Director: Renee Jordan. Previously unpublished scripts (any media or length) written by high school students (Junior Award) and college students (Senior Awards).

THE JANET HEIDINGER KAFKA PRIZE, English Department/Writers Workshop, 127 Lattimore Hall, University of Rochester, Rochester NY 14627. (716)275-2347. Chairman: Anne Ludlow. Administrative Secretary: Patty Miller. Book-length fiction (novel, short story or experimental writing) by U.S. woman citizen submitted by publishers.

MARC A. KLEIN PLAYWRITING AWARD, Department of Theatre, Case Western Reserve University, 2070 Adelbert Rd., Cleveland OH 44106. (216)368-2858. Unpublished, professionally unproduced full-length plays, evening of related short plays, or full-length musical by students in American college or university.

KNOWLEDGE INDUSTRY PUBLICATIONS, INC. AWARD FOR LIBRARY LITERATURE, donated by Knowledge Industry Publications, Inc., Administered by American Library Association, 50 E. Huron, Chicago IL 60611. (312)944-6780. Outstanding contribution to library literature.

RUTH LAKE MEMORIAL AWARD, Poetry Society of America, 15 Gramercy Park S., New York NY 10003. (212)254-9628. Contact: Award Director. Unpublished poem of retrospection.

LAMONT POETRY SELECTION, Academy of American Poets, 177 E. 87th St., New York NY 10128. (212)427-5665. Contest/Award Director: Nancy Schoenberger. Second book of unpublished poems by an American citizen, submitted by publisher in manuscript form.

‡THE HAROLD MORTON LANDON TRANSLATION PRIZE, The Academy of American Poets, 177 E. 87th St., New York NY 10128. (212)427-5665. Award Director: Nancy Schoenberger. Previously published translation of poetry from any language into English by an American translator.

ELIAS LIEBERMAN STUDENT POETRY AWARD, Poetry Society of America, 15 Gramercy Park S., New York NY 10003. (212)254-9628. Contact: Award Director. Unpublished poem by student (grades 9-12).

‡LINCOLN MEMORIAL ONE-ACT PLAYWRITING CONTEST, International Society of Dramatists, Box 1310, Miami FL 33153. Award Director: Renee Jordan. Unpublished one-act plays.

JOSEPH W. LIPPINCOTT AWARD, Donated by Joseph W. Lippincott, Jr., Administered by American Library Association, 50 E. Huron, Chicago IL 60611. (312)944-6780. For distinguished service to the profession of librarianship (notable published professional writing).

‡LOCKERT LIBRARY OF POETRY IN TRANSLATION, Princeton University Press, 41 William St., Princeton NJ 08540. (609)452-4900. Poetry Editor: Robert E. Brown. Book-length poetry translation of a single poet.

LOFT-MCKNIGHT WRITERS AWARD, The Loft, 2301 E. Franklin Ave., Minneapolis MN 55406. (612)341-0431. Director: Susan Broadhead. Eight awards for Minnesota writers of poetry and creative prose.

LOFT-MENTOR SERIES, The Loft, 2301 Franklin Ave., Minneapolis MN 55406. (612)341-0431. Director: Susan Broadhead. Poetry and fiction by Minnesota writers.

HOWARD R. MARRARO PRIZE IN ITALIAN HISTORY, Office of the Executive Director, American Historical Association, 400 A St. SE, Washington DC 20003. Work on any epoch of Italian history, Italian cultural history or Italian-American relations.

JOHN MASEFIELD MEMORIAL AWARD, Poetry Society of America, 15 Gramercy Park S., New York NY 10003. (212)254-9628. Contact: Award Director. Unpublished narrative poem in English.

MASSACHUSETTS ARTISTS FELLOWSHIP, The Artists Foundation, Inc., 110 Broad St., Boston MA 02110. (617)482-8100. Funded by the Massachusetts Council on the Arts and Humanities. Director: Lucine A. Folgueras. Poetry, fiction, nonfiction and playwriting by Massachusetts residents.

‡VIRGINIA MATSON MEMORIAL AWARD, Friends of Literature, % James Friend, 3415 W. Pratt, Lincolnwood IL 60645. (312)677-9218. Contest Director: James Friend. Fiction and nonfiction categories. For a book by a past or current resident of Chicago.

‡THE MAYFLOWER SOCIETY CUP COMPETITION, North Carolina Literary and Historical Association, 109 E. Jones St., Raleigh NC 27611. (919)733-7305. Award Director: Becky Myer. Previously published nonfiction by a North Carolina resident.

LUCILLE MEDWICK MEMORIAL AWARD, Poetry Society of America, 15 Gramercy Park S., New York NY 10003. (212)254-9628. Contact: Award Director. Original poem on a humanitarian theme. Members only.

THE EDWARD J. MEEMAN AWARDS, The Scripps Howard Foundation, 1100 Central Trust Tower, Cincinnati, OH 45202. (513)977-3036. Conservation Reporting.

MELCHER BOOK AWARD, Unitarian Universalist Association, 25 Beacon St., Boston MA 02108. Staff Liaison: Rev. Mark W. Harris. Previously published book on religious liberalism.

MENCKEN AWARDS, Free Press Association, Box 15548, Columbus OH 43215. (415)834-6880. FPA Executive Director: Michael Grossberg. Defense of human rights and individual liberties (news story or investigative report, feature story, editorial or op-ed column, editorial cartoon; and book).

KENNETH W. MILDENBERGER PRIZE, Modern Language Association, 10 Aster Place, New York NY 10003. Contact: Theresa Kirby, Research Programs. Outstanding research publication in the field of teaching foreign languages and literatures.

FRANK LUTHER MOTT-KAPPA TAU ALPHA RESEARCH AWARD IN JOURNALISM, 107 Sondra Ave., Columbia MO 65202. (314)443-3521. Executive Director, Central Office: William H. Taft. Research in journalism (book).

MS PUBLIC EDUCATION AWARDS CONTEST, National Multiple Sclerosis Society, 205 E. 42nd St., New York NY 10017. Contact: Public Relations Director. Reporting on facts and consequences of multiple sclerosis (newspaper, magazine, radio or TV).

‡NATIONAL AWARDS PROGRAM, Freedoms Foundation at Valley Forge, Box 706, Valley Forge PA 19087. (215)933-8825. Award Director: E. Katherine Wood. Nominated, previously published submissions focusing on the United States' social, political and economic system and suggesting solutions to basic problems, contribute to responsible citizenship, and strengthen an understanding of the fundamentals of a free society.

NATIONAL ONE-ACT PLAY CONTEST, Actors Theatre of Louisville, 316 W. Main St., Louisville KY 40202. (502)584-1265. Director: Michael Bigelow Dixon. Previously unproduced (professionally) one-act plays. "Entries must *not* have had an Equity or Equity-waiver production."

NATIONAL PLAY AWARD, Box 71011, Los Angeles CA 90071. (213)629-3762. Assistant Literary Manager: Emily Schiller. Unpublished, nonprofessionally produced plays.

NATIONAL SOCIETY OF PROFESSIONAL ENGINEERS JOURNALISM AWARDS, 1420 King St., Alexandria VA 22314. (703)684-2852. PR Director: Leslie Collins. Engineering and technology in contemporary life (articles in general interest magazines and newspapers).

‡NEW JERSEY STATE COUNCIL ON THE ARTS LITERARY ARTS FELLOWSHIPS, 109 West State St., CN306, Trenton NJ 08625. (609)292-6130. Contact: Literary Arts Coordinator. Fellowships for prose, poetry and playwriting by New Jersey residents.

NEW PLAY FESTIVAL, Colony/Studio Theatre, 1944 Riverside Dr., Los Angeles CA 90039. Literary Manager: Todd Nielsen. Unpublished, unproduced play.

NEW WRITERS AWARDS, Great Lakes Colleges Association, c/o English Department, Albion College, Albion MI 49224. (517)629-5511. Director: James W. Cook. Published poetry or fiction (first book).

NEW YORK STATE HISTORICAL ASSOCIATION MANUSCRIPT AWARD, Box 800, Cooperstown NY 13326. (607)547-2508. Director of Publications: Dr. Wendell Tripp. Unpublished book-length monograph on New York State history.

‡JOHN NEWBERY MEDAL, Association for Library Service to Children/American Library Association, 50 E. Huron St., Chicago IL 60611. (312)944-6780. Award Director: Ann Carlson Weeks. Previously published children's literature.

NEWCOMEN AWARDS IN BUSINESS HISTORY, c/o *Business History Review*, Harvard Business University, Gallatin D-126, Soldiers Field, Boston MA 02163. (617)495-6154. Editor: Richard S. Tedlow. Business history article.

‡OHIOANA BOOK AWARD, Ohioana Library Association, Room 1105, Ohio Departments Bldg., 65 S. Front St., Columbus OH 43215. (614)466-3831. Award Director: James P. Barry. Books published within the past 12 months by Ohioans or about Ohio and Ohioans.

OPEN CIRCLE THEATRE PLAYWRIGHTS AWARD, Goucher College, Towson MD 21204. Director: Barry Knower. Unpublished, unproduced plays. (50% of major roles must be for women.)

OSCARS IN AGRICULTURE, DEKALB Corp., 3100 Sycamore Rd., DeKalb IL 60115. (815)758-3461. Manager of Editorial Services, Corporate Public Relations: Deb DeGraff. Agricultural news reporting (newspaper, magazine, TV and radio).

THE ALICIA PATTERSON FOUNDATION FELLOWSHIP PROGRAM FOR JOURNALISTS, The Alicia Patterson Foundation, Suite 320, 655 15th St. NW, Washington DC 20005. (202)639-4203. Contest/Award Director: Helen McMaster Coulson. One-year grants awarded to working journalists with five year's experience to pursue independent projects of significant interest.

PEN MEDAL FOR TRANSLATION, PEN American Center, 568 Broadway, New York NY 10012. (212)334-1660. Translators nominated by the PEN Translation Committee.

PEN/NELSON ALGREN FICTION AWARD, PEN American Center, 568 Broadway, New York NY 10012. (212)334-1660. "For the best uncompleted novel or short story collection by an American writer who needs financial assistance to finish the work."

PEN PUBLISHER CITATION, PEN American Center, 568 Broadway, New York NY 10012. (212)334-1660. "Awarded every two years to a publisher who has throughout his career, given distinctive and continuous service." Nominated by the PEN Executive Board.

PEN/ROGER KLEIN AWARD FOR EDITING, PEN American Center, 568 Broadway, New York NY 10012. (212)334-1660. "Given every two years to an editor of trade books who has an outstanding record of recognizing talents." Nominated by authors, agents, publishers and editors.

PEN SYNDICATED FICTION PROJECT, PEN American Center, Box 6303, Washington DC 20008. (301)229-0933. Award Director: Richard Harteis. Unpublished short fiction by recipient of a fellowship, grant, national literary award or a member of PEN American Center.

PEN TRANSLATION PRIZES, PEN American Center, 568 Broadway, New York NY 10012. Contact: Chairman, Translation Committee. Two awards to book-length translations of poetry and of literary prose into English. (No technical, scientific or reference.)

PEN WRITING AWARDS FOR PRISONERS, PEN American Center, 568 Broadway, New York NY 10012. (212)334-1660. "Awarded to the authors of the best poetry, plays, short fiction and nonfiction received from prison writers in the U.S."

‡**PERKINS PLAYWRITING CONTEST,** International Society of Dramatists, Box 1310, Miami FL 33153. (305)756-8313. Award Director: Renee Jordan. Unproduced full-length plays.

‡**EDGAR ALLAN POE AWARDS,** Mystery Writers of America, 150 5th Ave., New York NY 10011. (212)255-7005. Contact: Mary A. Frisque. Previously published books, short stories and scripts in the mystery, crime and suspense fields.

‡**THE POET IN ALL OF US AWARD,** *Poet,* Box 44021, Shreveport LA 71134. Contest/Award Director: Peggy Cooper. Estab. 1985. Poetry published during the preceding year in the *Poet.*

‡**POETRY EDITOR'S AWARD,** *Poet,* Box 44021, Shreveport LA 71134. Contest/Award Director: Peggy Cooper. Estab. 1985. Poetry published during the preceeding year in the New American Poets section of *Poet.*

‡**POETRY MAGAZINE POETRY AWARDS,** Box 4348, 601 S. Morgan St., Chicago IL 60680. (312)996-7803. Contest/Award Director: Joseph Parisi, Editor. All poems published in *POETRY* are automatically considered for prizes. Poems should be submitted to the magazine.

RENATO POGGIOLI TRANSLATION AWARD, PEN American Center, 568 Broadway, New York NY 10012. (212)334-1660. "Given to encourage a beginning and promising translator who is working on a first book length translation from Italian into English."

‡**PRINCETON SERIES OF CONTEMPORARY POETS,** Princeton University Press, 41 William St., Princeton NJ 08540. (609)452-4900. Poetry Editor: Robert E. Brown. Book-length poetry mss.

‡**PRIX ALVINE-BELISLE,** ASTED, 7243, rue Saint-Denis, Montreal, Quebec H2R 2E3 Canada. Contact: Jean-Pierre Leduc. French-Canadian literature for children submitted by the publisher.

PULITZER PRIZES, Secretary, The Pulitzer Prize Board, 702 Journalism, Columbia University, New York NY 10027. Awards for journalism, letters, drama and music in U.S. newspapers, and in literature, drama and music by Americans.

PULP PRESS INTERNATIONAL 3-DAY NOVEL COMPETITION, Pulp Press (Vancouver) Publishers, Suite 202, 986 Homer St., Vancouver, British Columbia V6R 2P1 Canada. (604)687-4233. Director: F.H. Eger. Novel written in three days.

ERNIE PYLE AWARD, Scripps Howard Foundation, 1100 Central Trust Tower, Cincinnati OH 45202. (513)977-3036. Human-interest reporting.

‡SIR WALTER RALEIGH AWARD, North Carolina Literary and Historical Association, 109 E. Jones St., Raleigh NC 27611. (919)733-7305. Award Director: Becky Myer. Previously published fiction by a North Carolina writer.

REDBOOK'S NEW SHORT STORY CONTEST, Redbook Magazine, 224 W. 57th St., New York NY 10019. Fiction Editor: Kathy Sagan. Short stories by writers who have not previously published fiction in a major publication.

‡RHODE ISLAND STATE COUNCIL ON THE ARTS FELLOWSHIP, 312 Wickenden St., Providence RI 02903. (401)277-3880. Award Director: Robert Demers. Poetry, fiction or play be a resident of Rhode Island.

‡RHYME TIME CREATIVE WRITING COMPETITION, Rhyme Time/Story Time, Box 2377, Coeur d'Alene ID 83814. (208)667-7511. Award Director: Linda Hutton. Rhymed poetry, fiction and essays.

‡ROANOKE-CHOWAN AWARD FOR POETRY, North Carolina Literary and Historical Association, 109 E. Jones St., Raleigh NC 27611. (919)733-7305. Award Director: Becky Myer. Previously published poetry by a resident of North Carolina.

FOREST A. ROBERTS PLAYWRITING AWARD, In cooperation with Shiras Institute, Forest A. Roberts Theatre, Northern Michigan University, Marquette MI 49855. (906)227-2553. Award Director: Dr. James A. Panowski. Unpublished, unproduced plays.

MARY ROBERTS RINEHART FUND, English Department, George Mason University, 4400 University Dr., Fairfax VA 22030. (703)323-2220. Contact: Director of the Writing Program. Alternating awards for fiction, nonfiction, drama and poetry by unpublished writers nominated by an agent, editor or established writer.

THE CARL SANDBURG LITERARY ARTS AWARDS, The Friends of the Chicago Public Library, 78 E. Washington St., Chicago IL 60611. (812)269-2922. Chicago writers of fiction, nonfiction, poetry, and children's literature.

THE CHARLES M. SCHULZ AWARD, The Scripps-Howard Foundation, Box 5380, Cincinnati OH 45201. (513)977-3035. Cartoonists.

ROBERT LIVINGSTON SCHUYLER PRIZE, Committee Chairman, American Historical Association, 400 A St. SE, Washington DC 20003. Modern British, British Imperial, and British Commonwealth history by American citizen.

‡THE SCIENCE AWARD, Phi Beta Kappa (The United Chapters of Phi Beta Kappa), 1811 Q St. NW, Washington DC 20009. (202)265-3808. Contact: Aministrator, Phi Beta Kappa Book Awards. Interpretations of the physical or biological sciences or mathematics submitted by the publisher.

THE EDWARD WILLIS SCRIPPS AWARD, The Scripps Howard Foundation, Box 5380, Cincinnati OH 45201. (513)977-3036. Service to the First Amendment.

‡SEAL BOOKS FIRST NOVEL AWARD, Seal Books, 60 St. Clair Ave. E, #601, Toronto, Ontario M4T 1N5 Canada. (416)922-4970. Award Director: Janet Turnbull. Novel by an unpublished Canadian author.

‡SENIOR FELLOWSHIPS FOR LITERATURE, National Endowment for the Arts Literature Program, 1100 Pennsylvania Ave. NW, Washington DC 20506. (202)682-5451. Award Director: Frank Conroy. Not open to application. Nominated work of high critical acclaim.

‡SFWA NEBULA AWARDS, Science Fiction Writers of America, Inc., Box H, Wharton NJ 07885. Science fiction or fantasy in the categories of novel, novella, novelette and short story recommended by members.

MINA P. SHAUGHNESSY PRIZE, Modern Language Association, 10 Astor Place, New York NY 10003. Contact: Theresa Kirby, Administrative Assistant. Outstanding research publication in the field of teaching English language and literature.

SHELLEY MEMORIAL AWARD, Poetry Society of America, 15 Gramercy Park S., New York NY 10003. (212)254-9628. Contact: Award Director. By nomination only to a living American poet.

‡SIERRA REPERTORY THEATRE, Box 3030, Sonora CA 95370. (209)532-3120. Producer: Dennis C. Jones. Full-length, one-act plays.

BRYANT SPANN MEMORIAL PRIZE, % History Dept., Indiana State University, Terre Haute IN 47809. Social criticism in the tradition of Eugene V. Debs.

SPUR AWARDS (WESTERN WRITERS OF AMERICA, INC.), WWA, % Fairgrounds, Sheridan WY 82801. (307)742-3010. Director: Barbara Ketcham. Ten categories of western: novel, historical novel, nonfiction book, juvenile nonfiction, juvenile fiction, nonfiction article, fiction short story, best TV script, movie screenplay, cover art. Also, Medicine Pipe Bearer's Award for best first novel.

STANLEY DRAMA AWARD, Wagner College, Staten Island NY 10301. (212)390-3256. Unpublished and nonprofessionally produced full-length plays or related one-acts by American playwrights.

THE WALKER STONE AWARDS, The Scripps Howard Foundation, 1100 Central Trust Tower, Cincinnati OH 45202. (513)977-3036. Editorial writing.

MARVIN TAYLOR PLAYWRITING AWARD, Sierra Repertory Theatre, Box 3030, Sonora CA 95370. (209)532-3120. Producing Director: Dennis C. Jones. Full-length plays.

SYDNEY TAYLOR MANUSCRIPT CONTEST OF AJL, (formerly The Sidney Taylor Children's Book Awards), 15 Goldsmith St., Providence RI 02906. Contact: Lillian Schwartz. Unpublished Jewish book for ages 8-12.

THE TEN BEST "CENSORED" STORIES OF 1986, Project Censored—Sonoma State University, Rohnert Park CA 94928. (707)664-2149. Award Director: Carl Jensen, Ph.D. Current published, nonfiction stories of national social significance that have been overlooked or under-reported by the news media.

‡TEXAS BLUEBONNET AWARD, Texas Association of School Libraries and Children's Round Table, Suite 603, 3355 Bee Cave Rd., Austin TX 78746. (512)328-1518. Contact: Mrs. Ada Howard. Published books for children recommended by librarians, teachers and students.

‡THE THEATRE LIBRARY ASSOCIATION AWARD, 111 Amsterdam Ave., New York NY 10023. Awards Committee Chair: Martha R. Mahard, Harvard Theatre Collection, Harvard College Library, Cambridge MA 02138. Book published in the United States in the field of recorded performance, including motion pictures and television.

‡TOWSON STATE UNIVERSITY PRIZE FOR LITERATURE, College of Liberal Arts, Towson State University, Towson MD 21204. (301)321-2128. Award Director: Dean Annette Chappell. Book or book-length manuscript that has been accepted for publication, written by a Maryland author of no more than 40 years of age.

THE TRANSLATION CENTER AWARDS—NATIONAL & INTERNATIONAL, The Translation Center, 307A Mathematics Bldg., Columbia University, New York NY 10027. (212)280-2305. Executive Director: Diane G.H. Cook. Outstanding translations of a book-length literary work.

‡HARRY S. TRUMAN BOOK PRIZE, Harry S. Truman Library Institute, Independence MO 64050. Secretary of the Institute: Dr. Benedict K. Zobrist. Previously published book written within a two-year period dealing primarily with the history of the United States between April 12, 1945 and January 20, 1953, or with the public career of Harry S. Truman.

UFO RESEARCH AWARD, Fund for UFO Research, Box 277, Mt. Rainier MD 20712. (301)779-8683. Contact: Executive Committee, Fund for UFO Research. Unscheduled cash awards for published works on UFO phenomena research or public education.

‡VERBATIM ESSAY COMPETITION, Verbatim, The Language Quarterly, Box 668, Essex CT 06426. (203)767-8248. Award Director: Laurence Urdang. Unpublished articles on topic pertaining to language.

CELIA B. WAGNER AWARD, Poetry Society of America, 15 Gramercy Park St. S., New York NY 10003. (212)254-9628. Contact: Award Director. Unpublished poem.

EDWARD LEWIS WALLANT BOOK AWARD, Mrs. Irving Waltman, 3 Brighton Rd., West Hartford CT 06117. Published fiction with significance for the American Jew (novel or short stories).

WICHITA STATE UNIVERSITY PLAYWRITING CONTEST, Wichita State University Theatre, WSU, Box 31, Wichita KS 67208. (316)689-3185. Contest Director: Bela Kiralyfalvi. Two or three short, unpublished, unproduced plays or full-length plays by graduate or undergraduate U.S. college students.

‡**LAURA INGALLS WILDER AWARD**, Association for Library Service to Children/American Library Association, 50 E. Huron St., Chicago IL 60611. (312)944-6780. Contact: Award Director. Awarded every three years to a previously published nominated children's book.

BELL I. WILEY PRIZE, National Historical Society, 2245 Kohn Rd., Box 8200, Harrisburg PA 17105. (717)657-9555, ext. 3301. Civil War and Reconstruction nonfiction (book).

WILLIAM CARLOS WILLIAMS AWARD, Poetry Society of America, 15 Gramercy Park S., New York NY 10003. (212)254-9628. Contact: Award Director. Small press, nonprofit, or university press book of poetry submitted by publisher.

H.W. WILSON LIBRARY PERIODICAL AWARD, donated by H.W. Wilson Company, administered by the American Library Association, 50 E. Huron, Chicago IL 60611. (312)944-6780. Periodical published by a local, state, or regional library, library group, or association in U.S. or Canada.

WISCONSIN ARTS BOARD FELLOWSHIP PROGRAM, 107 S. Butler St., Madison WI 53703. (608)266-0190. Contact: Grants Coordinator. Awards for artistic works and activities for professional advancement by Wisconsin writers.

‡**WITTER BYNNER FOUNDATION FOR POETRY, INC. GRANTS**, Box 2188, Santa Fe NM 87504. (505)988-3251. Award Director: Steven D. Schwartz. Grants for poetry and poetry-related projects.

‡**WORK-IN-PROGRESS GRANT**, Society of Children's Book Writers and Judy Blume, Box 296 Mar Vista, Los Angeles CA 90066. Grant Coordinator: Eve Bunting, 1512 Rose Villa, Pasadena CA 91106. Two grants—one designated specifically for a contemporary novel for young people—to assist SCBW members in the completion of a specific project.

WRITERS GUILD OF AMERICA WEST AWARDS, Allen Rivkin, Public Relations, Writers Guild of America West, 8955 Beverly Blvd., Los Angeles CA 90048. Scripts (screen, TV and radio). Members only.

WRITERS OF THE FUTURE CONTEST, L. Ron Hubbard, #343, 2210 Wilshire Blvd., Santa Monica CA 90403. (213)466-3310. Award Director: Fred Harris of Author Services, Inc. Unpublished science fiction and fantasy.

‡**Y.E.S. (YEAR END SERIES) NEW PLAY FESTIVAL**, Northern Kentucky University, Highland Heights KY 41076. (606)572-5560. Project Director: Jack Wann. Previously unpublished plays, submitted May-December.

‡**THE YOUNGER POET AWARD**, *POET*, Box 44021, Shreveport LA 71134. Estab. 1985. Poetry published in The Younger Poet section of *POET* during a calendar year.

66 *On revision, test each sentence and paragraph, asking: Does this mean what I want it to mean? Is there a more precise way I can say it (which often means a simpler way)? Avoid repetition.* **99**

John Guinther

Appendix

The Business of Freelancing

> To make a book is as much a trade
> as to make a clock:
> Something more than intelligence
> is required to become an author.
> —La Bruyere

Even if you consider writing to be an art and believe yourself to be an artist, as a freelance writer you are also an independent business person. Independence is the most emphasized element of freelancing, but we must all recognize that independence brings responsibility.

As a responsible business person, you must learn the business thoroughly and be prepared for occasional—or even frequent—disappointment. Freelance writing is a highly competitive profession. Even the most successful writers invest time and money in research, manuscript preparation and marketing, with no guarantee that their work will sell. By buying this edition of *Writer's Market*, you have declared that you are serious about the business of freelancing. You aren't just ready to write; you're ready to *work* to give your submissions every advantage.

Management of your writing work begins with developing a strategy, gathering ideas, identifying markets and dealing with rejection slips. You need to acquire certain supplies and equipment. Before you put your finished product in the mail, you must know the rules for approaching editors and preparing your manuscripts.

Developing a strategy

Some writers decide to write about whatever interests *them* . . . and then look around for a publisher. While this is a common approach, it reduces your chances of success. Instead, try the following strategy.

Decide on a general writing category that interests you. Study the appropriate sections of *Writer's Market*. Pay special attention to the introductions to each market. They describe both general trends and specific details for submissions in each category. Select *several* listings that are good prospects for the writing you want to do. Then follow the suggestions in Approaching Your Markets later in this Appendix.

Develop *several* ideas. Based on a realistic estimate of getting your work published, make a list of the potential markets for each idea. Make the initial contact with the first market on your list, using its preferred method (query letter, outline/synopsis, manuscript, etc.). As you continue to develop each idea, keep copies of your writing and all correspondence related to it with your list of remaining markets.

If you exhaust your list of possibilities, don't give up. Re-evaluate the idea, revise it, or try another angle. If your idea didn't appeal to consumer magazines, it might be right for a trade publication. Freelance writing is a "numbers game." Your chances of success increase as the number of pieces you have "out" increases.

Continue developing ideas and approaching markets. When the first query or manuscript is mailed, begin work on another idea. Identify and rank potential markets for this idea and continue the process, but don't approach a market more than once until you've received a response to your first submission.

Prepare for rejection. When a submission is returned, check the file folder of potential markets for that idea. Cross off the current market and immediately mail an appropriate submission to the next market on your list. Remember, the first editor didn't reject *you*, but simply chose not to buy your product. When you choose not to buy a certain brand of shampoo, you don't intend to personally insult the president of the company that made it. Likewise, a rejection means only that your particular writing did not fit the particular needs of the market at this time. Your job is to find the *right* publisher for your writing. Submit the work again and go back to work on another idea.

Equipment and supplies

Like anyone involved in a trade or business, you need certain tools and supplies to produce your product or provide your service. Sharp pencils and yellow pads of paper will get you just so far as a freelance writer. The basic necessities for your writing business, plus some "extras" you may eventually want to have, include:

Typewriters. A well-maintained manual typewriter is adequate for many writers. Those who write fulltime often prefer an electric or electronic typewriter, which usually produce more uniform, clearer characters. Most typewriters are available in either pica or elite type. Pica type has ten characters to a horizontal inch and elite has twelve; both have six single-spaced, or three double-spaced, lines to a vertical inch. The slightly larger pica type is easier to read and many editors prefer it, though they don't object to elite.

Editors dislike—and often refuse to read—manuscripts typed in all caps or in an unusual type style—such as script, italics, or Old English. Reading such manuscripts is hard on the eyes. You should strive for clean, easy-to-read manuscripts and correspondence that reflect pride in your work and consideration for your reader.

Use a good black (never colored) typewriter ribbon and clean your keys frequently. If the enclosures of the letters a, b, d, e, g, etc., become inked-in, a cleaning is overdue.

Even the best typists make errors. *Occasional* retyping over erasures is acceptable, but strikeovers give your manuscript a sloppy, careless appearance. Hiding typos with large splotches of correction fluid makes your work look amateurish; use it sparingly. Some writers prefer to use typing correction film for final drafts and correction fluid for rough drafts. Better yet, a "self-correcting" electric typewriter with a correction tape makes typos nearly invisible. Whatever method you use, it's best to retype a page that has several noticeable corrections. Sloppy typing is taken by many editors as a hint of sloppy work habits—and the likelihood of careless research and writing.

Types of paper. The paper you use must measure 8½x11 inches. That's a standard size and editors are adamant—they don't want unusual colors or sizes. There's a wide range of white 8½x11 papers. The cheaper ones are made from wood pulp. They will suffice, but are not recommended. Editors also discourage the use of erasable bond for manuscripts; typewriter ribbon ink on erasable bond tends to smear when handled. Don't use less than a 16-pound bond paper; 20-pound is preferred. Your best bet is paper with a 25 percent cotton fiber content. Its texture shows type neatly and it holds up under erasing and corrections.

You don't need fancy letterhead stationery for your correspondence with editors. Plain bond paper is fine; just type your name, address, phone number and the date at the top of the page—centered or in the right-hand corner. If you decide to order letterhead, make it as simple and businesslike as possible. Never use letterhead for typing your manuscript.

Photocopies and carbons. Always make copies of your manuscripts and correspondence before putting them in the mail. Don't learn the hard way—as many writers have—that manuscripts get lost in the mail and publishers sometimes go out of business without returning submissions. While some writers continue to make carbon copies of their correspondence with editors, most depend on photocopy machines for duplicating manuscripts. In general, use carbon copies for your own records; never send a carbon to an editor unless the original correspondence has been lost.

You might want to make several copies of your manuscript while it is still clean and crisp. Some writers keep their original manuscript as a file copy and submit good quality photocopies. Submitting copies can save you the expense and effort of retyping a manuscript if it becomes lost in the mail. The quality of photocopies varies, so visit print shops in your area until you find one that makes perfect photocopies.

If you submit a copy, include a personal note explaining whether or not you are making a simultaneous or multiple submission. Many editors refuse to consider material they think is being submitted simultaneously. See Approaching Your Markets later in this Appendix.

Some writers include a self-addressed postcard with a photocopied submission; in their cover letter they suggest that if the editor is not interested in the manuscript, it may be tossed out and a reply returned on the postcard. This practice is often recommended for dealing with foreign markets. Submitting disposable photocopies costs the writer some photocopy expense, but saves on large postage bills.

The cost of personal photocopiers is coming down, but they remain much too expensive for most writers. If you need to make a large number of photocopies, you should ask your print shop about quantity discounts. One advantage of a personal computer is that it can quickly print copies of any text you have composed on it.

Computers and accessories. A personal computer can make a writer's work much more efficient. Writing, revising and editing are usually faster and easier on a computer than on a typewriter. Many writers rely on their computers to give them fresh, readable copy as they revise rough drafts into finished manuscripts. When a manuscript is written *on* a computer, it can come *out* of the computer in three ways: as "hard copy" from the computer's printer; stored on a removable electronic disk (often called a "floppy") that can be "read" by *some* other computers; or as an "electronic transfer" over telephone lines using a modem (a device that allows one computer to "talk" to another).

● Hard copy—Most editors are receptive to a computer printout submission if it looks like a neatly *typed* manuscript. Some of the older and less expensive printers produce only a low-quality "dot-matrix" printout with hard-to-read, poorly shaped letters and numbers. Not many editors are willing to read these manuscripts. New dot-matrix printers can produce "letter quality" printouts that are almost indistinguishable from a typewritten manuscript. When you submit hard copy to an editor, be sure that you use quality paper. Some computer printers use the standard bond paper you use in a typewriter. Others are equipped with a tractor-feed that pulls continuous form paper (with holes along the edges) through the machine. If you use continuous form paper, be sure to remove the perforated tabs on each side and separate the pages.

● Disk—You'll find that more publishers are accepting (or even requesting) electronic submissions on disk. If your disk can be read by the publisher's computer, the publisher won't need to have your manuscript typeset by another person—an expensive, time-consuming task.

● Modem—Some publishers who accept submissions on disk will also accept electronic submissions by modem. This is the fastest method of getting your manuscript to the publisher.

Before sending anything electronically, by either disk or modem, you'll need to query the publisher for details. Your computer and the publisher's must be compatible at some level. When you query about electronic submissions, include the name of your computer, its manufacturer and model; mention the operating system (CPM or MS-DOS) and word processing software you use. Because most editors prefer that you submit hard copy along with any electronic submission, you may wonder why you should even consider using disk or modem. Editors know they can revise manuscripts more quickly on a computer screen as well as save typesetting expenses. Best of all, some publishers are beginning to pay more for manuscripts submitted on disk or modem.

Assorted supplies. Where will you put all your manuscripts and correspondence? A two- or four-drawer filing cabinet with an ample supply of file folders is the obvious choice—but often too expensive. Many writers "make do" with used manila envelopes and cardboard boxes. The most important thing is to organize and label your correspondence, manuscripts, ideas, submission records, clippings, etc., so you can find them when you need them. See also the sections on Recording Your Submissions and Financial Records in this Appendix.

You will also need stamps and envelopes; see Mailing Your Submissions and Postage by the Page. If you decide to invest in a camera to increase your sales of nonfiction manuscripts, you'll find details in the sections on Approaching Your Markets and Mailing Your Submissions.

Approaching your markets

Before submitting a manuscript to a market, be sure you've done your homework.
• Know your market. Familiarize yourself with the publication or other type of market that interests you. Your first sales will probably be to markets you already know through your reading. If you find a listing in *Writer's Market* that seems a likely home for an idea you've been working on, study a sample copy or book catalog to see if your idea fits in with their current topics.
• Always request writer's guidelines, even if you can read a sample copy at the library. Guidelines give a publication's exact requirements for submissions, and will help focus your query letter or manuscript. If a publication has undergone editorial changes since this edition of *Writer's Market* went to press, those changes will usually be reflected in its writer's guidelines. The response to your request for guidelines can also tell you if a publication has folded or if it has an unreasonably long response time.
• Check submission requirements. A publication that accepts only queries may not respond at all to a writer who submits a manuscript and cover letter. Don't send an unpublished manuscript to a publication that publishes only reprints. If you're submitting photos, be sure the publication reviews prints or slides, and find out if they require model releases and captions. An editor is impressed when a writer has carefully studied a publication before making a submission.
• Always include SASE. With submissions or correspondence, enclose a stamped, self-addressed envelope. Editors appreciate the convenience and the savings in postage. Some editorial offices deal with such a large volume of mail that their policies will not allow them to respond to mail that does not include a SASE. If you're submitting to a foreign market, enclose a SAE with IRCs purchased from the post office.

Those are the basics; now you're ready to learn the details of what you should send as you contact an editor.

Query letters. A query letter is a brief, but detailed, letter written to convince an editor to consider your manuscript. Some beginners are hesitant to query, thinking an editor can more fairly judge an idea by seeing the entire manuscript. Actually most editors of nonfiction do prefer to be queried.

Do your best writing when you sit down to compose your query. There is no query formula that will guarantee success, but there are some points to consider before you begin:
• Queries are single-spaced business letters, usually limited to one page. Address the current editor by name, if possible. Do not immediately address an editor by a first name; some edi-

tors are offended by unwarranted familiarity. Wait until you receive a response and follow the editor's lead.
● Your major goal is to convince the editor that your idea would be of interest to his readership—and that you are the best writer for the job.
● Be sure you use a strong opening that will pique the editor's interest. Some queries begin with a paragraph that approximates the lead of the intended article. This beginning paragraph is double spaced; the rest of the query is single spaced.
● Briefly detail the structure of the article. Give some facts and anecdotes, and mention people you intend to interview. Give the editor enough information to make him want to know more—but don't reveal all your resources.
● Mention any special training or experience that qualifies you to write the article.
● If you have prior writing experience, you may mention this; if not, there's no need to call attention to the fact. Some editors will also look at clips of your published work. If possible, submit something related to your idea, either in topic or style.
● If photos are available, let the editor know.
● Your closing paragraph may include a direct request to do the article; it may specify the date the manuscript can be completed and an approximate length.
● Don't discuss fees or request advice from the editor.
● Fiction is rarely queried, but if a fiction editor requests a query, briefly describe the main theme and story line, including the conflict and resolution of your story.
● Some writers state politely in their query letter that after a specified date (slightly beyond the listed reporting time), they will assume the editor is not currently interested in their topic and will submit their query elsewhere.

Cover letters. A brief cover letter enclosed with your manuscript is helpful in personalizing a submission. If you have previously queried the editor on the article or book, the note should be a brief reminder: "Here is the piece on the city's missing funds, which we discussed previously. I look forward to hearing from you at your earliest convenience." Don't use the letter to make a sales pitch. Nothing you can say now will make the editor decide in your favor—the manuscript must stand alone.

If you are submitting to a market that considers complete manuscripts, your cover letter should tell the editor something about you—your publishing history, or any particular qualifications you have for writing the enclosed manuscript.

If the manuscript you are submitting is a photocopy, indicate whether it is a simultaneous submission. An editor may assume it is, unless you tell him otherwise—and some are offended by writers using this marketing technique. Only send simultaneous submissions to markets that state they will consider such submissions.

Book proposals. Book proposals are some combination of a cover letter, a synopsis, an outline and/or two or three sample chapters. The exact combination of these will depend on the publisher.

Some editors use the terms "synopsis" and "outline" interchangeably. If the publisher requests only a synopsis or an outline, not both, be sure you know which format the publisher prefers. Either a synopsis or outline is appropriate for a novel, but you may find an outline is more effective for a nonfiction book.
● A synopsis is a very brief summary of your book. Cover the basic plot or theme of your book and reveal the ending. Make sure your synopsis flows well, is interesting and easy to read.
● An outline covers the highlights of your book chapter-by-chapter. If your outline is for a novel, include all major characters, the main plot, subplots, and any pertinent details. An outline may run ten to thirty pages, depending upon the complexity and length of your book. Be sure your outline is clearly stated and doesn't become such a tangle of ideas and events that you lose your reader.
● Sample chapters are also requested by many editors. Some editors are interested in the first

two or three chapters to see how well you develop your book. Others want a beginning chapter, a chapter from the middle of your book, and the final chapter, so they can see how well you follow through.

Reprints. You can get more mileage—and money—out of your research and writing time by marketing your previously published material for reprint sales. You may use a photocopy of your original manuscript and/or tearsheets from the publication in which it originally appeared. With your reprint submission be sure to inform the editor that you are marketing this article as a reprint, especially if you're sending a photocopy without tearsheets. The editor will need to know when and in which publication it appeared.

If you are marketing for reprint an article that has not yet been published by the original purchaser, inform editors that it may not be used before it has made its initial appearance.

Photographs and slides. The availability of good quality photos can be the deciding factor when an editor is considering a manuscript. Some publications also offer additional pay for photos accepted with a manuscript. When submitting black and white prints, send 8x10 glossies, unless the editor indicates another preference. The universally accepted size for color transparencies is 35mm; few buyers will look at color prints.

On all your photos and slides, you should stamp or print your copyright notice and "Return to:" followed by your name, address and phone number. Rubber stamps are preferred for labeling photos as they are less likely to cause damage; you can order them from many stationery or office supply stores. If using a pen on photos, be careful not to damage them by pressing too hard or allowing ink to bleed through the paper.

● Captions should be typed on a sheet of paper and taped—with masking tape—to the bottom of the back of the prints. The caption should fold over the front of the photo so the buyer can fold the paper back for easy reading.

● Submit prints rather than negatives, and consider having duplicates made of your slides. Don't risk having your original negative or slide lost or damaged. Look for a photography lab that can make a high quality copy.

Manuscript mechanics

A unique work may be tossed aside by an editor who refuses to read a handwritten manuscript; and fancy typefaces, coffee stains, or dog-eared pages rarely make a favorable impression. Follow these basic rules of manuscript mechanics and you will present your work in its best form.

Manuscript format. Do not use a cover sheet or title page. Use a binder only if you are submitting a play or a television or movie script. You may use a paper clip to hold pages together, but never use staples.

The upper corners of the first page contain important information about you and your manuscript. This information is always single-spaced. In the upper left corner list your name, address, phone number and Social Security number. In the upper right corner indicate the approximate word count for the manuscript, the rights you are offering for sale and your copyright notice (© 1987 Chris Jones). A handwritten copyright symbol is acceptable. For a book manuscript do not specify the rights you are offering; that will be covered in your contract. Do not number the first page of your manuscript.

Center the title in capital letters one-third of the way down the page. To center, set the tabulator to stop halfway between the right and left edges of the page. Count the letters in the title, including spaces and punctuation, and backspace half that number. Type the title. Set your typewriter to double-space. Type "by" centered one double-space under your title, and type your name or pseudonym centered one double-space beneath that.

After the title and byline, drop down two double-spaces, paragraph indent, and begin the body of your manuscript. Paragraph indentation is five spaces. Margins should be about 1¼ inches on all sides of each full page of typewritten manuscript. You may lightly pencil in a line

Jones—2

Title of Manuscript (optional)

Begin the second page, and all following pages, in this manner—with a page-number line (as above) that includes your name, in case loose manuscript pages get shuffled by mistake. You may include the title of your manuscript or a shortened version of the title to identify the Jones manuscript this page 2 belongs to.

Chris Jones
1234 My Street
Anytown, State, Zip
Tel. 123/456-7890
Social Security Number

About 3,000 words
First Serial Rights
© 1987 Chris Jones

YOUR STORY OR ARTICLE TITLE HERE

by

Chris Jones

The manuscript begins here—about halfway down the first page. It should be cleanly typed, double-spaced, using either elite or pica type. Use one side of the paper only, and leave a margin of about 1¼ inches on all four sides.

To begin a new paragraph, drop down one double-space and indent. Don't put extra white space between paragraphs.

NEATNESS COUNTS. Here are sample pages of a manuscript ready for submission to an editor. If the author uses a pseudonym, it should be placed on the title page only in the byline position; the author's real name must always appear in the top left corner of the title page—for manuscript mailing and payment purposes. On subsequent pages, list the real name, then the pen name in parentheses, followed by a dash and the page number.

to remind you when you reach the bottom margin of your page, but be sure to erase it before submitting your manuscript.

On every page after the first, type your last name, a dash and the page number in the upper left corner. The title of your manuscript may, but need not, be typed beneath this. Page number two would read: Jones-2. If you are using a pseudonym, type your real name, followed by your pen name in parentheses, then a dash and the page number: Jones (Smith)-2. Then drop down two double-spaces and continue typing. Follow this format throughout your manuscript.

If you are submitting novel chapters, leave one-third of the first page of each chapter blank before typing the title. Subsequent pages should include the author's last name, the page number, a shortened form of the book's title, and a chapter number in the upper left margin. Use arabic numerals (1, 2, 3, etc.) for chapter numbers.

When submitting poetry, the poems should be typed single-spaced (double-space between stanzas), one poem per page. For a long poem requiring more than one page, paper clip the pages together.

On the final page of your manuscript, after you've typed your last word and period, skip three double spaces and center the words "The End" or, if it's nonfiction, use the old newspaper telegrapher's symbol —30— which indicates the same thing.

Estimating word count. To estimate word count in manuscripts of up to 25 pages, count the exact number of words on three full pages of your manuscript (not the first or last page). Count abbreviations and short words such as "a" and "by" as one word each. Divide this word count by three and multiply the result by the total number of pages. Round this number to the nearest 100 words. On manuscripts of more than 25 pages, count five pages instead of three and follow the same process, dividing by five.

Mailing your submissions

No matter what size manuscript you're mailing, always include sufficient return postage, and a self-addressed envelope large enough to contain your manuscript if it is returned.

A manuscript of fewer than six pages may be folded in thirds and mailed as if it were a letter, using a #10 (business-size) envelope. The enclosed SASE should be a #10 envelope folded in thirds (though these are sometimes torn when a letter opener catches in one of the folds), or a #9 envelope which will slip into the mailing envelope without being folded.

For a manuscript of six or more pages, use 9x12 envelopes for both mailing and return. The return SASE may be folded in half.

A book manuscript should be mailed in a sturdy, well-wrapped box. Your typing paper or envelope box is a suitable mailer. Enclose a self-addressed mailing label and paper clip your return postage stamps to the label.

Always mail photos and slides First Class. The rougher handling received by Fourth Class mail could damage your prints or slides. If you are concerned about their being lost, send them certified or registered mail. For any photo submission that is mailed separately from a manuscript, enclose a separate self-addressed label, adequate return postage, and an envelope. Never submit photos or slides mounted in glass.

To mail up to twenty prints, use photo mailers that are stamped "Photos—Do Not Bend" and contain two cardboard inserts to sandwich your prints. Or use a 9x12 manila envelope, write "Photos—Do Not Bend" and devise your own cardboard inserts. Some photography supply shops also carry heavy cardboard envelopes that are reusable.

When mailing numerous prints, such as 25 to 50 prints for a photo book, pack them in a sturdy cardboard box. A box for typing paper or photo paper is an adequate mailer. If, after packing both manuscript and photos, there's empty space in the box, slip in enough cardboard inserts to fill the box. Wrap the box securely.

To mail transparencies, first slip them into protective vinyl sleeves, then mail as you would prints. If you're mailing a number of sheets, use a cardboard box as for photos above.

Postage by the Page

by Carolyn Hardesty

Writers have the satisfaction of "finishing" their work several times. After the relief of completing the first draft, each revision and eventually the final typing give a temporary sensation of being done. But the *finishing* feels most complete when you seal the envelope, write *First Class* on it, and tuck it into the mail slot.

How often is this last stage delayed by a 20-minute wait behind customers who are stamp collectors or who have ten letters to certify? Writers, who have more ideas than time, don't need that added frustration. Try these suggestions.

For short manuscripts or long queries, use a business-size envelope and up to five pages with a 22¢ stamp. If you are including a business-size SASE (as you should), four pages is the limit. Another option for brief submissions is a 6x9 envelope. With SASE and up to seven sheets, it can be mailed for $.39. (The return envelope will need $.39 also, unless the manuscript is three or fewer pages). Some editors appreciate the ease in handling and reading a manuscript folded once instead of twice.

The chart below can simplify the postal process and save you time. Postage rates are listed by numbers of pages (using 20-pound paper) for First Class packages up to 12 ounces. After the first ounce (22¢), the increments are 17¢. The post office sells a convenient 39¢ stamp and also 17¢ stamps, so a stock of those denominations will allow you to stamp and mail your manuscripts in any dropbox as easily at midnight as noon.

First Class Postage Rates

ounces	9x12 envelope, 9x12 SASE number of pages	9x12 SASE (for return trips) number of pages	First Class Postage
under 2	. . .	1 to 2	$ .32*
2	1 to 4	3 to 8	.39
3	5 to 10	9 to 12	.56
4	11 to 16	13 to 19	.73
5	17 to 21	20 to 25	.90
6	22 to 27	26 to 30	1.07
7	28 to 32	31 to 35	1.24
8	33 to 38	36 to 41	1.41
9	39 to 44	42 to 46	1.58
10	45 to 49	47 to 52	1.75
11	50 to 55	53 to 57	1.92
12	56 to 61	58 to 63	2.09

*includes an assessment for over-sized mail that is light in weight

You'll have to go to the post office if your manuscript includes photos and cardboard insert or special cardboard envelope—or if you need any of the following services:
- First Class packages weighing more than 12 ounces are charged according to geographical zones. This is true also for all weights of Fourth Class (or book rate) mail.
- Insurance (for typing and production costs) is 50¢ for $25 liability; $1.10 covers costs to $50; and $1.40 provides insurance to $100.
- International Reply Coupons (IRCs) are essential for Canadian and overseas submissions but are generally available only at larger post offices.

Carolyn Hardesty, *as a freelance writer and graduate student, doesn't have time for post office lines. She is pursuing a Ph.D in American Studies at the University of Iowa and is editor of* Iowa Woman.

Types of mail service

● First Class is the most expensive way of mailing a manuscript, but many writers prefer it. First Class mail generally receives better handling and is delivered more quickly. Mail sent First Class is forwarded if the addressee has moved, and is returned automatically if it is undeliverable.

● Fourth Class rates are available for packages that weigh sixteen ounces or more and are to be delivered within the United States. Pack materials carefully when mailing Fourth Class as they will be handled the same as Parcel Post—roughly. If a letter is enclosed with your Fourth Class package, write "First Class Letter Enclosed" on the package and add adequate First Class postage for your letter. To make sure your package will be returned to you if it is undeliverable, print "Return Postage Guaranteed" under your address.

● Certified Mail must be signed for when it reaches its destination. If requested, a signed receipt is returned to the sender. There is a 75¢ charge for this service, in addition to the required postage.

● Registered Mail is a high security method of mailing. The package is signed in and out of every office it passes through, and a receipt is returned to the sender when the package reaches its destination. This service costs $3.60, in addition to the postage required for the item.

● United Parcel Service may be slightly cheaper than First Class postage if you drop the package off at UPS yourself. UPS cannot legally carry First Class mail, so your cover letter would need to be mailed separately. Check with UPS in your area for current rates. The cost depends on the weight of your package and the distance to its destination.

● Overnight mail services are provided by both the U.S. Postal Service and numerous private firms. These services can be useful if you find yourself in a situation where a manuscript or revisions *must* be at an editor's office. More information on next day service is available from the U.S. Post Office in your area, or check your telephone directory under "Delivery Service."

Other important details

● Money orders should be used if you are ordering sample copies or supplies and do not have checking services available to you. You'll have a receipt and money orders are traceable. Money orders for up to $25 can be purchased from the U.S. Postal Service for 75¢. Banks, savings and loans, and some commercial businesses also carry money orders; their fees vary.

● Insurance is available for items handled by the U.S. Postal Service, but is payable only on typing fees or the tangible value of the item in the package—such as typing paper—so your best insurance when mailing manuscripts is to keep a copy of what you send.

● When corresponding with foreign publications and publishers, International Reply Coupons (IRCs) must be used for return postage. Surface rates in foreign countries differ from those in the U.S., and U.S. postage stamps are of no use there. Currently, one IRC costs 65¢ and is sufficient for one ounce traveling at surface rate; two are recommended for air mail return. Many writers dealing with foreign publishers mail photocopies and direct the publisher to dispose of them if they're not appropriate for current editorial needs; when using this method, it's best to also set a deadline for withdrawing your manuscript from consideration.

● International money orders are also available from the post office at a slightly higher fee than those for domestic use.

Recording your submissions

An amazing number of writers seem to think once they've mailed a manuscript, the situation is out of their hands. They no longer have control of their work and all they can do is sit and wait. But submitting a manuscript doesn't mean you've lost control of it. Manage your writing business by keeping copies of all manuscripts and correspondence, and by recording the dates of submissions.

ARE YOU SERIOUS?

About learning to write better? Getting published? Getting paid for what you write?
If you're dedicated to your writing, **Writer's Digest School** can put you on the fast track to writing success.

STUDY WITH A PROFESSIONAL

When you enroll in a **Writer's Digest School** course, you get more than writing textbooks and assignments. You get a one-on-one relationship with a professional writer who is currently writing *and selling* the kind of material you're interested in. Your training as a writer is built around this personal guidance from an experienced pro who knows what it takes to succeed in the competitive literary marketplace.

FOUR COURSES AVAILABLE

Writer's Digest School offers four courses: Writing to Sell Nonfiction (Articles), Writing to Sell Fiction (Short Stories), Elements of Effective Writing, and Advanced Writer's Workshop. Each course is described in more detail on the reverse side.

WE'VE BEEN TEACHING CREATIVE PEOPLE SINCE 1920

Writer's Digest School was founded over 60 years ago by the same people who publish **Writer's Digest,** the world's leading magazine for writers, and **Writer's Market,** the indispensable annual reference directory for writers. When you enroll in a **Writer's Digest School** course, you get the quality and expertise that are the hallmarks of the **Writer's Digest** name.

If you're serious about your writing, you owe it to yourself to check out **Writer's Digest School.** Mail the coupon below today for *free* information!

- -

Yes, I'm Serious!

I want to learn to write and sell from the professionals at **Writer's Digest School.** Send me free information about the course I've checked below:

☐ Writing to Sell Nonfiction (Articles)   ☐ Advanced Writer's Workshop
☐ Writing to Sell Fiction (Short Stories)   ☐ Elements of Effective Writing

_____
NAME

_____
ADDRESS

_____
CITY   STATE   ZIP

Mail this card today! No postage needed   QWM7

Writer's Digest School has been teaching people like you to write for more than 60 years.

Writer's Digest School
9933 Alliance Road
Cincinnati, Ohio 45242

Four **Writer's Digest School** courses to help you write better and sell more:

- **Writing to Sell Nonfiction.** Master the fundamentals of writing/selling nonfiction articles: finding article ideas, conducting interviews, writing effective query letters and attention-getting leads, targeting your articles to the right publication, and other important elements of a salable article. Course includes 31 writing assignments and one complete article manuscript and its revision. Your instructor will critique each assignment and help you slant your article to a particular magazine.

- **Writing to Sell Fiction.** Learn the basics of writing/selling short stories: plotting, characterization, dialogue, theme, conflict, and other elements of a marketable short story. Course includes 31 writing assignments and one complete short story and its revision. Your instructor will critique each assignment and give you suggestions for selling your story.

- **Advanced Writer's Workshop.** Advanced course open to selected graduates of the Fiction and Nonfiction courses and equally qualified writers. Your professional instructor analyzes and evaluates your four short stories or articles, and gives you specific marketing suggestions. This is an intensive, six-month course for writers serious about publishing their work.

- **Elements of Effective Writing.** Refresher course covers the basics of grammar, punctuation and elements of composition. You review the nine parts of speech and their correct usage, and learn to write clearly and effectively. Course includes 12 lessons with a grammar exercise and writing assignment in each lesson.

Mail this card today for **free** information!

NO POSTAGE
NECESSARY
IF MAILED
IN THE
UNITED STATES

BUSINESS REPLY MAIL
FIRST CLASS   PERMIT NO. 17   CINCINNATI, OHIO

POSTAGE WILL BE PAID BY ADDRESSEE

WRITER'S DIGEST SCHOOL
9933 Alliance Road
Cincinnati, Ohio 45242-9990

One way to keep track of your manuscripts is to use a record of submissions that includes the date sent, title, market, editor, and enclosures (such as photos). You should also note the date of the editor's response and—if the manuscript was accepted—the publication date and payment information. You might want to keep a similar record just for queries.

Also remember to keep a separate file for each manuscript or idea along with its list of potential markets. You may want to keep track of expected reporting times on a calendar, too. Then you'll know when a market has been slow to respond.

Financial records

While visiting a small office or shop, you may have seen this sign: "We're a nonprofit business . . . We didn't intend to be, that's just the way it turned out." Whether you are profitable in your writing or not, you'll need to keep accurate financial records. Such records are necessary to let *you* know how you're doing. And, of course, the government is also interested in your financial activities.

Date	Description	Expense		Paid by	Income	
Jan.						
4	Box of floppies	$30	00	#303		
6	Supply Mart: 1 ream bond	$6	95	cash		
8	Economic Bulletin — March article				$550	00
11	Pat's Bookstore — 1987 Writer's Market	$21	95	Visa		
13	Wright Corp.- for editing 4th - quarter newsletter				$300	00
15	Renewal of WD subscription	#17	00	#304		
18	Pat's - 20 manila envelopes	$4	00	cash		
21	Mountain Press - for editing Survival Handbook				$575	00
21	Devphoto - for developing Photos for Am. Horse J. article	#11	95	#305		
23	1987 Poet's Market	$16	95	Visa		
28	Fee for Southern Writer's Conference	$30	00	#306		
30	American Horse Journal for special issue article				$275	00
	Jan. TOTALS	$138	80		$1,700	00

A typical single-entry page in a bookkeeping journal that records a freelance writer's income and expense transactions.

If you have another source of income, you should plan to keep separate records for all your writing expenses and income. Some writers open separate checking accounts used only for their writing-related expenses.

The best financial records are the ones that get used. Usually, the simpler the form the more likely it will be used regularly. Get in the habit of recording every transaction related to your writing. You can start at any time; it doesn't need to be on January 1. Because you're likely to have expenses long before you have any income, start keeping your record whenever you make your first purchase related to writing—such as this copy of *Writer's Market*.

A **simple bookkeeping system**. For most freelance writers, a simple type of "single-entry" bookkeeping is adequate. The heart of the single-entry system is the journal, an accounting book available at any stationery or office supply store. You record in the journal all of the financial transactions (expenses and income) of your writing business.

The single-entry journal's form is similar to a standard check register. Instead of withdrawals and deposits, you record expenses and income. You'll need to describe each transaction clearly—including the date; the source of the income (or the vendor of your purchase); a description of what was sold or bought; whether the payment was by cash, check or credit card; and the amount of the transaction.

Your receipt file. Keep all documentation pertaining to your writing expenses or income. This is true whether you have started a bookkeeping journal or not. For every payment you receive, you should have a check stub from the publisher's check, a cover letter stating the amount of payment, or your own bank records of the deposit. For every check you write to pay business expenses, you should have a record in your check register as well as a cancelled check. Keep credit card receipts, too. And for every cash purchase, you should have a receipt from the vendor—especially if the amount is over $25. For small expenses, you can usually keep a list if you don't record them in a journal.

Tax information

As we go to press with *Writer's Market '87*, the Federal Income Tax laws are undergoing substantial revision. While we cannot offer you tax advice or interpretations, we can suggest several sources for the most current information.

● Call your local IRS office. Look in the white pages of the telephone directory under U.S. Government—Internal Revenue Service. Someone will be able to respond to your request for IRS publications and tax forms or other information. Ask about the IRS Tele-tax service, a series of recorded messages you can hear by dialing on a touch-tone phone. If you need answers to complicated questions, ask to speak with a Taxpayer Service Specialist.

● Obtain the basic IRS publications. You can order them by phone or mail from any IRS office; most are available at libraries and some post offices. Start with *Your Federal Income Tax* (Publication 17) and *Tax Guide for Small Business* (Publication 334). These are both comprehensive, detailed guides—you'll need to find the regulations that apply to you and ignore the rest. You may also want to get copies of Publication 1163, which is about the Tele-Tax Service, and *Business Use of Your Home* (Publication 587).

● Consider other information sources. Many public libraries have detailed tax instructions available on tape. Some colleges and universities offer free assistance in preparing tax returns. And if you decide to consult a professional tax preparer, the fee is a deductible business expense on your tax return.

Rights and the writer

"We find that writers and editors define rights in different ways," said our letter inviting publications to be listed in this 1987 edition. "To eliminate any misinterpretations, make sure your answer is consistent with the following definitions."

Read on, and you'll see how we define each right—and you'll see the definitions upon which editors updated the *rights* information in their listings.

Every so often, we hear from a writer who is confused because an editor claims to not ever acquire or buy rights. The truth is, any time an editor buys a story or asks you for permission to publish a story in return for contributor copies, this editor is asking you for *rights* (even when he doesn't use the word, rights). Occasionally people start magazines related to their areas of expertise but they don't have extensive knowledge of publishing terms and practices. If you sense that an editor is interested in getting stories but doesn't seem to know what his and the writer's responsibilities are regarding rights, be wary. In such a case, you'll want to explain what rights you're offering (in *very* basic terms) and if you expect additional payment for subsequent use of your work. Writers may also experience a situation in which they agree to sell first rights, for example, to a magazine but then never receive a check for the manuscript and subsequent inquiries bring no response. In a case like this, we recommend that the writer send a certified letter, return receipt requested, notifying the magazine that the manuscript is being withdrawn from that publication for submission elsewhere. There is no industry standard for how long a writer should wait before using this procedure. The best bet is to check the *Writer's Market* listing for what the magazine lists as its usual reporting time and then, after a reasonable wait beyond that, institute the withdrawal.

Selling rights to your writing. The Copyright Law that went into effect January 1, 1978, said writers were only selling one-time rights to their work unless they—and the publisher— agreed otherwise in writing. In some cases, however, a writer may have little say in the rights sold to an editor. The beginning writer, in fact, can jeopardize a sale by arguing with an editor who is likely to have other writers on call who are eager to please. As long as there are more writers than there are markets, this situation will remain the same.

As a writer acquires skill, reliability, and professionalism on the job, he becomes more valued by editors—and rights become a more important consideration. Though a beginning writer will accept modest payment just to get in print, an experienced writer cannot afford to give away good writing just to see a byline. At this point a writer must become concerned with selling reprints of articles already sold to one market, or using sold articles as chapters in a book on the same topic, or seeking markets for the same material overseas, or offering work to TV or the movies. Such dramatic rights can be meaningful for both fiction and nonfiction writers.

You should strive to keep as many rights to your work as you can from the outset, because before you can resell any piece of writing you must own the rights to negotiate. If you have sold "all rights" to an article, for instance, it can be reprinted *without* your permission, and without additional payment to you. Many writers will not deal with editors who buy all rights. What an editor buys will determine whether you can resell your own work. Here is a list of the rights most editors and publishers seek. (Book rights will be covered by the contract submitted to the writer by a book publisher. The writer does not indicate any such rights offered on the first page of his manuscript.)

● First Serial Rights—The word serial does not mean publication in installments, as in a serialized novel, but refers to the fact that libraries call newspapers and magazines "periodicals" or "serials" because they are published in serial or continuing fashion. *First Serial Rights* means the writer offers the newspaper or magazine the right to publish the article, story or poem for the first time in any periodical. All other rights to the material belong to the writer. Variations on this right are, for example, First North American Serial Rights. Some magazines use this purchasing technique to obtain the right to publish first in both the U.S. and Canada since many U.S. magazines are circulated in Canada. If an editor had purchased only First U.S. Serial Rights, a Canadian magazine could come out with prior or simultaneous publication of the same material. When material is excerpted from a book scheduled to be published and it appears in a magazine or newspaper prior to book publication, this is also called First Serial Rights.

● First North American Serial Rights—Magazine publishers that distribute in both the United States and Canada frequently buy these first rights covering publication in both countries.

• One-Time Rights—This differs from First Serial Rights in that the buyer has no guarantee he will be the first to publish the work. One-time rights most often apply to photos, but occasionally writing, too.

• Second Serial (Reprint) Rights—This gives a newspaper or magazine the opportunity to print an article, poem or story after it has already appeared in another newspaper or magazine. The term is also used to refer to the sale of part of a book to a newspaper or magazine after a book has been published, whether or not there has been any first serial publication. Income derived from second serial rights to book material is often shared 50/50 by author and book publisher.

• All Rights—Some magazines buy All Rights, either because of the top prices they pay for material, or the fact that they have book publishing interests or foreign magazine connections. A writer who sells an article, story or poem to a magazine under these terms, forfeits the right to use his material in its present form elsewhere. If he signs a "work-for-hire" agreement, he signs away all rights and the copyright to the company making the assignment. If the writer thinks he may want to use his material later (perhaps in book form), he must avoid submitting to such markets, or refuse payment and withdraw his material if he discovers it later. Ask the editor whether he is willing to buy only first rights instead of all rights before you agree to an assignment or a sale. Some editors will reassign rights to a writer after a given period, such as one year. It's worth an inquiry in writing.

• Simultaneous Rights—This term covers articles and stories sold to publications (primarily religious magazines) that do not have overlapping circulations. A Catholic publication, for example, might be willing to buy Simultaneous Rights to a Christmas story they like very much, even though they know a Presbyterian magazine may be publishing the same story in one of its Christmas issues. Publications that buy simultaneous rights indicate this fact in their listings in *Writer's Market*. Always advise an editor when the material you are sending is a simultaneous submission. Type "Simultaneous submission" in the upper right corner of page 1 of your manuscript.

• Foreign Serial Rights—Can you resell a story you have had published in the U.S. or North America to a foreign magazine? If you sold only First U.S. Serial Rights or First North American rights, yes; you are free to market your story abroad. Of course, you must contact a foreign magazine that buys material that has previously appeared in U.S. or North American periodicals.

• Syndication Rights—This is a division of serial rights. For example, a book publisher may sell the rights to a newspaper syndicate to print a book in twelve installments in each of twenty U.S. newspapers. If they did this prior to book publication, they would be syndicating First Serial Rights to the book. If they did this after book publication, they would be syndicating Second Serial Rights to the book. In either case, the syndicate would be taking a commission on the sales it made to newspapers, so the remaining percentage would be split between author and publisher.

• Subsidiary Rights—The rights, other than book publication rights, that should be specified in a book contract. These may include various serial rights, dramatic rights, translation rights, etc. The contract lists what percentage of these sales goes to the author and what percentage to the publisher.

• Dramatic, Television and Motion Picture Rights—This means the writer is selling his material for use on the stage, in television, or in the movies. Often a one-year "option" to buy such rights is offered (generally for 10% of the total price). The interested party then tries to sell the idea to other people—actors, directors, studios or television networks, etc.—who become part of the project, which then becomes a script. Some properties are optioned over and over again, but fail to become dramatic productions. In such cases, the writer can sell his rights again and again—as long as there is interest in the material. Though dramatic, TV and motion picture rights are more important to the fiction writer than to the nonfiction writer, producers today are increasingly interested in "real-life" material; many biographies and articles are being dramatized.

Communicate and clarify. Before submitting material to a market, check its listing in this book to see what rights are purchased. Most editors will discuss rights they wish to purchase before an exchange of money occurs. Some buyers are adamant about what rights they will accept; others will negotiate. In any case, the rights purchased should be stated specifically *in writing* sometime during the course of the sale, usually in a letter or memo of agreement. If no rights are transferred in writing, and the material is sold for use in a collective work (a work that derives material from a number of contributors), you are authorizing unlimited use of your piece in that work or updates of that work or later collective works in the same series. Thus, you can't collect reprint fees if the rights weren't spelled out in advance, in writing.

Give as much attention to the rights you haven't sold as you do to the rights you have sold. Be aware of the rights you retain, with an eye for additional sales.

Regardless of the rights you sell or don't sell, make sure all parties involved in any sale understand the terms of the sale. Clarify what is being sold *before* any actual sale, and do it in writing. Communication, coupled with these guidelines and some common sense, will preclude misunderstandings with editors over rights. Keep in mind, too, that if there is a change in editors from the edition of *Writer's Market* you're using, the rights bought may also change.

Copyrighting your writing

The copyright law, effective since January 1, 1978, protects your writing, unequivocally recognizes you as its owner, and grants you all rights, benefits and *privileges* that ownership entails. In other words, the moment you finish a piece of writing—whether it is a short story, article, novel or poem—the law recognizes that only you can decide how it is to be used. This law gives you power in dealing with editors and publishers, but you should understand how to use that power. Certain circumstances can complicate and confuse the concept of ownership. You must be wary of these circumstances, or risk losing ownership of your work. Here are answers to frequently asked questions about copyright law:

To what rights am I entitled under copyright law? The law gives you, as creator of your work, the right to print, reprint and copy the work; to sell or distribute copies of the work; to prepare "derivative works"—dramatizations, translations, musical arrangement, novelizations, etc.; to record the work; and to perform or display literary, dramatic or musical works publicly. These rights give you control over how your work is used, and assure you (in theory) that you receive payment for any use of your work.

If, however, you create the work as a "work-for-hire," you *do not* own any of these rights. The person or company that commissioned the work-for-hire owns the copyright. The work-for-hire agreement will be discussed in more detail later.

When does copyright law take effect, and how long does it last? A piece of writing is copyrighted the moment it is put to paper. Protection lasts for the life of the author plus 50 years, thus allowing your heirs to benefit from your work. For material written by two or more people, protection lasts for the life of the last survivor plus 50 years. The life-plus-50 provision applies if the work was created or registered with the Copyright Office after January 1, 1978, when the updated copyright law took effect. The old law protected works for a 28-year term, and gave the copyright owner the option to renew the copyright for an additional 28 years at the end of that term. Works copyrighted under the old law that are in their second 28-year term automatically receive an additional 19 years of protection (for a total of 75 years). Works in their first term also receive the 19-year extension, but must still be renewed when the first term ends.

If you create a work anonymously or pseudonymously, protection lasts for 100 years after the work's creation, or 75 years after its publication, whichever is shorter. The life-plus-50 coverage takes effect, however, if you reveal your identity to the Copyright Office any time before the original term of protection runs out.

Works created on a for-hire basis are also protected for 100 years after the work's creation or 75 years after its publication, whichever is shorter. But the copyright is held by the publisher, not the writer.

Must I register my work with the Copyright Office to receive protection? No. Your work is copyrighted whether or not you register it, although registration offers certain advantages. For example, you must register the work before you can bring an infringement suit to court. You can register the work *after* an infringement has taken place, and *then* take the suit to court, but registering after the fact removes certain rights from you. You can sue for actual damages (the income or other benefits lost as a result of the infringement), but you can't sue for statutory damages and you can't recover attorney's fees unless the work has been registered with the Copyright Office *before* the infringement took place. Registering before the infringement also allows you to make a stronger case when bringing the infringement to court.

If you suspect that someone might infringe on your work, register it. If you doubt that an infringement is likely (and infringements are relatively rare), you might save yourself the time and money involved in registering the material.

I have an article that I want to protect fully. How do I register it? Request the proper form from the Copyright Office. Send the completed form, a $10 registration fee, and one copy (if the work is unpublished; two if it's published) of the work to the Register of Copyrights, Library of Congress, Washington, D.C. 20559. You needn't register each work individually. A group of articles can be registered simultaneously (for a single $10 fee) if they meet these requirements: They must be assembled in orderly form (simply placing them in a notebook binder is sufficient); they must bear a single title ("Works by Chris Jones," for example); they must represent the work of one person (or one set of collaborators); and they must be the subject of a single claim to copyright. No limit is placed on the number of works that can be copyrighted in a group.

If my writing is published in a "collective work"—such as a magazine—does the publication handle registration of the work? Only if the publication owns the piece of writing. Although the copyright notice carried by the magazine covers its contents, you must register any writing to which *you* own the rights if you want the additional protection registration provides.

Collective works are publications with a variety of contributors. Magazines, newspapers, encyclopedias, anthologies, etc., are considered collective works. If you sell something to a collective work, state specifically—*in writing*—what rights you're selling. If you don't, you are automatically selling the nonexclusive rights to use the writing in the collective work and in any succeeding issues or revisions of it. For example, a magazine that buys your article without specifying in writing the rights purchased can reuse the article in that magazine—without paying you. The same is true for other collective works, so always detail *in writing* what rights you are selling before actually making the sale.

When contributing to a collective work, ask that your copyright notice be placed on or near your published manuscript (if you still own the manuscript's rights). Prominent display of your copyright notice on published work has two advantages: It signals to readers and potential reusers of the piece that it belongs to you, and not to the collective work in which it appears; and it allows you to register all published work bearing such notice with the Copyright Office as a group for a single $10 fee. A published work *not* bearing notice indicating you as copyright owner can't be included in a group registration.

Display of copyright notice is especially important when contributing to an uncopyrighted publication—that is, a publication that doesn't display a copyright symbol and doesn't register with the Copyright Office. You risk losing copyright protection on material that appears in uncopyrighted publication. Also, you have no legal recourse against a person who infringes on something that is published without appropriate copyright notice. That person has been misled by the absence of the copyright notice and can't be held liable for his infringement.

Copyright protection remains in force on material published in an uncopyrighted publication without benefit of copyright notice if the notice was left off only a few copies, if you asked (in writing) that the notice be included and the publisher didn't comply, or if you register the work and make a reasonable attempt to place the notice on any copies that haven't been distributed after the omission was discovered.

Official notice of copyright consists of the symbol ©, the word "Copyright," or the abbreviation "Copr."; the name of the copyright owner or owners; and the year date of first publication (for example, "© 1987 by Chris Jones"). A hand-drawn copyright symbol is acceptable.

Under what circumstances should I place my copyright notice on unpublished works that haven't been registered? Place official copyright notice on the first page of *any* manuscript, a procedure intended not to stop a buyer from stealing your material (editorial piracy is very rare, actually), but to demonstrate to the editor that you understand your rights under copyright law, that you own that particular manuscript, and that you want to retain your ownership after the manuscript is published. Seeing this notice, an editor might be less apt to try to buy all rights from you. Remember, you want to retain your rights to any writing.

How do I transfer copyright? A transfer of copyright, like the sale of any property, is simply an exchange of the property for payment. The law stipulates, however, that the transfer of any exclusive rights (and the copyright is the most exclusive of exclusive rights) must be made in writing to be valid. Various types of exclusive rights exist, as outlined above. Usually it is best not to sell your copyright. If you do, you lose control over the use of the manuscript, and forfeit future income from its use.

What is a "work-for-hire assignment"? This is a work that another party commissions you to do. Two types of work-for-hire works exist: Work done as a regular employee of a company, and commissioned work that is specifically called a "work-for-hire" in writing at the time of assignment. The phrase "work-for-hire" or something close must be used in the written agreement, though you should watch for similar phrasings. The work-for-hire provision was included in the new copyright law so that no writer could unwittingly sign away his copyright. The phrase "work-for-hire" is a bright red flag warning the writer that the agreement he is about to enter into will result in loss of rights to any material created under the agreement.

Some editors offer work-for-hire agreements when making assignments, and expect writers to sign them routinely. By signing them, you forfeit the potential for additional income from a manuscript through reprint sales, or sale of other rights. Be careful, therefore, in signing away your rights in a "work-for-hire" agreement. Many articles written as works-for-hire or to which all rights have been sold are never resold, but if you retain the copyright, you might try to resell the article—something you wouldn't be motivated to do if you forfeited your rights to the piece.

Can I get my rights back if I sell all rights to a manuscript, or if I sell the copyright itself? Yes. You or certain heirs can terminate the transfer of rights 40 years after creation or 35 years after publication of a work by serving written notice to the person to whom you transferred rights within specified time limits. Consult the Copyright Office for the procedural details. This may seem like a long time to wait, but remember that some manuscripts remain popular (and earn royalties and other fees) for much longer than 35 years.

Must all transfers be in writing? Only work-for-hire agreements and transfers of exclusive rights *must* be in writing. However, getting any agreement in writing before the sale is wise. Beware of other statements about what rights the buyer purchases that may appear on checks, writer's guidelines or magazine mastheads. If the publisher makes such a statement elsewhere, you might insert a phrase like "No statement pertaining to purchase of rights other than the one detailed in this letter—including masthead statements or writer's guidelines—applies to this agreement" into the letter that outlines your rights agreement. Some publishers put their terms in writing on the back of a check that, when endorsed by the writer, becomes in their view a "contract." If the terms on the back of the check do not agree with the rights you are selling, then change the endorsement to match the rights you have sold before signing the check for deposit. Contact the editor to discuss this difference in rights.

Are ideas and titles copyrightable? No. Nor can "facts" be copyrighted. Only the actual expression of ideas or information can be copyrighted. You can't copyright the idea to do a solar energy story, and you can't copyright lists of materials for building solar energy converters. But you can copyright the article that results from that idea and that information.

Where can I get more information about copyright law? Write the Copyright Office (Library of Congress, Washington, D.C. 20559) for a free Copyright Information Kit. Call (not collect) the Copyright Public Information Office at (202)287-8700 weekdays between 8:30 a.m. and 5 p.m. if you need forms for registration of a claim to copyright. The Copyright Office will answer specific questions but won't provide legal advice. For more information about copyright and other laws, consult the latest edition of *Law and the Writer*, edited by Kirk Polking and Leonard S. Meranus (Writer's Digest Books).

How much should I charge?

Pet lovers who want to take a vacation often hesitate to send their dogs or cats to a kennel because of the stress a kennel sometimes generates in a pet. Instead they hire "pet sitters" to take care of their pets while they're away. Now freelance writers with pet-sitting sidelines have found a way to improve on that part-time job by writing "pet reports" to the owners. Their letters describe the pet's health and behavior. Some write them in the name of the pet itself and get cards and letters in return. Pet sitting, like house sitting, provides a small sideline income ($6-$10 per day) while the writer uses the time to work on his own writing projects.

People hire freelancers to write other kinds of letters too—letters to the editor of the local newspaper on an issue they feel strongly about; letters to a politician on a proposed bill; letters of complaint about a faulty appliance. One such freelancer charges $15 per hour for such work. Another charges $35-$70 for certain problem and complaint letters.

But letter writing is a very small part of the many opportunities open to you as a freelance writer in your local community.

What follows is a list of writing jobs you might want to consider—and rates that have been reported to us by freelancers doing similar work in various parts of the U.S. The rates in your own marketplace may be higher or lower, depending on demand and other local variables. Consider the rates quoted here as guidelines, not fixed fees.

How do you find out what the local going rate is? If possible, contact writers or friends in a related business or agency that employs freelancers to find out what has been paid for certain jobs in the past. Or try to get the prospective client to quote his budget for a specific project before you name your price.

When setting your own fees, keep two factors in mind: (1)how much you think the client is willing or able to pay for the job; and (2)how much you want to earn for your time. For example, if something you write helps a businessman get a $50,000 order or a school board to get a $100,000 grant, that may influence your fees. How much you want to earn for your time should take into consideration not only an hourly rate for the time you spend writing, but also the time involved in meeting with the client, doing research and, where necessary, handling details with a printer or producer. One way to figure your hourly rate is to determine what an annual salary might be for a staff person to do the same job you are bidding on, and figure an hourly wage on that. If, for example, you think the buyer would have to pay a staff person $20,000 a year, divide that by 2,000 (approximately 40 hours per week for 50 weeks) and you will arrive at $10 an hour. Then add another 20% to cover the amount of fringe benefits that an employer normally pays in Social Security, unemployment insurance, paid vacations, hospitalization, retirement funds, etc. Then add another dollars-per-hour figure to cover your actual overhead expense for office space, equipment, supplies; plus time spent on professional meetings, readings, and making unsuccessful proposals. (Add up one year's expense and divide by the number of hours per year you work on freelancing. In the beginning you may have to adjust this to avoid pricing yourself out of the market.)

Regardless of the method by which you arrive at your fee for the job, be sure to get a letter of agreement signed by both parties covering the work to be done and the fee to be paid.

You will, of course, from time to time handle certain jobs at less than desirable rates because they are for a cause you believe in, or because the job offers additional experience or exposure to some profitable client for the future. Some clients pay hourly rates; others pay flat fees for the job. Both kinds of rates are listed when the data were available so you have as many pricing options as possible. More details on many of the freelance jobs listed below are contained in *Freelance Jobs for Writers*, edited by Kirk Polking (Writer's Digest Books)—which tells how to get writing jobs, how to handle them most effectively, and how to get a fair price for your work.

Advertising copywriting: Advertising agencies and the advertising departments of large companies need part-time help in rush seasons. Newspapers, radio and TV stations also need copywriters for their smaller business customers who do not have agencies. Depending on the client and the job, the following rates could apply: $20-$75 per hour, $100 and up per day, $200 and up per week, $100-$500 as a monthly retainer. Flat-fee-per-ad rates could range from $25-$500 depending upon size and kind of client.

Annual reports: A brief report with some economic information and an explanation of figures, $20-$35 per hour; a report that must meet Securities and Exchange Commission (SEC) standards and reports that use legal language could bill at $40-$65 per hour. Some writers who provide copywriting and editing services charge flat fees ranging from $5,000-$10,000.

Anthology editing: Variable advance plus 3%-15% of royalties. Flat-fee-per-manuscript rates could range from $500-$5,000 or more if it consists of complex, technical material.

Article manuscript critique: 3,000 words, $30.

Arts reviewing: For weekly newspapers, $15-35; for dailies, $45 and up; for Sunday supplements, $100-$400; regional arts events summaries for national trade magazines, $35-$100.

Associations: Miscellaneous writing projects, small associations, $5-$15 per hour; larger groups, up to $60 per hour; or a flat fee per project, such as $250-$750 for 10-12 page magazine articles, or $500-$1,500 for a 10-page booklet.

Audio cassette scripts: $10-$50 per scripted minute, assuming written from existing client materials, with no additional research or meetings; otherwise $75-$100 per minute, $750 minimum.

Audiovisuals: For writing; $125-$250 per requested scripted minute; includes rough draft, editing conference with client, and final shooting script. For consulting, research, producing, directing, soundtrack oversight, etc., $300-$500 per day plus travel and expenses. Writing fee is sometimes 10% of gross production price as billed to client.

Book, as-told-to (ghostwriting): Author gets full advance and 50% of author's royalties; subject gets 50%. Hourly rate for subjects who are self-publishing ($10-$35 per hour).

Book, ghostwritten, without as-told-to credit: For clients who are either self-publishing or have no royalty publisher lined up, $5,000 to $30,000 with one-fourth down payment, one-fourth when book half finished, one-fourth at three quarters mark and last fourth of payment when manuscript completed; or chapter by chapter.

Book content editing: $10-$50 per hour and up; $600-$3,000 per manuscript, based on size and complexity of the project.

Book copyediting: $7.50-$20 per hour and up; occasionally $1 per page.

Book indexing: $8-$18 per hour; $25 per hour using computer indexing software programs that take fewer hours; $1.50-$2 per printed book page; 40-55¢ per line of index; or flat fee.

Book jacket blurb writing: $60-$75 for front cover copy plus inside and back cover copy summarizing content and tone of the book.

Book manuscript criticism: $125 for outline and first 20,000 words.

Book manuscript reading, nonspecialized subjects: $20-$50 for a half page summary and recommendation. *Specialized subject:* $100-$350 and up, depending on complexity of project.

Book proofreading: $6.50-$20 per hour and up; sometimes 75¢-$1 per page.

Book proposal consultation: $25-$35 per hour.

Book proposal writing: $300-$1,000 or more depending on length and whether client provides full information or writer must do some research.

Book query critique: $50 for letter to publisher and outline.

Book research: $5-$20 per hour and up, depending on complexity.

Book reviews: For byline and the book only, on small newspapers; to $25-$300 on larger publications.

Book rewriting: $12-$30 per hour; sometimes $5 per page. Some writers have combination ghostwriting and rewriting short-term jobs for which the pay could be $350 per day and up. Some participate in royalties on book rewrites.

Brochures: $200-$7,500 depending on client (small nonprofit organization to large corporation), length, and complexity of job.

Business booklets, announcement folders: Writing and editing, $25-$1,000 depending on size, research, etc.

Business facilities brochure: 12-16 pages, $1,000-$4,000.

Business letters: Such as those designed to be used as form letters to improve customer relations, $20 per hour for small businesses; $200-$500 per form letter for corporations.

Business meeting guide and brochure: 4 pages, $200; 8-12 pages, $400.

Business writing: On the local or national level, this may be advertising copy, collateral materials, speechwriting, films, public relations or other jobs—see individual entries on these subjects for details. General business writing rates could range from $20-$50 per hour; $100-$200 per day, plus expenses.

Business writing seminars: $10 per person, minimum of 20, for a half-day seminar, plus travel expenses.

Catalogs for business: $60-$75 per printed page; more if many tables or charts must be reworked for readability and consistency.

Collateral materials for business: See business booklets, catalogs, etc.

Comedy writing for night club entertainers: Gags only, $2-$25 each. Routines, $100-$1,000 per minute. Some new comics may try to get a five-minute routine for $150; others will pay $2,500 for a five-minute bit from a top writer.

Commercial reports for businesses, insurance companies, credit agencies: $6-$10 per page; $5-$20 per report on short reports.

Company newsletters and inhouse publications: Writing and editing 2-4 pages, $200-$500; 12-32 pages, $1,000-$2,000. Writing, $8-$40 per hour; editing, $8-$35 per hour.

Church history: $200-$1,000 for writing 15 to 50 pages.

Consultation on communications: $250 per day plus expenses for nonprofit, social service and religious organizations; $400 per day to others.

Consultation to business: On writing, PR, $25-$50 per hour.

Consumer complaint letters: $15 per hour; $25-70 per letter.

Contest judging: Short manuscripts, $5 per entry; with one-page critique, $10-$25. Overall contest judging: $100-$500.

Copyediting and content editing for other writers: $1 per page. (See also Manuscript consultation and Manuscript criticism.)

Corporate history: $1,000-$20,000, depending on length, complexity and client resources.

Corporate profile: Up to 3,000 words, $1,250-$2,500.

Dance criticism: $25-$400 per article. (See also Arts reviewing.)

Direct-mail catalog copy: $10-$50 per page for 3-20 blocks of copy per page of a 24-48 page catalog.

Direct-mail packages: Copywriting direct mail letter, response card, etc., $1,500-$5,000 depending on writer's skill, reputation.

Direct response card on a product: $250.

Editing: See Book editing, Company newsletters, Magazine editing, etc.

Educational consulting and educational grant and proposal writing: $250-$750 per day and sometimes up to 5-10% of the total grant funds depending on whether only writing is involved or also research and design of the project itself.

Encyclopedia articles: Entries in some reference books, such as biographical encyclopedias, 500-2,000 words; pay ranges from $60-$80 per 1,000 words. Specialists' fees vary.

English teachers—lay reading for: $4-$6 per hour.

Family histories: See Histories, family.

Filmstrip script: See Audiovisual.

Financial presentation for a corporation: 20-30 minutes, $1,500-$4,500.

Flyers for tourist attractions, small museums, art shows: $25 and up for writing a brief bio, history, etc.

Fund-raising campaign brochure: $5,000 for 20 hours' research and 30 hours to write a major capital campaign brochure, get it approved, lay out and produce with a printer. For a standard fund-raising brochure, many fund-raising executives hire copywriters for $50-$75 an hour to do research which takes 10-15 hours and 20-30 hours to write/produce.

Gags: see Comedy writing.

Genealogical research: $5-$25 per hour.

Ghostwriting: $15-$40 per hour; $5-$10 per page, $200 per day plus expenses. Ghostwritten professional and trade journal articles under someone else's byline, $250-$3,000. Ghostwritten books: see Book, as-told-to (ghostwriting) and Book, ghostwritten, without as-told-to credit.

Ghostwriting a corporate book: 6 months' work, $13,000-$25,000.

Ghostwriting speeches: See Speeches.

Government public information officer: Part-time, with local governments, $10-$15 per hour; or a retainer for so many hours per period.

Histories, family: Fees depend on whether the writer need only edit already prepared notes or do extensive research and writing; and the length of the work, $500-$5,000.

Histories, local: Centennial history of a local church, $25 per hour for research through final manuscript for printer.

House organ editing: See Company newsletters.

Industrial product film: $1,000 for 10-minute script.

Industrial promotions: $15-$40 per hour. See also Business writing.

Job application letters: $10-$25.

Lectures to local librarians or teachers: $50-$100.

Lectures to school classes: $25-$75; $150 per day; $250 per day if farther than 100 miles.

Lectures at national conventions by well-known authors: $1,500-$20,000 and up, plus expenses; less for panel discussions.

Lectures at regional writers' conferences: $300 and up, plus expenses.

Magazine, city, calendar of events column: $150.

Magazine column: 200 words, $25. Larger circulation publications pay fees related to their regular word rate.

Magazine editing: Religious publications, $200-$500 per month.

Magazine stringing: 20¢-$1 per word based on circulation. Daily rate: $100-$200 plus expenses; weekly rate: $750 plus expenses. Also $7.50-$35 per hour plus expenses.

Manuscript consultation: $25-$50 per hour.

Manuscript criticism: $20 per 16-line poem; $30 per article or short story of up to 3,000 words; book outlines and sample chapters of up to 20,000 words, $125.

Manuscript typing: 75¢-$2.50 per page with one copy; $15 per hour.

Market research survey reports: $10 per report; $15-$30 per hour; writing results of studies or reports, $500-$1,200 per day.
Medical editing: $15-$30 per hour.
Medical proofreading: $10-$20 per hour.
Medical writing: $15-$80 per hour.
New product release: $300-$500 plus expenses.
Newsletters: See Company newsletters and Retail business newsletters.
Newspaper column, local: 80¢ per column inch to $5 for a weekly; $7.50 for dailies of 4,000-6,000 circulation; $10-$12.50 for 7,000-10,000 dailies; $15-$20 for 11,000-25,000 dailies; and $25 and up for larger dailies.
Newspaper feature: 35¢ to $1.50 per column inch for a weekly.
Newspaper feature writing, part-time: $1,000 a month for an 18-hour week.
Newspaper reviews of art, music, drama: See Arts reviewing.
Newspaper stringing: 50¢-$2.50 per column inch up to $7.50 per column inch for some national publications. Also publications like *National Enquirer* pay lead fees up to $250 for tips on page one story ideas.
Newspaper ads for small business: $25 for a small, one-column ad, or $10 per hour and up.
Novel synopsis for film producer: $150 for 5-10 pages typed single-spaced.
Obituary copy: Where local newspapers permit lengthier than normal notices paid for by the funeral home (and charged to the family), $15. Writers are engaged by funeral homes.
Opinion research interviewing: $4-$6 per hour or $15-$25 per completed interview.
Party toasts, limericks, place card verses: $1.50 per line.
Permission fees to publishers to reprint article or story: $75-$500; 10¢-15¢ per word; less for charitable organizations.
Photo brochures: $700-$15,000 flat fee for photos and writing.
Poetry criticism: $20 per 16-line poem.
Political writing: See Public relations and Speechwriting.
Press background on a company: $500-$1,200 for 4-8 pages.
Press kits: $500-$3,000.
Press release: 1-3 pages, $50-$200.
Printers' camera-ready typewritten copy: Negotiated with individual printers, but see also Manuscript typing services.
Product literature: Per page, $100-$150.
Programmed instruction consultant fees: $300-$700 per day; $50 per hour.
Programmed instruction materials for business: $50 per hour for inhouse writing and editing; $500-$700 a day plus expenses for outside research and writing. Alternate method: $2,000-$5,000 per hour of programmed training provided, depending on technicality of subject.
Public relations for business: $200-$500 per day plus expenses.
Public relations for conventions: $500-$1,500 flat fee.
Public relations for libraries: Small libraries, $5-$10 per hour; larger cities, $35 an hour and up.
Public relations for nonprofit or proprietary organizations: Small towns, $100-$500 monthly retainers.
Public relations for politicians: Small town, state campaigns, $10-$50 per hour; incumbents, congressional, gubernatorial, and other national campaigns, $25-$100 per hour.
Public relations for schools: $10 per hour and up in small districts; larger districts have full-time staff personnel.
Radio advertising copy: Small towns, up to $5 per spot; $20-$65 per hour; $100-$250 per week for a four- to six-hour day; larger cities, $250-$400 per week.
Radio continuity writing: $5 per page to $150 per week, part-time.
Radio documentaries: $200 for 60 minutes, local station.

Radio editorials: $10-$30 for 90-second to two-minute spots.

Radio interviews: For National Public Radio, up to 3 minutes, $25; 3-10 minutes, $40-$75; 10-60 minutes, $125 to negotiable fees. Small radio stations would pay approximately 50% of the NPR rate; large stations, double the NPR rate.

Readings by poets, fiction writers: $25-$600 depending on the author.

Record album cover copy: $100-$250 flat fee.

Recruiting brochure: 8-12 pages, $500-$1,500.

Research for writers or book publishers: $10-$30 an hour and up. Some quote a flat fee of $300-$500 for a complete and complicated job.

Restaurant guide features: Short article on restaurant, owner, special attractions, $15; interior, exterior photos, $15.

Résumé writing: $50-$150 per résumé.

Retail business newsletters for customers: $175-$300 for writing four-page publications. Some writers work with a local printer and handle production details as well, billing the client for the total package. Some writers also do their own photography.

Rewriting: Copy for a local client, $27.50 per hour.

Sales brochure: 12-16 pages, $750-$3,000.

Sales letter for business or industry: $150-$500 for one or two pages.

Science writing: For newspapers $150-$500; magazines $2,000-$5,000; encyclopedias $1 per line; textbook editing $40 per hour; professional publications $500-$750 for 1,500-3,000 words.

Script synopsis for agent or film producer: $75 for 2-3 typed pages, single-spaced.

Scripts for nontheatrical films for education, business, industry: Prices vary among producers, clients, and sponsors and there is no standardization of rates in the field. Fees include $75-$120 per minute for one reel (10 minutes) and corresponding increases with each successive reel; approximately 10% of the production cost of films that cost the producer more than $1,500 per release minute.

Services brochure: 12-18 pages, $1,250-$2,000.

Shopping mall promotion: $500 monthly retainer up to 15% of promotion budget for the mall.

Short story manuscript critique: 3,000 words, $30.

Slide film script: See Audiovisuals.

Slide presentation: Including visual formats plus audio, $1,000-$1,500 for 10-15 minutes.

Slide/single image photos: $75 flat fee.

Slide/tape script: $75-$100 per minute, $750 minimum.

Software manual writing: $15-$50 per hour for research and writing.

Special news article: For a business's submission to trade publication, $250-$400 for 1,000 words.

Special occasion booklet: Family keepsake of a wedding, anniversary, Bar Mitzvah, etc., $115 and up.

Speech for government official: $4,000 for 20 minutes plus up to $1,000 travel and miscellaneous expenses.

Speech for owners of a small business: $100 for six minutes.

Speech for owners of larger businesses: $500-$3,000 for 10-30 minutes.

Speech for local political candidate: $150-$250 for 15 minutes.

Speech for statewide candidate: $500-$800.

Speech for national congressional candidate: $1,000 and up.

Syndicated newspaper column, self-promoted: $2-$8 each for weeklies; $5-$25 per week for dailies, based on circulation.

Teaching adult education course: $10-$60 per class hour.

Teaching adult seminar: $350 plus mileage and per diem for a 6- or 7-hour day; plus 40% of the tuition fee beyond the sponsor's breakeven point.

Teaching college course or seminar: $15-$70 per class hour.

Teaching creative writing in school: $15-$60 per hour of instruction, or $1,200 for a 10-session class of 25 students; less in recessionary times.

Teaching elementary and middle school teachers how to teach writing to students: $75-$100 for a 1-1½ hour session.

Teaching journalism in high school: Proportionate to salary scale for full-time teacher in the same school district.

Teaching home-bound students: $5 per hour.

Technical typing: $1-$4 per double-spaced page.

Technical writing: $20-$60 per hour, depending on degree of complexity and type of audience.

Trade journal ad copywriting: $250-$500.

Trade journal article: For business client, $500-$1,500.

Translation, commercial: Final draft in one of the common European languages, 6-20¢ per English word.

Translation for government agencies: $27-$79 per 1,000 foreign words into English.

Translation, literary: $50-$100 per thousand English words.

Translation through translation agencies: Less 33⅓% for agency commission.

TV documentary: 30-minute 5-6 page proposal outline, $250 and up; 15-17 page treatment, $1,000 and up; less in smaller cities.

TV editorials: $35 and up for 1-minute, 45 seconds (250-300 words).

TV information scripts: Short 5- to 10-minute scripts for local cable TV stations, $10-$15 per hour.

TV instruction taping: $150 per 30-minute tape; $25 residual each time tape is sold.

TV news film still photo: $3-$6 flat fee.

TV news story: $16-$25 flat fee.

TV filmed news and features: From $10-$20 per clip for 30-second spot; $15-$25 for 60-second clip; more for special events.

TV, national and local public stations: $35-$100 per minute down to a flat fee of $100-$500 for a 30- to 60-minute script.

TV scripts: (Teleplay only), 60 minutes, prime time, Writers Guild rates effective 3/1/86-2/28/87: $10,584; 30 minutes, $7,846.

Video script: See Audiovisuals.

Writer-in-schools: Arts council program, $130 per day; $475 per week. Personal charges vary from $25 per day to $100 per hour depending on school's ability to pay.

Writer's workshop: Lecturing and seminar conducting, $100 per hour to $500 per day plus expenses; local classes, $50 per student for 10 sessions.

Glossary

Key to symbols and abbreviations follows the **Using Writer's Market** *section at front of book.*

Advance. A sum of money that a publisher pays a writer prior to the publication of a book. It is usually paid in installments, such as one-half on signing the contract; one-half on delivery of a complete and satisfactory manuscript. The advance is paid against the royalty money that will be earned by the book.

All Rights. See "Rights and the Writer" in the appendix.

Assignment. Editor asks a writer to do a specific article for which he usually names a price for the completed manuscript.

B&W. Abbreviation for black & white photograph.

Bimonthly. Every two months. See also *semimonthly.*

Bionote. A sentence or brief paragraph about the writer at the bottom of the first or last page on which an article or short story appears in a publication. A bionote may also appear on a contributors' page where the editor discusses the writers contributing to that particular edition.

Biweekly. Every two weeks.

Book auction. Selling the rights (i.e. paperback, movie, etc.) of a hardback book to the highest bidder. A publisher or agent may initiate the auction.

Book packager. Draws all the elements of a book together, from the initial concept to writing and marketing strategies, then sells the book package to a book publisher and/or movie producer.

Broadside. An oversized sheet or a one-page poster with illustration and text (poetry, fiction or nonfiction).

Caption. Originally a title or headline over a picture but now a description of the subject matter of a photograph, including names of people where appropriate. Also called cutline.

Chapbook. A small booklet, usually paperback, of poetry, ballads or tales.

Clean copy. Free of errors, cross-outs, wrinkles, smudges.

Clippings. News items of possible interest to trade magazine editors.

Clips. Samples, usually from newspapers or magazines, of your *published* work.

Column inch. All the type contained in one inch of a typeset column.

Commissioned work. See *assignment.*

Compatible. The condition which allows one type of computer/word processor to share information or communicate with another type of machine.

Concept. A statement that summarizes a screenplay or teleplay—before the outline or treatment is written.

Contributor's copies. Copies of the issues of a magazine sent to an author in which his/her work appears.

Co-publishing. An arrangement in which author and publisher share publication costs and profits.

Copyediting. Editing a manuscript for grammar, punctuation and printing style, not subject content.

Copyright. A means to protect an author's work. See "Rights and the Writer."

Cover letter. A brief letter, accompanying a complete manuscript, especially useful if responding to an editor's request for a manuscript. A cover letter may also accompany a book proposal. (A cover letter is *not* a query letter; see "Approaching Your Markets.")

Cutline. See *caption.*

Diorama. An advertising term referring to an elaborate, three-dimensional, miniature display.

Disk. A round, flat magnetic plate on which computer data may be stored.

Docudrama. A fictional film rendition of recent newsmaking events and people.

Dot-matrix. Printed type where individual characters are composed of a matrix or pattern of tiny dots.

Epigram. A short, witty, sometimes paradoxical saying.

Erotica. Usually fiction that is sexually-oriented, although it could be art on the same theme.

Fair use. A provision of the copyright law that says short passages from copyrighted material may be used without infringing on the owner's rights.

Feature. An article giving the reader information of human interest rather than news. Also used by magazines to indicate a lead article or distinctive department.

Filler. A short item used by an editor to "fill" out a newspaper column or a page in a magazine. It could be a timeless news item, a joke, an anecdote, some light verse or short humor, a puzzle, etc.

First North American serial rights. See "Rights and the Writer."

Formula story. Familiar theme treated in a predictable plot structure—such as boy meets girl, boy loses girl, boy gets girl.

Genre. Refers either to a general classification of writing, such as the novel or the poem, or to the categories within those classifications, such as the problem novel or the sonnet. Genre fiction describes commercial novels, such as mysteries, romances, and science fiction.

Ghostwriter. A writer who puts into literary form an article, speech, story or book based on another person's ideas or knowledge.

Glossy. A black and white photograph with a shiny surface as opposed to one with a non-shiny matte finish.

Gothic novel. One in which the central character is usually a beautiful young girl, the setting is an old mansion or castle; there is a handsome hero and a real menace, either natural or supernatural.

Hard copy. The printed copy (usually on paper) of a computer's output.

Hardware. All the mechanically-integrated components of a computer that are not software. Circuit boards, transistors, and the machines that are the actual computer are the hardware.

Honorarium. Token payment—small amount of money, or a byline and copies of a publication.

Illustrations. May be photographs, old engravings, artwork. Usually paid for separately from the manuscript. See also *package sale.*

Interactive fiction. Works of fiction in book or computer software format in which the reader determines the path that the story will take. The reader chooses from several alternatives at the end of a "chapter," and this determines the structure of the story. Interactive fiction features multiple plots and endings.

Invasion of privacy. Writing about persons (even though truthfully) without their consent.

Kill fee. Fee for a complete article that was assigned but which was subsequently cancelled.

Letter-quality submission. Computer printout that looks like a typewritten manuscript.

Libel. A false accusation or any published statement or presentation that tends to expose another to public contempt, ridicule, etc. Defenses are truth; fair comment on the matter of public interest; and privileged communication—such as a report of legal proceedings or a client's communication to his lawyer.

Little magazine. Publications of limited circulation, usually on literary or political subject matter.

Mainstream fiction. Fiction that transcends popular novel categories such as mystery, romance, or science fiction. Using conventional methods, this kind of fiction tells stories about people and their conflicts with greater depth of characterization, background, etc., than more narrowly focused genre novels.

Mass market. Nonspecialized books of wide appeal directed toward an extremely large audience.

Microcomputer. A small-computer system capable of performing various specific tasks with data it receives. Personal computers are microcomputers.

Model release. A paper signed by the subject of a photograph (or his guardian, if a juvenile) giving the photographer permission to use the photograph, editorially or for advertising purposes or for some specific purpose as stated.

Modem. A small electrical box that plugs into the serial card of a computer, used to transmit data from one computer to another, usually via telephone lines.

Monograph. Thoroughly detailed and documented scholarly study concerning a singular subject.

Multiple submissions. Submissions of the same article, story or poem to several publishers at the same time. Some publishers refuse to consider such submissions. No multiple submission should be made to larger markets unless it is a query on a highly topical article requiring an immediate response and that fact is stated in your letter.

Newsbreak. A newsbreak can be a small newsworthy story added to the front page of a newspaper at press time or can be a magazine news item of importance to readers.

Novelette. A short novel, or a long short story; 7,000 to 15,000 words approximately.

Offprint. Copies of an author's article taken "out of issue" before a magazine is bound and given to the author in lieu of monetary payment. An offprint could then be used by the writer as a published writing sample.

One-time rights. See "Rights and the Writer."

Outline. Of a book is usually a summary of its contents in five to fifteen double-spaced pages; often in the form of chapter headings with a descriptive sentence or two under each one to show the scope of the book. Of a screenplay or teleplay is a scene-by-scene narrative description of the story (10-15 pages for a ½-hour teleplay; 15-25 pages for a 1-hour teleplay; 25-40 pages for a 90-minute teleplay; 40-60 pages for a 2-hour feature film or teleplay).

Over-the-transom. Unsolicited material submitted by a freelance writer.

Package sale. The editor buys manuscript and photos as a "package" and pays for them with one check.

Page rate. Some magazines pay for material at a fixed rate per published page, rather than per word.

Payment on acceptance. The editor sends you a check for your article, story or poem as soon as he reads it and decides to publish it.

Payment on publication. The editor doesn't send you a check for your material until it's published.

Pen name. The use of a name other than your legal name on articles, stories, or books where you wish to remain anonymous. Simply notify your post office and bank that you are using the name so that you'll receive mail and/or checks in that name.

Photo feature. Feature in which emphasis is on the photographs rather than accompanying written material.

Photocopied submissions. Submitting *photocopies* of an original manuscript is acceptable to some editors instead of the author's sending his original manuscript. Do not assume that an editor who accepts photocopies will also accept multiple or simultaneous submissions.

Plagiarism. Passing off as one's own the expression of ideas and words of another writer.

Public domain. Material which was either never copyrighted or whose copyright term has run out.

Publication not copyrighted. Publication of an author's work in such a publication places it in the public domain, and it cannot subsequently be copyrighted. See "Rights and the Writer."

Query. A letter to an editor aimed to get his interest in an article you want to write.

Rebus. Stories, quips, puzzles, etc., in juvenile magazines that convey words or syllables with pictures, objects, or symbols whose names resemble the sounds of the intended words.

Release. A statement that your idea is original, has never been sold to anyone else, and that you give up all rights to the idea upon payment of the check.

Remainders. Copies of a book that are slow to sell and sometimes purchased from the publisher at a reduced price. Depending on the author's book contract, a reduced royalty or no royalty is paid on remainder books.

Reporting time. The time it takes an editor to report to the author on his query or manuscript.

Reprint rights. See "Rights and the Writer."

Round-up article. Comments from, or interviews with, a number of celebrities or experts on a single theme.

Royalties, standard hardcover book. 10% of the retail price on the first 5,000 copies sold; $12\frac{1}{2}$% on the next 5,000 and 15% thereafter.

Royalties, standard mass paperback book. 4 to 8% of the retail price on the first 150,000 copies sold.

Royalties, trade paperback book. No less than 6% of list price on first 20,000 copies; $7\frac{1}{2}$% thereafter.

Screenplay. Script for a film intended to be shown in theatres.

Second serial rights. See "Rights and the Writer."

Semimonthly. Twice a month.

Semiweekly. Twice a week.

Serial. Published periodically, such as a newspaper or magazine.

Sidebar. A feature presented as a companion to a straight news report (or main magazine article) giving sidelights on human-interest aspects or sometimes elucidating just one aspect of the story.

Simultaneous submissions. See *multiple submissions*.

Slant. The approach or style of a story or article so it will appeal to the readers of a specific magazine. For example, does this magazine always like stories with an upbeat ending?

Slides. Usually called transparencies by editors looking for color photographs.

Slush pile. The stack of unsolicited, or misdirected manuscripts received by an editor or book publisher.

Software. Programs and related documentation for use with a particular computer system.

Speculation. The editor agrees to look at the author's manuscript with no assurance that it will be bought.

Style. The way in which something is written—for example, short, punchy sentences, or flowing narrative.

Subsidiary rights. All those rights, other than book publishing rights, included in a book contract—such as paperback, book club, movie rights, etc.

Subsidy publisher. A book publisher who charges the author for the cost to typeset and print his book, the jacket, etc., as opposed to a royalty publisher which pays the author.

Syndication rights. See "Rights and the Writer" in the appendix.

Synopsis. A brief summary of a story, novel or play. As part of a book proposal, it is a comprehensive summary condensed in a page or page and a half, single-spaced. See also *outline*.

Tabloids. Newspaper format publication on about half the size of the regular newspaper page, such as the *National Enquirer*.

Tagline. A caption for a photo, or comment added to a filler.

Tearsheet. Page from a magazine or newspaper containing your printed story, article, poem or ad.

Trade. Either a hardcover or paperback book; subject matter frequently concerns a special interest. Books are directed toward the layperson rather than the professional.

Transparencies. Positive color slides; not color prints.

Treatment. Synopsis of a television or film script (40-60 pages for a 2-hour feature film or teleplay).

Unsolicited manuscript. A story, article, poem or book that an editor did not specifically ask to see.

User friendly. Easy to handle and use. Refers to computer hardware designed with the user in mind.

Vanity publisher. See *subsidy publisher*.

Word processor. A computer that produces typewritten copy via automated typing, text-editing, and storage and transmission capabilities.

Work-for-hire. See "Rights and the Writer" in the appendix.

Index

H

H.P. Books 86
H.W.H. Creative Productions, Inc. 86
Hadassah Magazine 281
Hale Limited, Robert 86
Hamilton Institute, Alexander 86
Hancock House Publishers Ltd. 87
Handicap News 382
Handwoven 329
Hanley & Belfus, Inc. 87
Happi 784
Happy Times 365
Harbor House Publishers 87
Hardcopy 721
Hardware Merchandiser 782
Haring Prize, Clarence H. 1003
Harlequin Books 87
Harper & Row Junior Books Group 87
Harper & Row Publishers, Inc. 88
Harper's Magazine 297
Harris & Associates Publishing Division 951
Harrow and Heston 88
Harrowsmith Magazine 384
Hart Literary Enterprises, Thomas S. 977
Harvard Business Review 699
Harvard Common Press, The 88
Harvard University Press 88
Harvest House Publishers 89
Haseltine Memorial Fellowship in Science Writing, Nate 1003
Haunts 560
Hayden Book Co. 89
Hayes School Publishing Co., Inc. 885
Hazelden Foundation 89
Heacock Literary Agency, Inc. 977
Headquarters Detective 276
Health & Wealth 297
Health Foods Business 779
Health Foods Retailing 728
Health Magazine 308
Health Plex Magazine 309
Health Profession Division 89
Heart of the Lakes Publishing 89
Heath & Co., D.C. 89
Heating, Plumbing, Air Conditioning 851
Heating/Piping/Air Conditioning 851
Heidinger Kafka Prize, The Janet 1004
Heinle & Heinle Enterprises, Inc. 977
Heinle & Heinle Publishers, Inc. 90
Helicopters in Canada 688

Helitzer, Mel 934
Helix Press 90
Hemingway Foundation Award, Ernest 1003
Hemley Memorial Award, Cecil 1003
Hendrick, Jr., Charles 934
Hendrickson Publishers, Inc. 90
Herald Publishing House 90
Herb Quarterly 344
Here's Life Publishers, Inc. 91
Heritage Books, Inc. 91
Heritage Features Syndicate 951
Heyday Books 91
HHM Literary Agency 977
Hibiscus Magazine 403
Hicall 528
Hideaways Guide 646
High Adventure 365
High Country News 441
High Plains Journal 756
High Volume Printing 853
Highlander, The 281
Highlights for Children 365
High-Tech Manager's Bulletin 826
High-Tech Marketing 673
High-Tech Selling 673
Hill Associates, Frederick 978
Hillman Prize Award, Sidney 1003
Hilton Literary Agency, Alice 978
Hintz & Fitzgerald 978
His Magazine 259
Hispanic Link News Service 951
Hit Parader 433
Hochmann Books, John L. 978
Hogan, Wayne 934
Holiday House, Inc. 91
Holloway House Publishing Co. 91
Hollywood Inside Syndicate 951
Hollywood Reporter, The 750
Home Business News 244
Home Education Magazine 266
Home Furnishings 784
Home Health Care Business 728
Home Illustrated 344
Home Life 266
Home Lighting & Accessories 784
Home Magazine 345
Home Mechanix 329
Home Shop Machinist, The 330
Home Viewer 633
Home Work Digest and Directory and Sourcebook 244
Homeowner, The 345
Homestyles Magazine 345
Honolulu 482
Honolulu Magazine Fiction Contest 1003
Honolulu Theatre for Youth 910
Hoof Beats 585
Horizon 633

Horizon Air (see Air Wisconsin 353)
Horn Book Magazine, The 692
Horoscope Guide 226
Horror Show, The 560
Horse and Horseman 207
Horse & Rider Magazine 207
Horse Illustrated 208
Horsemen's Yankee Pedlar Newspaper 208
Horseplay 208
Horses All 209
Horses West 209
Horticulture 346
Hospital Gift Shop Management 786
Hospital Supervisor's Bulletin 786
Hot Bike 232
Hotel and Motel Management 789
Houghton Mifflin Co. 92
Houghton Mifflin Co., Children's Trade Books 92
Hounslow Press 92
House & Garden 346
House Beautiful 346
Houston City Magazine 508
Howard Awards, The Roy W. 1003
Howell, David R. 934
Howell-North Books 92
Hub Rail 586
Hudson Hills Press, Inc. 93
Hudson Review, The 403
Hudson Valley Magazine 499
Human Kinetics Publishers, Inc. 93
Humanics Limited 93
Humor News and Novelties 350
Humorous Poetry Award 1004
Humpty Dumpty's Magazine 366
Hunt, William E. 910
Hunter House, Inc., Publishers 93
Huntington House, Inc. 94
Huntington Playhouse 910
Hurtig Publishers Ltd. 94
Hyde Park Media 952
Hysteria 658

I

I Know You Know 384
IBM PC Update 721
Icom Inc. 885
Ideal School Supply Co. 886
Ideals Magazine 297
Ideals Publishing Corp. 94
Illinois Banker 767
Illinois Business 250
Illinois Entertainer 433
Illinois Magazine 483
Illinois State Fine Arts Playwriting Award 1004
Illinois Times 483

Record of Submissions

DATE SENT	TITLE	MARKET	EDITOR

PIX	DATE RET'D	DATE ACCEPT'D	DATE PUBL'D	COPY RECV'D	EXPENSES	PAYMENT

Other Books of Interest

General Writing Books

    Beginning Writer's Answer Book, edited by Polking and Bloss $14.95

    Getting the Words Right: How to Revise, Edit and Rewrite, by Theodore A. Rees Cheney $13.95

    How to Become a Bestselling Author, by Stan Corwin $14.95

    How to Get Started in Writing, by Peggy Teeters (paper) $8.95

    How to Write a Book Proposal, by Michael Larsen $9.95

    How to Write While You Sleep, by Elizabeth Ross $12.95

    If I Can Write, You Can Write, by Charlie Shedd $12.95

    International Writers' & Artists' Yearbook (paper) $12.95

    Law & the Writer, edited by Polking & Meranus (paper) $10.95

    Knowing Where to Look: The Ultimate Guide to Research, by Lois Horowitz $16.95

    Make Every Word Count, by Gary Provost (paper) $7.95

    Pinckert's Practical Grammar, by Robert C. Pinckert $12.95

    Teach Yourself to Write, by Evelyn Stenbock (paper) $9.95

    The 29 Most Common Writing Mistakes & How to Avoid Them, by Judy Delton $9.95

    Writer's Block & How to Use It, by Victoria Nelson $12.95

    Writer's Guide to Research, by Lois Horowitz $9.95

    Writer's Market, edited by Becky Williams $21.95

    Writer's Resource Guide, edited by Bernadine Clark $16.95

    Writing for the Joy of It, by Leonard Knott $11.95

    Writing From the Inside Out, by Charlotte Edwards (paper) $9.95

Magazine/News Writing

    Basic Magazine Writing, by Barbara Kevles $16.95

    How to Sell Every Magazine Article You Write, by Lisa Collier Cool $14.95

    How to Write & Sell the 8 Easiest Article Types, by Helene Schellenberg Barnhart $14.95

    Writing Nonfiction that Sells, by Samm Sinclair Baker $14.95

Fiction Writing

    Creating Short Fiction, by Damon Knight (paper) $8.95

    Fiction Writer's Help Book, by Maxine Rock $12.95

    Fiction Writer's Market, edited by Jean Fredette $18.95

    Handbook of Short Story Writing, by Dickson and Smythe (paper) $8.95

    How to Write & Sell Your First Novel, by Oscar Collier with Frances Spatz Leighton $14.95

    How to Write Short Stories that Sell, by Louise Boggess (paper) $7.95

    One Way to Write Your Novel, by Dick Perry (paper) $6.95

    Storycrafting, by Paul Darcy Boles $14.95

    Writing Romance Fiction—For Love And Money, by Helene Schellenberg Barnhart $14.95

    Writing the Novel: From Plot to Print, by Lawrence Block (paper) $8.95

Special Interest Writing Books

    Complete Book of Scriptwriting, by J. Michael Straczynski $14.95

    The Complete Guide to Writing Software User Manuals, by Brad M. McGehee (paper) $14.95

    The Craft of Comedy Writing, by Sol Saks $14.95

    The Craft of Lyric Writing, by Sheila Davis $18.95

    Guide to Greeting Card Writing, edited by Larry Sandman (paper) $8.95

    How to Make Money Writing About Fitness & Health, by Celia & Thomas Scully $16.95

    How to Make Money Writing Fillers, by Connie Emerson (paper) $8.95

    How to Write a Cookbook and Get It Published, by Sara Pitzer $15.95

    How to Write a Play, by Raymond Hull $13.95

    How to Write and Sell Your Personal Experiences, by Lois Duncan (paper) $9.95

    How to Write and Sell (Your Sense of) Humor, by Gene Perret (paper) $9.95

    How to Write "How-To" Books and Articles, by Raymond Hull (paper) $8.95

    How to Write the Story of Your Life, by Frank P. Thomas $12.95

    How You Can Make $50,000 a Year as a Nature Photojournalist, by Bill Thomas (paper) $17.95

    Mystery Writer's Handbook, by The Mystery Writers of America (paper) $8.95

    Nonfiction for Children: How to Write It, How to Sell It, by Ellen E.M. Roberts $16.95

    On Being a Poet, by Judson Jerome $14.95

    The Poet's Handbook, by Judson Jerome (paper) $8.95

    Poet's Market, by Judson Jerome $16.95

    Sell Copy, by Webster Kuswa $11.95

    Successful Outdoor Writing, by Jack Samson $11.95

Travel Writer's Handbook, by Louise Zobel (paper) $9.95
TV Scriptwriter's Handbook, by Alfred Brenner (paper) $9.95
Writing After 50, by Leonard L. Knott $12.95
Writing and Selling Science Fiction, by Science Fiction Writers of America (paper) $7.95
Writing for Children & Teenagers, by Lee Wyndham (paper) $9.95
Writing for the Soaps, by Jean Rouverol $14.95
Writing the Modern Mystery, by Barbara Norville $15.95
Writing to Inspire, by Gentz, Roddy, et al $14.95

The Writing Business
Complete Guide to Self-Publishing, by Tom & Marilyn Ross $19.95
Complete Handbook for Freelance Writers, by Kay Cassill $14.95
Editing for Print, by Geoffrey Rogers $14.95
Freelance Jobs for Writers, edited by Kirk Polking (paper) $8.95
How to Bulletproof Your Manuscript, by Bruce Henderson $9.95
How to Get Your Book Published, by Herbert W. Bell $15.95
How to Understand and Negotiate a Book Contract or Magazine Agreement, by Richard Balkin $11.95
How You Can Make $20,000 a Year Writing, by Nancy Hanson (paper) $6.95
Literary Agents: How to Get & Work with the Right One for You, by Michael Larsen $9.95
Professional Etiquette for Writers, by William Brohaugh $9.95

To order directly from the publisher, include $2.00 postage and handling for 1 book and 50¢ for each additional book. Allow 30 days for delivery.

Writer's Digest Books, Department B
9933 Alliance Road, Cincinnati OH 45242
Prices subject to change without notice.